PENNSYLVANIA TEACHER'S EDITION

PRENTICE HALL

MATHEMATICS

COURSE 3

PEARSON
Prentice
Hall

ISBN 0-13-203172-8
1 2 3 4 5 6 7 8 9 10 10 09 08 07 06

Pennsylvania Mathematics Teacher Handbook

Table of Contents

Scope and Sequence for the Pennsylvania Assessment Anchors

The following chart provides an overview of where within Prentice Hall Course 3 Mathematics the Eligible Content of the Pennsylvania Assessment Anchors is introduced,developed. and mastered.

M8.A NUMBERS AND OPERATIONS

Assessment Anchor M8.A.1 Demonstrate an understanding of numbers, ways of representing numbers, relationships among numbers, and number systems.				
M8.A.1.1	Represent numbers in equivalent forms.			
M8.A.1.1.1	Represent numbers using scientific notation and/or exponential forms.	2-7	2-7, 2-8	2-7, 2-8
M8.A.1.1.2	Find the square or cube of a whole number (single digit) and/or the square root of a perfect square (without a calculator).	2-7, 3-1	2-7, 3-1	2-7, 3-1
Assessment Anchor M8.A.2 Understand the meanings of operations, use operations, and understand how they relate to each other.				
M8.A.2.1	Complete calculations by applying the order of operations.			
M8.A.2.1.1	Simplify numeric expressions involving integers, using the order of operations. (May include all types of grouping symbols. No combining negatives with exponents or compound exponents.)	1-1, 1-4	1-4, 2-7	1-4, 2-7
M8.A.2.2	Represent or solve problems using rates, ratios, proportions, and/or percents.			
M8.A.2.2.1	Solve problems involving percents (e.g., tax, discounts, etc). Do not include percent increase or decrease.	5-2	5-3, 5-4	5-6
M8.A.2.2.2	Represent or solve rate problems (e.g., unit rates, simple interest, distance, etc.) Students may be asked to solve for any term (formulas provided on the reference sheet for distance and interest).	2-6	4-1, 4-3	5-7

KEY

Introduce	Develop	Master

M8.A NUMBERS AND OPERATIONS (cont.)				
Assessment Anchor M8.A.3 Compute accurately and fluently and make reasonable estimates.				
M8.A.3.1	Determine the appropriateness of overestimating, underestimating or calculating an exact answer in problem-solving situations.			
M8.A.3.1.1	Identify, use, and/or explain when it is appropriate to round up or round down	p. 630	1-6	4-1
M8.A.3.1.2	Identify, apply, and/or explain when an exact answer is needed or when estimation is appropriate.	1-6, 4-1	5-3, 5-4, 6-6	8-4, 8-8
M8.A.3.2	Use estimation strategies in problem-solving situations.			
M8.A.3.2.1	Estimate answers to problems involving percents (percents will be limited to: 1%, 10%, 15%, 20%, 25%, 50%, or 75%).	5-2	5-3, 5-4	5-5
M8.A.3.3	Compute and/or explain operations with integers, fractions and/or decimals.			
M8.A.3.3.1	Add, subtract, multiply, and/or divide integers, fractions, and/or decimals with and without a calculator (straight computation or word problems).	1-3	1-4, 2-4	2-5

M8.B MEASUREMENT

Assessment Anchor M8.B.1 Demonstrate an understanding of measurable attributes of objects and figures, and the units, systems, and processes of measurement.				
M8.B.1.1	Convert measurements.			
M8.B.1.1.1	Convert among metric measurements (milli, centi, kilo using meter, liter, and gram).	4-2	4-2	4-2
M8.B.1.1.2	Convert customary measurements up to 2 units above or below the given unit (e.g., inches to yards, pints to gallons).	4-2	4-2	4-2
M8.B.1.1.3	Convert time up to 2 units above or below given unit (e.g., seconds to hours).			
M8.B.1.1.4	Convert from Fahrenheit to Celsius or Celsius to Fahrenheit.	2-6a	2-6a	2-6a
Assessment Anchor M8.B.2 Apply appropriate techniques, tools, and formulas to determine measurements.				
M8.B.2.1	Determine the measurement of a missing side(s) or angle(s) in a polygon.			
M8.B.2.1.1	Determine the total number of degrees in the interior angles of a polygon in 3–8 sided figures.	7-5a	7-5	7-5
M8.B.2.1.2	Determine the measurement of one interior angle of a regular polygon (3–8 sided polygons).	7-5a	7-5	7-5
M8.B.2.1.3	Determine the number of sides of a polygon given the total number of degrees in the interior angles (3–8 sided polygons).	7-5a	7-5	7-5
M8.B.2.3	Use, describe, and/or develop procedures to determine measures of perimeter, circumference, area, surface area, and/or volume.			
M8.B.2.3.1	Calculate the surface area of cubes and rectangular prisms.	8-4	8-4	8-4
M8.B.2.3.2	Calculate the volume of cubes and rectangular prisms.	8-6	8-6	8-6
M8.B.2.3.3	Determine the appropriate type of measurement (circumference, perimeter, area, surface area, volume) for a given situation (e.g., which measurement is needed to determine the amount of carpeting for a room).	8-5	8-3	8-9

M8.C GEOMETRY

Assessment Anchor M8.C.1 Analyze characteristics and properties of two- and three-dimensional geometric shapes and demonstrate understanding of geometric relationships.

M8.C.1.1	Identify, use, and/or describe properties of angles, triangles, quadrilaterals, circles, pyramids, cubes, prisms, spheres, cones, and/or cylinders.			
M8.C.1.1.1	Match the three-dimensional figure with its net (cube, cylinder, cone, prism, pyramid). Any measurements used should be consistent in the stem and answer choices.	8-3	8-3	8-3
M8.C.1.1.2	Define, identify, and/or use properties of angles formed by intersecting lines (complementary, supplementary, adjacent, and/or vertical angles).	7-1	7-1	7-1
M8.C.1.1.3	Define, identify, and/or use properties of angles formed when two parallel lines are cut by a transversal (alternate interior, alternate exterior, vertical corresponding).	7-2	7-2	7-2
M8.C.1.2	Compute measures of sides of right triangles using the Pythagorean Theorem.			
M8.C.1.2.1	Use the Pythagorean Theorem to find the measure of a missing side of a right triangle.	3-2, 3-3	3-2, 3-3	3-2, 3-3

Assessment Anchor M8.C.3 Locate points or describe relationships using the coordinate plane.

M8.C.3.1	Plot and/or identify ordered pairs on a coordinate plane.			
M8.C.3.1.1	Plot, locate, or identify ordered pairs on a coordinate plane (the point may be a vertex of a polygon).	3-4b	3-5, 3-5b, 3-6	3-7, 3-8

M8.D ALGEBRAIC CONCEPTS

Assessment Anchor M8.D.1 Demonstrate an understanding of patterns, relations, and functions.				
M8.D.1.1	Analyze, extend, or develop descriptions of patterns or functions.			
M8.D.1.1.1	Continue a numeric or algebraic pattern (pattern must show 3 repetitions—may include up to 2 operations, squares, and square roots).	11-1	11-1	11-1
M8.D.1.1.2	Find missing elements in numeric or geometric patterns, and/or functions (may be given a table or rule—pattern must show 3 repetitions).	3-5	11-1	11-3
M8.D.1.1.3	Determine the rule of a function (given elements in an input-output table, chart, or list—limit to linear functions).	3-5	11-6, 3-5	11-6
Assessment Anchor M8.D.2 Represent and/or analyze mathematical situations using numbers, symbols, words, tables, and/or graphs.				
M8.D.2.1	Select and/or use a strategy to simplify an expression, solve an equation or inequality, and/or check the solution for accuracy.			
M8.D.2.1.1	Solve one- or two-step equations and inequalities (should not include absolute values—one variable only).	1-6	1-7, 6-1	6-5, 6-6
M8.D.2.1.2	Use substitution to check the accuracy of a given value for an equation or inequality (simple inequalities with one variable).	1-7	1-7, 6-5	1-7, 6-5
M8.D.2.1.3	Determine the value of an algebraic expression by simplifying and/or substituting a number for the variable.	1-1	1-4, 1-5	6-2
M8.D.2.2	Create and/or interpret expressions, equations, or inequalities that model problem situations.			
M8.D.2.2.1	Match a written situation to its numeric and/or algebraic expression, equation, or inequality (up to two variables in equations or expressions—one variable with inequalities).	1-1	1-6, 6-1, 6-2, 6-3	11-6, 6-5, 6-6
M8.D.2.2.2	Write and/or solve an equation for a given problem situation (one variable only).	1-6	6-1, 6-3	11-6
Assessment Anchor M8.D.3 Describe or use models to represent quantitative relationships.				
M8.D.3.1	Represent relationships with tables or graphs on the coordinate plane.			
M8.D.3.1.1	Graph a linear function based on an *x*/*y* table (integers only).	3-5a, 3-5, 3-5b	11-4, 11-5a, 11-5	11-6, 11-7b
M8.D.3.1.2	Match the graph of a linear function to its *x*/*y* table (integers only).	3-5a, 3-5, 3-5b	11-4, 11-5a, 11-5	11-6, 11-7b
M8.D.3.1.3	Match the linear equation ($y = mx + b$ form) to the *x*/*y* table (integers only in the table).	3-5a, 3-5, 3-5b	11-4, 11-5a, 11-5	11-6, 11-7b

M8.E DATA ANALYSIS AND PROBABILITY				
Assessment Anchor M8.E.1 Formulate or answer questions that can be addressed with data and/or organize, display, interpret, or analyze data.				
M8.E.1.1	Choose, display, or interpret data (tables, charts, graphs, etc.).			
M8.E.1.1.1	Choose and/or explain the correct representation (graph) for a set of data.	9-4	9-4, 9-9	9-9
M8.E.1.1.2	Analyze data and/or answer questions pertaining to data shown in multiple line graphs, circle graphs, or histograms.	p.642	9-2	9-8
M8.E.1.1.3	Interpret data shown in stem-and-leaf or box-and-whisker plots.	9-5, 9-6	9-5, 9-6	9-5, 9-6
Assessment Anchor M8.E.3 Select and/or use appropriate statistical methods to analyze data.				
M8.E.3.1	Calculate the probability of an event.			
M8.E.3.1.1	Find the probability for a mutually exclusive or an independent event (written as a fraction in simplest form).	10-1	10-2a, 10-4a	10-4
Assessment Anchor M8.E.3 Understand and/or apply basic concepts of probability or outcomes.				
M8.E.3.2	Determine the number of combinations and/or permutations for an event.			
M8.E.3.2.1	Determine/show the number of permutations and/or combinations for an event using up to four choices (e.g., organized list, etc.).	5-8	10-1, 10-4	10-1
Assessment Anchor M8.E.4 Develop and/or evaluate inferences and predictions or draw conclusions based on data or data displays.				
M8.E.4.1	Draw conclusions, make inferences, and/or evaluate hypotheses based on statistical and data displays.			
M8.E.4.1.1	Fit a line to a scatter plot and/or describe any correlation between the two variables (positive, negative, strong, weak, or none).	9-7	9-7	9-7
M8.E.4.1.2	Make predictions based on survey results or graphs (bar, line, circle, scatter plots, etc.).	9-7a	10-2	10-3

Pennsylvania Assessment Anchors and Eligible Content Correlation and Professional Development

Use these pages to acquaint yourself with selected Pennsylvania Assessment Anchors and Eligible Content with respect to where previous standards have brought the students and where this year's standards will lead their studies going forward.

Correlation

M8.A Numbers and Operations

	Eligible Content	Prentice Hall Course 3 Mathematics Lessons
M8.A.1.1.1.	Represent numbers using scientific notation and/or exponential forms.	2-7, 2-8
M8.A.2.1.1.	Simplify numeric expressions involving integers, using the order of operations. (May include all types of grouping symbols. No combining negatives with exponents or compound exponents.)	1-1, 1-4, 2-7
M8.A.2.2.1.	Solve problems involving percents (e.g., tax, discounts, etc). Do not include percent increase or decrease.	5-2, 5-3, 5-4, 5-6
M8.A.3.2.1.	Estimate answers to problems involving percents (percents will be limited to: 1%, 10%, 15%, 20%, 25%, 50% or 75%).	5-2

Professional Development

Professional Development

Math Background

A number expressed with an exponent is called a *power*. The exponent of a power tells how many times the base is used as a factor. For example, the expression 6^3 is a power of 6. The number 6 is the base, and 3 is the exponent.

$$6^3 = 6 \cdot 6 \cdot 6$$

Scientific notation is a method of expressing numbers that is useful when working with very large or very small measurements. A number in scientific notation is written as the product of two factors. One factor is greater than or equal to 1 and less than 10. The other factor is a power of 10. For example, the number 265,000 written in scientific notation is 2.65×10^5.

Math Progression

Prior Years

Students learned ways to recognize equal values and to compare decimals, percents, fractions, and integers. They also learned to follow the order of operations.

This Year

Recognition of numbers will include powers and numbers expressed in scientific notation. Students will use the order of operations as they work with more-complex numerical expressions.

Going Forward

Students will classify numbers as rational or irrational. They will use numbers written in scientific notation to solve problems. They will also learn to apply the laws of exponents.

Correlation

M8.B Measurement		
	Eligible Content	**Prentice Hall Course 3 Mathematics Lessons**
M8.B.2.2.1.	Calculate the surface area of cubes and rectangular prisms.	8-4a, 8-4
M8.B.2.2.2.	Calculate the volume of cubes and rectangular prisms.	8-6a, 8-6
M8.B.2.2.3.	Determine the appropriate type of measurement (circumference, perimeter, area, surface area, volume) for a given situation (e.g., which measurement is needed to determine the amount of carpeting for a room).	7-6, 7-7, 8-4a, 8-4, 8-6a, 8-6

Professional Development

Math Background

The *surface area* of a three-dimensional solid is the sum of the areas of its surfaces. Surface area is measured in square units, such as square feet or square centimeters. The amount of space enclosed by a three-dimensional solid is called its *volume*. Volume is measured in cubic units, like cubic yards or cubic inches.

The amount of wrapping paper needed to wrap a gift box is determined by its surface area. Similarly, the amount of water that a glass can hold is determined by its volume.

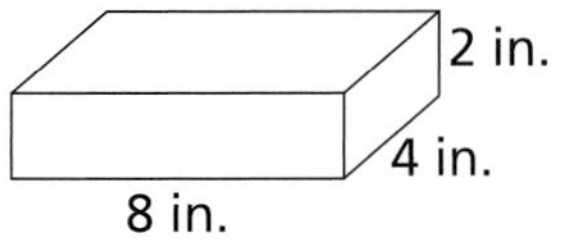

Rectangular Prism

Volume $= \ell \times w \times h = 8 \times 4 \times 2 = 64$ cubic inches

Surface area $= 2\ell w + 2\ell h + 2wh = 64 + 32 + 16 = 112$ square inches

Math Progression

Prior Years

Students focused on fundamental measurement concepts, such as making direct measurements of length, temperature, and capacity. They also used models to solve simple perimeter, area, and volume problems.

This Year

Students will expand their understanding as they learn to recognize whether given measurements are reasonable. They will compute the perimeter and area of more-complex figures, and they will find the surface area and volume of cubes, rectangular prisms, and other three-dimensional solids.

Going Forward

Students will investigate the degree of accuracy required in different measurement situations. They will continue to use models and formulas to solve measurement problems, such as those involving the surface area of three-dimensional objects.

Correlation

M8.C Geometry

Eligible Content		Prentice Hall Course 3 Mathematics Lessons
M8.C.1.1.1.	Match the three-dimensional figure with its net (cube, cylinder, cone, prism, pyramid). Any measurements used should be consistent in the stem and answer choices.	8-3
M8.C.1.1.3.	Define, identify, and/or use properties of angles formed when two parallel lines are cut by a transversal (alternate interior, alternate exterior, vertical corresponding).	7-2
M8.C.1.2.1.	Use the Pythagorean Theorem to find the measure of a missing side of a right triangle (whole numbers only).	3-2, 3-3
M8.C.3.1.1.	Plot, locate, or identify ordered pairs on a coordinate plane (the point may be a vertex of a polygon).	3-4

Professional Development

Math Background

In a right triangle, the *legs* are the two shortest sides. The *hypotenuse* is the longest side and is always opposite the right angle. The Pythagorean Theorem shows how the legs and hypotenuse of a right triangle are related.

The Pythagorean Theorem states that in any right triangle the sum of the squares of the lengths of the legs is equal to the square of the length of the hypotenuse.

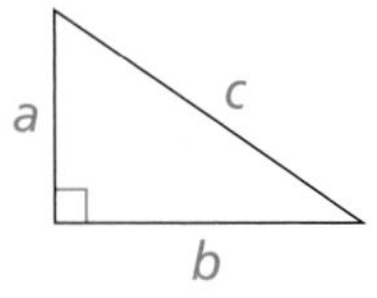

$a^2 + b^2 = c^2$

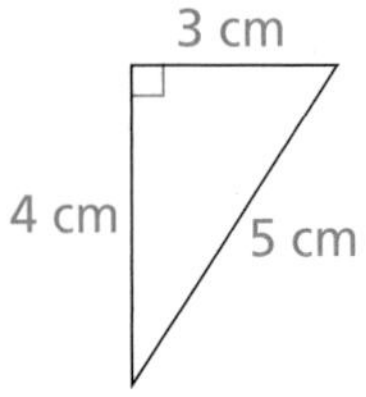

$3^2 + 4^2 = 5^2$

As a formula, the Pythagorean Theorem can be used to find the length of a side of a right triangle when the lengths of the other two sides are known.

Math Progression

Prior Years

Students focused on identifying congruent and similar figures. They used the properties of congruency and similarity to find missing measures and solve problems.

This Year

Students will be introduced to the Pythagorean Theorem as they explore the relationship between the lengths of the sides of a right triangle. They will use this theorem in a variety of problem-solving situations, including finding missing measures in right triangles.

Going Forward

Students will investigate the properties of special right triangles as well as the sine, cosine, and tangent ratios. They will combine these properties with their knowledge of the Pythagorean Theorem to solve a variety of real-world problems.

Correlation

M.8D Algebraic Concepts		
	Eligible Content	**Prentice Hall Course 3 Mathematics Lessons**
M8.D.1.1.2.	Find missing elements in numeric or geometric patterns and/or functions (may be given a table or rule–pattern must show 3 repetitions).	3-5, 11-1, 11-3
M8.D.2.1.1.	Solve one- or two-step equations and inequalities (should not include absolute values–one variable only).	1-6, 1-7, 6-1, 6-5, 6-6
M8.D.2.2.1.	Match a written situation to its numeric and/or algebraic expression, equation or inequality (up to two variables in equations or expressions–one variable with inequalities).	1-1, 1-6, 6-1, 6-2, 6-3, 6-5, 6-6, 11-6

Professional Development

Professional Development

Math Background

Students often need to be able to identify a sequence or pattern as well as determine missing terms. One way to do so is to write a rule that tells how to find the next term in a pattern based on the previous term. For example, the arithmetic sequence below can be described by the rule, "Start with 3 and add 3 repeatedly." If you wanted to find the 20th term of this sequence, you would need to apply this rule 20 times.

3, 6, 9, 12, . . .

A simpler way to find the 20th term of this sequence is to write a rule that can be used to find the value of any term based on the term number. To do so, make a function table in which the output values are the terms of the sequence and the input values are the term numbers.

Term Number	1	2	3	4
Term of Sequence	3	6	9	12

The table makes it clear that each term of the sequence is 3 times the term number. Therefore, the 20th term of the sequence is equal to 3 • 20, or 60.

Math Progression

Prior Years

Students focused on analyzing and extending sequences of numbers and geometric figures. They also described patterns and functions by using algebraic expressions and equations.

This Year

Students will examine arithmetic and geometric sequences and use algebraic expressions to predict terms of sequences. They will graph and solve one- and two-step equations and inequalities.

Going Forward

Students will identify the domain and range of functions and recognize whether a functional relationship exists between sets of data. They will also investigate how changing an equation's coefficients or constants affects the equation's graph.

Correlation

M8.E Data Analysis and Probability		
	Eligible Content	**Prentice Hall Course 3 Mathematics Lessons**
M8.E.1.1.3.	Interpret data shown in stem-and-leaf or box-and-whisker plots.	9-5, 9-6
M8.E.3.2.1.	Determine/show the number of permutations and/or combinations for an event using up to four choices (e.g., organized list, etc.).	5-8, 10-1, 10-4
M8.E.4.1.1.	Fit a line to a scatter plot and/or describe any correlation between the two variables (positive, negative, strong, weak or none).	9-7

Professional Development

Professional Development

Math Background

A *scatter plot* is a graph that shows the relationship between two sets of data, such as age and height of students. The two sets of data are plotted as ordered pairs on a coordinate grid, as shown below.

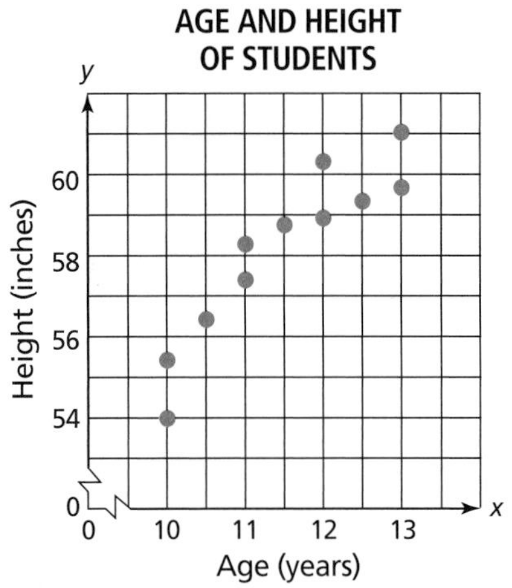

Sometimes the points plotted on a scatter plot show a trend. When the value of one variable tends to increase as the value of the other variable increases, the scatter plot shows a *positive trend*. When the value of one variable tends to decrease as the value of the other variable increases, the scatter plot shows a *negative trend.*

Math Progression

Prior Years

Students represented and analyzed data by using measures of central tendency and a variety of graphs. They distinguished between theoretical and experimental probability and determined the number of possible outcomes in a given situation.

This Year

Students will continue to build their critical thinking skills as they interpret displays of data and choose appropriate displays for given situations. They will determine the probability of compound events and use models to investigate combinations and permutations.

Going Forward

Students will determine whether the relationship between two sets of data is linear or nonlinear. They will estimate probability by using simulations, and they will distinguish between probability and odds.

Course 3 Pennsylvania Leveled Pacing Chart

This Pennsylvania Leveled Pacing Chart is provided as a guide to help you customize your course and to provide for differentiated instruction. This chart covers the content of the book and helps students cover the Eligible Content they need for success on the Pennsylvania System of School Assessment (PSSA).

The suggested number of days for each chapter is based on a traditional 45-minute class period and on a 90-minute block period. The total of 160 days of instruction leaves time for assessments, projects, assemblies, or other special days that vary from school to school.

- ✔ Content to prepare for the PSSA test
- ✔ Reviews the previous year
- ✔ Content to cover after the PSSA test or for Enrichment

Differentiated Instruction

		Assessment Anchors and Eligible Content	Core	Advanced
Chapter 1 Integers and Algebraic Expressions		**Traditional 14 days Block 7 days**		
1-1	Algebraic Expressions and the Order of Operations	M8.A.2.1.1, M8.D.2.1.3, M8.D.2.2.1	✔	✔
	• Vocabulary Builder: High-Use Academic Words		✔	
1-2	Integers and Absolute Value		✔	
1-2b	Activity Lab, Data Analysis: Integers and Differences		✔	
1-3a	Activity Lab: Adding Integers		✔	
1-3	Adding and Subtracting Integers	M8.A.3.3.1	✔	✔
1-4	Multiplying and Dividing Integers	M8.A.2.1.1, M8.A.3.3.1, M8.D.2.1.3	✔	✔
	• Guided Problem Solving: Solving Multiple-Step Problems	M8.D.2.2.2	✔	✔
1-5	Properties of Numbers	M8.D.2.1.3	✔	✔
1-6a	Activity Lab, Hands-On: Modeling Equations		✔	
1-6	Solving Equations by Adding and Subtracting	M8.D.2.1.1, M8.D.2.2.1, M8.D.2.2.2	✔	✔
1-6b	Activity Lab: Number Squares			✔
1-7	Solving Equations by Multiplying and Dividing	M8.D.2.1.1, M8.D.2.1.2	✔	✔
1-7b	Activity Lab, Algebra Thinking: The Cover-up Method	M8.D.2.2.2	✔	✔
	Problem Solving Application: Applying Integers	M8.A.2.1.1, M8.A.3.3.1, M8.D.2.1.3	✔	✔
	Pennsylvania Workout, p. PA5	M8.A.2.1.1, M8.A.3.3.1, M8.D.2.1.1, M8.D.2.1.2, M8.D.2.1.3, M8.D.2.2.1, M8.D.2.2.2	✔	✔
Chapter 2 Rational Numbers		**Traditional 15 days Block 8 days**		
2-1	Factors		✔	
2-2	Equivalent Forms of Rational Numbers	M8.A.1.1.1	✔	✔
2-2b	Activity Lab: Repeating Decimals			✔
2-3	Comparing and Ordering Rational Numbers		✔	
2-4	Adding and Subtracting Rational Numbers	M8.A.3.3.1	✔	✔
2-5a	Activity Lab, Hands On: Modeling Fraction Multiplication		✔	
2-5	Multiplying and Dividing Rational Numbers	M8.A.3.3.1	✔	✔
	• Vocabulary Builder: Learning Vocabulary	M8.A.3.3	✔	✔
	• Guided Problem Solving: Practice Solving Problems	M8.A.3.3.1	✔	✔
2-6a	Activity Lab, Algebra Thinking: Estimating Solutions	M8.A.3.1.1, M8.A.3.1.2	✔	✔
2-6	Formulas	M8.A.2.2.2	✔	
2-6b	Activity Lab, Technology: Using Formulas	M8.B.2	✔	✔
2-7	Powers and Exponents	M8.A.1.1.1, M8.A.1.1.2, M8.A.2.1.1	✔	✔
2-7b	Activity Lab, Technology: Evaluating Expressions	M8.A.1.1.1, M8.B.2	✔	✔
2-8a	Activity Lab: Multiplying by Powers of 10	M8.A.1.1.1	✔	✔
2-8	Scientific Notation	M8.A.1.1.1	✔	✔
2-8b	Activity Lab, Data Analysis: Writing Measurements	M8.A.1.1.1	✔	✔
	Problem Solving Applications: Applying Real Numbers	M8.A.1.1.1, M8.A.3.3.1	✔	✔
	Pennsylvania Workout, p. PA6	M8.A.1.1.1, M8.A.1.1.2, M8.A.2.1.1, M8.A.2.2.2, M8.A.3.3.1	✔	✔
	Pennsylvania Benchmark Test 1 in PA PMA, pp. 7–12			
Chapter 3 Real Numbers and the Coordinate Plane		**Traditional 15 days Block 8 days**		
3-1	Exploring Square Roots and Irrational Numbers	M8.A.1.1.2	✔	✔
3-2a	Activity Lab, Hands On: Exploring the Pythagorean Theorem	M8.A.1.1.2, M8.C.1.2.1	✔	✔
3-2	The Pythagorean Theorem	M8.C.1.2.1	✔	✔
	• Guided Problem Solving: Squares and Square Roots	M8.A.1.1.1, M8.C.1.2.1	✔	✔
3-3	Using the Pythagorean Theorem	M8.C.1.2.1	✔	✔
	• Extension: Analyzing Triangles			✔
3-4	Graphing in the Coordinate Plane	M8.C.3.1.1	✔	✔
3-4b	Activity Lab: Finding the Midpoint		✔	

	Assessment Anchors and Eligible Content	Core	Advanced
3-5a Activity Lab, Data Analysis: Tables and Graphs	M8.E.1.1.1	✔	✔
3-5 Equations, Tables, and Graphs	M8.D.1.1.2, M8.D.1.1.3	✔	✔
3-5b Activity Lab, Algebra Thinking: Matching Graphs	M8.D.1.1.2, M8.D.1.1.3	✔	✔
3-6 Translations		✔	
3-7a Activity Lab, Hands On: Exploring Reflections		✔	
3-7 Reflections and Symmetry		✔	
3-8a Activity Lab, Hands On: Exploring Rotations		✔	
3-8 Rotations		✔	
• Extension: Tessellations		✔	
Problem Solving Application: Applying Rate of Change	M8.C.3.1.1, M8.D.1.1.2, M8.D.1.1.3	✔	✔
Pennsylvania Workout, p. PA7	M8.A.1.1.2, M8.C.1.2.1, M8.C.3.1.1, M8.D.1.1.2, M8.D.1.1.3, M8.D.4.1.1	✔	✔
Chapter 4 Applications of Proportions	**Traditional 13 days Block 7 days**		
4-1 Ratios and Rates	M8.A.2.2.2	✔	✔
4-1b Activity Lab: Finding Rates		✔	
4-2a Activity Lab: Choosing Units		✔	
4-2 Converting Units	M8.B.1.1.1, M8.B.1.1.2	✔	✔
4-3a Activity Lab: Proportional and Nonproportional Relationships	M8.A.2.2	✔	✔
4-3 Solving Proportions	M8.A.2.2.2	✔	
• Guided Problem Solving: Using Rates and Proportions		✔	
4-4 Similar Figures and Proportions		✔	
4-4b Activity Lab: Ratios of Similar Figures		✔	
4-5a Activity Lab: Exploring Dilations			✔
4-5 Similarity Transformations		✔	
4-5b Activity Lab: Geometry Software and Dilations			✔
4-6 Scale Models and Maps		✔	
4-7a Activity Lab, Hands On: Using Similar Figures		✔	
4-7 Similarity and Indirect Measurement		✔	
Problem Solving Application: Applying Proportions	M8.A.2.2.2	✔	✔
Pennsylvania Workout, p. PA8	M8.A.2.2.2, M8.B.1.1.1, M8.B.1.1.2	✔	✔
Pennsylvania Benchmark Test 2 in PA PMA, pp. 13–18			
Chapter 5 Applications of Percent	**Traditional 13 days Block 7 days**		
5-1 Fractions, Decimals, and Percents		✔	
5-2 Estimating With Percents	M8.A.2.2.1, M8.A.3.2.1	✔	✔
5-3 Percents and Proportions	M8.A.2.2.1	✔	✔
5-3b Activity Lab, Data Analysis: Percents and Graphs	M8.A.2.2.1	✔	✔
5-4 Percents and Equations	M8.A.2.2.1	✔	✔
• Vocabulary Builder: High-Use Academic Words		✔	
5-5a Activity Lab, Data Analysis: Describing Change	M8.E.4.1	✔	✔
5-5 Percent of Change		✔	
5-6 Markup and Discount	M8.A.2.2.1	✔	✔
5-6b Activity Lab, Hands On: Using Percents	M8.A.2.2.1	✔	✔
• Guided Problem Solving: Practice Solving Problems	M8.A.2.2	✔	✔
5-7 Simple Interest	M8.A.2.2.2	✔	✔
5-8a Activity Lab, Hands On: Exploring Probability	M8.A.2.2.1, M8.E.3.1.1	✔	✔
5-8 Ratios and Probability	M8.E.3.1.1	✔	✔
Problem Solving Application: Applying Percents	M8.A.2.2.1, M8.E.4.1	✔	✔
Pennsylvania Workout, p. PA9	M8.A.2.2.1, M8.A.2.2.2, M8.A.3.2.1	✔	✔
Chapter 6 Equations and Inequalities	**Traditional 11 days Block 6 days**		
6-1a Activity Lab, Hands On: Modeling Multi-Step Equations	M8.D.2.1.1	✔	✔
6-1 Solving Two-Step Equations	M8.D.2.1.1, M8.D.2.2.1, M8.D.2.2.2	✔	✔
6-2a Activity Lab, Hands On: Modeling Expressions	M8.D.2.1.1	✔	✔
6-2 Simplifying Algebraic Expressions	M8.D.2.1.3, M8.D.2.2.1	✔	✔
6-3 Solving Multi-Step Equations	M8.D.2.2.1, M8.D.2.2.2	✔	✔
6-4 Solving Equations With Variables on Both Sides	M8.D.2.1.1	✔	✔
• Guided Problem Solving: Writing Equations	M8.D.2.1.1, M8.D.2.2	✔	✔
6-5a Activity Lab: Graphing Inequalities	M8.D.2.1.1	✔	✔
6-5 Solving Inequalities by Adding or Subtracting	M8.D.2.1.1, M8.D.2.1.2, M8.D.2.2.1	✔	✔
• Vocabulary Builder: High-Use Academic Words		✔	

		Assessment Anchors and Eligible Content	Core	Advanced
6-6a	Activity Lab: Inequalities and Negative Numbers	M8.D.2.1 M8.D.2.1.1	✔	✔
6-6	Solving Inequalities by Multiplying or Dividing	M8.D.2.1.1, M8.D.2.2.1	✔	✔
	Problem Solving Application: Applying Equations	M8.D.2.1.1, M8.D.2.2.1, M8.D.2.2.2	✔	✔
	Pennsylvania Workout, p. PA10	M8.D.2.1.1, M8.D.2.1.2, M8.D.2.1.3, M8.D.2.2.1, M8.D.2.2.2	✔	✔
	Pennsylvania Benchmark Test 3 in PA PMA, pp. 19–24			
Chapter 7 Geometry		**Traditional 15 days Block 7 days**		
7-1a	Activity Lab, Hands On: Exploring Pairs of Angles	M8.C.1.1.2, M8.C.1.1.3	✔	✔
7-1	Pairs of Angles	M8.C.1.1.2	✔	✔
7-2	Angles and Parallel Lines	M8.C.1.1.3	✔	✔
7-2b	Activity Lab, Algebra Thinking: Solving Angle Equations	M8.C.1.1.2	✔	✔
7-3	Congruent Polygons		✔	
7-4	Classifying Triangles and Quadrilaterals		✔	
	• Vocabulary Builder: Using Concept Maps			✔
7-5a	Activity Lab: Angle Sums	M8.B.2.1.3	✔	✔
7-5	Angles and Polygons	M8.B.2.1.1, M8.B.2.1.2	✔	✔
7-6	Areas of Polygons		✔	
	• Guided Problem Solving: Geoboard Area		✔	
7-7a	Activity Lab, Hands On: Estimating Area		✔	
7-7	Circumference and Area of a Circle		✔	
	• Extension: Arcs, Chords, and Semicircles	Prepares for M11.C.1.1.2		✔
7-8	Constructions	M8.C.1.1.2, M8.C.1.1.3	✔	✔
7-8b	Activity Lab, Technology: Geometry Software and Constructions	M8.C.1.1.2	✔	✔
	Problem Solving Application: Applying Geometry	M8.B.2.1.1, M8.B.2.1.2, M8.B.2.1.3	✔	✔
	Pennsylvania Workout, p. PA11	M8.B.2.1.2, M8.C.1.1.2, M8.C.1.1.3	✔	✔
Chapter 8 Measurement		**Traditional 16 days Block 8 days**		
8-1	Solids	M8.C.1.1	✔	✔
8-2	Drawing Views of Three-Dimensional Figures	M8.C.1.1.1	✔	✔
8-2b	Activity Lab: Sketching Solids	M8.C.1.1.1	✔	✔
8-3a	Activity Lab, Hands On: Making Solids From Nets	M8.C.1.1.1	✔	✔
8-3	Nets and Three-Dimensional Figures	M8.C.1.1.1	✔	✔
8-4a	Activity Lab, Hands On: Modeling Surface Area	M8.B.2.3	✔	✔
8-4	Surface Areas of Prisms and Cylinders	M8.B.2.3.1	✔	✔
8-5a	Activity Lab, Hands On: Surface Area of a Pyramid	M8.B.2.3.1	✔	✔
8-5	Surface Areas of Pyramids and Cones	M8.B.2.3.1	✔	✔
8-6a	Activity Lab, Hands On: Modeling Volume	M8.B.2.3	✔	✔
8-6	Volume of Prisms and Cylinders	M8.B.2.3.2	✔	✔
	• Guided Problem Solving: Using Formulas	M8.C.1.1	✔	✔
8-7a	Activity Lab, Hands On: Finding Volume Using Models	M8.C.1.1.1	✔	✔
8-7	Volumes of Pyramids and Cones	M8.B.2.3.3, M8.C.1.1	✔	✔
8-8	Spheres	M8.C.1.1	✔	✔
8-9a	Activity Lab: Changing Dimensions	M8.B.2.3.3	✔	✔
8-9	Exploring Similar Solids	M8.B.2.3.3	✔	✔
8-9b	Activity Lab, Data Analysis: Precision and Significant Digits			✔
	Problem Solving Application: Applying Measurement	M8.B.2.3, M8.C.1.1.1	✔	✔
	Pennsylvania Workout, p. PA12	M8.B.2.3.1, M8.B.2.3.2, M8.C.1.1.1	✔	✔
	Pennsylvania Benchmark Test 4 in PA PMA, pp. 25–30			
Chapter 9 Using Graphs to Analyze Data		**Traditional 15 days Block 7 days**		
9-1	Finding Mean, Median, and Mode		✔	
9-1b	Activity Lab, Data Collection: Comparing Mean and Median		✔	
9-2	Displaying Frequencies	M8.E.1.1.2	✔	✔
9-2b	Activity Lab, Technology: Making Histograms	M8.E.1.1.3	✔	✔
9-3	Venn Diagrams			✔
9-4a	Activity Lab, Data Analysis: Reading Graphical Displays	M8.E.4.1	✔	✔
9-4	Reading Graphs Critically	M8.E.1.1.1	✔	✔
9-4b	Activity Lab, Data Analysis: Making Graphs to Tell a Story	M8.E.1.1.1	✔	✔
9-5	Stem-and-Leaf Plots	M8.E.1.1.3	✔	✔
9-6	Box-and-Whisker Plots	M8.E.1.1.3	✔	✔
9-6b	Activity Lab, Technology: Making Box-and-Whisker Plots	M8.E.1.1.3	✔	✔

		Assessment Anchors and Eligible Content	Core	Advanced
9-7a	Activity Lab, Data Collection: Scatter Plots	M8.E.4.1.2	✔	✔
9-7	Making Predictions From Scatter Plots	M8.E.4.1.1, M8.E.4.1.2	✔	✔
9-7b	Activity Lab, Algebra Thinking: Plotting a Strategy	M8.E.4.1.1, M8.E.4.1.2	✔	✔
9-8	Circle Graphs	M8.E.1.1.2	✔	✔
	• Guided Problem Solving: Equations and Graphs	M8.E.1.1.2	✔	✔
9-9	Choosing an Appropriate Graph	M8.E.1.1.1	✔	✔
9-9b	Activity Lab, Technology: Graphing Data Using Spreadsheets			✔
	Problem Solving Application: Applying Data Analysis	M8.E.1.1.1	✔	✔
	Pennsylvania Workout, p. PA13	M8.E.1.1.1, M8.E.1.1.2, M8.E.1.1.3	✔	✔
Chapter 10 Probability		**Traditional 11 days Block 5 days**		
10-1	Theoretical and Experimental Probability	M8.E.3.1.1	✔	✔
10-2a	Activity Lab, Hands On: Fair Games	M8.E.2.1	✔	✔
10-2	Making Predictions	M8.E.4.1.2	✔	✔
	• Extension: Complements and Probability			✔
10-3	Conducting a Survey			✔
10-3b	Activity Lab, Technology: Simulations With Random Numbers			✔
10-4a	Activity Lab, Hands On: Comparing Types of Events	M8.E.2.1	✔	✔
10-4	Independent and Dependent Events	M8.E.3.1.1	✔	✔
10-5	Permutations	M8.E.3.2.1	✔	✔
10-6	Combinations	M8.E.3.2.1	✔	✔
	• Vocabulary Builder: Understanding Vocabulary		✔	
	• Guided Problem Solving: Permutations, Combinations, and Probability	M8.E.3.1.1	✔	✔
	Problem Solving Application: Applying Probability	M8.E.3.1.1	✔	✔
	Pennsylvania Workout, p. PA14	M8.E.3.1.1, M8.E.3.2.1, M8.E.4.1.2	✔	✔
Chapter 11 Functions		**Traditional 13 days Block 6 days**		
11-1	Sequences	M8.D.1.1.1, M8.D.1.1.2	✔	✔
11-1b	Activity Lab, Technology: Exploring Sequences	M8.D.1.1.1, M8.D.1.1.2	✔	✔
11-2	Relating Graphs to Events	M8.E.3.1.1	✔	✔
11-2b	Activity Lab, Data Collection: Line Graphs	M8.E.3.1.1	✔	✔
11-3	Functions	M8.D.1.1.2	✔	✔
11-4a	Activity Lab: Rate of Change		✔	
11-4	Understanding Slope	Prepares for M11.D.3.2.1		✔
	• Extension: Parallel and Perpendicular Lines	Prepares for M11.C.3.1.2		✔
11-5a	Activity Lab, Technology: Graphing Equations	M8.D.3.1.3	✔	✔
11-5	Graphing Linear Functions	M8.D.4.1.1	✔	✔
11-6	Writing Rules for Linear Functions	M8.D.1.1.3, M8.D.2.2.1, M8.D.2.2.2	✔	✔
	• Guided Problem Solving: Linear Functions	M8.D.3.1.3	✔	✔
11-7	Quadratic and Other Nonlinear Functions	M8.D.3.1	✔	✔
11-7b	Activity Lab, Data Analysis: Changing Representations	M8.D.2	✔	✔
	Problem Solving Application: Applying Quadratic Functions	M8.D.3.1	✔	✔
	Pennsylvania Workout, p. PA15	M8.D.1.1.1, M8.D.1.1.2, M8.D.2.2.1, M8.D.4.1.1	✔	✔
Chapter 12 Polynomials and Properties of Exponents		**Traditional 9 days Block 4 days**		
12-1a	Activity Lab, Algebra Thinking: Writing Expressions	M8.D.2.2.1, M8.D.2.2.2	✔	✔
12-1	Exploring Polynomials	Prepares for M11.D.2.2.1		✔
12-2	Adding and Subtracting Polynomials	Prepares for M11.D.2.2.1		✔
12-3a	Activity Lab: Exploring Exponents	M8.A.1.1.1	✔	✔
12-3	Exponents and Multiplication	M8.A.1.1.1	✔	✔
12-3b	Activity Lab, Technology: Scientific Notation	M8.A.1.1.1	✔	✔
12-4	Multiplying Polynomials	Prepares for M11.D.2.2.1		✔
12-5	Exponents and Division	M8.A.1.1.1	✔	✔
	• Extension: Power Rules	M8.A.1.1.1	✔	✔
	• Guided Problem Solving: Solving Equations	M8.A.2.2	✔	✔
	Problem Solving Application: Applying Scientific Notation	M8.A.1.1.1	✔	✔
	Pennsylvania Workout, p. PA16	M8.A.2.2.1, M8.C.1.1.2, M8.D.2.1.3, M8.D.2.2.1, M8.D.4.1.1, M8.E.1.1.2, M8.E.3.2.1	✔	✔
	Pennsylvania Benchmark Test 5 in PA PMA, pp. 31–38			

Pennsylvania Assessment Anchors and Eligible Content

The Pennsylvania Department of Education has worked hard to create the Assessment Anchors. The Anchors are designed to help you create and develop the tools you will need to be successful in school, the workplace, and your daily life. The Eligible Content within those Anchors helps you to identify specific skills.

M8.A. Numbers and Operations

There are three anchors in this reporting category (M8.A.1 to M8.A.3). The Eligible Content within them identifies 9 skills for you to master (M8.A.1.1.1 to M8.A.3.3.1).

What It Means To You

As you work to master these skills, you will develop a stronger number sense. For instance, you will learn to use scientific notation to represent very small and very large numbers. You will also continue to add, subtract, multiply, and divide integers and use the order of operations to simplify numeric and algebraic expressions, such as the one to the right. You will also gain the ability to estimate with percents and to determine when estimation is appropriate.

$$5 + 2 \times 3^3$$

M8.B Measurement

There are two anchors in this reporting category (M8.B.1 and M8.B.2). The Eligible Content within them identifies 10 skills for you to master (M8.B.1.1.1 to M8.B.2.3.3).

M8.C Geometry

There are three anchors in this reporting category (M8.C.1 to M8.C.3). The Eligible Content within them identifies five skills for you to master (M8.C.1.1.1 to M8.C.3.1.1).

What It Means To You

These skills are designed to encourage you to think geometrically. For instance, you will learn to represent three-dimensional figures with two-dimensional patterns called nets. You will also learn to identify and work with special pairs of angles formed when two parallel lines are cut by a transversal. In addition, you will learn to use the Pythagorean Theorem to solve problems associated with right triangles. For example, you will be able to find the distance across Mirror Lake, shown in the figure to the right. You will also be able to locate, identify, and plot ordered pairs on a coordinate plane.

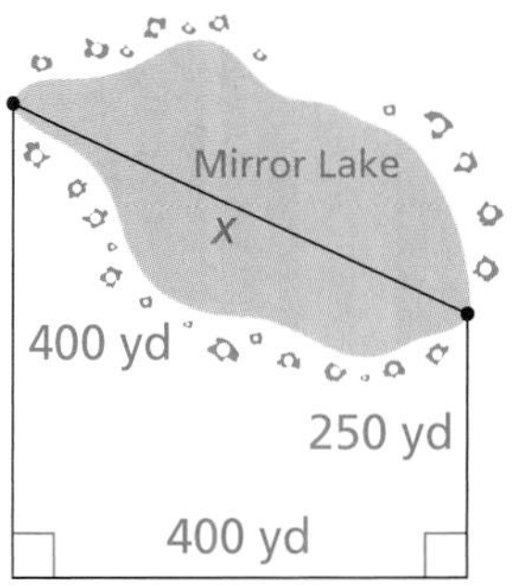

M8.D Algebraic Concepts

There are four anchors in this reporting category (M8.D.1 to M8.D.4). The Eligible Content within them identifies 11 skills for you to master (M8.D.1.1.1 to M8.D.4.1.4).

What It Means To You

As you work to develop these skills, you will begin to think algebraically. For instance, you will learn to represent a function expressed in table-form with a function rule written in equation-form, and you will also use substitution to solve problems and verify solutions. You will continue to solve two-step equations and inequalities, and you will also learn how to solve both multi-step equations and equations with variables on both sides. In addition, you will represent linear functions, such as the one to the right, with tables, equations, and graphs.

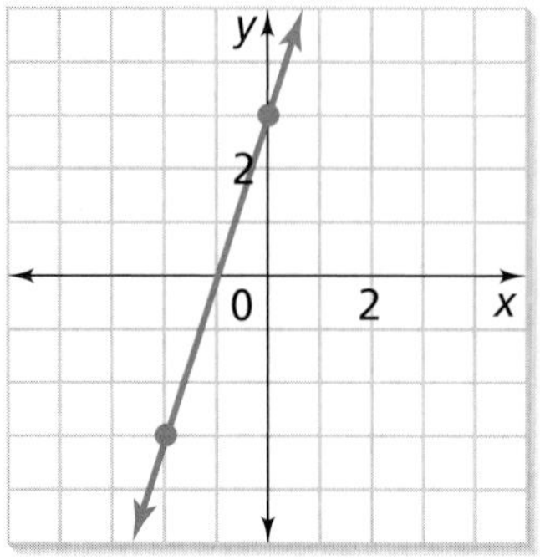

M8.E Data Analysis and Probability

There are four anchors in this reporting category (M8.E.1 to M8.E.4). The Eligible Content within them identifies 7 skills for you to master (M8.E.1.1.1 to M8.E.4.1.2).

What It Means To You

These skills are designed to help you work with data. For instance, you will learn to represent a set of data with the best type of data display. In addition, you will learn the difference between permutations and combinations how to calculate the number of permutations or combinations of a given event. You will also determine the probabilities of independent events, and you will gain the ability to fit a line to a scatter plot, like the one to the right.

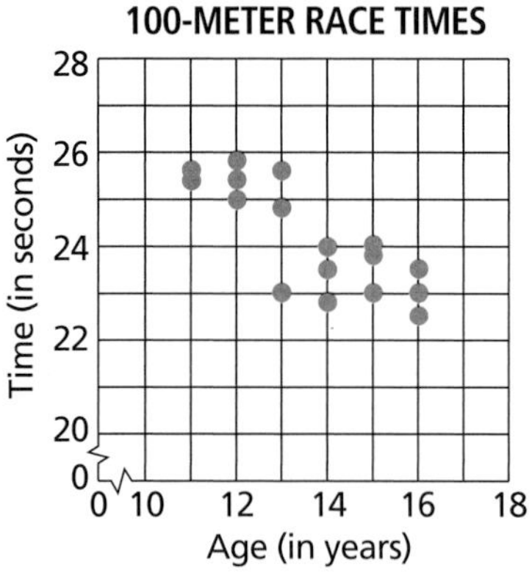

Workout for Pennsylvania Assessment Anchors and Eligible Content Mastery

Ready to go after Chapter 1

For help, go to the lesson in green.

1. What is the value of the expression $6 \bullet (n + 4) - 3$, when $n = 7$? **(Lesson 1-1)**

A 21
B 42
C 48
D 63

2. The state beach charges an entrance fee of \$4 for a vehicle with one person in it, and \$2 for each additional passenger. Which algebraic expression could be used to calculate the entrance cost for a vehicle with n passengers? **(Lesson 1-1)**

A $4 + 2(n - 1)$
B $4 + 2n - 1$
C $4 + 2n$
D $4(2n)$

3. As of 2000, the highest temperature recorded in the United States was 134° F and the lowest was −80° F. What is the difference between these highest and lowest temperatures? **(Lesson 1-3)**

A 254° F
B 214° F
C 154° F
D 54° F

4. During a winter storm, the outside temperature decreases 36 degrees in 3 hours. What is the average change of the temperature in degrees per hour? **(Lesson 1-4)**

A −33° F
B −12° F
C 12° F
D 33° F

5. Which of these expressions is equivalent to $n \bullet 84 - 25 \bullet 84$? **(Lesson 1-5)**

A $84(n - 25)$
B $84 - (n \bullet 25)$
C $(n \bullet 84) - 12$
D $n(84 - 25)$

6. What statement best describes how the following equation can be solved for k? **(Lesson 1-6)**

$k + 14 = -5$

A Add 14 to the left side, and subtract 14 from the right side.
B Subtract 14 from the left side, and add 14 to the right side.
C Add 14 to both sides of the equation.
D Subtract 14 from both sides of the equation.

7. Open-Ended Larry stated that the equation $\frac{t}{-4} = 60$ has a solution of −15.

A. Is Larry's statement correct? Explain the process you used to determine your answer.
B. How should Larry solve the equation? Show your work.
(Lesson 1-7)

PA **Assessment Anchors and Eligible Content**
M8.A.2.1.1, M8.A.3.3.1, M8.D.2.1.1, M8.D.2.1.2, M8.D.2.1.3, M8.D.2.2.1, M8.D.2.2.2

Chapter 1 Workout

Correlation to Pennsylvania Assessment Anchors and Eligible Content

Item	Assessment Anchors and Eligible Content
1	M8.A.2.1.1, M8.D.2.1.3
2	M8.D.2.2.1
3	M8.A.3.3.1
4	M8.A.2.1.1, M8.A.3.3.1
5	M8.D.2.1.3
6	M8.D.2.1.1
7	M8.D.2.1.1, M8.D.2.1.2, M8.D.2.1.3

Answers

1. D
2. A
3. B
4. B
5. A
6. D
7. A. No. Answers may vary. Sample answer: Check Larry's solution in the original equation $\frac{t}{-4} = 60$.

$\frac{-15}{-4} \stackrel{?}{=} 60$

$3.75 \neq 60$

B. $\frac{t}{-4} = 60$

$\frac{t}{-4} \times -4 = 60 \times -4$

$t = -240$

The correct solution is −240.

Prescribing Intervention

Item	Intervention	Item	Intervention
1	Lesson 1-1, Example 3	5	Lesson 1-5, Example 4
2	Lesson 1-1, Example 1	6	Lesson 1-6, Example 1
3	Lesson 1-3, Example 3	7	Lesson 1-7, Example 1
4	Lesson 1-4, Example 2		

Chapter 2 Workout

Correlation to Pennsylvania Assessment Anchors and Eligible Content

Item	Assessment Anchors and Eligible Content
1	M8.A.3.3.1
2	M8.A.3.3.1
3	M8.A.1.1.1, M8.A.1.1.2, M8.A.2.1.1
4	M8.A.1.1.1
5	M8.A.1.1.1
6	M8.A.1.1.1, M8.A.1.1.2, M8.A.2.1.1
7	M8.A.2.2.2

Answers

1. A
2. C
3. B
4. B
5. D
6. Yes. Answers may vary. Sample answer: The expression 3^4 is equal to $3 \bullet 3 \bullet 3 \bullet 3 = 81$. The expression $(-3)^4$ is equal to $(-3) \bullet (-3) \bullet (-3) \bullet (-3) = 9 \bullet 9 = 81$.
7. A. 60 miles per hour

$$d = rt$$
$$280 = r \bullet 4\frac{2}{3}$$
$$60 = r$$

B. $d = rt$, where d is the distance traveled, r is the rate of travel, and t is the time spent traveling. Substitute 280 for d and $4\frac{2}{3}$ for r. Divide both sides of the equation by $4\frac{2}{3}$.

Workout for Pennsylvania Assessment Anchors and Eligible Content Mastery

Ready to go after Chapter 2

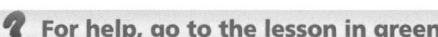

For help, go to the lesson in green.

1. The average yearly snowfall in Ashwood is $15\frac{7}{10}$ inches and $27\frac{3}{5}$ inches in Newton. On average, how many more inches of snow does Newton receive each year than Ashwood?
(Lesson 2-4)
A $11\frac{9}{10}$
B $11\frac{1}{10}$
C $12\frac{1}{10}$
D $12\frac{1}{5}$

2. A recipe for carrot bread calls for $1\frac{3}{4}$ cups of grated carrots. If Pilar only makes half as much, how many cups of carrots does she grate?
(Lesson 2-5)
A less than $\frac{1}{2}$ cup
B between $\frac{1}{2}$ cup and $\frac{3}{4}$ cup
C between $\frac{3}{4}$ cup and 1 cup
D more than 1 cup

3. What is the value of the expression $5 + 2 \bullet 3^3$?
(Lesson 2-7)
A 34
B 59
C 189
D 221

4. There are about 10,550 radio stations in the United States. Which of the following shows this number written in scientific notation?
(Lesson 2-8)
A 10.55×10^4
B 1.055×10^4
C 10.55×10^3
D 1.055×10^3

5. The table below shows the population of four counties.

COUNTY POPULATIONS

County	Population
Morris	1.54×10^6
Jones	2.9×10^5
Orange	1.34×10^6
Sterling	2.0×10^5

Which of these counties had the least population?
(Lesson 2-8)
A Morris
B Jones
C Orange
D Sterling

6. Short Open-Ended Is the expression $(-3)^4$ equivalent to the expression 3^4? Explain the process you used to determine your answer.
(Lesson 2-7)

7. Open-Ended Alan drove from Oxford to Morristown, a distance of about 280 miles. The drive took $4\frac{2}{3}$ hours.
A. What is Alan's average speed in miles per hour?
B. What formula was used? Explain all your work.
(Lesson 2-6)

PA **Assessment Anchors and Eligible Content**
M8.A.1.1.1, M8.A.1.1.2, M8.A.2.1.1, M8.A.2.2.2, M8A.3.3.1

Prescribing Intervention

Item	Intervention	Item	Intervention
1	Lesson 2-4, Example 3	5	Lesson 2-8, Example 1
2	Lesson 2-5, Example 1	6	Lesson 2-7, Example 2
3	Lesson 2-7, Example 2	7	Lesson 2-6, Example 2
4	Lesson 2-8, Example 2		

Workout for Pennsylvania Assessment Anchors and Eligible Content Mastery

Ready to go after Chapter 3

For help, go to the lesson in green.

1. What is the value of the expression $\sqrt{16}$? **(Lesson 3-1)**

A 4
B 8
C −8
D −16

2. Gwen lives 1.5 miles east of the library and 2 miles north of Karl's house. What is the distance from Karl's house to the library? **(Lesson 3-2)**

A 0.5 mile
B 1.8 miles
C 2.5 miles
D 3.1 miles

3. The cost of renting a van for one day can be determined by using the equation $c = 0.5m + 20$, where c is the cost in dollars and m is the number of miles driven. What is the cost of renting a van for one day if the van is driven 64 miles? **(Lesson 3-5)**

Number of miles, m	8	32	64	128
Cost of renting, c	24	36	?	84

A \$22
B \$42
C \$52
D \$88

4. An artist begins designing a logo by using a computer illustration program to draw $\angle JKL$. What are the coordinates of point J? **(Lesson 3-4)**

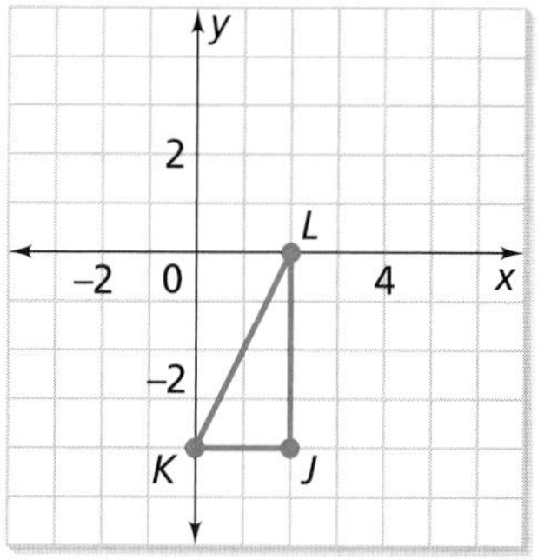

A (4, −2)
B (2, −4)
C (−2, 4)
D (−4, 2)

5. Open-Ended Marian wants to know the distance across Mirror Lake.

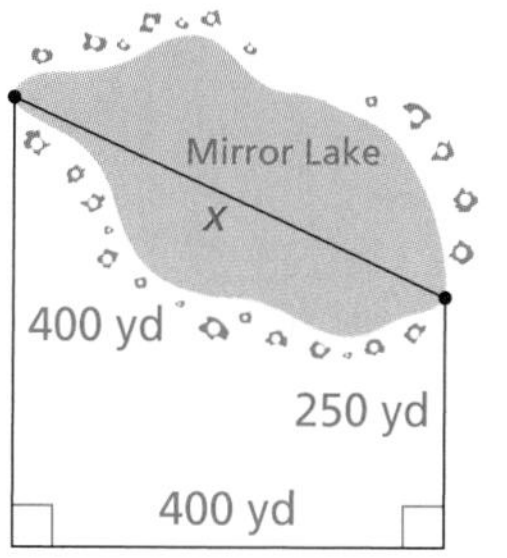

A. Write an equation that can be used to find the distance x. Explain all your work.
B. Solve your equation to find the distance across Mirror Lake to the nearest yard. Show all your work.
(Lesson 3-3)

PA Assessment Anchors and Eligible Content
M8.A.1.1.2, M8.C.1.2.1, M8.C.3.1.1, M8.D.1.1.2, M8.D1.1.3, M8.D.4.1.1

Prescribing Intervention

Item	Intervention	Item	Intervention
1	Lesson 3-1, Example 1	4	Lesson 3-4, Example 2
2	Lesson 3-2, Example 1	5	Lesson 3-3, Example 1
3	Lesson 3-5, Example 1		

Chapter 3 Workout

Correlation to Pennsylvania Assessment Anchors and Eligible Content

Item	Assessment Anchors and Eligible Content
1	M8.A.1.1.2
2	M8.C.1.2.1
3	M8.D.1.1.2, M8.D.1.1.3
4	M8.C.3.1.1
5	M8.C.1.2.1

Answers

1. A
2. C
3. C
4. B
5. A. $400^2 + (400 - 250)^2 = x^2$ or equivalent equation. Answers may vary. Sample answer: Divide the figure in the drawing into a right triangle and a rectangle. The length of the longer leg of the right triangle is 400 yards, and the length of the shorter leg is equal to (400 − 250) yards. Use the Pythagorean Theorem to find x, the length of the hypotenuse.
$a^2 + b^2 = c^2$
$400^2 + (400 - 250)^2 = x^2$

   B. 427 yards

Chapter 4 Workout

Correlation to Pennsylvania Assessment Anchors and Eligible Content

Item	Assessment Anchors and Eligible Content
1	M8.A.2.2.2
2	M8.B.1.1.2
3	M8.B.1.1.1, M8.B.1.1.2
4	M8.A.2.2.2
5	M8.A.2.2.2
6	M8.B.1.1.1, M8.B.1.1.2

Answers

1. C
2. D
3. B
4. A
5. B
6. A. 18 logs;

   $225 \times 12 = 2{,}700;$

   $\frac{2{,}700}{150} = 18$

   B. 144 logs;

   $225 \times 2 = 450;$

   $450 \times 12 = \frac{5{,}400}{150} = 36;$

   $36 \times 4 = 144$

Workout for Pennsylvania Assessment Anchors and Eligible Content Mastery

Ready to go after Chapter 4

For help, go to the lesson in green.

1. The table shows the weight and cost of four brands of strawberry jam. Which brand of jam represents the best buy?
(Lesson 4-1)

Brand	Weight (ounces)	Cost
A	8	$1.60
B	10	$1.75
C	14	$1.90
D	19	$3.00

A Brand A
B Brand B
C Brand C
D Brand D

2. A cheetah can run as fast as 93 feet per second. If one miles represents 5,280 feet, which best represents this speed in miles per hour?
(Lesson 4-2)

A 31 mi/h
B 52.8 mi/h
C 55.8 mi/h
D 63.4 mi/h

3. A faucet has a flow rate of 6 liters of water per minute. How many seconds will it take to fill a 2-liter pitcher from the faucet?
(Lesson 4-2)

A 10 seconds
B 20 seconds
C 30 seconds
D 40 seconds

4. A dozen daffodils cost $9.99. At this rate, how much would a bouquet of 20 daffodils cost?
(Lesson 4-3)

A $16.65
B $18.32
C $19.98
D $24.02

5. If 50 pennies has a mass of 0.125 kilogram, what is the mass of 1,000,000 pennies?
(Lesson 4-3)

A 2,000 kilograms
B 2,500 kilograms
C 4,000 kilograms
D 6,250 kilograms

6. Open-Ended Park rangers are building a log path across a wetland. The logs measure 150 inches in length. The diameters of the logs measure about 12 inches.

A. How many logs placed end-to-end will they need to span a distance of 225 feet? Show your work.
B. If the length of the path is doubled and the width is 4 feet, how many logs will they need? Show your work.
(Lesson 4-2)

PA Assessment Anchors and Eligible Content
M8.A.2.2.2, M8.B.1.1.1, M8.B.1.1.2

PA8 Pennsylvania Student Handbook

Prescribing Intervention

Item	Intervention	Item	Intervention
1	Lesson 4-1, Example 3	4	Lesson 4-3, Example 2
2	Lesson 4-2, Example 1	5	Lesson 4-3, Example 2
3	Lesson 4-2, Example 2	6	Lesson 4-2, Example 3

Workout for Pennsylvania Assessment Anchors and Eligible Content Mastery

Ready to go after Chapter 5

For help, go to the lesson in green.

1. About 36% of 164 contestants in a talent competition made it to the second round. Which is closest to the number of contestants who made it to the second round?
   (Lesson 5-2)
   A 75
   B 60
   C 45
   D 30

2. The number of people at this year's spring festival was 115% of the number who attended last year. If 320 people were at the festival last year, how many people attended this year?
   (Lesson 5-3)
   A 278
   B 335
   C 359
   D 368

3. A nutrition label says that 20% of the calories in a granola bar come from fat. If the granola bar has 25 calories from fat, what is the bar's total number of calories?
   (Lesson 5-4)
   A 50 calories
   B 80 calories
   C 125 calories
   D 150 calories

4. A store pays $35.00 for watches. The store marks up the price by 116%. What is the selling price of the watches?
   (Lesson 5-6)
   A $40.60
   B $56.00
   C $75.60
   D $91.00

5. Jalan deposits $150.00 into an account that earns 3% simple interest. What will be the balance of the account after 4 years?
   (Lesson 5-7)
   A $168.00
   B $162.00
   C $154.50
   D $151.20

6. Open-Ended Twelve percent of the band members play the trumpet. There are six trumpet players.
   A. Write a proportion to represent how many members, n, are in the band.
   B. What is the total number of band members? Show all your work.
   (Lesson 5-3)

PA Assessment Anchors and Eligible Content
M8.A.2.2.1, M8.A.2.2.2, M8.A.3.2.1

Prescribing Intervention

Item	Intervention	Item	Intervention
1	Lesson 5-2, Example 1	4	Lesson 5-6, Example 2
2	Lesson 5-3, Example 2	5	Lesson 5-7, Example 2
3	Lesson 5-4, Example 2	6	Lesson 5-3, Example 3

Chapter 5 Workout

Correlation to Pennsylvania Assessment Anchors and Eligible Content

Item	Assessment Anchors and Eligible Content
1	M8.A.2.2.1, M8.A.3.2.1
2	M8.A.2.2.1
3	M8.A.2.2.1
4	M8.A.2.2.1
5	M8.A.2.2.2
6	M8.A.2.2.1

Answers

1. B
2. D
3. C
4. C
5. A
6. A. $\frac{6}{n} = \frac{12}{100}$
   B. 50 band members;
   $\frac{6}{n} = \frac{12}{100}$
   $6 \times 100 = 12n$
   $\frac{600}{12} = \frac{12n}{12}$
   $50 = n$

Pennsylvania Workouts

Chapter 6 Workout

Correlation to Pennsylvania Assessment Anchors and Eligible Content

Item	Assessment Anchors and Eligible Content
1	M8.D.2.1.1, M8.D.2.2.1, M8.D.2.2.2
2	M8.D.2.1.1, M8.D.2.2.1, M8.D.2.2.2
3	M8.D.2.1.3
4	M8.D.2.2.1, M8.D.2.2.2
5	M8.D.2.2.1, M8.D.2.2.2
6	M8.D.2.1.1, M8.D.2.2.1
7	M8.D.2.1.1, M8.D.2.2.1
8	M8.D.2.1.1, M8.D.2.2.1, M8.D.2.2.2

Answers

1. A
2. C
3. B
4. D
5. B
6. A
7. C
8. A. $0.08n + 6 = 10$
$0.08n + 6 - 6 = 10 - 6$
$0.08n = 4$
$n = 50$ fliers

B. 75 more or 125 fliers total.
Sample answer:
$\$10 \div 0.08 = 125.$
$125 - 50 = 75.$

Workout for Pennsylvania Assessment Anchors and Eligible Content Mastery

Ready to go after Chapter 6

For help, go to the lesson in green.

1. A well-drilling company charges \$22 per foot of depth and \$500 for a well pump. The cost for a well, c, can be represented by the equation $c = 22d + 500$, where d is the depth of the well in feet. What is the depth of a well that costs \$7,650?
(Lesson 6-1)

A 325 feet **C** 575 feet
B 370 feet **D** 847 feet

2. Mrs. Hansen bought 6 cans of frozen lemonade. She used a coupon for \$0.70 off her total purchase and paid a total of \$7.40. What is the regular price of each can of lemonade?
(Lesson 6-1)

A \$1.12 **C** \$1.35
B \$1.23 **D** \$1.93

3. Which of these expressions is equivalent to $3(b - 4) + 2b$?
(Lesson 6-2)

A $5b - 4$ **C** $6b - 4$
B $5b - 12$ **D** $6b - 12$

4. A taxi ride costs \$3.50 for the first mile and \$1.50 for each additional mile. The equation $3.50 + 1.50(m - 1) = f$ can be used to determine the fare, f, for a taxi ride of m miles. If Natalya's fare for a taxi ride to the airport is \$14.00, how many miles was her trip?
(Lessons 6-3, 6-4)

A 14 miles **C** 10.5 miles
B 12 miles **D** 8 miles

5. What is the value of x that makes the equation $2x + 16 = -4x + 4$ true?
(Lesson 6-4)

A -20 **C** 2
B -2 **D** 20

6. At least 26 students must sign up for a painting class or it will be canceled. Eleven students have signed up. Which inequality best represents n, the number of additional students who must sign up to prevent the cancellation of the class?
(Lesson 6-5)

A $n \geq 15$ **C** $n \geq 37$
B $n \leq 15$ **D** $n \leq 37$

7. What is the solution of the inequality $-3b \geq 54$?
(Lesson 6-6)

A $b \leq -162$ **C** $b \leq -18$
B $b \geq -162$ **D** $b \geq -18$

8. Open-Ended To promote the school play, the drama club made one copy of a poster and multiple copies of a flyer. It costs \$6.00 to copy a poster and \$0.08 to copy a flyer. The clubs spent a total of \$10.00 on the poster and flyers.

A. Write an equation to find n, the number of flyers the club made. Solve the equation and show all your work.

B. How many more copies of the flyer could the club afford if they had chosen **not** to have the poster copied? Show all your work.
(Lessons 6-1, 6-3)

PA **Assessment Anchors and Eligible Content**
M8.D.2.1.1, M8.D.2.1.2, M8.D.2.1.3, M8.D.2.2.1, M8.D.2.2.2

Prescribing Intervention

Item	Intervention	Item	Intervention
1	Lesson 6-1, Example 1	5	Lesson 6-4, Example 1
2	Lesson 6-1, Example 2	6	Lesson 6-5, Example 2
3	Lesson 6-2, Example 3	7	Lesson 6-6, Example 3
4	Lesson 6-3, Example 2, Lesson 6-4, Example 2	8	Lesson 6-1, Example 2, Lesson 6-3, Example 1

Workout for Pennsylvania Assessment Anchors and Eligible Content Mastery

Ready to go after Chapter 7

For help, go to the lesson in green.

1. Use your protractor. What is the measure of the complement of $\angle RST$?
(Lesson 7-1)

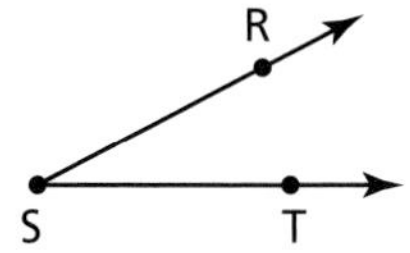

A 57°
B 63°
C 147°
D 153°

2. In the figure below, $\angle 1$ measures 38° and $\angle 2$ measures 61°. What is the measure of $\angle 3$?
(Lesson 7-1)

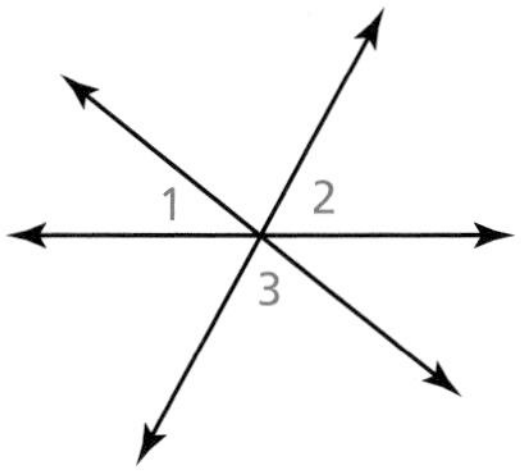

A 52°
B 61°
C 81°
D 99°

3. Angle *JKL* is an acute angle. Which must be true about the supplement of $\angle JKL$?
(Lesson 7-1)

A It is an obtuse angle.
B It is a right angle.
C It is congruent to $\angle JKL$.
D It measures less than $\angle JKL$.

4. The outdoor stage in a town park is in the shape of a regular octagon as shown. What is the value of *x*?
(Lesson 7-5)

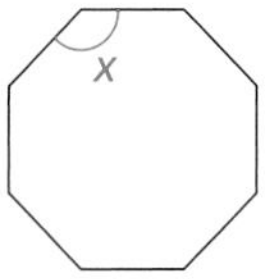

A 113°
B 135°
C 156°
D 203°

5. Open-Ended A train track runs parallel to a road. A second road intersects both of them, as shown.

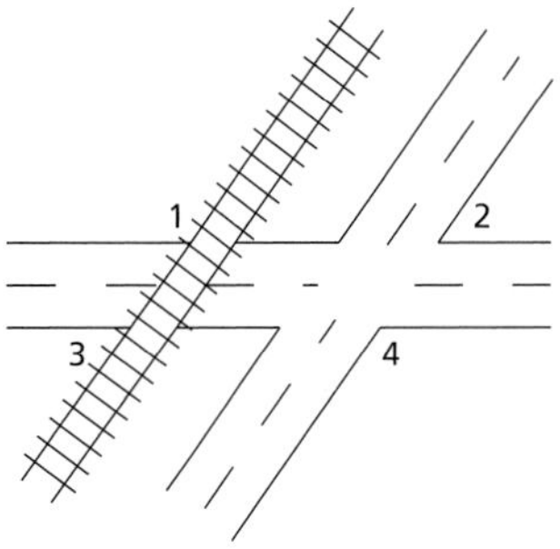

A. Which of the numbered angles are congruent? How do you know?
B. If the measure of $\angle 2$ is 54°, what is the measure of $\angle 1$? Explain all your work.
(Lesson 7-2)

Assessment Anchors and Eligible Content
M8.B.2.1.2, M8.C.1.1.2, M8.C.1.1.3

Prescribing Intervention

Item	Intervention	Item	Intervention
1	Lesson 7-1, Example 3	4	Lesson 7-5, Example 3
2	Lesson 7-1, Example 3	5	Lesson 7-2, Example 3
3	Lesson 7-1, Example 2		

Chapter 7 Workout

Correlation to Pennsylvania Assessment Anchors and Eligible Content

Item	Assessment Anchors and Eligible Content
1	M8.C.1.1.2
2	M8.C.1.1.2
3	M8.C.1.1.2
4	M8.B.2.1.2
5	M8.C.1.1.3

Answers

1. B
2. C
3. A
4. B
5. A. $\angle 2 \cong \angle 3$; $\angle 1 \cong \angle 4$; Answers may vary. Sample answer: Corresponding angles are congruent, and vertical angles are congruent.

   B. 126°; Answers may vary. Sample answer: Because corresponding angles are congruent, $\angle 1$ is congruent to the supplement to $\angle 2$. Therefore, $\angle 1$ and $\angle 2$ are supplementary and the sum of their measures is 180°.
   $m\angle 1 + m\angle 2 = 180°$
   $m\angle 1 + 54° = 180°$
   $m\angle 1 = 126°$

Chapter 8 Workout

Correlation to Pennsylvania Assessment Anchors and Eligible Content

Item	Assessment Anchors and Eligible Content
1	M8.C.1.1.1
2	M8.C.1.1.1
3	M8.B.2.3.1
4	M8.B.2.3.2
5	M8.B.2.3.2

Answers

1. D
2. A
3. A
4. B
5. A. 2,560 cubic feet; $40 \times 8 \times 8 = 2{,}560$

   B. $2{,}560 \times 0.45 = 1{,}152$; If the container is 45% full, it will hold 1,152 cubic feet of liquid.

Workout for Pennsylvania Assessment Anchors and Eligible Content Mastery

Ready to go after Chapter 8

For help, go to the lesson in green.

1. Which of these solid figures can be formed from the net shown?
   (Lesson 8-3)

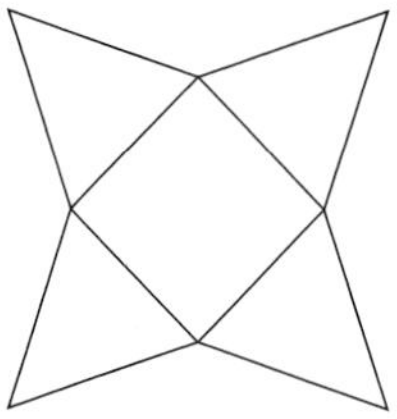

   A triangular prism
   B rectangular prism
   C triangular pyramid
   D rectangular pyramid

2. A sporting-goods company ships baseball bats in boxes shaped like pentagonal prisms. What shapes make up the net of one of the boxes?
   (Lesson 8-3)
   A 2 pentagons and 5 rectangles
   B 2 pentagons and 2 rectangles
   C 1 pentagon and 5 triangles
   D 1 pentagon and 4 triangles

3. A furniture designer is making cedar trunks shaped like a rectangular prism. Each trunk measures 32 inches in length, 24 inches in width, and 16 inches in depth. Which is the total surface area of each trunk?
   (Lesson 8-4)
   A 3,328 square inches
   B 6,656 square inches
   C 8,960 square inches
   D 12,288 square inches

4. A pool shaped like a rectangular prism measures 50 meters in length, 25 meters in width, and 2.5 meters in depth. To the nearest cubic meter, what volume of water does the pool hold when it is 95% full?
   (Lesson 8-6)
   A 2,679 cubic meters
   B 2,969 cubic meters
   C 3,125 cubic meters
   D 5,938 cubic meters

5. Open-Ended A cargo container shaped like a rectangular prism measures 40 feet in length, 8 feet in width, and 8 feet in depth.
   A. To the nearest cubic foot, what is the greatest amount of liquid the container can hold? Express your answer in cubic feet. Show all your work.
   B. To the nearest cubic foot, how much liquid does the container hold when it is 45% full? Show your work.
   (Lesson 8-6)

Assessment Anchors and Eligible Content
M8.B.2.3.1, M8.B.2.3.2, M8.C.1.1.1

PA12 Pennsylvania Student Handbook

Prescribing Intervention

Item	Intervention	Item	Intervention
1	Lesson 8-3, Example 2	4	Lesson 8-6, Example 1
2	Lesson 8-3, Example 1	5	Lesson 8-6, Example 1
3	Lesson 8-4, Example 1		

Workout for Pennsylvania Assessment Anchors and Eligible Content Mastery

Ready to go after Chapter 9

For help, go to the lesson in green.

1. The number of children in each of 18 families is shown in the line plot. What is the median number of children among these families?
(Lesson 9-2)

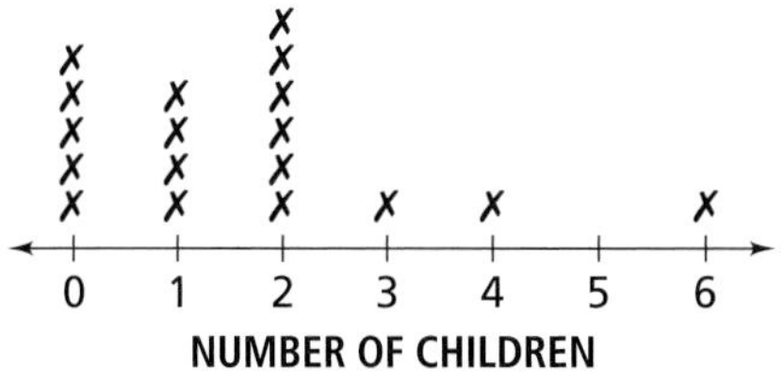

A 2.5	**C** 1.7
B 2.0	**D** 1.5

2. The graph shows ticket sales earned by the movies of a film studio last year. Which statement about the ticket sales is true?
(Lesson 9-4)

A *Waterfalls* earned 5 times as much as *Volcanoes*.

B *Abe* earned 10% more than *Volcanoes*.

C *Dino* earned $100,000 more than Exit.

D *Exit* earned $\frac{4}{5}$ of the amount earned by *Dino*.

3. The box-and-whisker plot shows the number of students enrolled at a community college between 1993 and 2003. Which is the best estimate of the range of the data in the plot?
(Lesson 9-6)

AVERAGE YEARLY ENROLLMENT 1993–2003

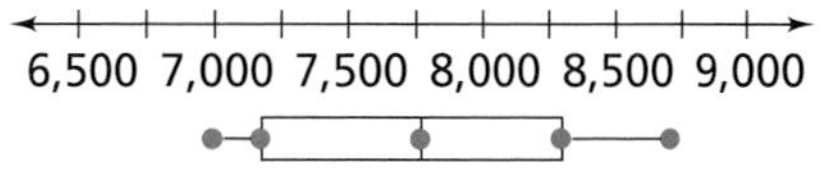

A 750 students	**C** 1,750 students
B 1,000 students	**D** 2,500 students

4. Which type of display would be most appropriate for the data in the table?
(Lesson 9-9)

U.S. CELLULAR TELEPHONE SUBSCRIBERS

Year	Millions of Subscribers
1990	5.3
1995	33.8
1999	86.0
2000	109.5
2001	128.4

A line graph	**C** line plot
B circle graph	**D** stem-and-leaf plot

5. Open-Ended The list shows the daily high temperatures in Central Park during the first two weeks of July 2003.

84° F 84° F 72° F 92° F 94° F 89° F 89° F

88° F 83° F 69° F 82° F 83° F 81° F 76° F

A. Make a stem-and-leaf plot for the data above.

B. Find the median and mode of the data from the stem-and-leaf plot.
(Lesson 9-5)

PA Assessment Anchors and Eligible Content M8.E.1.1.1, M8.E.1.1.2, M8.E.1.1.3

Chapter 9 Workout

Correlation to Pennsylvania Assessment Anchors and Eligible Content

Item	Assessment Anchors and Eligible Content
1	M8.E.1.1.2
2	M8.E.1.1.1
3	M8.E.1.1.3
4	M8.E.1.1.1
5	M8.E.1.1.3

Answers

1. D
2. B
3. C
4. A
5. A. Daily High Temperatures

6	9
7	2 6
8	1 2 3 3 4 4 8 9 9
9	2 4

Key: 6 | 9 means 69°

B. median: 83;
modes: 83, 84, 89

Pennsylvania Workouts

Prescribing Intervention

Item	Intervention	Item	Intervention
1	Lesson 9-2, Example 1	4	Lesson 9-9, Examples 1, 2
2	Lesson 9-4, Example 1	5	Lesson 9-5, Examples 1, 2
3	Lesson 9-6, Example 2		

Chapter 10 Workout

Correlation to Pennsylvania Assessment Anchors and Eligible Content

Item	Assessment Anchors and Eligible Content
1	M8.E.3.1.1
2	M8.E.4.1.2
3	M8.E.3.1.1
4	M8.E.3.2.1
5	M8.E.3.2.1
6	M8.E.3.2.1
7	M8.E.3.1.1

Answers

1. D
2. C
3. A
4. D
5. C
6. A
7. A. The number of winning caps should be 75 out of 600 bottles.

$\frac{\textit{number of winning caps}}{600} = \frac{1}{8}$

$\textit{number of winning caps} = 75$

B. Fifteen fewer bottles had winning caps than would be expected based on the theoretical probability.

Workout for Pennsylvania Assessment Anchors and Eligible Content Mastery

Ready to go after Chapter 10

For help, go to the lesson in green.

1. A spinner is divided into three equal sections numbered 1 to 3. Latrisha spins the pointer 50 times. Table shows the results. What is the experimental probability that Latrisha will spin a 2 on her next spin? **(Lesson 10-1)**

Outcome	1	2	3
Frequency	13	18	19

A $\frac{1}{3}$ C $\frac{9}{16}$
B $\frac{1}{9}$ D $\frac{9}{25}$

2. DJ Snap is shipping her promotional CDs. Based on a survey of customers that she took, the probability of a CD being defective is $\frac{1}{25}$. In a shipment of 140 CDs, how many are likely to be defective? **(Lesson 10-2)**

A 2 C 5
B 3 D 14

3. Kenji rolls a number cube twice. What is the probability that he rolls an even number on the second roll? **(Lesson 10-4)**

A $\frac{1}{3}$ C $\frac{1}{4}$
B $\frac{1}{4}$ D $\frac{1}{6}$

4. A television producer must decide the order in which four advertisements will be shown during the commercial break. In how many different orders can the four advertisements be shown? **(Lesson 10-5)**

A 8 C 16
B 10 D 24

5. A contestant on a game show must play 3 out of the 6 games the show offers. How many different combinations of three games can the contestant choose? **(Lesson 10-6)**

A 27
B 24
C 20
D 18

6. The students in Ms. Franklin's class completed 10 projects. Two projects will be entered in a science fair. How many different combinations of two projects are possible? **(Lesson 10-6)**

A 45
B 50
C 90
D 100

7. Open-Ended A juice company is having a prize giveaway. Some of their bottle caps are marked as winners. The company states that the theoretical probability of getting a bottle with a winning cap is $\frac{1}{8}$. A grocery store sells 600 bottles, but only 60 of them turn out to be winning caps.

A. Based on the company's statement, how many bottles at the grocery should have winning caps? Show your work.
B. How many fewer bottles have winning caps than would be expected based on the theoretical probability? **(Lesson 10-1)**

PA Assessment Anchors and Eligible Content M8.E.3.2.1, M8.E.3.1.1, M8.E.4.1.2

Prescribing Intervention

Item	Intervention	Item	Intervention
1	Lesson 10-1, Example 1	5	Lesson 10-6, Example 1
2	Lesson 10-2, Example 2	6	Lesson 10-6, Example 1
3	Lesson 10-4, Example 3	7	Lesson 10-1, Example 2
4	Lesson 10-5, Example 1		

Workout for Pennsylvania Assessment Anchors and Eligible Content Mastery

Ready to go after Chapter 11

For help, go to the lesson in green.

1. What is the next number in the sequence? **(Lesson 11-1)**

−1	2	−4	8

A −16
B −12
C 12
D 16

2. Which rule describes the following sequence? **(Lesson 11-1)**

1.6	3.2	4.8	6.4	8.0

A Start with 1.6 and add 2.4 repeatedly.
B Start with 1.6 and add 1.6 repeatedly.
C Start with 1.6 and multiply by 2 repeatedly.
D Start with 1.6 and multiply by 1.6 repeatedly.

3. The function rule $b = 500 + 2m$ represents the number of bonus points, b, a passenger earns for flying m miles. How many bonus points are earned for flying 1,500 miles? **(Lesson 11-3)**

A 500
B 3,000
C 3,500
D 7,500

4. The table shows how the number of points, p, a player receives for completing each level of a video game depends on n, the number of levels completed. Which describes the relationship in the table? **(Lesson 11-6)**

n	1	2	3	4
p	250	550	850	1,150

A $p = 200n + 50$
B $p = 300n - 50$
C $p = 250n$
D $p = 350n - 100$

5. Which function is graphed below? **(Lesson 11-6)**

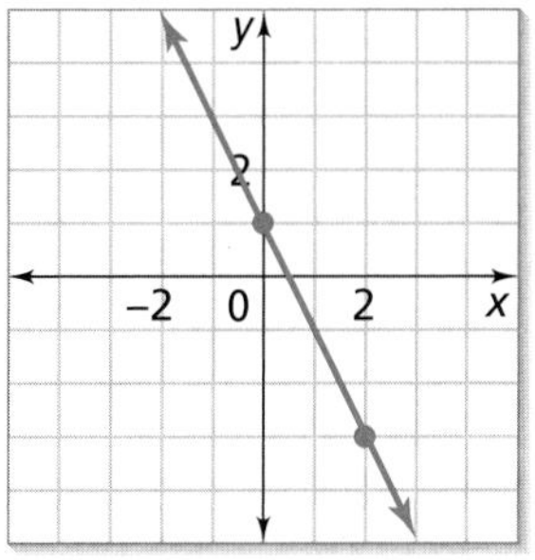

A $y = 2x + 1$
B $y = x - 2$
C $y = \frac{1}{2}x - 1$
D $y = -2x + 1$

6. Open-Ended Use the function rule $y = \frac{1}{2}x - 2$.

x	−2	0	2	4
y				

A. Complete the table. Explain how to use a table to graph a function.
B. Graph the function on a coordinate plane.
(Lesson 11-5)

PA Assessment Anchors and Eligible Content
M8.D.1.1.1, M8.D.1.1.2, M8.D.2.2.1, M8.D.4.1.1

Chapter 11 Workout

Correlation to Pennsylvania Assessment Anchors and Eligible Content

Item	Assessment Anchors and Eligible Content
1	M8.D.1.1.1
2	M8.D.1.1.1, M8.D.1.1.2
3	M8.D.1.1.2
4	M8.D.2.2.1
5	M8.D.1.1.1, M8.D.1.1.2
6	M8.D.4.1.1

Answers

1. A
2. B
3. C
4. B
5. D
6. A. The table should have y values, from left to right, of −3, −2, −1, and 0. Plot the ordered pairs in the coordinate plane. From the origin, move left or right based on the x-coordinate of each ordered pair. Then, move up or down based on the y-coordinate of each ordered pair..

   B. Check students' graphs. Students should graph the points determined by the ordered pairs in the table and connect them with a line.

Pennsylvania Workouts

Prescribing Intervention

Item	Intervention	Item	Intervention
1	Lesson 11-1, Example 1	4	Lesson 11-6, Example 2
2	Lesson 11-1, Example 1	5	Lesson 11-6, Example 3
3	Lesson 11-3, Example 2	6	Lesson 11-5, Example 2

Chapter 12 Workout

Correlation to Pennsylvania Assessment Anchors and Eligible Content

Item	Assessment Anchors and Eligible Content
1	M8.D.2.2.1
2	M8.A.2.2.1
3	M8.D.2.1.3, M8.D.2.2.1
4	M8.C.1.1.2
5	M8.E.1.1.2
6	M8.E.3.2.1
7	M8.D.4.1.1

Answers

1. A
2. B
3. B
4. B
5. C
6. C
7. A. Students' graphs should include a title, labels for the axes, and appropriate scales. Check that the line of the graph passes through the points (0, 15) and (1, 27).

   B. \$51.00; Answers may vary. Find y when $x = 3$.

   $y = 12x + 15$

   $y = 12(3) + 15$

   $y = 51$

Workout for Pennsylvania Assessment Anchors and Eligible Content Mastery

Ready to go after Chapter 12

For help, go to the lesson in green.

1. Which of these ordered pairs is a solution of the equation $y = 4x - 6$? **(Lesson 3-5)**

A $(-3, -18)$
B $(-1, -2)$
C $(2, 0)$
D $(6, 30)$

2. Andy is buying a shirt that costs \$15.00 and a pair of pants for \$24.50. The sales tax rate is 6%. What is the total cost of the two items, including sales tax? **(Lesson 5-4)**

A \$37.13
B \$41.87
C \$55.97
D \$63.20

3. Jan bought 2 rolls of tape and 2 pens. Wally bought 1 roll of tape and 3 pens. The total cost of their purchases is represented by $(2t + 2p) + (t + 3p)$: t represents the cost in dollars of a roll of tape and p represents the cost in dollars of a pen. If $t = 1.19$ and $p = 0.95$, what is the total cost of Jan's and Wally's items? **(Lesson 6-2)**

A \$8.80
B \$8.32
C \$8.08
D \$7.37

4. If ∠1 and ∠2 are vertical angles, which statement must be true? **(Lesson 7-1)**

A They share a side.
B They share a vertex.
C The sum of their measures is 90°.
D The sum of their measures is 180°.

5. The circle graph shows the results from a survey of 180 students about their favorite places to swim. How many of the students surveyed chose either rivers or lakes as their favorite place to swim? **(Lesson 9-8)**

FAVORITE PLACES TO SWIM

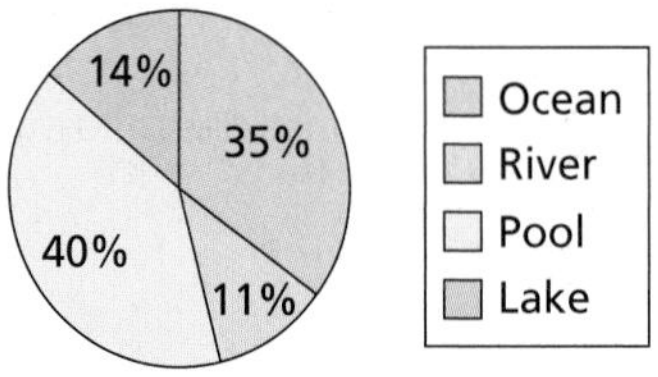

A 25 **C** 45
B 36 **D** 72

6. A restaurant's lasagna dinner comes with a choice of two appetizers, four side dishes, and two types of bread. How many different lasagna dinners can a customer choose from if they pick one appetizer, one side dish, and one type of bread? **(Lesson 10-5)**

A 8
B 9
C 16
D 32

7. **Open-Ended** The cost of renting a horse for trail riding can be represented by the function $y = 12x + 15$, where x is the number of hours the horse is rented.

A. Make a graph of the function. Be sure to title your graph and label the axes.
B. How much does it cost to rent a horse for three hours? Show all your work. **(Lesson 11-5)**

PA **Assessment Anchors and Eligible Content**
M8.A.2.2.1, M8.C.1.1.2, M8.D.2.1.3, M8.D.2.2.1, M8.D.4.1.1, M8.E.1.1.2, M8.E.3.2.1

Prescribing Intervention

Item	Intervention	Item	Intervention
1	Lesson 3-5, Example 1	5	Lesson 9-8, Example 1
2	Lesson 5-4, Example 1	6	Lesson 10-5, Example 1
3	Lesson 6-2, Example 2	7	Lesson 11-5, Example 1
4	Lesson 7-1, Example 1		

Randall I. Charles
Mark Illingworth
Bonnie McNemar
Darwin Mills
Alma Ramirez
Andy Reeves

PEARSON
Prentice Hall

Boston, Massachusetts
Upper Saddle River, New Jersey

Acknowledgments appear on pp. T709–T711, which constitute an extension of this copyright page.

PEARSON
Prentice Hall

ISBN 0-13-134002-6
1 2 3 4 5 6 7 8 9 10 10 09 08 07 06

Prentice Hall Math Course 3 Teacher's Edition Contents

Mathematics Teacher Handbook

Student Edition With Teacher Notes

Acknowledgments appear on p. 744, which constitutes an extension of this copyright page.

Dorling Kindersley (DK) is an international publishing company that specializes in the creation of high-quality, illustrated information books for children and adults. Dorling Kindersley's unique graphic presentation style is used in this program to motivate students in learning about real-world applications of mathematics. DK is part of the Pearson family of companies.

PEARSON
Prentice Hall

1 2 3 4 5 6 7 8 9 10   10 09 08 07 06

Authors

Series Author

Randall I. Charles, Ph.D.,is Professor Emeritus in the Department of Mathematics and Computer Science at San Jose State University, San Jose, California. He began his career as a high school mathematics teacher, and he was a mathematics supervisor for five years. Dr. Charles has been a member of several NCTM committees and is the former Vice President of the National Council of Supervisors of Mathematics. Much of his writing and research has been in the area of problem solving. He has authored more than 75 mathematics textbooks for kindergarten through college.
Scott Foresman-Prentice Hall Mathematics Series Author Kindergarten through Algebra 2

Program Authors

Mark Illingworth has taught in both elementary and high school math programs for more than twenty years. During this time, he received the Christa McAuliffe sabbatical to develop problem-solving materials and projects for middle grades math students, and he was granted the Presidential Award for Excellence in Mathematics Teaching. Mr. Illingworth's specialty is in teaching mathematics through applications and problem solving. He has written two books on these subjects and has contributed to math and science textbooks at Prentice Hall.

Bonnie McNemar is a mathematics educator with more than 30 years' experience in Texas schools as a teacher, administrator, and consultant. She began her career as a middle school mathematics teacher and served as a supervisor at the district, county, and state levels. Ms. McNemar was the director of the Texas Mathematics Staff Development Program, now known as TEXTEAMS, for five years, and she was the first director of the Teachers Teaching with Technology (T^3) Program. She remains active in both of these organizations as well as in several local, state, and national mathematics organizations, including NCTM.

Darwin Mills, an administrator for the public school system in Newport News, Virginia, has been involved in secondary level mathematics education for more than fourteen years. Mr. Mills has served as a high school teacher, a community college adjunct professor, a department chair, and a district level mathematics supervisor. He has received numerous teaching awards, including teacher of the year for 1999–2000 and an Excellence in Teaching award from the College of Wooster, Ohio, in 2002. He is frequent presenter at workshops and conferences. He believes that all students can learn mathematics if given the proper instruction.

Alma Ramirez is co-director of the Mathematics Case Project at WestEd, a nonprofit educational institute in Oakland, California. A former bilingual elementary and middle school teacher, Ms. Ramirez has considerable expertise in mathematics teaching and learning, second language acquisition, and professional development. She has served as a consultant on a variety of projects and has extensive experience as an author for elementary and middle grades texts. In addition, her work has appeared in the 2004 NCTM Yearbook. Ms. Ramirez is a frequent presenter at professional meetings and conferences.

Andy Reeves, Ph.D., teaches at the University of South Florida in St. Petersburg. His career in education spans 30 years and includes seven years as a middle grades teacher. He subsequently served as Florida's K–12 mathematics supervisor, and more recently he supervised the publication of The Mathematics Teacher, Mathematics Teaching in the Middle School, and Teaching Children Mathematics for NCTM. Prior to entering education, he worked as an engineer for Douglas Aircraft.

Contributing Author

Denisse R. Thompson, Ph.D., is a Professor of Mathematics Education at the University of South Florida. She has particular interests in the connections between literature and mathematics and in the teaching and learning of mathematics in the middle grades. Dr. Thompson contributed to the Guided Problem Solving features.

Reviewers

Course 1 Reviewers

Donna Anderson
Math Supervisor 7–12
West Hartford Public Schools
West Hartford, Connecticut

Nancy L. Borchers
West Clermont Local Schools
Cincinnati, Ohio

Kathleen Chandler
Walnut Creek Middle School
Erie, Pennsylvania

Jane E. Damaske
Lakeshore Public Schools
Stevensville, Michigan

Frank Greco
Parkway South Middle School
Manchester, Missouri

Rebecca L. Jones
Odyssey Middle School
Orlando, Florida

Marylee R. Liebowitz
H. C. Crittenden Middle School
Armonk, New York

Kathy Litz
K. O. Knudson Middle School
Las Vegas, Nevada

Don McGurrin
Wake County Public School System
Raleigh, North Carolina

Ron Mezzadri
K–12 Mathematics Supervisor
Fair Lawn School District
Fair Lawn, New Jersey

Sylvia O. Reeder-Tucker
Prince George's County Math Department
Upper Marlboro, Maryland

Julie A. White
Allison Traditional Magnet Middle School
Wichita, Kansas

Charles Yochim
Bronxville Middle School
Bronxville, New York

Course 2 Reviewers

Cami Craig
Prince William County Public Schools
Marsteller Middle School
Bristow, Virginia

Donald O. Cram
Lincoln Middle School
Rio Rancho, New Mexico

Pat A. Davidson
Jacksonville Junior High School
Jacksonville, Arkansas

Yvette Drew
DeKalb County School System
Open Campus High School
Atlanta, Georgia

Robert S. Fair
K–12 District Mathematics Coordinator
Cherry Creek School District
Greenwood Village, Colorado

Michael A. Landry
Glastonbury Public Schools
Glastonbury, Connecticut

Nancy Ochoa
Weeden Middle School
Florence, Alabama

Charlotte J. Phillips
Wichita USD 259
Wichita, Kansas

Mary Lynn Raith
Mathematics Curriculum Specialist
Pittsburgh Public Schools
Pittsburgh, Pennsylvania

Tammy Rush
Consultant, Middle School Mathematics
Hillsborough County Schools
Tampa, Florida

Judith R. Russ
Prince George's County Public Schools
Capitol Heights, Maryland

Tim Tate
Math/Science Supervisor
Lafayette Parish School System
Lafayette, Louisiana

Dondi J. Thompson
Alcott Middle School
Norman, Oklahoma

Candace Yamagata
Hyde Park Middle School
Las Vegas, Nevada

Course 3 Reviewers

Linda E. Addington
Andrew Lewis Middle School
Salem, Virginia

Jeanne Arnold
Mead Junior High School
Schaumburg, Illinois

Sheila S. Brookshire
A. C. Reynolds Middle School
Asheville, North Carolina

Jennifer Clark
Mayfield Middle School
Putnam City Public Schools
Oklahoma City, Oklahoma

Nicole Dial
Chase Middle School
Topeka, Kansas

Christine Ferrell
Lorin Andrews Middle School
Massillon, Ohio

Virginia G. Harrell
Education Consultant
Hillsborough County, Florida

Jonita P. Howard
Mathematics Curriculum Specialist
Lauderdale Lakes Middle School
Lauderdale Lakes, Florida

Patricia Lemons
Rio Rancho Middle School
Rio Rancho, New Mexico

Susan Noce
Robert Frost Junior High School
Schaumburg, Illinois

Carla A. Siler
South Bend Community School Corp.
South Bend, Indiana

Kathryn E. Smith-Lance
West Genesee Middle School
Camillus, New York

Kathleen D. Tuffy
South Middle School
Braintree, Massachusetts

Patricia R. Wilson
Central Middle School
Murfreesboro, Tennessee

Patricia Young
Northwood Middle School
Pulaski County Special School District
North Little Rock, Arkansas

Content Consultants

Ann Bell
Mathematics
Prentice Hall Consultant
Franklin, Tennessee

Blanche Brownley
Mathematics
Prentice Hall Consultant
Olney, Maryland

Joe Brumfield
Mathematics
Prentice Hall Consultant
Altadena, California

Linda Buckhalt
Mathematics
Prentice Hall Consultant
Derwood, Maryland

Andrea Gordon
Mathematics
Prentice Hall Consultant
Atlanta, Georgia

Eleanor Lopes
Mathematics
Prentice Hall Consultant
New Castle, Delaware

Sally Marsh
Mathematics
Prentice Hall Consultant
Baltimore, Maryland

Bob Pacyga
Mathematics
Prentice Hall Consultant
Darien, Illinois

Judy Porter
Mathematics
Prentice Hall Consultant
Fuquay Varena, North Carolina

Rose Primiani
Mathematics
Prentice Hall Consultant
Harbor City, New Jersey

Jayne Radu
Mathematics
Prentice Hall Consultant
Scottsdale, Arizona

Pam Revels
Mathematics
Prentice Hall Consultant
Sarasota, Florida

Barbara Rogers
Mathematics
Prentice Hall Consultant
Raleigh, North Carolina

Michael Seals
Mathematics
Prentice Hall Consultant
Edmond, Oklahoma

Margaret Thomas
Mathematics
Prentice Hall Consultant
Indianapolis, Indiana

CHAPTER 1

Algebra

Integers and Algebraic Expressions

Assessment and Test Prep

Student Support

Vocabulary

Go Online

GPS Guided Problem Solving

CHAPTER 2

Rational Numbers

Student Support

Vocabulary

Vocabulary Review 52, 57, 62, 66, 72, 81, 86, 92
New Vocabulary 52, 57, 62, 72, 81, 86, 92
Vocabulary Builder 77
Vocabulary Tip 58, 81, 86
Exercises 54, 59, 64, 74, 83, 88, 94

GO Online

Video Tutor Help 73
Active Math 63, 82
Homework Video Tutor 56, 60, 65, 68, 75, 84, 89, 95
Lesson Quiz 55, 59, 65, 69, 75, 83, 89, 95
Vocabulary Quiz 98
Chapter Test 100

GPS Guided Problem Solving

Exercises 55, 59, 64, 68, 75, 83, 88, 94
Practice Solving Problems 78
DK Applications: Applying Real Numbers, 102–103

Assessment and Test Prep

Table of Contents

CHAPTER 3

Real Numbers and the Coordinate Plane

Student Support

Vocabulary

Vocabulary Review 106, 112, 118, 124, 130, 136, 141, 146
New Vocabulary 106, 112, 124, 130, 136, 141, 146
Vocabulary Tip 108, 119, 131, 136
Exercises 108, 114, 120, 126, 132, 137, 143, 148

GO Online

Video Tutor Help 113
Active Math 107
Homework Video Tutor 109, 115, 121, 127, 133, 139, 144, 148
Lesson Quiz 109, 115, 121, 127, 133, 139, 143, 149
Vocabulary Quiz 152
Chapter Test 154
Math at Work 123

GPS Guided Problem Solving

Exercises 109, 114, 120, 126, 133, 138, 143, 148
Squares and Square Roots 116
DK Applications: Applying Rate of Change, 156–157

Assessment and Test Prep

CHAPTER 4

Applications of Proportions

Student Support

Vocabulary

Vocabulary Review 160, 166, 174, 181, 187, 192, 197
New Vocabulary 160, 166, 174, 181, 187, 192, 197
Vocabulary Tip 175, 183, 187
Exercises 162, 169, 176, 183, 189, 193, 198

GO Online

Video Tutor Help 161, 197
Active Math 160, 188
Homework Video Tutor 162, 170, 177, 184, 190, 195, 200
Lesson Quiz 163, 169, 177, 183, 189, 195, 199
Vocabulary Quiz 202
Chapter Test 204
Math at Work 171

GPS Guided Problem Solving

Exercises 162, 169, 177, 183, 189, 194, 199
Using Rates and Proportions 179
DK Applications: Applying Proportions, 206–207

Assessment and Test Prep

Table of Contents

CHAPTER 5

Applications of Percent

Student Support

Vocabulary

Vocabulary Review 210, 214, 218, 224, 230, 234, 242, 246
New Vocabulary 210, 230, 234, 242, 246
Vocabulary Builder 228
Vocabulary Tip 214, 243
Exercises 212, 232, 237, 243, 248

GO Online

Video Tutor Help 210, 219
Active Math 211, 220
Homework Video Tutor 213, 216, 221, 226, 233, 237, 244, 249
Lesson Quiz 213, 217, 221, 227, 233, 237, 243, 249
Vocabulary Quiz 252
Chapter Test 254

GPS Guided Problem Solving

Exercises 213, 216, 221, 226, 233, 237, 244, 249
Practice Solving Problems 240
DK Applications: Applying Percents, 256–257

Assessment and Test Prep

CHAPTER 6

Algebra

Equations and Inequalities

Student Support

Vocabulary

Vocabulary Review 261, 266, 271, 276, 282, 288
New Vocabulary 266, 282, 288
Vocabulary Builder 286
Vocabulary Tip 266, 282, 290
Exercises 268, 273, 284, 291

GO Online

Video Tutor Help 267, 283
Active Math 261, 290
Homework Video Tutor 263, 269, 274, 278, 285, 291
Lesson Quiz 263, 269, 275, 277, 285, 291
Vocabulary Quiz 294
Chapter Test 296
Math at Work 270

GPS Guided Problem Solving

Exercises 263, 268, 274, 278, 284, 291
Writing Equations 279
DK Applications: Applying Equations, 298–299

Assessment and Test Prep

CHAPTER 7

Geometry

Student Support

Vocabulary

Vocabulary Review 303, 307, 312, 318, 324, 328, 336, 341
New Vocabulary 303, 307, 312, 318, 324, 328, 341
Vocabulary Builder 322
Vocabulary Tip 303, 308, 313, 318, 319
Exercises 305, 314, 320, 326, 331, 338, 342

GO Online

Video Tutor Help 330, 336
Active Math 304, 325
Homework Video Tutor 306, 309, 316, 321, 327, 332, 339, 343
Lesson Quiz 305, 309, 315, 321, 327, 331, 339, 343
Vocabulary Quiz 346
Chapter Test 348
Math at Work 317

GPS Guided Problem Solving

Exercises 305, 309, 315, 320, 326, 331, 338, 343
Geoboard Area 333
DK Applications: Applying Geometry, 350–351

Assessment and Test Prep

CHAPTER 8

Measurement

Student Support

Vocabulary

Vocabulary Review 354, 358, 364, 368, 374, 380, 388, 393, 398
New Vocabulary 354, 358, 364, 368, 374, 380, 393, 398
Vocabulary Tip 354, 368
Exercises 356, 360, 365, 371, 377, 382, 395, 400

GO Online

Video Tutor Help 381, 389
Active Math 359, 382
Homework Video Tutor 357, 361, 366, 372, 378, 383, 391, 395, 401
Lesson Quiz 357, 361, 365, 371, 377, 383, 391, 395, 401
Vocabulary Quiz 404
Chapter Test 406
Math at Work 392

GPS Guided Problem Solving

Exercises 356, 360, 366, 371, 377, 383, 390, 395, 400
Using Formulas 385
DK Applications: Applying Measurement, 408–409

Assessment and Test Prep

CHAPTER 9

Using Graphs to Analyze Data

Student Support

Vocabulary

Vocabulary Review 412, 418, 424, 428, 433, 438, 444, 450, 456
New Vocabulary 412, 418, 424, 433, 438, 444, 450
Vocabulary Tip 412, 419, 436, 445
Exercises 414, 420, 425, 429, 435, 440, 446, 452, 457

GO Online

Video Tutor Help 421
Active Math 413, 418, 419, 435, 439
Homework Video Tutor 416, 421, 425, 431, 436, 441, 447, 453, 458
Lesson Quiz 415, 421, 425, 431, 437, 441, 447, 453, 459
Vocabulary Quiz 462
Chapter Test 464

GPS Guided Problem Solving

Exercises 415, 420, 425, 430, 436, 440, 446, 452, 458
Equations and Graphs 454
DK Applications: Applying Data Analysis, 466–467

Assessment and Test Prep

CHAPTER 10

Probability

Student Support

Vocabulary

GO Online

GPS Guided Problem Solving

Assessment and Test Prep

Table of Contents

Algebra

CHAPTER 11 Functions

Student Support

Vocabulary

Vocabulary Review 512, 518, 523, 528, 534, 540, 546
New Vocabulary 512, 523, 528, 534, 546
Vocabulary Tip 513, 524, 528, 529, 534
Exercises 514, 519, 525, 530, 536, 542, 548

GO Online

Video Tutor Help 514, 535
Active Math 518, 529, 546
Homework Video Tutor 515, 520, 525, 531, 537, 542, 549
Lesson Quiz 515, 521, 525, 531, 537, 543, 549
Vocabulary Quiz 552
Chapter Test 554

GPS Guided Problem Solving

Exercises 515, 520, 525, 531, 537, 542, 548
Linear Functions 544
DK Applications: Applying Quadratic Functions, 556–557

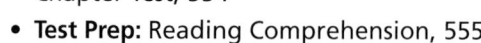

Assessment and Test Prep

CHAPTER 12

Algebra

Polynomials and Properties of Exponents

Student Support

Vocabulary

GO Online

GPS Guided Problem Solving

Assessment and Test Prep

Connect Your Learning

through problem solving, activities, and the Web

Applications: Real-World Applications

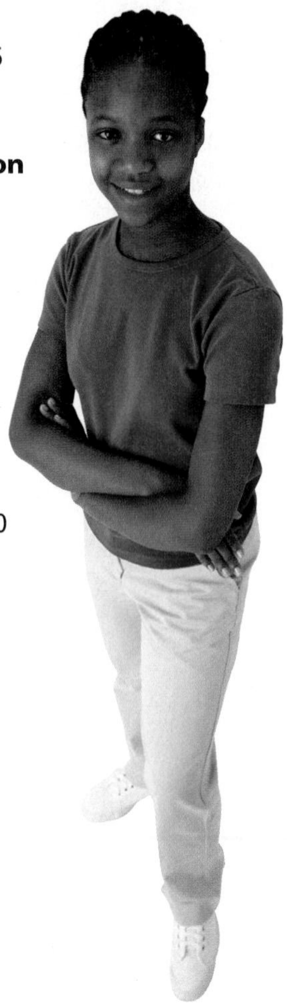

Applications: Math at Work and Careers

Applications: Interdisciplinary Applications

Activity Labs

Activity Labs: Hands On

Activity Labs: Technology

Activity Labs: **Data Analysis**

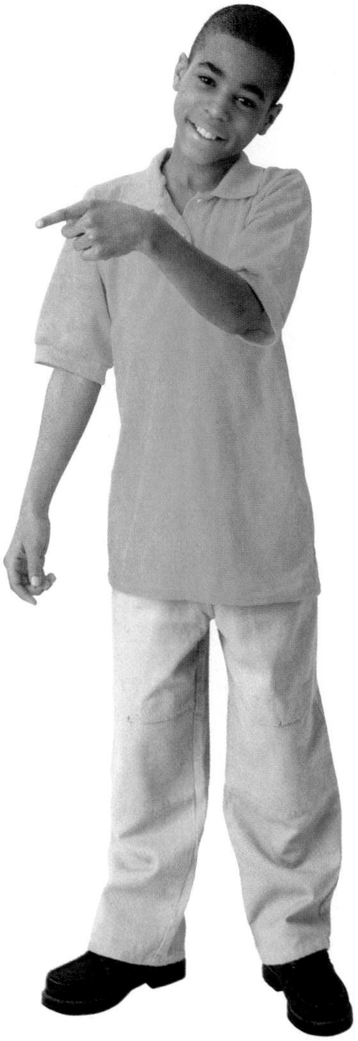

Activity Labs: Data Collection

Activity Labs: Algebra Thinking

Activities: **Chapter Projects**

Problem Solving Strategies

Guided Problem Solving features

GO Online

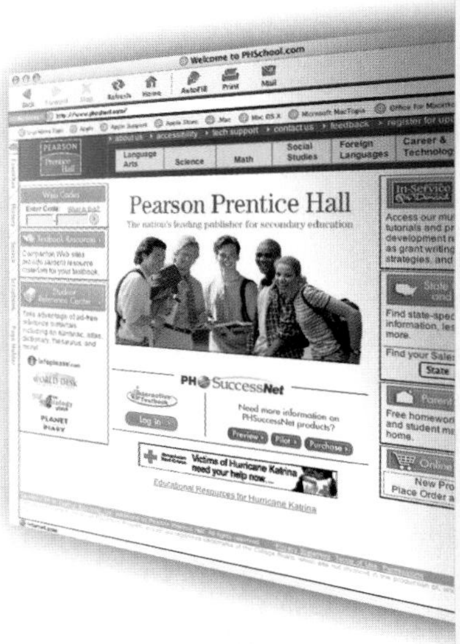

Throughout this book you will find links to the Prentice Hall Web site. Use the Web Codes provided with each link to gain direct access to online material. Here's how to *Go Online*:

1. Go to PHSchool.com
2. Enter the Web Code
3. Click Go!

Lesson Web Codes

Lesson Quiz Web Codes: There is an online quiz for every lesson. Access these quizzes with Web Codes asa-0101 through asa-1205 for Lesson 1-1 through Lesson 12-5. See page 7.

Lesson Quizzes
Web Code format: asa-0204 02 = Chapter 2 04 = Lesson 4

Homework Video Tutor Web Codes: For every lesson, there is additional support online to help students complete their homework. Access the Homework Video Tutors with Web Codes ase-0101 through ase-1205 for Lesson 1-1 through Lesson 12-5. See page 8.

Homework Video Tutor
Web Code format: ase-0605 06 = Chapter 6 05 = Lesson 5

Chapter Web Codes

Chapter	Vocabulary Quizzes	Chapter Tests	Chapter Projects
1	asj-0151	asa-0152	asd-0161
2	asj-0251	asa-0252	asd-0261
3	asj-0351	asa-0352	asd-0361
4	asj-0451	asa-0452	asd-0461
5	asj-0551	asa-0552	asd-0561
6	asj-0651	asa-0652	asd-0661
7	asj-0751	asa-0752	asd-0761
8	asj-0851	asa-0852	asd-0861
9	asj-0951	asa-0952	asd-0961
10	asj-1051	asa-1052	asd-1061
11	asj-1151	asa-1152	asd-1161
12	asj-1251	asa-1252	asd-1261
End-of-Course		asa-1254	

Additional Web Codes

Video Tutor Help:
Use Web Code ase-0775 to access engaging online instructional videos to help bring math concepts to life. See page 17.

Data Updates:
Use Web Code asg-9041 to get up-to-date government data for use in examples and exercises. See page 11.

Math at Work:
For information about each Math at Work feature, use Web Code asb-2031. See page 123.

Differentiate Instruction with Ease

Students develop and learn in different ways at different paces. Accessible content, presented in a variety of formats, acknowledges these unique differences while providing options for learning. The goal of *Prentice Hall Mathematics* is for all students to be successful and for you to have the tools you need to accomplish this. *Prentice Hall Mathematics* Grade 6 through Algebra 2 provides better solutions for meeting the needs of every student in the classroom by achieving two goals:

- Providing superior teacher support materials for planning how to effectively differentiate instruction
- Providing unique resources for the various populations of students.

Differentiated Instruction
Solutions for All Learners

Adapted Resources for Differentiating Instruction

In addition to the support provided in the Teacher's Editions, Prentice Hall has created resources developed uniquely for Below Level and Special Needs students.

ALL-IN-ONE
STUDENT WORKBOOK
ADAPTED VERSION
PRENTICE HALL
MATHEMATICS
COURSE 3
KEY FEATURES
• Daily Notetaking Guide pages for each lesson provide support for taking effective notes in class
• Guided Problem Solving pages give students the opportunity to work through a step-by-step solution to a problem from each lesson of the Student Edition
• Practice pages provide for additional practice of key concepts for every lesson
• Vocabulary and Study Skills pages include activities to increase reading and math understanding for each chapter

All-in-One Student Workbook Adapted Version

This resource includes adapted practice and adapted daily notetaking worksheets to support special needs students. By providing these critical resources ready for you to use, you can cover the same mathematical content with the students, but provide a more appropriate resource for them to take notes and practice the lesson's mathematics.

Differentiated Assessments

Prentice Hall Mathematics also recognizes the importance of not only differentiating instruction, but also differentiating the assessments used to monitor student progress and inform future instruction. To achieve this, three versions of each chapter test are provided: L2 for Below Level L3 for All Students and L4 for Advanced Learners.

ExamView® Assessment Suite

Exam*View* 5.0 Assessment Suite

To provide the ultimate flexibility in creating assessments and practice worksheets for all students, the *Prentice Hall Mathematics ExamView* Test Banks contain adapted items written exclusively for your Special Needs and Below Level students.

Prentice Hall Mathematics Teacher's Editions offer comprehensive support in differentiating instruction.

- L1 Special Needs
- L2 Below Level
- L3 All Students
- L4 Advanced Learners
- ELL English Language Learners

Prentice Hall Mathematics uses a consistent method for identifying resources for differentiating instruction. This consistency helps you to easily identify and choose the appropriate resources for your students.

Planning and Using Differentiated Resources
These chapter level support pages provide you an easy-to-read overview of the resources available and suggested ways in the instructional lesson to use the resources.

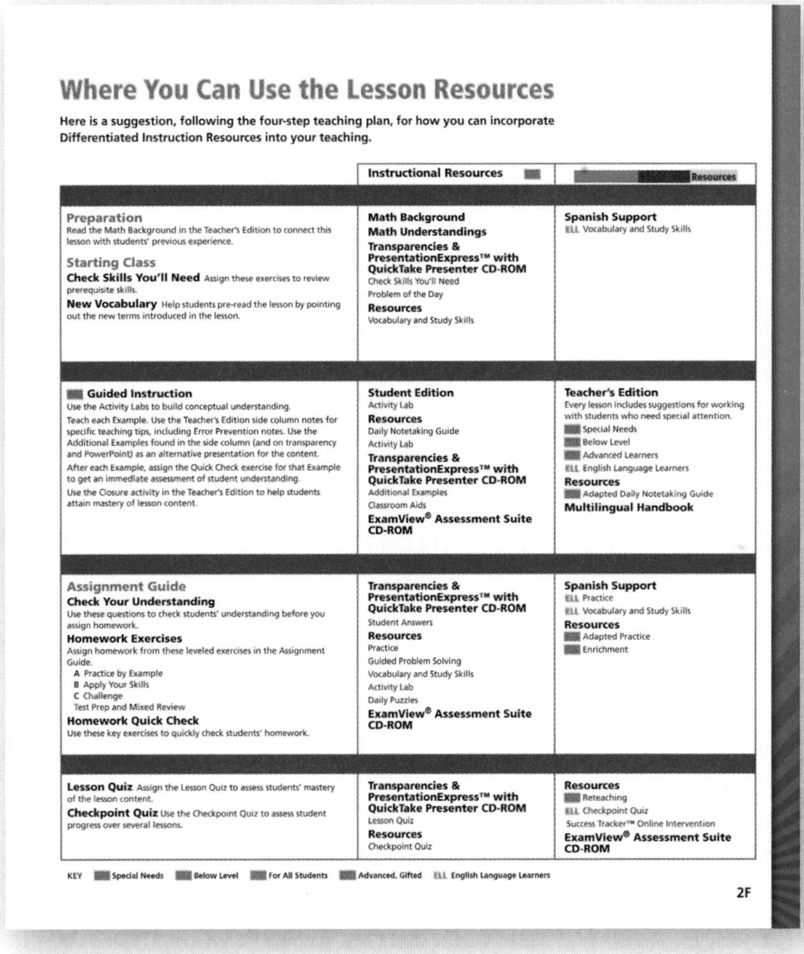

Where You Can Use the Lesson Resources

Here is a suggestion, following the four-step teaching plan, for how you can incorporate Differentiated Instruction Resources into your teaching.

	Instructional Resources	Resources
Preparation Read the Math Background in the Teacher's Edition to connect this lesson with students' previous experience. **Starting Class** **Check Skills You'll Need** Assign these exercises to review prerequisite skills. **New Vocabulary** Help students pre-read the lesson by pointing out the new terms introduced in the lesson.	**Math Background** **Math Understandings** **Transparencies & PresentationExpress™ with QuickTake Presenter CD-ROM** Check Skills You'll Need Problem of the Day **Resources** Vocabulary and Study Skills	**Spanish Support** ELL Vocabulary and Study Skills
Guided Instruction Use the Activity Labs to build conceptual understanding. Teach each Example. Use the Teacher's Edition side column notes for specific teaching tips, including Error Prevention notes. Use the Additional Examples found in the side column (and on transparency and PowerPoint) as an alternative presentation for the content. After each Example, assign the Quick Check exercise for that Example to get an immediate assessment of student understanding. Use the Closure activity in the Teacher's Edition to help students attain mastery of lesson content.	**Student Edition** Activity Lab **Resources** Daily Notetaking Guide Activity Lab **Transparencies & PresentationExpress™ with QuickTake Presenter CD-ROM** Additional Examples Classroom Aids **ExamView® Assessment Suite CD-ROM**	**Teacher's Edition** Every lesson includes suggestions for working with students who need special attention. Special Needs Below Level Advanced Learners ELL English Language Learners **Resources** Adapted Daily Notetaking Guide **Multilingual Handbook**
Assignment Guide **Check Your Understanding** Use these questions to check students' understanding before you assign homework. **Homework Exercises** Assign homework from these leveled exercises in the Assignment Guide. A Practice by Example B Apply Your Skills C Challenge Test Prep and Mixed Review **Homework Quick Check** Use these key exercises to quickly check students' homework.	**Transparencies & PresentationExpress™ with QuickTake Presenter CD-ROM** Student Answers **Resources** Practice Guided Problem Solving Vocabulary and Study Skills Activity Lab Daily Puzzles **ExamView® Assessment Suite CD-ROM**	**Spanish Support** ELL Practice ELL Vocabulary and Study Skills **Resources** Adapted Practice Enrichment
Lesson Quiz Assign the Lesson Quiz to assess students' mastery of the lesson content. **Checkpoint Quiz** Use the Checkpoint Quiz to assess student progress over several lessons.	**Transparencies & PresentationExpress™ with QuickTake Presenter CD-ROM** Lesson Quiz **Resources** Checkpoint Quiz	**Resources** Reteaching ELL Checkpoint Quiz Success Tracker™ Online Intervention **ExamView® Assessment Suite CD-ROM**

KEY Special Needs Below Level For All Students Advanced, Gifted ELL English Language Learners

2F

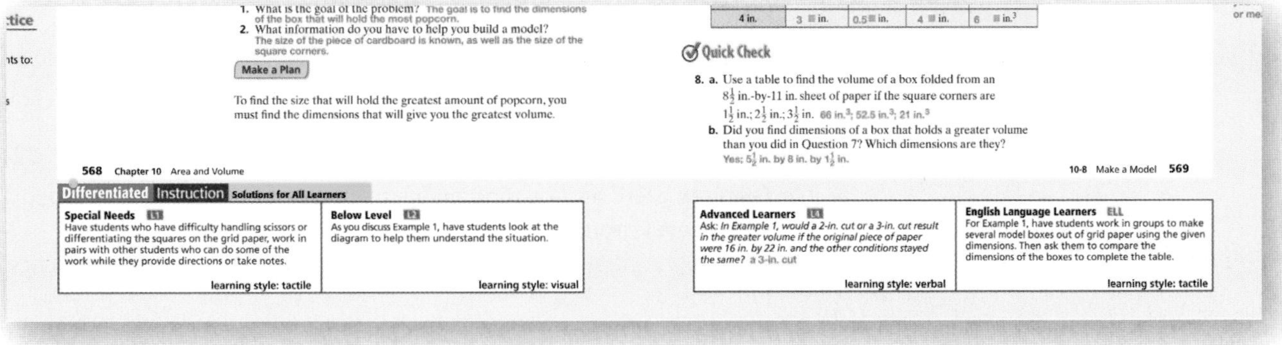

1. What is the goal of the problem? The goal is to find the dimensions of the box that will hold the most popcorn.
2. What information do you have to help you build a model? The size of the piece of cardboard is known, as well as the size of the square corners.

Make a Plan

To find the size that will hold the greatest amount of popcorn, you must find the dimensions that will give you the greatest volume.

568 Chapter 10 Area and Volume

Quick Check

8. a. Use a table to find the volume of a box folded from an $8\frac{1}{2}$ in.-by-11 in. sheet of paper if the square corners are $1\frac{1}{2}$ in.; $2\frac{1}{2}$ in.; $3\frac{1}{2}$ in. 66 in.^{3}; 52.5 in.^{3}; 21 in.^{3}
   b. Did you find dimensions of a box that holds a greater volume than you did in Question 7? Which dimensions are they? Yes; $5\frac{1}{2}$ in. by 8 in. by $1\frac{1}{2}$ in.

10-8 Make a Model 569

Differentiated Instruction Solutions for All Learners

Special Needs L1
Have students who have difficulty handling scissors or differentiating the squares on the grid paper, work in pairs with other students who can do some of the work while they provide directions or take notes.
learning style: tactile

Below Level L2
As you discuss Example 1, have students look at the diagram to help them understand the situation.
learning style: visual

Advanced Learners L4
Ask: *In Example 1, would a 2-in. cut or a 3-in. cut result in the greater volume if the original piece of paper were 16 in. by 22 in. and the other conditions stayed the same?* a 3-in. cut
learning style: verbal

English Language Learners ELL
For Example 1, have students work in groups to make several model boxes out of grid paper using the given dimensions. Then ask them to compare the dimensions of the boxes to complete the table.
learning style: tactile

Differentiated Instruction teaching notes
These useful notes help you differentiate the lesson for all learners, including Special Needs, Below Level, Advanced, and English Language Learners.

Assessment to Inform Instruction

Assessment is integral to mathematics instruction. Student assessment should occur often and with a variety of different measures. *Prentice Hall Mathematics* provides an ongoing assessment strand that addresses assessment *for* learning and assessment *of* learning. The formative assessment features (before and during instruction) offer a variety of methods for teachers to assess student understanding and inform future instruction. The summative assessment features (after instruction) document student mastery of mathematical concepts and skills and further prepare students for success in today's tests.

Instant Check System™ for Ongoing Assessment

This unique feature of *Prentice Hall Mathematics* ensures that students make progress every day, in every lesson. It helps teachers assess necessary prerequisite skills and monitor student understanding. The Instant Check System™ assessments include:

- Check Your Readiness – Assesses prerequisite skills for each chapter
- Check Skills You'll Need – Assesses prerequisite skills for each lesson
- Quick Check – Assesses student understanding after every example in the book
- Check Your Understanding – Assesses understanding before the homework exercises
- Check Point – Assesses understanding after completing lessons

Progress Monitoring Assessments

This comprehensive teacher support resource contains all the program assessments needed to evaluate student understanding, monitor student progress, and inform future instruction. The following assessments are included:

- Screening Test
- Benchmark Tests
- Test-Taking Strategy Practice
- Quarter, Mid-Course, and Final Tests – regular and below level versions
- Comprehensive Report Forms
- Answers to all of the tests

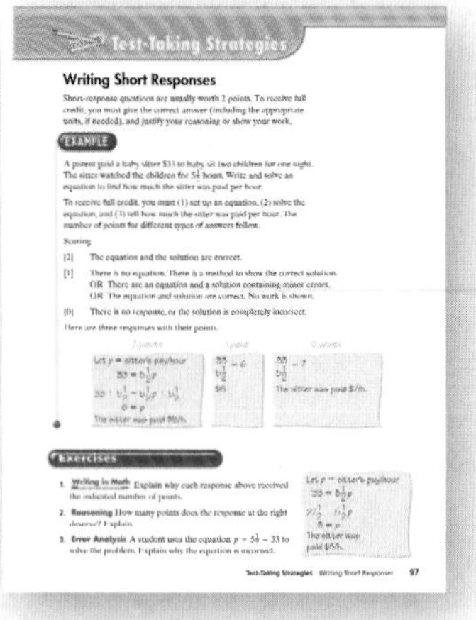

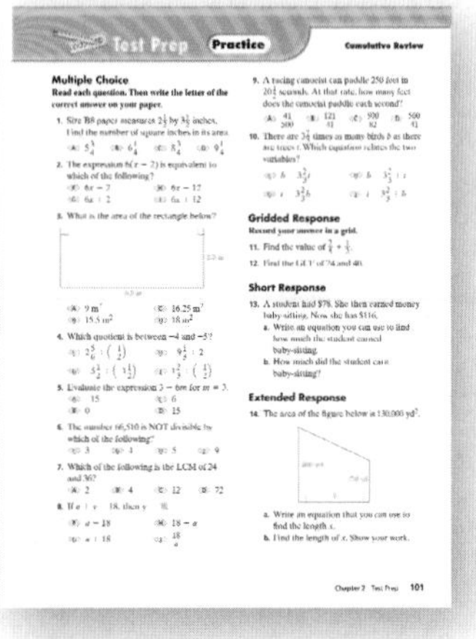

Preparation for High-Stakes Assessment

Prentice Hall Mathematics recognizes how critical it is for teachers to prepare every student for test success.

The following features help achieve this:

- Separate Test-Taking Strategy lessons focus on specific strategies necessary for test success.
- Test Prep exercises, focusing on all major question types, are included after every lesson.
- After every chapter, Test Prep review pages provide additional practice for students.

Help All Students Become Problem Solvers

One of the major goals of a mathematics program is to develop students' ability to solve problems in class, on assessments, in the context of real-world situations, and outside the classroom. *Prentice Hall Mathematics* helps support this goal by embedding problem-solving instruction in every lesson, providing targeted support for problem-solving strategies throughout the Student Edition, and including sufficient problems to help students practice and reinforce problem solving skills.

Guided Problem Solving Features

These features throughout the Student Edition provide scaffolded support in solving problems. The student walks through how to solve one representative problem, focusing on both the reasoning and the computation that must be done.

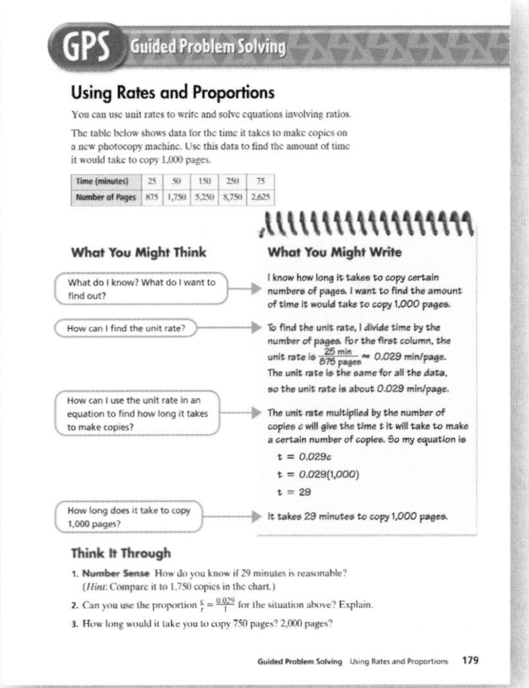
GPS Guided Problem Solving

Using Rates and Proportions

You can use unit rates to write and solve equations involving ratios.

The table below shows data for the time it takes to make copies on a new photocopy machine. Use this data to find the amount of time it would take to copy 1,000 pages.

Time (minutes)	25	50	150	250	75
Number of Pages	875	1,750	5,250	8,750	2,625

What You Might Think	What You Might Write
What do I know? What do I want to find out?	I know how long it takes to copy certain numbers of pages. I want to find the amount of time it would take to copy 1,000 pages.
How can I find the unit rate?	To find the unit rate, I divide time by the number of pages. For the first column, the unit rate is $\frac{25 \text{ min}}{875 \text{ pages}} \approx 0.029$ min/page. The unit rate is the same for all the data, so the unit rate is about 0.029 min/page.
How can I use the unit rate in an equation to find how long it takes to make copies?	The unit rate multiplied by the number of copies c will give the time t it will take to make a certain number of copies. So my equation is $t = 0.029c$, $t = 0.029(1{,}000)$, $t = 29$
How long does it take to copy 1,000 pages?	It takes 29 minutes to copy 1,000 pages.

Think It Through

1. **Number Sense** How do you know if 29 minutes is reasonable? (*Hint*: Compare it to 1,750 copies in the chart.)
2. Can you use the proportion $\frac{c}{t} = \frac{0.029}{1}$ for the situation above? Explain.
3. How long would it take you to copy 750 pages? 2,000 pages?

Guided Problem Solving Using Rates and Proportions 179

Activities and Activity Labs

Throughout the Student Edition are in-lesson activities and full feature Activity Labs. These provide students an opportunity to complete more in-depth problems and applications of the mathematical content they're learning.

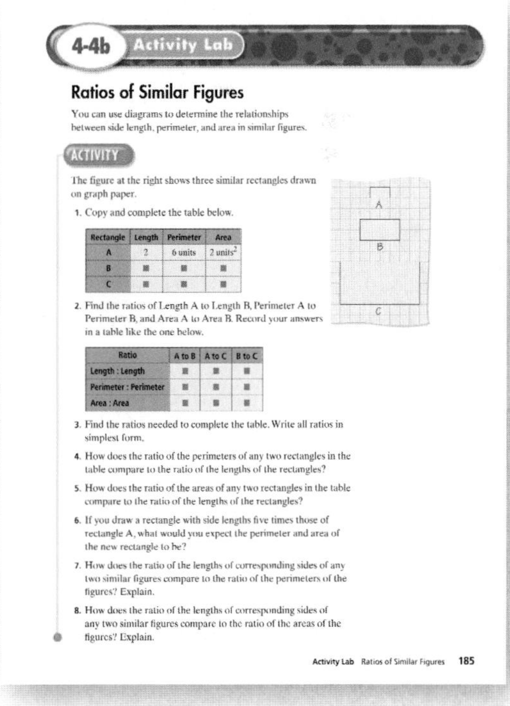
4-4b Activity Lab

Ratios of Similar Figures

You can use diagrams to determine the relationships between side length, perimeter, and area in similar figures.

ACTIVITY

The figure at the right shows three similar rectangles drawn on graph paper.

1. Copy and complete the table below.

Rectangle	Length	Perimeter	Area
A	2	6 units	2 units^2
B	■	■	■
C	■	■	■

2. Find the ratios of Length A to Length B, Perimeter A to Perimeter B, and Area A to Area B. Record your answers in a table like the one below.

Ratio	A to B	A to C	B to C
Length : Length	■	■	■
Perimeter : Perimeter	■	■	■
Area : Area	■	■	■

3. Find the ratios needed to complete the table. Write all ratios in simplest form.
4. How does the ratio of the perimeters of any two rectangles in the table compare to the ratio of the lengths of the rectangles?
5. How does the ratio of the areas of any two rectangles in the table compare to the ratio of the lengths of the rectangles?
6. If you draw a rectangle with side lengths five times those of rectangle A, what would you expect the perimeter and area of the new rectangle to be?
7. How does the ratio of the lengths of corresponding sides of any two similar figures compare to the ratio of the perimeters of the figures? Explain.
8. How does the ratio of the lengths of corresponding sides of any two similar figures compare to the ratio of the areas of the figures? Explain.

Activity Lab Ratios of Similar Figures 185

Problem Solving Practice

Every lesson in the Student Edition includes a comprehensive, leveled exercise set. This provides students the opportunity to solve a variety of problems and apply problem solving strategies on a daily basis. Furthermore, additional problems have been added to the end of each book in the Extra Skill and Word Problem Practice section.

Technology – not simply added, but added value

Take Learning to a New Level

StudentEXPRESS™ CD-ROM
A suite of learning tools to help students study, learn, and succeed in class. An interactive textbook with instructional videos, built-in activities, vocabulary support, and instant feedback assessments make this the most powerful student study tool available. Interactive Text also available online.

Homework Video Tutor and Online Active Math
Homework Video Tutors provide built-in homework help for every lesson. Narrated by real teachers, these engaging interactive tutorials cover the key concepts of each day's lesson. Additionally, Online Active Math interactivities provide an opportunity to explore math concepts.

Use Assessment Technology to Inform Instruction

Exam*View*® 5.0 Assessment Suite
The most powerful test generator available—with the most comprehensive test banks. Create and modify custom-made tests with ease. Access the Math Art Gallery to instantly add math images to your questions. Also-instantly translate any test into Spanish.

MindPoint® Quiz Show
This creative product allows teachers to involve the entire class in a fun, end-of-chapter review game.

Success Tracker™ Online
Personalized for each student with individual assessment, diagnosis, and remediation. Color-coded reports make it easy for teachers to monitor progress.

Superior Planning and Teaching Tools

TeacherEXPRESS™ CD-ROM—powered by LessonView® planning software
An Interactive Teacher's Edition, LessonView planning software, correlations to national and state standards, instructional tools, plus professional development to help teachers plan, teach, and assess.

PresentationEXPRESS™ CD-ROM with ExamView® QuickTake Presenter
This innovative component includes all the transparencies in interactive, PowerPoint format, making it easier for you to teach and to customize based on your teaching preferences. QuickTake assessments are embedded in every lesson, allowing teachers to quickly and easily monitor student progress.

Worksheets Online
All program worksheets are also conveniently posted online so you and your students can access them anywhere - one more way to make your planning and assignment management easier.

Professional Development
that meets your needs

In-Service On Demand

Now, you have the freedom to access your Prentice Hall in-service training online, anytime, anywhere, at PHSchool.com. This online tutorial library offers in-service training specifically for the Prentice Hall textbook and technology you're teaching with right now.

In-service designed around you!

In-Service On Demand is Prentice Hall's new Web site of in-service training tutorials for your Prentice Hall products. Now you can access the same training for using your Prentice Hall textbook and technology that you would learn in a traditional in-service—from the convenience of your computer!

In-Service for your Prentice Hall program!

The In-Service On Demand library features video-based tutorials to help you maximize the effectiveness of the Prentice Hall program you use. This extensive library is continually being updated with tutorials for Prentice Hall's newest products! Visit the site as often as you like!

In-Service is just a click away!

1. Go to PHSchool.com and click on In-Service On Demand.
2. Select mathematics and then select your *Prentice Hall Mathematics* book.
3. Watch the video-based tutorials and get the in-service training you need when and where it's convenient for you.
4. Download and print PDF tutorial guides on what you've just seen.

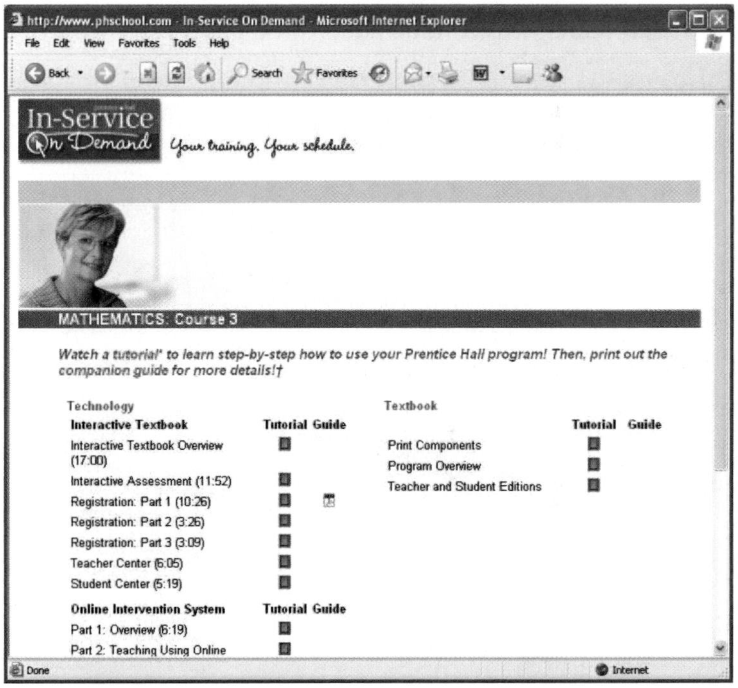

Day-to-Day Professional Development

Math Background in Teacher's Edition

Support instruction at the chapter and lesson level as every Chapter of Prentice Hall Mathematics begins with Math Background related to the content of the chapter in both middle school and high school.

Research-Based and Proven Effective

The stakes for mathematics educators are high. You are expected to raise student achievement. Prentice Hall Mathematics programs are backed by efficacy research to give you the confidence to meet this challenge.

In developing Prentice Hall programs, the use of research is a guiding, central construct. This research was conducted in three phases:

1 Exploratory Needs Assessment

(Quantitative and Qualitative)

Key research events include —

- Teacher interviews
- Classroom observations
- Mail surveys
- Reviews of educational research

2 Formative, Prototype Development and Field Testing

(Quantitative and Qualitative)

Key research events include —

- Field testing of prototypes
- Classroom observations
- Teacher reviews
- Supervisor reviews
- Educator advisory panels

3 Summative, Validation Research

(Experimental and Quasi-Experimental Study Designs & Qualitative Research)

Key research events include —

- Pre-publication learner verification research
- Post-publication efficacy studies
- Classroom observations
- Evaluation of in-market results on standardized tests
- Effect size studies

The facing page contains an example of the latest research carried out for Prentice Hall Middle School Mathematics.

2005 Research Results: Prentice Hall Middle School Mathematics

Independent research confirms Middle School students using Prentice Hall Mathematics achieve greater success in mathematics

Results of independent research indicate that students using Prentice Hall Mathematics Course 2 showed significant improvement, outperforming students using other mathematics programs.The randomized control trial, conducted by PRES Associates, Inc., a national educational evaluation firm with central offices in Jackson,WY, confirmed students using the Prentice Hall curricula showed greater improvement from pre- to post-tests than their counterparts using other programs as measured by two different standardized assessments. Improvement was evident on all mathematics objectives measured. Additionally, the program was especially effective with low-performing students.

The study is part of a multi-year research effort commissioned by the publisher and is one of many slated to evaluate the effectiveness of Prentice Hall's educational materials across disciplines and grade levels. Participants represented a mix of urban and urban-fringe districts with diverse socio-economic, ethnic, and academic backgrounds.

Among the key findings, PRES Associates reported:

- Student performance significantly improved from the beginning of the school year to its end as measured by the TerraNova Basic Multiple Assessment, chosen because it is aligned to national NCTM standards and has proven reliability and validity.
- Students using Prentice Hall Mathematics Course 2 improved to a greater extent in pre- to post-test scores than those using other programs.
- Assessment results suggest that Prentice Hall Mathematics Course 2 is particularly effective with low-performing students, as evidenced by the significant gains in low-performing student test scores.
- Prentice Hall Mathematics Course 2 students reported feeling significantly more comfortable with math than students using other programs.They also reported higher math aspirations (i.e., plans to take advanced math in high school).
- Teachers participating in the study reported that Prentice Hall Mathematics Course 2 provided significantly better assistance than other programs in the following areas (1) individualizing instruction, (2) reinforcing previously taught concepts, (3) providing test preparation, and (4) making connections to real-life.
- Teachers identified many aspects of the Prentice Hall program as effective, including the Guided Problem Solving workbook, Check Skills You'll Need exercises, and Check Understanding exercises.

The study was designed to fully meet the evidence criteria put forth by the What Works Clearinghouse, the Federal agency established in 2002 to provide the educators and the public with a trusted source of scientific evidence of what works in education.This study was designed so that accurate and appropriate inferences could be made regarding the effectiveness of the Prentice Hall Mathematics Course 2 program.

Visit PHSchool.com/MathResearch for the full report and additional research in support of Prentice Hall Mathematics programs.

Mathematics Strands

The following 10 strands are from the NCTM Principles and Standards. The Background and Progression sections highlight content students usually have mastered when they enter middle grades and the progression expected using *Prentice Hall Mathematics Courses 1, 2,* and *3*.

Number and Operations

- Understand numbers, ways of representing numbers, relationships among numbers, and number systems
- Understand meanings of operations and how they relate to one another
- Compute fluently and make reasonable estimates

Background and Progression Students usually enter middle grades with computational facility with whole numbers, and varying degrees of mastery of fractions and decimals.

In ***Course 1***, students reach mastery of all decimal and fraction operations. They work with percents and develop estimation skills. Concepts of scale and ratio are introduced. (Chapters 1, 5, 6, and 7)

In ***Course 2***, students reach mastery of integer operations, rates, and ratios. They work with percent applications and exponents. (Chapters 1, 2, 5, and 6)

In ***Course 3***, students reach mastery of percent and proportion applications. They continue to work with exponents, including using square roots. (Chapters 2, 3, and 4)

Algebra

- Understand patterns, relations, and functions
- Represent and analyze mathematical situations and structures using algebraic symbols
- Use mathematical models to represent and understand quantitative relationships
- Analyze change in various contexts

Background and Progression Students usually enter middle grades having represented patterns through words, tables, and graphs. They also have some experience with symbolic representation of unknown quantities.

In ***Course 1***, students use variables in equations and patterns. Models are introduced for percents, proportions, integers, and properties of equality. (Chapters 3, 7, and 11)

In ***Course 2***, students continue to use models, tables, graphs, and symbolic notation to represent algebraic relationships. They solve equations and interpret the slope of a line. (Chapters 4, 9, and 10)

In ***Course 3***, students solve equations and use equivalent forms for expressions containing parentheses, like terms, and exponents. They relate slope and y-intercept to graphs and linear relationships. (Chapters 1, 6, 11, and 12)

Geometry

- Analyze characteristics and properties of two- and three-dimensional geometric shapes and develop mathematical arguments about geometric relationships
- Specify locations and describe spatial relationships using coordinate geometry and other representational systems
- Apply transformations and use symmetry to analyze mathematical situations
- Use visualization, spatial reasoning, and geometric modeling to solve problems

Background and Progression Students entering middle grades have usually mastered names and characteristics of common polygons and simple solids.

In ***Course 1***, students use grids, nets, and block diagrams to build concepts of area and volume. They explore symmetry and transformations. The coordinate plane is introduced. (Chapters 8 and 9)

In ***Course 2***, students continue to use two-dimensional representations of three-dimensional figures. They study congruent and similar figures and transformations. (Chapters 5, 7, 8, and 10)

In ***Course 3***, students draw inferences about lengths, areas, and volumes of similar two- and three-dimensional figures. They study both reflectional and rotational symmetry. (Chapters 3, 7, and 8)

Measurement

- Understand measurable attributes of objects and the units, systems, and processes of measurement
- Apply appropriate techniques, tools, and formulas to determine measurements

Background and Progression Students entering middle grades have usually worked with customary and metric units. They often know formulas for the perimeter and area of simple figures.

In ***Course 1***, students choose units, convert units, and estimate measures within the customary and metric systems. They develop and use formulas related to polygons. They explore surface area and volume. (Chapters 6 and 9)

In ***Course 2***, students develop and use formulas to find areas of irregular figures, and to find surface area and volume of prisms and cylinders. (Chapters 5 and 8)

In ***Course 3***, students continue to convert units. They extend their understanding of formulas to include pyramids, cones, and spheres. (Chapters 4, 7, and 8)

Data Analysis and Probability

- Formulate questions that can be addressed with data and collect, organize, and display relevant data to answer them
- Select and use appropriate statistical methods to analyze data
- Understand and apply basic concepts of probability

Background and Progression Students in middle grades have experience with gathering, displaying, and analyzing data. They have used simple probabilities to express the likelihood of an event.

In ***Course 1***, students master measures of central tendency, simple line graphs, bar graphs, and probabilities. They make line plots, circle graphs, and stem-and-leaf plots. (Chapters 2, 7, and 10)

In ***Course 2***, students continue to study line plots, stem-and-leaf plots, and bar graphs. They analyze survey techniques for bias, and make scatter plots to analyze data. (Chapter 11)

In ***Course 3***, students place and interpret trend lines on scatter plots. They also develop probability concepts for compound events. (Chapters 9 and 10)

Problem Solving

- Build new mathematical knowledge through problem solving
- Solve problems that arise in mathematics and in other contexts
- Apply and adapt a variety of appropriate strategies to solve problems
- Monitor and reflect on the process of mathematical problem solving

Background and Progression *Throughout Prentice Hall Mathematics*, students use a consistent framework for problem solving, which identifies four phases: Understand the Problem, Make a Plan, Carry Out the Plan, Check the Answer.

In each course, students learn specific strategies and apply them to a variety of problems. They practice and apply these strategies through guided problem solving. (Problem Solving Handbook)

Reasoning and Proof

- Recognize reasoning and proof as fundamental aspects of mathematics
- Make and investigate mathematical conjectures
- Develop and evaluate mathematical arguments and proofs
- Select and use various types of reasoning and methods of proof

Background and Progression At the elementary level, students use mathematical reasoning in the development of number sense and classification skills.

In ***Prentice Hall Mathematics***, reasoning is an integral part of students' daily work. Every lesson contains a mix of Reasoning, Number Sense, and Error Analysis exercises. Students have the opportunity to explain their thinking using mathematical concepts and properties. Activities throughout the program provide students with opportunities to use inductive reasoning.

Communication

- Organize and consolidate their mathematical thinking through communication
- Communicate their mathematical thinking coherently and clearly to peers, teachers, and others
- Analyze and evaluate the mathematical thinking and strategies of others
- Use the language of mathematics to express mathematical ideas precisely

Background and Progression To effectively communicate mathematically, students need ample opportunity to express math in words, in symbols, through models, and orally.

Prentice Hall Mathematics integrates a vocabulary strand that includes short help tips related to vocabulary and symbols as well as full-page features.

Students also have opportunities to write about mathematics. Many exercises ask students to justify their work, explain a process, or draw a conclusion.

Connections

- Recognize and use connections among mathematical ideas
- Understand how mathematical ideas interconnect and build on one another to produce a coherent whole
- Recognize and apply mathematics in contexts outside of mathematics

Background and Progression By the upper elementary grades, most students are able to distinguish which one of several approaches might be best to solve a problem.

In ***Prentice Hall Mathematics***, students use alternative methods in More Than One Way features (every chapter). These situations give a rich mix of numeric, algebraic, geometric, and experimental approaches to problems. Each lesson also includes real-world Examples and exercises that provide contexts in mathematics.

Representation

- Create and use representations to organize, record, and communicate mathematical ideas
- Select, apply, and translate among mathematical representations to solve problems
- Use representations to model and interpret physical, social, and mathematical phenomena

Background and Progression Students entering middle grades have experience using concrete and visual models to help develop number concepts.

In ***Prentice Hall Mathematics***, visualization continues with consistent modeling of numbers, operations, and relationships.

Algebraic relationships are represented through tables, patterns, graphs, words, and notation. The use of variables is introduced gradually through the program.

By the end of ***Course 3***, students have learned to identify the most appropriate vehicle for presenting data, which means choosing among various types of graphs.

Course 3 Leveled Pacing Chart

This Leveled Pacing Chart is provided as a guide to help you customize your course and to provide for differentiated instruction. The suggested number of days for each chapter is based on a traditional 45-minute class period and on a 90-minute block period. The total of 160 days of instruction leaves time for assessments, projects, assemblies, or other special days that vary from school to school.

Differentiated Instruction
Solutions for All Learners

	Below Level L2	On Level	Advanced L4
Chapter 1 Integers and Algebraic Expressions Traditional 14 days Block 7 days			
1-1 Algebraic Expressions and the Order of Operations	✓	✓	✓
Vocabulary Builder: High-Use Use Academic Words	✓	✓	✓
1-2 Integers and Absolute Value	✓	✓	✓
1-2b Activity Lab, Data Analysis: Integers and Differences	✓	✓	✓
1-3a Activity Lab: Adding Integers	✓	✓	✓
1-3 Adding and Subtracting Integers	✓	✓	✓
1-4 Multiplying and Dividing Integers	✓	✓	✓
Guided Problem Solving: Solving Multiple-Step Problems	✓	✓	✓
1-5 Properties of Numbers	✓	✓	✓
1-6a Activity Lab, Hands-On: Modeling Equations	✓	✓	
1-6 Solving Equations by Adding and Subtracting	✓	✓	✓
1-6b Activity Lab: Number Squares	✓	✓	✓
1-7 Solving Equations by Multiplying and Dividing	✓	✓	✓
1-7b Activity Lab, Algebra Thinking: The Cover-up Method	✓	✓	✓
Problem Solving Application: Applying Integers	✓	✓	✓
Chapter 2 Rational Numbers Traditional 15 days Block 8 days			
2-1 Factors	✓	✓	✓
2-2 Equivalent Forms of Rational Numbers	✓	✓	✓
2-2b Activity Lab: Repeating Decimals	✓	✓	✓
2-3 Comparing and Ordering Rational Numbers	✓	✓	✓
2-4 Adding and Subtracting Rational Numbers	✓	✓	✓
2-5a Activity Lab: Modeling Fraction Multiplication	✓	✓	✓
2-5 Multiplying and Dividing Rational Numbers	✓	✓	✓
Vocabulary Builder: Learning Vocabulary	✓	✓	✓
Guided Problem Solving: Practice Solving Problems	✓	✓	✓
2-6a Activity Lab, Algebra Thinking: Estimating Solutions	✓	✓	✓
2-6 Formulas	✓	✓	✓
2-6b Activity Lab, Technology: Using Formulas		✓	✓
2-7 Powers and Exponents	✓	✓	✓
2-7b Activity Lab, Technology: Evaluating Expressions	✓	✓	✓
2-8a Activity Lab: Multiplying by Powers of 10	✓	✓	✓
2-8 Scientific Notation	✓	✓	✓
2-8b Activity Lab, Data Analysis: Writing Measurements	✓	✓	✓
Problem Solving Application: Applying Real Numbers	✓	✓	✓
Chapter 3 Real Numbers and the Coordinate Plane Traditional 15 days Block 8 days			
3-1 Exploring Square Roots and Irrational Numbers	✓	✓	✓
3-2a Activity Lab, Hands On: Exploring the Pythagorean Theorem	✓	✓	✓
3-2 The Pythagorean Theorem	✓	✓	✓
Guided Problem Solving: Squares and Square Roots	✓	✓	✓
3-3 Using the Pythagorean Theorem	✓	✓	✓
Extension: Analyzing Triangles			✓
3-4 Graphing in the Coordinate Plane	✓	✓	✓

	Below Level L2	On Level	Advanced L4
3-4b Activity Lab: Finding the Midpoint	✓	✓	✓
3-5a Activity Lab, Data Analysis: Tables and Graphs	✓	✓	✓
3-5 Equations, Tables, and Graphs	✓	✓	✓
3-5b Activity Lab, Algebra Thinking: Matching Graphs	✓	✓	✓
3-6 Translations	✓	✓	✓
3-7a Activity Lab, Hands On: Exploring Reflections	✓	✓	✓
3-7 Reflections and Symmetry	✓	✓	✓
3-8a Activity Lab, Hands On: Exploring Rotations	✓	✓	✓
3-8 Rotations	✓	✓	✓
Extension: Tessellations	✓	✓	✓
Problem Solving Application: Applying Rate of Change	✓	✓	✓
Chapter 4 Applications of Proportions Traditional 13 days Block 7 days			
4-1 Ratios and Rates	✓	✓	✓
4-1b Activity Lab: Finding Rates	✓	✓	✓
4-2a Activity Lab: Choosing Units	✓	✓	✓
4-2 Converting Units	✓	✓	✓
4-3a Activity Lab: Proportional and Nonproportional Relationships	✓	✓	✓
4-3 Solving Proportions	✓	✓	✓
Guided Problem Solving: Using Rates and Proportions	✓	✓	✓
4-4 Similar Figures and Proportions	✓	✓	✓
4-4b Activity Lab: Ratios of Similar Figures	✓	✓	✓
4-5a Activity Lab: Exploring Dilations	✓	✓	✓
4-5 Similarity Transformations	✓	✓	✓
4-5b Activity Lab, Technology: Geometry Software and Dilations			✓
4-6 Scale Models and Maps	✓	✓	✓
4-7a Activity Lab, Hands On: Using Similar Figures	✓	✓	
4-7 Similarity and Indirect Measurement	✓	✓	✓
Problem Solving Application: Applying Proportions	✓	✓	✓
Chapter 5 Applications of Percent Traditional 13 days Block 7 days			
5-1 Fractions, Decimals, and Percents	✓	✓	✓
5-2 Estimating With Percents	✓	✓	✓
5-3 Percents and Proportions	✓	✓	✓
5-3b Activity Lab, Data Analysis: Percents and Graphs	✓	✓	✓
5-4 Percents and Equations	✓	✓	✓
Vocabulary Builder: High-Use Academic Words	✓	✓	✓
5-5a Activity Lab: Describing Change	✓	✓	✓
5-5 Percent of Change	✓	✓	✓
5-6 Markup and Discount	✓	✓	✓
5-6b Activity Lab, Hands On: Using Percents	✓	✓	
Guided Problem Solving: Practice Solving Problems	✓	✓	✓
5-7 Simple Interest	✓	✓	✓
5-8a Activity Lab, Hands On: Exploring Probability	✓	✓	✓
5-8 Ratios and Probability			✓
Problem Solving Application: Applying Percents	✓	✓	✓
Chapter 6 Equations and Inequalities Traditional 11 days Block 6 days			
6-1a Activity Lab, Hands On: Modeling Multi-Step Equations	✓	✓	✓
6-1 Solving Two-Step Equations	✓	✓	✓
6-2a Activity Lab, Hands On: Modeling Expressions	✓	✓	
6-2 Simplifying Algebraic Expressions	✓	✓	✓
6-3 Solving Multi-Step Equations	✓	✓	✓
6-4 Solving Equations With Variables on Both Sides	✓	✓	✓
Guided Problem Solving: Writing Equations	✓	✓	✓
6-5a Activity Lab: Graphing Inequalities	✓	✓	✓
6-5 Solving Inequalities by Adding or Subtracting	✓	✓	✓

Differentiated Instruction

	Below Level L2	On Level	Advanced L4
Vocabulary Builder: High-Use Academic Words	✓	✓	✓
6-6a Activity Lab: Inequalities and Negative Numbers	✓	✓	✓
6-6 Solving Inequalities by Multiplying or Dividing	✓	✓	✓
Problem Solving Application: Applying Equations	✓	✓	✓
Chapter 7 Geometry Traditional 15 days Block 7 days			
7-1a Activity Lab, Hands On: Exploring Pairs of Angles	✓	✓	✓
7-1 Pairs of Angles	✓	✓	✓
7-2 Angles and Parallel Lines	✓	✓	✓
7-2b Activity Lab, Algebra Thinking: Solving Angle Equations	✓	✓	✓
7-3 Congruent Polygons	✓	✓	✓
7-4 Classifying Triangles and Quadrilaterals	✓	✓	✓
Vocabulary Builder: Using Concept Maps	✓	✓	✓
7-5a Activity Lab: Angle Sums	✓	✓	✓
7-5 Angles and Polygons	✓	✓	✓
7-6 Areas of Polygons	✓	✓	✓
Guided Problem Solving: Geoboard Area	✓	✓	✓
7-7a Activity Lab, Hands On: Estimating Area	✓	✓	
7-7 Circumference and Area of a Circle	✓	✓	✓
Extension: Arcs, Chords, and Semicircles			✓
7-8 Constructions		✓	✓
7-8b Activity Lab, Technology: Geometry Software and Constructions			✓
Problem Solving Application: Applying Geometry	✓	✓	✓
Chapter 8 Measurement Traditional 16 days Block 8 days			
8-1 Solids	✓	✓	✓
8-2 Drawing Views of Three-Dimensional Figures	✓	✓	✓
8-2b Activity Lab: Sketching Solids	✓	✓	✓
8-3a Activity Lab, Hands On: Making Solids From Nets	✓	✓	✓
8-3 Nets and Three-Dimensional Figures	✓	✓	✓
8-4a Activity Lab, Hands On: Modeling Surface Area	✓	✓	✓
8-4 Surface Areas of Prisms and Cylinders	✓	✓	✓
8-5a Activity Lab, Hands On: Surface Area of a Pyramid	✓	✓	✓
8-5 Surface Areas of Pyramids and Cones	✓	✓	✓
8-6a Activity Lab, Hands On: Modeling Volume	✓	✓	✓
8-6 Volume of Prisms and Cylinders	✓	✓	✓
Guided Problem Solving: Using Formulas	✓	✓	✓
8-7a Activity Lab, Hands On: Finding Volume Using Models	✓	✓	✓
8-7 Volumes of Pyramids and Cones	✓	✓	✓
8-8 Spheres	✓	✓	✓
8-9a Activity Lab: Changing Dimensions	✓	✓	✓
8-9 Exploring Similar Solids			✓
Activity Lab, Data Analysis: Precision and Significant Digits		✓	✓
Problem Solving Application: Applying Measurement	✓	✓	✓
Chapter 9 Using Graphs to Analyze Data Traditional 15 days Block 7 days			
9-1 Finding Mean, Median, and Mode	✓	✓	✓
9-1b Activity Lab, Data Collection: Comparing Mean and Median	✓	✓	✓
9-2 Displaying Frequency	✓	✓	✓
9-2b Activity Lab, Technology: Making Historgrams	✓	✓	✓
9-3 Venn Diagrams	✓	✓	✓
9-4a Activity Lab, Data Analysis: Reading Graphical Displays	✓	✓	✓
9-4 Reading Graphs Critically	✓	✓	✓
9-4b Activity Lab, Data Analysis: Making Graphs to Tell a Story	✓	✓	✓
9-5 Stem-and-Leaf Plots	✓	✓	✓
9-6 Box-and-Whisker Plots	✓	✓	✓

Differentiated Instruction

	Below Level L2	On Level	Advanced L4
9-6b Activity Lab, Technology: Making Box-and-Whisker Plots	✓	✓	✓
9-7a Activity Lab, Data Collection: Scatter Plots	✓	✓	✓
9-7 Making Predictions From Scatter Plots	✓	✓	✓
9-7b Activity Lab, Algebra Thinking: Plotting a Strategy	✓	✓	✓
9-8 Circle Graphs	✓	✓	✓
Guided Problem Solving: Equations and Graphs	✓	✓	✓
9-9 Choosing an Appropriate Graph		✓	✓
9-9b Activity Lab, Technology: Graphing Data Using Spreadsheets		✓	✓
Problem Solving Application: Applying Data Analysis	✓	✓	✓
Chapter 10 Probability Traditional 11 days Block 5 days			
10-1 Theoretical and Experimental Probability	✓	✓	✓
10-2a Activity Lab, Hands On: Fair Games	✓	✓	✓
10-2 Making Predictions	✓	✓	✓
Extension: Complements and Probability			✓
10-3 Conducting a Survey	✓	✓	✓
10-3b Activity Lab, Technology: Simulations With Random Numbers	✓	✓	✓
10-4a Activity Lab, Hands On: Comparing Types of Events	✓	✓	✓
10-4 Independent and Dependent Events	✓	✓	✓
10-5 Permutations	✓	✓	✓
10-6 Combinations		✓	✓
Vocabulary Builder: Understanding Vocabulary	✓	✓	✓
Guided Problem Solving: Permutation, Combinations, and Probability	✓	✓	✓
Problem Solving Application: Applying Probability	✓	✓	✓
Chapter 11 Functions Traditional 13 days Block 6 days			
11-1 Sequences	✓	✓	✓
11-1b Activity Lab, Technology: Exploring Sequences		✓	✓
11-2 Relating Graphs to Events		✓	✓
11-2b Activity Lab, Data Collection: Line Graphs	✓	✓	✓
11-3 Functions	✓	✓	✓
11-4a Activity Lab: Rate of Change	✓	✓	✓
11-4 Understanding Slope	✓	✓	✓
Extension: Parallel and Perpendicular Lines			✓
11-5a Activity Lab, Technology: Graphing Lines	✓	✓	✓
11-5 Graphing Linear Functions	✓	✓	✓
11-6 Writing Rules for Linear Functions	✓	✓	✓
Guided Problem Solving: Linear Functions	✓	✓	✓
11-7 Quadratic and Other Nonlinear Functions	✓	✓	✓
11-7b Activity Lab, Data Analysis: Changing Representations	✓	✓	✓
Problem Solving Application: Applying Quadratic Functions	✓	✓	✓
Chapter 12 Polynomials and Properties of Exponents Traditional 9 days Block 4 days			
12-1a Activity Lab, Algebra Thinking: Writing Expressions	✓	✓	✓
12-1 Exploring Polynomials		✓	✓
12-2 Adding and Subtracting Polynomials			✓
12-3a Activity Lab: Exploring Exponents	✓	✓	✓
12-3 Exponents and Multiplication	✓	✓	✓
12-3b Activity Lab, Technology: Scientific Notation	✓	✓	✓
12-4 Multiplying Polynomials			✓
12-5 Exponents and Division	✓	✓	✓
Extension: Power Rules			✓
Guided Problem Solving: Solving Equations	✓	✓	✓
Problem Solving Application: Applying Scientific Notation	✓	✓	✓

Using Your Book for Success

Welcome to *Prentice Hall Course 3*.
There are many features built into the daily lessons of this text that will help you learn the important skills and concepts you will need to be successful in this course. Look through the following pages for some study tips that you will find useful as you complete each lesson.

Getting Ready to Learn

Check Your Readiness

Complete the *Check Your Readiness* exercises to see what topics you may need to review before you begin the chapter.

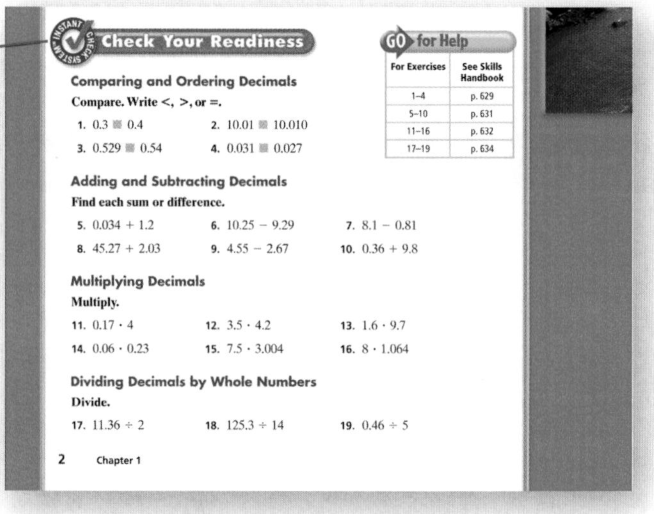
INSTANT CHECK SYSTEM Check Your Readiness

GO for Help

For Exercises	See Skills Handbook
1–4	p. 629
5–10	p. 631
11–16	p. 632
17–19	p. 634

Comparing and Ordering Decimals
Compare. Write <, >, or =.
1. 0.3 ■ 0.4
2. 10.01 ■ 10.010
3. 0.529 ■ 0.54
4. 0.031 ■ 0.027

Adding and Subtracting Decimals
Find each sum or difference.
5. 0.034 + 1.2
6. 10.25 − 9.29
7. 8.1 − 0.81
8. 45.27 + 2.03
9. 4.55 − 2.67
10. 0.36 + 9.8

Multiplying Decimals
Multiply.
11. 0.17 · 4
12. 3.5 · 4.2
13. 1.6 · 9.7
14. 0.06 · 0.23
15. 7.5 · 3.004
16. 8 · 1.064

Dividing Decimals by Whole Numbers
Divide.
17. 11.36 ÷ 2
18. 125.3 ÷ 14
19. 0.46 ÷ 5

2 Chapter 1

Check Skills You'll Need

Complete the *Check Skills You'll Need* exercises to make sure you have the skills needed to successfully learn the concepts in the lesson.

New Vocabulary

New Vocabulary is listed for each lesson, so you can pre-read the text. As each term is introduced, it is highlighted in yellow.

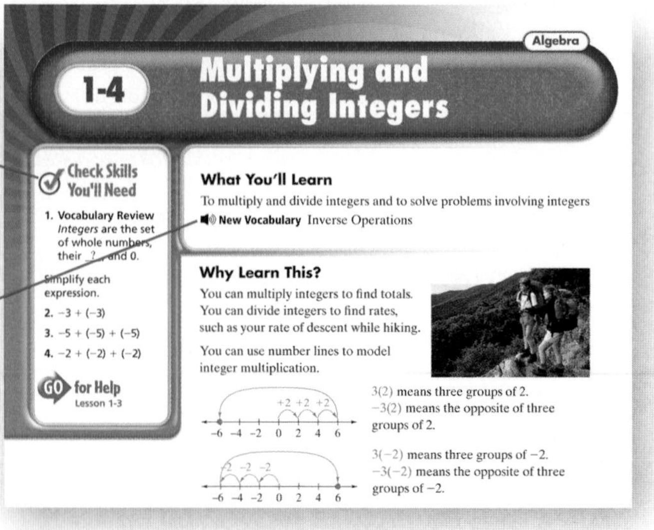
Algebra

1-4 Multiplying and Dividing Integers

Check Skills You'll Need
1. Vocabulary Review *Integers* are the set of whole numbers, their ?, and 0.
Simplify each expression.
2. −3 + (−3)
3. −5 + (−5) + (−5)
4. −2 + (−2) + (−2)
GO for Help Lesson 1-3

What You'll Learn
To multiply and divide integers and to solve problems involving integers
New Vocabulary Inverse Operations

Why Learn This?
You can multiply integers to find totals. You can divide integers to find rates, such as your rate of descent while hiking.

You can use number lines to model integer multiplication.

3(2) means three groups of 2.
−3(2) means the opposite of three groups of 2.

3(−2) means three groups of −2.
−3(−2) means the opposite of three groups of −2.

Built-In Help

Go for Help

Look for the green labels throughout your book that tell you where to "Go" for help. You'll see this built-in help in the lessons and in the homework exercises.

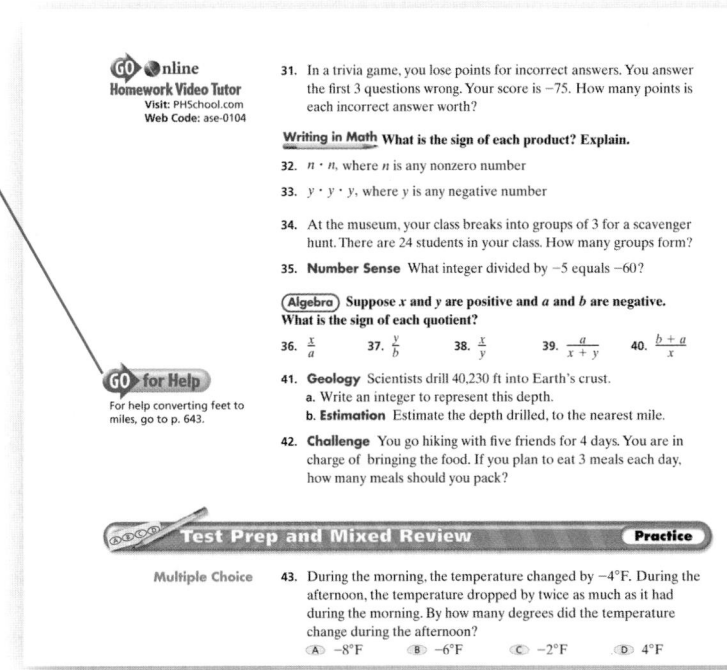

GO Online
Homework Video Tutor
Visit: PHSchool.com
Web Code: ase-0104

31. In a trivia game, you lose points for incorrect answers. You answer the first 3 questions wrong. Your score is −75. How many points is each incorrect answer worth?

Writing in Math **What is the sign of each product? Explain.**

32. $n \cdot n$, where n is any nonzero number

33. $y \cdot y \cdot y$, where y is any negative number

34. At the museum, your class breaks into groups of 3 for a scavenger hunt. There are 24 students in your class. How many groups form?

35. **Number Sense** What integer divided by −5 equals −60?

Algebra **Suppose x and y are positive and a and b are negative. What is the sign of each quotient?**

36. $\frac{x}{a}$ 37. $\frac{y}{b}$ 38. $\frac{x}{y}$ 39. $\frac{a}{x+y}$ 40. $\frac{b+a}{x}$

GO for Help
For help converting feet to miles, go to p. 643.

41. **Geology** Scientists drill 40,230 ft into Earth's crust.
a. Write an integer to represent this depth.
b. **Estimation** Estimate the depth drilled, to the nearest mile.

42. **Challenge** You go hiking with five friends for 4 days. You are in charge of bringing the food. If you plan to eat 3 meals each day, how many meals should you pack?

Test Prep and Mixed Review **Practice**

Multiple Choice

43. During the morning, the temperature changed by −4°F. During the afternoon, the temperature dropped by twice as much as it had during the morning. By how many degrees did the temperature change during the afternoon?
Ⓐ −8°F Ⓑ −6°F Ⓒ −2°F Ⓓ 4°F

Video Tutor Help

Go online to see engaging videos to help you better understand important math concepts.

GO Online

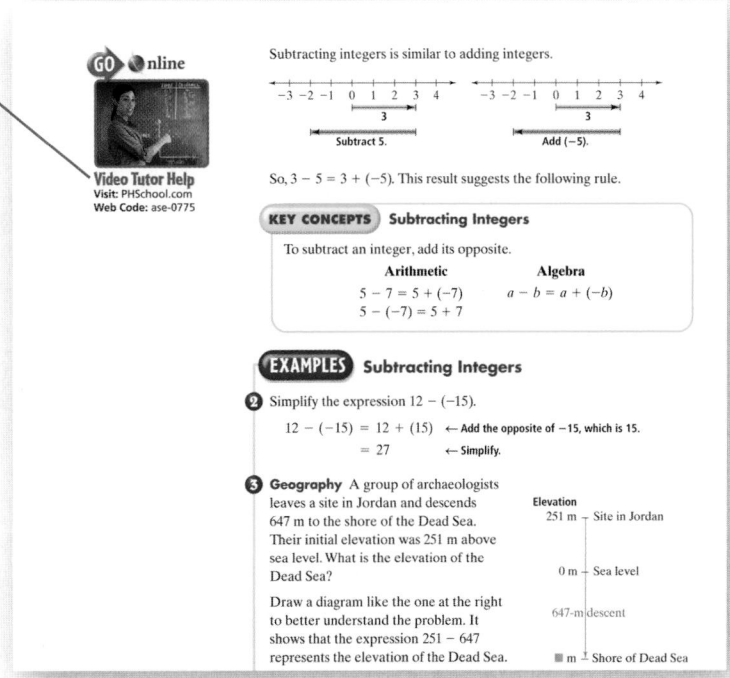

Video Tutor Help
Visit: PHSchool.com
Web Code: ase-0775

Subtracting integers is similar to adding integers.

−3 −2 −1 0 1 2 3 4 (3; Subtract 5.)   −3 −2 −1 0 1 2 3 4 (3; Add (−5).)

So, 3 − 5 = 3 + (−5). This result suggests the following rule.

KEY CONCEPTS **Subtracting Integers**

To subtract an integer, add its opposite.

Arithmetic	**Algebra**
5 − 7 = 5 + (−7)	$a - b = a + (-b)$
5 − (−7) = 5 + 7	

EXAMPLES **Subtracting Integers**

2. Simplify the expression 12 − (−15).

12 − (−15) = 12 + (15) ← Add the opposite of −15, which is 15.
= 27 ← Simplify.

3. **Geography** A group of archaeologists leaves a site in Jordan and descends 647 m to the shore of the Dead Sea. Their initial elevation was 251 m above sea level. What is the elevation of the Dead Sea?

Draw a diagram like the one at the right to better understand the problem. It shows that the expression 251 − 647 represents the elevation of the Dead Sea.

Elevation
251 m — Site in Jordan
0 m — Sea level
647-m descent
■ m — Shore of Dead Sea

Understanding the Mathematics

Quick Check

Every lesson includes numerous examples, each followed by a *Quick Check* question that you can do on your own to see if you understand the skill being introduced. Check your progress with the answers at the back of the book.

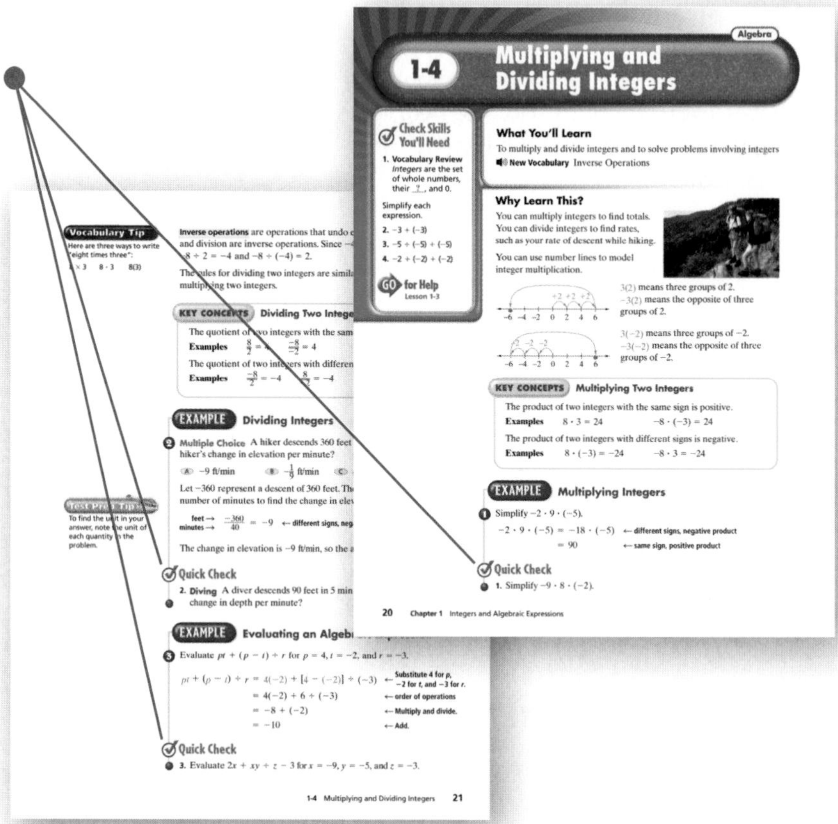
Algebra

1-4 Multiplying and Dividing Integers

Check Skills You'll Need

1. Vocabulary Review *Integers* are the set of whole numbers, their ?, and 0.

Simplify each expression.

2. $-3 + (-3)$
3. $-5 + (-5) + (-5)$
4. $-2 + (-2) + (-2)$

GO for Help Lesson 1-3

What You'll Learn

To multiply and divide integers and to solve problems involving integers

New Vocabulary Inverse Operations

Why Learn This?

You can multiply integers to find totals. You can divide integers to find rates, such as your rate of descent while hiking.

You can use number lines to model integer multiplication.

3(2) means three groups of 2. −3(2) means the opposite of three groups of 2.

3(−2) means three groups of −2. −3(−2) means the opposite of three groups of −2.

KEY CONCEPTS Multiplying Two Integers

The product of two integers with the same sign is positive.

Examples $8 \cdot 3 = 24$ $-8 \cdot (-3) = 24$

The product of two integers with different signs is negative.

Examples $8 \cdot (-3) = -24$ $-8 \cdot 3 = -24$

EXAMPLE Multiplying Integers

1 Simplify $-2 \cdot 9 \cdot (-5)$.

$-2 \cdot 9 \cdot (-5) = -18 \cdot (-5)$ ← different signs, negative product

$= 90$ ← same sign, positive product

Quick Check

1. Simplify $-9 \cdot 8 \cdot (-2)$.

20 Chapter 1 Integers and Algebraic Expressions

EXAMPLE Evaluating an Algebraic Expression

3 Evaluate $pt + (p - t) \div r$ for $p = 4$, $t = -2$, and $r = -3$.

Quick Check

3. Evaluate $2x + xy + z - 3$ for $x = -9$, $y = -5$, and $z = -3$.

1-4 Multiplying and Dividing Integers 21

Understanding Key Concepts

Frequent *Key Concept* boxes summarize important definitions, formulas, and properties. Use these to review what you've learned.

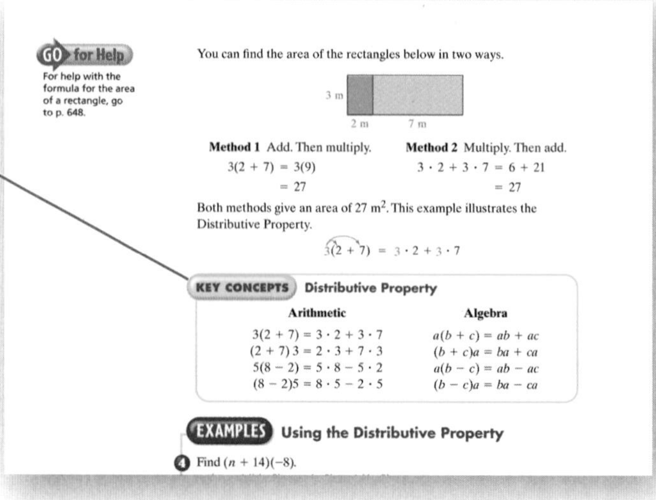
GO for Help For help with the formula for the area of a rectangle, go to p. 648.

You can find the area of the rectangles below in two ways.

Method 1 Add. Then multiply. $3(2 + 7) = 3(9) = 27$

Method 2 Multiply. Then add. $3 \cdot 2 + 3 \cdot 7 = 6 + 21 = 27$

Both methods give an area of 27 m^2. This example illustrates the Distributive Property.

$3(2 + 7) = 3 \cdot 2 + 3 \cdot 7$

KEY CONCEPTS Distributive Property

Arithmetic	Algebra
$3(2 + 7) = 3 \cdot 2 + 3 \cdot 7$	$a(b + c) = ab + ac$
$(2 + 7)3 = 2 \cdot 3 + 7 \cdot 3$	$(b + c)a = ba + ca$
$5(8 - 2) = 5 \cdot 8 - 5 \cdot 2$	$a(b - c) = ab - ac$
$(8 - 2)5 = 8 \cdot 5 - 2 \cdot 5$	$(b - c)a = ba - ca$

EXAMPLES Using the Distributive Property

4 Find $(n + 14)(-8)$.

Online Active Math

Make math come alive with these online activities. Review and practice important math concepts with these engaging online tutorials.

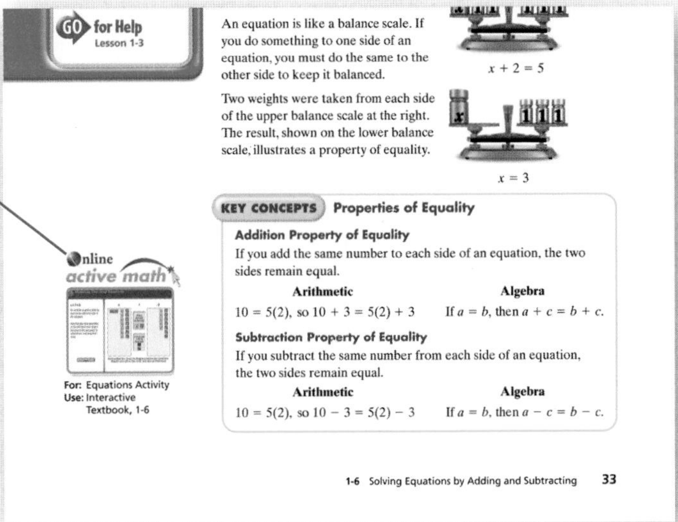
GO for Help
Lesson 1-3

An equation is like a balance scale. If you do something to one side of an equation, you must do the same to the other side to keep it balanced.

$x + 2 = 5$

Two weights were taken from each side of the upper balance scale at the right. The result, shown on the lower balance scale, illustrates a property of equality.

$x = 3$

Online active math

For: Equations Activity
Use: Interactive Textbook, 1-6

KEY CONCEPTS Properties of Equality

Addition Property of Equality
If you add the same number to each side of an equation, the two sides remain equal.

Arithmetic	Algebra
$10 = 5(2)$, so $10 + 3 = 5(2) + 3$	If $a = b$, then $a + c = b + c$.

Subtraction Property of Equality
If you subtract the same number from each side of an equation, the two sides remain equal.

Arithmetic	Algebra
$10 = 5(2)$, so $10 - 3 = 5(2) - 3$	If $a = b$, then $a - c = b - c$.

1-6 Solving Equations by Adding and Subtracting 33

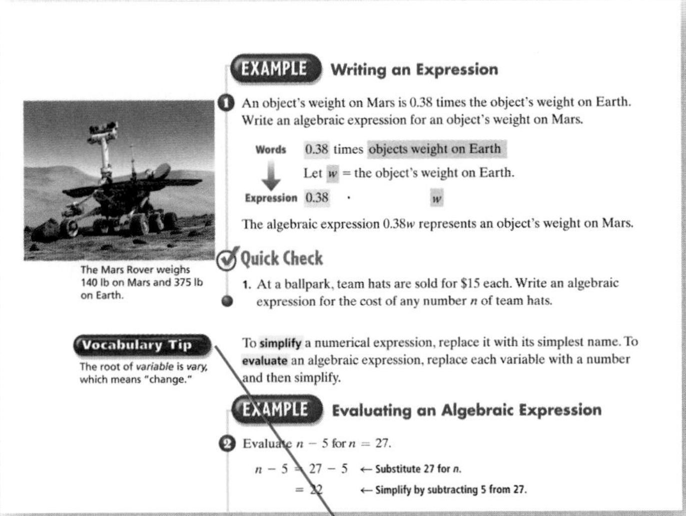
EXAMPLE Writing an Expression

1 An object's weight on Mars is 0.38 times the object's weight on Earth. Write an algebraic expression for an object's weight on Mars.

Words: 0.38 times objects weight on Earth
Let w = the object's weight on Earth.
Expression: $0.38 \cdot w$

The algebraic expression $0.38w$ represents an object's weight on Mars.

The Mars Rover weighs 140 lb on Mars and 375 lb on Earth.

Quick Check
1. At a ballpark, team hats are sold for $15 each. Write an algebraic expression for the cost of any number n of team hats.

Vocabulary Tip
The root of *variable* is *vary*, which means "change."

To **simplify** a numerical expression, replace it with its simplest name. To **evaluate** an algebraic expression, replace each variable with a number and then simplify.

EXAMPLE Evaluating an Algebraic Expression

2 Evaluate $n - 5$ for $n = 27$.

$n - 5 = 27 - 5$ ← Substitute 27 for n.
$= 22$ ← Simplify by subtracting 5 from 27.

Vocabulary Support

Understanding mathematical vocabulary is an important part of studying mathematics. *Vocabulary Tips* and *Vocabulary Builders* throughout the book help focus on the language of math.

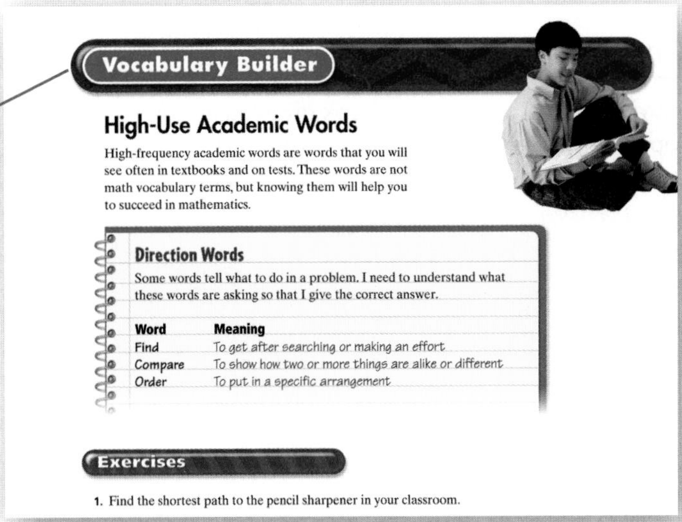
Vocabulary Builder

High-Use Academic Words

High-frequency academic words are words that you will see often in textbooks and on tests. These words are not math vocabulary terms, but knowing them will help you to succeed in mathematics.

Direction Words
Some words tell what to do in a problem. I need to understand what these words are asking so that I give the correct answer.

Word	Meaning
Find	To get after searching or making an effort
Compare	To show how two or more things are alike or different
Order	To put in a specific arrangement

Exercises

1. Find the shortest path to the pencil sharpener in your classroom.

Using Your Book for Success

Understanding the Mathematics

Guided Problem Solving

These features throughout your Student Edition provide practice in problem solving. Solved from a student's point of view, this feature focuses on the thinking and reasoning that goes into solving a problem.

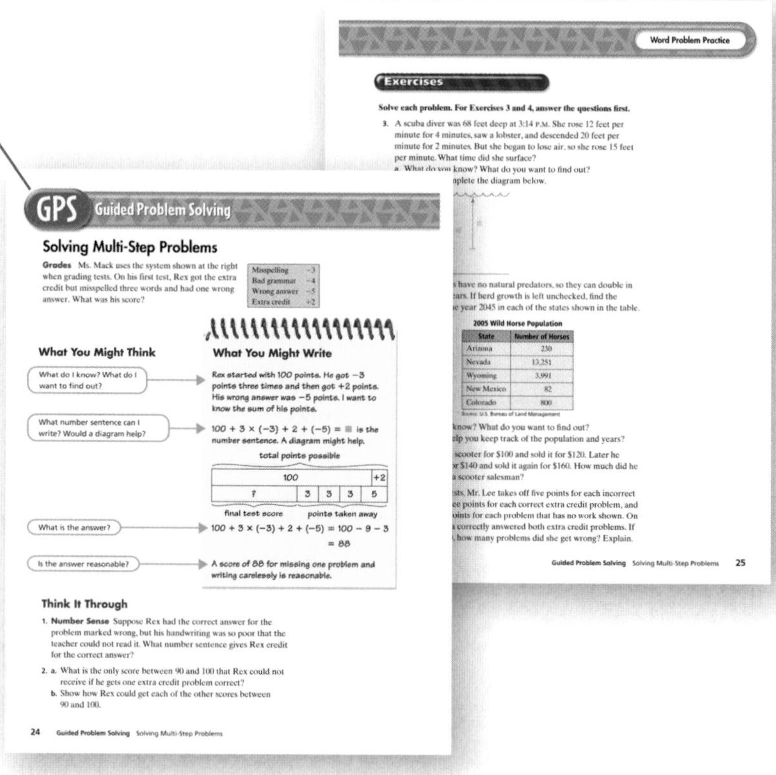
Word Problem Practice

Exercises

Solve each problem. For Exercises 3 and 4, answer the questions first.

3. A scuba diver was 68 feet deep at 3:14 P.M. She rose 12 feet per minute for 4 minutes, saw a lobster, and descended 20 feet per minute for 2 minutes. But she began to lose air, so she rose 15 feet per minute. What time did she surface?

25 Guided Problem Solving Solving Multi-Step Problems

GPS Guided Problem Solving

Solving Multi-Step Problems

Grades Ms. Mack uses the system shown at the right when grading tests. On his first test, Rex got the extra credit but misspelled three words and had one wrong answer. What was his score?

Misspelling	−3
Bad grammar	−4
Wrong answer	−5
Extra credit	+2

What You Might Think / **What You Might Write**

What do I know? What do I want to find out? → Rex started with 100 points. He got −3 points three times and then got +2 points. His wrong answer was −5 points. I want to know the sum of his points.

What number sentence can I write? Would a diagram help? → $100 + 3 \times (-3) + 2 + (-5) = ■$ is the number sentence. A diagram might help.

What is the answer? → $100 + 3 \times (-3) + 2 + (-5) = 100 - 9 - 3 = 88$

Is the answer reasonable? → A score of 88 for missing one problem and writing carelessly is reasonable.

Think It Through

1. **Number Sense** Suppose Rex had the correct answer for the problem marked wrong, but his handwriting was so poor that the teacher could not read it. What number sentence gives Rex credit for the correct answer?
2. a. What is the only score between 90 and 100 that Rex could not receive if he gets one extra credit problem correct?
   b. Show how Rex could get each of the other scores between 90 and 100.

24 Guided Problem Solving Solving Multi-Step Problems

Activity Labs

Activity Labs throughout the book give you an opportunity to explore a concept. Apply the skills you've learned in these engaging activities.

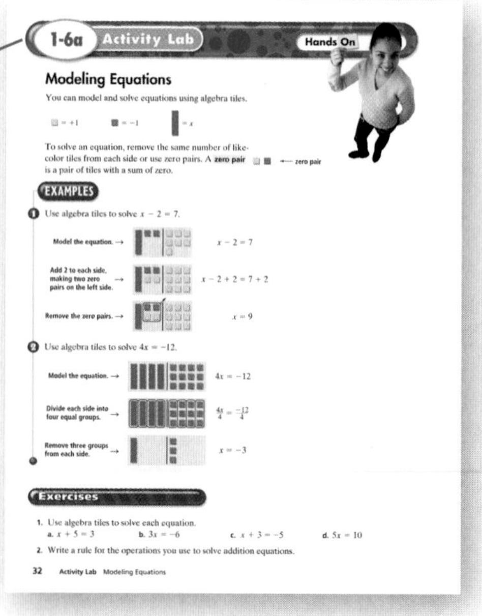
1-6a Activity Lab Hands On

Modeling Equations

You can model and solve equations using algebra tiles.

■ = +1   ■ = −1   ▮ = x

To solve an equation, remove the same number of like-color tiles from each side or use zero pairs. A **zero pair** is a pair of tiles with a sum of zero.

EXAMPLES

1. Use algebra tiles to solve $x - 2 = 7$.
   - Model the equation. → $x - 2 = 7$
   - Add 2 to each side, making two zero pairs on the left side. → $x - 2 + 2 = 7 + 2$
   - Remove the zero pairs. → $x = 9$
2. Use algebra tiles to solve $4x = -12$.
   - Model the equation. → $4x = -12$
   - Divide each side into four equal groups. → $\frac{4x}{4} = \frac{-12}{4}$
   - Remove three groups from each side. → $x = -3$

Exercises

1. Use algebra tiles to solve each equation.
   a. $x + 5 = 3$ b. $3x = -6$ c. $x + 3 = -5$ d. $5x = 10$
2. Write a rule for the operations you use to solve addition equations.

32 Activity Lab Modeling Equations

Practice What You've Learned

There are numerous exercises in each lesson that give you the practice you need to master the concepts in the lesson. The following exercises are included in each lesson.

Check Your Understanding

These exercises help you prepare for the Homework Exercises.

Practice by example

These exercises refer you back to the Examples in the lesson, in case you need help with completing these exercises.

Apply your skills

These exercises combine skills from earlier lessons to offer you richer skill exercises and multi-step application problems.

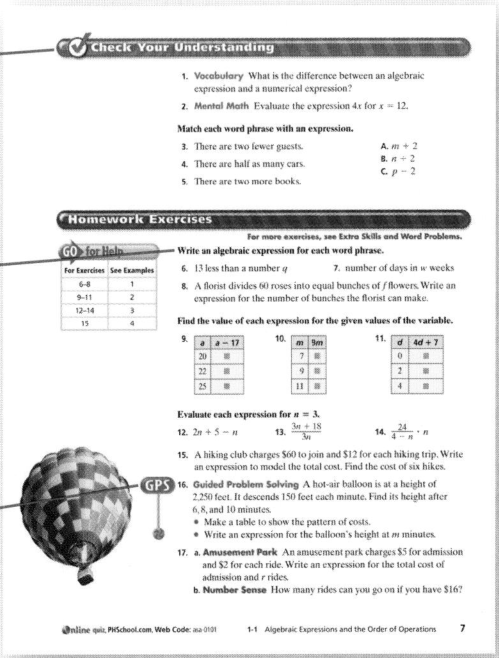

Check Your Understanding

1. **Vocabulary** What is the difference between an algebraic expression and a numerical expression?
2. **Mental Math** Evaluate the expression $4x$ for $x = 12$.

Match each word phrase with an expression.

3. There are two fewer guests.
4. There are half as many cars.
5. There are two more books.

A. $m + 2$
B. $n \div 2$
C. $p - 2$

Homework Exercises

For more exercises, see Extra Skills and Word Problems.

GO for Help

For Exercises	See Examples
6–8	1
9–11	2
12–14	3
15	4

Write an algebraic expression for each word phrase.

6. 13 less than a number q
7. number of days in w weeks
8. A florist divides 60 roses into equal bunches of f flowers. Write an expression for the number of bunches the florist can make.

Find the value of each expression for the given values of the variable.

9.

a	$a - 17$
20	■
22	■
25	■

10.

m	$9m$
7	■
9	■
11	■

11.

d	$4d + 7$
0	■
2	■
4	■

Evaluate each expression for $n = 3$.

12. $2n + 5 - n$
13. $\frac{3n + 18}{3n}$
14. $\frac{24}{4 - n} \cdot n$
15. A hiking club charges $60 to join and $12 for each hiking trip. Write an expression to model the total cost. Find the cost of six hikes.

GPS 16. **Guided Problem Solving** A hot-air balloon is at a height of 2,250 feet. It descends 150 feet each minute. Find its height after 6, 8, and 10 minutes.
- Make a table to show the pattern of costs.
- Write an expression for the balloon's height at m minutes.

17. a. **Amusement Park** An amusement park charges $5 for admission and $2 for each ride. Write an expression for the total cost of admission and r rides.
b. **Number Sense** How many rides can you go on if you have $16?

Online quiz, PHSchool.com, Web Code: asa-0101 1-1 Algebraic Expressions and the Order of Operations 7

Homework Video Tutor

These interactive tutorials provide you with homework help for *every lesson*.

Challenge

This exercise gives you an opportunity to extend and stretch your thinking.

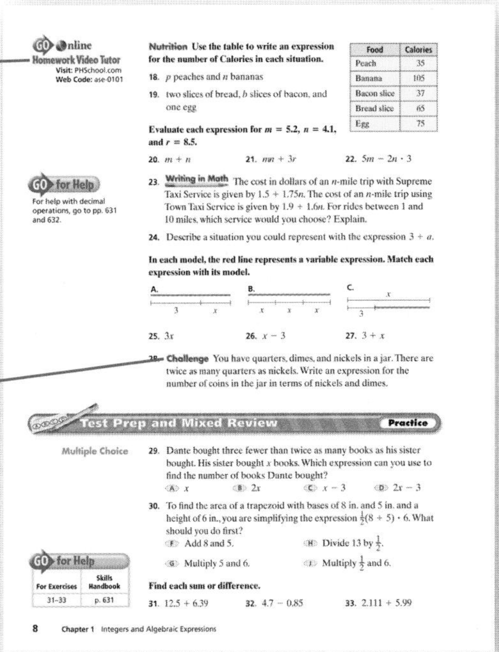

GO Online
Homework Video Tutor
Visit: PHSchool.com
Web Code: ase-0101

Nutrition Use the table to write an expression for the number of Calories in each situation.

Food	Calories
Peach	35
Banana	105
Bacon slice	37
Bread slice	65
Egg	75

18. p peaches and n bananas
19. two slices of bread, b slices of bacon, and one egg

Evaluate each expression for $m = 5.2$, $n = 4.1$, and $r = 8.5$.

20. $m + n$
21. $mn + 3r$
22. $5m - 2n \cdot 3$

GO for Help
For help with decimal operations, go to pp. 631 and 632.

23. **Writing in Math** The cost in dollars of an n-mile trip with Supreme Taxi Service is given by $1.5 + 1.75n$. The cost of an n-mile trip using Town Taxi Service is given by $1.9 + 1.6n$. For rides between 1 and 10 miles, which service would you choose? Explain.
24. Describe a situation you could represent with the expression $3 + a$.

In each model, the red line represents a variable expression. Match each expression with its model.

A. 3 x
B. x x x
C. x 3

25. $3x$
26. $x - 3$
27. $3 + x$
28. **Challenge** You have quarters, dimes, and nickels in a jar. There are twice as many quarters as nickels. Write an expression for the number of coins in the jar in terms of nickels and dimes.

Test Prep and Mixed Review Practice

Multiple Choice

29. Dante bought three fewer than twice as many books as his sister bought. His sister bought x books. Which expression can you use to find the number of books Dante bought?
(A) x (B) $2x$ (C) $x - 3$ (D) $2x - 3$
30. To find the area of a trapezoid with bases of 8 in. and 5 in. and a height of 6 in., you are simplifying the expression $\frac{1}{2}(8 + 5) \cdot 6$. What should you do first?
(F) Add 8 and 5. (H) Divide 13 by $\frac{1}{2}$.
(G) Multiply 5 and 6. (J) Multiply $\frac{1}{2}$ and 6.

GO for Help

For Exercises	Skills Handbook
31–33	p. 631

Find each sum or difference.

31. $12.5 + 6.39$
32. $4.7 - 0.85$
33. $2.111 + 5.99$

8 Chapter 1 Integers and Algebraic Expressions

GO for Help

Intervention This Diagnostic Test covers pre-course skills that students need to succeed in this math program. For intervention, direct students to the following pages from the Skills Handbook in the back of their textbooks.

Exercise	Page
1–5	628
6–9	629
10–13	630
14–17	631
18	632
19	633
20	634
21, 22	635
23	636
24	637
25–28	638
29–32	639
33–36	640
37, 38	641
39, 40	642

Beginning-of-Course Diagnostic Test

For Exercises 1–2, write the value of the underlined digit.

1. $842,\underline{9}76$ nine hundreds
2. $761.03\underline{2}5$ two thousandths
3. Write seven and ninety-six thousandths as a decimal. 7.096
4. Write 9.204 in words. nine and two hundred four thousandths
5. Write 0.000073 in words. seventy-three millionths

For Exercises 6–7, use <, >, or = to compare the decimals.

6. 0.008 __?__ 0.06 <
7. 0.000307 __?__ 0.003007 <

For Exercises 8–11, write the decimals in order from least to greatest.

8. 7.21 0.712 72.1 0.721 0.712, 0.721, 7.21, 72.1
9. 0.01010 0.10101 0.01001 0.00101
   0.00101, 0.01001, 0.01010, 0.10101
10. Round 15,763 to the nearest thousand. 16,000
11. Round 96.853 to the nearest tenth. 96.9

For Exercises 12–13, round to the place of the underlined digit.

12. $123.9\underline{8}47$ 123.98
13. $14\underline{7}.48$ 147

For Exercises 14–17, find each sum or difference.

14. $76.87 - 45.91$ 30.96
15. $21.283 + 9.72$ 31.003
16. $9 - 3.245$ 5.755
17. $1.309 + 2.46 + 2.6$ 6.369

For Exercises 18–24, multiply or divide.

18. 38.6×0.4 15.44
19. $0.0027 \cdot 0.04$ 0.000108
20. $16.8 \div 4$ 4.2
21. $7,354 \div 0.01$ 735,400
22. $5.697 \times 10,000$ 56,970
23. $3.813 \div 4.1$ 0.93
24. $0.002847 \div 0.73$ 0.0039

For Exercises 25–26, write each improper fraction as a mixed number.

25. $\frac{11}{3}$ $3\frac{2}{3}$
26. $\frac{48}{11}$ $4\frac{4}{11}$

For Exercises 27–28, write each mixed number as an improper fraction.

27. $6\frac{4}{7}$ $\frac{46}{7}$
28. $9\frac{1}{8}$ $\frac{73}{8}$

For Exercises 29–32, add or subtract. Write each answer in simplest form.

29. $\frac{9}{12} + \frac{5}{12}$ $1\frac{1}{6}$
30. $\frac{7}{14} - \frac{5}{14}$ $\frac{1}{7}$
31. $6\frac{3}{8} + 8\frac{5}{8}$ 15
32. $9\frac{8}{10} - 7\frac{3}{10}$ $2\frac{1}{2}$

For Exercises 33–34, measure each angle. Classify it as *acute, right, obtuse,* or *straight*.

33.

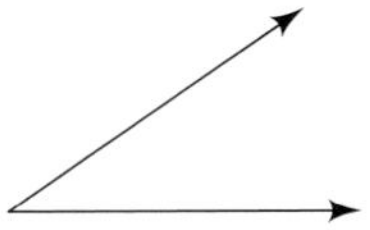

35°; acute

34.

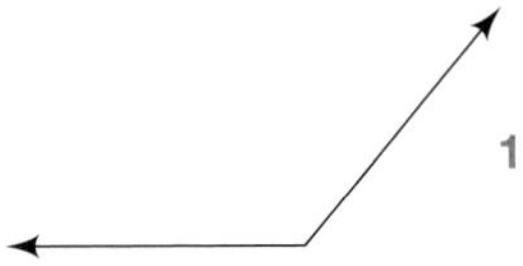

130°; obtuse

For Exercises 35–36, draw an angle with the given measure. 35–40. See margin.

35. 75°

36. 130°

37. Draw a bar graph for the data below.

Number of Movies Rented Per Month

Number of Movies	0	1	2	3	more than 3
Number of Rentals	2	3	7	5	8

38. Draw a double bar graph for the data below.

Favorite Vegetable in Ms. Green's Class

	Corn	Cabbage	Green Beans	Peas
Boys	8	5	6	1
Girls	5	7	6	3

39. Draw a line graph for the data below.

Forest Service Expenditures for Emergency Fire Suppression

Year	Cost Per Acre Burned
1	$388.40
2	$740.65
3	$545.45
4	$818.71
5	$487.56
6	$623.08
7	$575.87
8	$932.54
9	$376.12
10	$640.03
11	$716.67
12	$976.86

40. Draw a double line graph for the data below.

Average Temperatures

Month	Avg. High (°F)	Avg. Low (°F)
January	61	43
February	64	45
March	70	52
April	76	58
May	83	66
June	89	72
July	91	75
August	90	74
September	87	70
October	79	60
November	70	51
December	63	45

35. Check students' work; Sample:

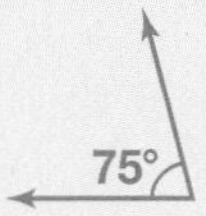

36. Check students' work; Sample:

37.

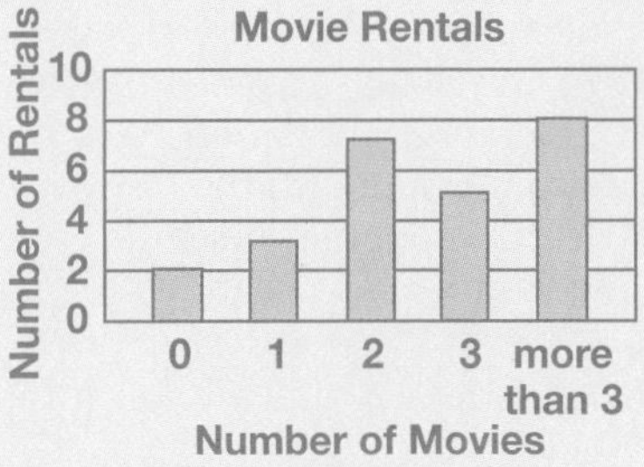

38.

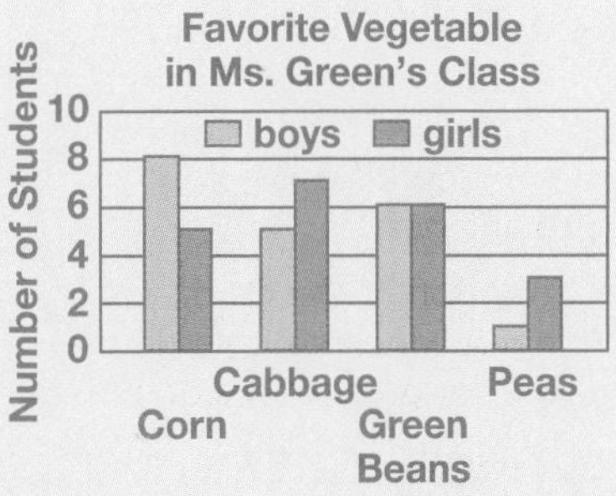

Diagnostic Test

39.

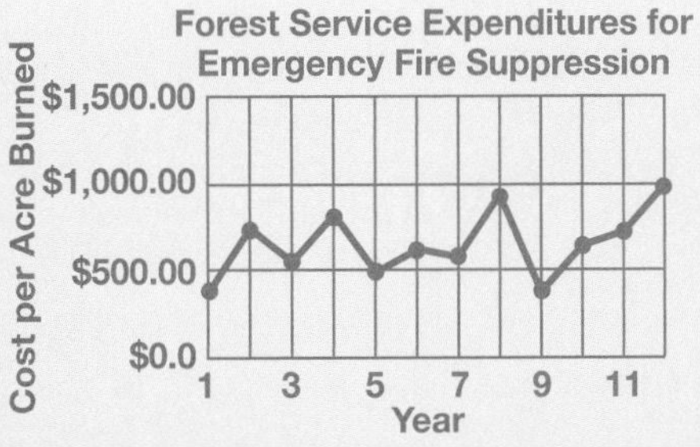

40.

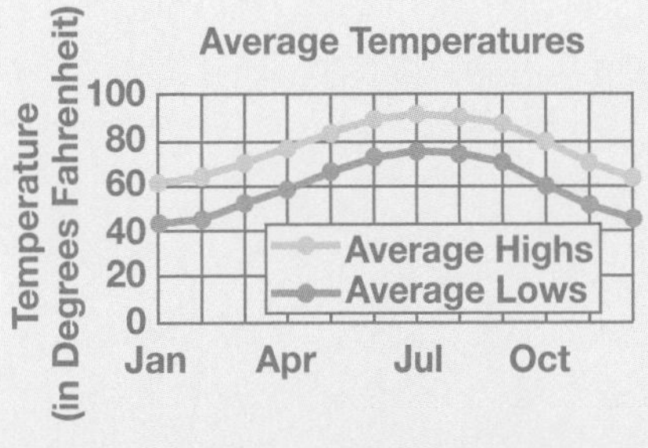

Using the Problem Solving Plan

Throughout this text, students will be encouraged to use the four-step problem-solving plan that is outlined in this lesson. This approach gives students a simple yet effective framework for organizing their work in the process of solving a problem. Rather than having students haphazardly approach the task of problem solving, this four-step plan gives them an organized procedure to follow for a wide range of problems.

Guided Instruction

Students should remember these key phrases: Understand the Problem; Make a Plan; Carry out the Plan; Check for Reasonableness.

Call attention to the list of problem-solving strategies in the text. Ask for an example of each.

Have students brainstorm strategies that they can use to solve real-world problems such as Make a Table. Write up their ideas on poster board and display them in the room for students' reference.

Error Prevention!

Students often focus on one condition of a problem and forget another. Stress the importance of checking that a proposed solution satisfies all the conditions of the problem.

Problem Solving Handbook

Using the Problem Solving Plan

One of the most important skills you can have is the ability to solve problems. An integral part of learning mathematics is how adept you become at unraveling problems and looking back to see how you found the solution. Maybe you don't realize it, but you solve problems every day—some problems are easy to solve, and others are challenging and require a good plan of action. In this Problem Solving Handbook you will learn how to work through mathematical problems using a simple four-step plan:

THE 4-STEP PLAN

1. **Understand** **Understand the problem.**
   Read the problem. Ask yourself, "What information is given? What is missing? What am I being asked to find or to do?"

2. **Plan** **Make a plan to solve the problem.**
   Choose a strategy. As you use problem solving strategies throughout this book, you will decide which one is best for the problem you are trying to solve.

3. **Carry Out** **Carry out the plan.**
   Solve the problem using your plan. Organize your work.

4. **Check** **Check the answer to be sure it is reasonable.**
   Look back at your work and compare it against the information and question(s) in the problem. Ask yourself, "Is my answer reasonable? Did I check my work?"

Problem Solving Strategies

Creating a good plan to solve a problem means that you will need to choose a strategy. What is the best way to solve that challenging problem? Perhaps drawing a diagram or making a table will lead to a solution. A problem might seem to have too many steps. Maybe working a simpler problem is the key. There are a number of strategies to choose from. You will decide which strategy is most effective.

As you work through this book, you will encounter many opportunities to improve your problem solving and reasoning skills. Working through mathematical problems using this four-step process will help you to organize your thoughts, develop your reasoning skills, and explain how you arrived at a particular solution.

Putting this problem solving plan to use will allow you to work through mathematical problems with confidence. Getting in the habit of planning and strategizing for problem solving will result in success in future math courses and high scores on those really important tests!

THE STRATEGIES

Here are some examples of problem solving strategies. Which one will work best for the problem you are trying to solve?

- **Draw a Picture**
- **Look for a Pattern**
- **Systematic Guess and Check**
- **Act It Out**
- **Make a Table**
- **Work a Simpler Problem**
- **Work Backward**
- **Write an Equation**

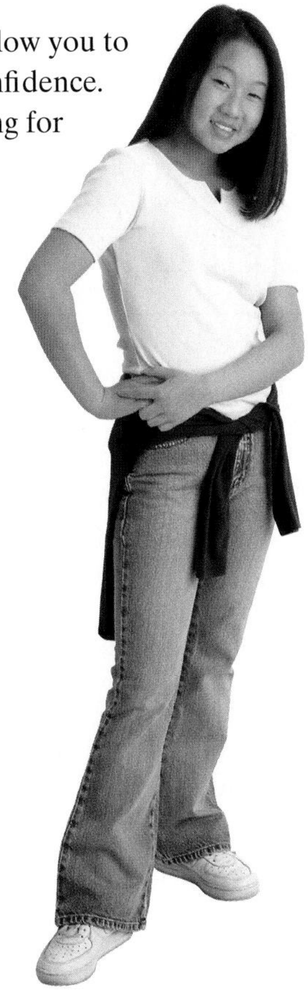

Good Luck!

Data Analysis Connection
Point out that problem-solving strategies are used to solve many types of problems, mathematical and non-mathematical.
Ask questions such as:

- *What are some real-world problems that scientists, mathematicians, professional athletes and coaches, or other professionals might need to analyze?* **Accept all reasonable answers.**

Differentiated Instruction

Visual Learners
To help students remember the four steps of the Problem-Solving Plan, display these phrases on a poster and have students suggest graphics to illustrate each. For instance, they might suggest a telescope to signal Check for Reasonableness.

Problem Solving Handbook

Draw a Picture

Draw a Picture is a visual problem-solving strategy that helps students clarify what information is known and what information remains unknown.

Guided Instruction

Use a concrete model. Cut a piece of cardboard into a rectangular shape (for example, 3 ft long and 4 in. wide). Explain that this represents a board *w* (for whole) feet long. Mark the board as if to cut off a segment *c* feet (for cut off) long. Ask students to represent the length that is left after the cut with an algebraic expression. $w - c$.

Elicit the problem solving steps:

- Understand the Problem
- Make a Plan
- Carry Out the Plan
- Check the Answer

Error Prevention!

Drawing a picture can also help students check the reasonableness of their answers by using their picture to remember to which measurements their answers refer.

Differentiated Instruction

Tactile Learners

Have students make models similar to the one you may have used for the demonstration. Ask how long the leftover piece is. Then discuss how to apply this thinking to the kite problem.

Draw a Picture

When to Use This Strategy Some word problems are hard to solve mentally. In such cases, you can *Draw a Picture* of the problem.

The tail of a kite steadies the kite in the air. One of the longest kites is a Chinese dragon kite. The length of one dragon kite, including its tail, is 21 ft. If the tail is 15 ft longer than the kite body, how long is the body of the kite?

Understand The combined length of the kite tail and body is 21 ft. The tail is 15 ft longer than the kite body. The goal is to find the length of the kite body.

Plan *Draw a Picture* to show that the kite with its tail is 21 ft long and the tail is 15 ft longer than the body.

Carry Out The diagram shows that the total length of 21 ft is equal to 15 ft plus two body lengths.

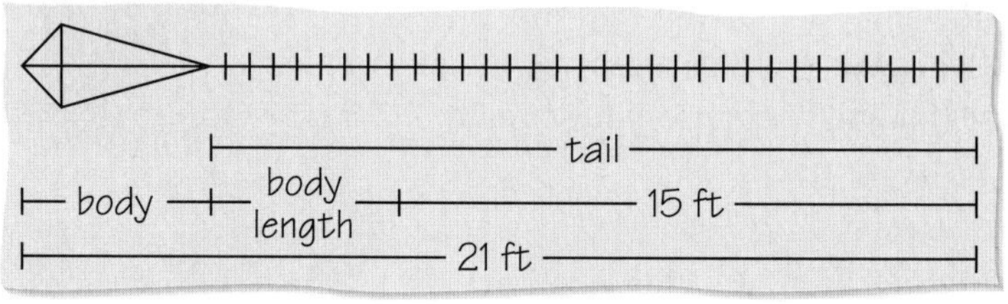

Subtracting 15 ft from 21 ft results in 6 ft, which is twice the body length. The kite's body length is 3 ft.

Check If the body is 3 ft, then the length of the tail is $3 \text{ ft} + 15 \text{ ft} = 18$ ft. The length of the kite is then $3 \text{ ft} + 18 \text{ ft} = 21$ ft. The answer checks.

Practice

1. Your aunt is building a garden in her backyard. She has 90 ft of fencing to surround it. If she wants the length to be 15 feet longer than the width, what should the dimensions of her garden be?
2. You bike 32 mi in two days. On the second day, you bike 9 mi more than on the first day. How many miles do you bike each day?
3. If you have 20 yards of ribbon and need to cut it into 2-yard lengths, how many cuts do you have to make?

1. 30 ft by 15 ft
2. 11.5 mi and 20.5 mi
3. 9 cuts

Look for a Pattern

When to Use This Strategy Sometimes you are given a few parts of a sequence and you are asked to predict how the sequence will continue. In such a problem, you can *Look for a Pattern* to help make your prediction.

A group in Spain built a human pyramid with ten levels. How many people were in the pyramid?

Understand A human pyramid has ten levels. The top level will have just one person. The bottom level will have ten people. The goal is to find the total number of people needed to form the pyramid.

Plan *Look for a Pattern* in pyramids with fewer levels and then extend the pattern to ten levels.

Carry Out Use a dot to represent each person. Draw one-, two-, three-, and four-level pyramids.

Number of People 1 $1 + 2 = 3$ $1 + 2 + 3 = 6$ $1 + 2 + 3 + 4 = 10$

The total number increases from 1, to $1 + 2 = 3$ to $1 + 2 + 3 = 6$, and to $1 + 2 + 3 + 4 = 10$. The total number for n-levels is the sum of the numbers from 1 to n. The sum of $1 + 2 + \ldots + 9 + 10$ is 55. So there were 55 people in the pyramid.

Check Draw a diagram of a ten-level pyramid. It has 55 dots.

Practice

1. In a tournament, each person plays one game against each of the other players. There are 20 players. How many games are played?
2. Starting with 1, multiply by 2. Then multiply the result by 3. Then continue to alternate multiplying by 2 and by 3. What is the ones digit after the twelfth multiplication?
3. A baby hamster weighs 4 g when it is born. It weighs 28 g at 4 weeks and 52 g at 8 weeks. Assume a constant rate of increase. How much will the hamster weigh at 14 weeks?

1. 190 games
2. 6
3. 88 g

Look for a Pattern

Looking for a pattern can help students develop reasoning skills. Assuming that the pattern will continue as it began, students use inductive reasoning to find successive numbers or figures, and predict future values. In some cases, the assumption may not be true, which underscores the importance of having students explain, justify, and check their ideas and conclusions.

Guided Instruction

Have a volunteer read the problem.

Elicit the problem solving steps:
- Understand the Problem
- Make a Plan
- Carry Out the Plan
- Check the Answer

Error Prevention!

To help students relate the diagrams to the pattern that develops, have them write the corresponding calculation and solution, such as $1 + 2 + 3 = 6$ under each diagram.

Alternative Method
Suggest that students record their observations in a table, and observe patterns in numbers across rows and down columns. Use column headings: Figure, Sum of Dots, and Total Number of Dots. For example, entries for row 2 would read: 2, $1 + 2$, and 3.

Differentiated Instruction

Tactile Learners
Have students model the problem with concrete objects, such as coins or chips.

Problem Solving Handbook

Systematic Guess and Check

Guessing possible solutions to a problem may initially give students an entry point to understanding the problem, but they may feel discouraged if they don't begin to see relevant connections to the problem. Being systematic about their trials—making choices, knowing why they made those choices, recording their trials and observing any patterns that emerge, and checking their solutions—can help students make reasonable estimates and more accurately solve problems.

Guided Instruction

Have a volunteer read the problem.

Elicit the problem solving steps:
- Understand the Problem
- Make a Plan
- Carry Out the Plan
- Check the Answer

Teaching Tip
Encourage students to try different strategies to solve problems and compare approaches with other students.

Differentiated Instruction

Tactile Learners
Have students use coins to model and make sense of the problem.

Systematic Guess and Check

When to Use This Strategy Use *Systematic Guess and Check* in situations where you can make a guess and then, based on the result, make a better guess.

Money Your friend used equal numbers of quarters and nickels in a vending machine to buy a drink for $1.20. How many quarters and how many nickels did your friend use?

Understand The drink cost $1.20. He paid with equal numbers of quarters and nickels. You need to find how many of each it will take to add up to $1.20.

Plan Use *Systematic Guess and Check* to find the answer. Make a table to record your guesses.

Carry Out Start the table with a guess. Suppose you use one quarter and one nickel. From the table, you can see how the result of each guess helps you make a better guess.

GUESS Number (n)	CHECK $n \times \$.25 + n \times \$.05 =$	RESULT Compare to $1.20
1	$1 \times \$.25 + 1 \times \$.05 = \$.30$	too low
2	$2 \times \$.25 + 2 \times \$.05 = \$.60$	too low
5	$5 \times \$.25 + 5 \times \$.05 = \$1.50$	too high
4	$4 \times \$.25 + 4 \times \$.05 = \$1.20$	correct

You friend used four quarters and four nickels to make $1.20.

Check Another way to think about this problem is to consider that one quarter and one nickel are worth $.30. How many times does 30 go into 120? The answer is 4 times, so you need four of each coin.

Practice

1. A groomer clips the claws of 40 dogs and birds. There are 110 feet among them. How many dogs and how many birds are there?
2. You can buy balloons in packs of 25 or packs of 75. Suppose you buy 8 packs and have 450 balloons in all. How many packs of each size do you buy?

1. 15 dogs, 25 birds
2. 5 packs of 75, 3 packs of 25

Act It Out

When to Use This Strategy For problems involving probability, you can *Act It Out* by conducting an experiment.

What is the probability of guessing all the answers correctly on a three-question true-or-false quiz?

Understand Your goal is to find the probability of guessing the answers to three questions correctly. The probability of guessing correctly for one question is $\frac{1}{2}$.

Plan Since the probability of guessing correctly for one question is $\frac{1}{2}$, you can *Act It Out* by tossing a coin. Let heads represent a correct guess and tails represent an incorrect guess. Three tosses represent the quiz. Simulate 30 quizzes by tossing a coin 90 times.

90 Tosses

HHT	TTH	HTH
(HHH)	TTH	THT
THH	HTH	TTT
HHT	HTT	(HHH)
TTT	THH	THT
HTT	HHT	THH
TTH	(HHH)	HTT
HTT	TTH	THT
THH	(HHH)	TTH
HTH	TTT	HTH

Carry Out The data at the left show the results from acting out 30 quizzes. Circle each instance of three heads. In 30 quiz simulations HHH occurs 4 times.

$$P(\text{3 correct guesses}) = \frac{\text{number of times HHH occurs}}{\text{total number of quizzes}}$$

$$= \frac{4}{30}, \text{ or about } 13\%$$

Check Compute the theoretical probability.

$$P(\text{3 correct}) = P(\text{1 correct}) \cdot P(\text{1 correct}) \cdot P(\text{1 correct}).$$

$$= \frac{1}{2} \cdot \frac{1}{2} \cdot \frac{1}{2} = \frac{1}{8}, \text{ or } 12.5\%$$

The theoretical probability is close to the result of acting it out.

Practice

1. Suppose a license plate contains four digits. The probability of a plate number having an even or an odd digit is the same. What is the probability of having a license plate with all even digits?
2. A true-or-false test has five questions. What is the probability of guessing exactly four out of the five answers correctly?
3. Your cat is expecting a litter of kittens. Suppose the probability of a male kitten is $\frac{1}{2}$. What is the probability that a litter of five kittens contains all male kittens?

1. $\frac{1}{16}$
2. $\frac{5}{32}$
3. $\frac{1}{32}$

Act It Out

Often there is more than one way to approach and solve a problem. Acting out, or simulating, a problem in more than one way can help students visualize and make sense of a problem, and choose a method that feels most comfortable to them.

Guided Instruction

Have a volunteer read the problem. Have students share ideas about how to organize and record their data when they act out the problem with coin tosses.

Elicit the problem solving steps:

- Understand the Problem
- Make a Plan
- Carry Out the Plan
- Check the Answer

Alternative Method
Have students make a tree diagram to find all possible outcomes.

Teaching Tip
Review how to convert a fraction into a percent.

Differentiated Instruction

Visual Learners
Have students write H for heads and T for tails on the result of each trial, in groups of 3 (for three questions). Have them circle each occurrence of HHH.

Problem Solving Handbook

Make a Table

The *Make a Table* strategy is useful for recording and organizing information. Tables also help students observe numerical patterns across rows or columns.

Guided Instruction

Have a volunteer read the problem. Discuss students' understanding of the goal.

Elicit the problem solving steps:

- Understand the Problem
- Make a Plan
- Carry Out the Plan
- Check the Answer

Teaching Tip

Encourage students who have difficulty translating flat diagrams into three-dimensional models to also use the problem-solving strategies *Draw a Picture* and *Act It Out.* Have students model the problem with several different boxes, each starting with a piece of paper that is 9 in. by 12 in. Have them measure dimensions and compare volumes.

Connection to Geometry

Review with students the relationships between dimensions length and width, and volume of a three-dimensional figure. Review units associated with each.

Make a Table

When to Use This Strategy You can *Make a Table* to help you keep track of possible solutions to a problem. A table can help you organize your data and compare solutions.

A company makes boxes without tops by cutting square corners out of the corners of rectangular sheets of cardboard. Each rectangular sheet is 7 in. by 10 in. Using whole-inch lengths only, find the dimensions of the box with the greatest possible volume.

Understand The goal is to find the dimensions of a box that will result in the greatest volume. The piece of cardboard used to make the box is 7 in. by 10 in.

Plan *Make a Table* to organize the information in the problem. Start with square cuts 1 in. on each side. Then increase the size 1 in. at a time.

Carry Out Let x represent the size of the squares. The length of the box is represented by $10 - 2x$. The width of the box is represented by $7 - 2x$. The expression $x(10 - 2x)(7 - 2x)$ represents volume.

Height (Size of Cut) x	Length $10 - 2x$	Width $7 - 2x$	Volume $x(10 - 2x)(7 - 2x)$
1 in.	8 in.	5 in.	40 $in.^3$
2 in.	6 in.	3 in.	36 $in.^3$
3 in.	4 in.	1 in.	12 $in.^3$

As the size of the square cut increases, the volume decreases. Square cuts of 1 in. result in the maximum volume of 40 $in.^3$.

Check A value of 4 for x makes the expression $(7 - 2x)$ negative, which is an impossible value for length. The possible lengths are 1, 2, and 3 in.

Practice

1. A dog owner has 200 ft of fencing and wants to enclose the greatest possible rectangular area for her dog. What dimensions should she use?
2. A customer gives a cashier a $100 bill for a $64 shirt. The customer will accept no more than six $1 bills. In what ways can the cashier give change using bills only? Assume that the cashier has no $2 bills.

2.

$20	$10	$5	$1
1	1		6
1	1	1	1
1		3	1
1		2	6
	3	1	1
	3		6
	2	2	6
	2	3	1
	1	4	6
	1	5	1
		6	6
		7	1

1. 50 ft by 50 ft
2. See above left.

Work a Simpler Problem

When to Use This Strategy A problem may have too many steps. When you *Work a Simpler Problem,* you can gain insight that can help with the more difficult problem.

A standard checkerboard has 8 squares on each side. How many squares of different sizes are there on a standard 8-by-8 board?

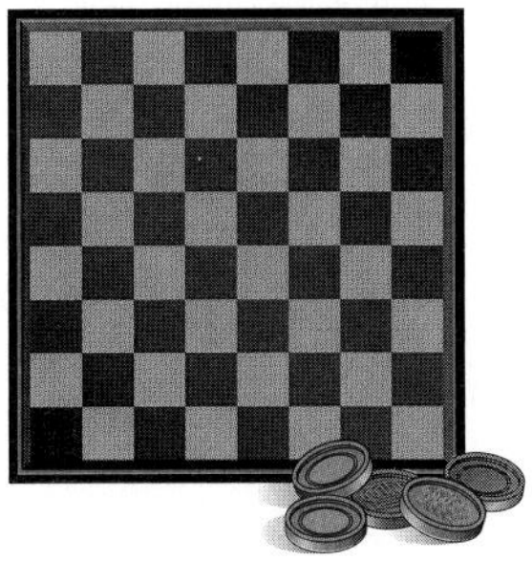

Understand The goal is to find the total number of squares on a checkerboard. Squares can be 1×1, 2×2, . . . 8×8.

Plan You can *Work a Simpler Problem* by examining boards that are 1×1, 2×2, and 3×3. Make a conjecture about the solution.

Carry Out Consider the simpler boards. Then organize your data.

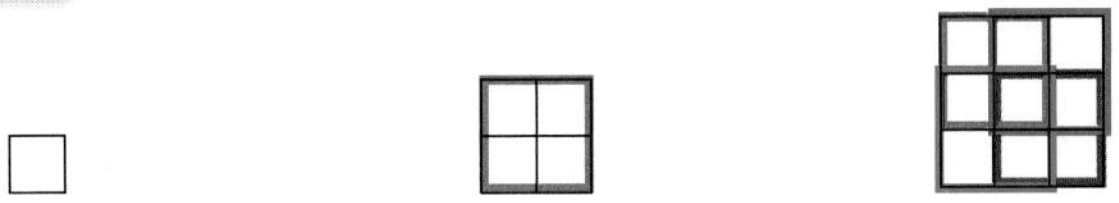

one 1×1 square	one 2×2 square four 1×1 squares	one 3×3 square four 2×2 squares nine 1×1 squares

Size of checkerboard	1×1	2×2	3×3
Number of squares	$1^2 = 1$	$1^2 + 2^2 = 5$	$1^2 + 2^2 + 3^2 = 14$

On an $n \times n$ checkerboard, the total number of squares is the sum of the squares of the positive integers from 1 to n $(1^2 + 2^2 + \ldots + n^2)$.

An 8×8 board has $1 + 4 + 9 + 16 + 25 + 36 + 49 + 64$, or 204 squares.

Check Test your conjecture by drawing a diagram of a 4×4 board.

Practice

Geometry Use the figure at the left.

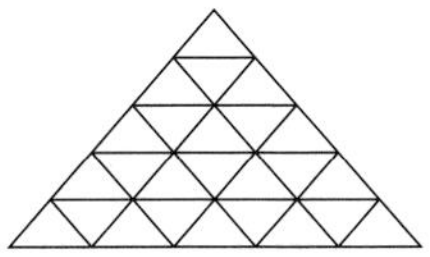

1. Find the number of small triangles.
2. How many small triangles will there be in the complete figure if you extend the figure to 10 rows? What about n rows?
3. The houses on one side of Hall Avenue are numbered with even numbers. Of the even house numbers from 140 to 224, how many have at least one 6?

Work a Simpler Problem

When a problem involves repetition and greater numbers, sometimes you can solve a simpler problem by beginning with lesser numbers and looking for a pattern.

Guided Instruction

Have a volunteer read the problem. Have another volunteer describe the game of checkers for those who have not played it.

Elicit the problem solving steps:
- Understand the Problem
- Make a Plan
- Carry Out the Plan
- Check the Answer

Teaching Tip
Have a few game boards available for students to use and compare. Have them sketch boards of various sizes on paper. They can use several colors to outline squares.

Connection to Algebra
Discuss squares of numbers, and how to recognize them. For example, 36 is 6^2.

1. 25 triangles
2. 100 triangles; n^2 triangles
3. 12 houses

Work Backward

Some problems truly do not have enough information to solve them. However, most have bits of information that need to be pieced together like a puzzle. Working backward can help students make sense of the gaps in a situation, such as, when a final amount is given in addition to a few midway values or events.

Guided Instruction

Have a volunteer read the problem. Discuss the meanings of monetary terms, such as *withdrawal* and *initial amount.*

Elicit the problem solving steps:

- Understand the Problem
- Make a Plan
- Carry Out the Plan
- Check the Answer

Teaching Tip
Before students begin to calculate, help them understand the situation. Have students act out the situation and model the problem with paper money.

Connection to Geography
Have students locate Paris, Cairo, and Istanbul on a world map.

Work Backward

When to Use This Strategy Use the *Work Backward* strategy to solve problems that give only a final result and ask you to find an initial value.

At the start of a mission, international spy Rex King withdrew half of the money in his bank account in Paris. Later, he withdrew $5,000 in Cairo. In Istanbul, he withdrew half of the remaining money. He had $7,500 left. What amount did he have at the start of the mission?

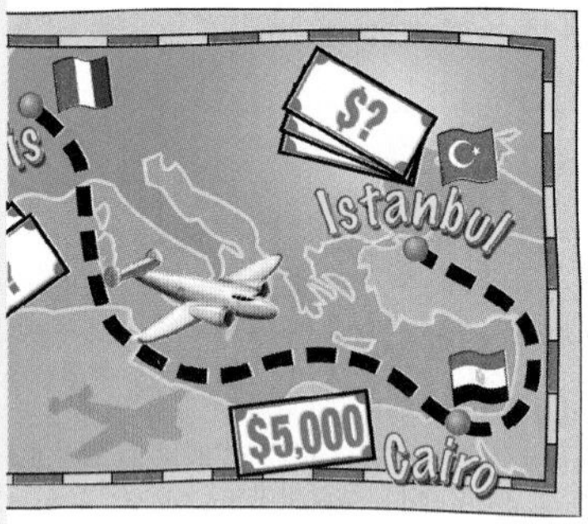

Understand The goal is to find the initial amount. Rex withdrew half the initial amount in Paris, $5,000 in Cairo, and half the remaining amount in Istanbul. He had $7,500 left.

Plan *Work Backward* by starting with what you know.

Carry Out Start with $7,500 and work backward.

- The final amount, $7,500, is half the amount in the bank before Rex went to Istanbul. So he had $15,000 when he arrived in Istanbul.
- He withdrew $5,000 in Cairo. So he left Paris with $20,000.
- At the start, he withdrew half of the amount he had. So at the start he had $40,000 in the bank account.

Check Start with $40,000 and work forward.

Paris		Cairo		Istanbul
$\frac{1}{2}$ of \$40,000 = \$20,000	→	\$20,000 − \$5,000 = \$15,000	→	$\frac{1}{2}$ of \$15,000 = \$7,500 ✔

Practice

1. You returned home from mowing lawns at 3:00 P.M. on Saturday. It took $1\frac{1}{2}$ hours to mow the first lawn. It took twice as long to mow the next lawn. After a half-hour lunch break, it took $1\frac{1}{4}$ hours to mow one more lawn. At what time did you start?

2. **Business** A salesperson bought a case of pens. On Monday, he sold $\frac{1}{2}$ of the pens. On Tuesday, he sold 30 more. On Wednesday, he sold $\frac{1}{3}$ of the pens that were left. On Thursday, he sold the remaining 40 pens. How many pens were originally in the case?

1. 8:45 A.M.
2. 180 pens

Write an Equation

When to Use This Strategy You can *Write an Equation* when a real-world situation involves two related variables.

You plan a party at a restaurant. A buffet dinner costs \$15 per person. For dessert, you plan to buy a birthday cake for \$30. You have \$275 to spend. How much will you have left if there are 16 people at the party?

Understand Your goal is to find out how much money you will have left out of \$275. You must spend \$15 for each person plus an additional \$30 for the cake.

Plan *Write an Equation* to represent the total cost of the party. Subtract the total cost from \$275 to see how much money you will have left.

Carry Out Write an equation to represent the total cost.

Words	total cost	is	cost per person	times	number of people	plus	cost of cake

Let t = the total cost.

Let p = the number of people.

Equation	t	$=$	15	$\cdot$	p	$+$	30

$$t = 15p + 30$$

Substitute 16 for p. This gives $t = 15 \cdot 16 + 30 = 240 + 30 = 270$. Now subtract the total cost from \$275. This gives \$275 − \$270 = \$5.

Check Estimate. The cost for 20 people would be \$300 + \$30 = \$330, which is more than \$270. Similarly, the cost for 10 people would be \$150 + \$30 = \$180, which is less than \$270. A cost of \$270 is reasonable.

Practice

1. You buy a belt for \$10 and some socks. Each pair of socks costs \$3. The total shipping cost is \$3. What is the total cost if you buy 11 pairs of socks?
2. You mix 8 oz of concentrate with 64 oz of water to make orange juice. If you need a total of 288 oz of juice, how much concentrate should you buy?

1. \$46
2. 32 oz

Write an Equation

Writing an equation from a real-world situation is an important mathematical and algebraic skill. However, getting from the words to the symbols is often quite a challenge. Writing a sentence that can help identify important values, as well as graphing the situation, can help students make the transition.

Guided Instruction

Have a volunteer read the problem. Ask students to identify key quantities and identify letters to represent quantities that are unknown.

Elicit the problem solving steps:
- Understand the Problem
- Make a Plan
- Carry Out the Plan
- Check the Answer

Alternative Method
Have students identify which quantities in the problem depend on each other. Cost depends on number of people. Have students use those quantities as axes and graph the situation for a few hypothetical values. Noticing a linear relationship can help students visualize and make sense of the problem.

Differentiated Instruction

Visual Learners
Have students highlight different parts of the sentence in different colors to help them associate corresponding parts of the equation.

1 Integers and Algebraic Expressions

Chapter at a Glance

Lesson Titles, Objectives, and Features	Assessment	NCTM Standards	Local Standards
1-1 Algebraic Expressions and the Order of Operations • To write algebraic expressions and evaluate them using the order of operations **Vocabulary Builder:** High-Use Academic Words	Lesson Quiz	1, 2, 6, 7, 8, 9, 10	
1-2 Integers and Absolute Value • To find the absolute values of integers and to use absolute value to compare integers **1-2b Activity Lab, Data Analysis:** Integers and Differences	Lesson Quiz Checkpoint Quiz 1	1, 2, 3, 4, 5, 6, 7, 8, 9, 10	
1-3a Activity Lab: Adding Integers **1-3 Adding and Subtracting Integers** • To add and subtract integers and to solve problems involving integers	Lesson Quiz	1, 2, 3, 6, 7, 8, 9, 10	
1-4 Multiplying and Dividing Integers • To multiply and divide integers and to solve problems involving integers **Guided Problem Solving:** Solving Multi-Step Problems	Lesson Quiz	1, 2, 3, 4, 6, 7, 8, 9, 10	
1-5 Properties of Numbers • To identify the properties of numbers and use the properties to solve problems **Math Games:** Integer Flip	Lesson Quiz Checkpoint Quiz 2	1, 2, 6, 7, 8, 9, 10	
1-6a Activity Lab, Hands On: Modeling Equations **1-6 Solving Equations by Adding and Subtracting** • To write and solve equations using addition and subtraction **1-6b Activity Lab:** Number Squares	Lesson Quiz	1, 2, 3, 6, 7, 8, 9, 10	
1-7 Solving Equations by Multiplying and Dividing • To write and solve equations using multiplication or division **1-7b Activity Lab, Algebra Thinking:** The Cover-up Method	Lesson Quiz	1, 2, 3, 6, 7, 8, 9, 10	
Problem Solving Application: Applying Integers			

NCTM Standards 2000
1 Number and Operations **2** Algebra **3** Geometry **4** Measurement **5** Data Analysis and Probability
6 Problem Solving **7** Reasoning and Proof **8** Communication **9** Connections **10** Representation

Correlations to Standardized Tests

All content for these tests is contained in *Prentice Hall Math*, Course 3. This chart reflects coverage in this chapter only.

	1-1	1-2	1-3	1-4	1-5	1-6	1-7
Terra Nova CAT6 (Level 18)							
Number and Number Relations	✔	✔	✔	✔	✔		
Computation and Numerical Estimation	✔		✔	✔		✔	✔
Operation Concepts	✔	✔	✔	✔	✔	✔	✔
Measurement							
Geometry and Spatial Sense							
Data Analysis, Statistics, and Probability							
Patterns, Functions, Algebra	✔	✔	✔	✔	✔	✔	✔
Problem Solving and Reasoning	✔	✔	✔	✔	✔	✔	✔
Communication	✔	✔	✔	✔	✔	✔	✔
Decimals, Fractions, Integers, Percent	✔	✔	✔	✔	✔	✔	✔
Order of Operations	✔						
Algebraic Operations	✔	✔	✔	✔	✔	✔	✔
Terra Nova CTBS (Level 18)							
Decimals, Fractions, Integers, Percents	✔	✔	✔	✔	✔	✔	✔
Order of Operations, Numeration, Number Theory	✔	✔	✔	✔	✔	✔	✔
Data Interpretation							
Measurement							
Geometry							
ITBS (Level 14)							
Number Properties and Operations	✔	✔	✔	✔	✔	✔	✔
Algebra	✔	✔	✔	✔	✔	✔	✔
Geometry							
Measurement							
Probability and Statistics							
Estimation							
SAT10 (Adv 1 Level)							
Number Sense and Operations	✔	✔	✔	✔	✔	✔	✔
Patterns, Relationships, and Algebra	✔	✔	✔	✔	✔	✔	✔
Data, Statistics, and Probability							
Geometry and Measurement							
NAEP							
Number Sense, Properties, and Operations		✔	✔	✔	✔		
Measurement							
Geometry and Spatial Sense							
Data Analysis, Statistics, and Probability							
Algebra and Functions	✔	✔		✔	✔	✔	✔

CAT6 California Achievement Test, 6th Ed.
CTBS Comprehensive Test of Basic Skills
ITBS Iowa Test of Basic Skills, Form M
SAT10 Stanford Achievement Test, 10th Ed.
NAEP National Assessment of Educational Progress 2005 Mathematics Objectives

Math Background

Professional Development

Skills Trace

BEFORE Chapter 1

Course 2 introduced algebraic expressions and operations with integers.

DURING Chapter 1

Course 3 reviews and applies algebraic expressions and integers to find absolute values, to simplify expressions with exponents, and to apply order of operations.

AFTER Chapter 1

Throughout this course students use algebraic expressions and integers.

1-1 Algebraic Expressions and the Order of Operations

Math Understandings

- An expression is in simplest form when there are no operations that can be performed and there is no equivalent expression that uses fewer symbols.
- To avoid the confusion of differing results when simplifying or evaluating a numerical expression, mathematicians use an agreed-upon order of operations.

A **variable** is a symbol that stands for one or more numbers. An **algebraic expression** is a mathematical phrase that uses numbers, variables, and operation symbols. To **simplify** a numerical expression, replace it with its simplest name. To **evaluate** an algebraic expression, replace each variable with a number and then simplify.

An incomplete order of operations is presented as follows:

Order of Operations

1. Work inside grouping symbols.
2. Multiply and divide in order from left to right.
3. Add and subtract in order from left to right.

Example: Evaluate $5(n + 4) - 2$ for $n = 6$.
$5(6 + 4) - 2 = 5(10) - 2 = 50 - 2 = 48$

1-2 Integers and Absolute Value

Math Understandings

- Zero is the only integer that is its own opposite. Zero is neither positive nor negative. The absolute value of zero is zero.
- A number and its opposite have the same absolute value.

Numbers that are the same distance from zero on a number line but in opposite directions are **opposites**, where 0 is its own opposite. 4 and -4 are opposites. **Integers** are the set of whole numbers and their opposites. A number's distance from zero on the number line is its **absolute value**. The absolute value of -4, written as $|-4|$, is 4, and $|4|$ is also 4.

1-3 Adding and Subtracting Integers

Math Understandings

- You can rewrite subtracting a number as adding the opposite of that number.
- The opposite of the opposite of a number is the number itself.

Two numbers whose sum is 0 are **additive inverses**.

Adding Integers

Same Sign The sum of two positive integers is positive. The sum of two negative integers is negative.
Different Signs Find the absolute value of each. Subtract the lesser absolute value from the greater. The sum has the sign of the integer with the greater absolute value. The sum of opposites is zero.

Subtracting Integers

To subtract an integer, add its opposite.
$a - b = c$ is equivalent to $a = b + c$
$a + (-b) = b + c + (-b) = c$, so $a - b = a + (-b)$

1-4 Multiplying and Dividing Integers

Math Understandings

- Inverse operations undo each other. Addition and subtraction are inverse operations. Multiplication and division are inverse operations.
- Dividing by a number is the same as multiplying by the reciprocal of that number.

Multiplying or Dividing Two Integers

The product or quotient of two integers with the same sign is positive.
The product or quotient of two integers with different signs is negative.

1-5 Properties of Numbers

Math Understandings

- The Distributive Property combines two operations: (1) multiplication; (2) either addition or subtraction.
- The Distributive Property can be written and used in several different forms.

Commutative Properties of Addition and Multiplication

$a + b = b + a$ $\quad$ $a \cdot b = b \cdot a$

Associative Properties of Addition and Multiplication

$(a + b) + c = a + (b + c)$ $\quad$ $(a \cdot b) \cdot c = a \cdot (b \cdot c)$

Identity Properties of Addition and Multiplication

$a + 0 = 0 + a = a$ $\quad$ $a \cdot 1 = 1 \cdot a = a$

Distributive Property

$a(b + c) = ab + ac$ $\quad$ $(b + c)a = ba + ca$

$a(b - c) = ab - ac$ $\quad$ $(b - c)a = ba - ca$

1-6 1-7 Solving Equations by Adding, Subtracting, Multiplying, and Dividing

Math Understandings

- Addition and subtraction are inverse operations that undo each other. Multiplication and division are also inverse operations that undo each other.
- When you solve an equation, any operation that you do to one side you must also do to the other.

A mathematical sentence with an equal sign is an **equation**. A **solution** to an equation is any value that makes the equation true. To find a solution of an equation, **isolate** the variable by using **inverse operations** (operations that undo each other) and the properties of equality.

Addition and Subtraction Properties of Equality

If you add the same number to each side of an equation, the two sides remain equal.

Arithmetic	**Algebra**
$10 = 5(2)$, so $10 + 3 = 5(2) + 3$	If $a = b$ then $a + c = b + c$.

If you subtract the same number from each side of an equation, the two sides remain equal.

Arithmetic	**Algebra**
$10 = 5(2)$, so $10 - 3 = 5(2) - 3$	If $a = b$ then $a - c = b - c$.

Additional Professional Development Opportunities

Professional Development

Math Background Notes for Chapter 1: Every lesson has a Math Background in the PLAN section.

Research Overview, Mathematics Strands
Additional support for these topics and more is in the front of the Teacher's Edition.

LessonLab
LessonLab, a Pearson Education company, offers comprehensive, facilitated professional development designed to help teachers to improve student achievement. To learn more please visit lessonlab.com.

Chapter 1 Resources

	1-1	1-2	1-3	1-4	1-5	1-6	1-7	For the Chapter
Print Resources								
L3 Practice	●	●	●	●	●	●	●	
L1 Adapted Practice	●	●	●	●	●	●	●	
L3 Guided Problem Solving	●	●	●	●	●	●	●	
L2 Reteaching	●	●	●	●	●	●	●	
L4 Enrichment	●	●	●	●	●	●	●	
L3 Daily Notetaking Guide	●	●	●	●	●	●	●	
L1 Adapted Daily Notetaking Guide	●	●	●	●	●	●	●	
L3 Vocabulary and Study Skills Worksheets	●		●	●	●		●	●
L3 Daily Puzzles	●	●	●	●	●	●	●	
L3 Activity Labs	●	●	●	●	●	●	●	
L3 Checkpoint Quiz		●			●			
L3 Chapter Project								●
L2 Below Level Chapter Test								●
L3 Chapter Test								●
L4 Alternative Assessment								●
L3 Cumulative Review								●
Spanish Resources ELL								
L3 Practice	●	●	●	●	●	●	●	
L3 Vocabulary and Study Skills Worksheets	●		●	●	●		●	●
L3 Checkpoint Quiz		●			●			
L2 Below Level Chapter Test								●
L3 Chapter Test								●
L4 Alternative Assessment								●
L3 Cumulative Review								●
Transparencies								
Check Skills You'll Need	●	●	●	●	●	●	●	
Additional Examples	●	●	●	●	●	●	●	
Problem of the Day	●	●	●	●	●	●	●	
Classroom Aid	●	●	●	●		●	●	
Student Edition Answers	●	●	●	●	●	●	●	●
Lesson Quiz	●	●	●	●	●	●	●	
Test-Taking Strategies								●
Technology								
Interactive Textbook Online	●	●	●	●	●	●	●	●
StudentExpress™ CD-ROM	●	●	●	●	●	●	●	●
Success Tracker™ Online Intervention	●	●	●	●	●	●	●	●
TeacherExpress™ CD-ROM	●	●	●	●	●	●	●	●
PresentationExpress™ with QuickTake Presenter	●	●	●	●	●	●	●	●
ExamView® Assessment Suite CD-ROM	●	●	●	●	●	●	●	●
MindPoint® Quiz Show CD-ROM								●
Prentice Hall Web Site: PHSchool.com	●	●	●	●	●	●	●	●

Also Available: **Prentice Hall Assessment System**
- Progress Monitoring Assessments
- Skills and Concepts Review
- Test Prep Workbook

Other Resources
Algebra Readiness Tests
All-in-One Student Workbook
All-in-One Student Workbook, Adapted Version
Multilingual Handbook

Solution Key
Math Notes Study Folder
Spanish Cumulative Assessment

Where You Can Use the Lesson Resources

Here is a suggestion, following the four-step teaching plan, for how you can incorporate Differentiated Instruction Resources into your teaching.

	Instructional Resources L3	Differentiated Instruction Resources
1. Plan		
Preparation Read the Math Background in the Teacher's Edition to connect this lesson with students' previous experience. **Starting Class** **Check Skills You'll Need** Assign these exercises to review prerequisite skills. **New Vocabulary** Help students pre-read the lesson by pointing out the new terms introduced in the lesson.	**Math Background** **Math Understandings** **Transparencies & PresentationExpress™ with QuickTake Presenter** Check Skills You'll Need Problem of the Day **Resources** Vocabulary and Study Skills	**Spanish Support** ELL Vocabulary and Study Skills
2. Teach		
L3 **Guided Instruction** Use the Activity Labs to build conceptual understanding. Teach each Example. Use the Teacher's Edition side column notes for specific teaching tips, including Error Prevention notes. Use the Additional Examples found in the side column (and on transparency and PowerPoint) as an alternative presentation for the content. After each Example, assign the Quick Check exercise for that Example to get an immediate assessment of student understanding. Use the Closure activity in the Teacher's Edition to help students attain mastery of lesson content.	**Student Edition** Activity Lab **Resources** Daily Notetaking Guide Activity Lab **Transparencies & PresentationExpress™ with QuickTake Presenter** Additional Examples Classroom Aids **ExamView® Assessment Suite CD-ROM**	**Teacher's Edition** Every lesson includes suggestions for working with students who need special attention. L1 Special Needs L2 Below Level L4 Advanced Learners ELL English Language Learners **Resources** L1 Adapted Daily Notetaking Guide **Multilingual Handbook**
3. Practice		
Assignment Guide **Check Your Understanding** Use these questions to check students' understanding before you assign homework. **Homework Exercises** Assign homework from these leveled exercises in the Assignment Guide. **A** Practice by Example **B** Apply Your Skills **C** Challenge Test Prep and Mixed Review **Homework Quick Check** Use these key exercises to quickly check students' homework.	**Transparencies & PresentationExpress™ with QuickTake Presenter** Student Answers **Resources** Practice Guided Problem Solving Vocabulary Masters with Study Skills Activity Lab Daily Puzzles **ExamView® Assessment Suite CD-ROM**	**Spanish Support** ELL Practice ELL Vocabulary and Study Skills **Resources** L1 Adapted Practice L4 Enrichment
4. Assess & Reteach		
Lesson Quiz Assign the Lesson Quiz to assess students' mastery of the lesson content. **Checkpoint Quiz** Use the Checkpoint Quiz to assess student progress over several lessons.	**Transparencies & PresentationExpress™ with QuickTake Presenter** Lesson Quiz **Resources** Checkpoint Quiz	**Resources** L2 Reteaching ELL Checkpoint Quiz Success Tracker™ Online Intervention **ExamView® Assessment Suite CD-ROM**

KEY L1 Special Needs L2 Below Level L3 For All Students L4 Advanced, Gifted ELL English Language Learners

CHAPTER 1

Integers and Algebraic Expressions

Check Your Readiness

Answers for students are in the back of the textbook.

For intervention, direct students to:

Comparing and Ordering Decimals
Skills Handbook, p. 629

Adding and Subtracting Decimals
Skills Handbook, p. 631

Multiplying Decimals
Skills Handbook, p. 632

Dividing Decimals by Whole Numbers
Skills Handbook, p. 634

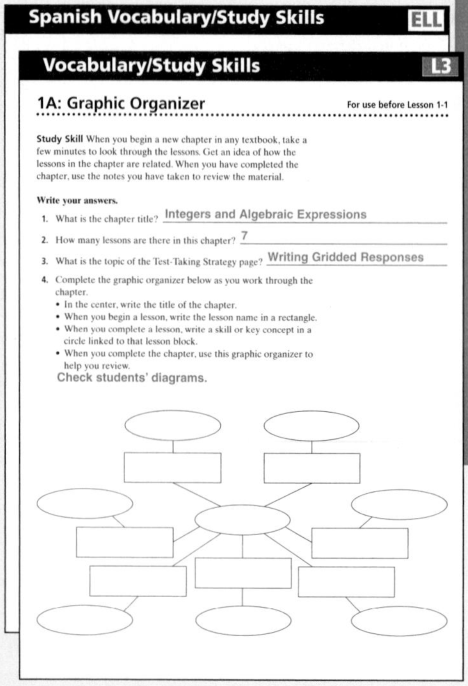
Spanish Vocabulary/Study Skills ELL

Vocabulary/Study Skills L3

1A: Graphic Organizer — For use before Lesson 1-1

Study Skill When you begin a new chapter in any textbook, take a few minutes to look through the lessons. Get an idea of how the lessons in the chapter are related. When you have completed the chapter, use the notes you have taken to review the material.

Write your answers.

1. What is the chapter title? Integers and Algebraic Expressions
2. How many lessons are there in this chapter? 7
3. What is the topic of the Test-Taking Strategy page? Writing Gridded Responses
4. Complete the graphic organizer below as you work through the chapter.
   - In the center, write the title of the chapter.
   - When you begin a lesson, write the lesson name in a rectangle.
   - When you complete a lesson, write a skill or key concept in a circle linked to that lesson block.
   - When you complete the chapter, use this graphic organizer to help you review.

   Check students' diagrams.

Algebra

CHAPTER 1 Integers and Algebraic Expressions

What You've Learned

- In a previous course, you learned to compare and order decimals.
- You used addition, subtraction, multiplication, and division to solve problems involving decimals.
- You simplified numerical expressions involving order of operations.

Check Your Readiness

GO for Help

For Exercises	See Skills Handbook
1–4	p. 629
5–10	p. 631
11–16	p. 632
17–19	p. 634

Comparing and Ordering Decimals

Compare. Write <, >, or =.

1. 0.3 ■ 0.4 < **2.** 10.01 ■ 10.010 =

3. 0.529 ■ 0.54 < **4.** 0.031 ■ 0.027 >

Adding and Subtracting Decimals

Find each sum or difference.

5. $0.034 + 1.2$ 1.234 **6.** $10.25 - 9.29$ 0.96 **7.** $8.1 - 0.81$ 7.29

8. $45.27 + 2.03$ 47.3 **9.** $4.55 - 2.67$ 1.88 **10.** $0.36 + 9.8$ 10.16

Multiplying Decimals

Multiply.

11. $0.17 \cdot 4$ 0.68 **12.** $3.5 \cdot 4.2$ 14.7 **13.** $1.6 \cdot 9.7$ 15.52

14. $0.06 \cdot 0.23$ 0.0138 **15.** $7.5 \cdot 3.004$ 22.53 **16.** $8 \cdot 1.064$ 8.512

Dividing Decimals by Whole Numbers

Divide.

17. $11.36 \div 2$ 5.68 **18.** $125.3 \div 14$ 8.95 **19.** $0.46 \div 5$ 0.092

Chapter 1 Overview

In this chapter, students evaluate and write algebraic expressions. They use the concept of absolute value to add and subtract integers. They also multiply and divide integers. In addition, they use properties of numbers and solve simple equations.

Activating Prior Knowledge

In this chapter, students build on and extend their knowledge of the order of operations, number properties, and integers. Students apply their knowledge to algebraic expressions and simple equations involving integers. They also draw upon their understanding of mental math strategies.

Ask questions such as:

- *Is $2 + 3 = 3 + 2$?* yes
- *Is $2 - 3 = 3 - 2$?* no
- *What does $4 + 6 \times 3$ simplify to?* 22

What You'll Learn Next

- In this chapter, you will learn to compare and order integers.
- You will use appropriate operations to solve problems involving integers.
- You will learn and use the properties of numbers.
- You will find solutions to application problems using equations.

Problem Solving Application On pages 48 and 49, you will work an extended activity involving lakes.

Key Vocabulary

- absolute value (p. 10)
- additive inverses (p. 16)
- algebraic expression (p. 4)
- associative properties (p. 26)
- commutative properties (p. 26)
- Distributive Property (p. 28)
- evaluate (p. 5)
- identity properties (p. 26)
- integers (p. 10)
- inverse operations (p. 21)
- isolate (p. 34)
- opposites (p. 10)
- order of operations (p. 5)
- simplify (p. 5)
- solution (p. 34)
- variable (p. 4)

1-1

1. Plan

Objective
To write algebraic expressions and evaluate them using the order of operations

Examples
1 Writing an Expression
2 Evaluating an Algebraic Expression
3 Using the Order of Operations
4 Application: Fitness

Math Understandings: p. 2C

Professional Development

Math Background
You can use any letter to represent a variable. So it may help to choose a letter that relates to the meaning of the symbol, such as *h* for the number of hours. An algebraic expression can be *simplified* without having any value for the variable. To *evaluate* an expression, a value for the variable is necessary.

More Math Background: p. 2C

Lesson Planning and Resources
See p. 2E for a list of the resources that support this lesson.

PowerPoint

Bell Ringer Practice
Check Skills You'll Need
Use student page, transparency, or PowerPoint. For intervention, direct students to:
Multiplying Decimals
Skills Handbook, p. 632

Algebra

1-1 Algebraic Expressions and the Order of Operations

Check Skills You'll Need
1. **Vocabulary Review** Which expression does not use multiplication: 3 · 4, $\frac{3}{4}$, 3 × 4, or 3(4)? $\frac{3}{4}$

Multiply.

2. 12 · 8 96
3. 2.5 · 4 10
4. 7.4 · 6 44.4
5. 0.6 · 5 3

GO for Help Skills Handbook p. 632

What You'll Learn
To write algebraic expressions and evaluate them using the order of operations

New Vocabulary variable, algebraic expression, simplify, evaluate, order of operations

Why Learn This?

Values such as an astronaut's weight on the moon and on Earth follow a pattern or relationship. You can use tables and symbols to show relationships between numbers.

The table below shows the relationship between an astronaut's weight on the moon and the astronaut's weight on Earth.

Weight on Earth (lb)	Weight on Moon (lb)
100	0.16 · 100
120	0.16 · 120
140	0.16 · 140
160	0.16 · 160
w	0.16 · *w*

The second column gives a numerical expression for each weight on the moon.

variable representing weight on Earth → *w*

algebraic expression for weight on the moon → 0.16 · *w*

A **variable** is a symbol that stands for one or more numbers. An **algebraic expression** is a mathematical phrase that uses numbers, variables, and operation symbols.

You can translate word phrases into algebraic expressions.

Word Phrase	Algebraic Expression
3 more than a number a number increased by 3	$x + 3$
the quotient of a number and 8	$k \div 8$ or $\frac{k}{8}$
6 times a number the product of 6 and a number	$6 \cdot y$ or $6y$
15 less than a number 15 subtracted from a number	$z - 15$

Differentiated Instruction Solutions for All Learners

Special Needs L1
Students highlight parts of an expression in different colors, according to the order of operations, keeping track of the order of the colors used.

learning style: visual

Below Level L2
Review *numbers, variables,* and *operation symbols.* Students provide examples of each. Then students write algebraic expressions using their examples.

learning style: verbal

EXAMPLE Writing an Expression

1 An object's weight on Mars is 0.38 times the object's weight on Earth. Write an algebraic expression for an object's weight on Mars.

Words 0.38 times object's weight on Earth

Let w = the object's weight on Earth.

Expression $0.38 \cdot w$

The algebraic expression $0.38w$ represents an object's weight on Mars.

The Mars Rover weighs 140 lb on Mars and 375 lb on Earth.

Quick Check

1. At a ballpark, team hats are sold for $15 each. Write an algebraic expression for the cost of any number n of team hats. $15n$

Vocabulary Tip

The root of *variable* is *vary*, which means "change."

To **simplify** a numerical expression, replace it with its simplest name. To **evaluate** an algebraic expression, replace each variable with a number and then simplify.

EXAMPLE Evaluating an Algebraic Expression

2 Evaluate $n - 5$ for $n = 27$.

$n - 5 = 27 - 5$ ← **Substitute 27 for *n*.**

$= 22$ ← **Simplify by subtracting 5 from 27.**

Quick Check

2. Evaluate $7 - m$ for $m = 2$. 5

Here is an expression simplified in two ways, with different results.

$16 - 4 \cdot 3$	$16 - 4 \cdot 3$
$12 \cdot 3$	$16 - 12$
36 ✘	4 ✔

To avoid confusion when simplifying an expression, mathematicians have established a standard **order of operations.**

KEY CONCEPTS **Order of Operations**

Work inside grouping symbols.

1. Multiply and divide in order from left to right.
2. Add and subtract in order from left to right.

2. Teach

Activity Lab

Use before the lesson.

All in One Teaching Resources

Activity Lab 1-1: Tik-Tak-Toe Algebra

Guided Instruction

Example 1

Ask: *Why would it be incorrect to write the expression 38w?* **The numbers 38 and 0.38 are different. While 38 is a whole number, 0.38 is a decimal number less than 1.**

Error Prevention!

In Example 1, students may interpret the variable w in $0.38w$ (0.38 times w) as a single digit placeholder, such as 5 in 0.385. Remind them that a numeral written next to a letter is an algebraic expression and not the same as digits written next to each other.

Alternative Method

Invite a student to write the expression $16 - 4 \cdot 3$ on the board twice. Then have them add parentheses to make clear the contradictory sets of steps for simplifying the expression. **$(16 - 4) \cdot 3$, $16 - (4 \cdot 3)$**

PowerPoint

Additional Examples

1 A student earns $5 an hour babysitting. The hours vary from week to week. Define a variable. Write an algebraic expression for how much the student earns in a week. $5h$

2 Evaluate $p - 23$ for $p = 10$. -13

Advanced Learners L4

Students research the force of gravity on Mars or Venus and write an algebraic expression for weight on each of these planets.

learning style: verbal

English Language Learners ELL

Make sure students understand that the expression $16 - 4 \cdot 3$ has just one (correct) value: $16 - 12 = 4$. The other solution (36) is an example of an incorrect simplification.

learning style: verbal

Guided Instruction

Example 3
Remind students that the value for the variable is substituted in *every* place the variable occurs.

Example 4
Ask students to identify the labels for each row and column of the table. Have them create their own tables, properly labeled, for Additional Example 4 below.

PowerPoint

Additional Examples

3 Evaluate the expression $t + (12 - t) \div 2$ for $t = 6$. 9

4 An Internet service provider charges $25 for a connection fee and then $16 per month. Write an expression to model the total cost and then evaluate the expression for 1 to 5 months of Internet access. $25 + 16m$; $41, $57, $73, $89, $105

All in One Teaching Resources

- Daily Notetaking Guide 1-1 L3
- Adapted Notetaking 1-1 L1

Closure

- *How do you evaluate an algebraic expression?* Replace each variable with a number and then simplify.
- *What does the order of operations state?* Simplify within grouping symbols first, and then, in order from left to right, multiply and divide, and finally, add and subtract.

The symbols ( ) and [ ] are grouping symbols. A fraction bar is also a grouping symbol. So $\frac{5+4}{3+6} = (5+4) \div (3+6)$.

EXAMPLE Using the Order of Operations

3 Evaluate $n + (13 - n) \div 5$ for $n = 3$.

$$\begin{aligned} n + (13 - n) \div 5 &= 3 + (13 - 3) \div 5 && \leftarrow \text{Substitute 3 for } n.\\ &= 3 + 10 \div 5 && \leftarrow \text{Work inside parentheses.}\\ &= 3 + 2 && \leftarrow \text{Divide.}\\ &= 5 && \leftarrow \text{Add.} \end{aligned}$$

Quick Check

3. Evaluate $3x + x \div 3$ for $x = 12$. 40

The value of an algebraic expression can vary, or change, depending upon the value you give the variable.

EXAMPLE Application: Fitness

4 A fitness club charges $100 to join and $33 for each month. Write an expression for the total cost. Find the cost for 6 months of membership.

Make a Table to show the pattern of costs by month.

Number of Months	Cost to Join	Monthly Cost	Total
1	100	33(1)	100 + 33(1)
2	100	33(2)	100 + 33(2)
3	100	33(3)	100 + 33(3)
m	100	33(m)	100 + 33m

Use m to represent any number of months. → m; **total for m months** ← $100 + 33m$

The expression $100 + 33m$ models the total cost.

$$\begin{aligned} 100 + 33m &= 100 + 33(6) && \leftarrow \text{Substitute 6 for } m \text{ to evaluate for 6 months.}\\ &= 100 + 198 && \leftarrow \text{Multiply.}\\ &= 298 && \leftarrow \text{Add.} \end{aligned}$$

The total cost for 6 months is $298.

Quick Check

4. The monthly cost increases to $35. Write an expression to model the total cost. Find the cost for 12 months of membership.
$100 + 35m$; $520

Check Your Understanding

1. Answers may vary. Sample: An algebraic expression may use variables. A numerical expression does not.

1. **Vocabulary** What is the difference between an algebraic expression and a numerical expression? See left.
2. **Mental Math** Evaluate the expression $4x$ for $x = 12$. 48

Match each word phrase with an expression.

3. There are two fewer guests. C
4. There are half as many cars. B
5. There are two more books. A

A. $m + 2$
B. $n \div 2$
C. $p - 2$

Homework Exercises

For more exercises, see Extra Skills and Word Problems.

GO for Help

For Exercises	See Examples
6–8	1
9–11	2
12–14	3
15	4

A **Write an algebraic expression for each word phrase.**

6. 13 less than a number q $q - 13$
7. number of days in w weeks $7w$
8. A florist divides 60 roses into equal bunches of f flowers. Write an expression for the number of bunches the florist can make. $60 \div f$ or $\frac{60}{f}$

Find the value of each expression for the given values of the variable.

9.

a	$a - 17$	
20	■	3
22	■	5
25	■	8

10.

m	$9m$	
7	■	63
9	■	81
11	■	99

11.

d	$4d + 7$	
0	■	7
2	■	15
4	■	23

Evaluate each expression for $n = 3$.

12. $2n + 5 - n$ 8
13. $\frac{3n + 18}{3n}$ 3
14. $\frac{24}{4 - n} \cdot n$ 72

15. A hiking club charges \$60 to join and \$12 for each hiking trip. Write an expression to model the total cost. Find the cost of six hikes. $60 + 12h$; \$132

B

16. **GPS** **Guided Problem Solving** A hot-air balloon is at a height of 2,250 feet. It descends 150 feet each minute. Find its height after 6, 8, and 10 minutes. 1,350 ft; 1,050 ft; 750 ft
    - Make a table to show the pattern of heights.
    - Write an expression for the balloon's height at m minutes.

17. **GPS** a. **Amusement Park** An amusement park charges \$5 for admission and \$2 for each ride. Write an expression for the total cost of admission and r rides. $5 + 2r$
    b. **Number Sense** How many rides can you go on if you have \$16? 5 rides

3. Practice

Assignment Guide

Check Your Understanding

Go over Exercises 1–5 in class before assigning the Homework Exercises.

Homework Exercises

A	Practice by Example	6–15
B	Apply Your Skills	16–27
C	Challenge	28
	Test Prep and Mixed Review	29–33

Homework Quick Check

To check students' understanding of key skills and concepts, go over Exercises 7, 10, 17, 19, and 23.

Differentiated Instruction Resources

Adapted Practice 1-1 L1

Practice 1-1 Algebraic Expressions and the Order of Ope… L3

Write an algebraic expression for each word phrase.

1. 5 less than a number n $n - 5$
2. 15 more than the absolute value of a number $|n| + 15$
3. the number of minutes in n hours $60n$
4. 5 more than a number, divided by 9 $\frac{x + 5}{9}$
5. 3 more than the product of 8 and a number $8y + 4$
6. 3 less than the absolute value of a number, times 4 $4(|n| - 3)$

Write an algebraic expression for each situation. Explain what the variable represents.

7. the amount of money Waldo has if he has \$10 more than Jon
   $j + 10$; j = the amount of money Jon has
8. the amount of money that Mika has if she has some quarters
   $25q$ or $\$.25q$; q = the number of quarters
9. how much weight Kirk can lift if he lifts 30 lb more than his brother
   $w + 30$; w = the amount of weight Kirk's brother can lift
10. how fast Rya runs if she runs 5 mi/h slower than Danae
    $s - 5$; s = Danae's running speed

Write a word phrase that can be represented by each variable expression.

11. $n \div (4)$ a number divided by 4
12. $n + 4$ 4 more than a number
13. $3n$ the product of a number and 3
14. $n - 8$ 8 less than a number

Evaluate each expression for $n = 5.6$, $x = 2.4$, and $y = 4$.

15. $6(n + 8)$ 81.6
16. $29y - 15$ 101
17. $(x + n) \div y$ 2
18. $(24 \div x) + 18$ 28
19. $(6 \cdot 8 + y) \cdot n$ 291.2
20. $xn + y$ 17.44
21. $6 \cdot 8 + y \cdot n$ 70.4
22. $6(8 + y) \cdot n$ 403.2
23. $12 \div x + xy$ 14.6
24. $4n + x(y + 1)$ 34.4

1-1 • Guided Problem Solving GPS L3

GPS Student Page 7, Exercise 17:

a. **Amusement Park** An amusement park charges \$5 for admission and \$2 for each ride. Write an expression for the total cost.

b. **Number Sense** How many rides can you go on if you have \$16?

Understand

1. What information is given in the problem? The cost for entering the amusement park and the cost per ride.
2. What are you being asked to do? a) Write an expression for the total cost. b) Determine how many rides you can go on for \$16.
3. What does it cost to enter the park? \$5
4. What does a ride cost? \$2

Plan and Carry Out

5. Write an expression for riding r rides costing \$2 each, after paying the cost for the admission. $5 + 2r$
6. Using your expression, how many rides can you go on with \$16? $5 + 2(5) = 15$; 5 rides

Check

7. Is your expression reasonable? Does the expression check? Sample answer: Yes, the expression checks. $\$15 \le \$16$.

Solve Another Problem

8. A car-rental agency charges \$35 per day and \$.25 per mile. Write an expression for the cost of renting a car for one day and driving m miles. How many miles could you drive if you have only \$50?
   $35 + .25m$; 60 miles, since $35 + .25(60) = 50$

4. Assess & Reteach

PowerPoint

Lesson Quiz

1. Write an expression for the number of months in y years. $12y$
2. Evaluate your expression in Item 1 for 7 years. 84 months
3. Evaluate $5n - n \div 2$ for $n = 10$. 45
4. Evaluate $3c - 5$ for $c = 2, 4,$ and 6. 1, 7, 13

Reteaching 1-1 — Algebraic Expressions and the Order of O[...]s — L2

A *variable* represents a number. An *algebraic expression* is formed from numbers, variables, and operations.

To evaluate an algebraic expression, substitute a number for each variable. Then follow the order of operations.

	Evaluate $4(n + 2)$ for $n = 3$.	Evaluate $n + 12 \div (3 \times m)$ for $n = 4$ and $m = 2$.
① Substitute for each variable.	$4(3 + 2)$	$4 + 12 \div (3 \times 2)$
② Work inside grouping symbols.	$= 4(5)$	$= 4 + 2 \div 6$
③ Multiply and divide from left to right.	$= 20$	$= 4 + 2$
④ Add and subtract from left to right.		$= 6$

Evaluate each expression for $g = 4$, $k = 2$, and $t = 9$.

1. $4t$ 36
2. $3k$ 6
3. $5t + 7$ 52
4. $4(g - 1)$ 12
5. $3t - g$ 23
6. $gt \div k$ 18
7. $g + 12 - 3 \times k$ 10
8. $32 \div g \times k$ 16
9. $(20 \div g) \times k$ 10
10. $4g + t - k$ 23
11. $2g + 2 \times 3$ 14
12. $kt - 3$ 15
13. The formula for the perimeter of a rectangle is $P = 2l + 2w$. If $l = 2$ in. and $w = 4$ in., what operation(s) would you do first? $P = 2(2) + 2(4)$; multiply 2 by 2 in. and 2 by 4 in.

Enrichment 1-1 — Algebraic Expressions and the Order of O[...]s — L4

Patterns in Algebra

Notice the pattern that results when you substitute the positive integers 1, 2, 3, and 4 for the variable in the algebraic expression $2x$.

x	1	2	3	4
$2x$	2	4	6	8

One way to describe the pattern formed by the algebraic expression $2x$ is: The numbers start at 2 and increase by 2.

1. Write the next 3 numbers in the pattern of $2x$. 10, 12, 14

Substitute the integers 1, 2, 3, and 4 for x to find the resulting first four numbers in each algebraic expression. Study the number pattern. Describe the pattern in words. Then continue each pattern by writing the next three numbers.

2. $5x$ The numbers increase by 5; 5, 10, 15, 20, 25, 30, 35
3. $6x + 1$ The numbers increase by 6; 7, 13, 19, 25, 31, 37, 43
4. x^2 The numbers increase by 2 more than the previous increase; 1, 4, 9, 16, 25, 36, 49; or the numbers are the value multiplied by itself.
5. $2x^2 + 5$ The numbers increase by 4 more than the previous increase; 7, 13, 23, 37, 55, 77, 103; or the numbers are the value multiplied by itself, doubled, and added to 5.
6. Write the expression for this pattern: 3, 9, 19, 33, 51, 73. $2x^2 + 1$

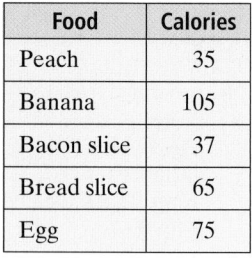

GO Online
Homework Video Tutor
Visit: PHSchool.com
Web Code: ase-0101

Nutrition **Use the table to write an expression for the number of Calories in each situation.**

Food	Calories
Peach	35
Banana	105
Bacon slice	37
Bread slice	65
Egg	75

18. p peaches and n bananas $35p + 105n$
19. two slices of bread, b slices of bacon, and one egg $37b + 205$

Evaluate each expression for $m = 5.2$, $n = 4.1$, and $r = 8.5$.

20. $m + n$ 9.3
21. $mn + 3r$ 46.82
22. $5m - 2n \cdot 3$ 1.4

GO for Help

For help with decimal operations, go to pp. 631 and 632.

23. **Writing in Math** The cost in dollars of an n-mile trip with Supreme Taxi Service is given by $1.5 + 1.75n$. The cost of an n-mile trip using Town Taxi Service is given by $1.9 + 1.6n$. For rides between 1 and 10 miles, which service would you choose? Explain. See left.
24. Describe a situation you could represent with the expression $3 + a$. See below left.

23. Answers may vary. Sample: I would choose Supreme Taxi if I knew I would be going 2 mi or less, because Supreme is cheaper for less than 3 mi. For any trips 3 mi or over, Town Taxi is cheaper.

24. Answers may vary. Sample: You have a pencils, and you buy 3 more.

In each model, the red line represents a variable expression. Match each expression with its model.

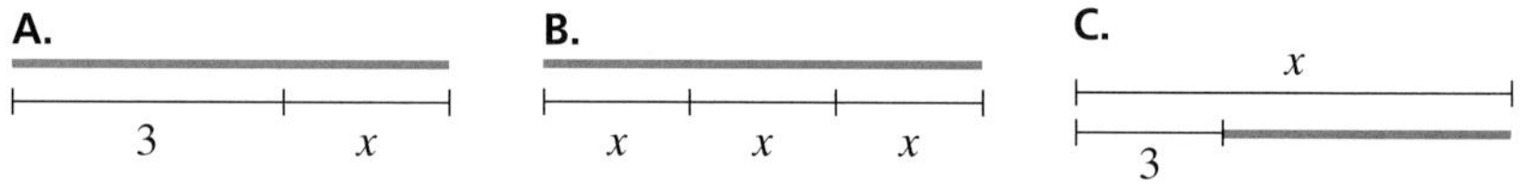

25. $3x$ B
26. $x - 3$ C
27. $3 + x$ A

C 28. **Challenge** You have quarters, dimes, and nickels in a jar. There are twice as many quarters as nickels. Write an expression for the number of coins in the jar in terms of nickels and dimes. $3n + d$

Test Prep and Mixed Review — Practice

Multiple Choice

29. Dante bought three fewer than twice as many books as his sister bought. His sister bought x books. Which expression can you use to find the number of books Dante bought? D
    - A x
    - B $2x$
    - C $x - 3$
    - D $2x - 3$
30. To find the area of a trapezoid with bases of 8 in. and 5 in. and a height of 6 in., you are simplifying the expression $\frac{1}{2}(8 + 5) \cdot 6$. What should you do first? F
    - F Add 8 and 5.
    - G Multiply 5 and 6.
    - H Divide 13 by $\frac{1}{2}$.
    - J Multiply $\frac{1}{2}$ and 6.

GO for Help

For Exercises	Skills Handbook
31–33	p. 631

Find each sum or difference.

31. $12.5 + 6.39$ 18.89
32. $4.7 - 0.85$ 3.85
33. $2.111 + 5.99$ 8.101

Test Prep

Resources
For additional practice with a variety of test item formats:
- Test Taking Strategies, p. 43
- Test Prep, p. 47
- Test-Taking Strategies with Transparencies

Alternative Assessment

Students write an expression involving the variable m on a piece of paper, such as $3m + 5$. They trade papers with a partner and evaluate the expression for $m = 1, 2,$ and 5.

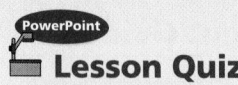

High-Use Academic Words

High-frequency academic words are words that you will see often in textbooks and on tests. These words are not math vocabulary terms, but knowing them will help you to succeed in mathematics.

Direction Words

Some words tell what to do in a problem. I need to understand what these words are asking so that I give the correct answer.

Word	Meaning
Find	To get after searching or making an effort
Compare	To show how two or more things are alike or different
Order	To put in a specific arrangement

Exercises

1. Find the shortest path to the pencil sharpener in your classroom. **1–3. Check students' work.**
2. Compare the path you take to the pencil sharpener to the path your friend takes.
3. Order your five favorite foods from the food you like most to the food you like least.
4. Decorated notepads cost $1.25 each. Find the number of notepads you can buy if you have $5.25. **4 notepads**
5. Three printed T-shirts cost $21.60. Five plain T-shirts cost $25. Compare the cost of a printed T-shirt to the cost of a plain T-shirt. **$7.20 > $5**
6. Order the following numbers from least to greatest: 1.71, 1.17, 7.11, 1.7, 7.1. **1.17, 1.7, 1.71, 7.1, 7.11**
7. **Word Knowledge** Think about the word *represent.* **7a–c. Check students' work.**
   a. Choose the letter for how well you know the word.
      A. I know its meaning.
      B. I've seen it, but I don't know its meaning.
      C. I don't know it.
   b. **Research** Look up and write the definition of *represent.*
   c. Use the word in a sentence involving mathematics.

High-Use Academic Words

This feature focuses on vocabulary words that are not specifically mathematical terms but are frequently used in mathematical and scientific explanations. Students study the definitions of these words and apply them in everyday contexts as well as in mathematical contexts.

Guided Instruction

Before students read the definitions, ask them to use their own words to define *find, compare,* and *order*. Have students compare their definitions to the definitions given.

Exercises
Have two volunteers from different sides of the classroom each get up and complete Exercise 1. For Exercise 2, ask different students to compare the paths taken by the first two volunteers.

Differentiated Instruction

Advanced Learners L4
Have students use the word *represent* in two sentences, one illustrating an everyday use and the second illustrating a mathematical use of the word.

Resources

- Vocabulary and Study Skills Worksheet

1-2

1. Plan

Objective
To find the absolute values of integers and to use absolute value to compare integers

Examples
1 Finding Absolute Value
2 Comparing and Ordering Integers
3 Absolute Value in Algebraic Expressions

Math Understandings: p. 2C

Professional Development

Math Background

Integers consist of the counting numbers (1, 2, 3, . . .), their opposites (−1, −2, −3, . . .), and zero (0). Any positive integer is greater than zero or any negative integer. When comparing any two integers, the one to the right on a number line is always greater. The absolute value of an integer is the magnitude of its distance from zero, without regard to direction.

More Math Background: p. 2C

Lesson Planning and Resources

See p. 2E for a list of the resources that support this lesson.

PowerPoint

Bell Ringer Practice

Check Skills You'll Need
Use student page, transparency, or PowerPoint. For intervention, direct students to:
Algebraic Expressions and Order of Operations
Lesson 1-1
Extra Skills and Word Problems Practice, Ch. 1

Algebra

1-2 Integers and Absolute Value

Check Skills You'll Need

1. **Vocabulary Review** What is an *algebraic expression*? See below.

Evaluate each expression for $x = 4$.

2. $2x + 3$ 11
3. $5(x - 1)$ 15
4. $7x - 4x$ 12

GO for Help Lesson 1-1

Vocabulary Tip
Ellipses (. . .) indicate that the list continues. You read . . . as "and so on."

Check Skills You'll Need

1. An algebraic expression is a mathematical phrase that uses numbers, variables, and operation symbols.

What You'll Learn

To find absolute values of integers and to use absolute value to compare integers

New Vocabulary opposites, integers, absolute value

Why Learn This?

You probably have heard some temperatures described as "below zero." You can use integers to describe and compare numbers that are less than zero.

Numbers that are the same distance from zero on a number line but in opposite directions are **opposites.**

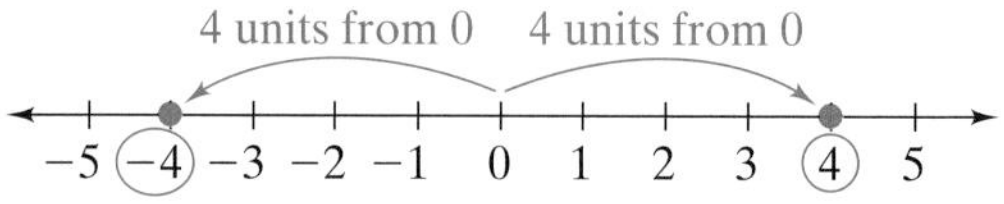

−4 and 4 are opposites.

Recall that 0, 1, 2, 3, . . . are whole numbers. **Integers** are the set of whole numbers and their opposites. Zero is its own opposite.

Integers: . . . −5, −4, −3, −2, −1, 0, 1, 2, 3, 4, 5, . . .

negative integers ← zero → positive integers

A number's distance from zero on the number line is its **absolute value.** You write "the absolute value of negative 6" as $|-6|$.

EXAMPLE Finding Absolute Value

1 Find $|-6|$.

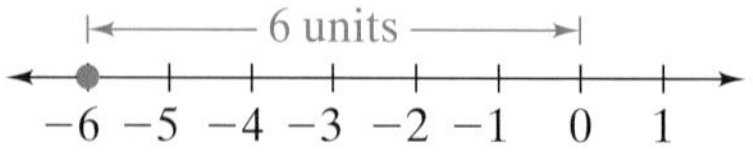

On the number line, −6 is 6 units from 0. So $|-6| = 6$.

Quick Check

1. Find $|7|$ and $|-7|$. 7, 7

Differentiated Instruction Solutions for All Learners

Special Needs L1
Students highlight the distance between zero and any given integer. Then they use their fingers to point to and count each unit from zero. Ensure that students understand the last number they say is the absolute value of that integer.
learning style: tactile

Below Level L2
Students graph positive and negative numbers on a number line. Ask: *How are 3 and negative 3 similar?* Both are 3 units from 0.
learning style: visual

You can use a number line to compare and order integers. Numbers increase from left to right on a number line. You can also order negative integers by finding their absolute values. The negative integer with the greatest absolute value is the least integer.

EXAMPLES Comparing and Ordering Integers

2 Order −2, 3, and −6 from least to greatest.

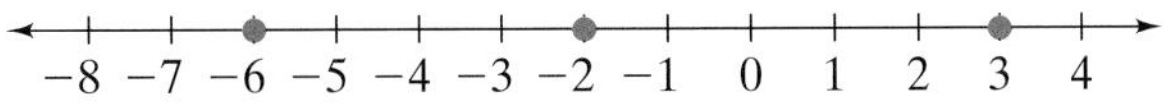

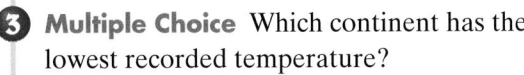

← **Put the integers on the same number line.**

The numbers from left to right are −6, −2, and 3.

3 **Multiple Choice** Which continent has the lowest recorded temperature?

(A) Africa (C) Antarctica
(B) Asia (D) South America

Find the negative integer with the greatest absolute value.

The greatest absolute value is $|-129|$.

The correct answer is Antarctica, choice C.

Lowest Recorded Temperatures

Continent	°F
Africa	−11
Antarctica	−129
Asia	−90
South America	−27

SOURCE: National Climatic Data Center. Go to **www.PHSchool.com** for a data update. Web Code: asg-9041

Not all penguins live in Antarctica. Some types are found in South Africa and South America.

Quick Check

2. Order 0, −5, and 4 from least to greatest. **−5, 0, 4**
3. Which has the lower recorded temperature: Asia or South America? **Asia**

Like parentheses, absolute value symbols are grouping symbols.

EXAMPLE Absolute Value in Algebraic Expressions

Test Prep Tip
Write out each step to be sure that you are using the correct order of operations.

4 Evaluate $|2b| - 6$ for $b = 4$.

$|2b| - 6 = |2(4)| - 6$ ← **Substitute 4 for *b*.**
$= |8| - 6$ ← **Work within grouping symbols first. Multiply.**
$= 8 - 6$ ← **Find the absolute value.**
$= 2$ ← **Subtract.**

Quick Check

4. Evaluate $3|s|$ for $s = -5$. **15**

Advanced Learners L4 Students write a real-world problem that involves the absolute value of integers. **learning style: verbal**	**English Language Learners** ELL Students count the units from 0 to −3, and then count the units from 0 to 3. Elicit the fact that a number's distance from zero is its absolute value. **learning style: verbal**

2. Teach

Activity Lab

Use before the lesson.

All in One Teaching Resources

Activity Lab 1-2: Integers and Absolute Value

Guided Instruction

Error Prevention!

Students sometimes have the incorrect idea that "absolute value" means the same as "opposite." They may think that $|4|$ is −4 rather than the correct value of 4.

Diversity
Ask students what unit is used for the temperatures in Example 3. **Fahrenheit, °F** Discuss what they know about other units for temperature, such as Celsius, which is used in countries that use the metric system.

PowerPoint
Additional Examples

1 Find each absolute value.
a. $|3|$ **3** **b.** $|-2|$ **2**

2 Order −7, 5, and −4 from least to greatest. **−7, −4, 5**

3 The lowest recorded temperature in Asia is −90°F; in North America it is −81°F. Which continent has the lower recorded temperature? **Asia**

4 Evaluate $5|z|$ for $z = -2.4$. **12**

All in One Teaching Resources
- Daily Notetaking Guide 1-2 L3
- Adapted Notetaking 1-2 L1

Closure

- *How do you find the absolute value of an integer?* **Find its distance from zero on a number line.**
- *How do you compare and order a set of negative integers without graphing them?* **Find their absolute values. The least integer has the greatest absolute value.**

3. Practice

Assignment Guide

Check Your Understanding

Go over Exercises 1–5 in class before assigning the Homework Exercises.

Homework Exercises

A Practice by Example	6–18
B Apply Your Skills	19–30
C Challenge	31
Test Prep and Mixed Review	32–35

Homework Quick Check

To check students' understanding of key skills and concepts, go over Exercises 8, 12, 20, 29, and 30.

Differentiated Instruction Resources

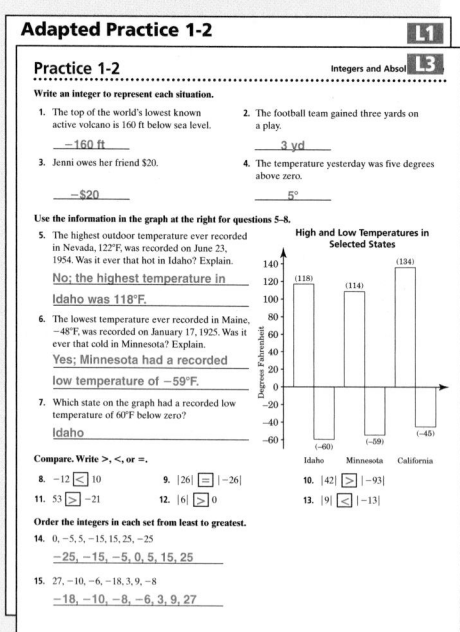

Adapted Practice 1-2 L1

Practice 1-2 Integers and Absol L3

Write an integer to represent each situation.

1. The top of the world's lowest known active volcano is 160 ft below sea level. −160 ft
2. The football team gained three yards on a play. 3 yd
3. Jenni owes her friend \$20. −\$20
4. The temperature yesterday was five degrees above zero. 5°

Use the information in the graph at the right for questions 5–8.

5. The highest outdoor temperature ever recorded in Nevada, 122°F, was recorded on June 23, 1954. Was it ever that hot in Idaho? Explain. No; the highest temperature in Idaho was 118°F.
6. The lowest temperature ever recorded in Maine, −48°F, was recorded on January 17, 1925. Was it ever that cold in Minnesota? Explain. Yes; Minnesota had a recorded low temperature of −59°F.
7. Which state on the graph had a recorded low temperature of 60°F below zero? Idaho

High and Low Temperatures in Selected States

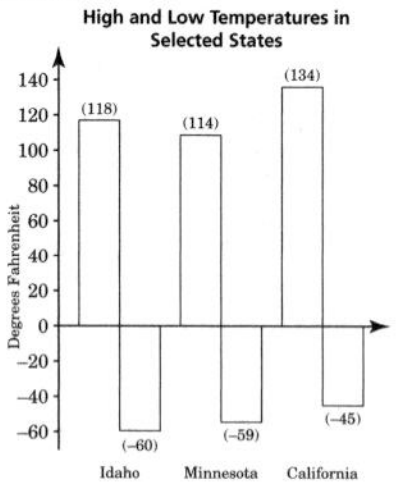

Compare. Write >, <, or =.

8. −12 [<] 10
9. |26| [=] |−26|
10. |42| [>] |−93|
11. 53 [>] −21
12. |6| [>] 0
13. |9| [<] |−13|

Order the integers in each set from least to greatest.

14. 0, −5, 5, −15, 15, 25, −25
−25, −15, −5, 0, 5, 15, 25
15. 27, −10, −6, −18, 3, 9, −8
−18, −10, −8, −6, 3, 9, 27

1-2 • Guided Problem Solving GPS L3

GPS **Student Page 12, Exercise 20:**

Golf In golf, the lowest score wins. One golfer finishes a course at −9. A second golfer finishes at −12.

a. Which golfer wins?

b. By how much does the winner beat the other golfer?

Understand

1. What information in the problem do you need? the score of the two golfers
2. How is the winner determined in golf? The player with the lowest score wins.
3. What two things are you asked to find? which golfer wins, by how much

Plan and Carry Out

4. How could you compare the two scores? Plot them on a number line.

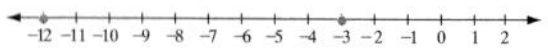

5. Plot the two scores on the number line.
6. Which score is farther to the left of zero? −12
7. What is the difference between the two scores? 3
8. By how much does the golfer win? 3 strokes

Check

9. Is your answer reasonable? Is there another method you could use to check the problem? Sample Answer: Yes, since the scores are negative find the answer with the largest absolute value.

Solve Another Problem

10. A diver located 250 feet below sea level spots a whale at 135 feet below sea level. Who is deeper and by how much? the diver; 115 feet

Check Your Understanding

1. **Vocabulary** How are whole numbers different from integers?
1. Answers may vary. Sample: Integers include whole numbers and their opposites.

Write the letter for the point on the number line that describes each temperature.

Temperature (°F)

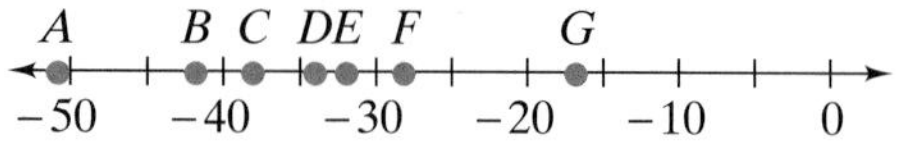

2. Coventry, Connecticut
January 22, 1961: −32°F E
3. Vanderbilt, Michigan
February 9, 1934: −51°F A
4. Mt. Mitchell, North Carolina
January 21, 1985: −34°F D
5. Smethport, Pennsylvania
January 5, 1904: −42°F B

Homework Exercises

For more exercises, see Extra Skills and Word Problems.

GO for Help

For Exercises	See Examples
6–9	1
10–14	2–3
15–18	4

A **Find each absolute value. You may find a number line helpful.**

6. $|-52|$ 52
7. $|26|$ 26
8. $|0|$ 0
9. $|-200|$ 200

Order the integers in each set from least to greatest.

10. −9, 5, 2, −8, 0, 10, −12
−12, −9, −8, 0, 2, 5, 10
11. −13, −16, 11, −6, 7, 2, −4
−16, −13, −6, −4, 2, 7, 11
12. −9, −2, −12, −6, −15, −1
−15, −12, −9, −6, −2, −1
13. −33, 33, −19, 19, 27, −27
−33, −27, −19, 19, 27, 33
14. Order the elements in the table at the right from least to greatest boiling point.
14. helium, neon, nitrogen, oxygen, radon, chlorine, iodine

Boiling Point (at sea level)

Element	°F
Chlorine	−29
Helium	−452
Iodine	364
Neon	−411
Nitrogen	−320
Oxygen	−297
Radon	−79

Evaluate each expression for the given value.

15. $8|w|$ for $w = -6$ 48
16. $5 + |t|$ for $t = -8$ 13
17. $10|a|$ for $a = -7$ 70
18. $|3z|$ for $z = 62$ 186

B GPS 19. **Guided Problem Solving** Mount Kilimanjaro has an altitude of 19,340 ft. The lowest point in the Dead Sea has an altitude of −1,312 ft. Which altitude is farther from sea level? Mount Kilimanjaro

- The integer ■ represents sea level.
- To compare the distances from sea level, use their _?_.

20. **Golf** In golf, the lowest score wins. One golfer finishes a course at GPS −9. A second golfer finishes at −12.
a. Which golfer wins? The second golfer wins.
b. By how much does the winner beat the other golfer? by three

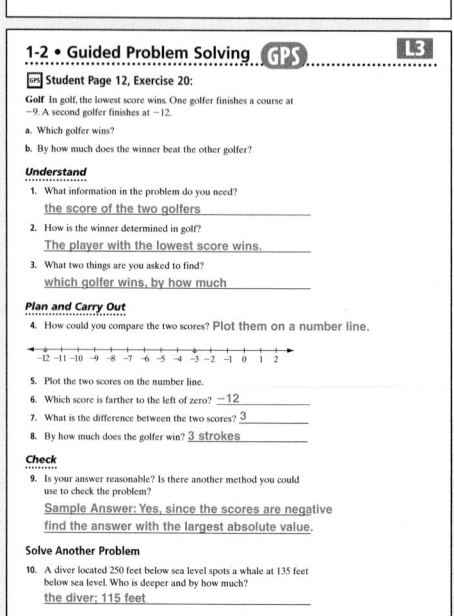

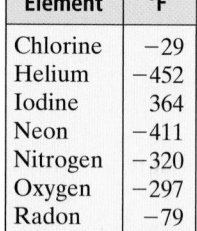

Go Online Homework Video Tutor
Visit: PHSchool.com
Web Code: ase-0102

21. **Number Sense** Which is greater, $-5|x|$ or $5|-x|$? $5|-x|$

Data Analysis **Use the graph at the right.**

22. Which state had the lower temperature? Colorado

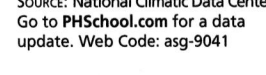

23. The lowest temperature ever recorded in Illinois was −38°C. Was it ever that cold in Kansas? Explain.

23. Yes; the record in Kansas is −40°C, which is colder than −38°C.

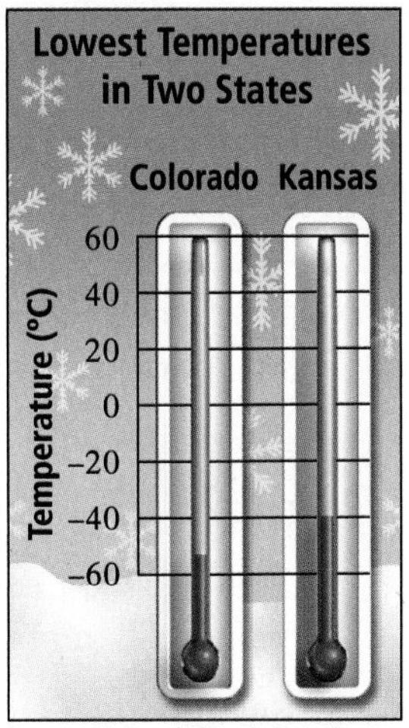

SOURCE: National Climatic Data Center. Go to **PHSchool.com** for a data update. Web Code: asg-9041

Compare. Write <, >, or =.

24. $|-12|$ ■ $|12|$ =
25. $|3|$ ■ $|-4|$ <
26. $|-19|$ ■ $|-7|$ >
27. $|6|$ ■ $|-9|$ <

28. **Open-Ended** Write an integer that is greater than 10 and less than $|-15|$. 11, 12, 13, or 14

29. **Writing in Math** Suppose a and b are integers, and $|a| > |b|$. Must a be greater than b? Use examples to support your answer. No; for example, $|-5| > |1|$, but $-5 < 1$.

30. **Reasoning** Do decimals have opposites? Explain. See left.

30. Yes; answers may vary. Sample: −1.5 and 1.5 are the same distance from 0 on a number line.

C 31. **Challenge** For what values of x does $|x| = -x$? for all non-positive values of x

Test Prep and Mixed Review

Practice

Multiple Choice

32. Which integer is greater than −6 and less than −3? C
 (A) 4 (B) −2 (C) −5 (D) −7

33. Kyle's family drove 40.8 miles east to visit his grandmother, and then 5.2 miles farther east to a restaurant. His family then drove west to return home. How many miles did his family travel in all?
 (F) 46 (G) 81.6 (H) 86.8 (J) 92 J

34. Refer to the table. Which expression represents the cost of t tickets? B
 (A) $21.00 - 5.25t$
 (B) $5.25t$
 (C) $\frac{5.25}{t}$
 (D) $5.25 + t$

Tickets	Cost ($)
1	5.25
2	10.50
3	15.75
4	21.00

Go for Help

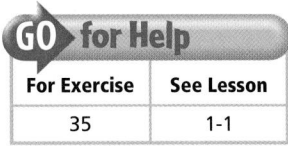

For Exercise	See Lesson
35	1-1

35. **Cable Service** A cable company charges a $25 setup fee and $34.95 each month for basic service. Write an expression to model these charges. Find the costs for 1, 3, and 6 months.
 $25 + 34.95m$; $59.95; $129.85; $234.70

Online lesson quiz, PHSchool.com, Web Code: asa-0102

4. Assess & Reteach

PowerPoint

Lesson Quiz

Compare. Write <, >, or =.

1. $|7|$ ■ $|-8|$ <
2. $|-1|$ ■ $|-6|$ <
3. $|-5|$ ■ $|5|$ =
4. $|-10|$ ■ -2 >
5. 14 ■ $|14|$ =
6. 9 ■ $|-9|$ =

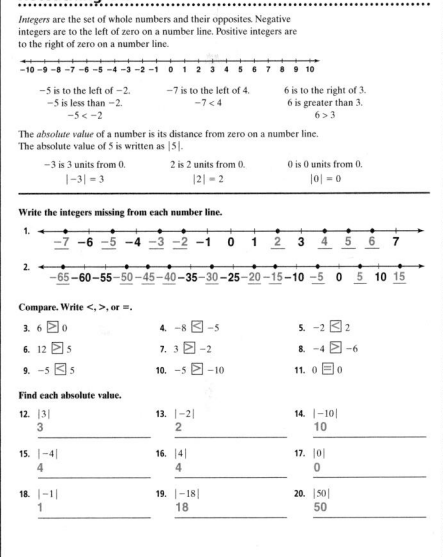

Reteaching 1-2

Integers and Absolu… L2

Integers are the set of whole numbers and their opposites. Negative integers are to the left of zero on a number line. Positive integers are to the right of zero on a number line.

−10 −9 −8 −7 −6 −5 −4 −3 −2 −1 0 1 2 3 4 5 6 7 8 9 10

−5 is to the left of −2.
−5 is less than −2.
$-5 < -2$

−7 is to the left of 4.
$-7 < 4$

6 is to the right of 3.
6 is greater than 3.
$6 > 3$

The *absolute value* of a number is its distance from zero on a number line. The absolute value of 5 is written as $|5|$.

−3 is 3 units from 0.
$|-3| = 3$

2 is 2 units from 0.
$|2| = 2$

0 is 0 units from 0.
$|0| = 0$

Write the integers missing from each number line.

1. −7 −6 −5 −4 −3 −2 −1 0 1 2 3 4 5 6 7
2. −65 −60 −55 −50 −45 −40 −35 −30 −25 −20 −15 −10 −5 0 5 10 15

Compare. Write <, >, or =.

3. 6 > 0
4. −8 < −5
5. −2 < 2
6. 12 > 5
7. 3 > −2
8. −4 > −6
9. −5 < 5
10. −5 > −10
11. 0 = 0

Find each absolute value.

12. $|3|$ 3
13. $|-2|$ 2
14. $|-10|$ 10
15. $|-4|$ 4
16. $|4|$ 4
17. $|0|$ 0
18. $|-1|$ 1
19. $|-18|$ 18
20. $|50|$ 50

Enrichment 1-2

Integers and Absol… L4

Critical Thinking

In golf, each hole on a course is designated by a *par*, the number of shots a professional golfer should take for that hole.

- If the number of shots a golfer takes is *above par*, then the score is designated by a positive number.
- If the number of shots a golfer takes is *below par*, the score is designated by a negative number.
- A golfer's final score is the sum of the score for all 18 holes on the course.

EXAMPLES

① If a golfer takes 4 shots to get the ball in the hole on a par 5 hole, the golfer's score is a −1 for that hole.

② If a golfer takes 7 shots on a par 5 hole, then the score is a +2 for that hole.

③ If a golfer shoots par, then the score is a 0 for that hole.

Solve.

1. The table below shows a golfer's score on the first day of a professional tournament in 2002. Find the score for each hole. Then complete the Status row, or running total of the score, for each hole.

Hole	1	2	3	4	5	6	7	8	9	10	11	12	13	14	15	16	17	18	TOT
Par	4	3	4	4	4	3	4	4	5	4	3	4	4	4	5	4	4	3	70
Rnd 1	4	2	4	4	5	2	4	5	4	4	2	4	4	4	5	5	4	4	70
Score on hole	0	−1	0	0	+1	−1	0	+1	−1	0	−1	0	0	0	0	+1	0	+1	
Status	0	−1	−1	−1	0	−1	−1	0	−1	−1	−2	−2	−2	−2	−2	−1	−1	0	0

Tiger Woods's scorecard for the first round of the 2005 British Open Tournament is shown below.

Hole	1	2	3	4	5	6	7	8	9	10	11	12	13	14	15	16	17	18	TOT
Par	4	4	4	4	5	4	4	3	4	4	3	4	4	5	4	4	4	4	72
Rnd 1	4	4	4	3	4	4	3	3	3	3	2	3	5	5	4	5	4	3	66
Score on hole	0	0	0	−1	−1	0	−1	0	−1	−1	−1	−1	+1	0	+1	0	0	−1	
Status	0	0	0	−1	−2	−2	−3	−3	−4	−5	−6	−7	−6	−6	−6	−5	−5	−6	−6

2. On how many holes did Tiger shoot over par? Under par? 2 holes; 8 holes
3. Fill in the rest of the table, and find Tiger's final score for the day. −6

Alternative Assessment

In small groups, students write an explanation of how to find the absolute value of both positive and negative integers.

Test Prep

Resources

For additional practice with a variety of test item formats:
- Test-Taking Strategies, p. 43
- Test Prep, p. 47
- Test-Taking Strategies with Transparencies

Activity Lab

Integers and Differences

Students use a business graph to visualize positive and negative integers and the change (difference) between them.

Guided Instruction

Teaching Tip
Have volunteers read the account values for various months of the year. Ask: *Did the value of the account increase or decrease over the period shown?* increase

Differentiated Instruction

Special Needs L1
Review absolute values by sketching an ocean scene with the water line as the x-axis. Draw a vertical line for the y-axis and label from -5 to $+5$. Show a point at -4 where fish might be. Show a point at $+4$ where a bird might be. Elicit the fact that the fish and the bird are the same distance from the water line.

Checkpoint Quiz

Use this Checkpoint Quiz to check students' understanding of the skills and concepts of Lessons 1-1 through 1-2.

Resources

- All in One Teaching Resources Checkpoint Quiz 1
- ExamView Assessment Suite CD-ROM
- Success Tracker Online Intervention

1-2b Activity Lab — Data Analysis

Integers and Differences

In finance, negative values represent debts or losses. The graph shows the month-to-month account of one business. The year begins with a negative value because Chantal borrowed money to pay startup costs.

Chantal's Web-Site Business

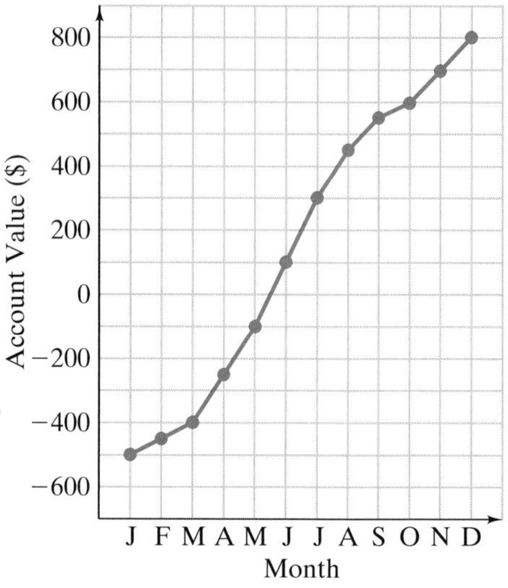

ACTIVITY

1. Write an expression to calculate the amount of money Chantal made from August to October. 600 − 450
2. Simplify the expression. Explain why you chose to use a particular operation. Check students' work; 150.
3. Write a subtraction expression to find how much money Chantal made during the year. 800 − (−500)
4. Explain how to simplify the expression by applying absolute value to one of the numbers. 4–5. See margin.
5. Describe a procedure for simplifying 225 − (−315).

Checkpoint Quiz 1

Lessons 1-1 through 1-2

Write an algebraic expression for each phrase.

1. the product of −3 and a number s $-3s$
2. a number v divided by 12 $v \div 12$ or $\frac{v}{12}$
3. the quotient of a number m and 10 $m \div 10$ or $\frac{m}{10}$
4. the sum of 4 and a number f $4 + f$

Simplify each expression.

5. $|-304|$ 304
6. $|15|$ 15
7. $2 \cdot |8|$ 16
8. $6 - |-3|$ 3

Evaluate each expression for the given values.

9. $3|c|$ for $c = -3.5$ 10.5
10. $|f \cdot g|$ for $f = 4$ and $g = 7$ 28
11. $|x| + y$ for $x = -4.2$ and $y = 3$ 7.2
12. A mechanic charges $168 for parts and $35 per hour for labor. Write an expression for the total charge. Evaluate the expression to find the total charge for 3 hours of labor. $168 + 35h$; $273

Activity Lab

4. Add the absolute value of −500 to 800.
5. Answers may vary. Sample: Add the absolute value of −315 to 225.

1-3a Activity Lab

Adding Integers

You can use number lines to add integers. Start at 0. Move right on the number line to add positive integers and left to add negative integers.

EXAMPLE Using Number Lines

1 Use a number line to find the sum $-5 + 7$.

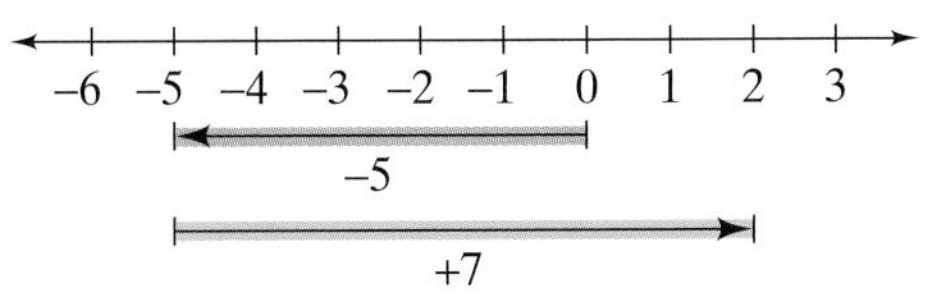

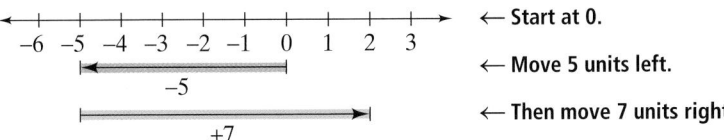

← **Start at 0.**
← **Move 5 units left.**
← **Then move 7 units right.**

After moving 7 units right, you are at 2. The number line shows that $-5 + 7 = 2$.

Exercises

1. Find the sum modeled by each number line.

a.

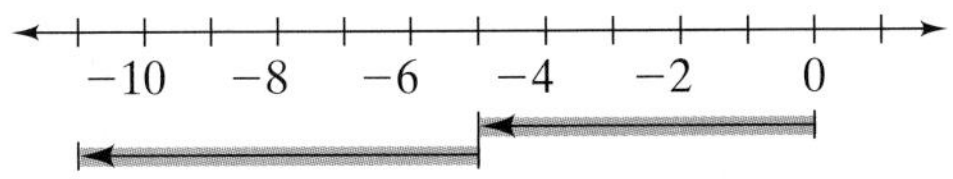

−11

b.

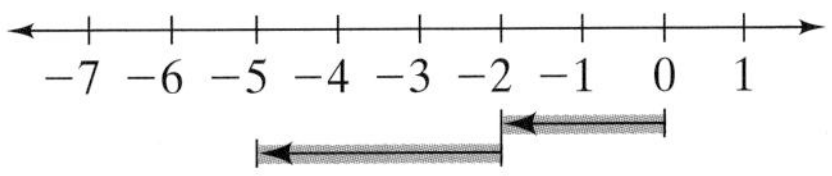

−5

2. A *conjecture* is a prediction that suggests what can be expected to happen. Make a conjecture about the sign of the sum of two negative integers. Use a number line to support your conjecture. **Answers may vary. Sample: The sign of the sum of two neg. integers is neg.**

3. Write an addition expression modeled by each number line. Then find the sum.

a.

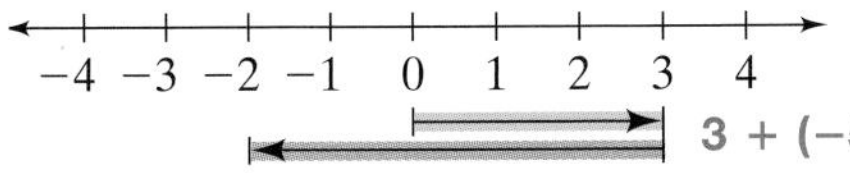

3 + (−5); −2

b.

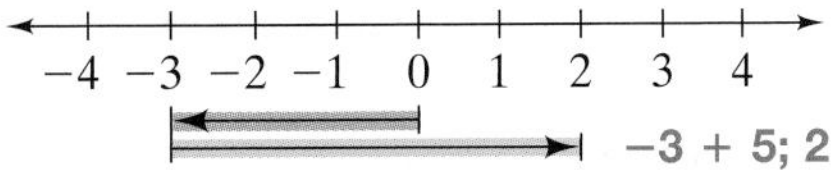

−3 + 5; 2

4. Use a number line to find each sum.

a. $-4 + 5$ **1** **b.** $8 + (-4)$ **4** **c.** $2 + (-6)$ **−4** **d.** $-9 + 2$ **−7**

5. When is the sum of a positive integer and a negative integer positive? Use a number line to support your answer. **Answers may vary. Sample: When the absolute value of the pos. number is greater than the absolute value of the neg. number.**

6. When is the sum of a positive integer and a negative integer negative? Use a number line to support your answer. **See margin.**

6. **Answers may vary. Sample: When the absolute value of the pos. number is less than the absolute value of the neg. number.**

Activity Lab

Adding Integers

This Activity Lab gives students a way to visualize adding and subtracting integers by using a number line. Starting from 0, they move to the right when adding positive numbers and to the left when adding negative numbers.

Guided Instruction

Before beginning the activity, be sure students understand that positive numbers are represented by movement to the right, and negative numbers by movement to the left, along the number line.

Ask: *Would you get the same sum if you moved 7 units right from 0 first and then 5 units left?* **Yes; changing the order does not change the sum (commutative property).**

Exercises

After students do Exercises 1–3 individually, have them work with a partner to complete Exercise 4. One partner predicts the sum. The other uses the number line to find the sum. Have the pairs make up examples to verify their answers for Exercises 5 and 6.

For an extension, ask students if this statement is true: *The sum of three integers always has the sign of the number with the greatest absolute value.* **No** Have them give a counter example using the number line. **Sample: −8 + 7 + 2.**

Resources

- Activity Lab 1–3: Adding and Subtracting Integers
- number lines numbered from −10 to 10

1-3

1. Plan

Objective
To add and subtract integers and to solve problems involving integers

Examples
1 Adding Integers
2 Subtracting Integers

Math Understandings: p. 2C

Professional Development

Math Background

Subtracting a negative integer is a concept that students may find somewhat confusing. This concept may be modeled in English as in "She is not untalented." The meaning of this double negative is that she *is* talented.

More Math Background: p. 2C

Lesson Planning and Resources

See p. 2E for a list of the resources that support this lesson.

PowerPoint

Bell Ringer Practice

Check Skills You'll Need
Use student page, transparency, or PowerPoint. For intervention, direct students to:
Algebraic Expressions and Order of Operations
Lesson 1-1
Extra Skills and Word Problems Practice, Ch. 1

Algebra

1-3 Adding and Subtracting Integers

Check Skills You'll Need

1. **Vocabulary Review** How is *simplifying* an expression different from *evaluating* an expression? See below.

Evaluate each expression for $x = 7$.

2. $x + 12$ 19
3. $x - 5$ 2
4. $7x - 11$ 38
5. $\frac{12 + 9}{x}$ 3

GO for Help Lesson 1-1

Check Skills You'll Need

1. Answers may vary. Sample: When you simplify an expression, you write its simplest name. When you evaluate an expression, you replace each variable with a number and then simplify.

What You'll Learn

To add and subtract integers and to solve problems involving integers

New Vocabulary additive inverses

Why Learn This?

You can add and subtract integers to describe changes, such as a football team's movement on the field.

If a team loses 9 yards and then gains 9 yards, it is back where it started: $-9 + 9 = 0$. Two numbers whose sum is 0 are **additive inverses.**

The following rules explain how to add two integers.

KEY CONCEPTS **Adding Integers**

Same Sign The sum of two positive integers is positive. The sum of two negative integers is negative.

Different Signs Find the absolute value of each integer. Subtract the lesser absolute value from the greater. The sum has the sign of the integer with the greater absolute value.

Online active math

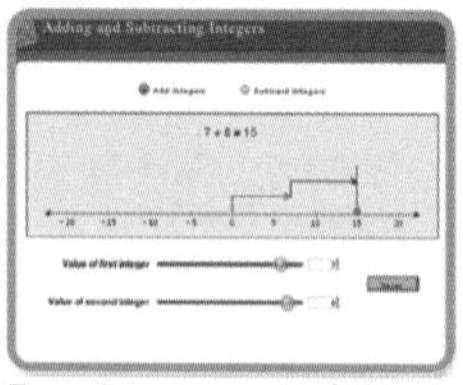

For: Integers Activity
Use: Interactive Textbook, 1-3

EXAMPLE **Adding Integers**

1 Simplify $6 + (-15)$.

$|6| = 6$ and $|-15| = 15$ ← **Find the absolute value of each integer.**

$15 - 6 = 9$ ← **Subtract 6 from 15 because $|6| < |-15|$.**

$6 + (-15) = -9$ ← **The sum has the same sign as -15.**

Quick Check

1. Simplify each expression.
   a. $-12 + 30$ 18
   b. $-12 + (-3)$ -15

Differentiated Instruction Solutions for All Learners

Special Needs L1
Students use one color for movement in the positive direction and another color for movement in the negative direction when they use number lines to add integers.
learning style: visual

Below Level L2
Using floor tiles, students walk the addition and subtraction of integers. Use forward for positive, backward for negative, and movement in the opposite direction for subtraction.
learning style: tactile

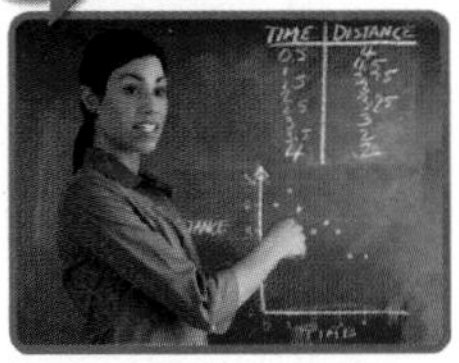

Go Online

Video Tutor Help
Visit: PHSchool.com
Web Code: ase-0775

Subtracting integers is similar to adding integers.

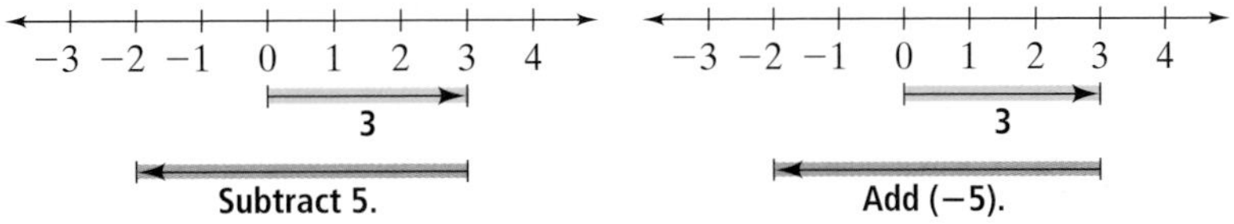

So, $3 - 5 = 3 + (-5)$. This result suggests the following rule.

KEY CONCEPTS **Subtracting Integers**

To subtract an integer, add its opposite.

Arithmetic	Algebra
$5 - 7 = 5 + (-7)$	$a - b = a + (-b)$
$5 - (-7) = 5 + 7$	$a - (-b) = a + b$

EXAMPLES Subtracting Integers

2 Simplify the expression $12 - (-15)$.

$12 - (-15) = 12 + (15)$ ← Add the opposite of −15, which is 15.

$= 27$ ← Simplify.

3 **Geography** A group of archaeologists leaves a site in Jordan and descends 647 m to the shore of the Dead Sea. Their initial elevation was 251 m above sea level. What is the elevation of the Dead Sea?

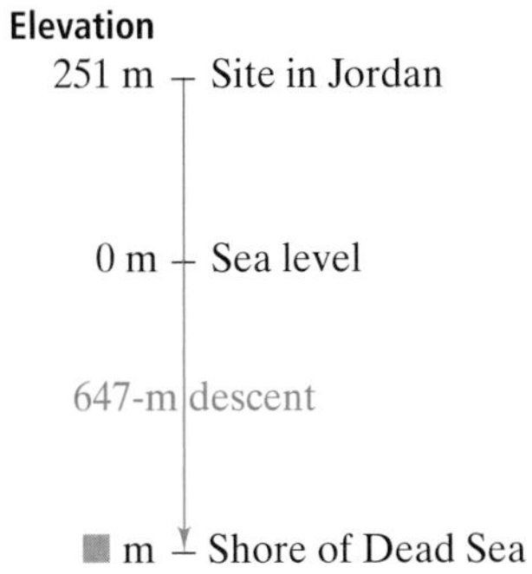

Draw a diagram like the one at the right to better understand the problem. It shows that the expression $251 - 647$ represents the elevation of the Dead Sea.

$251 - 647 = 251 + (-647)$ ← Add the opposite of 647, which is −647.

$= -396$ ← Use the rule for adding integers with different signs.

The elevation of the Dead Sea is −396 m, or 396 m below sea level.

Quick Check

2. Simplify each expression.
   a. $8 - (-4)$ 12 b. $-23 - (-11)$ −12 c. $-140 - 60$ −200

3. −181 ft, or 181 ft below the surface

3. **Diving** A scuba diver goes 94 ft below the surface of the ocean, and then descends 87 ft farther. What is the diver's depth?

2. Teach

Activity Lab

Use before the lesson.
Student Edition Activity Lab 1-3a, Adding Integers, p. 15

All in One Teaching Resources

Activity Lab 1-3: Adding and Subtracting Integers

Guided Instruction

Example 1
Suggest that, before they begin their calculations, students ask themselves this question: *Are the signs alike or different?*

Diversity
Have students locate the Dead Sea, which is mentioned in Example 3, on a map. **It is on the border between Jordan and Israel and the lowest point on Earth.**

PowerPoint
Additional Examples

1 Simplify each expression.
  a. $-7 + (-7)$ −14
  b. $8 + (-32)$ −24

2 Simplify the expression $10 - 17$ −7

3 The elevation of the Dead Sea is 396 m below sea level. A group of archaeologists leaves the shore of the Dead Sea. They stop after ascending 500 m. What is their elevation? **104 m above sea level**

All in One Teaching Resources
- Daily Notetaking Guide 1-3 L3
- Adapted Notetaking 1-3 L1

Closure

- Explain how to add any two integers. **If the signs are the same, add the integers and retain the sign. If the signs are different, use a number line.**
- Explain how to subtract any two integers. **To subtract an integer, add its opposite.**

Advanced Learners L4
Ask if this statement is true: *To subtract a negative number, rewrite subtraction as addition.* **Not true—statement must include,** ***and the negative number becomes positive.***

learning style: verbal

English Language Learners ELL
In Example 2, students may read the expression $12 - (-15)$ as *12 minus negative 15.* Point out that they can also read this expression as *12 plus the opposite of negative 15.*

learning style: verbal

3. Practice

Assignment Guide

Check Your Understanding

Go over Exercises 1–10 in class before assigning the Homework Exercises.

Homework Exercises

A	Practice by Example	11–26
B	Apply Your Skills	27–34
C	Challenge	35
Test Prep and Mixed Review		36–41

Homework Quick Check

To check students' understanding of key skills and concepts, go over Exercises 12, 20, 29, 30, and 33.

Differentiated Instruction Resources

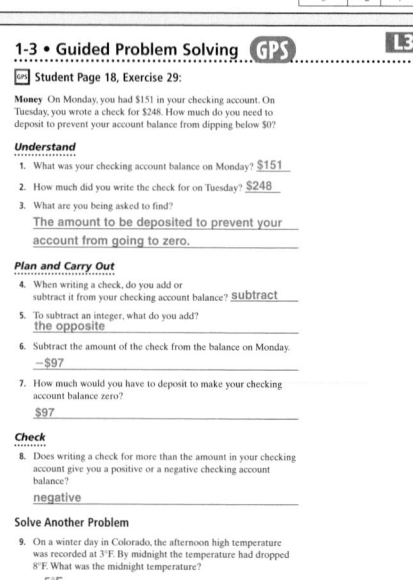

Adapted Practice 1-3 L1

Practice 1-3 Adding and Subtracting L3

Write the addition expression that is suggested by each model.

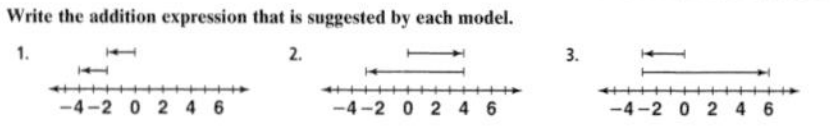

1. $-2 + (-2) = -4$
2. $4 + (-7) = -3$
3. $-3 + 9 = 6$

Write an algebraic expression to find the sum for each situation.

4. The varsity football team gained 7 yd on one play and then lost 4 yd. $7 + (-4) = 3$
5. The airplane descended 140 ft and then rose 112 ft. $(-140) + 112 = -28$
6. The squirrel climbed 18 in. up a tree, slipped back 4 in., and then climbed up 12 in. more. $18 + (-4) + 12 = 26$
7. The temperature was 72°F at noon. At midnight a cold front moved in, dropping the temperature 12°F. $72 + (-12) = 60$

Simplify each expression.

8. $8 + (7)$ 15
9. $9 + (-4)$ 5
10. $-6 + (-8)$ −14
11. $9 + (-17)$ −8
12. $-15 + (-11)$ −26
13. $-23 + 18$ −5
14. $27 + 34$ 61
15. $-8 + (-17)$ −25
16. $19 + (-8)$ 11
17. $-14 - 33$ −47
18. $-32 - (-18)$ −14
19. $-15 - (-26)$ 11
20. $-19 - (-12)$ −7
21. $-16 - (-21)$ 5
22. $27 - 19$ 8

Evaluate each expression for $x = 5$, $y = -6$, and $z = -7$.

23. $x + y$ −1
24. $15 - z$ 22
25. $y - z$ 1
26. $y - 15 + x$ −16
27. $32 - z + x$ 44
28. $|x| - |y|$ −1
29. Jill and Joe are playing a game. The chart at the right shows the points gained or lost on each round.
    a. Who has the most points after the fifth round? Jill
    b. To win, a player must have 20 points. How many points does each player need to win? Jill, 4 points; Joe, 6 points

Round	Jill	Joe
1	10	12
2	−2	3
3	6	−8
4	4	0
5	−2	7

1-3 • Guided Problem Solving GPS L3

GPS **Student Page 18, Exercise 29:**

Money On Monday, you had $151 in your checking account. On Tuesday, you wrote a check for $248. How much do you need to deposit to prevent your account balance from dipping below $0?

Understand

1. What was your checking account balance on Monday? $151
2. How much did you write the check for on Tuesday? $248
3. What are you being asked to find? The amount to be deposited to prevent your account from going to zero.

Plan and Carry Out

4. When writing a check, do you add or subtract it from your checking account balance? subtract
5. To subtract an integer, what do you add? the opposite
6. Subtract the amount of the check from the balance on Monday. −$97
7. How much would you have to deposit to make your checking account balance zero? $97

Check

8. Does writing a check for more than the amount in your checking account give you a positive or a negative checking account balance? negative

Solve Another Problem

9. On a winter day in Colorado, the afternoon high temperature was recorded at 3°F. By midnight the temperature had dropped 8°F. What was the midnight temperature? −5°F.

Check Your Understanding

1. **Vocabulary** What is the additive inverse of 0? Explain. 0; $0 + 0 = 0$

Vocabulary Tip

The parentheses around negative numbers help avoid confusion with subtraction signs.

Mental Math Determine whether each expression equals a *positive* or a *negative* number.

2. $2 + (-6)$ negative
3. $-1 + (-4)$ negative
4. $-5 + 9$ positive

Simplify each expression.

5. $6 + 2$ 8
6. $-8 + 3$ −5
7. $-7 + 5$ −2
8. $4 - 1$ 3
9. $4 + (-3)$ 1
10. $-4 - 4$ −8

Homework Exercises

For more exercises, see Extra Skills and Word Problems.

GO for Help

For Exercises	See Examples
11–19	1
20–26	2 and 3

A Simplify each expression. You may find a number line helpful.

11. $-3 + (-5)$ −8
12. $49 + (-13)$ 36
13. $-15 + 14$ −1
14. $3 + (-12)$ −9
15. $-25 + (-7)$ −32
16. $-17 + 18$ 1
17. $-23 + 35$ 12
18. $215 + (-117)$ 98
19. $-508 + 507$ −1
20. $-5 - 8$ −13
21. $-3 - (-7)$ 4
22. $6 - 18$ −12
23. $21 - (-15)$ 36
24. $-38 - 38$ −76
25. $-23 - (-23)$ 0
26. **Temperature** The temperature was 2°F. By midnight, the temperature had dropped 7°F. What was the temperature at midnight? −5°F

B GPS

27. **Guided Problem Solving** The graph shows temperatures at various altitudes. How much colder is it at 6,000 m than at 4,000 m?
    - What is the temperature at 4,000 m?
    - What is the temperature at 6,000 m?
    - What is the difference in temperature? 13°C

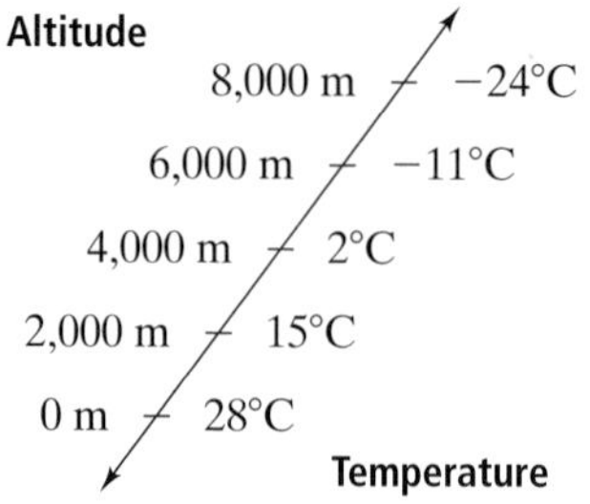

28. **Golf** In a golf tournament, a player scores −8 on the first day and +5 on the second day. What is the player's overall score? −3
29. **Money** On Monday, you had $151 in your checking account. On Tuesday, you wrote a check for $248. How much money should you deposit to prevent your account balance from going below $0? $97 (GPS)

Go Online
Homework Video Tutor
Visit: PHSchool.com
Web Code: ase-0103

Reasoning **Is each statement *sometimes, always,* or *never* true? Explain.**

30. The sum of a number and its opposite is negative. never; it is always 0

31. The difference of a number and its opposite is negative. sometimes; $2 - (-2) = 4$ and $-2 - 2 = -4$

Math in the Media **Use the cartoon below for Exercises 32 and 33.**

32. What would you add to 8 to get the sum 7? −1

33. **Writing in Math** Is the statement Calvin's father makes in the last frame always true? Explain.

33. No; you can add a negative integer and come out with less than you started with.

34. Evaluate $x + y - z$ for $x = 2$, $y = -2$, and $z = -3$. 3

C **35.** **Challenge** For what integer values of x is $|x + 1| - 2$ positive? all integers greater than 1 or less than −3

Test Prep and Mixed Review

Practice

Multiple Choice

36. A stock price was \$43 on Monday morning. That week, the value of the stock gained \$3, lost \$5, lost \$1, gained \$2, and gained \$4. What was the stock price at the end of the day on Friday? C

A \$28 B \$37 C \$46 D \$58

37. In a trivia game, you earn 15 points for a correct answer and lose 10 points for an incorrect answer. With −45 points, you answer the next question wrong. Which expression describes your new score? H

F $-45 + 15$ H $-45 - 10$
G $-45 - 15$ J $10 - 45$

38. At a library, copies cost \$0.15 each. You made 8 copies and paid \$1.25 for overdue books. Which expression can you use to find the amount you spent at the library? B

A $0.15 + 1.25$ C $1.25 - 0.15(8)$
B $0.15(8) + 1.25$ D $0.15 + 1.25(8)$

Go for Help

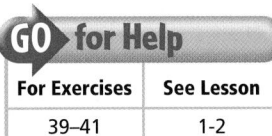

For Exercises	See Lesson
39–41	1-2

Compare. Write <, >, or =.

39. −14 ■ 12 <
40. −3 ■ −4 >
41. −6 ■ −10 >

4. Assess & Reteach

PowerPoint

Lesson Quiz

Simplify each expression.

1. $11 - 17$ −6
2. $8 + (-6)$ 2
3. $-1 - (-20)$ 19
4. $15 - 12$ 3
5. $-4 + (-6)$ −10
6. $9 - (-2)$ 11

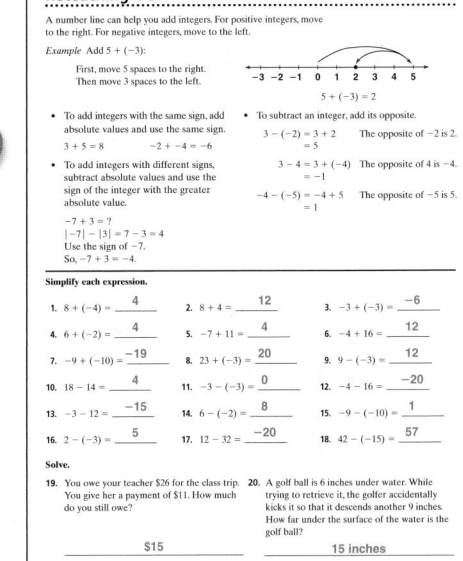

Reteaching 1-3
Adding and Subtracting L2

A number line can help you add integers. For positive integers, move to the right. For negative integers, move to the left.

Example Add $5 + (-3)$:

First, move 5 spaces to the right.
Then move 3 spaces to the left.

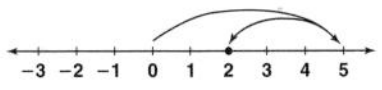

$5 + (-3) = 2$

- To add integers with the same sign, add absolute values and use the same sign.
  $3 + 5 = 8$ $-2 + -4 = -6$
- To add integers with different signs, subtract absolute values and use the sign of the integer with the greater absolute value.
  $-7 + 3 = ?$
  $|-7| - |3| = 7 - 3 = 4$
  Use the sign of −7.
  So, $-7 + 3 = -4$.
- To subtract an integer, add its opposite.
  $3 - (-2) = 3 + 2 = 5$ The opposite of −2 is 2.
  $3 - 4 = 3 + (-4) = -1$ The opposite of 4 is −4.
  $-4 - (-5) = -4 + 5 = 1$ The opposite of −5 is 5.

Simplify each expression.

1. $8 + (-4) =$ 4
2. $8 + 4 =$ 12
3. $-3 + (-3) =$ −6
4. $6 + (-2) =$ 4
5. $-7 + 11 =$ 4
6. $-4 + 16 =$ 12
7. $-9 + (-10) =$ −19
8. $23 + (-3) =$ 20
9. $9 - (-3) =$ 12
10. $18 - 14 =$ 4
11. $-3 - (-3) =$ 0
12. $-4 - 16 =$ −20
13. $-3 - 12 =$ −15
14. $6 - (-2) =$ 8
15. $-9 - (-10) =$ 1
16. $2 - (-3) =$ 5
17. $12 - 32 =$ −20
18. $42 - (-15) =$ 57

Solve.

19. You owe your teacher \$26 for the class trip. You give her a payment of \$11. How much do you still owe? \$15

20. A golf ball is 6 inches under water. While trying to retrieve it, the golfer accidentally kicks it so that it descends another 9 inches. How far under the surface of the water is the golf ball? 15 inches

Enrichment 1-3
Adding and Subtracting L4

Critical Thinking

The Dow Jones Industrial Average (also called "The Dow") measures the prices of important stocks on the New York Stock Exchange. Suppose the Dow Jones Average at the end of a week is 5,602.10. The average lost 8.70 points on Monday, gained 37.70 on Tuesday, lost 11.25 on Wednesday, gained 24.90 on Thursday, and gained 27.15 on Friday. What was the Dow Jones Average at the start of the week?

1. What was the Dow Jones Average at the end of the week? 5,602.10
2. How many changes were made during the week? 5
3. What are you asked to find? the Dow Jones average at the start of the week
4. Which of the changes would be considered positive? negative? positive: 37.70, 24.90, 27.15; negative: 8.70, 11.25
5. Let x represent the Dow Jones Average at the start of the week. Write an equation to show the change from the start of the week to the end of the week. $x - 8.70 + 37.70 - 11.25 + 24.90 + 27.15 = 5{,}602.10$
6. Solve the equation you wrote in Exercise 5. What was the Dow Jones Average at the start of the week? 5,532.30
7. On January 29, the Dow closed at 7,989.65 points. The high for the day was 8,088.89 points and the low was 7,951.37 points.
   a. What was the difference between the Dow's high and low on January 29? 137.52
   b. Find the average of the three given points. Did the day close at a value greater than or less than the average? How much greater than or less than? The Dow closed at a value less than the average; 20.32 points less.

Alternative Assessment

Students write two integers. They exchange papers with partners who add the integers. Students then subtract the first integer from the second.

Test Prep

Resources
For additional practice with a variety of test item formats:
- Test-Taking Strategies, p. 43
- Test Prep, p. 47
- Test-Taking Strategies with Transparencies

1-4

1. Plan

Objective
To multiply and divide integers and to solve problems involving integers

Examples
1 Multiplying Integers
2 Dividing Integers
3 Evaluating an Algebraic Expression

Math Understandings: p. 2D

Professional Development

Math Background

Multiplication can be thought of as repeated addition. For example, $5 \cdot (-2)$ can be rewritten as $(-2) + (-2) + (-2) + (-2) + (-2)$, which is -10. However, this approach is less obvious when the multiplier itself is a negative, as for example $(-4) \cdot (-3)$. This example could be rewritten as $(-1) \cdot 4 \cdot (-1) \cdot (3)$. If $(-1) \cdot (-1)$ is thought of as "take the opposite of the opposite of 1," then it makes sense that the product of $(-4) \cdot (-3)$ is 12.

More Math Background: p. 2D

Lesson Planning and Resources

See p. 2E for a list of the resources that support this lesson.

PowerPoint

Bell Ringer Practice

Check Skills You'll Need
Use student page, transparency, or PowerPoint. For intervention, direct students to:
Adding and Subtracting Integers
Lesson 1-3
Extra Skills and Word Problems Practice, Ch. 1

Algebra

1-4 Multiplying and Dividing Integers

Check Skills You'll Need

1. **Vocabulary Review** *Integers* are the set of whole numbers, and their ? . opposites

Simplify each expression.

2. $-3 + (-3)$ -6
3. $-5 + (-5) + (-5)$ -15
4. $-2 + (-2) + (-2)$ -6

GO for Help Lesson 1-3

What You'll Learn

To multiply and divide integers and to solve problems involving integers

New Vocabulary inverse operations

Why Learn This?

You can multiply integers to find totals. You can divide integers to find rates, such as your rate of descent while hiking.

You can use number lines to model integer multiplication.

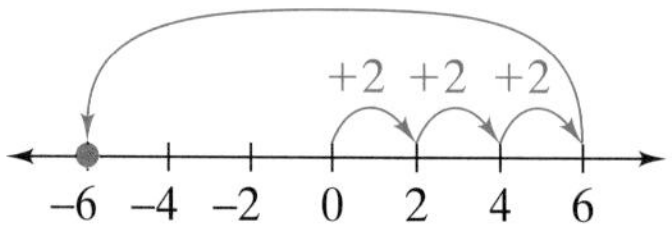

3(2) means three groups of 2.
−3(2) means the opposite of three groups of 2.

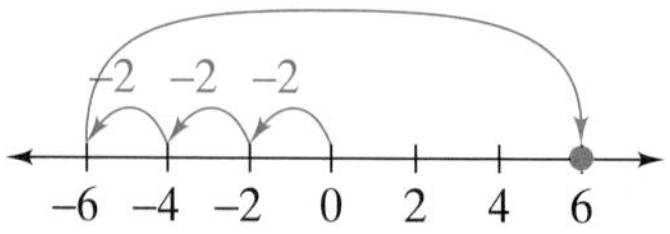

3(−2) means three groups of −2.
−3(−2) means the opposite of three groups of −2.

KEY CONCEPTS **Multiplying Two Integers**

The product of two integers with the same sign is positive.

Examples $8 \cdot 3 = 24$ $-8 \cdot (-3) = 24$

The product of two integers with different signs is negative.

Examples $8 \cdot (-3) = -24$ $-8 \cdot 3 = -24$

EXAMPLE **Multiplying Integers**

1 Simplify $-2 \cdot 9 \cdot (-5)$.

$-2 \cdot 9 \cdot (-5) = -18 \cdot (-5)$ ← different signs, negative product

$= 90$ ← same sign, positive product

Quick Check

1. Simplify $-9 \cdot 8 \cdot (-2)$. 144

Differentiated Instruction Solutions for All Learners

Special Needs L1	**Below Level** L2
Students use number lines to find the answers to Example 1 and related problems. For example, $8 \cdot (-3)$ can be found by circling 8 lengths, each 3 units long, starting with 0 to −3, −3 to −6, up to −21 to −24. **learning style: visual**	Students work in pairs with flash cards to review the basic facts for multiplication and division up to (−15). **learning style: verbal**

Vocabulary Tip

Here are three ways to write "eight times three":

8×3 $8 \cdot 3$ $8(3)$

Inverse operations are operations that undo each other. Multiplication and division are inverse operations. Since $-4 \cdot 2 = -8$, it follows that $-8 \div 2 = -4$ and $-8 \div (-4) = 2$.

The rules for dividing two integers are similar to the rules for multiplying two integers.

KEY CONCEPTS Dividing Two Integers

The quotient of two integers with the same sign is positive.

Examples $\frac{8}{2} = 4$ $\frac{-8}{-2} = 4$

The quotient of two integers with different signs is negative.

Examples $\frac{-8}{2} = -4$ $\frac{8}{-2} = -4$

EXAMPLE Dividing Integers

2 **Multiple Choice** A hiker descends 360 feet in 40 minutes. What is the hiker's change in elevation per minute?

Ⓐ −9 ft/min Ⓑ $-\frac{1}{9}$ ft/min Ⓒ $\frac{1}{9}$ ft/min Ⓓ 9 ft/min

Let −360 represent a descent of 360 feet. Then divide the descent by the number of minutes to find the change in elevation per minute.

$$\frac{-360}{40} = -9$$

feet → numerator, minutes → denominator; ← different signs, negative quotient

The change in elevation is −9 ft/min, so the answer is A.

Test Prep Tip

To find the unit in your answer, note the unit of each quantity in the problem.

Quick Check

2. **Diving** A diver descends 90 feet in 5 minutes. What is the diver's change in depth per minute? −18 ft/min

EXAMPLE Evaluating an Algebraic Expression

3 Evaluate $pt + (p - t) \div r$ for $p = 4$, $t = -2$, and $r = -3$.

$pt + (p - t) \div r = 4(-2) + [4 - (-2)] \div (-3)$ ← Substitute 4 for *p*, −2 for *t*, and −3 for *r*.

$= 4(-2) + 6 \div (-3)$ ← order of operations

$= -8 + (-2)$ ← Multiply and divide.

$= -10$ ← Add.

Quick Check

3. Evaluate $2x + xy \div z - 3$ for $x = -9$, $y = -5$, and $z = -3$. −36

2. Teach

Activity Lab

Use before the lesson.

All in One Teaching Resources

Activity Lab 1-4: Multiplying and Dividing Integers

Guided Instruction

Example 2

Ask: *How are the rules for multiplying integers similar to the rules for dividing integers?* Signs same, answer is positive; signs different, answer is negative.

Error Prevention!

To help prevent errors with signs in Example 3, particularly when substituting a negative value for the variable, suggest that students form the habit of always writing the value of the variable in parentheses when substituting.

PowerPoint

Additional Examples

1. Simplify $-11 \cdot 2 \cdot (-1)$. 22

2. A diver descended 80 ft in 4 min. What was the rate of this descent? 20 ft/min

3. Evaluate $y \div (x - y) - zy$ for $x = 6$, $y = 9$, and $z = -2$. 15

All in One Teaching Resources

- Daily Notetaking Guide 1-4 L3
- Adapted Notetaking 1-4 L1

Closure

- *What is the sign of the sum of two negative integers?* negative
- *What is the sign of the product of two negative integers?* positive
- *If two integers have the same sign, what is the sign of their sum?* the same as the sign of the two integers
- *If two integers have the same sign, what is the sign of their quotient?* positive

Advanced Learners L4	**English Language Learners** ELL
Students write an explanation for a friend why the product of two negative numbers is a positive number. learning style: verbal	Students work on the examples in pairs. Have them use the language of this section to describe each expression. For example, in Example 1, $-2 \cdot 9$ is *the opposite of two groups of 9*, which equals −18. Then, $-18 \cdot (-5)$ is *the opposite of 18 groups of −5*, which equals 90. learning style: verbal

3. Practice

Assignment Guide

Check Your Understanding

Go over Exercises 1–9 in class before assigning the Homework Exercises.

Homework Exercises

A	Practice by Example	10–28
B	Apply Your Skills	29–41
C	Challenge	42
Test Prep and Mixed Review		43–49

Homework Quick Check

To check students' understanding of key skills and concepts, go over Exercises 15, 24, 32, 39, and 41.

Differentiated Instruction Resources

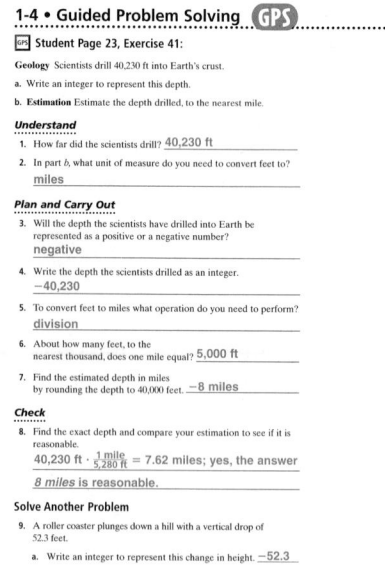

Adapted Practice 1-4 L1

Practice 1-4 Multiplying and Dividing L3

Simplify each expression.

1. $-4 \cdot 8$ −32
2. $-7 \cdot (-9)$ 63
3. $-5 \cdot (-11)$ 55
4. $2(-3)(-3)$ 18
5. $(-4)(-4)(-4)$ −64
6. $(5)(2)(-20)$ −200
7. $-63 \div 7$ −9
8. $81 \div (-9)$ −9
9. $\frac{96}{-12}$ −8
10. $\frac{-54}{-6}$ 9
11. $-1000 \div (-100)$ 10
12. $\frac{-120}{10}$ −12
13. The value of Jim's telephone calling card decreases 12 cents for every minute he uses it. Yesterday he used the card to make a 6-minute call. What was the change in the value of the card? −72 cents
14. One day the temperature in Lone Grove, Oklahoma, fell 15 degrees in 5 hours. What was the average temperature change per hour? 3°

Evaluate each expression for $x = -4$ and $y = 6$.

15. $2x + xy$ −32
16. $(y - x) + 7x$ −18
17. $4 + 2y \div x$ 1
18. $\frac{x - y - 11}{-7}$ 3

1-4 • Guided Problem Solving GPS L3

GPS **Student Page 23, Exercise 41:**

Geology Scientists drill 40,230 ft into Earth's crust.

a. Write an integer to represent this depth.

b. **Estimation** Estimate the depth drilled, to the nearest mile.

Understand

1. How far did the scientists drill? 40,230 ft
2. In part *b*, what unit of measure do you need to convert feet to? miles

Plan and Carry Out

3. Will the depth the scientists have drilled into Earth be represented as a positive or a negative number? negative
4. Write the depth the scientists drilled as an integer. −40,230
5. To convert feet to miles what operation do you need to perform? division
6. About how many feet, to the nearest thousand, does one mile equal? 5,000 ft
7. Find the estimated depth in miles by rounding the depth to 40,000 feet. −8 miles

Check

8. Find the exact depth and compare your estimation to see if it is reasonable. $40{,}230 \text{ ft} \cdot \frac{1 \text{ mile}}{5{,}280 \text{ ft}} = 7.62$ miles; yes, the answer *8 miles* is reasonable.

Solve Another Problem

9. A roller coaster plunges down a hill with a vertical drop of 52.3 feet.
   a. Write an integer to represent this change in height. −52.3
   b. Estimate the vertical change, to the nearest yard. −17 yd

Check Your Understanding

1. **Vocabulary** $-5(3)$ means the opposite of five groups of ■. three

2. **Number Sense** Which product is greater, a negative number multiplied by a negative number or a negative number multiplied by a positive number? Explain. See left.

2. A negative times a negative; a negative times a negative is always positive, and a negative times a positive is always negative.

Mental Math **Compare. Write <, >, or =.**

3. $-3 \cdot 6$ ■ $9 \cdot 5$ <
4. $6(-7)$ ■ $-2(-8)$ <
5. $12 \cdot 4$ ■ $8(-11)$ >

Simplify each expression.

6. $8 \cdot 3$ 24
7. $7(-5)$ −35
8. $\frac{24}{6}$ 4
9. $\frac{-12}{-3}$ 4

Homework Exercises

For more exercises, see Extra Skills and Word Problems.

GO for Help

For Exercises	See Examples
10–15	1
16–22	2
23–28	3

A **Simplify each expression.**

10. $3 \cdot (-15) \cdot 2$ −90
11. $-8 \cdot (-5) \cdot 4$ 160
12. $-7(-2)(-1)$ −14
13. $-1 \cdot 3 \cdot 2 \cdot (-6)$ 36
14. $-3(-1)(-4)(-7)$ 84
15. $2(-4)(-8)(-6)$ −384
16. $\frac{-45}{9}$ −5
17. $\frac{50}{5}$ 10
18. $-64 \div 8$ −8
19. $\frac{35}{-7}$ −5
20. $-72 \div 9$ −8
21. $\frac{-48}{-6}$ 8
22. **Elevators** An elevator descends 1,000 feet in 8 seconds. What is the change in height per second? −125 ft per sec

Evaluate each expression for $c = -2$ and $d = 5$.

23. $cd - 5d$ −35
24. $dc + (c - d)$ −17
25. $d + 3c \div 2$ 2
26. $(2d - c) \div [4(d + c)]$ 1
27. $\frac{d - c + 8}{5}$ 3
28. $\frac{12d}{c - 4}$ −10

B **GPS**

29. **Guided Problem Solving** You withdraw $260 from your bank account in 5 trips to the ATM. What is the average change in your account balance for each trip? −$52
   - What integer represents the amount of money you withdraw?
   - What integer represents the number of trips made to the ATM?
   - Do you need to multiply or divide?

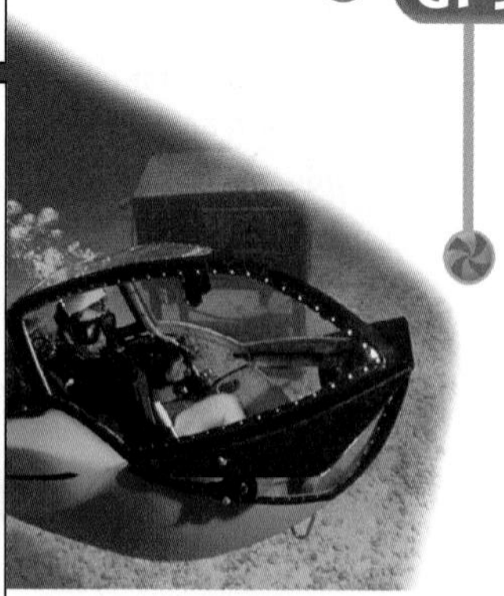

30. **Measurement** A submarine descends 60 ft/min. What depth below the water's surface will the submarine reach in 4 min after leaving the surface? −240 ft

GO Online
Homework Video Tutor
Visit: PHSchool.com
Web Code: ase-0104

31. In a trivia game, you lose points for incorrect answers. You answer the first 3 questions wrong. Your score is −75. How many points is each incorrect answer worth? −25 points

Writing in Math **What is the sign of each product? Explain.**

32. $n \cdot n$, where n is any nonzero number
Positive; the signs are the same.

33. $y \cdot y \cdot y$, where y is any negative number
Negative; there are three negative factors.

34. At the museum, your class breaks into groups of 3 for a scavenger hunt. There are 24 students in your class. How many groups form?
8 groups

35. **Number Sense** What integer divided by −5 equals −60? 300

Algebra **Suppose x and y are positive and a and b are negative. What is the sign of each quotient?**

36. $\frac{x}{a}$ negative
37. $\frac{y}{b}$ negative
38. $\frac{x}{y}$ positive
39. $\frac{a}{x + y}$ negative
40. $\frac{b + a}{x}$ negative

GO for Help
For help converting feet to miles, go to p. 643.

41. **Geology** Scientists drill 40,230 ft into Earth's crust.
GPS **a.** Write an integer to represent this depth. −40,230
b. **Estimation** Estimate the depth drilled, to the nearest mile.
Answers may vary. Sample: 8 mi

C **42.** **Challenge** You go hiking with five friends for 4 days. You are in charge of bringing the food. If you plan to eat 3 meals each day, how many meals should you pack? 72 meals

Test Prep and Mixed Review

Practice

Multiple Choice

43. During the morning, the temperature changed by −4°F. During the afternoon, the temperature dropped by twice as much as it had during the morning. By how many degrees did the temperature change during the afternoon? A

Ⓐ −8°F Ⓑ −6°F Ⓒ −2°F Ⓓ 4°F

44. Which set of integers is in order from least to greatest? H

Ⓕ 8, 5, 3, −1, −6, −9
Ⓗ −13, −7, −2, −1, 1, 4
Ⓖ −1, 2, 5, −6, 8, −9
Ⓙ −3, −10, −12, 0, 4, 18

45. A 165-foot ship was sunk off an island in Hawaii to make an artificial reef. It is located 90 feet below the ocean's surface. If the elevation at the ocean's surface is 0, which integer best represents the elevation of the ship? B

Ⓐ −165 Ⓑ −90 Ⓒ 90 Ⓓ 165

GO for Help

For Exercises	See Lesson
46–49	1-3

Simplify each expression.

46. 8 + (−5) 3
47. −13 + 7 −6
48. −10 − 3 −13
49. 2 − (−6) 8

Online lesson quiz, **PHSchool.com**, **Web Code:** asa-0104

4. Assess & Reteach

PowerPoint

Lesson Quiz

Simplify each expression.

1. 7(−4) −28
2. 10(2) 20
3. (−3)(6) −18
4. (−5)(−9)(−2) −90
5. $\frac{-21}{-3}$ 7
6. $\frac{18}{-2}$ −9

Alternative Assessment

Each student in a pair writes two positive integers and two negative integers, each number on a separate index card. Students mix the cards and place them facedown. Each student picks a card. Together they do a multiplication and a division using the numbers. They mix cards and repeat the activity.

Test Prep

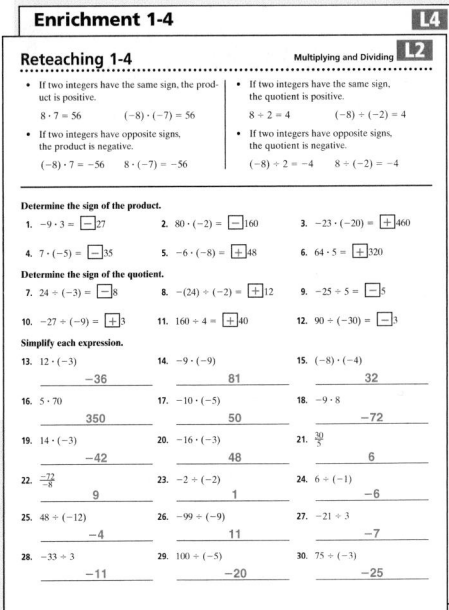

Resources
For additional practice with a variety of test item formats:
- Test-Taking Strategies, p. 43
- Test Prep, p. 47
- Test-Taking Strategies with Transparencies

Enrichment 1-4 L4

Reteaching 1-4 Multiplying and Dividing L2

- If two integers have the same sign, the product is positive.
  8 · 7 = 56 (−8) · (−7) = 56
- If two integers have opposite signs, the product is negative.
  (−8) · 7 = −56 8 · (−7) = −56
- If two integers have the same sign, the quotient is positive.
  8 ÷ 2 = 4 (−8) ÷ (−2) = 4
- If two integers have opposite signs, the quotient is negative.
  (−8) ÷ 2 = −4 8 ÷ (−2) = −4

Determine the sign of the product.

1. −9 · 3 = [−] 27
2. 80 · (−2) = [−] 160
3. −23 · (−20) = [+] 460
4. 7 · (−5) = [−] 35
5. −6 · (−8) = [+] 48
6. 64 · 5 = [+] 320

Determine the sign of the quotient.

7. 24 ÷ (−3) = [−] 8
8. −(24) ÷ (−2) = [+] 12
9. −25 ÷ 5 = [−] 5
10. −27 ÷ (−9) = [+] 3
11. 160 ÷ 4 = [+] 40
12. 90 ÷ (−30) = [−] 3

Simplify each expression.

13. 12 · (−3) −36
14. −9 · (−9) 81
15. (−8) · (−4) 32
16. 5 · 70 350
17. −10 · (−5) 50
18. −9 · 8 −72
19. 14 · (−3) −42
20. −16 · (−3) 48
21. $\frac{30}{5}$ 6
22. $\frac{-72}{-8}$ 9
23. −2 ÷ (−2) 1
24. 6 ÷ (−1) −6
25. 48 ÷ (−12) −4
26. −99 ÷ (−9) 11
27. −21 ÷ 3 −7
28. −33 ÷ 3 −11
29. 100 ÷ (−5) −20
30. 75 ÷ (−3) −25

Solving Multi-Step Problems

Most real-world problems require several steps to solve. This feature helps students analyze these types of problems. They note each step and consider which strategy—such as an equation, a diagram, or a chart—can help them solve it.

Guided Instruction

Read the problem with students. Elicit from students different ways they might approach the problem. Then restate their approaches in terms of the problem-solving steps in the feature.

Teaching Tip
Work through the solution strategy beginning with the key steps: identifying what you know and what you want to find out.

Ask:

- *Normally, what score does everyone start with on a test?* **100 points or 100%**
- *How can writing a number sentence help you find Rex's score?* **Sample: The number sentence helps you keep track of all the points that were added and taken off to get the final score.**

Alternative Method
Discuss the second method, which might help students solve the problem. Visual learners may benefit from seeing the diagram, showing the points to be added on the top and the points to be subtracted on the bottom.

2b. Answers may vary. Sample:

$100 + 2 - 3 = 99$
$100 + 2 - 4 = 98$
$100 + 2 - 5 = 97$
$100 + 2 - 3 - 3 = 96$
$100 + 2 - 3 - 4 = 95$
$100 + 2 - 4 - 4 = 94$
$100 + 2 - 4 - 5 = 93$
$100 + 2 - 5 - 5 = 92$
$100 + 2 - 3 - 4 - 4 = 91$
$100 + 2 - 3 - 4 - 5 = 90$

GPS Guided Problem Solving

Solving Multi-Step Problems

Grades Ms. Mack uses the system shown at the right when grading tests. On his first test, Rex got the extra credit but misspelled three words and had one wrong answer. What was his score?

Misspelling	−3
Bad grammar	−4
Wrong answer	−5
Extra credit	+2

What You Might Think / What You Might Write

What do I know? What do I want to find out? → Rex started with 100 points. He got −3 points three times and then got +2 points. His wrong answer was −5 points. I want to know the sum of his points.

What number sentence can I write? Would a diagram help? → $100 + 3 \times (-3) + 2 + (-5) = \blacksquare$ is the number sentence. A diagram might help.

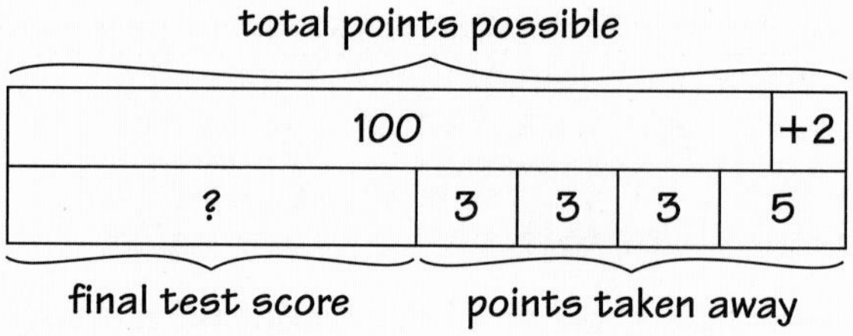

What is the answer? → $100 + 3 \times (-3) + 2 + (-5) = 100 - 9 - 3$
$= 88$

Is the answer reasonable? → A score of 88 for missing one problem and writing carelessly is reasonable.

Think It Through

1. **Number Sense** Suppose Rex had the correct answer for the problem marked wrong, but his handwriting was so poor that the teacher could not read it. What number sentence gives Rex credit for the correct answer? **Answers may vary. Sample: $100 + 3 \times (-3) + 2$**

2. a. What is the only score from 90 to 100 that Rex could not receive if he gets one extra credit problem correct? **100**
   b. Show how Rex could get each of the other scores between 90 and 100. **See margin.**

Exercises

Solve each problem. For Exercises 3 and 4, answer the questions first.

3. A scuba diver was 68 feet deep at 3:14 P.M. She rose 12 feet per minute for 4 minutes, saw a lobster, and descended 20 feet per minute for 2 minutes. But she began to lose air, so she rose 15 feet per minute. What time did she surface? **3:24 P.M.**
   a. What do you know? What do you want to find out?
   b. Copy and complete the diagram below.

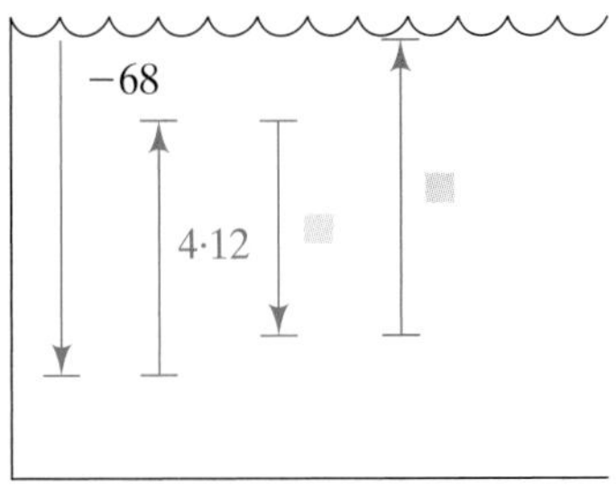

4. Wild horse herds have no natural predators, so they can double in size every five years. If herd growth is left unchecked, find the population by the year 2045 in each of the states shown in the table.

2005 Wild Horse Population

State	Number of Horses
Arizona	230
Nevada	13,251
Wyoming	3,991
New Mexico	82
Colorado	800

SOURCE: U.S. Bureau of Land Management

4. AZ: 58,880; NV: 3,392,256; WY: 1,021,696; NM: 20,992; CO: 204,800

   a. What do you know? What do you want to find out?
   b. Will a table help you keep track of the population and years?

5. A man bought a scooter for $100 and sold it for $120. Later he bought it back for $140 and sold it again for $160. How much did he make or lose as a scooter salesman? **He made $40.**

6. When grading tests, Mr. Lee takes off five points for each incorrect answer, adds three points for each correct extra credit problem, and takes off three points for each problem that has no work shown. On the last test, Sara correctly answered both extra credit problems. If her score was 90, how many problems did she get wrong? Explain. **See right.**

6. 2; the highest possible test score was 106, 16 points more than Sara received. Since 16 ÷ 5 = 3*R*1, Sara got two problems wrong and had 3 points taken off two times for not showing her work.

Guided Instruction

Error Prevention!

Review the order of operations with students when simplifying the number sentence in the given example.

Exercises

For Exercises 3 and 4, discuss the answers to questions *a* and *b*, before students find each answer. Ask: *How can you extend the table in Exercise 4 to help you solve the problem?* **Sample: Insert another column for each 5-year period. Add columns for the years 2010, 2015, 2020, 2025, 2030, 2035, 2040, and 2045.**

Differentiated Instruction

Visual Learners

Help students who are visual learners understand Exercise 5 by drawing a diagram. The diagram might look like this:

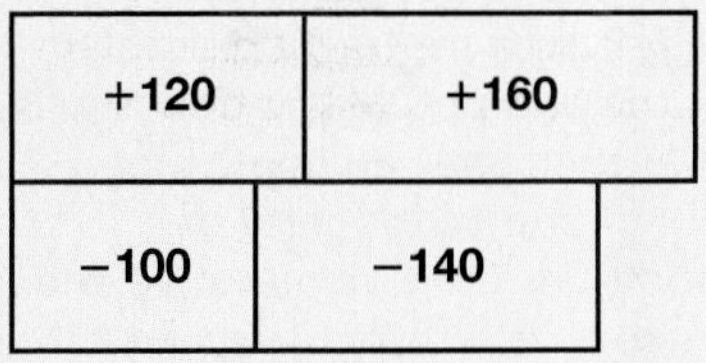

1-5

1. Plan

Objective
To identify the properties of numbers and use the properties to solve problems

Examples
1 Using Mental Math
2 Using the Distributive Property

Math Understandings: p. 2D

Professional Development

Math Background

One of the consequences of rewriting a subtraction problem as the addition of the opposite is that then you can apply the Commutative Property of Addition. The Commutative and Associative Properties make it possible to rearrange and regroup expressions, facilitating estimation and mental math procedures.

More Math Background: p. 2D

Lesson Planning and Resources

See p. 2E for a list of the resources that support this lesson.

PowerPoint

Bell Ringer Practice

Check Skills You'll Need
Use student page, transparency, or PowerPoint. For intervention, direct students to:
Multiplying and Dividing Integers
Lesson 1-4
Extra Skills and Word Problems Practice, Ch. 1

1-5 Properties of Numbers

Check Skills You'll Need

1. **Vocabulary Review** What does it mean to *simplify* an expression?
See below.

Simplify each expression.

2. $23 + 15 + 73 - 12$ 99
3. $5 \cdot 7 + 5 \cdot 13$ 100
4. $6 \cdot 7 + (-9) \cdot 7$ -21
5. $8(-1) - 8(-5)$ 32

GO for Help Lesson 1-4

Check Skills You'll Need
1. To simplify an expression means to replace it with its simplest name.

What You'll Learn

To identify the properties of numbers and use the properties to solve problems

New Vocabulary commutative properties, associative properties, identity properties, Distributive Property

Why Learn This?

When you go shopping, you might find the cost mentally to be sure you have enough money. Understanding operations with numbers can help you make calculations easily and quickly.

You can add or multiply two numbers in any order and get the same result. For example, $7 + 2 = 2 + 7$ and $7 \cdot 2 = 2 \cdot 7$. You can also change the grouping of numbers before you add or multiply them.

KEY CONCEPTS Properties of Operations

Commutative Properties of Addition and Multiplication

Arithmetic	Algebra
$7 + 12 = 12 + 7$	$a + b = b + a$
$7 \cdot 12 = 12 \cdot 7$	$a \cdot b = b \cdot a$

Associative Properties of Addition and Multiplication

Arithmetic	Algebra
$(4 + 7) + 3 = 4 + (7 + 3)$	$(a + b) + c = a + (b + c)$
$(4 \cdot 7) \cdot 3 = 4 \cdot (7 \cdot 3)$	$(a \cdot b) \cdot c = a \cdot (b \cdot c)$

Adding 0 and multiplying by 1 do not change the value of a number.

KEY CONCEPTS Identity Properties

Arithmetic	Algebra
$6 + 0 = 0 + 6 = 6$	$a + 0 = 0 + a = a$
$6 \cdot 1 = 1 \cdot 6 = 6$	$a \cdot 1 = 1 \cdot a = a$

Differentiated Instruction Solutions for All Learners

Special Needs L1
Students "prove" that $(4 + 7) + 3 = 4 + (7 + 3)$ by simplifying each side, using the order of operations. They do the same to "prove" the other associative and commutative properties.

learning style: verbal

Below Level L2
Students insert ( ) to make equations true. This can illustrate specific properties as shown below.
$2 \cdot (5 + 4) = 18$
Distributive Prop. $2 \cdot 5 + 2 \cdot 4 = 18$

learning style: visual

You can use mental math and the properties of numbers to simplify expressions.

EXAMPLES Using Mental Math

1 Mental Math Use mental math to simplify $2.5 + 5.3 + 7.5$.

What you think

I should look for numbers that are easy to add: $2.5 + 7.5 = 10$. Then I can add 5.3: $10 + 5.3 = 15.3$.

Why it works

$2.5 + 5.3 + 7.5 = 2.5 + 7.5 + 5.3$ ← Commutative Property of Addition

$= 10 + 5.3$ ← order of operations

$= 15.3$ ← Simplify.

2 Mental Math Use mental math to simplify $58 - 73$.

What you think

I can make the problem easier by splitting 58 into 5 and 53. First, I should find $53 - 73$, which equals -20. Then, I can add the rest of 58: $5 + (-20) = -15$.

Why it works

$58 - 73 = (5 + 53) - 73$ ← Write 58 as 5 + 53.

$= 5 + (53 - 73)$ ← Associative Property of Addition

$= 5 + (-20)$ ← order of operations

$= -15$ ← Simplify.

Test Prep Tip
You can use mental math as a quick way to check an answer.

3 Mental Math Use mental math to simplify $-5 \cdot 7 \cdot 8$.

What you think

It is easy to multiply with multiples of 10. I should multiply -5 by 8 to get -40. Then I can multiply by 7: $-40 \cdot 7 = -280$.

Why it works

$-5 \cdot 7 \cdot 8 = -5 \cdot 8 \cdot 7$ ← Commutative Property of Addition

$= -40 \cdot 7$ ← order of operations

$= -280$ ← Simplify.

Quick Check

Use mental math to simplify each expression.

1. $26 + (-12) + 34$ 48
2. $46 - 92$ -46
3. $-4 \cdot 121 \cdot (-5)$ 2,420

2. Teach

Activity Lab

Use before the lesson.

All in One Teaching Resources

Activity Lab 1-5: The Distributive Property

Guided Instruction

Example 1
Remind students to look for combinations that add to 10.

Teaching Tip
Ask a student to explain, in Example 2, why 58 was expressed as 5 + 53, instead of, for example, 50 + 8. This was done because the other number is -73, and 53 and -73 add to -20.

Error Prevention!

Help students identify properties by first asking them to carefully pronounce each name aloud, perhaps making a rhythmic song or poem. Suggest they use these questions for identifying the property: 1) Is it all addition or all multiplication? 2) Is the order of the items changed? 3) Are the items grouped differently?

PowerPoint

Additional Examples

1 2 Use mental math to simplify each expression.

a. $3.8 + 17 + 6.2$ 27

b. $89 - 67$ 22

3 Use mental math to simplify $-2 \cdot 13 \cdot 5$. -130

Advanced Learners L4
Students write a set of questions about a property, with yes-or-no answers, that will lead to correct identification of the property.
learning style: verbal

English Language Learners ELL
Students write the addition symbol and the words *sum* and *addends* on a card to remind themselves that these go together. They write the multiplication symbol and the words *factors* and *product* on another card. They include examples of each term on the cards.
learning style: visual

Guided Instruction

Example 4
Students may forget to multiply the second number in the parentheses by the multiplier. Suggest that, before they begin to calculate, they draw arrows to pair the multiplier with each term in the parentheses.

PowerPoint
Additional Examples

4 Find each product.

a. $7(t - 5)$ $7t - 35$

b. $(d + 23)(-4)$ $-4d - 92$

5 A student buys 11 CDs that cost \$6.10 each. How much will the CDs cost? \$67.10

All in One Teaching Resources
- Daily Notetaking Guide 1-5 L3
- Adapted Notetaking 1-5 L1

Closure

- Give an example for each property:
  Commutative Property of Addition $5 + 9 = 9 + 5$
  Commutative Property of Multiplication $5 \cdot 3 = 3 \cdot 5$
  Associative Property of Addition $(3 + 4) + 5 = 3 + (4 + 5)$
  Associative Property of Mulitplication $(3 \cdot 4) \cdot 5 = 3 \cdot (4 \cdot 5)$
  Identity Property of Addition $5 + 0 = 5$
  Identity Property of Multiplication $5 \cdot 1 = 5$
  Distributive Property $5(2 + x) = 10 + 5x$
- *How does the Distributive Property differ from the other properties?* Sample: It always involves two operations and parentheses.

GO for Help
For help with the formula for the area of a rectangle, go to p. 648.

You can find the area of the rectangles below in two ways.

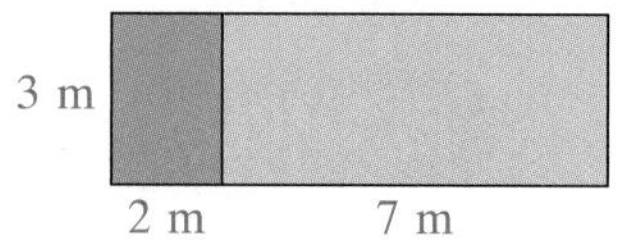

Method 1 Add. Then multiply.

$3(2 + 7) = 3(9)$
$= 27$

Method 2 Multiply. Then add.

$3 \cdot 2 + 3 \cdot 7 = 6 + 21$
$= 27$

Both methods give an area of 27 m^2. This example illustrates the Distributive Property.

$$3(2 + 7) = 3 \cdot 2 + 3 \cdot 7$$

KEY CONCEPTS Distributive Property

Arithmetic	Algebra
$3(2 + 7) = 3 \cdot 2 + 3 \cdot 7$	$a(b + c) = ab + ac$
$(2 + 7)3 = 2 \cdot 3 + 7 \cdot 3$	$(b + c)a = ba + ca$
$5(8 - 2) = 5 \cdot 8 - 5 \cdot 2$	$a(b - c) = ab - ac$
$(8 - 2)5 = 8 \cdot 5 - 2 \cdot 5$	$(b - c)a = ba - ca$

EXAMPLES Using the Distributive Property

4 Find $(n + 14)(-8)$.

$(n + 14)(-8) = n(-8) + 14(-8)$ ← **Distributive Property**
$= -8n + (-112)$ ← **Simplify.**
$= -8n - 112$ ← **Rewrite as a subtraction expression.**

5 **Art Supplies** A teacher orders supply kits for a class of 20 students. Each kit costs \$5.90. What is the total cost?

$20(5.9) = 20(6 - 0.1)$ ← **Replace 5.9 with 6 − 0.1.**
$= 20(6) - 20(0.1)$ ← **Distributive Property**
$= 120 - 2$ ← **Multiply.**
$= 118$ ← **Subtract.**

The total cost is \$118.

Quick Check

4. Find $6(m + 3)$. $6m + 18$

5. A large supply kit costs \$8.10. What is the cost of 20 large kits? \$162

Check Your Understanding

1. **Vocabulary** By the Identity Property of Multiplication, multiplying a number by ■ does not change the number's value. 1

Identify each property.

2. $-19.1 + 0 = -19.1$ Ident. Prop. of Add.
3. $6(-8) = (-8)6$ Comm. Prop. of Mult.
4. $(9 + 10) + 20 = 9 + (10 + 20)$ Assoc. Prop. of Add.
5. $-6.2 + 7.9 = 7.9 + (-6.2)$ Comm. Prop. of Add.
6. $4(wx) = (4w)x$ Assoc. Prop. of Mult.
7. $m \cdot 1 = m$ Ident. Prop. of Mult.

Use mental math to simplify each expression.

8. $3.5 + 9 + 6.5$ 19
9. $14 - 31$ −17
10. $-4 \cdot 6 \cdot (-25)$ 600

11. Use the Distributive Property to rewrite $27 \cdot 2 + 73 \cdot 2$. $(27 + 73)2$

Homework Exercises

For more exercises, see Extra Skills and Word Problems.

GO for Help

For Exercises	See Examples
12–20	1–3
21–26	4
27–30	5

A **Mental Math** **Use mental math to simplify each expression.**

12. $67 + 63 + 25$ 155
13. $87 + 32 + 13$ 132
14. $178 + 288 + 22$ 488
15. $13 - 67$ −54
16. $38 - 59$ −21
17. $24 - 46$ −22
18. $5 \cdot 245 \cdot 20$ 24,500
19. $-2(43)(-5)$ 430
20. $20(34)(-5)$ −3,400

Find each product.

21. $5(a + 6)$ $5a + 30$
22. $7(b - 9)$ $7b - 63$
23. $-4(t + 3)$ $-4t - 12$
24. $(v - 2)9$ $9v - 18$
25. $(8 + r)4$ $32 + 4r$
26. $(-11 + w)(-2)$ $-2w + 22$
27. $6(2.5)$ 15
28. $5(0.9)$ 4.5
29. $4(1.98)$ 7.92

30. **School Supplies** At the school store, notebooks cost \$3.49. How much will you pay for 4 notebooks? \$13.96

B **GPS**

31. **Guided Problem Solving** At the bakery, you want to buy 3 loaves of bread for \$1.99 each and 2 muffins for \$.89 each. You have \$7 to spend. Do you have enough money? no
   - To find the cost of the bread, replace 1.99 with ■ − ■.
   - Multiply by 3 using the __?__ Property.

32. **Tickets** Four students sell 38 tickets each to a school play. The school auditorium can seat 150 people. Are there enough seats? no

33. Find the total cost of buying 4 pairs of candles for \$2.97 per pair, 3 cards for \$1.99 each, and 5 colored markers for \$.99 each. \$22.80 (GPS)

3. Practice

Assignment Guide

Check Your Understanding

Go over Exercises 1–11 in class before assigning the Homework Exercises.

Homework Exercises

A Practice by Example	12–30
B Apply Your Skills	31–40
C Challenge	41
Test Prep and Mixed Review	42–47

Homework Quick Check

To check students' understanding of key skills and concepts, go over Exercises 17, 26, 33, 38, and 39.

Differentiated Instruction Resources

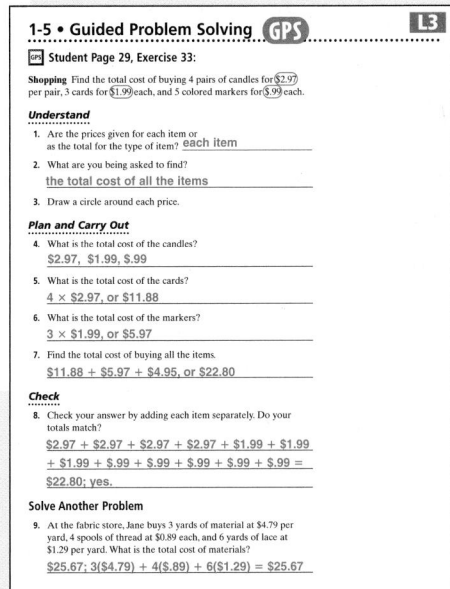

Adapted Practice 1-5 L1

Practice 1-5 Properties of N... L3

Determine whether each equation is true or false.

1. $9 \cdot 8 + 6 = 9 \cdot 6 + 8$ false
2. $-7(11 - 4) = 7(15)$ false
3. $12 \cdot 7 = 10 \cdot 7 + 2 \cdot 7$ true
4. $15 + (-17) = -17 + 15$ true
5. $93 \cdot (-8) = -93 \cdot 8$ true
6. $53 + (-19) = -53 + 19$ false

Use mental math to simplify each expression.

7. $8 + (-2) + 7 + (-5)$ 8
8. $65 + 23 + 35$ 123
9. $17 + (-9) + 18 + (-11)$ 15
10. $220 + 343 + 80$ 643
11. $21 - 74$ −53
12. $36 - 63$ −27
13. $(-5)(38)(-20)$ 3,800
14. $2 \cdot 83 \cdot (-5)$ −830
15. $4 \cdot (25 \cdot 27)$ 2,700

Find each product.

16. $25(-99)$ −2,475
17. $19(-6)$ −114
18. $6 \cdot \$2.99$ \$17.94
19. $102 \cdot \$21$ \$2,142
20. $19 \cdot 21$ 399
21. $26 \cdot 97$ 2,522
22. $21 \cdot (-11)$ −231
23. $9 \cdot \$4.98$ \$44.82
24. $103 \cdot \$32$ \$3,296

The table to the right shows daily changes in temperature over a 5-day period.

25. Which two-day period had the greatest change in temperature? Monday and Tuesday
26. On Sunday the temperature was 20°F. What was the temperature at the end of the day on Friday? 9°F

Day	Change in Temperature
Mon	−12°F
Tues	+6°F
Wed	−4°F
Thurs	−9°F
Fri	+8°F

1-5 • Guided Problem Solving GPS L3

Student Page 29, Exercise 33:

Shopping Find the total cost of buying 4 pairs of candles for \$2.97 per pair, 3 cards for \$1.99 each, and 5 colored markers for \$.99 each.

Understand

1. Are the prices given for each item or as the total for the type of item? each item
2. What are you being asked to find? the total cost of all the items
3. Draw a circle around each price.

Plan and Carry Out

4. What is the total cost of the candles? \$2.97, \$1.99, \$.99
5. What is the total cost of the cards? 4 × \$2.97, or \$11.88
6. What is the total cost of the markers? 3 × \$1.99, or \$5.97
7. Find the total cost of buying all the items. \$11.88 + \$5.97 + \$4.95, or \$22.80

Check

8. Check your answer by adding each item separately. Do your totals match? \$2.97 + \$2.97 + \$2.97 + \$2.97 + \$1.99 + \$1.99 + \$1.99 + \$.99 + \$.99 + \$.99 + \$.99 + \$.99 = \$22.80; yes.

Solve Another Problem

9. At the fabric store, Jane buys 3 yards of material at \$4.79 per yard, 4 spools of thread at \$0.89 each, and 6 yards of lace at \$1.29 per yard. What is the total cost of materials? \$25.67; 3(\$4.79) + 4(\$.89) + 6(\$1.29) = \$25.67

4. Assess & Reteach

PowerPoint

Lesson Quiz

Use the Distributive Property to rewrite each expression.

1. $8(a + 2)$ $8a + 16$
2. $-2(3x + 1)$ $-6x - 2$
3. $4 \cdot 3 + 6 \cdot 3$ $(4 + 6)3$
4. $(6 - r)(-4)$ $-24 + 4r$
5. $5 \cdot 1 + 5 \cdot 9$ $5(1 + 9)$

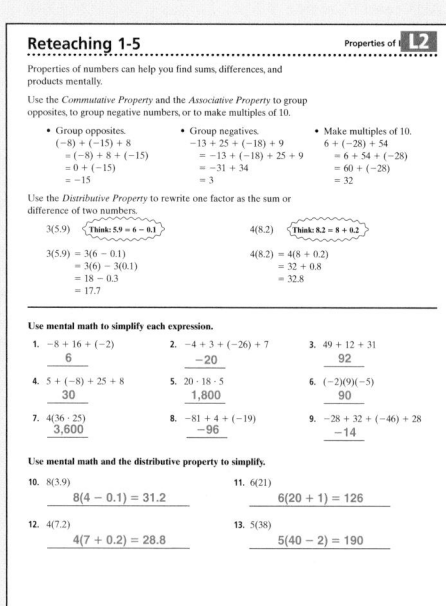

Reteaching 1-5 Properties of [N] **L2**

Properties of numbers can help you find sums, differences, and products mentally.

Use the *Commutative Property* and the *Associative Property* to group opposites, to group negative numbers, or to make multiples of 10.

- Group opposites.
  $(-8) + (-15) + 8$
  $= (-8) + 8 + (-15)$
  $= 0 + (-15)$
  $= -15$
- Group negatives.
  $-13 + 25 + (-18) + 9$
  $= -13 + (-18) + 25 + 9$
  $= -31 + 34$
  $= 3$
- Make multiples of 10.
  $6 + (-28) + 54$
  $= 6 + 54 + (-28)$
  $= 60 + (-28)$
  $= 32$

Use the *Distributive Property* to rewrite one factor as the sum or difference of two numbers.

3(5.9) **Think: 5.9 = 6 − 0.1**

$3(5.9) = 3(6 - 0.1)$
$= 3(6) - 3(0.1)$
$= 18 - 0.3$
$= 17.7$

4(8.2) **Think: 8.2 = 8 + 0.2**

$4(8.2) = 4(8 + 0.2)$
$= 32 + 0.8$
$= 32.8$

Use mental math to simplify each expression.

1. $-8 + 16 + (-2)$ 6
2. $-4 + 3 + (-26) + 7$ −20
3. $49 + 12 + 31$ 92
4. $5 + (-8) + 25 + 8$ 30
5. $20 \cdot 18 \cdot 5$ 1,800
6. $(-2)(9)(-5)$ 90
7. $4(36 \cdot 25)$ 3,600
8. $-81 + 4 + (-19)$ −96
9. $-28 + 32 + (-46) + 28$ −14

Use mental math and the distributive property to simplify.

10. 8(3.9) $8(4 - 0.1) = 31.2$
11. 6(21) $6(20 + 1) = 126$
12. 4(7.2) $4(7 + 0.2) = 28.8$
13. 5(38) $5(40 - 2) = 190$

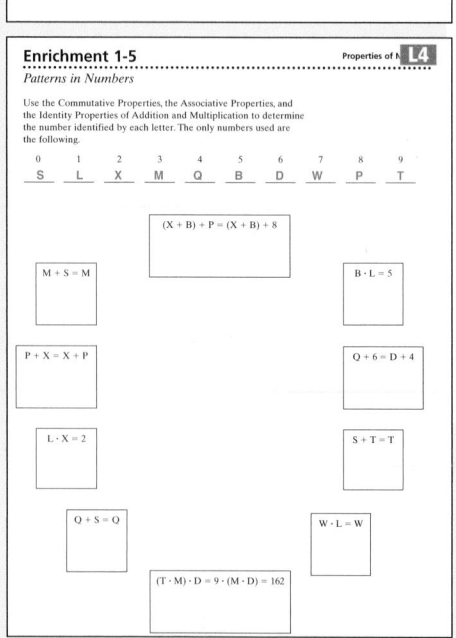

Enrichment 1-5 Properties of [N] **L4**

Patterns in Numbers

Use the Commutative Properties, the Associative Properties, and the Identity Properties of Addition and Multiplication to determine the number identified by each letter. The only numbers used are the following.

0	1	2	3	4	5	6	7	8	9
S	L	X	M	Q	B	D	W	P	T

$(X + B) + P = (X + B) + 8$

$M + S = M$ $B \cdot L = 5$

$P + X = X + P$ $Q + 6 = D + 4$

$L \cdot X = 2$ $S + T = T$

$Q + S = Q$ $W \cdot L = W$

$(T \cdot M) \cdot D = 9 \cdot (M \cdot D) = 162$

GO Online
Homework Video Tutor
Visit: PHSchool.com
Web Code: ase-0105

35. Answers may vary. Sample: mental math; $4(5.98) = 4(6 - 0.02) = 24 - 0.08 = 23.92$

34. You have \$3 to spend on lunch. You want to buy a sandwich for \$1.95, a carton of milk for \$.40, and a banana for \$.60.
    a. Do you have enough money for lunch? yes
    b. If so, how much change do you get? If not, how much more money do you need? \$.05 change

35. **Choose a Method** Four picture frames cost \$5.98 each. Which would you use to find the total cost—mental math or paper and pencil? Explain your choice. See left.

Use mental math to simplify each expression.

36. $-50 + 2 + 108 + (-450)$ −390
37. $(40)(-2)(29)(-10)$ 23,200

38. **Track** In a women's 4×100 m relay race, a team's times for the legs of the race are 11.92 seconds, 12.20 seconds, 12.08 seconds, and 11.86 seconds. What is the difference between the team's total time and the world record time of 41.37 seconds? 6.69 s

39. **Writing in Math** Explain how to use the properties of numbers to simplify $(-68) + 6(-99) + (-32)$. See margin.

40. **Error Analysis** A student claims that $7 \cdot 6 + 4 = 7 \cdot 4 + 6$ by the Commutative Property of Addition. Explain the student's error. See margin.

C 41. **Challenge** A volunteer at a food bank is packing boxes with cans of fruit. Each box must weigh 20 lb or less. Can the volunteer put two dozen 15-oz cans in the box? Explain. (*Hint:* 1 lb = 16 oz) No; 20 lb is 320 oz. Two dozen cans weigh 360 oz.

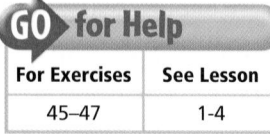

Test Prep and Mixed Review

Practice

Multiple Choice

42. Scarlet bought 1 box of markers for \$3.49, 1 package of lined paper for \$1.19, and 2 packages of folders for \$0.79 each. To make sure she had enough money, Scarlet estimated the total cost. Which is a reasonable estimate for this situation? C
    (A) \$5.50 (B) \$5.75 (C) \$6.30 (D) \$7.00

43. On a 100-point exam, you got 4 questions wrong. Each question was worth 5 points. What would you do to find your score? G
    (F) Multiply and add. (H) Divide and subtract.
    (G) Multiply and subtract. (J) Add and subtract.

44. Which group of numbers is in order from least to greatest? D
    (A) 7, 3, −15, −7, −1, 1 (C) −1, −7, −15, 1, 3,7
    (B) −1, 1, 3, −7, 7, −15 (D) −15, −7, −1, 1, 3, 7

GO for Help

For Exercises	See Lesson
45–47	1-4

Simplify each expression.

45. $-6 \cdot (-2) \cdot 3$ 36
46. $3(-4) \cdot 2$ −24
47. $-2 \cdot 5 \cdot (-1) \cdot 6$ 60

Test Prep

Resources

For additional practice with a variety of test item formats:
- Test-Taking Strategies, p. 43
- Test Prep, p. 47
- Test-Taking Strategies with Transparencies

Alternative Assessment

Students work in pairs and take turns. One student names a property. The partner gives a numerical example. Then students take turns writing a numerical example of a property and challenging the partner to name the property.

Checkpoint Quiz 2

Lessons 1-3 through 1-5

Simplify each expression.

1. $-79 + 15$ −64
2. $23 - (-14)$ 37
3. $-32 - 11$ −43
4. $-4 \div (-1)$ 4
5. $-30 \div (-3 \cdot 2)$ 5
6. $7 - (-9) \cdot 2$ 25

Mental Math **Use mental math to simplify each expression.**

7. $70 + 19 + 30$ 119
8. $540 + 160 - 280 - 10$ 410
9. An animal shelter purchases dog food for \$15.98 per bag. Use the Distributive Property to find how much the shelter will pay for 4 bags of dog food. \$63.92
10. **Fishing** A fishing boat sets its net 37 ft below the ocean's surface. Then it lowers the net an additional 16.5 ft. Write an expression to represent the new depth of the net. $-37 - 16.5$ or $-37 + (-16.5)$

MATH GAMES

Integer Flip

What You'll Need

- 25 index cards numbered from 1 to 25
- 25 index cards numbered from −1 to −25

How To Play

- Shuffle the two piles of index cards together. Deal the same number of cards face down to each player.
- Each player keeps his or her pile face down. All players turn over two cards at a time.
- The player whose cards have the largest sum wins all of the cards that are face up.
- The winner of the game is the player who wins all of the cards.

31

Checkpoint Quiz

Use this Checkpoint Quiz to check students' understanding of the skills and concepts of Lessons 1-3 through 1-5.

Resources

- All in One Teaching Resources Checkpoint Quiz 2
- ExamView Assessment Suite CD-ROM
- Success Tracker Online Intervention

MATH GAMES

Integer Flip

In this game, students practice comparing and adding integers. As players turn over their cards simultaneously, the player whose sum is the greatest wins.

Guided Instruction

Before students play the game, remind them that the greatest of two or more integers is the one that is farthest to the right on the number line.

Ask: *Are all positive integers greater than any negative integer?* yes

Resources

- 25 index cards numbered from 1 to 25
- 25 index cards numbered from −1 to −25

Exercises, p. 30

39. Answers may vary. Sample: I would use the Comm. Prop. of Add. to get $(-68) + (-32) + 6(-99)$. This simplifies to $-100 + 6(-99)$. Then I would use the Dist. Prop. to get $-100 + (-594)$. This simplifies to -694.

40. Answers may vary. Sample: The Comm. Prop. of Add. applies only if all the operations are addition.

Activity Lab

Modeling Equations

The experience of using concrete materials to model mathematical concepts helps many students to better understand the concept. In this activity, students solve addition and subtraction equations using algebra tiles.

Guided Instruction

Read the introduction with students. Be sure they know that the yellow tiles represent −1, the red tiles represent −1, and the long green tiles represent the variable or "unknown" *x*.

Teaching Tip
Have student work in pairs as they manipulate tiles as shown in Example 1. Ask: *Why are two +1 tiles placed on the left side of the equation?* Sample: So the side with the variable only has zero pairs added to it. *Why are two +1 tiles also placed on the right side of the equation?* Sample: So the two sides are still equal.

For Example 2, remind students that division involves making equal groups. Since the left side has *four x*'s, they must divide the right side into *four* equal groups. Ask: *What is the value of each group?* −3

Differentiated Instruction

Auditory Learners
Have students explain their steps to their partner. Suggest that each person explains one addition and one multiplication example aloud.

Resources

- Activity Lab 1-6: Cryptarithm
- algebra tiles

1-6a Activity Lab — Hands On

Modeling Equations

You can model and solve equations using algebra tiles.

▢ = +1 ■ = −1 ▮ = *x*

To solve an equation, remove the same number of like-color tiles from each side or use zero pairs. A **zero pair** is a pair of tiles with a sum of zero. ▢■ ← zero pair

EXAMPLES

1 Use algebra tiles to solve $x - 2 = 7$.

Model the equation. →

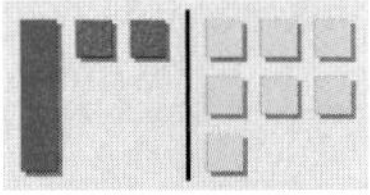

$x - 2 = 7$

Add 2 to each side, making two zero pairs on the left side. →

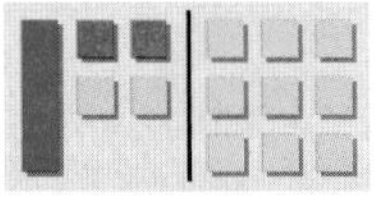

$x - 2 + 2 = 7 + 2$

Remove the zero pairs. →

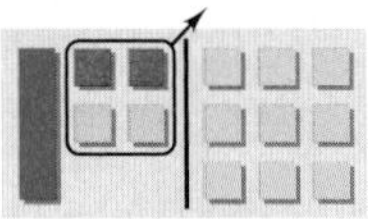

$x = 9$

2 Use algebra tiles to solve $4x = -12$.

Model the equation. →

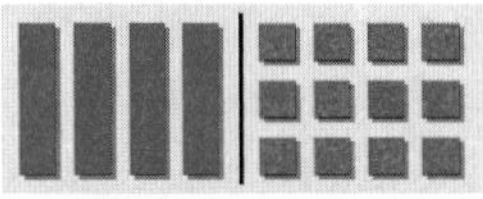

$4x = -12$

Divide each side into four equal groups. →

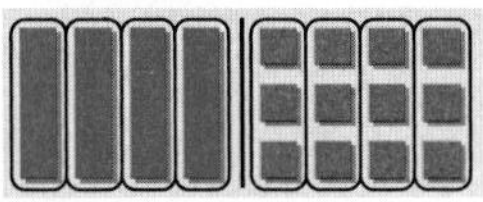

$\frac{4x}{4} = \frac{-12}{4}$

Remove three groups from each side. →

$x = -3$

Exercises

1. Use algebra tiles to solve each equation.
   a. $x + 5 = 3$ −2 b. $3x = -6$ −2 c. $x + 3 = -5$ −8 d. $5x = 10$ 2
2. Write a rule for the operations you use to solve addition equations. See above.

2. Answers may vary. Sample: Add the same neg. number to each side. For example, if $x + 5 = 1$, add −5 to each side to get $x = -4$.

Algebra

1-6 Solving Equations by Adding and Subtracting

Check Skills You'll Need

1. **Vocabulary Review** 4 and −4 are *additive* ___?___. inverses

Simplify each expression.

2. $-4 + (-7)$ −11
3. $12 + (-12)$ 0
4. $3 - 10$ −7
5. $-5 - 1$ −6

GO for Help Lesson 1-3

What You'll Learn

To write and solve equations using addition and subtraction

New Vocabulary equation, Addition Property of Equality, Subtraction Property of Equality, solution, isolate

Why Learn This?

You have probably used the library to find information for a project. In math, you often solve equations to find unknown information, such as account balances or altitudes.

An **equation** is a mathematical sentence with an equal sign.

An equation is like a balance scale. If you do something to one side of an equation, you must do the same to the other side to keep it balanced.

$x + 2 = 5$

Two weights were taken from each side of the upper balance scale at the right. The result, shown on the lower balance scale, illustrates a property of equality.

$x = 3$

KEY CONCEPTS Properties of Equality

Addition Property of Equality

If you add the same number to each side of an equation, the two sides remain equal.

Arithmetic	Algebra
$10 = 5(2)$, so $10 + 3 = 5(2) + 3$	If $a = b$, then $a + c = b + c$.

Subtraction Property of Equality

If you subtract the same number from each side of an equation, the two sides remain equal.

Arithmetic	Algebra
$10 = 5(2)$, so $10 - 3 = 5(2) - 3$	If $a = b$, then $a - c = b - c$.

Online active math

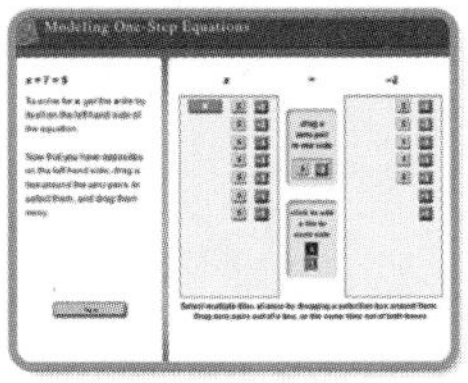

For: Equations Activity
Use: Interactive Textbook, 1-6

Differentiated Instruction Solutions for All Learners

Special Needs L1
In Example 2, students circle the answer they want to find (the plane's original altitude), and the variable (a), using the same color. This can help them make the connection between the unknown and the variable when the words are translated to symbols.
learning style: visual

Below Level L2
Draw a balanced scale on the board. Write 2 + 3 on one side and 5 on the other. Redraw the balance scale to show how one side drops when 4 is added to it. Redraw the scale a third time to show how the scales are balanced again when 4 is added to the number(s) on the other side.
learning style: verbal

1-6

1. Plan

Objective
To write and solve equations using addition and subtraction

Example
1 Solving Equations

Math Understandings: p. 2D

Professional Development

Math Background

An equation must have a verb (such as *equals* or *is*) just as a complete sentence must. Equations can be simplified and solved by undoing what has been done to the variable using inverse operations, such as undoing addition with subtraction. To maintain the balance, or truth, of an equation, the same operation must always be carried out on both sides of the equation.

More Math Background: p. 2D

Lesson Planning and Resources

See p. 2E for a list of the resources that support this lesson.

PowerPoint

Bell Ringer Practice

Check Skills You'll Need
Use student page, transparency, or PowerPoint. For intervention, direct students to:
Adding and Subtracting Integers
Lesson 1-3
Extra Skills and Word Problems Practice, Ch. 1

2. Teach

Activity Lab

Use before the lesson.
Student Edition Activity Lab, Hands On 1-6a, Modeling Equations, p. 32

All in One Teaching Resources

Activity Lab 1-6: Cryptarithm

Guided Instruction

Error Prevention!

Have students begin by drawing a circle around the variable for which they are solving. This may help to avoid confusion about which operation is needed to isolate the variable.

PowerPoint

Additional Examples

1 Solve $-3 = m - 16$. $m = 13$

2 After Vida adds 17 new shells to her collection, she has a total of 52 shells. Write and solve an equation to find how many shells she had before adding the new ones.
$s + 17 = 52$; $s = 35$

All in One Teaching Resources

- Daily Notetaking Guide 1-6 L3
- Adapted Notetaking 1-6 L1

Closure

- *When you solve an equation that has a variable plus or minus a number on one side of the equation, and a number on the other side of the equation, how do you know which operation to choose to isolate the variable?* Decide what has been done to the variable and use the inverse operation. For example, if one side of the equation has a variable plus a number, subtract that number from both sides of the equation to isolate the variable.

A **solution** to an equation is any value that makes the equation true. To find a solution, **isolate** the variable, or get it alone on one side. Use inverse operations, which are operations that undo each other.

Addition Undoes Subtraction		**Subtraction Undoes Addition**
$2 - 8 + 8 = 2$	← arithmetic →	$5 + 7 - 7 = 5$
$n - 6 + 6 = n$	← algebra →	$n + 9 - 9 = n$

After you solve an equation, check your solution by substituting it for the variable in the original equation.

EXAMPLES Solving Equations

1 Solve $-2 = k - 14$.

$-2 = k - 14$
$-2 + 14 = k - 14 + 14$ ← Isolate the variable. Use the Addition Property of Equality.
$12 = k$ ← Simplify.
Check $-2 = k - 14$ ← Check the solution in the original equation.
$-2 \stackrel{?}{=} 12 - 14$ ← Substitute 12 for *k*.
$-2 = -2$ ✔ ← Subtract.

Vocabulary Tip

Read the equation $-2 \stackrel{?}{=} 12 - 14$ as the question, "Is -2 equal to $12 - 14$?"

2 **Altitude** An airplane climbs 7,900 ft during a flight. The airplane's altitude is then 13,220 ft. What was the airplane's original altitude?

Words original altitude plus climb = new altitude

Let a = the original altitude.

Equation $a + 7{,}900 = 13{,}220$

$a + 7{,}900 = 13{,}220$
$a + 7{,}900 - 7{,}900 = 13{,}220 - 7{,}900$ ← Isolate the variable. Use the Subtraction Property of Equality.
$a = 5{,}320$ ← Simplify.

Before climbing, the airplane was 5,320 feet above the ground.

Check for Reasonableness Round 7,900 to 8,000 and 5,320 to 5,000. Since $8{,}000 + 5{,}000 = 13{,}000$, and 13,000 is close to 13,220, the answer is reasonable.

Careers An air-traffic controller monitors both the direction and altitude of a plane.

Quick Check

1. Solve $x - 7 = -10$. -3
2. Yesterday an official mailed some notices for a meeting. Today she mailed 8 more notices. She mailed 52 notices in all. Write and solve an equation to find the number of notices mailed yesterday.

2. $x + 8 = 52$; 44

Differentiated Instruction Solutions for All Learners

Advanced Learners L4
Students describe the difference between numbers that are opposites and operations that are inverses.
learning style: verbal

English Language Learners ELL
In Example 1, elicit the fact that 14 is added to both sides of the equation because adding 14 to -14 gives a sum of zero, leaving the variable isolated on one side of the equation. Ask: *What is the inverse of subtraction?* addition
learning style: verbal

Check Your Understanding

1. Answers may vary. Sample: An equation has an equal sign, but an expression does not.

1. **Vocabulary** How is an expression different from an equation?
2. **Mental Math** What is the solution to $m - 9 = 8$? 17
3. Your friend made y bracelets. After she gave four away, she had eight bracelets left. Write an equation to model the situation. $y - 4 = 8$

Mental Math For each equation, determine whether −3 is a solution.

4. $a + 4 = 7$ no
5. $w - 7 = -10$ yes
6. $-1 + c = 4$ no
7. $z - 3 = 0$ no
8. $7 + p = 4$ yes
9. $r + 3 = 0$ yes

Homework Exercises

For more exercises, see Extra Skills and Word Problems.

GO for Help

For Exercises	See Examples
10–18	1
19–28	2

A **Solve each equation. Check the solution.**

10. $p - 1 = -12$ −11
11. $a - 9 = 45$ 54
12. $-37 = y - 2$ −35
13. $b - 2 = -2$ 0
14. $-36 = t - 14$ −22
15. $m - 45 = 1$ 46
16. $23 = q - 12$ 35
17. $d - 15 = -31$ −16
18. $w - 32 = -5$ 27
19. $a + 15 = 10$ −5
20. $x + 1 = 22$ 21
21. $v + 9 = -2$ −11
22. $r + 27 = -52$ −79
23. $b + 61 = 27$ −34
24. $-10 = 3 + c$ −13
25. $19 + g = 32$ 13
26. $f + 47 = 100$ 53
27. $h + 21 = -50$ −71
28. **Money** You deposit \$450 into a bank account. The new balance is \$512. Write and solve an equation to find the original balance. $x + 450 = 512$; \$62

B **GPS**

29. **Guided Problem Solving** Between 1950 and 2000, the population of Kansas increased by 783,000. Use the graph to find the population of Kansas in 1950. 1,905,000 people

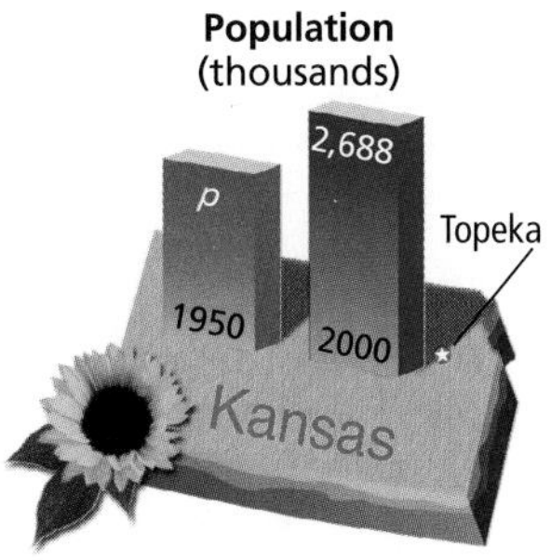

- What operation should you use to show the change in population from 1950 to 2000?
- What equation models the situation?
- How can you check your answer for reasonableness?

30. The temperature at 6:00 P.M. was 12°F. At 6:00 A.M., it was 15 degrees cooler. What was the temperature at 6:00 A.M.? −3°F

3. Practice

Assignment Guide

Check Your Understanding

Go over Exercises 1–9 in class before assigning the Homework Exercises.

Homework Exercises

A Practice by Example	10–28
B Apply Your Skills	29–39
C Challenge	40
Test Prep and Mixed Review	41–47

Homework Quick Check

To check students' understanding of key skills and concepts, go over Exercises 15, 28, 34, 35, and 36.

Differentiated Instruction Resources

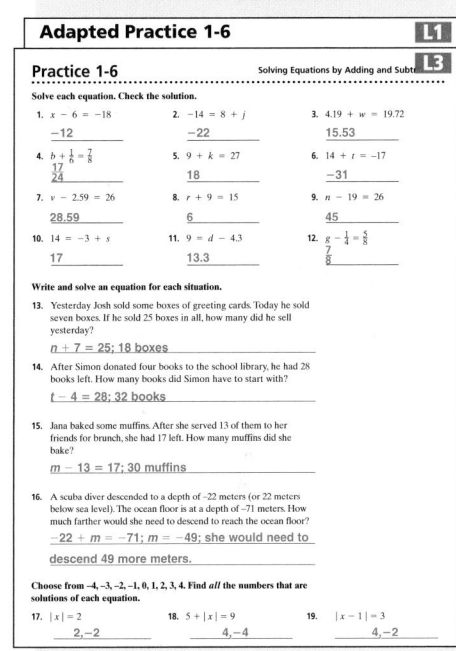

Adapted Practice 1-6 L1

Practice 1-6 — Solving Equations by Adding and Subtracting L3

Solve each equation. Check the solution.

1. $x - 6 = -18$ −12
2. $-14 = 8 + j$ −22
3. $4.19 + w = 19.72$ 15.53
4. $b + \frac{1}{6} = \frac{7}{8}$ $\frac{17}{24}$
5. $9 + k = 27$ 18
6. $14 + t = -17$ −31
7. $v - 2.59 = 26$ 28.59
8. $r + 9 = 15$ 6
9. $n - 19 = 26$ 45
10. $14 = -3 + s$ 17
11. $9 = d - 4.3$ 13.3
12. $g - \frac{1}{4} = \frac{5}{8}$ $\frac{7}{8}$

Write and solve an equation for each situation.

13. Yesterday Josh sold some boxes of greeting cards. Today he sold seven boxes. If he sold 25 boxes in all, how many did he sell yesterday? $n + 7 = 25$; 18 boxes
14. After Simon donated four books to the school library, he had 28 books left. How many books did Simon have to start with? $t - 4 = 28$; 32 books
15. Jana baked some muffins. After she served 13 of them to her friends for brunch, she had 17 left. How many muffins did she bake? $m - 13 = 17$; 30 muffins
16. A scuba diver descended to a depth of −22 meters (or 22 meters below sea level). The ocean floor is at a depth of −71 meters. How much farther would she need to descend to reach the ocean floor? $-22 + m = -71$; $m = -49$; she would need to descend 49 more meters.

Choose from −4, −3, −2, −1, 0, 1, 2, 3, 4. Find *all* the numbers that are solutions of each equation.

17. $|x| = 2$ 2, −2
18. $5 + |x| = 9$ 4, −4
19. $|x - 1| = 3$ 4, −2

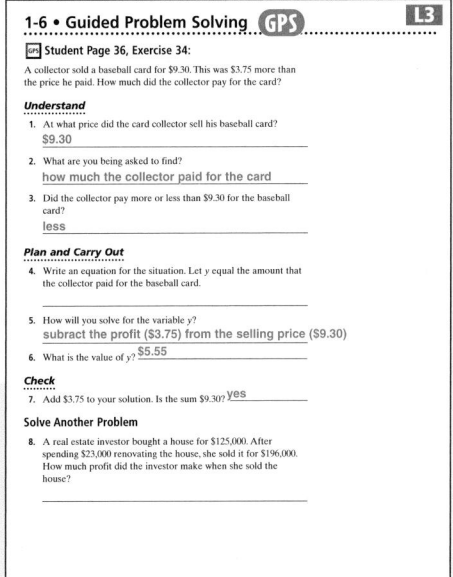

1-6 • Guided Problem Solving GPS L3

GPS Student Page 36, Exercise 34:

A collector sold a baseball card for \$9.30. This was \$3.75 more than the price he paid. How much did the collector pay for the card?

Understand

1. At what price did the card collector sell his baseball card? \$9.30
2. What are you being asked to find? how much the collector paid for the card
3. Did the collector pay more or less than \$9.30 for the baseball card? less

Plan and Carry Out

4. Write an equation for the situation. Let y equal the amount that the collector paid for the baseball card.
5. How will you solve for the variable y? subract the profit (\$3.75) from the selling price (\$9.30)
6. What is the value of y? \$5.55

Check

7. Add \$3.75 to your solution. Is the sum \$9.30? yes

Solve Another Problem

8. A real estate investor bought a house for \$125,000. After spending \$23,000 renovating the house, she sold it for \$196,000. How much profit did the investor make when she sold the house?

4. Assess & Reteach

PowerPoint

Lesson Quiz

1. $8 = -7 + m$ 15
2. $-61 + t = 23$ 84
3. $n - 15 = -12$ 3
4. $-82 = r - 36$ −46

Alternative Assessment

Students write two equations, each one involving addition and subtraction. Students exchange papers with a partner, solve the equations, and then check each other's work.

Reteaching 1-6 Solving Equations by Adding and Sub L2

To solve one-step equations:

① Use opposite, or inverse, operations to isolate the variable.
② Simplify.
③ Check by substituting your answer for the variable.

Solve and check each equation.

$x + 7 = 34$
$x + 7 - 7 = 34 - 7$ ← Subtract 7 from each side.
$x = 27$ ← Simplify.
Check: $x + 7 = 34$
$27 + 7 \stackrel{?}{=} 34$
$34 = 34$ ✔

$n - 5 = 37$
$n - 5 + 5 = 37 + 5$ ← Add 5 to each side.
$n = 42$ ← Simplify.
Check: $n - 5 = 37$
$42 - 5 \stackrel{?}{=} 37$
$37 = 37$ ✔

Show your steps to solve each equation. Then check.

1. $n + 5 = 11$
$n + 5 - \boxed{5} = 11 - \boxed{5}$
$n = \boxed{6}$
Check: $n + 5 = 11$
$\boxed{6} + 5 \stackrel{?}{=} 11$
$\boxed{11} = 11$

2. $13 + b = 27$
$13 + b - \boxed{13} = 27 - \boxed{13}$
$b = \boxed{14}$
Check: $13 + b = 27$
$13 + \boxed{14} \stackrel{?}{=} 27$
$\boxed{27} = 27$

3. $y - 18 = 24$
$y - 18 + 18 = 24 + 18$;
$y = 42$
Check: $y - 18 = 24$;
$42 - 18 \stackrel{?}{=} 24$;
$24 = 24$

Solve.

4. $6 = f + 12$ $f =$ −6
5. $-18 = s + (-23)$ $s =$ 5
6. $w + 4 = \frac{1}{2}$ $w =$ $-3\frac{1}{2}$
7. $b - 29 = -3$ $b =$ 26
8. $9 = k + 17$ $k =$ −8
9. $14 + m = -7$ $m =$ −21
10. $27 = j - 13$ $j =$ 40
11. $-14 + t = -5$ $t =$ 9
12. $x - 7 = -24$ $x =$ −17

Enrichment 1-6 Solving Equations by Adding and Sub L4

Patterns in Algebra

Study the following figures and the table below the figures.
Then complete the questions.

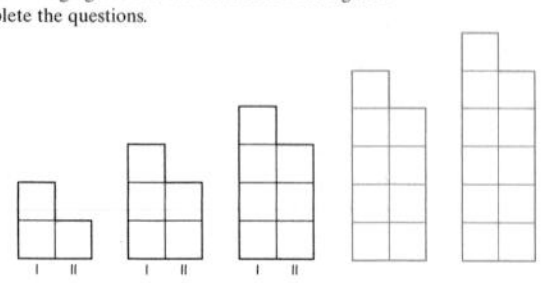

Column I	2	3	4	5	6
Column II	1	2	3	4	5

1. Sketch the next two figures in the pattern above. Then complete the next two sections in the table.
2. How many squares are in the figure that has 10 squares in Column I?
19 squares
Sketch the drawing in the space at the right.

3. Let n represent the number in Column I.
   a. Write an expression for the number of squares in Column II for any figure in the pattern.
   $n - 1$
   b. Write an equation that shows the total number of squares for any figure in the pattern. Hint: Add the squares in Column I to the squares in Column II.
   $n + (n - 1) = 2n - 1$
4. How many squares will be in a figure with 50 squares in Column I?
99 squares
5. Now complete the missing numbers in the pattern in this table. Use n to write an expression to represent each number in Column II.

Column I	1	2	3	4	5	6	10	50	n
Column II	6	7	8	9	10	11	15	55	$n + 5$

GO Online
Homework Video Tutor
Visit: PHSchool.com
Web Code: ase-0106

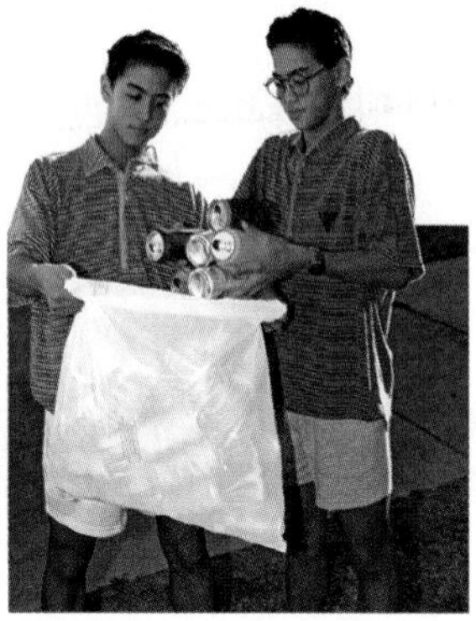

Number Sense Choose from −3, −2, −1, 0, 1, 2, and 3. Find *all* the numbers that are solutions of each equation.

31. $-|n| = -3$ −3, 3
32. $|n| + 1 = 2$ −1, 1
33. $|n + 1| = 2$ −3, 1

34. A collector sold a baseball card for \$9.30. This was \$3.75 more than the price he paid. How much did the collector pay for the card? \$5.55 (GPS)

35. **Recycling** In one weekend, a student collected p lb of cans to take to the recycling center. After delivering 5.2 lb of cans, the student still had 7.8 lb of cans. How many pounds of cans did the student collect? 13 lb

36. **Writing in Math** Describe a problem that could be solved using the equation $a + 8.40 = 11.55$. See margin.

Solve each equation.

37. $w - 2.45 = 3.1$ 5.55
38. $h - (-7) = 4.3$ −2.7
39. $-12 = -6.4 + m$ −5.6

40. (C) **Challenge** For what values of x is $x + 15 = x + 6 + 9$ true? Explain. See margin.

Test Prep and Mixed Review — Practice

Multiple Choice

41. Which problem situation matches the equation $x + 96 = 102$? D
    (A) Nathan rented two movies with run times of 96 minutes and 102 minutes. What is x, the time it took to watch both movies?
    (B) A class sells 96 concert tickets. They earn \$102. What is x, the price of each ticket?
    (C) On her last two math exams, Kathy got scores of 96 and 102. What is x, her average score?
    (D) Together, Joey and his cat weigh 102 pounds. Alone, Joey weighs 96 pounds. What is x, the weight of Joey's cat?

42. Three friends agreed to split a dinner bill equally. The dinner cost \$81, and tax was an additional \$4.05. They left a \$15 tip. Which expression can be used to find how much each person paid? F
    (F) $\frac{81 + 4.05 + 15}{3}$
    (G) $3 \div (81 + 4.05 + 15)$
    (H) $3(81 + 4.05 + 15)$
    (J) $\frac{8 + 15}{3 + 4.05}$

43. A basketball team has 18 points. The team then scores six 2-point baskets and two 3-point baskets. What is the team's score? D
    (A) 23 (B) 26 (C) 31 (D) 36

GO for Help

For Exercises	See Lesson
44–47	1-3

Simplify each expression.

44. $3 + (-12)$ −9
45. $-15 + (-6)$ −21
46. $-21 - 37$ −58
47. $-24 - (-9)$ −15

Test Prep

Resources

For additional practice with a variety of test item formats:
- Test-Taking Strategies, p. 43
- Test Prep, p. 47
- Test-Taking Strategies with Transparencies

36. Check students' work. Sample: You have an amount of money a. After you get another \$8.40, you have a total of \$11.55. How much did you start with?

40. All values of x; by the Subtr. Prop. of Eq., $x + 15 - 15 = x + 6 + 9 - 15$. So $x = x$. This statement is true for all values of x.

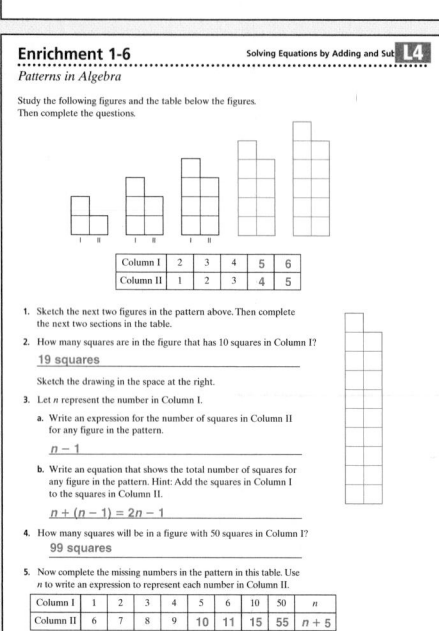

1-6b Activity Lab

Number Squares

A number square is a square table with the same number of rows as columns. Each row, column, and main diagonal in the square has the same sum. Each entry in the square is a different number. At the right is a 3-by-3 number square. The sum of each row, column, and main diagonal is 15.

8	3	4
1	5	9
6	7	2

EXAMPLE

Write and solve an equation to find each missing value in the square at the right.

−4	−6	b
6	−2	−10
a	2	0

Step 1 Use a row, column, or diagonal without variables to find the sum.
$6 + (-2) + (-10) = -6$

Step 2 Write and solve two equations.

First column:
$$-4 + 6 + a = -6$$
$$a + 2 = -6$$
$$a + 2 - 2 = -6 - 2$$
$$a = -8$$

First row:
$$-4 + (-6) + b = -6$$
$$b - 10 = -6$$
$$b - 10 + 10 = -6 + 10$$
$$b = 4$$

Exercises

Write and solve an equation to find the value of each variable.
1–3. See margin.

1.

2	b	−2
a	−1	c
0	1	−4

2.

17	x	7
12	22	z
w	y	27

3.

−6	4	5	−9
2	m	−1	−3
−5	1	n	0
p	−7	−8	z

4. Use the number square at the top of the page. Add −5 to each number. Is the result still a number square? Explain. See right.

5. **Writing in Math** In a 3-by-3 square, what is the least number of values you must know before you can write equations to complete the square? Explain. See margin.

4. Yes; you just added 3(−5) or −15 to each column, row, and diagonal.

Activity Lab

Number Squares

This activity shows students what number squares are. It presents a way to find the missing entries in number squares by writing and solving equations.

Guided Instruction

Guide students to notice the difference between the first number square and the one in the Example. Variables are used to represent missing entries.

Emphasize the key first step of identifying the square's "special sum." After finding the sum of the second row, ask, *Look at the number square. How else could you have found this sum?* by adding the integers in the diagonal: $-4 + (-2) + 0 = -6$, or the middle column: $-6 + (-2) + 2 = -6$

Activity

Have students work in pairs to make their own number squares, with or without variables. Invite pairs to share the strategies they used to make their puzzles.

Differentiated Instruction

Visual Learners and Auditory Learners
Some students may not be familiar with number squares. Have a volunteer read the opening paragraph while another volunteer builds the number square on the board.

Resources

- blank 3-by-3 number squares

1. $2 + a + 0 = -3$, $a = -5$;
$2 + b + (-2) = -3$,
$b = -3$;
$-2 + c + (-4) = -3$, $c = 3$

2. $17 + 12 + w = 66$,
$w = 37$;
$17 + x + 7 = 66$, $x = 42$;
$42 + 22 + y = 66$, $y = 2$;
$7 + z + 27 = 66$, $z = 32$

3. $4 + m + 1 + (-7) = -6$,
$m = -4$;
$5 + (-1) + n + (-8) = -6$,
$n = -2$;
$-6 + 2 + (-5) + p = -6$,
$p = 3$;
$-9 + (-3) + 0 + z = -6$,
$z = 6$

5. 4; you need to have 3 numbers in one row, column, or diagonal to figure out the sum of each and one other number.

1-7

1. Plan

Objective
To write and solve equations using multiplication and division

Examples
1 Solving by Multiplying
2 Solving by Dividing

Math Understandings: p. 2D

Professional Development

Math Background

In the previous lesson, the equations could be simplified and solved using addition to undo subtraction, and subtraction to undo addition. In this lesson, multiplication or division are required to isolate the variable. Division undoes multiplication, and multiplication undoes division. As with addition and subtraction, the balance, or truth, of the equation is maintained by performing the multiplication or division on both sides of the equation.

More Math Background: p. 2D

Lesson Planning and Resources

See p. 2E for a list of the resources that support this lesson.

PowerPoint

Bell Ringer Practice

Check Skills You'll Need
Use student page, transparency, or PowerPoint. For intervention, direct students to:
Multiplying and Dividing Integers
Lesson 1-4
Extra Skills and Word Problems Practice, Ch. 1

1-7 Solving Equations by Multiplying and Dividing

Check Skills You'll Need

1. **Vocabulary Review** *Inverse operations* are operations that __?__ each other. undo

Simplify each expression.

2. $6 \cdot 4$ 24
3. $-7 \cdot 3$ −21
4. $\frac{10}{-5}$ −2
5. $\frac{-27}{-9}$ 3

GO for Help Lesson 1-4

What You'll Learn

To write and solve equations using multiplication and division

New Vocabulary Multiplication Property of Equality, Division Property of Equality

Why Learn This?

Some equations model the relationships between sizes of groups. When you can solve multiplication and division equations, you can find unknown values such as the number of people in an audience or school.

KEY CONCEPTS Properties of Equality

Multiplication Property of Equality If you multiply each side of an equation by the same number, the two sides remain equal.

Arithmetic	Algebra
$20 = \frac{40}{2}$, so $2(20) = 2\left(\frac{40}{2}\right)$	If $a = b$, then $ac = bc$.

Division Property of Equality If you divide each side of an equation by the same nonzero number, the two sides remain equal.

Arithmetic	Algebra
$30 = 3(10)$, so $\frac{30}{6} = \frac{3(10)}{6}$	If $a = b$ and $c \neq 0$, then $\frac{a}{c} = \frac{b}{c}$.

Vocabulary Tip
The symbol ≠ means "does not equal."

EXAMPLE Solving by Multiplying

1 Solve $\frac{x}{-7} = 15$.

$-7 \cdot \left(\frac{x}{-7}\right) = -7 \cdot 15$ ← **Isolate the variable. Use the Multiplication Property of Equality.**

$x = -105$ ← **Simplify.**

Quick Check

1. Solve $\frac{t}{8} = -5$. −40

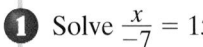

Differentiated Instruction Solutions for All Learners

Special Needs L1
Students compare Daryl's Method with Tina's Method. Elicit the fact that both methods end with multiplying $5 \cdot 112$ to find the answer. Then they use both methods to solve the Choose a Method problem.
learning style: verbal

Below Level L2
Draw a balanced scale on the board. Write 2 + 3 on one side and 5 on the other. Redraw the balance scale to show how one side drops when the number(s) are multiplied by 2. Redraw the scale a third time to show how the scales are balanced again when the other side is multiplied by 2.
learning style: verbal

EXAMPLE Solving by Dividing

GO for Help

For help multiplying and dividing integers, go to Lesson 1-4, Examples 1 and 2.

2 Solve $816 = 8c$.

$\frac{816}{8} = \frac{8c}{8}$ ← Isolate the variable. Use the Division Property of Equality.

$102 = c$ ← Simplify.

Check $816 \stackrel{?}{=} 8(102)$ ← Check the solution in the original equation. Substitute 102 for *c*.

$816 = 816$ ✔ ← Multiply.

Quick Check

2. Solve $3y = -12$. -4

More Than One Way

One out of every five people attending a town rock concert came to support the local high school rock band. The band had 112 supporters. How many people were in the audience?

Daryl's Method

I see that 112 supporters equal one out of five audience members. I know there are five groups of 112 people in the audience.

So, there are $5 \cdot 112$, or 560 audience members.

Tina's Method

I can represent the number of people in the audience as *p*. The number of supporters is *p* divided by 5. I can write the equation as $\frac{p}{5} = 112$ and solve for *p*.

$$\frac{p}{5} = 112$$

$$5\left(\frac{p}{5}\right) = 5(112)$$

$$p = 560$$

There are 560 people in the audience.

Choose a Method

One out of three students at a school likes gym. If 120 students like gym, how many students go to the school? Explain your method.

360 students; check students' work.

2. Teach

Activity Lab

Use before the lesson.

All-in-One Teaching Resources

Activity Lab 1-7: Dividing Integers

Guided Instruction

Teaching Tip

Have students test the Multiplication and Division Properties of Equality by multiplying each side of $8 = (-2)(-4)$ by -3 and dividing each side of $8 = (-2)(-4)$ by -2 to verify that the resulting equations are still true.

Error Prevention!

Make sure students realize that to isolate the variable is to get the variable alone (with no negative sign) on either the right or left side of the equation.

PowerPoint

Additional Examples

1 Solve $\frac{y}{-3} = 14$. $y = -42$

2 Solve $265 = -5x$. $x = -53$

All-in-One Teaching Resources

- Daily Notetaking Guide 1-7 L3
- Adapted Notetaking 1-7 L1

Closure

- *When you solve an equation, how do you know which operation to choose to isolate the variable?* Decide what has been done to the variable and use the inverse operation.

Advanced Learners L4	**English Language Learners** ELL
Students discuss why the Division Property of Equality specifies that *c* must be nonzero. learning style: verbal	Make sure students understand what is being done in Example 1 by asking *Why did we multiply both sides of the equation by −7?* To isolate the variable *x*. For Example 2, ask *Why did we divide both sides of the equation by 8?* To isolate the variable *c*. learning style: verbal

3. Practice

Assignment Guide

Check Your Understanding
Go over Exercises 1–11 in class before assigning the Homework Exercises.

Homework Exercises

A	Practice by Example	12–30
B	Apply Your Skills	31–41
C	Challenge	42
	Test Prep and Mixed Review	43–48

Homework Quick Check
To check students' understanding of key skills and concepts, go over Exercises 18, 30, 33, 34, and 41.

Differentiated Instruction Resources

Adapted Practice 1-7 L1

Practice 1-7 Solving Equations by Multiplying and L3

Solve each equation. Check the solution.

1. $\frac{a}{-6} = 2$ −12
2. $18 = \frac{y}{-1.8}$ −32.4
3. $46 = 2.3m$ 20
4. $-114 = -6k$ 19
5. $0 = \frac{b}{19}$ 0
6. $136 = 8y$ 17
7. $0.6j = -1.44$ −2.4
8. $\frac{q}{7.4} = 8.3$ 61.42
9. $28b = -131.6$ −4.7
10. $\frac{n}{-9} = -107$ 963
11. $37c = -777$ −21
12. $\frac{n}{-1.28} = 4.96$ −6.3488

Write and solve an equation for each situation.

13. Skylar spent \$90.65 on books that cost \$12.95 each. How many books did Skylar buy?
$n = \frac{\$90.65}{\$12.95}; n = 7$
14. Eugenio has five payments left to make on his computer. If each payment is \$157.90, how much does he still owe?
$n = 5(\$157.90); n = \$789.50$
15. Judy spent \$83.86 to buy T-shirts for the 14 members of the Chess Club. How much did each T-shirt cost?
$n = \frac{\$83.86}{14}; n = \$5.99$
16. Alison uses a total of 94.5 cups of dog food each week to feed her three dogs. Each dog eats the same amount. How much does each dog eat in one day?
$n = \frac{94.5}{7 \cdot 3}; n = 4.5$

Choose from −4, −3, −2, −1, 0, 1, 2, 3, 4. Find *all* the numbers that are solutions of each equation.

17. $|x| = 4$ 4, −4
18. $5 + |x| = 6$ 1, −1
19. $|x - 2| = 2$ 4, 0

1-7 • Guided Problem Solving GPS L3

GPS Student Page 40, Exercise 30:

Surveys In a survey, 124 students reported they do community service. This is four times as many as those who reported they are in the band. How many students surveyed are in the band?

Understand

1. How many students reported that they do community service?
124
2. Is this four times more or less than the number of students who said they are in the band?
more
3. What are you being asked to find?
the number of students surveyed who are in the band

Plan and Carry Out

4. Write an equation for the situation. Let x equal the number of students in the band.
$4x = 124$
5. How will you solve for the variable x?
Divide the total number of students surveyed by 4.
6. What is the value of x?
$x = 31$

Check

7. Multiply your solution by 4. Is the product 124?
yes; $4x = 124$; $4(31) = 124$; $124 = 124$

Solve Another Problem

8. There are 288 animal crackers in a package. If each child in the after-school program gets a dozen crackers, how many students are in the after-school program?
$12x = 288$; $x = 24$; 24 students

Check Your Understanding

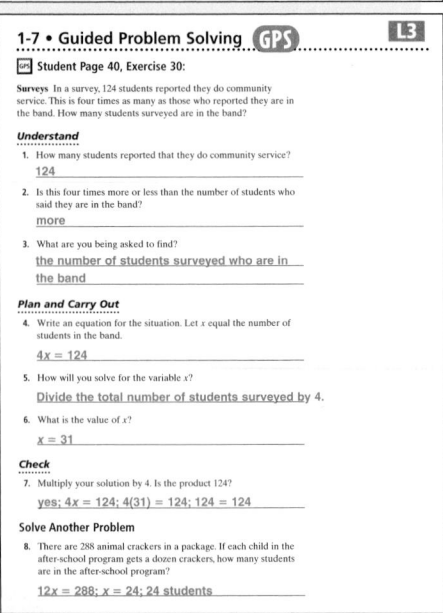

1. A value is a solution if it makes the equation true.

1. **Vocabulary** When is a value a solution to an equation?

Which property of equality does each equation illustrate?

2. $\frac{24}{4} = \frac{8(3)}{4}$ Div. Prop. of Eq.
3. $36 + (-10) = 4(9) + (-10)$ Add. Prop. of Eq.
4. $8(-7) = \left(\frac{-56}{-7}\right)(-7)$ Mult. Prop. of Eq.
5. $-5(6) - 13 = -30 - 13$ Subtr. Prop. of Eq.

Mental Math For each equation, find whether −5 is a solution.

6. $25v = -5$ no
7. $\frac{15}{m} = -3$ yes
8. $10 = -2t$ yes
9. $-5p = 25$ yes
10. $7 = \frac{35}{w}$ no
11. $\frac{-45}{z} = -9$ no

Homework Exercises

For more exercises, see Extra Skills and Word Problems.

GO for Help

For Exercises	See Examples
12–20	1
21–30	2

A Solve each equation. Check the solution.

12. $\frac{d}{10} = 34$ 340
13. $\frac{x}{5} = -1$ −5
14. $-17 = \frac{w}{9}$ −153
15. $-52 = \frac{a}{-11}$ 572
16. $\frac{h}{-9} = 3$ −27
17. $\frac{k}{-7} = 5$ −35
18. $-1.4 = \frac{g}{7}$ −9.8
19. $2.5 = \frac{c}{24}$ 60
20. $\frac{m}{-3.25} = -8$ 26
21. $-6y = -30$ 5
22. $4t = 432$ 108
23. $3w = -99$ −33
24. $-2p = 1$ $-\frac{1}{2}$
25. $-24k = 144$ −6
26. $20b = -460$ −23
27. $-16 = -8d$ 2
28. $112h = 336$ 3
29. $-85 = 17j$ −5

30. **Surveys** In a survey, 124 students reported they do community service. This is four times as many as those who reported they are in the band. How many of the students surveyed are in the band? 31 students

B GPS 31. **Guided Problem Solving** A bicycle has 44 teeth on the front gear. This is four times the number of teeth on the rear gear. Write and solve an equation to find the number of teeth on the rear gear.
- Translate the words into an equation. $4r = 44$;
  Words: four times ? equals ?
  Equation: 4 · ■ = ■

32. 47.6 kilograms

32. **Animals** A zoo has six adult tigers. Their caretaker orders a total of 40.8 kilograms of meat for them each day. Each tiger receives the same amount. How much meat does a single tiger eat in a week?

Go Online
Homework Video Tutor
For: PHSchool.com
Web Code: ase-0107

33. **Writing in Math** Explain why the Division Property of Equality includes the statement "$c \neq 0$." Division by zero is undefined.

34. a. **Open-Ended** Write an equation that you can solve using the Multiplication Property of Equality. Check students' work.
    b. Describe a real-world situation that you can solve using the equation you wrote in part (a). Check students' work.

Savings **Use the picture at the left for Exercises 35 and 36.**

35. You plan to buy the bodyboard nine weeks from now. How much money must you save per week? $5.34

36. Your friend saves $12 per week. How many weeks will it take your friend to save enough to buy the bodyboard? 4 weeks

Solve each equation.

37. $-1 = \frac{-b}{7}$ 7
38. $-p = 29.16$ −29.16
39. $0.4f = 300$ 750
40. $-8.1 = \frac{r}{-5.2}$ 42.12

41. **Choose a Method** Your class sold raffle tickets. Out of every 15 tickets, 14 tickets did not win. There were 24 winners. How many tickets were sold? Explain why you chose the method you used. 360 tickets; check students' work.

C 42. **Challenge** Twice as many students go to the park than to the theater. Five more students go to the theater than to the museum. If 16 students go to the park, how many students go to the museum? 3 students

Test Prep and Mixed Review

Practice

Multiple Choice

43. A woodcarver made a model of a chair. The equation $0.08h = 3$ can be used to find the actual height h of the chair in inches. What was the actual height of the chair? D
    A 0.24 in. B 3.75 in. C 24 in. D 37.5 in.

44. Holly is simplifying the expression $-39 + 1.5(-24)$ to estimate the wind chill when the air temperature is −24°F and the wind speed is 20 miles per hour. What should she do first? J
    F Add −39 and 1.5. H Add −39 and −24.
    G Subtract −24 from 1.5. J Multiply 1.5 and −24.

45. Brian has four fewer than twice as many sports cards as Miles, who has c cards. Write an expression for the number of Brian's cards. A
    A $2c - 4$ B $4c + 2$ C $-4 - 2c$ D $4 - 2c$

GO for Help

For Exercises	See Lesson
46–48	1-5

Use mental math to simplify each expression.

46. $5(0.98)$ 4.9
47. $7(1.2)$ 8.4
48. $3.1(9)$ 27.9

4. Assess & Reteach

PowerPoint

Lesson Quiz

1. $-12w = -60$ 5
2. $\frac{n}{-3} = 9$ −27
3. $5x = -20$ −4
4. $-2 = \frac{r}{-16}$ 32

Alternative Assessment

Students write two equations, each one involving multiplication and division. Have students exchange papers with a partner, solve the equations, and then check each other's work.

Reteaching 1-7 Solving Equations by Multiplying and L2

To solve one-step equations:
① Use opposite, or inverse, operations to isolate the variable.
② Simplify.
③ Check by substituting your answer for the variable.

Solve and check each equation.

$7y = 84$
$\frac{7y}{7} = \frac{84}{7}$ ← Divide each side by 7.
$y = 12$ ← Simplify.
Check: $7y = 84$
$7 \cdot 12 \stackrel{?}{=} 84$
$84 = 84$ ✔

$\frac{w}{5} = 20$
$5 \cdot \frac{w}{5} = 5 \cdot 20$ ← Multiply each side by 5.
$w = 100$ ← Simplify.
Check: $\frac{w}{5} = 20$
$\frac{100}{5} \stackrel{?}{=} 20$
$20 = 20$ ✔

Show your steps to solve each equation. Then check.

1. $3x = 18$
   $\frac{3x}{3} = \frac{18}{3}$
   $x = 6$
   Check: $3x = 18$
   $3 \cdot 6 \stackrel{?}{=} 18$
   $18 = 18$

2. $\frac{y}{-5} = -13$
   $\frac{y}{-5} \cdot -5 = -13 \cdot -5$
   $y = 65$
   Check: $\frac{y}{-5} = -13$
   $\frac{65}{-5} \stackrel{?}{=} -13$
   $-13 = -13$

3. $y \cdot 8 = 24$
   $\frac{y \cdot 8}{8} = \frac{24}{8}$
   $y = 3$
   Check: $y \cdot 8 = 24$
   $3 \cdot 8 \stackrel{?}{=} 24$
   $24 = 24$

Solve.

4. $-16 = -8x$ $x =$ 2
5. $\frac{b}{0.4} = 1.6$ $b =$ 0.64
6. $7.5 = 1.5c$ $c =$ 5
7. $\frac{b}{17} = -3$ $b =$ −51
8. $9 = -k$ $k =$ −9
9. $-14m = -70$ $m =$ 5
10. $-0.4 = \frac{j}{22}$ $j =$ −8.8
11. $-13t = -91$ $t =$ 7
12. $4.5x = 27$ $x =$ 6

Enrichment 1-7 Solving Equations by Multiplying and L4

Critical Thinking

One out of every five fans that attended the Houston Rodeo went to the Rodeo Carnival to ride the rides. The carnival attracted 9,000 people in all. What was the total number of people who attended the rodeo?

1. How do you find the number of people who attended the rodeo?
   Multiply the number of fans attracted to the carnival by 5.
2. What was the total number of people who went to the carnival?
   9,000
3. Were there more people at the rodeo or at the carnival?
   the rodeo
4. Write an equation for this situation, using the variable x to represent the number of people who attended the rodeo.
   $\frac{1}{5}x = 9{,}000$
5. Solve the equation you wrote in Exercise 4. How many people went to the rodeo?
   $x = 5(9{,}000)$ or 45,000
6. What is another strategy you could use to solve the problem?
   Sample Answer: Add fire groups of 9,000:
   9,000 + 9,000 + 9,000 + 9,000 + 9,000 = 45,000
7. Which method do you prefer? Explain why.
   Sample Answer: Multiplication, because there are fewer steps to perform.

Test Prep

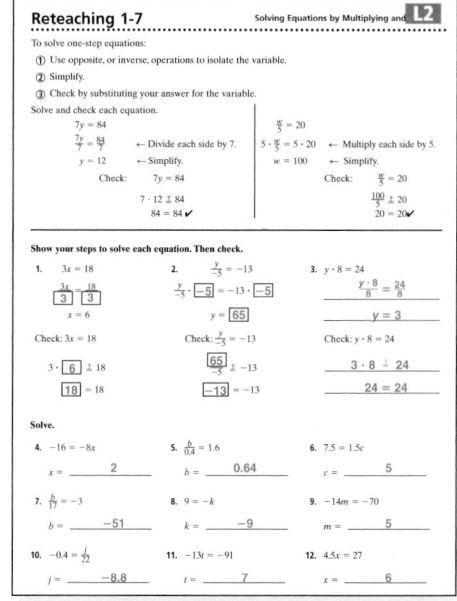

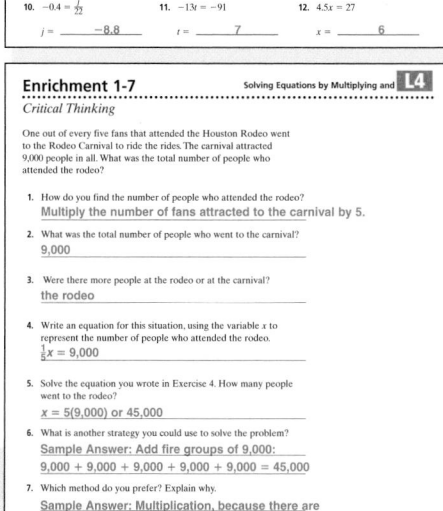

Resources
For additional practice with a variety of test item formats:
- Test-Taking Strategies, p. 43
- Test Prep, p. 47
- Test-Taking Strategies with Transparencies

Activity Lab

The Cover-up Method

Students cover up the variable and ask a "what number" question, then use their number sense to solve the equation.

Guided Instruction

This method has students use their knowledge of inverse operations.

Example 2

Have students give examples of other ways to frame the questions that can be used to solve the equation in Example 2. Students might ask, "What number can you subtract $4\frac{1}{2}$ from to get an answer of $20\frac{1}{2}$?" Emphasize that there is more than one correct question that can be asked to get the same answer.

Exercises

For Exercises 1 and 2, have volunteers state the question they might ask to solve the equation. For Exercise 1, students might ask, "What number divided by 3 is 40?" For Exercise 2, a possible question is "The sum of 11 and what number is 71?"

Differentiated Instruction

Special Needs L1

Elicit from students the meanings of the terms *sum*, *difference*, *product*, *factor*, *divisor*, and *quotient*.

The Cover-Up Method

You can use the cover-up method to solve some equations. Number sense is involved.

EXAMPLES

1 Solve $6x = -48$.

$6\blacksquare = -48$ ← Cover up *x*. Ask, "What number times 6 is −48?"

$\blacksquare = -8$ ← 6 × 8 is 48, so 6 × (−8) = −48.

The answer is −8.

2 Solve $y - 4\frac{1}{2} = 20\frac{1}{2}$.

$\blacksquare - 4\frac{1}{2} = 20\frac{1}{2}$ ← Cover up *y*. Ask, "What number, less $4\frac{1}{2}$, is $20\frac{1}{2}$?"

$\blacksquare = 25$ ← Use mental math. $25 - 4\frac{1}{2} = 20\frac{1}{2}$.

The answer is 25.

Exercises

Solve each equation using the cover-up method or paper and pencil. Explain why you chose the method you used.

1. $\frac{x}{3} = 40$ 120
2. $x + 11 = 71$ 60
3. $y - 45 = 110$ 155
4. $25x = 175$ 7
5. $\frac{y}{2} = 62$ 124
6. $y - 17\frac{1}{2} = 33\frac{1}{2}$ 51
7. $x + 29\frac{1}{2} = 89\frac{1}{2}$ 60
8. $y - 1.7 = 1.3$ 3
9. $0.5x = 3.5$ 7
10. $15x = 225$ 15
11. **Error Analysis** Aimee says that the solution to the equation $x + 43 = 103$ is 146. Ivan says that the solution is 60. Explain how you know who is correct without solving the equation.
12. A homeowner enlarged the fenced-in area of a yard to be a square 10 ft by 10 ft. The length of the new fenced-in area is twice that of the original square. Write and solve an equation to find the area of the original fenced-in area. 25 ft^2

11. Answers may vary. Sample: If *x* plus a pos. number is 103, then *x* must be less than 103.

Writing Gridded Responses

Some test questions have answers with gridded responses. To answer these questions, first find a numerical answer. Then write your answer at the top of the grid. Fill in the corresponding bubbles.

EXAMPLE

Chad walks his dog the same distance every week. If he walks his dog a total of 42 miles in 8 weeks, how many miles does he walk each week? Record your answer and fill in the bubbles. Be sure to use the correct place value.

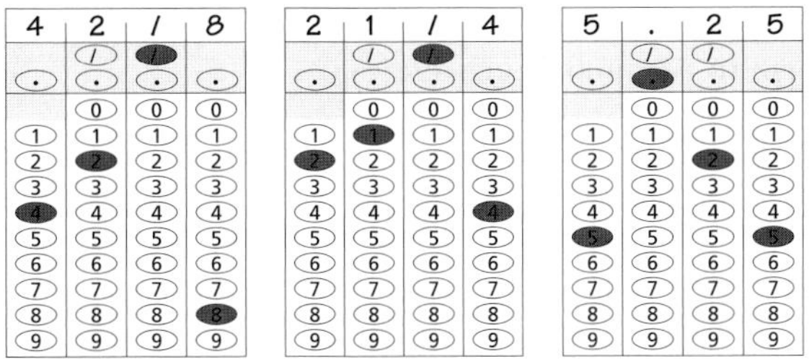

The answer is $\frac{42}{8}$. You can grid this as $\frac{42}{8}$, $\frac{21}{4}$ or 5.25.

Exercises

Find each answer. If you have a grid, record your answer and fill in the bubbles. Be sure to use the correct place value.

1. A play is 90 minutes long. There is a 15-minute intermission. How many hours should you plan to be at the theater? 1.75
2. Megan rides her bike to work. She bikes 3.2 miles to work, 1.3 miles to a coffee shop, 2.7 miles to the library, and then 3.6 miles home. How many miles does Megan bike? 10.8
3. At a movie theater, tickets cost \$9 each and parking costs \$4. The expression $9t + 4$ models the cost of going to the movies, where t represents the number of movie tickets. In dollars, how much would it cost you and three friends to go to the movies in one car? 40
4. You have \$11.27. You want to buy a book that costs \$14.95. In dollars, how much money do you need to save before you can buy the book? 3.68

Writing Gridded Responses

This strategy provides students with examples that demonstrate how to correctly enter an answer for test questions using a griddable form.

Guided Instruction

Teaching Tip
Emphasize that fully completing a griddable-response test question involves two distinct parts:
(1) writing the answer in the top row, one digit or symbol to a column, and (2) filling in the bubble in each column that corresponds to the digit or symbol written at the top of that column.

Resources

Test-Taking Strategies with Transparencies
- Transparency 2
- Practice sheet, p. 25

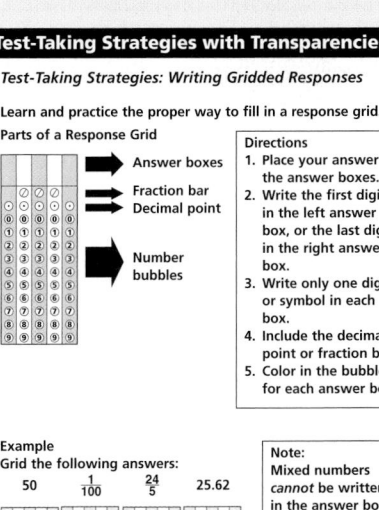

Test-Taking Strategies with Transparencies

Test-Taking Strategies: Writing Gridded Responses

Learn and practice the proper way to fill in a response grid.

Parts of a Response Grid

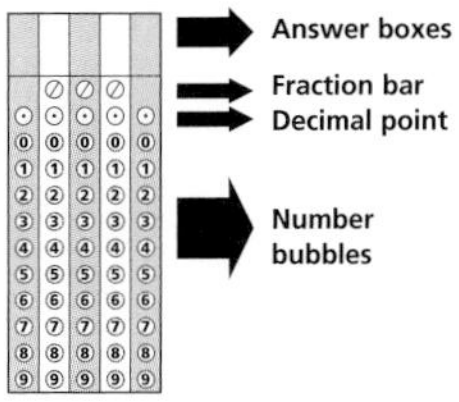

Directions
1. Place your answer in the answer boxes.
2. Write the first digit in the left answer box, or the last digit in the right answer box.
3. Write only one digit or symbol in each box.
4. Include the decimal point or fraction bar.
5. Color in the bubble for each answer box.

Example
Grid the following answers:
50   $\frac{1}{100}$ $\frac{24}{5}$ 25.62

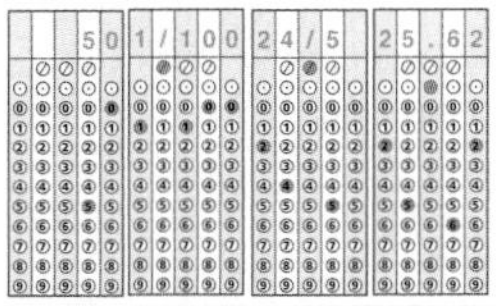

Note:
Mixed numbers *cannot* be written in the answer box. You must convert the answer to an improper fraction.

So, $4\frac{4}{5}$ must be gridded as $\frac{24}{5}$.

Resources

Student Edition
Extra Skills and Word Problems Practice, Ch. 1, p. 604
English/Spanish Glossary, p. 650
Formulas and Properties, p. 648
Tables, p. 643

All in One Teaching Resources
- Vocabulary and Study Skills 1F **L3**

Differentiated Instruction

Spanish Vocabulary Workbook with Study Skills **ELL**
Interactive Textbook
- Audio Glossary

Online Vocabulary Quiz

Success Tracker™
Online at PHSchool.com

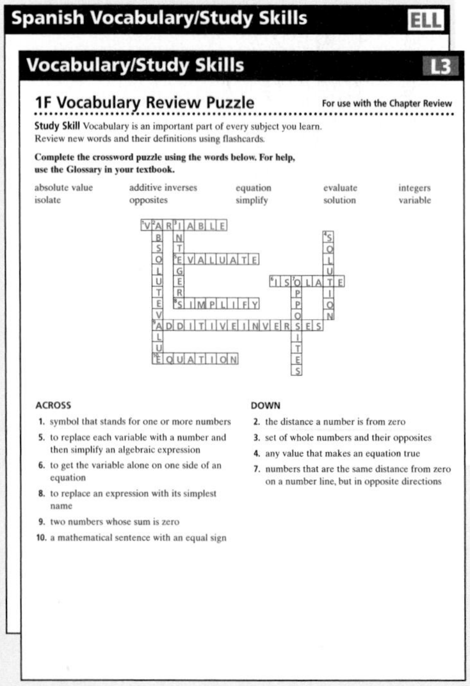

Spanish Vocabulary/Study Skills **ELL**

Vocabulary/Study Skills **L3**

1F Vocabulary Review Puzzle For use with the Chapter Review

Study Skill Vocabulary is an important part of every subject you learn. Review new words and their definitions using flashcards.

Complete the crossword puzzle using the words below. For help, use the Glossary in your textbook.

absolute value, additive inverses, equation, evaluate, integers, isolate, opposites, simplify, solution, variable

ACROSS
1. symbol that stands for one or more numbers
5. to replace each variable with a number and then simplify an algebraic expression
6. to get the variable alone on one side of an equation
8. to replace an expression with its simplest name
9. two numbers whose sum is zero
10. a mathematical sentence with an equal sign

DOWN
2. the distance a number is from zero
3. set of whole numbers and their opposites
4. any value that makes an equation true
7. numbers that are the same distance from zero on a number line, but in opposite directions

Chapter 1 Review

Vocabulary Review

absolute value (p. 10)
Addition Property of Equality (p. 33)
additive inverses (p. 16)
algebraic expression (p. 4)
Associative Property of Addition (p. 26)
Associative Property of Multiplication (p. 26)
Commutative Property of Addition (p. 26)
Commutative Property of Multiplication (p. 26)
Distributive Property (p. 28)
Division Property of Equality (p. 38)
equation (p. 33)
evaluate (p. 5)
Identity Property of Addition (p. 26)
Identity Property of Multiplication (p. 26)
integers (p. 10)
inverse operations (p. 21)
isolate (p. 34)
Multiplication Property of Equality (p. 38)
opposites (p. 10)
order of operations (p. 5)
simplify (p. 5)
solution (p. 34)
Subtraction Property of Equality (p. 33)
variable (p. 4)

Choose the correct term to complete each sentence.

1. You __?__ $4 + 4 \cdot 2$ as 12. simplify
2. The __?__ of a number is its distance from zero on a number line. absolute value
3. The statement $5(a + 6) = 5a + 30$ shows the __?__. Distributive Property
4. A value that makes an equation true is a(n) __?__. solution
5. Use __?__ to isolate a variable in an equation. inverse operations
6. A(n) __?__ is a symbol that stands for one or more numbers. variable
7. The set of whole numbers and their opposites are __?__. integers
8. A mathematical sentence with an equal sign is a(n) __?__. equation

Go Online PHSchool.com
For: Online Vocabulary Quiz
Web Code: asj-0151

Skills and Concepts

Lesson 1-1

- To write algebraic expressions and evaluate them using the order of operations

To **simplify** a numerical expression, use the **order of operations.** To **evaluate** an **algebraic expression,** replace each variable with a number and then simplify.

Evaluate each expression for $x = 2$.

9. $6(x - 1)$ 6
10. $-42 \div x + 5.5$ −15.5
11. $-42 \div (x + 5.5)$ −5.6

Write an algebraic expression for each word phrase.

12. the sum of 27 and a number g $27 + g$
13. the quotient of a number y and 4 $\frac{y}{4}$
14. the number of pages in r reams of paper if each ream has 500 pages $500r$

Alternative Assessment — L4

Alternative Assessment — Form C

Chapter 1

MAKE THE BANKER GO BROKE

Play the game "Make the Banker Go Broke" to practice your math. The rules of the game are as follows:

- The banker starts with \$500. Each player starts with a zero balance.
- Each player draws a card from a stack of cards.
- If the number or expression on the card is positive, the banker gives that amount of money to the player.
- If the number or expression on the card is negative, the player gives that amount of money to the banker.
- If the number or expression on the card is zero, skip to the next player.
- Players are allowed to have a negative balance.
- Players continue to choose cards until the banker has a zero balance. The player with the most money then wins the game.
- The deck of cards contains one card for each integer from −20 through 20. The deck also has the cards shown below.

$-15 - 8$	$-4 - 12$	$-8 + 22$	$28 - 4$	$-1 + 17$	$-7 + 7$
8×-1	-4×-4	-5×-5	0×-20	-6×4	-4×-5
$\frac{-33}{3}$	$\frac{48}{-2}$	$\frac{-40}{-2}$	$\frac{-12}{-1}$	$\frac{20}{-2}$	$\frac{0}{15}$

Show all of your work on a separate sheet of paper.

1. Suppose you have the opportunity to pick any five cards you want. Which five cards would get you the most money? (Don't forget the cards with the integers.)
2. Which five cards would put you the most in debt?
3. On the first round, four players each drew a card representing the same amount. Which cards could they have chosen?
4. After choosing his first two cards, Loren had a zero balance. Which two cards could he have picked?

Lesson 1-2

- To find the absolute values of integers and to use absolute value to compare integers

Integers are the set of whole numbers, their **opposites,** and zero. The **absolute value** of a number is its distance from zero on the number line.

Compare. Write <, >, or =.

15. -18 ■ -11 < **16.** -37 ■ 2 < **17.** $|-34|$ ■ 21 > **18.** $|-4|$ ■ $|4|$ =

19. The lowest recorded temperature in Australia was −9°F. The lowest recorded temperature in North America was −81°F. Which continent has the lower recorded temperature? North America

Lessons 1-3, 1-4

- To add and subtract integers and to solve problems involving integers
- To multiply and divide integers and to solve problems involving integers

Two numbers are **additive inverses** if their sum is zero. The sum of two positive numbers is positive. The sum of two negative integers is negative.

The product or quotient of two integers with the same sign is positive. The product or quotient of two integers with different signs is negative.

Simplify each expression.

20. $-9 + (-3)$ −12 **21.** $-11 - (-5)$ −6 **22.** $-34 \div (-2)$ 17

23. $4(-10)$ −40 **24.** $-5 - 2$ −7 **25.** $39 \div (-3)$ −13

26. Kai has \$315 in her bank account. She withdraws \$65 for a new jacket and another \$13 for lunch with her friends. She deposits \$26. What is the balance in Kai's account? \$263

Lesson 1-5

- To identify the properties of numbers and use the properties to solve problems

You can use the commutative, associative, identity, and distributive properties to simplify an expression.

Mental Math **Use mental math to simplify each expression.**

27. $(-5)(168)(20)$ −16,800 **28.** $125 + 394 + 575$ 1,094 **29.** $4(-18)(25)$ −1,800

Find each product.

30. $3(p - 7)$ $3p - 21$ **31.** $(m + 4)8$ $8m + 32$ **32.** $-5(-2 - k)$ $10 + 5k$

Lessons 1-6, 1-7

- To write and solve equations using addition and subtraction
- To write and solve equations using multiplication and division

A value of the variable that makes an **equation** true is a **solution.** You can solve an equation using **inverse operations** and the properties of equality to **isolate** the variable.

Solve each equation. Check the solution.

33. $d - 7 = 23$ 30 **34.** $6 = r + 3$ 3 **35.** $8 = -3 + a$ 11

36. $7p = 49$ 7 **37.** $\frac{h}{-4} = -12$ 48 **38.** $\frac{z}{5} = 0.4$ 2

Resources

- ExamView Assessment Suite CD-ROM
  - Ch. 1 Ready-Made Test
  - Make your own Ch. 1 test
- MindPoint Quiz Show CD-ROM
  - Chapter 1 Review

Differentiated Instruction

All in One Teaching Resources

- Below Level Chapter 1 Test L2
- Chapter 1 Test L3
- Chapter 1 Alternative Assessment L4

Spanish Assessment Resources ELL

- Below Level Chapter 1 Test L2
- Chapter 1 Test L3
- Chapter 1 Alternative Assessment L4

ExamView Assessment Suite CD-ROM

- Special Needs Test L1
- Special Needs Practice Bank L1

Online Chapter 1 Test at www.PHSchool.com L3

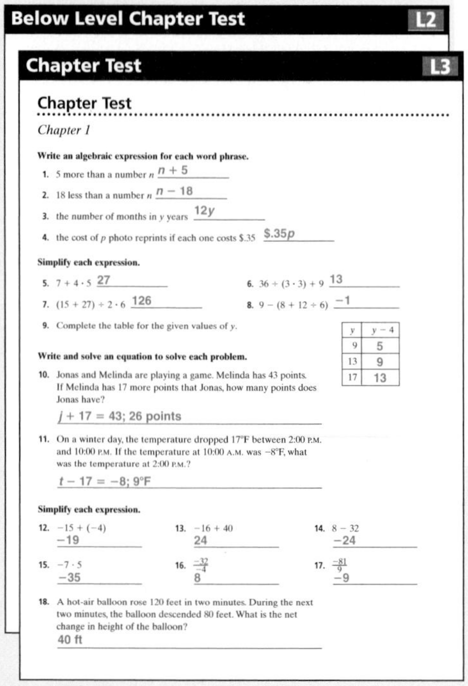

Below Level Chapter Test L2

Chapter Test L3

Chapter Test

Chapter 1

Write an algebraic expression for each word phrase.

1. 5 more than a number n $n + 5$
2. 18 less than a number n $n - 18$
3. the number of months in y years $12y$
4. the cost of p photo reprints if each one costs \$.35 $\$.35p$

Simplify each expression.

5. $7 + 4 \cdot 5$ 27
6. $36 \div (3 \cdot 3) + 9$ 13
7. $(15 + 27) \div 2 \cdot 6$ 126
8. $9 - (8 + 12 \div 6)$ −1
9. Complete the table for the given values of y.

y	$y - 4$
9	5
13	9
17	13

Write and solve an equation to solve each problem.

10. Jonas and Melinda are playing a game. Melinda has 43 points. If Melinda has 17 more points that Jonas, how many points does Jonas have? $j + 17 = 43$; 26 points
11. On a winter day, the temperature dropped 17°F between 2:00 P.M. and 10:00 P.M. If the temperature at 10:00 A.M. was −8°F, what was the temperature at 2:00 P.M.? $t - 17 = -8$; 9°F

Simplify each expression.

12. $-15 + (-4)$ −19
13. $-16 + 40$ 24
14. $8 - 32$ −24
15. $-7 \cdot 5$ −35
16. $\frac{-32}{-4}$ 8
17. $\frac{-81}{9}$ −9
18. A hot-air balloon rose 120 feet in two minutes. During the next two minutes, the balloon descended 80 feet. What is the net change in height of the balloon? 40 ft

Chapter 1 Test

Go Online PHSchool.com For: Online chapter test Web Code: asa-0152

Write an algebraic expression for each word phrase.

1. the sum of a number v and 18 $v + 18$
2. the number of miles a motorcycle gets per gallon if you use g gallons to travel 462 miles $\frac{462}{g}$
3. the number of years equal to d days $\frac{d}{365}$
4. the number of seconds equal to m minutes $60m$

Simplify each expression.

5. $6 + 3 \cdot 5$ 21
6. $18 \div (3 \cdot 2) + 3$ 6
7. $(10 + 14) \div 4 \cdot 2$ 12
8. $5 - (8 + 6 \div 2)$ −6
9. $9 - 5 + 2 \cdot 4$ 12
10. $5 \div (1 + 4) \cdot 6$ 6
11. Find the value of each expression for the given values of b in the table at the right.

b	$b + 7$	
8	■	15
12	■	19
20	■	27

Evaluate each expression for the given value.

12. $|c|$ for $c = -15$ 15
13. $5 + |h|$ for $h = 8$ 13
14. $-|3v|$ for $v = -7$ −21
15. $6 - |-t|$ for $t = 9$ −3
16. $4|y|$ for $y = -3$ 12
17. $|5f|$ for $f = 16$ 80

Simplify each expression.

18. $-14 + 60$ 46
19. $7 - 24$ −17
20. $\frac{-15}{5}$ −3
21. $-4 \cdot 3$ −12
22. $-9(-8)$ 72
23. $(-2)(-2)(-2)$ −8
24. **Football** A football team gained 6 yd on a play. On the next play, the team lost 9 yd. What is the net yardage for the team? −3 yd

Order the integers in each set from least to greatest.

25. −2, 0, 3, −4, −9
−9, −4, −2, 0, 3
26. −17, −14, 8, −13
−17, −14, −13, 8
27. 4, −3, −10, −7, −1
−10, −7, −3, −1, 4
28. −21, 22, −17, 5, 2
−21, −17, 2, 5, 22

Evaluate each expression for $m = -4$ and $p = 2$.

29. $mp - 5p$ −18
30. $(4p - m) \div 4$ 3
31. $\frac{p - m + 3}{5}$ 1.8
32. $m + p \cdot (-7)$ −18
33. **Writing in Math** Explain how positive and negative integers can be used to describe changes in depth. See margin.

Identify each property. 34–37. See margin.

34. $3(ck) = (3c)k$
35. $j = j \cdot 1$
36. $-7 + 5 = 5 + (-7)$
37. $(x + 5)2 = x \cdot 2 + 5 \cdot 2$

Mental Math **Use mental math to simplify each expression.**

38. $30(12)$ 360
39. $6 \cdot 32$ 192
40. $4(8.8)$ 35.2

Solve each equation.

41. $m - 45 = 10$ 55
42. $\frac{a}{-2} = 2.5$ −5
43. $3h = -18$ −6
44. $x + 4 = -1.2$ −5.2
45. $w + 7 = 18$ 11
46. $2 + y = -7$ −9
47. **Hiking** A hiker begins a hike in Death Valley National Park at the park's lowest point. She climbs 11,331 feet to the park's highest point, 11,049 feet above sea level. Find the elevation of Death Valley's lowest point. 282 ft below sea level
48. A store sells bicycles for \$250 each. In one week the store had \$1,250 in bicycle sales. How many bicycles did the store sell? 5 bicycles
49. Write an addition expression modeled by the number line below. $4 + (-9)$

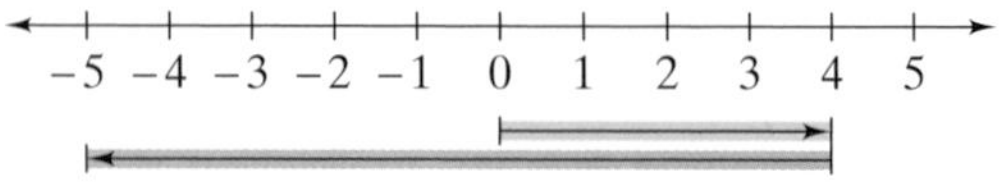

33. Answers may vary. Sample: Positive integers can show a change from deeper to less deep and negative integers show a change from deep to deeper.
34. Assoc. Prop. of Mult.
35. Ident. Prop. of Mult.
36. Comm. Prop. of Add.
37. Dist. Prop.

Reading Comprehension

Read each passage and answer the questions that follow.

Moore Power Computers keep getting more and more powerful; not long after you buy one, there is likely to be a more powerful model available for the same price. A "law" called Moore's Law was created to express this trend. It says the amount of computer power you can buy for a fixed price will double about every 18 months. This law has been remarkably accurate for more than 35 years, and most computer experts think it will continue to hold for several decades more.

1. Suppose you have $750 to spend on a computer. According to Moore's Law, about how much more powerful a computer will you be able to buy for the amount if you wait $1\frac{1}{2}$ years to make your purchase? B
   - A 1.5 times
   - B 2 times
   - C 3 times
   - D 18 times

2. About how much more powerful are computers that sell for $1,000 today than those that sold for $1,000 only 3 years ago? H
   - F 2 times
   - G 3 times
   - H 4 times
   - J 6 times

3. If Moore's Law continues to hold, about how much more powerful will computers be in around $4\frac{1}{2}$ years? C
   - A 4 times
   - B 6 times
   - C 8 times
   - D 16 times

4. According to Moore's Law, how long will it take before computers are 128 times as powerful as they are today? G
   - F 7 years
   - G 10.5 years
   - H 12 years
   - J 25 years

Perfect 10 The Pythagorean Greeks were fascinated by properties of numbers. They discovered that some numbers were equal to the sum of their lesser whole-number divisors. They called these numbers "perfect." For example, 6 is a perfect number because its divisors less than 6 are 1, 2, and 3, which add up to 6. The number 8 is "deficient" because the sum of its lesser divisors (1 + 2 + 4) is less than the number itself. The number 12 is "abundant" because the sum of its lesser divisors (1 + 2 + 3 + 4 + 6) is greater than it is.

5. According to the article, which number is a deficient number? A
   - A 15
   - B 20
   - C 36
   - D 48

6. According to the article, the number 18 is F
   - F abundant.
   - G deficient.
   - H divisible.
   - J perfect.

7. What is the sum of the divisors of 28? C
   - A 24
   - B 27
   - C 28
   - D 32

8. According to the article, which number is an abundant number? J
   - F 9
   - G 16
   - H 32
   - J 40

Test Prep

Resources

Test Prep Workbook

All in One Teaching Resources
- Cumulative Review L3

ExamView Assessment Suite CD-ROM
- Standardized Test Practice

Differentiated Instruction

Spanish Assessment Resources
- Spanish Cumulative Review ELL

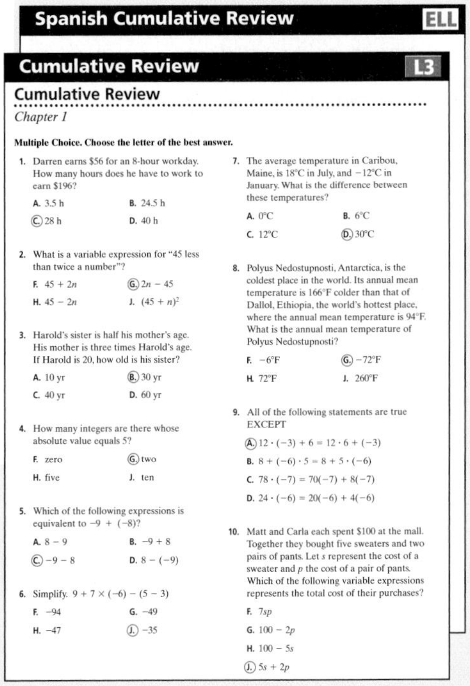

Spanish Cumulative Review ELL

Cumulative Review L3

Cumulative Review

Chapter 1

Multiple Choice. Choose the letter of the best answer.

1. Darren earns $56 for an 8-hour workday. How many hours does he have to work to earn $196?
   A. 3.5 h B. 24.5 h C. 28 h D. 40 h
2. What is a variable expression for "45 less than twice a number"?
   F. $45 + 2n$ G. $2n - 45$ H. $45 - 2n$ J. $(45 + n)^2$
3. Harold's sister is half his mother's age. His mother is three times Harold's age. If Harold is 20, how old is his sister?
   A. 10 yr B. 30 yr C. 40 yr D. 60 yr
4. How many integers are there whose absolute value equals 5?
   F. zero G. two H. five J. ten
5. Which of the following expressions is equivalent to $-9 + (-8)$?
   A. $8 - 9$ B. $-9 + 8$ C. $-9 - 8$ D. $8 - (-9)$
6. Simplify. $9 + 7 \times (-6) - (5 - 3)$
   F. −94 G. −49 H. −47 J. −35
7. The average temperature in Caribou, Maine, is 18°C in July, and −12°C in January. What is the difference between these temperatures?
   A. 0°C B. 6°C C. 12°C D. 30°C
8. Polyus Nedostupnosti, Antarctica, is the coldest place in the world. Its annual mean temperature is 166°F colder than that of Dallol, Ethiopia, the world's hottest place, where the annual mean temperature is 94°F. What is the annual mean temperature of Polyus Nedostupnosti?
   F. −6°F G. −72°F H. 72°F J. 260°F
9. All of the following statements are true EXCEPT
   A. $12 \cdot (-3) + 6 = 12 \cdot 6 + (-3)$
   B. $8 + (-6) \cdot 5 = 8 + 5 \cdot (-6)$
   C. $78 \cdot (-7) = 70(-7) + 8(-7)$
   D. $24 \cdot (-6) = 20(-6) + 4(-6)$
10. Matt and Carla each spent $100 at the mall. Together they bought five sweaters and two pairs of pants. Let s represent the cost of a sweater and p the cost of a pair of pants. Which of the following variable expressions represents the total cost of their purchases?
   F. $7sp$ G. $100 - 2p$ H. $100 - 5s$ J. $5s + 2p$

Problem Solving

Applying Integers

Students will use data from these two pages to answer the questions posed in the Activity.

Activating Prior Knowledge

Review and discuss the meaning of latitude and longitude with students. Have students use a map to approximate these coordinates for where you live and for other locations they choose.

Guided Instruction

Have a volunteer read aloud the information about the global positioning system (GPS) and the other information presented on page 48.

Guide students to select and use benchmarks to help them better understand a speed of 17,000 mph, an orbit that is 12,660 miles high, or a weight of 230,000 pounds.

History Connection
Encourage interested students to research the history of the submersibles that have been used to explore the oceans and ocean floors.

Science Connection
Invite students interested in sound detection of depth to find out what sonar (sound navigation ranging) is, when it was discovered, and how it works. Have them share what they learn with classmates.

DK Problem Solving Application

Applying Integers

Treasure Hunt For centuries, explorers used a compass and a sextant to plot expeditions. Today, global positioning system (GPS) satellites find locations accurately, even when the sun or stars are not visible. On Earth's surface, two coordinates define a position. In the air or the oceans, a third coordinate, elevation above or below Earth's surface, joins the first two.

What's Up There?
Space near Earth contains meteoroids and man-made debris traveling at speeds of about 17,000 mi/h. At that speed, even tiny particles can cause damage.

Global Positions
GPS satellites orbit 12,660 mi above Earth. Coordinating signals from three satellites can tell your position on or above Earth to within about 300 ft.

Half Rocket, Half Airplane
At lift-off, the space shuttle weighs about 4.5 million lb. When it lands, it weighs only about 230,000 lb.

Go Online PHSchool.com
For: Information about navigation
Web Code: ase-0153

1a. The sub starts at an elevation of 0 (on the surface) and at a horizontal position of 0.

b. The horizontal position increases (+5) because the sub goes forward (to the right). The vertical position decreases as the sub dives below the surface.

2. B to C:
vertical: −15 + (−20) = −35
horizontal: 5 + 20 = 25
C to D.
vertical: −35 + (−5) = −40
horizontal: 25 + 10 = 35
D to E.
vertical: −40 + 20 = −20
horizontal: 35 + 15 = 50
E to F.
vertical: −20 + 0 = −20

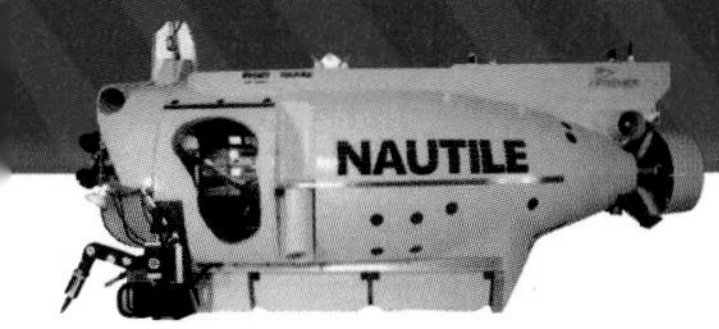

Submersible Vehicles

Although the ocean is about 36,000 ft deep at its deepest point, a submersible designed to operate at 20,000 ft can reach 98% of the ocean floor.

Sound Detection

Submarines determine the depth of the ocean beneath them by bouncing sound waves off the ocean floor and analyzing the echoes.

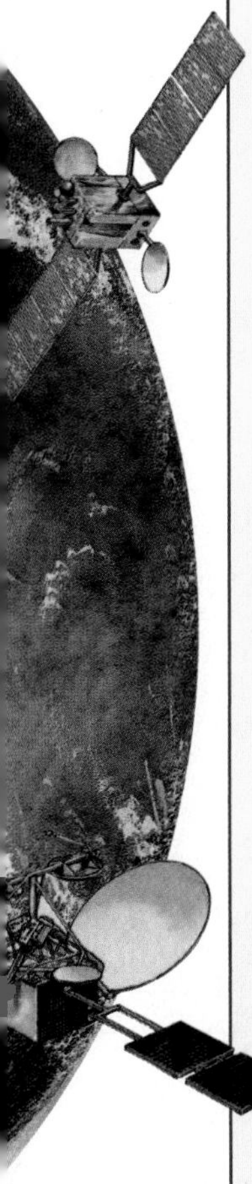

Put It All Together

Materials graph paper

Suppose you are navigating a treasure-hunting submarine. The sub starts on the ocean surface outside a cave (point *A*). Plot a course through the cave to the treasure, marked with an *X*.

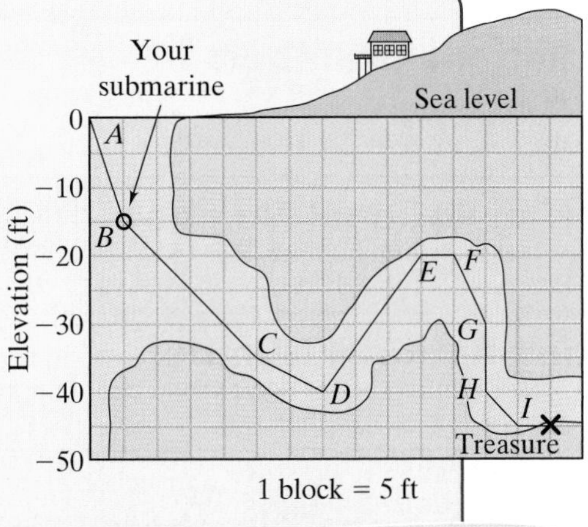

1. The Navigation Instruction Sheet shows how to get from point *A* to point *B*.
   a. Why are the entries for the initial horizontal and vertical positions each 0?
   b. Why is the horizontal change a positive number while the vertical change is a negative number?
2. Use the map. Follow the style of the Navigation Instruction Sheet to write instructions to reach the treasure.

Navigation Instruction Sheet

From point:	A			To point:	B
	initial	+	change	=	end
Vertical	0	+	−15		−15
Horizontal	0	+	+5		+5

3. a. **Open-Ended** Draw an underwater cave on a piece of graph paper and put a treasure somewhere inside it. Make sure that a sub can reach the treasure in eight moves or less.
   b. Draw a course that the sub could follow to reach the treasure. Write a set of instructions for the course.
   c. **Writing in Math** Exchange instructions with a classmate. Follow your classmate's instructions on a blank grid. When you finish, check your work with your classmate. Did you find the treasure? Explain.

Put It All Together

Have students work in pairs to answer the navigation questions. Discuss that in this activity, students will write instructions for locating and reaching points on the coordinate grid.

Exercise 1 Carefully work through the steps for using the Navigation Instruction Sheet to get from Point *A* to Point *B*. Guide students to see that the grid map shows that the submarine is 15 feet below sea level (−15).

Exercise 2 Guide pairs of students to understand that they need to navigate from point to point to get *A* from *I*. Have them record their movements in a table that shows movement from *A* to *B*, from *B* to *C*, from *C* to *D*, and so on.

Exercise 3c Clarify for students that there may be more than one course a sub can follow to reach the treasure.

Differentiated Instruction

Special Needs L1

As needed, review positive and negative integers. Ask: *Why is the vertical change negative?* **The movement in elevation is down from sea level.**

horizontal: 50 + 5 = 55
F to G.
vertical: −20 + (−10) = −30
horizontal: 55 + 5 = 60
G to H.
vertical: −30 + (−10) = −40
horizontal: 60 + 0 = 60
H to I.
vertical: −40 + (−5) = −45
horizontal: 60 + 5 = 65

3a–c. Check students' work.

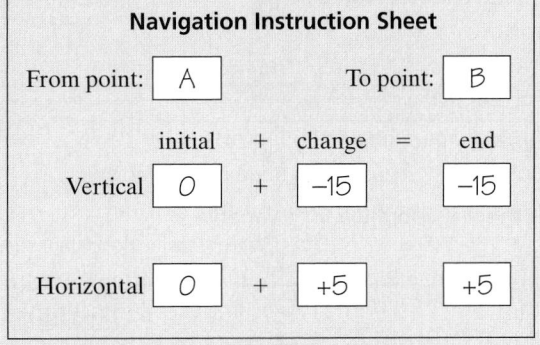

2 Rational Numbers

Chapter at a Glance

Lesson Titles, Objectives, and Features	Assessment	NCTM Standards	Local Standards
2-1 Factors • To identify prime and composite numbers and to find the greatest common factor	Lesson Quiz	1, 2, 3, 6, 7, 8, 9, 10	
2-2 Equivalent Forms of Rational Numbers • To write equivalent fractions and decimals **2-2b Activity Lab:** Repeating Decimals	Lesson Quiz	1, 2, 5, 6, 7, 8, 9, 10	
2-3 Comparing and Ordering Rational Numbers • To use least common denominators, decimals, and number lines to compare and order rational numbers	Lesson Quiz	1, 2, 3, 6, 7, 8, 9, 10	
2-4 Adding and Subtracting Rational Numbers • To add and subtract fractions and mixed numbers and to solve problems involving rational numbers	Lesson Quiz Checkpoint Quiz 1	1, 2, 6, 7, 8, 9, 10	
2-5a Activity Lab: Modeling Fraction Multiplication **2-5 Multiplying and Dividing Rational Numbers** • To multiply and divide fractions and mixed numbers and to solve problems involving rational numbers **Vocabulary Builder:** Learning Vocabulary **Guided Problem Solving:** Practice Solving Problems	Lesson Quiz	1, 2, 3, 6, 7, 8, 9, 10	
2-6a Activity Lab, Algebra Thinking: Estimating Solutions **2-6 Formulas** • To use formulas to solve problems and to solve a formula for a variable **2-6b Activity Lab, Technology:** Using Formulas	Lesson Quiz	1, 2, 3, 4, 6, 7, 8, 9, 10	
2-7 Powers and Exponents • To write, simplify, and evaluate expressions involving exponents **2-7b Activity Lab, Technology:** Evaluating Expressions	Lesson Quiz Checkpoint Quiz 2	1, 2, 3, 4, 6, 7, 8, 9, 10	
2-8a Activity Lab: Multiplying by Powers of 10 **2-8 Scientific Notation** • To write numbers in both standard form and scientific notation **2-8b Activity Lab, Data Analysis:** Writing Measurements	Lesson Quiz	1, 2, 4, 6, 7, 8, 9, 10	
Problem Solving Application: Applying Real Numbers			

NCTM Standards 2000
1 Number and Operations **2** Algebra **3** Geometry **4** Measurement **5** Data Analysis and Probability
6 Problem Solving **7** Reasoning and Proof **8** Communication **9** Connections **10** Representation

Correlations to Standardized Tests

All content for these tests is contained in *Prentice Hall Math*, Course 3. This chart reflects coverage in this chapter only.

	2-1	2-2	2-3	2-4	2-5	2-6	2-7	2-8
Terra Nova CAT6 (Level 18)								
Number and Number Relations	✔	✔	✔	✔	✔	✔	✔	✔
Computation and Numerical Estimation	✔	✔	✔	✔	✔	✔	✔	✔
Operation Concepts	✔			✔	✔	✔	✔	✔
Measurement								
Geometry and Spatial Sense								
Data Analysis, Statistics, and Probability								
Patterns, Functions, and Algebra						✔		
Problem Solving and Reasoning	✔	✔	✔	✔	✔	✔	✔	✔
Communication	✔	✔	✔	✔	✔	✔	✔	✔
Decimals, Fractions, Integers, Percent	✔	✔	✔	✔	✔	✔	✔	✔
Order of Operations								
Algebraic Operations								
Terra Nova CTBS (Level 18)								
Decimals, Fractions, Integers, and Percents	✔	✔	✔	✔	✔	✔	✔	✔
Order of Operations, Numeration, Number Theory	✔	✔	✔	✔	✔	✔	✔	✔
Data Interpretation								
Measurement								
Geometry								
ITBS (Level 14)								
Number Properties and Operations	✔	✔	✔	✔	✔	✔	✔	✔
Algebra						✔		
Geometry								
Measurement								
Probability and Statistics								
Estimation								
SAT10 (Adv 1 Level)								
Number Sense and Operations	✔	✔	✔	✔	✔	✔	✔	✔
Patterns, Relationships, and Algebra						✔		
Data, Statistics, and Probability								
Geometry and Measurement								
NAEP								
Number Sense, Properties, and Operations	✔	✔	✔	✔	✔		✔	✔
Measurement								
Geometry and Spatial Sense								
Data Analysis, Statistics, and Probability								
Algebra and Functions						✔		

CAT6 California Achievement Test, 6th Ed. **CTBS** Comprehensive Test of Basic Skills **ITBS** Iowa Test of Basic Skills, Form M
SAT10 Stanford Achievement Test, 10th Ed. **NAEP** National Assessment of Educational Progress 2005 Mathematics Objectives

Math Background

Professional Development

Skills Trace

BEFORE Chapter 2

Course 2 introduced rational and irrational numbers.

DURING Chapter 2

Course 3 extends the study of rational numbers to include comparing, adding, subtracting, multiplying, and dividing.

AFTER Chapter 2

Throughout this course students work with rational numbers to find probabilities and solve real-world problems.

2-1 Factors

Math Understandings

- A number that is divisible by *n* is also divisible by each factor of *n*. For example, any number divisible by 12 is also divisible by 2, 3, 4, and 6.
- The fundamental theorem of arithmetic states that every integer greater than 1 can be expressed as a product of prime factors in one and only 1 way, except for the order of the factors.
- The number 1 is neither prime nor composite. The number 2 is the only even prime number.

A number is **divisible** by a second number if the number can be divided by the second number with a remainder of 0. A **prime number** is a whole number greater than 1 with exactly two factors, 1 and the number itself. A **composite number** is a whole number greater than 1 with more than two factors.

A composite number written as a product of prime numbers is the **prime factorization** of the number. The **greatest common factor** (*GCF*) of two or more numbers is the largest number that is a factor of all the numbers.

Example: $84 = 2 \times 2 \times 3 \times 7$
$308 = 2 \times 2 \times 7 \times 11$

The GCF of 84 and 308 is $2 \times 2 \times 7$, or 28.

2-2 Equivalent Forms of Rational Numbers

Math Understandings

- Dividing the numerator and denominator of a rational number by common factors relies on two properties: $\frac{a}{a} = 1$ and $a \times 1 = a$.
- Terminating decimals and repeating decimals are rational numbers. Non-terminating decimals that do not repeat, such as π and $\sqrt{3}$, are irrational numbers.

A **rational number** is a number that can be written in the form $\frac{a}{b}$, where *a* is an integer and *b* is any nonzero integer. Two integers *a* and *b* are **relatively prime** if 1 is their only common factor. A fraction $\frac{a}{b}$ is in simplest form when *a* and *b* are relatively prime. A **terminating decimal** is a decimal that stops. A decimal that repeats the same digit or group of digits forever is a **repeating decimal**.

Example: $\frac{1}{3} = 0.333\ldots = 0.\overline{3}$
$\frac{5}{12} = 0.41666\ldots = 0.41\overline{6}$

2-3 2-4 Comparing, Ordering, Adding, and Subtracting Rational Numbers

Math Understandings

- You can always find a common denominator for two fractions by multiplying the two denominators, but this may not be the least common denominator.
- When two rational numbers have a common positive denominator, the greater numerator identifies the greater rational number.
- We add or subtract rational numbers with unlike denominators by changing to a simple calculation with like denominators.

The **least common multiple (LCM)** of two or more numbers is the smallest multiple that is common to all of the numbers. The LCM of the denominators is called the **least common denominator (LCD)**. To add, subtract, or compare fractions, rewrite them with a common denominator. You can find the LCM directly with some calculators, such as the TI-34 II or TI-73.

Example: Find the LCD for $\frac{3}{10}$ and $\frac{5}{12}$.

For $\frac{3}{10}$ and $\frac{5}{12}$, the product of the denominators (120) is a common denominator. However, the least common multiple (LCM) of 10 and 12 is 60, so the LCD is 60.

2-5 Multiplying and Dividing Rational Numbers

Math Understandings

- You can multiply mixed numbers by writing each as an improper fraction.
- Dividing by a fraction is the same as multiplying by the reciprocal of the fraction.

To find the product of rational numbers that are fractions, multiply the numerators and multiply the denominators. Two numbers whose product is 1 are called **reciprocals**. The reciprocal of a number is also called its **multiplicative inverse**.

2-6 Formulas

Math Understandings

- When you solve a formula for a variable, you use inverse operations and the properties of equality.
- When you can substitute a value for all but one of the variables in a formula, you can then solve for the remaining unknown value.

A **formula** is an equation that shows a relationship between two or more quantities. Some commonly used formulas include:

$A = \ell w$, $P = 2\ell + 2w$, $d = rt$, $C = 2\pi r$, and $A = \pi r^2$.

2-7 Powers and Exponents

Math Understandings

- An exponent applies only to its base so $(-3)^2$ is 9 but -3^2 is -9.

A **factor** is an integer that divides another integer with a remainder of 0. An **exponent** tells how many times a number, or **base**, is used as a factor. An expression that uses a base and an exponent is called a **power**. You can extend the order of operations to include powers.

Order of Operations

1. Work inside grouping symbols.
2. Simplify the powers.
3. Multiply and divide from left to right.
4. Add and subtract from left to right.

2-8 Scientific Notation

Math Understandings

- Scientific notation is a brief way to write very large or very small numbers.
- To multiply a number by 10^p, when $p > 0$, you move the decimal point in the number p places to the right to increase the size of the number. When $p < 0$, move the decimal point in the number $|p|$ places to the left to decrease the size of the number.
- To write the number 10^p without an exponent, $p > 0$, you write 1 followed by p zeros.

A number is in **scientific notation** if the first factor is greater than or equal to 1 and less than 10 and the second factor is a power of 10.

Example:	Standard Form	Scientific Notation
	14,830	1.483×10^4
	1,483	1.483×10^3
	148.3	1.483×10^2
	14.83	1.483×10^1
	1.483	1.483×10^0
	0.1483	1.483×10^{-1}
	0.01483	1.483×10^{-2}
	0.001483	1.483×10^{-3}

Additional Professional Development Opportunities

Professional Development

Math Background Notes for Chapter 2: Every lesson has a Math Background in the PLAN section.

Research Overview, Mathematics Strands
Additional support for these topics and more is in the front of the Teacher's Edition.

LessonLab
LessonLab, a Pearson Education company, offers comprehensive, facilitated professional development designed to help teachers to improve student achievement. To learn, more please visit lessonlab.com.

Chapter 2 Resources

	2-1	2-2	2-3	2-4	2-5	2-6	2-7	2-8	For the Chapter
Print Resources									
L3 Practice	●	●	●	●	●	●	●	●	
L1 Adapted Practice	●	●	●	●	●	●	●	●	
L3 Guided Problem Solving	●	●	●	●	●	●	●	●	
L2 Reteaching	●	●	●	●	●	●	●	●	
L4 Enrichment	●	●	●	●	●	●	●	●	
L3 Daily Notetaking Guide	●	●	●	●	●	●	●	●	
L1 Adapted Daily Notetaking Guide	●	●	●	●	●	●	●	●	
L3 Vocabulary and Study Skills Worksheets	●		●	●		●		●	●
L3 Daily Puzzles	●	●	●	●	●	●	●	●	
L3 Activity Labs	●	●	●	●	●	●	●	●	
L3 Checkpoint Quiz				●			●		
L3 Chapter Project									●
L2 Below Level Chapter Test									●
L3 Chapter Test									●
L4 Alternative Assessment									●
L3 Cumulative Review									●
Spanish Resources ELL									
L3 Practice	●	●	●	●	●	●	●	●	●
L3 Vocabulary and Study Skills Worksheets	●		●	●		●		●	●
L3 Checkpoint Quiz				●			●		
L2 Below Level Chapter Test									●
L3 Chapter Test									●
L4 Alternative Assessment									●
L3 Cumulative Review									●
Transparencies									
Check Skills You'll Need	●	●	●	●	●	●	●	●	
Additional Examples	●	●	●	●	●	●	●	●	
Problem of the Day	●	●	●	●	●	●	●	●	
Classroom Aid	●	●	●	●	●	●	●	●	
Student Edition Answers	●	●	●	●	●	●	●	●	●
Lesson Quiz	●	●	●	●	●	●	●	●	
Test-Taking Strategies									●
Technology									
Interactive Textbook Online	●	●	●	●	●	●	●	●	●
StudentExpress™ CD-ROM	●	●	●	●	●	●	●	●	●
Success Tracker™ Online Intervention	●	●	●	●	●	●	●	●	●
TeacherExpress™ CD-ROM	●	●	●	●	●	●	●	●	●
PresentationExpress™ with QuickTake Presenter CD-ROM	●	●	●	●	●	●	●	●	●
ExamView® Assessment Suite CD-ROM	●	●	●	●	●	●	●	●	●
MindPoint® Quiz Show CD-ROM									●
Prentice Hall Web Site: PHSchool.com	●	●	●	●	●	●	●	●	●

Also available: **Prentice Hall Assessment System**
- Progress Monitoring Assessments
- Skills and Concepts Review
- Test Prep Workbook

Other Resources
Algebra Readiness Tests
All-in-One Student Workbook
All-in-One Student Workbook, Adapted Version
Multilingual Handbook
Solution Key
Math Notes Study Folder
Spanish Cumulative Assessment

Where You Can Use the Lesson Resources

Here is a suggestion, following the four-step teaching plan, for how you can incorporate Differentiated Instruction Resources into your teaching.

	Instructional Resources L3	Differentiated Instruction Resources
1. Plan		
Preparation Read the Math Background in the Teacher's Edition to connect this lesson with students' previous experience. **Starting Class** **Check Skills You'll Need** Assign these exercises to review prerequisite skills. **New Vocabulary** Help students pre-read the lesson by pointing out the new terms introduced in the lesson.	**Math Background** **Math Understandings** **Transparencies & PresentationExpress™ with QuickTake Presenter CD-ROM** Check Skills You'll Need Problem of the Day **Resources** Vocabulary and Study Skills	**Spanish Support** ELL Vocabulary and Study Skills
2. Teach		
L3 **Guided Instruction** Use the Activity Labs to build conceptual understanding. Teach each Example. Use the Teacher's Edition side column notes for specific teaching tips, including Error Prevention notes. Use the Additional Examples found in the side column (and on transparency and PowerPoint) as an alternative presentation for the content. After each Example, assign the Quick Check exercise for that Example to get an immediate assessment of student understanding. Use the Closure activity in the Teacher's Edition to help students attain mastery of lesson content.	**Student Edition** Activity Lab **Resources** Daily Notetaking Guide Activity Lab **Transparencies & PresentationExpress™ with QuickTake Presenter CD-ROM** Additional Examples Classroom Aids **ExamView® Assessment Suite CD-ROM**	**Teacher's Edition** Every lesson includes suggestions for working with students who need special attention. L1 Special Needs L2 Below Level L4 Advanced Learners ELL English Language Learners **Resources** L1 Adapted Daily Notetaking Guide **Multilingual Handbook**
3. Practice		
Assignment Guide **Check Your Understanding** Use these questions to check students' understanding before you assign homework. **Homework Exercises** Assign homework from these leveled exercises in the Assignment Guide. A Practice by Example B Apply Your Skills C Challenge Test Prep and Mixed Review **Homework Quick Check** Use these key exercises to quickly check students' homework.	**Transparencies & PresentationExpress™ with QuickTake Presenter CD-ROM** Student Answers **Resources** Practice Guided Problem Solving Vocabulary and Study Skills Activity Lab Daily Puzzles **ExamView® Assessment Suite CD-ROM**	**Spanish Support** ELL Practice ELL Vocabulary and Study Skills **Resources** L1 Adapted Practice L4 Enrichment
4. Assess & Reteach		
Lesson Quiz Assign the Lesson Quiz to assess students' mastery of the lesson content. **Checkpoint Quiz** Use the Checkpoint Quiz to assess student progress over several lessons.	**Transparencies & PresentationExpress™ with QuickTake Presenter CD-ROM** Lesson Quiz **Resources** Checkpoint Quiz	**Resources** L2 Reteaching ELL Checkpoint Quiz Success Tracker™ Online Intervention **ExamView® Assessment Suite CD-ROM**

KEY L1 Special Needs L2 Below Level L3 For All Students L4 Advanced, Gifted ELL English Language Learners

CHAPTER 2

Rational Numbers

Check Your Readiness

Answers for students are in the back of the textbook.

For intervention, direct students to:

Evaluating Algebraic Expressions
Lesson 1-1
Extra Skills and Word Problems Practice, Ch. 1

Comparing and Ordering Integers
Lesson 1-2
Extra Skills and Word Problems Practice, Ch. 1

Adding and Subtracting Integers
Lesson 1-3
Extra Skills and Word Problems Practice, Ch. 1

Multiplying and Dividing Integers
Lesson 1-4
Extra Skills and Word Problems Practice, Ch. 1

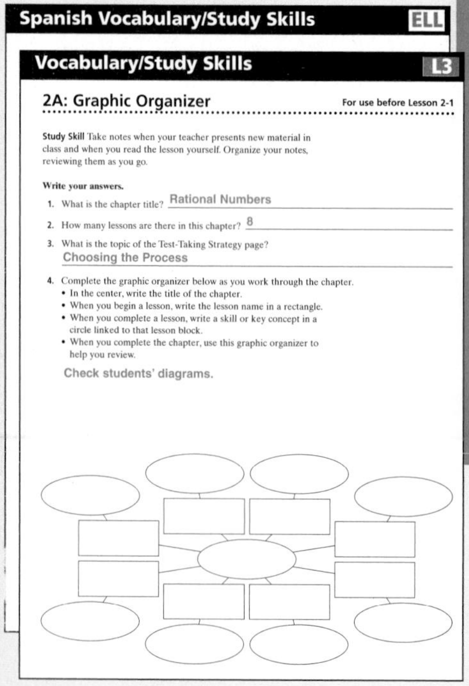
Spanish Vocabulary/Study Skills ELL

Vocabulary/Study Skills L3

2A: Graphic Organizer — For use before Lesson 2-1

Study Skill Take notes when your teacher presents new material in class and when you read the lesson yourself. Organize your notes, reviewing them as you go.

Write your answers.

1. What is the chapter title? Rational Numbers
2. How many lessons are there in this chapter? 8
3. What is the topic of the Test-Taking Strategy page? Choosing the Process
4. Complete the graphic organizer below as you work through the chapter.
   - In the center, write the title of the chapter.
   - When you begin a lesson, write the lesson name in a rectangle.
   - When you complete a lesson, write a skill or key concept in a circle linked to that lesson block.
   - When you complete the chapter, use this graphic organizer to help you review.

   Check students' diagrams.

CHAPTER 2 Rational Numbers

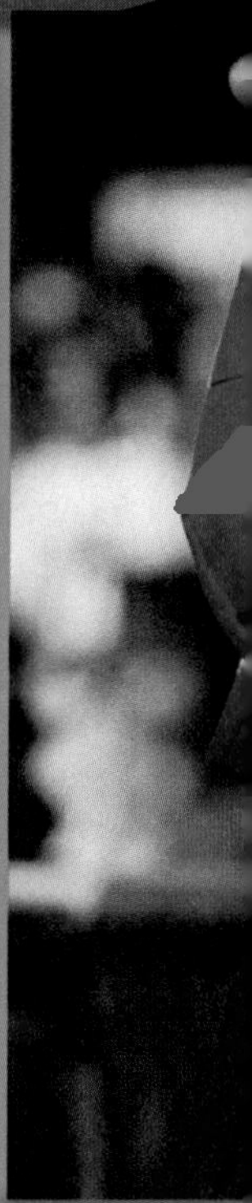

What You've Learned

- In a previous course, you solved problems involving fractions.
- In Chapter 1, you compared and ordered rational numbers, including integers.
- You used addition, subtraction, multiplication, and division to solve problems involving integers.

Check Your Readiness

GO for Help

For Exercises	See Lessons
1–4	1-1
5–8	1-2
9–12	1-3
13–16	1-4

Evaluating Algebraic Expressions

Evaluate each expression for $n = 4$.

1. $3(n + 2) - n$ 14 **2.** $3n + 2 \cdot 5$ 22

3. $\frac{3}{n + 2} \cdot n$ 2 **4.** $\frac{3 + 5}{n}$ 2

Comparing and Ordering Integers

Order the integers in each set from least to greatest.

5. $-4, 3, 0, -11$ $-11, -4, 0, 3$ **6.** $8, -6, -9, 13$ $-9, -6, 8, 13$

7. $-21, -8, 9, 16$ $-21, -8, 9, 16$ **8.** $-35, -3, 22, -17$ $-35, -17, -3, 22$

Adding and Subtracting Integers

Simplify each expression.

9. $-5 + 8$ 3 **10.** $16 - 29$ -13 **11.** $-23 + (-14)$ -37 **12.** $-36 - (-11)$ -25

Multiplying and Dividing Integers

Simplify each expression.

13. $4 \cdot (-12)$ -48 **14.** $\frac{-54}{9}$ -6 **15.** $-7 \cdot 2 \cdot (-3)$ 42 **16.** $\frac{-108}{-12}$ 9

Chapter 2 Overview

In this chapter, students draw upon their prior knowledge of fractions and of integers as they learn how to compare, order, and simplify rational numbers, and to add, subtract, multiply, and divide them. They also work with exponents and scientific notation where they use both positive and negative powers of ten.

Activating Prior Knowledge

In this chapter, students build on their knowledge of operations with fractions and with integers in order to compute with rational numbers. Ask questions such as:

- *Solve:* $-12 + (-5)$. -17
- *Solve:* $4n + 2 = 20$. $n = 4.5$

What You'll Learn Next

- In this chapter, you will compare and order rational numbers, including positive and negative fractions and decimals.
- You will use addition, subtraction, multiplication, and division to solve problems involving rational numbers.
- You will write and use numbers with exponents, including numbers in scientific notation.

Problem Solving Application On pages 102 and 103, you will work an extended activity on frequency.

Key Vocabulary

- base (p. 86)
- composite number (p. 52)
- divisible (p. 52)
- exponent (p. 86)
- factor (p. 52)
- formula (p. 81)
- greatest common factor (p. 53)
- least common denominator (p. 62)
- least common multiple (p. 62)
- multiplicative inverse (p. 73)
- power (p. 86)
- prime factorization (p. 53)
- prime number (p. 52)
- rational number (p. 57)
- reciprocals (p. 73)
- relatively prime (p. 57)
- scientific notation (p. 92)

2-1

1. Plan

Objective
To identify prime and composite numbers and to find the greatest common factor

Examples
1 Prime and Composite Numbers
2 Finding Prime Factorization
3 Finding the GCF by Listing
4 Finding the GCF with Prime Factorization

Math Understandings: p. 50C

Professional Development

Math Background

Every counting number greater than 1 is either a prime number, or it can be written as the product of prime numbers. Writing a number (that is not prime) as the product of its prime factors is called *factoring* that number.

More Math Background: p. 50C

Lesson Planning and Resources

See p. 50E for a list of the resources that support this lesson.

PowerPoint

Bell Ringer Practice

Check Skills You'll Need
Use student page, transparency, or PowerPoint. For intervention, direct students to:
Multiplying and Dividing Integers
Lesson 1-4
Extra Skills and Word Problems Practice, Ch. 1

2-1 Factors

Check Skills You'll Need

1. **Vocabulary Review** When you multiply two numbers, the result is called the _?_. product

Simplify each expression.

2. −10(10) −100
3. −8(−7) 56
4. 5(−4)(−2) 40
5. −1 · 1 · 0 0

GO for Help Lesson 1-4

What You'll Learn

To identify prime and composite numbers and to find the greatest common factor

New Vocabulary divisible, factor, prime number, composite number, prime factorization, greatest common factor (GCF)

Why Learn This?

Sometimes you want to arrange items or people in groups. You can use factors to help you find the size of each group.

A number is **divisible** by a second number if the number can be divided by the second number with a remainder of 0. You can use divisibility tests to see if one number is divisible by another.

Divisible by	Divisibility Test
2	The ones digit is 0, 2, 4, 6, or 8.
3	The sum of the digits is divisible by 3.
4	The last two digits are divisible by 4.
5	The ones digit is 0 or 5.
9	The sum of the digits is divisible by 9.
10	The ones digit is 0.

An integer that divides another integer with a remainder of 0 is a **factor.** A **prime number** is a whole number greater than 1 with exactly two factors, 1 and the number itself. A **composite number** is a whole number greater than 1 with more than two factors. The number 1 is neither prime nor composite.

EXAMPLE Prime and Composite Numbers

1 Identify 2,727 as prime or composite. Explain.

The sum of the digits is 18, which is divisible by 3.
Since 2,727 is divisible by 3, it is composite.

Quick Check

1. Identify 15,482 as *prime* or *composite.* Explain. composite; divisible by 2

Differentiated Instruction Solutions for All Learners

Special Needs L1
Students who have a difficult time drawing the branches on a factor tree can pair up with, and check the calculations of, students who can draw the trees.
learning style: visual

Below Level L2
Explain that a number divisible by 6 is also divisible by all other factors of 6: 1, 2, and 3. Have students test whether 30 is divisible by all the factors of 30 to reinforce the definition of divisible.
learning style: verbal

A composite number written as a product of prime numbers is the **prime factorization** of the number. There is only one prime factorization for a number, regardless of the order of the factors. For example, the prime factorization $2 \cdot 3$ is the same as $3 \cdot 2$.

You can use divisibility tests and a factor tree to find the prime factorization of a number.

EXAMPLE Finding Prime Factorization

2 Use a factor tree to find the prime factorization of 54.

The number 54 is divisible by 2 because it is an even number. Begin the factor tree with $2 \cdot 27$.

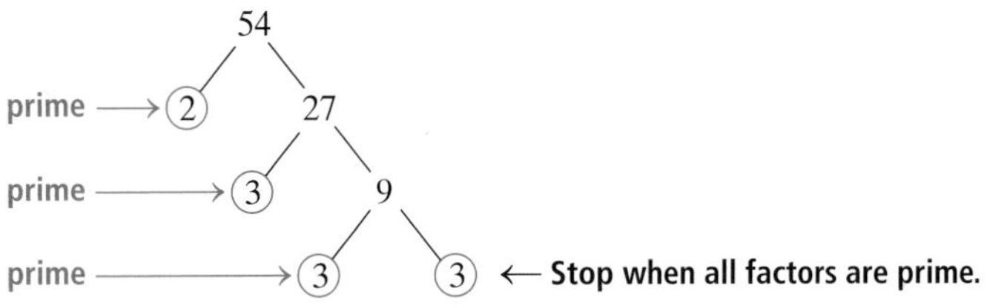

The prime factorization of 54 is $2 \cdot 3 \cdot 3 \cdot 3$.

Quick Check

2. Use a factor tree to find the prime factorization of each number.
a. 96 $2 \cdot 2 \cdot 2 \cdot 2 \cdot 2 \cdot 3$ **b.** 240 $2 \cdot 2 \cdot 2 \cdot 2 \cdot 3 \cdot 5$

The **greatest common factor (GCF)** of two or more numbers is the greatest number that is a factor of all of the numbers. You can list factors to find the GCF of two numbers.

EXAMPLE Finding the GCF by Listing

3 Find the GCF of 42 and 36.

Begin by finding the factors of 42 and 36.

42: 1, 2, 3, 6, 7, 14, 21, 42

36: 1, 2, 3, 4, 6, 9, 12, 18, 36

The factors 1, 2, 3, and 6 are common to both numbers. So the GCF of 42 and 36 is 6.

Test Prep Tip
When listing the factors of a number, begin with 1 and continue in order until a factor is repeated.

Quick Check

3. Find the GCF of each pair of numbers by listing their factors.
a. 54, 63 9 **b.** 18, 42 6

2. Teach

Activity Lab

Use before the lesson.

All-in-One Teaching Resources

Activity Lab 2-1: Consecutive Numbers

Guided Instruction

Example 2
Connect the language of mathematics to the plain language that students use by explaining that x is divisible by y if y goes into x evenly, with nothing left over.

Error Prevention!

In listing the prime factors for a number in Example 2, students may omit one or more repetitions of a repeated factor. Have them check their work by multiplying the factors in the final list to verify that the product is equal to the original number.

Technology Tip
Students can also use a calculator to investigate and verify the divisibility of one number by another.

PowerPoint
Additional Examples

1 Identify each number as *prime* or *composite*. Explain.
- **a.** 57 composite; divisible by 3
- **b.** 1,354 composite; divisible by 2
- **c.** 43 prime; divisible only by 43 and 1
- **d.** 975 composite; divisible by 5

2 Use a factor tree to find the prime factorization of 588. $2^2 \cdot 3 \cdot 7^2$

3 Find the GCF of 55 and 231. 11

Advanced Learners L4	**English Language Learners** ELL
Have students find the GCF of each set of numbers. 120, 240, 320 40 24, 36, 48 12 72, 15, 36 3 96, 16, 25 1 **learning style: visual**	Elicit the definition of *greatest common factor* by having students consider the meaning of each word, then putting it all together. Sample: The greatest common factor is the greatest factor that numbers share. **learning style: verbal**

PowerPoint

Additional Examples

4 A band with 36 members is marching with a 32-member band. If the two bands are to have the same number of columns, what is the greatest possible number of columns in which you could arrange the two bands? 4

All in One Teaching Resources

- Daily Notetaking Guide 2-1 L3
- Adapted Notetaking 2-1 L1

Guided Instruction

Example 4

Provide students with a blank grid from **Test-Taking Strategies with Transparencies**. Students check their work by asking themselves this question: *Have I listed any factor that is still divisible by a number other than 1 and itself?* Then, after listing the prime factorization for each number, students circle the prime factors common to both lists to help them find the GCF.

Closure

- Explain how to find the greatest common factor of two numbers. Sample: List the prime factors for each of the numbers. Then circle all the factors that occur in both lists and multiply those factors to find the greatest common factor of the two numbers.

You can also use prime factorization to find the GCF of two numbers.

EXAMPLE Finding the GCF with Prime Factorization

4 **Gridded Response** A parade director wants two bands to have the same number of people in every row. One band has 24 members. The other has 60. What is the greatest possible number of people in a row?

Step 1 Find the prime factorization of each number.

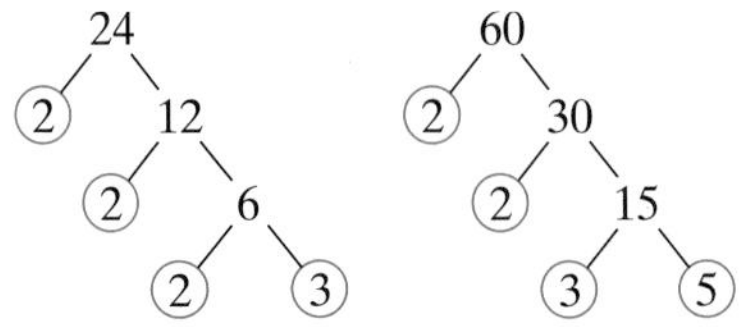

Step 2 Find the product of the common prime factors of each number.

$24 = 2 \cdot 2 \cdot 2 \cdot 3$

$60 = 2 \cdot 2 \cdot 3 \cdot 5$

The common prime factors are 2, 2, and 3. The GCF of 24 and 60 is $2 \cdot 2 \cdot 3 = 12$.

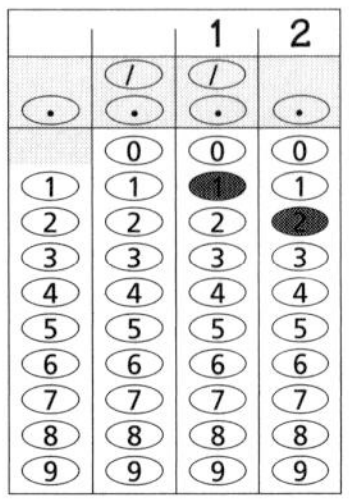

Test Prep Tip

Remember, whole numbers go to the left of the decimal point when writing your answer in the grid.

Quick Check

4. Two pipes have lengths 63 ft and 84 ft. You cut them into pieces of equal length with nothing left over. What is the greatest possible length of the pieces? 21 ft

Check Your Understanding

1. **Vocabulary** The greatest number that is a factor of two or more numbers is the __?__ of the numbers. GCF

2. Find the factors of 54. 1, 2, 3, 6, 9, 18, 27, 54

Is the first number divisible by the second? Explain. 3–6. See left.

3. 105; 2 **4.** 91; 5 **5.** 123; 3

6. **Error Analysis** Whose work is correct? Explain.

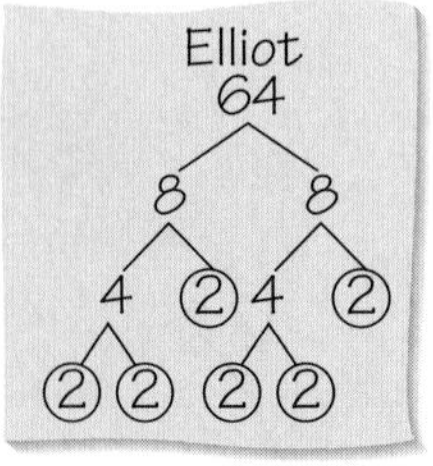

3. No; the ones digit is not 0, 2, 4, 6, or 8.
4. No; the ones digit is not 0 or 5.
5. Yes; the sum of the digits is 6, which is divisible by 3.
6. Elliot's, all factors are prime.

Homework Exercises

For more exercises, see Extra Skills and Word Problems.

GO for Help

For Exercises	See Examples
7–14	1
15–22	2
23–30	3
31–39	4

A **Identify each number as *prime* or *composite*. Explain.**

7–14. See left.

7. 48 **8.** 25 **9.** 73 **10.** 79

11. 99 **12.** 250 **13.** 101 **14.** 1011

Use a factor tree to find the prime factorization of each number.

15–22. See margin.

15. 20 **16.** 12 **17.** 16 **18.** 400

19. 27 **20.** 26 **21.** 56 **22.** 39

Find the GCF of each pair of numbers by listing their factors.

23. 6, 18 6 **24.** 15, 54 3 **25.** 42, 72 6 **26.** 21, 63 21

27. 52, 78 26 **28.** 38, 82 2 **29.** 44, 68 4 **30.** 30, 50 10

Use prime factorization to find the GCF of each pair of numbers.

31. 14, 35 7 **32.** 27, 36 9 **33.** 30, 45 15 **34.** 32, 48 16

35. 44, 66 22 **36.** 62, 93 31 **37.** 86, 94 2 **38.** 57, 76 19

39. Students are cleaning a local park in groups. There are 50 boys and 75 girls. Each group has the same number of boys and the same number of girls. What is the greatest possible number of groups? 25

B **GPS**

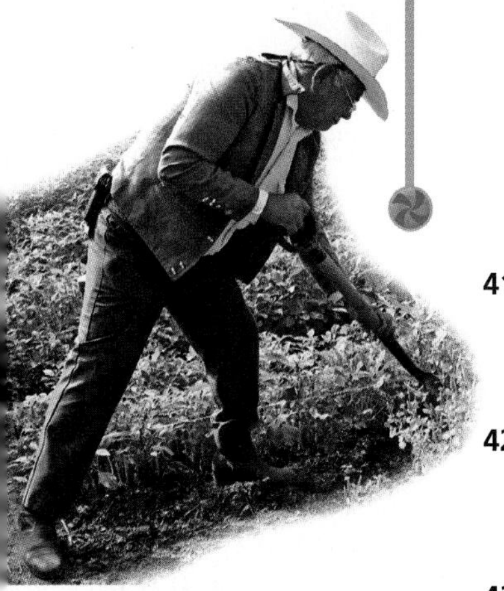

40. Guided Problem Solving You are dividing a community garden 35 m long by 15 m wide into equal-sized square gardens. Find the greatest possible dimensions of each square. 5 m by 5 m

- **Make a Plan** Draw a picture to help you visualize the problem. Then find the GCF.
- **Carry Out the Plan** The GCF is ■. The largest possible dimensions of each square are ■ m by ■ m.

41. The cafeteria has 144 bananas, 36 pears, and 72 apples. Each student gets the same number of pieces of each fruit. What is the greatest number of students who can receive fruit? 36

42. Reasoning Use factor trees starting with $6 \cdot 16$ and $8 \cdot 12$ to find the prime factorization of 96. Explain why the prime factorization of 96 is the same for both factor trees. See left.

43. Performances The 48 members of a chorus will sit in rows in front of the 300 members of the audience. All the rows have the same number of chairs. What is the greatest possible number of chairs in each row? 12

7. composite; $2 \cdot 2 \cdot 2 \cdot 2 \cdot 3$
8. composite; $5 \cdot 5$
9. prime
10. prime
11. composite; $3 \cdot 3 \cdot 11$
12. composite; $2 \cdot 5 \cdot 5 \cdot 5$
13. prime
14. composite; $3 \cdot 337$
15. $2 \cdot 2 \cdot 5$
16. $2 \cdot 2 \cdot 3$
17. $2 \cdot 2 \cdot 2 \cdot 2$
18. $2 \cdot 2 \cdot 2 \cdot 2 \cdot 5 \cdot 5$

42. Regardless of the method used, the prime factorization of a number consists of only prime numbers.

Online lesson quiz, PHSchool.com, Web Code: asa-0201

15–18. See above left.
19. $n = 4.5$ 20. $2 \cdot 13$
21. $2 \cdot 2 \cdot 2 \cdot 7$ 22. $3 \cdot 13$

3. Practice

Assignment Guide

Check Your Understanding
Go over Exercises 1–6 in class before assigning the Homework Exercises.

Homework Exercises

A	Practice by Example	7–39
B	Apply Your Skills	40–51
C	Challenge	52
	Test Prep and Mixed Review	53–58

Homework Quick Check
To check students' understanding of key skills and concepts, go over Exercises 21, 36, 42, 47, and 48.

Differentiated Instruction Resources

Adapted Practice 2-1 L1

Practice 2-1 L3

List all the factors of each number.

1. 36 1, 2, 3, 4, 6, 9, 12, 18, 36 2. 42 1, 2, 3, 6, 7, 14, 21, 42 3. 50 1, 2, 5, 10, 25, 50 4. 41 1, 41

Tell whether the first number is a factor of the second.

5. 2; 71 no 6. 1; 18 yes 7. 3; 81 yes 8. 4; 74 no
9. 9; 522 yes 10. 8; 508 no 11. 13; 179 no 12. 17; 3,587 yes

Identify each number as *prime* or *composite*. If the number is *composite*, use a factor tree to find its prime factorization.

13. 74 composite $2 \cdot 37$ 14. 83 prime 15. 23 prime
16. 73 prime 17. 91 composite $7 \cdot 13$ 18. 109 prime

Write the prime factorization of each number.

19. 70 $2 \cdot 5 \cdot 7$ 20. 92 $2^2 \cdot 23$ 21. 120 $2^3 \cdot 3 \cdot 5$
22. 200 $2^3 \cdot 5^2$ 23. 180 $2^2 \cdot 3^2 \cdot 5$ 24. 360 $2^3 \cdot 3^2 \cdot 5$
25. 187 $11 \cdot 17$ 26. 364 $2^2 \cdot 7 \cdot 13$ 27. 1,287 $3^2 \cdot 11 \cdot 13$

Find the GCF by finding the prime factorization.

28. 24, 40 8 29. 20, 42 2 30. 56, 63 7
31. 18, 24, 36 6 32. 20, 45, 75 5 33. 120, 150, 180 30

34. Mr. Turner distributed some supplies in his office. He distributed 120 pencils, 300 paper clips, and 16 pens. What is the greatest number of people there can be in the office if each person received the same number of items? 4 people

35. The baseball league bought new equipment for the teams. The managers bought 288 baseballs, 40 bats, and 24 equipment bags. What is the greatest number of teams there can be if all the new equipment is distributed equally among the teams? 8 teams

2-1 • Guided Problem Solving GPS L3

GPS Student Page 56, Exercise 48:

Art The art teacher hands out her entire inventory of art supplies, listed at the right. Each class gets the same number of each item.

paintbrushes 120
boxes of markers 78
pads of paper 24
sets of watercolors 54

a. How many classes receive supplies?
b. How many of each item does each class get?

Understand

1. What are you being asked to do? Determine the number of classes that can receive supplies and how many of each item each class gets.

Plan and Carry Out

2. Write the prime factorization of 120. $2^3 \cdot 3 \cdot 5$
3. Write the prime factorization of 78. $2 \cdot 3 \cdot 13$
4. Write the prime factorization of 24. $2^3 \cdot 3$
5. Write the prime factorization of 54. $2 \cdot 3^3$
6. What is the product of the common prime factors of each number? 6; $2 \cdot 3$
7. What is the greatest number of classes that can receive supplies? 6
8. How many of each item will each class receive? 20 paintbrushes, 13 boxes of markers, 4 pads of paper, and 9 sets of watercolors

Check

9. Is your answer reasonable? Yes, since 6 is the greatest number that will divide evenly into the number of each item.

Solve Another Problem

10. You have three pieces of string with lengths of 42 inches, 63 inches, and 77 inches. You need to cut pieces of equal length from these three pieces of string. How long should each piece be, and how many pieces can you get from each length of string? Each piece will be 7 inches long; 42-inch piece: 6 pieces; 63-inch piece: 9 pieces; 77-inch piece: 11 pieces; total: 26 pieces

4. Assess & Reteach

Lesson Quiz

Write the prime factorization of each number.

1. 24 $2^3 \cdot 3$ **2.** 27 3^3 **3.** 31 31

Find the GCF of each pair of numbers.

4. 4 and 14 2 **5.** 18 and 27 9

Alternative Assessment

In small groups, each student writes a digit to create a multiple-digit number, such as 4,575. Then group members determine if the number is prime or composite. If it is composite, they work together to write its prime factorization.

Reteaching 2-1 L2

A *prime number* is a number with only two factors, 1 and itself.

The number 17 is prime.
Its only factors are 1 and 17.

Use a factor tree to find prime factors. The product of prime factors is called the *prime factorization.*

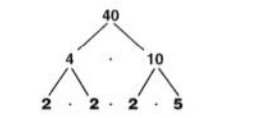

The prime factorization of 40 is $2 \cdot 2 \cdot 2 \cdot 5$ or $2^3 \cdot 5$.

The *greatest common factor (GCF)* of a set of numbers is the greatest factor common to the numbers.

Find the GCF of 20 and 30.

① Use factor trees to find prime factors.

② Circle the common factors. The product of the common factors is the GCF.

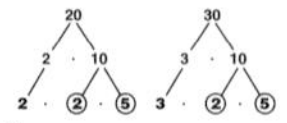

$2 \cdot 5 = 10$
The GCF of 20 and 30 is 10.

Complete these factor trees. Write the prime factorization for each number.

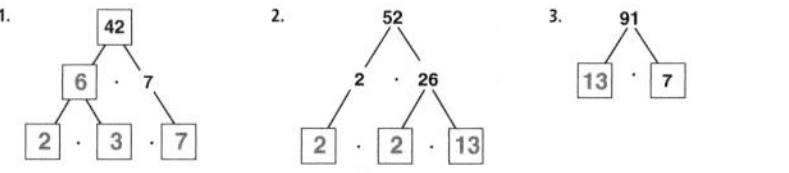

1. $42 = 2 \cdot 3 \cdot 7$
2. $52 = 2^2 \cdot 13$
3. $91 = 13 \cdot 7$

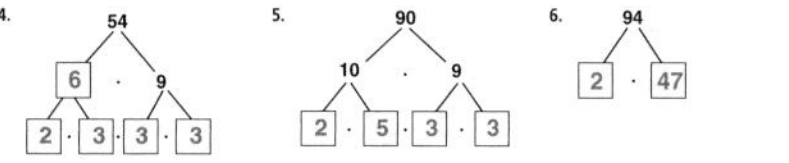

4. $54 = 2 \cdot 3^3$
5. $90 = 2 \cdot 5 \cdot 3^2$
6. $94 = 2 \cdot 47$

Find the GCF by finding the prime factorization.

7. 10, 12
2

8. 15, 8
1

9. 12, 18
6

10. 27, 18
9

Enrichment 2-1 L4

Critical Thinking

The set of factors for an integer is all the numbers that can be evenly divided into the integer. The *proper factors* of an integer include all these numbers *except* the integer itself.

Example: The set of factors for 12 are 1, 2, 3, 4, 6, and 12. The proper factors are 1, 2, 3, 4, and 6.

A positive integer is *perfect* if the sum of its proper factors is equal to the integer itself.

- It is *abundant* if the sum is greater than the integer.
- It is *deficient* if the sum is less than the integer.

To see if 12 is a perfect, abundant, or deficient number

① Add its proper factors: $1 + 2 + 3 + 4 + 6 = 16$.

② Then compare the sum and the integer. Since 16 is greater than 12, 12 is an abundant number.

Complete the table to identify perfect, abundant, and deficient integers.

	Integer	Proper Factors	Sum	Type of Integer
1.	6	1, 2, 3	6	perfect
2.	15	1, 3, 5	9	deficient
3.	16	1, 2, 4, 8	15	deficient
4.	17	1	1	deficient
5.	18	1, 2, 3, 6, 9	21	abundant
6.	19	1	1	deficient
7.	20	1, 2, 4, 5, 10	22	abundant
8.	21	1, 3, 7	11	deficient
9.	22	1, 2, 11	14	deficient

10. Write a perfect number greater than 22.
Sample answer: 28

11. Write an abundant number greater than 22.
Sample answer: 24

12. Write a deficient number greater than 22.
Sample answer: 23

13. Write 24 as the sum of two abundant numbers.
Sample answer: 12 + 12

14. There are exactly two ways to write 36 as the sum of two abundant numbers. Write both ways.
12 + 24; 18 + 18

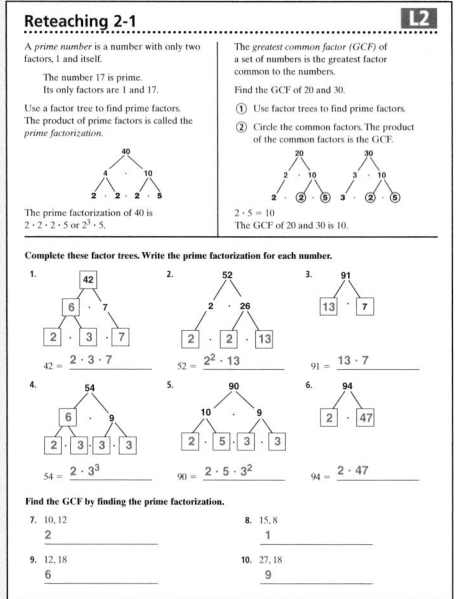

GO Online
Homework Video Tutor
Visit: PHSchool.com
Web Code: ase-0201

Find the GCF.

44. 22, 33, 44 11 **45.** 27, 45, −81 9 **46.** 12, −24, 36 12

47. In 1742, the mathematician Christian Goldbach made a conjecture that every even number greater than 2 can be expressed as the sum of two prime numbers. Write the number 60 as the sum of two prime numbers.

47. Answers may vary. Samples are given. 7 + 53; 13 + 47; 17 + 43; 19 + 41; 23 + 37; 29 + 31

48. Art (GPS) The art teacher hands out her entire inventory of art supplies, listed at the right. Each class gets the same number of each item.
a. How many classes receive supplies?
b. How many of each item does each class get?

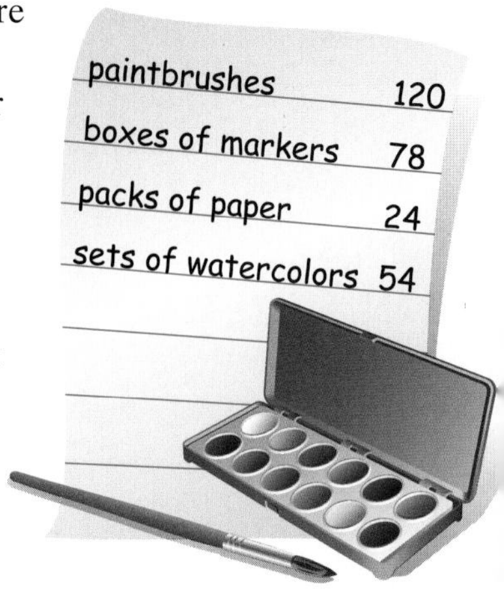

48a. 6 classes
b. 20 paintbrushes, 13 boxes of markers, 4 packs of paper, 9 watercolors

49. Reasoning If w is divisible by 2, what can you conclude about the factors of $w + 2$? It is also divisible by 2.

50. Writing in Math What is the GCF of any two prime numbers? Explain.

50. 1; the factors of any prime number are 1 and the number.

51. (Algebra) Show that the expression $-x^2 + 7x + 7$ is a prime number when $x = 0$, $x = 2$, and $x = 3$. 7, 17, and 19 are prime.

Ⓒ **52. Challenge** What is the least number that has exactly five factors? List the factors. 16; 1, 2, 4, 8, 16

Test Prep and Mixed Review

Practice

Gridded Response

53. Max bought $2\frac{1}{2}$ ft of ribbon. He used 18 in. to wrap a gift. How many feet of ribbon did he have left? 1

54. The amount c Jeff spends on juice and muffins during the week can be found using the equation $c = 5(1.25) + x(1.45)$, where x represents the number of muffins Jeff ate during the week. Find the total cost, in dollars, for a week in which Jeff ate 3 muffins. 10.60

55. On Rita's science test, the first 10 questions were worth 3 points each, the next 6 questions were worth 4 points each, and the last 4 questions were worth 5 points each. If Rita answered each question correctly, how many points did she score on the test? 74

GO for Help

For Exercises	See Lesson
56–58	1-5

Choose a Method **Use paper and pencil, number lines, or mental math to simplify each expression.**

56. $3.4 + 5.6 + 8.3$ 17.3 **57.** $6 \cdot -7 \cdot 5$ −210 **58.** $12(8.1)$ 97.2

Test Prep

Resources

For additional practice with a variety of test item formats:
- Test-Taking Strategies, p. 97
- Test Prep, p. 101
- Test-Taking Strategies with Transparencies

2-2 Equivalent Forms of Rational Numbers

Check Skills You'll Need

1. **Vocabulary Review** Write the *prime factorization* of 100. 2 · 2 · 5 · 5

Find the GCF of each pair of numbers.

2. 6, 12 6
3. 8, 12 4
4. 25, 50 25
5. 36, 40 4

GO for Help Lesson 2-1

What You'll Learn

To write equivalent fractions and decimals

New Vocabulary rational number, relatively prime, terminating decimal, repeating decimal

Why Learn This?

The baseball standings at the right use both decimals and fractions. Decimals and fractions are rational numbers.

Team Standings

	W	L	PCT	GB
Houston	24	14	.632	—
St. Louis	19	19	.500	5
Milwaukee	17	20	.459	$6\frac{1}{2}$
Chicago	17	20	.459	$6\frac{1}{2}$
Pittsburgh	15	23	.395	9
Cincinnati	14	25	.359	$10\frac{1}{2}$

A **rational number** is a number that can be written in the form $\frac{a}{b}$, where a is an integer and b is any nonzero integer. Two integers a and b are **relatively prime** if 1 is their only common factor. A fraction $\frac{a}{b}$ is in simplest form when a and b are relatively prime.

EXAMPLES Simplifying a Fraction

1 Write $\frac{36}{40}$ in simplest form using the GCF.

The GCF of 36 and 40 is 4.

$\frac{36}{40} = \frac{36 \div 4}{40 \div 4}$ ← **Divide the numerator and denominator by the GCF.**

$= \frac{9}{10}$ ← **Simplify.**

2 Write $\frac{54}{60}$ in simplest form using prime factorization.

$\frac{54}{60} = \frac{2 \cdot 3 \cdot 3 \cdot 3}{2 \cdot 2 \cdot 3 \cdot 5}$ ← **Write the prime factorizations of the numerator and denominator.**

$= \frac{{}^{1}\cancel{2} \cdot 3 \cdot \cancel{3}^{1} \cdot 3}{{}_{1}\cancel{2} \cdot 2 \cdot \cancel{3}_{1} \cdot 5}$ ← **Divide the common factors.**

$= \frac{9}{10}$ ← **Simplify.**

Quick Check

1. Write $\frac{12}{20}$ in simplest form using the GCF. $\frac{12 \div 4}{20 \div 4} = \frac{3}{5}$
2. Write $\frac{27}{45}$ in simplest form using prime factorization. $\frac{3 \cdot 3 \cdot 3}{3 \cdot 3 \cdot 5} = \frac{3}{5}$

Differentiated Instruction Solutions for All Learners

Special Needs L1	**Below Level** L2
Review with students how to divide a greater number into a lesser one before they convert fractions to decimals. learning style: verbal	Have students use long division to divide 1 by 3 $0.\overline{3}$; 2 by 3 $0.\overline{6}$; and 2 by 9 $0.\overline{2}$. Have students describe the quotients. Sample: In each example, the same digit repeats forever. learning style: verbal

2-2

1. Plan

Objective

To write equivalent fractions and decimals

Examples

1. Simplifying a Fraction
2. Writing an Equivalent Decimal
3. Writing an Equivalent Fraction

Math Understandings: p. 50C

Professional Development

Math Background

The name for the set of rational numbers comes from the fact that a **ratio**nal number can be expressed as a **ratio** of integers. All decimals are rational if they end or repeat a group of digits forever. They can be written as fractions with integers in each numerator and denominator.

More Math Background: p. 50C

Lesson Planning and Resources

See p. 50E for a list of the resources that support this lesson.

PowerPoint

Bell Ringer Practice

Check Skills You'll Need

Use student page, transparency, or PowerPoint. For intervention, direct students to:

Factors

Lesson 2-1

Extra Skills and Word Problems Practice, Ch. 2

2. Teach

Activity Lab

Use before the lesson.

All in One Teaching Resources

Activity Lab 2-2: Converting Fractions to Decimals

Guided Instruction

Alternative Method

For Example 1, students can also rewrite $\frac{36}{40}$ as $\frac{4 \cdot 9}{4 \cdot 10}$, which is $\frac{4}{4} \cdot \frac{9}{10}$ or $1 \cdot \frac{9}{10}$ or $\frac{9}{10}$.

Error Prevention!

Explain that a decimal that goes on forever can have a pattern and still not be a repeating decimal. For instance, in 0.121121112 . . . you can predict the next digit, but there is no single group of digits that repeats.

PowerPoint

Additional Examples

1. Write $\frac{138}{150}$ in simplest form using the GCF. $\frac{23}{25}$
2. Write $\frac{60}{126}$ in simplest form using prime factorization. $\frac{10}{21}$
3. Write each batting average as a decimal.
   a. Joe made 4 hits in 20 times at bat. .200
   b. Pat made 6 hits in 33 times at bat. .182
4. Write 3.225 as a mixed number. $3\frac{9}{40}$

All in One Teaching Resources

- Daily Notetaking Guide 2-2 L3
- Adapted Notetaking 2-2 L1

Closure

- *Explain which types of decimals can be written as the ratio of two integers.* Sample: every terminating decimal and every non-terminating decimal that repeats one digit or the same group of digits

Vocabulary Tip

The fraction $\frac{a}{b}$ means $a \div b$. You can write the fraction $\frac{a}{b}$ as $a \div b$.

You can represent a rational number as a fraction. You can write a fraction as a decimal by dividing the numerator by the denominator.

If the division results in a decimal that stops, the decimal is called a **terminating decimal.** If the division results in a decimal that repeats the same digit or group of digits forever, the decimal is a **repeating decimal.** A bar indicates the repeating digits. So $0.\overline{3} = 0.3333\ldots$

EXAMPLE 3 Writing an Equivalent Decimal

Baseball In baseball, a player's batting average is $\frac{\text{number of hits}}{\text{number of times at bat}}$. A batting average is rounded to three decimal places and is written without the leading 0.

a. Find the batting average of a hitter with 36 hits in 125 times at bat.

$\frac{36}{125}$ ← **Write the batting average as a fraction.**

0.288 ← **Divide. This is a terminating decimal.**

The player's batting average is .288.

b. Find the batting average of a hitter with 27 hits in 99 times at bat.

$\frac{27}{99}$ ← **Write the batting average as a fraction.**

$0.27272727\ldots = 0.\overline{27}$ ← **Divide. This is a repeating decimal.**

The player's batting average is about .273.

Quick Check

3. Find the batting average of a hitter with 39 hits in 85 times at bat. .459

You can write a terminating decimal as a fraction by multiplying both the numerator and the denominator by the same power of 10.

EXAMPLE 4 Writing an Equivalent Fraction

Write 1.345 as a mixed number in simplest form.

$1.345 = \frac{1.345}{1}$ ← **Write as a fraction with the denominator 1.**

$= \frac{1{,}345}{1{,}000}$ ← **Since there are 3 digits to the right of the decimal, multiply the numerator and the denominator by 1,000.**

$= \frac{1{,}345 \div 5}{1{,}000 \div 5}$ ← **Divide the numerator and the denominator by the GCF, 5.**

$= \frac{269}{200} = 1\frac{69}{200}$ ← **Simplify. Write as a mixed number.**

Quick Check

4. Write 1.42 as a mixed number in simplest form. $1\frac{21}{50}$

Differentiated Instruction Solutions for All Learners

Advanced Learners L4

Have students write each fraction as a decimal using a bar to indicate repeating digits.

$\frac{1}{6}$ $0.1\overline{6}$ $\frac{1}{9}$ $0.\overline{1}$ $\frac{1}{11}$ $0.\overline{09}$

learning style: verbal

English Language Learners ELL

Review the math meaning of the word *prime* with students before defining *relatively prime.* Students define the word *ratio,* then connect it to the term *rational number.*

learning style: verbal

Check Your Understanding

1. **Vocabulary** Since 123 is a rational number, it can be written in the form $\frac{123}{■}$. $\frac{123}{1}$

2. **Number Sense** A player has 15 hits in 34 times at bat and then gets another hit. Did the batting average increase? Explain. Yes; it increased from .441 to .457.

Match each fraction with its equivalent decimal.

3. $\frac{1}{4}$ D
4. $\frac{3}{10}$ C
5. $\frac{1}{2}$ A
6. $\frac{2}{5}$ B

A. 0.5
B. 0.4
C. 0.3
D. 0.25

Homework Exercises

For more exercises, see Extra Skills and Word Problems.

GO for Help

For Exercises	See Examples
7–14	1 and 2
15–23	3
24–31	4

A **Write each fraction in simplest form.**

7. $\frac{15}{20}$ $\frac{3}{4}$
8. $\frac{48}{64}$ $\frac{3}{4}$
9. $-\frac{40}{60}$ $-\frac{2}{3}$
10. $-\frac{12}{54}$ $-\frac{2}{9}$
11. $\frac{20}{100}$ $\frac{1}{5}$
12. $\frac{18}{81}$ $\frac{2}{9}$
13. $-\frac{4}{14}$ $-\frac{2}{7}$
14. $\frac{12}{60}$ $\frac{1}{5}$

Write each fraction as a decimal. Round to three decimal places.

15. $\frac{2}{3}$ 0.667
16. $\frac{8}{25}$ 0.320
17. $\frac{17}{16}$ 1.063
18. $\frac{16}{17}$ 0.941
19. $-\frac{13}{7}$ −1.857
20. $\frac{9}{45}$ 0.200
21. $\frac{5}{13}$ 0.385
22. $-\frac{28}{35}$ −0.800

23. **Sports** A baseball player has 34 hits in 102 times at bat. Another baseball player has 24 hits in 96 times at bat. Write each player's batting average. .333; .250

Write each decimal as a mixed number or fraction in simplest form.

24. 1.4 $1\frac{2}{5}$
25. 0.33 $\frac{33}{100}$
26. 0.24 $\frac{6}{25}$
27. 4.44 $4\frac{11}{25}$
28. 2.8 $2\frac{4}{5}$
29. 0.05 $\frac{1}{20}$
30. 0.005 $\frac{1}{200}$
31. 7.32 $7\frac{8}{25}$

B GPS

32. **Guided Problem Solving** At a chili festival over the past few years, Restaurant A won 56 out of 98 contests. Restaurant B won 84 out of 147 contests. Which restaurant has the better record?
    - What fraction represents the wins for Restaurant A?
    - What fraction represents the wins for Restaurant B?

    They have the same record.

33. **Population** In 2003, 0.219 of the people in the United States were younger than 15 years old. Write the decimal as a fraction. $\frac{219}{1{,}000}$ (GPS)

3. Practice

Assignment Guide

Check Your Understanding

Go over Exercises 1–6 in class before assigning the Homework Exercises.

Homework Exercises

A Practice by Example	7–31
B Apply Your Skills	32–37
C Challenge	38
Test Prep and Mixed Review	39–45

Homework Quick Check

To check students' understanding of key skills and concepts, go over Exercises 16, 30, 33, 34, and 37.

Differentiated Instruction Resources

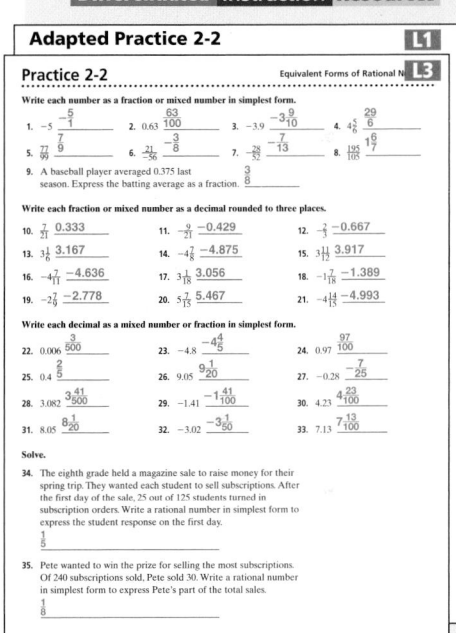

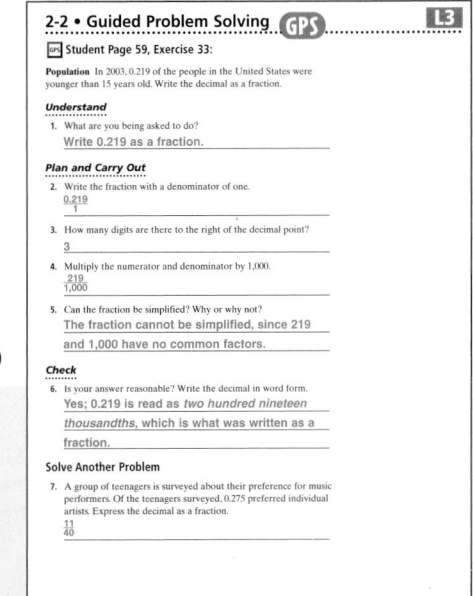

Adapted Practice 2-2 L1

Practice 2-2 Equivalent Forms of Rational N L3

Write each number as a fraction or mixed number in simplest form.

1. −5 $\frac{-5}{1}$
2. 0.63 $\frac{63}{100}$
3. −3.9 $-3\frac{9}{10}$
4. $4\frac{5}{6}$ $\frac{29}{6}$
5. $\frac{77}{99}$ $\frac{7}{9}$
6. $\frac{21}{-56}$ $-\frac{3}{8}$
7. $-\frac{28}{52}$ $-\frac{7}{13}$
8. $\frac{195}{105}$ $1\frac{6}{7}$
9. A baseball player averaged 0.375 last season. Express the batting average as a fraction. $\frac{3}{8}$

Write each fraction or mixed number as a decimal rounded to three places.

10. $\frac{7}{21}$ 0.333
11. $-\frac{9}{21}$ −0.429
12. $-\frac{2}{3}$ −0.667
13. $3\frac{1}{6}$ 3.167
14. $-4\frac{7}{8}$ −4.875
15. $3\frac{11}{12}$ 3.917
16. $-4\frac{7}{11}$ −4.636
17. $3\frac{1}{18}$ 3.056
18. $-1\frac{7}{18}$ −1.389
19. $-2\frac{7}{9}$ −2.778
20. $5\frac{7}{15}$ 5.467
21. $-4\frac{14}{15}$ −4.993

Write each decimal as a mixed number or fraction in simplest form.

22. 0.006 $\frac{3}{500}$
23. −4.8 $-4\frac{4}{5}$
24. 0.97 $\frac{97}{100}$
25. 0.4 $\frac{2}{5}$
26. 9.05 $9\frac{1}{20}$
27. −0.28 $-\frac{7}{25}$
28. 3.082 $3\frac{41}{500}$
29. −1.41 $-1\frac{41}{100}$
30. 4.23 $4\frac{23}{100}$
31. 8.05 $8\frac{1}{20}$
32. −3.02 $-3\frac{1}{50}$
33. 7.13 $7\frac{13}{100}$

Solve.

34. The eighth grade held a magazine sale to raise money for their spring trip. They wanted each student to sell subscriptions. After the first day of the sale, 25 out of 125 students turned in subscription orders. Write a rational number in simplest form to express the student response on the first day. $\frac{1}{5}$

35. Pete wanted to win the prize for selling the most subscriptions. Of 240 subscriptions sold, Pete sold 30. Write a rational number in simplest form to express Pete's part of the total sales. $\frac{1}{8}$

2-2 • Guided Problem Solving GPS L3

GPS Student Page 59, Exercise 33:

Population In 2003, 0.219 of the people in the United States were younger than 15 years old. Write the decimal as a fraction.

Understand

1. What are you being asked to do?
   Write 0.219 as a fraction.

Plan and Carry Out

2. Write the fraction with a denominator of one.
   $\frac{0.219}{1}$
3. How many digits are there to the right of the decimal point?
   3
4. Multiply the numerator and denominator by 1,000.
   $\frac{219}{1{,}000}$
5. Can the fraction be simplified? Why or why not?
   The fraction cannot be simplified, since 219 and 1,000 have no common factors.

Check

6. Is your answer reasonable? Write the decimal in word form.
   Yes; 0.219 is read as *two hundred nineteen thousandths,* which is what was written as a fraction.

Solve Another Problem

7. A group of teenagers is surveyed about their preference for music performers. Of the teenagers surveyed, 0.275 preferred individual artists. Express the decimal as a fraction.
   $\frac{11}{40}$

4. Assess & Reteach

PowerPoint

Lesson Quiz

Write each as a fraction in simplest form.

1. $\frac{30}{42}$ $\frac{5}{7}$
2. $-\frac{12}{18}$ $-\frac{2}{3}$
3. Write $\frac{2}{16}$ as a decimal. 0.125

Write each decimal as a mixed number or fraction in simplest form.

4. 2.75 $2\frac{3}{4}$
5. 0.4 $\frac{2}{5}$

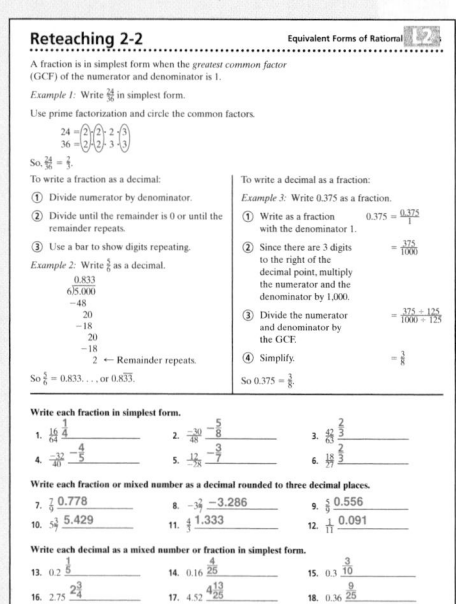

Reteaching 2-2

Equivalent Forms of Rational Numbers L2

A fraction is in simplest form when the *greatest common factor* (GCF) of the numerator and denominator is 1.

Example 1: Write $\frac{24}{36}$ in simplest form.

Use prime factorization and circle the common factors.

$24 = 2 \cdot 2 \cdot 2 \cdot 3$
$36 = 2 \cdot 2 \cdot 3 \cdot 3$

So, $\frac{24}{36} = \frac{2}{3}$.

To write a fraction as a decimal:

① Divide numerator by denominator.
② Divide until the remainder is 0 or until the remainder repeats.
③ Use a bar to show digits repeating.

Example 2: Write $\frac{5}{6}$ as a decimal.

$6\overline{)5.000} = 0.833$
−48
20
−18
20
−18
2 ← Remainder repeats.

So $\frac{5}{6} = 0.833\ldots$, or $0.8\overline{33}$.

To write a decimal as a fraction:

Example 3: Write 0.375 as a fraction.

① Write as a fraction with the denominator 1. $0.375 = \frac{0.375}{1}$
② Since there are 3 digits to the right of the decimal point, multiply the numerator and the denominator by 1,000. $= \frac{375}{1000}$
③ Divide the numerator and denominator by the GCF. $= \frac{375 \div 125}{1000 \div 125}$
④ Simplify. $= \frac{3}{8}$

So $0.375 = \frac{3}{8}$.

Write each fraction in simplest form.

1. $\frac{16}{64}$ $\frac{1}{4}$
2. $\frac{-30}{48}$ $-\frac{5}{8}$
3. $\frac{42}{63}$ $\frac{2}{3}$
4. $\frac{-32}{40}$ $-\frac{4}{5}$
5. $\frac{12}{-28}$ $-\frac{3}{7}$
6. $\frac{18}{27}$ $\frac{2}{3}$

Write each fraction or mixed number as a decimal rounded to three decimal places.

7. $\frac{7}{9}$ 0.778
8. $-3\frac{2}{7}$ −3.286
9. $\frac{5}{9}$ 0.556
10. $5\frac{3}{7}$ 5.429
11. $\frac{4}{3}$ 1.333
12. $\frac{1}{11}$ 0.091

Write each decimal as a mixed number or fraction in simplest form.

13. 0.2 $\frac{1}{5}$
14. 0.16 $\frac{4}{25}$
15. 0.3 $\frac{3}{10}$
16. 2.75 $2\frac{3}{4}$
17. 4.52 $4\frac{13}{25}$
18. 0.36 $\frac{9}{25}$

Enrichment 2-2

Equivalent Forms of Rational Numbers L4

Critical Thinking

Place each number shown below in the correct column(s) in the table. Be careful: Some numbers might go into more than one column.

$\frac{4}{5}, \frac{9}{25}, 4, -50, -\frac{1}{2}, \frac{6}{20}, 2\frac{7}{10}, -3\frac{4}{5}, 0.36, -1, 16, 0.8, 0.3, 2.7, -3\frac{8}{10}, 25, -\frac{250}{5}$

1.

Whole Numbers	Integers	Rational Numbers	
4	4	4	$\frac{4}{5}$
16	16	16	$\frac{9}{25}$
25	25	25	$-\frac{1}{2}$
	−1	−1	$\frac{6}{20}$
	−50	−50	$2\frac{7}{10}$
		0.36	$-3\frac{4}{5}$
		0.8	$-3\frac{8}{10}$
		0.3	$-\frac{250}{5}$
		2.7	

2. There are 6 pairs of equivalent rational numbers in the table. List them below in order from smallest to largest.
   a. $-\frac{250}{5}$, −50
   b. $-3\frac{4}{5}$, $-3\frac{8}{10}$
   c. $\frac{6}{20}$, 0.3
   d. $\frac{9}{25}$, 0.36
   e. $\frac{4}{5}$, 0.8
   f. $2\frac{7}{10}$, 2.7

GO Online
Homework Video Tutor
Visit: PHSchool.com
Web Code: ase-0202

34. 0.25; $0.\overline{3}$; $0.1\overline{6}$; 0.25

34. The circle graph at the right shows the sizes of American households. Write a decimal for the fraction of households in each category.

Households by Size

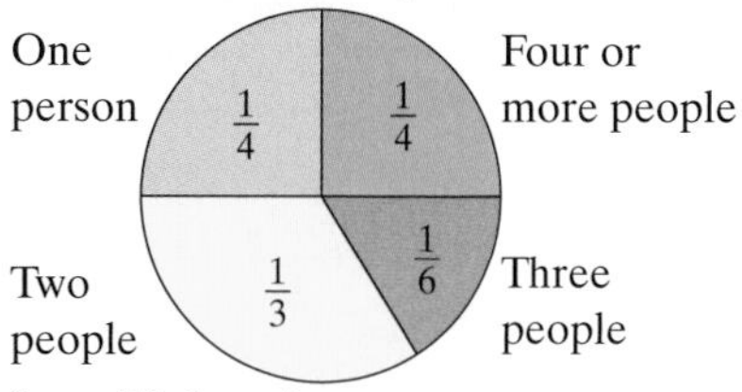

Source: U.S. Census Bureau

35. **Algebra** Evaluate $\frac{1 + a}{2b}$ for $a = 3$ and $b = -5$. Write your answer in simplest form. $-\frac{2}{5}$

Math in the Media **Refer to the cartoon below.**

36. If Leroy Lockhorn missed one of Loretta Lockhorn's birthdays in 25 years, what would his "batting average" be? .960

THE LOCKHORNS

"SO I MISSED ONE OF YOUR BIRTHDAYS IN 25 YEARS OF MARRIAGE. WHAT'S WRONG WITH A .980 BATTING AVERAGE?"

37. Answers may vary. Sample: He cannot forget just $\frac{1}{2}$ of a birthday.

37. **Writing in Math** Explain why, in 25 years of marriage, Leroy Lockhorn could never have a "batting average" of .980.

38. **Challenge** The number 77 is what fractional part of 7,777? $\frac{1}{101}$

Test Prep and Mixed Review

Practice

Multiple Choice

39. Tyler reads for 3 hours each day. There are 24 hours in a day. What fraction of each day does he spend reading? A
    Ⓐ $\frac{1}{8}$ Ⓑ $\frac{1}{21}$ Ⓒ $\frac{1}{27}$ Ⓓ $\frac{1}{72}$

40. Which list shows the numbers in order from least to greatest? J
    Ⓕ 1, 5, −11, −3 Ⓗ −3, −11, 1, 5
    Ⓖ 1, −3, 5, −11 Ⓙ −11, −3, 1, 5

41. Brandon simplified an expression as shown below.

$$4 + 16 \div 4 \times 2 - 6 \times 2 - 1$$

Step 1: $4 + 16 \div 8 - 6 \times 2 - 1$
Step 2: $4 + 16 \div 8 - 6 \times 1$
Step 3: $4 + 16 \div 8 - 6$
Step 4: $4 + 2 - 6$
Step 5: 0

In which step did Brandon make his first mistake? A
Ⓐ Step 1 Ⓑ Step 2 Ⓒ Step 3 Ⓓ Step 4

GO for Help

For Exercises	See Lesson
42–45	1-3

Simplify each expression.

42. $-19 + (-6)$ −25
43. $-11 + 20$ 9
44. $-25 - 25$ −50
45. $19 - (-15)$ 34

Test Prep

Resources

For additional practice with a variety of test item formats:

- Test-Taking Strategies, p. 97
- Test Prep, p. 101
- Test-Taking Strategies with Transparencies

Alternative Assessment

In small groups, students choose a digit from 1–9. Members use the digits to form a decimal to 3 places, such as 15.124. Then students work together to write the decimal as a fraction in simplest form. $15\frac{31}{250}$

2-2b Activity Lab

Repeating Decimals

In Lesson 2-2, you learned how to write a terminating decimal as a fraction. You use algebra to write a repeating decimal as a fraction.

EXAMPLE Writing a Repeating Decimal as a Fraction

In a recent survey, $0.\overline{45}$ of those asked chose blue as their favorite color. Write $0.\overline{45}$ as a fraction in simplest form.

Step 1 Represent the given decimal with a variable.

$n = 0.\overline{45}$

Step 2 Multiply by 10^n, where $n =$ the number of digits that repeat. In this case, multiply by 10^2, or 100, because the repeating part of the decimal is 45.

$100n = 45.\overline{45}$

Step 3 Subtract to eliminate the repeating part.

$$\begin{aligned} 100n &= 45.454545\ldots \\ -\ \ n &= -\ \ 0.454545\ldots && \leftarrow \text{Use the Subtraction Property of Equality.} \\ \hline 99n &= 45.000000\ldots && \leftarrow \text{Simplify.} \\ 99n &= 45 \end{aligned}$$

Step 4 Solve the new equation.

$$\frac{99n}{99} = \frac{45}{99} \qquad \leftarrow \text{Divide each side by 99.}$$

$$n = \frac{45}{99} = \frac{5}{11} \qquad \leftarrow \text{Simplify using the GCF, 9.}$$

The repeating decimal $0.\overline{45}$ equals $\frac{5}{11}$.

Exercises

Write each repeating decimal as a fraction in simplest form.

1. $0.\overline{5}$ $\frac{5}{9}$
2. $0.\overline{7}$ $\frac{7}{9}$
3. $0.\overline{24}$ $\frac{8}{33}$
4. $0.\overline{15}$ $\frac{5}{33}$
5. $0.\overline{135}$ $\frac{5}{37}$
6. $0.\overline{282}$ $\frac{94}{333}$
7. **Writing in Math** Explain why a repeating decimal is a rational number. Justify your answer with an example. See margin.

Activity Lab

Repeating Decimals

In this Activity, students learn to write a repeating decimal as a fraction.

Guided Instruction

Read through the Example with students. In Step 2 of this Example, make sure students understand that 100 is chosen as the mutiplier because there are two decimal places in the repeating portion. Multiplying by 10 two times will line up the repeating parts so they subtract to zero. Explain that you would multiply by 1,000 if the decimal were, for instance, $0.\overline{234}$.

Extend the activity to patterns that repeat for 6 digits. Have students write $\frac{1}{13}$, $\frac{2}{13}$, and $\frac{3}{13}$ as decimals.
$0.\overline{076923}$, $0.\overline{153846}$, $0.\overline{230769}$
Then have them predict what decimal is equivalent to $\frac{6}{13}$.
$0.\overline{461538}$

Technology Tip
Have students check their answers by dividing the numerator by the denominator using a calculator.

Differentiated Instruction

Visual Learners
In order to see patterns for repeating decimals, have students make a table showing the fractions $\frac{1}{11}, \frac{2}{11}, \frac{3}{11}, \cdots$ to $\frac{10}{11}$ and their equivalent decimals.

Resources

- a calculator

7. A repeating number is a rational number, because it can be written in the form $\frac{a}{b}$, where $b \neq 0$. For example, $0.\overline{1} = \frac{1}{9}$.

2-3

1. Plan

Objective
To use least common denominators, decimals, and number lines to compare and order rational numbers

Examples
1 Comparing Using the LCD
2 Comparing Using Decimals
3 Ordering Rational Numbers

Math Understandings: p. 50C

Professional Development

Math Background

You can compare fractions by using least common denominators. So $\frac{1}{3} > \frac{1}{4}$ because $\frac{4}{12} > \frac{3}{12}$. Because two fractions are represented as parts of the same whole, the fraction that represents the larger part is greater.

When you compare parts of *different* wholes (such as $\frac{1}{4}$ of 12 books 3 to $\frac{1}{3}$ of 6 books 2), you see that $\frac{1}{4}$ of 12 is greater. This is introduced in Example 2.

More Math Background: p. 50C

Lesson Planning and Resources

See p. 50E for a list of the resources that support this lesson.

PowerPoint

Bell Ringer Practice

Check Skills You'll Need
Use student page, transparency, or PowerPoint. For intervention, direct students to:

Equivalent Forms of Rational Numbers
Lesson 2-2
Extra Skills and Word Problems Practice, Ch. 2

2-3 Comparing and Ordering Rational Numbers

Check Skills You'll Need

1. **Vocabulary Review** Explain what the *numerator* of a fraction represents. See below.

Use the GCF to write each fraction in simplest form.

2. $\frac{12}{20}$ $\frac{3}{5}$
3. $\frac{15}{55}$ $\frac{3}{11}$
4. $\frac{16}{64}$ $\frac{1}{4}$
5. $\frac{50}{550}$ $\frac{1}{11}$

GO for Help Lesson 2-2

Check Skills You'll Need

1. The numerator represents a part of the whole.

What You'll Learn

To use least common denominators, decimals, and number lines to compare and order rational numbers

New Vocabulary least common multiple (LCM), least common denominator (LCD)

Why Learn This?

When you conduct a survey or do research, you often want to analyze and compare your results. The data you collect will be in the form of rational numbers.

You can compare rational numbers by finding a common denominator and then comparing the numerators. A common denominator is any common multiple of two denominators.

The **least common multiple (LCM)** of two or more numbers is the least multiple that is common to all of the numbers. The LCM of the denominators is called the **least common denominator (LCD).**

EXAMPLE Comparing Using the LCD

1 Which is greater, $\frac{4}{9}$ or $\frac{5}{12}$?

List multiples of each denominator to find their LCD.

Multiples of 9: 9, 18, 27, 36
Multiples of 12: 12, 24, 36

The LCM of 9 and 12 is 36. So the LCD of the fractions is 36.

$\frac{4}{9} = \frac{4 \cdot 4}{9 \cdot 4}$ ← Multiply the numerator and denominator by 4.
$= \frac{16}{36}$ ← Simplify.

$\frac{5}{12} = \frac{5 \cdot 3}{12 \cdot 3}$ ← Multiply the numerator and denominator by 3.
$= \frac{15}{36}$ ← Simplify.

Since $\frac{16}{36} > \frac{15}{36}$, $\frac{4}{9} > \frac{5}{12}$.

Quick Check

1. Rewrite $\frac{1}{6}$ and $\frac{1}{9}$ using their LCD. Which fraction is greater?

$\frac{3}{18}, \frac{2}{18}; \frac{1}{6}$ is greater.

Differentiated Instruction Solutions for All Learners

Special Needs L1	Below Level L2
Help students find the approximate locations of decimal numbers on a number line. Then have them characterize the numbers as less than zero, closest to 1, and so on, to help them grasp their relative value. learning style: visual	Have students cut 3 index cards into thirds, fourths, and eighths, and compare to see that a greater denominator means a smaller part. learning style: visual

When it is not easy to find a common denominator, you can write equivalent decimals.

EXAMPLE Comparing Using Decimals

2 **Surveys** A random group of middle-school students from two schools was asked which types of movies they preferred. Which school had the greater fraction of students who preferred adventure movies?

Change each fraction to a decimal. Compare the decimals.

School A: $\frac{37}{58} \approx 0.6379310$

School B: $\frac{45}{71} \approx 0.6338028$

} **Divide. Use a calculator.**

Since 0.637 > 0.633, School A had the greater fraction of students who preferred adventure movies.

Quick Check

2. At the local pet store, 7 out of 10 cats are male, and 12 out of 17 dogs are male. Which animal has the greater fraction of males? dogs; $\frac{12}{17} > \frac{7}{10}$

To order a set of rational numbers, write each number as a decimal.

EXAMPLE Ordering Rational Numbers

3 Order $\frac{5}{8}$, -0.37, 1, $-\frac{29}{40}$ and 0.3 from least to greatest.

Write each fraction as a decimal.

$\frac{5}{8} = 0.625$

$-\frac{29}{40} = -0.725$

Then graph each decimal on a number line.

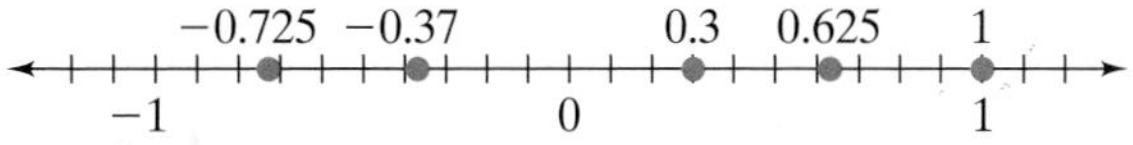

The order of the points from left to right gives the order of the numbers from least to greatest.

$-0.725 < -0.37 < 0.3 < 0.625 < 1$

So $-\frac{29}{40} < -0.37 < 0.3 < \frac{5}{8} < 1$.

Quick Check

3. Order $\frac{8}{5}$, $1\frac{1}{2}$, -0.625, $-\frac{7}{8}$, and 1.61 from least to greatest. $-\frac{7}{8}$, -0.625, $1\frac{1}{2}$, $\frac{8}{5}$, 1.61

Online active math

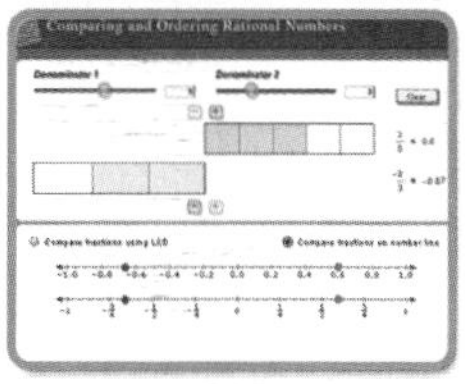

For: Rational Numbers Activity
Use: Interactive Textbook, 2-3

Advanced Learners L4

Have students quickly compare fractions by mentally comparing each fraction to $\frac{1}{2}$.

$\frac{475}{910}$ ■ $\frac{395}{823}$ > $\frac{147}{299}$ ■ $\frac{161}{314}$ <

$\frac{5{,}270}{9{,}615}$ ■ $\frac{30{,}421}{62{,}932}$ > $\frac{74}{136}$ ■ $\frac{21}{46}$ >

learning style: verbal

English Language Learners ELL

Students read LCM and LCD as least *common multiple* and *least common denominator* to help them keep track of the meaning of the abbreviations.

learning style: verbal

2. Teach

Activity Lab

Use before the lesson.

All in One Teaching Resources

Activity Lab 2-3: Comparing Fractions to Decimals

Guided Instruction

Example 1

Some students might observe that 5 > 4 and 12 > 9 and falsely conclude that $\frac{5}{12} > \frac{4}{9}$. Remind them that the fractions must have common denominators before they can compare numerators.

Alternative Method

Have students also compare fractions and decimals by converting all numbers to fractions.

PowerPoint

Additional Examples

1 Which is greater, $\frac{7}{18}$ or $\frac{5}{12}$? $\frac{5}{12}$

2 The Eagles won 7 out of 11 games while the Seals won 8 out of 12 games. Which team has the better record? Seals

3 Order -0.175, $\frac{2}{3}$, $-\frac{5}{8}$, 1.7, and -0.95 from least to greatest. -0.95, $-\frac{5}{8}$, -0.175, $\frac{2}{3}$, 1.7

All in One Teaching Resources

- Daily Notetaking Guide 2-3 L3
- Adapted Notetaking 2-3 L1

Closure

- *How do you compare two rational numbers when the denominators are alike?* The greater number has the greater numerator.
- *How do you compare two rational numbers when the denominators are different?* Sample: Find a common denominator and compare numerators or change each fraction into a decimal and compare them on a number line.

3. Practice

Assignment Guide

Check Your Understanding

Go over Exercises 1–6 in class before assigning the Homework Exercises.

Homework Exercises

A	Practice by Example	7–23
B	Apply Your Skills	24–33
C	Challenge	34
Test Prep and Mixed Review		35–40

Homework Quick Check

To check students' understanding of key skills and concepts, go over Exercises 15, 20, 25, 30, and 33.

Exercises

Remind students that comparing negative fractions or decimals is similar to comparing negative integers. The fraction or decimal with the greatest absolute value is the least.

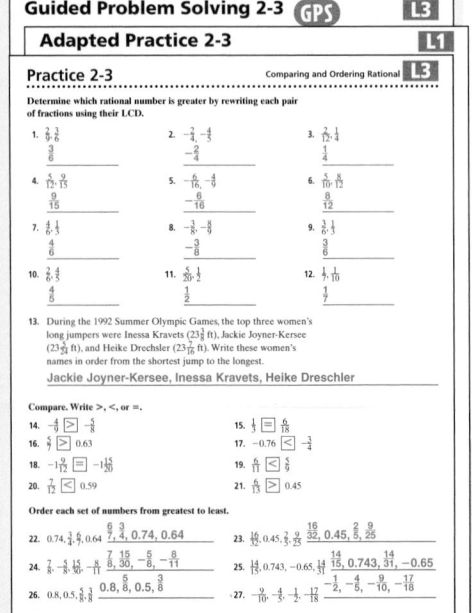

Differentiated Instruction Resources

Guided Problem Solving 2-3 GPS L3

Adapted Practice 2-3 L1

Practice 2-3 Comparing and Ordering Rational L3

Determine which rational number is greater by rewriting each pair of fractions using their LCD.

1. $\frac{2}{9}, \frac{3}{6}$ $\frac{3}{6}$
2. $-\frac{2}{4}, -\frac{4}{5}$ $-\frac{2}{4}$
3. $\frac{2}{12}, \frac{1}{4}$ $\frac{1}{4}$
4. $\frac{5}{12}, \frac{9}{15}$ $\frac{9}{15}$
5. $-\frac{6}{16}, -\frac{4}{9}$ $-\frac{6}{16}$
6. $\frac{5}{10}, \frac{8}{12}$ $\frac{8}{12}$
7. $\frac{4}{6}, \frac{1}{3}$ $\frac{4}{6}$
8. $-\frac{3}{8}, -\frac{8}{9}$ $-\frac{3}{8}$
9. $\frac{3}{6}, \frac{1}{3}$ $\frac{3}{6}$
10. $\frac{2}{6}, \frac{4}{5}$ $\frac{4}{5}$
11. $\frac{5}{20}, \frac{1}{2}$ $\frac{1}{2}$
12. $\frac{1}{7}, \frac{1}{10}$ $\frac{1}{7}$
13. During the 1992 Summer Olympic Games, the top three women's long jumpers were Inessa Kravets ($23\frac{3}{8}$ ft), Jackie Joyner-Kersee ($23\frac{5}{24}$ ft), and Heike Drechsler ($23\frac{7}{16}$ ft). Write these women's names in order from the shortest jump to the longest.
Jackie Joyner-Kersee, Inessa Kravets, Heike Dreschler

Compare. Write >, <, or =.

14. $-\frac{4}{9} > -\frac{5}{8}$
15. $\frac{1}{3} = \frac{6}{18}$
16. $\frac{5}{7} > 0.63$
17. $-0.76 < -\frac{3}{4}$
18. $-1\frac{9}{12} = -1\frac{15}{20}$
19. $\frac{6}{11} < \frac{5}{9}$
20. $\frac{7}{12} < 0.59$
21. $\frac{6}{13} > 0.45$

Order each set of numbers from greatest to least.

22. $0.74, \frac{3}{4}, \frac{6}{7}, 0.64$ $\frac{6}{7}, \frac{3}{4}, 0.74, 0.64$
23. $\frac{16}{32}, 0.45, \frac{2}{5}, \frac{9}{25}$ $\frac{16}{32}, 0.45, \frac{2}{5}, \frac{9}{25}$
24. $\frac{7}{8}, -\frac{5}{8}, \frac{15}{30}, -\frac{8}{11}$ $\frac{7}{8}, \frac{15}{30}, -\frac{5}{8}, -\frac{8}{11}$
25. $\frac{14}{15}, 0.743, -0.65, \frac{14}{31}$ $\frac{14}{15}, 0.743, \frac{14}{31}, -0.65$
26. $0.8, 0.5, \frac{5}{8}, \frac{3}{8}$ $0.8, \frac{5}{8}, 0.5, \frac{3}{8}$
27. $-\frac{9}{10}, -\frac{4}{5}, -\frac{1}{2}, -\frac{17}{18}$ $-\frac{1}{2}, -\frac{4}{5}, -\frac{9}{10}, -\frac{17}{18}$

Check Your Understanding

1. The LCM is the smallest number that is a multiple of both numbers.

1. **Vocabulary** What is the difference between a multiple of two numbers and the LCM of two numbers?
2. Is $\frac{15}{28}$ greater or less than $\frac{1}{2}$? Justify your answer. greater; $\frac{15}{28} > \frac{14}{28}$

Determine which rational number is greater by rewriting each pair of fractions with a common denominator.

3. $\frac{2}{9}, \frac{1}{7}$ $\frac{2}{9}$
4. $\frac{5}{7}, \frac{2}{3}$ $\frac{5}{7}$
5. $\frac{3}{4}, \frac{4}{5}$ $\frac{4}{5}$
6. Which rational number is the greatest: $-\frac{5}{12}$, -0.4, $-\frac{1}{2}$, or $-\frac{4}{9}$? -0.4

Homework Exercises

For more exercises, see Extra Skills and Word Problems.

GO for Help

For Exercises	See Examples
7–14	1
15–19	2
20–23	3

A **Determine which rational number is greater by rewriting each pair of fractions using their LCD.**

7. $\frac{2}{15}, \frac{4}{25}$ $\frac{4}{25}$
8. $\frac{2}{5}, \frac{4}{11}$ $\frac{2}{5}$
9. $-\frac{10}{21}, -\frac{5}{14}$ $-\frac{5}{14}$
10. $\frac{7}{8}, \frac{6}{7}$ $\frac{7}{8}$
11. $\frac{3}{8}, \frac{5}{12}$ $\frac{5}{12}$
12. $-\frac{6}{26}, -\frac{9}{39}$ equal
13. $-\frac{13}{22}, -\frac{14}{33}$ $-\frac{14}{33}$
14. $-\frac{9}{20}, -\frac{7}{15}$ $-\frac{9}{20}$
15. **Surveys** A survey found that 13 out of 108 men and 23 out of 233 women were left-handed. Which group had the greater fraction of left-handed people? men; $\frac{13}{108} > \frac{23}{233}$

Calculator **Which fraction is greater?**

16. $\frac{9}{13}, \frac{19}{28}$ $\frac{9}{13}$
17. $\frac{29}{17}, \frac{19}{11}$ $\frac{19}{11}$
18. $-\frac{11}{8}, -\frac{41}{30}$ $-\frac{41}{30}$
19. $-\frac{12}{19}, -\frac{17}{27}$ $-\frac{17}{27}$

Order each set of numbers from least to greatest.

20. $\frac{10}{13}, \frac{15}{19}, 0.8, -3.13$
21. $\frac{1}{3}, \frac{3}{10}, 0.03, 0.33$ $0.03, \frac{3}{10}, 0.33, \frac{1}{3}$
22. $-4, -3.9, -\frac{2}{9}, \frac{2}{11}$
23. $\frac{5}{7}, \frac{5}{3}, \frac{5}{6}, \frac{5}{2}$ $\frac{5}{7}, \frac{5}{6}, \frac{5}{3}, \frac{5}{2}$

20. $-3.13, \frac{10}{13}, \frac{15}{19}, 0.8$

22. $-4, -3.9, -\frac{2}{9}, \frac{2}{11}$

B GPS

24. **Guided Problem Solving** During lunch period A, 26 out of 52 students ate turkey sandwiches. During lunch period B, 21 out of 49 students ate turkey sandwiches. Which lunch period had a greater fraction of students who ate turkey sandwiches? A
    - The fraction of students from Lunch A who ate turkey sandwiches was ■.
    - The fraction of students from Lunch B who ate turkey sandwiches was ■.
25. **Number Sense** If 1 is added to the numerator and denominator of $\frac{5}{12}$, is the new number greater than or less than $\frac{5}{12}$? Explain.

25. Greater; check student's explanation.

30. Answers may vary. Sample: Change the fraction to a decimal and compare it to 0.5.

32. $\frac{5}{8}, \frac{5}{7}, \frac{5}{4}, \frac{5}{3}$; when the numerators are the same, the larger the denominator is, the smaller the value.

Online Homework Video Tutor
Visit: PHSchool.com
Web Code: ase-0203

Compare. Write <, >, or =.

26. $\frac{1}{8}$ ■ $\frac{5}{7}$ <

27. $-\frac{3}{8}$ ■ -0.375 =

28. $\frac{1}{4}$ ■ 0.025 >

29. -1 ■ $-\frac{9}{11}$ <

30. **Writing in Math** Explain how you can tell if a fraction is greater or less than $\frac{1}{2}$. See margin.

31. **Video Games** In a video game, you successfully completed 30 out of 55 levels. Your friend completed all but 7 out of 46 levels of another game. Who completed a greater fraction of a game? your friend

32. **Reasoning** Order $\frac{5}{3}$, $\frac{5}{8}$, $\frac{5}{4}$, and $\frac{5}{7}$ from least to greatest. Explain how you would order fractions with the same numerator *without* writing them as decimals or finding the LCD. See margin.

33. GPS Erika worked from 4:55 P.M. to 5:30 P.M. Maria worked $\frac{2}{3}$ of an hour. Who worked longer? Maria

34. C **Challenge** In the repeating decimal $0.\overline{365} = 0.365365365\ldots$, which digit is 100 places to the right of the decimal point? 3

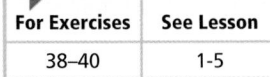

Test Prep and Mixed Review — Practice

Multiple Choice

35. The table shows the number of eighth-graders taught by four teachers, and the number of eighth-graders in each teacher's school. Which teacher taught the greatest fraction of his or her school's eighth-graders? D

Teacher	Mr. Alpert	Ms. Bee	Mr. Coe	Ms. Drew
Students Taught	7	20	12	37
Students in School	42	80	36	74

(A) Mr. Alpert (B) Ms. Bee (C) Mr. Coe (D) Ms. Drew

36. Adrianna spent 3 of the 7 dollars she had. Paul spent 4 of his 9 dollars. Jennifer spent 2 of her 4 dollars. Brian spent 5 of his 11 dollars. Who spent the third-greatest fraction of their money? J

(F) Adrianna (G) Brian (H) Jennifer (J) Paul

37. In the morning, the temperature was 58°F. By noon, the temperature had risen 14°F. After an afternoon rain, the temperature dropped 4°F, and then rose 2°F. The temperature rose 1°F just before sunset. What was the temperature at sunset? C

(A) 63°F (B) 67°F (C) 71°F (D) 79°F

GO for Help

For Exercises	See Lesson
38–40	1-5

Find each product.

38. $9(r - 7)$ $9r - 63$

39. $-8(-6 + b)$ $48 - 8b$

40. $(t - 4)10$ $10t - 40$

Online lesson quiz, PHSchool.com, Web Code: asa-0203

4. Assess & Reteach

PowerPoint Lesson Quiz

Compare. Use <, >, or =.

1. $\frac{5}{12}$ ■ $\frac{8}{15}$ <
2. $\frac{4}{5}$ ■ $\frac{8}{11}$ >
3. $\frac{15}{50}$ ■ $\frac{36}{120}$ =
4. $\frac{7}{20}$ ■ 0.35 =
5. Order 0.17, $\frac{1}{5}$, −0.3, 0, and $-\frac{1}{4}$ from least to greatest. $-0.3, -\frac{1}{4}, 0, 0.17, \frac{1}{5}$.
6. A survey found that 75 out of 125 men and 88 out of 136 women prefer comedy films over action films. Which group prefers comedy over action films more? women

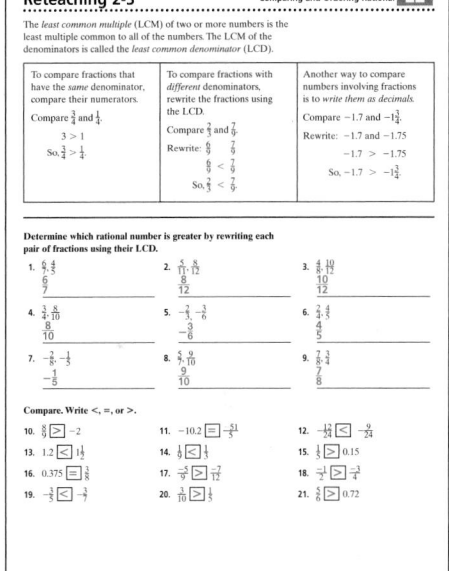

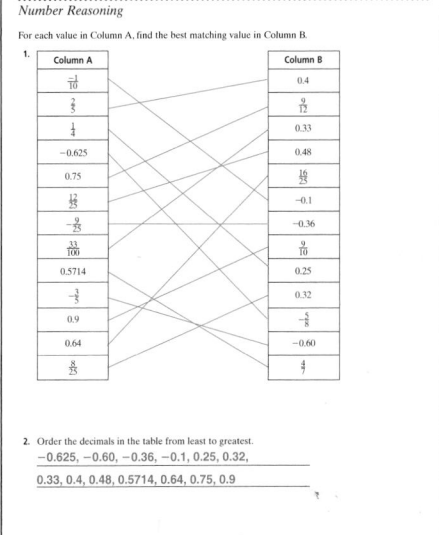

Reteaching 2-3 Comparing and Ordering Rational L2

The *least common multiple* (LCM) of two or more numbers is the least multiple common to all of the numbers. The LCM of the denominators is called the *least common denominator* (LCD).

To compare fractions that have the *same* denominator, compare their numerators. Compare $\frac{3}{4}$ and $\frac{1}{4}$. $3 > 1$ So, $\frac{3}{4} > \frac{1}{4}$.	To compare fractions with *different* denominators, rewrite the fractions using the LCD. Compare $\frac{2}{3}$ and $\frac{7}{9}$. Rewrite: $\frac{6}{9}$ $\frac{7}{9}$ $\frac{6}{9} < \frac{7}{9}$ So, $\frac{2}{3} < \frac{7}{9}$.	Another way to compare numbers involving fractions is to *write them as decimals.* Compare −1.7 and $-1\frac{3}{4}$. Rewrite: −1.7 and −1.75 $-1.7 > -1.75$ So, $-1.7 > -1\frac{3}{4}$.

Determine which rational number is greater by rewriting each pair of fractions using their LCD.

1. $\frac{6}{7}, \frac{4}{5}$ $\frac{6}{7}$
2. $\frac{5}{11}, \frac{8}{12}$ $\frac{8}{12}$
3. $\frac{4}{8}, \frac{10}{12}$ $\frac{10}{12}$
4. $\frac{3}{4}, \frac{8}{10}$ $\frac{8}{10}$
5. $-\frac{2}{3}, -\frac{3}{6}$ $-\frac{3}{6}$
6. $\frac{2}{4}, \frac{4}{5}$ $\frac{4}{5}$
7. $-\frac{2}{8}, -\frac{1}{5}$ $-\frac{1}{5}$
8. $\frac{5}{7}, \frac{9}{10}$ $\frac{9}{10}$
9. $\frac{7}{8}, \frac{3}{4}$ $\frac{7}{8}$

Compare. Write <, =, or >.

10. $\frac{8}{9}$ [>] -2
11. -10.2 [=] $\frac{-51}{5}$
12. $-\frac{12}{24}$ [<] $-\frac{9}{24}$
13. 1.2 [<] $1\frac{1}{2}$
14. $\frac{1}{9}$ [<] $\frac{1}{3}$
15. $\frac{1}{5}$ [>] 0.15
16. 0.375 [=] $\frac{3}{8}$
17. $\frac{-5}{9}$ [>] $\frac{-7}{12}$
18. $\frac{-1}{2}$ [>] $\frac{-3}{4}$
19. $-\frac{3}{5}$ [<] $-\frac{3}{7}$
20. $\frac{3}{10}$ [>] $\frac{1}{5}$
21. $\frac{5}{6}$ [>] 0.72

Enrichment 2-3 Comparing and Ordering Rational L4

Number Reasoning

For each value in Column A, find the best matching value in Column B.

1.

Column A	Column B
$\frac{-1}{10}$	0.4
$\frac{2}{5}$	$\frac{9}{12}$
$\frac{1}{4}$	0.33
−0.625	0.48
0.75	$\frac{16}{25}$
$\frac{12}{25}$	−0.1
$-\frac{9}{25}$	−0.36
$\frac{33}{100}$	$\frac{9}{10}$
0.5714	0.25
$-\frac{3}{5}$	0.32
0.9	$-\frac{5}{8}$
0.64	−0.60
$\frac{8}{25}$	$\frac{4}{7}$

2. Order the decimals in the table from least to greatest.
−0.625, −0.60, −0.36, −0.1, 0.25, 0.32,
0.33, 0.4, 0.48, 0.5714, 0.64, 0.75, 0.9

Alternative Assessment

Students write a paragraph identifying which method they prefer to use to compare fractions—using a least common denominator or using decimals. Then they justify their choice.

Test Prep

Resources
For additional practice with a variety of test item formats:
- Test-Taking Strategies, p. 97
- Test Prep, p. 101
- Test-Taking Strategies with Transparencies

2-4

1. Plan

Objective
To add and subtract fractions and mixed numbers and to solve problems involving rational numbers

Examples
1 Adding and Subtracting Fractions
2 Adding Mixed Numbers
3 Subtracting Mixed Numbers

Math Understandings: p. 50C

Professional Development

Math Background

Unlike multiplying two fractions, adding or subtracting fractions requires a common denominator. Using the LCD makes the calculations easier.

More Math Background: p. 50C

Lesson Planning and Resources

See p. 50E for a list of the resources that support this lesson.

PowerPoint

Bell Ringer Practice

Check Skills You'll Need
Use student page, transparency, or PowerPoint. For intervention, direct students to:
Adding and Subtracting Integers
Lesson 1-3
Extra Skills and Word Problems Practice, Ch. 1

2-4 Adding and Subtracting Rational Numbers

Check Skills You'll Need

1. **Vocabulary Review** Which numbers are *integers*: 2, 4.5, 0, −6, $\frac{1}{3}$? 2, 0, −6

Simplify each expression.

2. −9 − 1 −10
3. 10 − 100 −90
4. 12 + (−2) 10

GO for Help Lesson 1-3

What You'll Learn

To add and subtract fractions and mixed numbers and to solve problems involving rational numbers

Why Learn This?

Understanding how to add and subtract fractions allows you to make more accurate measurements. Carpenters, electricians, plumbers, and tailors all use fractions in their work.

To add or subtract fractions, rewrite them with a common denominator. You can use the LCD to make calculations easier.

EXAMPLES Adding and Subtracting Fractions

1 A cake recipe calls for $\frac{5}{8}$ cup of walnuts and $\frac{1}{2}$ cup of pecans. How many cups of nuts do you need?

$$\frac{5}{8} + \frac{1}{2} = \frac{5}{8} + \frac{1 \cdot 4}{2 \cdot 4} \quad \leftarrow \text{Write equivalent fractions with the same denominator.}$$

$$= \frac{5}{8} + \frac{4}{8} \quad \leftarrow \text{Simplify.}$$

$$= \frac{9}{8} \quad \leftarrow \text{Add the numerators.}$$

You need $\frac{9}{8}$, or $1\frac{1}{8}$, cups of nuts.

2 Find $\frac{1}{6} - \frac{4}{9}$.

The LCM of 6 and 9 is 18, so the LCD of $\frac{1}{6}$ and $\frac{4}{9}$ is 18.

$$\frac{1}{6} - \frac{4}{9} = \frac{3}{18} - \frac{8}{18} \quad \leftarrow \text{Write equivalent fractions using the LCD.}$$

$$= \frac{3-8}{18} = -\frac{5}{18} \quad \leftarrow \text{Subtract the numerators.}$$

Quick Check

1. Find $\frac{2}{15} + \frac{1}{10}$ by using $15 \cdot 10 = 150$ as the common denominator. $\frac{7}{30}$
2. Find $\frac{1}{10} - \frac{1}{4}$. $-\frac{3}{20}$

Differentiated Instruction Solutions for All Learners

Special Needs L1	Below Level L2
Before working on Examples 3 and 4, write a mixed number on the board and have students describe how to write this number as an improper fraction. learning style: verbal	Have students change between mixed numbers and improper fractions, and describe how they did this, with exercises such as these: $3\frac{1}{2}$ $\frac{7}{2}$ $5\frac{2}{3}$ $\frac{17}{3}$ $\frac{8}{3}$ $2\frac{2}{3}$ learning style: verbal

You can add or subtract mixed numbers by writing improper fractions. You can also add or subtract the integers and fractions separately.

EXAMPLE Adding Mixed Numbers

3 Find $3\frac{2}{3} + 5\frac{1}{2}$.

Estimate $3\frac{2}{3} + 5\frac{1}{2} \approx 4 + 6 = 10$

$3\frac{2}{3} + 5\frac{1}{2} = \frac{11}{3} + \frac{11}{2}$ ← Write each mixed number as an improper fraction.

$= \frac{22}{6} + \frac{33}{6}$ ← Write equivalent fractions using the LCD, 6.

$= \frac{55}{6}$ ← Add the numerators.

$= 9\frac{1}{6}$ ← Change the improper fraction to a mixed number.

Check for Reasonableness Since $9\frac{1}{6} \approx 10$, the answer is reasonable.

GO for Help
See Skills Handbook p. 638 for writing mixed numbers as improper fractions.

Quick Check

3. Find $4\frac{1}{5} + 2\frac{3}{4}$. $6\frac{19}{20}$

EXAMPLE Subtracting Mixed Numbers

4 **Multiple Choice** A spool holds 60 ft of TV cable. Installation for a house uses 23 ft 5 in. of cable. Which equation can be used to find the amount t of cable left?

Ⓐ $t = 60 + 23\frac{5}{12}$ Ⓒ $t = 60 - 23\frac{5}{12}$

Ⓑ $t = 23\frac{5}{12} + 60$ Ⓓ $t = 23\frac{5}{12} - 60$

To find the amount left, you *subtract* the amount used from the original amount. Since 5 in. $= \frac{5}{12}$ ft, the amount left is $60 - 23\frac{5}{12}$ ft.

The answer is C. You can find the amount left on the roll by subtracting.

$60 - 23\frac{5}{12} = 59\frac{12}{12} - 23\frac{5}{12}$ ← Rewrite 60 as $59 + \frac{12}{12}$, or 1.

$= 36\frac{7}{12}$ ← Subtract the integers: $59 - 23$. Then subtract the fractions: $\frac{12}{12} - \frac{5}{12}$.

The amount of cable left is $36\frac{7}{12}$ ft.

Test Prep Tip
Use estimation to check that your answer is reasonable.

Quick Check

4. **Weather** In 2000, a single storm dropped $20\frac{3}{10}$ in. of snow in North Carolina. The previous record was $17\frac{4}{5}$ in. in 1927. Write and solve an equation to find how much more snow fell in 2000 than in 1927.
$17\frac{4}{5} + x = 20\frac{3}{10}$; $x = 2\frac{1}{2}$ in.

2. Teach

Activity Lab

Use before the lesson.

All in One Teaching Resources

Activity Lab 2-4: Adding and Subtracting Rational Numbers

Guided Instruction

Example 1
Emphasize that you cannot add $\frac{5}{8}$ and $\frac{1}{2}$ without rewriting them both in terms of the same denominator.

Example 4
To help visual learners, draw a line segment on the board labeled 60 ft. Label one portion of the segment 23 ft 5 in., and the remaining portion *t*.

PowerPoint

Additional Examples

1. A recipe calls for $\frac{1}{3}$ cup white flour and $\frac{3}{4}$ cup wheat flour. How many total cups of flour are used? $1\frac{1}{12}$ c
2. Find $\frac{9}{10} - \frac{3}{4}$. $\frac{3}{20}$
3. Find $6\frac{3}{4} + 8\frac{2}{3}$. $15\frac{5}{12}$
4. On a 50-ft roll of cable, $15\frac{3}{4}$ ft are left. How many feet of cable were used? $34\frac{1}{4}$ ft

All in One Teaching Resources

- Daily Notetaking Guide 2-4 L3
- Adapted Notetaking 2-4 L1

Closure

- *How do you add or subtract fractions with different denominators?* Sample: Rewrite fractions using a least common denominator and add or subtract numerators.
- *How do you add or subtract mixed numbers?* Sample: Change the mixed numbers to improper fractions, find a least common denominator, add or subtract, and change the improper fraction to a mixed number if necessary.

Advanced Learners L4
Have students rewrite $\frac{1}{a} + \frac{1}{b}$ as a single fraction. Have students show their work and justify each step.
$\frac{1}{a} + \frac{1}{b} = \frac{b}{ab} + \frac{a}{ab} = \frac{a+b}{ab}$

learning style: verbal

English Language Learners ELL
For Example 4, help students identify the correct equation by having them identify what they know and what they are trying to find. Have them ask themselves these same questions as they complete the next problem independently.

learning style: verbal

3. Practice

Assignment Guide

Check Your Understanding
Go over Exercises 1–7 in class before assigning the Homework Exercises.

Homework Exercises

A	Practice by Example	8–28
B	Apply Your Skills	29–40
C	Challenge	41
	Test Prep and Mixed Review	42–46

Homework Quick Check
To check students' understanding of key skills and concepts, go over Exercises 10, 22, 30, 37, and 40.

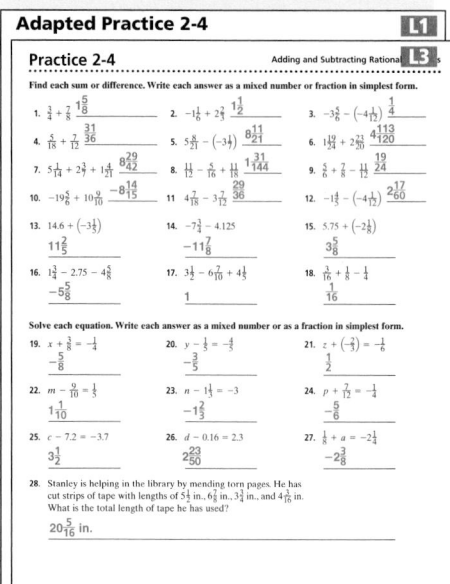

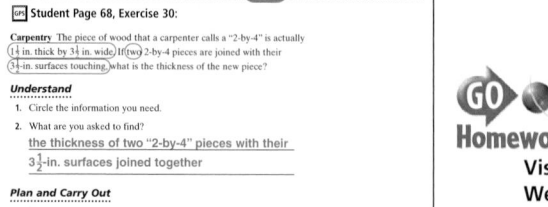

Differentiated Instruction Resources

Adapted Practice 2-4 L1

Practice 2-4 — Adding and Subtracting Rationals L3

Find each sum or difference. Write each answer as a mixed number or fraction in simplest form.

1. $\frac{3}{4} + \frac{7}{8}$ $1\frac{5}{8}$
2. $-1\frac{1}{6} + 2\frac{2}{3}$ $1\frac{1}{2}$
3. $-3\frac{5}{6} - \left(-4\frac{1}{12}\right)$ $\frac{1}{4}$
4. $\frac{5}{18} + \frac{7}{12}$ $\frac{31}{36}$
5. $5\frac{8}{21} - \left(-3\frac{1}{7}\right)$ $8\frac{11}{21}$
6. $1\frac{19}{24} + 2\frac{23}{20}$ $4\frac{113}{120}$
7. $5\frac{1}{14} + 2\frac{3}{7} + 1\frac{4}{21}$ $8\frac{29}{42}$
8. $\frac{11}{12} - \frac{5}{16} + \frac{11}{18}$ $1\frac{31}{144}$
9. $\frac{5}{6} + \frac{7}{8} - \frac{11}{12}$ $\frac{19}{24}$
10. $-19\frac{5}{6} + 10\frac{9}{10}$ $-8\frac{14}{15}$
11. $4\frac{7}{18} - 3\frac{7}{12}$ $\frac{29}{36}$
12. $-1\frac{4}{5} - \left(-4\frac{1}{12}\right)$ $2\frac{17}{60}$
13. $14.6 + \left(-3\frac{1}{5}\right)$ $11\frac{2}{5}$
14. $-7\frac{3}{4} - 4.125$ $-11\frac{7}{8}$
15. $5.75 + \left(-2\frac{1}{8}\right)$ $3\frac{5}{8}$
16. $1\frac{3}{4} - 2.75 - 4\frac{5}{8}$ $-5\frac{5}{8}$
17. $3\frac{1}{2} - 6\frac{7}{10} + 4\frac{1}{5}$ 1
18. $\frac{3}{16} + \frac{1}{8} - \frac{1}{4}$ $\frac{1}{16}$

Solve each equation. Write each answer as a mixed number or as a fraction in simplest form.

19. $x + \frac{3}{8} = -\frac{1}{4}$ $-\frac{5}{8}$
20. $y - \frac{1}{5} = -\frac{4}{5}$ $-\frac{3}{5}$
21. $z + \left(-\frac{2}{3}\right) = -\frac{1}{6}$ $\frac{1}{2}$
22. $m - \frac{9}{10} = \frac{1}{5}$ $1\frac{1}{10}$
23. $n - 1\frac{1}{3} = -3$ $-1\frac{2}{3}$
24. $p + \frac{7}{12} = -\frac{1}{4}$ $-\frac{5}{6}$
25. $c - 7.2 = -3.7$ $3\frac{1}{2}$
26. $d - 0.16 = 2.3$ $2\frac{23}{50}$
27. $\frac{1}{8} + a = -2\frac{1}{4}$ $-2\frac{3}{8}$
28. Stanley is helping in the library by mending torn pages. He has cut strips of tape with lengths of $5\frac{1}{2}$ in., $6\frac{7}{8}$ in., $3\frac{3}{4}$ in., and $4\frac{3}{16}$ in. What is the total length of tape he has used? $20\frac{5}{16}$ in.

2-4 • Guided Problem Solving GPS L3

GPS Student Page 68, Exercise 30:

Carpentry The piece of wood that a carpenter calls a "2-by-4" is actually $1\frac{1}{2}$ in. thick by $3\frac{1}{2}$ in. wide. If two 2-by-4 pieces are joined with their $3\frac{1}{2}$-in. surfaces touching, what is the thickness of the new piece?

Understand

1. Circle the information you need.
2. What are you asked to find? the thickness of two "2-by-4" pieces with their $3\frac{1}{2}$-in. surfaces joined together

Plan and Carry Out

3. What operation needs to be performed with the fractions? addition
4. Write an expression to show the operation that is to be performed. $1\frac{1}{2} + 1\frac{1}{2}$
5. Do the fractions have a common denominator? yes
6. Add the whole numbers and add the fractions. $(1 + 1) + (\frac{1}{2} + \frac{1}{2})$
7. Simplify and change the improper fraction to a mixed number. $2 + \frac{2}{2} = 2 + 1 = 3$ inches

Check

8. Does your answer make sense? Could you do the problem another way? Yes; you could multiply $2 \times 1\frac{1}{2} = 3$ in.

Solve Another Problem

9. It rained $5\frac{1}{2}$ inches in June and $4\frac{1}{4}$ inches in July. What was the total rainfall for the months of June and July? $5\frac{1}{2} + 4\frac{1}{4} = 5\frac{2}{4} + 4\frac{1}{4} = 9\frac{3}{4}$ inches

Check Your Understanding

Find the LCD for each pair of fractions.

1. $\frac{1}{2}, \frac{1}{10}$ 10
2. $\frac{1}{3}, \frac{1}{5}$ 15
3. $\frac{1}{4}, \frac{1}{14}$ 28

Find each sum or difference. Write your answer in simplest form.

4. $\frac{5}{8} + \left(-\frac{7}{8}\right)$ $-\frac{1}{4}$
5. $\frac{5}{6} - \frac{2}{6}$ $\frac{1}{2}$
6. $3\frac{1}{3} + 2\frac{4}{5}$ $6\frac{2}{15}$
7. **Reasoning** Without simplifying the expression, determine whether $\frac{1}{50} - \frac{1}{51}$ is a positive or a negative number. Explain.

7. Positive; $51 > 50$, so $\frac{1}{51} < \frac{1}{50}$, and $\frac{1}{50} - \frac{1}{51}$ is positive.

Homework Exercises

For more exercises, see Extra Skills and Word Problems.

GO for Help

For Exercises	See Examples
8–19	1 and 2
20–27	3
28	4

A **Use common denominators to find each sum or difference.**

8. $\frac{1}{7} + \frac{2}{3}$ $\frac{17}{21}$
9. $\frac{7}{8} + \frac{1}{5}$ $1\frac{3}{40}$
10. $-\frac{2}{7} + \left(-\frac{2}{5}\right)$
11. $\frac{2}{5} + \frac{2}{3}$ $1\frac{1}{15}$
12. $\frac{1}{10} + \frac{1}{9}$ $\frac{19}{90}$
13. $-\frac{1}{9} + \left(-\frac{5}{6}\right)$
14. $\frac{5}{12} + \frac{1}{9}$ $\frac{19}{36}$
15. $\frac{2}{3} - \frac{2}{9}$ $\frac{4}{9}$
16. $\frac{2}{7} - \frac{2}{21}$ $\frac{4}{21}$
17. $\frac{9}{10} - \frac{4}{5}$ $\frac{1}{10}$
18. $\frac{2}{15} - \frac{1}{10}$ $\frac{1}{30}$
19. $\frac{3}{10} - \frac{11}{15}$ $-\frac{13}{30}$

10. $-\frac{24}{35}$
13. $-\frac{17}{18}$

Find each sum or difference. Write your answer in simplest form.

20. $3\frac{5}{6} - \left(-\frac{2}{3}\right)$
21. $\frac{3}{4} - \left(-2\frac{5}{12}\right)$
22. $1\frac{1}{15} - \left(-\frac{5}{60}\right)$
23. $-2\frac{1}{8} - 4\frac{1}{4}$
24. $-4\frac{2}{3} - 6\frac{1}{4}$
25. $-5\frac{1}{2} + 8\frac{2}{3}$
26. $-7\frac{2}{5} + \left(-\frac{3}{4}\right)$
27. $7\frac{4}{5} + 11\frac{1}{3}$

20–27. See left.

20. $4\frac{1}{2}$
21. $3\frac{1}{6}$
22. $1\frac{3}{20}$
23. $-6\frac{3}{8}$
24. $-10\frac{11}{12}$
25. $3\frac{1}{6}$
26. $-8\frac{3}{20}$
27. $19\frac{2}{15}$

28. **Weather** It snowed $6\frac{3}{5}$ in. during the first three months of the year. It didn't snow again until December. The total snowfall for the year was $7\frac{1}{2}$ in. Find the December snowfall. $\frac{9}{10}$ in.

B GPS

29. **Guided Problem Solving** A group of students was asked which computer activity occupied the most time: e-mailing, playing games, or burning CDs. One half of the students chose e-mailing, and $\frac{1}{10}$ of the students chose burning CDs. What fraction of the students chose playing games? $\frac{2}{5}$
   - **Understand the Problem** Read the problem again. What information is given? What information is missing?
   - **Check Your Answer** Look at your work and compare it against the information in the problem. Is your answer reasonable?

30. **Carpentry** The piece of wood that a carpenter calls a "2-by-4" is actually $1\frac{1}{2}$ in. thick by $3\frac{1}{2}$ in. wide. If two 2-by-4 pieces are joined with their $3\frac{1}{2}$-in. surfaces touching, what is the thickness of the new piece? 3 in.

GPS

GO Online
Homework Video Tutor
Visit: PHSchool.com
Web Code: ase-0204

Algebra **Solve each equation for x when $a = \frac{1}{2}$, $b = \frac{1}{3}$, and $c = \frac{1}{4}$. Write each answer in simplest form.**

31. $a + x = 3$ $2\frac{1}{2}$

32. $2\frac{1}{6} + x = -b$ $-2\frac{1}{2}$

33. $c + x = \frac{1}{8}$ $-\frac{1}{8}$

34. $x - a = c$ $\frac{3}{4}$

35. $-5\frac{1}{2} + x = 2 + a$ 8

36. $x - 1\frac{1}{2} = b$ $1\frac{5}{6}$

39. Answers may vary. Sample: $\frac{1}{2} + \frac{1}{3} = \frac{5}{6}$; $\frac{1}{2+3} = \frac{1}{5}$

37. Student Council The student council needs $\frac{2}{3}$ of its members to vote favorably for a motion in order for it to pass. Currently, $\frac{2}{7}$ of the members are in favor of a certain motion. What additional fraction of the council needs to be in favor of the motion in order for it to pass? $\frac{8}{21}$

38. Golf The diameter of a golf ball is $1\frac{2}{3}$ in., and the diameter of a hole is $4\frac{1}{4}$ in. Find the difference between the two diameters. $2\frac{7}{12}$ in.

39. Error Analysis A student adds $\frac{1}{a} + \frac{1}{b}$ and says the answer is $\frac{1}{a+b}$. Give an example that shows the student is incorrect. See left.

40. Writing in Math Explain why you do *not* have to change mixed numbers to improper fractions before you find the LCD. See left.

40. You can rewrite all of the fractions using the LCD. Then add the integers together and add the fractions together. Simplify.

Ⓒ **41. Challenge** If $b = a + \frac{1}{3}$, what is the value of $b - 1$ in terms of a? $a - \frac{2}{3}$

Test Prep and Mixed Review

Practice

Multiple Choice

42. Miguel recorded the distance he ran each day last week. What is the total number of miles he ran last week? C

Ⓐ $9\frac{1}{4}$ Ⓒ $9\frac{7}{20}$

Ⓑ $9\frac{3}{10}$ Ⓓ $9\frac{2}{5}$

Day	Distance (mi)
Monday	$1\frac{1}{2}$
Tuesday	$2\frac{1}{10}$
Wednesday	$\frac{3}{4}$
Thursday	$3\frac{1}{5}$
Friday	$1\frac{4}{5}$

43. How many integers are greater than $\frac{9}{37}$ and less than $\frac{37}{9}$? H

Ⓕ 2 Ⓗ 4

Ⓖ 3 Ⓙ 5

44. Emilio is marking a flagpole using colored tape. The red tape is halfway up the pole. The blue tape is $\frac{7}{11}$ of the way up the pole. The white tape is $\frac{5}{9}$ of the way up the pole. The green tape is $\frac{4}{5}$ of the way up the pole. What color tape is highest on the flagpole? B

Ⓐ Blue Ⓑ Green Ⓒ Red Ⓓ White

GO for Help

For Exercises	See Lesson
45–46	2-3

Order each set of numbers from least to greatest.

45. $0.8, \frac{1}{125}, 0.808, \frac{22}{25}$

$\frac{1}{125}, 0.8, 0.808, \frac{22}{25}$

46. $-2\frac{33}{50}, -2\frac{3}{50}, -2.006, -2.6$

$-2\frac{33}{50}, -2.6, -2\frac{3}{50}, -2.006$

Alternative Assessment

Each student in a pair writes a mixed number. Partners add the numbers and write the sum in simplest form. Then partners use the original mixed numbers to write and solve a subtraction problem.

Test Prep

Resources

For additional practice with a variety of test item formats:

- Test-Taking Strategies, p. 97
- Test Prep, p. 101
- Test-Taking Strategies with Transparencies

4. Assess & Reteach

PowerPoint

Lesson Quiz

Find each sum or difference.

1. $\frac{8}{9} - \frac{5}{9}$ $\frac{1}{3}$
2. $\frac{4}{5} + \frac{2}{3}$ $1\frac{7}{15}$
3. $\frac{7}{8} - \frac{1}{2}$ $\frac{3}{8}$
4. $4\frac{5}{6} - 1\frac{1}{4}$ $3\frac{7}{12}$
5. It snowed $2\frac{1}{2}$ in. on top of $4\frac{1}{2}$ in. of snow already on the ground. How deep is the snow now? 7 in.

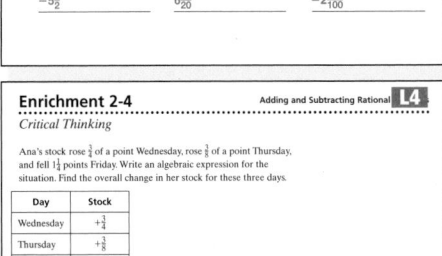

Reteaching 2-4

Adding and Subtracting Rational **L2**

To add or subtract fractions and mixed numbers with unlike denominators, first rewrite the fractions using the least common denominator (LCD).

Subtract: $2\frac{3}{4} - 5\frac{1}{3}$

$2\frac{3}{4} - 5\frac{1}{3} = \frac{11}{4} - \frac{16}{3}$

$= \frac{33}{12} - \frac{64}{12}$ ← The LCD is 12.

$= \frac{-31}{12}$ ← Subtract numerators.

$= -2\frac{7}{12}$ ← Simplify.

$2\frac{3}{4} - 5\frac{1}{3} = -2\frac{7}{12}$

You can use addition or subtraction to solve equations with rational numbers.

Solve: $h - \frac{3}{8} = \frac{1}{6}$

$h - \frac{3}{8} + \frac{3}{8} = \frac{1}{6} + \frac{3}{8}$ ← Add $\frac{3}{8}$.

$h = \frac{4}{24} + \frac{9}{24}$ ← The LCD is 24.

$h = \frac{13}{24}$

Find each sum or difference as a fraction or mixed number in simplest form.

1. $6\frac{1}{4} - 2\frac{3}{8}$ $3\frac{7}{8}$
2. $\frac{5}{6} + \left(-\frac{1}{2}\right)$ $\frac{1}{3}$
3. $\frac{1}{8} - \left(-\frac{1}{6}\right)$ $\frac{7}{24}$
4. $-1\frac{3}{8} - 4\frac{1}{12}$ $-5\frac{11}{24}$
5. $1\frac{5}{8} - \left(-2\frac{1}{2}\right)$ $4\frac{1}{8}$
6. $-2\frac{1}{3} - \left(-1\frac{5}{12}\right)$ $-\frac{11}{12}$
7. $1\frac{1}{3} - 4\frac{3}{4}$ $-3\frac{5}{12}$
8. $9 + \left(-6\frac{5}{9}\right)$ $2\frac{4}{9}$
9. $-2\frac{5}{6} - 5\frac{5}{12}$ $-8\frac{1}{4}$

Solve each equation. Write each answer as a mixed number or as a fraction in simplest form.

10. $y + \frac{7}{8} = -\frac{1}{4}$ $-1\frac{1}{8}$
11. $c + -\frac{3}{5} = \frac{1}{2}$ $1\frac{1}{10}$
12. $m - 3\frac{2}{3} = 1\frac{1}{6}$ $4\frac{5}{6}$
13. $x - 2\frac{1}{4} = -3$ $-\frac{3}{4}$
14. $n + \frac{1}{2} = -2\frac{5}{6}$ $-3\frac{1}{3}$
15. $\frac{1}{2} + d = -3\frac{1}{5}$ $-3\frac{7}{10}$
16. $7.3 + g = 1\frac{4}{5}$ $-5\frac{1}{2}$
17. $y - 4.1 = 2\frac{3}{4}$ $6\frac{17}{20}$
18. $z + 2.6 = 0.37$ $-2\frac{23}{100}$

Enrichment 2-4

Adding and Subtracting Rational **L4**

Critical Thinking

Ana's stock rose $\frac{3}{4}$ of a point Wednesday, rose $\frac{3}{8}$ of a point Thursday, and fell $1\frac{1}{4}$ points Friday. Write an algebraic expression for the situation. Find the overall change in her stock for these three days.

Day	Stock
Wednesday	$+\frac{3}{4}$
Thursday	$+\frac{3}{8}$
Friday	$-1\frac{1}{4}$

1. Would a rising stock price be a positive or a negative number? positive
2. Would a falling stock price be a positive or a negative number? negative
3. Write an expression for the change in stock price. Sample answer: $\frac{3}{4} + \frac{3}{8} + (-1\frac{1}{4})$
4. Simplify your expression. $-\frac{1}{8}$
5. What is the overall change in stock price? down $\frac{1}{8}$ of a point
6. The following week Ana's stock fell $\frac{1}{8}$ of a point on Monday and rose $\frac{3}{4}$ of a point on Tuesday. Write an expression for the change in stock price on Monday and Tuesday. Sample answer: $-\frac{1}{8} + \frac{3}{4}$
7. Simplify your expression. $\frac{5}{8}$
8. Write and simplify an expression for the change in stock price from Wednesday to Tuesday. Sample answer: $\frac{3}{4} + \frac{3}{8} + (-1\frac{1}{4}) + (-\frac{1}{8}) + \frac{3}{4}$; $\frac{1}{2}$

Checkpoint Quiz

Use this Checkpoint Quiz to check students' understanding of the skills and concepts of Lessons 2-1 through 2-4.

Resources

- All in One Teaching Resources Checkpoint Quiz 1
- ExamView Assessment Suite CD-ROM
- Success Tracker Online Intervention

MATH GAMES

Force Out!

In this game, students use mental math to name composite numbers and their factors.

Guided Instruction

Before students play the game, review composite and prime numbers with them.

Ask:

- *What is a number called if its only factors are the number itself and 1?* a prime number
- *What is a number called if it has more than two factors?* a composite number

Checkpoint Quiz 1

Lessons 2-1 through 2-4

1. Find the prime factorization of 504. $2 \cdot 2 \cdot 2 \cdot 3 \cdot 3 \cdot 7$
2. What is the GCF of 99 and 132? 33
3. **Baseball** Find the batting average of a hitter with 8 hits in 27 times at bat. .296
4. Write 0.56 as a fraction in simplest form. $\frac{14}{25}$
5. Order the following numbers from least to greatest: $\frac{8}{25}, -\frac{15}{7}, 0.35, 2, -2.6$ $-2.6, -\frac{15}{7}, \frac{8}{25}, 0.35, 2$

Simplify each expression.

6. $\frac{2}{3} + \frac{1}{9}$ $\frac{7}{9}$
7. $5 - \frac{2}{5}$ $4\frac{3}{5}$
8. $-2\frac{1}{6} + \frac{5}{24}$ $-1\frac{23}{24}$
9. $2\frac{4}{5} - 5\frac{1}{4}$ $-2\frac{9}{20}$
10. **Cooking** A cook needs $1\frac{1}{2}$ cups of sugar. The cook has $\frac{3}{8}$ cup. How many more cups of sugar does the cook need? $1\frac{1}{8}$ cups

MATH GAMES

Force Out!

What You'll Need

Three or more players

How To Play

- The first player says a composite number.
- The next player chooses a factor of the previous player's number that is less than the number.
- The second player subtracts the factor from the number and says the result.
- The game continues with each player subtracting a factor from the previous player's number.
- The game ends when a player says "one." That player wins.

Player Thinks	Player Says
18	"eighteen"
$18 = 6 \cdot 3$ $18 - 6 = 12$	"twelve"
$12 = 4 \cdot 3$ $12 - 3 = 9$	"nine"

2-5a Activity Lab

Modeling Fraction Multiplication

You can shade grids to model fraction multiplication. Use one color to represent the first fraction. Use another color to represent the second fraction. The overlap represents the product.

EXAMPLE Multiplying Rational Numbers

Use models to multiply $\frac{3}{4}$ by $\frac{9}{10}$.

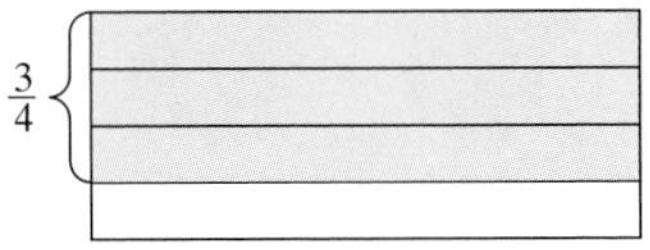

← **Shade 3 out of 4 rows red to model $\frac{3}{4}$.**

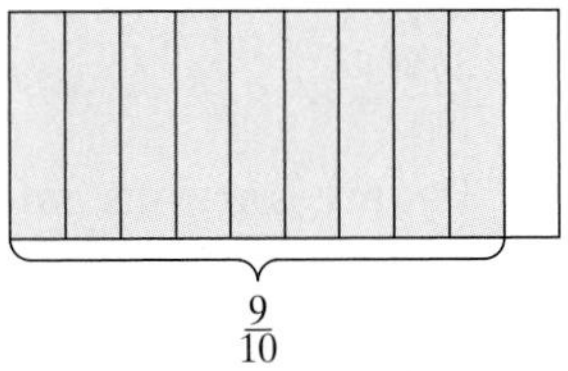

← **Shade 9 out of 10 columns blue to model $\frac{9}{10}$.**

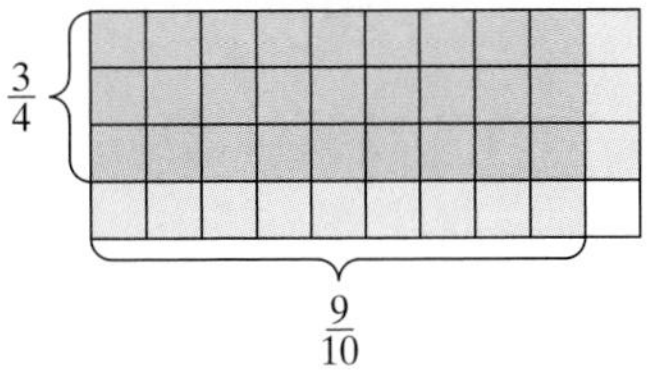

← **To find the product, model both fractions in one rectangle. 27 out of 40 squares are purple.**

So $\frac{3}{4} \cdot \frac{9}{10} = \frac{27}{40}$.

Exercises

6. $\frac{2}{5} \cdot \frac{3}{7} = \frac{6}{35}$

Use models to find each product.

1. $\frac{1}{2} \cdot \frac{5}{6}$ $\frac{5}{12}$
2. $\frac{3}{4} \cdot \frac{1}{5}$ $\frac{3}{20}$
3. $\frac{2}{3} \cdot \frac{3}{8}$ $\frac{1}{4}$
4. $\frac{3}{10} \cdot \frac{4}{9}$ $\frac{2}{15}$
5. $\frac{1}{4} \cdot \frac{1}{4}$ $\frac{1}{16}$
6. Write a numeric equation to represent the model at the right. See above.
7. Write a multiplication expression for the numerator of the product of $\frac{3}{4}$ and $\frac{9}{10}$. $3 \cdot 9 = 27$
8. Write a multiplication expression for the denominator of the product of $\frac{3}{4}$ and $\frac{9}{10}$. $4 \cdot 10 = 40$

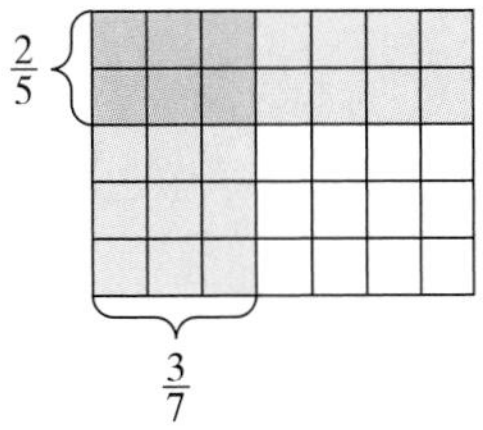

Activity Lab

Modeling Fraction Multiplication

Students use rectangles drawn on grid paper to model fraction multiplication.

Guided Instruction

Example

Model the Example by sketching the 4-unit × 10-unit grid on the chalkboard. Use crosshatching in one direction to "shade" $\frac{3}{4}$, and crosshatching in another direction for $\frac{9}{10}$. The product is shown by the part of the rectangle that has cross-hatching in both directions.

Teaching Tip

Have students draw rectangles on grid paper using the denominators of the fractions they are multiplying as the dimensions of the rectangle. For example, to model Exercise 1, students will use a 2-unit × 6-unit rectangle.

Differentiated Instruction

Visual Learners

Ask: *How does this model show that the product of two fractions less than 1 will always be less than 1?* Sample: When you shade both factors, the overlapping area will always be smaller than the whole rectangle, so it is less than 1.

Resources

- Activity Lab 2-5: Multiplying Rational Numbers
- grid paper

2-5

1. Plan

Objective
To multiply and divide fractions and mixed numbers and to solve problems involving rational numbers

Examples
1 Multiplying Rational Numbers
2 Dividing Rational Numbers
3 Solving Equations by Multiplying

Math Understandings: p. 50D

Professional Development

Math Background

Students often find multiplying fractions easier than dividing them. To divide by a fraction, change the divisor to its reciprocal and then multiply. Dividing by fractions is often less intuitive than multiplying. When multiplying or dividing mixed numbers, first rewrite each number as an improper fraction.

More Math Background: p. 50D

Lesson Planning and Resources

See p. 50E for a list of the resources that support this lesson.

PowerPoint

Bell Ringer Practice

Check Skills You'll Need
Use student page, transparency, or PowerPoint. For intervention, direct students to:
Equivalent Forms of Rational Numbers
Lesson 2-2
Extra Skills and Word Problems Practice, Ch. 2

2-5 Multiplying and Dividing Rational Numbers

Check Skills You'll Need

1. **Vocabulary Review** A *rational number* can be written in the form ■, where $b \neq 0$. $\frac{a}{b}$

Write each fraction in simplest form.

2. $\frac{7}{21}$ $\frac{1}{3}$
3. $\frac{12}{20}$ $\frac{3}{5}$
4. $\frac{9}{81}$ $\frac{1}{9}$
5. $\frac{36}{66}$ $\frac{6}{11}$

GO for Help Lesson 2-2

What You'll Learn

To multiply and divide fractions and mixed numbers and to solve problems involving rational numbers

New Vocabulary reciprocals, multiplicative inverse

Why Learn This?

Sometimes objects need to be divided into smaller pieces. For example, when you divide 3 apples into four sections each, you get 12 smaller pieces. Dividing 3 by $\frac{1}{4}$ is the same as multiplying 3 by 4.

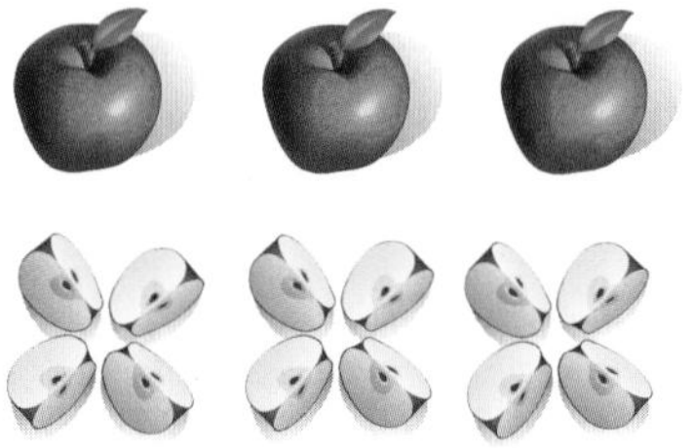

To find the product of rational numbers that are fractions, multiply the numerators and multiply the denominators.

EXAMPLES Multiplying Rational Numbers

1 Find $-\frac{5}{8} \cdot \frac{7}{15}$.

$$-\frac{5}{8} \cdot \frac{7}{15} = -\frac{5 \cdot 7}{8 \cdot 15} \quad \leftarrow \text{Multiply the numerators. Multiply the denominators.}$$

$$= -\frac{\cancel{5}^{1} \cdot 7}{8 \cdot \cancel{15}_{3}} \quad \leftarrow \text{Divide the numerator and denominator by their GCF, 5.}$$

$$= -\frac{7}{24} \quad \leftarrow \text{Simplify.}$$

2 Find the product $-2\frac{1}{4} \cdot \left(-3\frac{3}{5}\right)$.

$$-2\frac{1}{4} \cdot \left(-3\frac{3}{5}\right) = -\frac{9}{4} \cdot \left(-\frac{18}{5}\right) \quad \leftarrow \text{Write as improper fractions.}$$

$$= \frac{9 \cdot \cancel{18}^{9}}{{}_{2}\cancel{4} \cdot 5} \quad \leftarrow \text{Divide the numerator and denominator by their GCF, 2.}$$

$$= \frac{81}{10} = 8\frac{1}{10} \quad \leftarrow \text{Simplify. Write as a mixed number.}$$

Quick Check

Find each product. Write the answer in simplest form.

1. $-\frac{4}{5} \cdot \left(-\frac{3}{8}\right)$ $\frac{3}{10}$
2. $2\frac{1}{10} \cdot \left(-1\frac{2}{5}\right)$ $-2\frac{47}{50}$

Differentiated Instruction Solutions for All Learners

Special Needs L1	**Below Level** L2
Students practice finding the reciprocal of fractions, including fractions equal to or greater than whole numbers. Then they multiply a number and its reciprocal. Elicit the fact that the product of a fraction and its reciprocal is always 1. learning style: verbal	Ask: *To find $\frac{1}{2}$ of a number, you divide by what number?* 2 *To find $\frac{1}{3}$, divide by what number?* 3 *To find $\frac{2}{3}$, divide by 3 and multiply by what number?* 2 learning style: verbal

Two numbers with a product of 1 are called **reciprocals.** The reciprocal of $\frac{a}{b}$ is $\frac{b}{a}$, where $a \neq 0$ and $b \neq 0$. The reciprocal of a number is also called its **multiplicative inverse.** Remember that dividing by a fraction is the same as multiplying by the reciprocal of the fraction.

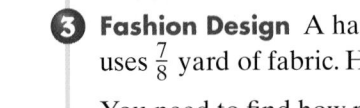

GO Online

Video Tutor Help
Visit: PHSchool.com
Web Code: ase-0775

EXAMPLE Dividing Rational Numbers

3 **Fashion Design** A handbag designer has $15\frac{1}{2}$ yards of fabric. Each bag uses $\frac{7}{8}$ yard of fabric. How many bags can the designer make?

You need to find how many $\frac{7}{8}$-yard pieces there are in $15\frac{1}{2}$ yards. Divide $15\frac{1}{2}$ by $\frac{7}{8}$.

$15\frac{1}{2}$			
$\frac{7}{8}$	$\frac{7}{8}$	. . .	$\frac{7}{8}$

$15\frac{1}{2} \div \frac{7}{8} = \frac{31}{2} \div \frac{7}{8}$ ← Write the mixed number as an improper fraction.

$= \frac{31}{2} \cdot \frac{8}{7}$ ← Multiply by the reciprocal of $\frac{7}{8}$.

$= \frac{248}{14}$ ← Multiply.

$= 17\frac{5}{7}$ ← Write as a mixed number.

Since no one can make $\frac{5}{7}$ of a bag, the designer can make only 17 bags.

Check for Reasonableness Round $15\frac{1}{2}$ to 16 and $\frac{7}{8}$ to 1. Then $16 \div 1 = 16$, which is close to 17. The answer is reasonable.

Quick Check

3. **Sewing** You have $13\frac{3}{4}$ yards of material to cut into $2\frac{1}{2}$-yard lengths. How many lengths can you cut from the material? 5 lengths

You can use reciprocals to solve equations involving multiplication.

EXAMPLE Solving Equations by Multiplying

4 Solve $\frac{4}{5}x = -\frac{9}{10}$.

$\frac{4}{5}x = -\frac{9}{10}$

$\frac{^1\cancel{5}}{_1\cancel{4}} \cdot \frac{\cancel{4}^1}{\cancel{5}_1}x = \frac{^1\cancel{5}}{4} \cdot \left(-\frac{9}{\cancel{10}_2}\right)$ ← Multiply each side by the reciprocal of $\frac{4}{5}$.

$1x = -\frac{1 \cdot 9}{4 \cdot 2}$ ← Multiply the numerators and the denominators.

$x = -\frac{9}{8} = -1\frac{1}{8}$ ← Simplify. Write the fraction as a mixed number.

Quick Check

4. Solve the equation $\frac{3}{7}p = 3\frac{1}{2}$. $8\frac{1}{6}$

2. Teach

Activity Lab

Use before the lesson.
Student Edition
Activity Lab 2-5a, Modeling Fraction Multiplication, p. 71

All in One Teaching Resources

Activity Lab 2-5: Multiplying Rational Numbers

Guided Instruction

Example 1
Review using the GCF to simplify or "cancel" fractions when multiplying.

Example 2
Ask:
- *What is the sign for the product of two numbers with unlike signs?* negative
- *What is the sign for the product of two numbers with like signs?* positive

Example 3
Ask:
- *What is the product if you multiply a number and its multiplicative inverse?* one
- *What is another name for the multiplicative inverse of a number?* reciprocal

Error Prevention!

Watch for students who multiply by the reciprocal of the dividend instead of the divisor.

PowerPoint

Additional Examples

1 Find $\frac{5}{12} \cdot (-\frac{4}{7})$. $-\frac{5}{21}$

2 Find the product $-3\frac{1}{3} \cdot (-2\frac{5}{6})$. $9\frac{4}{9}$

3 One bow takes $\frac{3}{4}$ yard of ribbon. How many bows could you make from a roll of ribbon that is $12\frac{1}{2}$ yards long? 16 bows

4 Solve $\frac{3}{4}y = -\frac{1}{8}$. $y = -\frac{1}{6}$

Advanced Learners L4
Ask: *What is the reciprocal of* $1\frac{1}{2}$? $\frac{2}{3}$ $\frac{5}{7}$? $\frac{7}{5}$ or $1\frac{2}{5}$ $2\frac{3}{4}$? $\frac{4}{11}$ *23?* $\frac{1}{23}$ *Does every number have a reciprocal?* every number except zero

learning style: verbal

English Language Learners ELL
For the *More Than One Way* problem, some students use *Nicole's Method* and the others use *Eric's Method.* Then students discuss in small groups why they prefer a particular method.

learning style: verbal

Guided Instruction

Alternative Method
Use models such as fraction bars or index cards cut into halves to help students convince themselves that dividing a number by two is the same as finding one half of that number, and that dividing by one-half is the same as multiplying by 2. Have students make models and demonstrate the same principle with multiplying by three and dividing by one third.

Differentiated Instruction

Auditory Learners
So that students can recognize incorrect answers, have them quietly give a rough estimate for an answer before calculating. For example: "Since each bag takes a little less than a yard, the designer can make more than 15 bags."

All in One Teaching Resources

- Daily Notetaking Guide 2-5 L3
- Adapted Notetaking 2-5 L1

Closure

- Explain how to rewrite division by a rational number using multiplication. Sample: Dividing by a rational number is the same as multiplying by the reciprocal of that number, so rewrite the division as multiplication by the reciprocal.

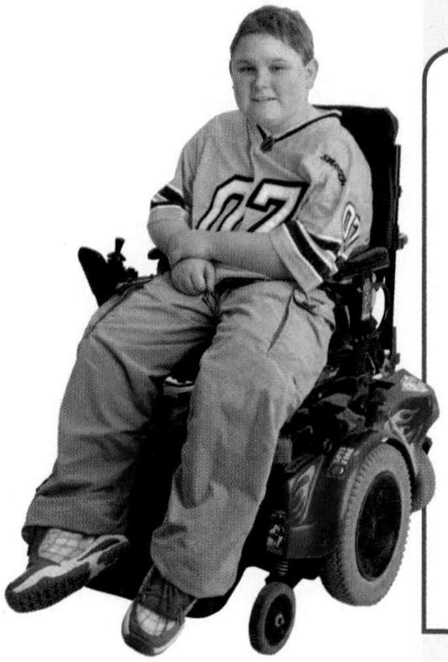

More Than One Way

A pancake recipe calls for $1\frac{2}{3}$ cups of flour to make about 20 pancakes. You have 13 cups of flour. Do you have enough for 100 pancakes?

Eric's Method

I'll divide 13 cups by $1\frac{2}{3}$ cups to find how many times I can make the recipe.

$13 \div 1\frac{2}{3} = 13 \div \frac{5}{3}$ ← **Write the mixed number as an improper fraction.**

$= 13 \cdot \frac{3}{5}$ ← **Multiply the reciprocal of $\frac{5}{3}$.**

$= \frac{39}{5} = 7\frac{4}{5}$ ← **Multiply. Write as a mixed number.**

I can make the recipe 7 times. Since $7 \cdot 20 = 140$, I have enough flour to make 100 pancakes.

Nicole's Method

For 100 pancakes, I need 5 times the amount of flour for one recipe.

$5 \cdot 1\frac{2}{3} = 5 \cdot \frac{5}{3}$ ← **Change the mixed number to an improper fraction.**

$= \frac{25}{3} = 8\frac{1}{3}$ ← **Multiply. Write as a mixed number.**

I need $8\frac{1}{3}$ cups, so I have plenty of flour.

Choose a Method
Your dog eats $1\frac{1}{2}$ cups of food per day. You have 50 cups of food. Do you have enough for 40 days? Explain why you chose the method you used.
No, you only have enough for 33 days; check students' work.

Check Your Understanding

1. **Vocabulary** The reciprocal of a number is also called its ? . multiplicative inverse
2. **Estimation** Estimate the solution of $\frac{6}{7}x = 2\frac{4}{5}$. $x \approx 3$

Copy and complete each equation.

3. $\frac{3}{5} \cdot \frac{5}{3} = ■$ 1
4. $-\frac{7}{2} \cdot ■ = 1$ $-\frac{2}{7}$
5. $■ \cdot \left(-\frac{1}{5}\right) = 1$ −5

Homework Exercises

For more exercises, see Extra Skills and Word Problems.

GO for Help

For Exercises	See Examples
6–14	1 and 2
15–25	3
26–31	4

A **Find each product. Write the answer in simplest form.**

6. $-\frac{4}{5} \cdot \left(-\frac{1}{2}\right)$ $\frac{2}{5}$
7. $\frac{9}{10} \cdot \left(-\frac{2}{3}\right)$ $-\frac{3}{5}$
8. $-\frac{34}{35} \cdot \left(-\frac{7}{2}\right)$ $3\frac{2}{5}$
9. $-\frac{5}{6} \cdot \frac{1}{4}$ $-\frac{5}{24}$
10. $-\frac{1}{2} \cdot \frac{2}{3}$ $-\frac{1}{3}$
11. $\frac{8}{9} \cdot \left(-\frac{3}{4}\right)$ $-\frac{2}{3}$
12. $-1\frac{1}{2} \cdot \left(-4\frac{1}{2}\right)$ $6\frac{3}{4}$
13. $3\frac{3}{4} \cdot 2\frac{1}{3}$ $8\frac{3}{4}$
14. $\left(-2\frac{3}{4}\right) \cdot 4$ -11

Find each quotient. Write the answer in simplest form.

15. $\frac{1}{2} \div \left(-\frac{3}{4}\right)$ $-\frac{2}{3}$
16. $-\frac{8}{9} \div \frac{1}{6}$ $-5\frac{1}{3}$
17. $8 \div \frac{8}{17}$ 17
18. $-\frac{7}{9} \div \left(-\frac{9}{7}\right)$ $\frac{49}{81}$
19. $\frac{100}{101} \div 100$ $\frac{1}{101}$
20. $-3\frac{3}{10} \div \frac{1}{10}$ -33
21. $\frac{1}{4} \div \left(-\frac{1}{3}\right)$ $-\frac{3}{4}$
22. $3\frac{3}{5} \div (-9)$ $-\frac{2}{5}$
23. $\frac{2}{7} \div 1\frac{2}{7}$ $\frac{2}{9}$

24. **Running** A jogger is running around a $\frac{1}{4}$-mile track. How many laps does the jogger have to run in order to go $5\frac{1}{2}$ miles? 22 laps

25. **Trail Mix** You have $6\frac{2}{3}$ lb of raisins to divide evenly among 5 bags of trail mix. How many pounds of the raisins will go in each bag? $1\frac{1}{3}$ lb

Solve each equation.

26. $\frac{1}{2}j = 12\frac{1}{2}$ 25
27. $\frac{2}{3}y = \frac{2}{5}$ $\frac{3}{5}$
28. $\frac{1}{2}m = 1\frac{1}{3}$ $2\frac{2}{3}$
29. $-\frac{2}{7}b = 1\frac{1}{14}$ $-3\frac{3}{4}$
30. $1\frac{1}{3}p = -4\frac{1}{3}$ $-3\frac{1}{4}$
31. $-\frac{1}{3}u = 6\frac{1}{3}$ -19

B **GPS** 32. **Guided Problem Solving** Justin needs to make cardboard signs. He has $50\frac{4}{5}$ ft of cardboard, and each sign uses $3\frac{1}{10}$ ft of board. Write and solve an equation to find how many signs he can make. Use estimation to check your answer. $50\frac{4}{5} \div 3\frac{1}{10}$; 16

- **Understand the Problem** To find how many signs he can make, should you multiply or divide?
- **Check Your Answer** To check your answer, what values can you substitute in the problem?

33. **Recycling** A family uses $14\frac{1}{2}$ pounds of paper in a week and recycles about $\frac{3}{4}$ of its waste. How many pounds of paper does the family recycle? $10\frac{7}{8}$ lb (GPS)

34. **Choose a Method** A hiking trail is $43\frac{5}{9}$ mi long. There is a cabin every $4\frac{1}{2}$ mi. How many cabins are along the trail? Explain why you chose the method you used. 9; check students' work.

GO Online
Homework Video Tutor
Visit: PHSchool.com
Web Code: ase-0205

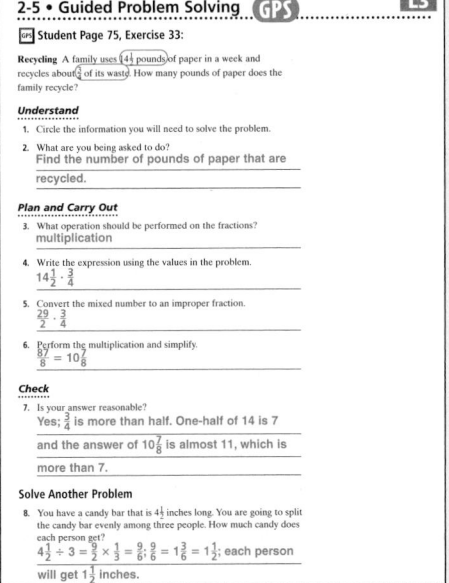

3. Practice

Assignment Guide

Check Your Understanding

Go over Exercises 1–5 in class before assigning the Homework Exercises.

Homework Exercises

A Practice by Example	6–31
B Apply Your Skills	32–41
C Challenge	42
Test Prep and Mixed Review	43–48

Homework Quick Check

To check students' understanding of key skills and concepts, go over Exercises 8, 18, 33, 38, and 39.

Differentiated Instruction Resources

Adapted Practice 2-5 L1

Practice 2-5 Multiplying and Dividing Rational N L3

Find each product or quotient. Write each answer as a fraction or mixed number in simplest form.

1. $-\frac{1}{6} \cdot 2\frac{3}{4}$ $\frac{-11}{24}$
2. $\frac{3}{16} \div \left(-\frac{1}{8}\right)$ $-1\frac{1}{2}$
3. $-5\frac{7}{12} \div 12$ $\frac{-67}{144}$
4. $-8 \div \frac{1}{4}$ -32
5. $8\frac{3}{4} \cdot 3\frac{7}{8}$ $33\frac{29}{32}$
6. $-\frac{11}{12} \div \frac{5}{6}$ $-1\frac{1}{10}$
7. $-1\frac{1}{15} \div 15$ $\frac{-16}{225}$
8. $-3 \div \frac{3}{4}$ -4
9. $-2\frac{7}{8} \div 3\frac{3}{4}$ $\frac{-23}{30}$
10. $-\frac{23}{24} \cdot (-8)$ $7\frac{2}{3}$
11. $\frac{7}{8} \cdot \left(-\frac{2}{7}\right)$ $\frac{-1}{4}$
12. $-7 \div \frac{1}{9}$ -63
13. $-6\frac{5}{6} \div \frac{1}{6}$ -41
14. $-8 \cdot 3\frac{3}{4}$ -30
15. $\frac{7}{10} \cdot \left(-3\frac{1}{4}\right)$ $-2\frac{11}{40}$
16. $5 \cdot \left(-3\frac{5}{6}\right)$ $-19\frac{1}{6}$
17. $-\frac{8}{9} \div \left(-3\frac{2}{3}\right)$ $\frac{8}{33}$
18. $2\frac{1}{3} \div \frac{2}{3}$ $3\frac{1}{2}$

Solve each equation.

19. $\frac{1}{3}a = \frac{3}{10}$ $\frac{9}{10}$
20. $-\frac{3}{4}b = 9$ -12
21. $-\frac{7}{8}c = 4\frac{2}{3}$ $-5\frac{1}{3}$
22. $\frac{5}{6}n = -3\frac{3}{4}$ $-4\frac{1}{2}$
23. $-\frac{3}{5}x = 12$ -20
24. $-2\frac{2}{3}y = 3\frac{1}{3}$ $-1\frac{1}{4}$
25. $\frac{7}{12}y = -2\frac{4}{5}$ $-4\frac{4}{5}$
26. $2\frac{1}{4}z = -\frac{1}{9}$ $\frac{-4}{81}$
27. $2\frac{1}{5}d = -\frac{1}{2}$ $\frac{-5}{22}$

28. One pound of flour contains about four cups. A recipe calls for $2\frac{1}{4}$ c of flour. How many full recipes can you make from a two-pound bag of flour? 3 recipes
29. Kim needs $2\frac{1}{2}$ ft of wrapping paper to wrap each package. She has five packages to wrap. How many packages can she wrap with a 12-ft roll of wrapping paper? 4 packages
30. Gina and Paul are making pizza for the cast and crew of the school play. They estimate that the boys in the cast and crew will eat $\frac{1}{2}$ pizza each. They estimate that the girls will each eat $\frac{1}{3}$ of a pizza. There are 7 boys and 10 girls working on the play. How many pizzas do they need to make? 7 pizzas

2-5 • Guided Problem Solving GPS L3

GPS Student Page 75, Exercise 33:

Recycling A family uses $14\frac{1}{2}$ pounds of paper in a week and recycles about $\frac{3}{4}$ of its waste. How many pounds of paper does the family recycle?

Understand

1. Circle the information you will need to solve the problem.
2. What are you being asked to do? Find the number of pounds of paper that are recycled.

Plan and Carry Out

3. What operation should be performed on the fractions? multiplication
4. Write the expression using the values in the problem. $14\frac{1}{2} \cdot \frac{3}{4}$
5. Convert the mixed number to an improper fraction. $\frac{29}{2} \cdot \frac{3}{4}$
6. Perform the multiplication and simplify. $\frac{87}{8} = 10\frac{7}{8}$

Check

7. Is your answer reasonable? Yes; $\frac{3}{4}$ is more than half. One-half of 14 is 7 and the answer of $10\frac{7}{8}$ is almost 11, which is more than 7.

Solve Another Problem

8. You have a candy bar that is $4\frac{1}{2}$ inches long. You are going to split the candy bar evenly among three people. How much candy does each person get? $4\frac{1}{2} \div 3 = \frac{9}{2} \times \frac{1}{3} = \frac{9}{6}$; $\frac{9}{6} = 1\frac{3}{6} = 1\frac{1}{2}$; each person will get $1\frac{1}{2}$ inches.

4. Assess & Reteach

PowerPoint

Lesson Quiz

1. $\frac{5}{8} \cdot \left(-\frac{4}{5}\right)$ $-\frac{1}{2}$
2. $2\frac{1}{3} \cdot \left(-1\frac{1}{8}\right)$ $-2\frac{5}{8}$
3. $-\frac{1}{6} \div \left(-\frac{3}{4}\right)$ $\frac{2}{9}$
4. $\left(-1\frac{7}{8}\right) \div \left(1\frac{1}{2}\right)$ $-1\frac{1}{4}$
5. Solve the equation. $1\frac{2}{3}r = \frac{5}{6}$ $\frac{1}{2}$
6. Megan has $3\frac{1}{2}$ quarts of punch. One serving is $\frac{1}{4}$ quart. Does she have enough to serve 15 guests? No

Reteaching 2-5

Multiplying and Dividing Rational Numbers **L2**

To multiply rational numbers in fraction form, multiply numerators, then multiply denominators.

Multiply: $\frac{7}{12} \cdot 1\frac{4}{5}$

$\frac{7}{12} \cdot \frac{9}{5}$ ← fraction form

$\frac{7 \cdot 9}{12 \cdot 5}$ ← Multiply numerators. ← Multiply denominators.

$\frac{63}{60} = 1\frac{3}{60} = 1\frac{1}{20}$ ← Simplify.

To divide, multiply by the reciprocal of the divisor.

Divide: $-3\frac{1}{8} \div \frac{2}{3}$

$\frac{-25}{8} \div \frac{2}{3}$ ← fraction form

$\frac{-25}{8} \cdot \frac{3}{2}$ ← reciprocal of divisor

$\frac{-25 \cdot 3}{8 \cdot 2} = \frac{-75}{16}$ ← Multiply.

$= -4\frac{11}{16}$ ← Simplify.

Find each product. Write each answer as a fraction or mixed number in simplest form.

1. $\frac{8}{9} \cdot \left(-\frac{3}{4}\right)$ $-\frac{2}{3}$
2. $-\frac{1}{2} \cdot \frac{4}{5}$ $-\frac{2}{5}$
3. $\frac{5}{6} \cdot \frac{3}{7}$ $\frac{5}{14}$
4. $\frac{3}{4} \cdot \left(-\frac{2}{3}\right)$ $-\frac{1}{2}$
5. $-5\frac{1}{2} \cdot 1\frac{3}{4}$ $-9\frac{5}{8}$
6. $-2\frac{1}{8} \cdot (-3)$ $6\frac{3}{8}$
7. $\frac{13}{15} \cdot \frac{5}{6}$ $\frac{13}{18}$
8. $-3\frac{2}{5} \cdot 2\frac{1}{2}$ $-8\frac{1}{2}$
9. $-5 \cdot \left(-2\frac{1}{4}\right)$ $11\frac{1}{4}$
10. $-\frac{5}{8} \cdot 4\frac{2}{3}$ $-2\frac{11}{12}$
11. $-5 \cdot 3\frac{3}{10}$ $-16\frac{1}{2}$
12. $-2\frac{3}{5} \cdot \left(-3\frac{1}{3}\right)$ $8\frac{2}{3}$

Find each quotient. Write the answer in simplest form.

13. $\frac{5}{6} \div \frac{3}{5}$ $1\frac{7}{18}$
14. $-\frac{3}{8} \div \left(-\frac{1}{2}\right)$ $\frac{3}{4}$
15. $-6 \div \frac{3}{4}$ -8
16. $4 \div \left(-\frac{2}{3}\right)$ -6
17. $5\frac{1}{4} \div 1\frac{1}{2}$ $3\frac{1}{2}$
18. $-\frac{3}{4} \div \left(-1\frac{1}{2}\right)$ $\frac{1}{2}$
19. $-1\frac{3}{5} \div \frac{1}{4}$ $-6\frac{2}{5}$
20. $-\frac{5}{9} \div \left(-\frac{2}{3}\right)$ $\frac{5}{6}$
21. $-6 \div 3\frac{5}{8}$ $-1\frac{19}{29}$

Enrichment 2-5

Multiplying and Dividing Rationals **L4**

Reasoning

Some say that the average ratio of inches of snow to inches of water is 10 to 1. If the snow is equivalent to $2\frac{7}{8}$ inches of water, how many inches of snow are there? Explain your reasoning.

1. What is the average ratio of inches of snow to inches of water? 10 to 1
2. Write $2\frac{7}{8}$ as a decimal. 2.875
3. Let x represent inches of snow. Write a proportion for the problem using 10 to 1 and x. $\frac{10}{1} = \frac{x}{2.875}$
4. Why would you use a proportion to solve this problem? A proportion shows the relationship between inches of snow and rain. Solving the proportion will give the missing measurement.
5. Solve for x to find the number of inches of snow equivalent to $2\frac{7}{8}$ inches of water. Write your answer in a complete sentence. 28.75 in. of snow is equivalent to $2\frac{7}{8}$ inches of water.
6. Could you have found your answer using an improper fraction? Explain. Yes; convert the mixed number to an improper fraction, write the proportion, and solve for x.
7. Which method is easier, using decimals or improper fractions? Explain. Sample answer: Using decimals is easier because you can easily multiply the decimal by 10 just by moving the decimal point.
8. Write a rule explaining how to convert inches of water to inches of snow and vice versa. If you know the inches of water, multiply the value by 10 to get inches of snow. If you know the inches of snow, divide the value by 10 to get inches of water.

Algebra **Evaluate each expression for $x = 1$, $y = 2$, and $z = 3$.**

35. $\left(x + \frac{x}{5}\right) \div \frac{1}{5}$ 6
36. $\frac{x}{y}\left(\frac{y}{z} - x\right)$ $-\frac{1}{6}$
37. $3 \div \left(\frac{y}{z} - \frac{x}{yz}\right)$ 6

38. **Baking** You are making apple pies for a school fundraiser. You have 4 baskets of apples, and each basket contains 11 apples. Each pie requires $3\frac{1}{5}$ cups of apples. One apple fills about $\frac{1}{2}$ cup.
    a. How many cups of apples do you have? 22 cups
    b. How many pies can you make? 6 pies
39. **Reasoning** When you divide a positive number by a fraction that is between 0 and 1, the answer is always greater than the positive number. Explain why. See left.
40. **Writing in Math** Explain the difference between dividing 10 by 4 and dividing 10 by $\frac{1}{4}$. Use diagrams to support your answer. See margin.
41. The school band uses $1\frac{3}{4}$ yd of blue fabric and $\frac{3}{8}$ yd of gold fabric to make one banner. How many yards of fabric does the band need to make 5 banners? $10\frac{5}{8}$ yd
42. **Challenge** Your uncle has 36 coins in nickels and quarters. The value of his nickels is $\frac{1}{15}$ of the value of his quarters. Find the number of nickels. 9 nickels

39. Dividing by a fraction is the same as multiplying by its reciprocal. The reciprocal of a number less than 1 is a number greater than 1, so the answer will be greater.

Test Prep and Mixed Review

Practice

Multiple Choice

43. Ali is tiling a bathroom that is $10\frac{1}{3}$ ft by $10\frac{1}{3}$ ft. How many tiles like the one at the right will fit along one side of the bathroom? C

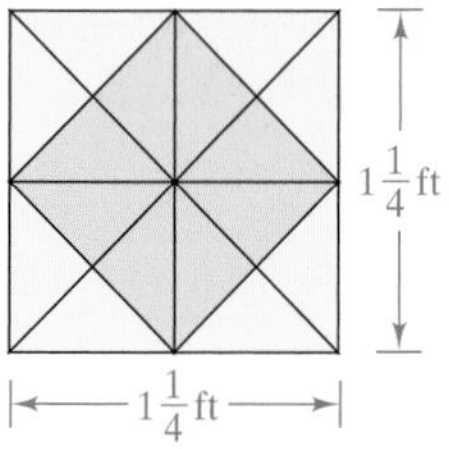

    A $7\frac{1}{2}$ C $8\frac{4}{15}$
    B $8\frac{1}{3}$ D $12\frac{11}{12}$

44. Shelly keeps track of the time she spends on her cell phone. Today she made three calls that lasted 3.2 minutes, $12\frac{1}{2}$ minutes, and 20 minutes 15 seconds. How many minutes did Shelly spend on the phone today? J
    F 35.55 min G 35.75 min H 35.85 min J 35.95 min
45. Scott is twice as old as Ben. Donna is 6 years older than Ben. The sum of their ages is 34. Which expression can you use to represent the sum of ages? D
    A $x + 2x - 6x$
    B $x + 2x + 6x$
    C $x + 2x + (x - 6)$
    D $x + 2x + (x + 6)$

GO for Help

For Exercises	See Lesson
46–48	1-6

Solve each equation.

46. $a + 12 = -31$ -43
47. $-9 = b - 16$ 7
48. $-36 = c - 36$ 0

Test Prep

Resources

For additional practice with a variety of test item formats:
- Test-Taking Strategies, p. 97
- Test Prep, p. 101
- Test-Taking Strategies with Transparencies

Alternative Assessment

Working in pairs, one partner writes a positive mixed number; the other writes a negative mixed number. Together they first multiply the numbers, then divide them. Students must agree on the solutions.

Vocabulary Builder

Learning Vocabulary

Your textbook has vocabulary terms that may be new.
Make your own mathematics dictionary in a notebook.
Use the following ideas to write your definitions.

- Write the vocabulary term and its definition. Include any symbols.
- If possible, draw a diagram.
- Give one or more examples of the term.
- Give one or more nonexamples and explain how they are different.
- Include details, using other related terms you know.

Here is a possible entry for your dictionary.

> Two numbers are reciprocals if their product is 1.
>
> 10 and $\frac{1}{10}$ are reciprocals, because their product is 1.
>
> 2 and -2 are not reciprocals, because their product is -4.
>
> reciprocals: $2, \frac{1}{2}$; $-1, -1$
>
> not reciprocals: $2, 0.2$; $3, -\frac{1}{3}$

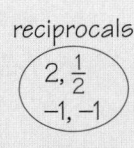

EXAMPLE A Dictionary Entry

a. What term is being defined? *reciprocal*

b. Why do 10 and $\frac{1}{10}$ satisfy the definition? *Their product is 1.*

c. Why do 2 and -2 not satisfy the definition? *Their product is not 1.*

d. What does the diagram show? *It shows examples of reciprocals and nonreciprocals.*

Exercises

1. Write a dictionary entry for *multiplicative inverse.*
2. **Error Analysis** A student wrote the definition for *prime factorization* at the right. Which parts are incorrect? Explain.
   1–2. See margin.

> When a number is written in prime factorization, it is written as the product of two factors.
>
> The prime factorization of 14 is $1 \cdot 2 \cdot 7$ because 1, 2, and 7 are prime numbers.
>
> The prime factorization of 20 is not $4 \cdot 5$, because 4 is not a prime number.

Vocabulary Builder

Learning Vocabulary

Students who grasp the precision of math vocabulary will improve their ability to understand and share mathematical ideas. In this feature, students learn a strategy for acquiring the new mathematics vocabulary they come across in their texts.

Guided Instruction

Call students' attention to the Table of Symbols and the Illustrated English/Spanish Glossary in the back of their texts.

Ask:

- *How will it help to show examples of reciprocals and examples that are not reciprocals?* **Sample: to show more clearly what a reciprocal is**
- *Why are 3 and $-\frac{1}{3}$ not reciprocals?* **The product is −1. Reciprocals have a product of 1.**

Teaching Tip
Make an effort to use new math vocabulary often as you work through the textbook lessons. This practice gives students, particularly English language learners, a chance to hear the words spoken correctly and in the right context.

Exercises
Have students share dictionary entries with a partner. Invite pairs to discuss ways to improve each other's entries.

Resources

- Vocabulary and Study Skills Worksheet
- a notebook

Exercises, p. 76

40. **Answers may vary. Sample: Dividing by 4 will give an answer that is smaller than 10. Dividing by $\frac{1}{4}$ will give an answer greater than 10 because it is the same as multiplying by 4.**

Vocabulary Builder

1. **The multiplicative inverse is the number by which you multiply a given number to get a product of 1.**
2. **The first sentence is wrong. The prime factorization can have more than two factors. The second sentence is also wrong. The number 1 is not a prime number.**

GPS Guided Problem Solving

Practice Solving Problems

Drawing a diagram can help students better understand, and solve, a problem. In this feature, students study and use diagrams to illustrate word problems. Then they compute the answer without a diagram and compare results.

Guided Instruction

Begin by reviewing the key elements of identifying what you know and what you want to find out.

Teaching Tip
Help students understand how the diagram depicts the situation in the word problem.

Ask:

- *What does the rectangle represent?* the whole collection
- *Why is the rectangle divided into thirds?* The art collector sold $\frac{1}{3}$ of his collection. Dividing the rectangle into thirds makes it easy to indicate the amount sold and the amount left.
- *What part of the diagram represents the amount that was left after the sale?* the $\frac{2}{3}$ of the rectangle on the right
- *What does the shaded part of the rectangle represent?* $\frac{1}{2}$ of the $\frac{2}{3}$ of the rectangle left after the sale is the amount the art collector donated to a museum. This shaded portion represents $\frac{1}{3}$ of the collectors original collection.

GPS Guided Problem Solving

Practice Solving Problems

Collections An art collector sold $\frac{1}{3}$ of his collection to a friend. The collector then donated $\frac{1}{2}$ of what was left to a museum. What part of the original collection did the collector have left?

What You Might Think	What You Might Write
What do I know? What do I want to find out?	The collector sold $\frac{1}{3}$, so he had $\frac{2}{3}$ left. He gave away $\frac{1}{2}$ of that. How much was left?
How do I show the main idea?	I can draw a diagram.

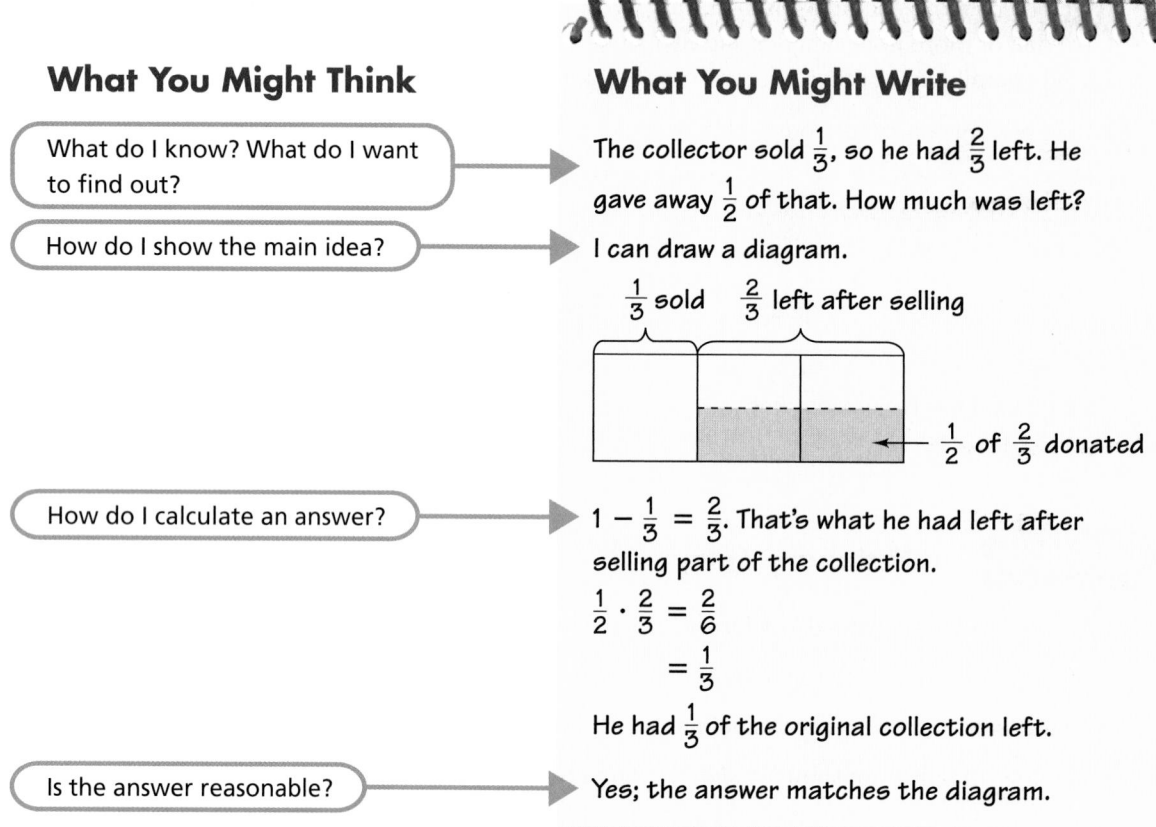

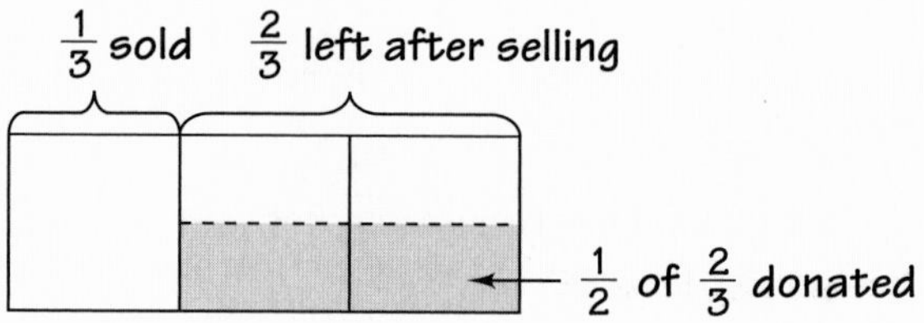

What You Might Think	What You Might Write
How do I calculate an answer?	$1 - \frac{1}{3} = \frac{2}{3}$. That's what he had left after selling part of the collection. $\frac{1}{2} \cdot \frac{2}{3} = \frac{2}{6} = \frac{1}{3}$ He had $\frac{1}{3}$ of the original collection left.
Is the answer reasonable?	Yes; the answer matches the diagram.

Think It Through

1–2. Answers may vary. Samples are given.

1. How does the diagram show $\frac{1}{2} \cdot \frac{2}{3} = \frac{2}{6}$? Explain. 1. When you divide $\frac{2}{3}$ by 2, the result is 2 of the 6 pieces in the whole.
2. **Reasoning** If the collector had donated $\frac{1}{2}$ of $\frac{2}{3}$ of the collection, is the amount he had left the same as the amount he donated? Use the diagram to explain how you know the answer without calculating. 2. No; he will have the remaining $\frac{4}{6}$ left.
3. You can find $\frac{1}{2}$ of $\frac{2}{3}$ using a similar diagram, but without dividing the rectangle horizontally into halves. Draw another diagram you can use to find the answer. Which method do you prefer? Check students' work.

Exercises

Solve each problem. For Exercises 4 and 5, answer parts (a) and (b) first.

4. Julio feeds his dog $1\frac{1}{3}$ cans of dog food each day Monday through Saturday. On Sunday, he feeds his dog half as much. How many cans of dog food does Julio feed his dog in a week? $8\frac{2}{3}$ cans

a. What do you know, and what do you want to find out?

b. Use the diagram at the right. Make a similar diagram to show six times $1\frac{1}{3}$ cans of dog food plus half of $1\frac{1}{3}$. Calculate $6 \cdot 1\frac{1}{3} + \frac{1}{2} \cdot 1\frac{1}{3}$. Do your answers match?

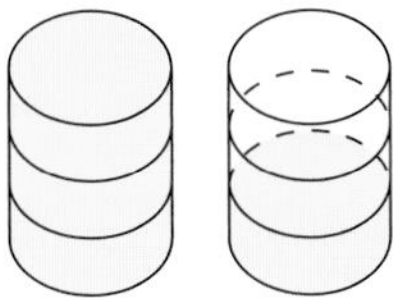

5. Kendra ordered pizzas for a party. After the party, she had $2\frac{3}{4}$ pizzas left. She estimates that $\frac{1}{2}$ of a pizza is one meal. How many meals does she have left? $5\frac{1}{2}$ meals

a. What do you know, and what do you want to find out?

b. Copy and complete the diagram below. Explain how the drawing matches the number sentence for the problem.

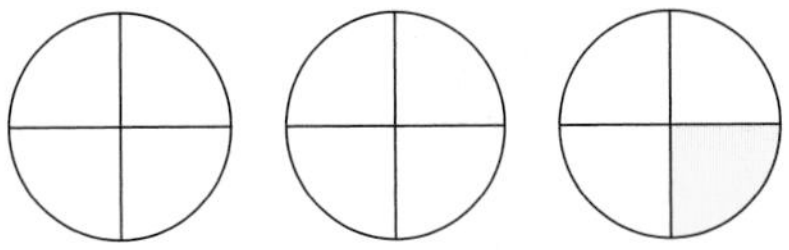

6. Max has published a book. He earns \$5.50 as a royalty for each copy of the book that is sold. The royalties for the first five months of the year are shown in the graph below. He expects similar royalties for the rest of year. How much should Max expect to earn in royalties during the year? about \$1,000

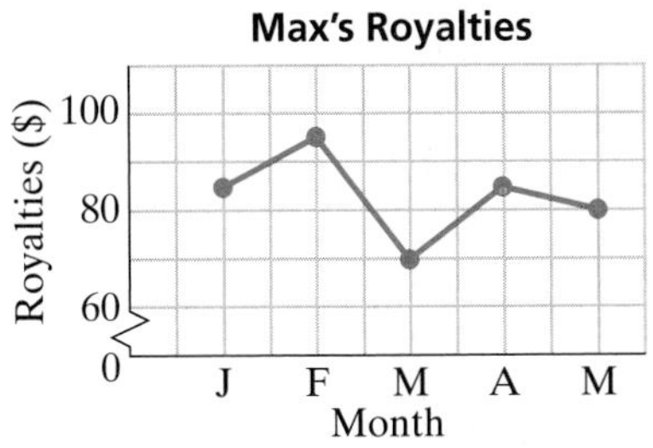

7. Melita had some hardboiled eggs. She gave away $\frac{1}{2}$ of the eggs, plus $\frac{1}{2}$ an egg, to Sam. She then gave away $\frac{1}{2}$ of what she had left, plus $\frac{1}{2}$ an egg, to Alonzo. After she gave $\frac{1}{2}$ of what she had left, plus $\frac{1}{2}$ an egg, to Jacquelyn, she had no eggs left. How many eggs did Melita have before giving any away? 7 eggs

Guided Instruction

Error Prevention!

Be sure students realize that $\frac{1}{2}$ of $\frac{2}{3}$ is the same as $\frac{1}{2} \times \frac{2}{3}$ or $\frac{2}{3} \times \frac{1}{2} = \frac{1}{3}$. Some students may be tempted to interpret $\frac{1}{2}$ of $\frac{2}{3}$ incorrectly as $\frac{2}{3} \div \frac{1}{2}$. Elicit from them that taking half of something is the same as dividing the amount by 2 (not $\frac{1}{2}$).

Exercises

You may want to have students work in pairs to solve the exercises. Then call on volunteers to share their solutions. One member of the pair can draw the diagram while the second explains their reasoning in solving the problem.

Differentiated Instruction

Special Needs L1

Remind students of how a diagram can show multiplication. Draw a simple rectangle of 3 rows and 4 columns. Shade 1 row with diagonal lines going in one direction. Ask: *How much of the rectangle has been shaded with these lines?* $\frac{1}{3}$ Then shade 3 columns with diagonal lines that are perpendicular to the other diagonal lines. Ask: *How much of the rectangle has been shaded with these lines?* $\frac{3}{4}$ Elicit from the students that the overlapping areas of shading represent $\frac{1}{3} \times \frac{3}{4} = \frac{3}{12} = \frac{1}{4}$.

Activity Lab

Estimating Solutions

In this Activity, students estimate solutions to equations and formulas. They can compare the estimates with the original equations' solutions to evaluate the solutions' reasonableness.

Guided Instruction

Discuss the Examples with students.

For Example 1, ask: *Why were the numbers not rounded to the nearest whole number, for example, 32 and 728?* Sample: It is easier to calculate with numbers rounded to the nearest ten, and the estimate is still reasonable.

Alternative Method
In Example 2, students might use compatible numbers by rounding 32 to 27 and multiplying by $\frac{5}{9}$.

$C \approx \frac{5}{9} \times (0 - 27)$
$C \approx \frac{5}{9} \times (-27)$
$C \approx 5 \times (-3) = -15$

Differentiated Instruction

Special Needs L1
Review fractions that might reasonably be rounded to 1, such as $\frac{9}{10}, \frac{5}{6}, \frac{13}{16}, \frac{2}{3}$. Review fractions that might be rounded to $\frac{1}{2}$, such as $\frac{6}{10}, \frac{5}{9}, \frac{4}{7}, \frac{9}{20}$.

Resources

- Activity Lab 2-6: Using a Volume Formula

Estimating Solutions

Estimating solutions helps you solve equations. You can round the numbers in an equation or formula to estimate the solution. Then you can compare your solution of the original equation to the estimated solution and decide whether your answer is reasonable.

EXAMPLE Estimating a Solution

1 Your friend says the solution of the equation $x + 31\frac{2}{3} = 727\frac{5}{8}$ is $x = 596\frac{3}{4}$. Is the solution reasonable?

$x + 30 \approx 730$ ← Round $31\frac{2}{3}$ to 30 and $727\frac{5}{8}$ to 730.

$x \approx 700$ ← Use mental math: 700 + 30 = 730.

The value of x is about 700. Your friend's solution is not reasonable.

EXAMPLE Estimating With a Formula

2 The formula to convert from Fahrenheit to Celsius is $C = \frac{5}{9}(F - 32)$. Estimate the Celsius temperature for 0°F.

$C \approx \frac{1}{2}(F - 30)$ ← Round $\frac{5}{9}$ to $\frac{1}{2}$ and −32 to 30.

$\approx \frac{1}{2}(0 - 30)$ ← Substitute 0 for *F*.

$\approx \frac{1}{2}(-30) = -15$ ← Subtract. Multiply.

The Celsius temperature for 0°F is about −15°C.

1–6. Answers may vary. Samples are given.
1. yes; 84 + 19 = 103
2. no; (−40)(5) ≠ −400
3. yes; $\frac{140}{50} \approx 3$
4. no; −56 − 35 ≠ −21
5. about 165
6. about 170

Exercises

Decide whether the solution to each equation is reasonable. Explain. 1–6. See above.

1. $y + 19\frac{1}{4} = 102\frac{3}{5}; y = 83\frac{7}{20}$
2. $-39\frac{5}{6}z = -401; z = 5\frac{1}{6}$
3. $\frac{t}{48} = 2\frac{9}{10}; t = 139\frac{2}{10}$
4. $m - 34\frac{7}{8} = -21\frac{1}{3}; m = -56\frac{5}{24}$
5. Estimate the maximum heart rate for a $13\frac{10}{12}$-year-old male using the formula $M = \frac{4}{5}(220 - A)$, where A represents his age.
6. Estimate the maximum heart rate for a $13\frac{10}{12}$-year-old female using the formula $F = \frac{4}{5}(226 - A)$, where A represents her age.

2-6 Formulas

Check Skills You'll Need

1. **Vocabulary Review** According to the *order of operations,* you multiply and divide before you _?_ and _?_. add; subtract

Evaluate each expression for $w = 2$ and $t = -3$.

2. $4w + t$ 5
3. $4(w + t)$ −4
4. $4w + 4t$ −4
5. $-4t - w$ 10

GO for Help Lesson 1-1

What You'll Learn

To use formulas to solve problems and to solve a formula for a variable

New Vocabulary formula

Why Learn This?

Understanding formulas allows you to find quantities such as area, distance, rate, and time. You can use these formulas in aviation and sports.

A **formula** is a rule that shows a relationship between two or more quantities. The variables represent the quantities.

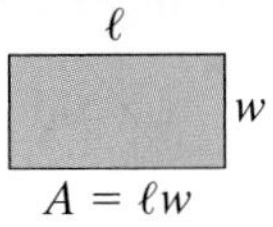

Recall that the perimeter of a figure is the distance around it. The area of a figure is the amount of space that it encloses. The diagram at the right shows the relationship between the area of a rectangle and its two dimensions. You use the formula $A = \ell w$ to find the area.

EXAMPLE Using Formulas to Solve Problems

1 Find the area of the trapezoid at the right.

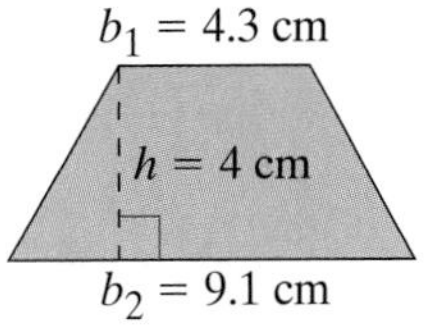

$A = \frac{1}{2}h(b_1 + b_2)$ ← **Use the formula for the area of a trapezoid.**

$= \frac{1}{2}(4)(4.3 + 9.1)$ ← **Substitute.**

$= \frac{1}{2}(4)(13.4)$ ← **Add within the parentheses.**

$= 2(13.4)$ ← **Multiply from left to right.**

$= 26.8$ ← **Simplify.**

The area of the trapezoid is 26.8 cm^2.

Vocabulary Tip

The variables b_1 and b_2 stand for "base 1" and "base 2." The lowered numbers 1 and 2 are called subscripts.

Quick Check

1. Find the area of each figure.
   a. trapezoid: $h = 4.2$ cm, $b_1 = 1.4$ cm, $b_2 = 4.6$ cm 12.6 cm^2
   b. rectangle: $\ell = \frac{2}{3}$ yd, $w = 3$ yd 2 yd^2

Differentiated Instruction Solutions for All Learners

Special Needs L1

In Example 3, draw a square and assign a numerical value, such as 8, to the perimeter. Help students work through the formulas to see which is appropriate for finding the length of one side, given what is known about the sides and perimeter of a square.

learning style: visual

Below Level L2

Have students draw a rectangle and color its perimeter red and its interior area blue. Then have them do the same coloring activity for a trapezoid.

learning style: visual

2-6

1. Plan

Objective

To use formulas to solve problems and to solve a formula for a variable

Examples

1 Using Formulas to Solve Problems
2 Application: Sports
3 Isolating a Variable

Math Understandings: p. 50D

Professional Development

Math Background

A *formula* is an equation that shows a relationship between two or more variables. A familiar example is the formula for the area of a rectangle: $A = \ell w$.

More Math Background: p. 50D

Lesson Planning and Resources

See p. 50E for a list of the resources that support this lesson.

PowerPoint

Bell Ringer Practice

Check Skills You'll Need

Use student page, transparency, or PowerPoint. For intervention, direct students to:

Algebraic Expressions and Order of Operations
Lesson 1-1
Extra Skills and Word Problems Practice, Ch. 1

2. Teach

Activity Lab

Use before the lesson.
Student Edition Activity Lab 2-6a, Algebra Thinking, Estimating Solutions, p. 80

All in One Teaching Resources

Activity Lab 2-6: Using a Volume Formula

Guided Instruction

In Example 1, remind students that a trapezoid is a four-sided figure with exactly one pair of parallel sides.

Diversity
In Example 2, students can apply the distance formulas to other races. Have them describe other famous races. Sample: Tour de France bicycle race

Error Prevention!

In Example 3, have students compare and contrast the formula for the perimeter of a square with the formula for its area. Sample: Area is measured in square units and is the product of length times width. Perimeter is measured in linear units and is the sum of all four sides.

PowerPoint

Additional Examples

1. Find the area of a trapezoid with height of 6 cm and bases of 5.2 cm and 7.5 cm. 38.1 cm^2

2. Find the time it takes a sled dog team to go 95 miles if their average rate is 19 mph. 5 h

3. Which formula can be used to find the diameter d of a circle, given the circumference C? $d = \frac{C}{\pi}$

All in One Teaching Resources

- Daily Notetaking Guide 2-6 L3
- Adapted Notetaking 2-6 L1

Closure

- Describe how to solve a formula for any variable. Sample: Use the properties of equality to get that variable alone on one side.

You can use formulas to solve some real-world problems.

EXAMPLE Application: Sports

2 The Iditarod is a 1,159-mile dog-sled race from Anchorage, Alaska, to Nome, Alaska. Susan Butcher won the race four times. Her time for one race was 11 days. Find the average distance she went each day.

Use the distance formula $d = rt$, where d is the distance traveled, r is the rate of travel, and t is the time spent traveling.

$d = rt$ ← **Use the distance formula.**

$1{,}159 = r \cdot 11$ ← **Substitute 1,159 for *d* and 11 for *t*.**

$\frac{1{,}159}{11} = \frac{r \cdot 11}{11}$ ← **Divide each side by 11 to isolate *r* on the right.**

$\frac{1{,}159}{11} = r$ ← **Simplify.**

1,159 [÷] 11 [=] 105.36364 ← **Use a calculator.**

Susan Butcher traveled about 105 miles per day.

Check for Reasonableness Round 1,159 to 1,000 and 11 to 10. $1{,}000 \approx r \cdot 10$, so $r \approx 100$. The answer is reasonable.

Online active math

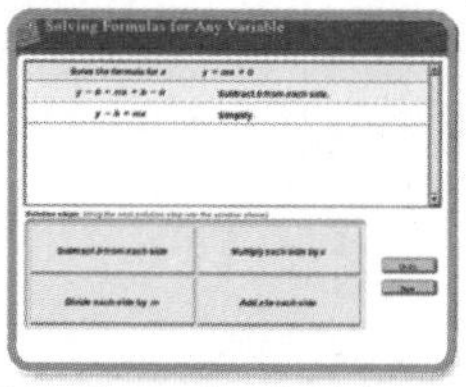

For: Formulas Activity
Use: Interactive Textbook, 2-6

Quick Check

2. In 1900, Johann Hurlinger walked 870 miles on his hands. He did this in 55 ten-hour shifts, or 550 hours. Find his rate in miles per hour. 1.58 mi/h

You can use the properties of equality to isolate a variable in a formula.

EXAMPLE Isolating a Variable

3 **Multiple Choice** Which formula can be used to find the side length s of a square, given the perimeter P?

(A) $P = \frac{s}{4}$ (B) $s = 4P$ (C) $s = \frac{P}{4}$ (D) $s = \frac{4}{P}$

$P = 4s$ ← **Use the perimeter formula for a square.**

$\frac{P}{4} = \frac{4s}{4}$ ← **Divide each side by 4 to isolate the variable *s*.**

$\frac{P}{4} = s$ ← **Simplify.**

The formula for the side of a square is $s = \frac{P}{4}$, so the answer is C.

Test Prep Tip

Circle the variable you are isolating so that you don't solve for the wrong variable by mistake.

Quick Check

3. Solve $A = w - 5$ for w. $w = A + 5$

Differentiated Instruction Solutions for All Learners

Advanced Learners L4
Have students write a formula for finding the number of seconds in H hours and the number of seconds in w weeks. $s = 3{,}600H$; $s = 604{,}800w$

learning style: verbal

English Language Learners ELL
Students read the formulas in this lesson using words. For instance, Example 1 should be read as: *The area of a trapezoid is half the height times the sum of base 1 and base 2.*

learning style: verbal

Check Your Understanding

1. ℓ is the length; w is the width.
2. Solve the formula $d = rt$ for r by dividing both sides of the equation by t.

1. **Vocabulary** In the formulas $A = \ell w$ and $P = 2\ell + 2w$, what do the variables ℓ and w represent?
2. **Reasoning** Suppose you know a friend's distance and time for a race. How would you find your friend's rate of travel?

Use the formula $A = \ell w$ to find the area of each rectangle.

3. $\ell = 1.75$ cm, $w = 0.5$ cm $\frac{7}{8}$ cm^2
4. $\ell = 2\frac{1}{3}$ ft, $w = 1\frac{1}{4}$ in. 35 in.^{2}

Name each formula and identify its variables. 5–7. See margin.

5. $A = \frac{1}{2}h(b_1 + b_2)$
6. $d = rt$
7. $P = 4s$

Homework Exercises

For more exercises, see Extra Skills and Word Problems.

GO for Help

For Exercises	See Examples
8–12	1
13	2
14–19	3

A **Find the area of each figure.**

8. 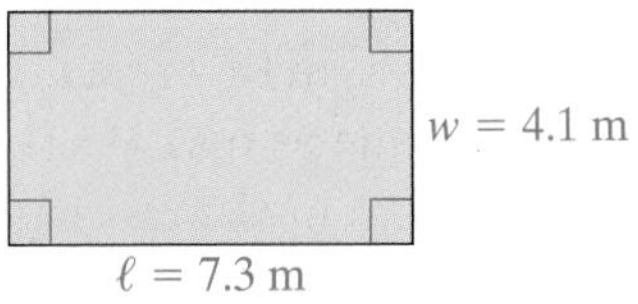

29.93 m^2

9. 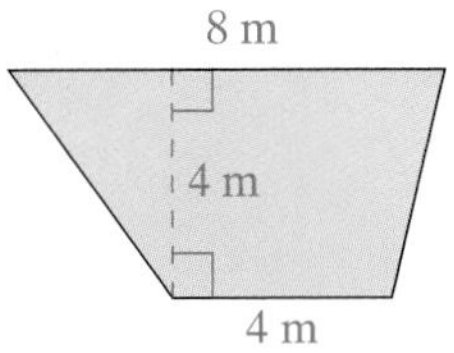

24 m^2

10. 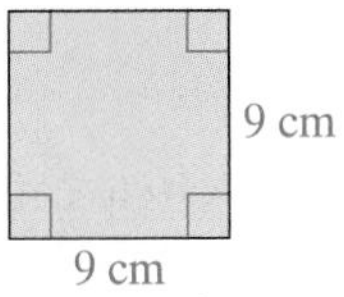

81 cm^2

11. 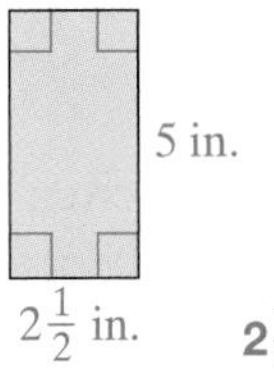

$2\frac{1}{2}$ in.^{2}

12. 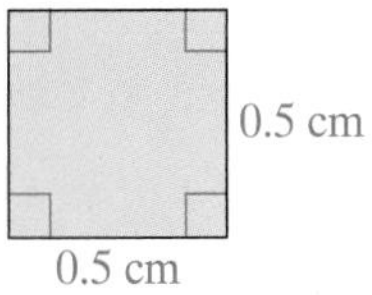

0.25 cm^2

13. Charles Lindbergh flew nonstop across the Atlantic Ocean in 1927. He flew 3,610 miles in 33.5 hours. Find his rate of travel. about 108 mi/h

Algebra **Solve each formula for the variable indicated in red.**

14. $V = \ell wh$ $h = \frac{V}{\ell w}$
15. $d = rt$ $t = \frac{d}{r}$
16. $C = 2\pi r$ $r = \frac{C}{2\pi}$
17. $K = C + 273$ $C = K - 273$
18. $V = \frac{1}{3}Bh$ $h = \frac{3V}{B}$
19. $W = g - 25$ $g = W + 25$

B **GPS**

20. **Guided Problem Solving** A black mamba travels 20 mi/h for $\frac{1}{4}$ mile. How many seconds does it take the snake to travel $\frac{1}{4}$ mile?
    - Solve the distance formula for time. For which variables in the formula should you substitute 20 and $\frac{1}{4}$?
    - How many seconds are in an hour? 45 seconds

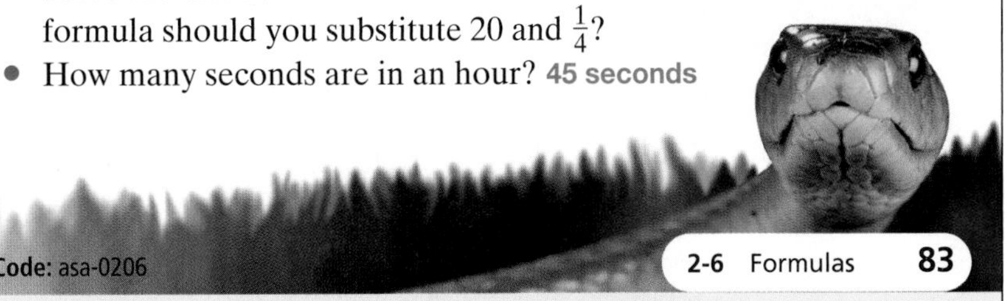

5. Area of a trapezoid; h is the height; b_1 and b_2 are the bases.
6. Distance formula; d is the distance, r is the rate, and t is the time.
7. Perimeter of a square; s is the side length.

3. Practice

Assignment Guide

Check Your Understanding

Go over Exercises 1–7 in class before assigning the Homework Exercises.

Homework Exercises

A Practice by Example	8–19
B Apply Your Skills	20–25
C Challenge	26
Test Prep and Mixed Review	27–32

Homework Quick Check

To check students' understanding of key skills and concepts, go over Exercises 12, 18, 23, 24, and 25.

Differentiated Instruction Resources

Adapted Practice 2-6 L1

Practice 2-6 L3

Find the area and the perimeter of each figure.

1. 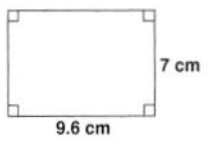

$P = 2l + 2w$; $A = l \cdot w$
$P = 33.2$ cm; $A = 67.2$ cm^2

2. 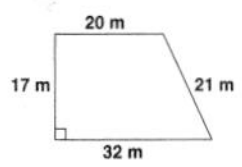

$P = a + b + c + d$;
$A = \frac{1}{2}h(b_1 + b_2)$;
$P = 90$ m; $A = 442$ m^2

Write an equation to find the the solution for each problem. Use the formula $d = rt$. Solve the equation. Then give the solution for the problem.

3. Kent left college at 7:00 A.M. and drove to his parents' house 400 mi away. He arrived at 3:00 P.M. What was his average speed?
   $8r = 400$; 50 mi/h
4. An airplane flew for 4 h 30 min at an average speed of 515 mi/h. How far did it fly?
   $4.5 \times 515 = d$; 2,317.5 mi
5. Marcia rowed her boat 18 mi downstream at a rate of 12 mi/h. How long did the trip take?
   $12t = 18$; 1.5 h

In exercises 6–9, use the formula $F = \frac{9}{5}C + 32$ or $C = \frac{5}{9}(F - 32)$ to find a temperature in either degrees Fahrenheit, °F, or degrees Celsius, °C.

6. What is the temperature in degrees Fahrenheit when it is 0°C?
   32°F
7. What is the temperature in degrees Fahrenheit when it is 100°C?
   212°F
8. What is the temperature in degrees Celsius when it is −4°F?
   −20°C
9. What is the temperature in degrees Celsius when it is 77°F?
   25°C

2-6 • Guided Problem Solving GPS L3

GPS Student Page 84, Exercise 23:

Find the height h of a cone with a radius of 3 ft and a volume of 27 ft^3. Use the formula $V = \frac{1}{3}\pi r^2 h$.

Understand

1. What formula are you given?
   $V = \frac{1}{3}\pi r^2 h$
2. What are you being asked to do?
   Find the height h of the cone.

Plan and Carry Out

3. What do you do first?
   Multiply by $\frac{3}{\pi r^2}$ to isolate h.
4. What is the next step?
   Plug in values and solve for h. $h = \frac{3V}{\pi r^2} \approx \frac{3(27)}{3.14(3^2)} \approx 2.87$

Check

5. How can you check to see if your answer is correct?
   Substitute h into the given formula and solve for V.
   $V = \frac{1}{3}\pi r^2 h \approx \frac{1}{3} \cdot 3.14 \cdot 3^2 \cdot 2.87 = 3.14 \times 3 \times 2.87 \approx 27$

Solve Another Problem

6. For adults, a blood pressure reading around $\frac{120}{80}$ is considered normal. The upper number measures the force of the blood pushing against the walls of the arteries and is called the systolic pressure. An estimate of a person's systolic pressure, P, can be found with the formula $P = 100 + \frac{a}{2}$, where a is age. Solve the formula for a.
   $P = 100 + \frac{a}{2}$; $P - 100 = \frac{a}{2}$; $2(P - 100) = a$

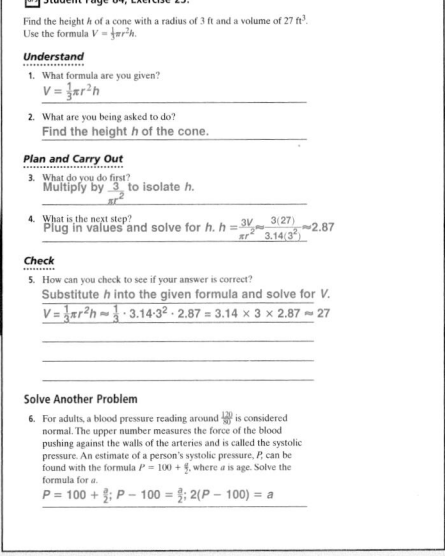

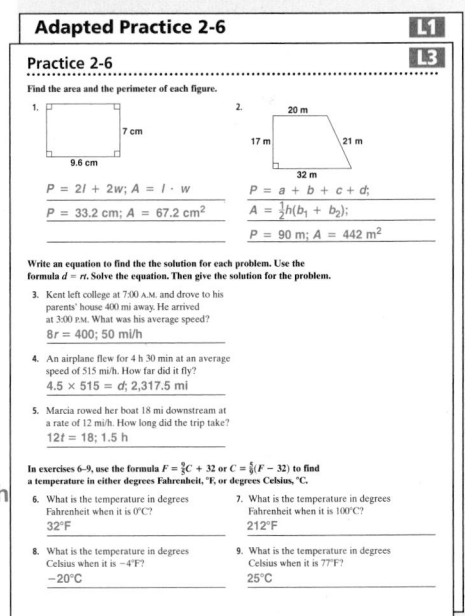

4. Assess & Reteach

PowerPoint

Lesson Quiz

1. Find the area of a triangle whose base is 18 cm and height is 3 cm. **27 cm²**
2. Amina purchased a circular glass tabletop. The radius of the tabletop is 6.5 inches. Find the area of the tabletop. Use $A = \pi r^2$ and let $\pi = 3$. **126.75 square inches**
3. Solve for w in the formula $V = \ell wh$. $w = \frac{V}{\ell h}$
4. Tyrone drove 1,570 miles in 4 days. Find the average distance he drove each day. **392.5 miles**

25a. 2,220 ft

b. The difference between the dew point and air temperature will grow larger, and the height of the base of the cloud will increase. Examples:

$H = 222(80 - 70) =$ 2,220 ft

$H = 222(80 - 60) =$ 4,440 ft

Enrichment 2-6 L4

Reteaching 2-6 L2

You can use a *formula* to find the area of a figure.

Example: Find the area of a square with side length 1.2 m.

$A = s \cdot s$ ← Write the formula.
$A = (1.2)(1.2)$ ← Substitute known values.
$A = 1.44$ ← Simplify.

The area of the square is 1.44 m².

Area Formulas
Rectangle: A = length · width; $A = \ell w$
Square: A = side length · side length; $A = s \cdot s$
Trapezoid: $A = \frac{1}{2}$ height (sum of bases); $A = \frac{1}{2}h(b_1 + b_2)$

Knowing how to *transform a formula* by solving for one of its variables can be useful.

Write a formula to find the width of a rectangle.

Use $A = \ell w$. Solve for w.

$\frac{A}{\ell} = \frac{\ell w}{\ell}$

$\frac{A}{\ell} = w$; or $w = \frac{A}{\ell}$

Find the area of each figure.

1. Square: side 3.4 ft — $A = 11.56$ ft²
2. Rectangle: 6 m × 2.3 m — $A = 13.8$ m²
3. Trapezoid: $b_1 = 6$ m, $b_2 = 12$ m, $h = 4.2$ m — $A = 37.8$ m²

Solve each formula for the variable indicated.

4. Solve for r. $d = rt$ — $r = \frac{d}{t}$
5. Solve for ℓ. $w = \ell - 6$ — $l = w + 6$
6. Solve for b. $y = rx + b$ — $b = y - rx$

Use the formula $d = rt$ to find each of the following.

7. time for $d = 500$ miles and $r = 50$ mi/h — $t = 10$ h
8. rate for $d = 52.5$ miles and $t = 1.5$ hours — 35 mi/h
9. time for $d = 75$ km and $r = 25$ km/h — 3 h

GO Online
Homework Video Tutor
Visit: PHSchool.com
Web Code: ase-0206

24. You use properties of equality; instead of getting a number for an answer, you get an equation.

Use the formula $d = rt$ to find each of the following.

21. r for $d = 12$ mi and $t = 0.5$ h **24 mi/h**
22. t for $d = 120$ km and $r = 45$ km/h **$2\frac{2}{3}$ h**

23. **(Algebra)** GPS Find the height h of a cone with a radius of 3 ft and a volume of 27 ft³. Use the formula $V = \frac{1}{3}\pi r^2 h$. **$\frac{9}{\pi}$ ft**

24. **Writing in Math** How is transforming a formula similar to solving an equation with just one variable? How is it different? **See left.**

25. **Clouds** Cumulus clouds have flat bases and lumpy tops. The tops are usually about 1 mile above sea level. To find the height in feet of the base of a cumulus cloud, you can use the formula
height = 222(air temperature − dew-point temperature).
The air and dew-point temperatures are in degrees Fahrenheit.
a. Find the height of the base of a cumulus cloud when the air temperature is 80°F and the dew-point temperature is 70°F.
b. **Number Sense** Suppose the dew point drops and the air temperature remains constant. What happens to the height of the base of the cloud? Explain. **25a–b. See margin.**

(C) 26. **Challenge** The length of a rectangle is 5 cm. The area of the rectangle is the same as that of a square whose side measures 4 cm. Find the width of the rectangle. **3.2 cm**

Test Prep and Mixed Review

Practice

Multiple Choice

27. The circumference C of a circle can be found using the formula $C = 2\pi r$, where r represents the radius of the circle. What should Olivia do to write a formula to find the radius of a circle? **C**
 (A) Subtract 2π from C and $2\pi r$.
 (B) Multiply C and $2\pi r$ by r.
 (C) Divide C and $2\pi r$ by 2π.
 (D) Divide C and $2\pi r$ by r.

28. Jose is sharing half of a pizza with two friends. Which expression can be used to find the fraction of a whole pizza each person will get, if they split what they have evenly? **G**
 (F) $\frac{1}{2} \cdot 3$
 (G) $\frac{1}{2} \cdot \frac{1}{3}$
 (H) $2 \cdot 3$
 (J) $2 \cdot \frac{1}{3}$

29. Your school is having three speakers on career day. One fifth of the students are going to hear Speaker A, and $\frac{2}{3}$ are going to hear Speaker B. What fraction of students are going to hear Speaker C? **B**
 (A) $\frac{1}{15}$
 (B) $\frac{2}{15}$
 (C) $\frac{1}{5}$
 (D) $\frac{4}{15}$

GO for Help

For Exercises	See Lesson
30–32	2-1

Use prime factorization to find the GCF of each pair of numbers.

30. 32, 48 **16**
31. 51, 68 **17**
32. 84, 90 **6**

Test Prep

Resources

For additional practice with a variety of test item formats:
- Test-Taking Strategies, p. 97
- Test Prep, p. 101
- Test-Taking Strategies with Transparencies

Alternative Assessment

Given a rectangle with a perimeter of 22 m and a width of 3 m, students find the length and then the area of the rectangle. **8 m; 24 m²**

Using Formulas

Use the LIST key on a graphing calculator to evaluate a formula.

EXAMPLE

Evaluate the formula $P = 2\ell + 2w$ for $\ell = 3$ and for whole-number values of w from 8 to 11.

Step 1 Press STAT 1 to open the stat list editor window. If columns are not clear, use the arrow keys to go to the top of each column. Press CLEAR ENTER.

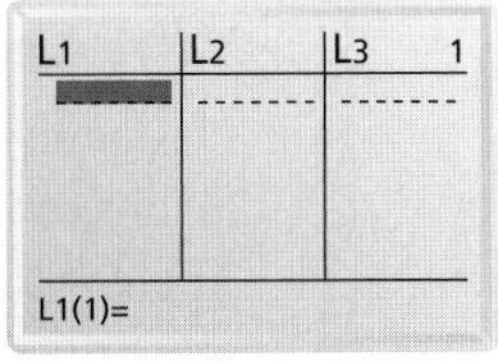

Step 2 In the column labeled L1, enter the four values of ℓ. In this example, each value of ℓ is 3. In the column labeled L2, enter the four values of w from 8 to 11.

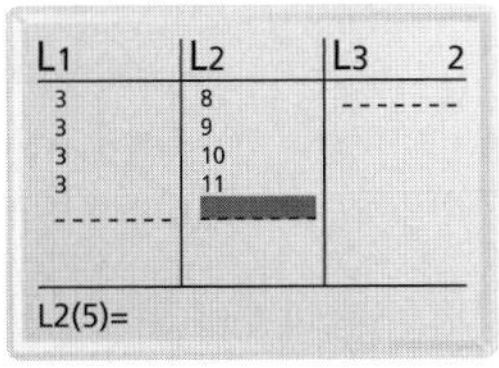

Step 3 Go to the top of the column marked L3 and highlight L3. To enter the formula $P = 2\ell + 2w$, think L3 = 2 · L1 + 2 · L2. Use these keystrokes.
2 × 2nd STAT 1 + 2 × 2nd STAT 2
Press ENTER. The calculator automatically calculates the value of the perimeters.
Hint: Before starting a new exercise, clear the columns.

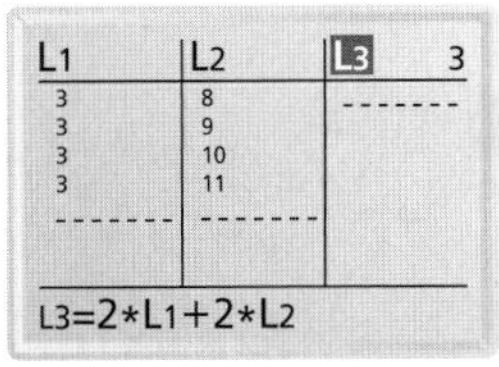

Exercises

Suppose the values of *a* and *b* are listed in L1 and L2 of a graphing calculator. Write the keystrokes you would use to enter each formula in L3.

1. $P = a + b$
   L3 = $L_1 + L_2$
2. $X = 3a + 5b$
   L3 = $3 \times L_1 + 5 \times L_2$
3. $A = 0.5ab$
   L3 = $0.5 \times L_1 \times L_2$
4. $T = a^2$
   L3 = L_1^2
5. **Calculator** Evaluate the formula $A = \frac{1}{2}bh$ for the given values.
   a. $b = 8$; $h = 10, 11, 12, 13, 14, 15$
   40, 44, 48, 52, 56, 60
   b. $b = 8, 9, 10, 11, 12$; $h = 10$
   40, 45, 50, 55, 60
6. **Patterns** Enter the numbers 1 through 7 in L1. Enter the formula L2 = $\frac{L1}{9}$. What number pattern do you see in L2? $0.\overline{1}, 0.\overline{2}, \ldots 0.\overline{7}$
7. Enter the numbers 1 through 7 in L1. Enter L2 = L1^2 − L1 + 41. Are all the numbers in L2 prime? yes

Activity Lab

Using Formulas

In this Activity, students use a graphing calculator to evaluate formulas, such as the one used for finding the perimeter of a rectangle.

Guided Instruction

Example

Work with small groups of students to help them understand the uses of the keys on their calculators. Provide time for practice. As needed, begin this lesson by evaluating a simpler formula, such as $A = \ell w$ or $d = rt$.

Then have students work in pairs. Partners can compare and discuss formulas, evaluate formulas, and find number patterns. Invite pairs to choose other formulas to evaluate: one partner can select the formula and the other can name number values to enter.

Differentiated Instruction

Auditory Learners
Review and have students repeat the mathematical meanings of the terms *evaluate* and *perimeter*. Invite students to add these terms to their mathematics dictionaries. Also, make sure students understand what it means to "scroll," and what a "column" is in this context.

Resources

- any graphing calculator

2-7

1. Plan

Objective
To write, simplify, and evaluate expressions involving exponents

Examples
1 Writing with Exponents
2 Simplifying Expressions
3 Evaluating Expressions

Math Understandings: p. 50D

Professional Development

Math Background

Just as multiplication can be thought of as repeated addition, so exponentiation is a way of indicating repeated multiplication. The exponent tells how many times the base is used as a factor. An exponent applies only to its base or to the contents in the parentheses to which it is attached. For example, $13 - 3^2$ is 4 because the base (3) is squared. So -3^2 equals -9, and $(-3)^2$ equals 9.

More Math Background: p. 50D

Lesson Planning and Resources

See p. 50E for a list of the resources that support this lesson.

PowerPoint

Bell Ringer Practice

Check Skills You'll Need
Use student page, transparency, or PowerPoint. For intervention, direct students to:
Factors
Lesson 2-1
Extra Skills and Word Problems Practice, Ch. 2

2-7 Powers and Exponents

Check Skills You'll Need

1. **Vocabulary Review** A _?_ is an integer that divides another integer with a remainder of 0. factor

Find the GCF.

2. 12, 16 4
3. 24, 30 6
4. 32, 48 16
5. 120, 144 24
6. 80, 256 16

GO for Help Lesson 2-1

What You'll Learn

To write, simplify, and evaluate expressions involving exponents

New Vocabulary exponent, base, power

Why Learn This?

Designing a bridge or other large structure involves many calculations and measurements. You can use exponents to represent some of these numbers.

An **exponent** tells how many times a number, or **base,** is used as a factor. An expression using a base and an exponent is a **power.**

$$2^5 = \underbrace{2 \cdot 2 \cdot 2 \cdot 2 \cdot 2}_{5 \text{ factors of } 2} = 32$$

power → 2^5; base: 2; exponent: 5; 32 ← value of the expression

A power with an exponent of 1 means that the base is used as a factor only once. For example, $3^1 = 3$.

EXAMPLE Writing With Exponents

1 Write $3 \cdot 3 \cdot 5 \cdot 5 \cdot 5$ using exponents.

$3^2 \cdot 5^3$ ← 3 is a factor 2 times, and 5 is a factor 3 times.

Vocabulary Tip
You read 3^2 as "3 to the second power" or "3 squared." You read 5^3 as "5 to the third power" or "5 cubed."

Quick Check

1. Write $6 \cdot 6 \cdot 7 \cdot 7 \cdot 7 \cdot 7 \cdot 7 \cdot 7$ using exponents. $6^2 \cdot 7^6$

You can extend the order of operations to include powers.

KEY CONCEPTS Order of Operations

1. Work inside grouping symbols.
2. Simplify the powers.
3. Multiply and divide from left to right.
4. Add and subtract from left to right.

Differentiated Instruction Solutions for All Learners

Special Needs L1
Highlight the base in 5^3 and say: *5 is the base.* Circle the exponent and say: *3 is the exponent. The 3 tells you to use 5 as a factor 3 times:* 5 x 5 x 5. Have students identify the base and exponent of 4^3 and explain what 4^3 means.
learning style: visual

Below Level L2
Have students describe how repeated additions compare with repeated multiplications using the example $5 + 5 + 5 = 5 \cdot 3 = 15$ and $2 \cdot 2 \cdot 2 \cdot 2 = 2^4 = 16$.
learning style: verbal

The expression $(-5)^4$ means the fourth power of −5. The expression -5^4 means the opposite of the fourth power of 5.

EXAMPLES Simplifying Expressions

Calculator Tip

You can use the exponent key ^ on your calculator to find the value of any power. To evaluate $(-5)^4$, press ((−) 5) ^ 4 ENTER.

2 Simplify $(-5)^4$.

$(-5)^4 = (-5)(-5)(-5)(-5)$ ← **The base is −5.**

$= 625$ ← **Multiply.**

3 Simplify -5^4.

$-5^4 = -(5 \cdot 5 \cdot 5 \cdot 5)$ ← **The base is 5.**

$= -625$ ← **Multiply.**

4 Simplify $26 - (2 \cdot 5)^2$.

$26 - (2 \cdot 5)^2 = 26 - (10)^2$ ← **Work inside the grouping symbols.**

$= 26 - 100$ ← **Simplify the power.**

$= -74$ ← **Subtract.**

Quick Check

Simplify each expression.

2. $(-7)^3$ −343 **3.** -7^3 −343 **4.** $-4 + 6 \cdot 3^2$ 50

You can evaluate algebraic expressions using the order of operations.

EXAMPLE Evaluating Expressions

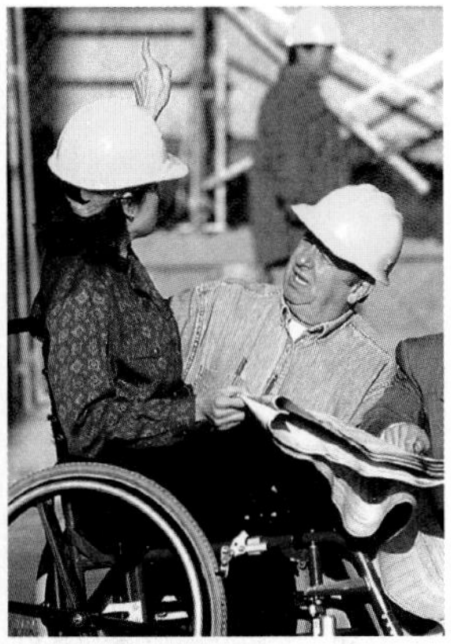

Careers Architects design a wide variety of buildings and complexes.

5 **Architecture** You can find the radius of the arch in a doorway with the expression $\frac{s^2 + h^2}{2h}$. Find the radius r of a doorway with dimensions $s = 4$ ft and $h = 2$ ft.

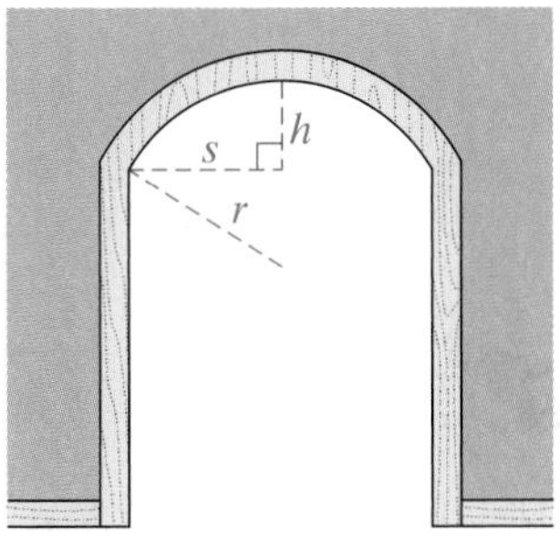

$\frac{s^2 + h^2}{2h} = \frac{4^2 + 2^2}{2 \cdot 2}$ ← **Substitute 4 for *s* and 2 for *h*.**

$= \frac{16 + 4}{2 \cdot 2}$ ← **Simplify the powers in the numerator.**

$= \frac{20}{4} = 5$ ← **Simplify. Then divide.**

The radius of the arch is 5 ft.

Quick Check

5. Find the radius r of a doorway with dimensions $s = 5$ m and $h = 3$ m. $5\frac{2}{3}$ m

2. Teach

Activity Lab

Use before the lesson.

All-in-One Teaching Resources

Activity Lab 2-7: Powers and Exponents

Guided Instruction

Error Prevention!

Some students may see 3^2 as $3 \cdot 2$. Discuss the fact that an exponent is always to the right of its base, always raised, and always a smaller-sized number.

PowerPoint

Additional Examples

1 Write $2 \cdot 2 \cdot 2 \cdot 7 \cdot 7$ using exponents. **a.** $2^3 \cdot 7^2$

Simplify the expression.

2 $(-2)^6$ 64

3 $-(2)^6$ −64

4 $38 - (3 \cdot 2)^2$ 2

5 Use the expression $\frac{s^2 + h^2}{2h}$ to find the radius of a doorway that has the dimensions $s = 3$ ft and $h = 1$ ft. 5 ft

All-in-One Teaching Resources

- Daily Notetaking Guide 2-7 L3
- Adapted Notetaking 2-7 L1

Closure

- *How can you recognize an exponent, and what does it mean?* An exponent is "raised" to the upper right of a base. It is a shorthand notation for indicating how many times the base is multiplied by itself.
- *When, in the order of operations, do you calculate the value of expressions with exponents?* after calculations in grouping symbols and before the multiplications and divisions are performed

Advanced Learners L4

Have students use patterns to make conjectures about the meaning of 0 and −1 as exponents.

learning style: verbal

English Language Learners ELL

Students write the order of operations using symbols and words. For example: **1.** ( ) parentheses; **2.** a^3 exponents; **3.** × or ÷ multiply or divide; **4.** + or − add or subtract.

learning style: visual

3. Practice

Assignment Guide

Check Your Understanding

Go over Exercises 1–10 in class before assigning the Homework Exercises.

Homework Exercises

A Practice by Example	11–31
B Apply Your Skills	32–41
C Challenge	42
Test Prep and Mixed Review	43–49

Homework Quick Check

To check students' understanding of key skills and concepts, go over Exercises 16, 25, 38, 39, and 40.

Differentiated Instruction Resources

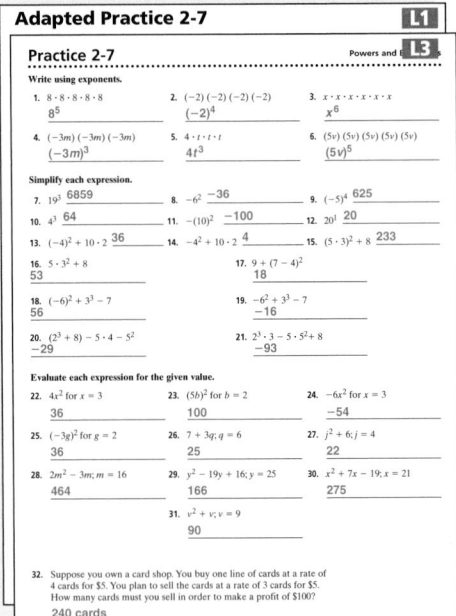

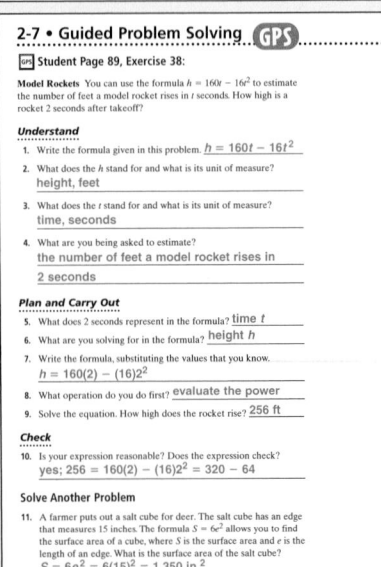

Adapted Practice 2-7 L1

Practice 2-7 Powers and E[...]s L3

Write using exponents.

1. $8 \cdot 8 \cdot 8 \cdot 8 \cdot 8$ 8^5
2. $(-2)(-2)(-2)(-2)$ $(-2)^4$
3. $x \cdot x \cdot x \cdot x \cdot x \cdot x$ x^6
4. $(-3m)(-3m)(-3m)$ $(-3m)^3$
5. $4 \cdot t \cdot t \cdot t$ $4t^3$
6. $(5v)(5v)(5v)(5v)(5v)$ $(5v)^5$

Simplify each expression.

7. 19^3 6859
8. -6^2 −36
9. $(-5)^4$ 625
10. 4^3 64
11. $-(10)^2$ −100
12. 20^1 20
13. $(-4)^2 + 10 \cdot 2$ 36
14. $-4^2 + 10 \cdot 2$ 4
15. $(5 \cdot 3)^2 + 8$ 233
16. $5 \cdot 3^2 + 8$ 53
17. $9 + (7 - 4)^2$ 18
18. $(-6)^2 + 3^3 - 7$ 56
19. $-6^2 + 3^3 - 7$ −16
20. $(2^3 + 8) - 5 \cdot 4 - 5^2$ −29
21. $2^3 \cdot 3 - 5 \cdot 5^2 + 8$ −93

Evaluate each expression for the given value.

22. $4x^2$ for $x = 3$ 36
23. $(5b)^2$ for $b = 2$ 100
24. $-6x^2$ for $x = 3$ −54
25. $(-3g)^2$ for $g = 2$ 36
26. $7 + 3q; q = 6$ 25
27. $j^2 + 6; j = 4$ 22
28. $2m^2 - 3m; m = 16$ 464
29. $y^2 - 19y + 16; y = 25$ 166
30. $x^2 + 7x - 19; x = 21$ 275
31. $v^2 + v; v = 9$ 90

32. Suppose you own a card shop. You buy one line of cards at a rate of 4 cards for $5. You plan to sell the cards at a rate of 3 cards for $5. How many cards must you sell in order to make a profit of $100? 240 cards

2-7 • Guided Problem Solving GPS L3

Student Page 89, Exercise 38:

Model Rockets You can use the formula $h = 160t - 16t^2$ to estimate the number of feet a model rocket rises in t seconds. How high is a rocket 2 seconds after takeoff?

Understand

1. Write the formula given in this problem. $h = 160t - 16t^2$
2. What does the h stand for and what is its unit of measure? height, feet
3. What does the t stand for and what is its unit of measure? time, seconds
4. What are you being asked to estimate? the number of feet a model rocket rises in 2 seconds

Plan and Carry Out

5. What does 2 seconds represent in the formula? time t
6. What are you solving for in the formula? height h
7. Write the formula, substituting the values that you know. $h = 160(2) - (16)2^2$
8. What operation do you do first? evaluate the power
9. Solve the equation. How high does the rocket rise? 256 ft

Check

10. Is your expression reasonable? Does the expression check? yes; $256 = 160(2) - (16)2^2 = 320 - 64$

Solve Another Problem

11. A farmer puts out a salt cube for deer. The salt cube has an edge that measures 15 inches. The formula $S = 6e^2$ allows you to find the surface area of a cube, where S is the surface area and e is the length of an edge. What is the surface area of the salt cube? $S = 6e^2 = 6(15)^2 = 1{,}350$ in.^{2}

Check Your Understanding

Vocabulary **Match the variable(s) with the correct term.**

1. 3^x C
2. m^5 A
3. y^z B

A. base
B. power
C. exponent

4. **Reasoning** Is $x^2 \cdot x^3$ the same as x^5? Explain. Yes; $x^2 \cdot x^3 = x \cdot x \cdot x \cdot x \cdot x$, which is x^5.

Write using exponents.

5. $9 \cdot 9 \cdot 9 \cdot x$ $9^3 \cdot x$
6. $4 \cdot 4 \cdot 4 \cdot 4 \cdot 4$ 4^5
7. $z \cdot z \cdot z \cdot z \cdot z \cdot z$ z^6

Simplify each expression.

8. -8^2 −64
9. $(-8)^2$ 64
10. $(-1)^2 - 2 \cdot 4$ −7

Homework Exercises

For more exercises, see Extra Skills and Word Problems.

GO for Help

For Exercises	See Examples
11–16	1
17–24	2 and 3
25–30	4
31	5

A **Write using exponents.**

11. $4 \cdot 4 \cdot 8 \cdot 8 \cdot 8 \cdot 8$ $4^2 \cdot 8^4$
12. $6 \cdot 6 \cdot 6 \cdot 11$ $6^3 \cdot 11$
13. $5 \cdot 5 \cdot x \cdot x \cdot x \cdot y$ $5^2 \cdot x^3 \cdot y$
14. $9 \cdot a \cdot a \cdot b \cdot c \cdot c \cdot c$ $9 \cdot a^2 \cdot b \cdot c^3$
15. $m \cdot p \cdot m \cdot p \cdot p$ $m^2 \cdot p^3$
16. $7 \cdot w \cdot t \cdot 7 \cdot t$ $7^2 \cdot t^2 \cdot w$

Simplify each expression.

17. $(-2)^5$ −32
18. -2^5 −32
19. $(-6)^3$ −216
20. -6^3 −216
21. -15^2 −225
22. $(-15)^2$ 225
23. $(-3)^4$ 81
24. -3^4 −81
25. $(-3)^2 + 12 \cdot 4$ 57
26. $-3^2 + 12 \cdot 5$ 51
27. $(3 \cdot 2)^2 + 5$ 41
28. $3^2 \cdot 2 + 5$ 23
29. $4 + (8 - 6)^2$ 8
30. $4 + 8 - 6^2$ −24

31. **Geometry** The formula for the volume of a cylinder is $V = \pi r^2 h$, where r is the radius of the base, and h is the height of the cylinder. Find the volume of the cylinder with a radius of 6 cm and a height of 30 cm. Use $\pi = 3.14$. 3,391.2 cm^3

B **GPS** 32. **Guided Problem Solving** The formula for the area of a square is $A = s^2$. The formula for the area of a circle is $A = \pi r^2$. What is the difference in the areas of the figures if the square has a side length of 10 units and the circle has a radius length of 10 units? Use $\pi \approx 3.14$. 214 square units
- What is the area of the square?
- What is the area of the circle?

Exercises, p. 89

39. No; the product of any number and itself is always positive. For example, $3^2 = 3 \cdot 3 = 9$, and $(-3)^2 = -3 \cdot -3 = 9$.

41. yes; when $a = 0$ or $b = 0$, and when $a = 1$

Online Homework Video Tutor
Visit: PHSchool.com
Web Code: ase-0207

Evaluate each expression for $n = -3$.

33. $5n^2 - 5(2n - 3)^2$ −360

34. $(4n)^2 + 48 \div (-4n)$ 148

35. $\frac{n^2 + 9}{n^2}$ 2

36. $5(2n - 3)^2$ 405

37. **Skydiving** The formula $d = 16t^2$ describes the number of feet d a skydiver falls in t seconds of free fall assuming there is no air resistance. How far does a skydiver fall between the third and fourth seconds? 112 ft

38. **Model Rockets** (GPS) You can use the formula $h = 160t - 16t^2$ to estimate the number of feet a model rocket rises in t seconds. How high is a rocket 2 seconds after takeoff? 256 ft.

39. **Writing in Math** Can the square of a number be negative? Explain. See margin.

40. The formula for the volume of a cone is $V = \frac{1}{3}\pi r^2 h$, where r is the radius, and h is the height. The formula for the volume of a sphere is $V = \frac{4}{3}\pi r^3$, where r = the radius. How many fewer cubic units of space does a sphere with a radius of 3 units occupy than a cone with a radius of 6 units and a height of 9 units? Use $\pi \approx 3.14$. 226.08 cubic units

41. **Reasoning** Does $(ab)^2 = ab^2$ for any values of a and b? Explain. See margin.

(C) 42. **Challenge** Write an expression for 100 using five 5's. Sample answer: $5 \cdot 5 \cdot 5 - 5 \cdot 5$

Test Prep and Mixed Review — Practice

Multiple Choice

43. The number of square feet that represent the area of a square is twice the number of feet that represents the perimeter of the square. Which of the following could be the area of the square? D
(A) 4 ft^2 (B) 16 ft^2 (C) 36 ft^2 (D) 64 ft^2

44. In science class, Julian learned that he can use the formula $C = \frac{5}{9}(F - 32)$ to convert between degrees Celsius C and degrees Fahrenheit F. If the temperature outside is 95°F, what is the temperature in degrees Celsius? F
(F) 35°C (G) 63°C (H) 113°C (J) 203°C

45. In Amanda's CD collection, $\frac{1}{3}$ of the CDs are pop and $\frac{1}{5}$ are rock. Of her rock CDs, $\frac{1}{2}$ of the artists are bands and $\frac{1}{4}$ are solo female singers. The rest of her CDs are movie soundtracks. What fraction of Amanda's CDs are soundtracks? C
(A) $\frac{1}{15}$ (B) $\frac{1}{8}$ (C) $\frac{7}{15}$ (D) $\frac{8}{15}$

GO for Help

For Exercises	See Lesson
46–49	2-2

Write each decimal as a fraction in simplest form.

46. 0.3 $\frac{3}{10}$

47. 6.36 $6\frac{9}{25}$

48. 0.003 $\frac{3}{1000}$

49. 0.45 $\frac{9}{20}$

4. Assess & Reteach

PowerPoint Lesson Quiz

1. Write $a \cdot a \cdot a \cdot b \cdot b$ using exponents. a^3b^2
2. Simplify $(-4)^3$. −64
3. Simplify -2^5. −32
4. Simplify $(-8 \cdot 5)^2 - 9^2$. 1,519
5. Evaluate $10 - (5x)^2$ for $x = -2$. −90
6. Find the volume of a child's wading pool that has a diameter of 6 feet and a height of 1 foot. Use the formula $V = \pi r^2 h$. Use $\pi = 3$. 27 cubic feet

Reteaching 2-7 — Powers and E… L2

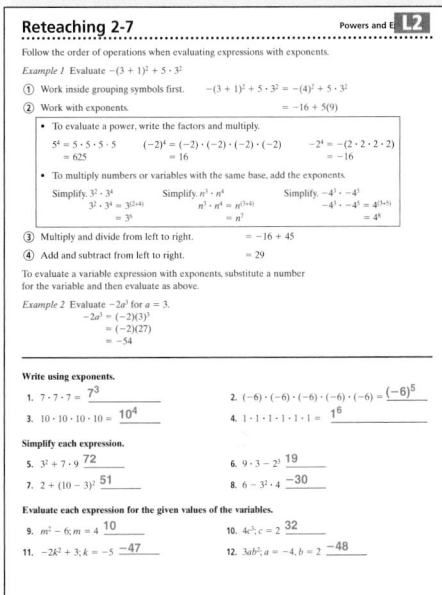

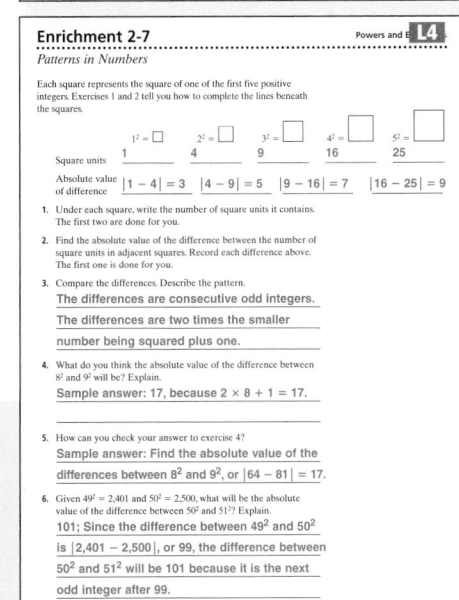

Follow the order of operations when evaluating expressions with exponents.

Example 1 Evaluate $-(3 + 1)^2 + 5 \cdot 3^2$

① Work inside grouping symbols first. $-(3 + 1)^2 + 5 \cdot 3^2 = -(4)^2 + 5 \cdot 3^2$

② Work with exponents. $= -16 + 5(9)$

- To evaluate a power, write the factors and multiply.
  $5^4 = 5 \cdot 5 \cdot 5 \cdot 5 = 625$ $(-2)^4 = (-2) \cdot (-2) \cdot (-2) \cdot (-2) = 16$ $-2^4 = -(2 \cdot 2 \cdot 2 \cdot 2) = -16$
- To multiply numbers or variables with the same base, add the exponents.
  Simplify. $3^2 \cdot 3^4$: $3^2 \cdot 3^4 = 3^{(2+4)} = 3^6$ Simplify. $n^3 \cdot n^4$: $n^3 \cdot n^4 = n^{(3+4)} = n^7$ Simplify. $-4^3 \cdot -4^5$: $-4^3 \cdot -4^5 = 4^{(3+5)} = 4^8$

③ Multiply and divide from left to right. $= -16 + 45$

④ Add and subtract from left to right. $= 29$

To evaluate a variable expression with exponents, substitute a number for the variable and then evaluate as above.

Example 2 Evaluate $-2a^3$ for $a = 3$.
$-2a^3 = (-2)(3)^3 = (-2)(27) = -54$

Write using exponents.

1. $7 \cdot 7 \cdot 7 =$ 7^3
2. $(-6) \cdot (-6) \cdot (-6) \cdot (-6) \cdot (-6) =$ $(-6)^5$
3. $10 \cdot 10 \cdot 10 \cdot 10 =$ 10^4
4. $1 \cdot 1 \cdot 1 \cdot 1 \cdot 1 \cdot 1 =$ 1^6

Simplify each expression.

5. $3^2 + 7 \cdot 9$ 72
6. $9 \cdot 3 - 2^3$ 19
7. $2 + (10 - 3)^2$ 51
8. $6 - 3^2 \cdot 4$ −30

Evaluate each expression for the given values of the variables.

9. $m^2 - 6; m = 4$ 10
10. $4c^3; c = 2$ 32
11. $-2k^2 + 3; k = -5$ −47
12. $3ab^2; a = -4, b = 2$ −48

Enrichment 2-7 — Powers and E… L4

Patterns in Numbers

Each square represents the square of one of the first five positive integers. Exercises 1 and 2 tell you how to complete the lines beneath the squares.

	$1^2 =$ □	$2^2 =$ □	$3^2 =$ □	$4^2 =$ □	$5^2 =$ □
Square units	1	4	9	16	25
Absolute value of difference	$\|1 - 4\| = 3$	$\|4 - 9\| = 5$	$\|9 - 16\| = 7$	$\|16 - 25\| = 9$	

1. Under each square, write the number of square units it contains. The first two are done for you.
2. Find the absolute value of the difference between the number of square units in adjacent squares. Record each difference above. The first one is done for you.
3. Compare the differences. Describe the pattern.
   The differences are consecutive odd integers. The differences are two times the smaller number being squared plus one.
4. What do you think the absolute value of the difference between 8^2 and 9^2 will be? Explain.
   Sample answer: 17, because $2 \times 8 + 1 = 17$.
5. How can you check your answer to exercise 4?
   Sample answer: Find the absolute value of the differences between 8^2 and 9^2, or $|64 - 81| = 17$.
6. Given $49^2 = 2{,}401$ and $50^2 = 2{,}500$, what will be the absolute value of the difference between 50^2 and 51^2? Explain.
   101; Since the difference between 49^2 and 50^2 is $|2{,}401 - 2{,}500|$, or 99, the difference between 50^2 and 51^2 will be 101 because it is the next odd integer after 99.

Alternative Assessment

Students list the formulas used in this lesson. Then, working in pairs, one student selects an equation and numbers for all but one of the variables. The second student evaluates the expression.

Test Prep

Resources
For additional practice with a variety of test item formats:
- Test-Taking Strategies, p. 97
- Test Prep, p. 101
- Test-Taking Strategies with Transparencies

Activity Lab

Evaluating Expressions

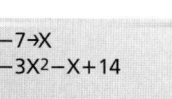

Like scientific calculators, graphing calculators can be an invaluable tool for math students. In this Activity, students use a graphing calculator to evaluate algebraic expressions containing integers and exponents.

Guided Instruction

Discuss with students the similarities and differences between features of basic calculators, scientific calculators, and graphing calculators.

Examples

Work with small groups of students to help them understand the uses of the keys on their graphing calculators. Provide time for exploration and practice using the most frequently-used keys. Also, as needed, review what an expression is and what it means to evaluate an expression.

Error Prevention!

Students may press the keys in the wrong order. To help remediate, have students work through the examples, using the keystrokes shown to find the answers. Next, have students use their calculators to evaluate the expressions *without* looking at the examples.

Differentiated Instruction

Below Level L2

Before students do Exercise 1, ask them to say the keystrokes to evaluate the expression in Exercise 1.

Resources

- a graphing calculator

Evaluating Expressions

You can use a graphing calculator to evaluate any expression. Note that on a graphing calculator, [–] means subtract, while [(–)] means the opposite of a number.

EXAMPLE Evaluating for One Value

1 Use a graphing calculator to evaluate $-3x^2 - x + 14$ for $x = -7$.

Keystrokes

[(–)] 7 [STO▶] [x] [ENTER] ← **Store the value −7 to the variable *x*. Use the negative key [(–)].**

[(–)] 3 [x] [x^2] [–] [x] [+] 14 [ENTER] ← **Evaluate the expression.**

Screen

```
-7→X            -7
-3X²-X+14     -126
```

The value of the expression when $x = -7$ is -126.

EXAMPLE Evaluating for Many Values

2 Evaluate the expression in Example 1 for integer values of x from 1 to 7.

Step 1 Press [Y=]. Next to Y1, enter the expression $-3x^2 - x + 14$.

```
Plot 1  Plot 2  Plot 3
\Y1=-3X²-X+14
\Y2=
\Y3=
\Y4=
```

Step 2 Press [2nd] [WINDOW] and set TblStart = 1 and ΔTbl = 1.

```
TABLE SETUP
 TblStart=1
 ΔTbl=1
Indpnt: Auto Ask
Depend: Auto Ask
```

Step 3 Press [2nd] [GRAPH] to view the table.

X	Y1
1	10
2	0
3	−16
4	−38
5	−66
6	−100
7	−140

X=1

Exercises

Use a graphing calculator to evaluate each expression for the given value.

1. $x^2 - 2x + 5$ for $x = -10$ 125

2. $\frac{5}{9}(x - 32)$ for $x = 98.6$ 37

3. $-4x^2 + 34x - 6$ for $x = 25$ −1656

4. Use a graphing calculator to evaluate the expression $4x^2 - 7x + 19$ for integer values of x from 1 to 7. 16; 21; 34; 55; 84; 121; 166

Checkpoint Quiz 2

Lessons 2-5 through 2-7

Find each product or quotient. Write the answer in simplest form.

1. $\frac{2}{5} \cdot (-7)$ $-2\frac{4}{5}$
2. $1\frac{1}{3} \cdot 1\frac{1}{3}$ $1\frac{7}{9}$
3. $1\frac{2}{3} \div 3\frac{4}{7}$ $\frac{7}{15}$
4. $-\frac{1}{6} \div 4\frac{3}{4}$ $-\frac{2}{57}$

Simplify each expression.

5. $10 - 2^4 \cdot 3$ -38
6. $(-5)^2 - 6 \cdot 4^2$ -71
7. $(3^2 + 1)^2$ 100
8. $(3 + 2)^3 - 8 \cdot 4$ 93
9. Solve the formula $T = \frac{1}{3}ab$ for b. $b = \frac{3T}{a}$
10. The formula for the area of a trapezoid is $A = \frac{1}{2}h(b_1 + b_2)$. Find A for a trapezoid with height $2\frac{1}{3}$ cm and bases $4\frac{3}{4}$ cm and $3\frac{5}{6}$ cm. $A = 10\frac{1}{72}$ cm^2
11. The formula for the volume of a cone is $V = \frac{1}{3}\pi r^2 h$, where r is the radius, and h is the height. Find the height h of a cone with a radius of 6 cm and a volume of 48 cm^3. $h = \frac{4}{\pi}$ cm

2-8a Activity Lab

Multiplying by Powers of 10

ACTIVITY

1. Copy and complete the table. See margin.

$6.71 \times 10^6 = 6.71 \times 1{,}000{,}000$	= ■
$6.71 \times 10^5 = 6.71 \times 100{,}000$	= ■
$6.71 \times 10^4 = 6.71 \times 10{,}000$	= ■
$6.71 \times 10^3 = 6.71 \times$ ■	= ■
$6.71 \times 10^2 = 6.71 \times 100$	= ■
$6.71 \times 10^1 = 6.71 \times$ ■	= ■

2. The exponent of 10 is equal to the number of zeros in the number being multiplied by 6.71.
3. The decimal point moves to the right the number of places equal to the exponent.
4. When you multiply by a positive power of 10, move the decimal point to the right the number of places equal to the exponent.

2. **Patterns** What relationship do you see between the exponent of 10 and the number being multiplied by 6.71?
3. Explain what happens in your table as the exponent of 10 increases.
4. **Writing in Math** Write a rule for multiplying by powers of 10.

Checkpoint Quiz

Use this Checkpoint Quiz to check students' understanding of the skills and concepts of Lessons 2-5 through 2-7.

Resources

- All in One Teaching Resources Checkpoint Quiz 1
- ExamView Assessment Suite CD-ROM
- Success Tracker Online Intervention

Activity Lab

Multiplying by Powers of 10

Students view patterns of powers of ten on a table in preparation for using scientific notation to write very large and very small numbers.

Guided Instruction

To make sure that students find the patterns in the table, have them describe what they see in each column. Point out the changes between each row. You may want to return to this pattern when students learn about negative exponents in Lesson 2-8.

Resources

- Activity Lab 2-8: Notation Concentration

Activity Lab

1.

$6.71 \times 10^6 = 6.71 \times 1{,}000{,}000$	= 6,710,000
$6.71 \times 10^5 = 6.71 \times 100{,}000$	= 671,000
$6.71 \times 10^4 = 6.71 \times 10{,}000$	= 67,100
$6.71 \times 10^3 = 6.71 \times 1{,}000$	= 6,710
$6.71 \times 10^2 = 6.71 \times 100$	= 671
$6.71 \times 10^1 = 6.71 \times 10$	= 67.1

2-8

1. Plan

Objective
To write numbers in both standard form and scientific notation

Examples
1 Writing in Standard Form
2 Writing in Scientific Notation
3 Negative Exponents
4 Numbers Less Than 1

Math Understandings: p. 50D

Professional Development

Math Background

The "center" of decimal notation is the units place together with the decimal point. To the right of the decimal point is one-tenth; to the left of the decimal point is ten. A number is written in *scientific notation* when it is expressed as the product of $c \times 10^d$ where $1 \leq c < 10$ and d is an integer.

More Math Background: p. 50D

Lesson Planning and Resources

See p. 50E for a list of the resources that support this lesson.

PowerPoint

Bell Ringer Practice

Check Skills You'll Need
Use student page, transparency, or PowerPoint. For intervention, direct students to:
Multiplying Whole Numbers and Decimals
Skills Handbook, p. 634

2-8 Scientific Notation

Check Skills You'll Need

1. **Vocabulary Review** An expression using a base and an exponent is a ? . **power**

Multiply.

2. 2×10 **20**
3. 4.51×100 **451**
4. $1.5 \times 1{,}000$ **1,500**
5. $1.803 \times 10{,}000$ **18,030**
6. $2.39 \times 1{,}000{,}000$ **2,390,000**

GO for Help Skills Handbook p. 635

What You'll Learn

To write numbers in both standard form and scientific notation

New Vocabulary scientific notation

Why Learn This?

When you are dealing with very large or very small numbers in science, it is helpful to be able to write them in a shorter form.

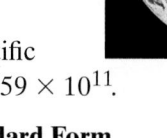

Written in standard form, or standard notation, the volume of Earth is about 259,000,000,000 cubic miles. Using scientific notation, you can write the number as 2.59×10^{11}.

Scientific Notation		Standard Form
2.59×10^{11}	=	259,000,000,000

KEY CONCEPTS Scientific Notation

A number is in **scientific notation** if the first factor is greater than or equal to 1 and less than 10 and the second factor is a power of 10.

Examples 1×10^8 1.54×10^7 9.99×10^4

Multiplying a number by 10^n, when n is positive, moves the decimal point n places to the right.

EXAMPLE Writing in Standard Form

Calculator Tip
1.55E6 on a calculator means 1.55×10^6.

1 **Science** The temperature at the sun's core is about 1.55×10^6 degrees Celsius. Write the temperature in standard form.

$$1.55 \times 10^6 = 1.550000. \leftarrow \text{Move the decimal point 6 places to the right. Insert zeros as necessary.}$$
$$= 1{,}550{,}000$$

The temperature at the sun's core is 1,550,000°C.

Quick Check

1. Write 7.66×10^6 km^2, the area of Australia, in standard form. **7,660,000 km^2**

Differentiated Instruction Solutions for All Learners

Special Needs L1	Below Level L2
Give some students index cards with greater numbers written in standard form. Give others the same numbers written in scientific notation. Have students find their "match" and then prove how they know they are correct. learning style: visual	Have students multiply 7.9 by 10, 100, 1,000, and 10,000 and describe what happens to the location of the decimal point. **79, 790, 7,900, 79,000; moves as many places as there are zeros in the multiple of 10** learning style: verbal

To write a number in scientific notation, determine the first factor. Then write the second factor as a power of 10.

EXAMPLE Writing in Scientific Notation

2 A supercomputer can perform 135,300,000,000,000 operations per second. Write this quantity in scientific notation.

$135{,}300{,}000{,}000{,}000 = 1.35{,}300{,}000{,}000{,}000.$ ← **Move the decimal point 14 places to the left.**

$= 1.353 \times 10^{14}$ ← **Use 14 as the exponent of 10.**

The supercomputer can perform 1.353×10^{14} operations per second.

Quick Check

2. Write 3,476,000 m, the moon's diameter, in scientific notation. 3.476×10^6 m

Numbers in scientific notation can have negative exponents. Multiplying a number by 10^n, when n is negative, moves the decimal point n places to the left.

EXAMPLE Negative Exponents

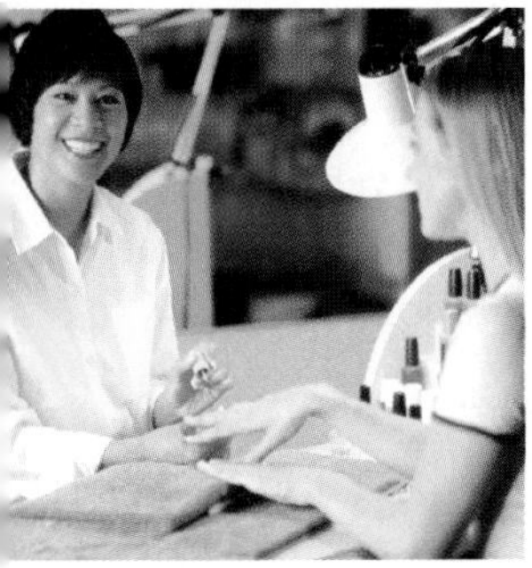

3 **Biology** Fingernails grow about 1.23×10^{-2} centimeters per day. Write this rate in standard form.

$1.23 \times 10^{-2} = .01.23$ ← **Move the decimal point 2 places to the left to make 1.23 less than 1.**

Fingernails grow about 0.0123 centimeters per day.

Quick Check

3. Write 2.5×10^{-4} inches, the diameter of a cell, in standard form. 0.00025 in.

To write a number that is less than 1 in scientific notation, determine the first factor by moving the decimal point. Then write the second factor as a power of ten with a negative exponent.

EXAMPLE Numbers Less Than 1

4 Write the quantity 0.0000076 in scientific notation.

$0.0000076 = 0.000007.6$ ← **Move the decimal point 6 places to the right to get a factor greater than 1 but less than 10.**

$= 7.6 \times 10^{-6}$ ← **Use −6 as the exponent of 10.**

Quick Check

4. Write 0.0000035 in scientific notation. 3.5×10^{-6}

2. Teach

Activity Lab

Use before the lesson.
Student Edition Activity Lab 2-8a, Multiplying by Powers of 10, p. 91

All in One Teaching Resources

Activity Lab 2-8: Notation Concentration

Guided Instruction

Error Prevention!

When writing a number in scientific notation, some students may incorrectly find the exponent of 10 by counting all the digits or by counting just the zeros. Have them cover the first digit and count the remaining digits.

Technology Tip
Many calculators automatically display in scientific notation results that require more than 10 digits.

PowerPoint

Additional Examples

1 At one point, the distance from the Earth to the moon is 1.513431×10^{10} in. Write this number in standard form. 15,134,310,000

2 The diameter of the planet Jupiter is about 142,800 km. Write this number in scientific notation. 1.428×10^5

3 Write 4.86×10^{-3} in standard form. 0.00486

4 Write 0.0000059 using scientific notation. 5.9×10^{-6}

All in One Teaching Resources
- Daily Notetaking Guide 2-8 L3
- Adapted Notetaking 2-8 L1

Closure

- Use an example to explain the differences between standard form and scientific notation. Answers will vary but should include the fact that a number in scientific notation is the product of a number ≥ 1 and < 10 times a power of 10.

Advanced Learners L4
Ask: *How can you add $6 \times 10^3 + 4.2 \times 10^4$ without writing each number in standard form?* Sample: Change 4.2×10^4 to 42×10^3. Then add 42 + 6 to get 48×10^3, which is 4.8×10^4.

learning style: verbal

English Language Learners ELL
Students explain why moving a decimal point left (or right) in the first factor of a number in scientific notation requires adding to (or subtracting from, respectively) the exponent of 10. For example, $82 = 8.2 \times 10^1$ and $0.5 = 5 \times \frac{1}{10} = 5 \times 10^{-1}$.

learning style: verbal

3. Practice

Assignment Guide

Check Your Understanding

Go over Exercises 1–4 in class before assigning the Homework Exercises.

Homework Exercises

A	Practice by Example	5–25
B	Apply Your Skills	26–36
C	Challenge	37
	Test Prep and Mixed Review	38–43

Homework Quick Check

To check students' understanding of key skills and concepts, go over Exercises 11, 16, 33, 34, and 36.

Differentiated Instruction Resources

Adapted Practice 2-8 L1

Practice 2-8 Scientific L3

Write each number in scientific notation.

1. 45 4.5×10^1
2. 250 2.5×10^2
3. 90 9×10^1
4. 670 6.7×10^2
5. 4,100 4.1×10^3
6. 500 5×10^2
7. 43,200 4.32×10^4
8. 97,100 9.71×10^4
9. 38,050 3.805×10^4
10. 480,000 4.8×10^5
11. 960,000 9.6×10^5
12. 8,750,000 8.75×10^6

Write each number in standard form.

13. 3.1×10^1 31
14. 8.07×10^2 807
15. 4.501×10^4 45,010
16. 9.7×10^6 9,700,000
17. 2.86×10^5 286,000
18. 3.58×10^6 3,580,000
19. 8.1×10^1 81
20. 9.071×10^2 907.1
21. 4.83×10^9 4,830,000,000
22. 2.73×10^8 273,000,000
23. 2.57×10^5 257,000
24. 8.09×10^4 80,900

Order each set of numbers from least to greatest.

25. $8.9 \times 10^2, 6.3 \times 10^3, 2.1 \times 10^4, 7.8 \times 10^5$
    $8.9 \times 10^2, 6.3 \times 10^3, 2.1 \times 10^4, 7.8 \times 10^5$
26. $2.1 \times 10^4, 2.12 \times 10^3, 3.46 \times 10^5, 2.112 \times 10^2$
    $2.112 \times 10^2, 2.12 \times 10^3, 2.1 \times 10^4, 3.46 \times 10^5$
27. A mulberry silkworm can spin a single thread that measures up to 3,900 ft in length. Write the number in scientific notation.
    3.9×10^3

Write each number in scientific notation.

28. 0.025 2.5×10^{-2}
29. 0.00003 3×10^{-5}
30. 0.00197 1.97×10^{-3}
31. 0.000407 4.07×10^{-4}

Write each number in standard form.

32. 8.1×10^{-3} 0.0081
33. 3.42×10^{-5} 0.0000342
34. 9.071×10^{-6} 0.000009071
35. 2.57×10^{-4} 0.000257

2-8 • Guided Problem Solving GPS L3

GPS **Student Page 95, Exercise 33:**

Astronomy When the sun emits a solar flare, the blast wave can travel through space at 3×10^6 km/h. Use the formula $d = rt$ to find how far the wave will travel in 30 min.

Understand

1. What does each of the variables stand for in the formula?
   d = distance, r = rate, and t = time
2. What is it that you are being asked to find?
   how far the solar flare will go in 30 minutes

Plan and Carry Out

3. Which variable are you solving for in the formula? d, distance
4. To write the rate in standard form, which way and how many places will you move the decimal point? What is the rate in standard form?
   6 places to the right; 3,000,000 km/h
5. Convert 30 minutes to hours. 30 min ÷ 60 min/h = $\frac{1}{2}$ h
6. Substitute what you know into the formula and solve.
   $d = 3{,}000{,}000$ km/h $\cdot \frac{1}{2}$h; $d = 1{,}500{,}000$ km
7. Write the distance back into scientific notation. Which way will you move the decimal point and how many places?
   6 places to the left; 1.5×10^6 km

Check

8. How can you check to see if your answer is reasonable?
   Sample answer: Half of 3 is one and one half; the exponent on 10 will not change.

Solve Another Problem

9. A state animal shelter had 4.2×10^4 unwanted animals dropped off last year. If the goal of the shelter is to decrease the number by one-sixth this year, how many fewer animals will enter the shelter? Write your answer in scientific notation.
   $\frac{1}{6} \times 4.2 \times 10^4 = 0.7 \times 10^4 = 7 \times 10^3$ animals

Check Your Understanding

1. **Vocabulary** A number is in scientific notation if the first factor is greater than or equal to _?_ and less than 10. 1
2. **Reasoning** Explain why 1.55×10^6 does not have six zeros when it is written in standard form. See left.
3. **Number Sense** Is 8.1×10^{-5} greater than or less than 0? Explain. See left.
4. When 123.4 and 654.321 are written in scientific notation, will the exponents of 10 be the same? Explain. See margin.

2. When you move the decimal point 6 places to the right, it takes 2 moves to get to the right of 0.55.
3. greater than 0, because the number remains positive even though the decimal point moves 5 places to the left

Homework Exercises

For more exercises, see Extra Skills and Word Problems.

GO for Help

For Exercises	See Examples
5–9	1
10–14	2
15–19	3
20–25	4

A **Write each number in standard form.**

5. 3.2×10^3 3,200
6. 5.08×10^4 50,800
7. 4.1×10^8 410,000,000
8. 7.145×10^9 7,145,000,000
9. **Whales** Write the average weight of a blue whale, 2.6×10^5 lb, in standard form. 260,000 lb

Write each number in scientific notation.

10. 4,800 4.8×10^3
11. 17,200 1.72×10^4
12. 180,000 1.8×10^5
13. 343,502 3.43502×10^5
14. **Space Travel** NASA's Apollo program lasted nine years (1963–1972) and included six moon landings. Write the cost of the Apollo project, $25,000,000,000, in scientific notation. $\$2.5 \times 10^{10}$

Write each number in standard form.

15. 2.5×10^{-3} 0.0025
16. 5.12×10^{-5} 0.0000512
17. 1.05×10^{-2} 0.0105
18. 3.14×10^{-7} 0.000000314
19. Write the size of a grain of very fine sand, about 9.35×10^{-3} cm, in standard form. 0.00935 cm

Write each number in scientific notation. 20–25. See left.

20. 0.00581
21. 0.00105
22. 0.0000078
23. 0.000027
24. 0.000000132
25. 0.000000009

20. 5.81×10^{-3}
21. 1.05×10^{-3}
22. 7.8×10^{-6}
23. 2.7×10^{-5}
24. 1.32×10^{-7}
25. 9×10^{-9}

Retina Cells

B GPS 26. **Guided Problem Solving** The human eye's retina has about 130 million light-sensitive cells. Write this number in scientific notation. 1.3×10^8

- What is 130 million written in standard form?
- Should you move the decimal point to the right or to the left?
- How many places should you move the decimal point?

4. Yes; the decimal point in each number needs to move 2 places to the left.

Exercises, p. 95

41. −135 42. 63 43. −18

Go Online
Homework Video Tutor
Visit: PHSchool.com
Web Code: ase-0208

Find each value of n.

27. $1.0035 \times 10^n = 100{,}350{,}000$ 8

28. $56{,}194 = n \times 10^4$ 5.6194

29. $0.0000083 = 8.3 \times 10^n$ −6

30. $n \times 10^{-9} = 0.000000004802$ 4.802

31. The population of the United States is expected to be 392 million people by 2050. Write this number in scientific notation. 3.92×10^8

32. Error Analysis Explain how you know that 492×10^5 is not in scientific notation. because 492 is not between 1 and 10

33. Astronomy (GPS) When the sun emits a solar flare, the blast wave can travel through space at 3×10^6 km/h. Use the formula $d = rt$ to find how far the wave will travel in 30 min. 1.5×10^6 km

34. Which number is greater, 3.14×10^{99} or 3×10^{100}? 3×10^{100}

35. Heat For a 10-minute shower, you use about 5,500 kilocalories to heat 50 gallons of water. (The prefix *kilo-* means 1,000 or 10^3.)
a. About how many calories do you use in a 5-minute shower?
b. Write your answer to part (a) in scientific notation. 35a–b. See left.

35a. 2,750,000 calories
b. 2.75×10^6 calories

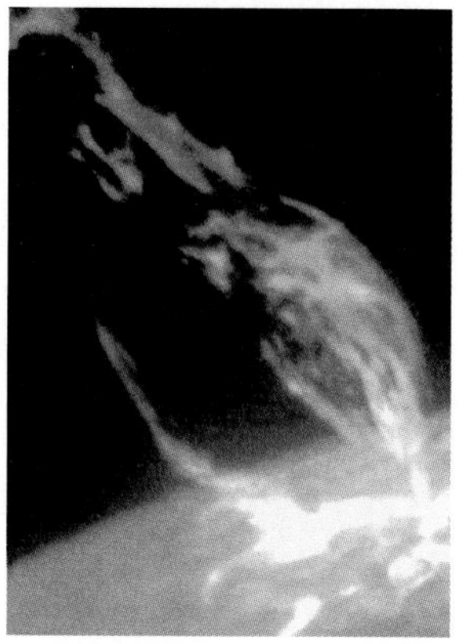

36. Writing in Math A number written in scientific notation is multiplied by 100. Explain what happens to the exponent of 10. It increases by two.

(C) **37. Challenge** Write $10^{29} - 10^{28}$ in scientific notation. 9×10^{28}

Test Prep and Mixed Review — Practice

Multiple Choice

38. The moon is about 380,000 kilometers from Earth. Which expression represents this measurement in scientific notation? C
(A) 3.8×10^3 km
(B) 3.8×10^4 km
(C) 3.8×10^5 km
(D) 3.8×10^6 km

39. In Brett's class, there are $2\frac{1}{2}$ times as many people who eat meat as people who don't. If 10 people in his class eat meat, which equation can be used to find the number of people v who do not? G
(F) $v = 2\frac{1}{2} \times 10$
(G) $v = 10 \div 2\frac{1}{2}$
(H) $v = 2\frac{1}{2} \div 10$
(J) $v = 2\frac{1}{2} + 10$

40. Maya wants to find the width of a rectangular trunk using the formula $v = \ell wh$, where $v = 24$ ft^3, $\ell = 4$ ft, and $h = 2$ ft. To solve the formula for w, D
(A) Multiply both sides by 6.
(B) Multiply both sides by 8.
(C) Divide both sides by 6.
(D) Divide both sides by 8.

Go for Help

For Exercises	See Lesson
41–43	2-7

Find each value of y for $x = 3$. 41–43. See margin.

41. $y = x^3 + x^4 - x^5$ **42.** $y = 3x^3 - 2x^2$ **43.** $y = x^2 - x^3$

Online lesson quiz, PHSchool.com, Web Code: asa-0208

4. Assess & Reteach

PowerPoint

Lesson Quiz

1. Write 7.304×10^2 in standard form. 730.4
2. Write 41,700,000,000 in scientific notation. 4.17×10^{10}
3. Write 3.03×10^{-5} in standard form. 0.0000303
4. Write 0.00000127 using scientific notation. 1.27×10^{-6}

Reteaching 2-8 Scientific L2

To write a number such as 67,000 in *scientific notation,* move the decimal point to form a number between 1 and 10. The number of places moved shows which power of 10 to use.

- Write 67,000 in scientific notation.

 6.7 is between 1 and 10. So, move the decimal point in 67,000 to the left 4 places and multiply by 10^4.

 $67{,}000 = 6.7 \times 10^4$

To write scientific notation in *standard form,* look at the exponent. The exponent shows the number of places and the direction to move the decimal point.

- Write 8.5×10^5 in standard form.

 The exponent is positive 5, so move the decimal point 5 places to the right.

 $8.5 \times 10^5 = 850{,}000$

Write each number in scientific notation.

1. 6,500 6.5×10^3
2. 65,000 6.5×10^4
3. 6,520 6.52×10^3
4. 345 3.45×10^2
5. 29,100 2.91×10^4
6. 93,000,000 9.3×10^7
7. 200 2×10^2
8. 2,300 2.3×10^3
9. 23,000 2.3×10^4

Write each number in standard form.

10. 4×10^4 40,000
11. 4×10^5 400,000
12. 3.6×10^3 3,600
13. 4.85×10^4 48,500
14. 4.05×10^2 405
15. 7.1×10^5 710,000
16. 4×10^2 400
17. 1.3×10^2 130
18. 7×10^1 70
19. 1.81×10^3 1,810
20. Jupiter orbits at an average of 7.783×10^8 kilometers from the Sun. 778,300,000 km

Which number is greater?

21. 5×10^2 or 2×10^5 2×10^5
22. 2.1×10^3 or 2.1×10^6 2.1×10^6
23. 6×10^{10} or 3×10^9 6×10^{10}
24. 3.6×10^1 or 3.6×10^3 3.6×10^3

Enrichment 2-8 Scientific L4

Critical Thinking

A Russian cosmonaut spent 439 days in space, returning to Earth in March of 1995.

a. How many hours did he spend in space? Write your answer in standard notation.
b. How many minutes did he spend in space? Write this answer in scientific notation.

1. What are you asked to do? Find the number of hours and minutes in 439 days.
2. How can you find how many hours are in
 a. 2 days? 2×24 b. 439 days? 439×24
3. How can you find how many minutes are in
 a. 2 days? $2(60 \times 24)$ b. 439 days? $439(60 \times 24)$
4. How many hours did the cosmonaut spend in space? 10,536 hours
5. How many minutes did the cosmonaut spend in space? 632,160 minutes
6. Write the number of minutes in scientific notation. 6.3216×10^5
7. Kate's birthday is February 29. She was born in a leap year.
 a. How many days does she have to wait between birthdays? Write this answer in standard notation. 1,460 days
 b. How many minutes does she have to wait between birthdays? Write this answer in scientific notation. 2.1024×10^6 min

Alternative Assessment

Each partner in a pair writes a positive integer with six to ten digits. Partners exchange papers and write six to ten zeros to the left or right of the number. Partners exchange papers again and write in scientific notation the number they see.

Test Prep

Resources

For additional practice with a variety of test item formats:
- Test-Taking Strategies, p. 97
- Test Prep, p. 101
- Test-Taking Strategies with Transparencies

Activity Lab

Writing Measurements

Students extend their understanding of scientific notation to using metric prefixes as an alternative way to write greater and lesser numbers in various scientific contexts.

Guided Instruction

Students are introduced to metric prefixes, their symbols, and their meanings. Read the table with them. Explain that these words and symbols are used extensively in science.

Connection to Science
You may wish to have examples from scientific literature of numbers using the metric prefixes and/or their abbreviations.

Exercise
Have students complete Exercises 1–4. Have volunteers share their responses. Then have students work in groups to find data on animals or insects for Exercise 5 and post their charts on a bulletin board where the class can see and discuss them.

Differentiated Instruction

Special Needs L1
Before working on the Activity, elicit from students the standard form of the powers of ten represented by the metric prefixes: 10^6, 10^3, 10^{-2}, 10^{-3}, and 10^{-6}. 1,000,000; 1,000; 0.01; 0.001; 0.000001

Resources

- science books and magazines
- animal or insect books
- almanacs

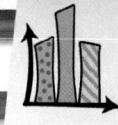

2-8b Activity Lab — Data Analysis

Writing Measurements

When you write very large or very small numbers in scientific notation, you write the numbers as multiples of powers of ten. In the metric system of measurement, you can use prefixes to indicate powers of ten. The table shows common prefixes and their meanings.

For example, the prefix *kilo-* means 10^3. You can write 2 kilometers as 2×10^3, or 2,000, meters. Similarly, you can write 4,000 meters as 4×10^3 meters, or 4 kilometers. Note that the symbol for kilo- is *k*, so the abbreviation for kilometers is km.

Prefix	Symbol	Meaning
micro-	μ	10^{-6}
milli-	m	10^{-3}
centi-	c	10^{-2}
kilo-	k	10^{3}
mega-	M	10^{6}

ACTIVITY

1. Use a metric prefix to write 3,100 grams (g) in kilograms (kg). 3.1 kg
2. Use a metric prefix to write 0.0052 meters (m) in millimeters (mm). 5.2 mm
3. Use a metric prefix to write 64,200,000 bytes (b) in megabytes (Mb). 64.2 Mb
4. Copy the table below. Fill in each of the facts about Thomson's gazelles using both scientific notation and metric prefixes. See margin.

Thomson's Gazelles

Characteristic	Measure	Scientific Notation	Metric Prefixes
Average weight	21,500 g	■ g	■
Average height	0.63 m	■ m	■
Possible diameter of a single hair	0.00005 m	■ m	■
Distance a herd can travel in a day	16,000 m	■ m	■

5. Make a table like the one above for an animal or insect of your choice. Write all measures using both scientific notation and metric prefixes. Check students' work.
6. The average diameter of a human hair is about 80 micrometers. Use scientific notation or measurements with metric prefixes to compare it to the diameter of a gazelle's hair. Explain your choice.
7. Suppose you want to compare the weight of an elephant to the weight of a whale. Would you write the measures in scientific notation or using metric prefixes? Explain your choice. Check students' work.

6. The human's hair is thicker; 8×10^{-5} m > 5×10^{-5} m; check students' work.

4.

Measure	Scientific Notation	Metric Prefixes
21,500 g	2.15×10^4 g	21.5 kg
0.63 m	6.3×10^{-1} m	63 cm
0.00005 m	5×10^{-5} m	50 μm
16,000 m	1.6×10^4 m	16 km

Test-Taking Strategies

Writing Short Responses

Short-response questions are usually worth 2 points. To receive full credit, you must give the correct answer (including the appropriate units, if needed), and justify your reasoning or show your work.

EXAMPLE

A parent paid a baby sitter \$33 to baby-sit two children for one night. The sitter watched the children for $5\frac{1}{2}$ hours. Write and solve an equation to find how much the sitter was paid per hour.

To receive full credit, you must (1) set up an equation, (2) solve the equation, and (3) tell how much the sitter was paid per hour. The number of points for different types of answers follow.

Scoring

[2] The equation and the solution are correct.

[1] There is no equation. There *is* a method to show the correct solution.
OR There are an equation and a solution containing minor errors.
OR The equation and solution are correct. No work is shown.

[0] There is no response, or the solution is completely incorrect.

Here are three responses with their points.

2 points

Let p = sitter's pay/hour
$33 = 5\frac{1}{2}p$
$33 \div 5\frac{1}{2} = 5\frac{1}{2}p \div 5\frac{1}{2}$
$6 = p$
The sitter was paid \$6/h.

1 point

$\frac{33}{5\frac{1}{2}} = 6$
\$6

0 points

$\frac{33}{5\frac{1}{2}} = 7$
The sitter was paid \$7/h.

Exercises

1–3. See margin.

1. **Writing in Math** Explain why each response above received the indicated number of points.
2. **Reasoning** How many points does the response at the right deserve? Explain.
3. **Error Analysis** A student uses the equation $p \div 5\frac{1}{2} = 33$ to solve the problem. Explain why the equation is incorrect.

Let p = sitter's pay/hour
$33 = 5\frac{1}{2}p$
$27\frac{1}{2} = 5\frac{1}{2}p$
$5 = p$
The sitter was paid \$5/h.

Writing Short Responses

This strategy provides students with a rubric and an example showing how to get full credit for answers to short-response questions.

Guided Instruction

Teaching Tip
Have students compare the 1-point response with 2-point response to note similarities and differences. Ask: *Although both yield the correct answer, why is the 2-point answer deserving of a higher score?* Students should point to the identification of the variable for hours worked, to the equation written and solved, step-by-step, and to the answer expressed in a complete sentence.

Resources

Test-Taking Strategies with Transparencies
- Transparency 3
- Practice sheet, p. 26

Test-Taking Strategies with Transparencies

Test-Taking Strategies: Writing Short Responses

Estimate 98.57 × 206. Write your estimate and explain in writing how you got it.

Scoring Guide
2 Explains method, with answer that matches method.
1 Gives estimate with no explanation, OR gives explanation with no answer, OR shows computation, OR rounds first, but not enough to make computation easy.
0 Computes exact answer, then rounds, OR gives incorrect response.

Answer earning 2 points
Round: 98.57 → 100
206 → 200
Estimate = 20,000
First round, then multiply the rounded numbers.

Answer earning 1 point
Estimate: 98.57 206
206
× 99
1854
1854
20394

Answer earning 0 points
98.57
2 06
591 42
19714
20305.42
20305

Resources

Student Edition

Extra Skills and Word Problem Practice, Ch. 2, p. 606

English/Spanish Glossary, p. 650

Formulas and Properties, p. 648

Tables, p. 643

All in One Teaching Resources

- Vocabulary and Study Skills 2F L3

Differentiated Instruction

Spanish Vocabulary Workbook with Study Skills ELL

Interactive Textbook

- Audio Glossary

Online Vocabulary Quiz

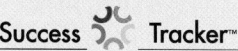

Success Tracker™

Online at PHSchool.com

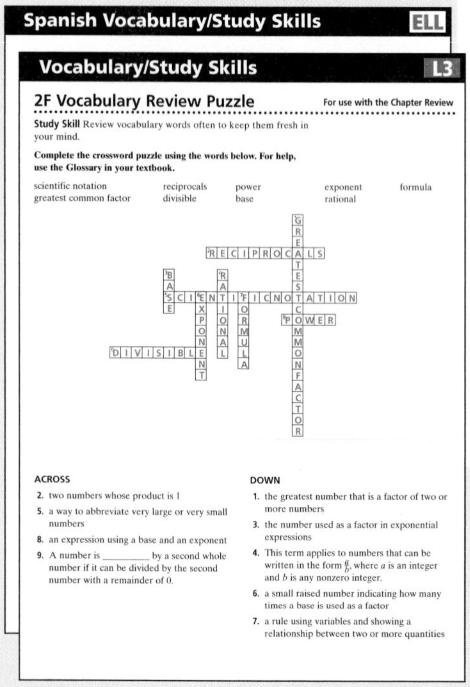
Spanish Vocabulary/Study Skills ELL

Vocabulary/Study Skills L3

2F Vocabulary Review Puzzle — For use with the Chapter Review

Study Skill Review vocabulary words often to keep them fresh in your mind.

Complete the crossword puzzle using the words below. For help, use the Glossary in your textbook.

scientific notation	reciprocals	power	exponent	formula
greatest common factor	divisible	base	rational	

ACROSS

2. two numbers whose product is 1
5. a way to abbreviate very large or very small numbers
8. an expression using a base and an exponent
9. A number is ________ by a second whole number if it can be divided by the second number with a remainder of 0.

DOWN

1. the greatest number that is a factor of two or more numbers
3. the number used as a factor in exponential expressions
4. This term applies to numbers that can be written in the form $\frac{a}{b}$, where a is an integer and b is any nonzero integer.
6. a small raised number indicating how many times a base is used as a factor
7. a rule using variables and showing a relationship between two or more quantities

Chapter 2 Review

Vocabulary Review

base (p. 86)
composite number (p. 52)
divisible (p. 52)
exponent (p. 86)
factor (p. 52)
formula (p. 81)
greatest common factor (GCF) (p. 53)
least common denominator (LCD) (p. 62)
least common multiple (LCM) (p. 62)
multiplicative inverse (p. 73)
power (p. 86)
prime factorization (p. 53)
prime number (p. 52)
rational number (p. 57)
reciprocals (p. 73)
relatively prime (p. 57)
repeating decimal (p. 58)
scientific notation (p. 92)
terminating decimal (p. 58)

Go Online PHSchool.com

For: Online Vocabulary Quiz
Web Code: asj-0251

Choose the correct vocabulary term above to complete each sentence.

1. _?_ is used when writing very large or very small numbers. scientific notation
2. Two numbers whose product is one are called _?_. reciprocals or multiplicative inverses
3. The _?_ of 15 and 25 is 75. LCM
4. The expression $3^2 \cdot 7$ is the _?_ of 63. prime factorization
5. An expression like 12^8 is a(n) _?_. power
6. A(n) _?_ shows the relationship between two or more quantities. formula
7. The numbers 8 and 9 are _?_ because 1 is their only common factor. relatively prime
8. The number 0.3589402 is a _?_. terminating decimal
9. The _?_ of 15 and 25 is 5. GCF
10. The expression 5^3 has a(n) _?_ of 3 and a(n) _?_ of 5. exponent; base

Skills and Concepts

Lessons 2-1, 2-2

- To identify prime and composite numbers and to find the greatest common factor
- To write equivalent fractions and decimals

15. $2^2 \cdot 3^3 \cdot 5 \cdot 13$

The **greatest common factor** of two numbers is the greatest **factor** that is common to both numbers. A **rational number** can be written in the form $\frac{a}{b}$, where a is an integer and b is any nonzero integer.

Use a factor tree to find the prime factorization of each number.

11. 260 $2^2 \cdot 5 \cdot 13$
12. 700 $2^2 \cdot 5^2 \cdot 7$
13. 378 $2 \cdot 3^3 \cdot 7$
14. 139 $1 \cdot 139$
15. 7,020

16. **Surveys** In a survey about favorite subjects in school, 0.16 of the students surveyed liked math the most. What fraction of the students surveyed chose math as their favorite subject? $\frac{4}{25}$

Alternatice Assessment L4

Alternative Assessment Form C

Chapter 2

TELEVISIONS FOR SALE

Ira was saving to buy a television for his grandmother. He was trying to decide what size he should buy. He measured the screen of his family's TV set. It was about 16 in. by 20 in. He wanted a TV about that size or smaller. Then he looked in the newspaper and saw the advertisements below.

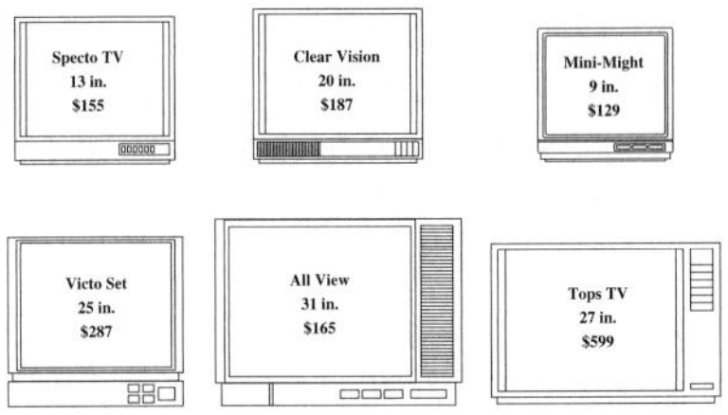

Show all of your work on a separate sheet of paper.

1. Ira wanted to compare the sizes of these TV sets to the size of his family's TV set. Describe a method he could use to do this.
2. Which of the six sets is closest in size to Ira's family's TV? Explain.
3. Next, Ira wanted to compare the prices of the sets, while taking into account their sizes. Describe a method he could use.
4. Compare the prices of the sets that are about the same size or smaller than his family's set. Which TV is the best buy, based on the size of the screen?

Lesson 2-3

- To use least common denominators, decimals, and number lines to compare and order rational numbers

You can compare rational numbers by rewriting the fractions with a common denominator or by changing each fraction to a decimal.

Compare. Write <, >, or =.

17. $\frac{3}{5}$ ■ $\frac{7}{9}$ <　　**18.** -4 ■ $-\frac{14}{3}$ >　　**19.** 0.625 ■ $\frac{5}{8}$ =

Lessons 2-4, 2-5

- To add and subtract fractions and mixed numbers and to solve problems involving rational numbers
- To multiply and divide fractions and mixed numbers and to solve problems involving rational numbers

To add or subtract fractions, write equivalent fractions using a common multiple of the denominators or the **least common denominator (LCD).** To multiply fractions, multiply both the numerators and denominators. To divide, multiply by the **reciprocal** of the divisor.

Simplify.

20. $-\frac{7}{8} + \frac{3}{4}$ $-\frac{1}{8}$　　**21.** $-2\frac{4}{5} - \left(-1\frac{3}{10}\right)$ $-1\frac{1}{2}$　　**22.** $-3\frac{1}{6} + 2\frac{1}{2}$ $-\frac{2}{3}$

23. $-\frac{1}{6} \cdot \left(-\frac{3}{8}\right)$ $\frac{1}{16}$　　**24.** $2\frac{1}{2} \div \frac{10}{13}$ $3\frac{1}{4}$　　**25.** $-4\frac{2}{3} \div 2\frac{2}{9}$ $-2\frac{1}{10}$

26. A carpenter cuts a $7\frac{1}{2}$-ft board into $2\frac{1}{2}$-ft pieces. How many pieces does he have? 3

Lesson 2-6

- To use formulas to solve problems and to solve a formula for a variable

A **formula** is an equation that shows a relationship between two or more quantities. A common formula for finding distance is $d = rt$.

27. Find the average rate of travel if a car travels 270 miles in 6 hours. 45 mi/h

Solve each formula for the variable shown in red.

28. $A = \frac{1}{2}bh$ $b = \frac{2A}{h}$　　**29.** $y = mx + b$ $b = y - mx$　　**30.** $d = rt$ $r = \frac{d}{t}$

Lessons 2-7, 2-8

- To write, simplify, and evaluate expressions involving exponents
- To write numbers in both standard form and scientific notation

An **exponent** tells how many times a number, or **base,** is used as a factor. To simplify a numerical expression, use the order of operations.

A number is in **scientific notation** if the first factor is greater than or equal to 1 and less than 10 and the second factor is a **power** of 10.

Simplify each expression.

31. $(4 \cdot 2)^2 - 3$ 61　　**32.** $5^2 \cdot 2 + 4$ 54　　**33.** $-8 + 2 \cdot 4^2$ 24

Write each number in scientific notation.

34. 3,500 3.5×10^3　　**35.** 801,000 8.01×10^5　　**36.** 0.000205 2.05×10^{-4}　　**37.** 0.000000081 8.1×10^{-8}

38. The moon is about 3.8×10^8 m from Earth. Write this number in standard form. 380,000,000

Resources

- ExamView Assessment Suite CD-ROM
  - Ch. 2 Ready-Made Test
  - Make your own Ch. 2 test
- MindPoint Quiz Show CD-ROM
  - Chapter 2 Review

Differentiated Instruction

All in One Teaching Resources

- Below Level Chapter 2 Test L2
- Chapter 2 Test L3
- Chapter 2 Alternative Assessment L4

Spanish Assessment Resources ELL

- Below Level Chapter 2 Test L2
- Chapter 2 Test L3
- Chapter 2 Alternative Assessment L4

ExamView Assessment Suite CD-ROM

- Special Needs Test L1
- Special Needs Practice Bank L1

Online Chapter 2 Test at www.PHSchool.com L3

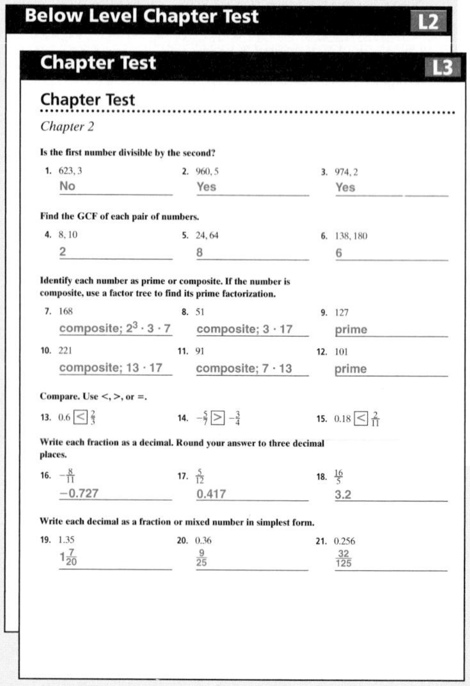

Below Level Chapter Test L2

Chapter Test L3

Chapter Test

Chapter 2

Is the first number divisible by the second?

1. 623, 3 No
2. 960, 5 Yes
3. 974, 2 Yes

Find the GCF of each pair of numbers.

4. 8, 10 2
5. 24, 64 8
6. 138, 180 6

Identify each number as prime or composite. If the number is composite, use a factor tree to find its prime factorization.

7. 168 composite; $2^3 \cdot 3 \cdot 7$
8. 51 composite; $3 \cdot 17$
9. 127 prime
10. 221 composite; $13 \cdot 17$
11. 91 composite; $7 \cdot 13$
12. 101 prime

Compare. Use <, >, or =.

13. $0.6 \; \boxed{<} \; \frac{2}{3}$
14. $-\frac{5}{7} \; \boxed{>} \; -\frac{3}{4}$
15. $0.18 \; \boxed{<} \; \frac{2}{11}$

Write each fraction as a decimal. Round your answer to three decimal places.

16. $-\frac{8}{11}$ −0.727
17. $\frac{5}{12}$ 0.417
18. $\frac{16}{5}$ 3.2

Write each decimal as a fraction or mixed number in simplest form.

19. 1.35 $1\frac{7}{20}$
20. 0.36 $\frac{9}{25}$
21. 0.256 $\frac{32}{125}$

Chapter 2 Test

Go Online PHSchool.com For: Online chapter test Web Code: asa-0252

Find the GCF of each pair of numbers.

1. 12, 16 **4**
2. 32, 48 **16**
3. 144, 192 **48**

Use a factor tree to find the prime factorization of each number.

4. 90 $2 \cdot 3^2 \cdot 5$
5. 432 $2^4 \cdot 3^3$
6. 47 $1 \cdot 47$
7. 280 $2^3 \cdot 5 \cdot 7$

Compare. Write <, >, or =.

8. $\frac{3}{8} \;\blacksquare\; 0.4$ **<**
9. $-\frac{1}{2} \;\blacksquare\; -\frac{5}{12}$ **<**
10. $-0.89 \;\blacksquare\; -\frac{9}{10}$ **>**
11. $\frac{4}{9} \;\blacksquare\; 0.\overline{4}$ **=**

Write each fraction as a decimal. Round to three decimal places.

12. $\frac{2}{5}$ **0.400**
13. $-\frac{27}{8}$ **−3.375**
14. $\frac{19}{15}$ **1.267**
15. $\frac{7}{11}$ **0.636**

Write each decimal as a fraction or mixed number in simplest form.

16. 0.64 $\frac{16}{25}$
17. $0.\overline{6}$ $\frac{2}{3}$
18. 0.471 $\frac{471}{1,000}$
19. $0.\overline{282}$ $\frac{94}{333}$

20. **Sports** Each time a ball hits the ground, it bounces back to $\frac{2}{3}$ of its previous height. On its second bounce, the ball reaches a height of 12 in. What was the ball's original height? **27 in.**

21. **Running** A runner jogs on a $\frac{1}{4}$-mi track. How many miles does the runner jog in 18 laps? **$4\frac{1}{2}$ mi**

Simplify each expression. Write the answer as a fraction or mixed number in simplest form.

22. $-\frac{3}{5} - \frac{1}{3}$ $-\frac{14}{15}$
23. $\frac{1}{12} - \frac{5}{12}$ $-\frac{1}{3}$
24. $\frac{5}{12} + \frac{5}{9}$ $\frac{35}{36}$
25. $3\frac{1}{4} - 2\frac{2}{3}$ $\frac{7}{12}$
26. $\frac{11}{12} - \frac{3}{4}$ $\frac{1}{6}$
27. $2\frac{1}{5} - 3\frac{1}{3}$ $-1\frac{2}{15}$
28. $-2\frac{3}{4} \cdot \frac{8}{9}$ $-2\frac{4}{9}$
29. $\frac{5}{8} \div \left(-\frac{1}{2}\right)$ $-1\frac{1}{4}$
30. $-\frac{2}{5} \cdot \frac{7}{8}$ $-\frac{7}{20}$
31. $-1\frac{1}{2} \div \frac{5}{12}$ $-3\frac{3}{5}$
32. $1\frac{1}{4} \cdot -\frac{5}{9}$ $-\frac{25}{36}$
33. $\frac{21}{50} \div \frac{21}{50}$ 1

34. **Writing in Math** Write what you would say to a classmate who asked you to explain why -4^2 is equal to −16. **See margin.**

Simplify each expression.

35. $(-2)^4$ **16**
36. -2^4 **−16**
37. $3^3 + 5^2$ **52**
38. $4^2 \cdot 2 + 8$ **40**
39. $(9 - 3)^2$ **36**
40. $22 - 7^2$ **−27**

Evaluate each expression for $m = -4$ and $p = 2$.

41. $m^2 - p + 12$ **26**
42. $2p^2 - (m - 1)^2$ **−17**
43. $3(5m - 1)^2$ **1,323**
44. $\frac{m^2 + 16}{m^2}$ **2**

Write each number in scientific notation.

45. 23,000,000 2.3×10^7
46. 1,500,000 1.5×10^6
47. 450,000,000 4.5×10^8
48. 0.00007 7.0×10^{-5}
49. 0.0089 8.9×10^{-3}
50. 0.0401 4.01×10^{-2}

Write each number in standard form.

51. 4.1×10^5 **410,000**
52. 8.02×10^4 **80,200**
53. 5×10^{-3} **0.005**
54. 8.8×10^{-6} **0.0000088**

55. **Number Sense** Which number is greater, 5×10^{-6} or 6×10^{-5}? Explain. **See margin.**

56. **Aviation** In 2002, Erik Lindbergh, the grandson of aviator Charles Lindbergh, flew 3,756 miles in 17.7 hours. Find his average speed. Use the formula $d = rt$. **about 212 mi/h**

57. Find the area of a rectangle with a length of $2\frac{1}{4}$ in. and a width of $\frac{7}{8}$ in. Use the formula $A = \ell w$. **$1\frac{31}{32}$ in.²**

Solve each formula for the variable shown in red.

58. $L = 2\pi r h$ $r = \frac{L}{2\pi h}$
59. $V = Bh$ $B = \frac{V}{h}$
60. $S = a + 2b$ $a = S - 2b$
61. $C = -5d + p$ $p = C + 5d$

34. Answers may vary. Sample: The exponent 2 only applies to the number 4, not −4.

55. 6×10^{-5}; $\frac{6}{100,000} > \frac{5}{1,000,000}$

Multiple Choice

Read each question. Then write the letter of the correct answer on your paper.

1. Size B8 paper measures $2\frac{1}{2}$ by $3\frac{1}{2}$ inches. Find the number of square inches in its area. C
   Ⓐ $5\frac{3}{4}$ Ⓑ $6\frac{1}{4}$ Ⓒ $8\frac{3}{4}$ Ⓓ $9\frac{1}{4}$

2. The expression $6(x - 2)$ is equivalent to which of the following? H
   Ⓕ $6x - 2$ Ⓗ $6x - 12$
   Ⓖ $6x + 2$ Ⓙ $6x + 12$

3. What is the area of the rectangle below? C

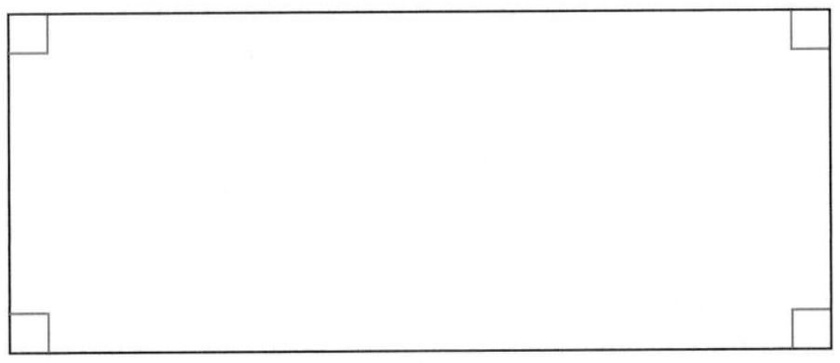

   Ⓐ 9 m^2 Ⓒ 16.25 m^2
   Ⓑ 15.5 m^2 Ⓓ 18 m^2

4. Which quotient is between −4 and −5? H
   Ⓕ $2\frac{5}{6} \div \left(-\frac{1}{2}\right)$ Ⓗ $-9\frac{1}{3} \div 2$
   Ⓖ $-5\frac{1}{2} \div \left(-1\frac{1}{2}\right)$ Ⓙ $1\frac{2}{3} \div \left(-\frac{1}{2}\right)$

5. Evaluate the expression $3 - 6m$ for $m = 3$. A
   Ⓐ −15 Ⓒ 6
   Ⓑ 0 Ⓓ 15

6. The number 66,510 is NOT divisible by which of the following? G
   Ⓕ 3 Ⓖ 4 Ⓗ 5 Ⓙ 9

7. Which of the following is the LCM of 24 and 36? D
   Ⓐ 2 Ⓑ 4 Ⓒ 12 Ⓓ 72

8. If $a + y = 18$, then $y =$ ■. H
   Ⓕ $a - 18$ Ⓗ $18 - a$
   Ⓖ $a + 18$ Ⓙ $\frac{18}{a}$

9. A racing canoeist can paddle 250 feet in $20\frac{1}{2}$ seconds. At that rate, how many feet does the canoeist paddle each second? D
   Ⓐ $\frac{41}{500}$ Ⓑ $\frac{121}{41}$ Ⓒ $\frac{500}{82}$ Ⓓ $\frac{500}{41}$

10. There are $3\frac{2}{3}$ times as many birds b as there are trees t. Which equation relates the two variables? F
   Ⓕ $b = 3\frac{2}{3}t$ Ⓗ $b = 3\frac{2}{3} + t$
   Ⓖ $t = 3\frac{2}{3}b$ Ⓙ $t = 3\frac{2}{3} + b$

Gridded Response

Record your answer in a grid.

11. Find the value of $\frac{2}{5} + \frac{1}{2}$. $\frac{9}{10}$

12. Find the GCF of 24 and 40. 8

Short Response 13–14. See margin.

13. A student had \$78. She then earned money baby-sitting. Now she has \$116.
   a. Write an equation you can use to find how much the student earned baby-sitting.
   b. How much did the student earn baby-sitting?

Extended Response

14. The area of the figure below is $130{,}000\text{ yd}^2$.

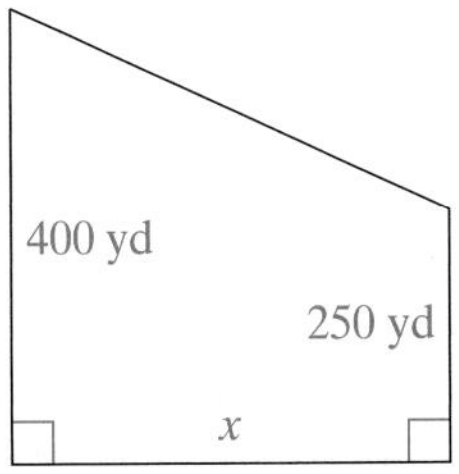

   a. Write an equation that you can use to find the length x.
   b. Find the length of x. Show your work.

Item	1	2	3	4	5	6	7	8	9	10	11	12	13	14
Lesson	2-5	1-5	Skills Handbook p. 632	2-5	1-1	2-1	2-3	1-6	2-5	1-7	2-4	2-1	1-6	1-7

Test Prep

Resources

Test Prep Workbook

All in One **Teaching Resources**
- Cumulative Review **L3**

ExamView Assessment Suite CD-ROM
- Standardized Test Practice

Differentiated Instruction

Spanish Assessment Resources
- Spanish Cumulative Review **ELL**

13. [2] a. $78 + b = 116$
    b. \$38
    [1] one part correct

14. [4] a. $130{,}000 = \frac{1}{2}x(400 + 250)$
    b. $130{,}000 = \frac{1}{2}x(650)$
    $130{,}000 = 325x$
    $400 = x$
    [3] correct equation and minor error in solving for x
    [2] correct equation with incorrect value for x OR incorrect equation but value for x follows correctly from equation
    [1] correct value for x without work shown and no equation

Problem Solving

Applying Real Numbers

Students will use data from these two pages to answer the questions posed here in Put It All Together.

Activating Prior Knowledge

Invite students who play musical instruments to talk about how they create different sounds and effects with their instruments. Have them share what is hardest and easiest about playing their instrument, and have them describe what they like most about it. Invite students to demonstrate, by playing, to help clarify their answers to these questions.

Guided Instruction

If possible, begin this activity in the music room. Invite a volunteer or the music teacher to show the keyboard and the piano action (the mechanism that makes the key hit the string and make the sound). Give students the opportunity to see how the instrument works. Similarly, have volunteers show the key parts of the violin and guitar and explain what is important about each part and why each looks as it does.

History Connection
Inform students that before the advent of the phonograph and the radio, families commonly made their own music. Many families had pianos and frequently used them.

Careers
Piano tuning is one of the many jobs in the field of music. Ask students if any have watched a piano tuner at work, and have them describe what they witnessed. Then have students find out what skills, talents, and study are essential for those interested in becoming a piano tuner.

Problem Solving Application

Applying Real Numbers

Frequency and Math Vibrations produce sounds. When a series of vibrations makes pleasing combinations of sounds, the result is called music.

The *frequency* of a sound is the number of vibrations, or cycles, per second that produce the sound. The greater the frequency, the higher the pitch. The *period* of a sound is the duration of one cycle in seconds. For example, one part of a telephone's dial tone uses a frequency of 350 cycles per second. This sound has a period of $\frac{1}{350}$ s.

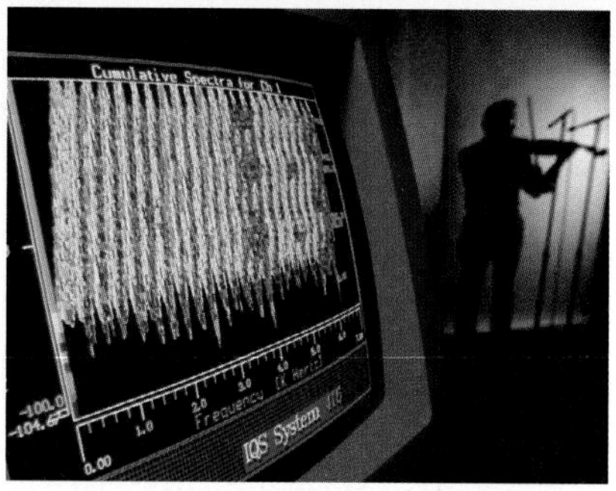

Analyzing Sound
A spectrum analyzer measures the sound of a violin.

Exploding Glass
If you tap a delicate glass, it produces a high-pitched tone. This is the "natural frequency" of the glass. A very steady, very loud sound with this frequency can break the glass by causing it to vibrate until it shatters.

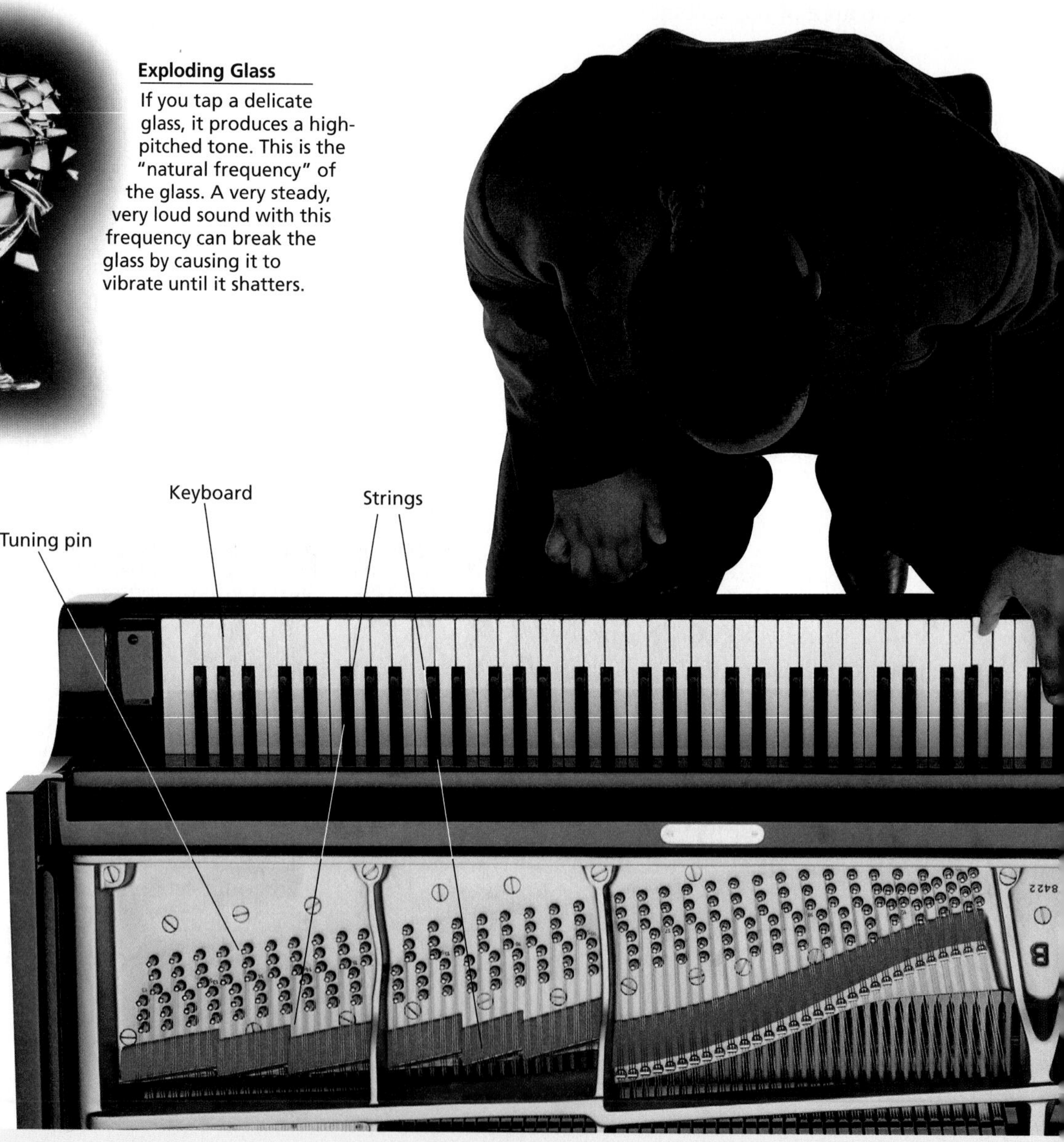

1a. 50 cycles per second

b. $\frac{1}{50}$ s

2.

Sound	Approximate Frequency (cycles per second)	Period (seconds)
Lowest sound	20	0.05
Lowest note	82	0.012
Highest note	1,568	0.00064
Highest sound	20,000	0.00005

Put It All Together

1. **a.** What is the frequency of a piano string that vibrates 50 times per second?
   b. What is the period of the note?
2. Copy and complete the table. Write each period in decimal form.

Sound	Approximate Frequency (cycles per second)	Period (seconds)
Lowest sound audible to humans	20	■
Lowest note on a guitar	82	■
Highest note on an oboe	1,568	■
Highest sound audible to humans	20,000	■

3. **Reasoning** People often associate trumpet-like sounds with elephants. Scientists have discovered that elephants communicate using "sounds" with periods as long as $\frac{1}{10}$ s. Why do you think these communications weren't discovered until recently?
4. **a. Language** Bats use ultrasonic frequencies to help them navigate and locate food. Use a dictionary to find the definition of *ultrasonic*.
   b. Open-Ended Give an example of the period of an ultrasonic frequency.
5. **Research** Prepare a report about animals who make sounds with frequencies that humans cannot hear.

Acoustic Guitar

This acoustic guitar has a hollow body and six strings. Plucking or strumming the strings produces vibrations. The guitar's body amplifies the vibrations.

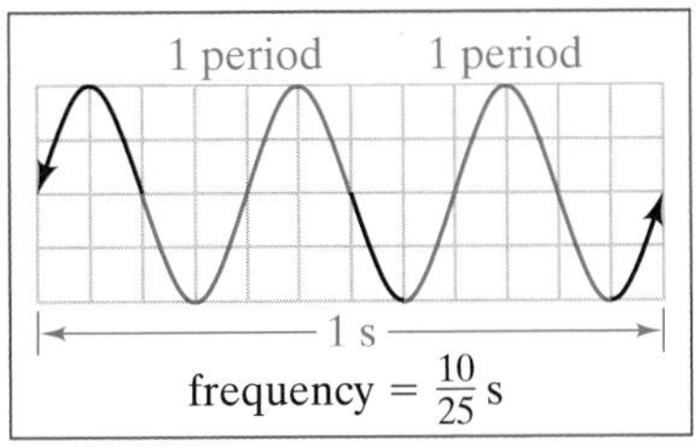

Sound Waves

The period of a sound wave is one complete "wave" of the sound. The frequency is the length, or duration, of the period.

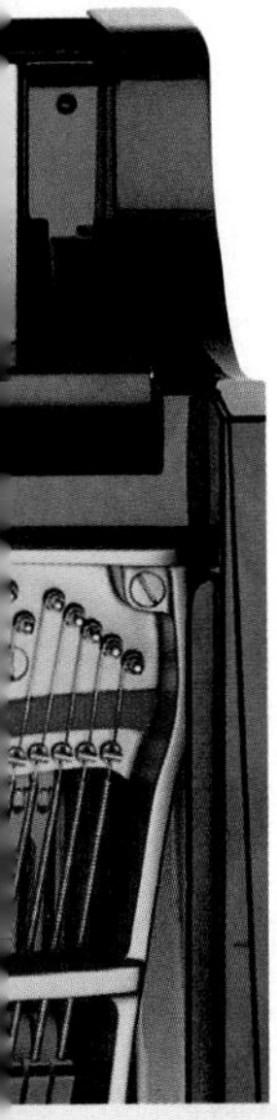

Piano Strings

A grand piano (shown) has 88 keys and about 230 strings running parallel to the floor. The strings of an upright piano run perpendicular to the floor.

Go Online
PHSchool.com
For: Information about sound
Web Code: ase-0253

Put It All Together

Have students work in pairs to answer the questions and complete the table.

Exercise 1 Help students understand that period is the reciprocal of the frequency. Ask: *If there are 50 vibrations in one second, what would be the time in seconds for one vibration?* $\frac{1}{50}$ s

Exercise 5 Guide students to use tables or graphs to show their findings most effectively.

Science Connection
Tell students that the values for human hearing range vary with age. Tell them that the *lower* range is sometimes identified as 16Hz. Discuss that the older people get, the lower the *upper* limit of their hearing becomes. For adults, the upper limit ranges from about 15,000 Hz to about 18,000 Hz.

Differentiated Instruction

English Language Learners ELL
Music has its own specialized vocabulary, as all students who play instruments know. Review and discuss the key words in the activity related to making sound: *vibrations, frequency, pitch, keys, tone, tune, note, wave,* and *audible*.

3. Answer may vary. Sample: The period of $\frac{1}{10}$ s corresponds to a frequency of 10 cycles per second, which is below the range of human hearing. People could not hear these elephant communications.

4. Answers may vary. Samples are given.
   a. ultrasonic: a frequency of vibration above the range of human hearing
   b. A frequency of 40,000 cycles per second has a period of = 0.000025 s.

5. Check students' work.

3 Real Numbers and the Coordinate Plane

Chapter at a Glance

Lesson Titles, Objectives, and Features	Assessment	NCTM Standards	Local Standards
3-1 Exploring Square Roots and Irrational Numbers • To find and estimate square roots and to classify numbers as rational or irrational	Lesson Quiz	1, 2, 3, 6, 7, 8, 9, 10	
3-2a Activity Lab, Hands On: Exploring the Pythagorean Theorem **3-2 The Pythagorean Theorem** • To use the Pythagorean Theorem to find the length of the hypotenuse of a right triangle **Guided Problem Solving:** Squares and Square Roots	Lesson Quiz	1, 2, 3, 4, 6, 7, 8, 9, 10	
3-3 Using the Pythagorean Theorem • To use the Pythagorean Theorem to find missing measurements of triangles **Extension:** Analyzing Triangles	Lesson Quiz Checkpoint Quiz 1	1, 2, 3, 4, 6, 7, 8, 9, 10	
3-4 Graphing in the Coordinate Plane • To graph points and to use the Pythagorean Theorem to find distances in the coordinate plane **3-4b Activity Lab:** Finding the Midpoint	Lesson Quiz	1, 2, 3, 6, 7, 8, 9, 10	
3-5a Activity Lab, Data Analysis: Tables and Graphs **3-5 Equations, Tables, and Graphs** • To use tables, equations, and graphs to solve problems **3-5b Activity Lab, Algebra Thinking:** Matching Graphs	Lesson Quiz	1, 2, 3, 6, 7, 8, 9, 10	
3-6 Translations • To graph and describe translations in the coordinate plane	Lesson Quiz Checkpoint Quiz 2	1, 2, 3, 6, 7, 8, 9, 10	
3-7a Activity Lab, Hands On: Exploring Reflections **3-7 Reflections and Symmetry** • To graph reflections in the coordinate plane and to identify lines of symmetry	Lesson Quiz	1, 2, 3, 6, 7, 8, 9, 10	
3-8a Activity Lab, Hands On: Exploring Rotations **3-8 Rotations** • To graph rotations and to identify rotational symmetry **Extension:** Tessellations	Lesson Quiz	1, 2, 3, 4, 5, 6, 7, 8, 9, 10	
Problem Solving Application: Applying Rate of Change			

NCTM Standards 2000
1 Number and Operations
2 Algebra
3 Geometry
4 Measurement
5 Data Analysis and Probability
6 Problem Solving
7 Reasoning and Proof
8 Communication
9 Connections
10 Representation

Correlations to Standardized Tests

All content for these tests is contained in *Prentice Hall Math,* Course 3. This chart reflects coverage in this chapter only.

	3-1	3-2	3-3	3-4	3-5	3-6	3-7	3-8
Terra Nova CAT6 (Level 18)								
Number and Number Relations	✔							
Computation and Numerical Estimation	✔							
Operation Concepts								
Measurement								
Geometry and Spatial Sense		✔	✔			✔	✔	✔
Data Analysis, Statistics, and Probability								
Patterns, Functions, and Algebra				✔	✔			
Problem Solving and Reasoning	✔	✔	✔	✔	✔	✔	✔	✔
Communication	✔	✔	✔	✔	✔	✔	✔	✔
Decimals, Fractions, Integers, and Percent								
Order of Operations								
Algebraic Operations								
Terra Nova CTBS (Level 18)								
Decimals, Fractions, Integers, Percents								
Order of Operations, Numeration, Number Theory	✔							
Data Interpretation								
Measurement								
Geometry		✔	✔			✔	✔	✔
ITBS (Level 14)								
Number Properties and Operations	✔							
Algebra				✔	✔			
Geometry		✔	✔			✔	✔	✔
Measurement								
Probability and Statistics								
Estimation								
SAT10 (Adv 1 Level)								
Number Sense and Operations	✔							
Patterns, Relationships, and Algebra	✔			✔	✔			
Data, Statistics, and Probability								
Geometry and Measurement		✔	✔			✔	✔	✔
NAEP								
Number Sense, Properties, and Operations	✔							
Measurement								
Geometry and Spatial Sense		✔	✔	✔		✔	✔	✔
Data Analysis, Statistics, and Probability								
Algebra and Functions				✔	✔			

CAT6 California Achievement Test, 6th Ed. **CTBS** Comprehensive Test of Basic Skills **ITBS** Iowa Test of Basic Skills, Form M
SAT10 Stanford Achievement Test, 10th Ed. **NAEP** National Assessment of Educational Progress 2005 Mathematics Objectives

Math Background

Professional Development

Skills Trace

BEFORE Chapter 3

Course 2 introduced the Pythagorean Theorem and graphing in the coordinate plane.

DURING Chapter 3

Course 3 reviews and extends graphing in the coordinate plane and has students apply the Pythagorean Theorem.

AFTER Chapter 3

Throughout this course students make and interpret graphs of two-variable problems.

3-1 Exploring Square Roots and Irrational Numbers

Math Understandings

- The square root of a negative number is undefined in the real number system. (These roots are defined in the complex number system.)
- Mathematicians have agreed that the symbol $\sqrt{\ }$, or radical sign, indicates the nonnegative square root of a number, if it exists.
- Only squares of whole numbers are called perfect squares.

A number like 16, which is the square of the whole number 4, is a **perfect square**. So, while it is true that $1.2 \times 1.2 = 1.44$, 1.44 is not called a perfect square. The **square root** of a number is a number that when multiplied by itself is equal to the given number. There are two values for the square root of 9, 3, and −3. However, $\sqrt{9}$ is defined as only the positive square root, 3. **Irrational numbers** are numbers that cannot be written as the ratio $\frac{a}{b}$, where *a* is any integer and *b* is any nonzero integer. Together, rational and irrational numbers form the set of **real numbers.**

3-2 The Pythagorean Theorem
3-3 Using the Pythagorean Theorem

Math Understandings

- The converse of the Pythagorean Theorem is also true: A triangle with sides *a, b,* and *c* is a right triangle if the equation $a^2 + b^2 = c^2$ is true.
- In general, $\sqrt{a^2 + b^2}$ is not equal to $a + b$.

In a right triangle, the two shortest sides are **legs**. The longest side, which is opposite the right angle, is the **hypotenuse**. The **Pythagorean Theorem,** $a^2 + b^2 = c^2$ relates the lengths of the legs (*a* and *b*) and hypotenuse (*c*) of any right triangle.

3-4 Graphing in the Coordinate Plane
3-5 Equations, Tables, and Graphs

Math Understandings

- Linear equations can have an infinite number of solutions.
- Every point that is a solution for an equation lies on the graph of that equation, and every point on the graph of an equation is a solution to the equation.

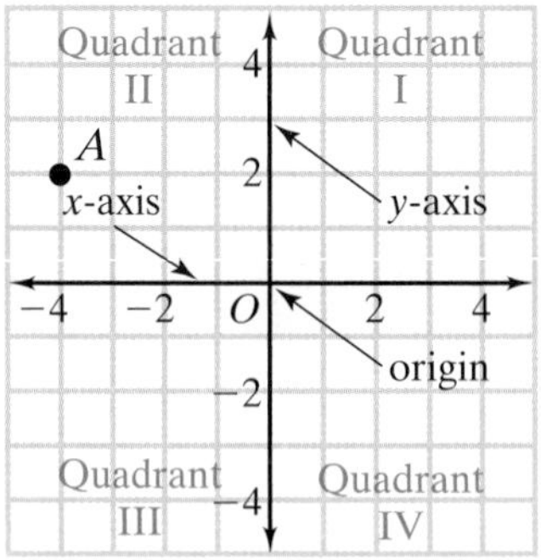

You can use a coordinate system to name points in a plane. A **coordinate plane** is a grid formed by the intersection of two number lines at right angles. An **ordered pair** gives the coordinates of the location of a point. In the graph, point *A* has the coordinates (−4, 2). The ***x*-coordinate** (−4 for point *A*) tells the number of horizontal units a point is from *O*. The ***y*-coordinate** (2 for point A) tells the number of vertical units a point is from *O*. Any ordered pair that makes an equation true is a **solution** of the equation. A linear equation such as $y = 3x - 5$ has many solutions, all of which lie on a line that is the graph of the equation.

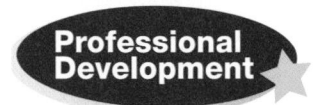

3-6 Translations

Math Understandings

- Three types of transformations that change a figure's position, but not its size or shape, are translations, reflections, and rotations (also known as slides, flips, and turns).
- A translation is described by the distance and direction that each point in the original figure moves to create the image.

A **transformation** is a change in the position, shape, or size of a figure. A **translation** is a transformation that moves each point of a figure the same distance and in the same direction.

The figure you get after a transformation (of point A, for example) is an **image** of the original figure (indicated by A', read as "A prime"). You can show this translation by writing $A \rightarrow A'$, read as "point A goes to point A prime."

3-7 Reflections and Symmetry

Math Understandings

- A reflection requires a line of reflection over which the original figure flips to form the image.
- A segment joining a point and its reflection image is perpendicular to the line of reflection.
- A figure can have zero, one, or more than one lines of symmetry.

A **reflection** is a transformation that flips a figure over a line. This line is the **line of reflection**. If a figure can be reflected over a line so that its image matches the original figure, the figure has **reflectional symmetry**. If you fold a figure along a **line of symmetry**, the two halves match exactly.

Transformations

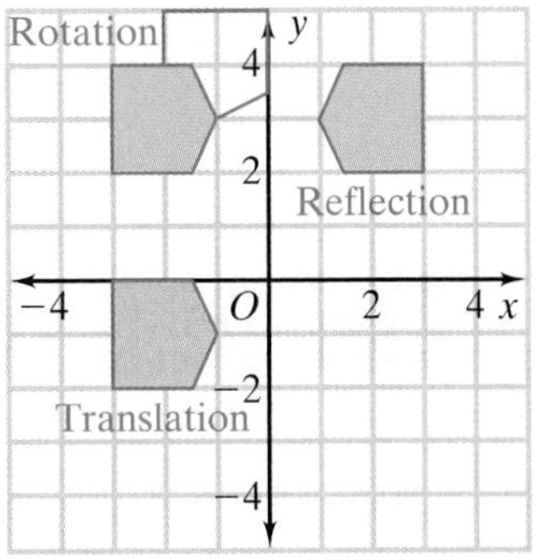

3-8 Rotations

Math Understandings

- Every figure can be rotated 360° to match its original figure exactly.
- Rotating a figure 180° produces the same image as a reflection over the x-axis or y-axis.

A **rotation** is a transformation that turns a figure about a fixed point. This fixed point is called the **center of rotation**. The **angle of rotation** is the number of degrees the figure rotates. In this book, all rotations are counterclockwise.

A figure has **rotational symmetry** if it can be rotated 180° or less and exactly matches its original figure. For rotational symmetry, the angle of rotation is the fewest number of degrees the figure must be rotated to match the original figure. A complete rotation has 360°.

Example: Both figures below have rotational symmetry.

The angle of rotation is 72°.

The angle of rotation is 60°.

Additional Professional Development Opportunities

Professional Development

Math Background Notes for Chapter 3: Every lesson has a Math Background in the PLAN section.

Research Overview, Mathematics Strands
Additional support for these topics and more is in the front of the Teacher's Edition.

LessonLab
LessonLab, a Pearson Education company offers comprehensive, facilitated professional development designed to help teachers to improve student achievement. To learn more please visit lessonlab.com.

Chapter 3 Resources

	3-1	3-2	3-3	3-4	3-5	3-6	3-7	3-8	For the Chapter
Print Resources									
Lesson Plans	●	●	●	●	●	●	●	●	
L3 Practice	●	●	●	●	●	●	●	●	
L1 Adapted Practice	●	●	●	●	●	●	●	●	
L3 Guided Problem Solving	●	●	●	●	●	●	●	●	
L2 Reteaching	●	●	●	●	●	●	●	●	
L4 Enrichment	●	●	●	●	●	●	●	●	
L3 Daily Notetaking Guide	●	●	●	●	●	●	●	●	
L1 Adapted Daily Notetaking Guide	●	●	●	●	●	●	●	●	
L3 Vocabulary and Study Skills Worksheets	●		●	●		●		●	●
L3 Daily Puzzles	●	●	●	●	●	●	●	●	
L3 Activity Labs	●	●	●	●	●	●	●	●	
L3 Checkpoint Quiz			●			●			
L3 Chapter Project									●
L2 Below Level Chapter Test									●
L3 Chapter Test									●
L4 Alternative Assessment									●
L3 Cumulative Review									●
Spanish Resources ELL									
L3 Practice	●	●	●	●	●	●	●	●	
L3 Vocabulary and Study Skills Worksheets	●		●	●		●		●	●
L3 Checkpoint Quiz			●			●			
L2 Below Level Chapter Test									●
L3 Chapter Test									●
L4 Alternative Assessment									●
L3 Cumulative Review									●
Transparencies									
Check Skills You'll Need	●	●	●	●	●	●	●	●	
Additional Examples	●	●	●	●	●	●	●	●	
Problem of the Day	●	●	●	●	●	●	●	●	
Classroom Aid	●	●	●	●	●	●	●	●	
Student Edition Answers	●	●	●	●	●	●	●	●	●
Lesson Quiz	●	●	●	●	●	●	●	●	
Test-Taking Strategies									●
Technology									
Interactive Textbook Online	●	●	●	●	●	●	●	●	●
StudentExpress™ CD-ROM	●	●	●	●	●	●	●	●	●
Success Tracker™ Online Intervention	●	●	●	●	●	●	●	●	●
TeacherExpress™ CD-ROM	●	●	●	●	●	●	●	●	●
PresentationExpress™ with QuickTake Presenter CD-ROM	●	●	●	●	●	●	●	●	●
ExamView® Assessment Suite CD-ROM	●	●	●	●	●	●	●	●	●
MindPoint® Quiz Show CD-ROM									●
Prentice Hall Web Site PHSchool.com	●	●	●	●	●	●	●	●	●

Also available: **Prentice Hall Assessment System**
- Progress Monitoring Assessments
- Skills and Concepts Review
- Test Prep Workbook

Other Resources
Algebra Readiness Tests
All-in-One Student Workbook
All-in-One Student Workbook, Adapted Version
Multilingual Handbook
Solution Key
Math Notes Study Folder
Spanish Cumulative Assessment

Where You Can Use the Lesson Resources

Here is a suggestion, following the four-step teaching plan, for how you can incorporate Differentiated Instruction Resources into your teaching.

	Instructional Resources L3	Differentiated Instruction Resources
1. Plan		
Preparation Read the Math Background in the Teacher's Edition to connect this lesson with students' previous experience. **Starting Class** **Check Skills You'll Need** Assign these exercises to review prerequisite skills. **New Vocabulary** Help students pre-read the lesson by pointing out the new terms introduced in the lesson.	**Math Background** **Math Understandings** **Transparencies & PresentationExpress™ with QuickTake Presenter CD-ROM** Check Skills You'll Need Problem of the Day **Resources** Vocabulary and Study Skills	**Spanish Support** ELL Vocabulary and Study Skills
2. Teach		
L3 **Guided Instruction** Use the Activity Labs to build conceptual understanding. Teach each Example. Use the Teacher's Edition side column notes for specific teaching tips, including Error Prevention notes. Use the Additional Examples found in the side column (and on transparency and PowerPoint) as an alternative presentation for the content. After each Example, assign the Quick Check exercise for that Example to get an immediate assessment of student understanding. Use the Closure activity in the Teacher's Edition to help students attain mastery of lesson content.	**Student Edition** Activity Lab **Resources** Daily Notetaking Guide Activity Lab **Transparencies & PresentationExpress™ with QuickTake Presenter CD-ROM** Additional Examples Classroom Aids **ExamView® Assessment Suite CD-ROM**	**Teacher's Edition** Every lesson includes suggestions for working with students who need special attention. L1 Special Needs L2 Below Level L4 Advanced Learners ELL English Language Learners **Resources** L1 Adapted Daily Notetaking Guide **Multilingual Handbook**
3. Practice		
Assignment Guide **Check Your Understanding** Use these questions to check students' understanding before you assign homework. **Homework Exercises** Assign homework from these leveled exercises in the Assignment Guide. A Practice by Example B Apply Your Skills C Challenge Test Prep and Mixed Review **Homework Quick Check** Use these key exercises to quickly check students' homework.	**Transparencies & PresentationExpress™ with QuickTake Presenter CD-ROM** Student Answers **Resources** Practice Guided Problem Solving Vocabulary Masters with Study Skills Activity Lab Daily Puzzles **ExamView® Assessment Suite CD-ROM**	**Spanish Support** ELL Practice ELL Vocabulary and Study Skills **Resources** L1 Adapted Practice L4 Enrichment
4. Assess & Reteach		
Lesson Quiz Assign the Lesson Quiz to assess students' mastery of the lesson content. **Checkpoint Quiz** Use the Checkpoint Quiz to assess student progress over several lessons.	**Transparencies & PresentationExpress™ with QuickTake Presenter CD-ROM** Lesson Quiz **Resources** Checkpoint Quiz	**Resources** L2 Reteaching ELL Checkpoint Quiz Success Tracker™ Online Intervention **ExamView® Assessment Suite CD-ROM**

KEY L1 Special Needs L2 Below Level L3 For All Students L4 Advanced, Gifted ELL English Language Learners

CHAPTER 3

Real Numbers and the Coordinate Plane

Check Your Readiness

Answers for students are in the back of the textbook.

For intervention, direct students to:

Evaluating and Simplifying Expressions
Lessons 1-1, 1-3
Extra Skills and Word Problems Practice, Ch. 1

Fractions and Decimals
Lesson 2-2
Extra Skills and Word Problems Practice, Ch. 2

Formulas
Lesson 2-6
Extra Skills and Word Problems Practice, Ch. 2

Exponents
Lesson 2-7
Extra Skills and Word Problems Practice, Ch. 2

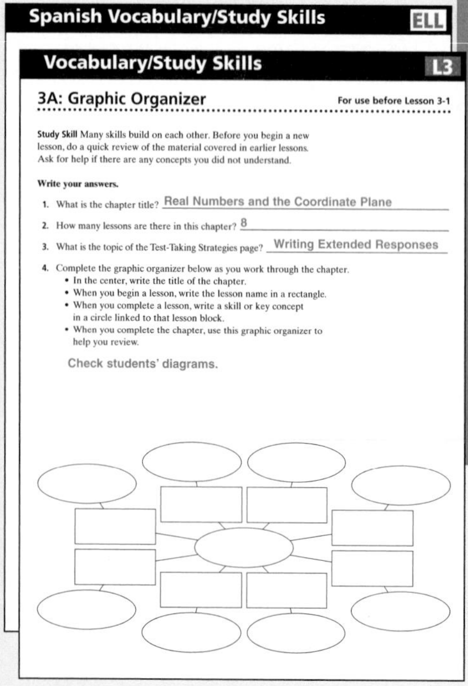

Spanish Vocabulary/Study Skills ELL

Vocabulary/Study Skills L3

3A: Graphic Organizer — For use before Lesson 3-1

Study Skill Many skills build on each other. Before you begin a new lesson, do a quick review of the material covered in earlier lessons. Ask for help if there are any concepts you did not understand.

Write your answers.

1. What is the chapter title? Real Numbers and the Coordinate Plane
2. How many lessons are there in this chapter? 8
3. What is the topic of the Test-Taking Strategies page? Writing Extended Responses
4. Complete the graphic organizer below as you work through the chapter.
   - In the center, write the title of the chapter.
   - When you begin a lesson, write the lesson name in a rectangle.
   - When you complete a lesson, write a skill or key concept in a circle linked to that lesson block.
   - When you complete the chapter, use this graphic organizer to help you review.

Check students' diagrams.

CHAPTER 3 Real Numbers and the Coordinate Plane

What You've Learned

- In Chapter 1, you wrote and solved algebraic equations.
- In Chapter 2, you used appropriate operations to solve problems involving rational numbers.

Check Your Readiness

GO for Help

For Exercises	See Lessons
1–2	1-1
3–5	1-3
6–9	2-2
10–12	2-6
13–15	2-7

Evaluating and Simplifying Expressions

(Algebra) **Evaluate each expression for $s = 4$ and $t = -3$.**

1. $5s + 16t$ −28 **2.** $44 - 2st$ 68

Simplify each expression.

3. $-11 + 2$ −9 **4.** $15 + (-2)$ 13 **5.** $5 - (-5)$ 10

Fractions and Decimals

Write each fraction as a decimal. Round to three decimal places.

6. $\frac{5}{6}$ 0.833 **7.** $\frac{16}{40}$ 0.4 **8.** $\frac{21}{13}$ 1.615 **9.** $\frac{19}{22}$ 0.864

Formulas

(Algebra) **Solve each formula for the variable indicated in red.**

10. $c = a + b$
$b = c - a$

11. $d = 16t$
$t = \frac{d}{16}$

12. $s = 200 + T$
$T = s - 200$

Exponents

Simplify each expression.

13. $3^2 + 4^2$ 25 **14.** $5^2 - 2^2$ 21 **15.** $9^2 + 10^2$ 181

Chapter 3 Overview

In this chapter, students use exponents and square roots to explore the Pythagorean Theorem. They graph points and linear equations in the coordinate plane. In addition, they learn to translate, reflect, and rotate figures.

Activating Prior Knowledge

Students use their knowledge of rational numbers and exponents to learn and apply the Pythagorean Theorem. They also build on their work writing and solving one-step equations to graph and solve linear equations.

What You'll Learn Next

- In this chapter, you will approximate the value of irrational numbers and use the Pythagorean Theorem to solve real-world problems.
- You will graph points and lines in the coordinate plane.
- You will translate, reflect, and rotate figures.

Key Vocabulary

- coordinate plane (p. 124)
- image (p. 136)
- irrational numbers (p. 107)
- linear equation (p. 131)
- ordered pair (p. 124)
- perfect square (p. 106)
- Pythagorean Theorem (p. 112)
- quadrants (p. 124)
- real numbers (p. 107)
- reflectional symmetry (p. 142)
- rotational symmetry (p. 146)
- solution (p. 131)
- square root (p. 106)
- transformation (p. 136)
- translation (p. 136)

Problem Solving Application On pages 156 and 157, you will work an extended activity on mountain slopes.

3-1

1. Plan

Objective
To find and estimate square roots and to classify numbers as rational or irrational

Examples
1 Finding Square Roots of Perfect Squares
2 Estimating a Square Root
3 Application: Skydiving
4 Classifying Real Numbers

Math Understandings: p. 104C

Professional Development

Math Background

The equation $x^2 = 9$ has two possible solutions: $x = 3$ and $x = -3$. However, there is only one solution to $x = \sqrt{9}$, $x = 3$. By convention, the radical sign, $\sqrt{\ }$, means the nonnegative square root only. *Nonnegative* describes all positive numbers and zero.

More Math Background p. 104C

Lesson Planning and Resources

See p. 104E for a list of the resources that support this lesson.

PowerPoint

Bell Ringer Practice

Check Skills You'll Need
Use student page, transparency, or PowerPoint. For intervention, direct students to:
Powers and Exponents
Lesson 2-7
Extra Skills and Word Problems Practice, Ch. 2

3-1 Exploring Square Roots and Irrational Numbers

Check Skills You'll Need

1. **Vocabulary Review** In a power, the __?__ tells how many times a base is used as a factor. exponent

Evaluate the expression x^2 for each value of x.

2. 2 4 **3.** −2 4

4. −6 36 **5.** 10 100

GO for Help Lesson 2–7

What You'll Learn

To find and estimate square roots and to classify numbers as rational or irrational

New Vocabulary perfect square, square root, irrational numbers, real numbers

Why Learn This?

Not every situation can be modeled using the four basic operations. For example, you need square roots to relate the time and distance a skydiver falls.

A number that is the square of a whole number is a **perfect square.** The **square root** of a number is another number that when multiplied by itself is equal to the given number.

In the diagram at the right, 16 square tiles form a square with 4 tiles on each side. Since $4 \cdot 4 = 16$ and $-4 \cdot (-4) = 16$, 16 has two square roots, 4 and −4. Since $4^2 = 16$, 16 is a perfect square.

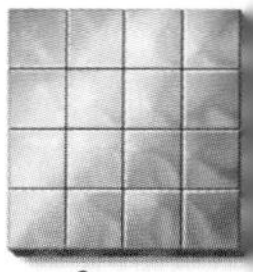

$4^2 = 16$

EXAMPLE **Finding Square Roots of Perfect Squares**

Perfect Squares

n	n^2
0	0
1	1
2	4
3	9
4	16
5	25
6	36
7	49
8	64
9	81
10	100
11	121
12	144

1 Find the two square roots of 25.

$5 \cdot 5 = 25$ and $-5 \cdot (-5) = 25$

The square roots of 25 are 5 and −5.

Quick Check

1. Find the square roots of each number.
   a. 36 6, −6 **b.** 1 1, −1 **c.** $\frac{1}{16}$ $\frac{1}{4}, -\frac{1}{4}$

The symbol $\sqrt{\ }$ means the square root of a number. In this book, $\sqrt{\ }$ means the positive square root, unless stated otherwise. So $\sqrt{9}$ means the positive square root of 9, or 3, and $-\sqrt{9}$ means the opposite of the positive square root of 9, or −3.

Differentiated Instruction **Solutions for All Learners**

Special Needs L1
Students draw a 3 × 3 square and a 6 × 6 square on grid paper. They count the square units. 9 and 36 Then they try to draw a square with 6 square units. Elicit the fact that some numbers cannot be drawn as perfect whole-number squares.
learning style: visual

Below Level L2
Students are asked to notice what the sign should be in multiplications such as the ones below. Then, students identify which can be re-written as a number squared, and rewrite them.
(−2)(−2) positive, $(-2)^2$ (−5)(5) negative
learning style: visual

To estimate the square root of a number that is not a perfect square, use the square root of the nearest perfect square.

EXAMPLE Estimating a Square Root

2 Estimate the value of $\sqrt{28}$ to the nearest integer.

Since 28 is closer to 25 than it is to 36, $\sqrt{28}$ is closer to 5 than to 6. You can write $\sqrt{28} \approx 5$.

Quick Check

2. Estimate the value of $\sqrt{38}$ to the nearest integer. 6

Finding a number's square root is the inverse operation of finding the number's square. So $\sqrt{3^2} = 3$.

EXAMPLE Application: Skydiving

3 The formula $d = 16t^2$ represents the approximate distance d in feet a skydiver falls in t seconds before opening the parachute. The formula assumes there is no air resistance. Find the time a skydiver takes to fall 816 feet before opening the parachute.

$d = 16t^2$ ← **Use the formula for distance and time.**

$816 = 16t^2$ ← **Substitute 816 for *d*.**

$\frac{816}{16} = t^2$ ← **Divide each side by 16 to isolate *t*.**

$51 = t^2$ ← **Simplify.**

$\sqrt{51} = \sqrt{t^2}$ ← **Find the positive square root of each side.**

[√] 51 [=] 7.1414284285 ← **Use a calculator.**

$7.1 \approx t$ ← **Round to the nearest tenth.**

The skydiver takes about 7.1 seconds to fall 816 feet.

Quick Check

3. Find the time a skydiver takes to fall each distance. Round to the nearest tenth of a second.

a. 480 ft 5.5 s **b.** 625 ft 6.3 s

Irrational numbers are numbers that cannot be written in the form $\frac{a}{b}$, where a is any integer and b is any nonzero integer. Rational and irrational numbers form the set of **real numbers.**

Online active math

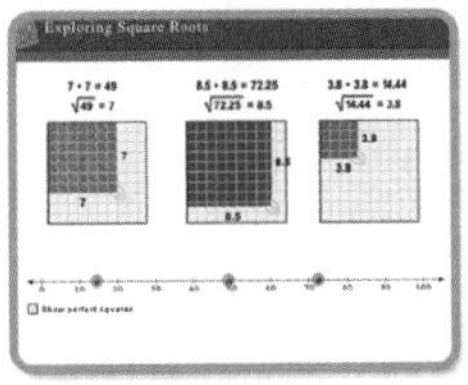

For: Square Roots Activity
Use: Interactive Textbook, 3-1

GO for Help

For help in using formulas, go to Lesson 2-6, Example 1.

2. Teach

Activity Lab

Use before the lesson.

All in One Teaching Resources

Activity Lab 3-1: Powerful Patterns

Guided Instruction

Example 1
To help students recognize perfect squares, have them make a table showing the squares of integers from 2 through 25.

Example 2
Remind students that the symbol ≈ means *approximately equal to.*

Error Prevention!

Students may confuse squaring a number with multiplying a number by 2. To clarify this, write 3^2 and $3 \cdot 2$ on the board. Elicit the fact that the first means $3 \cdot 3$ which is not the same as $3 \cdot 2$. Have students find the values for both expressions, and write them on the board. $3^2 = 9$; $3 \cdot 2 = 6$

Technology Tip
Note that, when presenting Example 3, on some calculators, taking the square root may be a 2nd function. This involves first pressing the [2nd] key and then the [√] key before entering the number. On other calculators, you may first enter the number and then press the [√] key. Have students experiment with finding $\sqrt{9}$ to see what keystrokes their calculators require.

PowerPoint

Additional Examples

1 Find the two square roots of 81 9 and −9

2 Estimate the value of $-\sqrt{70}$ to the nearest integer. $-\sqrt{70} \approx -8$

3 The math class drops a small ball from the top of a stairwell. They measure the distance to the basement as 48 feet. Use the formula $d = 16t^2$ to find how long it takes the ball to fall. $t \approx 1.7$ s

Advanced Learners L4
Students find the side of a square with the given area:
81 9 121 11 400 20
learning style: verbal

English Language Learners ELL
Students draw a 2-column table on an index card and label the table *Real Numbers.* They label the columns *Rational Numbers* and *Irrational Numbers,* respectively. Have them provide examples of rational numbers in one column and irrational numbers in the other.
learning style: verbal

Guided Instruction

Connection to Physics
The formula $d = 16t^2$ in Example 3 is the same for objects of any size and weight. So, in the absence of air resistance, a feather and a hammer fall the same distance in a specified time. This was demonstrated by an astronaut on the moon.

PowerPoint

Additional Examples

4 Identify each number as *rational* or *irrational*. Explain.

a. $-9.333\overline{3}$ Rational; the decimal repeats.

b. $4\frac{7}{9}$ Rational; the ratio is $\frac{43}{9}$.

c. $\sqrt{90}$ Irrational; 90 is not a perfect square.

d. 6.36366366636666 . . . Irrational; the decimal does not terminate or repeat a group of digits.

All in One Teaching Resources

- Daily Notetaking Guide 3-1 L3
- Adapted Notetaking 3-1 L1

Closure

- *What is the square root of a given number?* A number that when multiplied by itself is equal to the given number.
- Give several examples of irrational numbers. Sample: $\sqrt{3}$, 1.343344333444 . . ., $\sqrt{12}$
- Give several examples of rational numbers. Sample: $\frac{3}{7}$, $\sqrt{25}$, $0.6666\overline{6}$

Vocabulary Tip

The word *rational* has the word *ratio* in it.

The word *irrational* means "not rational."

The diagram below shows the relationships among sets of numbers.

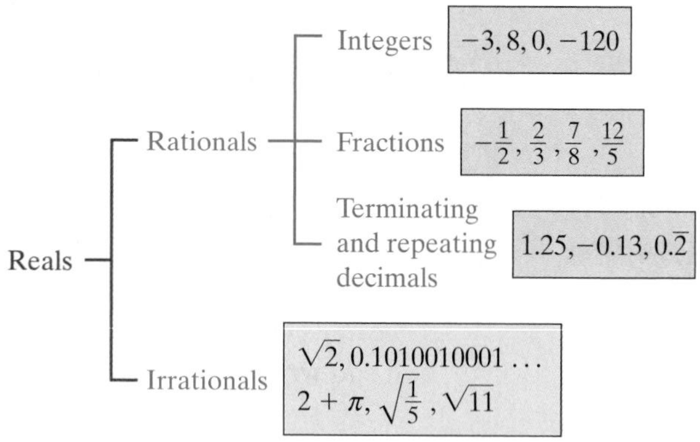

The decimal digits of irrational numbers do not terminate or repeat. The decimal digits of $\pi = 3.14159265359\ldots$ do not terminate or repeat, because π is an irrational number. Irrational numbers can also include decimals that have a pattern in their digits, like 0.02022022202222 . . .

For any integer n that is not a perfect square, $\sqrt{n}$ is irrational.

GO for Help

For help with terminating and repeating decimals, go to Lesson 2-2, Example 3.

EXAMPLE Classifying Real Numbers

4 Is each number *rational* or *irrational*? Explain.

a. 0.818118111 . . . Irrational; the decimal does not terminate or repeat.

b. $-0.\overline{81}$ Rational; the decimal repeats.

c. $1\frac{2}{9}$ Rational; the number can be written as the ratio $\frac{11}{9}$.

d. $\sqrt{5}$ Irrational; 5 is not a perfect square.

Quick Check

4. Is $0.\overline{6}$ *rational* or *irrational*? Explain. Rational; the decimal repeats.

Check Your Understanding

Vocabulary **Write all the possible names for each number. Choose from the terms at the right.**

1. $\sqrt{6}$ irrational, real
2. $-0.\overline{6}$ rational, real
3. $\frac{1}{6}$ rational, real
4. 25 rational, real, perfect square

A. rational number
B. irrational number
C. real number
D. perfect square

Find the positive and negative square roots of each number.

5. 4 2, −2
6. $\frac{1}{4}$ $\frac{1}{2}, -\frac{1}{2}$
7. 100 10, −10
8. $\frac{1}{100}$ $\frac{1}{10}, -\frac{1}{10}$

Homework Exercises

For more exercises, see Extra Skills and Word Problems.

GO for Help

For Exercises	See Examples
9–13	1
14–21	2
22–25	3
26–31	4

A **Find the square roots of each number.**

9. 49 $7, -7$
10. 900 $30, -30$
11. $\frac{1}{36}$ $\frac{1}{6}, -\frac{1}{6}$
12. $\frac{1}{121}$ $\frac{1}{11}, -\frac{1}{11}$
13. $\frac{4}{25}$ $\frac{2}{5}, -\frac{2}{5}$

Estimate the value of each expression to the nearest integer.

14. $\sqrt{3}$ 2
15. $\sqrt{10}$ 3
16. $-\sqrt{22}$ -5
17. $\sqrt{88}$ 9
18. $-\sqrt{54}$ -7
19. $-\sqrt{105}$ -10
20. $\sqrt{150}$ 12
21. $-\sqrt{120}$ -11

Use $s = 20\sqrt{273 + T}$ to estimate the speed of sound s in meters per second for each Celsius temperature T. Round to the nearest integer.

22. 0°C 330 m/s
23. 20°C 342 m/s
24. −10°C 324 m/s
25. 70°C 370 m/s

Is each number *rational* or *irrational*? Explain. 26–31. See margin.

26. −0.6
27. $\sqrt{40}$
28. 0.606606660 . . .
29. $-\sqrt{144}$
30. $\sqrt{12}$
31. 0.0203040506 . . .

B **GPS**

32. **Guided Problem Solving** The area of a square postage stamp is $\frac{81}{100}$ in.^{2}. What is the side length of the stamp?
    - What is the formula for the area of a square?
    - How can you use the formula to find the side length of a square? $\frac{9}{10}$ in.

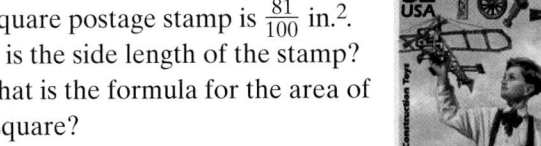

33. **Boxing** The area of a square boxing ring is 484 ft^2. What is the perimeter of the boxing ring? 88 ft

34. **Geometry** A tile is shown at the right. The area of the larger square is 49 in.^{2}. Find the area of the smaller square. 9 in.^{2}

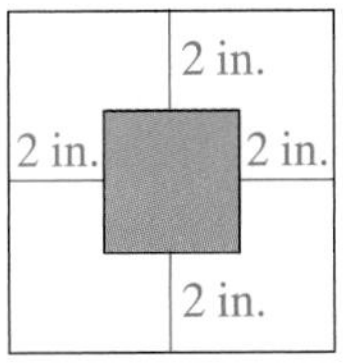

35. **Open-Ended** Give an example of an irrational number that is less than 2 and greater than 1.5. Explain how you know the number is irrational. Answers may vary. Sample: $\sqrt{3}$; 3 is not a perfect square.

36. **Writing in Math** Explain how you can approximate $\sqrt{30}$. See left.

37. The Closure Property states that a set of numbers is closed under a given operation if the result of the operation is in the same set of numbers. For example, the set of rational numbers is closed under addition, because the sum of any two rational numbers is a rational number. Is each set of numbers closed under addition? Explain.
    a. even numbers
    b. irrational numbers
    c. prime numbers
    37a–c. See left.

GO Online
Homework Video Tutor
Visit: PHSchool.com
Web Code: ase-0301

36. Find the closest perfect square to 30, which is 25. Then take the square root of 25, which is 5.

37a. Yes; the sum of even numbers is an even number.

b. Yes; the sum of two irrational numbers is an irrational number.

c. No; the sum of two prime numbers can be a composite number.

26. Rational; the decimal terminates.
27. Irrational; 40 is not a perfect square.
28. Irrational; the decimal does not terminate or repeat.
29. Rational; 144 is a perfect square.
30. Irrational; 12 is not a perfect square.
31. Irrational; the decimal does not terminate or repeat.

3. Practice

Assignment Guide

Check Your Understanding

Go over Exercises 1–8 in class before assigning the Homework Exercises.

Homework Exercises

A Practice by Example	9–31
B Apply Your Skills	32–49
C Challenge	50
Test Prep and Mixed Review	51–56

Homework Quick Check

To check students' understanding of key skills and concepts, go over Exercises 23, 27, 34, 36, and 47.

Differentiated Instruction Resources

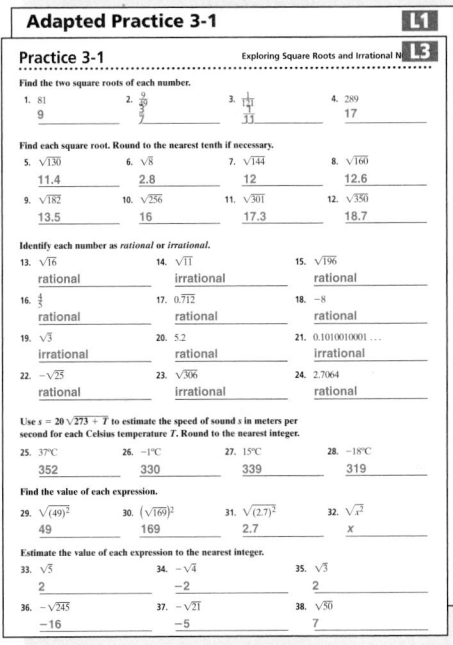

Adapted Practice 3-1 L1

Practice 3-1 Exploring Square Roots and Irrational N[umbers] L3

Find the two square roots of each number.

1. 81 — 9
2. $\frac{9}{49}$ — $\frac{3}{7}$
3. $\frac{1}{121}$ — $\frac{1}{11}$
4. 289 — 17

Find each square root. Round to the nearest tenth if necessary.

5. $\sqrt{130}$ — 11.4
6. $\sqrt{8}$ — 2.8
7. $\sqrt{144}$ — 12
8. $\sqrt{160}$ — 12.6
9. $\sqrt{182}$ — 13.5
10. $\sqrt{256}$ — 16
11. $\sqrt{301}$ — 17.3
12. $\sqrt{350}$ — 18.7

Identify each number as *rational* or *irrational*.

13. $\sqrt{16}$ — rational
14. $\sqrt{11}$ — irrational
15. $\sqrt{196}$ — rational
16. $\frac{4}{5}$ — rational
17. $0.\overline{712}$ — rational
18. −8 — rational
19. $\sqrt{3}$ — irrational
20. 5.2 — rational
21. 0.1010010001 . . . — irrational
22. $-\sqrt{25}$ — rational
23. $\sqrt{306}$ — irrational
24. 2.7064 — rational

Use $s = 20\sqrt{273 + T}$ to estimate the speed of sound s in meters per second for each Celsius temperature T. Round to the nearest integer.

25. 37°C — 352
26. −1°C — 330
27. 15°C — 339
28. −18°C — 319

Find the value of each expression.

29. $\sqrt{(49)^2}$ — 49
30. $(\sqrt{169})^2$ — 169
31. $\sqrt{(2.7)^2}$ — 2.7
32. $\sqrt{x^2}$ — x

Estimate the value of each expression to the nearest integer.

33. $\sqrt{5}$ — 2
34. $-\sqrt{4}$ — −2
35. $\sqrt{3}$ — 2
36. $-\sqrt{245}$ — −16
37. $-\sqrt{21}$ — −5
38. $\sqrt{50}$ — 7

3-1 • Guided Problem Solving GPS L3

GPS Student Page 110, Exercise 47:

Ferris Wheels The formula $d = 1.23\sqrt{h}$ represents the distance in miles d you can see from h feet above ground. On the London Eye Ferris wheel, you are 450 ft above ground. To the nearest tenth of a mile, how far can you see?

Understand

1. What are you being asked to find?
   the distance in miles that one can see from 450 ft above ground on the London Eye Ferris Wheel

Plan and Carry Out

2. What is the formula?
   $d = 1.23\sqrt{h}$
3. What is the height?
   450 ft
4. Substitute known values into the formula.
   $d = 1.23\sqrt{450}$
5. Simplify using a calculator. Round to the nearest tenth.
   26.1 mi

Check

6. Use estimation to check your answer.
   $d \approx 1.25 \times 21 \approx (1 \times 21) + (\frac{1}{4} \times 21) \approx$
   $21 + 5.25 \approx 26.25$; It checks.

Solve Another Problem

7. The formula $d = 1.23\sqrt{h}$ represents the distance in miles d you can see from h feet above ground. At the top of the Ferris wheel at Cedar Point, you are 140 ft above ground. To the nearest tenth of a mile, how far can you see?
   14.6 mi

4. Assess & Reteach

PowerPoint

Lesson Quiz

1. Find the two square roots of 400. 20 and −20
2. Estimate $\sqrt{34}$ to the nearest integer. 6
3. Using $d = 16t^2$, find how long it takes a skydiver to fall 676 ft from an airplane. 6.5 s
4. Is $\frac{\sqrt{64}}{5}$ rational or irrational? Explain. Rational; it can be written as $\frac{8}{5}$.

Reteaching 3-1 — Exploring Square Roots and Irrational — L2

- The *square* of 5 is 25.
  $5 \cdot 5 = 5^2 = 25$
- The *square root* of 25 is 5 because $5^2 = 25$.

$\sqrt{25} = 5$

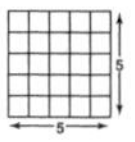

$1^2 = 1$, $2^2 = 4$, $3^2 = 9$, $4^2 = 16$, $5^2 = 25$ } *perfect squares*

Example: You can use a calculator to find square roots.
Find $\sqrt{36}$ and $\sqrt{21}$ to the nearest tenth.

36 [√] = 6   21 [√] ≈ 4.5825757 ≈ 4.6

You can estimate square roots like $\sqrt{52}$ and $\sqrt{61}$.

Perfect squares: 49, 52, 64 — Estimate — $\sqrt{49} = 7$, $\sqrt{52} \approx 7$, $\sqrt{64} = 8$ — Estimate — $\sqrt{49} = 7$, $\sqrt{61} \approx 8$, $\sqrt{64} = 8$

Find each square root. Estimate to the nearest integer if necessary. Use ≈ to show that a value is estimated.

1. $\sqrt{16}$ 4	2. $\sqrt{85}$ ≈ 9	3. $\sqrt{26}$ ≈ 5	4. $\sqrt{36}$ 6
5. $\sqrt{98}$ ≈ 10	6. $\sqrt{40}$ ≈ 6	7. $\sqrt{100}$ 10	8. $\sqrt{18}$ ≈ 4
9. $\sqrt{5}$ ≈ 2	10. $\sqrt{121}$ 11	11. $\sqrt{68}$ ≈ 8	12. $\sqrt{144}$ 12
13. $\sqrt{29}$ ≈ 5	14. $\sqrt{64}$ 8	15. $\sqrt{37}$ ≈ 6	16. $\sqrt{75}$ ≈ 9

17. If a whole number is not a perfect square, its square root is an *irrational number.* List the numbers from exercises 1–16 that are irrational.
$\sqrt{85}, \sqrt{26}, \sqrt{98}, \sqrt{40}, \sqrt{18}, \sqrt{5}, \sqrt{68}, \sqrt{29}, \sqrt{37}, \sqrt{75}$

Enrichment 3-1 — Exploring Square Roots and Irrational — L4

Patterns in Numbers

Use a calculator or a table of square roots to find the square root of each integer below. Round each answer to the nearest thousandth. The first ten are done for you.

N	$\sqrt{N}$	*N*	$\sqrt{N}$	*N*	$\sqrt{N}$
2	1.414	12	3.464	22	4.690
3	1.732	13	3.606	23	4.796
4	2.000	14	3.742	24	4.899
5	2.236	15	3.873	25	5.000
6	2.449	16	4.000	26	5.099
7	2.646	17	4.123	27	5.196
8	2.828	18	4.243	28	5.292
9	3.000	19	4.359	29	5.385
10	3.162	20	4.472	30	5.477
11	3.317	21	4.583	31	5.568

1. Use the square roots in the table to find each product. Round the product to the nearest thousandth.
   a. $\sqrt{2} \times \sqrt{3}$ 2.449 b. $\sqrt{2} \times \sqrt{4}$ 2.828 c. $\sqrt{2} \times \sqrt{5}$ 3.162
   d. $\sqrt{3} \times \sqrt{4}$ 3.464 e. $\sqrt{3} \times \sqrt{5}$ 3.873 f. $\sqrt{2} \times \sqrt{13}$ 5.099
2. Look at your answers in Exercise 1. Compare them to the square roots of other numbers in the table. Describe the pattern you see.
   Sample answer: The product of the square roots of two integers is equal to the square root of the product of the two integers.
3. Choose two pairs of two numbers from the table. Multiply to see if your conjecture is true for these numbers.
   Sample answer: $\sqrt{2} \times \sqrt{11} = 1.414 \times 3.317 = 4.960 = \sqrt{22}$
   $\sqrt{5} \times \sqrt{5} = 2.236 \times 2.236 = 5.000 = \sqrt{25}$

Find the value of each expression.

38. $(\sqrt{36})^2$ 36 39. $\sqrt{(10)^2}$ 10 40. $\sqrt{(3.2)^2}$ 3.2 41. $(\sqrt{a})^2$ $|a|$

A number that is used as a factor three times is the cube root of the product. Since $2^3 = 8$, 2 is the cube root of 8. Find each cube root *n*.

42. $n^3 = 27$ 3 43. $n^3 = 64$ 4 44. $n^3 = 125$ 5 45. $n^3 = -8$ −2

46. The area of a square is $\frac{25}{36}$ in.^{2}. What is the length of its side? $\frac{5}{6}$ in.

GPS 47. **Ferris Wheels** The formula $d = 1.23\sqrt{h}$ represents the distance in miles *d* you can see from *h* feet above ground. On the London Eye Ferris Wheel, you are 450 ft above ground. To the nearest tenth of a mile, how far can you see? 26.1 mi

48. **Number Sense** For what values of *n* is $\sqrt{n}$ a rational number? when *n* is a perfect square, including 0

49. **Error Analysis** A student evaluated the expression $\sqrt{4 + 9}$ and got the answer 5. What error did the student make? See margin.

C 50. **Challenge** Explain how you know that the number 123,456,789,101,112 cannot be a perfect square. (*Hint:* What is the units digit?) No integer multiplied by itself ends in 2.

Test Prep and Mixed Review — Practice

Multiple Choice

51. The area of a square is 150 square centimeters. Which best represents the side length of the square? B
    (A) 11.7 cm (B) 12.2 cm (C) 2.9 cm (D) 13 cm

52. The diameter of a human hair is about 1.7×10^{-5} meters. Which of the following represents this number in standard notation? F
    (F) 0.000017 (G) 0.00017 (H) 17,000 (J) 170,000

53. Which problem situation matches the equation $2x + 5 = 20$? C
    (A) Jacob travels 5 more than twice as many miles to work as Carrie travels. If Carrie travels 20 miles to work, how many miles *x* does Jacob travel?
    (B) Dana's arm is 5 inches longer than Collin's arm. If Dana's arm is 20 inches long, what is twice the length *x* of Collin's arm?
    (C) Joel made a $20 phone call to Spain. The call cost $2 per minute plus a $5 connection fee. How many minutes *x* did the call last?
    (D) Alondra invited 20 people to a party. Two people arrived late, and five people could not go. How many people *x* arrived on time for the party?

GO for Help

For Exercises	See Lesson
54–56	2-8

Write each number in scientific notation.

54. 18,000 1.8×10^4 55. 6,038,000 6.038×10^6 56. 49,700 4.97×10^4

Test Prep

Resources

For additional practice with a variety of test item formats:
- Test-Taking Strategies, p. 151
- Test Prep, p. 155
- Test-Taking Strategies with Transparencies

Alternative Assessment

Each student in a pair writes an irrational number. Then each partner decides which two whole numbers the other partner's value falls between.

49. The student took the square root of 4 and added it to the square root of 9. You must add 4 + 9 first and then take the square root.

Hands On

Exploring the Pythagorean Theorem

ACTIVITY

Step 1 Use centimeter grid paper to draw a right triangle. The right angle should be included between sides that are 3 cm and 4 cm long.

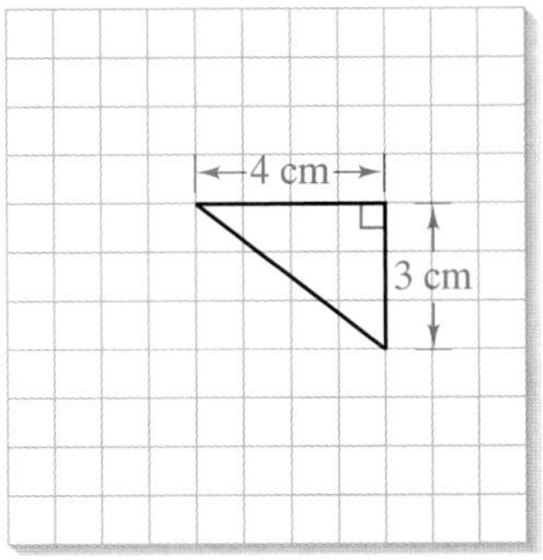

Step 2 Draw a 3-by-3 square along the side that is 3 cm long. Label the square A. Draw a 4-by-4 square along the side that is 4 cm long. Label the square B.

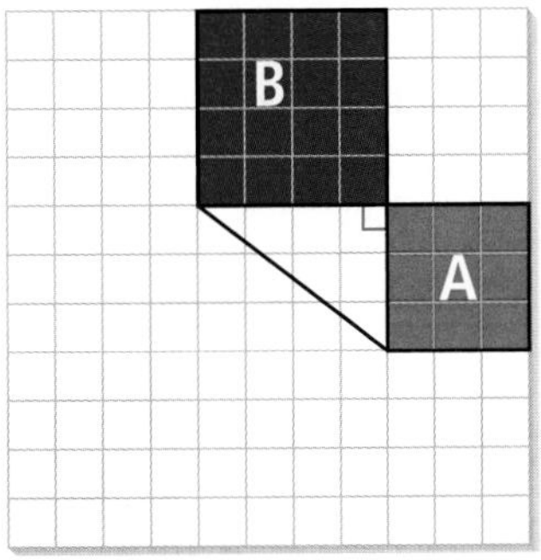

Step 3 Cut out another piece of grid paper to make a square on the side opposite the right angle. Label the square C.

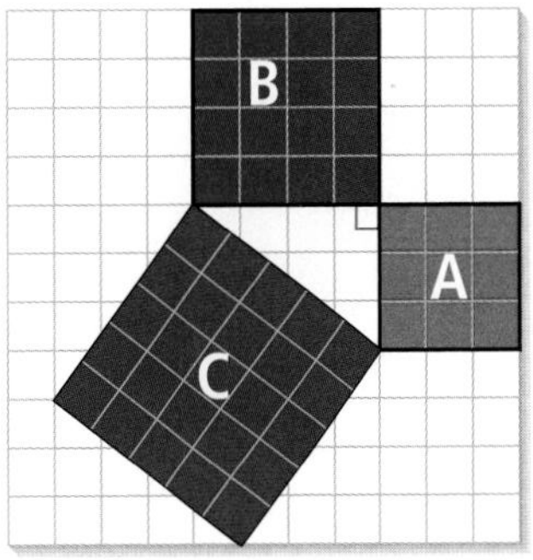

Exercises

1–2. See margin.

1. a. Repeat the activity for the triangles shown in the table. Copy and complete the table.
   b. **Patterns** What is the relationship between the areas of the two smaller squares (A and B) and the area of the largest square (C)?
2. **Algebra** Use variables to write an equation that relates the side lengths of a right triangle.

Sides of Triangle	Area of Square A	Area of Square B	Area of Square C
3, 4, 5	9	16	25
5, 12, ■	■	■	■
6, 8, ■	■	■	■
9, 12, ■	■	■	■

Activity Lab

Exploring the Pythagorean Theorem

Students use geometry to explore the basis of the Pythagorean Theorem. They cut out squares using grid paper to form the edges of a right triangle and analyze patterns in side lengths.

Guided Instruction

Before beginning the activity, students should review how squares are related to triangles and to exponents. Ask questions such as:

- *How many right triangles make up a square? How do the side lengths of the triangles compare to the side lengths of the square they make up?* 2; they are the same
- *What do you know about the angles of a right triangle?* one angle always measures 90°, the other two are less than 90°, they all add up to 180°
- *How do you find the area of a square?* "square" the length of a side

Differentiated Instruction

Special Needs L1

Help students identify the hypotenuse as the longest side and the side opposite the right angle. Draw several right triangles of different sizes and orientations on the board. Have students identify each hypotenuse.

Resources

- Activity Lab 3-2: Sporting Distances
- centimeter grid paper

1a.

Sides of Triangle	Area of Square A	Area of Square B	Area of Square C
3, 4, 5	9	16	25
5, 12, 13	25	144	169
6, 8, 10	36	64	100
9, 12, 15	81	144	225

b. The sum of the areas of the two smaller squares (A and B) is equal to the area of the largest square (C).

2. $a^2 + b^2 = c^2$, where a and b are the lengths of the shorter sides, and c is the length of the longest side.

3-2

1. Plan

Objective
To use the Pythagorean Theorem to find the length of the hypotenuse of a right triangle

Example
1 Finding the Hypotenuse

Math Understandings: p. 104C

Professional Development

Math Background

In a right triangle, the longest side, or *hypotenuse*, lies opposite the largest angle, which is 90°. The two other sides are called *legs*. The Pythagorean Theorem, $a^2 + b^2 = c^2$, relates the lengths of the legs (a and b) to the length of the hypotenuse (c).

More Math Background: p. 104C

Lesson Planning and Resources

See p. 104E for a list of the resources that support this lesson.

PowerPoint

Bell Ringer Practice

Check Skills You'll Need
Use student page, transparency, or PowerPoint. For intervention, direct students to:
Exploring Square Roots and Irrational Numbers
Lesson 3-1
Extra Skills and Word Problems Practice, Ch. 3

3-2 The Pythagorean Theorem

Check Skills You'll Need

1. **Vocabulary Review** What is the *square root* of a number? See below.

Estimate the value of each expression to the nearest integer.

2. $\sqrt{60}$ 8 3. $\sqrt{111}$ 11
4. $\sqrt{80}$ 9 5. $\sqrt{22}$ 5

GO for Help Lesson 3-1

Check Skills You'll Need

1. a number that when multiplied by itself is equal to the given number

What You'll Learn

To use the Pythagorean Theorem to find the length of the hypotenuse of a right triangle

New Vocabulary legs, hypotenuse, Pythagorean Theorem

Why Learn This?

The Pythagorean Theorem describes the special relationship among the sides of a right triangle. You can use the theorem to find the side lengths of right triangles in structures such as bridges.

In a right triangle, the two shortest sides are **legs.** The longest side, which is opposite the right angle, is the **hypotenuse.** The **Pythagorean Theorem** is an equation that shows the relationship between the legs and the hypotenuse.

KEY CONCEPTS **The Pythagorean Theorem**

In any right triangle, the sum of the squares of the lengths of the legs is equal to the square of the length of the hypotenuse.

$$a^2 + b^2 = c^2$$

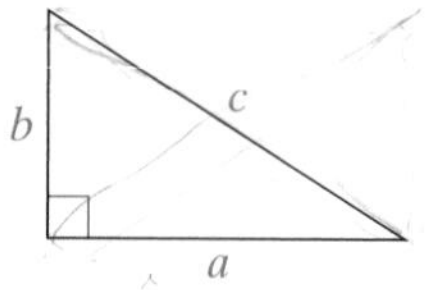

You can use the Pythagorean Theorem to find the length of the hypotenuse of a right triangle if you know the lengths of the two legs.

Differentiated Instruction Solutions for All Learners

Special Needs L1
Students are given pictures of several right triangles of different sizes. Students highlight the legs of each right triangle in one color and the hypotenuse in another color. Then they measure each side with a ruler. Elicit the fact that the hypotenuse is always the longest side.
learning style: visual

Below Level L2
Students state each expression, and then find the sum. For example, "3 squared plus 5 squared means 3 times 3 plus 5 times 5."

$3^2 + 5^2$ 34 $4^2 + 11^2$ 137
$1^2 + 7^2$ 50 $2^2 + 6^2$ 40

learning style: verbal

EXAMPLES Finding the Hypotenuse

1 Find the length of the hypotenuse of the triangle below.

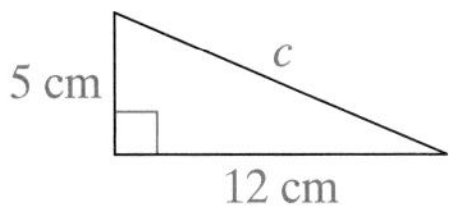

$a^2 + b^2 = c^2$ ← **Use the Pythagorean Theorem.**

$5^2 + 12^2 = c^2$ ← **Substitute 5 for *a* and 12 for *b*.**

$25 + 144 = c^2$ ← **Simplify.**

$169 = c^2$ ← **Add.**

$\sqrt{169} = \sqrt{c^2}$ ← **Find the positive square root of each side.**

$13 = c$ ← **Simplify.**

The length of the hypotenuse is 13 cm.

2 **Gridded Response** An architect drew the sketch of a bridge shown below. The bridge has 12-ft-long horizontal members and 24-ft-long vertical members. What is the length in feet of each diagonal member? Round to the nearest foot.

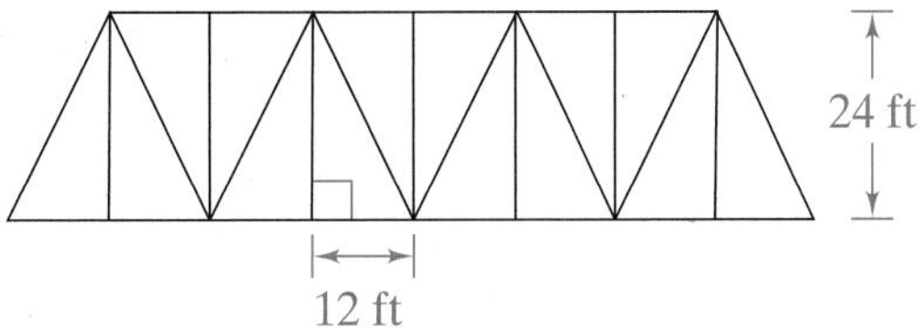

Each diagonal member is the hypotenuse of a right triangle.

$a^2 + b^2 = c^2$ ← **Use the Pythagorean Theorem.**

$12^2 + 24^2 = c^2$ ← **Substitute 12 for *a* and 24 for *b*.**

$144 + 576 = c^2$ ← **Simplify.**

$720 = c^2$ ← **Add.**

$\sqrt{720} = \sqrt{c^2}$ ← **Find the positive square root of each side.**

√ 720 = 26.83281573 ← **Use a calculator.**

$27 \approx c$ ← **Simplify.**

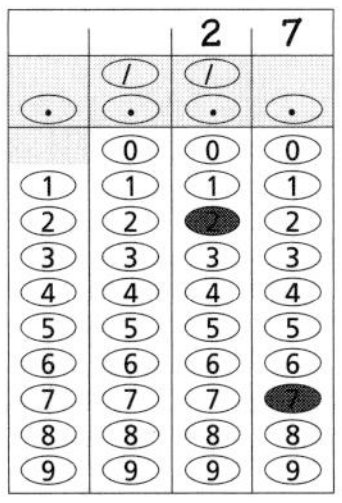

The length of each diagonal member is about 27 ft.

Quick Check

1. Find the length of the hypotenuse of a right triangle with legs of 12 cm and 16 cm. 20 cm
2. A bridge has 22-ft horizontal members and 25-ft vertical members. Find the length of each diagonal member to the nearest foot. 33 ft

GO Online

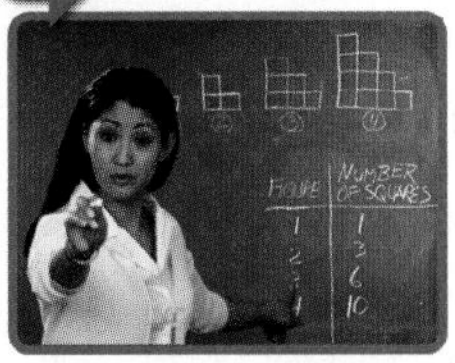

Video Tutor Help
Visit: PHSchool.com
Web Code: ase-0775

Test Prep Tip

Draw and label a picture of a right triangle like the one below to match the problem situation.

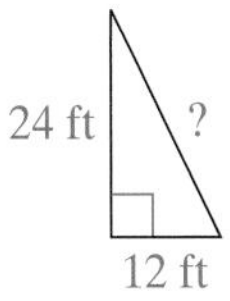

2. Teach

Activity Lab

Use before the lesson.
Student Edition Activity Lab, Hands On 3-2a, Exploring the Pythagorean Theorem, p. 111

All in One Teaching Resources

Activity Lab 3-2: Sporting Distances

Guided Instruction

Error Prevention!

Students may sometimes forget to find the square root of c^2. Point out that the hypotenuse is always the longest side and that $a + b$ must always be greater than c.

Example 2
Provide students with a blank grid from TAKS **Strategies with Transparencies.**

PowerPoint

Additional Examples

1 Find the hypotenuse of a right triangle whose legs are 6 ft and 8 ft. 10 ft

2 A wheelchair ramp that leads into an apartment building doorway is 5 feet above the ground. The horizontal distance from the entrance to the end of the ramp is 16 feet. What is the length in feet of the ramp? Round to the nearest foot. 17 feet

All in One Teaching Resources
- Daily Notetaking Guide 3-2 L3
- Adapted Notetaking 3-2 L1

Closure

- *What does the Pythagorean Theorem state?* Sample: In a right triangle, the longest side squared equals the sum of the squares of the other two sides.
- *If you know the length of two legs of a right triangle, how would you find the hypotenuse?* Sample: Find the sum of the squares of the side lengths, and then take the square root.

Advanced Learners L4
Ask: *Is $4^2 + 5^2$ equal to $(4 + 5)^2$? Explain.* Sample: No; exponentiation cannot be distributed over addition.

learning style: verbal

English Language Learners ELL
The words *hypotenuse* and *triangle* are difficult to pronounce for many English learners. While they learn to say the words correctly, have students agree on a shortcut way to say them, such as *tri* or *hyp.*

learning style: verbal

3. Practice

Assignment Guide

Check Your Understanding

Go over Exercises 1–2 in class before assigning the Homework Exercises.

Homework Exercises

A Practice by Example	3–13
B Apply Your Skills	14–23
C Challenge	24
Test Prep and Mixed Review	25–30

Homework Quick Check

To check students' understanding of key skills and concepts, go over Exercises 6, 13, 15, 20, and 21.

Differentiated Instruction Resources

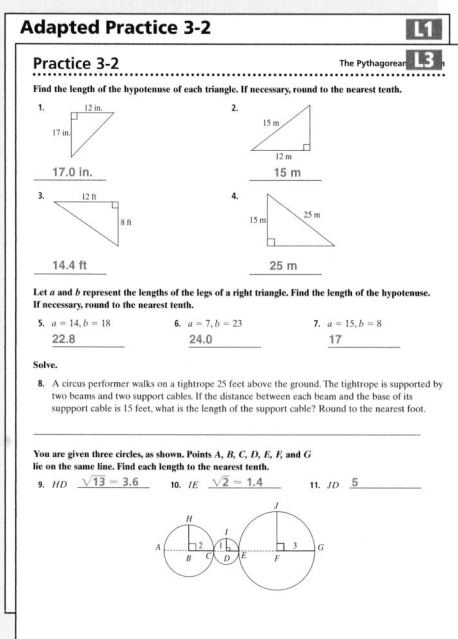

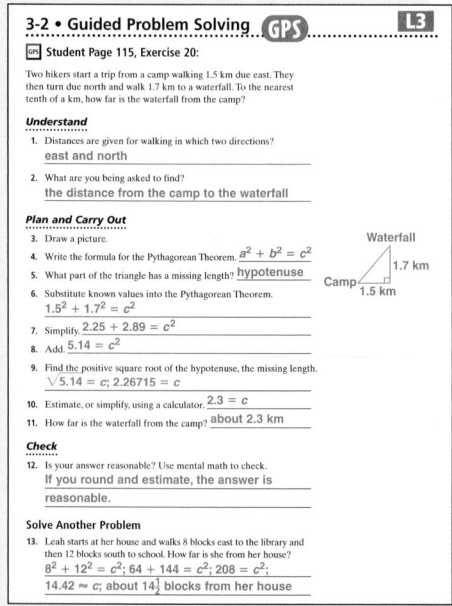

Adapted Practice 3-2 L1

Practice 3-2 The Pythagorean Theorem L3

Find the length of the hypotenuse of each triangle. If necessary, round to the nearest tenth.

1. 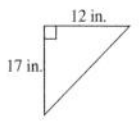

17.0 in.

2. 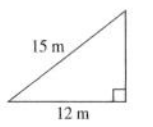

15 m

3. 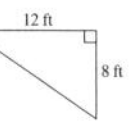

14.4 ft

4. 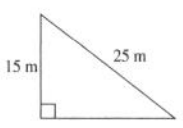

25 m

Let a and b represent the lengths of the legs of a right triangle. Find the length of the hypotenuse. If necessary, round to the nearest tenth.

5. $a = 14, b = 18$ 22.8
6. $a = 7, b = 23$ 24.0
7. $a = 15, b = 8$ 17

Solve.

8. A circus performer walks on a tightrope 25 feet above the ground. The tightrope is supported by two beams and two support cables. If the distance between each beam and the base of its suppport cable is 15 feet, what is the length of the support cable? Round to the nearest foot.

You are given three circles, as shown. Points $A, B, C, D, E, F,$ and G lie on the same line. Find each length to the nearest tenth.

9. HD $\sqrt{13} \approx 3.6$
10. IE $\sqrt{2} \approx 1.4$
11. JD 5

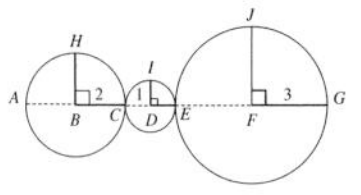

3-2 • Guided Problem Solving GPS L3

Student Page 115, Exercise 20:

Two hikers start a trip from a camp walking 1.5 km due east. They then turn due north and walk 1.7 km to a waterfall. To the nearest tenth of a km, how far is the waterfall from the camp?

Understand

1. Distances are given for walking in which two directions? east and north
2. What are you being asked to find? the distance from the camp to the waterfall

Plan and Carry Out

3. Draw a picture.

4. Write the formula for the Pythagorean Theorem. $a^2 + b^2 = c^2$
5. What part of the triangle has a missing length? hypotenuse
6. Substitute known values into the Pythagorean Theorem. $1.5^2 + 1.7^2 = c^2$
7. Simplify. $2.25 + 2.89 = c^2$
8. Add. $5.14 = c^2$
9. Find the positive square root of the hypotenuse, the missing length. $\sqrt{5.14} = c$; $2.26715 = c$
10. Estimate, or simplify, using a calculator. $2.3 = c$
11. How far is the waterfall from the camp? about 2.3 km

Check

12. Is your answer reasonable? Use mental math to check. If you round and estimate, the answer is reasonable.

Solve Another Problem

13. Leah starts at her house and walks 8 blocks east to the library and then 12 blocks south to school. How far is she from her house? $8^2 + 12^2 = c^2$; $64 + 144 = c^2$; $208 = c^2$; $14.42 \approx c$; about $14\frac{1}{2}$ blocks from her house

Check Your Understanding

1. **Vocabulary** The side lengths of a right triangle are 5, 12, and 13. How do you know that the length of the hypotenuse is 13? Explain. The hypotenuse is the longest side.
2. Fill in the blanks for each step to find the missing hypotenuse length of the triangle below.

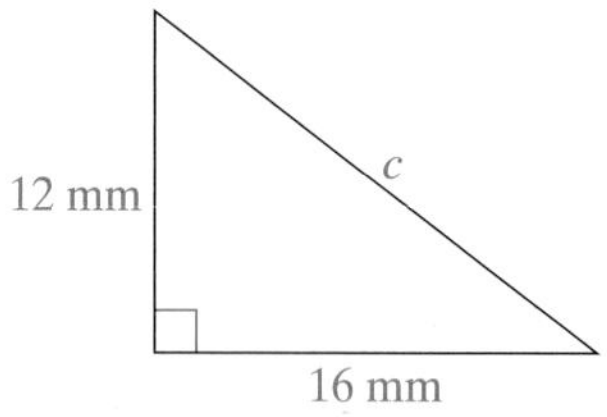

   a. $12^2 + ■^2 = c^2$ 16
   b. $■ + 256 = c^2$ 144
   c. $■ = c^2$ 400
   d. $■ = c$ 20

Homework Exercises

For more exercises, see Extra Skills and Word Problems.

GO for Help

For Exercises	See Examples
3–13	1, 2

A **Find the length of the hypotenuse of each triangle. For Exercises 7–12, a and b represent the lengths of the two legs. If necessary, round to the nearest tenth.**

3. 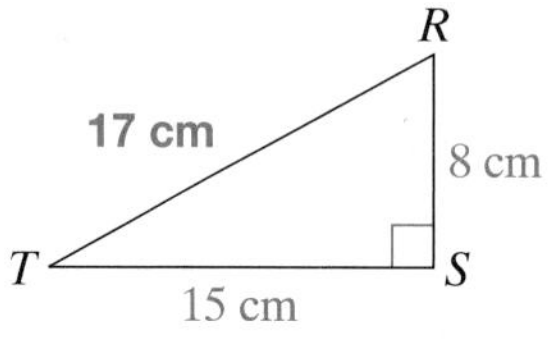

4. 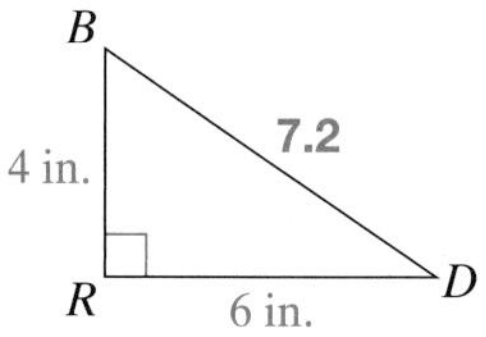

5. 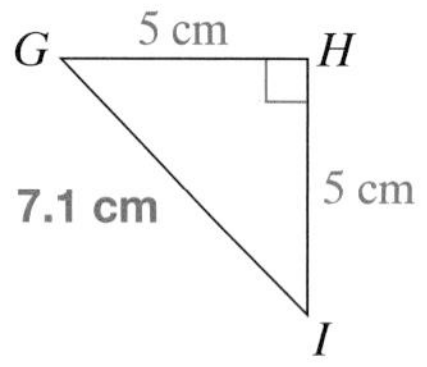

6. 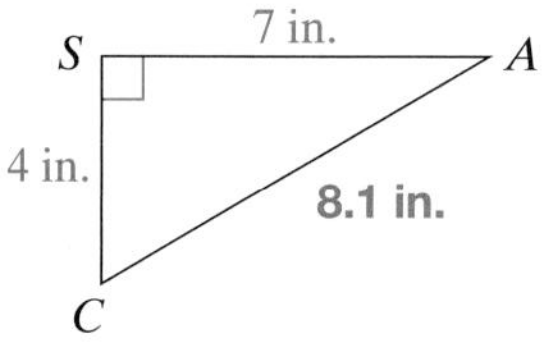

7. $a = 3, b = 4$ 5
8. $a = 9, b = 12$ 15
9. $a = 7, b = 24$ 25
10. $a = 6, b = 5$ 7.8
11. $a = 11, b = 14$ 17.8
12. $a = 18, b = 22$ 28.4

13. **Ramps** A ramp is 1 ft high. The base of the ramp extends 14 ft along the side of a building. How long is the sloped part of the ramp to the nearest hundredth of a foot? 14.04 ft

B GPS 14. **Guided Problem Solving** Find the perimeter of a right triangle with legs of 6 cm and 8 cm. 24 cm
- **Make a Plan** First use the Pythagorean Theorem to find the length of the hypotenuse. Then find the perimeter of the triangle.
- **Carry Out the Plan** The hypotenuse is ■ cm long. The perimeter of the triangle is ■ cm.

GO Online
Homework Video Tutor
Visit: PHSchool.com
Web Code: ase-0302

15. **Television** A television is measured by the diagonal dimension of its screen. For example, a 24-in. television has a diagonal measure of 24 in.
   a. A television screen is 16 in. high and 22 in. wide. What is its diagonal dimension to the nearest integer? 27 in.
   b. Find the dimensions of a television screen with the same diagonal measure as the one in part (a), but with a different height and width. Answers may vary. Sample: 20 in. by 18 in.

The legs of a right triangle are equal. Given the length of the legs, find the length of the hypotenuse. Round to the nearest tenth.

16. 5 cm 7.1 cm 17. 2 cm 2.8 cm 18. 10 in. 14.1 in. 19. 12 m 17.0 m

20. (GPS) Two hikers start a trip from a camp walking 1.5 km due east. They turn due north and walk 1.7 km to a waterfall. To the nearest tenth of a kilometer, how far is the waterfall from the camp? 2.3 km

21. **Writing in Math** Explain how you would find the distance AB across the lake at the right. Then find AB to the nearest foot. See back of book.

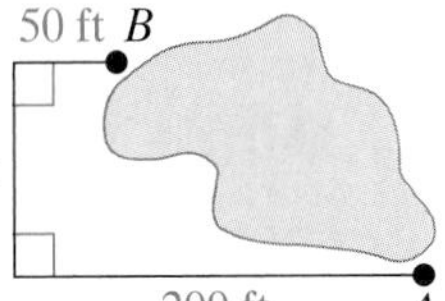

22. **Reasoning** If $\sqrt{w}$ is an integer, how many values of w are between 20 and 120? 6 values

23. **Algebra** Is $m = 3$ a solution to $m^2 + (m + 1)^2 = (m + 2)^2$? See margin.

(C) 24. **Challenge** The sum of the squares of the lengths of all three sides of a right triangle is 200. What is the length of the hypotenuse? 10

Test Prep and Mixed Review — Practice

Gridded Response

25. A carpenter is attaching a brace to the back of the frame shown at the right. What is the length, in inches, of the brace? 50

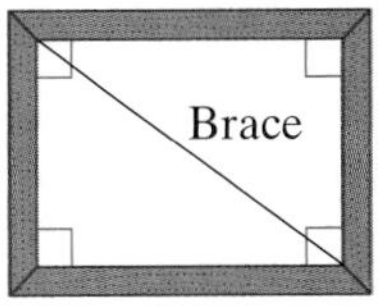

26. Nicole wrote the equation $b = \frac{5}{8}a$ to estimate the number of baskets b she makes for the number of free throw attempts a she makes. If she attempts 24 free throws, how many baskets is she likely to make? 15

27. Ms. Santiago wrote a 20-question math test. It took her 35 seconds to answer each question. Ms. Santiago expects her students to spend three times as long as she did on each question. How many minutes should her students take to complete the test? 35

GO for Help

For Exercises	See Lesson
28–30	2-8

Write each number in standard form.

28. 2.97×10^3 2,970 29. 1.02×10^5 102,000 30. 8.11×10^4 81,100

Online lesson quiz, PHSchool.com, Web Code: asa-0302

4. Assess & Reteach

PowerPoint

Lesson Quiz

1. Find the hypotenuse of a right triangle with legs of 9 in. Round to the nearest inch. 13 in.
2. A right triangle has legs of 5 cm and 18 cm. What is the length of its hypotenuse? Round to the nearest centimeter. 19 cm
3. A staircase is 20 ft high. The horizontal distance from one end of the staircase to the other end is 24 ft. What is the distance from the top of the staircase to the bottom of the staircase? Round to the nearest foot. 31 ft
4. A book is leaning with one end at the top edge of a bookend. The bookend is 6 in. high. The distance along the shelf from the edge of the book to the bottom of the bookend is 4 in. How long is the book? Round to the nearest inch. 7 in.

23. yes; $3^2 + (3 + 1)^2 \stackrel{?}{=} (3 + 2)^2$
$3^2 + 4^2 \stackrel{?}{=} 5^2$
$9 + 16 \stackrel{?}{=} 25$
$25 = 25$

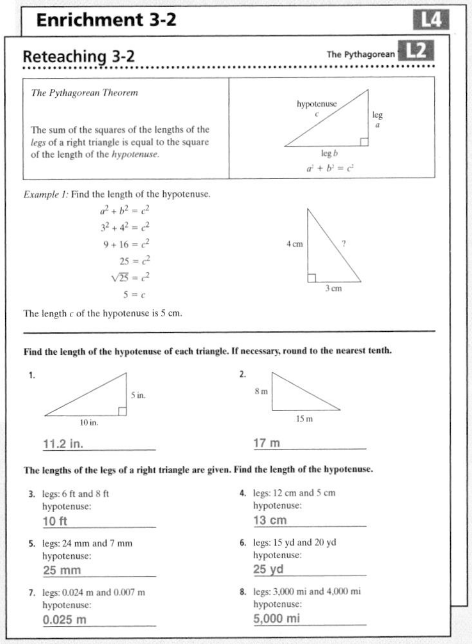

Enrichment 3-2 L4

Reteaching 3-2 The Pythagorean L2

The Pythagorean Theorem

The sum of the squares of the lengths of the *legs* of a right triangle is equal to the square of the length of the *hypotenuse*.

hypotenuse c, leg a, leg b

$a^2 + b^2 = c^2$

Example 1: Find the length of the hypotenuse.

$a^2 + b^2 = c^2$
$3^2 + 4^2 = c^2$
$9 + 16 = c^2$
$25 = c^2$
$\sqrt{25} = c^2$
$5 = c$

4 cm, 3 cm, ?

The length c of the hypotenuse is 5 cm.

Find the length of the hypotenuse of each triangle. If necessary, round to the nearest tenth.

1. 5 in., 10 in. — 11.2 in.
2. 8 m, 15 m — 17 m

The lengths of the legs of a right triangle are given. Find the length of the hypotenuse.

3. legs: 6 ft and 8 ft hypotenuse: 10 ft
4. legs: 12 cm and 5 cm hypotenuse: 13 cm
5. legs: 24 mm and 7 mm hypotenuse: 25 mm
6. legs: 15 yd and 20 yd hypotenuse: 25 yd
7. legs: 0.024 m and 0.007 m hypotenuse: 0.025 m
8. legs: 3,000 mi and 4,000 mi hypotenuse: 5,000 mi

Alternative Assessment

Each student in a pair picks two numbers to represent the legs of a right triangle. Each partner finds the hypotenuse of the other partner's triangle.

Test Prep

Resources
For additional practice with a variety of test item formats:
- Test-Taking Strategies, p. 151
- Test Prep, p. 155
- Test-Taking Strategies with Transparencies

Squares and Square Roots

Students read a guided real-world problem to develop problem-solving and reasoning skills. In the left-hand column, they read questions they could ask themselves to make sense of the problem. In the right-hand column, they read the steps for setting up and solving equations used to describe the situation.

Guided Instruction

Have students work through the problem, rather than just read. Have them identify any steps that are unclear or that don't match their own work.

Error Prevention!

Some students may interpret "add $\frac{1}{10}$ of that number" as simply adding the fraction $\frac{1}{10}$ instead of adding $\frac{1}{10}$ **of the number.** Have them think about $\frac{1}{10}$ as 10 percent. Remind them that they can consider 1 a whole. Ask: *By what do you need to multiply a number to increase it by a percentage?* 1 and a fraction, in this case $1\frac{1}{10}$

Alternative Method

The equation that represents the situation can also be written to more closely match the English wording, using parentheses: $w = (g^2 \times \ell) \div 800 + \frac{1}{10}((g^2 \times \ell) \div 800)$.

1. Answers may vary. Sample: Multiplying by 1.1 is the same as multiplying by $1 + 0.1$. By the Distributive Property, a number multiplied by $1 + 0.1$ equals that number plus $\frac{1}{10}$ of that number.

2. Answers may vary. Sample: Rounding 47 and 78 up increases the weight, while ignoring "adding $\frac{1}{10}$" decreases the weight.

Squares and Square Roots

To estimate the weight, in pounds, of a large fish, fishermen square the girth, multiply by the length, divide by 800, and then add $\frac{1}{10}$ of that number. What is the weight of the tarpon below?

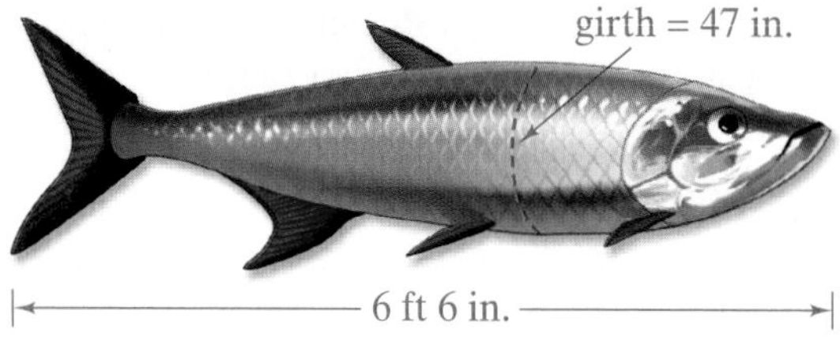

What You Might Think / What You Might Write

What You Might Think	What You Might Write
What do I know? What do I want to find out?	The girth g is 47 inches, and the length ℓ is 6 ft 6 in. or 78 inches. I know the formula is $w = (g^2 \times \ell) \div 800 \times 1\frac{1}{10}$.
How do I estimate an answer?	Round 47 to 50 and 78 to 80. Then ignore the extra $\frac{1}{10}$ to compensate for rounding up. $(50^2 \times 80) \div 800 = 250$. The fish weighs about 250 pounds.
How do I calculate an answer?	$w = (47^2 \times 78) \div 800 \times 1\frac{1}{10}$ $= (2{,}209 \times 78) \div 800 \times 1.1$ ≈ 236.9
What is the answer?	The fish weighs about 237 pounds.
Is the answer reasonable?	Yes; 237 pounds is close to the 250-pound estimate.

Think It Through 1–2. See margin.

1. **Reasoning** Why is multiplying by 1.1 the same as adding $\frac{1}{10}$ of a number to that number?
2. **Number Sense** When you estimated, why did rounding up 47 and 78 compensate for ignoring "add $\frac{1}{10}$"?

Exercises

Solve each problem. For Exercises 3 and 4, answer the questions first.

3. A jogger runs around the city park shown below. Her friend cuts through the park on a diagonal. In miles, how far does each jogger run on a five-lap jog? **The jogger runs 15,000 ft. Her friend runs 13,090 ft.**

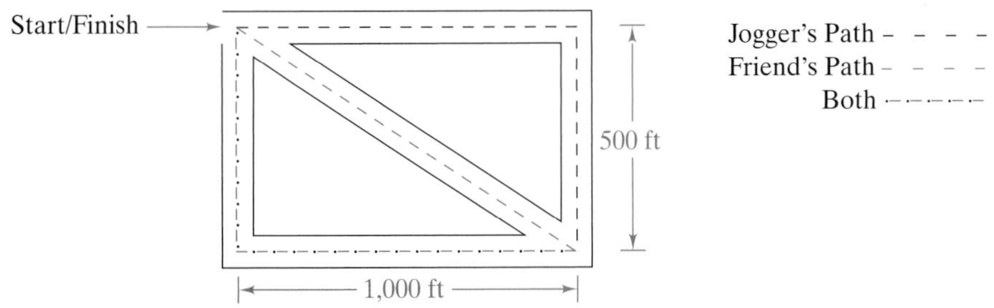

   a. What do you know and what do you want to find out?
   b. How will the Pythagorean Theorem help you?

4. Ignoring air resistance, the distance d in feet an object falls in t seconds is $d = 16t^2$. The Sears Tower is 1,450 ft tall. If a window washer at the top of the tower drops his squeegee, about how much time passes before the squeegee hits the sidewalk below? **9.5 s**
   a. What do you know and what do you want to find out?
   b. **Number Sense** To estimate, why might you round 1,450 ft to 1,600 ft? Explain.

5. A car washing business uses the equation $m = -4p^2 + 40p$ to predict the amount of money m they can make with the price p of a car wash. For example, if the price of one wash is \$1, the amount of money they make is $m = -4(1)^2 + 40(1)$, or \$36.
   a. Complete the table at the right. **See margin.**
   b. At which price does the business earn the most money? The least? **\$5; \$1**

Car Wash Business

p (dollars)	1	2	3	4	5	6	7
m (dollars)	■	■	■	■	■	■	■

6. Carpenters have a simple way to tell if a wall forms a 90° angle with the floor. They mark a point at the base of the wall. Then they measure 3 ft up the wall and mark a point. They also mark a point on the floor 4 ft away from the base of the wall. If the wall forms a right angle, what is the distance from the point on the wall to the point on the floor? How do you know? **5 ft; the distance from the point on the wall to the point on the floor is the hypotenuse of a right triangle with legs of lengths 3 ft and 4 ft.**

Guided Instruction

Teaching Tip
Have students ask themselves the same or similar questions as in the example as they work through the Exercises.

Exercises
Checking the reasonableness of an answer is an important skill. For Exercise 4, review estimation methods. For Exercise 6, have students practice justifying their answers. Compare different students' explanations.

Differentiated Instruction

Visual Learners
Help students identify important measurements in the given problem by having them draw and label a diagram.

Tactile Learners
Work on Exercise 6 with students. They measure and "mark" points on the wall and the floor with pieces of tape. Then they measure the distance between the two points with a measuring tape.

5a.

Car Wash Business

p (dollars)	1	2	3	4	5	6	7
m (dollars)	36	64	84	96	100	96	84

3-3

1. Plan

Objective
To use the Pythagorean Theorem to find missing measurements of triangles

Examples
1 Finding a Leg of a Right Triangle
2 Application: Satellites

Math Understandings: p. 104C

Professional Development

Math Background

The Pythagorean Theorem gives the length of the hypotenuse for given lengths of legs in a right triangle, $a^2 + b^2 = c^2$. If you know the length of the hypotenuse and only one leg, you can find the other leg using this formula. A reasonable answer for the length of a leg will always be less than the hypotenuse.

More Math Background: p. 104C

Lesson Planning and Resources

See p. 104E for a list of the resources that support this lesson.

PowerPoint

Bell Ringer Practice

Check Skills You'll Need
Use student page, transparency, or PowerPoint. For intervention, direct students to:
The Pythagorean Theorem
Lesson 3-2
Extra Skills and Word Problems Practice, Ch. 3

3-3 Using the Pythagorean Theorem

Check Skills You'll Need

1. **Vocabulary Review** State the *Pythagorean Theorem.* See below.

Find the length of the hypotenuse given the lengths of the two legs, *a* and *b*. Round to the nearest tenth.

2. $a = 3, b = 4$ 5
3. $a = 7, b = 5$ 8.6

GO for Help Lesson 3-2

Check Skills You'll Need

1. The Pythagorean Theorem states that in any right triangle, the sum of the squares of the lengths of the legs (*a* and *b*) is equal to the square of the length of the hypotenuse: $a^2 + b^2 = c^2$.

What You'll Learn

To use the Pythagorean Theorem to find missing measurements of triangles

Why Learn This?

You can use the Pythagorean Theorem to find distances without measuring, including distances in space.

When you know the length of one leg and the hypotenuse of a right triangle, you can use the Pythagorean Theorem to find the length of the other leg.

EXAMPLE Finding a Leg of a Right Triangle

1 Find the missing leg length of the triangle below.

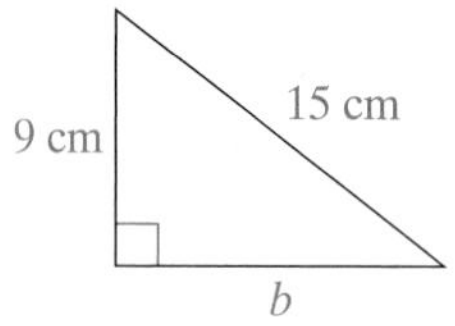

$a^2 + b^2 = c^2$ ← Use the Pythagorean Theorem.

$9^2 + b^2 = 15^2$ ← Substitute 9 for *a* and 15 for *c*.

$81 + b^2 = 225$ ← Simplify.

$b^2 = 144$ ← Subtract 81 from each side.

$\sqrt{b^2} = \sqrt{144}$ ← Find the positive square root of each side.

$b = 12$ ← Simplify.

The length of the other leg is 12 cm.

Quick Check

1. The hypotenuse of a right triangle is 20.2 ft long. One leg is 12.6 ft long. Find the length of the other leg to the nearest tenth. 15.8 ft

Differentiated Instruction Solutions for All Learners

Special Needs L1	Below Level L2
Students label the sides of each triangle *a, b,* and *c* so they know which length corresponds to which variable. They may highlight or circle the leg whose distance they need to find. learning style: visual	Students draw triangles and assign reasonable lengths for the hypotenuse and one leg. Then they set up the Pythagorean Theorem for each triangle and draw arrows from values in the equation to corresponding elements of their diagrams. learning style: visual

You can substitute the known leg length for either a or b in the Pythagorean Theorem.

EXAMPLE Application: Satellites

2 **Multiple Choice** Satellites that relay television signals to Earth cruise at a distance of about 22,200 miles above Earth's surface. The radius of Earth is about 4,000 miles. Find the distance a from the satellite to point T in the diagram below. Round to the nearest hundred miles.

(A) 22,500 mi (C) 25,900 mi
(B) 26,000 mi (D) 670,440 mi

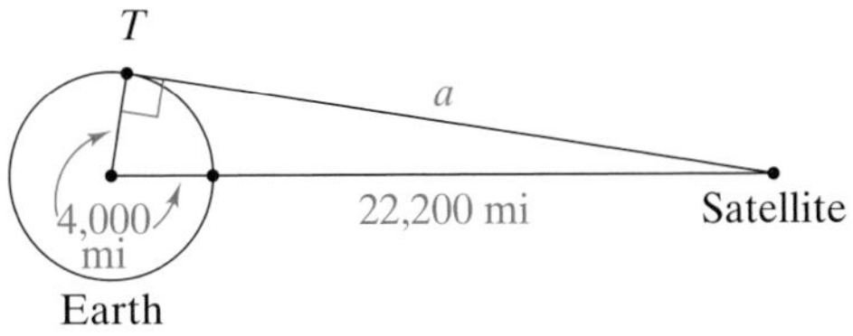

Vocabulary Tip

The *radius* of a circle is a segment that connects the center to the circle.

The diagram above shows a right triangle with a hypotenuse of 22,200 miles + 4,000 miles, or 26,200 miles. The length of the known leg is 4,000 miles. The variable a represents the length of the other leg.

$a^2 + b^2 = c^2$	← **Use the Pythagorean Theorem.**
$a^2 + 4{,}000^2 = 26{,}200^2$	← **Substitute 4,000 for *b* and 26,200 for *c*.**
$a^2 + 16{,}000{,}000 = 686{,}440{,}000$	← **Find $4{,}000^2$ and $26{,}200^2$.**
$a^2 = 670{,}440{,}000$	← **Subtract 16,000,000 from each side.**
$\sqrt{a^2} = \sqrt{670{,}440{,}000}$	← **Find the positive square root of each side.**
[√] 670,440,000 [=] 25892.85616	← **Use a calculator.**
$a \approx 25{,}900$	← **Round to the nearest hundred.**

The distance from the satellite to the horizon is about 25,900 mi. The answer is C.

Test Prep Tip

You can eliminate Choice D, because the leg of a right triangle cannot be longer than its hypotenuse.

Quick Check

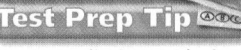

2. **Construction** The bottom of an 18-ft ladder is 5 ft from the side of a house. Find the distance from the top of the ladder to the ground. Round to the nearest tenth. 17.3 ft

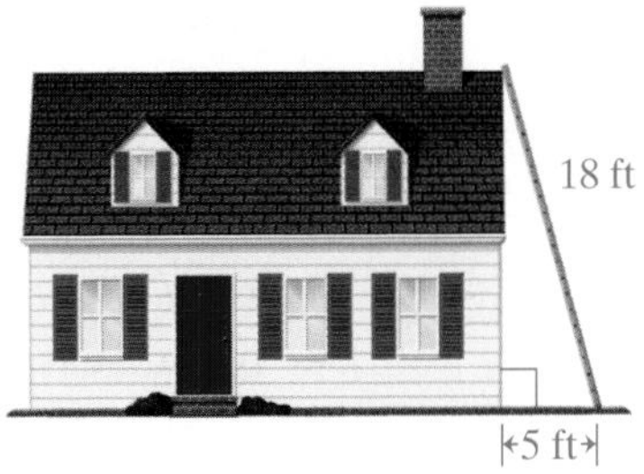

2. Teach

Activity Lab

Use before the lesson.

All in One Teaching Resources

Activity Lab 3-3: Patterns in Geometry

Guided Instruction

Alternative Method

Some students might prefer to see the value they want to find on the left side of the equals sign. To find a leg, rewrite the Pythagorean Theorem before substituting values: $a^2 = c^2 - b^2$.

PowerPoint

Additional Examples

1 Find the missing leg length of the triangle. 5 cm

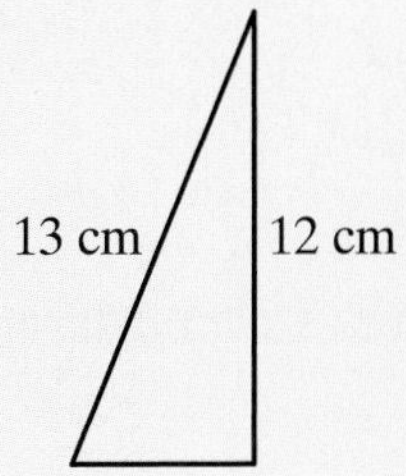

2 The bottom of a 10-ft ladder is 2.5 ft from the side of a wall. How far, to the nearest tenth, is the top of the ladder from the ground? 9.7 ft

All in One Teaching Resources

- Daily Notetaking Guide 3-3 L3
- Adapted Notetaking 3-3 L1

Closure

- *If you know the lengths of the hypotenuse and one leg of a right triangle, how would you find the other leg?* **Sample: Subtract the square of the leg from the square of the hypotenuse, and then take the square root.**
- When you find the value of a leg given the hypotenuse and another leg, explain how you can check if your answer is reasonable. **Sample: The hypotenuse is the longest side, so the leg should be less than the hypotenuse.**

Advanced Learners L4

If a triangle has lengths of 7 in., 25 in., and 24 in., how could you tell if it is a right triangle? **Sample: The Pythagorean Theorem only applies to right triangles. Substitute the values and check that the equation is true.**

learning style: verbal

English Language Learners ELL

The exercises for this lesson require extensive reading, writing, and speaking skills. Students work in pairs on the exercises so that they can talk about what they understand and ask questions about what they do not understand.

learning style: verbal

3. Practice

Assignment Guide

Check Your Understanding

Go over Exercises 1–2 in class before assigning the Homework Exercises.

Homework Exercises

A Practice by Example	3–13
B Apply Your Skills	14–20
C Challenge	21
Test Prep and Mixed Review	22–28

Homework Quick Check

To check students' understanding of key skills and concepts, go over Exercises 4, 13, 18, 19, and 20a.

Differentiated Instruction Resources

Adapted Practice 3-3 L1

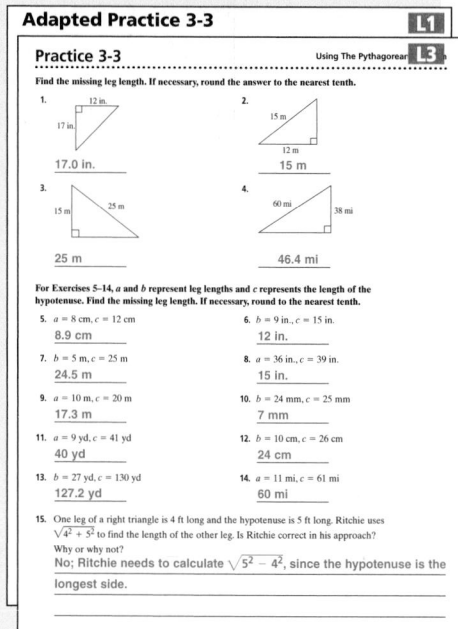

Practice 3-3 Using The Pythagorean Theorem L3

Find the missing leg length. If necessary, round the answer to the nearest tenth.

1. 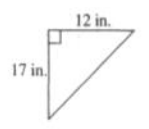

17.0 in.

2. 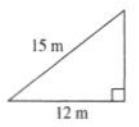

15 m

3. 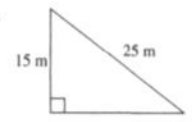

25 m

4. 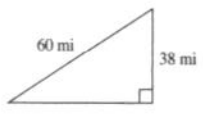

46.4 mi

For Exercises 5–14, *a* and *b* represent leg lengths and *c* represents the length of the hypotenuse. Find the missing leg length. If necessary, round to the nearest tenth.

5. $a = 8$ cm, $c = 12$ cm 8.9 cm
6. $b = 9$ in., $c = 15$ in. 12 in.
7. $b = 5$ m, $c = 25$ m 24.5 m
8. $a = 36$ in., $c = 39$ in. 15 in.
9. $a = 10$ m, $c = 20$ m 17.3 m
10. $b = 24$ mm, $c = 25$ mm 7 mm
11. $a = 9$ yd, $c = 41$ yd 40 yd
12. $b = 10$ cm, $c = 26$ cm 24 cm
13. $b = 27$ yd, $c = 130$ yd 127.2 yd
14. $a = 11$ mi, $c = 61$ mi 60 mi
15. One leg of a right triangle is 4 ft long and the hypotenuse is 5 ft long. Ritchie uses $\sqrt{4^2 + 5^2}$ to find the length of the other leg. Is Ritchie correct in his approach? Why or why not?
No; Ritchie needs to calculate $\sqrt{5^2 - 4^2}$, since the hypotenuse is the longest side.

3-3 • Guided Problem Solving GPS L3

GPS **Student Page 120, Exercise 13:**

A 10-ft-long slide is attached to a deck that is 5 ft high. Find the distance from the bottom of the deck to the bottom of the slide to the nearest tenth.

Understand

1. What two lengths are given in the problem? the height of the deck and the length of the slide
2. What are you being asked to find? the distance from the bottom of the deck to the bottom of the slide

Plan and Carry Out

3. Draw a picture of the slide, deck, and ground.
4. What kind of a triangle is formed by the picture? right triangle

5. Is the unknown length a leg or hypotenuse of the triangle? leg
6. Write down the formula for the Pythagorean Theorem. $a^2 + b^2 = c^2$
7. Substitute values from your picture into the Pythagorean Theorem. $(5\text{ ft})^2 + b^2 = (10\text{ ft})^2$
8. Simplify. $b^2 = 75\text{ ft}^2$
9. Use a calculator to find the square root. Round to the nearest tenth. $b = \sqrt{75}\text{ ft} \approx 8.7$ ft
10. What is the distance from the bottom of the deck to the bottom of the slide? approximately 8.7 ft

Check

11. Use the Pythagorean Theorem to check the length of the slide based on your answer, and the height of the deck. Is your answer the same as the given slide length? Why or why not?
It is close but not exactly correct, because of rounding errors.

Solve Another Problem

12. Mason is on the southwest corner of a 90° intersection. One street in the intersection is 23 ft wide. If Mason crosses diagonally to the northeast corner, he will walk 34 ft. Find the width of the other street. If necessary, round your answer to the nearest tenth. 25.0 ft

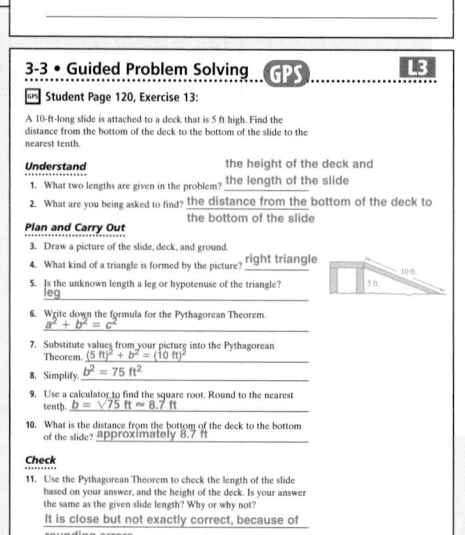

Check Your Understanding

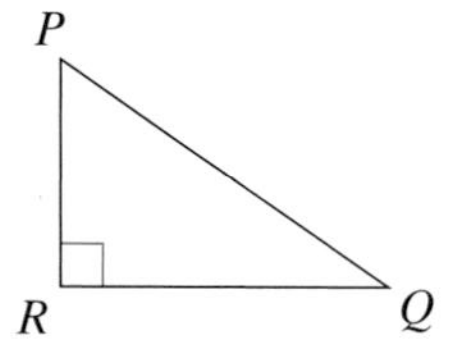

1. **Vocabulary** Name the two legs and the hypotenuse of the triangle at the left. $\overline{PR}$ and $\overline{RQ}$; $\overline{PQ}$

2. Fill in the blanks for each step to find the missing leg length of the triangle below.

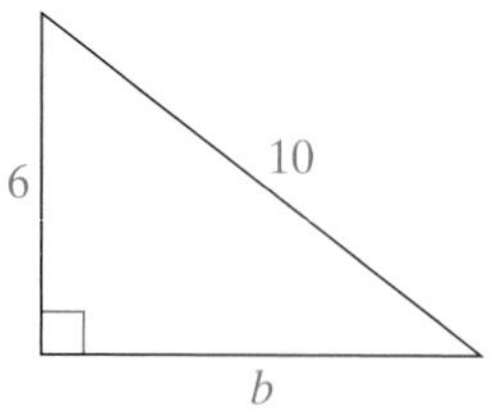

a. $6^2 + b^2 = \blacksquare^2$ 10

b. $\blacksquare + b^2 = 100$ 36

c. $b^2 = \blacksquare$ 64

d. $b = \blacksquare$ 8

Homework Exercises

For more exercises, see Extra Skills and Word Problems.

GO for Help

For Exercises	See Examples
3–13	1, 2

A **Find the missing leg length. For Exercises 7–12, *a* and *b* represent leg lengths and *c* represents the length of the hypotenuse. If necessary, round to the nearest tenth.**

3. 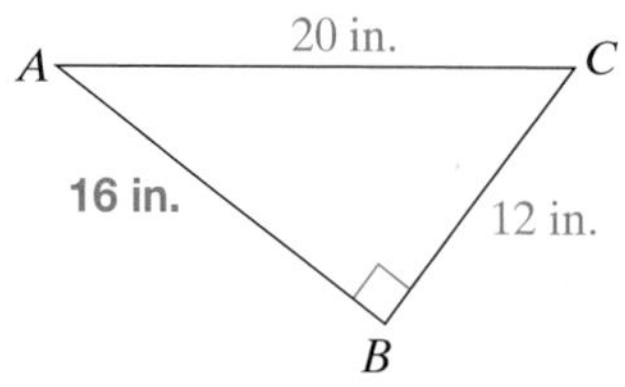

4. 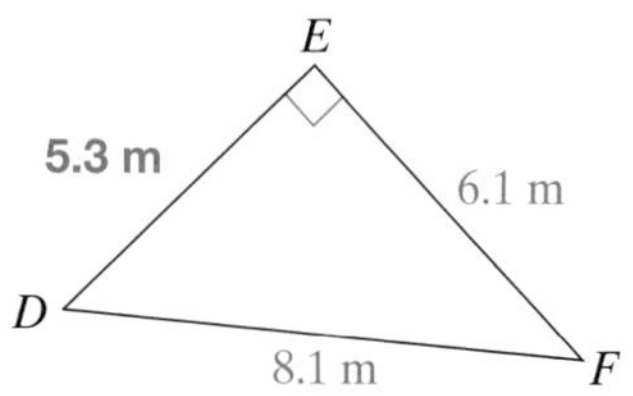

5. 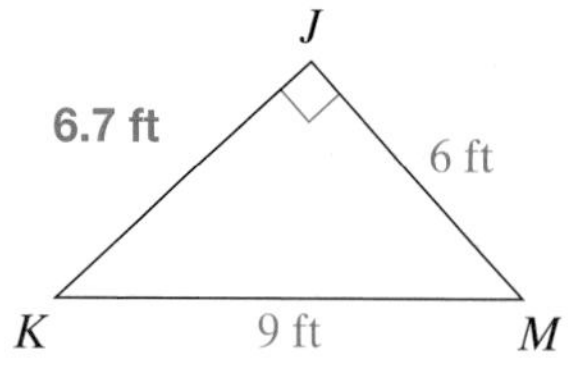

6. 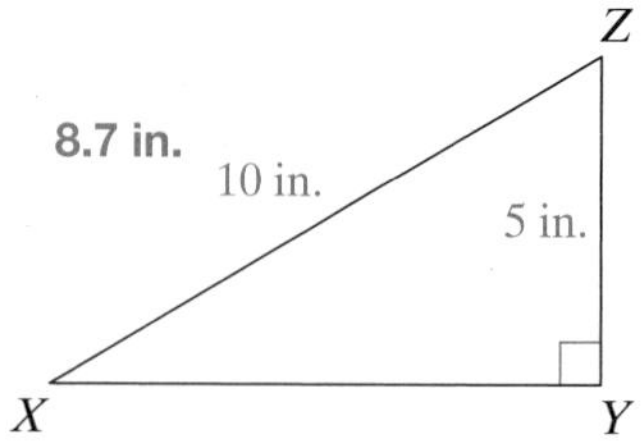

7. $a = 5, c = 12$ 10.9
8. $a = 7, c = 25$ 24
9. $b = 10.5, c = 20.1$ 17.1
10. $a = 3.4, c = 6.7$ 5.8
11. $b = 8.3, c = 16.9$ 14.7
12. $b = 11, c = 15$ 10.2

GPS 13. A 10-ft-long slide is attached to a deck that is 5 ft high. Find the distance from the bottom of the deck to the bottom of the slide to the nearest tenth. 8.7 ft

B GPS 14. **Guided Problem Solving** A computer screen has a diagonal length of 17 in. and a height of 9 in. To the nearest tenth, what is the area of the screen? 129.6 in.^{2}

- To the nearest tenth, what is the width of the computer screen?
- What is the formula for the area of a rectangle?

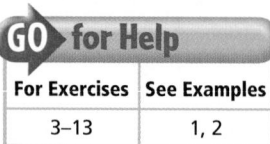

GO Online
Homework Video Tutor
Visit: PHSchool.com
Web Code: ase-0303

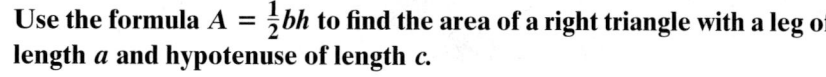

Use the formula $A = \frac{1}{2}bh$ to find the area of a right triangle with a leg of length a and hypotenuse of length c.

15. $a = 4, c = 5$ 6
16. $a = 8.6, c = 10$ 21.9
17. $a = 7.3, c = 9.1$ 19.8

18. Diving A diver swims 20 m under water to the anchor of a buoy that is 10 m below the surface of the water. On the surface, how far is the buoy located from the place where the diver started? Round to the nearest meter. 17 m

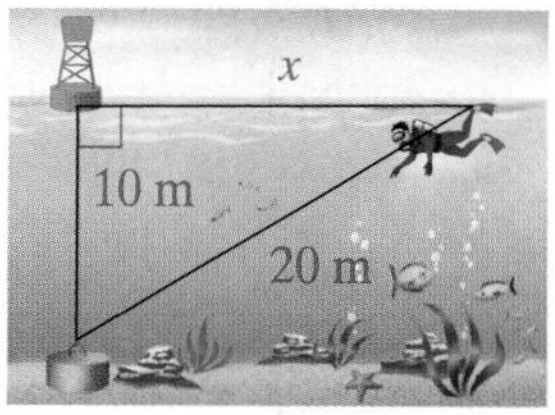

19. The student added 3^2 to 4^2 instead of subtracting it from 4^2. You must find $\sqrt{4^2 - 3^2}$.

19. Error Analysis One leg of a right triangle is 3 cm and the hypotenuse is 4 cm. A student evaluates $\sqrt{3^2 + 4^2}$ to find the length of the other leg. What error did the student make? See left.

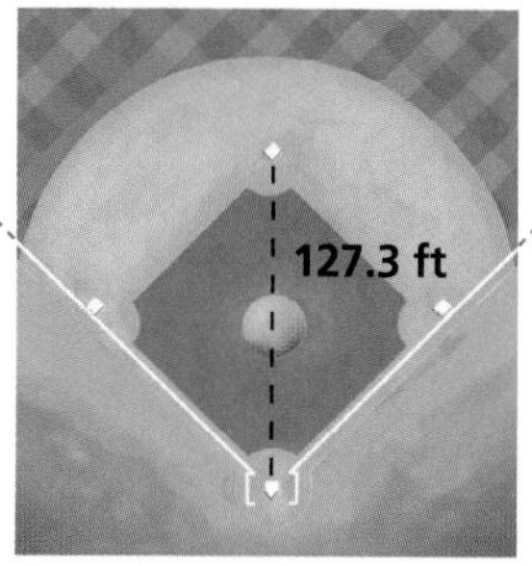

20. The distance from home plate to second base is about 127.3 ft.
a. **Writing in Math** Explain how you would find the distance between the bases. See margin.
b. **Estimation** Estimate the distance between the bases to the nearest foot. 90 ft
c. When you hit a home run, you run around all the bases. How far do you run? 360 ft

Ⓒ **21. Challenge** The sides of a right triangle are labelled a, b, and c. Can $a + b = c$? Explain. no; $(a + b)^2 \neq a^2 + b^2$

Test Prep and Mixed Review

Practice

Multiple Choice

22. The top of a badminton net is 5 feet high. Ropes connect the top of each pole to stakes in the ground. The ropes are 8.5 feet long. Which is closest to the distance from a stake to the base of a pole? B

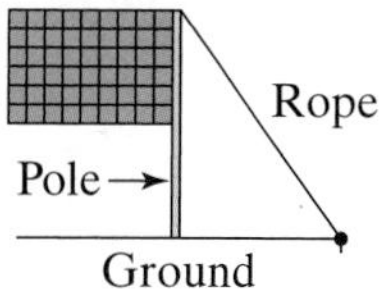

Ⓐ 4 ft Ⓑ 7 ft Ⓒ 9 ft Ⓓ 15 ft

23. Which integer is closest to $\sqrt{10}$? G
Ⓕ 2 Ⓖ 3 Ⓗ 4 Ⓙ 5

24. Oliver is buying three items that cost \$4.95, \$6.99, and \$1.05. He gives the cashier a \$20 bill. How much change should he receive? B
Ⓐ \$5.95 Ⓑ \$7.01 Ⓒ \$8.06 Ⓓ \$12.99

GO for Help

For Exercises	See Lesson
25–28	2-3

Compare. Use <, >, or =.

25. $\frac{5}{6}$ ■ $\frac{9}{11}$ >
26. $\frac{1}{8}$ ■ 0.1 >
27. $\frac{4}{20}$ ■ 0.2 =
28. $\frac{3}{7}$ ■ $\frac{4}{10}$ >

4. Assess & Reteach

PowerPoint

Lesson Quiz

1. A triangle has a hypotenuse of 17 in. and one of its legs is 8 in. What is the length of the other leg? 15 in.
2. The bottom of a 12-ft ladder is 4 ft from the side of a house. Find the height of the top of the ladder above the ground to the nearest tenth. 11.3 ft
3. An artist is measuring a rectangular canvas. Its length is 30 in. The distance from one corner of the canvas to the other (along the diagonal) is 34 in. What is its width? 16 in.
4. The legs of a right triangle have the same length. Its hypotenuse is 30 ft. How long is each leg? If necessary, round to the nearest foot. 21 ft

20a. The distance d between the bases is the same, and the angles in a baseball diamond are right angles. You can use the Pythagorean Theorem: $d^2 + d^2 = 127.3^2$. Then solve for d.

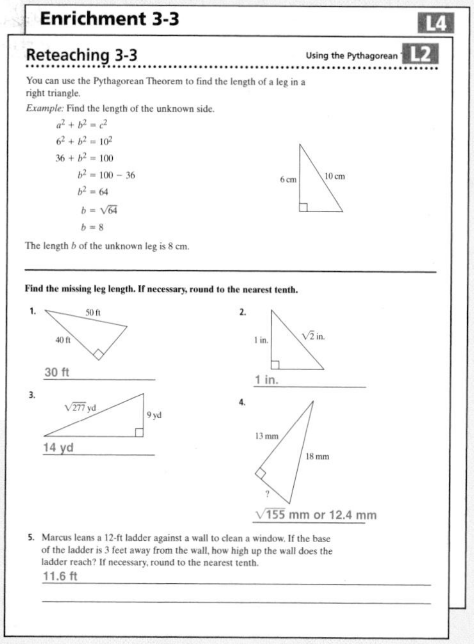

Enrichment 3-3 L4

Reteaching 3-3 Using the Pythagorean L2

You can use the Pythagorean Theorem to find the length of a leg in a right triangle.

Example: Find the length of the unknown side.

$a^2 + b^2 = c^2$
$6^2 + b^2 = 10^2$
$36 + b^2 = 100$
$b^2 = 100 - 36$
$b^2 = 64$
$b = \sqrt{64}$
$b = 8$

6 cm, 10 cm

The length b of the unknown leg is 8 cm.

Find the missing leg length. If necessary, round to the nearest tenth.

1. 50 ft, 40 ft — 30 ft
2. 1 in., $\sqrt{2}$ in. — 1 in.
3. $\sqrt{277}$ yd, 9 yd — 14 yd
4. 13 mm, 18 mm, ? — $\sqrt{155}$ mm or 12.4 mm
5. Marcus leans a 12-ft ladder against a wall to clean a window. If the base of the ladder is 3 feet away from the wall, how high up the wall does the ladder reach? If necessary, round to the nearest tenth. 11.6 ft

Alternative Assessment

Each student in a pair picks two different numbers. They use the greater number for the hypotenuse and the lesser number for a leg. Each partner uses the Pythagorean Theorem to solve for the other partner's missing leg length.

Test Prep

Resources
For additional practice with a variety of test item formats:
- Test-Taking Strategies, p. 151
- Test Prep, p. 155
- Test-Taking Strategies with Transparencies

Extension

Analyzing Triangles

Students explore the Triangle Inequality Theorem and use the converse of the Pythagorean Theorem to identify right triangles.

Guided Instruction

Before beginning, have students state the Pythagorean Theorem. Ask questions such as:

- *To which types of triangles does the Pythagorean Theorem apply?* right triangles
- *If you know the lengths of the legs of a right triangle, what can you find? If you know the lengths of one leg and the hypotenuse, what can you find?* hypotenuse; the other leg
- *Which is the longest side in a right triangle?* hypotenuse

Error Prevention!

Students often expect to see an answer accompanying an expression. In Example 2, students may calculate $a^2 + b^2$ and write c^2 on the right side of the equals sign as if the statement must be true. Help students reason by setting up a two-column table with the headings $a^2 + b^2$ and c^2. When they have calculated the values for each column, ask them if the value on the left side is equal to the value on the right side. This strategy is especially helpful when the equation is not true.

Exercises

In Exercise 4, remind students that the Triangle Inequality Theorem states that the sum of the measures of any two sides of any triangle is greater than the measure of the third side.

Resources

- a ruler

Extension | **For Use With Lesson 3-3**

Analyzing Triangles

The **Triangle Inequality Theorem** states that the sum of the lengths of any two sides of a triangle is greater than the length of the third side.

EXAMPLE Side Measurements of a Triangle

1 Is it possible to construct a triangle with side lengths 6 in., 10 in., and 20 in.? Explain.

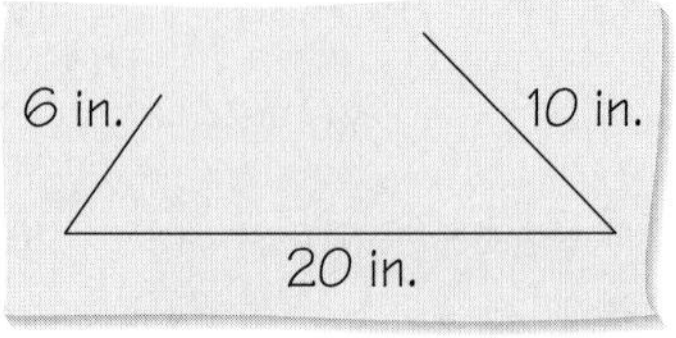

Since $6 + 10 < 20$, it is not possible.

If the equation $a^2 + b^2 = c^2$ is true for the lengths of the sides of a triangle, then the triangle is a right triangle. This is called the converse of the Pythagorean Theorem.

EXAMPLE Identifying a Right Triangle

2 Is a triangle with sides 7 in., 25 in., and 24 in. a right triangle? Explain.

$a^2 + b^2 = c^2$ ← Use the Pythagorean Theorem.

$7^2 + 24^2 \stackrel{?}{=} 25^2$ ← The longest side, 25 in., is the hypotenuse. Substitute $a = 7$, $b = 24$, and $c = 25$.

$49 + 576 = 625$ ✓ ← Simplify.

The equation is true, so the triangle is a right triangle.

Exercises

Is it possible for a triangle to have sides with the given lengths? Explain. 1–3. See above.

1. 15 cm, 35 cm, 40 cm
2. 7 mi, 15 mi, 6 mi
3. $1\frac{1}{2}$ in., $2\frac{1}{2}$ in., $3\frac{1}{2}$ in.

1. yes; $15 + 35 > 40$; $50 > 40$

2. no; $7 + 6 < 15$; $13 < 15$

3. yes; $1\frac{1}{2} + 2\frac{1}{2} > 3\frac{1}{2}$; $4 > 3\frac{1}{2}$

4. **Measurement** Draw a triangle with side lengths of your choice. Use a ruler to test the Triangle Inequality Theorem. Check students' work.

Is a triangle with the given side lengths a right triangle? Explain. 5–7. See margin.

5. 6 cm, 8 cm, 10 cm
6. 10 in., 24 in., 26 in.
7. 16 km, 63 km, 65 km

8. **Number Sense** How do you know a triangle with side lengths $\sqrt{1}$, $\sqrt{2}$, and $\sqrt{3}$ is a right triangle? Explain. $(\sqrt{1})^2 + (\sqrt{2})^2 = (\sqrt{3})^2$; $1 + 2 = 3$; $3 = 3$. The equation $a^2 + b^2 = c^2$ is true, so the triangle is a right triangle.

5. yes; $6^2 + 8^2 = 10^2$; $36 + 64 = 100$; $100 = 100$

6. yes; $10^2 + 24^2 = 26^2$; $100 + 576 = 676$; $676 = 676$

7. yes; $16^2 + 63^2 = 65^2$; $256 + 3{,}969 = 4{,}225$; $4{,}225 = 4{,}225$

Checkpoint Quiz 1

Lessons 3-1 through 3-3

1. Estimate the value of $\sqrt{85}$ to the nearest integer. 9

Is each number *rational* or *irrational*? Explain.

2. $\sqrt{13}$ Irrational; 13 is not a perfect square.
3. $\frac{13}{28}$ Rational; the number is a ratio of two integers.
4. 1.231241251261271 . . . 4. Irrational; the decimal does not terminate or repeat.

Find the missing length in each right triangle. If necessary, round to the nearest tenth.

5. leg = 9 cm, leg = 12 cm 15 cm.
6. leg = 8 ft, leg = 21 ft 22.5 ft
7. leg = 7 in., hypotenuse = 25 in. 24 in.
8. leg = 15 m, leg = 19 m 24.2 m
9. **Diving** You stand at the edge of a 4-m-high diving platform. A beach ball is exactly 8 m from the base of the platform. To the nearest tenth of a meter, what is the distance d from the top of the platform to the beach ball? 8.9 m

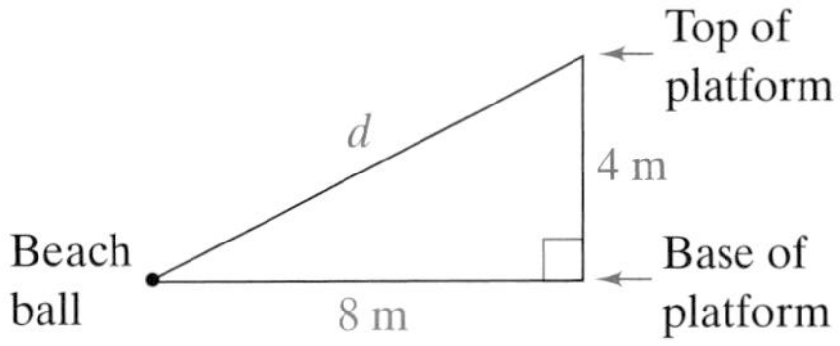

MATH AT WORK

Civil Engineer

Civil engineers design and build structures. They specialize in areas such as transportation, construction, and the environment.

Civil engineers who work in transportation use geometry and their knowledge of maps to plan and build roadways. Some, who specialize in construction, design structures such as buildings, bridges, and dams. Civil engineers who work with the environment build facilities such as water treatment plants that make water safe to drink.

Go Online PHSchool.com **For:** Information on Civil Engineers **Web Code:** asb-2031

Checkpoint Quiz

Use this Checkpoint Quiz to check students' understanding of the skills and concepts of Lessons 3-1 through 3-3.

Resources

- All in One Teaching Resources Checkpoint Quiz 1
- ExamView Assessment Suite CD-ROM
- Success Tracker Online Intervention

MATH AT WORK

Civil Engineering

This feature introduces students to a career that incorporates the math topics of this chapter into its work. Students learn about what civil engineers do.

Guided Instruction

Have students discuss examples of architecture and construction in life. Ask questions such as:

- *Where do you see right triangles in buildings, bridges, vehicles, and other examples of construction and transportation?*
- *How might the Pythagorean Theorem be useful in construction and architecture?*

3-4

1. Plan

Objective
To graph points and to use the Pythagorean Theorem to find distances in the coordinate plane

Examples
1 Graphing Points
2 Finding Distance on a Coordinate Plane

Math Understandings: p. 104C

Professional Development

Math Background

The *coordinate plane* is a grid created by a horizontal number line and a vertical number line—the *x*-axis and *y*-axis respectively. These number lines intersect at the *origin,* designated by the ordered pair (0, 0). Ordered pairs, such as (0, 0) and (3, −2) are used to locate points in the coordinate plane. The first number in the pair is the *x*-coordinate and the second number is the *y*-coordinate. The *x*-coordinate describes a point's location to the left or right of the origin. The *y*-coordinate describes a point's location up or down from the origin.

More Math Background: p. 104C

Lesson Planning and Resources

See p. 104E for a list of the resources that support this lesson.

PowerPoint

Bell Ringer Practice

Check Skills You'll Need
Use student page, transparency, or PowerPoint. For intervention, direct students to:

Integers and Absolute Value
Lesson 1-2
Extra Skills and Word Problems Practice, Ch. 1

3-4 Graphing in the Coordinate Plane

Check Skills You'll Need

1. **Vocabulary Review** How can you tell whether two numbers on a number line are *opposites*? See below.

Order the integers in each set from least to greatest.

2. 3, −5, −1, −3
−5, −3, −1, 3
3. 9, 2, −4, −6
−6, −4, 2, 9
4. −8, 6, 0, −10
−10, −8, 0, 6
5. −2, 7, −5, 4
−5, −2, 4, 7

GO for Help Lesson 1-2

Check Skills You'll Need

1. They are the same distance from zero on a number line but on opposite sides of zero.

What You'll Learn

To graph points and to use the Pythagorean Theorem to find distances in the coordinate plane

New Vocabulary coordinate plane, *y*-axis, *x*-axis, quadrants, origin, ordered pair, *x*-coordinate, *y*-coordinate

Why Learn This?

Mapmakers use a coordinate grid system for maps. The coordinate plane is another type of grid system. You can use coordinate planes to help you find distances, design projects, and read building plans.

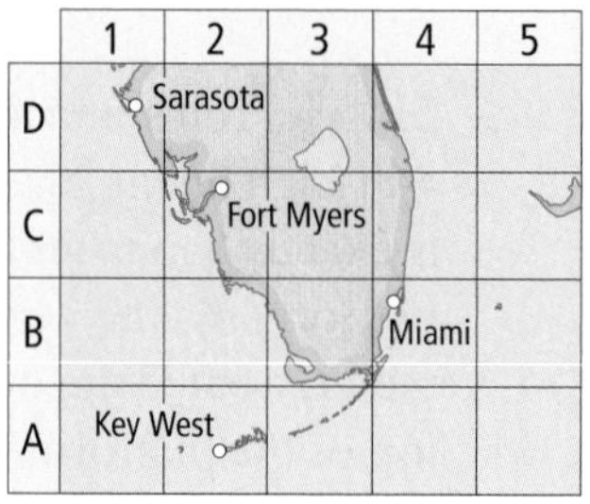

A **coordinate plane** is a grid formed by the intersection of two number lines. You can use a coordinate plane to locate and name points.

The **y-axis** is a vertical number line.

The **x-axis** is a horizontal number line.

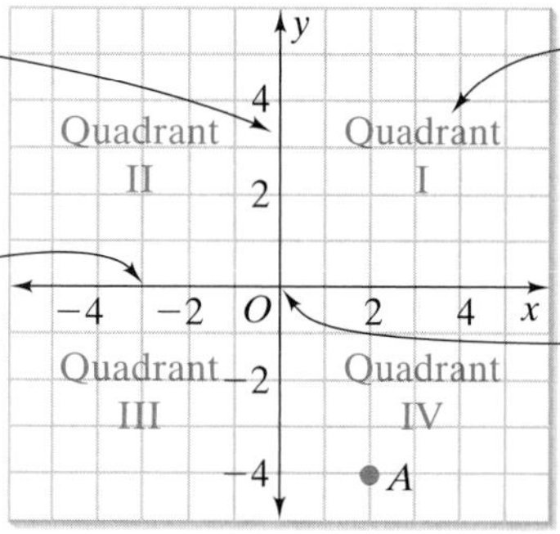

The axes divide the plane into four **quadrants.**

O indicates the **origin,** where the axes intersect.

An **ordered pair** (*x*, *y*) gives the coordinates of the location of a point. In the graph above, point *A* has coordinates (2, −4).

(2, −4)

The **x-coordinate** tells the number of horizontal units a point is from the origin.

The **y-coordinate** tells the number of vertical units a point is from the origin.

You can graph a point when you know its coordinates.

Differentiated Instruction Solutions for All Learners

Special Needs L1
Students graph points with a partner. Pair students who need help graphing points with those who can graph without assistance. Those students needing assistance can read the points to a partner who can then graph them.
learning style: tactile

Below Level L2
Make sure students can identify the *x*- and *y*-coordinates in ordered pairs. Have them say, "*x* comma *y*" or "*x*-coordinate, *y*-coordinate" or "*x* comes before *y*" to help them graph the following points: *A*(4, 3), *B*(−3, 2), *D*(−1, −2). Check students' graphs.
learning style: verbal

EXAMPLE Graphing Points

1 Graph point $A\left(2\frac{1}{2}, -3\right)$ on a coordinate plane.

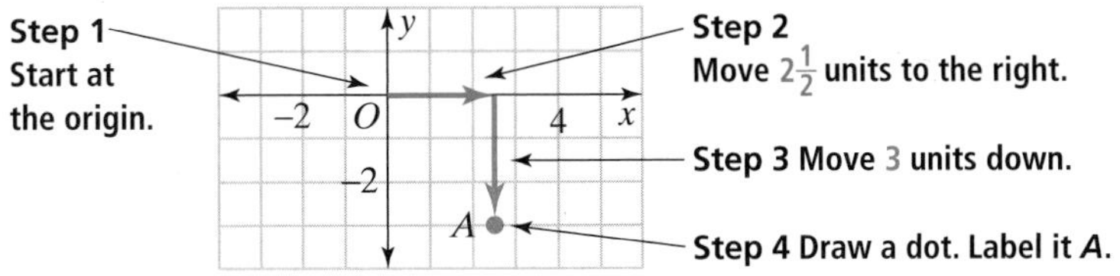

Quick Check

1. Graph $R(4, -2)$ and $S\left(-4, 2\frac{1}{2}\right)$ on the same coordinate plane. See back of book.

You can use the Pythagorean Theorem to find distances in the coordinate plane.

EXAMPLE Finding Distance on a Coordinate Plane

2 **Multiple Choice** The library is 5 miles north of your house. The post office is 6 miles east of your house. To the nearest mile, how far is the library from the post office?

(A) 7 mi (B) 8 mi (C) 9 mi (D) 10 mi

Graph the three locations on a coordinate plane. Place your home at the origin. Notice that you can draw a right triangle. The x-coordinate and the y-coordinate are the lengths of the legs of the right triangle.

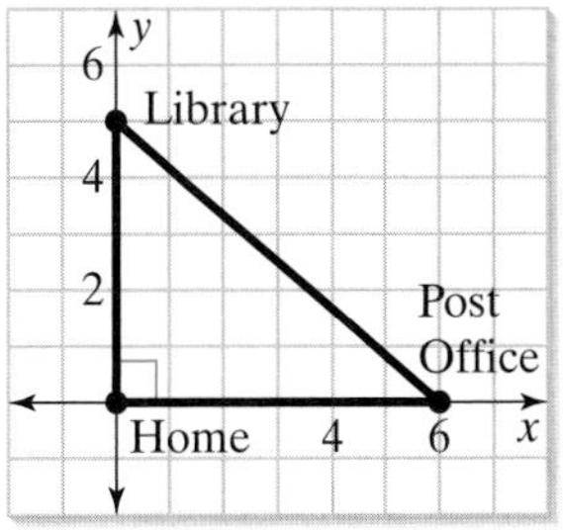

$a^2 + b^2 = c^2$ ← Use the Pythagorean Theorem.

$5^2 + 6^2 = c^2$ ← Substitute.

$25 + 36 = c^2$ ← Simplify.

$61 = c^2$ ← Add.

$\sqrt{61} = \sqrt{c^2}$ ← Find the positive square root of each side.

[√] 61 [=] 7.810249676 ← Use a calculator.

$c \approx 8$

The answer is B.

Quick Check

2. Your school is 3 miles south of your house. The general store is 5 miles east of your school. To the nearest mile, how far is your house from the general store? 6 mi

Test Prep Tip

Be careful to follow the order of operations when solving for a variable in the Pythagorean Theorem.

2. Teach

Activity Lab

Use before the lesson.

All in One Teaching Resources

Activity Lab 3-4: Similar Lines

Guided Instruction

Example 1

Have students say *right two and a half,* and *down three* as they graph point *A*. Saying *left* or *right* with each first coordinate and then *up* or *down* (depending on the sign) with the second coordinate will help students remember which way to move first.

PowerPoint

Additional Examples

1 Graph $P(-3, 2\frac{1}{2})$ on a coordinate plane.

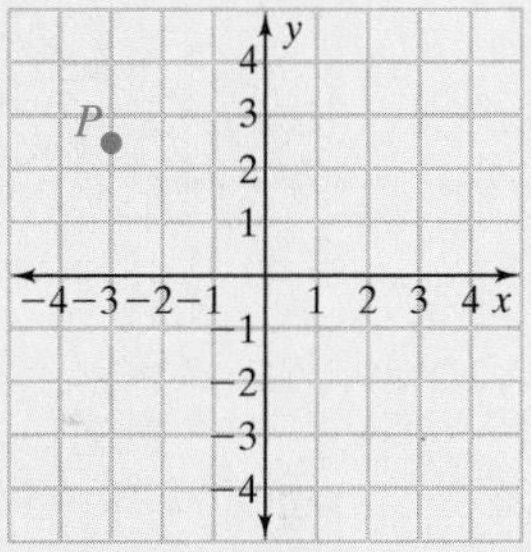

2 The mall is 5 miles north of the library. The roller skating rink is 12 miles east of the library. To the nearest mile, how far is the mall from the roller skating rink? 13 miles

All in One Teaching Resources

- Daily Notetaking Guide 3-4 L3
- Adapted Notetaking 3-4 L1

Closure

- Explain how an ordered pair locates a point in the coordinate plane. Sample: The first coordinate in an ordered pair tells the number of horizontal units the point is from the origin. The second coordinate tells the number of vertical units a point is from the origin.

Advanced Learners L4

A rectangle has opposite vertices at points with coordinates (4, 3) and (−4, −3). What are the coordinates of the other vertices? (−4, 3), (4, −3)

learning style: verbal

English Language Learners ELL

In problems requiring the use of the Pythagorean Theorem, make sure students can identify and label the origin, the legs, and the hypotenuse as they would be drawn on a coordinate plane. Ask: *Which length are you trying to find? Is that a leg or the hypotenuse?*

learning style: verbal

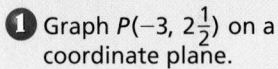

3. Practice

Assignment Guide

Check Your Understanding
Go over Exercises 1–10 in class before assigning the Homework Exercises.

Homework Exercises

A	Practice by Example	11–23
B	Apply Your Skills	24–30
C	Challenge	31
Test Prep and Mixed Review		32–38

Homework Quick Check
To check students' understanding of key skills and concepts, go over Exercises 16, 23, 25, 27, and 30.

Differentiated Instruction Resources

Adapted Practice 3-4 L1

Practice 3-4 Graphing in the Coordinate Plane L3

Name the coordinates of each point in the graph.

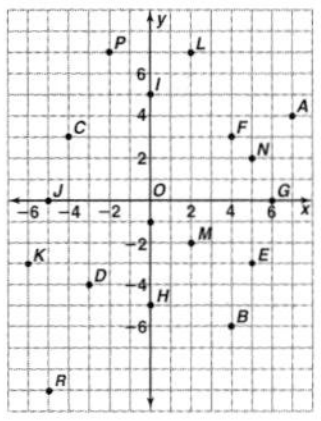

1. J (–5, 0)
2. R (–5, –9)
3. K (–6, –3)
4. M (2, –2)
5. I (0, 5)
6. P (–2, 7)
7. N (5, 2)
8. L (2, 7)

In which quadrant or on which axis is each point located?

9. $(-3, -2)$ III
10. $(7, 0)$ x-axis
11. $(4, 0)$ x-axis
12. $(-3, -9)$ III
13. $(4, -7)$ IV
14. $(7, -5)$ IV
15. $(2, 9)$ I
16. $(-3, 2)$ y-axis

17. Arnie plotted points on the graph below. He placed his pencil point at A. He can move either right or down any whole number of units until he reaches point B. In how many ways can he do this?
10 ways

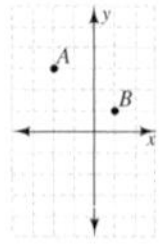

18. Marika had to draw $\triangle ABC$ that fit several requirements.
    a. It must fit in the box shown.
    b. The endpoints of $\overline{AB}$ have coordinates $A(-2, 0)$ and $B(2, 0)$.
    c. Point C must be on the y-axis and its y-coordinate is an integer.
    Name all the points that could be point C.
    (0, 5), (0, 4), (0, 3), (0, 2), (0, 1), (0, –1), (0, –2), (0, –3), (0, –4), (0, –5)

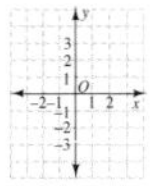

3-4 • Guided Problem Solving GPS L3

GPS **Student Page 126, Exercise 25:**

a. Graph each of these points on a coordinate plane: $(-2, -2), (-5, 3), (-3, 3), (-1, 0), (1, 3), (3, 3), (0, -2), (0, -7), (-2, -7), (-2, -2)$.

b. Connect the points in order and describe the figure formed.

Understand

1. How many points are you to plot? nine
2. Given an ordered pair, the x-coordinate is the first number; the y-coordinate is the second number.
3. What is it that you are asked to do after plotting the points? Connect the points in order, and describe the figure that is formed.

Plan and Carry Out

4. What does the x-coordinate indicate? the number of horizontal units a point is from zero

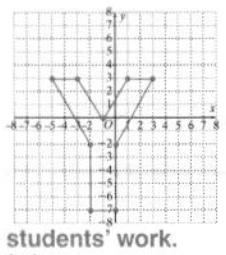

5. What does the y-coordinate indicate? the number of vertical units a point is from zero
6. Plot the points on the graph. Check students' work.
7. Which quadrant is the first point in? third
8. Connect the points in order. Check students' work.
9. What shape is formed? the letter Y

Check

10. Is every point plotted correctly to create the figure? Yes, the letter Y is made.

Solve Another Problem

11. Plot the following points on the grid at the right. Connect the points in order, connecting the last point to the first. What shape is formed?
$(-3, -2), (0, 4), (3, -2), (-3, 2), (3, 2)$

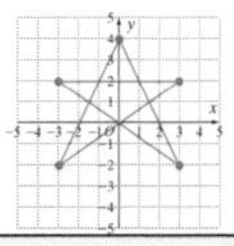

Check Your Understanding

Vocabulary Match each ordered pair with the appropriate quadrant.

1. $(-4, 2)$ B
2. $(3, 5)$ A
3. $(12, -6)$ D
4. $(-7, -1)$ C

A. Quadrant I
B. Quadrant II
C. Quadrant III
D. Quadrant IV

Name the coordinates of each point in the graph.

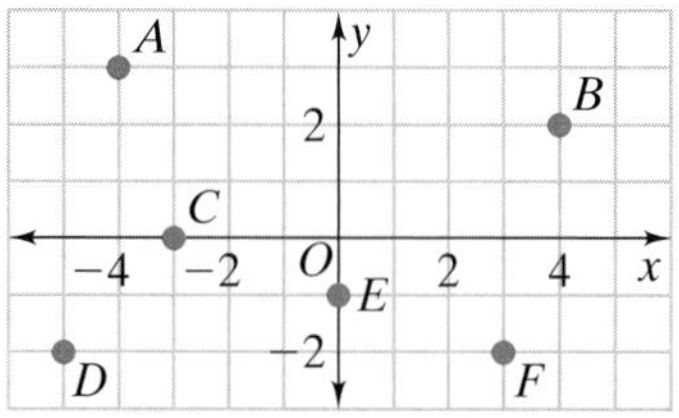

5. A (–4, 3)
6. B (4, 2)
7. C (–3, 0)
8. D (–5, –2)
9. E (0, –1)
10. F (3, –2)

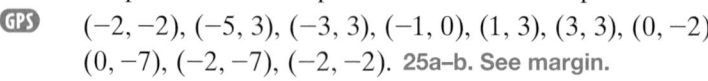

Homework Exercises

For more exercises, see Extra Skills and Word Problems.

GO for Help

For Exercises	See Examples
11–22	1
23	2

A Graph each point on the same coordinate plane. 11–18. See back of book.

11. $A(4, -5)$
12. $B(3, 4)$
13. $C(5, 0)$
14. $D(0, -3)$
15. $E(-5, 1)$
16. $F(-2, -4)$
17. $G(-2, 0)$
18. $H(6, 2)$

Name the point with the given coordinates in the graph at the right.

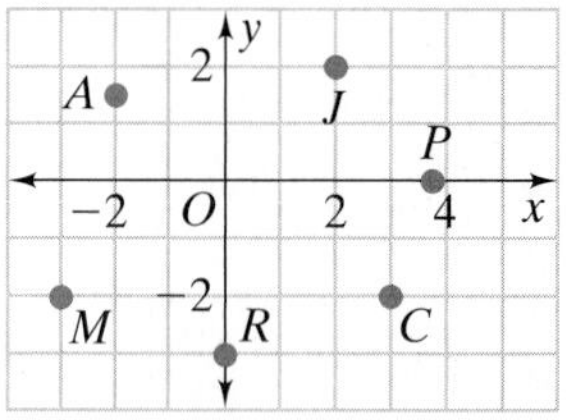

19. $(3, -2)$ C
20. $(-3, -2)$ M
21. $\left(3\frac{3}{4}, 0\right)$ P
22. $(-2, 1.5)$ A

23. **Softball** A softball diamond has the shape of a square. The distance from home plate to second base is about 85 ft. Find the distance a player would run going from first base to second base. about 60 ft

B GPS 24. **Guided Problem Solving** Find the length of the hypotenuse to the nearest tenth. 7.1 units
- The length of $\overline{AC}$ is ▪ units.
- The length of $\overline{BC}$ is ▪ units.
- Using the Pythagorean Theorem, the length of $\overline{AB}$ is the square root of $▪^2 + ▪^2$.

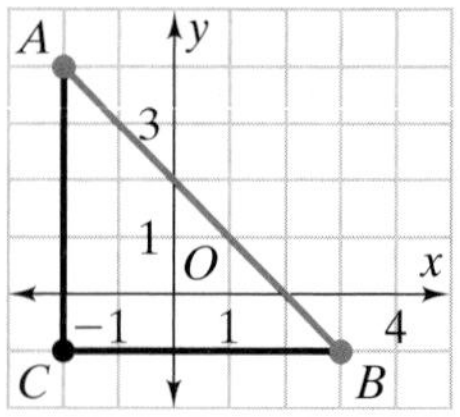

25. a. Graph each of these points on a coordinate plane: $(-2, -2), (-5, 3), (-3, 3), (-1, 0), (1, 3), (3, 3), (0, -2), (0, -7), (-2, -7), (-2, -2)$. 25a–b. See margin.
GPS b. Connect the points in order and describe the figure formed.

25a–b. See back of book.

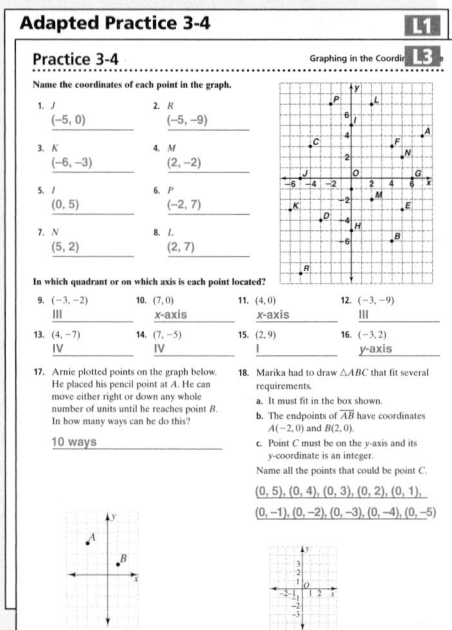

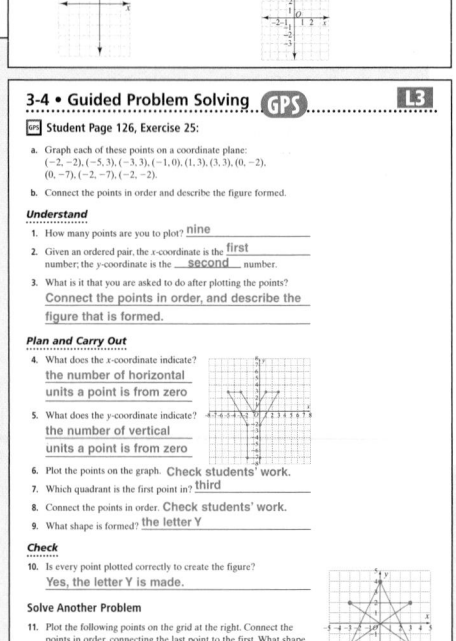

Online Homework Video Tutor
Visit: PHSchool.com
Web Code: ase-0304

26. On a graph, the points (4, −2), (7, −2), (9, −5), and (2, −5) are connected in order to form a trapezoid. To the nearest tenth, what is its perimeter? 17.2 units

27. **Geography** Degrees of longitude and latitude indicate locations on a map. The longitude of Chicago is about 88° W, and the latitude is about 42° N. Estimate the longitude and latitude of St. Paul and Lincoln.
93° W, 45° N; 97° W, 41° N

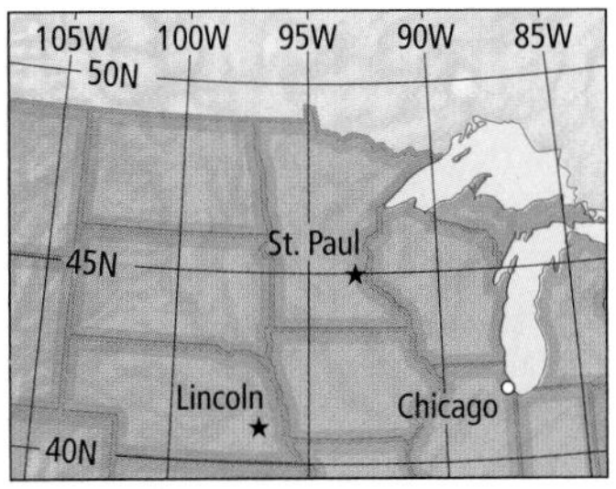

In which quadrant is each point located?

28. (x, y) if $x > 0$ and $y < 0$ Quadrant IV

29. (x, y) if $x > 0$ and $y > 0$ Quadrant I

30. **Writing in Math** Use coordinates to write directions that will get the mouse to the cheese in the maze at the right. See back of book.

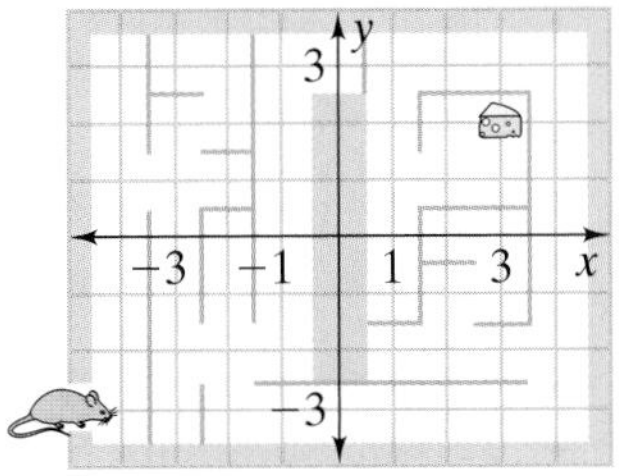

31. **Challenge** Graph and connect the points (3, 2), (−2, 2), (−2, 7), (3, 7), and (3, 2) in order. Then graph and connect the points (3, −2), (−2, −2), (−2, −7), (3, −7), and (3, −2) in order. How are these two figures related? See back of book.

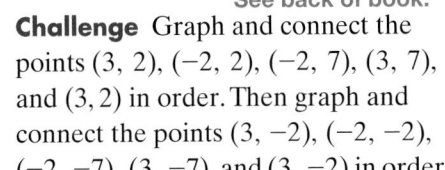

Test Prep and Mixed Review

Practice

Multiple Choice

32. What are the coordinates of point P at the right? C
   - (A) (1.5, −2)
   - (B) (−1.5, 2)
   - (C) (−2, 1.5)
   - (D) (2, −1.5)

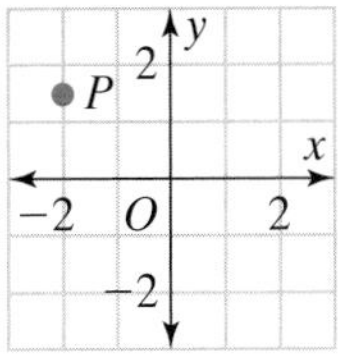

33. Oscar grew 3 inches each year for 5 years, until he was 18 years old. What additional information is necessary to find Oscar's height at age 18? H
   - (F) the average height of an 18-year-old
   - (G) how quickly he grew from age 0 to age 6
   - (H) how tall Oscar was when he was 13
   - (J) Oscar's weight when he turned 18

34. Sarah walks across a rectangular field as shown. Which is the closest to the distance she walks? C
   - (A) 100 ft
   - (B) 90 ft
   - (C) 70 ft
   - (D) 50 ft

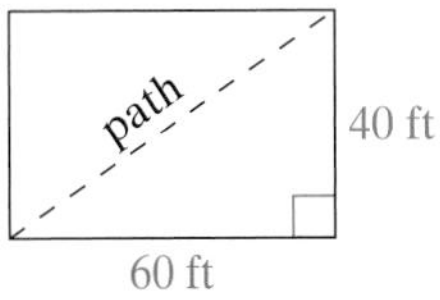

GO for Help

For Exercises	See Lesson
35–38	3-1

Find each square root. Where necessary, round to the nearest tenth.

35. $\sqrt{50}$ 7.1

36. $-\sqrt{\frac{1}{6}}$ −0.4

37. $\sqrt{7}$ 2.6

38. $\sqrt{0.18}$ 0.4

Online lesson quiz, PHSchool.com, Web Code: asa-0304

4. Assess & Reteach

PowerPoint

Lesson Quiz

1. Graph the points $A(2, 2)$, $B(-3, 1)$, and $C(2, 1.5)$ on the same coordinate plane. See graph below.

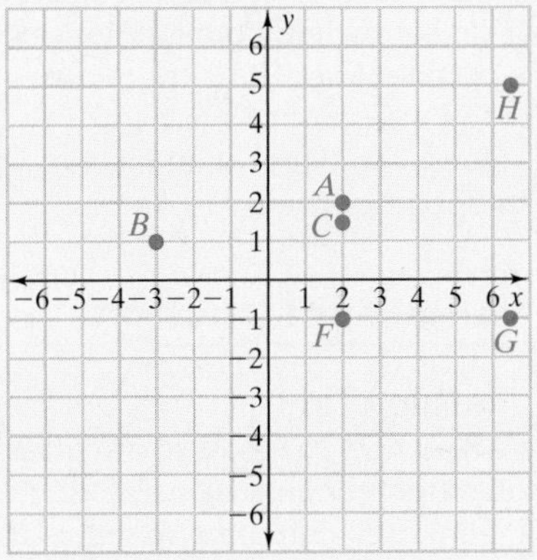

2. Graph the points $F(2, -1)$, $G(6.5, -1)$, and $H(6.5, 5)$ on the same coordinate plane. See graph above.

3. Find the length of the hypotenuse of △FGH. 7.5 units

4. On a soccer field, one goalpost is 25 yards west of a second goalpost. The gymnasium is 20 yards north of the second goalpost. How far is the gymnasium from the first goalpost? 32 yards

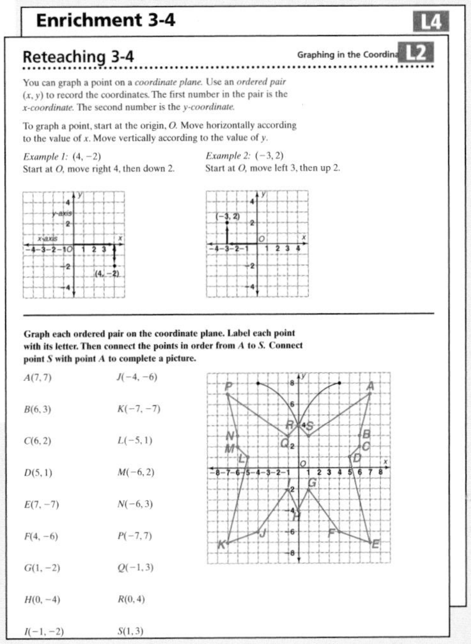
Enrichment 3-4 L4
Reteaching 3-4 Graphing in the Coordina... L2
You can graph a point on a coordinate plane. Use an ordered pair (x, y) to record the coordinates. The first number in the pair is the x-coordinate. The second number is the y-coordinate.
To graph a point, start at the origin, O. Move horizontally according to the value of x. Move vertically according to the value of y.
Example 1: (4, −2) Start at O, move right 4, then down 2.
Example 2: (−3, 2) Start at O, move left 3, then up 2.
Graph each ordered pair on the coordinate plane. Label each point with its letter. Then connect the points in order from A to S. Connect point S with point A to complete a picture.
A(7, 7) J(−4, −6)
B(6, 3) K(−7, −7)
C(6, 2) L(−5, 1)
D(5, 1) M(−6, 2)
E(7, −7) N(−6, 3)
F(4, −6) P(−7, 7)
G(1, −2) Q(−1, 3)
H(0, −4) R(0, 4)
I(−1, −2) S(1, 3)

Alternative Assessment

Pairs of students draw a right triangle with horizontal and vertical legs, and each of its endpoints in different quadrants. They list the coordinates of the endpoints. They then find the length of the hypotenuse.

Test Prep

Resources
For additional practice with a variety of test item formats:
- Test-Taking Strategies, p. 151
- Test Prep, p. 155
- Test-Taking Strategies with Transparencies

Activity Lab

Finding the Midpoint

A midpoint of a line segment lies exactly halfway between the two endpoints, or equidistant from each endpoint. Finding midpoints on a coordinate plane is similar to finding midpoints on a number line. The *x*-coordinate is the midpoint of the two *x*-values. The *y*-coordinate is the midpoint of the two *y*-values.

Guided Instruction

Teaching Tip
Review how to measure distances on a number line. Discuss the meaning of *midpoint,* in terms of equal distances from *A* to *B* and from *B* to *C.*

Error Prevention!

In Exercise 2, remind students that midpoints of slanted lines need to be calculated by using both the distance between the *x*-values and the distance between the *y*-values. Help them picture the horizontal and vertical distances by having them draw a dotted vertical line from one endpoint to the gridline on which the other endpoint sits, and a horizontal line from there to the other endpoint.

Resources

- graph paper

5. Add x_1 and x_2 and divide by 2. This is the *x*-coordinate of the midpoint. Add y_1 and y_2 and divide by 2. This is the *y*-coordinate of the midpoint.

3-4b Activity Lab

Finding the Midpoint

The **midpoint** of a line segment is the point that divides the segment into two segments of equal length.

ACTIVITY

In the diagram below, the midpoint of $\overline{AC}$ is point *B*.

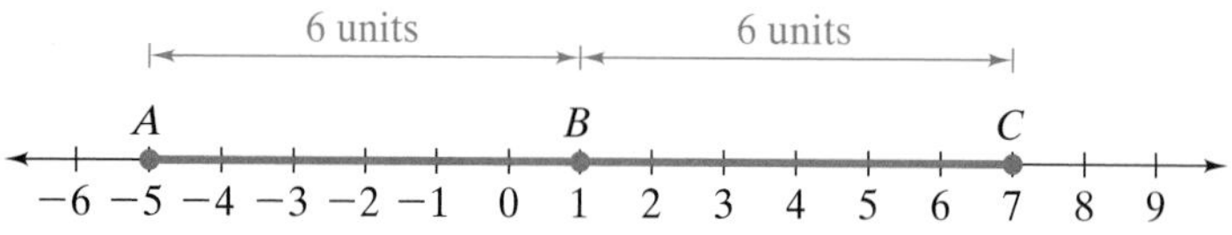

1. On the number line above, the value at point *B* is 1. Describe how you could use the values at points *A* and *C* to find the value at *B*.
2. Suppose point *E* is located at 27 on the number line above. Point *D* is the midpoint between *C* and *E*. Use what you learned in Exercise 1 to find the value at point *D*. 17

1. Answers may vary. Sample: Add the values of points *A* and *C*, then divide by 2.

Exercises

For Exercises 1 and 2, use the diagram at the right.

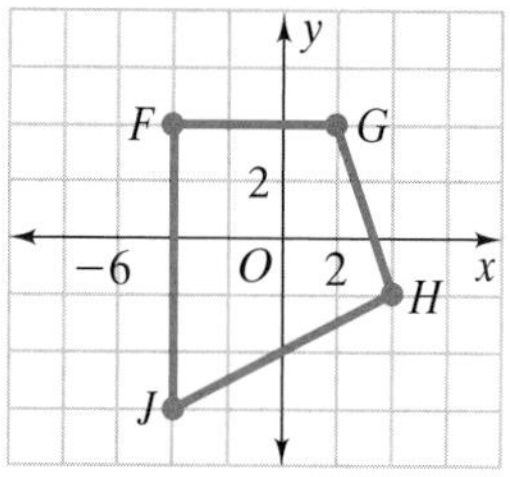

1. **a.** What are the coordinates of the midpoint of $\overline{FG}$? (−1, 4)
   b. What are the coordinates of the midpoint of $\overline{FJ}$? (−4, −1)
2. Find the coordinates of the midpoints of $\overline{GH}$ and $\overline{HJ}$. Use the same technique you used in Exercise 1, but use it once to find the *x*-coordinate and once to find the *y*-coordinate. (3, 1); (0, −4)
3. The coordinates of the four corners of a square are (8, 12), (12, 4), (0, 8), and (4, 0). Find the coordinates of the midpoint of each side. (2, 4); (8, 2); (10, 8); (4,10)
4. **a.** Suppose you are traveling from Los Angeles, California to Chicago, Illinois along Route 66. Use the photo at the right. If you are 150 miles from Los Angeles, how far are you from Adrian, Texas? 989 mi
   b. How far are you from Chicago? 2,128 mi
5. **Writing in Math** The coordinates of points *W* and *Z* in the coordinate plane are (x_1, y_1) and (x_2, y_2) respectively. Explain how you can find the *x*- and *y*-coordinates of the midpoint of $\overline{WZ}$. See margin.

Tables and Graphs

Words, data tables, and graphs are three different ways to show the same information. You can use one representation to generate another representation.

ACTIVITY

For Exercises 1 and 2, describe the pattern shown in each graph. Then copy and complete each table. 1–2. See margin.

1. The graph at the right shows how the earnings of a lifeguard change with the number of hours she works.

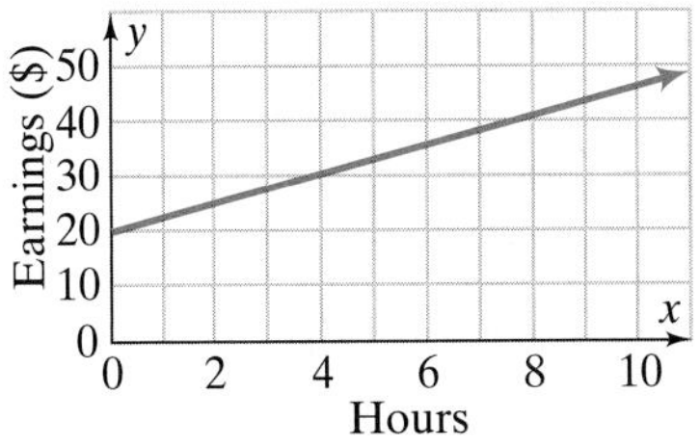

Hours	0	4	8	12	24
Earnings ($)	20	30	40	■	■

2. The graph at the right shows how the total cost of a cookout changes with the number of guests.

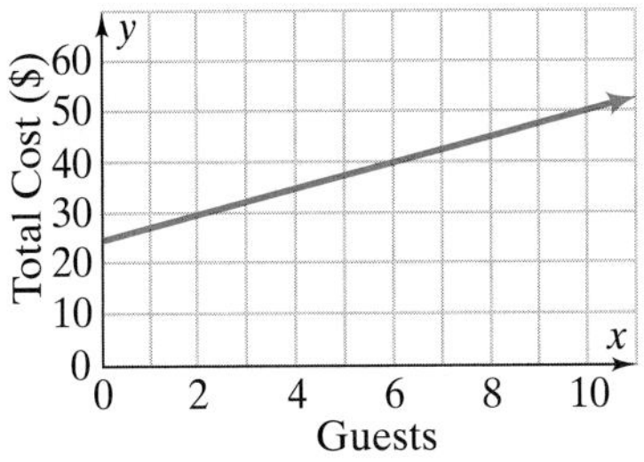

Guests	6	9	12	30	120
Cost ($)	45	55	■	■	■

3. The students in the skateboarding club at Orchard Middle School had a fundraiser to raise money to build a new skate park. The club began with 180 raffle tickets to sell. Every day, they sold 9 tickets.

a. Copy and complete the table below. 3a–b. See back of book.

Number of Days	0	1	2	3	■
Tickets Remaining	■	■	■	■	0

b. Use the data in the table to draw a graph showing how the number of tickets remaining changes with the number of days the club has been selling tickets.

4. (Algebra) You can also use an algebraic equation to represent data. Use Exercise 3 to write an equation relating the number of days the club has been selling tickets to the number of tickets remaining. Let x be the number of days and y be the number of tickets. Answers may vary. Sample: $y = 180 - 9x$

Activity Lab

Tables and Graphs

In this activity, students practice showing the same information using words, tables, and graphs. The final exercise challenges students to represent the data in Exercise 3 as an equation.

Guided Instruction

Teaching Tip
Have students describe the steepness of each graph, tell whether it is increasing or decreasing, and describe the relationship each graph displays.

Error Prevention!

In the Exercises 1–3, help students keep track of which values correspond to which axes. For example, for Exercise 1 ask: *On which axis are hours shown?* x-axis *On which axis are earnings shown?* y-axis

Differentiated Instruction

Visual Learners
To complete a table of values given a graph, have students draw a colored or dotted vertical line from a value on the x-axis up to the graph (line), and then horizontally over to the corresponding value on the y-axis.

Resources

- Activity Lab 3-5: Hidden Equation
- graph paper

1. Pattern: Answers may vary. Earnings increase by $10 as the number of hours worked increases by 4. Table:

Hours	0	4	8	12	24
Earnings ($)	20	30	40	50	80

2. Pattern: Answers may vary. Sample: Total cost increases by $10 as the number of guests increases by 3. Table:

Guests	6	9	12	30	120
Cost ($)	45	55	65	125	425

3-5

1. Plan

Objective
To use tables, equations, and graphs to solve problems

Examples
1 Making Tables and Writing Equations
2 Graphing Linear Equations

Math Understandings: p. 104C

Professional Development

Math Background

The solutions of an equation in two variables, such as $y + x = 5$, can be graphed on a coordinate plane as a line formed by an infinite set of ordered pairs. Tables can be used to represent a set of x- and y-coordinates that satisfy the equation. The set of x-values is known as the domain and the set of corresponding y-values is known as the range. In real-world linear situations, the domain and range must be reasonable values.

More Math Background: p. 104C

Lesson Planning and Resources

See p. 104E for a list of the resources that support this lesson.

PowerPoint

Bell Ringer Practice

Check Skills You'll Need
Use student page, transparency, or PowerPoint. For intervention, direct students to:
Algebraic Expressions and Order of Operations
Lesson 1-1
Extra Skills and Word Problems Practice, Ch. 1

3-5 Equations, Tables, and Graphs

Check Skills You'll Need

1. **Vocabulary Review** What do you call a symbol that stands for one or more numbers? variable

Evaluate for $a = 4$.

2. $6a - 21$ 3
3. $13 + 2a$ 21
4. $5a + 8$ 28

GO for Help Lesson 1-1

What You'll Learn

To use tables, equations, and graphs to solve problems

New Vocabulary solution, linear equation

Why Learn This?

You can use equations, tables, and graphs to represent the same data. For example, you can use a table of values for plant growth to write an equation or make a graph.

Given a word problem, you can sometimes make a table of data. Then you can write an equation to model the situation.

GO for Help
For help making a table of data, go to Lesson 1-1, Example 4.

EXAMPLE Making Tables and Writing Equations

1 Suppose you save \$3 each week. Make a table and write an equation to represent your total savings after a given number of weeks.

Number of Weeks	Total Savings (dollars)	Expression
0	0	3(0)
1	3	3(1)
2	6	3(2)
3	9	3(3)
w	t	$3(w)$

Let w represent the number of weeks.

Let t represent your total savings.

Look for a pattern in the table. Your total savings for a given week is 3 times the number of weeks you have been saving.

The equation $t = 3w$ models your total savings.

Quick Check

1. You buy CDs from a music store. Each CD costs \$15. Make a table and write an equation to represent the total cost of buying a given number of CDs. See back of book.

Differentiated Instruction Solutions for All Learners

Special Needs L1	Below Level L2
Students work in pairs. Match those who have difficulty graphing equations on the grids with those who can do so more easily. The first student can make the data tables while the partner can graph the equations. Then partners can check each other's work. **learning style: visual**	To help students remember the order of a coordinate pair, have them write x over the first value and y over the second value. **learning style: visual**

Vocabulary Tip

The term *linear* means "relating to a line."

Any ordered pair that makes an equation true is a **solution** of the equation. For example, (2, 6) is a solution of $y = 3x$ because $6 = 3(2)$. An equation with two variables can have many solutions. You can show these solutions on a graph. An equation is a **linear equation** if all of its solutions lie on a line.

EXAMPLE Graphing Linear Equations

2 Jerrod keeps track of how much dry food is in his cat's feeder. Graph the linear equation $y = -\frac{1}{2}x + 12$, where y represents the cups of food left and x represents the number of days since he filled the twelve-cup feeder.

Step 1 Make a table.

x	$y = -\frac{1}{2}x + 12$
0	$-\frac{1}{2}(0) + 12 = 12$
4	$-\frac{1}{2}(4) + 12 = 10$
9	$-\frac{1}{2}(9) + 12 = 7\frac{1}{2}$
16	$-\frac{1}{2}(16) + 12 = 4$

Step 2 Graph the ordered pairs and draw a line through the points.

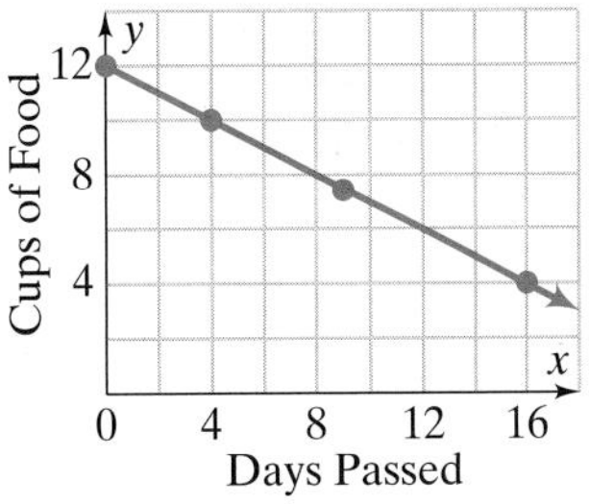

Each point (x, y) on the graph represents a solution of the equation. For example, the point (4, 10) means that after 4 days, 10 cups are left.

Quick Check

2. Graph the linear equation $y = 5x + 50$, where y represents the temperature in °F of a chemical solution after x minutes.
See back of book.

More Than One Way

A plant is 4 cm tall and grows 2 cm per day. Predict how tall the plant will be after 8 days.

Roberto's Method

I can make a table of data.

Height of Plant

Days Passed	0	1	2	3	4	5	6	7	8
Height	4	6	8	10	12	14	16	18	20

After 8 days, the plant will be 20 cm tall.

2. Teach

Activity Lab

Use before the lesson.
Student Edition Activity Lab, Data Analysis 3-5a, Tables and Graphs, p. 129

All in One Teaching Resources

Activity Lab 3-5: Hidden Equation

PowerPoint

Additional Examples

1 Suppose you buy a bag of food for your pet dog every week. Dog food costs \$4 per bag. Make a table and write an equation to represent the total cost of buying dog food for any number of weeks.
$c = 4w$

Number of Weeks	1	2	3	4	w
Cost of Dog Food	4	8	12	16	c

2 Graph the linear equation $y = -x + 3$, where y represents the pressure inside a deflating balloon after x seconds.

Seconds	0	1	2	3
Pressure	3	2	1	0

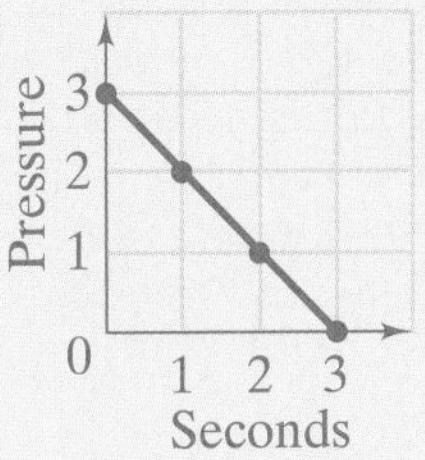

Advanced Learners L4
The equation $y = 6 - 3x$ represents the height of water in a bottle pouring out over time. Do all of its solutions apply to the graph of the equation? **no**
Which of the solutions to the equation should be shown on the graphed line? **Sample: the positive values, including zero**
learning style: verbal

English Language Learners ELL
Students may be comfortable mentally calculating the answer for the *Choose a Method* example since the numbers are small integers. Stress that the tables and graphs also allow them to make predictions, whether the numbers are easy or hard to mentally calculate.
learning style: verbal

Guided Instruction

Example 1

Ask:

- *How do the x-values change as you move down the table?* increase by 1
- *How do the y-values change?* increase by 3
- *If this pattern continues, what would be the next ordered pair in the table?* (4, 12)

Error Prevention!

In a real-world situation, students need to consider not only coordinates that are solutions to the equation, but values that are reasonable for the situation. Ask: *Why would you **not** choose negative values for x in Example 2?* There cannot be a negative number of days.

All in One Teaching Resources

- Daily Notetaking Guide 3-5 L3
- Adapted Notetaking 3-5 L1

Closure

- *How do you graph a linear equation in two variables?* Sample: Make a table of values by choosing several *x*-values and substituting them into the equation and simplifying. Graph the resulting ordered pairs and connect them in a straight line.
- *In many cases when a linear equation represents a real-world situation, such as height vs. age, which values cannot apply to the situation? In which quadrant will the graph be shown?* negative nonzero *x*- and *y*-values; first quadrant

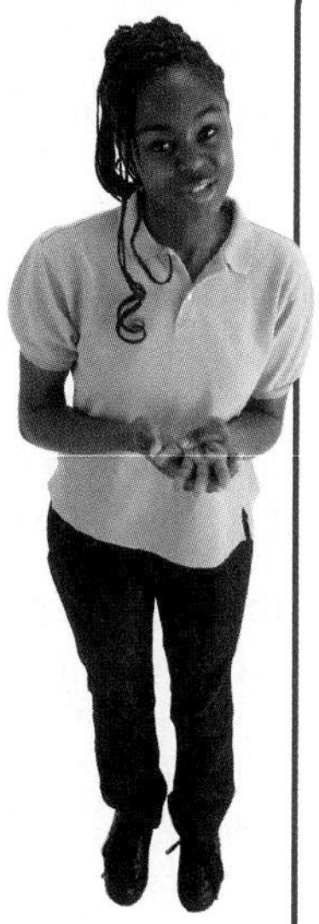

Jasmine's Method

I can make a graph. Let x represent the number of days that have passed. Let y represent the height of the plant.

Height of Plant

Days Passed (x)	1	2	3
Height (y)	6	8	10

I can make a table of solutions. Three points on the graph are (1, 6), (2, 8), and (3, 10).

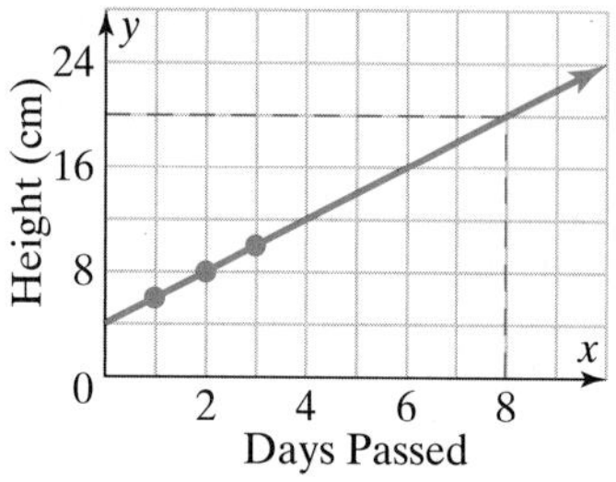

I can draw a line through the points. Then I can use the graph to find the height y when $x = 8$.

After 8 days, the plant will be 20 cm tall.

Choose a Method

A bag of rice weighs 80 oz. If a serving of rice is 2 oz, how much rice will be left after you prepare 10 servings? Explain why you chose the method you used. 60 oz; check students' methods.

Check Your Understanding

1. **Vocabulary** Which statement about linear equations is *not* true? C
   - (A) The graph of a linear equation is a line.
   - (B) Every point on the graph of a linear equation is a solution.
   - (C) A point that does not lie on the graph of a linear equation may still be a solution of the equation.
   - (D) You can write solutions of a linear equation as ordered pairs.

2. A leaky pipe loses 0.75 gallons of water every minute. Complete the data table below. See margin.

Water Loss

Number of Minutes (t)	1	2	3	4
Gallons of Water Lost (g)	■	■	■	■

3. Use the table from Exercise 2. Write a linear equation to represent the amount of water lost from the leaky pipe. $g = 0.75t$

4. Suppose you wanted to graph the equation in Exercise 3. Use the table from Exercise 2 to name four points that lie on the graph.

4. (1, 0.75), (2, 1.5), (3, 2.25), (4, 3)

2.

Water Loss

Number of Minutes (t)	1	2	3	4
Gallons of Water Lost (g)	0.75	1.5	2.25	3

Homework Exercises

For more exercises, see Extra Skills and Word Problems.

GO for Help

For Exercises	See Examples
5–6	1
7–8	2

A 5. In 2000, about four babies were born world-wide every second. Make a table and write an equation to represent the total number of babies born over time. See margin.

6. The temperature drops 2°F every hour. Make a table and write an equation to represent the total temperature drop over time. See margin.

7. For a certain repair, an auto shop charges a \$20 fee for materials plus \$40 per hour for labor. Graph the linear equation $y = 40x + 20$, where y represents the total cost and x represents the hours of labor. 7–8. See back of book.

8. On a 100-point test, each question is worth 5 points. Partial answers receive partial credit. Graph the linear equation $y = 100 - 5x$, where y represents your score and x represents the number of incorrect answers.

B **GPS** 9. **Guided Problem Solving** In the design at the right, 12 squares surround a row of 3 circles. Predict the number of squares needed to surround a row of 10 circles.

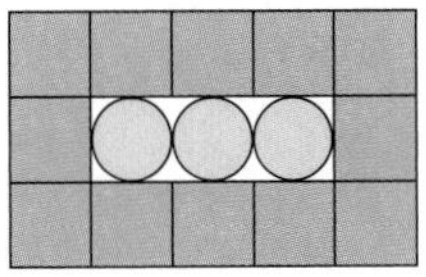

- **Make a Plan** Make a table of values. 26 squares
  Graph the ordered pairs from the table and draw a line through the points. Then use the graph to find the answer.
- **Carry Out the Plan** Complete the table below.

Number of Circles (x)	1	2	3	4	5	6
Number of Squares (y)	■	■	■	■	■	■

Graph each linear equation. 10–12. See back of book.

10. $y = -\frac{2}{3}x + 3$
11. $y = -\frac{3}{5}x - 2$
12. $y = 1.5x + 4$

13. **Writing in Math** Four of the five points below are solutions of the same linear equation. Which one is not? Explain. See left.
$A(2, 1)$ $B(0, -4)$ $C(1, -2)$ $D(4, 4)$ $E(3, 2)$

14. The table below shows the cost of buying class mugs online. Write an equation to model the data. See left.

Number of Mugs	1	2	3	4	5
Total Cost	13	21	29	37	45

15. **GPS** Engraving a key chain costs \$10 plus \$1.50 for each engraved letter. You can only spend \$20. What is the maximum number of letters you can engrave? Solve by making a table and writing an equation. See back of book.

13. A; A is not on the line passing through the other points.

14. Let m = the number of mugs. Let t = the total cost. $t = 8m + 5$

GO Online
Homework Video Tutor
Visit: PHSchool.com
Web Code: ase-0305

5–6. See back of book.

3. Practice

Assignment Guide

Check Your Understanding

Go over Exercises 1–4 in class before assigning the Homework Exercises.

Homework Exercises

A Practice by Example	5–8
B Apply Your Skills	9–17
C Challenge	18
Test Prep and Mixed Review	19–24

Homework Quick Check

To check students' understanding of key skills and concepts, go over Exercises 6, 7, 13, 15, and 16.

Differentiated Instruction Resources

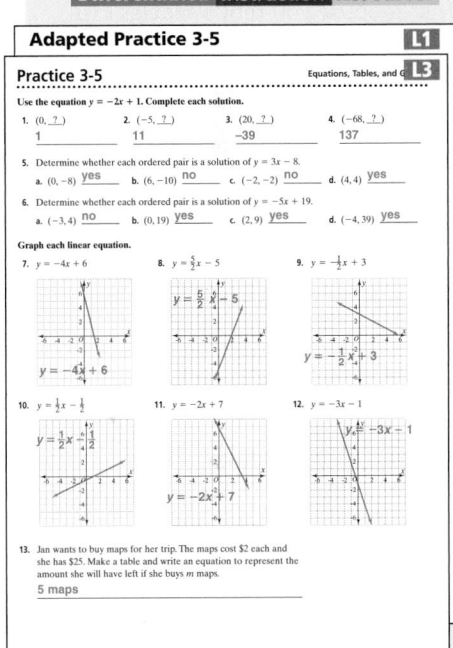

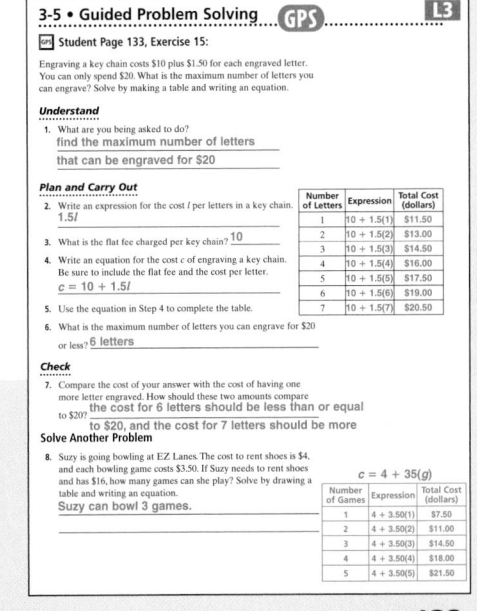

Adapted Practice 3-5 L1

Practice 3-5 Equations, Tables, and G L3

Use the equation $y = -2x + 1$. Complete each solution.

1. (0, ?) 1
2. (−5, ?) 11
3. (20, ?) −39
4. (−68, ?) 137

5. Determine whether each ordered pair is a solution of $y = 3x - 8$.
a. (0, −8) yes b. (6, −10) no c. (−2, −2) no d. (4, 4) yes

6. Determine whether each ordered pair is a solution of $y = -5x + 19$.
a. (−3, 4) no b. (0, 19) yes c. (2, 9) yes d. (−4, 39) yes

Graph each linear equation.

7. $y = -4x + 6$

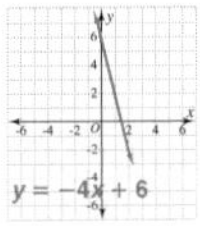

8. $y = \frac{5}{2}x - 5$

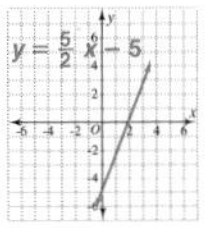

9. $y = -\frac{1}{2}x + 3$

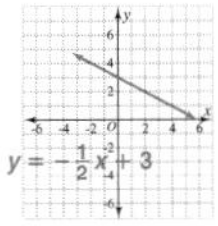

10. $y = \frac{1}{2}x - \frac{1}{2}$

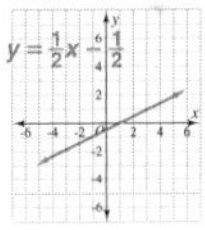

11. $y = -2x + 7$

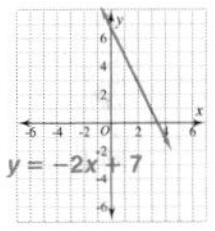

12. $y = -3x - 1$

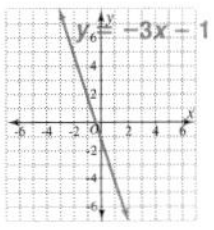

13. Jan wants to buy maps for her trip. The maps cost \$2 each and she has \$25. Make a table and write an equation to represent the amount she will have left if she buys m maps.
5 maps

3-5 • Guided Problem Solving GPS L3

GPS Student Page 133, Exercise 15:

Engraving a key chain costs \$10 plus \$1.50 for each engraved letter. You can only spend \$20. What is the maximum number of letters you can engrave? Solve by making a table and writing an equation.

Understand

1. What are you being asked to do?
find the maximum number of letters that can be engraved for \$20

Plan and Carry Out

2. Write an expression for the cost l per letters in a key chain.
$1.5l$
3. What is the flat fee charged per key chain? 10
4. Write an equation for the cost c of engraving a key chain. Be sure to include the flat fee and the cost per letter.
$c = 10 + 1.5l$
5. Use the equation in Step 4 to complete the table.

Number of Letters	Expression	Total Cost (dollars)
1	10 + 1.5(1)	\$11.50
2	10 + 1.5(2)	\$13.00
3	10 + 1.5(3)	\$14.50
4	10 + 1.5(4)	\$16.00
5	10 + 1.5(5)	\$17.50
6	10 + 1.5(6)	\$19.00
7	10 + 1.5(7)	\$20.50

6. What is the maximum number of letters you can engrave for \$20 or less? 6 letters

Check

7. Compare the cost of your answer with the cost of having one more letter engraved. How should these two amounts compare to \$20? the cost for 6 letters should be less than or equal to \$20, and the cost for 7 letters should be more

Solve Another Problem

8. Suzy is going bowling at EZ Lanes. The cost to rent shoes is \$4, and each bowling game costs \$3.50. If Suzy needs to rent shoes and has \$16, how many games can she play? Solve by drawing a table and writing an equation.
Suzy can bowl 3 games.

$c = 4 + 35(g)$

Number of Games	Expression	Total Cost (dollars)
1	4 + 3.50(1)	\$7.50
2	4 + 3.50(2)	\$11.00
3	4 + 3.50(3)	\$14.50
4	4 + 3.50(4)	\$18.00
5	4 + 3.50(5)	\$21.50

4. Assess & Reteach

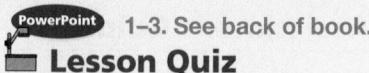

PowerPoint 1–3. See back of book.

Lesson Quiz

1. Suppose you make \$8 per hour at an after-school job. Make a table and write an equation to represent your total pay after 6 hours of work.
2. Membership at a video store costs \$5 per month, plus \$1.50 to rent each movie. Graph the linear equation $y = 5 + 1.50x$, where y represents the total cost in a month and x represents the number of movies rented each month.
3. Suppose you rent 6 movies in a month, in the situation above. Make a table that represents your total costs.
4. The air pressure in a tire is 32 pounds per square inch. Every hour, air is leaking out at the rate of 3 pounds per square inch. Write an equation that describes this situation. Sample: $p = 32 - 3h$

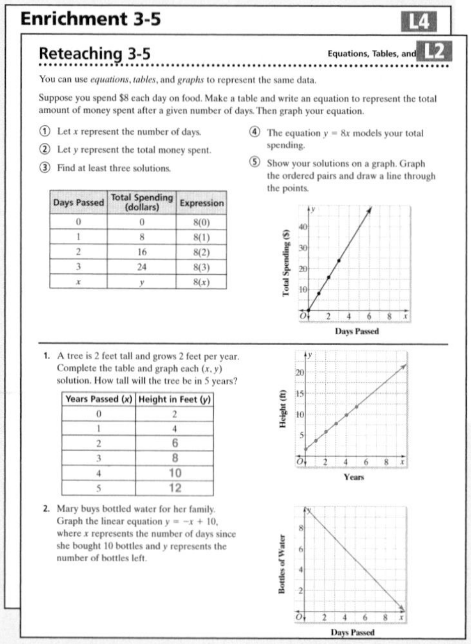
Enrichment 3-5 L4

Reteaching 3-5 Equations, Tables, and L2

You can use *equations*, *tables*, and *graphs* to represent the same data.

Suppose you spend \$8 each day on food. Make a table and write an equation to represent the total amount of money spent after a given number of days. Then graph your equation.

① Let x represent the number of days.
② Let y represent the total money spent.
③ Find at least three solutions.
④ The equation $y = 8x$ models your total spending.
⑤ Show your solutions on a graph. Graph the ordered pairs and draw a line through the points.

Days Passed	Total Spending (dollars)	Expression
0	0	8(0)
1	8	8(1)
2	16	8(2)
3	24	8(3)
x	y	8(x)

1. A tree is 2 feet tall and grows 2 feet per year. Complete the table and graph each (x, y) solution. How tall will the tree be in 5 years?

Years Passed (x)	Height in Feet (y)
0	2
1	4
2	6
3	8
4	10
5	12

2. Mary buys bottled water for her family. Graph the linear equation $y = -x + 10$, where x represents the number of days since she bought 10 bottles and y represents the number of bottles left.

17. Gina; the graph drawn by Gina's father shows the amount owed after Gina gives him \$40 each week, not \$20.

16. **Choose a Method** You start an exercise routine by lifting 3 lb and increase the weight by 2 lb per month. Predict how much weight you will lift after 5 months. Explain why you chose the method you used. 13 lb; check students' methods.

17. **Error Analysis** Gina owes her father \$200. During each week, she pays \$20. They both draw graphs to represent the money she owes. Who is correct? Explain. See left.

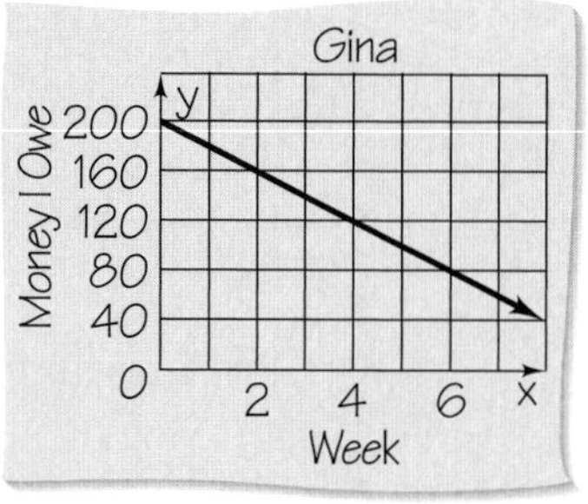

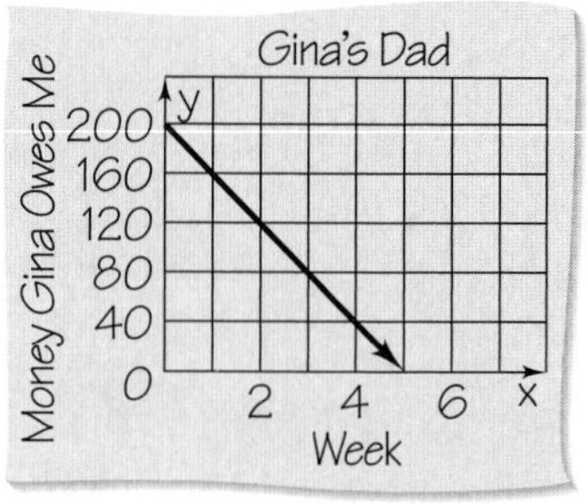

Ⓒ 18. **Challenge** A club sells calendars for \$4 each. It spends \$2 to make each calendar and \$20 on film. Write and graph two equations to represent income and expenses. Where do the graphs intersect? See back of book.

Test Prep and Mixed Review

Practice

Multiple Choice

19. The graph of $y = \frac{1}{2}x + 1$ is shown on the coordinate grid at the right. Which table of ordered pairs contains only points on this line? B

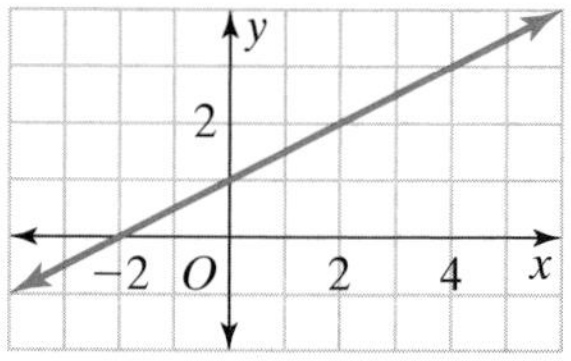

Ⓐ

x	y
−4	1
2	2
3	2.5

Ⓑ

x	y
−2	0
1	1.5
4	3

Ⓒ

x	y
0	−2
1	0
2	2

Ⓓ

x	y
−3	−1.5
0	2
5	3.5

20. Audrey bought a box of cereal and some bananas for \$4.69. If the cereal cost \$3.99 and the bananas were on sale for \$0.28 per pound, how many pounds of bananas did Audrey buy? H
Ⓕ 0.42 lb Ⓖ 2.2 lb Ⓗ 2.5 lb Ⓙ 4.2 lb

21. A ferry travels at 20 knots, which is about 23 miles per hour. How should Sam find the number of miles per hour that equals 1 knot? B
Ⓐ Divide 20 by 23.
Ⓑ Divide 23 by 20.
Ⓒ Divide 3 by 20.
Ⓓ Divide 3 by 23.

GO for Help

For Exercises	See Lesson
22–24	1-6

Solve each equation.

22. $b + 6 = 10$ 4
23. $k - 1 = 24$ 25
24. $-4 + n = 40$ 44

Test Prep

Resources

For additional practice with a variety of test item formats:

- Test-Taking Strategies, p. 151
- Test Prep, p. 155
- Test-Taking Strategies with Transparencies

Alternative Assessment

Students write a paragraph explaining how to graph the following situation in the coordinate plane: A scientist is releasing 20 drops of liquid from a tube every 10 seconds. Students write an equation that describes the situation and draw the graph.

Matching Graphs

Graphs in algebra can tell a story, just as graphs in the real world do.

EXAMPLE Matching Graphs And Descriptions

Mary and Marty both get the same allowance. Match each description of how they spend their allowance with one graph shown below. Explain your choice.

1. Mary gets her allowance once a week and spends it all.
2. Marty gets his allowance once a week. He saves half and spends half.

Graph A

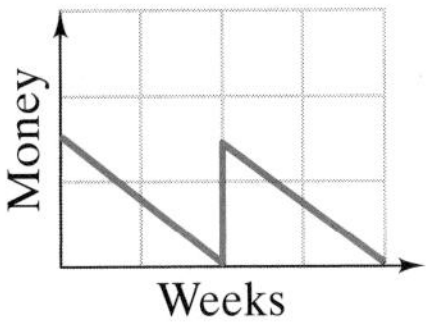

Graph B

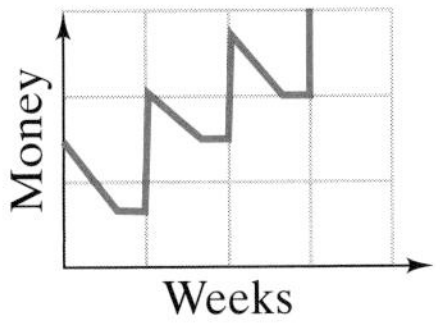

Graph C

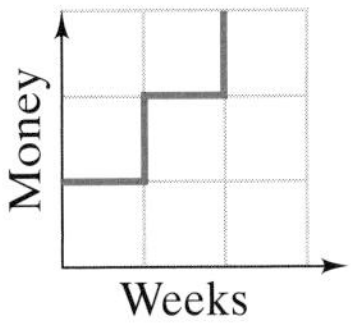

Graph D

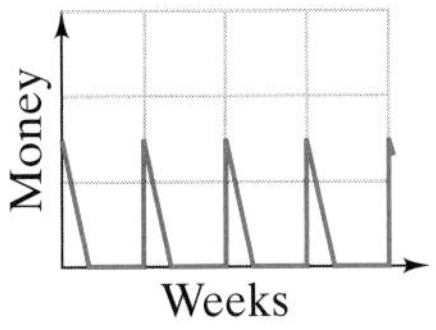

Graph D represents Mary, because during each week, the amount of money drops to zero. Graph B represents Marty because the graph shows half the money staying constant before Marty gets his allowance again.

Exercises

Sketch a graph to match each description. Label the x- and y-axes.

1–4. Check students' work.

1. The energy level of a puppy whose family leaves at 8 A.M., returns at 5 P.M., goes to bed at 10 P.M., and wakes up at 6 A.M. The x-axis shows the time for three days.
2. The number of students on your school grounds during a typical school day. The x-axis is labeled 8 A.M., 2 P.M., 10 P.M., and 4 A.M. for three days.
3. Your interest level in watching television over a 1-week period during the school year. The x-axis shows the seven days with times each day labeled 8 A.M., 2 P.M., 6 P.M., and 2 A.M.
4. Make a story and graph to match. Pick an activity for which your interest level varies over time. Make a graph, label both axes, draw the graph, and write a paragraph that explains the graph.

Activity Lab

Matching Graphs

Relationships can be represented with words, tables, graphs, and equations. In this activity, students focus on graphs. They analyze real-world situations and match or sketch graphs that describe the situations.

Guided Instruction

Example

Students should review how to graph real-world situations. Ask:

- *What does the x-axis represent? What does the y-axis represent?* in these examples, it represents time; in these examples, the level of allowance or number of students in school, for example, depending upon the time
- *Which values depend on each other?* y-values depend on x-values

Error Prevention!

Students may sketch graphs that reverse the axes. Remind students that the y-values depend on the x-values. Have them first decide and set up the units by which values are increasing on the x-axis. Then, have them consider where the y-coordinates lie in relation to the x-coordinates.

Alternative Method

Have students analyze the relationship described in each problem. Ask:

- *As the quantity of x increases, does the quantity of y increase or decrease?*
- *Does this change at different points in the situation?*

3-6

1. Plan

Objective
To graph and describe translations in the coordinate plane

Examples
1 Graphing a Translation
2 Describing a Translation

Math Understandings: p. 104D

Professional Development

Math Background

A *transformation* is a change in the position, shape, or size of a figure. A *translation* moves each point of a figure the same distance in the same direction. The resulting figure is an *image* of the original figure. Prime notation is used to identify images. For instance, the image of point C is C' and read as "C prime." Arrow notation can be used to describe a translation. For example, $C(2, 5) \rightarrow C'(3, 9)$ describes a translation of point C 1 unit right and 4 units up in a coordinate grid. The rule for this translation would be $(x, y) \rightarrow (x + 1, y + 4)$.

More Math Background: p. 104D

Lesson Planning and Resources

See p. 104E for a list of the resources that support this lesson.

PowerPoint

Bell Ringer Practice

Check Skills You'll Need
Use student page, transparency, or PowerPoint. For intervention, direct students to:
Graphing in the Coordinate Plane
Lesson 3-4
Extra Skills and Word Problems Practice, Ch. 3

3-6 Translations

Check Skills You'll Need

1. **Vocabulary Review** In what *quadrant* is (−3, 5) located?
Quadrant II

Name the coordinates of each point.

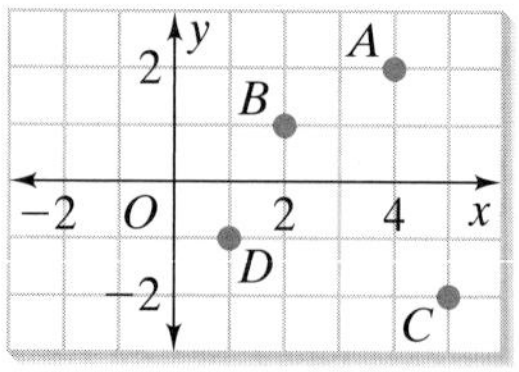

2. A (4, 2) 3. B (2, 1)
4. C (5, −2) 5. D (1, −1)

GO for Help Lesson 3-4

What You'll Learn

To graph and describe translations in the coordinate plane

New Vocabulary transformation, translation, image

Why Learn This?

Translations are used in games and in the arts. You can use translations to plan a winning chess strategy or choreograph a figure-skating routine.

A **transformation** is a change in the position, shape, or size of a figure. A **translation** is a transformation that moves each point of a figure the same distance and in the same direction.

The figure you get after a transformation is an **image** of the original figure. To identify the image of point A, use prime notation (A'). You read A' as "A prime."

Vocabulary Tip
Each corner of a triangle is a *vertex*. The plural of vertex is *vertices*.

EXAMPLE Graphing a Translation

1 **Multiple Choice** If $\triangle PQR$ below is translated 6 units to the right and 3 units down, what are the coordinates of point P'?

Ⓐ $P'(-1, -2)$ Ⓑ $P'(-2, 1)$ Ⓒ $P'(-2, -1)$ Ⓓ $P'(1, -2)$

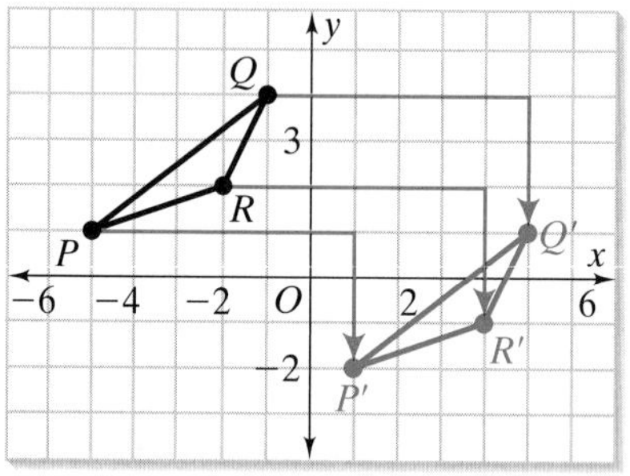

Slide each vertex right 6 units and down 3 units. Label and connect the images of the vertices.

The answer is D.

Quick Check

1. $\triangle JKL$ has vertices $J(0, 2)$, $K(3, 4)$, and $L(5, 1)$. Translate $\triangle JKL$ 4 units to the left and 5 units up. What are the coordinates of J'?
See back of book.

Differentiated Instruction Solutions for All Learners

Special Needs L1	Below Level L2
Students trace the "slide" of each vertex in Examples 1 and 2 with a finger. As they slide the finger to the right, have them say *6 units right,* and as they slide the finger down, have them say *3 units down.* learning style: tactile	Students draw horizontal and vertical arrows along the grids to show the translations. This will help them recognize both the direction and the distance of a translation. learning style: visual

You can use arrow notation to describe the translation in Example 1. The translation of each point is shown below.

$P(-5, 1) \rightarrow P'(1, -2)$ ← **Read $P \rightarrow P'$ as "point P goes to point P prime."**

$Q(-1, 4) \rightarrow Q'(5, 1)$

$R(-2, 2) \rightarrow R'(4, -1)$

The arrow notation for the translation of the image is $\triangle PQR \rightarrow \triangle P'Q'R'$.

You can use arrow notation to write a general rule that describes a translation. For example, $(x, y) \rightarrow (x - 1, y + 5)$ shows the ordered pair (x, y) and describes a translation to the left 1 unit and up 5 units.

EXAMPLE Describing a Translation

2 Write a rule to describe the translation of the black triangle to the blue triangle.

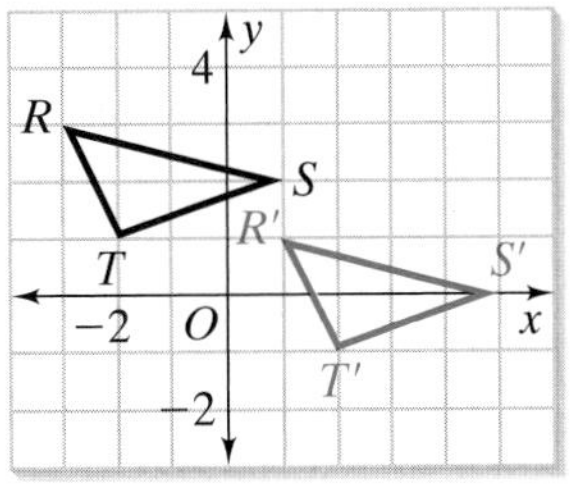

Each point has moved 4 units to the right and 2 units down. So the translation adds 4 to the x-coordinate and subtracts 2 from the y-coordinate.

The rule is $(x, y) \rightarrow (x + 4, y - 2)$.

Test Prep Tip

Draw arrows from each original point to its image to help you see the translation.

Quick Check

2. Write a rule that describes the translation shown on the graph at the right.
$(x, y) \rightarrow (x + 6, y + 2)$

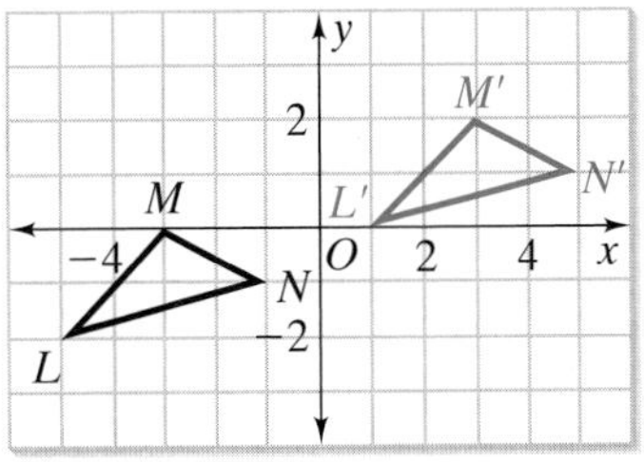

Check Your Understanding

1. **Vocabulary** A (transformation, image) is a change in the position, shape, or size of a figure. transformation
2. **Sports** The graph at the left shows an ice skater moving across the ice. How far and in what direction does the skater move?
6 units right

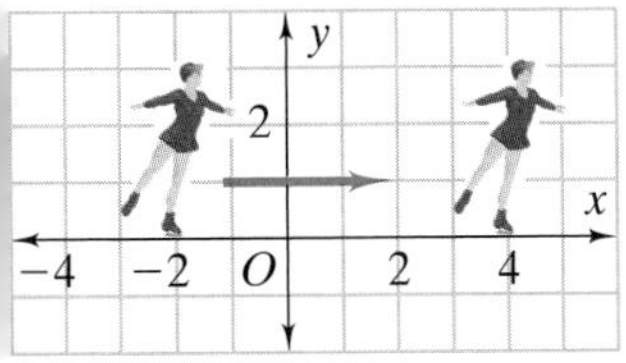

Graph each point and its image after the given translation. 3–6. See back of book.

3. $T(1, 3)$, left 2 units
4. $V(-4, 4)$, down 6 units
5. $S(4, 0)$, right 1 unit, down 3 units
6. $X(0, -2)$, right 7 units

2. Teach

Activity Lab

Use before the lesson.

All in One Teaching Resources

Activity Lab 3-6: Transformations I

Guided Instruction

Error Prevention!

Remind students a translation is measured as a combination of movements in the horizontal direction (the number of x-units moved) and the vertical direction (the number of y-units moved).

PowerPoint

Additional Examples

1 $\triangle ABC$ has vertices $A(1, -3)$, $B(3, 0)$, and $C(4, -2)$. Graph $\triangle ABC$ and its image after a translation to the left 3 units and up 2 units. What are the coordinates of its image?
See back of book.

2 Write a rule to describe the translation of $G(-5, 3)$ to $G'(-1, -2)$.
$(x, y) \rightarrow (x + 4, y - 5)$

All in One Teaching Resources

- Daily Notetaking Guide 3-6 L3
- Adapted Notetaking 3-6 L1

Closure

- *When a triangle is translated, what stays the same and what changes?* The shape and size stay the same but the coordinates of all the points of the triangle may change.
- *How can you find a general rule to describe a translation?* Find how many units a figure moves left or right and down or up. Add (right and up) or subtract (left and down) these amounts from the respective x- and y-coordinates.

Advanced Learners L4

Students use the same translation rule twice: once to a figure and a second time to its translated image. What image rule directly gives the second image? twice the first rule

learning style: verbal

English Language Learners ELL

Make a connection between translated images and translated words. Say: *When we translate words, we are saying the same thing, just in another language. When we translate an image, we have the same image, just in a different place on the grid.*

learning style: verbal

3. Practice

Assignment Guide

Check Your Understanding

Go over Exercises 1–6 in class before assigning the Homework Exercises.

Homework Exercises

A	Practice by Example	7–14
B	Apply Your Skills	15–21
C	Challenge	22
Test Prep and Mixed Review		23–26

Homework Quick Check

To check students' understanding of key skills and concepts, go over Exercises 10, 12, 16, 19, and 21.

Differentiated Instruction Resources

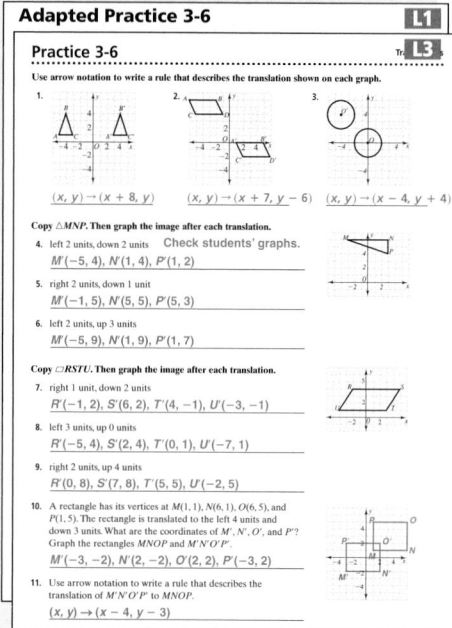

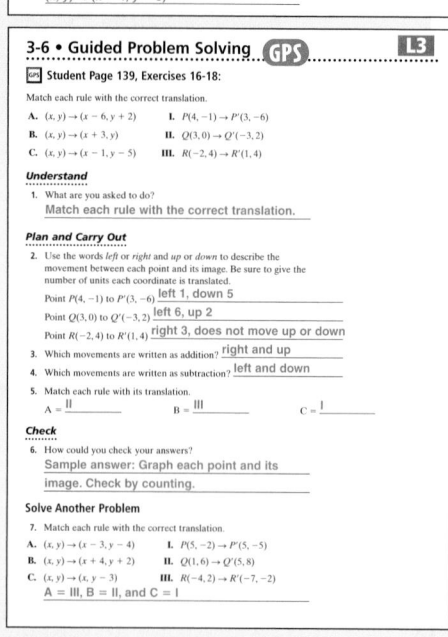

Adapted Practice 3-6 L1

Practice 3-6 L3

Use arrow notation to write a rule that describes the translation shown on each graph.

1. 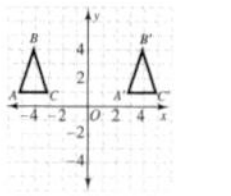
(x, y) → (x + 8, y)

2. 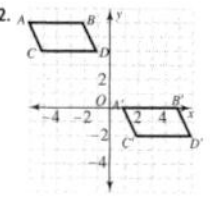
(x, y) → (x + 7, y − 6)

3. 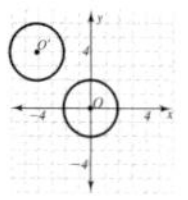
(x, y) → (x − 4, y + 4)

Copy △MNP. Then graph the image after each translation.

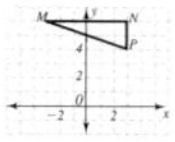

4. left 2 units, down 2 units Check students' graphs.
M′(−5, 4), N′(1, 4), P′(1, 2)
5. right 2 units, down 1 unit
M′(−1, 5), N′(5, 5), P′(5, 3)
6. left 2 units, up 3 units
M′(−5, 9), N′(1, 9), P′(1, 7)

Copy ▱RSTU. Then graph the image after each translation.

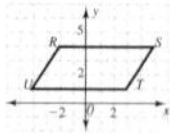

7. right 1 unit, down 2 units
R′(−1, 2), S′(6, 2), T′(4, −1), U′(−3, −1)
8. left 3 units, up 0 units
R′(−5, 4), S′(2, 4), T′(0, 1), U′(−7, 1)
9. right 2 units, up 4 units
R′(0, 8), S′(7, 8), T′(5, 5), U′(−2, 5)
10. A rectangle has its vertices at M(1, 1), N(6, 1), O(6, 5), and P(1, 5). The rectangle is translated to the left 4 units and down 3 units. What are the coordinates of M′, N′, O′, and P′? Graph the rectangles MNOP and M′N′O′P′.
M′(−3, −2), N′(2, −2), O′(2, 2), P′(−3, 2)

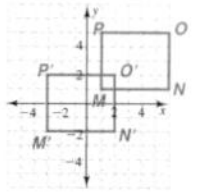

11. Use arrow notation to write a rule that describes the translation of M′N′O′P′ to MNOP.
(x, y) → (x − 4, y − 3)

3-6 • Guided Problem Solving GPS L3

Student Page 139, Exercises 16-18:

Match each rule with the correct translation.

A. (x, y) → (x − 6, y + 2) I. P(4, −1) → P′(3, −6)
B. (x, y) → (x + 3, y) II. Q(3, 0) → Q′(−3, 2)
C. (x, y) → (x − 1, y − 5) III. R(−2, 4) → R′(1, 4)

Understand

1. What are you asked to do?
Match each rule with the correct translation.

Plan and Carry Out

2. Use the words *left* or *right* and *up* or *down* to describe the movement between each point and its image. Be sure to give the number of units each coordinate is translated.
Point P(4, −1) to P′(3, −6) left 1, down 5
Point Q(3, 0) to Q′(−3, 2) left 6, up 2
Point R(−2, 4) to R′(1, 4) right 3, does not move up or down
3. Which movements are written as addition? right and up
4. Which movements are written as subtraction? left and down
5. Match each rule with its translation.
A = II B = III C = I

Check

6. How could you check your answers?
Sample answer: Graph each point and its image. Check by counting.

Solve Another Problem

7. Match each rule with the correct translation.
A. (x, y) → (x − 3, y − 4) I. P(5, −2) → P′(5, −5)
B. (x, y) → (x + 4, y + 2) II. Q(1, 6) → Q′(5, 8)
C. (x, y) → (x, y − 3) III. R(−4, 2) → R′(−7, −2)
A = III, B = II, and C = I

Homework Exercises

For more exercises, see Extra Skills and Word Problems.

GO for Help

For Exercises	See Examples
7–10	1
11–14	2

7. 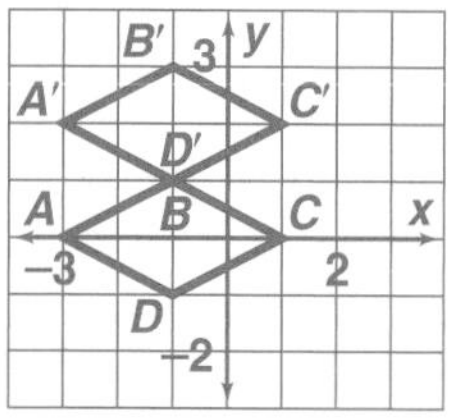

A **Copy each figure. Then graph the image after the given translation.** 8–10. See margin.

7. up 2 units See left.

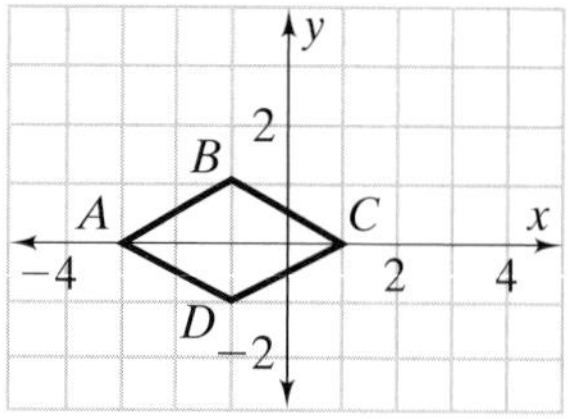

8. left 3 units, down 4 units

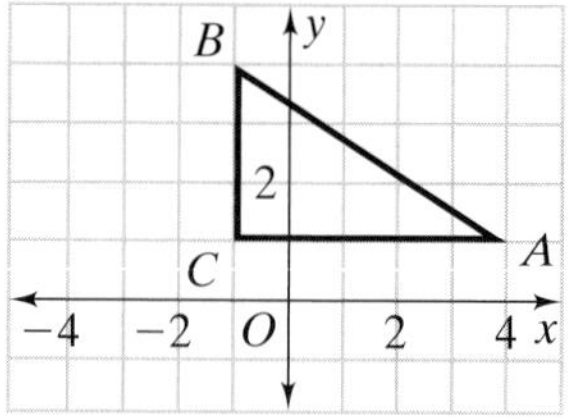

9. right 4 units, up 3 units

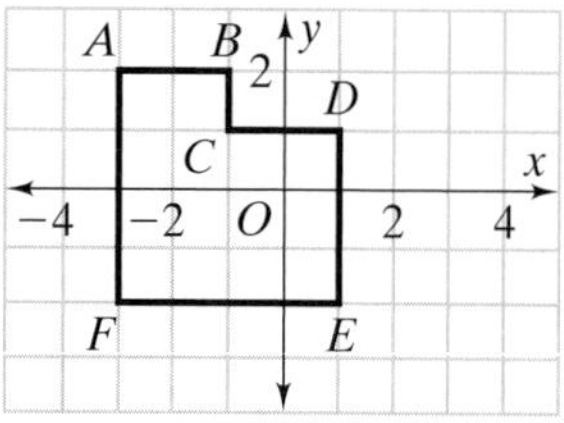

10. left 2 units, up 1 unit

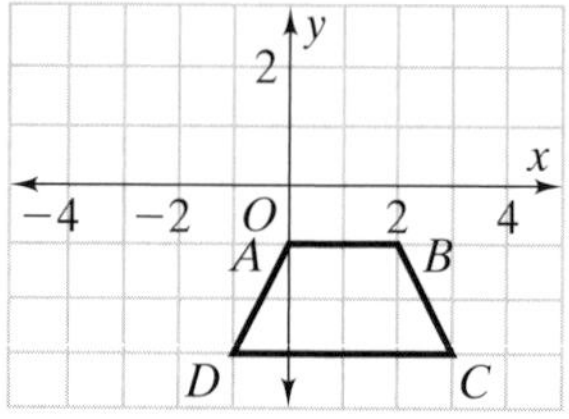

Write a rule that describes the translation shown on each graph.

11. 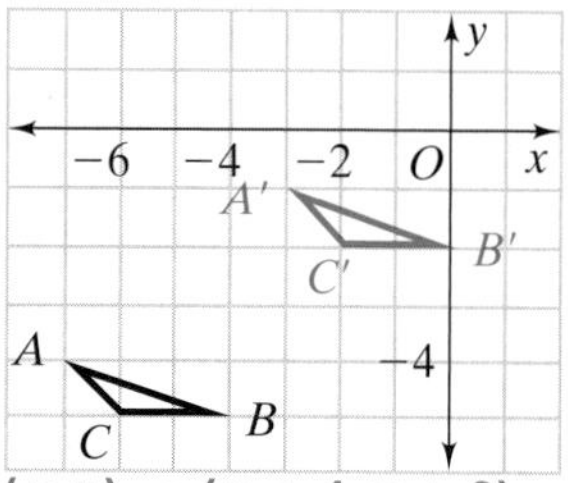
(x, y) → (x + 4, y + 3)

12. 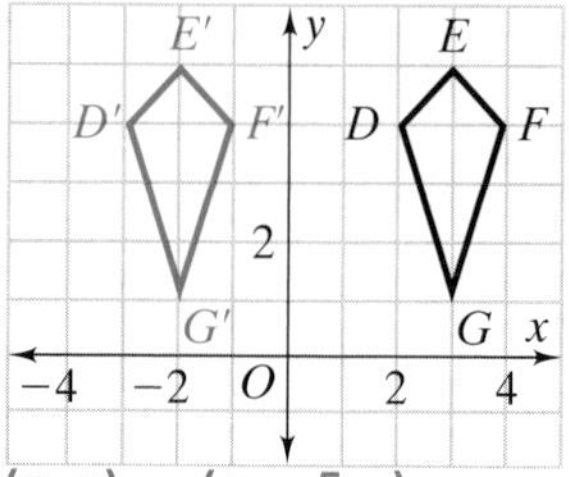
(x, y) → (x − 5, y)

13. 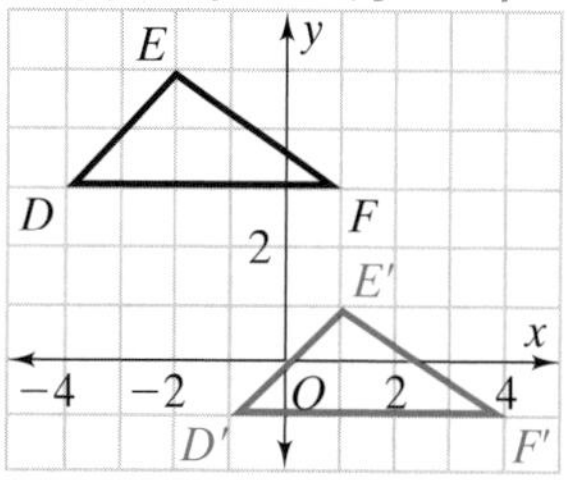
(x, y) → (x + 3, y − 4)

14. 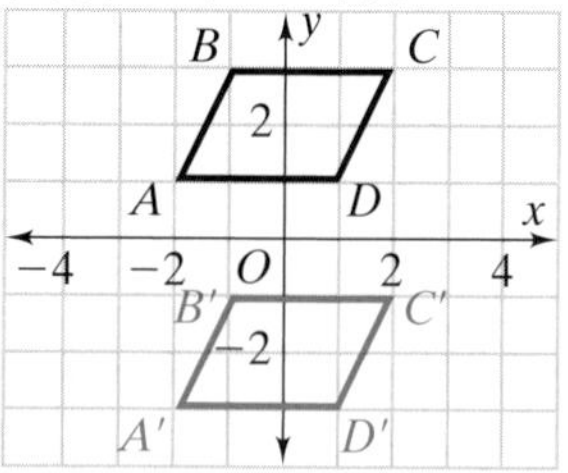
(x, y) → (x, y − 4)

B GPS 15. **Guided Problem Solving** Suppose the figure at the right is translated 6 units to the right and 5 units down. Without graphing, what are the coordinates of the image points? See left.

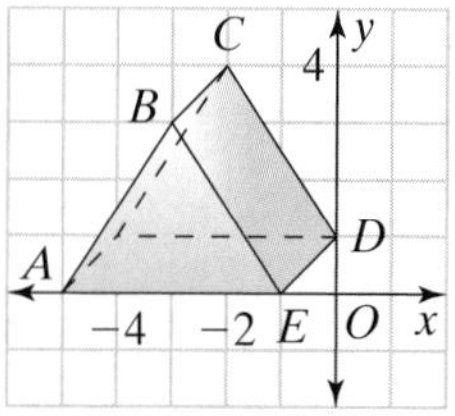

- What are the coordinates of the vertices?
- To translate to the right, do you add to or subtract from the x-coordinate?
- To translate down, do you add to or subtract from the y-coordinate?

15. A′(1, −5), B′(3, −2), C′(4, −1), D′(6, −4), E′(5, −5)

8. 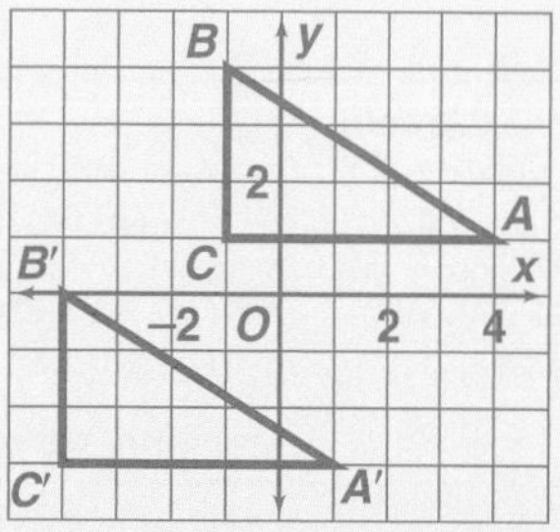

9. 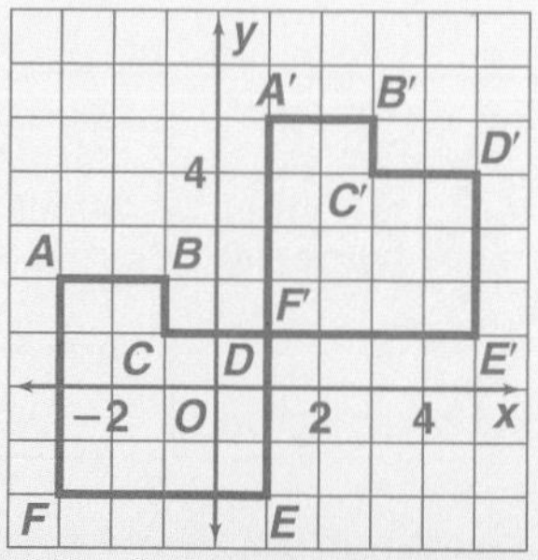

10. 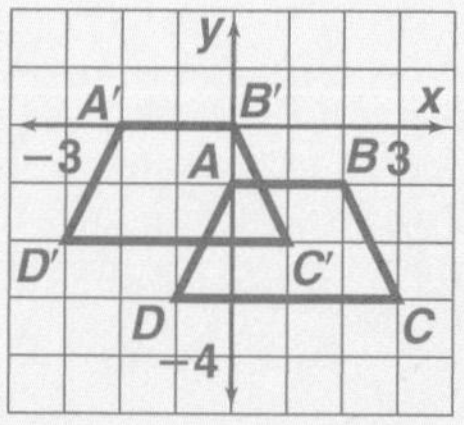

GO Online
Homework Video Tutor
Visit: PHSchool.com
Web Code: ase-0306

GPS Match each rule with the correct translation.

16. $(x, y) \rightarrow (x - 6, y + 2)$ B
17. $(x, y) \rightarrow (x + 3, y)$ C
18. $(x, y) \rightarrow (x - 1, y - 5)$ A

A. $P(4, -1) \rightarrow P'(3, -6)$
B. $Q(3, 0) \rightarrow Q'(-3, 2)$
C. $R(-2, 4) \rightarrow R'(1, 4)$

19. Answers may vary. Sample:

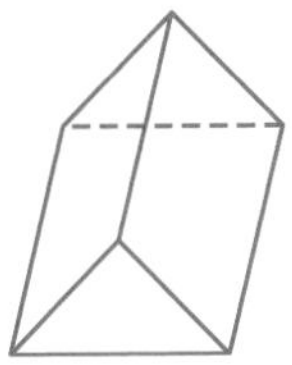

19. You can use translations to draw three-dimensional figures. Use the steps below to draw a three-dimensional figure starting with a triangle. See left.

Step 1	Step 2	Step 3	Step 4
Draw a figure on graph paper.	Translate the figure.	Connect each vertex with its image.	Use dashes for sides that are not visible.

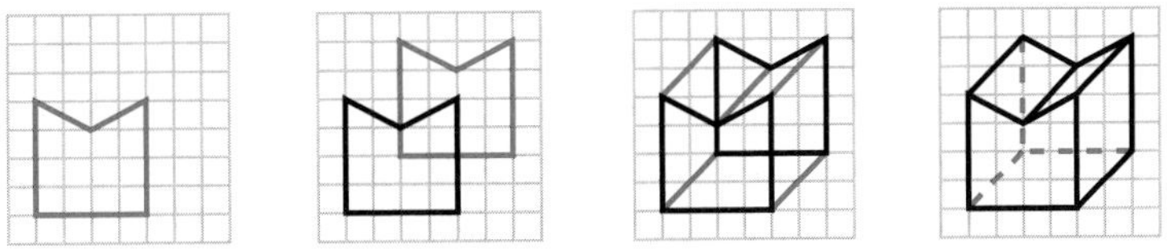

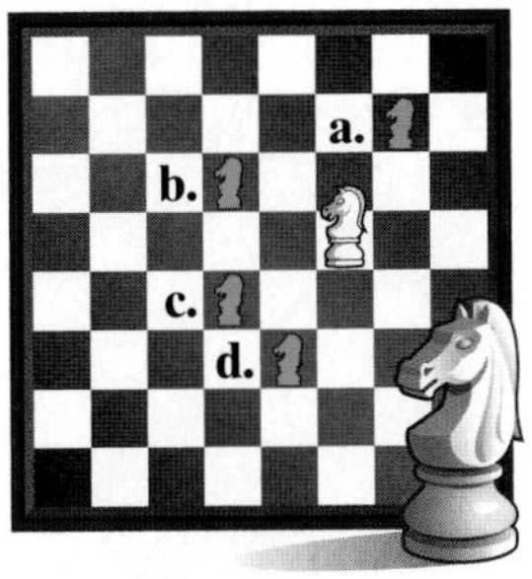

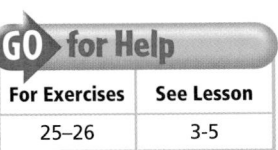

20. **Games** The chessboard at the left shows four possible moves for the white knight. Write a rule to describe each move as a translation, using the knight's original position as the origin. See margin.

21. **Writing in Math** Suppose you translate a point to the left 1 unit and up 3 units. Describe what you would do to the coordinates of the original point to find the coordinates of the image. Subtract 1 from the *x*-coordinate and add 3 to the *y*-coordinate.

C 22. **Challenge** Graph the equation $y = \frac{1}{2}x$. Translate the line right 2 units and up 4 units. See back of book.

Test Prep and Mixed Review

Practice

Multiple Choice

23. Point $A(2, 3)$ is translated 2 units to the right and 4 units down. What are the coordinates of point A'? D

   A (0, 0) B (0, −1) C (4, 0) D (4, −1)

24. Javier drew a right triangle on graph paper with legs of length 9 and 12. He then drew squares as shown. What was the area of the square opposite the right angle? J

   F 15 units^2 H 81 units^2
   G 144 units^2 J 225 units^2

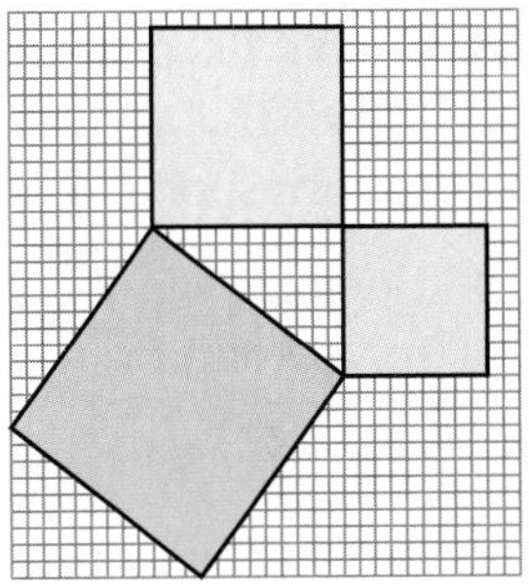

GO for Help

For Exercises	See Lesson
25–26	3-5

Graph each linear equation. 25–26. See back of book.

25. $y = \frac{1}{3}x$ 26. $y = -5x + 2$

Alternative Assessment

One student in a pair graphs a figure on the coordinate plane. The second student in the pair translates this figure to another location. The first student writes a rule that describes the translation. The second student writes a rule that describes the translation from the image back to the original figure. Partners compare the rules.

Test Prep

Resources
For additional practice with a variety of test item formats:
- Test-Taking Strategies, p. 151
- Test Prep, p. 155
- Test-Taking Strategies with Transparencies

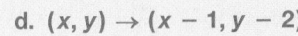

4. Assess & Reteach

PowerPoint

Lesson Quiz

1. Three points form a triangle: $P(0, 4)$, $Q(-1, 2)$, and $R(3, -3)$. What are the coordinates of its image after a translation left 4 units and down 3 units?
   $P'(-4, 1)$, $Q'(-5, -1)$, $R'(-1, -6)$
2. Write a rule to describe the translation of $K(-6, 4)$ to $K'(1, -8)$.
   $(x, y) \rightarrow (x + 7, y - 12)$
3. What are the coordinates of the image of $\triangle PQR$ (from question 1) after a translation right 3 units and up 1 unit?
   $P'(3, 5)$, $Q'(2, 3)$, $R'(6, -2)$
4. Write a rule to describe the translation in quiz question 1.
   $(x, y) \rightarrow (x - 4, y - 3)$

20a. $(x, y) \rightarrow (x + 1, y + 2)$
b. $(x, y) \rightarrow (x - 2, y + 1)$
c. $(x, y) \rightarrow (x - 2, y - 1)$
d. $(x, y) \rightarrow (x - 1, y - 2)$

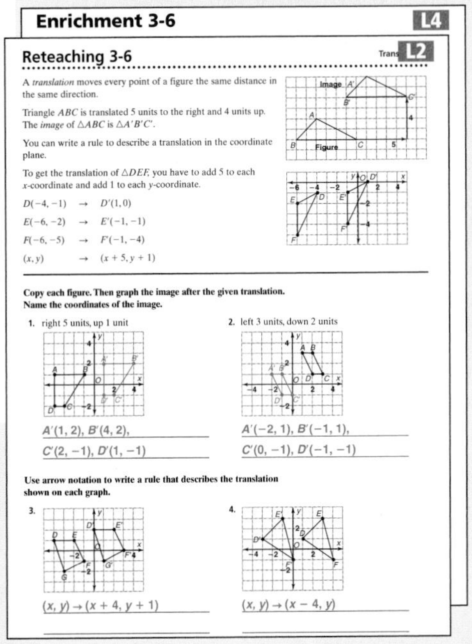
Enrichment 3-6 L4

Reteaching 3-6 Trans L2

A *translation* moves every point of a figure the same distance in the same direction.

Triangle ABC is translated 5 units to the right and 4 units up. The *image* of $\triangle ABC$ is $\triangle A'B'C'$.

You can write a rule to describe a translation in the coordinate plane.

To get the translation of $\triangle DEF$, you have to add 5 to each x-coordinate and add 1 to each y-coordinate.

$D(-4, -1) \rightarrow D'(1, 0)$
$E(-6, -2) \rightarrow E'(-1, -1)$
$F(-6, -5) \rightarrow F'(-1, -4)$
$(x, y) \rightarrow (x + 5, y + 1)$

Copy each figure. Then graph the image after the given translation. Name the coordinates of the image.

1. right 5 units, up 1 unit
   $A'(1, 2)$, $B'(4, 2)$, $C'(2, -1)$, $D'(1, -1)$
2. left 3 units, down 2 units
   $A'(-2, 1)$, $B'(-1, 1)$, $C'(0, -1)$, $D'(-1, -1)$

Use arrow notation to write a rule that describes the translation shown on each graph.

3. $(x, y) \rightarrow (x + 4, y + 1)$
4. $(x, y) \rightarrow (x - 4, y)$

Checkpoint Quiz

Use this Checkpoint Quiz to check students' understanding of the skills and concepts of Lessons 3-4 through 3-6.

Resources

- All in One Teaching Resources Checkpoint Quiz 1
- ExamView Assessment Suite CD-ROM
- Success Tracker Online Intervention

Activity Lab

Exploring Reflections

Reflections are sometimes difficult to visualize. Students use tracing paper to see what is actually happening when a figure is reflected. They then compare the image to the original figure.

Guided Instruction

Alternative Method
Students can also explore the idea of reflection by holding a small rectangular mirror upright along the line of reflection to see what the reflected image looks like.

Error Prevention!
Reflections may be difficult for some students to visualize. To help them see the change, make sure students label not only the sides (I and II), but also the points corresponding to $\triangle DEF$ and $\triangle D'E'F'$.

Resources

- Activity Lab 3-7: Reflections
- tracing paper

Checkpoint Quiz 2

Lessons 3-4 through 3-6

Graph each point on the same coordinate plane. 1–5. See margin.

1. $A(6, 1)$ **2.** $B(4, -3)$ **3.** $C(0, 2)$ **4.** $D(-5, -3)$ **5.** $E(-4, 2)$

6. Copy $\triangle JKL$ at the right. Graph the image after a translation to the left 3 units and up 4 units. What are the coordinates of J', K', and L'? 6–8. See back of book.

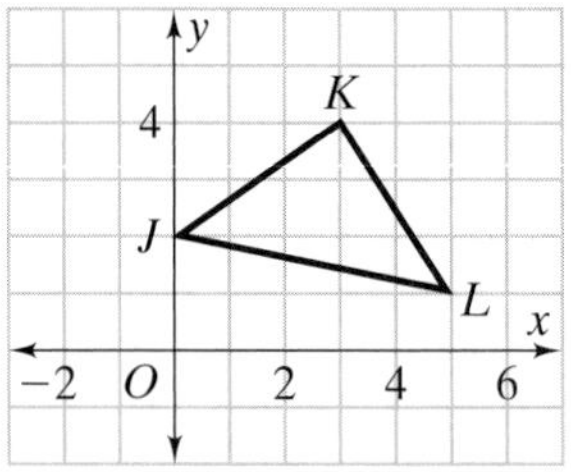

7. Write a rule to describe the translation in Exercise 6.

8. You do an exercise for 3 minutes. At the end of your workout, you stretch for 5 minutes. Make a table and write an equation to represent the total time spent for x exercises.

3-7a Activity Lab Hands On

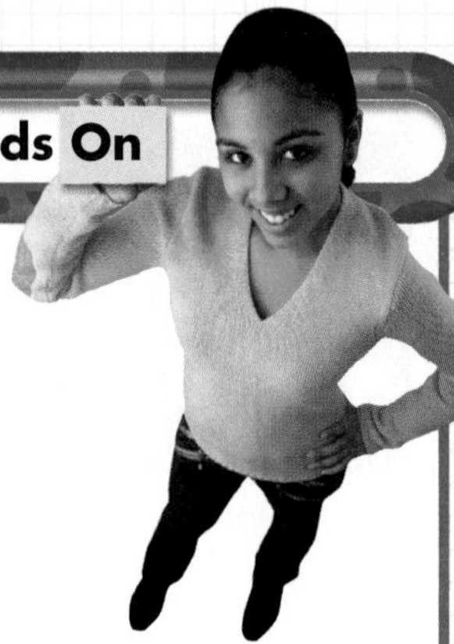

Exploring Reflections

1. Fold a piece of tracing paper in half. Unfold the paper. Label the halves I and II. Draw $\triangle DEF$ on half I.

2. Refold the paper. Trace the triangle on the back of half II.

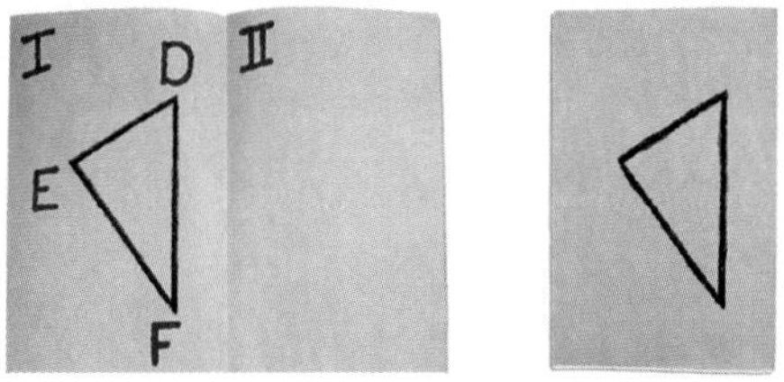

3. Unfold the paper and trace the second triangle onto the front of half II. Label the vertices of the last triangle D', E', and F' to correspond to the vertices of $\triangle DEF$.

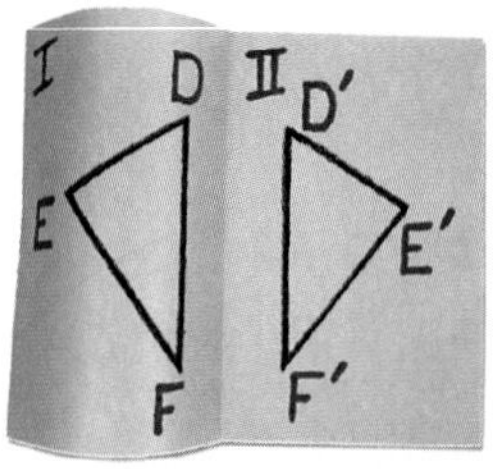

4. Compare the distances of D and D' from the fold. Do the same for the other vertices. What appears to be true?
D and D′ are the same distance from the fold; the same is true for the other vertices.

1–5.

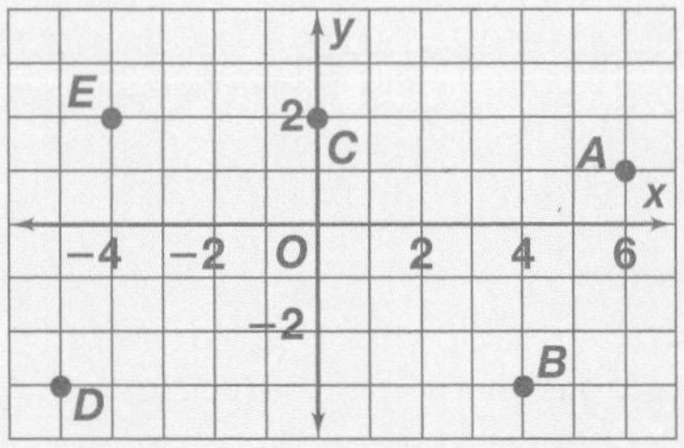

3-7 Reflections and Symmetry

What You'll Learn

To graph reflections in the coordinate plane and to identify lines of symmetry

New Vocabulary reflection, line of reflection, reflectional symmetry, line of symmetry

Why Learn This?

Reflections appear everywhere in the world around us. You can see reflections in a mirror or a pool of water, or in shapes in art and nature.

A **reflection** is a transformation that flips a figure over a line. This line is the **line of reflection.** Like translations, reflections change the position of a figure but not its size or shape.

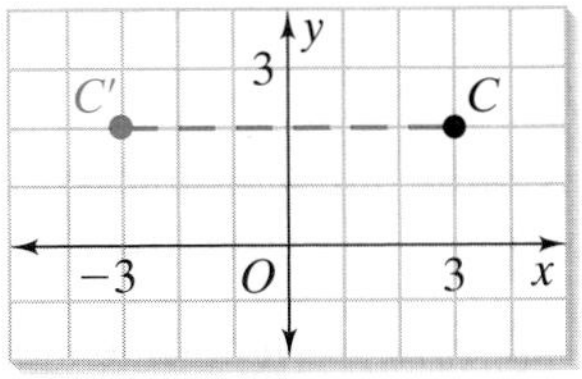

In the diagram at the left, C and C' are the same distance from the line of reflection, the y-axis.

EXAMPLE Graphing Reflections of a Point

1 Graph the point $A(3, 2)$. Then graph its image after it is reflected over the x-axis. Name the coordinates of A'.

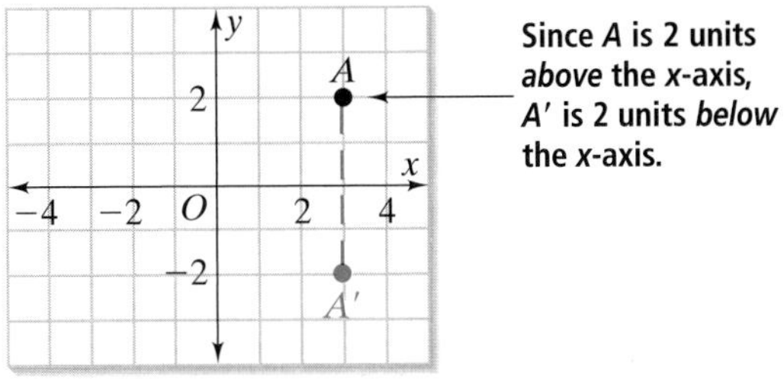

The coordinates of A' are $(3, -2)$.

Quick Check

1. Graph the point $D(-2, 1)$. Then graph its image after it is reflected over the y-axis. Name the coordinates of D'. See left.

Check Skills You'll Need

1. **Vocabulary Review** A *translation* moves each point in a figure the same ? in the same direction. distance

Graph the point $A(2, 4)$ and its image after the given translation. 2–5. See back of book.

2. left 2 units
3. up 4 units
4. down 1 unit, left 4 units
5. up 2 units, right 3 units

GO for Help Lesson 3-6

1.

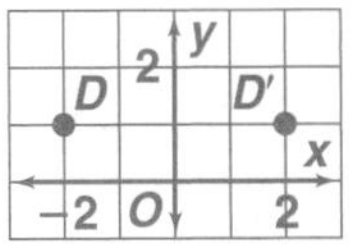

$D'(2, 1)$

3-7

1. Plan

Objective

To graph reflections in the coordinate plane and to identify lines of symmetry

Examples

1 Graphing Reflections of a Point
2 Graphing Reflections of a Shape
3 Identifying Lines of Symmetry

Math Understandings: p. 104D

Professional Development

Math Background

A reflection flips a figure over a line called the *line of reflection*. To reflect a figure, reflect each vertex in the figure and connect the image points. If a figure can be reflected over a line that passes through the figure and its image matches the original, the figure has *reflectional symmetry*. The line of reflection for reflectional symmetry is called the *line of symmetry*.

More Math Background: p. 104D

Lesson Planning and Resources

See p. 104E for a list of the resources that support this lesson.

PowerPoint

Bell Ringer Practice

Check Skills You'll Need
Use student page, transparency, or PowerPoint. For intervention, direct students to:
Translations
Lesson 3-6
Extra Skills and Word Problems Practice, Ch. 3

Differentiated Instruction Solutions for All Learners

Special Needs L1
Students draw the figures in this lesson on grid paper. They fold the paper along the lines of reflection—using the grid as a guide—and see how the image reflects. For Example 1, students fold the grid along the x-axis so they can see how the point A (3, 2) is reflected.
learning style: tactile

Below Level L2
Students reflect a letter such as S or B in a mirror. Elicit the fact that the image is reversed.
learning style: visual

2. Teach

Activity Lab

Use before the lesson.
Student Edition Activity Lab, Hands On 3-7a, Exploring Reflections, p. 140

All in One Teaching Resources

Activity Lab 3-7: Reflections

Guided Instruction

Teaching Tip
Point out, in Example 3, that reflecting one half of an object in a mirror reconstructs the image of the whole object. So the line of reflection is also a line of symmetry for the figure.

Additional Examples

1 Graph the point $H(-4, 5)$. Then graph its image after it is reflected over the *y*-axis. Name the coordinates of H'.
$H'(4, 5)$

2 $\triangle BCD$ has vertices $B(-3, 1), C(-2, 5)$, and $D(-5, 4)$. Graph $\triangle BCD$ and its image after a reflection over the *x*-axis. Name the coordinates of the vertices of $\triangle B'C'D'$.
See back of book.

3 Draw the lines of symmetry in the figure below.

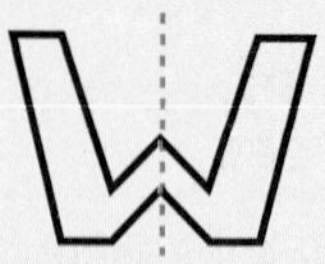

All in One Teaching Resources
- Daily Notetaking Guide 3-7 L3
- Adapted Notetaking 3-7 L1

Closure

- Explain how to graph the reflection of a triangle over a line. Find and graph the coordinates of the reflection of each vertex. Join them to form the image.

When you reflect a figure over a line, reflect the vertices first. Then connect the image points.

GO for Help
For help with graphing points, go to Lesson 3-4, Example 1.

EXAMPLE Graphing Reflections of a Shape

2 Graph $\triangle BCD$ and its image after it is reflected over the line through $(1, 3)$ and $(1, 0)$. Name the coordinates of the vertices of $\triangle B'C'D'$.

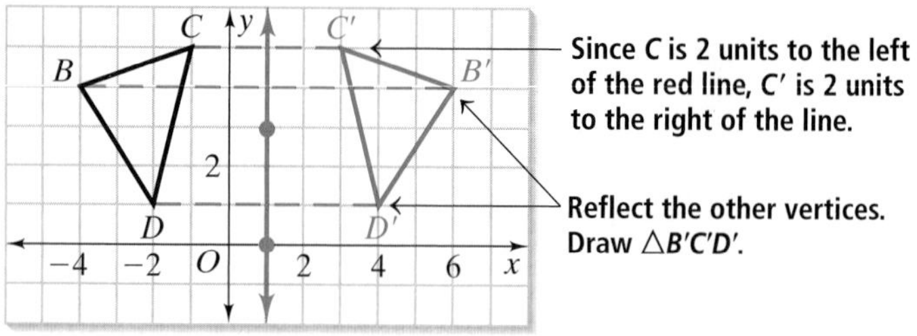

The coordinates of the vertices are $B'(6, 4)$, $C'(3, 5)$, and $D'(4, 1)$.

Quick Check

2. $\triangle EFG$ has vertices $E(4, 3)$, $F(3, 1)$, and $G(1, 2)$. Graph $\triangle EFG$ and its image after it is reflected over the *x*-axis. Name the coordinates of the vertices of $\triangle E'F'G'$. See back of book.

If a figure can be reflected over a line so its image matches the original figure, the figure has **reflectional symmetry.** The line that divides the figure into mirror images is called a **line of symmetry.**

Many shapes in nature have reflectional symmetry. In the leaf at the left, the black line approximates a line of symmetry.

EXAMPLE Identifying Lines of Symmetry

3 Draw the lines of symmetry for the snowflake below.

There are six ways to fold the figure so both halves match. The figure has six lines of symmetry.

Quick Check

3. Copy the flag at the right. Draw the lines of symmetry. See back of book.

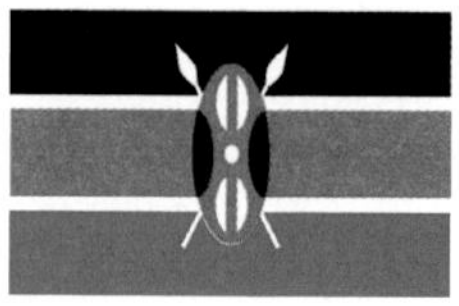

Differentiated Instruction Solutions for All Learners

Advanced Learners L4	English Language Learners ELL
Students draw figures that have 0, 1, 2, 3, 4, and 5 lines of symmetry. Label them for display in the classroom. learning style: visual	In the *Vocabulary* question for Check Your Understanding, pairs of students write and refine an explanation of how to decide whether a line is a line of symmetry. Partners read their explanation to the class so students can suggest clarifications. learning style: verbal

Check Your Understanding

1. Line *a* is a line of symmetry if one half of the figure matches the other half exactly when the figure is reflected over line *a*.

1. **Vocabulary** Line *a* divides a figure into two halves. How can you tell whether *a* is a line of symmetry?

Use the graph at the right. Match each point with its image after a reflection over the given axis.

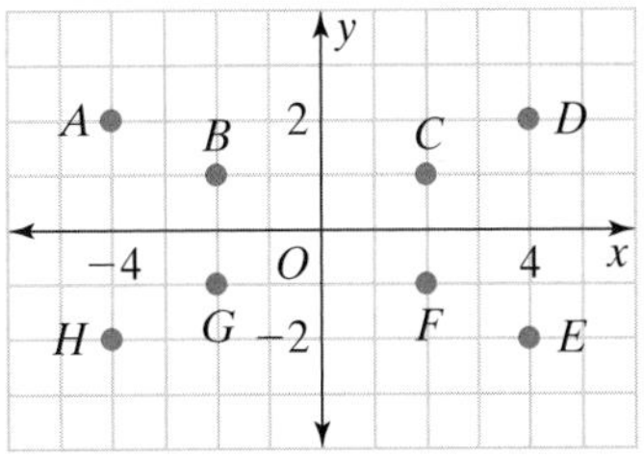

2. *A*, *y*-axis **D**
3. *B*, *x*-axis **G**
4. *H*, *y*-axis **E**
5. *F*, *y*-axis **G**
6. *E*, *x*-axis **D**
7. *C*, *x*-axis **F**

Homework Exercises

For more exercises, see Extra Skills and Word Problems.

GO for Help

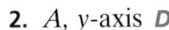

For Exercises	See Examples
8–13	1
14–16	2
17–19	3

A **Graph the given point and its image after each reflection over the given axis. Name the coordinates of the reflected point.** 8–13. See back of book.

8. $H(-3, 2)$, *x*-axis
9. $G(2, 4)$, *y*-axis
10. $B(-3, -4)$, *y*-axis
11. $D(0, -2)$, *x*-axis
12. $C(4, -3)$, *x*-axis
13. $M(5, 0)$, *y*-axis

$\triangle MPS$ has vertices $M(4, 5)$, $P(1, 2)$, and $S(5, 1)$. Graph $\triangle MPS$ and its image after a reflection over each line. Name the new coordinates. 14–16. See back of book.

14. *x*-axis
15. *y*-axis
16. line through $(1, -2)$ and $(4, -2)$

Copy each figure that has reflectional symmetry. Draw the lines of symmetry. Write *no reflectional symmetry* where applicable. 17–19. See margin.

17.
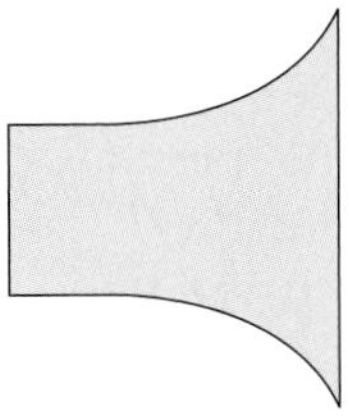

18.
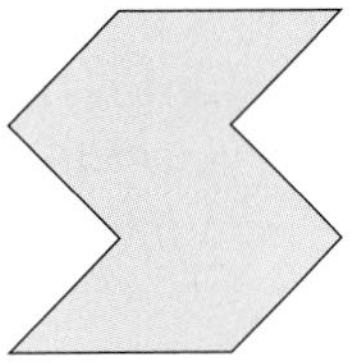

19.
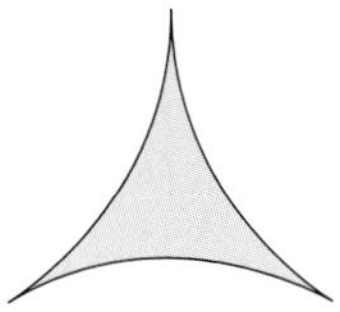

B **GPS** 20. **Guided Problem Solving** Does the flag at the right have reflectional symmetry? If so, state how many lines of symmetry it has. Yes; 1 line

- **Understand the Problem** Find whether you can fold the figure so both halves match.
- **Make a Plan** Copy the figure and try folding it in different ways.

21. The word **COB** has reflectional symmetry. Which capital letters in the alphabet have reflectional symmetry? A, B, C, D, E, H, I, K, M, O, T, U, V, W, X, Y

17.
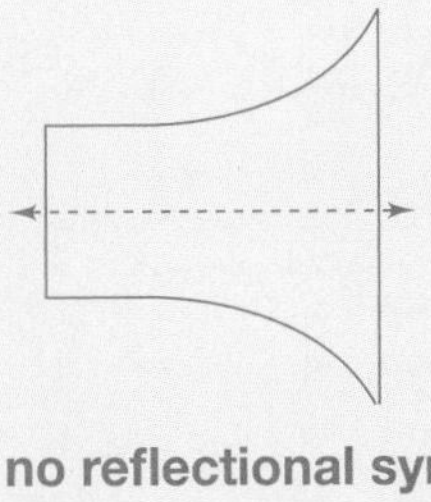

19.
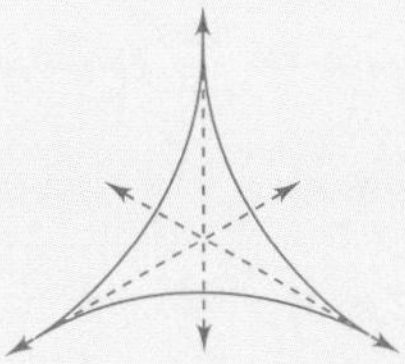

18. no reflectional symmetry

3. Practice

Assignment Guide

Check Your Understanding

Go over Exercises 1–7 in class before assigning the Homework Exercises.

Homework Exercises

A Practice by Example	8–19
B Apply Your Skills	20–27
C Challenge	28
Test Prep and Mixed Review	29–34

Homework Quick Check

To check students' understanding of key skills and concepts, go over Exercises 15, 19, 20, 22, and 27.

Differentiated Instruction Resources

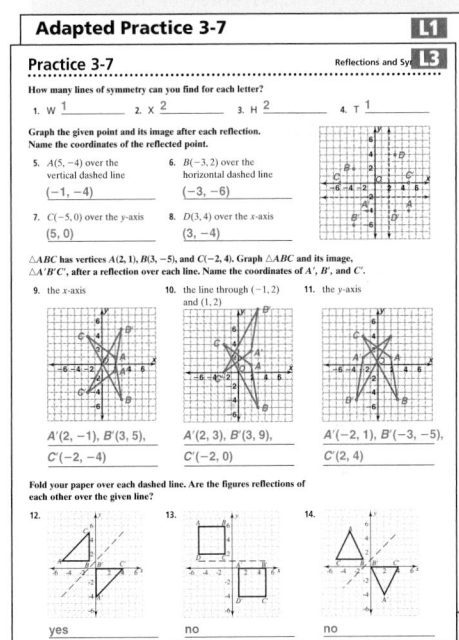

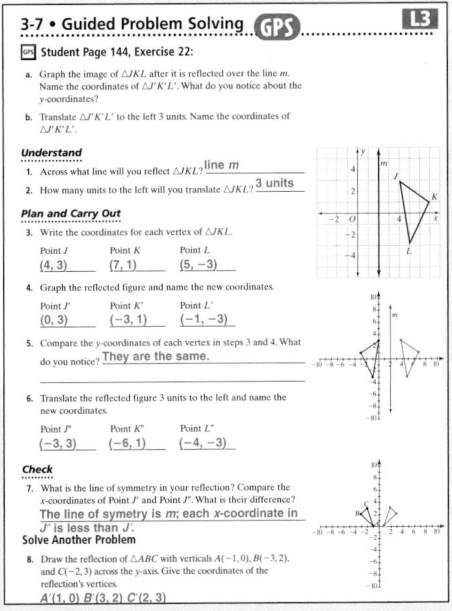

Adapted Practice 3-7 L1

Practice 3-7 Reflections and Sy… L3

How many lines of symmetry can you find for each letter?

1. W 1
2. X 2
3. H 2
4. T 1

Graph the given point and its image after each reflection. Name the coordinates of the reflected point.

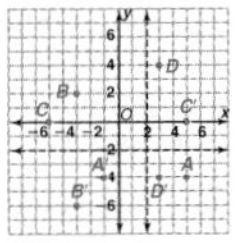

5. $A(5, -4)$ over the vertical dashed line $(-1, -4)$
6. $B(-3, 2)$ over the horizontal dashed line $(-3, -6)$
7. $C(-5, 0)$ over the *y*-axis $(5, 0)$
8. $D(3, 4)$ over the *x*-axis $(3, -4)$

$\triangle ABC$ has vertices $A(2, 1)$, $B(3, -5)$, and $C(-2, 4)$. Graph $\triangle ABC$ and its image, $\triangle A'B'C'$, after a reflection over each line. Name the coordinates of A', B', and C'.

9. the *x*-axis
10. the line through $(-1, 2)$ and $(1, 2)$
11. the *y*-axis

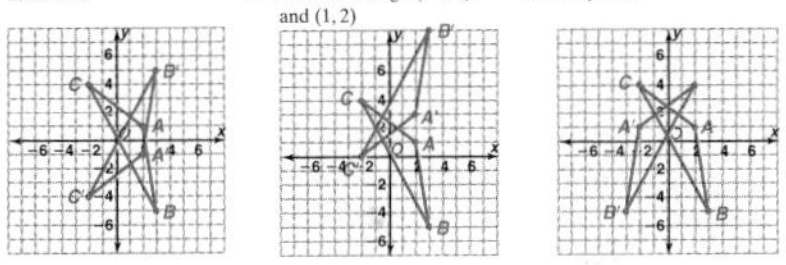

9. $A'(2, -1)$, $B'(3, 5)$, $C'(-2, -4)$
10. $A'(2, 3)$, $B'(3, 9)$, $C'(-2, 0)$
11. $A'(-2, 1)$, $B'(-3, -5)$, $C'(2, 4)$

Fold your paper over each dashed line. Are the figures reflections of each other over the given line?

12. 13. 14.

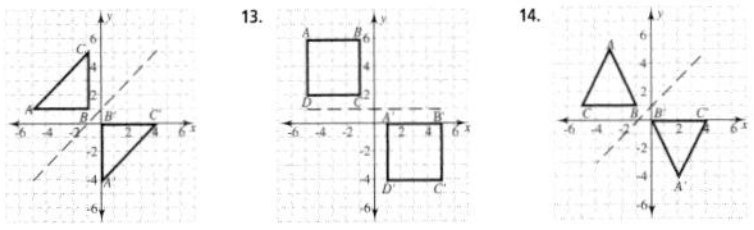

12. yes
13. no
14. no

3-7 • Guided Problem Solving GPS L3

Student Page 144, Exercise 22:

a. Graph the image of $\triangle JKL$ after it is reflected over the line *m*. Name the coordinates of $\triangle J'K'L'$. What do you notice about the *y*-coordinates?

b. Translate $\triangle J'K'L'$ to the left 3 units. Name the coordinates of $\triangle J'K'L'$.

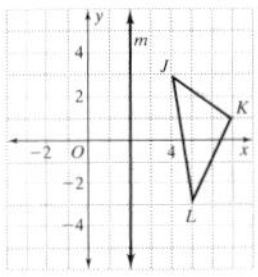

Understand

1. Across what line will you reflect $\triangle JKL$? line *m*
2. How many units to the left will you translate $\triangle JKL$? 3 units

Plan and Carry Out

3. Write the coordinates for each vertex of $\triangle JKL$.

Point *J* (4, 3) Point *K* (7, 1) Point *L* (5, −3)

4. Graph the reflected figure and name the new coordinates.

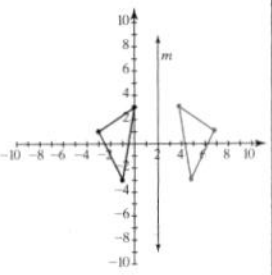

Point J' (0, 3) Point K' (−3, 1) Point L' (−1, −3)

5. Compare the *y*-coordinates of each vertex in steps 3 and 4. What do you notice? They are the same.

6. Translate the reflected figure 3 units to the left and name the new coordinates.

Point J'' (−3, 3) Point K'' (−6, 1) Point L'' (−4, −3)

Check

7. What is the line of symmetry in your reflection? Compare the *x*-coordinates of Point J' and Point J''. What is their difference? The line of symetry is *m*; each *x*-coordinate in J'' is less than J'.

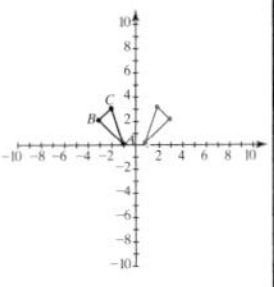

Solve Another Problem

8. Draw the reflection of $\triangle ABC$ with verticals $A(-1, 0)$, $B(-3, 2)$, and $C(-2, 3)$ across the *y*-axis. Give the coordinates of the reflection's vertices. $A'(1, 0)$ $B'(3, 2)$ $C'(2, 3)$

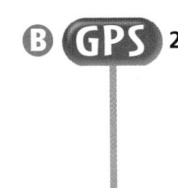

4. Assess & Reteach

PowerPoint

Lesson Quiz

1. $\triangle VQM$ has vertices $V(-3, 1)$, $Q(0, 0)$, and $M(4, 4)$. Name the coordinates of the vertices of $\triangle V'Q'M'$ after a reflection over the x-axis.
   $(-3, -1)$, $(0, 0)$, $(4, -4)$
2. List all capital letters of the alphabet that have two or more lines of symmetry.
   H, I, O, X
3. Name the coordinates of point $S(-5, 2)$ after a reflection about the line that passes through $(-1, 4)$ and $(-1, 0)$.
   $(3, 2)$
4. How many lines of symmetry does a regular hexagon have?
   6

Alternative Assessment

Students draw a triangle or rectangle on a paper. Then they fold the paper and draw the reflection of the figure over the line created by the fold.

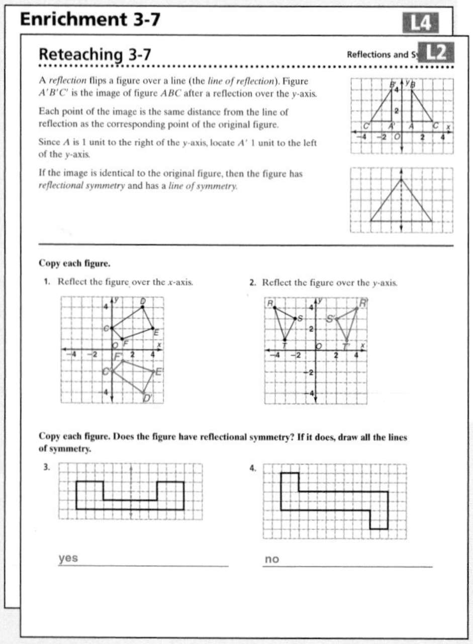
Enrichment 3-7 L4

Reteaching 3-7 Reflections and Sy L2

A *reflection* flips a figure over a line (the *line of reflection*). Figure $A'B'C'$ is the image of figure ABC after a reflection over the y-axis.

Each point of the image is the same distance from the line of reflection as the corresponding point of the original figure.

Since A is 1 unit to the right of the y-axis, locate A' 1 unit to the left of the y-axis.

If the image is identical to the original figure, then the figure has *reflectional symmetry* and has a *line of symmetry*.

Copy each figure.

1. Reflect the figure over the x-axis.
2. Reflect the figure over the y-axis.

Copy each figure. Does the figure have reflectional symmetry? If it does, draw all the lines of symmetry.

3. yes
4. no

GO Online
Homework Video Tutor
Visit: PHSchool.com
Web Code: ase-0307

22. a. Graph the image of $\triangle JKL$ after it is reflected over the red line. Name the coordinates of $\triangle J'K'L'$. What do you notice about the y-coordinates?
    b. Translate $\triangle J'K'L'$ to the left 3 units. Name the coordinates of $\triangle J''K''L''$.
    22a. See back of book.
    b. $J''(-3, 3)$, $K''(-6, 1)$, $L''(-4, -3)$

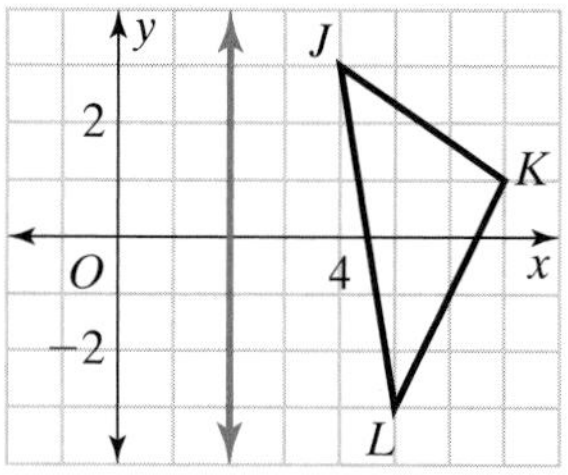

Figure *EFGH* has vertices $E(2, 5)$, $F(4, 5)$, $G(6, 1)$, and $H(3, 1)$. Graph figure *EFGH* and its image after a reflection over each line. Name the coordinates of the vertices of the reflected figure. 23–25. See back of book.

23. y-axis
24. x-axis
25. line through $(0, 2)$ and $(-3, 2)$

26.
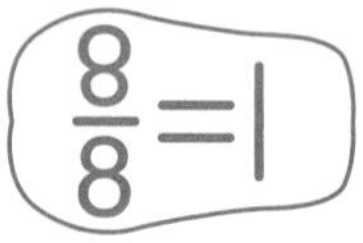

26. **Art** The figure at the right is folded along a red line of symmetry. Copy the figure and sketch the unfolded figure. See left.

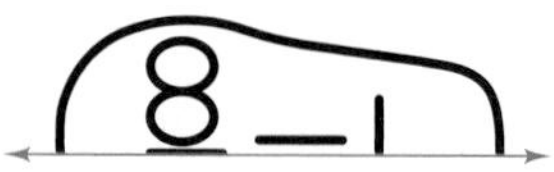

27. **Writing in Math** How many lines of symmetry does a circle have? Explain your answer. An infinite number; any line passing through the center of a circle is a line of symmetry.
28. **Challenge** When connected in order, the points $(-3, -3)$, $(-4, -1)$, $(-1, 2)$, $(2, 5)$, and $(4, 4)$ form half of a figure. The line of symmetry of the complete figure is $y = x$. Draw the complete figure. See back of book.

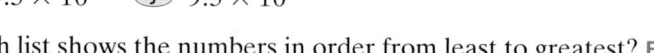

Test Prep and Mixed Review

Practice

Multiple Choice

29. If $\triangle ABC$ is reflected over the x-axis, what are the coordinates of C'? B
    A $(2, -4)$ C $(-2, 4)$
    B $(4, -2)$ D $(-4, 2)$

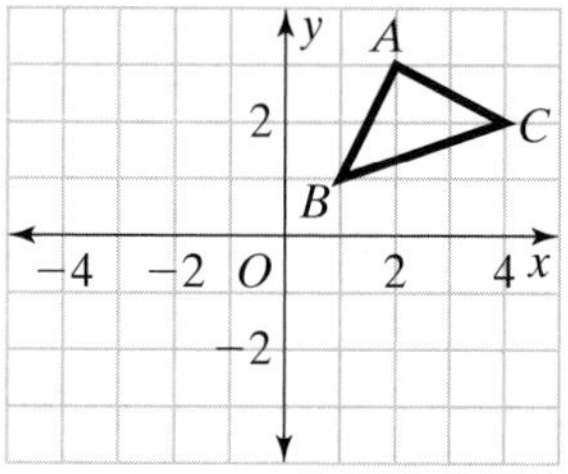

30. Earth is about 93,000,000 miles from the sun. Which expression represents this number in scientific notation? J
    F 9.3×10^{-7} H 9.3×10^{6}
    G 9.3×10^{-6} J 9.3×10^{7}
31. Which list shows the numbers in order from least to greatest? B
    A $\sqrt{5}$, 2.4, $\frac{7}{3}$, $\sqrt{2}$
    C $\sqrt{5}$, $\frac{7}{3}$, 2.4, $\sqrt{2}$
    B $\sqrt{2}$, $\sqrt{5}$, $\frac{7}{3}$, 2.4
    D $\sqrt{2}$, 2.4, $\sqrt{5}$, $\frac{7}{3}$

GO for Help

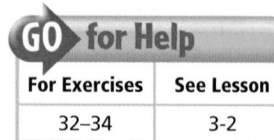

For Exercises	See Lesson
32–34	3-2

Given the lengths of two legs of a right triangle, find the length of the hypotenuse.

32. $a = 6$, $b = 8$ 10
33. $a = 5$, $b = 12$ 13
34. $a = 7$, $b = 24$ 25

Test Prep

Resources
For additional practice with a variety of test item formats:
- Test-Taking Strategies, p. 151
- Test Prep, p. 155
- Test-Taking Strategies with Transparencies

Exploring Rotations

ACTIVITY

Begin with a square piece of paper that has 4-inch sides.

Step 1 Place the piece of paper over the figure below. Trace everything in black: the center point, the kite, and the vertices of $\triangle ABC$.

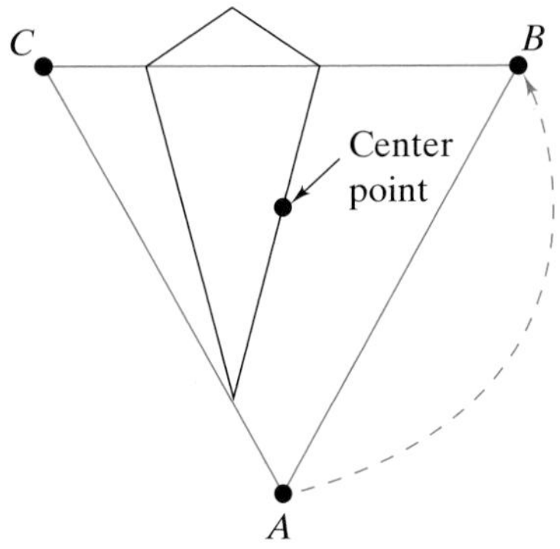

Step 2 Place the point of your pencil on the center point. Rotate the paper until vertex A overlaps vertex B. Trace the kite in its new location.

Step 3 Repeat Step 2, but this time, rotate the paper until vertex A overlaps vertex C.

3.

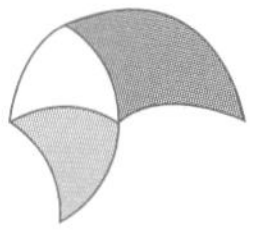

Exercises

1. The *angle of rotation* is the number of degrees a figure rotates. What is the angle of rotation of the kite in Step 2? 120°
2. Make a new design using a square rather than $\triangle ABC$. What angle do you rotate the figure for each vertex of the square? Check students' work; the angle of rotation is 90°.

The diagram at the right was made by rotating and copying a figure.

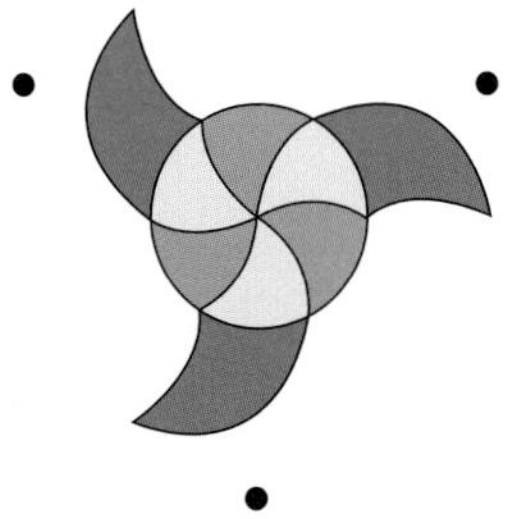

3. Make a sketch of the original figure. See right.
4. **Reasoning** Describe how to make the completed figure using the steps in the activity above. Rotate the original figure 120° about the center point.

Activity Lab

Exploring Rotations

Students analyze and make designs by rotating figures, using the center point and a central triangle for reference. They also find angles of rotation and notice patterns among the angles in figures that have rotational symmetry.

Guided Instruction

Before beginning the activity, review geometry facts on circles. Ask questions such as:

- *How many degrees are there in a circle?* 360
- *Into how many equal arcs do points A, B, and C divide the circle?* 3
- *As you rotate from A to B (counterclockwise), how many degrees are you turning?* 120

Activity

The angle of rotation is measured from an imaginary line of reference. For Exercise 1, have students draw a vertical dotted line from the center point through vertex *A*, from which they will measure the angle. If they do not recognize angles, have students use protractors.

Error Prevention!

Remind students that figures rotate about a center point. Remind them to note their starting and ending locations carefully, and to place their pencil on the center point as they rotate figures.

Resources

- white or tracing paper
- scissors
- protractors

3-8

1. Plan

Objective
To graph rotations and identify rotational symmetry.

Examples
1 Rotational Symmetry
2 Graphing Rotations

Professional Development

Math Background

A rotation is a transformation that turns a figure about a fixed point. As a reflection must specify a line of reflection, a rotation must specify a fixed point that is the *center of rotation.*

The *angle of rotation* is the number of degrees the figure rotates. In this text, rotations are assumed to be counterclockwise. A complete rotation is 360°. A figure has *rotational symmetry* if it can be rotated 180° or less and exactly match its original figure. Figures can have both rotational symmetry and reflectional symmetry.

More Math Background: p. 104D

Lesson Planning and Resources

See p. 104E for a list of the resources that support this lesson.

PowerPoint

Bell Ringer Practice

Check Skills You'll Need
Use student page, transparency, or PowerPoint. For intervention, direct students to:
Classifying Angles
Skills Handbook, p. 640

3-8 Rotations

Check Skills You'll Need

1. **Vocabulary Review** When a figure has *reflectional symmetry,* one half _?_ the other half exactly. matches

Classify each angle as *acute, right, obtuse,* or *straight.*

2. 180° straight
3. 150° obtuse
4. 95° obtuse
5. 20° acute
6. 35° acute
7. 90° right

GO for Help Skills Handbook, p. 640

What You'll Learn

To graph rotations and to identify rotational symmetry

New Vocabulary rotation, center of rotation, angle of rotation, rotational symmetry

Why Learn This?

When you learn to recognize rotational symmetry, you can see it in everything from art and nature to architecture and science.

A **rotation** is a transformation that turns a figure about a fixed point called the **center of rotation.** A figure has **rotational symmetry** if it can be rotated 180° or less and exactly matches its original figure.

Rotations change the position of a figure but not its size or shape. The **angle of rotation** is the number of degrees the figure rotates. A complete rotation is 360°.

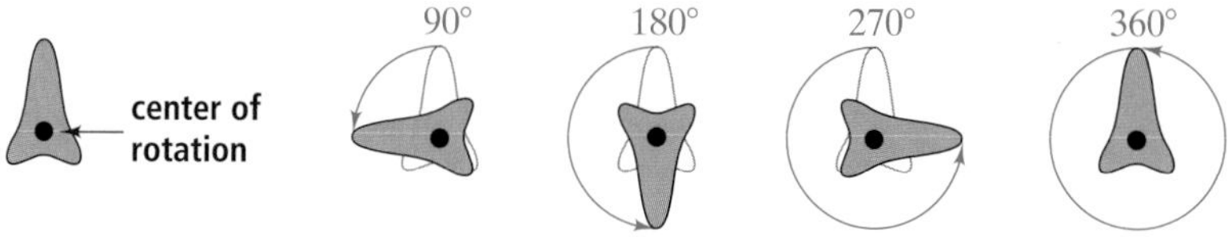

EXAMPLE Rotational Symmetry

1 **Nature** Find the angle of rotation of the figure.

The image matches the original after $\frac{1}{5}$ of a complete rotation.

$\frac{1}{5} \cdot 360° = 72°$

The angle of rotation is 72°.

Quick Check

1. If the figure at the right has rotational symmetry, find the angle of rotation. If it does not, write *no rotational symmetry.* 72°

Differentiated Instruction Solutions for All Learners

Special Needs L1	Below Level L2
Students work on the examples in pairs. Match students who have difficulty holding a pencil down with those who can do so more easily. The first student can rotate the figure while the other holds the pencil and verifies any rotational symmetry. **learning style: tactile**	Students use protractors to review measuring angles in degrees. Students draw and label angles on the coordinate plane, and represent counterclockwise by following the direction with their fingers. **learning style: tactile**

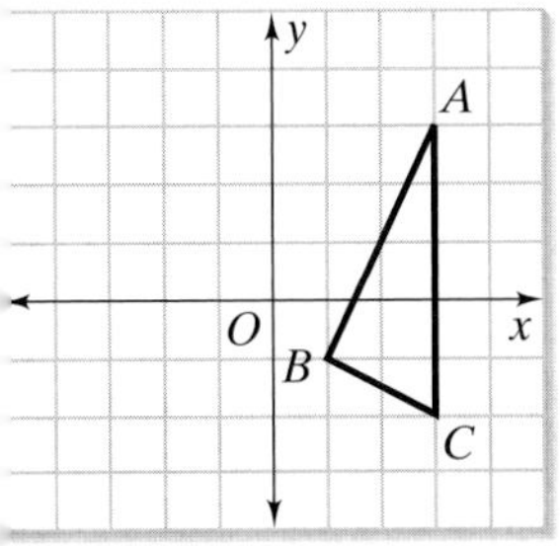

You can use the coordinate plane to graph rotations. In this book, all rotations are counterclockwise.

EXAMPLE Graphing Rotations

2 Draw the image of $\triangle ABC$ after a rotation of 90° about the origin.

Step 1 Draw and trace.

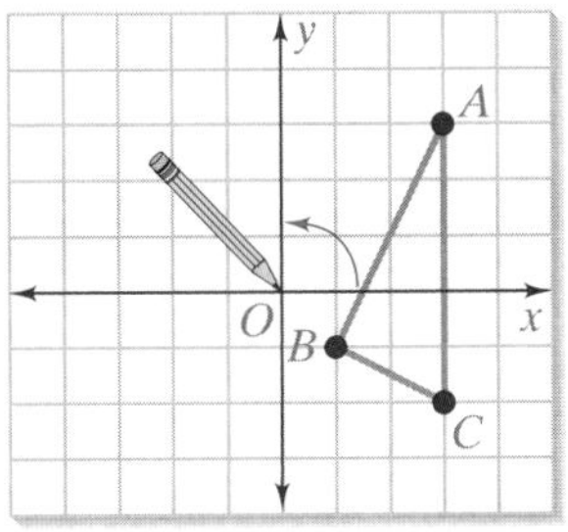

- Draw $\triangle ABC$ on a piece of graph paper. Place a piece of tracing paper over your graph.
- Trace the vertices of the triangle, the x-axis, and the y-axis, as shown in blue.
- Place your pencil at the origin to rotate the paper.

Step 2 Rotate and mark each vertex.

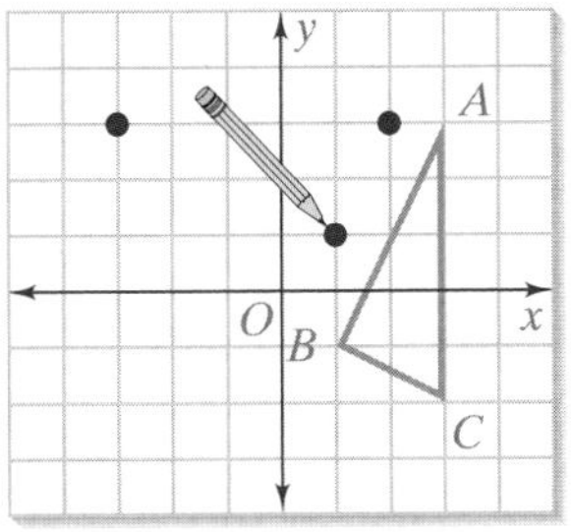

- Rotate the tracing paper 90° counterclockwise. The axes should line up.
- Mark the position of each vertex by pressing your pencil through the paper.

Step 3 Complete the new figure.

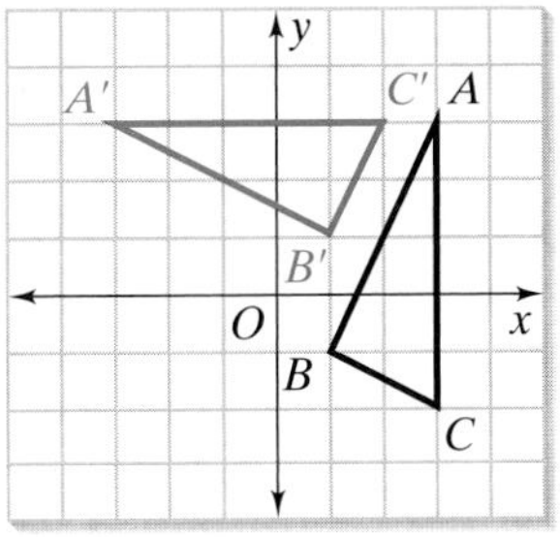

- Remove the tracing paper.
- Draw the triangle.
- Label the vertices to complete the figure.

Quick Check

2. Copy $\triangle ABD$. Draw the image of $\triangle ABD$ after a rotation of the given number of degrees about the origin.
   a. 180°
   b. 270°
   2a–b. See back of book.

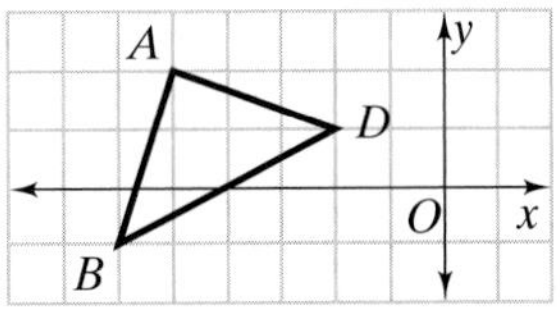

Advanced Learners L4
Students rotate a point, such as (2, 3), about the origin for 90°, 180°, 270°, 360°, 450°, 540°, 630°, and 720°. Ask them what they notice. If the point is rotated 360° or greater, its image is the same as a point with an angle measure that is 360° smaller.
learning style: tactile

English Language Learners ELL
Students demonstrate clockwise and counterclockwise motions with their hands. They draw lines at 0°, 90°, 180°, 270°, and 360° around the origin on a graph to help them calculate angles of rotation.
learning style: tactile

2. Teach

Activity Lab

Use before the lesson.
Student Edition Activity Lab, Hands On 3-8a, Exploring Rotations, p. 145

All in One Teaching Resources

Activity Lab 3-8: Transformations II

Guided Instruction

Error Prevention!

Students may assume that the center of a figure is always the center of rotation. Demonstrate how a triangle can be rotated about one of its vertices.

PowerPoint

Additional Examples

1 Find the angle of rotation for the figure below. 45°

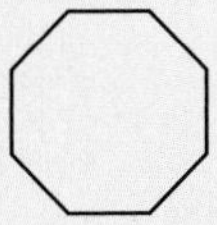

2 Draw the image of rectangle *ABCD* after a rotation of 90° about the origin.

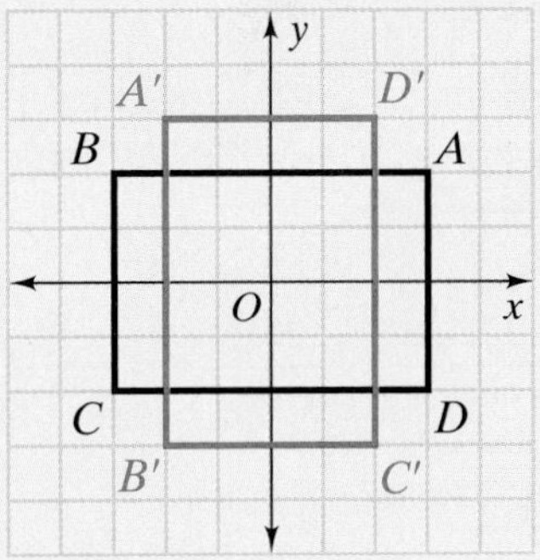

All in One Teaching Resources

- Daily Notetaking Guide 3-8 L3
- Adapted Notetaking 3-8 L1

Closure

- Describe a rotation. A transformation that turns a figure about a fixed point, called the center of rotation.
- Describe a figure with rotational symmetry. A figure is rotated a specified number of degrees less than 180°, and the image exactly matches the original.

3. Practice

Assignment Guide

Check Your Understanding

Go over Exercises 1–4 in class before assigning the Homework Exercises.

Homework Exercises

A Practice by Example	5–10
B Apply Your Skills	11–19
C Challenge	20
Test Prep and Mixed Review	23–27

Homework Quick Check

To check students' understanding of key skills and concepts, go over Exercises 6, 10, 12, 13, and 17.

Differentiated Instruction Resources

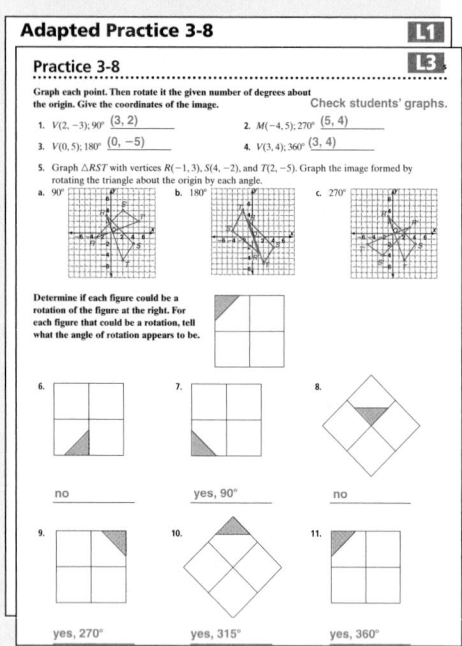

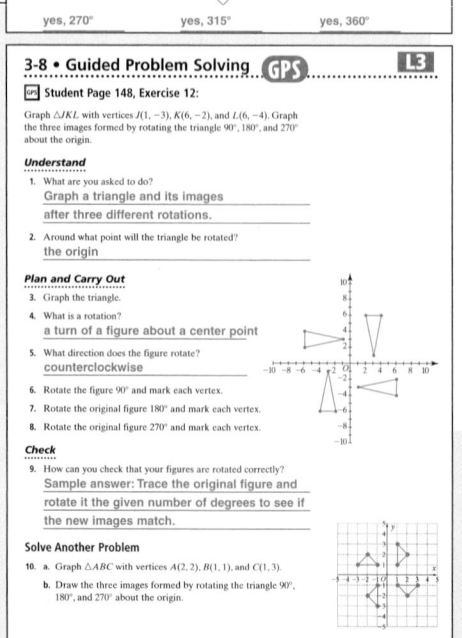

Adapted Practice 3-8 L1

Practice 3-8 L3

Graph each point. Then rotate it the given number of degrees about the origin. Give the coordinates of the image. Check students' graphs.

1. $V(2, -3)$; 90° (3, 2)
2. $M(-4, 5)$; 270° (5, 4)
3. $V(0, 5)$; 180° (0, −5)
4. $V(3, 4)$; 360° (3, 4)
5. Graph $\triangle RST$ with vertices $R(-1, 3)$, $S(4, -2)$, and $T(2, -5)$. Graph the image formed by rotating the triangle about the origin by each angle.

a. 90° b. 180° c. 270°

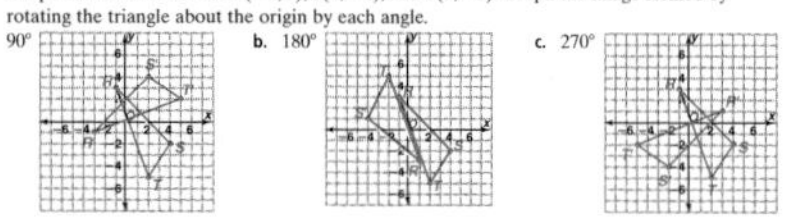

Determine if each figure could be a rotation of the figure at the right. For each figure that could be a rotation, tell what the angle of rotation appears to be.

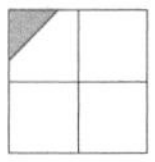

6.
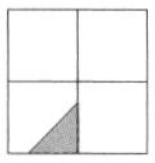
no

7.
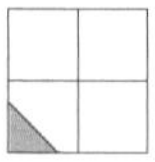
yes, 90°

8.
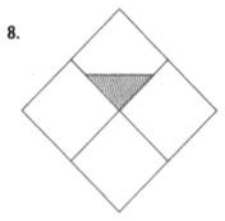
no

9.
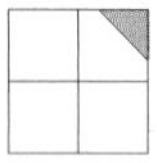
yes, 270°

10.
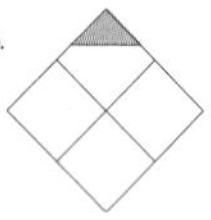
yes, 315°

11.
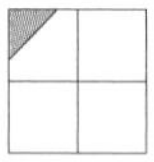
yes, 360°

3-8 • Guided Problem Solving GPS L3

GPS **Student Page 148, Exercise 12:**

Graph $\triangle JKL$ with vertices $J(1, -3)$, $K(6, -2)$, and $L(6, -4)$. Graph the three images formed by rotating the triangle 90°, 180°, and 270° about the origin.

Understand

1. What are you asked to do?
   Graph a triangle and its images after three different rotations.
2. Around what point will the triangle be rotated?
   the origin

Plan and Carry Out

3. Graph the triangle.
4. What is a rotation?
   a turn of a figure about a center point
5. What direction does the figure rotate?
   counterclockwise
6. Rotate the figure 90° and mark each vertex.
7. Rotate the original figure 180° and mark each vertex.
8. Rotate the original figure 270° and mark each vertex.

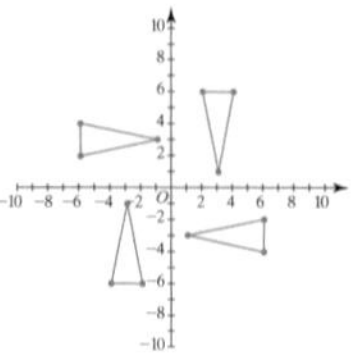

Check

9. How can you check that your figures are rotated correctly?
   Sample answer: Trace the original figure and rotate it the given number of degrees to see if the new images match.

Solve Another Problem

10. a. Graph $\triangle ABC$ with vertices $A(2, 2)$, $B(1, 1)$, and $C(1, 3)$.
    b. Draw the three images formed by rotating the triangle 90°, 180°, and 270° about the origin.

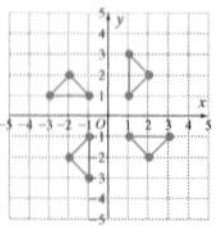

Check Your Understanding

1. **Vocabulary** A figure has rotational symmetry if it can be rotated ■ degrees or less and exactly match its original figure. 180

Graph each point. Then rotate it the given number of degrees about the origin. Give the coordinates of the image. See back of book for graphs.

2. $L(3, 3)$, 90° $L'(-3, 3)$
3. $M(-4, -2)$, 270° $M'(-2, 4)$
4. $N(3, -5)$, 180° $N'(-3, 5)$

Homework Exercises

For more exercises, see Extra Skills and Word Problems.

GO for Help

For Exercises	See Examples
5–7	1
8–10	2

A **Determine whether each figure has rotational symmetry. If it does, find the angle of rotation. Write *no rotational symmetry* if applicable.**

5.
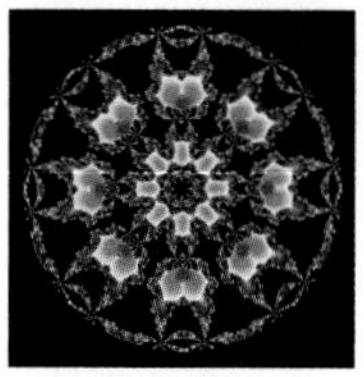
yes; 45°

6.

yes; 72°

7.

no rotational symmetr

Copy $\triangle PQR$. Draw the image of $\triangle PQR$ after a rotation of the given number of degrees about the origin. 8–10. See back of book.

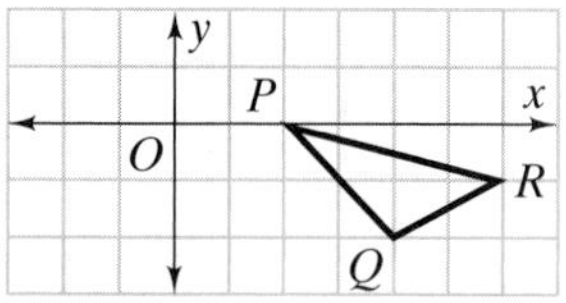

8. 90°
9. 180°
10. 270°

B GPS 11. **Guided Problem Solving** Figure B is an image formed by rotating Figure A. Give the angle of rotation for Figure B. 180°
- Draw Figure A on graph paper. Be sure to graph the center of the figure on the origin.
- Trace Figure A onto tracing paper and rotate counterclockwise.

Figure A

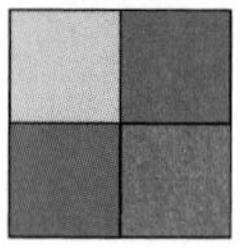
Figure B

12. Graph $\triangle JKL$ with vertices $J(1, -3)$, $K(6, -2)$, and $L(6, -4)$. GPS Graph the three images formed by rotating the triangle 90°, 180°, and 270° about the origin. See margin.

13. **Error Analysis** A square has rotational symmetry because it can be rotated 180° so that its image matches the original. Your friend says the angle of rotation is 180° ÷ 4 = 45°. What is wrong with this statement? A complete rotation has 360°. A square can be rotated 360° ÷ 4 or 90°.

GO Online
Homework Video Tutor
Visit: PHSchool.com
Web Code: ase-0308

12. See back of book.

14.
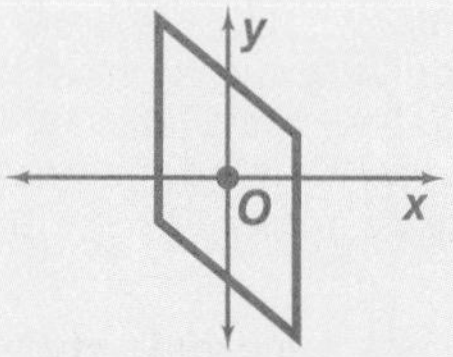

15.
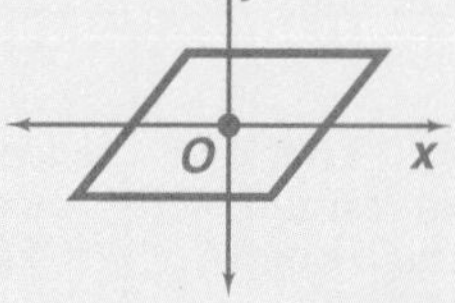

16.
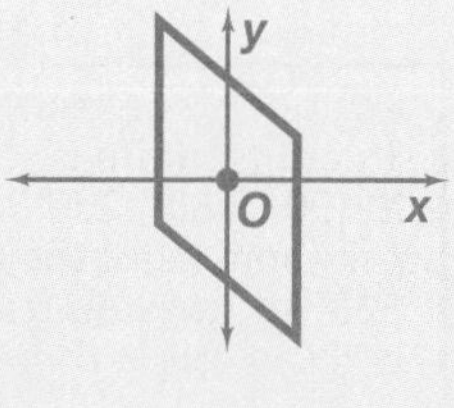

Draw the image of the figure at the right after the following rotations. 14–16. See margin.

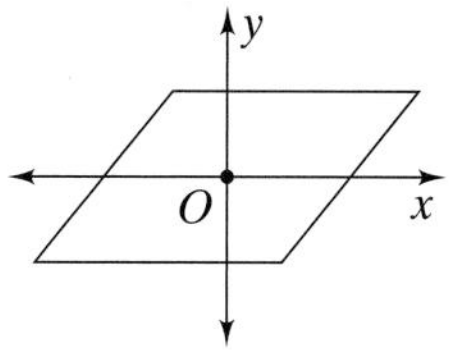

14. 90° **15.** 180° **16.** 270°

17. **Writing in Math** Explain how the design in the tie at the left can be made by using rotations and translations. Answers may vary. Sample: The repeating figure is rotated 90° and translated. It is then rotated 270° and translated.

Copy each figure. Then draw the image of the figure after the given rotation about the origin. 18–19. See margin.

18. 180°

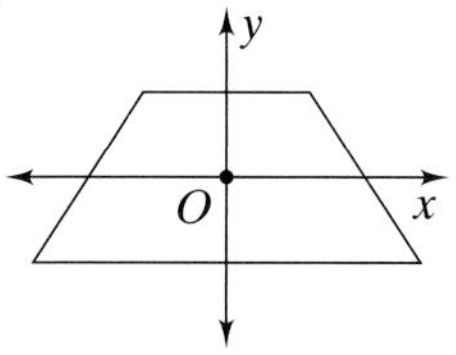

19. 270°

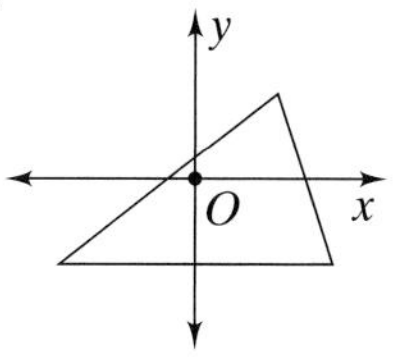

C **20.** **Challenge** Graph $\triangle PQR$ with vertices $P(3, 2)$, $Q(1, 0)$, and $R(3, -2)$. Draw the triangle after it is reflected across the y-axis. How can you get the same image using a rotation? Explain. See margin.

Test Prep and Mixed Review

Practice

Multiple Choice

21. Look at the pattern. What is the eighth figure in the pattern? D

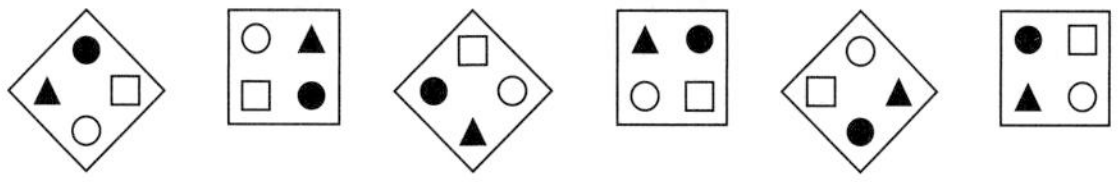

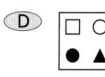

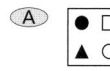

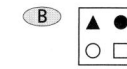

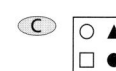

22. Plastic cups cost \$4.50 per bag, plastic plates cost \$4.30 per package, and plastic utensils cost \$2.25 per box. Scott buys 2 bags of cups, 1 package of plates, and 2 boxes of utensils. How much will he pay after using a coupon for half off his entire purchase? G

(F) \$5.53 (G) \$8.90 (H) \$9.15 (J) \$18.30

23. Alejandro wants to buy a digital audio player for \$124. His mother will pay $\frac{1}{3}$ of the cost. Alejandro has \$32.74. How much more money does he need to make the purchase? B

(A) \$8.59 (B) \$49.93 (C) \$60.84 (D) \$74.07

GO for Help

For Exercises	See Lesson
24–25	3-6

For $M(0, -3)$, give the coordinates of its image after each translation.

24. right 2 units and down 1 unit
$M'(2, -4)$

25. left 3 units and up 3 units
$M'(-3, 0)$

...mage.
(−6, 1), (−1, −6), (6, −1)

3. The points $T(0, 0)$, $U(-3, 0)$, and $V(-3, 5)$ form a triangle. Name the coordinates of the image of $\triangle T'U'V'$ after a rotation of 90° about the origin.
$T'(0, 0)$, $U'(0, -3)$, $V'(-5, -3)$

4. What is the angle of rotation for a square? 90°

18.

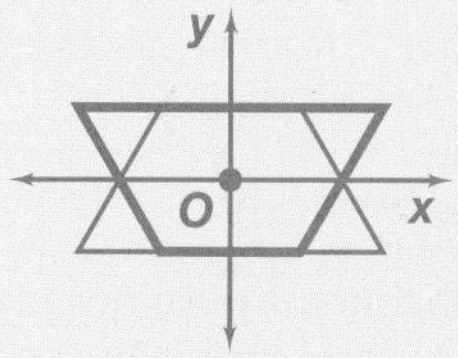

19.

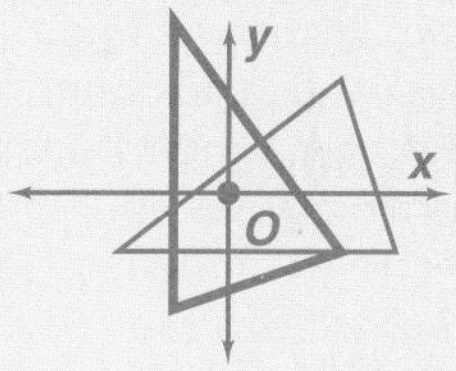

20. See back of book.

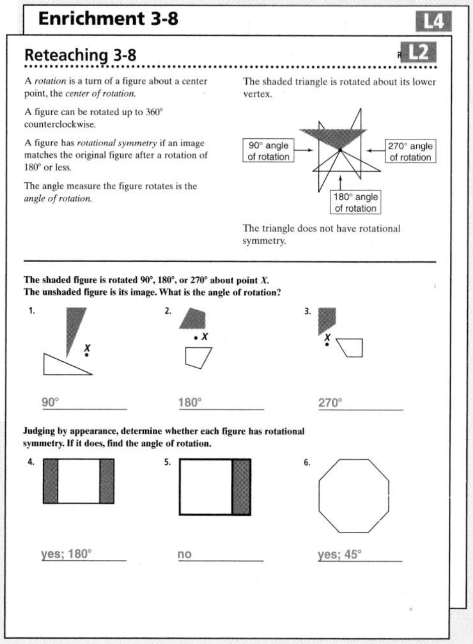

Enrichment 3-8 L4

Reteaching 3-8 L2

A *rotation* is a turn of a figure about a center point, the *center of rotation*.

A figure can be rotated up to 360° counterclockwise.

A figure has *rotational symmetry* if an image matches the original figure after a rotation of 180° or less.

The angle measure the figure rotates is the *angle of rotation*.

The shaded triangle is rotated about its lower vertex.

90° angle of rotation; 270° angle of rotation; 180° angle of rotation

The triangle does not have rotational symmetry.

The shaded figure is rotated 90°, 180°, or 270° about point X. The unshaded figure is its image. What is the angle of rotation?

1. 90°
2. 180°
3. 270°

Judging by appearance, determine whether each figure has rotational symmetry. If it does, find the angle of rotation.

4. yes; 180°
5. no
6. yes; 45°

Alternative Assessment

Teams of students compete to list one common representation of rotational symmetry for as many different angle measures as possible. They research road signs, letters of the alphabet, and classroom objects.

Test Prep

Resources

For additional practice with a variety of test item formats:

- Test-Taking Strategies, p. 151
- Test Prep, p. 155
- Test-Taking Strategies with Transparencies

ns

rotations,
nd/or reflections to
ting designs. Students
ich figures can form
lations and make their own
ssellating diagrams.

Guided Instruction

In Exercises 1–4, students draw figures on graph paper to determine which ones tessellate. They may also cut out the figures and place them in repeated positions. Review the types of transformations they can use. Ask:

- *In which directions can a figure translate?* horizontal and vertical
- *In which directions can you reflect a figure?* horizontal, vertical, or about a different line
- *How do you know how much to rotate a figure?* decide on an angle of rotation

Error Prevention!

Simply placing a figure next to itself may not always generate a tessellation. The way a figure is repeated must be consistent for every repetition. When students place or draw figures adjacent to each other, remind them to focus on a type of transformation, and to repeat that transformation exactly with each repetition.

Connection to Art
Have students research examples of tessellations in art and architecture.

Resources

- graph paper
- scissors

Tessellations

A **tessellation** is a repeating pattern of congruent shapes that completely cover a plane without gaps or overlaps. The Dutch artist M. C. Escher (1898–1972) was famous for using tessellations in his art. Many of his designs, like the one at the right, are based on polygons that tessellate.

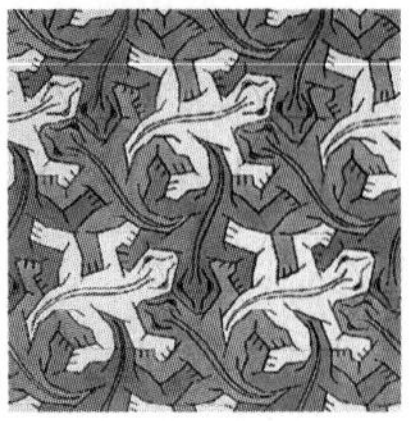

You can make a tessellation by repeatedly translating, rotating, or reflecting a figure.

EXAMPLE

Show how the figure at the right can form a tessellation.

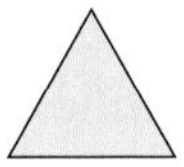

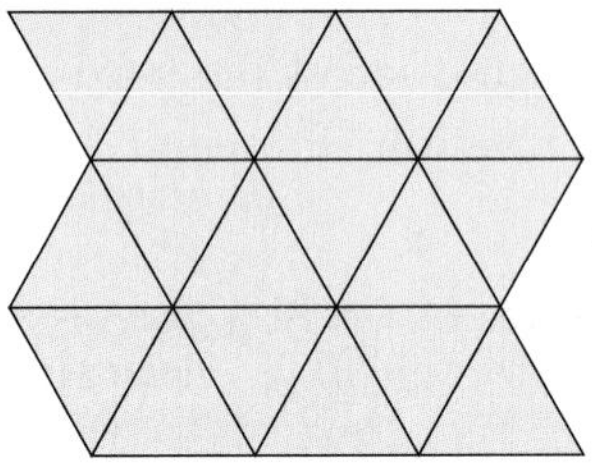

← Rotate, translate, and reflect the figure to cover the plane.

Exercises

Make multiple copies of each figure on graph paper. Determine whether each figure can form a tessellation. If it can, show the tessellation. 1–4. See margin.

1. 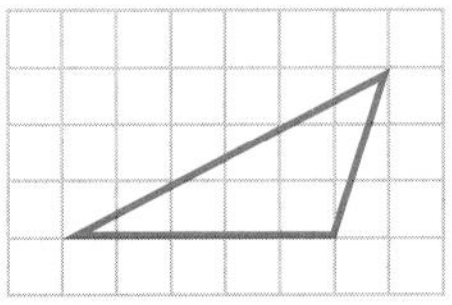
2. 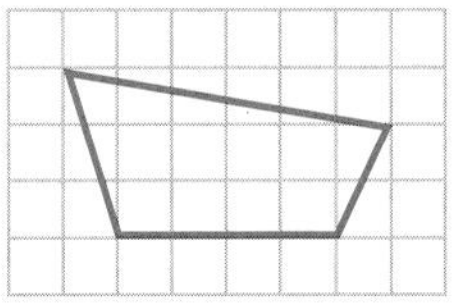
3. 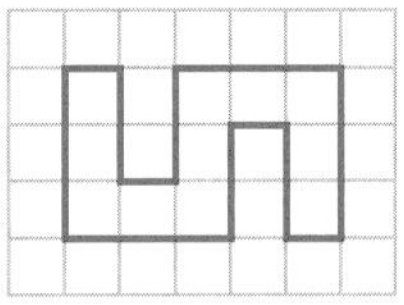
4. 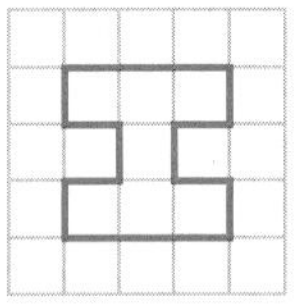

5. The diagrams below show how to construct a repeating figure for a tessellation. Follow the steps shown to make your own tessellation. 5–6. Check students' work.

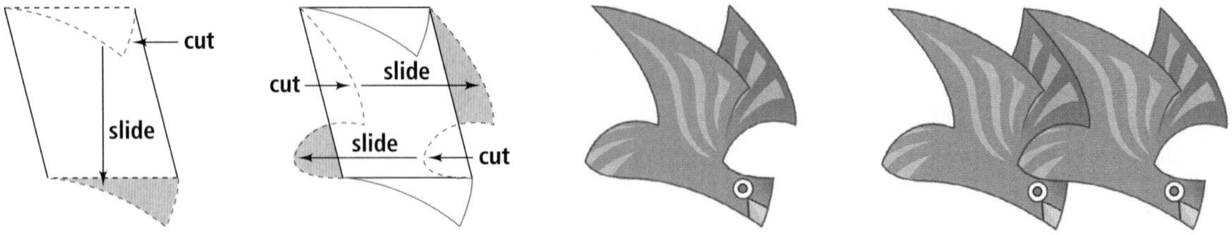

6. **Open-Ended** Make and decorate a tessellation, starting with a square.

1. 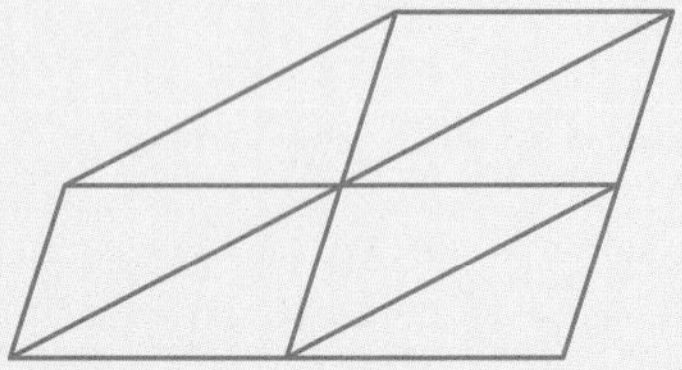

2. 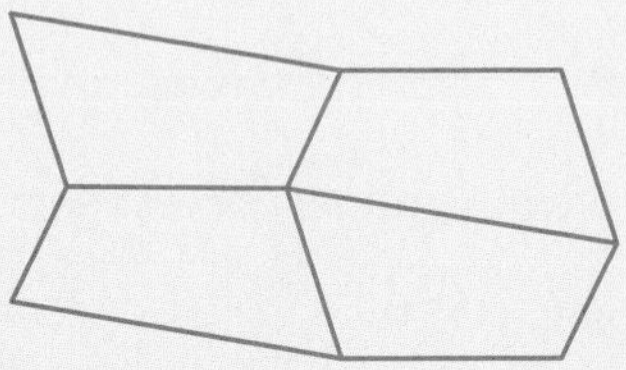

3. 

4. 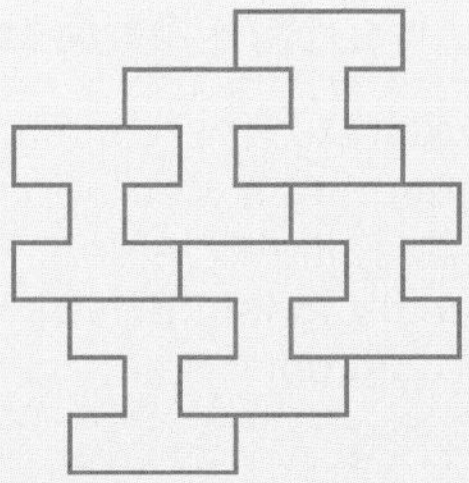

Writing Extended Responses

Extended-response questions have multiple parts. To receive full credit, you need to answer each part and show your work or justify your reasoning.

EXAMPLE

A machine to make buttons costs $12, and each blank costs $.50. Each button sells for $2. Write and graph equations to find how many buttons you must sell for income and expenses to be equal, or *to break even.*

Here are four students' responses and the points they received.

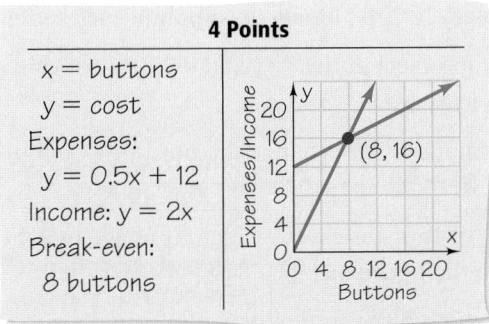

4 Points

x = buttons
y = cost
Expenses:
$y = 0.5x + 12$
Income: $y = 2x$
Break-even:
8 buttons

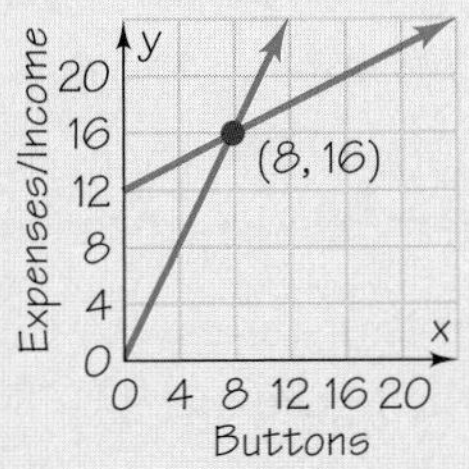

The equations, the graphs, and the solution are correct.

3 Points

x = buttons
y = cost
Expenses:
$y = 0.5x + 12$
Income: $y = 2x$
Break-even:
16 buttons

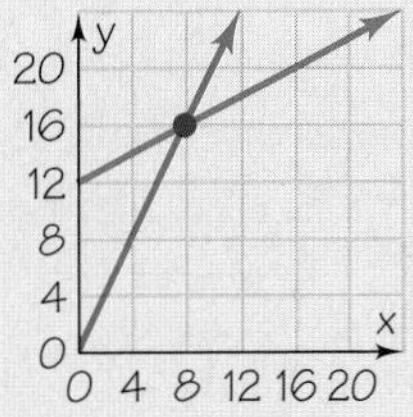

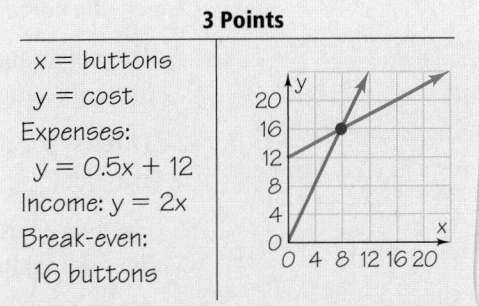

The equations and graphs are correct, but the solution is incorrect.

2 Points

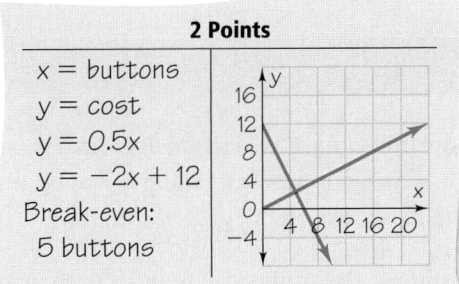

x = buttons
y = cost
$y = 0.5x$
$y = -2x + 12$
Break-even:
5 buttons

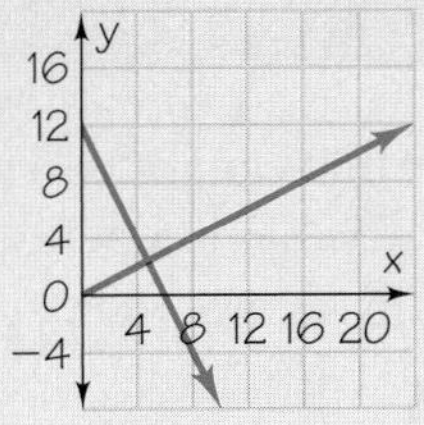

The equations are incorrect, but the graphs for the student's equations are correct.

1 Point

I need to sell 8 buttons in order to break even.

The solution is correct, but no work is shown.

For the question to receive 0 points, there is either no response, or it is completely incorrect.

Exercises

1. Tim can type 40 words per min. Bo can type 50 words per min. Tim has already typed 30 words. Write and graph equations to find how many minutes pass before Tim and Bo type the same number of words. See margin.

1. Answers may vary. Sample:
x = minutes
y = words
Tim: $y = 40x + 30$
Bo: $y = 50x$
Answer: 3 min

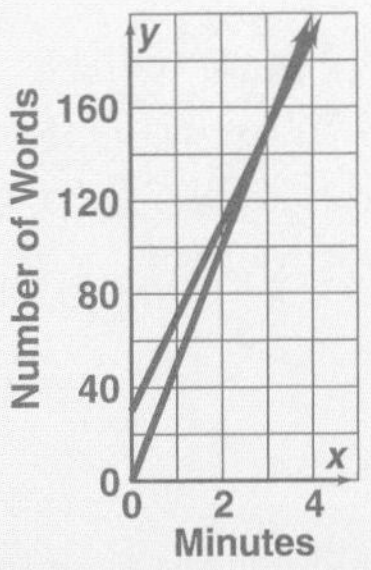

Writing Extended Responses

This strategy shows students what is required to get full credit on extended-response test questions.

Guided Instruction

Go over each of the four responses. Have students explain why each of the responses shown received the scores indicated.

Differentiated Instruction

English Learners
Using plain language, help students to understand the difference between answers that get full credit and those that get partial credit. Also, make sure that students fully understand what break even means as well as the meanings of the key terms variable, equation, graph and solution.

Resources

Test-Taking Strategies with Transparencies
- Transparency 4
- Practice sheet, p. 27

Test-Taking Strategies with Transparencies

Test-Taking Strategies: Writing Extended Responses

1. Draw and label two rectangles of different lengths and widths, each with a perimeter of 20 units.

Scoring Guide
- 4 Draws 2 rectangles of different lengths and widths, with perimeter 20 units indicated by labels on sides.
- 3 Draws 2 identical rectangles, with perimeter 20 units, OR draws 2 rectangles of different widths and lengths, only 1 with perimeter 20 units.
- 2 Draws 1 or 2 rectangles, whose perimeters are not 20 units.
- 1 Draws 1 or 2 non-rectangles. Does not label the sides.
- 0 Answers inappropriately or not at all.

2. The Athletic Council is hosting a sports banquet. It costs $300 to rent a hall, plus $8 per person for food. Between 50 and 90 people will attend. What are the least and greatest amounts of money the banquet could cost? Explain.

Scoring Guide
- 4 Correctly computes least and greatest costs, AND explains adequately.
- 3 Correctly computes least and greatest costs, but explanation is inadequate.
- 2 Computes least cost incorrectly, OR computes greatest cost incorrectly, OR explains inadequately.
- 1 Computes both costs incorrectly, OR computes one cost correctly, but explains inadequately.
- 0 Answers inappropriately or not at all.

Chapter 3 Review

Chapter 3 Review

Resources

Student Edition
Extra Skills and Word Problems Practice, Ch. 3, p. 608
English/Spanish Glossary, p. 650
Formulas and Properties, p. 648
Tables, p. 643

All in One Teaching Resources
Vocabulary and Study Skills 3F L3

Differentiated Instruction
Spanish Vocabulary and Study Skills 3F ELL
Interactive Textbook
- Audio Glossary

Online Vocabulary Quiz

Success Tracker™
Online at PHSchool.com

Vocabulary Review

angle of rotation (p. 146)
center of rotation (p. 146)
coordinate plane (p. 124)
hypotenuse (p. 112)
image (p. 136)
irrational numbers (p. 107)
legs (p. 112)
line of reflection (p. 141)
line of symmetry (p. 142)
linear equation (p. 131)
ordered pair (p. 124)
origin (p. 124)
perfect square (p. 106)
Pythagorean Theorem (p. 112)
quadrants (p. 124)
real numbers (p. 107)
reflection (p. 141)
reflectional symmetry (p. 142)
rotation (p. 146)
rotational symmetry (p. 146)
solution (p. 131)
square root (p. 106)
transformation (p. 136)
translation (p. 136)
***x*-axis** (p. 124)
***x*-coordinate** (p. 124)
***y*-axis** (p. 124)
***y*-coordinate** (p. 124)

Choose the correct vocabulary term(s) above to complete each sentence.

1. The x-axis and the __?__ intersect at the __?__ and divide a coordinate plane into four __?__. y-axis; origin; quadrants
2. Three types of transformations that change the position of a figure are __?__, __?__, and __?__. translations; reflections; rotations
3. If a figure has a(n) __?__ of 180° or less for which its image matches the original figure, then the figure has __?__. angle of rotation; rotational symmetry
4. A number such as 25, which is the square of a whole number, is a __?__. perfect square
5. The __?__ is the longest side of a right triangle. hypotenuse

Go Online
PHSchool.com
For: Online Vocabulary Quiz
Web Code: asj-0351

Skills and Concepts

Lesson 3-1

- To find and estimate square roots and to classify numbers as rational or irrational

Irrational numbers are numbers that cannot be written as fractions using integers. The square of a whole number is a **perfect square.** The opposite of squaring a number is finding its **square root.**

For a circle, use $A = 3r^2$ to estimate the radius r in feet for each area A in square feet. Round to the nearest tenth.

6. 21 square feet 2.6 ft
7. 240 square feet 8.9 ft
8. 570 square feet 13.8 ft

Is each number *rational* or *irrational*? Explain. 9–13. See margin.

9. $\sqrt{196}$
10. $-\sqrt{\frac{25}{36}}$
11. $\sqrt{57}$
12. $\sqrt{1.6}$
13. $\sqrt{225}$

9. Rational; 196 is a perfect square.
10. Rational; $\frac{25}{36}$ is a perfect square.
11. Irrational; 57 is not a perfect square.
12. Irrational; 1.6 is not a perfect square.
13. Rational; 225 is a perfect square.

Spanish Vocabulary/Study Skills ELL

Vocabulary/Study Skills L3

3F: Vocabulary Review Puzzle

For use with the Chapter Review

Vocabulary and Study Skills

Study Skill Taking short breaks can help you stay focused. Every 30 minutes, take a 5-minute break, then return to studying.

I. Match the term in Column A with its definition in Column B.

Column A	Column B
1. quadrant C	A. a transformation that turns a figure about a fixed point
2. origin D	B. the longest side in a right triangle, which is opposite the right angle
3. hypotenuse B	C. any one of the four sections into which the coordinate plane is divided
4. real numbers G	D. the point where the x-axis and the y-axis intersect, indicated by the ordered pair (0, 0)
5. Pythagorean Theorem F	E. a transformation that moves each point of a figure the same distance and in the same direction
6. translation E	F. a formula that describes the relationship of length between the legs and the hypotenuse, in a right triangle
7. rotation A	G. the set of numbers that includes rational and irrational numbers

II. Match the term in Column A with its definition in Column B.

Column A	Column B
1. perfect square D	A. numbers that cannot be written in the form $\frac{a}{b}$, where a is any integer and b is any nonzero integer
2. coordinate plane G	B. an equation whose solutions all lie on a line
3. ordered pair F	C. a transformation that flips a figure over a line
4. linear equation B	D. a number that is the square of a whole number
5. reflection C	E. a line that divides a figure into mirror images
6. line of symmetry E	F. gives the coordinates of the location of a point
7. irrational numbers A	G. a grid formed by the intersection of two number lines

Lessons 3-2, 3-3

- To use the Pythagorean Theorem to find the length of the hypotenuse of a right triangle
- To use the Pythagorean Theorem to find missing measurements of triangles

The **Pythagorean Theorem** states that if a and b are the lengths of the **legs** of a right triangle, and c is the length of the **hypotenuse,** then $a^2 + b^2 = c^2$.

Find the length of the hypotenuse given the lengths of the two legs. If necessary, round to the nearest tenth.

14. $a = 6,\ b = 8$ 10 **15.** $a = 12,\ b = 6$ 13.4 **16.** $a = 24,\ b = 40$ 46.6

17. The base of a 24-ft ladder is 6 ft from the base of a house. To the nearest tenth, how far up the house does the ladder reach? 23.2 ft

Lesson 3-4

- To graph points and to use the Pythagorean Theorem to find distances in the coordinate plane

An **ordered pair** describes the location of a point on a **coordinate plane.** The first number is the ***x*-coordinate.** The second is the ***y*-coordinate.**

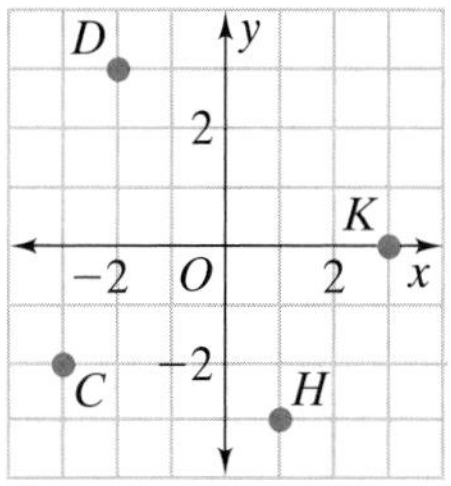

Name the coordinates of each point in the graph at the right.

18. C (−3, −2) **19.** D (−2, 3) **20.** H (1, −3)

In which quadrant or on which axis is each point? 21–23. See margin.

21. (7, −4) **22.** (0, −2) **23.** (−6, 5)

Lesson 3-5

- To use tables, equations, and graphs to solve problems

When the values in an ordered pair make an equation with two variables true, the ordered pair is a **solution** of the equation. To graph a **linear equation,** graph several solutions and draw a line through the points.

Graph each linear equation. 24–27. See margin.

24. $y = x + 3$ **25.** $y = \frac{1}{4}x - 1$ **26.** $y = -2x + 1$ **27.** $y = -\frac{2}{3}x$

Lessons 3-6, 3-7, 3-8

- To graph and describe translations in the coordinate plane
- To graph reflections in the coordinate plane and to identify lines of symmetry
- To graph rotations and to identify rotational symmetry

A **transformation** is a change in the position, shape, or size of a figure. The figure you get after a transformation is called the **image.** You can transform figures in a plane by a **translation,** a **reflection,** or a **rotation.**

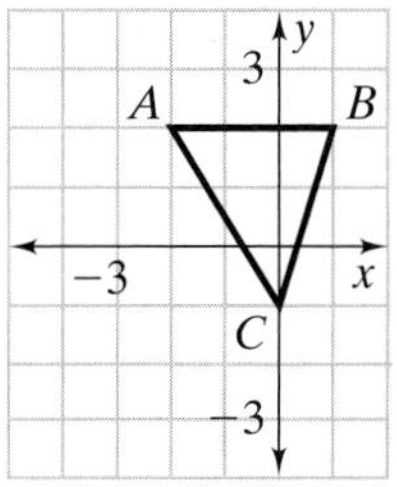

Copy △*ABC* for Exercises 28–30. Graph the image of △*ABC* after each transformation. 28–30. See back of book.

28. translation 2 units left and 1 unit up

29. reflection over the x-axis

30. rotation of 90° about the origin

21. Quadrant IV
22. y-axis
23. Quadrant II

24.

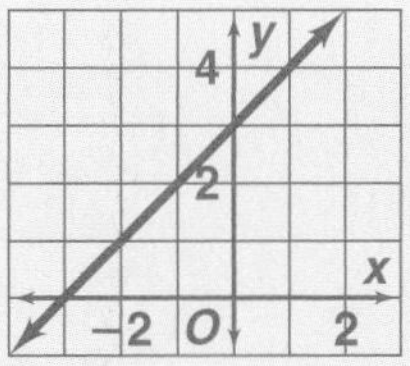

25.

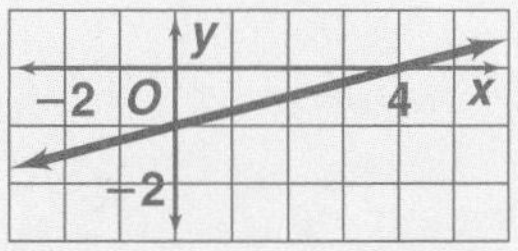

26.

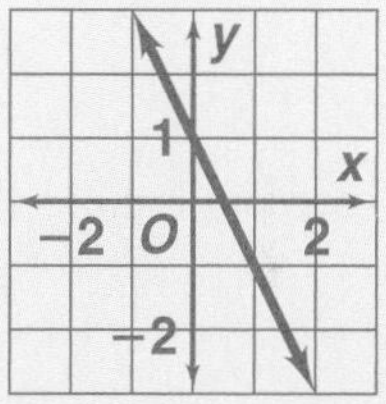

27.

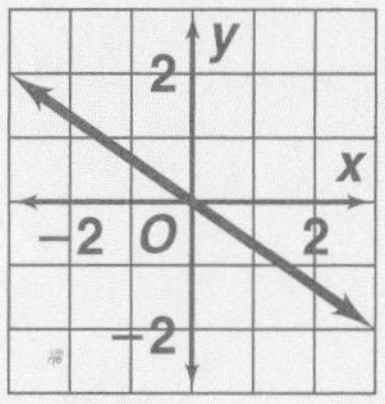

Alternative Assessment L4

Alternative Assessment Form C

Chapter 3

NEWSPAPER ROUTE

Julia just got a job delivering newspapers on her bicycle. Below are the names and addresses of the customers on her route. Notice that all of the roads on Julia's route are called either "streets" or "avenues."

Name	Address	Name	Address
Anderson	421 NE 6th St.	Keel	763 NE 6th St.
Baker	310 SE 8th St.	Lin	490 SW 3rd Ave.
Cohen	333 SW 6th Ave.	Mason	167 SW 8th St.
Dunken	551 NW 2nd Ave.	Norland	323 NW 8th St.
Ellis	134 SE 7th St.	Orson	778 SE 5th Ave.
Franklin	350 SW 6th St.	Pearson	590 SE 7th Ave.
Gross	379 NE 6th Ave.	Quill	462 SE 3rd St.
Hiedorn	810 NW 7th Ave.	Richards	605 NW 8th Ave.
Ingstrom	554 SW 8th St.	Sassor	45 SW 7th St.
Jackson	718 NE 1st St.		

Julia first wanted to determine the best route to follow when delivering the papers. She began by drawing a grid. Then, using the list of her customers' addresses, she started marking points to show where each customer lives. She used the first letter of each customer's name to label that customer's address on the grid.

The following information explains how Julia located each address. Consider this information while you study the grid on the following page.

- The four quadrants represent the NE, NW, SW, and SE sections of her route.
- The vertical grid lines are the streets, and the horizontal grid lines are the avenues.
- Each house address number is based on the two roads the house lies between. For example, if a house address on a street is a number between 200 and 300, then it lies between 2nd Avenue and 3rd Avenue. If a house address on an avenue is a number between 400 and 500, then it lies between 4th Street and 5th Street.

Spanish Quarter 1 Test — Forms A, B ELL

Quarter 1 Test — Forms D, E L2

Quarter 1 Test — Forms A, B L3

Quarter 1 Test Form A

Chapters 1–3

1. Evaluate $x(4 + 5y)$ for $x = 3$ and $y = 2.4$.
2. A company sells its product for \$16 per unit. How many units would have to be sold in order for the company to earn \$528?
3. Compare. Write $<$, $>$, or $=$. $|11|$ __?__ $|-13|$
4. Jared hiked from 132 feet above sea level to 6 feet below sea level. Write an integer to express the difference in these elevations.
5. Evaluate the expression $\frac{13}{-30 - a}$ for $a = -4$.
6. Simplify. $8 + 9 - 2^3$
7. Evaluate the expression $3x^3 + 5$ for $x = -2$.
8. Simplify. $-4(m - 6)$
9. Simplify. $(-22)(18 - 7)$
10. Rewrite this expression using exponents. $3 \cdot 3 \cdot 3 \cdot 3 \cdot x \cdot x \cdot x \cdot y \cdot y$

For Exercises 11–13, solve each equation.

11. $15 = x + 26$
12. $\frac{n}{4} = 11$
13. $7p = -105$
14. Simplify. $5x + 8(x - 5)$
15. Write the composite numbers in the list below. 37, 43, 47, 26, 32, 2, 17, 40, 16
16. Find the GCF of 35 and 90.
17. Explain how to write the fraction $\frac{81}{108}$ in simplest form.
18. Sam was at bat 20 times and had 14 hits. Write his batting average as a decimal.
19. Write 1.35 as a mixed number in simplest form.
20. Write $-3\frac{2}{5}$ as a decimal.
21. Write the repeating decimal $0.\overline{4}$ as a fraction in simplest form.
22. Use a factor tree to find the prime factorization of 126.
23. Order $\frac{3}{8}$, −1.25, $-2\frac{4}{5}$, 0.34, −0.63 from least to greatest.
24. Compare. Write $<$, $>$, or $=$. $\frac{3}{16}$ __?__ 0.2
25. You are making bread that requires $3\frac{1}{2}$ cups of whole wheat flour and $2\frac{1}{2}$ cups of white flour. How many cups of flour is that in all?
26. Subtract. $8\frac{7}{16} - 2\frac{1}{3}$
27. Multiply. $4\frac{1}{2} \times 1\frac{1}{3}$
28. Divide. $3\frac{3}{4} \div 1\frac{1}{2}$
29. Use the formula $P = 2l + 2w$ to find P when $l = 12$ and $w = 7$.
30. Find x.

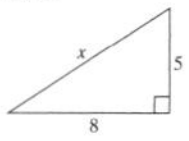

Chapter 3 Test

Resources

- ExamView Assessment Suite CD-ROM
  - Ch. 3 Ready-Made Test
  - Make your own Ch. 3 test
- MindPoint Quiz Show CD-ROM
  - Chapter 3 Review

Differentiated Instruction Resources

All in One Teaching Resources
- Below Level Chapter 3 Test L2
- Chapter 3 Test L3
- Chapter 3 Alternative Assessment L4

Spanish Assessment Resources ELL
- Below Level Chapter 3 Test L2
- Chapter 3 Test L3
- Chapter 3 Alternative Assessment L4

ExamView Assessment Suite CD-ROM
- Special Needs Test L1
- Special Needs Practice Bank L1

Online Chapter 3 Test at www.PHSchool.com L3

7. rational 8. irrational
9. rational 10. irrational
11. rational

Below Level Chapter Test L2

Chapter Test L3

Chapter Test Form A
Chapter 3

Find the two square roots of each number.

1. 289 ±17 2. 196 ±14 3. 81 ±9 4. 36 ±6

Determine whether each number is rational or irrational.

5. 5.010010001... irrational 6. $5.\overline{01}$ rational 7. $-\sqrt{16}$ rational
8. $-4\frac{2}{9}$ rational 9. $\sqrt{20}$ irrational 10. π irrational

The lengths of two sides of a right triangle are given. Find the third length. The variable *c* represents the length of the hypotenuse.

11. $a = 6, b = 8$ 10 12. $c = 13, b = 12$ 5 13. $c = 17, a = 8$ 15

Graph each point on the same coordinate plane.

14. $A(4, 0)$ 15. $B(0, 5)$
16. $C(-5, 5)$ 17. $D(-4, -4)$
18. $E(0, -1)$ 19. $F(1, 4)$
20. $G(-2, 0)$ 21. $H(3, -1)$

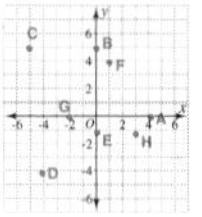

In which quadrant or on which axis is each point located?

22. (–6, 20) II 23. (5, 0) no quadrant; on *x*-axis 24. (–3, –1.2) III 25. (6, 35) I

$\triangle ABC$ has vertices $A(0, 6)$, $B(7, 6)$ and $C(2, 1)$. What are the coordinates of the new vertices after each transformation?

26. translation 2 units right $A'(2, 6), B'(9, 6), C'(4,1)$
27. translation 3 units up $A'(0, 9), B'(7, 9), C'(2, 4)$
28. translation 4 units left and 1 unit down $A'(-4, 5), B'(3, 5), C'(-2, 0)$
29. reflection over the *x*-axis $A'(0, -6), B'(7, -6), C'(2, -1)$
30. reflection over the *y*-axis $A'(0, 6), B'(-7, 6), C'(-2, 1)$
31. reflection over the line through (1, 1) and (5, 5) $A'(6, 0), B'(6, 7), C'(1, 2)$

Chapter 3 Test

Go Online PHSchool.com **For:** Online chapter test **Web Code:** asa-0352

Find the two square roots of each number.

1. 144 12, −12 2. 256 16, −16 3. 400 20, −20

Simplify.

4. $\sqrt{100}$ 10 5. $\sqrt{0}$ 0 6. $-\sqrt{1}$ −1

Determine whether each number is *rational* or *irrational*. 7–11. See margin.

7. $2.\overline{79}$ 8. $-\sqrt{10}$ 9. $-1\frac{5}{6}$
10. 0.717117111 . . . 11. $\sqrt{49}$

12. **Writing in Math** Describe the difference between rational and irrational numbers. See margin.

Find the missing length, where *a* and *b* are the leg lengths, and *c* is the hypotenuse length.

13. $c = 5, a = 3$ 4 14. $b = 30, c = 34$ 16
15. $a = 5, b = 12$ 13 16. $a = 48, c = 60$ 36

17. **Sailboats** In the diagram of a sailboat at the right, the length of the luff is 17 ft. The length of the foot is 10 ft. What is the length of the leech to the nearest foot? 20 ft

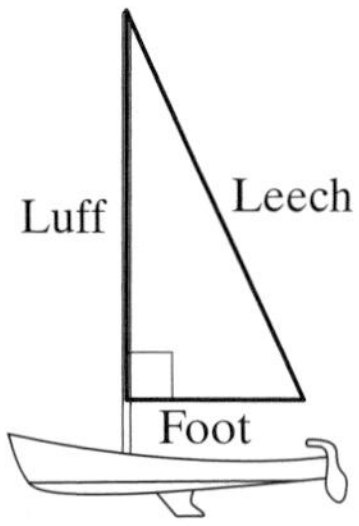

Match each equation with its graph at the right.

18. $y = 3x + 2$ v
19. $y = -3x - 2$ t
20. $y = \frac{1}{2}x - 3$ s

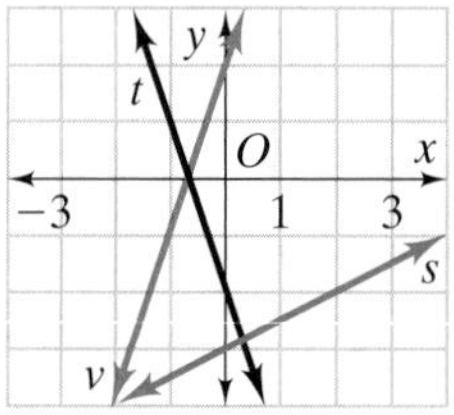

Graph all the points on the same coordinate plane. 21–23. See margin.

21. $A(4, -2)$ 22. $B(0, 5)$ 23. $C(-3, 2)$

In which quadrant or on which axis is each point located?

24. $(-4, -2)$ Quadrant III 25. $(5, -3.7)$ Quadrant IV 26. $(128, 0)$ *x*-axis

27. A bowling alley charges $2.00 for shoe rental and $4.00 for each game. Write and graph an equation that represents the total cost to bowl *x* games. 27–34. See back of book.

28. **Business** You want to make a game. You spend $20 for setup costs and $5 for the materials for each game. Make a table and write an equation to represent the total cost of making *x* games.

$\triangle JKL$ has vertices $J(4, 5)$, $K(6, 2)$, and $L(3, 2)$. Graph $\triangle JKL$ and its image after each transformation.

29. translation 6 units left
30. translation 3 units left and 3 units down
31. reflection over the *y*-axis
32. reflection over the line through $(1, -2)$ and $(1, 2)$
33. rotation of 90° about the origin
34. rotation of 180° about the origin

35. Write a rule to describe the translation at the right.

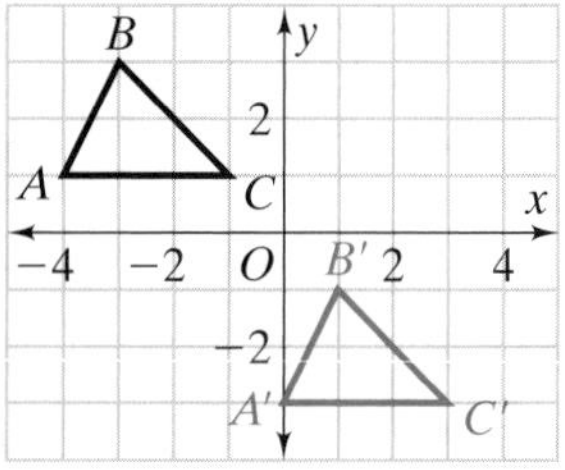

$(x, y) \rightarrow (x + 4, y - 4)$

36. **Open-Ended** Draw and describe a figure that has exactly three lines of symmetry. Check students' work.

37. After a certain reflection, the image of $P(3, -1)$ is $P'(-1, -1)$. What are the coordinates of the image of $Q(-2, 4)$ after the same reflection? $Q'(4, 4)$

12. A rational number can be expressed as $\frac{a}{b}$, where *a* and *b* are integers, $b \neq 0$. An irrational number cannot be expressed in that way. Rational numbers are terminating or repeating decimals. Irrational numbers are nonterminating, nonrepeating decimals.

21–23.

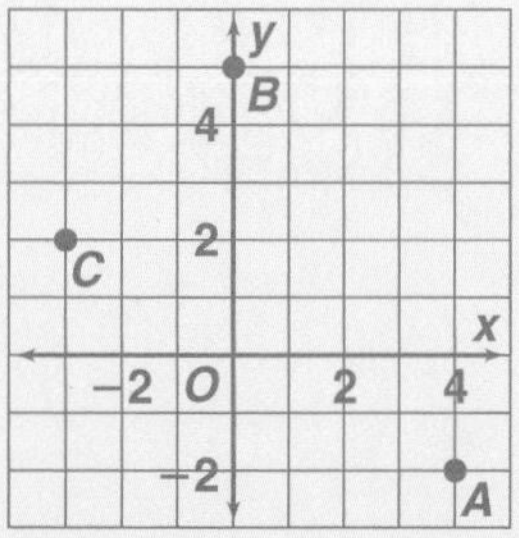

154

Test Prep Practice

Reading Comprehension

Read each passage and answer the questions that follow.

Just Kidding Mrs. Kidd likes to invite the neighbors for a cookout and then hide the food in various places around the backyard. Guests start at the center of the yard and then follow her clues to find their food. Here is one set of clues: "Meat at (3, 3). Vegetables at (−5, −12). Beverages at (5, −12). All measurements are in fathoms."

1. Treat the yard as a coordinate plane with the origin at the center. In which quadrant are the vegetables located? C
   Ⓐ I Ⓑ II Ⓒ III Ⓓ IV

2. Mrs. Kidd also gives this clue: "Dessert is 2 fathoms to the right and 5 fathoms below the meat." What is the location of dessert? G
   Ⓕ (2, −5) Ⓗ (−5, 2)
   Ⓖ (5, −2) Ⓙ (5, 2)

3. How far must guests walk to go directly from the vegetables to the beverages? A
   Ⓐ 10 fathoms Ⓒ 24 fathoms
   Ⓑ 12 fathoms Ⓓ 26 fathoms

4. Mrs. Kidd hints, "Potatoes are at the reflection of the meat over the y-axis." What are the coordinates of the potatoes? F
   Ⓕ (−3, 3) Ⓗ (−3, −3)
   Ⓖ (3, −3) Ⓙ (3, 3)

Piano Movers The Singhs are deciding where to put a new piano. They take graph paper and draw an outline of the room, using one square to represent 1 foot. With the origin at the center of the room, the room's corners fall at (8, 10), (−8, 10), and (−8, −10). The piano is 5 ft long and 3 ft wide.

5. Mr. Singh wants the piano to be along the left wall, but there is a window from (−8, 3) to (−8, 6) and from (−8, −6) to (−8, −3). D Will the piano fit between the windows?
   Ⓐ No, there is only 3 ft of space.
   Ⓑ No, there is only 4 ft of space.
   Ⓒ Barely, there is exactly 5 ft of space.
   Ⓓ Easily, there is 6 ft of space.

6. Suppose the piano's corners are at (0, 0), (5, 0), (5, 3) and (0, 3). If the piano is pushed straight back along the y-axis to the wall, where will the (0, 0) corner end up? G
   Ⓕ (7, 0) Ⓖ (0, 7) Ⓗ (0, 8) Ⓙ (0, 0)

7. If one corner of the piano is in the center of the room, which point could NOT be the location of another corner of the piano? D
   Ⓐ (5, 0) Ⓒ (−5, −3)
   Ⓑ (3, 5) Ⓓ (3, 3)

8. Suppose the piano has the same location that it had at the start of Exercise 6. The (0, 0) corner stays where it is, but the piano is turned to face the opposite direction. Which ordered pair will NOT be the new coordinates of a corner? J
   Ⓕ (−5, 0) Ⓗ (−5, −3)
   Ⓖ (0, −3) Ⓙ (0, 3)

Test Prep

Resources

Test Prep Workbook

All in One Teaching Resources
- Cumulative Review L3

ExamView Assessment Suite CD-ROM
- Standardized Test Practice

Differentiated Instruction

Spanish Assessment Resources
- Spanish Cumulative Review ELL

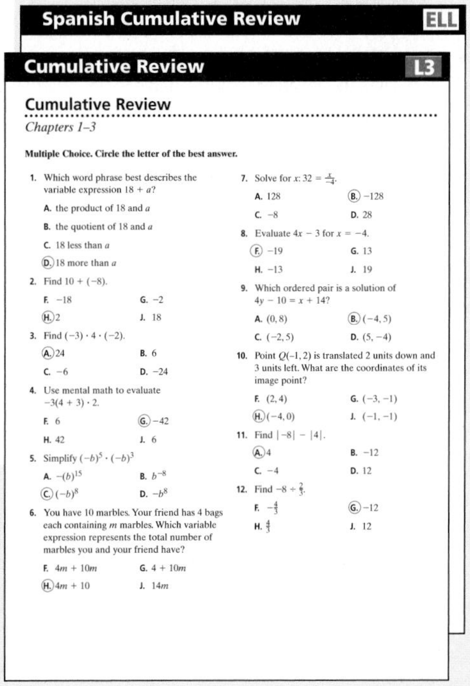

Spanish Cumulative Review ELL

Cumulative Review L3

Cumulative Review

Chapters 1–3

Multiple Choice. Circle the letter of the best answer.

1. Which word phrase best describes the variable expression $18 + a$?
   A. the product of 18 and a
   B. the quotient of 18 and a
   C. 18 less than a
   (D.) 18 more than a
2. Find $10 + (-8)$.
   F. −18 G. −2
   (H.) 2 J. 18
3. Find $(-3) \cdot 4 \cdot (-2)$.
   (A.) 24 B. 6
   C. −6 D. −24
4. Use mental math to evaluate $-3(4 + 3) \cdot 2$.
   F. 6 (G.) −42
   H. 42 J. 6
5. Simplify $(-b)^5 \cdot (-b)^3$
   A. $-(b)^{15}$ B. b^{-8}
   (C.) $(-b)^8$ D. $-b^8$
6. You have 10 marbles. Your friend has 4 bags each containing m marbles. Which variable expression represents the total number of marbles you and your friend have?
   F. $4m + 10m$ G. $4 + 10m$
   (H.) $4m + 10$ J. $14m$
7. Solve for x: $32 = \frac{x}{-4}$.
   A. 128 (B.) −128
   C. −8 D. 28
8. Evaluate $4x - 3$ for $x = -4$.
   (F.) −19 G. 13
   H. −13 J. 19
9. Which ordered pair is a solution of $4y - 10 = x + 14$?
   A. (0, 8) (B.) (−4, 5)
   C. (−2, 5) D. (5, −4)
10. Point $Q(-1, 2)$ is translated 2 units down and 3 units left. What are the coordinates of its image point?
    F. (2, 4) G. (−3, −1)
    (H.) (−4, 0) J. (−1, −1)
11. Find $|-8| - |4|$.
    (A.) 4 B. −12
    C. −4 D. 12
12. Find $-8 \div \frac{2}{3}$.
    F. $-\frac{4}{3}$ (G.) −12
    H. $\frac{4}{3}$ J. 12

Problem Solving

Mountain Slopes

Students will use data from these two pages to answer the questions posed here in Put It All Together.

Activating Prior Knowledge

Have students share any experiences they have had mountain climbing. Invite them to discuss what was hardest, easiest, and most and least enjoyable for them. In addition, ask them to explain how to prepare for such an excursion—how to dress and what to eat, as well as what provisions and equipment to bring along on a climb.

Guided Instruction

Have volunteers read the various paragraphs about Mt. Washington.

History Connection
Have students research the contribution to the sport of mountain climbing made by Sir Edmund Hillary. Hillary and his Sherpa guide Tenzing Norgay were the first people to reach Earth's highest point, the summit of Mount Everest in the Himalayas. They reached the top on May 29, 1953.

Physical Education Connection
Have students learn more about the challenging sport of rock climbing. Have some volunteers find out about the skills, training, and equipment needed. Have others find out which mountains or rock faces draw the world's most devoted climbers.

Problem Solving Application

Applying Rate of Change

Mountain Slopes Mt. Washington, in New Hampshire, is the highest mountain in the northeastern United States. Although it is shorter than many mountains in the western United States, it still offers some challenging hiking. One part of its Great Gulf Trail rises 1,600 ft in 0.8 mi! When you plan a hike, you need to consider elevation gain as well as the length of the trail.

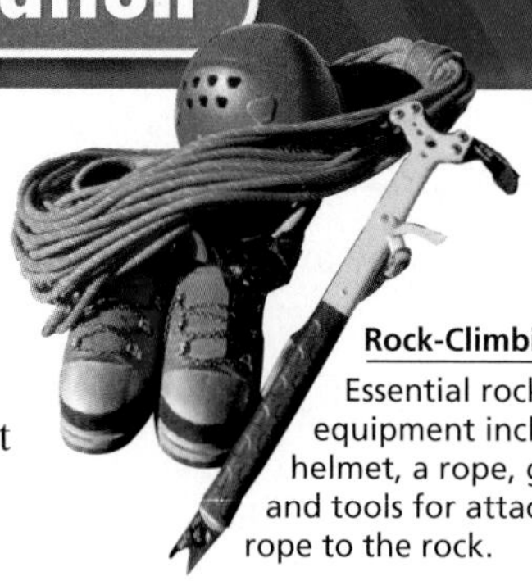

Rock-Climbing Gear

Essential rock-climbing equipment includes a helmet, a rope, good shoes, and tools for attaching your rope to the rock.

Ice on the Mt. Washington Observatory

In certain weather conditions, fog droplets freeze on rocks, trees, and the outside of the observatory. Crystal-like ice deposits can grow as tall as 10 ft! Weather observers break up the ice once an hour to keep it from interfering with the instruments at the observatory.

Windy Weather

Mt. Washington, with an elevation of 6,288 ft, is one of the windiest places on Earth. The annual mean wind speed is 35.1 mi/h, and the mountain holds the world record for greatest wind gust, 231 mi/h (April 12, 1934). Hurricane-force winds occur, on average, 100 days a year.

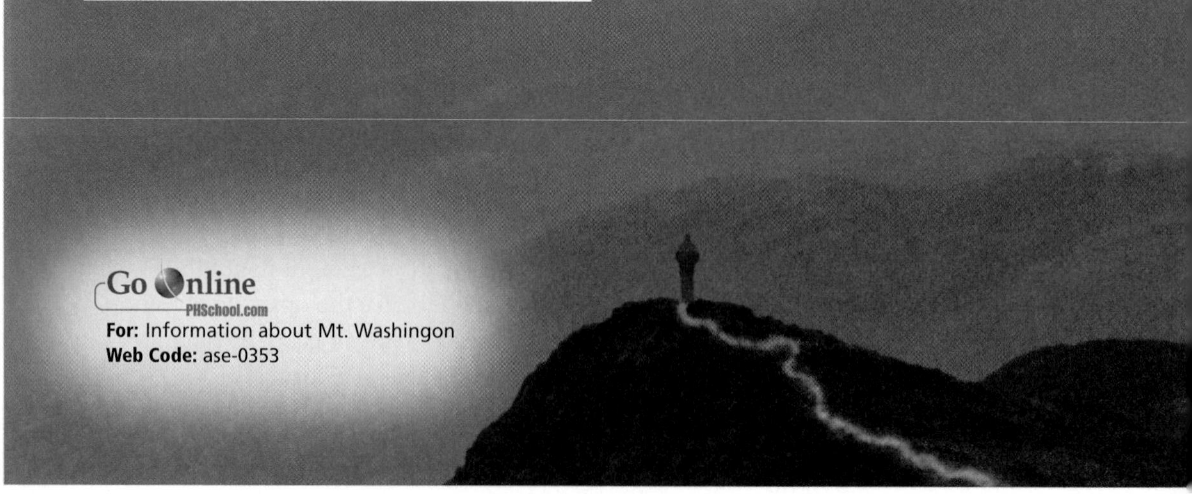

Go Online
PHSchool.com
For: Information about Mt. Washingon
Web Code: ase-0353

Put It All Together

Materials graph paper, ruler, watch or timer

Routes to the Top of Mount Washington

Route	Distance (mi)	Elevation Gain (ft)	Guidebook Time
Tuckerman Ravine Trail	4.2	4,300	4 h 15 min
Boott Spur Trail	5.4	4,300	4 h 50 min
Ammonoosuc Ravine Trail	4.5	3,800	4 h 10 min
Great Gulf Trail	7.9	5,000	6 h 25 min

SOURCE: Appalachian Mountain Club

1. The table shows four popular routes to the top of Mt. Washington.
  a. Why do some trails have different elevation gains even though they all end up at the top of Mt. Washington?
  b. Why do some trails have the same elevation gain but take different lengths of time to climb?
  c. **Reasoning** What does an elevation gain of 0 mean?

2. Make a graph to show the average elevation gain per hour for each trail. Place time on the x-axis and elevation gain on the y-axis. Label each line.

3. a. **Measurement** Measure the height of a flight of stairs. (*Hint:* If your home is on one level, measure a flight somewhere else.)
  b. Time yourself as you walk up the flight of stairs. How long does it take?
  c. Using your results from part (b), calculate the time it would take to gain 4,000 ft of elevation at the same rate.
  d. Add the stair-climbing data to your graph.
  e. **Writing in Math** How does your stair-climbing rate compare with the guidebook times in the table? Explain any differences.

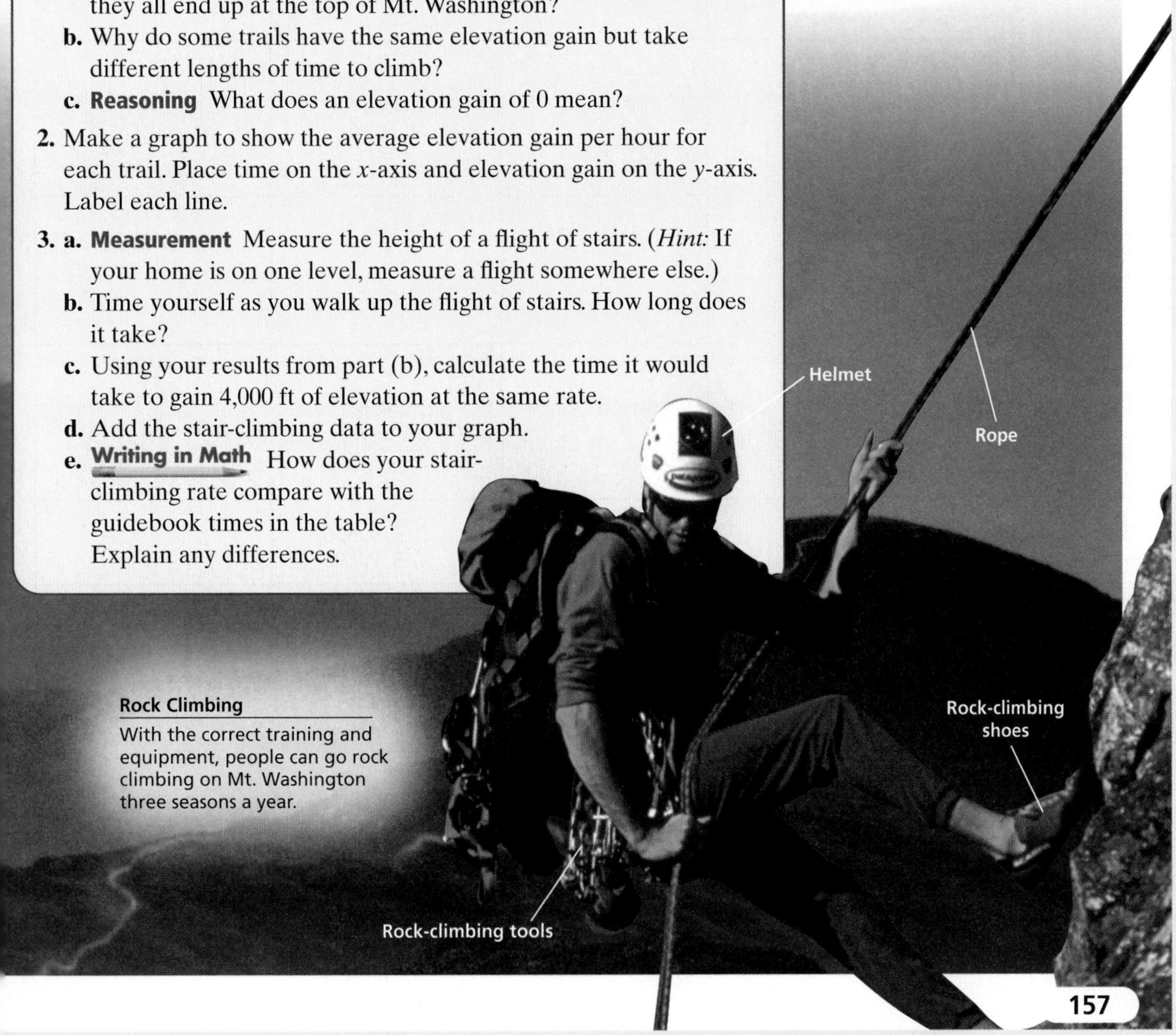

Rock Climbing
With the correct training and equipment, people can go rock climbing on Mt. Washington three seasons a year.

Activity

Have students work in pairs to answer the questions. Guide them to record data as they measure and accumulate it.

Exercise 2 Challenge students to use their number sense to pick the trail with the greatest elevation gain per hour. Elicit from them that the Tuckerman Ravine Trail will have the greatest elevation gain per hour, since hikers reach the same height as they do on Boott Spur Trail but in less time.

Exercise 3 Students use proportional reasoning when they use their stair climbs to determine how long it would take to climb 4,000 feet. You may wish to point out that in long climbs, fatigue and the need for rest can cause hiking speeds to decrease.

Differentiated Instruction

Special Needs L1
As needed, help students read the data in the table. Guide them to understand the distinction between trail distance and elevation gain. Ask questions such as:
- *Which is the longest trail?* Great Gulf
- *Which two trails have the same elevation gain?* Tuckerman Ravine and Boott Spur

1a. Different trails may start at a different number of feet above sea level.
b. Some trails wind around more and are longer. Some trails may be slower because they have particularly steep or difficult sections.
c. An elevation gain of 0 means that the starting elevation and ending elevation are the same. The trail between the start and finish may have hills and valleys.

2.
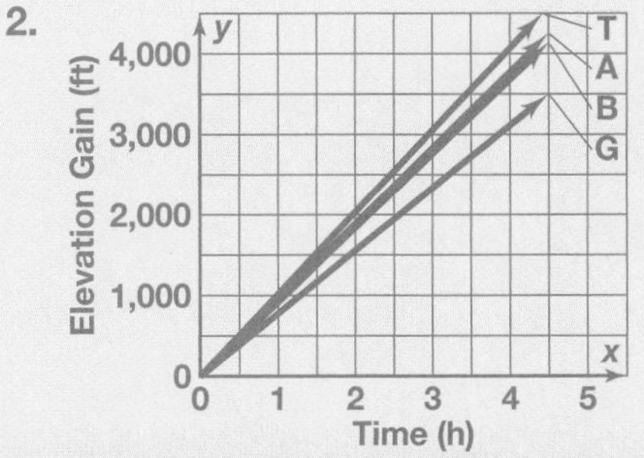

3a. Check students' work.
b. Answers will vary. Sample: about 1.5 ft/s
c. Answers will vary. Sample: about 44 min
d. Check students' work.
e. Check students' work.

4 Applications of Proportions

Chapter at a Glance

Lesson Titles, Objectives, and Features	Assessment	NCTM Standards	Local Standards
4-1 Ratios and Rates • To write ratios and unit rates and to use rates to solve problems **4-1b Activity Lab:** Finding Rates	Lesson Quiz	1, 2, 4, 5, 6, 7, 8, 9, 10	
4-2a Activity Lab: Choosing Units **4-2 Converting Units** • To convert units within and between the customary and metric systems	Lesson Quiz Checkpoint Quiz 1	1, 4, 6, 7, 8, 9, 10	
4-3a Activity Lab: Proportional and Nonproportional Relationships **4-3 Solving Proportions** • To identify and solve proportions **Guided Problem Solving:** Using Rates and Proportions	Lesson Quiz	1, 2, 3, 4, 6, 7, 8, 9, 10	
4-4 Similar Figures and Proportions • To identify similar figures and to use proportions to find missing measurements in similar figures **4-4b Activity Lab:** Ratios of Similar Figures	Lesson Quiz Checkpoint Quiz 2	1, 2, 3, 4, 6, 7, 8, 9, 10	
4-5a Activity Lab: Exploring Dilations **4-5 Similarity Transformations** • To graph dilations and to determine the scale factor of a dilation **4-5b Activity Lab, Technology:** Geometry Software and Dilations	Lesson Quiz	1, 2, 3, 4, 5, 6, 7, 8, 9, 10	
4-6 Scale Models and Maps • To use proportions to solve problems involving scale	Lesson Quiz	1, 2, 3, 4, 5, 6, 7, 8, 9, 10	
4-7a Activity Lab, Hands On: Using Similar Figures **4-7 Similarity and Indirect Measurement** • To use proportions and similar figures to solve problems	Lesson Quiz	1, 2, 3, 4, 6, 7, 8, 9, 10	
Problem Solving Application: Applying Proportions			

NCTM Standards 2000
1 Number and Operations **2** Algebra **3** Geometry **4** Measurement **5** Data Analysis and Probability
6 Problem Solving **7** Reasoning and Proof **8** Communication **9** Connections **10** Representation

Correlations to Standardized Tests

All content for these tests is contained in *Prentice Hall Math,* Course 3. This chart reflects coverage in this chapter only.

	4-1	4-2	4-3	4-4	4-5	4-6	4-7
Terra Nova CAT6 (Level 18)							
Number and Number Relations	✔		✔	✔		✔	✔
Computation and Numerical Estimation	✔	✔	✔	✔		✔	✔
Operation Concepts							
Measurement		✔				✔	✔
Geometry and Spatial Sense				✔	✔	✔	✔
Data Analysis, Statistics, and Probability							
Patterns, Functions, Algebra	✔		✔	✔		✔	
Problem Solving and Reasoning	✔	✔	✔	✔	✔	✔	✔
Communication	✔	✔	✔	✔	✔	✔	✔
Decimals, Fractions, Integers, Percent							
Order of Operations							
Algebraic Operations	✔		✔	✔		✔	
Terra Nova CTBS (Level 18)							
Decimals, Fractions, Integers, Percents							
Order of Operations, Numeration, Number Theory	✔		✔	✔		✔	✔
Data Interpretation							
Measurement		✔				✔	
Geometry				✔	✔	✔	✔
ITBS (Level 14)							
Number Properties and Operations	✔		✔	✔		✔	✔
Algebra	✔		✔	✔		✔	✔
Geometry				✔	✔	✔	✔
Measurement		✔					
Probability and Statistics							
Estimation		✔					
SAT10 (Adv 1 Level)							
Number Sense and Operations	✔		✔	✔		✔	✔
Patterns, Relationships, and Algebra	✔		✔	✔		✔	✔
Data, Statistics, and Probability							
Geometry and Measurement		✔		✔	✔	✔	✔
NAEP							
Number Sense, Properties, and Operations	✔	✔	✔	✔		✔	✔
Measurement		✔					✔
Geometry and Spatial Sense				✔	✔	✔	✔
Data Analysis, Statistics, and Probability							
Algebra and Functions			✔				

CAT6 California Achievement Test, 6th Ed. **CTBS** Comprehensive Test of Basic Skills **ITBS** Iowa Test of Basic Skills, Form M
SAT10 Stanford Achievement Test, 10th Ed. **NAEP** National Assessment of Educational Progress 2005 Mathematics Objectives

Math Background

Professional Development

Skills Trace

BEFORE Chapter 4

Course 2 introduced basic ratios, unit rates, and proportions.

DURING Chapter 4

Course 3 reviews and extends ratios, rates, and proportions to applications of similar figures and indirect measurement.

AFTER Chapter 4

Throughout this course students apply proportional reasoning to solve real-world problems.

4-1 Ratios and Rates

Math Understandings

- Ratios can compare a part to a part, a part to the whole, or the whole to a part.
- All ratios can be written in fraction form $\frac{a}{b}$.
- All fractions are ratios but not all ratios are fractions.
- Unit rates and unit prices are special kinds of ratios that are useful in making comparisons.

Ratio	
A ratio is a comparison of two quantities by division.	
Arithmetic	**Algebra**
5 to 8 $\frac{5}{8}$ 5 : 8	a to b $\frac{a}{b}$ $a : b$ *where* $b \neq 0$

A **rate** is a ratio that compares quantities measured in different units, such as miles to gallons or feet to seconds. A **unit rate** is the rate for one unit of a given quantity. The unit rate of an item for sale, called the unit price, is useful when you compare to find the best buy.

Example: Find the unit rate for typing 114 words in 3 minutes.

$$\frac{\text{words}}{\text{min}} = \frac{114 \text{ words}}{3 \text{ min}}$$
$$= 38 \text{ words/min}$$

4-2 Converting Units

Math Understandings

- Units can give a feeling for the size of the quantity.
- You can convert between units within the customary system or the metric system. You can also convert between the two systems.
- When you use a conversion factor, you are multiplying by 1, which results in an equivalent expression.

The rates $\frac{3 \text{ ft}}{1 \text{ yd}}$ and $\frac{1 \text{ yd}}{3 \text{ ft}}$ are **conversion factors,** which are rates equal to 1. **Dimensional analysis** is the process of analyzing units to decide which conversion factor(s) to use. Sometimes you need to use two or more conversion factors.

Example: Use dimensional analysis to find an equal rate in inches per minute.

$$\frac{15 \text{ ft}}{1 \text{ s}} = \frac{15 \text{ ft}}{1 \text{ s}} \cdot \frac{12 \text{ in.}}{1 \text{ ft}} \cdot \frac{60 \text{ s}}{1 \text{ min}} = 10{,}800 \text{ in./min}$$

4-3 Solving Proportions and 4-4 Similar Figures and Proportions

Math Understandings

- The Cross Products Property is true because of the Multiplication Property of Equality.
- When you write a proportion to solve a problem, both ratios must make the same kind of comparison, either part to part, part to whole, or whole to part.
- Two congruent figures are always similar, while two similar figures are not necessarily congruent.

A **proportion** is an equation stating that two ratios are equal. For two ratios, the **cross products** are found by multiplying the denominator of each ratio by the numerator of the other ratio.

Cross Products Property	
For two ratios, the cross products are found by multiplying the denominator of each ratio by the numerator of the other ratio.	
Arithmetic	**Algebra**
$\frac{6}{10} = \frac{9}{15}$	$\frac{a}{b} = \frac{c}{d}$, where $b \neq 0$ and $d \neq 0$
$6 \cdot 15 = 10 \cdot 9$	$ad = bc$

Figures that have the same shape but not necessarily the same size are **similar figures.** Angles that have equal measures are called **congruent angles.** If two polygons are similar, then corresponding angles are congruent and lengths of corresponding sides are in proportion.

4-5 Similarity Transformations

Math Understandings

- Translations, reflections, and rotations change a figure's position, but not its size or shape. A dilation transformation changes the size but not the shape.
- To define a dilation, you need to know the scale factor and the point that is the center of dilation.

A **dilation** is a transformation in which a figure and its image are similar. The ratio of the new image to the original figure is called the **scale factor.** A dilation with a scale factor greater than 1 is called an **enlargement.** The image of an enlargement is larger than the original figure. A dilation with a scale factor less than 1 is called a **reduction.** The image of a reduction is smaller than the original figure.

4-6 Scale Models and Maps

Math Understandings

- A scale model can be smaller or larger than the object that it represents.
- You can use the scale of a map to find actual distances between locations.

A **scale model** is similar to the actual object it represents.
Example:

The scale of a map is 1 in. : 12 mi. The actual miles a $5\frac{3}{4}$ in. measure represents is about 69 miles as shown.

$\frac{1}{12} = \frac{5.75}{x}$
$x = 12 \cdot 5.75$
$x = 69$

4-7 Similarity and Indirect Measurement

Math Understandings

- Using indirect measurement to determine the height of objects uses the properties of similar triangles.

Indirect measurement is the method of determining length or distance using a proportion without measuring directly.

Example: A person 6 ft tall casts a 10-ft shadow. A building nearby casts a 74-ft shadow. The building is about 44 ft tall.

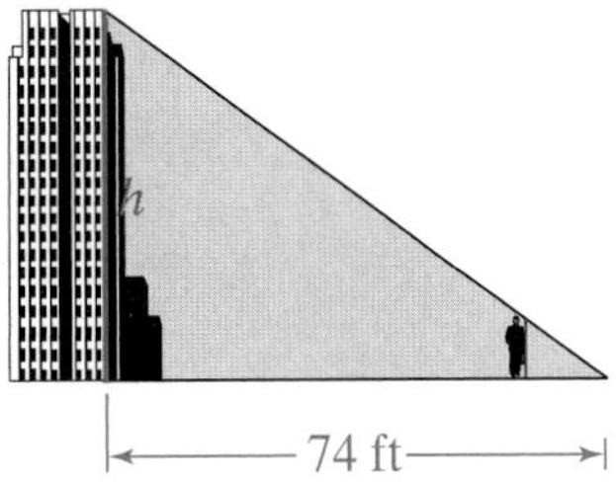

Additional Professional Development Opportunities

Professional Development

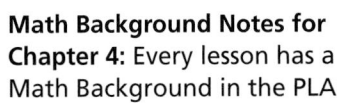

Math Background Notes for Chapter 4: Every lesson has a Math Background in the PLAN section.

Research Overview, Mathematics Strands
Additional support for these topics and more is in the front of the Teacher's Edition.

LessonLab
LessonLab, a Pearson Education company, offers comprehensive, facilitated professional development designed to help teachers to improve student achievement. To learn more, please visit lessonlab.com.

Chapter 4 Resources

	4-1	4-2	4-3	4-4	4-5	4-6	4-7	For the Chapter
Print Resources								
L3 Practice	●	●	●	●	●	●	●	
L1 Adapted Practice	●	●	●	●	●	●	●	
L3 Guided Problem Solving	●	●	●	●	●	●	●	
L2 Reteaching	●	●	●	●	●	●	●	
L4 Enrichment	●	●	●	●	●	●	●	
L3 Daily Notetaking Guide	●	●	●	●	●	●	●	
L1 Adapted Daily Notetaking Guide	●	●	●	●	●	●	●	
L3 Vocabulary and Study Skills Worksheets	●		●	●	●		●	●
L3 Daily Puzzles	●	●	●	●	●	●	●	
L3 Activity Labs	●	●	●	●	●	●	●	
L3 Checkpoint Quiz		●		●				
L3 Chapter Project								●
L2 Below Level Chapter Test								●
L3 Chapter Test								●
L4 Alternative Assessment								●
L3 Cumulative Review								●
Spanish Resources ELL								
L3 Practice	●	●	●	●	●	●	●	●
L3 Vocabulary and Study Skills Worksheets	●		●	●	●		●	●
L3 Checkpoint Quiz		●		●				
L2 Below Level Chapter Test								●
L3 Chapter Test								●
L4 Alternative Assessment								●
L3 Cumulative Review								●
Transparencies								
Check Skills You'll Need	●	●	●	●	●	●	●	
Additional Examples	●	●	●	●	●	●	●	
Problem of the Day	●	●	●	●	●	●	●	
Classroom Aid	●	●	●		●		●	
Student Edition Answers	●	●	●	●	●	●	●	●
Lesson Quiz	●	●	●	●	●	●	●	
Test-Taking Strategies								●
Technology								
Interactive Textbook Online	●	●	●	●	●	●	●	●
StudentExpress™ CD-ROM	●	●	●	●	●	●	●	●
Success Tracker™ Online Intervention	●	●	●	●	●	●	●	●
TeacherExpress™ CD-ROM	●	●	●	●	●	●	●	●
PresentationExpress™ with QuickTake Presenter CD-ROM	●	●	●	●	●	●	●	●
ExamView® Assessment Suite CD-ROM	●	●	●	●	●	●	●	●
MindPoint® Quiz Show CD-ROM								●
Prentice Hall Web Site: PHSchool.com	●	●	●	●	●	●	●	●

Also available: **Prentice Hall Assessment System**
- Progress Monitoring Assessments
- Skills and Concepts Review
- Test Prep Workbook

Other Resources
Algebra Readiness Tests
All-in-One Student Workbook
All-in-One Student Workbook, Adapted Version
Multilingual Handbook
Solution Key
Math Notes Study Folder
Spanish Cumulative Assessment

Where You Can Use the Lesson Resources

Here is a suggestion, following the four-step teaching plan, for how you can incorporate Differentiated Instruction Resources into your teaching.

	Instructional Resources L3	Differentiated Instruction Resources
1. Plan		
Preparation Read the Math Background in the Teacher's Edition to connect this lesson with students' previous experience. **Starting Class** **Check Skills You'll Need** Assign these exercises to review prerequisite skills. **New Vocabulary** Help students pre-read the lesson by pointing out the new terms introduced in the lesson.	**Math Background** **Math Understandings** **Transparencies & PresentationExpress™ with QuickTake Presenter CD-ROM** Check Skills You'll Need Problem of the Day **Resources** Vocabulary and Study Skills	**Spanish Support** ELL Vocabulary Masters with Study Skills
2. Teach		
L3 **Guided Instruction** Use the Activity Labs to build conceptual understanding. Teach each Example. Use the Teacher's Edition side column notes for specific teaching tips, including Error Prevention notes. Use the Additional Examples found in the side column (and on transparency and PowerPoint) as an alternative presentation for the content. After each Example, assign the Quick Check exercise for that Example to get an immediate assessment of student understanding. Use the Closure activity in the Teacher's Edition to help students attain mastery of lesson content.	**Student Edition** Activity Lab **Resources** Daily Notetaking Guide Activity Lab **Transparencies & PresentationExpress™ with QuickTake Presenter CD-ROM** Additional Examples Classroom Aids **ExamView® Assessment Suite CD-ROM**	**Teacher's Edition** Every lesson includes suggestions for working with students who need special attention. L1 Special Needs L2 Below Level L4 Advanced Learners ELL English Language Learners **Resources** L1 Adapted Daily Notetaking Guide **Multilingual Handbook**
3. Practice		
Assignment Guide **Check Your Understanding** Use these questions to check students' understanding before you assign homework. **Homework Exercises** Assign homework from these leveled exercises in the Assignment Guide. **A** Practice by Example **B** Apply Your Skills **C** Challenge Test Prep and Mixed Review **Homework Quick Check** Use these key exercises to quickly check students' homework.	**Transparencies & PresentationExpress™ with QuickTake Presenter CD-ROM** Student Answers **Resources** Practice Guided Problem Solving Vocabulary and Study Skills Activity Lab Daily Puzzles **ExamView® Assessment Suite CD-ROM**	**Spanish Support** ELL Practice ELL Vocabulary and Study Skills **Resources** L1 Adapted Practice L4 Enrichment
4. Assess & Reteach		
Lesson Quiz Assign the Lesson Quiz to assess students' mastery of the lesson content. **Checkpoint Quiz** Use the Checkpoint Quiz to assess student progress over several lessons.	**Transparencies & PresentationExpress™ with QuickTake Presenter CD-ROM** Lesson Quiz **Resources** Checkpoint Quiz	**Resources** L2 Reteaching ELL Checkpoint Quiz Success Tracker™ Online Intervention **ExamView® Assessment Suite CD-ROM**

KEY L1 Special Needs L2 Below Level L3 For All Students L4 Advanced, Gifted ELL English Language Learners

CHAPTER 4

Applications of Proportions

Check Your Readiness

Answers for students are in the back of the textbook.

For intervention, direct students to:

Equivalent Forms of Rational Numbers
Lesson 2-2
Extra Skills and Word Problems Practice, Ch. 2

Multiplying and Dividing Rational Numbers
Lesson 2-5
Extra Skills and Word Problems Practice, Ch. 2

The Pythagorean Theorem
Lesson 3-3
Extra Skills and Word Problems Practice, Ch. 3

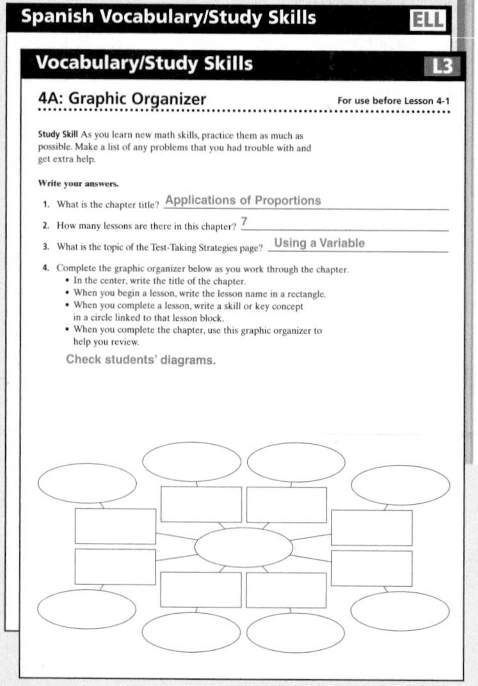
Spanish Vocabulary/Study Skills ELL

Vocabulary/Study Skills L3

4A: Graphic Organizer — For use before Lesson 4-1

Study Skill As you learn new math skills, practice them as much as possible. Make a list of any problems that you had trouble with and get extra help.

Write your answers.

1. What is the chapter title? Applications of Proportions
2. How many lessons are there in this chapter? 7
3. What is the topic of the Test-Taking Strategies page? Using a Variable
4. Complete the graphic organizer below as you work through the chapter.
   - In the center, write the title of the chapter.
   - When you begin a lesson, write the lesson name in a rectangle.
   - When you complete a lesson, write a skill or key concept in a circle linked to that lesson block.
   - When you complete the chapter, use this graphic organizer to help you review.

   Check students' diagrams.

CHAPTER 4 Applications of Proportions

What You've Learned

- In Chapter 1, you used equations to solve problems.
- In Chapter 3, you used the Pythagorean Theorem to find missing measurements in triangles.
- You also graphed translations, reflections, and rotations in the coordinate plane.

Check Your Readiness

GO for Help

For Exercises	See Lessons
1–9	2-2
10–15	2-5
16–18	3-3

Equivalent Forms of Rational Numbers

Write each fraction in simplest form.

1. $\frac{34}{68}$ $\frac{1}{2}$ **2.** $\frac{32}{112}$ $\frac{2}{7}$ **3.** $\frac{45}{63}$ $\frac{5}{7}$ **4.** $\frac{66}{120}$ $\frac{11}{20}$

Write each fraction as a decimal. Round to three decimal places.

5. $\frac{17}{27}$ 0.630 **6.** $\frac{49}{12}$ 4.083 **7.** $\frac{10}{31}$ 0.323 **8.** $\frac{19}{7}$ 2.714 **9.** $\frac{18}{35}$ 0.514

Algebra Multiplying and Dividing Rational Numbers

Solve each equation.

10. $\frac{1}{2}k = 28$ 56 **11.** $3b = \frac{3}{4}$ $\frac{1}{4}$ **12.** $\frac{3}{4}t = \frac{5}{8}$ $\frac{5}{6}$

13. $2y = \frac{9}{8}$ $\frac{9}{16}$ **14.** $\frac{5}{6}r = \frac{7}{2}$ $4\frac{1}{5}$ **15.** $\frac{1}{3}x = 10$ 30

The Pythagorean Theorem

Find the missing side length. Round to the nearest tenth.

16.
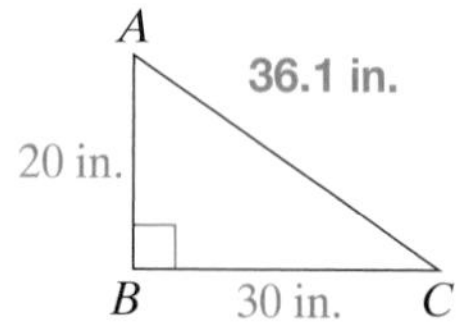

17.
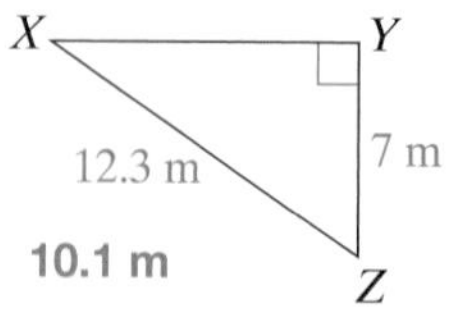

18.
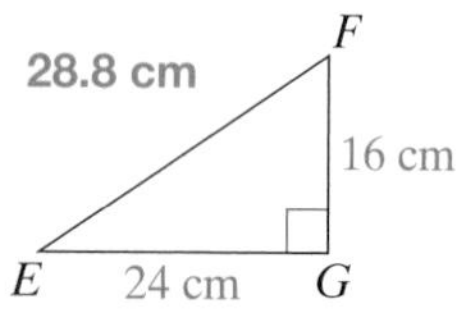

Chapter 4 Overview

In this chapter, students learn about ratios, rates, and proportions. They learn how to use proportions to solve problems involving similar polygons, scale models, and indirect measurement.

Activating Prior Knowledge

In this chapter, students build on their knowledge of rational numbers, of transformations, and of writing and solving equations to further investigate ratios and to write and solve proportions in order to solve a variety of problems. Ask questions such as:

- *Write the following in order from least to greatest:* $-3, 6, 4\frac{1}{2}, -1.5$. $-3, -1.5, 4\frac{1}{2}, 6$
- *Which of the following fractions is expressed in simplest form?* $\frac{4}{6}, \frac{8}{21}, \frac{3}{12}, \frac{9}{36}$ $\frac{8}{21}$
- *Solve* $3n + 15 = 39$. $n = 8$

What You'll Learn Next

- In this chapter, you will solve problems involving ratios, rates, and proportions.
- You will use proportions in real-world applications, including scale models and indirect measurements.
- You will graph dilations in the coordinate plane.

Problem Solving Application On pages 206 and 207, you will work an extended activity on burning Calories.

Key Vocabulary

- congruent angles (p. 181)
- conversion factor (p. 167)
- cross products (p. 175)
- dilation (p. 187)
- enlargement (p. 188)
- indirect measurement (p. 197)
- proportion (p. 174)
- rate (p. 161)
- reduction (p. 188)
- scale (p. 192)
- scale factor (p. 187)
- scale model (p. 192)
- similar figures (p. 181)
- similar polygons (p. 181)
- unit rate (p. 161)

4-1

1. Plan

Objective
To write ratios and unit rates and to use rates to solve problems

Examples
1 Writing a Ratio in Simplest Form
2 Finding a Unit Rate
3 Application: Consumer Prices

Math Understandings: p. 158C

Professional Development

Math Background

A ratio compares two quantities by division. A ratio can be expressed in three different forms: 1 to 3, 1 : 3, and $\frac{1}{3}$. Although a ratio is commonly stated in the form of a fraction (as in $\frac{3}{2}$), a ratio can also be a whole number (as in $\frac{6}{1}$ or 6).

A *rate* is a type of ratio in which two quantities are measured in different units, such as 50 miles per hour. Miles per hour is an example of a *unit rate* because it is a rate for one unit of a given quantity (hours). So, unit rates are commonly expressed as decimals or whole numbers instead of fractions with a denominator of 1.

More Math Background: p. 158C

Lesson Planning and Resources

See p. 158E for a list of the resources that support this lesson.

PowerPoint

Bell Ringer Practice

Check Skills You'll Need
For intervention, direct students to:
Comparing and Ordering Rational Numbers
Lesson 2-3
Extra Skills and Word Problems Practice, Ch. 2

4-1 Ratios and Rates

Check Skills You'll Need

1. **Vocabulary Review** What is the *least common denominator* of two rational numbers? See below.

Determine which rational number is greater.

2. $\frac{3}{9}, \frac{1}{6}$ $\frac{3}{9}$
3. $\frac{15}{25}, \frac{4}{5}$ $\frac{4}{5}$
4. $\frac{45}{54}, \frac{2}{3}$ $\frac{45}{54}$
5. $\frac{4}{7}, \frac{7}{12}$ $\frac{7}{12}$

GO for Help Lesson 2-3

Check Skills You'll Need

1. The least common denominator is the smallest multiple the denominators have in common.

What You'll Learn

To write ratios and unit rates and to use rates to solve problems

New Vocabulary rate, unit rate

Why Learn This?

When you shop, you make decisions based on both price and quantity. You can use ratios to compare quantities of different products.

KEY CONCEPTS Ratio

A ratio is a comparison of two quantities by division. You can write a ratio in three ways.

Arithmetic	Algebra
5 to 8 $\quad \frac{5}{8} \quad$ 5 : 8	a to b $\quad \frac{a}{b} \quad$ $a : b$ where $b \neq 0$

To write a ratio in simplest form, first write it as a fraction. Then find the simplest form of the fraction. The simplest form of a ratio can be a whole number.

EXAMPLE Writing a Ratio in Simplest Form

1 Write the ratio 50 seconds : 2 minutes in simplest form.

$\frac{50 \text{ s}}{2 \text{ min}} = \frac{50 \not{s}}{120 \not{s}}$ ← Convert minutes to seconds so that both measures are in the same units. Divide the common units.

$\frac{50}{120} = \frac{50 \div 10}{120 \div 10}$ ← Divide the numerator and the denominator by the GCF, 10.

$= \frac{5}{12}$ ← Simplify.

The ratio of 50 seconds : 2 minutes is $\frac{5}{12}$.

Quick Check

1. Write the ratio $\frac{30 \text{ s}}{3 \text{ min}}$ in simplest form. $\frac{1}{6}$

Online active math

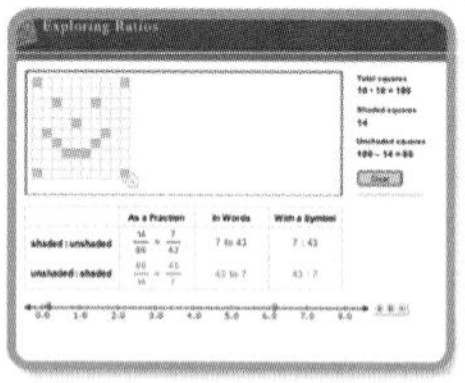

For: Exploring Ratios Activity
Use: Interactive Textbook, 4-1

Differentiated Instruction Solutions for All Learners

Special Needs L1	Below Level L2
On the board, write a (1) next to *oz* in the unit rates used in Example 3. Make sure students understand that dividing $2.99 by 64 ounces gives them the cost for one ounce. learning style: visual	Students use counters or tiles in two colors to model ratios 2 : 5, 5 : 4 and 2 : 1. Then they write each ratio three different ways, such as 2 : 5, 2 to 5, and $\frac{2}{5}$. learning style: tactile

A **rate** is a ratio that compares quantities measured in different units, such as miles to gallons or feet to seconds. A **unit rate** is the rate for one unit of a given quantity.

If a car travels 120 mi on 4 gal of gasoline, then the rate is $\frac{120\text{ mi}}{4\text{ gal}}$. The unit rate is $\frac{30\text{ mi}}{1\text{ gal}}$, or 30 mi/gal.

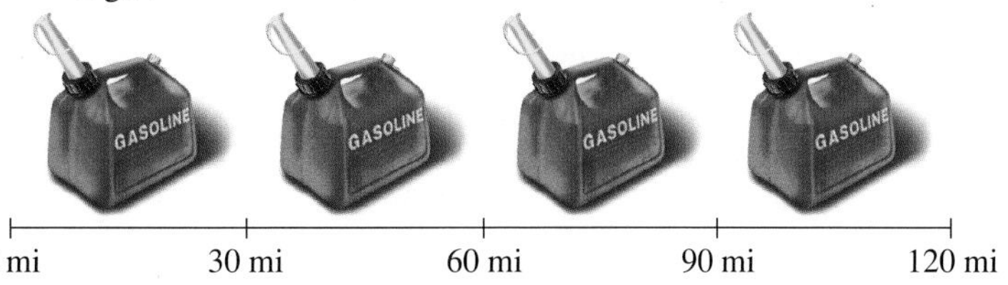

GO Online

Video Tutor Help
Visit: PHSchool.com
Web Code: ase-0775

EXAMPLE **Finding a Unit Rate**

2 **Cycling** A team finished the 200-lap Indiana Little 500 race in 2 hours and 4 minutes, or about 2.07 hours. Find the unit rate of laps per hour.

$\frac{\text{number of laps}}{\text{number of hours}} = \frac{200\text{ laps}}{2.07\text{ hours}}$ ← **Write a rate comparing laps to hours.**

≈ 96.6 laps/hour ← **Divide. Round to the nearest tenth.**

The unit rate is about 96.6 laps per hour.

Quick Check

2. Find the unit rate for 52 deliveries in 8 hours. **6.5 deliveries/h**

At a grocery store, the unit rate, or unit cost, is posted for each item. Unit costs help consumers compare prices of items in different sizes.

EXAMPLE **Application: Consumer Prices**

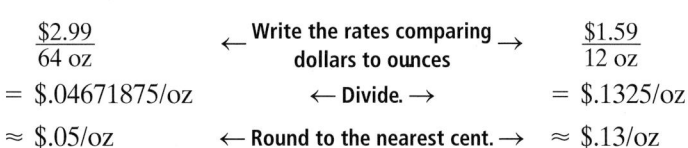

3 Find the unit cost for each bottle. Which size bottle is the better buy?

$\frac{\$2.99}{64\text{ oz}}$ ← **Write the rates comparing dollars to ounces** → $\frac{\$1.59}{12\text{ oz}}$

$= \$.04671875/\text{oz}$ ← **Divide.** → $= \$.1325/\text{oz}$

$\approx \$.05/\text{oz}$ ← **Round to the nearest cent.** → $\approx \$.13/\text{oz}$

The 64-oz bottle has the lower unit cost. This size is the better buy.

Check for Reasonableness $\$.05 \cdot 64 = \$3.20$ and $\$3.20 \approx \$2.99$. Also, $\$.13 \cdot 12 = \$1.56$ and $\$1.56 \approx \$1.59$. The answers are reasonable.

Quick Check

3. The cost of a 20-oz box of cereal is $4.29. A 12-oz box of the same cereal costs $3.59. Which box of cereal is a better buy? **the 20-oz box**

2. Teach

Activity Lab

Use before the lesson.

All in One Teaching Resources

Activity Lab 4-1: Ratios and Rates

Guided Instruction

Teaching Tip
Explain that 96.6 laps/1 hour can be written as 96.6 laps/hour.

Error Prevention!

Students may try to simplify a ratio, for instance, writing $\frac{3}{2}$ as a mixed number. Remind students that a ratio is a comparison which is easy to see when the ratio is written as a fraction, even an improper fraction.

PowerPoint

Additional Examples

1 Write the ratio 36 seconds to 12 minutes in simplest form. $\frac{36}{720} = \frac{1}{20}$

2 Computer time costs $4.50 for 30 min. What is the unit rate? **$.15 per minute**

3 Keneesha drove her car 267 miles using 11 gallons of gas. Vanessa drove her car 210 mi using 9 gal. Give the unit rate for each. **Keneesha, about 24.3 mi/gal, Vanessa, about 23.3 mi/gal** Which car got more miles per gallons of gas? **Keneesha's car**

All in One Teaching Resources
- Daily Notetaking Guide 4-1 **L3**
- Adapted Notetaking 4-1 **L1**

Closure

- Explain the differences among a ratio, a rate, and a unit rate. **Sample: A ratio compares two quantities. A rate is a ratio that compares quantities with different units. A unit rate is a rate that has 1 unit as the denominator.**

Advanced Learners L4	**English Language Learners** ELL
Students use food product labels to make a table comparing the unit rate of Calories per serving for some of their favorite foods. **learning style: verbal**	Explicitly tell students that every unit rate has a denominator of 1. Also, have students discuss the meaning of "a better buy." Make sure they understand that a larger amount is not necessarily a better buy. **learning style: verbal**

3. Practice

Assignment Guide

Check Your Understanding

Go over Exercises 1–7 in class before assigning the Homework Exercises.

Homework Exercises

A	Practice by Example	8–21
B	Apply Your Skills	22–29
C	Challenge	30
	Test Prep and Mixed Review	31–37

Homework Quick Check

To check students' understanding of key skills and concepts, go over Exercises 17, 21, 23, 25, and 29.

Differentiated Instruction Resources

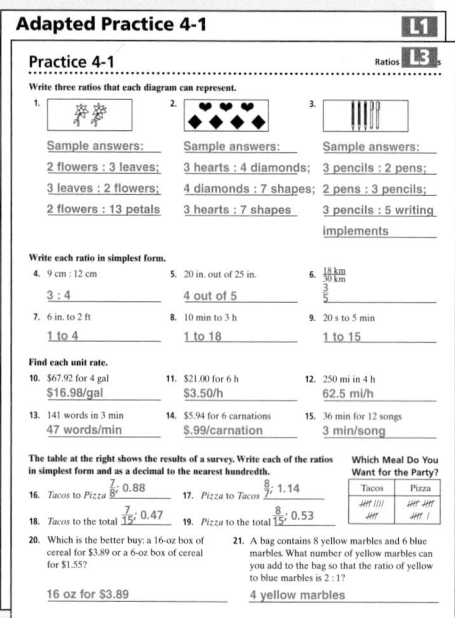

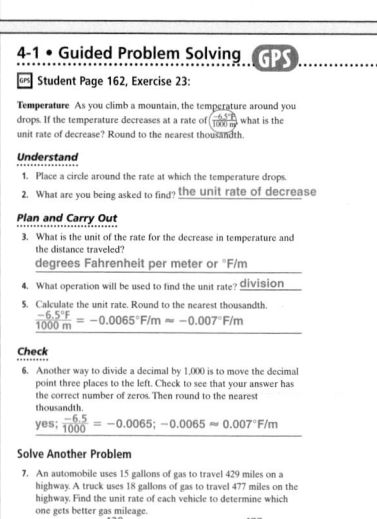

Adapted Practice 4-1 L1

Practice 4-1 Ratios L3

Write three ratios that each diagram can represent.

1. 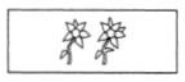
Sample answers:
2 flowers : 3 leaves;
3 leaves : 2 flowers;
2 flowers : 13 petals

2. 
Sample answers:
3 hearts : 4 diamonds;
4 diamonds : 7 shapes;
3 hearts : 7 shapes

3. 
Sample answers:
3 pencils : 2 pens;
2 pens : 3 pencils;
3 pencils : 5 writing implements

Write each ratio in simplest form.

4. 9 cm : 12 cm 3 : 4
5. 20 in. out of 25 in. 4 out of 5
6. $\frac{18\text{ km}}{30\text{ km}}$ $\frac{3}{5}$
7. 6 in. to 2 ft 1 to 4
8. 10 min to 3 h 1 to 18
9. 20 s to 5 min 1 to 15

Find each unit rate.

10. \$67.92 for 4 gal \$16.98/gal
11. \$21.00 for 6 h \$3.50/h
12. 250 mi in 4 h 62.5 mi/h
13. 141 words in 3 min 47 words/min
14. \$5.94 for 6 carnations \$.99/carnation
15. 36 min for 12 songs 3 min/song

The table at the right shows the results of a survey. Write each of the ratios in simplest form and as a decimal to the nearest hundredth.

Which Meal Do You Want for the Party?

Tacos	Pizza
卌 |||| 卌	卌 卌 卌 |

16. *Tacos* to *Pizza* $\frac{7}{8}$; 0.88
17. *Pizza* to *Tacos* $\frac{8}{7}$; 1.14
18. *Tacos* to the total $\frac{7}{15}$; 0.47
19. *Pizza* to the total $\frac{8}{15}$; 0.53
20. Which is the better buy: a 16-oz box of cereal for \$3.89 or a 6-oz box of cereal for \$1.55? 16 oz for \$3.89
21. A bag contains 8 yellow marbles and 6 blue marbles. What number of yellow marbles can you add to the bag so that the ratio of yellow to blue marbles is 2 : 1? 4 yellow marbles

4-1 • Guided Problem Solving GPS L3

GPS Student Page 162, Exercise 23:

Temperature As you climb a mountain, the temperature around you drops. If the temperature decreases at a rate of $\frac{-6.5°F}{1000\text{ m}}$, what is the unit rate of decrease? Round to the nearest thousandth.

Understand

1. Place a circle around the rate at which the temperature drops.
2. What are you being asked to find? the unit rate of decrease

Plan and Carry Out

3. What is the unit of the rate for the decrease in temperature and the distance traveled? degrees Fahrenheit per meter or °F/m
4. What operation will be used to find the unit rate? division
5. Calculate the unit rate. Round to the nearest thousandth. $\frac{-6.5°F}{1000\text{ m}} = -0.0065°F/m \approx -0.007°F/m$

Check

6. Another way to divide a decimal by 1,000 is to move the decimal point three places to the left. Check to see that your answer has the correct number of zeros. Then round to the nearest thousandth. yes; $\frac{-6.5}{1000} = -0.0065$; $-0.0065 \approx 0.007°F/m$

Solve Another Problem

7. An automobile uses 15 gallons of gas to travel 429 miles on a highway. A truck uses 18 gallons of gas to travel 477 miles on the highway. Find the unit rate of each vehicle to determine which one gets better gas mileage. automobile: $\frac{429}{15} = 28.6$ mi/gal; truck: $\frac{477}{18} = 26.5$ mi/gal. The automobile gets better gas mileage.

Check Your Understanding

1. A rate is a ratio that compares quantities measured in different units. The quantities 6 and 23 have the same unit of students.

1. **Vocabulary** How do you know that the ratio *6 students out of 23 students* is not a rate?

Write each ratio using the ladybugs and ants.

2. ants to all insects 4 : 7
3. ladybugs to ants 3 : 4
4. ladybugs to all insects 3 : 7

Write each ratio in simplest form.

5. 16 cm : 8 cm $\frac{2}{1}$
6. 10 s to 2 min $\frac{1}{12}$
7. $\frac{32\text{ in.}}{4\text{ ft}}$ $\frac{2}{3}$

Homework Exercises

For more exercises, see Extra Skills and Word Problems.

GO for Help

For Exercises	See Examples
8–13	1
14–21	2 and 3

A **Write each ratio in simplest form.**

8. 50 m : 30 m $\frac{5}{3}$
9. $\frac{28\text{ s}}{2\text{ min}}$ $\frac{7}{30}$
10. $\frac{80\text{ yd}}{120\text{ ft}}$ $\frac{2}{1}$
11. 22 in. to 3 ft $\frac{11}{18}$
12. 6 ft to 6 yd $\frac{1}{3}$
13. 36 cm : 132 cm $\frac{3}{11}$

Find each unit rate.

14. 36 gal in 12 min 3 gal/min
15. \$42 for 3 books \$14/book
16. 300 ft in 48 s 6.25 ft/s
17. \$21.60 for 12 roses \$1.80/rose
18. 200 m in 16 s 12.5 m/s
19. 676 mi in 13 h 52 mi/h
20. **Water** A water pump moves 330 gallons of water in 22 minutes. Find the unit rate. 15 gal/min
21. **Food** A 32-oz container of yogurt costs \$2.69. An 8-oz container of the same yogurt costs \$.75. Find the unit cost of each container. Which container of yogurt is the better buy? \$.08/oz; \$.09/oz; the 32-oz container

B GPS

22. **Guided Problem Solving** *Apollo 11* traveled about 237,000 miles to the moon in about 103 hours. *Apollo 12* made the same trip in about 123 hours. Find the difference in the rates of travel of the two spacecraft. Round to the nearest whole number. 374 mi/h
   - What ratio represents the rate of *Apollo 11*?
   - What ratio represents the rate of *Apollo 12*?

GO Online
Homework Video Tutor
Visit: PHSchool.com
Web Code: ase-0401

23. **Temperature** As you climb a mountain, the temperature of the air (GPS) around you drops. If the temperature decreases at a rate of $\frac{-6.5°C}{1{,}000\text{ m}}$, what is the unit rate of decrease? Round to the nearest thousandth. −0.007°C/m

Write each ratio as a fraction in simplest form.

24. $11\frac{1}{3}$ out of $50\frac{2}{3}$ $\frac{17}{76}$ **25.** $5\frac{1}{4}$ out of $20\frac{3}{4}$ $\frac{21}{83}$ **26.** $28\frac{1}{2} : 30\frac{1}{4}$ $\frac{114}{121}$

27. Travel During a 7.5-hour drive, a car's mileage indicator starts at 18,560 mi and ends at 18,980 mi. What is the car's rate of travel? 56 mi/h

28. Syrup Each year in Vermont, about 1,200 farmers produce about 410,000 gal of maple syrup. A typical farmer collects about 8,750 gal of sap. The sap produces 250 gal of syrup, which sells for about \$4.50 per half pint. 28a. 35 : 1 b. about 342 gal/grower c. \$72

a. Write a ratio, in simplest form, of the number of gallons of sap a grower collects to the number of gallons of syrup produced.

b. Find the unit rate of the number of gallons of maple syrup produced per year to the number of maple growers in Vermont.

c. Suppose a gallon of syrup has the same unit cost as a half pint. How much does a gallon of maple syrup cost? (1 gal = 8 pt)

Careers Farmers manage their crops and estimate how much profit they will make.

29. Writing in Math Your friend is 16 years old and her sister is 12 years old. In 3 years, will the ratio of their ages change? Explain. See left.

29. The ratio will change from $\frac{16}{12}$ to $\frac{19}{15}$, which is not the same.

Ⓒ **30. Challenge** A bag contains 7 red marbles and 5 black marbles. You add 60 marbles to the bag while keeping the ratio of red marbles to black marbles the same. How many of each color should you add? 25 black and 35 red

Test Prep and Mixed Review

Practice

Multiple Choice

31. Ryan mows a 4,000-square-foot lawn in 30 minutes. Which is closest to the number of square feet Ryan cuts in 1 minute? A

Ⓐ $133\frac{1}{3}$ ft^2 Ⓑ $133\frac{2}{3}$ ft^2 Ⓒ $134\frac{1}{3}$ ft^2 Ⓓ $134\frac{2}{3}$ ft^2

32. If figure $ABCD$ is translated 3 units to the left and 2 units down, what are the coordinates of point C'? G

Ⓕ (0, 0) Ⓗ (−1, 1)
Ⓖ (1, −1) Ⓙ (1, 1)

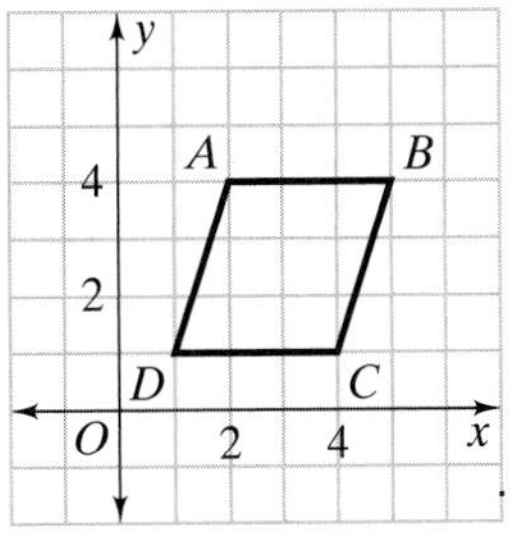

33. Tony leaves his house and bikes west 3.3 miles to the movie theater. He then turns south and bikes 4.1 miles to the pet store. About how far is the pet store from his house? B

Ⓐ 3.8 mi Ⓑ 5.3 mi Ⓒ 7.4 mi Ⓓ 27.7 mi

GO for Help

For Exercises	See Lesson
34–37	3-1

Find the positive square root of each number.

34. 225 15 **35.** $\frac{1}{625}$ $\frac{1}{25}$ **36.** $\frac{25}{400}$ $\frac{1}{4}$ **37.** $\frac{121}{196}$ $\frac{11}{14}$

Alternative Assessment

Each student in a pair writes a positive integer. Partners use their integers to write two different ratios in simplest form.

Test Prep

Resources

For additional practice with a variety of test item formats:

- Test-Taking Strategies, p. 201
- Test Prep, p. 205
- Test-Taking Strategies with Transparencies

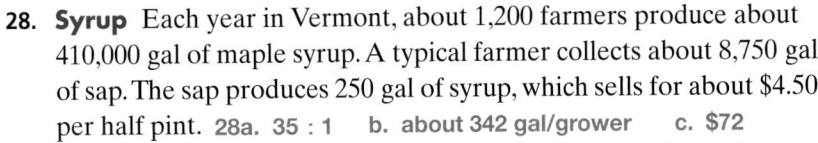

4. Assess & Reteach

PowerPoint

Lesson Quiz

Express each ratio in simplest form.

1. 27 laps : 81 minutes $\frac{1}{3}$
2. 12 minutes : 3 hours $\frac{1}{15}$
3. Carli walked 16 miles in 5 hours. Find the unit rate. 3.2 mi/h
4. A 21-oz bottle of shampoo costs \$2.80. A 12-oz bottle costs \$1.35. Which has the better unit rate? 12-oz bottle

Reteaching 4-1

Ratios L2

A *ratio* is a comparison between two quantities. Suppose that an apple pie is cut into 12 pieces, with 8 to be served hot and 4 to be served cold. Two possible ratios are:

$\frac{\text{hot}}{\text{cold}} = \frac{8}{4}\ \frac{(part)}{(part)}$ $\frac{\text{hot}}{\text{total}} = \frac{8}{12}\ \frac{(part)}{(whole)}$

Example 1: Write the ratios in simplest form.

$\frac{8}{4} = \frac{8 \div 4}{4 \div 4} = \frac{2}{1}$ $\frac{8}{12} = \frac{8 \div 4}{12 \div 4} = \frac{2}{3}$

A *rate* compares two different types of quantities. To find a unit rate, divide both the numerator and the denominator by the denominator.

Example 2: Find the unit rate for 150 miles in 6 hours.

① Compare. $\frac{\text{miles}}{\text{hours}} = \frac{150}{6}$
② Divide. $= \frac{150 \div 6}{6 \div 6}$
③ Simplify. $= \frac{25}{1}$

The unit rate is 25 miles per hour, or 25 mi/h.

Write each ratio in simplest form.

1. 8 in. to 10 in. 4 to 5
2. $\frac{16 \text{ cm}}{12 \text{ cm}}$ $\frac{4}{3}$
3. 15 m : 18 m 5 : 6
4. $\frac{16 \text{ yd}}{24 \text{ yd}}$ $\frac{2}{3}$
5. 30 ft : 10 ft 3 : 1
6. $\frac{9 \text{ mi}}{15 \text{ mi}}$ $\frac{3}{5}$
7. $\frac{12 \text{ ft}}{28 \text{ ft}}$ $\frac{3}{7}$
8. 12 cm to 9 cm 4 to 3
9. 6 m : 16 m 3 : 8

Use a calculator, paper and pencil, or mental math to find each unit rate.

10. \$3.75 for 3 pounds of bird seed \$1.25/lb
11. 270 miles for 12 gallons of gas 22.5 mi/gal
12. 45 minutes for 15 songs 3 min/song
13. \$10.50 for 3 pairs of socks \$3.50/pair
14. 72 plants in 9 planters 8 plants/planter
15. 192 jars in 8 cases 24 jars/case

Enrichment 4-1

Ratios L4

Patterns in Numbers

Finding equal ratios can help you identify patterns.

1. Write the powers of 2 from 2^0 through 2^6. 1, 2, 4, 8, 16, 32, 64
2. Describe the ratio of each power of 2 and the preceding power of 2. 2 to 1
3. Write the powers of 3 from 3^0 through 3^6. 1, 3, 9, 27, 81, 243, 729
4. Describe the ratio of each power of 3 and the preceding power of 3. 3 to 1
5. Find each product below.
   a. $2^0 \times 3^1 =$ 3
   b. $2^1 \times 3^2 =$ 18
   c. $2^2 \times 3^3 =$ 108
   d. $2^3 \times 3^4 =$ 648
   e. $2^4 \times 3^5 =$ 3,888
   f. $2^5 \times 3^6 =$ 23,328
6. Describe the patterns you see in the exercises for Exercise 5.
   Sample answer: The base numbers are 2 and 3. The exponent for 2 is one less than the exponent for 3.
7. Find the ratio of each product and the preceding product in Exercise 5.
   b : a 18 : 3, or 6 : 1
   c : b 108 : 18, or 6 : 1
   d : c 648 : 108, or 6 : 1
   e : d 3,888 : 648, or 6 : 1
   f : e 23,328 : 3,888, or 6 : 1
8. Describe the pattern of ratios.
   Sample answer: The ratio is 6 : 1 for each pair. Six is the product of the base numbers 3 and 5. The prediction is valid.
9. Predict the ratio of each product to the preceding product for the following sequence: $3^0 \times 5^1, 3^1 \times 5^2, 3^2 \times 5^3, 3^3 \times 5^4, 3^4 \times 5^5, 3^5 \times 5^6$. On what did you base your prediction? Check your prediction to verify its validity.
   Sample answer: 15 : 1; 15 is the product of the base numbers 3 and 5. The prediction is valid.

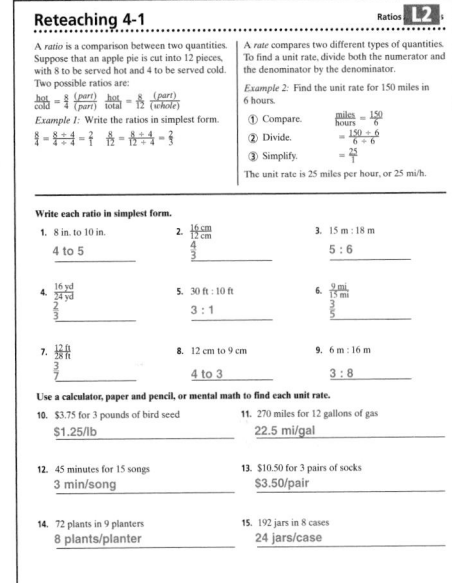

Activity Lab

Finding Rates

Students find unit rates and use them to calculate costs related to owning a car. They also use a table and bar graph to analyze yearly expenses.

Guided Instruction

Alternative Method
Help students think about unit rates by considering lesser numbers with which they are already familiar. Ask: *If you drive 100 miles in 2 hours, how long does it take to drive 50 miles?* 1 hour *What operation are you using to find the answer?* dividing the distance (miles) by 2

Connection to Data Analysis
Using bar graphs is a helpful way to analyze information. Discuss the meaning of values on each axis and how to interpret the information. Ask: *How does the height of the bar relate to the value on the x-axis? On the y-axis?* It identifies the amount of money (*y*-value) for that specific category (*x*-value).

Differentiated Instruction

English Language Learners ELL
Discuss the meaning of *per* in everyday language. Tell students that *per* in math usually indicates division. Have students write a division expression for some rates, such as $\frac{\text{miles}}{\text{gallon}}$, to represent miles per gallon, which means the number of miles for 1 gallon.

Resources

- graph paper

4-1b Activity Lab

Finding Rates

In a few years, you will be driving. Suppose your parents have offered to buy you a used car as long as you agree to pay for the expenses that go along with owning a car. You should estimate your expenses so that you will know what you are getting into.

ACTIVITY

1. Suppose your parents buy a car that gets 24 miles per gallon. If you plan to drive about 15,000 miles each year, how many gallons of gas would you use each year? 625 gallons
2. What is the cost per gallon of gasoline these days? This is the unit rate, or unit cost, for gasoline. 2–3. Check students' work.
3. To find how much you should expect to spend on gasoline each year, multiply the unit rate by the number of gallons you plan on using in a year.
4. Suppose four new tires cost \$350. The tires will last 60,000 miles. How many years will the tires last if you plan on driving 15,000 miles per year? Use this information to find the cost per year for tires. 4 years; \$87.50/yr
5. Use all of your calculations and the information in the table below to find the amount you will need to pay for all expenses for one year (not including the price of the car). 5–8. Check students' work.

Annual Car Expenses

Expense	Cost
Registration	\$70
Insurance	\$1,300
Repairs	\$800

6. Make a bar graph showing the different categories of annual expenses you will have if you own a car. Place the categories on the horizontal axis. Place the amount of money on the vertical axis.
7. Using your bar graph, compare the amount you would spend in each category. In which category would you spend the most money each year? In which would you spend the least?
8. How much money will you have to earn *per month* to pay for all of the expenses for the car?

Choosing Units

When you measure, you need to know which units to use. The table shows some common units of measurement in the customary and metric systems.

Customary Units

	Name	Approximate Comparison
Length	Inch	Length of a soda bottle cap
	Foot	Length of an adult maleís foot
	Yard	Length across a door
	Mile	Length of 14 football fields
Weight	Ounce	Weight of a slice of bread
	Pound	Weight of a loaf of bread
	Ton	Weight of two grand pianos
Capacity	Fluid ounce	Amount in mouthful of mouthwash
	Cup	Amount of milk in a single-serving carton
	Pint	Amount in a container of cream
	Quart	Amount in a bottle of fruit punch
	Gallon	Amount in a large can of paint

Metric Units

	Name	Approximate Comparison
Length	Centimeter	Length of a button
	Meter	Length of a baseball bat
	Kilometer	Length of 11 football fields
Mass	Gram	Mass of a small paper clip
	Kilogram	Mass of 4 videocassettes
Capacity	Milliliter	Amount of water in 2 dewdrops
	Liter	Amount in a bottle of fruit punch—about a quart

EXAMPLES Customary and Metric Units

1 Choose an appropriate customary unit for the weight of a truck.

Since a truck is quite heavy, tons would be the best units to use.

2 Choose an appropriate metric unit for the capacity of a jug of cider.

A jug of cider is large, so you should use liters.

4. kilometers
5. milliliters
6. kilograms

Exercises

Choose an appropriate customary unit.

1. length of a pencil inches
2. weight of a plum ounces
3. capacity of a car's gas tank gallons

Choose an appropriate metric unit. 4–6. See above right.

4. distance from Dallas to Reno
5. capacity of a small glass
6. mass of an adult

Activity Lab

Choosing Units

Students consider the relative lengths, capacities, weights, and masses of common objects. They determine appropriate customary and metric units for each object.

Guided Instruction

Error Prevention!

The magnitude of a unit may not always be obvious from the prefix. For example, a kilogram is greater than a gram, but a milliliter is less than a liter.

Teaching Tip
Have students measure classroom objects to get a better sense of relative size/length/weight/capacity. For example, ask:

- *Which would you measure in inches: a pencil, a book, a desk, the teacher's desk, the length across the room?* pencil, book, desk, possibly teacher's desk
- *Which object is difficult to measure in inches?* length of the room *What is the next greater unit?* feet (yards are reasonable, too)

Differentiated Instruction

Tactile Learners
Show and let students handle as many measuring instruments as possible, including measures of volume and weight. Explain that volume and capacity are different names for measuring the same amount.

Resources

- Activity Lab 4-2: Converting Units
- measuring instruments (e.g., measuring cups, cooking spoons, rulers, balance scale)

4-2

1. Plan

Objective
To convert units within and between the customary and metric systems

Examples
1 Converting Measurements
2 Application: Rowing
3 Converting Using Compatible Numbers
4 Converting Between Systems

Math Understandings: p. 158C

Professional Development

Math Background

Unit conversions are especially common in the sciences. Conversions are needed when anyone wants to change between and within systems of units. For instance, when changing from inches to feet, you multiply the given measurement in inches by the ratio $\frac{1\text{ ft}}{12\text{ in.}}$. Because 1 ft = 12 in., $\frac{1\text{ ft}}{12\text{ in.}}$ is a rate equal to 1 and is an example of a conversion factor. You can convert from one unit to another by multiplying a given measure by the corresponding conversion factor, which always equals 1.

More Math Background: p. 158C

Lesson Planning and Resources

See p. 158E for a list of the resources that support this lesson.

PowerPoint

Bell Ringer Practice

Check Skills You'll Need
Use student page, transparency, or PowerPoint. For intervention, direct students to:
Multiplying and Dividing Rational Numbers
Lesson 2-5
Extra Skills and Word Problems Practice, Ch. 2

4-2 Converting Units

Check Skills You'll Need

1. **Vocabulary Review** What is the product of a number and its *reciprocal*? 1

Find each product. Write the answer in simplest form.

2. $\frac{10}{3} \cdot \frac{1}{4}$ $\frac{5}{6}$
3. $\frac{4}{6} \cdot \frac{5}{6}$ $\frac{5}{9}$
4. $\frac{4}{9} \cdot \frac{3}{2}$ $\frac{2}{3}$
5. $\frac{6}{7} \cdot \frac{8}{3}$ $2\frac{2}{7}$

GO for Help
Lesson 2-5

What You'll Learn

To convert units within and between the customary and metric systems

New Vocabulary conversion factor

Why Learn This?

In 1999, the Mars orbiter was lost because the units of measure used to program the orbiter were not converted.

The table below shows equivalent measurements within the customary and metric systems.

Units of Measurement

Type	Unit	Equivalent
Length (customary)	inch (in.) foot (ft) yard (yd) mile (mi)	 1 ft = 12 in. 1 yd = 3 ft 1 mi = 5,280 ft
Length (metric)	centimeter (cm) meter (m) kilometer (km)	 1 m = 100 cm 1 km = 1,000 m
Capacity (customary)	fluid ounce (fl oz) cup (c) pint (pt) quart (qt) gallon (gal)	 1 c = 8 fl oz 1 pt = 2 c 1 qt = 2 pt 1 gal = 4 qt
Capacity (metric)	milliliter (mL) liter (L)	 1 L = 1,000 mL
Weight (customary)	ounce (oz) pound (lb) ton (t)	 1 lb = 16 oz 1 t = 2,000 lb
Mass (metric)	gram (g) kilogram (kg)	 1 kg = 1,000 g

Differentiated Instruction Solutions for All Learners

Special Needs L1
Make sure students understand that "m" stands for meters in Example 2. Show them a meter stick, and remind them that it takes 1,000 meter sticks to cover a 1-kilometer distance.

learning style: visual

Below Level L2
Students find the reciprocals of $\frac{2}{3}$ $\frac{3}{2}$, 4 $\frac{1}{4}$, and $\frac{1}{2}$ 2, then multiply $\frac{3}{4}$ by $\frac{2}{3}$ $\frac{1}{2}$, 5 by $\frac{3}{5}$ 3, and $1\frac{1}{2}$ by $\frac{1}{2}$ $\frac{3}{4}$.
Remind them to write mixed numbers as improper fractions.

learning style: visual

You can change one unit of measure to another by multiplying by a conversion factor. A **conversion factor** is a rate equal to 1. For example, 12 in. = 1 ft, so $\frac{12 \text{ in.}}{1 \text{ ft}} = 1$. Since conversion factors equal 1, multiplying by them does not change the value of a measurement.

EXAMPLE Converting Measurements

1 Convert 1.2 miles to feet.

Since 5,280 ft = 1 mi, use the conversion factor $\frac{5{,}280 \text{ ft}}{1 \text{ mi}}$.

$1.2 \text{ mi} = \frac{1.2 \text{ mi}}{1} \cdot \frac{5{,}280 \text{ ft}}{1 \text{ mi}}$ ← **Multiply by the conversion factor,** $\frac{5{,}280 \text{ ft}}{1 \text{ mi}}$.

$= \frac{(1.2)(5{,}280) \text{ ft}}{1}$ ← **Simplify.**

$= 6{,}336 \text{ ft}$ ← **Simplify.**

There are 6,336 ft in 1.2 miles.

Test Prep Tip

Check that the units cancel when you multiply by the conversion factor.

Quick Check

1. Convert $2\frac{1}{4}$ mi to feet. 11,880 ft

Sometimes you need to use two or more conversion factors.

EXAMPLE Application: Rowing

2 **Gridded Response** Community Rowing Inc., a nonprofit club, participated in the annual Head of the Charles Regatta rowing race in Boston, Massachusetts. The team completed the 2,000-m course at a rate of about 1.92 m/s. Convert this rate to kilometers per minute (km/min). Round your answer to hundredths.

Multiply by the conversion factors $\frac{60 \text{ s}}{1 \text{ min}}$ and $\frac{1 \text{ km}}{1{,}000 \text{ m}}$.

$\frac{1.92 \text{ m}}{1 \text{ s}} = \frac{1.92 \text{ m}}{1 \text{ s}} \cdot \frac{60 \text{ s}}{1 \text{ min}} \cdot \frac{1 \text{ km}}{1{,}000 \text{ m}}$

$= \frac{(1.92)(60)(1) \text{ km}}{(1)(1{,}000)(1) \text{ min}}$ ← **Simplify.**

$= 0.1152$ ← **Use a calculator.**

The team raced at a rate of about 0.12 km/min.

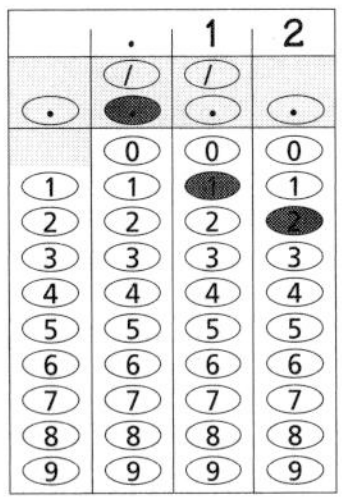

Check for Reasonableness Round 1.92 to 2. Then $2 \cdot 60 \div 1{,}000 = 0.12$. The answer 0.12 km/min matches the estimate. The answer is reasonable.

Quick Check

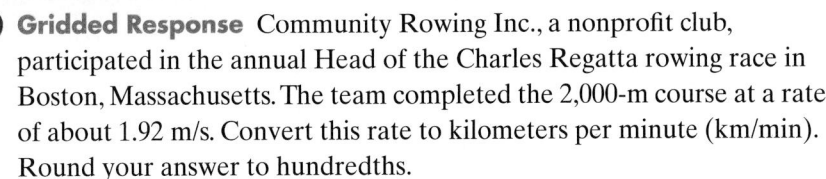

2. You ran at a rate of 0.15 mi/min. Convert the rate to feet per second. 13.2 ft/s

2. Teach

Activity Lab

Use before the lesson.
Student Edition Activity Lab 4-2a, Choosing Units, p. 165

All in One Teaching Resources

Activity Lab 4-2: Converting Units

Guided Instruction

Example 1
Explain that the conversion factor will have the unit of the desired measurement in the numerator and the given measurement in the denominator so the unit *miles* cancels.

Example 2
Provide students with a blank grid.

Teaching Tip
In Example 2, ask:
- *What conversion factor changes meters to kilometers?* $\frac{1 \text{ km}}{1{,}000 \text{ m}}$
- *What conversion factor changes minutes to seconds?* $\frac{60 \text{ s}}{1 \text{ min}}$

Math Tip
In Example 3, ask: *Why is 48 compatible with 8?* 6×8 is a basic fact and the division can be done easily with mental math.

Error Prevention!

In Examples 1, 3, and 4, show students how the given unit divides out (or cancels to 1) with the denominator of the conversion fraction. The desired unit must be in the numerator of the conversion fraction.

PowerPoint
Additional Examples

1 Convert 0.7 mi to ft. 3,696 ft

2 A rowing team completed a 2000-m course at a rate of 6.84 m/s. Convert this rate to kilometers per minute. 0.4104 km/min

Advanced Learners L4
Students find unit rates in minutes for their heartbeat and breath. They count the number of beats or breaths in 15 seconds and use that ratio to calculate unit rates per minute.

learning style: verbal

English Language Learners ELL
For Example 1, ask: *Since you are converting 1.2 miles to feet, will the resulting number be greater or less than 1.2?* Greater Have students explain their reasoning.

learning style: verbal

Additional Examples

3 Use compatible numbers to estimate the number of gallons in 33 quarts. about 8 gal

4 Convert 650 g to ounces. about 22.9 oz

All in One Teaching Resources

- Daily Notetaking Guide 4-2 L3
- Adapted Notetaking 4-2 L1

Closure

- Explain how to choose a conversion factor when you use dimensional analysis. Sample: Choose a conversion factor (a rate that equals 1) that causes the units you have to cancel and the units you want to remain.

You can estimate conversions by using compatible numbers.

EXAMPLE Converting Using Compatible Numbers

3 Use compatible numbers to estimate the number of cups in 50 fl oz.

The conversion factor for changing fluid ounces to cups is $\frac{1 \text{ c}}{8 \text{ fl oz}}$.

$$50 \text{ fl oz} \approx 48 \text{ fl oz}$$ ← **Round to the nearest number divisible by 8.**

$$= \frac{48 \cancel{\text{fl oz}}}{1} \cdot \frac{1 \text{ c}}{8 \cancel{\text{fl oz}}}$$ ← **Multiply by the conversion factor, $\frac{1 \text{ c}}{8 \text{ fl oz}}$.**

$$= \frac{48}{8} \text{ cups}$$ ← **Simplify.**

$$= 6 \text{ cups}$$ ← **Divide.**

There are about 6 cups in 50 fl oz.

Quick Check

3. Use compatible numbers to estimate.

a. 14,120 lb is about ■ t. 7 **b.** 9.8 c is about ■ pt. 5

You can convert between the metric system and the customary system using conversion factors. The table below shows the relationship between measurements in the two systems.

Type	Customary Units and Metric Units
Length	1 in. = 2.54 cm 1 mi ≈ 1.61 km 1 ft ≈ 0.3 m
Capacity	1 qt ≈ 0.94 L
Weight and Mass	1 oz ≈ 28.4 g 1 lb ≈ 0.45 kg

EXAMPLE Converting Between Systems

4 Convert 36 cm to inches. Round to the nearest tenth.

$$36 \text{ cm} = \frac{36 \cancel{\text{cm}}}{1} \cdot \frac{1 \text{ in.}}{2.54 \cancel{\text{cm}}}$$ ← **Multiply by the conversion factor, $\frac{1 \text{ in.}}{2.54 \text{ cm}}$.**

$$= \frac{(36)(1)\text{in.}}{2.54}$$ ← **Simplify.**

$$\approx 14.2 \text{ in.}$$ ← **Divide using a calculator.**

There are about 14.2 in. in 36 cm.

Quick Check

4. Convert 15 L to quarts. Round to the nearest tenth. 16.0 qt

Check Your Understanding

1. **Vocabulary** What conversion factor would you use to convert feet to inches? $\frac{12 \text{ in.}}{1 \text{ ft}}$

Choose the correct conversion factor to convert each measure.

2. 130 in. to feet E
3. 48 lb to ounces A
4. 9 km to meters D
5. 36 ft to inches B
6. 70 oz to pounds C

A. $\frac{16 \text{ oz}}{1 \text{ lb}}$

B. $\frac{12 \text{ in.}}{1 \text{ ft}}$

C. $\frac{1 \text{ lb}}{16 \text{ oz}}$

D. $\frac{1{,}000 \text{ m}}{1 \text{ km}}$

E. $\frac{1 \text{ ft}}{12 \text{ in.}}$

Homework Exercises

For more exercises, see Extra Skills and Word Problems.

GO for Help

For Exercises	See Examples
7–14	1–2
15–18	3
19–24	4

A Convert each measure. Round to the nearest tenth, if necessary.

7. 32 in. = ■ ft 2.7
8. 2,500 cm = ■ m 25
9. 15,000 g = ■ kg 15

Find an equivalent rate.

10. 90 in./min = ■ ft/min 7.5
11. $27/h = $■ /min 0.45
12. 12 cm/day = ■ cm/h 0.5
13. 12 qt/min = ■ gal/min 3

14. **Sports** Some pitchers can throw a baseball as fast as 100 mi/h. What is this rate in feet per second? 146.67 ft/s

Estimation **Use compatible numbers to estimate.**

15. 148 in. is about ■ ft. 12
16. 82 oz is about ■ lb. 5
17. 500 min is about ■ h. 8
18. 3,980 mm is about ■ m. 4

Convert each measure. Round to the nearest tenth, if necessary.

19. 25 cm = ■ in. 9.8
20. 18 qt = ■ L 16.9
21. 55 lb = ■ kg 24.8
22. 23 in. = ■ cm 58.4
23. 10 kg = ■ lb 22.2
24. 16 L = ■ qt 17.0

B GPS

25. **Guided Problem Solving** The cheetah can run as fast as 93 ft/s. Estimate the number of meters the cheetah can run in 7 seconds.
    - What conversion factor can you use for changing feet to meters?
    - How can you change the conversion factor to a number compatible with 93? Answers may vary. Sample: 217 m

26. The radius of a wheel is 14 in. Estimate the radius in centimeters. 35 cm

3. Practice

Assignment Guide

Check Your Understanding

Go over Exercises 1–6 in class before assigning the Homework Exercises.

Homework Exercises

A Practice by Example	7–24
B Apply Your Skills	25–38
C Challenge	39
Test Prep and Mixed Review	40–45

Homework Quick Check

To check students' understanding of key skills and concepts, go over Exercises 15, 24, 34, 37, and 38.

Differentiated Instruction Resources

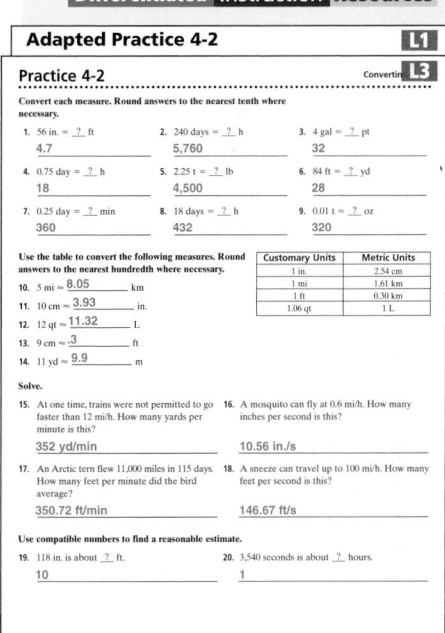

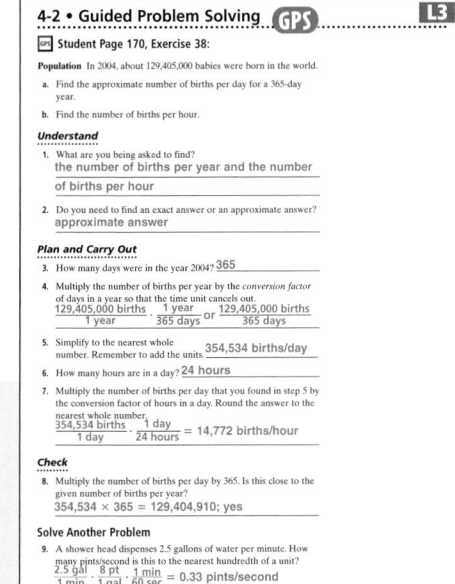

Adapted Practice 4-2 L1

Practice 4-2 Convertin[g Units] L3

Convert each measure. Round answers to the nearest tenth where necessary.

1. 56 in. = ? ft 4.7
2. 240 days = ? h 5,760
3. 4 gal = ? pt 32
4. 0.75 day = ? h 18
5. 2.25 t = ? lb 4,500
6. 84 ft = ? yd 28
7. 0.25 day = ? min 360
8. 18 days = ? h 432
9. 0.01 t = ? oz 320

Use the table to convert the following measures. Round answers to the nearest hundredth where necessary.

Customary Units	Metric Units
1 in.	2.54 cm
1 mi	1.61 km
1 ft	0.30 km
1.06 qt	1 L

10. 5 mi ≈ 8.05 km
11. 10 cm ≈ 3.93 in.
12. 12 qt ≈ 11.32 L
13. 9 cm ≈ .3 ft
14. 11 yd ≈ 9.9 m

Solve.

15. At one time, trains were not permitted to go faster than 12 mi/h. How many yards per minute is this? 352 yd/min
16. A mosquito can fly at 0.6 mi/h. How many inches per second is this? 10.56 in./s
17. An Arctic tern flew 11,000 miles in 115 days. How many feet per minute did the bird average? 350.72 ft/min
18. A sneeze can travel up to 100 mi/h. How many feet per second is this? 146.67 ft/s

Use compatible numbers to find a reasonable estimate.

19. 118 in. is about ? ft. 10
20. 3,540 seconds is about ? hours. 1

4-2 • Guided Problem Solving GPS L3

GPS Student Page 170, Exercise 38:

Population In 2004, about 129,405,000 babies were born in the world.

a. Find the approximate number of births per day for a 365-day year.
b. Find the number of births per hour.

Understand

1. What are you being asked to find? the number of births per year and the number of births per hour
2. Do you need to find an exact answer or an approximate answer? approximate answer

Plan and Carry Out

3. How many days were in the year 2004? 365
4. Multiply the number of births per year by the *conversion factor* of days in a year so that the time unit cancels out. $\frac{129{,}405{,}000 \text{ births}}{1 \text{ year}} \cdot \frac{1 \text{ year}}{365 \text{ days}}$ or $\frac{129{,}405{,}000 \text{ births}}{365 \text{ days}}$
5. Simplify to the nearest whole number. Remember to add the units. 354,534 births/day
6. How many hours are in a day? 24 hours
7. Multiply the number of births per day that you found in step 5 by the conversion factor of hours in a day. Round the answer to the nearest whole number. $\frac{354{,}534 \text{ births}}{1 \text{ day}} \cdot \frac{1 \text{ day}}{24 \text{ hours}} = 14{,}772$ births/hour

Check

8. Multiply the number of births per day by 365. Is this close to the given number of births per year? $354{,}534 \times 365 = 129{,}404{,}910$; yes

Solve Another Problem

9. A shower head dispenses 2.5 gallons of water per minute. How many pints/second is this to the nearest hundredth of a unit? $\frac{2.5 \text{ gal}}{1 \text{ min}} \cdot \frac{8 \text{ pt}}{1 \text{ gal}} \cdot \frac{1 \text{ min}}{60 \text{ sec}} = 0.33$ pints/second

4. Assess & Reteach

PowerPoint

Lesson Quiz

1. Convert 0.75 hours to seconds. 2,700 seconds
2. \$150 per hour is how much per minute? \$2.50 per min
3. 69.2 cm is about how many meters? 0.7 m
4. Convert 12 qt to liters. about 11.3 L

Reteaching 4-2

Convert L2

To convert units of measure, multiply by a *conversion factor*, or a ratio equal to 1.

Example: Convert 4.5 c to fluid ounces.

From the table, you know that 1 c = 8 fl oz, so $\frac{8 \text{ fl oz}}{1 \text{ c}} = 1$.

$\frac{8 \text{ fl oz}}{1 \text{ c}}$ is the conversion factor.

To convert cups to ounces, multiply by $\frac{8 \text{ fl oz}}{1 \text{ c}}$.

$4.5 \text{ c} = \frac{4.5 \text{ c}}{1} \cdot \frac{8 \text{ fl oz}}{1 \text{ c}} = \frac{(4.5)(8) \text{ fl oz}}{1} = 36 \text{ fl oz}$

So 4.5 cups equals 36 fluid ounces.

Equivalent Units of Measurement

Customary	Metric
1 ft = 12 in.	1 m = 100 cm
1 yd = 3 ft	1 km = 1,000 m
1 mi = 5,280 ft	
1 c = 8 fl oz	1 L = 1,000 mL
1 pt = 2 c	
1 qt = 2 pt	
1 gal = 4 qt	
1 lb = 16 oz	1 kg = 1,000 g
1 t = 2,000 lb	

Convert each measure.

1. 48 in. = _?_ ft 4
2. 8,400 cm = _?_ m 84
3. 6 km = _?_ m 6,000
4. 14.7 t = _?_ lb 29,400

Use compatible numbers to estimate.

5. 15 qt is about _?_ c. 60
6. 32,688 g is about _?_ kg. 33
7. 88 oz is about _?_ lb. 5.5
8. 45.2 gal = _?_ qt 180

Find an equivalent rate.

9. 35 mi/h = _?_ ft/h 184,800
10. 45 L/h = _?_ L/day 1,080
11. 12 ft/min = _?_ in./min 1
12. 5,400 m/sec = _?_ m/min 324,000

Convert each measure.

13. 4 in./sec = _?_ ft/h 12,000
14. 1,500 m/day = _?_ km/h 0.065

Enrichment 4-2

Convert L4

Critical Thinking

Twenty Thousand Leagues Under the Sea is a famous novel by Jules Verne. A league is about 3.45 miles. Convert the title of the book to feet.

1. How many miles are in one league? 3.45 miles/league
2. What number are you being asked to convert to feet? 20,000 leagues
3. Write a conversion factor changing 20,000 leagues to miles. 20,000 leagues × $\frac{3.45 \text{ miles}}{1 \text{ league}}$ ≈ 69,000 miles
4. When you convert leagues to miles, will your answer be less than or greater than 20,000? Explain. The answer will be greater than 20,000 because there are 3.45 miles per one league, so you multiply 20,000 by 3.45.
5. How many miles are in 20,000 leagues? 69,000 miles
6. How many feet are in one mile? 5,280 feet
7. Write a conversion factor changing miles to feet. 69,000 miles × $\frac{5,280 \text{ feet}}{1 \text{ mile}}$ ≈ 364,320,000 feet
8. How many feet are in 20,000 leagues? 364,320,000 feet
9. Write the title of Verne's novel using feet in place of leagues. *Three Hundred Sixty-Four Million, Three Hundred Twenty Thousand Feet Under the Sea*
10. Check to see if your answer makes sense. Show your work. 20,000 × 4 = 80,000; 80,000 × 5,000 = 400,000,000
11. To the nearest whole number, how many leagues are in 550,000,000 feet? 30,193 leagues

GO Online
Homework Video Tutor
Visit: PHSchool.com
Web Code: ase-0402

37. Answers may vary. Sample: Count the number of times you blink in a minute, multiply by $\frac{60 \text{ minutes}}{1 \text{ hour}} \times \frac{24 \text{ hours}}{1 \text{ day}}$. To find the number of times in a week, multiply the result by $\frac{7 \text{ days}}{1 \text{ week}}$.

38a. about 354,534 births/day

b. about 14,772 births/h

Convert each measure. Round to the nearest tenth, if necessary.

27. $1\frac{1}{2}$ mi/h = ■ ft/day 190,080
28. $64\frac{2}{3}$ yd/h = ■ in./s 0.6

Use the formulas $F = \frac{9}{5}C + 32$ and $C = \frac{5}{9}(F - 32)$ to convert temperatures between Celsius and Fahrenheit.

29. 28°C 82.4°F
30. 14°C 57.2°F
31. 32°F 0°C
32. 0°F −17.8°C

Use the table to match the activity with the Calories burned per minute.

33. 3.8 Cal/min swimming
34. 4.4 Cal/min cycling
35. 2.9 Cal/min dancing
36. 6.2 Cal/min aerobics

Activity	Calories/h
Aerobics (moderate)	371
Cycling (10 mi/h)	262
Dancing (moderate)	171
Jumping rope	342
Running (7 mi/h)	513
Swimming (25 yd/min)	228
Walking (4.5 mi/h)	257

SOURCE: *Principles & Labs*

37. **Writing in Math** Explain how you would estimate the number of times you blink your eyes in a day and in a week. See left.

38. **Population** In 2004, about 129,405,000 babies were born in the world. 38a–b. See left.
   a. Find the approximate number of births per day for a 365-day year.
   b. Find the number of births per hour.

C 39. **Challenge** Simplify 4 ft 7 in. − 3 ft 9 in. + 2 ft 5 in. Write the answer in simplest form. 3 ft 3 in.

Test Prep and Mixed Review

Practice

Gridded Response

40. Grace is a member of her school's track team. In one race, she ran 10 feet per second. What was her rate in miles per hour? Round to the nearest tenth. 6.8

41. Suppose △*ABC* at the right is reflected over the *y*-axis. What is the *x*-coordinate of *A*′? 2

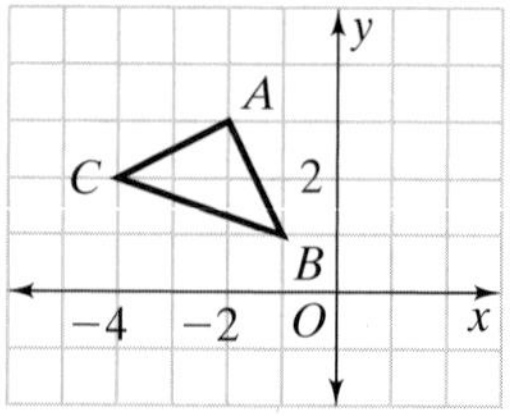

42. Mia rented a car with an odometer reading of 12,382.4 miles. When she returned the car, the odometer reading was 12,424.9 miles. If Mia was charged \$22.10 for the mileage she put on the car, how much in dollars, did the rental company charge per mile? 0.52

GO for Help

For Exercises	See Lesson
43–45	3-5

Graph each linear equation. 43–45. See back of book.

43. $y = -x + 3$
44. $y = \frac{3}{4}x - 5$
45. $y = -\frac{2}{5}x - 2$

Test Prep

Resources
For additional practice with a variety of test item formats:
- Test-Taking Strategies, p. 201
- Test Prep, p. 205
- Test-Taking Strategies with Transparencies

Alternative Assessment

Pairs of students measure the length of a school corridor in yards. They convert that length to feet, and then to meters. They repeat the activity with other objects and units of measure.

Checkpoint Quiz 1

Lessons 4-1 through 4-2

Write each ratio in simplest form.

1. $\frac{48 \text{ s}}{12 \text{ min}}$ $\frac{1}{15}$
2. 81 in. to 27 ft $\frac{1}{4}$
3. 90 m : 15 m 6 : 1
4. $\frac{18 \text{ yd}}{72 \text{ ft}}$ $\frac{3}{4}$

Find each unit rate.

5. $84 for 7 books $12/book
6. 96 m in 8 s 12 m/s
7. 57 gal in 19 min 3 gal/min
8. 232 mi in 29 h 8 mi/h

Convert each measure. If necessary, round to the nearest tenth.

9. $12/h = $■ /min 0.20
10. 9 kg = ■ lb 20
11. 16 L = ■ qt 17.0
12. 20 cm = ■ in. 7.9
13. The speed limit on some highways is 65 mi/h. What is this rate in kilometers per hour? 104.7 km/h
14. It costs $38 to have 8 pages of notes typed. Find the unit rate. $4.75/page
15. An airplane is flying at 455 miles per hour. What is its speed in kilometers per minute? 12.2 km/min

MATH AT WORK

Automotive Mechanic

Automotive mechanics diagnose and repair mechanical problems. An automotive mechanic must inspect a car and analyze its problems to determine the necessary adjustments to make.

The ability to reason is a skill that an auto mechanic uses to diagnose problems quickly and accurately. Mechanics also use estimating skills to determine the approximate cost of repairs. The mechanic wants to make sure that he or she charges enough for the work, yet does not overcharge the customer.

Go Online PHSchool.com **For:** Information on Automotive Mechanics **Web Code:** asb-2031

Checkpoint Quiz

Use this Checkpoint Quiz to check students' understanding of the skills and concepts of Lessons 4-1 through 4-2.

Resources

- All in One Teaching Resources Checkpoint Quiz 1
- ExamView Assessment Suite CD-ROM
- Success Tracker Online Intervention

MATH AT WORK

Automotive Mechanic

This feature describes how a mechanic uses math to calculate amounts and to make reasonable business decisions.

Guided Instruction

Have students discuss how a mechanic uses math. Ask questions such as:

- *What do mechanics need to calculate?* Sample: how much to charge for repairs, including charges for parts and labor (time spent working); how long it will take to make a repair
- *What kind of math do they use?* Sample: adding, subtracting, multiplying, and dividing real numbers; use estimation; understanding how to read a graph or table

Proportional and Nonproportional Relationships

Students observe a series of squares shaded in a particular pattern and then analyze those patterns in tables and graphs. They compare ratios of shaded area to total area to determine proportionality.

Guided Instruction

Activity

Have students shade blocks on graph paper. Review the meaning of ratio. Ask: *How can you tell if two ratios are proportional?* **Sample: Check whether the cross products are equal, or check whether the values of the ratios are equal.**

After students complete the first table, discuss any patterns they see in the tables. Begin with row 3, which shows the constant ratio. Make sure they see that this ratio is the result of dividing the value in row 1 by the value in row 2. In the first table, help them see the pattern in the first row. Ask: *How do the values in row 1 relate to corresponding values in each column of row 2?* **multiply the values in row 1 by 4**

Error Prevention!

Some students may have difficulty noticing patterns in tables. Here are some questions they can ask themselves to guide their observations: *What factors do the numbers in a column have in common? Is there a number by which I can multiply the number in one row to get the number in the next row? Is there a basic operation that results in the values in (some of) the columns or rows?*

Proportional and Nonproportional Relationships

A relationship is proportional if it can be described by ratios that are equivalent. If the ratios are not equivalent, the relationship is said to be nonproportional.

ACTIVITY

The figure below shows a series of squares drawn on graph paper with some blocks shaded.

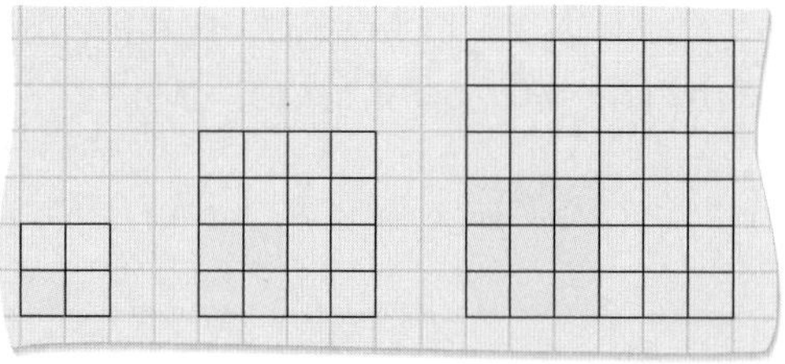

1.

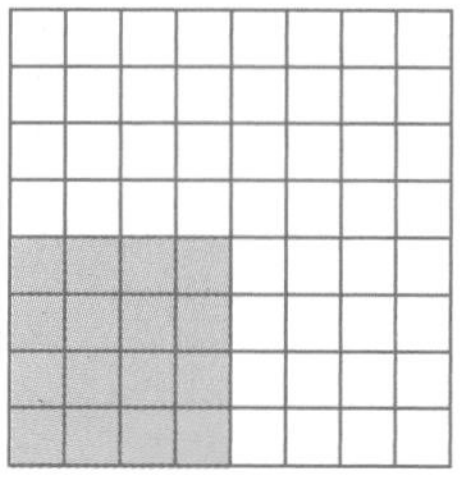

1. Draw an 8-by-8 square on a piece of graph paper. Shade the number of blocks needed to follow the pattern in this series of squares. **See above right.**
2. Complete the table below. Draw the next few squares on your graph paper as needed. Write all ratios in simplest form. **See margin.**

Shaded Blocks	1	4	9	16	25	■
Total Blocks	4	16	36	■	■	144
Ratio $\frac{\text{shaded}}{\text{total}}$	■	$\frac{4}{16} = \frac{1}{4}$	■	■	■	■

3. Look at the ratios you calculated in the table. Is the relationship between the number of shaded blocks and the total number of blocks proportional? Explain. **Yes; all ratios equal $\frac{1}{4}$.**
4. You can also use a graph to determine proportional and nonproportional relationships. Use the ordered pairs (number of shaded blocks, number of total blocks) to draw a graph for this series of squares on a coordinate plane. **See back of book.**
5. Describe the graph. What is its shape? Where does it intersect the y-axis? **The shape of the graph is a line. It intersects the y-axis at (0, 0).**
6. Use your graph to predict the total number of blocks in a square with 64 shaded blocks. **256 total blocks**

2.

Shaded Blocks	1	4	9	16	25	36
Total Blocks	4	16	36	64	100	144
Ratio $\frac{\text{shaded}}{\text{total}}$	$\frac{1}{4}$	$\frac{1}{4}$	$\frac{1}{4}$	$\frac{1}{4}$	$\frac{1}{4}$	$\frac{1}{4}$

ACTIVITY

A different series of figures is shown below.

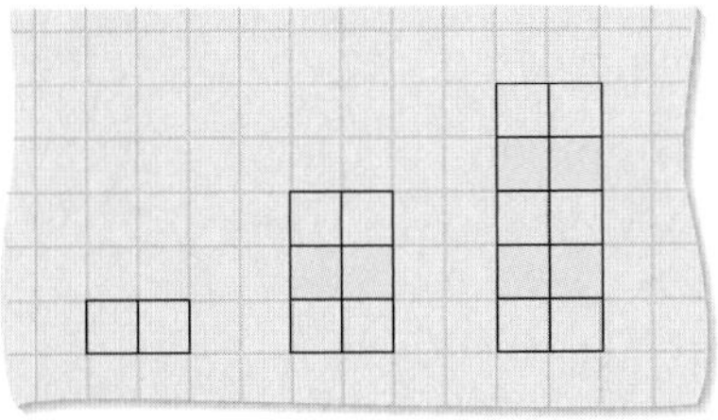

7. 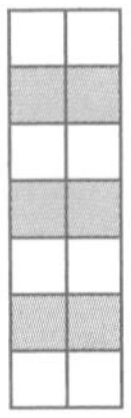

7. Draw a 7-by-2 rectangle on a piece of graph paper. Shade the number of blocks needed to follow the pattern in this series of rectangles. **See above right.**

8. Complete the table below. Draw the next few rectangles on your graph paper as needed. Write all ratios in simplest form. **See margin.**

Shaded Blocks	0	2	4	6	8	■
Total Blocks	2	6	10	■	■	22
Ratio $\frac{\text{shaded}}{\text{total}}$	$\frac{0}{2} = 0$	■	■	■	■	■

9. Is this relationship between the number of shaded blocks and the total number of blocks proportional? Explain. **No; the ratios are not equivalent.**

10. Use the ordered pairs (number of shaded blocks, number of total blocks) to draw a graph for this series of figures. What is its shape? Where does it intersect the *y*-axis? **See margin.**

11. Compare the graphs for the two different series of figures. How are the graphs alike? How are they different? **See margin.**

12. Draw a series of figures using shaded blocks. Is the relationship between shaded and total blocks proportional or nonproportional? **Check students' work.**

Exercises

Tell whether each table represents a proportional or nonproportional relationship. Explain.

1. **Yes; all ratios equal $\frac{1}{5}$.**

Shaded Blocks	1	2	3	10	100
Total Blocks	5	10	15	50	500

2. **No; the ratios are not equivalent.**

Shaded Blocks	3	4	5	9	11
Total Blocks	11	14	17	29	35

Teaching Tip
In Exercises 4–6, remind students to consider which value should be plotted on which axis. If they are accustomed to using vertical *x*-*y* tables, have them rewrite the rows labeled Shaded Blocks and Total Blocks as columns in a new table.

Alternative Method
Some students might find it easier to write the ratios in row 3 of the tables without simplifying them. This may help students remember where the ratios came from. Then, have them write the simplified form underneath so they can determine proportionality.

10. 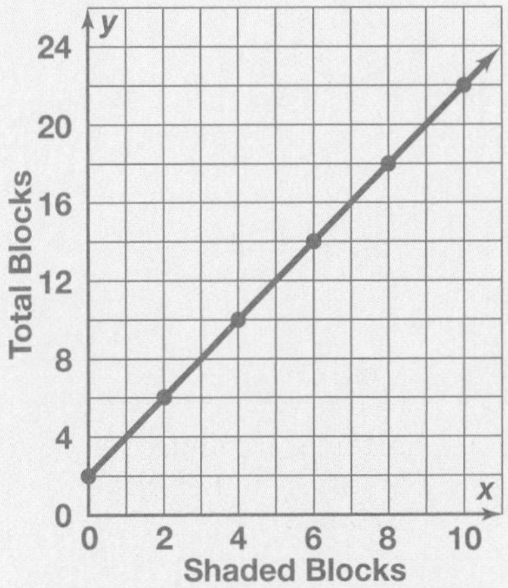

The graph is a line. It intersects the *y*-axis at (0, 2).

11. **Answers may vary. Sample: In both graphs, the number of shaded blocks increases as the total number of blocks increases. However, the *x*- and *y*-values in the first graph are proportional, while in the second graph they are not.**

Resources

- Activity Lab 4-3: Solving Proportions
- graph paper
- colored pencils or markers

8.

Shaded Blocks	0	2	4	6	8	10
Total Blocks	2	6	10	14	18	22
Ratio $\frac{\text{shaded}}{\text{total}}$	0	$\frac{1}{3}$	$\frac{2}{5}$	$\frac{3}{7}$	$\frac{4}{9}$	$\frac{5}{11}$

4-3

1. Plan

Objective
To identify and solve proportions

Examples
1 Identifying Proportions
2 Using Cross Products

Math Understandings: p. 158C

Professional Development

Math Background

A proportion is a comparison between ratios, in the form $\frac{a}{b} = \frac{c}{d}$, where *a*, *b*, *c*, and *d* are rational numbers. To show students why it is necessary to state that *b* and *d* cannot equal zero in the general statement of a proportion, remind them that, for instance, in $\frac{10}{0} = x$, there is no value for *x* that will make 0 times *x* equal to 10.

More Math Background: p. 158C

Lesson Planning and Resources

See p. 158E for a list of the resources that support this lesson.

PowerPoint

Bell Ringer Practice

Check Skills You'll Need
Use student page, transparency, or PowerPoint. For intervention, direct students to:
Equivalent Forms of Rational Numbers
Lesson 2-3
Extra Skills and Word Problems Practice, Ch. 2

Algebra

4-3 Solving Proportions

Check Skills You'll Need

1. **Vocabulary Review** Is the fraction $\frac{a+2}{b+2}$ in *simplest form*? Explain.

Write each fraction in simplest form.

2. $\frac{30}{99}$ $\frac{10}{33}$
3. $\frac{42}{12}$ $3\frac{1}{2}$
4. $\frac{132}{602}$ $\frac{66}{301}$
5. $\frac{70}{25}$ $2\frac{4}{5}$

GO for Help Lesson 2-2

Check Skills You'll Need

1. Yes; there is no common factor between the numerator and denominator.

What You'll Learn

To identify and solve proportions

New Vocabulary proportion, cross products

Why Learn This?

Exchange rates between currencies change daily. You can use equal ratios to find the value of the U.S. dollar at any time.

The rectangles below have the same amount shaded, so the ratios $\frac{12}{32}$ and $\frac{3}{8}$ are equal. The equation $\frac{12}{32} = \frac{3}{8}$ is a proportion.

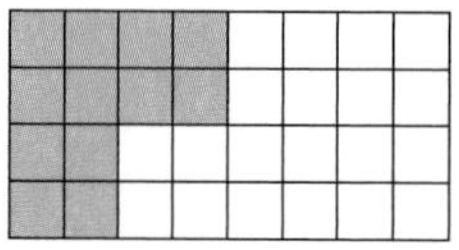

$\frac{12}{32}$ ← shaded / ← total

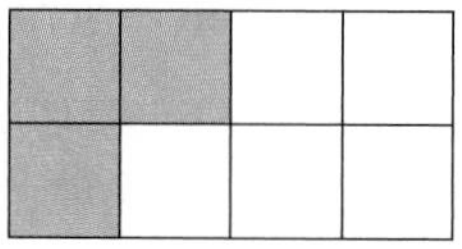

$\frac{3}{8}$ ← shaded / ← total

KEY CONCEPTS **Proportion**

A **proportion** is an equation stating that two ratios are equal.

Arithmetic	Algebra
$\frac{6}{10} = \frac{9}{15}$	$\frac{a}{b} = \frac{c}{d}$, where $b \neq 0$ and $d \neq 0$

EXAMPLE **Identifying Proportions**

1 Do $\frac{4}{5}$ and $\frac{12}{15}$ form a proportion? Explain.

$\frac{4}{5} \stackrel{?}{=} \frac{12}{15}$ ← **Write as a proportion.**

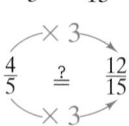

$\frac{4}{5} \stackrel{?}{=} \frac{12}{15}$ (× 3 on numerator and denominator) ← **Use number sense to find a common multiplier.**

Since $\frac{4}{5} = \frac{12}{15}$, they form a proportion.

Quick Check

1. Do $\frac{6}{7}$ and $\frac{23}{28}$ form a proportion? Explain. no; $\frac{6}{7} \neq \frac{23}{28}$

Differentiated Instruction Solutions for All Learners

Special Needs L1
After Example 1, give students a drawing of two congruent rectangles. (One rectangle is divided into 7 equal columns, the other into 7 equal columns and 4 equal rows.) Have them shade $\frac{6}{7}$ of the first rectangle, and $\frac{24}{28}$ of the second rectangle. Ask: *Is the same amount shaded?* yes **learning style: visual**

Below Level L2
Students use cross products to verify that ratios are equivalent with examples such as these.

$\frac{2}{3} = \frac{4}{6}$ $2 \cdot 6 = 3 \cdot 4$

$\frac{10}{2} = \frac{5}{1}$ $10 \cdot 1 = 2 \cdot 5$

learning style: visual

You can use the Multiplication Property of Equality to show an important property of all proportions.

Vocabulary Tip

Read $\frac{6}{10} = \frac{9}{15}$ as "The ratio of 6 to 10 equals the ratio of 9 to 15" or "6 is to 10 as 9 is to 15."

$\frac{6}{10} = \frac{9}{15}$		$\frac{a}{b} = \frac{c}{d}$
$\frac{6}{10}(10 \cdot 15) = \frac{9}{15}(10 \cdot 15)$	← **Multiply each side by the denominators.** →	$\frac{a}{b}(b \cdot d) = \frac{c}{d}(b \cdot d)$
$\frac{6 \cdot \cancel{10}^{1} \cdot 15}{{}_{1}\cancel{10}} = \frac{9 \cdot 10 \cdot \cancel{15}^{1}}{{}_{1}\cancel{15}}$	← **Divide the common factors.** →	$\frac{a \cdot \cancel{b}^{1} \cdot d}{{}_{1}\cancel{b}} = \frac{c \cdot b \cdot \cancel{d}^{1}}{{}_{1}\cancel{d}}$
$6 \cdot 15 = 9 \cdot 10$	← **Simplify.** →	$a \cdot d = c \cdot b$
or $6 \cdot 15 = 10 \cdot 9$		or $a \cdot d = b \cdot c$

KEY CONCEPTS **Cross Products Property**

The **cross products** of two ratios are two products found by multiplying the denominator of each ratio by the numerator of the other ratio. In a proportion, the cross products are equal.

Arithmetic	**Algebra**
$\frac{6}{10} = \frac{9}{15}$	$\frac{a}{b} = \frac{c}{d}$, where $b \neq 0$ and $d \neq 0$
$6 \cdot 15 = 10 \cdot 9$	$ad = bc$

You can use cross products to solve a proportion.

EXAMPLE Using Cross Products

2 **Money** Recently, the exchange rate for Mexican pesos to U.S. dollars was 10.737 pesos = 1 dollar. If you were vacationing in Mexico and had 250 pesos left, how many dollars would you receive?

Let d = the number of dollars.

$\frac{10.737}{1} = \frac{250}{d}$ ← **Write the proportion** $\frac{\text{pesos}}{\text{dollars}}$.

$10.737 \cdot d = 1 \cdot 250$ ← **Write the cross products.**

$\frac{10.737d}{10.737} = \frac{250}{10.737}$ ← **Divide each side by 10.737.**

$d = 23.28397131$ ← **Use a calculator.**

You would receive \$23.28.

Check for Reasonableness Round 10.737 to 10. Then $250 \div 10 = 25$. The answer 23.28 is close to the estimate 25. The answer is reasonable.

Quick Check

2. Recently, the exchange rate for Swiss francs to U.S. dollars was 1.2450 Swiss francs = 1 dollar. If you were leaving Switzerland for the United States with 300 francs left, how many dollars would you receive? **\$240.96**

2. Teach

Activity Lab

Use before the lesson.

Student Edition Activity Lab 4-3a, Proportional and Nonproportional Relationships, p. 172

All in One Teaching Resources

Activity Lab 4-3: Solving Proportions

Guided Instruction

Math Tip

Explain to students that when you write the proportion in Example 1, you are testing whether or not the two ratios are really equal. So you must put a question mark over the equal sign until you are sure that the cross products have the same value.

Technology Tip

You can use a calculator to determine whether ratios form a proportion. In Example 1, one method is to calculate one cross product, store the result, calculate the other cross product, and subtract your stored result. If the answer is 0, the ratios are proportional. Another method is to find the decimal equivalents of both $\frac{4}{5}$ and $\frac{12}{15}$ and then compare them. If they are the same, the values are equal and the statement is a proportion.

Teaching Tip

Make sure students realize that they could write the proportion in Example 2 in a different form, such as $\frac{d}{250} = \frac{1}{10.737}$ or $\frac{10.737}{250} = \frac{1}{d}$, and get the same result. Help students keep track of what they are comparing by having them indicate the units.

PowerPoint

Additional Examples

1 Do $\frac{4}{9}$ and $\frac{8}{18}$ form a proportion? Explain. **Yes, since $\frac{4}{9}$ and $\frac{8}{18}$ are equal, they form a proportion.**

2 The fixed rate of conversion is 1 euro = 0.7876 Irish pounds. How many euros would you receive for 125 Irish pounds? **158.71 euros**

Advanced Learners L4

Ask: *What is the cost of a T-shirt marked 15 euros if the current exchange rate is \$.95 = 1 euro?* **\$14.25**

learning style: verbal

English Language Learners ELL

Discuss Daryl's method. *Why did Daryl write a g over the 915?* **Because g stands for the number of goalies in the league, and the ratio $\frac{g}{915}$ equals the ratio $\frac{2}{30}$.**

learning style: verbal

Guided Instruction

Alternative Method
The method of solving proportions using a common multiplier is sometimes called the "factor of change" method. You can scale a ratio up or down to an equivalent ratio by multiplying its terms by a common multiplier, just as you can generate equivalent fractions by multiplying the numerator and denominator of a fraction by a common multiplier.

Error Prevention!

Remind students why you can only use cross multiplication with a proportion and not when adding (as in $\frac{1}{3} + \frac{2}{4}$) or multiplying (as in $\frac{3}{4} \cdot \frac{1}{6}$) fractions.

All in One Teaching Resources
- Daily Notetaking Guide 4-3 L3
- Adapted Notetaking 4-3 L1

Closure

- Explain how to solve a proportion. Sample: Find the cross products and then divide each side of the equation by the number that is the multiplier of the variable.

More Than One Way

Hockey In the National Hockey League, the ratio of goalies to the total number of players on a team is about 2 to 30. If the league has 915 players, about how many goalies are in the league?

Daryl's Method

I'll set up a proportion and use the cross products property. I'll let g stand for the number of goalies in the league.

$$\frac{2}{30} = \frac{g}{915}$$
$$2 \cdot 915 = 30 \cdot g$$
$$1{,}830 = 30g$$
$$\frac{1{,}830}{30} = \frac{30g}{30}$$
$$61 = g$$

There are about 61 goalies in the league.

Michelle's Method

I see that 2 out of every 30 players is a fraction of the total. Since there are 915 players in the league, I just need to multiply $\frac{2}{30}$ by 915 to find the number of goalies g in the whole league.

$$g = \frac{2}{30} \cdot 915$$
$$g = 61$$

There are about 61 goalies in the league.

Choose a Method
The ratio of defense players to the total number of players in the National Hockey League is about 9 to 30. If the league has 890 players, about how many defense players are in the league? Explain why you chose the method you used. Methods may vary. About 267 players play defense.

Check Your Understanding

1. **Vocabulary** You can find the __?__ of two ratios by multiplying the denominator of each ratio by the numerator of the other ratio. cross products

Number Sense **Do the ratios form a proportion? Explain.** 2–4. See left.

2. $\frac{5}{6}$ and $\frac{15}{18}$
3. $\frac{6}{27}$ and $\frac{2}{9}$
4. $\frac{3}{13}$ and $\frac{4}{14}$

2. yes; $\frac{5}{6} = \frac{15}{18}$
3. yes; $\frac{6}{27} = \frac{2}{9}$
4. no; $\frac{3}{13} \neq \frac{4}{14}$

Homework Exercises

For more exercises, see Extra Skills and Word Problems.

GO for Help

For Exercises	See Examples
5–12	1
13–21	2

5. no; $\frac{1}{4} \neq \frac{2}{10}$
6. yes; $\frac{30}{4} = \frac{15}{2}$
7. yes; $\frac{7}{6} = \frac{28}{24}$
8. no; $\frac{3}{8} \neq \frac{4}{10}$
9. no; $\frac{11}{18} \neq \frac{22}{32}$

A **Do the ratios form a proportion? Explain.** 5–9. See left.

5. $\frac{1}{4}$ and $\frac{2}{10}$ **6.** $\frac{30}{4}$ and $\frac{15}{2}$ **7.** $\frac{7}{6}$ and $\frac{28}{24}$ **8.** $\frac{3}{8}$ and $\frac{4}{10}$

9. $\frac{11}{18}$ and $\frac{22}{32}$ **10.** $\frac{25}{40}$ and $\frac{5}{8}$ yes; $\frac{25}{40} = \frac{5}{8}$ **11.** $\frac{15}{27}$ and $\frac{5}{9}$ yes; $\frac{15}{27} = \frac{5}{9}$ **12.** $\frac{2}{5}$ and $\frac{40}{100}$ yes; $\frac{2}{5} = \frac{40}{100}$

Solve each proportion.

13. $\frac{2}{9} = \frac{10}{a}$ 45 **14.** $\frac{k}{4} = \frac{21}{12}$ 7 **15.** $\frac{45}{15} = \frac{y}{1}$ 3 **16.** $\frac{12}{t} = \frac{8}{6}$ 9

17. $\frac{20}{b} = \frac{15}{9}$ 12 **18.** $\frac{12}{9} = \frac{w}{12}$ 16 **19.** $\frac{x}{63} = \frac{9}{14}$ 40.5 **20.** $\frac{3}{c} = \frac{5}{9}$ 5.4

21. You are visiting friends in Estonia. Suppose the exchange rate is 12.68 kroons = 1 dollar. How many Estonian kroons will you receive if you have $500? 6,340 kroons

B **GPS**

22. **Guided Problem Solving** For each crate of apples on display in a market, $\frac{1}{3}$ crate of oranges should be on display. If $2\frac{1}{4}$ crates of apples are on display, how many crates of oranges do you need? $\frac{3}{4}$ crate

- **Make a Plan** Write a proportion comparing crates of apples and crates of oranges.
- **Carry Out the Plan** Solve the proportion.

GO Online
Homework Video Tutor
Visit: PHSchool.com
Web Code: ase-0403

Recently, the exchange rate for Japanese yen to U.S. dollars was 1 yen = $.0093. Find the number of yen you would receive for each dollar amount.

23. $450 48,387 yen **24.** $40 4,301 yen **25.** $210 22,581 yen **26.** $175 18,817 yen

Solve each proportion. Justify each step in the solution. 27–28. See margin.

27. $\frac{x+3}{2} = \frac{5}{4}$ **28.** $\frac{6}{9} = \frac{x+4}{12}$

29. **Error Analysis** In 3 hours, Jim can walk 14 miles. To find the time he would take to walk 25 miles, he wrote the proportion $\frac{3}{14} = \frac{25}{h}$. Explain his error. *h* and 25 are reversed.

30. Determine whether the shaded regions below are proportional. yes

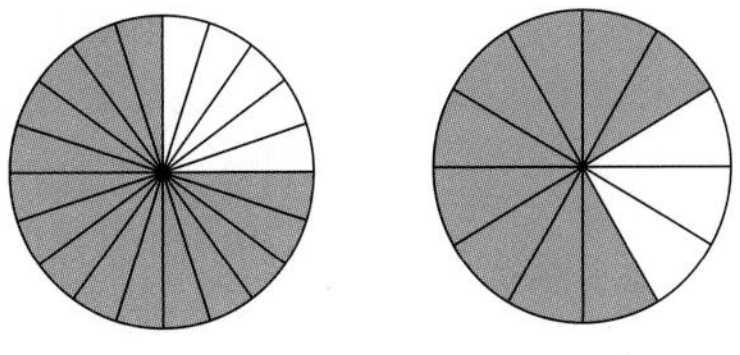

31. about 3 grams; methods may vary.

31. **Choose a Method** A 354-gram box of granola contains 20 grams of fat. The recommended serving size of granola is 55 grams. How many grams of fat does the recommended serving size contain? Explain why you chose the method you used. See left.

27.
$\frac{x+3}{2} = \frac{5}{4}$
$(x + 3)4 = 5 \cdot 2$ Write the cross products.
$4x + 12 = 10$ Multiply.
$4x = -2$ Subtract 12 from each side.
$\frac{4x}{4} = \frac{-2}{4}$ Divide each side by 4.
$x = -\frac{1}{2}$ Simplify.

28.
$\frac{6}{9} = \frac{x+4}{12}$
$6 \cdot 12 = 9(x + 4)$ Write the cross products.
$72 = 9x + 36$ Multiply.
$36 = 9x$ Subtract 36 from each side.
$\frac{36}{9} = \frac{9x}{9}$ Divide each side by 9.
$x = 4$ Simplify.

3. Practice

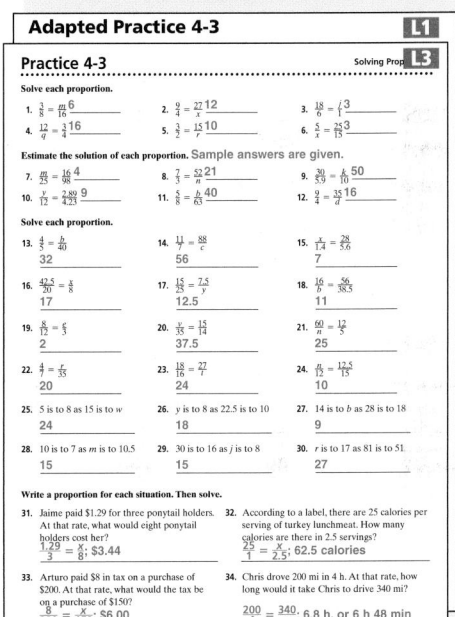

Assignment Guide

Check Your Understanding

Go over Exercises 1–4 in class before assigning the Homework Exercises.

Homework Exercises

A	Practice by Example	5–21
B	Apply Your Skills	22–39
C	Challenge	40
	Test Prep and Mixed Review	41–46

Homework Quick Check

To check students' understanding of key skills and concepts, go over Exercises 8, 18, 29, 35, and 39.

Differentiated Instruction Resources

Adapted Practice 4-3 L1

Practice 4-3 Solving Prop L3

Solve each proportion.

1. $\frac{3}{8} = \frac{m}{16}$ 6 2. $\frac{9}{4} = \frac{27}{x}$ 12 3. $\frac{18}{6} = \frac{j}{1}$ 3
4. $\frac{12}{q} = \frac{3}{4}$ 16 5. $\frac{3}{2} = \frac{15}{r}$ 10 6. $\frac{5}{x} = \frac{25}{15}$ 3

Estimate the solution of each proportion. Sample answers are given.

7. $\frac{m}{25} = \frac{16}{98}$ 4 8. $\frac{7}{3} = \frac{52}{n}$ 21 9. $\frac{30}{5.9} = \frac{k}{10}$ 50
10. $\frac{y}{12} = \frac{2.89}{4.23}$ 9 11. $\frac{5}{8} = \frac{b}{63}$ 40 12. $\frac{9}{4} = \frac{35}{d}$ 16

Solve each proportion.

13. $\frac{4}{5} = \frac{b}{40}$ 32 14. $\frac{11}{7} = \frac{88}{c}$ 56 15. $\frac{x}{1.4} = \frac{28}{5.6}$ 7
16. $\frac{42.5}{20} = \frac{x}{8}$ 17 17. $\frac{15}{25} = \frac{7.5}{y}$ 12.5 18. $\frac{16}{b} = \frac{56}{38.5}$ 11
19. $\frac{8}{12} = \frac{e}{3}$ 2 20. $\frac{v}{35} = \frac{15}{14}$ 37.5 21. $\frac{60}{n} = \frac{12}{5}$ 25
22. $\frac{4}{7} = \frac{r}{35}$ 20 23. $\frac{18}{16} = \frac{27}{t}$ 24 24. $\frac{n}{12} = \frac{12.5}{15}$ 10
25. 5 is to 8 as 15 is to *w* 24 26. *y* is to 8 as 22.5 is to 10 18 27. 14 is to *b* as 28 is to 18 9
28. 10 is to 7 as *m* is to 10.5 15 29. 30 is to 16 as *j* is to 8 15 30. *r* is to 17 as 81 is to 51 27

Write a proportion for each situation. Then solve.

31. Jaime paid $1.29 for three ponytail holders. At that rate, what would eight ponytail holders cost her? $\frac{1.29}{3} = \frac{x}{8}$; $3.44
32. According to a label, there are 25 calories per serving of turkey lunchmeat. How many calories are there in 2.5 servings? $\frac{25}{1} = \frac{x}{2.5}$; 62.5 calories
33. Arturo paid $8 in tax on a purchase of $200. At that rate, what would the tax be on a purchase of $150? $\frac{8}{200} = \frac{x}{150}$; $6.00
34. Chris drove 200 mi in 4 h. At that rate, how long would it take Chris to drive 340 mi? $\frac{200}{4} = \frac{340}{x}$; 6.8 h, or 6 h 48 min

4-3 • Guided Problem Solving GPS L3

Student Page 178, Exercise 35:

Money Before a trip to Quebec, you want to exchange 1,500 U.S. dollars for Canadian dollars. The exchange rate for U.S. dollars to Canadian dollars is 0.7975 U.S. dollar = 1 Canadian dollar from one bank and 0.8352 U.S. dollar = 1 Canadian dollar from another bank. How many more Canadian dollars will you receive from the first bank than from the second bank?

Understand

1. How much money do you want to exchange? 1,500 U.S. dollars
2. What are the 2 exchange rates from the banks? 0.7975 U.S. dollar = 1 Canadian dollar; 0.8352 U.S. dollar = 1 Canadian dollar
3. Underline what you are being asked to determine.

Plan and Carry Out

4. Let *C* represent the number of Canadian dollars. Write and solve a proportion of American dollars to Canadian dollars equal to the rate of the first bank. $\frac{C}{1{,}500} = \frac{0.7975}{1}$; $C = \$1{,}881.88$
5. Let *C* represent the number of Canadian dollars. Write and solve a proportion of American dollars to Canadian dollars equal to the rate of the second bank. $\frac{C}{1{,}500} = \frac{0.8352}{1}$; $C = \$1{,}795.97$
6. How do you find how much more money you received? Subtract to find the difference between the 2 banks, $85.91.

Check

7. Multiply the exchange rate at the first bank by your answer to step 4. The product should equal the amount of U.S. dollars you started with. $0.7975 \times \$1{,}881.88 = \$1{,}500$

Solve Another Problem

8. Two friends are running in a marathon. One runner averages 6.12 minutes per mile. The other runner averages 6.39 minutes per mile. What will be the difference in their finish times (rounded to the nearest hundredth of a minute) for the 26.2-mile race? $6.12 \times 26.2 = 160.34$; $6.39 \times 26.2 = 167.42$; $167.42 - 160.34 = 7.08$ minutes

4. Assess & Reteach

PowerPoint

Lesson Quiz

1. Is $\frac{5}{8}$ is proportional to $\frac{10}{24}$? Explain. No, because the fractions are not equal.

Solve each proportion.

2. $\frac{w}{12} = \frac{3}{4}$ 9
3. $\frac{4}{5} = \frac{20}{r}$ 25
4. Suppose the exchange rate for dollars to Indian rupees is 0.02. How many rupees should you receive for $100? 5,000 rupees

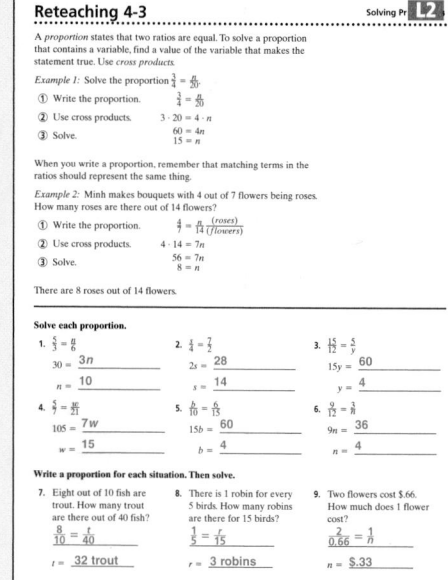

Reteaching 4-3

Solving Pr L2

A *proportion* states that two ratios are equal. To solve a proportion that contains a variable, find a value of the variable that makes the statement true. Use *cross products*.

Example 1: Solve the proportion $\frac{3}{4} = \frac{n}{20}$.

① Write the proportion. $\frac{3}{4} = \frac{n}{20}$

② Use cross products. $3 \cdot 20 = 4 \cdot n$

③ Solve. $60 = 4n$
$15 = n$

When you write a proportion, remember that matching terms in the ratios should represent the same thing.

Example 2: Minh makes bouquets with 4 out of 7 flowers being roses. How many roses are there out of 14 flowers?

① Write the proportion. $\frac{4}{7} = \frac{n}{14} \frac{(roses)}{(flowers)}$

② Use cross products. $4 \cdot 14 = 7n$

③ Solve. $56 = 7n$
$8 = n$

There are 8 roses out of 14 flowers.

Solve each proportion.

1. $\frac{5}{3} = \frac{n}{6}$
   $30 =$ $3n$
   $n =$ 10
2. $\frac{s}{4} = \frac{7}{2}$
   $2s =$ 28
   $s =$ 14
3. $\frac{15}{12} = \frac{5}{y}$
   $15y =$ 60
   $y =$ 4
4. $\frac{5}{7} = \frac{w}{21}$
   $105 =$ $7w$
   $w =$ 15
5. $\frac{b}{10} = \frac{6}{15}$
   $15b =$ 60
   $b =$ 4
6. $\frac{9}{12} = \frac{3}{n}$
   $9n =$ 36
   $n =$ 4

Write a proportion for each situation. Then solve.

7. Eight out of 10 fish are trout. How many trout are there out of 40 fish?
   $\frac{8}{10} = \frac{t}{40}$
   $t =$ 32 trout
8. There is 1 robin for every 5 birds. How many robins are there for 15 birds?
   $\frac{1}{5} = \frac{r}{15}$
   $r =$ 3 robins
9. Two flowers cost $.66. How much does 1 flower cost?
   $\frac{2}{0.66} = \frac{1}{n}$
   $n =$ $.33

Enrichment 4-3

Solving Pr L4

Visual Thinking

A custom skylight company will soon be selling triangular-shaped skylights for homes. One of the skylights has a perimeter of 56 in. The sides of the skylight are in a ratio of 6 : 5 : 3. What is the length of each side?

1. How do you determine the perimeter of a triangle?
   Add the lengths of each side.
2. Are the side lengths of the skylight the same? Explain how you know.
   No; the given ratio of the side lengths tells you that the side lengths of the skylight are different.
3. What is the total measure of the side lengths of the skylight?
   56 in.
4. What is sum of the ratios?
   14
5. Write a perimeter ratio.
   56 : 14
6. How can you use proportions to determine the lengths of the sides of the skylight?
   Set each number in the given ratio equal to the perimeter ratio, 56 : 14.
7. Write and solve three proportions to find the lengths of the sides.
   $\frac{56}{14} = \frac{x}{6} = \frac{y}{5} = \frac{z}{3}$; $x = 24$, $y = 20$, $z = 12$
8. What are the lengths of the sides of the skylight?
   24 in., 20 in., and 12 in.
9. Explain how can you confirm that the side lengths of the skylight are in a ratio of 6 : 5 : 3.
   The greatest common factor of the three values is 4. If you divide 24, 20, and 12 by 4, you get a ratio of 6 : 5 : 3.

Estimate the solution of each proportion. 32–34. Answers may vary. Samples are given.

32. $\frac{k}{20} = \frac{12}{47}$ 5 **33.** $\frac{h}{22.3} = \frac{4}{55}$ 2 **34.** $\frac{1.5}{r} = \frac{3}{4.97}$ 2.5

At Quebec's Le Chateau Frontenac hotel, a room can cost $399 in Canadian dollars, or about $321 in U.S. dollars.

35. Money Before a trip to Quebec, you want to exchange 1,500 U.S. dollars to Canadian dollars. The exchange rate for U.S. dollars to Canadian dollars is 0.7975 U.S. dollar = 1 Canadian dollar from one bank and 0.8352 U.S. dollar = 1 Canadian dollar from another bank. How many more Canadian dollars will you get from the first bank than from the second bank? about $85

GPS

Solve each proportion for *x*.

36. $\frac{x}{\frac{1}{2}} = \frac{12}{9}$ $\frac{2}{3}$ **37.** $\frac{8}{x+1} = \frac{1}{2}$ 15 **38.** $\frac{\frac{5}{1}}{3} = \frac{6}{x}$ $\frac{2}{5}$

39. Writing in Math Explain why the ratios $\frac{x}{y}$ and $\frac{x+z}{y}$ form a proportion only when $z = 0$. Answers may vary. Sample: x will only equal $x + z$ when z is 0.

Ⓒ **40. Challenge** The scale shown at the right is balanced when $a : y = b : x$. Suppose a 50-lb weight rests 29 in. from the fulcrum. How far from the fulcrum must a 30-lb weight be placed to maintain balance? 48.3 in.

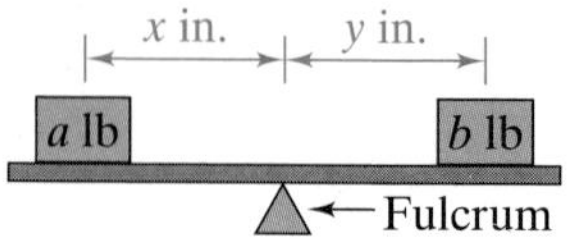

Test Prep and Mixed Review

Practice

Multiple Choice

41. Jocelyn has a 16-page presentation that she needs to give to 5 different teachers. A print shop charges $7.20 for the entire print job. How much does it cost her to print each page? C

Ⓐ $0.45 Ⓑ $0.05 Ⓒ $0.09 Ⓓ $1.44

42. Which quadrant only contains points with a positive *x*-coordinate and a negative *y*-coordinate? J

Ⓕ Quadrant I Ⓗ Quadrant III
Ⓖ Quadrant II Ⓙ Quadrant IV

43. For every 2 points that Lisa's team scored during a basketball game, Kiana's team scored 3 points. What additional information is needed to find the number of points Lisa's team scored? A

Ⓐ Kiana's team's score
Ⓑ The score after the first quarter
Ⓒ The number of players on Lisa's team
Ⓓ The number of players on both teams

GO for Help

For Exercises	See Lesson
44–46	1-3

Simplify each expression.

44. $-11 + (-5)$ -16 **45.** $-25 + 6$ -19 **46.** $-13 - 14$ -27

Test Prep

Resources
For additional practice with a variety of test item formats:
- Test-Taking Strategies, p. 201
- Test Prep, p. 205
- Test-Taking Strategies with Transparencies

Alternative Assessment

Pairs of students invent a new country, name the currency, and decide on an exchange rate to dollars that is not 1 : 1. They determine how much of the new currency they would receive for $1, $5, $10, $20, and $100.

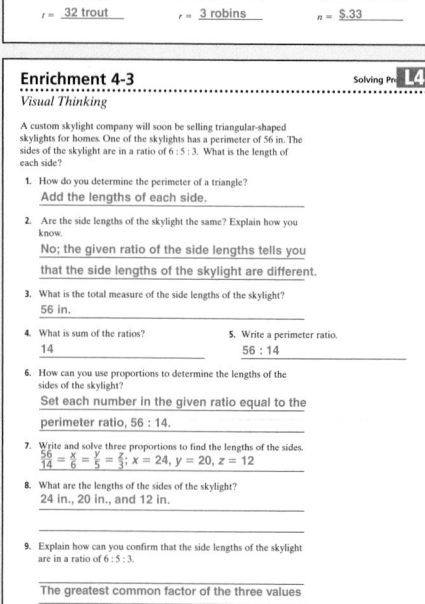

GPS Guided Problem Solving

Using Rates and Proportions

You can use unit rates to write and solve equations involving ratios.

The table below shows data for the time it takes to make copies on a new photocopy machine. Use this data to find the amount of time it would take to copy 1,000 pages.

Time (minutes)	25	50	150	250	75
Number of Pages	875	1,750	5,250	8,750	2,625

What You Might Think

What do I know? What do I want to find out?

What You Might Write

I know how long it takes to copy certain numbers of pages. I want to find the amount of time it would take to copy 1,000 pages.

How can I find the unit rate?

To find the unit rate, I divide time by the number of pages. For the first column, the unit rate is $\frac{25 \text{ min}}{875 \text{ pages}} \approx 0.029$ min/page. The unit rate is the same for all the data, so the unit rate is about 0.029 min/page.

How can I use the unit rate in an equation to find how long it takes to make copies?

The unit rate multiplied by the number of copies c will give the time t it will take to make a certain number of copies. So my equation is

$t = 0.029c$

$t = 0.029(1{,}000)$

$t = 29$

How long does it take to copy 1,000 pages?

It takes 29 minutes to copy 1,000 pages.

Think It Through

1. **Number Sense** How do you know if 29 minutes is reasonable? See margin. (*Hint*: Compare it to 1,750 copies in the chart.)
2. Can you use the proportion $\frac{c}{t} = \frac{0.029}{1}$ for the situation above? Explain. No, $\frac{c}{t} = \frac{1}{0.029}$.
3. How long would it take you to copy 750 pages? 2,000 pages? about 22 min; 58 min

1. Answer may vary. Sample: The unit rate is about 0.029 min/page, which is about $\frac{1}{33}$. Since $\frac{1}{33}$ of 1,000 is about 30, 29 minutes is reasonable.

GPS Guided Problem Solving

Using Rates and Proportions

Students read a guided real-world problem to develop problem solving and reasoning skills. In the left-hand column, they read questions they could ask themselves to make sense of the problem. In the right-hand column, they read the steps for setting up and solving equations used to describe the situation.

Guided Instruction

Have students work through the problem, rather than just read it. Have them identify any steps that are unclear or that don't match their own work.

Error Prevention!

Students might not know which unit rate to use. Help them understand the meaning of unit rate by calculating both $\frac{25 \text{ min}}{875 \text{ pages}}$ and $\frac{875 \text{ pages}}{25 \text{ min}}$. 0.029 min/page, 35 pages/min

Discuss the difference between the two ratios, and the meaning of each. The first ratio is the number of minutes to copy one page; the second ratio is the number of pages that can be copied in one min. Ask: *Why is 0.029 min/page used in this problem?* The unit rate 0.029 minutes per page helps you find the time it takes to copy any number of pages. *If the problem asked for the number of pages that could be printed in 500 minutes, which unit rate would be more useful?* 35 pages/min

Alternative Method

Ask students how they would set up the problem using a proportion instead of a unit rate. Sample: $\frac{25 \text{ min}}{875 \text{ pages}} = \frac{t}{1{,}000 \text{ pages}}$

Guided Instruction

Teaching Tip
Have students ask themselves the same or similar questions as in the example as they work through the Exercises.

Connection to Economics
Encourage students to research data on businesses they know at the National Better Business Bureau Web site. Have them compare rates of compliments and rates of complaints for these businesses.

Differentiated Instruction

Auditory Learners
To help students keep track of values they are comparing, have them describe the unit ratios aloud. For example, "25 minutes per 875 pages, or about 0.029 minutes per page, or 0.029 minutes to copy one page."

Exercises

Solve each problem. For Exercises 4 and 5, answer the questions first.

4. Data from the Council of Better Business Bureaus shows that customers filed approximately 28,000 complaints about cell phones in 2004. About how many complaints would this be per week?
   a. What are you trying to find?
   b. Use the diagram below to write a proportion for this situation.

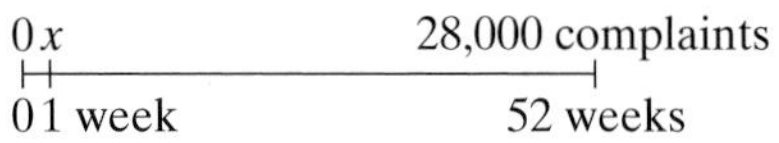

about 538 complaints/week

5. In an opinion poll, 600 teenagers were asked if basic money management skills should be taught in high school. The ratio of yes to no votes was 4 to 1. How many students voted yes and how many voted no? **480 students voted yes; 120 voted no.**
   a. Suppose someone says that 4 students voted yes and 1 voted no. Is that the best answer? Explain.
   b. Use the diagram below to write an equation for this situation.

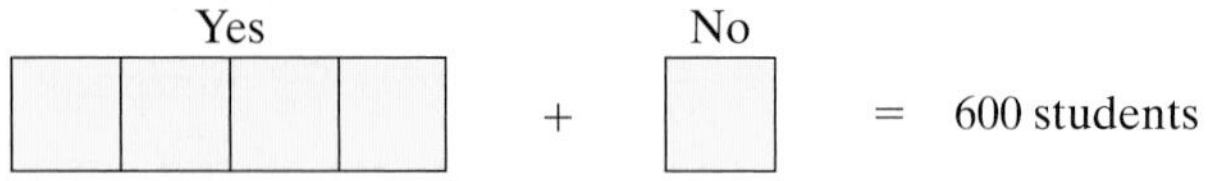

6. The graph at the right shows the enrollment in American Sign Language classes in various years. Compared to the number of students in 1995, how many times greater was the number of students that enrolled in American Sign Language classes in 2002? **about 14 times**

Students Enrolled in American Sign Language Classes

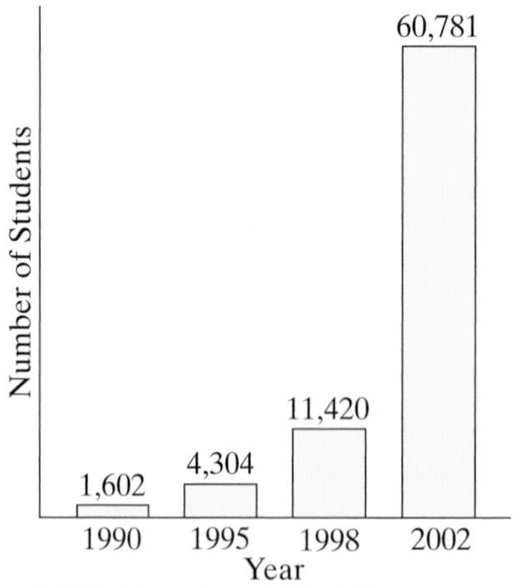

SOURCE: Modern Language Association

7. In a study of 6,349 public libraries in 2002, the average spending per person in the community was $30.32. Suppose you live in a community of 25,000 people and the annual budget is $437,500 for the library. Is this above or below the average found in the study? Explain. **Below; according to the study, your community would need to spend $758,000.**

Algebra

4-4 Similar Figures and Proportions

Check Skills You'll Need

1. **Vocabulary Review** What are the *cross products* for $\frac{10}{15} = \frac{2}{3}$? $10 \cdot 3 = 15 \cdot 2$

Solve each proportion.

2. $\frac{7}{13} = \frac{21}{t}$ 39
3. $\frac{k}{50} = \frac{22}{10}$ 110
4. $\frac{16}{25} = \frac{324}{m}$ $506\frac{1}{4}$

GO for Help Lesson 4-3

What You'll Learn

To identify similar figures and to use proportions to find missing measurements in similar figures

New Vocabulary similar figures, congruent angles, similar polygons

Why Learn This?

Sometimes you want an image to be larger or smaller than the original.

Similar figures have the same shape but not necessarily the same size. **Congruent angles** have equal measures. The ratios of the lengths of corresponding sides in similar figures are proportional.

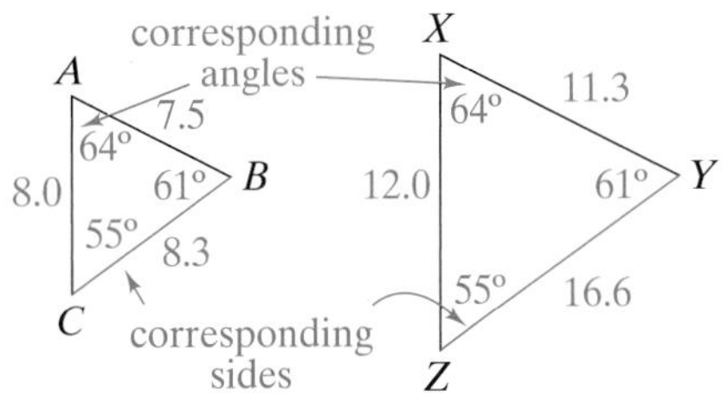

The symbol ~ means "is similar to."
The symbol ≅ means "is congruent to."

If two polygons are **similar polygons**, then corresponding angles are congruent and the lengths of corresponding sides are in proportion.

EXAMPLE Identifying Similar Polygons

1 Is rectangle *LMNO* similar to rectangle *HIJK*? Explain.

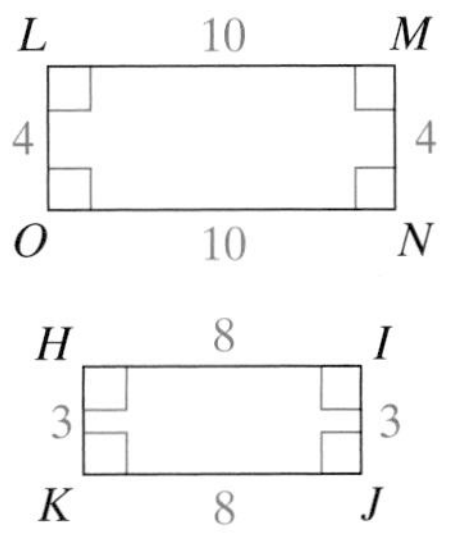

$\angle L \cong \angle H \quad \angle M \cong \angle I \quad \angle N \cong \angle J \quad \angle O \cong \angle K$

$\frac{MN}{IJ} \stackrel{?}{=} \frac{LM}{HI}$ ← **Write a proportion.**

$\frac{4}{3} \stackrel{?}{=} \frac{10}{8}$ ← **Substitute.**

$4 \cdot 8 \stackrel{?}{=} 3 \cdot 10$ ← **Write the cross products.**

$32 \neq 30$ ← **Simplify.**

The corresponding angles are congruent, but the corresponding sides are not in proportion. So the rectangles are *not* similar.

Quick Check

1. Rectangle *EFGH* has side lengths of 18 and 27. Rectangle *LMNO* has side lengths of 36 and 54. Are the rectangles similar? Explain. See left.

1. Yes; the corresponding angles are congruent and the corresponding side lengths are proportional.

Differentiated Instruction Solutions for All Learners

Special Needs L1	Below Level L2
Students draw the rectangles described in the *Quick Check* for Example 1. They label the sides; then write a proportion and check for similarity. **learning style: visual**	Review naming angles and identifying the vertex of an angle for different polygons. **learning style: verbal**

4-4

1. Plan

Objective

To identify similar figures and to use proportions to find missing measurements in similar figures

Examples

1 Identifying Similar Polygons
2 Application: Design
3 Overlapping Similar Triangles

Math Understandings: p. 158C

Professional Development

Math Background

Figures that have the same shape but not necessarily the same size are called *similar figures.* Similar polygons must satisfy two conditions: corresponding angles are congruent, and lengths of corresponding sides are in proportion. *Congruent angles* are angles that have equal measures. The symbol ≅ means *is congruent to.* The symbol ~ means *is similar to.* In order to identify similar polygons, it is necessary to understand how to identify corresponding parts of polygons. One method is to make the orientation of the polygons the same.

More Math Background: p. 158C

Lesson Planning and Resources

See p. 158E for a list of the resources that support this lesson.

PowerPoint

Bell Ringer Practice

Check Skills You'll Need
Use student page, transparency, or PowerPoint. For intervention, direct students to:
Solving Proportions
Lesson 4-3
Extra Skills and Word Problems Practice, Ch. 4

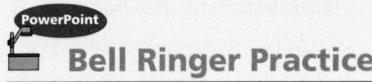

2. Teach

Activity Lab

Use before the lesson.

All in One Teaching Resources

Activity Lab 4-4: Similar Figures and Proportions

Guided Instruction

Error Prevention!

To help students write correct proportions, have them name the similar figures using the corresponding angles.

PowerPoint

Additional Examples

1. Is rectangle *ABCD* similar to rectangle *RSTU*? Explain why or why not.

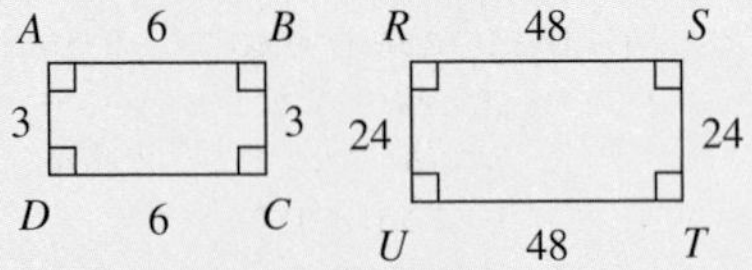

See back of book.

2. A stonemason's sketch of a carving to be made on a building includes the letter "E" shown below. If the width of the actual letter in the arrangement is 22 in., what is the height? 40 in.

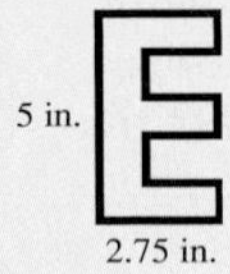

3. $\triangle RST \sim \triangle PSU$. Find the value of *d*. 24.5

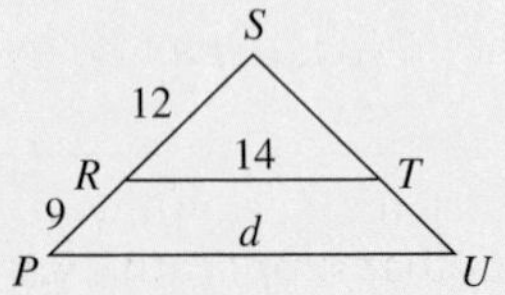

All in One Teaching Resources

- Daily Notetaking Guide 4-4 L3
- Adapted Notetaking 4-4 L1

Closure

- *When are two figures similar?* Their corresponding angles are congruent and corresponding sides are in proportion.

You can use proportions to find unknown lengths in similar figures.

EXAMPLE Application: Design

2 You are designing a poster. A sketch for the letter H is shown. The letter will be 9 in. tall on the poster. If the two letters are similar, what is the width on the poster?

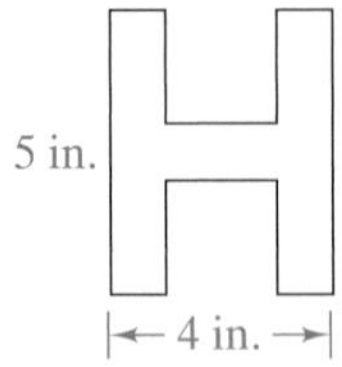

$\frac{5 \text{ in.}}{9 \text{ in.}} = \frac{4 \text{ in.}}{w}$ ← **Write a proportion.**

$5 \cdot w = 9 \cdot 4$ ← **Write the cross products.**

$5w = 36$ ← **Simplify.**

$\frac{5w}{5} = \frac{36}{5}$ ← **Divide each side by 5.**

$x = 7.2$ ← **Simplify.**

The width of the letter is 7.2 inches.

Quick Check

2. If the letter H on the poster has a height of 14 in., what is its width? 11.2 in.

When similar figures overlap, you can separate them.

EXAMPLE Overlapping Similar Triangles

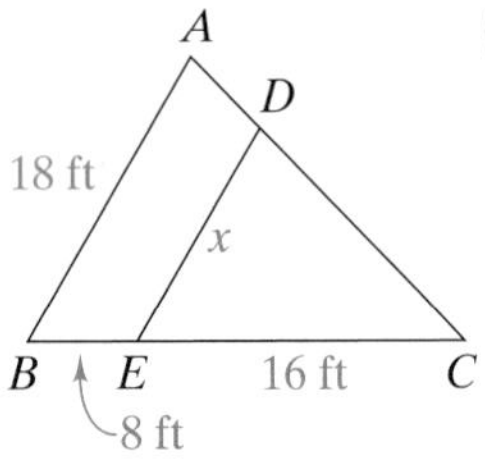

3 **Multiple Choice** In the figure at the left, $\triangle ABC \sim \triangle DEC$. Find the value of *x*.

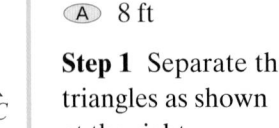

Ⓐ 8 ft Ⓑ 9 ft Ⓒ 12 ft Ⓓ 18 ft

Step 1 Separate the triangles as shown at the right.

Step 2 Write a proportion using corresponding sides of the triangles.

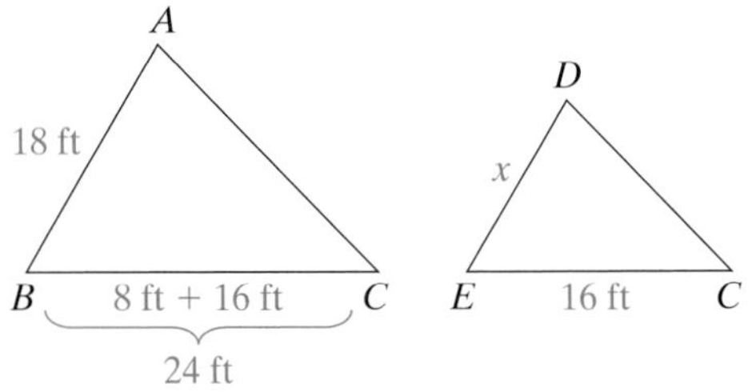

$\frac{18}{x} = \frac{24}{16}$ ← **Write a proportion.**

$18 \cdot 16 = 24 \cdot x$ ← **Write the cross products.**

$288 = 24x$ ← **Simplify.**

$\frac{288}{24} = \frac{24x}{24}$ ← **Divide each side by 24.**

$12 = x$ ← **Simplify.**

The value of *x* is 12 ft. The correct answer is choice C.

Test Prep Tip

You can reduce $\frac{24}{16}$ in the first step. This uses more steps but makes calculations easier.

Quick Check

3. If *DC* is 14 ft, what is the length of $\overline{AC}$? 21 ft

Differentiated Instruction Solutions for All Learners

Advanced Learners L4	**English Language Learners** ELL
Students explain why similar figures are not always congruent. In congruent figures, all sides and angles must be congruent. Similarity only requires the angles to be congruent and the sides to be in proportion. learning style: verbal	Students identify the corresponding sides of similar polygons that have different orientations. Make sure that students understand that corresponding sides are not a function of orientation. learning style: visual

Check Your Understanding

Vocabulary Tip

The notation PQ means the length of $\overline{PQ}$.

1. **Vocabulary** Can a triangle and square be similar figures? Explain. No; similar figures must have the same shape.

Complete each statement for the similar figures at the right.

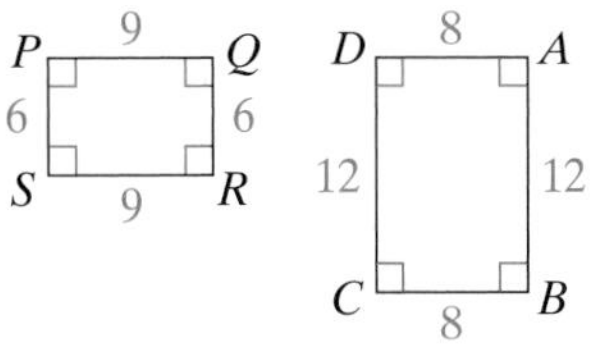

2. $\angle P \cong \angle A$, $\angle R \cong \angle$ ■ C

3. $\angle Q \cong \angle B$, $\angle S \cong \angle$ ■ D

4. $\frac{PQ}{AB} = \frac{■}{BC}$ QR

Homework Exercises

For more exercises, see Extra Skills and Word Problems.

GO for Help

For Exercises	See Examples
5–6	1
7–9	2
10–11	3

5. Yes; the angles are all congruent and the sides are proportional.

6. No; $\frac{ON}{QT} \neq \frac{MN}{TS}$.

A **Are the figures in each pair similar? Explain.** 5–6. See left.

5.

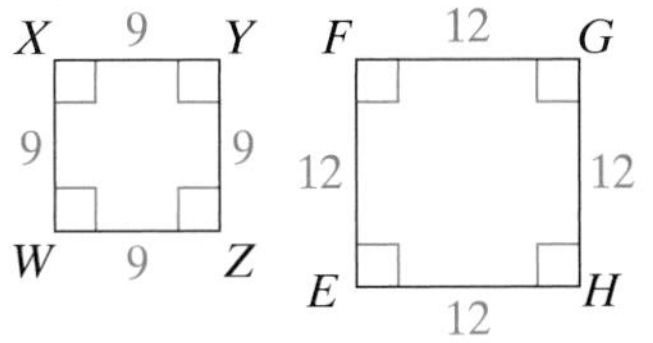

6.

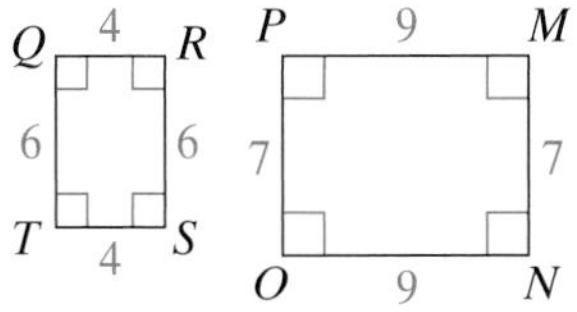

Exercises 7–8 show pairs of similar figures. Find the unknown lengths.

7. 5

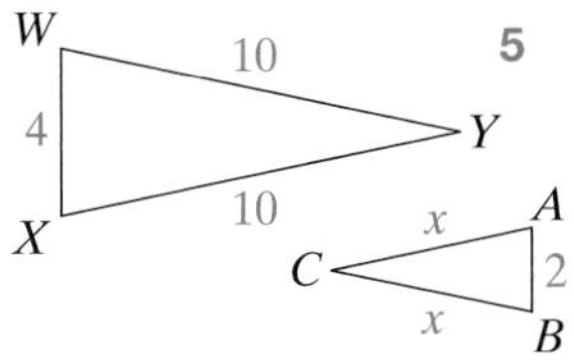

8. 32

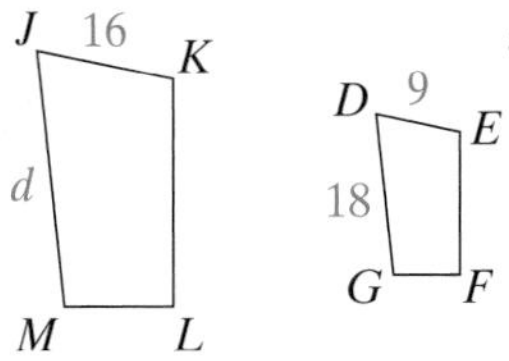

9. **Movies** A frame of movie film is 35 mm wide and 26.25 mm high. The film projects an image 8 m wide. How high is the image? 6 m

Exercises 10–11 show similar figures. Find the unknown lengths.

10. 20

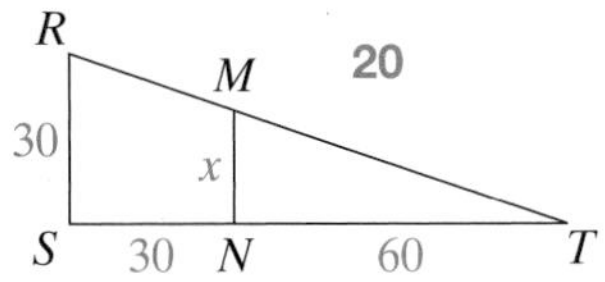

11. 48

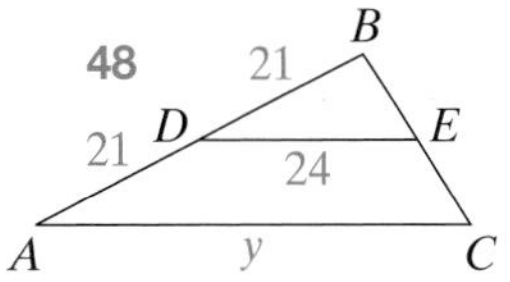

B **GPS** 12. **Guided Problem Solving** You have a class photo that is 10 in. long and 8 in. wide. If you want to enlarge your photo to be 15 in. long, how wide will the photo be? 12 in.

- **Understand the Problem** You know the dimensions of the original photo and the length of the enlarged photo. Find the width of the enlarged photo.
- **Make a Plan** Draw the figures and label their sides.

3. Practice

Assignment Guide

Check Your Understanding

Go over Exercises 1–4 in class before assigning the Homework Exercises.

Homework Exercises

A Practice by Example	5–11
B Apply Your Skills	12–18
C Challenge	19
Test Prep and Mixed Review	20–26

Homework Quick Check

To check students' understanding of key skills and concepts, go over Exercises 8, 10, 15, 16, and 17.

Differentiated Instruction Resources

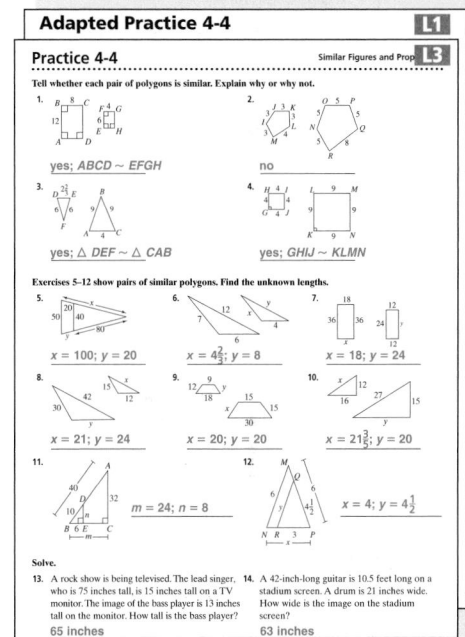

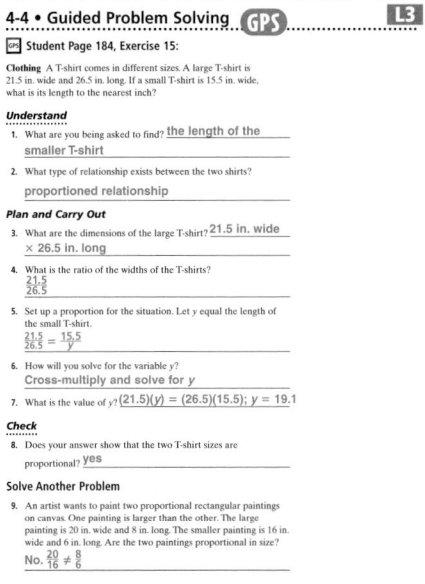

Adapted Practice 4-4 L1

Practice 4-4 Similar Figures and Prop L3

Tell whether each pair of polygons is similar. Explain why or why not.

1. yes; $ABCD \sim EFGH$
2. no

3. yes; $\triangle DEF \sim \triangle CAB$
4. yes; $GHIJ \sim KLMN$

Exercises 5–12 show pairs of similar polygons. Find the unknown lengths.

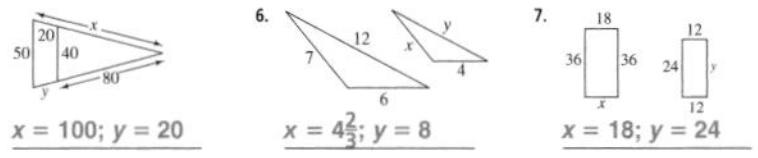

5. $x = 100$; $y = 20$
6. $x = 4\frac{2}{3}$; $y = 8$
7. $x = 18$; $y = 24$

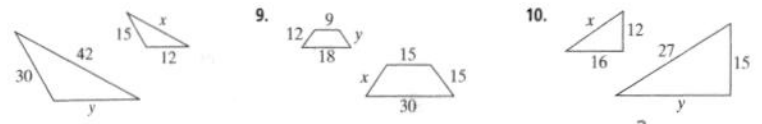

8. $x = 21$; $y = 24$
9. $x = 20$; $y = 20$
10. $x = 21\frac{3}{5}$; $y = 20$

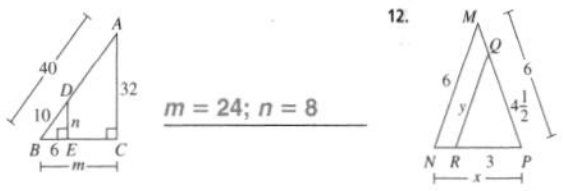

11. $m = 24$; $n = 8$
12. $x = 4$; $y = 4\frac{1}{2}$

Solve.

13. A rock show is being televised. The lead singer, who is 75 inches tall, is 15 inches tall on a TV monitor. The image of the bass player is 13 inches tall on the monitor. How tall is the bass player? 65 inches

14. A 42-inch-long guitar is 10.5 feet long on a stadium screen. A drum is 21 inches wide. How wide is the image on the stadium screen? 63 inches

4-4 • Guided Problem Solving GPS L3

GPS Student Page 184, Exercise 15:

Clothing A T-shirt comes in different sizes. A large T-shirt is 21.5 in. wide and 26.5 in. long. If a small T-shirt is 15.5 in. wide, what is its length to the nearest inch?

Understand

1. What are you being asked to find? the length of the smaller T-shirt
2. What type of relationship exists between the two shirts? proportioned relationship

Plan and Carry Out

3. What are the dimensions of the large T-shirt? 21.5 in. wide × 26.5 in. long
4. What is the ratio of the widths of the T-shirts? $\frac{21.5}{26.5}$
5. Set up a proportion for the situation. Let y equal the length of the small T-shirt. $\frac{21.5}{26.5} = \frac{15.5}{y}$
6. How will you solve for the variable y? Cross-multiply and solve for y
7. What is the value of y? $(21.5)(y) = (26.5)(15.5)$; $y = 19.1$

Check

8. Does your answer show that the two T-shirt sizes are proportional? yes

Solve Another Problem

9. An artist wants to paint two proportional rectangular paintings on canvas. One painting is larger than the other. The large painting is 20 in. wide and 8 in. long. The smaller painting is 16 in. wide and 6 in. long. Are the two paintings proportional in size? No. $\frac{20}{16} \neq \frac{8}{6}$

4. Assess & Reteach

PowerPoint

Lesson Quiz

1. Are the triangles similar? Explain.

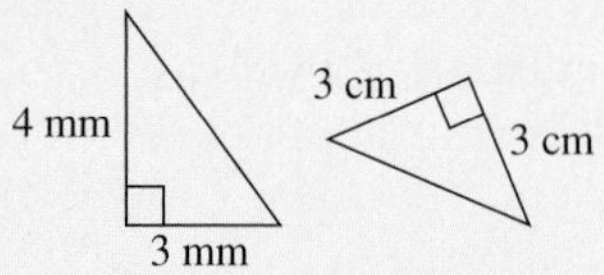

No; their sides are not proportional.

2. A model of a building is 18 in. tall and 24 in. wide. The building is 30 ft tall. How wide is the building? 40 ft

3. In the figure below, $\triangle MNO \sim \triangle LNP$. Find the value of a. 18

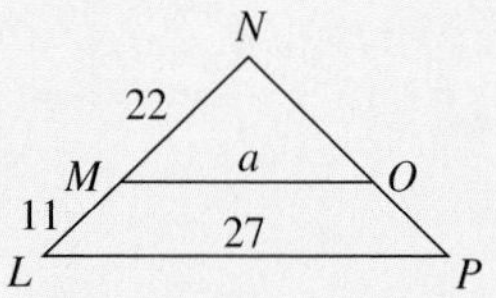

4. If all the lengths in item 3 are doubled, are the triangles still similar? Explain why or why not. Yes. Corresponding values are multiplied by the same factor.

16. Yes; the angles are always 90° and the lengths of the sides will always be proportional.

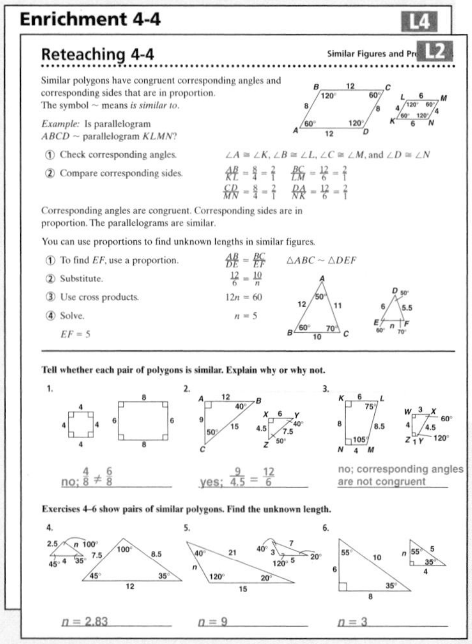

Enrichment 4-4 L4

Reteaching 4-4 — Similar Figures and Pr… L2

Similar polygons have congruent corresponding angles and corresponding sides that are in proportion.
The symbol ~ means *is similar to.*

Example: Is parallelogram $ABCD \sim$ parallelogram $KLMN$?

① Check corresponding angles. $\angle A \cong \angle K$, $\angle B \cong \angle L$, $\angle C \cong \angle M$, and $\angle D \cong \angle N$

② Compare corresponding sides. $\frac{AB}{KL} = \frac{8}{4} = \frac{2}{1}$ $\frac{BC}{LM} = \frac{12}{6} = \frac{2}{1}$ $\frac{CD}{MN} = \frac{8}{4} = \frac{2}{1}$ $\frac{DA}{NK} = \frac{12}{6} = \frac{2}{1}$

Corresponding angles are congruent. Corresponding sides are in proportion. The parallelograms are similar.

You can use proportions to find unknown lengths in similar figures.

① To find EF, use a proportion. $\frac{AB}{DE} = \frac{BC}{EF}$ $\triangle ABC \sim \triangle DEF$

② Substitute. $\frac{12}{6} = \frac{10}{n}$

③ Use cross products. $12n = 60$

④ Solve. $n = 5$

$EF = 5$

Tell whether each pair of polygons is similar. Explain why or why not.

1. no; $\frac{4}{8} \neq \frac{6}{8}$

2. yes; $\frac{9}{4.5} = \frac{12}{6}$

3. no; corresponding angles are not congruent

Exercises 4–6 show pairs of similar polygons. Find the unknown length.

4. $n = 2.83$

5. $n = 9$

6. $n = 3$

GO Online
Homework Video Tutor
Visit: PHSchool.com
Web Code: ase-0404

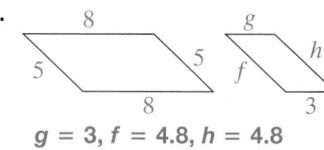

Exercises 13–14 show pairs of similar figures. Find the unknown lengths.

13. 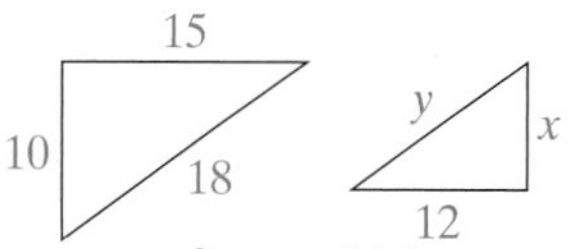

$x = 8$, $y = 14.4$

14. 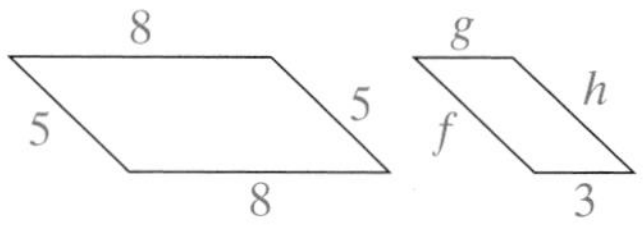

$g = 3$, $f = 4.8$, $h = 4.8$

15. **Clothing** A T-shirt comes in different sizes. A large T-shirt is 21.5 in. wide and 26.5 in. long. If a small youth T-shirt is 15.5 in. wide, what is its length to the nearest inch? about 19 inches

GPS

16. **Writing in Math** Are squares always similar? Explain. See margin.

17. **Multiple Choice** Which statement is *true*? D
    - Ⓐ Corresponding sides of similar polygons are equal.
    - Ⓑ Not all circles are similar.
    - Ⓒ Corresponding sides of similar polygons are congruent.
    - Ⓓ Not all rectangles are similar.

For Exercises 18–19 use the similar triangles shown below.

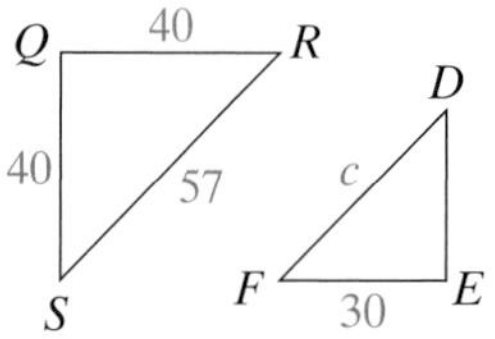

18. Find the length of side c. 42.75

Ⓒ 19. **Challenge** Find the ratio of corresponding sides and the ratio of the perimeters. What do you notice? They are the same.

Test Prep and Mixed Review

Practice

Multiple Choice

20. The figures shown at the right are similar. What is the value of w? B
    - Ⓐ 4.0
    - Ⓑ 4.4
    - Ⓒ 6.3
    - Ⓓ 8.0

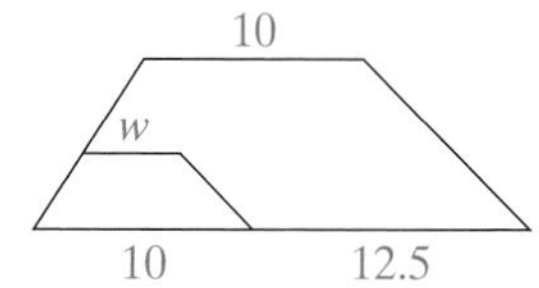

21. Javier and Daisy threw a dinner party for 38 people. The party cost \$920. Which proportion can be used to find the cost c of throwing a similar party with 25 people? F
    - Ⓕ $\frac{38}{25} = \frac{920}{c}$
    - Ⓗ $\frac{38}{920} = \frac{c}{25}$
    - Ⓖ $\frac{13}{38} = \frac{c}{920}$
    - Ⓙ $\frac{13}{25} = \frac{c}{920}$

22. Judy spends 3 more than twice as many hours studying for history as she does for math. She studies 4 hours for history. Which equation can be used to find x, the number of hours she studies for math? D
    - Ⓐ $3x + 3 = 4$
    - Ⓒ $2x + 2 = 4$
    - Ⓑ $3x + 2 = 4$
    - Ⓓ $2x + 3 = 4$

GO for Help

For Exercises	See Lesson
23–26	2-3

Compare. Use <, >, or =.

23. $\frac{16}{20}$ ■ 0.8 = 24. $\frac{7}{8}$ ■ 0.85 > 25. $\frac{18}{12}$ ■ −1.5 > 26. $\frac{5}{14}$ ■ $0.\overline{3}$ >

Test Prep

Resources
For additional practice with a variety of test item formats:
- Test-Taking Strategies, p. 201
- Test Prep, p. 205
- Test-Taking Strategies with Transparencies

Alternative Assessment

Have students write a statement explaining how they know that all squares are similar to each other.

4-4b Activity Lab

Ratios of Similar Figures

You can use diagrams to determine the relationships between side length, perimeter, and area in similar figures.

ACTIVITY

The figure at the right shows three similar rectangles drawn on graph paper.

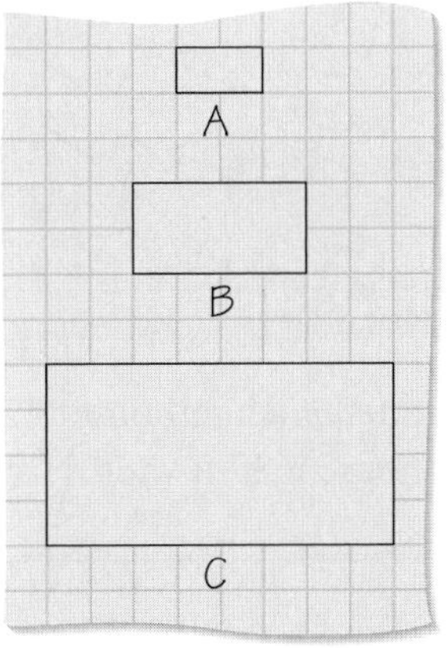

1. Copy and complete the table below. **See margin.**

Rectangle	Length	Perimeter	Area
A	2	6 units	2 units^2
B	■	■	■
C	■	■	■

2. Find the ratios of Length A to Length B, Perimeter A to Perimeter B, and Area A to Area B. Record your answers in a table like the one below. **2–3. See margin.**

Ratio	A to B	A to C	B to C
Length : Length	■	■	■
Perimeter : Perimeter	■	■	■
Area : Area	■	■	■

6. 30 units and 50 units^2; the perimeter would be 5 times the perimeter of rectangle A, and the area would be 5^2, or 25, times the area of rectangle A.

3. Find the ratios needed to complete the table. Write all ratios in simplest form.
4. How does the ratio of the perimeters of any two rectangles in the table compare to the ratio of the lengths of the rectangles? **They are the same.**
5. How does the ratio of the areas of any two rectangles in the table compare to the ratio of the lengths of the rectangles? **The ratio of the areas is the same as the ratio of the lengths squared.**
6. If you draw a rectangle with side lengths five times those of rectangle A, what would you expect the perimeter and area of the new rectangle to be? **See above right.**
7. How does the ratio of the lengths of corresponding sides of any two similar figures compare to the ratio of the perimeters of the figures? Explain. **Explanations may vary. Sample: They are the same because perimeter varies directly with length.**
8. How does the ratio of the lengths of corresponding sides of any two similar figures compare to the ratio of the areas of the figures? Explain. **Explanations may vary. Sample: The ratio of the areas is the same as the ratio of the sides squared; if you double the length, the area quadruples.**

Activity Lab

Ratios of Similar Figures

Students compare the lengths, perimeters, and areas of similar rectangles. They find and use the ratios of these measurements to make conjectures about relationships between the lengths of the sides of similar figures and their perimeters or areas.

Guided Instruction

Before beginning the activity, review similar figures with students. Ask: *What is equal in similar figures?* measures of corresponding angles *What is proportional in similar figures?* lengths of corresponding sides *How can you tell which sides or measurements correspond to each other?* Place figures in the same orientation and compare lengths, widths, or distances between corresponding endpoints.

Activity

Help students keep track of the quantities they are comparing by having them write the category next to the numerators and denominators of their ratios. For example, $\frac{\text{length A}}{\text{length B}} = \frac{2}{4} = \frac{1}{2}$.

Alternative Method
Some students may find it easier to remember where their ratios came from if they write them in the table without simplifying them. Then they can write the simplified form below each entry for their comparisons.

Resources

- graph paper
- colored pencils or markers

1.

Rectangle	Length	Perimeter	Area
A	2	6 units	2 units^2
B	4	12 units	8 units^2
C	8	24 units	32 units^2

2–3.

Ratio	A : B	A : C	B : C
Length/Length	1 : 2	1 : 4	1 : 2
Perimeter/Perimeter	1 : 2	1 : 4	1 : 2
Area/Area	1 : 4	1 : 16	1 : 4

Checkpoint Quiz

Use this Checkpoint Quiz to check students' understanding of the skills and concepts of Lessons 4-3 through 4-4.

Resources

- All in One Teaching Resources Checkpoint Quiz 2
- ExamView Assessment Suite CD-ROM
- Success Tracker Online Intervention

Activity Lab

Exploring Dilations

Students graph points on the coordinate plane that form similar triangles. This activity introduces students to the concept of dilation, stretching or shrinking an object so the object and its image are similar.

Guided Instruction

Students use the coordinate plane to draw and compare triangles. Ask: *Is the image triangle a stretching (enlargement) or a shrinking (reduction) of the original triangle?* a stretching (enlargement) *How does the distance from A′ to C′ compare to the distance from A to C?* twice the original *Are the other sides of △A′B′C′ in the same proportion as the image to the original?* yes

Resources

- Activity Lab 4-5: Similarity Transformations
- graph paper
- rulers
- colored pencils or markers

Checkpoint Quiz 2

Lessons 4-3 through 4-4

Solve each proportion.

1. $\frac{k}{6} = \frac{19}{3}$ 38 **2.** $\frac{15}{t} = \frac{5}{7}$ 21 **3.** $\frac{16}{12} = \frac{w}{6}$ 8 **4.** $\frac{5}{13} = \frac{20}{a}$ 52 **5.** $\frac{2}{5} = \frac{n}{15}$ 6 **6.** $\frac{0.7}{m} = \frac{7}{28}$ 2.8

7. Recently, the exchange rate for U.S. dollars to Indian rupees was $1 = 43.43 rupees. How many dollars would you get for 860 rupees? about $19.80

Exercises 8–9 show pairs of similar polygons. Find the unknown lengths.

8.

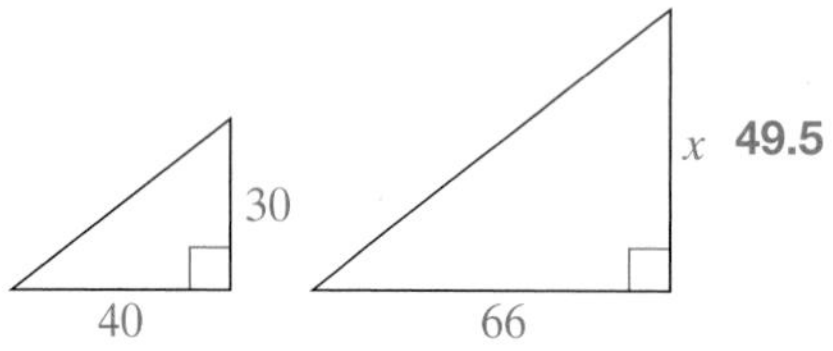

49.5

9.

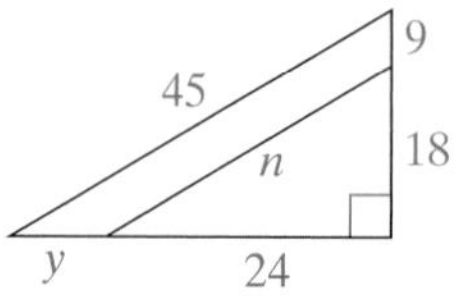

$n = 30$; $y = 12$

10. A model of a lighthouse is 25 cm wide and 75 cm high. The original lighthouse is 17 ft wide. How high is the original lighthouse? 51 ft

4-5a Activity Lab

Exploring Dilations

1. Draw triangles using the following instructions.
- Graph points $A(4, 2)$, $B(8, 2)$, $C(4, 5)$, and $O(0, 0)$ on graph paper. Draw $\triangle ABC$. Check students' work.
- Use a different color to draw rays $\overrightarrow{OA}$, $\overrightarrow{OB}$, and $\overrightarrow{OC}$.
- Use a ruler to locate A' on $\overrightarrow{OA}$ so that $\overline{OA} = \overline{AA'}$, as shown.
- Locate points B' and C'. Then draw $\triangle A'B'C'$.

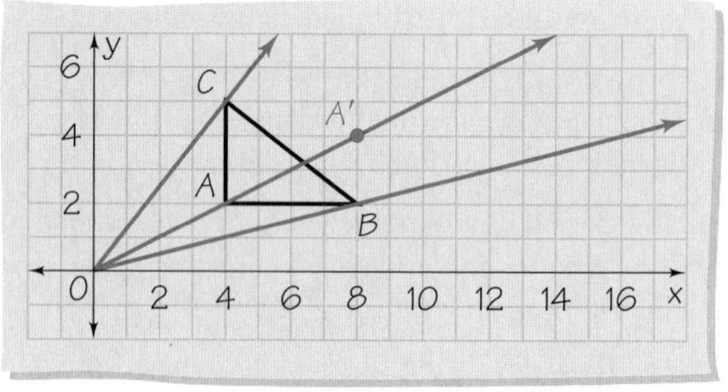

2. What appears to be true about $\triangle ABC$ and $\triangle A'B'C'$? Explain. Explanations may vary. Sample: $\triangle A'B'C'$ is twice as big as $\triangle ABC$; all the new coordinates are double the original coordinates.

4-5 Similarity Transformations

Check Skills You'll Need

1. **Vocabulary Review** The first coordinate in an *ordered pair* is the _?_ - coordinate. *x*

Graph each point on a coordinate plane. 2–5. See back of book.

2. $A(3, 6)$ **3.** $B(-2, 7)$

4. $C(5, -1)$ **5.** $D(-3, 0)$

GO for Help Lesson 3-4

What You'll Learn

To graph dilations and to determine the scale factor of a dilation

New Vocabulary dilation, scale factor, enlargement, reduction

Why Learn This?

Photos can be enlarged or reduced using scale factors.

A **dilation** is a transformation in which a figure and its image are similar. The ratio of a length in the image to the corresponding length in the original figure is the **scale factor.**

EXAMPLE Finding a Dilation

Vocabulary Tip

Dilate means "to make wider or larger." In math, a dilation can enlarge or reduce a figure.

1 Find the image of $\triangle ABC$ below after a dilation with center A and a scale factor of $\frac{1}{2}$.

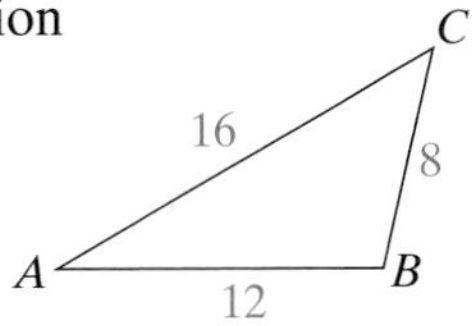

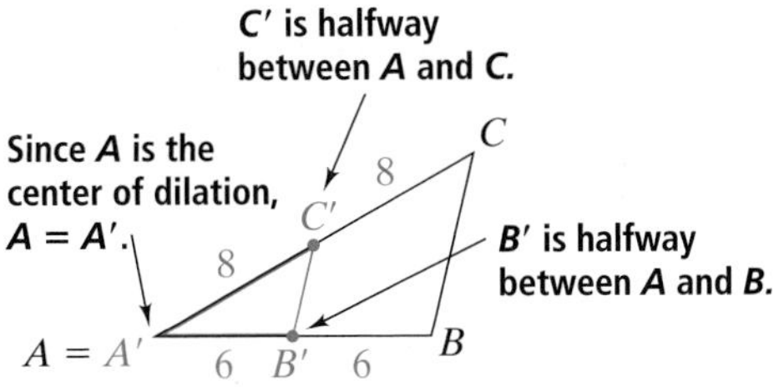

$\triangle A'B'C'$ is the image of $\triangle ABC$ after a dilation with a scale factor of $\frac{1}{2}$.

$\triangle ABC \sim \triangle A'B'C'$.

Quick Check

1. Find the image of $\triangle DEF$ with vertices $D(-2, 2)$, $E(1, -1)$, and $F(-2, -1)$ after a dilation with center D and a scale factor of 2. See back of book.

Unless otherwise noted, in this text, dilations in a coordinate plane have $(0, 0)$ as the center of dilation. To find the image of a figure in a coordinate plane after a dilation, you multiply the x- and y-coordinates by the scale factor.

Differentiated Instruction Solutions for All Learners

Special Needs L1	**Below Level** L2
Students who need help graphing the dilated images work with partners in class. learning style: tactile	Students plot the following points: $A(-1, -1)$, $B(1, 2)$, $C(3, 5)$, $D(2, -2)$, and $E(6, -3)$. They identify the polygons formed by drawing lines from A to C, C to E, E to A, and B to D. two similar triangles $\triangle ABD$ and $\triangle ACE$, one inside the other learning style: tactile

4-5

1. Plan

Objective

To graph dilations and to determine the scale factor of a dilation

Examples

1 Finding a Dilation
2 Graphing Dilation Images
3 Application: City Planning

Math Understandings: p. 158D

Professional Development

Math Background

A *dilation* is a transformation in which a figure and its image are similar. A dilation is *not* a rigid motion because the size of the figure changes.

To perform a dilation (either an enlargement or a reduction), you must know the amount of change, called the *scale factor,* and the point that is the *center of dilation.*

The scale factor is defined as the ratio of the new image to the original figure. In this lesson, the center of dilation is (0, 0), the origin.

More Math Background: p. 158D

Lesson Planning and Resources

See p. 158E for a list of the resources that support this lesson.

PowerPoint

Bell Ringer Practice

Check Skills You'll Need
Use student page, transparency, or PowerPoint. For intervention, direct students to:

Graphing in the Coordinate Plane
Lesson 3-4
Extra Skills and Word Problems Practice, Ch. 3

2. Teach

Activity Lab

Use before the lesson.
Student Edition Activity Lab 4-5a, Exploring Dilations, p. 186

All in One Teaching Resources

Activity Lab 4-5: Similarity Transformations

Guided Instruction

Error Prevention!

In Example 2, some students may multiply only one coordinate of each point by the scale factor. Point out that for the figures to remain similar, the scale factor must be applied to both coordinates.

PowerPoint

Additional Examples

1 Find the image of $\triangle ABC$ after a dilation with center A and a scale factor of 3.
See back of book.

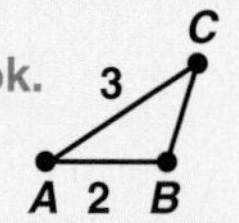

2 Find the coordinates of the image of quadrilateral $KLMN$ after a dilation with a scale factor of $\frac{1}{2}$. Quadrilateral $KLMN$ has vertices $K(-2, -1)$, $L(0, 2)$, $M(4, 2)$, and $N(4, -1)$.
$K'(-1, -\frac{1}{2})$; $L'(0, 1)$; $M'(2, 1)$; $N'(2, -\frac{1}{2})$

3 The figure below, $\triangle PQR$, shows the outline of a playing field. A city planner dilates the design to show the area available for community youth to play sports. Find the scale factor. Is it an enlargement or a reduction?

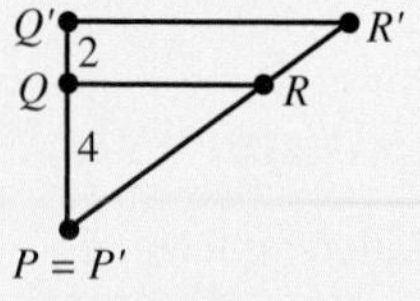

1.5; enlargement

All in One Teaching Resources

- Daily Notetaking Guide 4-5 L3
- Adapted Notetaking 4-5 L1

For: Similar Figures Activity
Use: Interactive Textbook, 4-5

EXAMPLE Graphing Dilation Images

2 Find the coordinates of the image of quadrilateral $KLMN$ after a dilation with a scale factor of $\frac{3}{2}$.

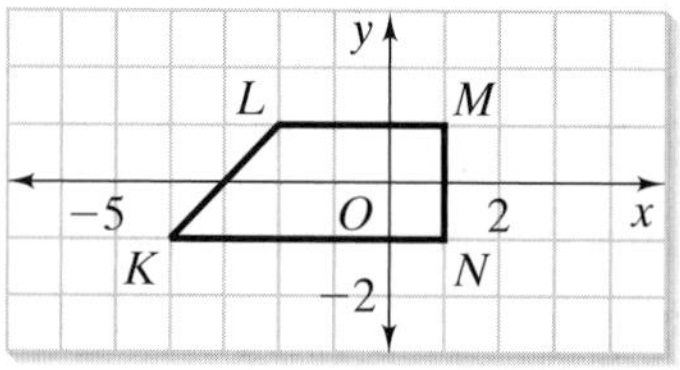

Step 1 Multiply the coordinates of each point by $\frac{3}{2}$.

$K(-4, -1) \rightarrow K'\left(-6, -\frac{3}{2}\right)$

$L(-2, 1) \rightarrow L'\left(-3, \frac{3}{2}\right)$

$M(1, 1) \rightarrow M'\left(\frac{3}{2}, \frac{3}{2}\right)$

$N(1, -1) \rightarrow N'\left(\frac{3}{2}, -\frac{3}{2}\right)$

Step 2 Graph the image.

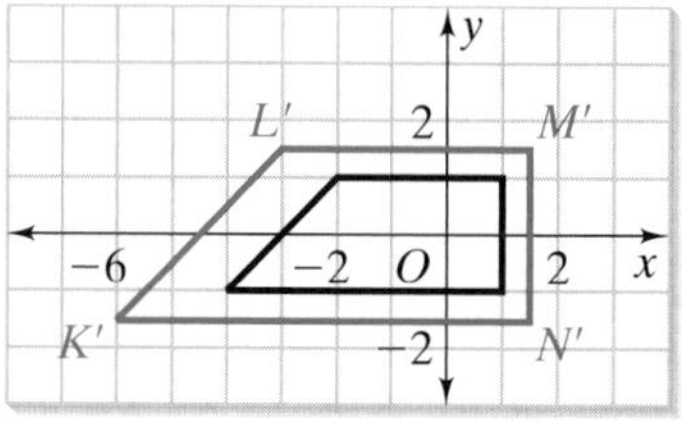

Quick Check

2. Find the coordinates of the image of $ABCD$ with vertices $A(0, 0)$, $B(0, 3)$, $C(3, 3)$, and $D(3, 0)$ after a dilation with a scale factor of $\frac{4}{3}$.
$A'(0, 0)$, $B'(0, 4)$, $C'(4, 4)$, $D'(4, 0)$

A dilation with a scale factor greater than 1 is called an **enlargement.** The image is bigger than the original. A dilation with a scale factor less than 1 is called a **reduction.** The image is smaller than the original.

EXAMPLE Application: City Planning

3 Figure $TRSV$ shows the outline of a park. A city planner dilates the figure to show the area of the park that can be used for concerts. Find the scale factor. Is it an enlargement or a reduction?

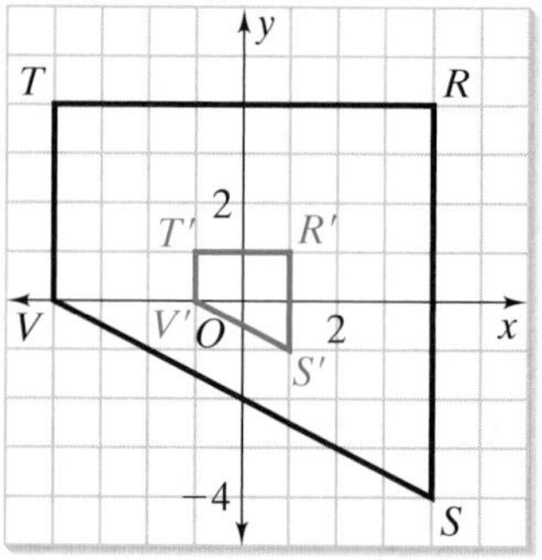

$$\begin{matrix}\text{image} \rightarrow \\ \text{original} \rightarrow\end{matrix} \frac{T'R'}{TR} = \frac{2}{8} = \frac{1}{4}$$

The scale factor is $\frac{1}{4}$. It is less than 1, so the dilation is a reduction.

Quick Check

3. 3; enlargement

3. The blue figure at the left shows the outline of a yard. The black figure is a doghouse. The blue figure is a dilation of the black figure. Find the scale factor. Is it an enlargement or a reduction?

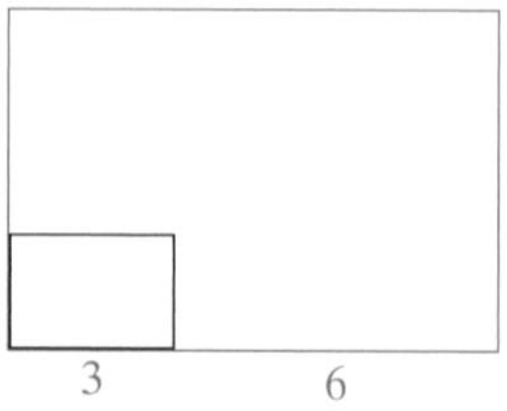

Differentiated Instruction Solutions for All Learners

Advanced Learners L4
Students use a copy machine to enlarge and reduce a right triangle with sides 3 in., 4 in., and 5 in., and then write a description of the results.
learning style: visual

English Language Learners ELL
Students talk with a partner about how photographs, maps, and models of buildings are real life examples of enlargements and reductions.
learning style: verbal

Check Your Understanding

1. **Vocabulary** A rectangle is dilated with a scale factor of 0.6. Is the image a reduction or an enlargement? Explain. Reduction; the dilation has a scale factor less than 1.

Use the diagram for Exercises 2 and 3. The blue figure is a dilation of the original figure.

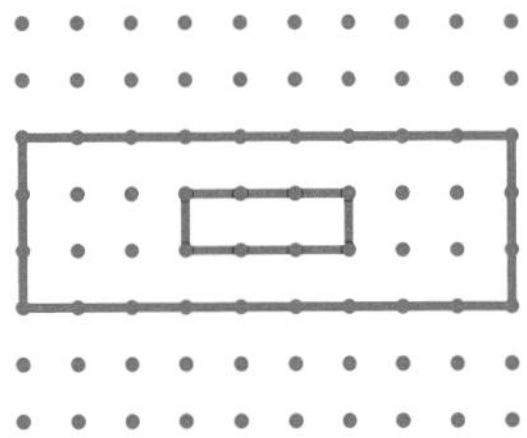

2. Is the blue figure an enlargement or a reduction of the original figure? enlargement
3. What is the scale factor? 3

Homework Exercises

For more exercises, see Extra Skills and Word Problems.

GO for Help

For Exercises	See Examples
4–5	1
6–7	2
8–10	3

A **In each exercise, find the image of $\triangle ABC$ after a dilation with the given center and scale factor.**

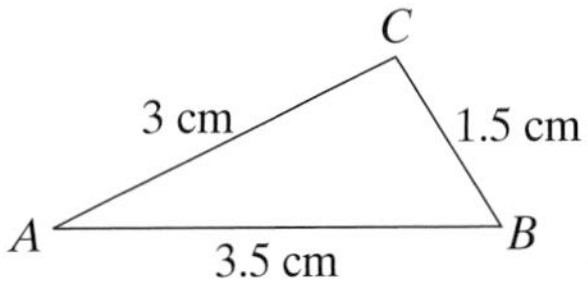

4–5. See left.

4. center C, scale factor $\frac{1}{2}$
5. center B, scale factor 2

4. 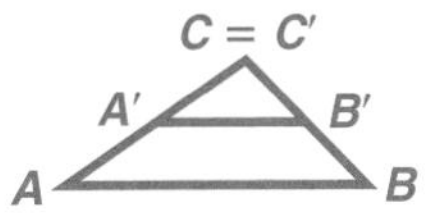

5. 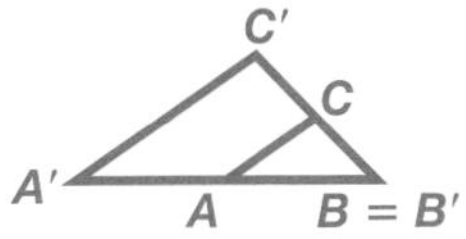

Find the coordinates of the image of quadrilateral $ABCD$ after a dilation with the given scale factor. Graph the image.

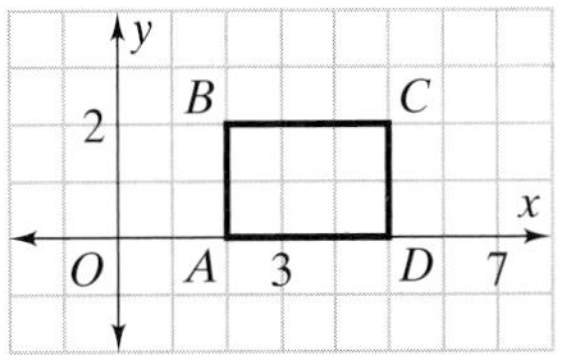

6–7. See margin.

6. scale factor 2
7. scale factor $\frac{1}{2}$

Each blue figure is a dilation of the original figure. Find the scale factor. Classify each dilation as an *enlargement* or a *reduction*.

8. 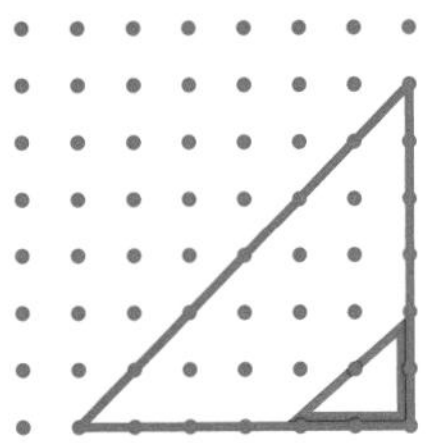
3; enlargement

9. 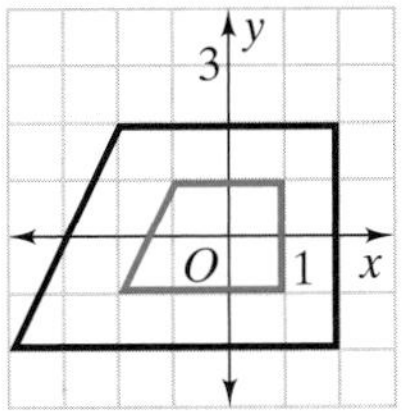

$\frac{1}{2}$; reduction

10. 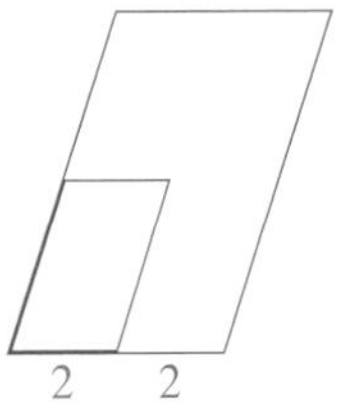

2; enlargement

B GPS 11. **Guided Problem Solving** You are reducing a digital photo that is 2 in. high and 3 in. wide. If the reduced photo is $1\frac{1}{4}$ in. high, what is its width? Write your answer as a mixed number in simplest form. $1\frac{7}{8}$ in.

- **Understand the Problem** You know the height and width of the original photo and the height of the reduced photo. You want to find the length of the reduced photo.
- **Make a Plan** Draw and label the original photo and the reduced photo next to each other. Label the missing width w.

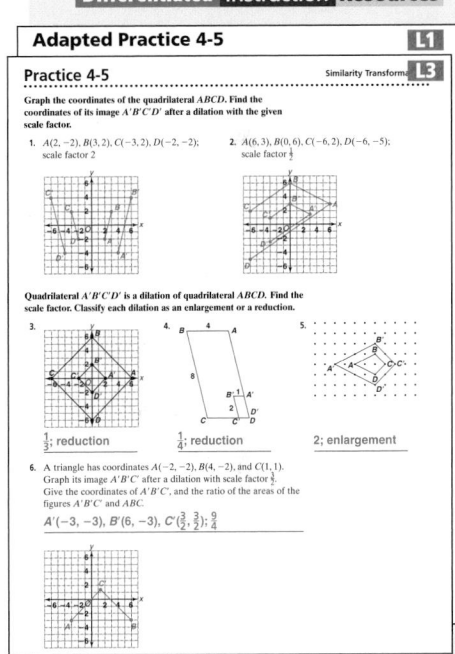

6. $A'(4, 0), B'(4, 4), C'(10, 4), D'(10, 0)$

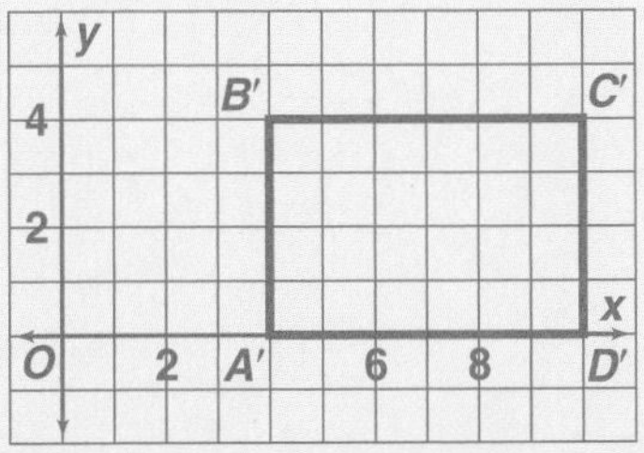

7. $A'(1, 0), B'(1, 1), C'(2.5, 1), D'(2.5, 0)$

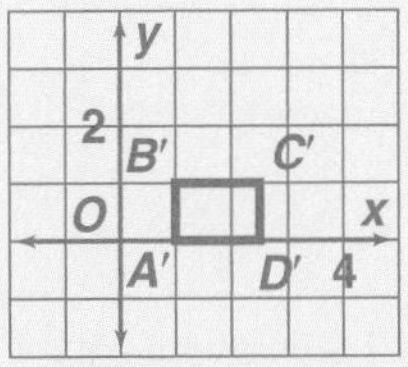

3. Practice

Assignment Guide

Check Your Understanding

Go over Exercises 1–3 in class before assigning the Homework Exercises.

Homework Exercises

A	Practice by Example	4–10
B	Apply Your Skills	11–17
C	Challenge	18
	Test Prep and Mixed Review	19–23

Homework Quick Check

To check students' understanding of key skills and concepts, go over Exercises 7, 9, 14, 15, and 17.

Differentiated Instruction Resources

Adapted Practice 4-5 L1

Practice 4-5 Similarity Transforma... L3

Graph the coordinates of the quadrilateral $ABCD$. Find the coordinates of its image $A'B'C'D'$ after a dilation with the given scale factor.

1. $A(2, -2), B(3, 2), C(-3, 2), D(-2, -2)$; scale factor 2

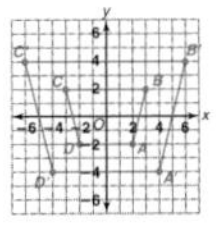

2. $A(6, 3), B(0, 6), C(-6, 2), D(-6, -5)$; scale factor $\frac{1}{2}$

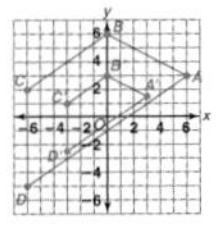

Quadrilateral $A'B'C'D'$ is a dilation of quadrilateral $ABCD$. Find the scale factor. Classify each dilation as an enlargement or a reduction.

3. 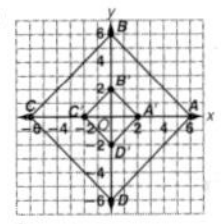
$\frac{1}{3}$; reduction

4. 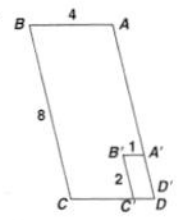

$\frac{1}{4}$; reduction

5. 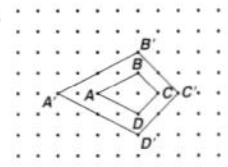

2; enlargement

6. A triangle has coordinates $A(-2, -2)$, $B(4, -2)$, and $C(1, 1)$. Graph its image $A'B'C'$ after a dilation with scale factor $\frac{3}{2}$. Give the coordinates of $A'B'C'$, and the ratio of the areas of the figures $A'B'C'$ and ABC.
$A'(-3, -3), B'(6, -3), C'(\frac{3}{2}, \frac{3}{2}); \frac{9}{4}$

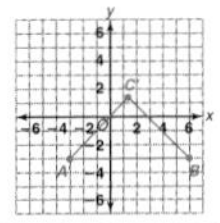

4-5 • Guided Problem Solving GPS L3

GPS Student Page 190, Exercise 15:

Computers A window on a computer screen is $1\frac{1}{2}$ in. high and 2 in. wide. After you click the "size reduction" button, the window is reduced to $1\frac{1}{8}$ in. high and $1\frac{1}{2}$ in. wide. What is the scale factor?

Understand

1. Place circles around the heights of the window and squares around the widths of the window.
2. What are you being asked to find?
the scale factor

Plan and Carry Out

3. Use the width dimension to find the scale factor by placing the values in the formula $\frac{\text{image}}{\text{original}}$.
$\frac{1\frac{1}{2}}{2}$
4. Simplify the fraction to find the scale factor.
$\frac{1\frac{1}{2}}{2} = \frac{3}{2} \div 2 = \frac{3}{2} \cdot \frac{1}{2} = \frac{3}{4}$

Check

5. Use the height dimension to find the scale factor. Does the value match your answer to Step 4?
$\frac{3}{4}$; yes, $\frac{3}{4} = \frac{3}{4}$

Solve Another Problem

6. A picture frame has an opening that is 12 in. by 15 in. If a matting is placed inside the frame to create an opening that is $7\frac{1}{2}$ in. by $9\frac{3}{8}$ in., what is the scale factor of the reduction?
Sample answer: $\frac{7\frac{1}{2}}{12} = \frac{15}{2} \div \frac{12}{1} = \frac{15}{2} \cdot \frac{1}{12} = \frac{5}{2} \cdot \frac{1}{4} = \frac{5}{8}$

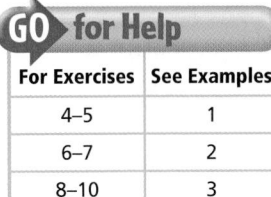

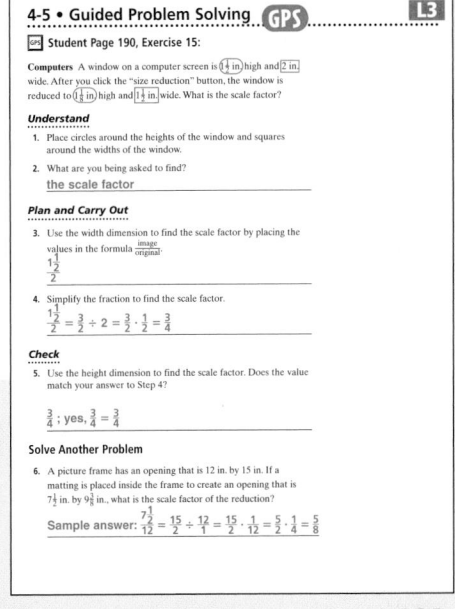

4. Assess & Reteach

PowerPoint

Lesson Quiz

$\triangle ABC$ has coordinates $A(0, 0)$, $B(10, 0)$, and $C(5, 5)$. Find the coordinates of the image of $\triangle ABC$ after a dilation with each scale factor.

1. $\frac{1}{5}$ $A'(0, 0)$, $B'(2, 0)$, $C'(1, 1)$
2. 4 $A'(0, 0)$, $B'(40, 0)$, $C'(20, 20)$
3. Figure ABCD shows the outline of a porch. The figure $A'B'C'D'$ is the outline of a table formed by dilating $ABCD$. Find the scale factor. Is it an enlargement or a reduction? $\frac{1}{3}$; reduction

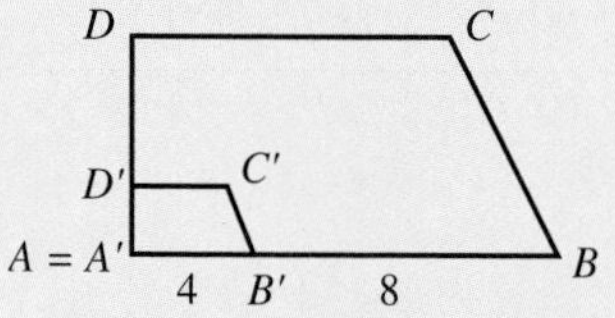

Alternative Assessment

In pairs, each student draws a triangle and its dilated image on a coordinate plane. Students then trade graphs to determine the scale factor of their partner's drawings.

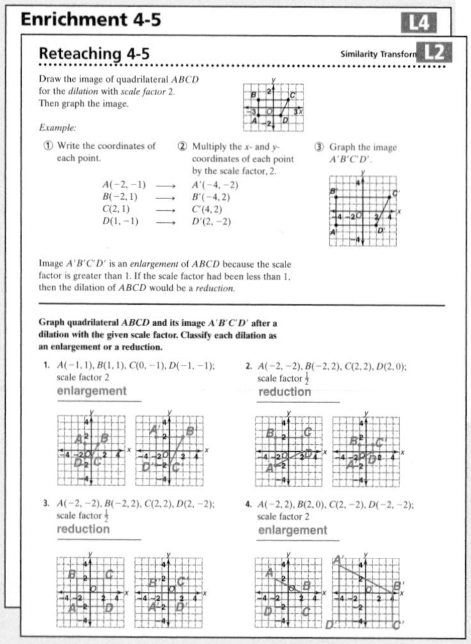

Enrichment 4-5 L4

Reteaching 4-5 Similarity Transform L2

Draw the image of quadrilateral $ABCD$ for the *dilation* with *scale factor* 2. Then graph the image.

Example:

① Write the coordinates of each point.
② Multiply the x- and y-coordinates of each point by the scale factor, 2.
③ Graph the image $A'B'C'D'$.

$A(-2, -1) \longrightarrow A'(-4, -2)$
$B(-2, 1) \longrightarrow B'(-4, 2)$
$C(2, 1) \longrightarrow C'(4, 2)$
$D(1, -1) \longrightarrow D'(2, -2)$

Image $A'B'C'D'$ is an *enlargement* of $ABCD$ because the scale factor is greater than 1. If the scale factor had been less than 1, then the dilation of $ABCD$ would be a *reduction*.

Graph quadrilateral $ABCD$ and its image $A'B'C'D'$ after a dilation with the given scale factor. Classify each dilation as an enlargement or a reduction.

1. $A(-1, 1), B(1, 1), C(0, -1), D(-1, -1)$; scale factor 2
enlargement
2. $A(-2, -2), B(-2, 2), C(2, 2), D(2, 0)$; scale factor $\frac{1}{2}$
reduction
3. $A(-2, -2), B(-2, 2), C(2, 2), D(2, -2)$; scale factor $\frac{1}{2}$
reduction
4. $A(-2, 2), B(2, 0), C(2, -2), D(-2, -2)$; scale factor 2
enlargement

GO Online
Homework Video Tutor
Visit: PHSchool.com
Web Code: ase-0405

Graph the coordinates of quadrilateral *EFGH*. Find the coordinates of its image after a dilation with the given scale factor. Graph the image.
12–14. See back of book.

12. $E(-2, -1)$, $F(2, 0)$, $G(2, 2)$, $H(-1, 2)$; scale factor of 2
13. $E(-3, 0)$, $F(1, -4)$, $G(5, 0)$, $H(1, 4)$; scale factor of $\frac{1}{2}$
14. $E(3, 0)$, $F(0, -2)$, $G(-3, 1)$, $H(2, 3)$; scale factor of 1.5

15. **Computers** A window on a computer screen is $1\frac{1}{2}$ in. high and 2 in. wide. After you click the "size reduction" button, the window is reduced to $1\frac{1}{8}$ in. high and $1\frac{1}{2}$ in. wide. What is the scale factor? $\frac{3}{4}$
16. $\triangle A'B'C'$ is the image of $\triangle ABC$ after a dilation. $AB = 7$ cm, $AC = 10$ cm, $A'B' = 28$ cm, and $B'C' = 24$ cm. What is the ratio of the perimeter of $\triangle ABC$ to the perimeter of $\triangle A'B'C'$? $\frac{1}{4}$
17. **Writing in Math** Explain the steps involved in dilating a figure in a coordinate plane. See left.

17. Answers may vary. Sample: To dilate a figure on a coordinate plane, find the coordinates of each vertex and multiply each coordinate by the scale factor. Then plot each of these points on the coordinate plane.

18. **Challenge** $\triangle ABC$ has three angles of 60° and three sides that measure 60 cm each. What scale factor should you use to create $\triangle A'B'C'$ with side lengths of 21 cm? 0.35

Test Prep and Mixed Review

Practice

Multiple Choice

19. The blue figure is a dilation of the original figure. What is the scale factor? A

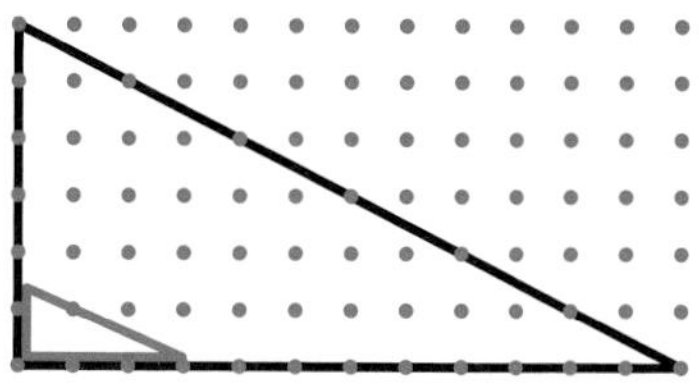

Ⓐ $\frac{1}{4}$ Ⓑ $\frac{1}{2}$ Ⓒ 2 Ⓓ 4

20. The number of people a restaurant can hold is proportional to the area of its floor space. A restaurant has a length of 45 feet, a width of 40 feet, and a height of 25 feet. It can hold 115 people. Which information will NOT help find the space needed for 200 people? H
Ⓕ The length of the restaurant
Ⓖ The number of people the restaurant can hold
Ⓗ The height of the restaurant
Ⓙ The width of the restaurant
21. Cory is putting tape along the diagonals of windows to prepare for a storm. Each window is 54 inches high and 40 inches wide. Which is closest to the amount of tape Cory needs to cover 12 windows? C
Ⓐ 11 ft Ⓑ 67 ft Ⓒ 134 ft Ⓓ 185 ft

GO for Help

For Exercises	See Lesson
22–23	3-2

The legs of a right triangle are given. Find the hypotenuse.

22. 16 cm, 12 cm 20 cm
23. 57 in., 76 in. 95 in.

Test Prep

Resources

For additional practice with a variety of test item formats:

- Test-Taking Strategies, p. 201
- Test Prep, p. 205
- Test-Taking Strategies with Transparencies

4-5b **Activity Lab** Technology

Geometry Software and Dilations

You can use the dilation command from geometry software to dilate a figure. The software asks you to specify a center of dilation and a scale factor. Use the origin (0, 0) for the center of dilation.

ACTIVITY

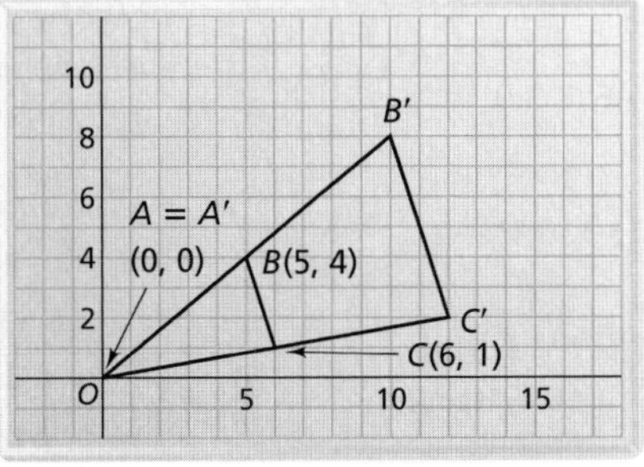

Draw $\triangle ABC$ with the following vertices: $A(0, 0)$, $B(5, 4)$, and $C(6, 1)$. Find the image of $\triangle ABC$ after a dilation with a scale factor of 2. Then find the coordinates of the image of $\triangle ABC$.

Step 1 Plot points A, B, and C. Construct the triangle.

Step 2 Use the *Dilate* command. Enter 2 for the scale factor. The results are shown at the right.

1. Find the image of $\triangle ABC$ after a dilation with a scale factor of 2.5. **Check students' work.**
2. Find the coordinates of the image of $\triangle ABC$. **$A'(0, 0)$, $B'(12.5, 10)$, $C'(15, 2.5)$**

Exercises

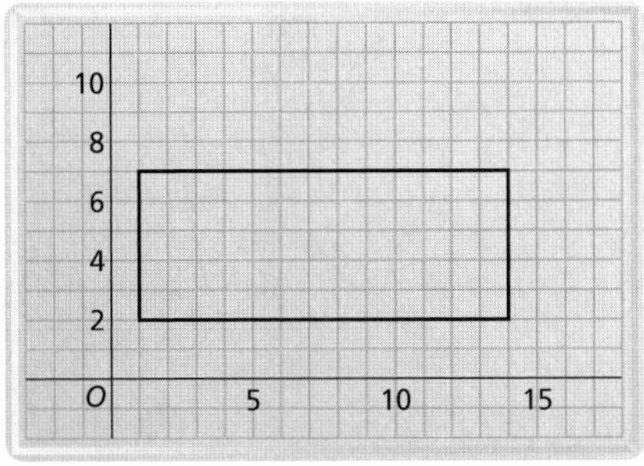

Use the figure at the right for Exercises 1–4. Rectangle *HIJK* is shown at the right. **1–2. Check students' work.**

1. Graph the coordinates of rectangle $HIJK$ with vertices $H(1, 2)$, $I(1, 7)$, $J(14, 7)$, and $K(14, 2)$. Label the vertices.
2. Find the image of rectangle $HIJK$ after a dilation with a scale factor of 0.5. Label the image $LMNO$.
3. Describe the relationship between the perimeters of rectangle $HIJK$ and of rectangle $LMNO$. Write a ratio to compare the perimeters. **It is the same as the scale factor; $\frac{18}{36}$, or $\frac{1}{2}$.**
4. a. Use the Area tool to find the areas of $HIJK$ and $LMNO$. Write a ratio to compare the areas. **65, 16.25, $\frac{16.25}{65}$**

   b. **Reasoning** What conclusions can you make about the ratio of the areas with a scale factor of 0.5? **The ratio of areas is 0.25, or $\frac{1}{4}$.**

Activity Lab

Technology: Geometry Software and Dilations

Learning about transformations in a computer-based environment helps students visualize two-dimensional figures and understand important geometric properties. In this activity, students use geometry software to make dilations.

Guided Instruction

Before beginning the activity, review the meanings of the terms *dilation, scale factor, enlargement,* and *reduction.*

Activity

Have students familiarize themselves with the software, such as computer commands and procedures, before doing the activity.

Teaching Tip
Challenge students to make generalizations about the impact of using different scale factors on the area and perimeter of the original figure.

Differentiated Instruction

Visual Learners
Have students graph a few of the exercises with paper and pencil, then graph the same exercises using the software.

Resources

- any dynamic software tool that can make transformations
- graph paper

4-6

1. Plan

Objective
To use proportions to solve problems involving scale

Examples
1 Using Proportion to Solve Problems
2 Application: Geography

Math Understandings: p. 158D

Professional Development

Math Background

A scale model may be either a reduction or an enlargement of the real object. For instance, engineers working on microchips may be designing on a screen at a scale on the order of 400 to 1.

More Math Background: p. 158D

Lesson Planning and Resources

See p. 158E for a list of the resources that support this lesson.

PowerPoint

Bell Ringer Practice

Check Skills You'll Need
Use student page, transparency, or PowerPoint. For intervention, direct students to:
Multiplying Decimals
Skills Handbook, p. 632

4-6 Scale Models and Maps

Check Skills You'll Need

1. **Vocabulary Review** A *product* is the result of which operation? multiplication

Multiply.

2. 4 × 3.2 12.8
3. 7.6 × 5.9 44.84
4. 1.8 × 22 39.6
5. 13 × 6.5 84.5

GO for Help Skills Handbook, page 632

What You'll Learn
To use proportions to solve problems involving scale

New Vocabulary scale model, scale

Why Learn This?

When building a large object, such as a car, you can make a scale model first to get an idea of what the object will look like.

A **scale model** is a model similar to the actual object it represents. The **scale** of a model is the ratio of the length of the model to the corresponding length of the actual object.

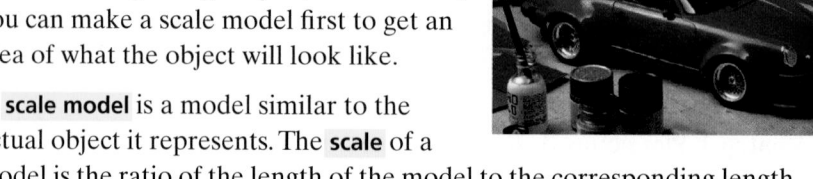

EXAMPLE Using Proportions to Solve Problems

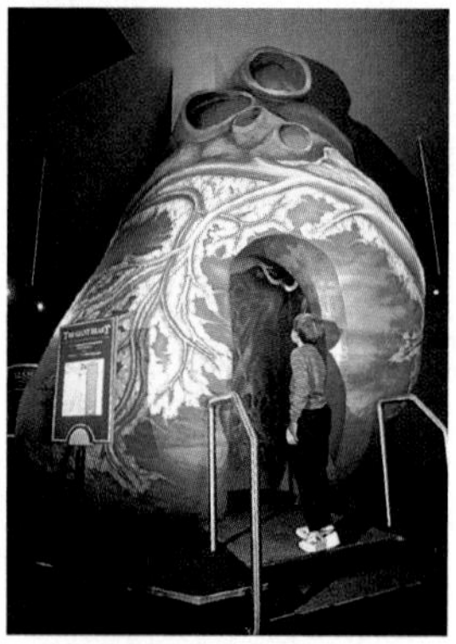

This model heart would fit in a person who is 28 stories tall!

1 **Museums** The Museum of Science and Industry in Chicago has a scale model of a human heart that is large enough for people to walk through. The height of the model is 16 ft. The scale used is 1 ft : $\frac{9}{32}$ in. What is the height of the actual heart on which the model is based?

Let h = the height of the actual heart.

model height (ft) → / actual height (in.) → $\frac{1}{\frac{9}{32}} = \frac{16}{h}$ ← model height (ft) / ← actual height (in.)

$1 \cdot h = 16 \cdot \frac{9}{32}$ ← **Write the cross products.**

$h = \overset{1}{\cancel{16}} \cdot \frac{9}{\cancel{32}_2}$ ← **Divide 16 and 32 by the GCF.**

$h = \frac{9}{2}$ ← **Simplify.**

$h = 4\frac{1}{2}$ ← **Write the improper fraction as a mixed number.**

The height of the actual heart is $4\frac{1}{2}$ in.

Quick Check

1. In Example 1, suppose the width of the scale model is 10 ft. What is the width of the actual heart? $2\frac{13}{16}$ in.

Differentiated Instruction Solutions for All Learners

Special Needs L1	Below Level L2
Students practice measuring the distance between several points on actual maps. Then they calculate the actual distances between those points.	Review and distinguish between fraction multiplication and solving proportions. Solve problems such as these: $\frac{3}{4} \times \frac{2}{3}$ $\frac{1}{2}$ $\frac{3}{4} = \frac{9}{x}$ 12 $\frac{5}{6} \times 18$ 15 $6 = \frac{2}{x}$ $\frac{1}{3}$
learning style: visual	learning style: visual

You can use the scale of a map to find actual distances between locations.

EXAMPLE **Application: Geography**

2 **Multiple Choice** Find the map distance from Columbus, Georgia, to Birmingham, Alabama. Which is closest to the actual distance?

Ⓐ 120 mi Ⓒ 140 mi
Ⓑ 130 mi Ⓓ 150 mi

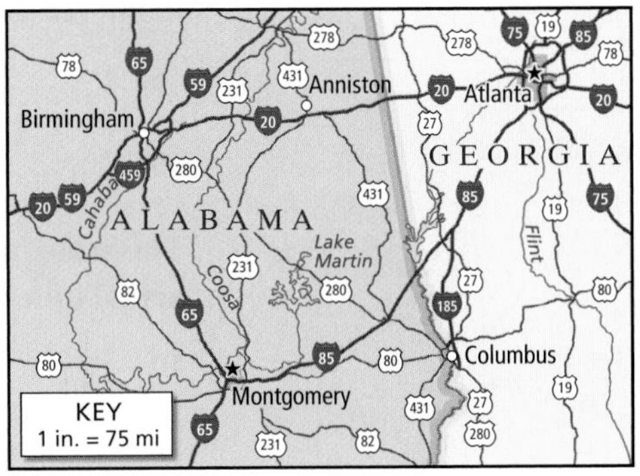

The map distance is about $1\frac{3}{4}$ in., or 1.75 in.

Let x = the actual distance.

$$\begin{array}{r} \text{map (in.)} \rightarrow \\ \text{actual (mi)} \rightarrow \end{array} \frac{1}{75} = \frac{1.75}{x} \begin{array}{l} \leftarrow \text{map (in.)} \\ \leftarrow \text{actual (mi)} \end{array}$$

$1 \cdot x = 75 \cdot 1.75$ ← **Write the cross products.**

$x = 131.25$ ← **Simplify.**

The distance from Birmingham to Columbus is about 130 mi. The correct answer is choice B.

Test Prep Tip

You can also solve this problem by multiplying 1.75 by the unit rate $\frac{75 \text{ mi}}{1 \text{ in.}}$.

Quick Check

2. Use the map in Example 2 and an inch ruler. Find the actual distance from Montgomery, Alabama, to Atlanta, Georgia. about 140 mi

Check Your Understanding

1. **Vocabulary** What does the scale on a map tell you about map distance and actual distance? The scale is the ratio of map distance to actual distance.
2. **Mental Math** Suppose a distance on the map in Example 2 is 2 in. Find the actual distance without using proportions. 150 mi
3. **Reasoning** Consider two models of the same object. The models have scales of 1 : 2 and of 1 : 3. Which model is larger? Explain. 1 : 2; the model is half as large as the object, compared to a third as large.

The scale of a model car is 1 in. : $2\frac{1}{2}$ ft. The length of the model is 6 in. The width of the model is 2.3 in.

4. Use the proportion $\frac{1 \text{ in.}}{2\frac{1}{2} \text{ ft}} = \frac{\blacksquare \text{ in.}}{x \text{ ft}}$ to find the actual length of the car. 6; 15 ft
5. Use the proportion $\frac{1 \text{ in.}}{2\frac{1}{2} \text{ ft}} = \frac{\blacksquare \text{ in.}}{y \text{ ft}}$ to find the actual width of the car. 2.3; 5.75 ft

2. Teach

Activity Lab

Use before the lesson.

All in One Teaching Resources

Activity Lab 4-6: Scale Models and Maps

Guided Instruction

Teaching Tip
Before students begin the exercises, have them practice simplifying complex fractions like those shown below.

$$\frac{3\frac{1}{3}}{1} = \frac{\frac{10}{3}}{1} = \frac{10}{3}$$

$$\frac{1}{2\frac{1}{4}} = \frac{1}{\frac{9}{4}} = \frac{4}{9}$$

Connection to Industry
Have students bring examples of scale models to class, such as dollhouse furniture, model cars, and model planes. Ask them to find or estimate the scales for the models.

PowerPoint

Additional Examples

1 On a blueprint, the cellar is 4 in. by 3 in. The scale is $\frac{1}{2}$ in. = 8 ft. What are the length and width of the actual cellar? 64 ft by 48 ft

2 The map distance from El Paso, Texas, to Chihuahua, Mexico, measures about 7.5 cm. The scale is 1 cm = 50 km. What is the actual distance? 375 km

All in One Teaching Resources

- Daily Notetaking Guide 4-6 L3
- Adapted Notetaking 4-6 L1

Closure

- Write a proportion using words that you can use to find an actual distance when you know the map distance. Sample:

$$\frac{\text{one inch on the map}}{\text{actual miles represented by one inch}} = \frac{\text{measured map distance in inches}}{\text{actual distance in miles}}$$

Advanced Learners L4
Students draw a scale diagram of a 3 ft-by-5 ft rug. They double each dimension by drawing a 6 ft-by-10 ft rug. *How much larger is the second rug?* 4 times larger in area

learning style: visual

English Language Learners ELL
To help students make sense of the answer, in Example 1, provide them with a scale model of a heart borrowed from a science class, or a picture of a heart drawn to scale.

learning style: visual

3. Practice

Assignment Guide

Check Your Understanding

Go over Exercises 1–5 in class before assigning the Homework Exercises.

Homework Exercises

A	Practice by Example	6–20
B	Apply Your Skills	21–26
C	Challenge	27
Test Prep and Mixed Review		28–33

Homework Quick Check

To check students' understanding of key skills and concepts, go over Exercises 9, 19, 23, 25, and 26.

Differentiated Instruction Resources

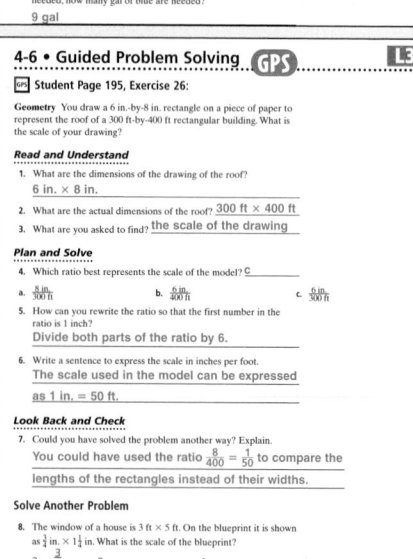

Adapted Practice 4-6 L1

Practice 4-6 Scale Models a... L3

The scale of a map is 1 in. : 40 mi. How many actual miles does each measurement on the map represent?

1. 3 in. 120 mi
2. 1.5 in. 60 mi
3. $7\frac{3}{4}$ in. 310 mi

Suppose you want to make a map with scale 1 in. : 12 mi. How many inches does each distance occupy on the map?

4. 60 mi 5 in.
5. 9 mi $\frac{3}{4}$
6. 40 mi $3\frac{1}{3}$

Solve.

7. Two cities on a map were $2\frac{1}{4}$ in. apart. The cities are actually 56.25 mi apart. What scale was used to draw the map? 1 in. : 25 mi
8. Four ounces of a certain perfume cost $20.96. How much would six ounces of perfume cost? $31.44
9. The human brain weighs about 1 lb for each 100 lb of body weight. What is the approximate weight to the nearest ounce of the brain of a person weighing 85 lb? 14 oz
10. Two towns are 540 km apart. If the scale on the map is 2 cm to 50 km, how far apart are the towns on the map? 21.6 cm
11. Cans of tuna cost $1.59 for $6\frac{1}{2}$ oz. At that rate, how much would 25 oz of tuna cost? $6.12
12. Students are building a model of a volcano. The volcano is about 8,000 ft tall. The students want the model to be 18 in. tall. What scale should they use? 1 in. : 444.4 ft
13. A certain shade of paint requires 3 parts of blue to 2 parts of yellow to 1 part of red. If 18 gal of that shade of paint are needed, how many gal of blue are needed? 9 gal

4-6 • Guided Problem Solving GPS L3

GPS **Student Page 195, Exercise 26:**

Geometry You draw a 6 in.-by-8 in. rectangle on a piece of paper to represent the roof of a 300 ft-by-400 ft rectangular building. What is the scale of your drawing?

Read and Understand

1. What are the dimensions of the drawing of the roof? 6 in. × 8 in.
2. What are the actual dimensions of the roof? 300 ft × 400 ft
3. What are you asked to find? the scale of the drawing

Plan and Solve

4. Which ratio best represents the scale of the model? C

a. $\frac{8 \text{ in.}}{300 \text{ ft}}$ b. $\frac{6 \text{ in.}}{400 \text{ ft}}$ c. $\frac{6 \text{ in.}}{300 \text{ ft}}$

5. How can you rewrite the ratio so that the first number in the ratio is 1 inch? Divide both parts of the ratio by 6.
6. Write a sentence to express the scale in inches per foot. The scale used in the model can be expressed as 1 in. = 50 ft.

Look Back and Check

7. Could you have solved the problem another way? Explain. You could have used the ratio $\frac{8}{400} = \frac{1}{50}$ to compare the lengths of the rectangles instead of their widths.

Solve Another Problem

8. The window of a house is 3 ft × 5 ft. On the blueprint it is shown as $\frac{3}{4}$ in. × $1\frac{1}{4}$ in. What is the scale of the blueprint? $\frac{3}{1} = \frac{\frac{3}{4}}{x}$; $3x = \frac{3}{4}$; $x = 4$, so 1 ft = $\frac{1}{4}$ in.

Homework Exercises

For more exercises, see Extra Skills and Word Problems.

GO for Help

For Exercises	See Examples
6–9	1
10–20	2

6. 30 in.; 6 in.
7. 15 in.; 3 in.
8. 22.5 in.; 4.5 in.
9. 12.5 in.; 2.5 in.

Test Prep Tip

Always choose efficient tools for measuring. This key relates inches to miles, so use an inch ruler.

A **A builder wants to make a model of the silo shown at the right. Find the height and diameter of the model silo for each scale.** 6–9. See left.

6. 1 in. : $2\frac{1}{2}$ ft **7.** 1 in. : 5 ft

8. 1 in. : $3\frac{1}{3}$ ft **9.** 1 in. : 6 ft

The scale of a map is 1 in. : 10 mi. How many actual miles does each measurement on the map represent?

10. $3\frac{1}{4}$ in. 32.5 mi **11.** $2\frac{1}{2}$ in. 25 mi **12.** 4.4 in. 44 mi **13.** 5.3 in. 53 mi

Suppose you want to make a map with a scale 1 in. : 4 mi. How many inches does each distance occupy on the map?

14. 22 mi 5.5 in. **15.** 86 mi 21.5 in. **16.** 92 mi 23 in. **17.** 39 mi 9.75 in.

Maps **Use the map below and an inch ruler for Exercises 18–20.**

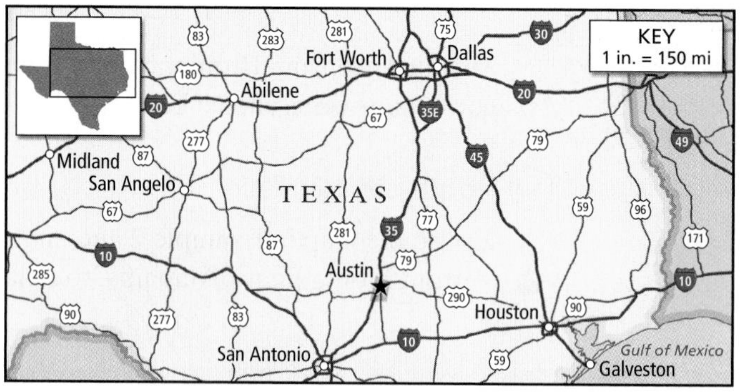

18. a. What is the map distance between Abilene and Houston? $2\frac{1}{8}$ in.
b. Find the actual distance in miles using a proportion. 318.75 mi

19. What is the actual distance from Midland to Austin? 300 mi

20. Which two cities on the map are about 300 mi from Fort Worth? Midland and Galveston

B GPS **21.** **Guided Problem Solving** Model trains built on the HO scale are $\frac{1}{80}$ the size of real trains. Models built on the N scale are $\frac{1}{160}$ the size of real trains. A full-size passenger car is 80 ft long. A model of the car is $\frac{1}{2}$ ft long. On which scale is the model made? N

- Solve the proportion $\frac{1}{80} = \frac{\blacksquare}{80}$ for the HO scale.
- Solve the proportion $\frac{1}{160} = \frac{\blacksquare}{80}$ for the N scale.

22. **Open-Ended** Make a scale drawing of a calculator or a pen. Be sure to include the scale. Check students' work.

GO Online
Homework Video Tutor
Visit: PHSchool.com
Web Code: ase-0406

Architecture **For Exercises 23–25, use the blueprint and an inch ruler.**

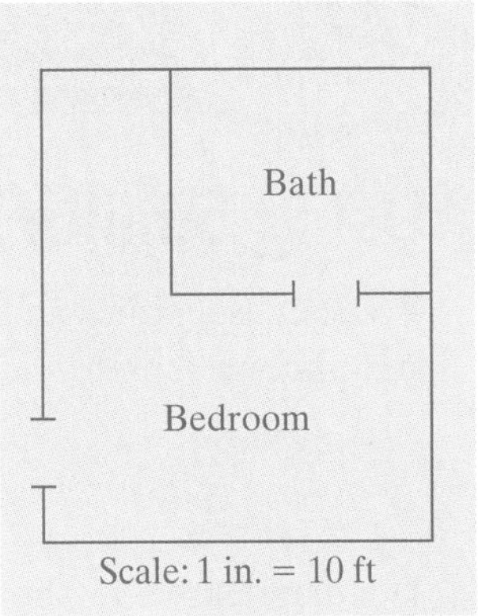

23. How many feet wide are the doors leading into the bedroom? 2.5 ft

24. What is the actual length of the right wall shared by the bedroom and bath? 17.5 ft

25. **Writing in Math** Could a bed 6 ft long and 3 ft wide fit into the narrow section of the bedroom? Explain. See left.

25. Yes; the narrow section of the bedroom is 5 ft wide by 7.5 ft long.

26. **Geometry** You draw a 6 in.-by-8 in. rectangle on a piece of paper to represent the roof of a 300 ft-by-400 ft rectangular building. What is the scale of your drawing? 1 in. : 50 ft

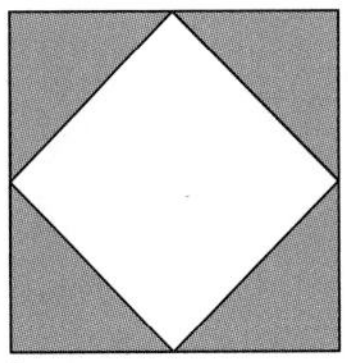

27. **Challenge** Make a scale drawing of the figure at the right for the scale 1 in. : $\frac{1}{3}$ in. Check students' work.

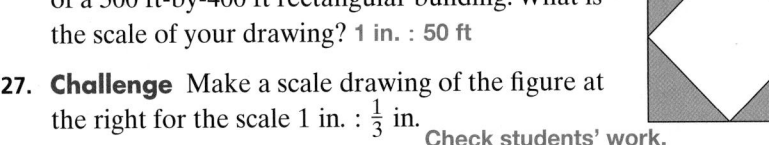

Test Prep and Mixed Review

Practice

Multiple Choice

28. An architect made a model building to scale so that 1 inch represents 40 feet. If the height of the model is $3\frac{1}{2}$ inches, what is the height of the actual building? D
    - A 11.4 ft
    - B 36 ft
    - C 125 ft
    - D 140 ft

29. Which number has the greatest value? H
    - F $-\frac{3}{2}$
    - G -2
    - H $-\frac{1}{4}$
    - J -0.38

30. The figures below have a repeating pattern. Which shows a 180° rotation of the 14th figure in the pattern? B

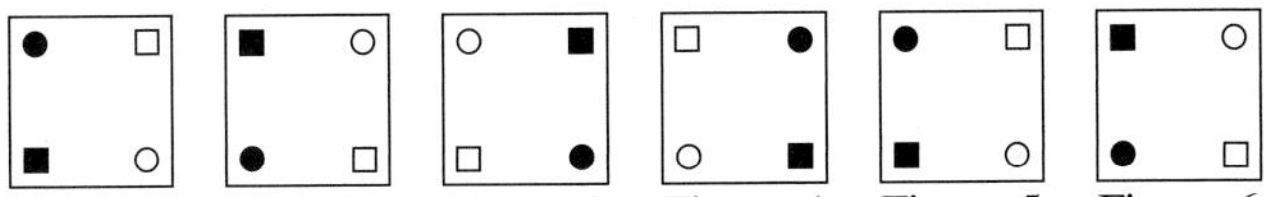

Figure 1 Figure 2 Figure 3 Figure 4 Figure 5 Figure 6

A 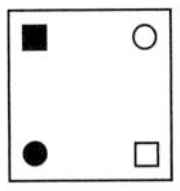
B 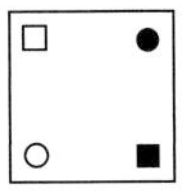
C 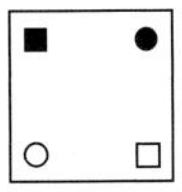
D 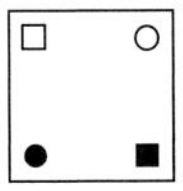

GO for Help

For Exercises	See Lesson
31–33	2-7

Evaluate each expression for $x = -1$ and $y = 1$.

31. $x^2 - 10(x - y^3)$ 21
32. $(x^5 + x^8)(y^7 - y^5)$ 0
33. $x + y - x^2 - y^2$ −2

4. Assess & Reteach

PowerPoint

Lesson Quiz

1. A 6-ft man is designing a new chair that would make him feel like a 2.5-ft child. The seat of a normal chair is 1.5 ft high. How high should he make the seat in his new chair? 3.6 ft

2. A map scale shows 4 cm to represent 6 km. Two intersections measure 1 cm apart on the map. What is the actual distance? 1.5 km

A tennis court is 36 ft wide. A drawing of the court is $2\frac{1}{4}$ in. long and 1 in. wide.

3. Find the scale used. 1 in. = 36 ft

4. Find the actual length of the court. 81 ft

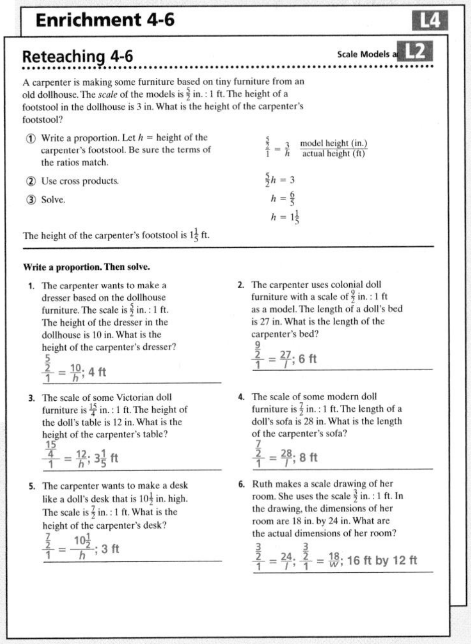

Enrichment 4-6 L4

Reteaching 4-6 Scale Models a L2

A carpenter is making some furniture based on tiny furniture from an old dollhouse. The *scale* of the models is $\frac{5}{2}$ in. : 1 ft. The height of a footstool in the dollhouse is 3 in. What is the height of the carpenter's footstool?

① Write a proportion. Let h = height of the carpenter's footstool. Be sure the terms of the ratios match. $\frac{\frac{5}{2}}{1} = \frac{3}{h}$ $\frac{\text{model height (in.)}}{\text{actual height (ft)}}$

② Use cross products. $\frac{5}{2}h = 3$

③ Solve. $h = \frac{6}{5}$, $h = 1\frac{1}{5}$

The height of the carpenter's footstool is $1\frac{1}{5}$ ft.

Write a proportion. Then solve.

1. The carpenter wants to make a dresser based on the dollhouse furniture. The scale is $\frac{5}{2}$ in. : 1 ft. The height of the dresser in the dollhouse is 10 in. What is the height of the carpenter's dresser? $\frac{\frac{5}{2}}{1} = \frac{10}{h}$; 4 ft

2. The carpenter uses colonial doll furniture with a scale of $\frac{9}{2}$ in. : 1 ft as a model. The length of a doll's bed is 27 in. What is the length of the carpenter's bed? $\frac{\frac{9}{2}}{1} = \frac{27}{l}$; 6 ft

3. The scale of some Victorian doll furniture is $\frac{15}{4}$ in. : 1 ft. The height of the doll's table is 12 in. What is the height of the carpenter's table? $\frac{\frac{15}{4}}{1} = \frac{12}{h}$; $3\frac{1}{5}$ ft

4. The scale of some modern doll furniture is $\frac{7}{2}$ in. : 1 ft. The length of a doll's sofa is 28 in. What is the length of the carpenter's sofa? $\frac{\frac{7}{2}}{1} = \frac{28}{l}$; 8 ft

5. The carpenter wants to make a desk like a doll's desk that is $10\frac{1}{2}$ in. high. The scale is $\frac{7}{2}$ in. : 1 ft. What is the height of the carpenter's desk? $\frac{\frac{7}{2}}{1} = \frac{10\frac{1}{2}}{h}$; 3 ft

6. Ruth makes a scale drawing of her room. She uses the scale $\frac{3}{2}$ in. : 1 ft. In the drawing, the dimensions of her room are 18 in. by 24 in. What are the actual dimensions of her room? $\frac{\frac{3}{2}}{1} = \frac{24}{l}$; $\frac{\frac{3}{2}}{1} = \frac{18}{w}$; 16 ft by 12 ft

Alternative Assessment

Students time how long it takes to count 30 pages in their math text. Then they write a proportion to see how many pages they could count in 3 minutes.

Test Prep

Resources

For additional practice with a variety of test item formats:
- Test-Taking Strategies, p. 201
- Test Prep, p. 205
- Test-Taking Strategies with Transparencies

Activity Lab

Using Similar Figures

Indirect measurement is a useful way to estimate the lengths of objects that may be difficult to measure. Students use proportions and similar figures to find measurements of objects.

Guided Instruction

Activity

If possible, take the class outside and use the measurement method described in the activity with large objects, such as trees, a flagpole, or buildings.

Error Prevention!

Help students set up a proportion using a diagram. Have them label quantities that are known and use a letter to label what's missing.

Connection to Algebra
Letters with subscripts are commonly used in algebra to refer to values that are related but unknown. In Exercises 3–4, tell students that d_1 and d_2 both represent distances.

Differentiated Instruction

Visual Learners
Have students redraw each diagram, labeling the sides and coloring corresponding sides.

Resources

- Activity Lab 4-7: Similarity and Indirect Measurement
- rulers
- colored pencils or markers

4-7a Activity Lab

Hands On

Using Similar Figures

You can use a ruler and similar triangles to estimate an unknown length.

ACTIVITY

The diagram below shows how to measure the length of a pond indirectly.

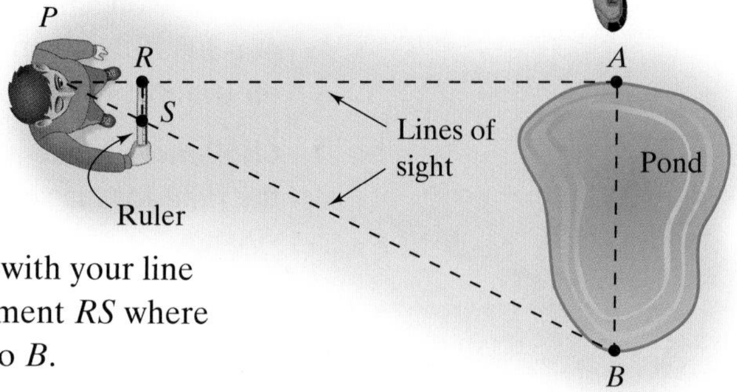

Step 1 Stand back and close one eye. Use the other hand to hold a ruler away from your face, parallel to the unknown length represented by $\overline{AB}$.

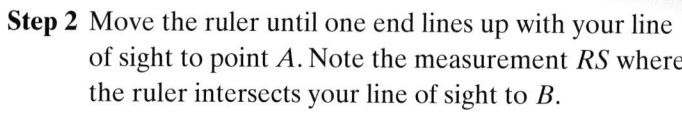

Step 2 Move the ruler until one end lines up with your line of sight to point A. Note the measurement RS where the ruler intersects your line of sight to B.

Step 3 Find the distance PR from your eye to the ruler and the distance PA from you to point A.

1. Which triangle is similar to $\triangle PRS$? $\triangle PAB$
2. Write a proportion you can use to find the length of the pond. Which three of the measurements in this proportion are known? Answers may vary. Sample: $\frac{RS}{AB} =$ RS, PR, and PA are known.
3. Solve the proportion from Exercise 2 to find the unknown distance if $RS = 0.75$ ft, $PA = 110$ ft, $PR = 1.5$ ft. 55 ft

Exercises

The diagram at the right shows how to estimate a vertical length.

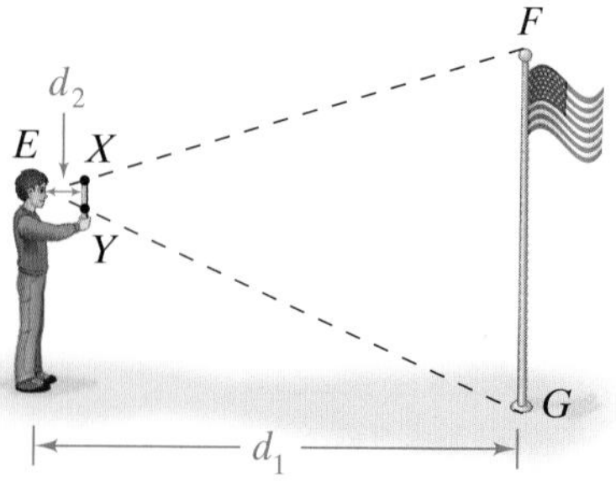

1. Which two triangles are similar? $\triangle EXY \sim \triangle EFG$
2. Write a proportion you can use to find the height of the flagpole. Answers may vary. Sample: $\frac{XY}{FG} = \frac{d_2}{d_1}$
3. Solve the proportion from Exercise 2 to find the unknown distance if $d_2 = 14$ in., $d_1 = 88$ ft, $XY = 8$ in. 603.43 in. or 50.3 ft
4. In Exercise 3, is it necessary to use the same units for all three measurements? Explain. No, only corresponding sides must have the same units.

4-7 Similarity and Indirect Measurement

Check Skills You'll Need

1. **Vocabulary Review** *Similar figures* have the same __?__ but not necessarily the same size. shape
2. If $\triangle ABC \sim \triangle XYZ$, which angle is congruent to $\angle B$? $\angle Y$

GO for Help Lesson 4-4

What You'll Learn

To use proportions and similar figures to solve problems

New Vocabulary indirect measurement

Why Learn This?

When measuring large objects, such as trees, it is not practical to use tools such as rulers.

Indirect measurement uses proportions and similar triangles to measure distances that would be difficult to measure directly.

GO Online

Video Tutor Help
Visit: PHSchool.com
Web Code: ase-0775

EXAMPLE Measuring Indirectly

1 A student is 5 ft tall and casts a shadow 15 ft long. A nearby tree casts a shadow 75 ft long. Find the height h of the tree.

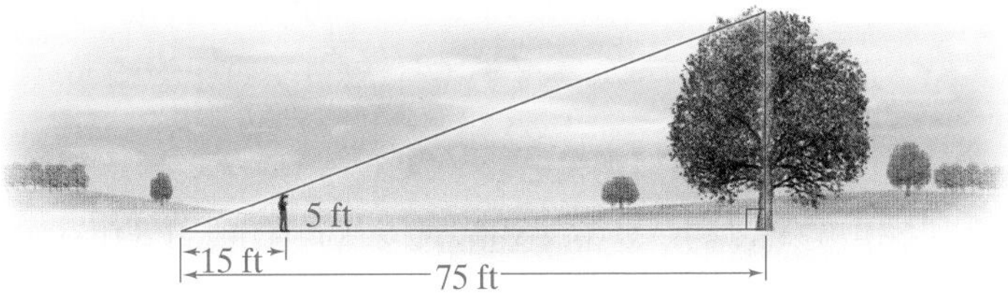

Use similar triangles to set up a proportion.

tree's height → / student's height → $\frac{h}{5} = \frac{75}{15}$ ← length of tree's shadow / ← length of student's shadow

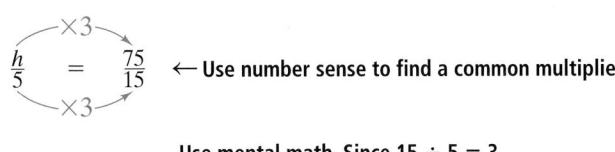

$\frac{h}{5} = \frac{75}{15}$ (×3) ← **Use number sense to find a common multiplier.**

$h = 25$ ← **Use mental math. Since $15 \div 5 = 3$, divide 75 by 3 to find h.**

The height of the tree is 25 ft.

Quick Check

1. A school 40 ft high casts a 160-ft shadow. A nearby cellular phone tower casts a 210-ft shadow. Find the height of the tower. 52.5 ft

4-7

1. Plan

Objective
To use proportions and similar figures to solve problems

Examples
1 Measuring Indirectly
2 Application: Surveying

Math Understandings: p. 158D

Professional Development

Math Background

One way to indirectly measure the thickness of one sheet of paper might be to use a ruler and measure the thickness of a stack of 100 sheets of paper. Another method of indirect measurement involves using similar triangles as presented in this lesson.

More Math Background: p. 158D

Lesson Planning and Resources

See p. 158E for a list of the resources that support this lesson.

PowerPoint

Bell Ringer Practice

Check Skills You'll Need
Use student page, transparency, or PowerPoint. For intervention, direct students to:
Similar Figures and Proportions
Lesson 4-4
Extra Skills and Word Problems Practice, Ch. 4

Differentiated Instruction Solutions for All Learners

Special Needs L1	Below Level L2
Students find the height of a flagpole or tree, as in Example 1, using their own heights and the lengths of their shadows as part of the proportion. learning style: visual	Students practice naming the corresponding angles and sides for several pairs of similar triangles, such as triangles with sides of 3, 4, 5 and 6, 8, 10. learning style: verbal

2. Teach

Activity Lab

Use before the lesson.
Student Edition Activity Lab, Hands-On 4-7a, Using Similar Figures, p. 196

All in One Teaching Resources

Activity Labs 4-7: Similarity and Indirect Measurement

Guided Instruction

Error Prevention!

In Example 2, help students identify corresponding sides using colored pencils or identifying marks.

PowerPoint

Additional Examples

1 When a 6-ft student casts a 17-ft shadow, a flagpole casts a shadow that is 51 ft long. Find the height of the flagpole. 18 ft

2 In the figure below, $\triangle ABC \sim \triangle EDC$. Find d. 188 m

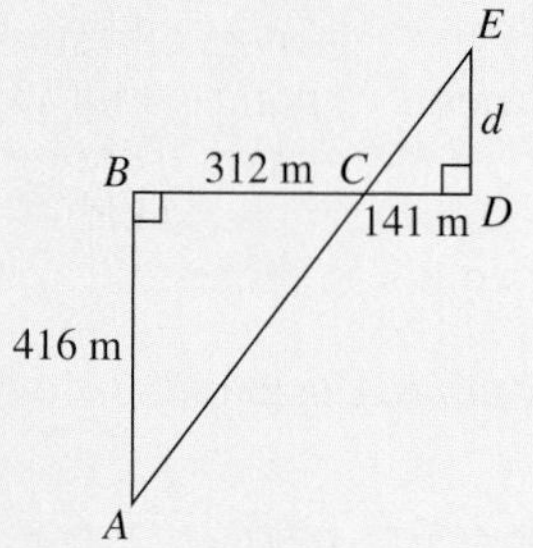

All in One Teaching Resources

- Daily Notetaking Guide 4-7 L3
- Adapted Notetaking 4-7 L1

Closure

- Explain how you can use similar triangles to indirectly measure the height of your house. Sample: Find the length of the shadow cast by the house and the length of the shadow of a yardstick held upright. Write a proportion so that $\frac{\text{house shadow in ft}}{\text{yardstick shadow in ft}} = \frac{n}{3}$.

You can use similar triangles to measure distances across canyons and rivers.

EXAMPLE **Application: Surveying**

2 A civil engineer took the measurements shown in the figure at the right, where $\triangle JKL \sim \triangle NML$. Find d, the distance across the river.

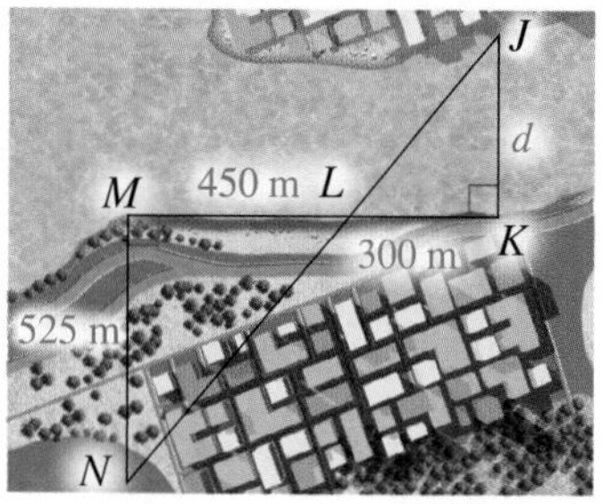

Use similar triangles to set up a proportion.

$$\frac{JK}{NM} = \frac{KL}{ML}$$

Estimate Round 450 and 525 to 500.
Then $\frac{d}{500} = \frac{300}{500}$. So $d \approx 300$.

$\frac{d}{525} = \frac{300}{450}$ ← **Substitute using actual measurements.**

$450 \cdot d = 525 \cdot 300$ ← **Write the cross products.**

$450d = 157{,}500$ ← **Simplify.**

$\frac{450d}{450} = \frac{157{,}500}{450}$ ← **Divide each side by 450.**

157,500 ÷ 450 = 350 ← **Use a calculator.**

The distance across the river is 350 m.

Check for Reasonableness The answer 350 m is close to the estimate 300 m. The answer is reasonable.

Quick Check

2. In Example 2, NL is about 691 m. Find LJ. Round to the nearest tenth. about 460.7 m

Check Your Understanding

Vocabulary **Which would you use to measure the height of the object—direct measurement or indirect measurement?**

1. flagpole indirect
2. lamp direct
3. Eiffel Tower indirect
4. rabbit direct

In the figure, $\triangle ABC \sim \triangle EDC$. Use the figure for Exercises 5 and 6.

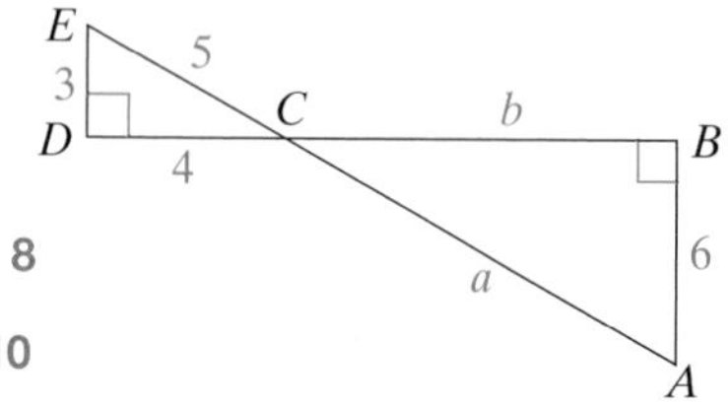

5. Use the proportion $\frac{b}{4} = \frac{6}{■}$ to find b. 8

6. Find a using the proportion $\frac{a}{5} = \frac{■}{3}$. 10

Differentiated Instruction Solutions for All Learners

Advanced Learners L4
Students use flashlights to investigate the relationship between the length of a shadow and the angle of the light.

learning style: visual

English Language Learners ELL
Make sure that students understand that *direct* and *indirect* are opposites. Students give examples of objects that are practical to measure directly, and objects that are not practical to measure directly. Note that a word meaning "not practical" is *impractical*.

learning style: verbal

Homework Exercises

For more exercises, see Extra Skills and Word Problems.

GO for Help

For Exercises	See Examples
7–8	1
9–14	2

A 7. A tower 15 m high casts a shadow 30 m long. A nearby telephone pole casts a shadow 16 m long. Find the height of the telephone pole. 8 m

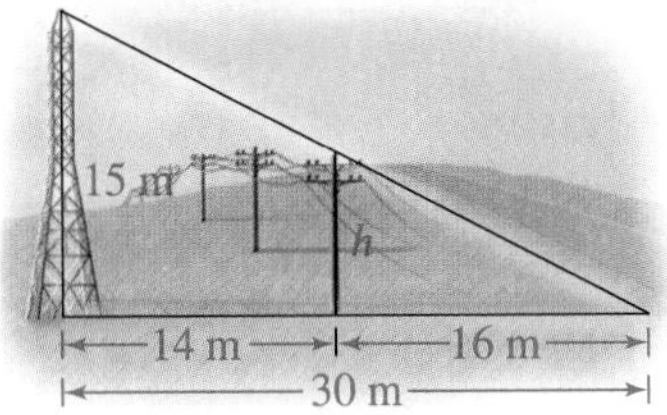

8. A telephone booth 7 ft tall casts a shadow 20 ft long. At the same time, a nearby fire hydrant casts a shadow 8 ft long. Find the height of the fire hydrant. 2.8 ft

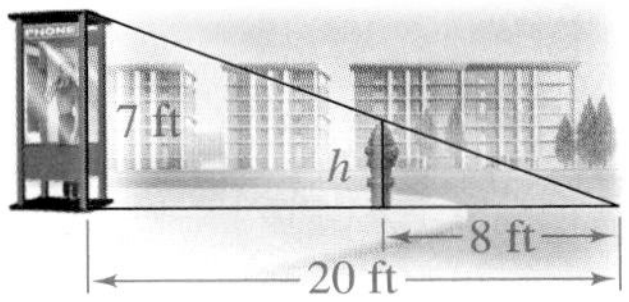

In the figure below, $\triangle PQR \sim \triangle TSR$.

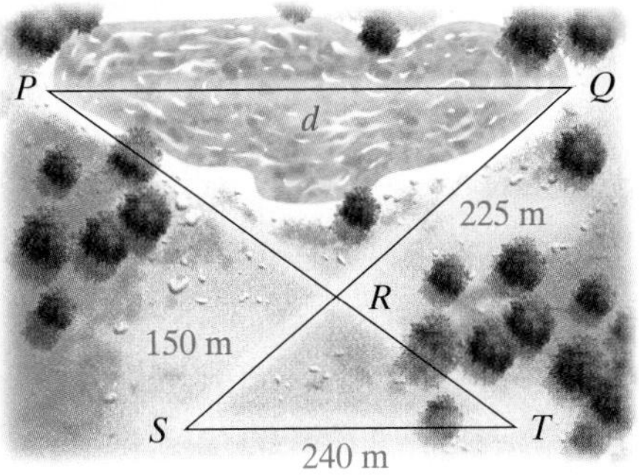

9. Find d. 360 m

10. $PR = 255$ m. Find RT. 170 m

In the figure, $\triangle ABC \sim \triangle EDC$. Round each answer to the nearest tenth.

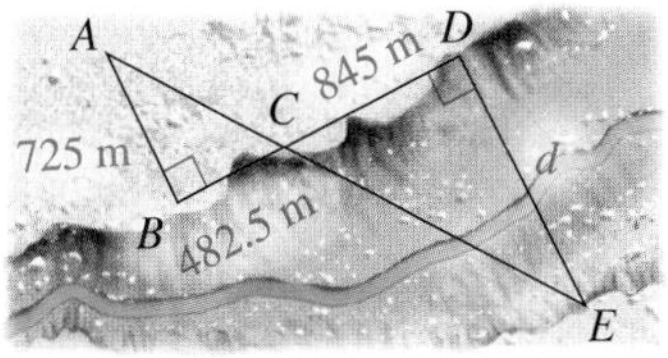

11. Find d. 1,269.7 m

12. $AC = 870$ m. Find CE. 1,523.6 m

Each figure shows similar triangles. Find h. Round to the nearest tenth.

13.

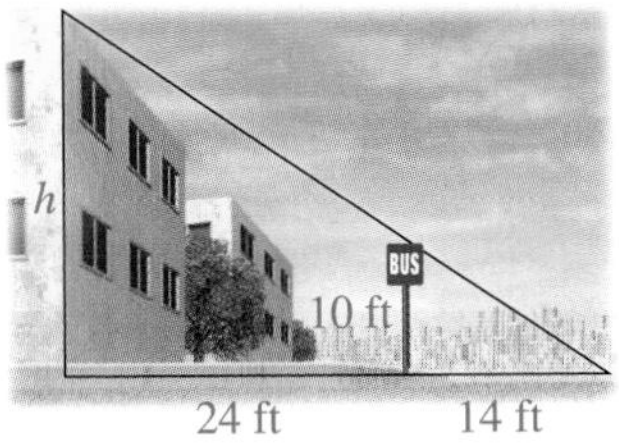

27.1 ft

14.

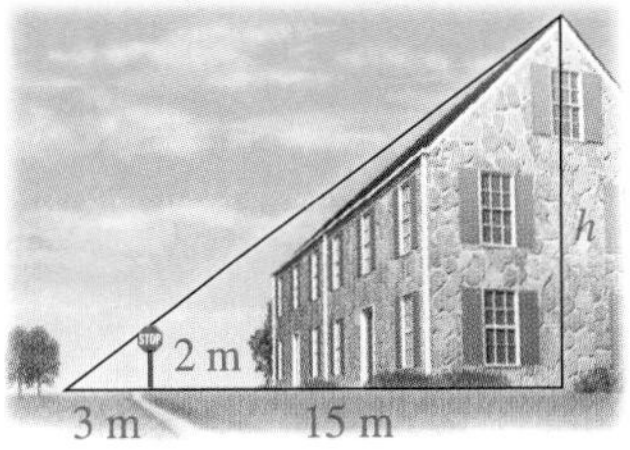

12 m

B **GPS** 15. **Guided Problem Solving** The Washington Monument casts a shadow 200 m long. At the same time, a nearby van that is 2.1 m high casts a shadow 2.5 m long. How tall is the monument? 168 m

- **Make a Plan** Draw and label a diagram. Write a proportion.
- **Carry Out the Plan** Solve the proportion $\frac{2.5}{200} = \frac{\blacksquare}{h}$.

3. Practice

Assignment Guide

Check Your Understanding

Go over Exercises 1–6 in class before assigning the Homework Exercises.

Homework Exercises

A Practice by Example	7–14
B Apply Your Skills	15–20
C Challenge	21
Test Prep and Mixed Review	22–26

Homework Quick Check

To check students' understanding of key skills and concepts, go over Exercises 10, 11, 16, 17, and 18.

Differentiated Instruction Resources

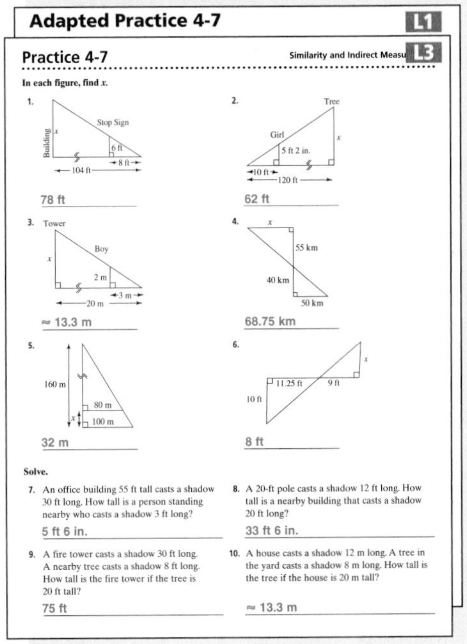

Adapted Practice 4-7 L1

Practice 4-7 — Similarity and Indirect Measu[rement] L3

In each figure, find x.

1. 78 ft

2. 62 ft

3. ≈ 13.3 m

4. 68.75 km

5. 32 m

6. 8 ft

Solve.

7. An office building 55 ft tall casts a shadow 30 ft long. How tall is a person standing nearby who casts a shadow 3 ft long? 5 ft 6 in.

8. A 20-ft pole casts a shadow 12 ft long. How tall is a nearby building that casts a shadow 20 ft long? 33 ft 6 in.

9. A fire tower casts a shadow 30 ft long. A nearby tree casts a shadow 8 ft long. How tall is the fire tower if the tree is 20 ft tall? 75 ft

10. A house casts a shadow 12 m long. A tree in the yard casts a shadow 8 m long. How tall is the tree if the house is 20 m tall? ≈ 13.3 m

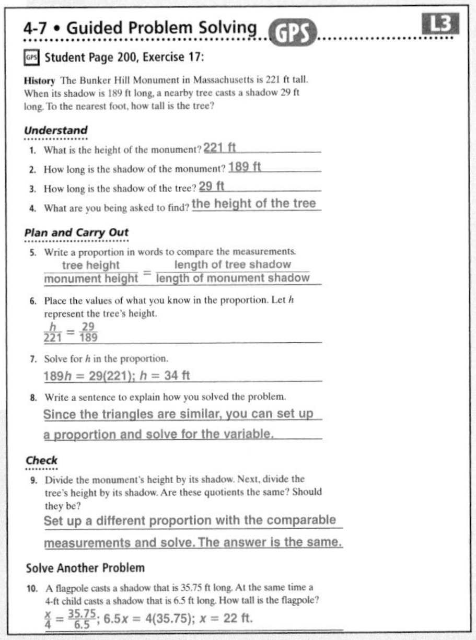

4-7 • Guided Problem Solving GPS L3

GPS Student Page 200, Exercise 17:

History The Bunker Hill Monument in Massachusetts is 221 ft tall. When its shadow is 189 ft long, a nearby tree casts a shadow 29 ft long. To the nearest foot, how tall is the tree?

Understand

1. What is the height of the monument? 221 ft
2. How long is the shadow of the monument? 189 ft
3. How long is the shadow of the tree? 29 ft
4. What are you being asked to find? the height of the tree

Plan and Carry Out

5. Write a proportion in words to compare the measurements.
$\frac{\text{tree height}}{\text{monument height}} = \frac{\text{length of tree shadow}}{\text{length of monument shadow}}$
6. Place the values of what you know in the proportion. Let h represent the tree's height.
$\frac{h}{221} = \frac{29}{189}$
7. Solve for h in the proportion.
$189h = 29(221)$; $h = 34$ ft
8. Write a sentence to explain how you solved the problem.
Since the triangles are similar, you can set up a proportion and solve for the variable.

Check

9. Divide the monument's height by its shadow. Next, divide the tree's height by its shadow. Are these quotients the same? Should they be?
Set up a different proportion with the comparable measurements and solve. The answer is the same.

Solve Another Problem

10. A flagpole casts a shadow that is 35.75 ft long. At the same time a 4-ft child casts a shadow that is 6.5 ft long. How tall is the flagpole?
$\frac{x}{4} = \frac{35.75}{6.5}$; $6.5x = 4(35.75)$; $x = 22$ ft.

4. Assess & Reteach

PowerPoint

Lesson Quiz

1. A 5-ft tall student casts a 12-ft shadow. A tree casts a 27-ft shadow. How tall is the tree? **11.25 ft tall**
2. A 6-ft man casts a 9-ft shadow. A sculpture casts a 45-ft shadow. How tall is the sculpture? **30 ft**

Use the diagram for Exercise 3.
$\triangle EFG \sim \triangle JHG$

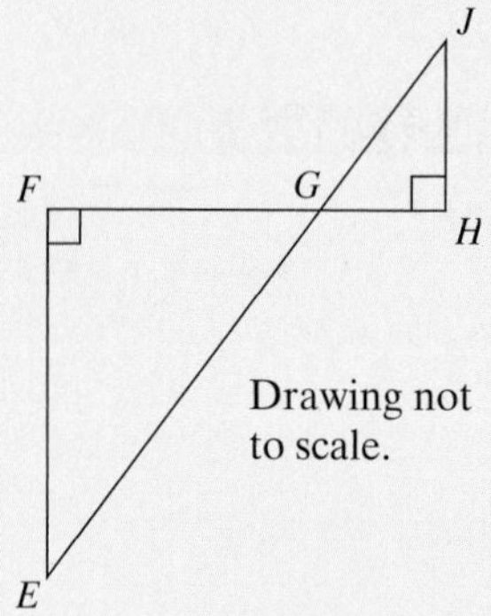

3. The diagram shows an outline of a village green $\triangle EFG$ next to a small park $\triangle JHG$. The length of $\overline{JH}$ is 47.4 m, $\overline{FG}$ is 31 m, and $\overline{HG}$ is 15.8 m. Find the length of $\overline{EF}$. **93 m**

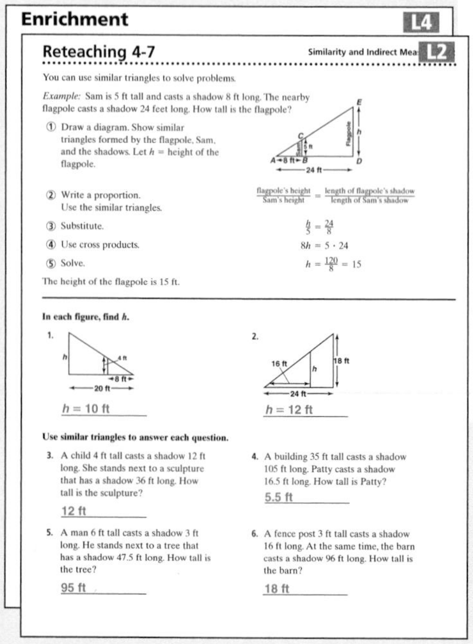
Enrichment L4

Reteaching 4-7 — Similarity and Indirect Mea[surement] L2

You can use similar triangles to solve problems.

Example: Sam is 5 ft tall and casts a shadow 8 ft long. The nearby flagpole casts a shadow 24 feet long. How tall is the flagpole?

① Draw a diagram. Show similar triangles formed by the flagpole, Sam, and the shadows. Let h = height of the flagpole.

② Write a proportion. Use the similar triangles. $\frac{\text{flagpole's height}}{\text{Sam's height}} = \frac{\text{length of flagpole's shadow}}{\text{length of Sam's shadow}}$

③ Substitute. $\frac{h}{5} = \frac{24}{8}$

④ Use cross products. $8h = 5 \cdot 24$

⑤ Solve. $h = \frac{120}{8} = 15$

The height of the flagpole is 15 ft.

In each figure, find h.

1. $h = 10$ ft
2. $h = 12$ ft

Use similar triangles to answer each question.

3. A child 4 ft tall casts a shadow 12 ft long. She stands next to a sculpture that has a shadow 36 ft long. How tall is the sculpture? 12 ft
4. A building 35 ft tall casts a shadow 105 ft long. Patty casts a shadow 16.5 ft long. How tall is Patty? 5.5 ft
5. A man 6 ft tall casts a shadow 3 ft long. He stands next to a tree that has a shadow 47.5 ft long. How tall is the tree? 95 ft
6. A fence post 3 ft tall casts a shadow 16 ft long. At the same time, the barn casts a shadow 96 ft long. How tall is the barn? 18 ft

GO Online
Homework Video Tutor
Visit: PHSchool.com
Web Code: ase-0407

16. Answers may vary. Sample: Measure the height of a tower by measuring its shadow and the shadow of an object of known height.

16. **Writing in Math** Describe an everyday situation in which you might measure a distance indirectly. See left.

17. **History** The Bunker Hill Monument in Massachusetts is 221 ft tall. GPS When its shadow is 189 ft long, a nearby tree casts a shadow 29 ft long. To the nearest foot, how tall is the tree? **34 ft**

In the diagram of the lake below, $\triangle BDC \sim \triangle AEC$.

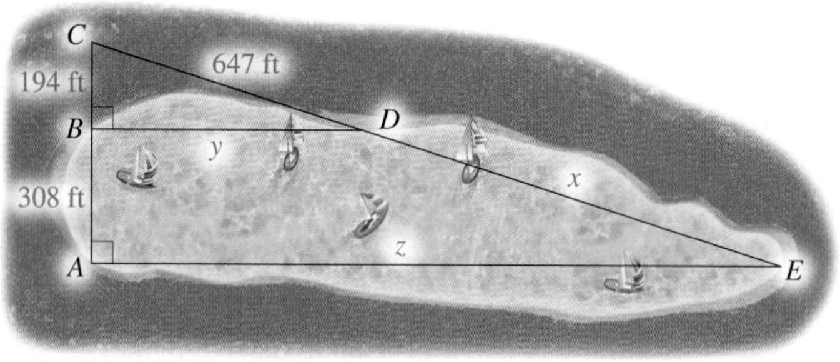

GO for Help

For help with the Pythagorean Theorem, go to Lesson 3-3, Example 1.

18. Use similar triangles to find the value of x. **about 1,027 ft**
19. Use the Pythagorean Theorem to find the value of y. **about 617 ft**
20. Find the value of z. **about 1,597 ft**

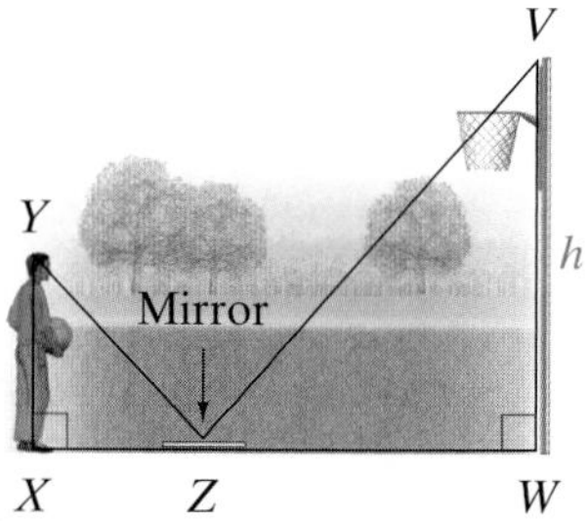

C 21. **Challenge** The figure at the right shows a method of indirect measurement. The triangles are similar. Once you have placed the mirror on the ground, how do you know where to stand? Answers may vary. Sample: Stand where you can see the basketball hoop in the mirror.

Test Prep and Mixed Review — Practice

Multiple Choice

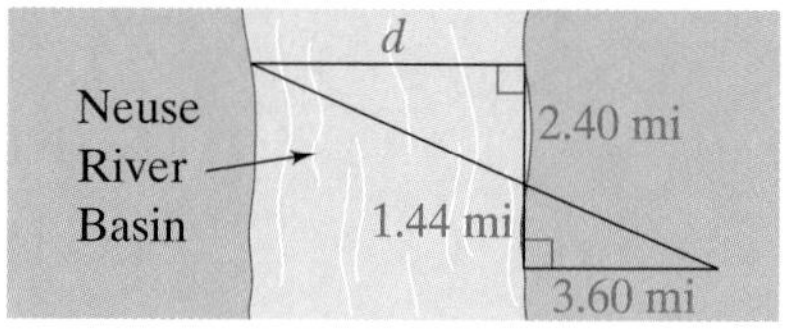

22. In the figure at the right, the triangles shown are similar. Find the distance d across this section of the river basin. **D**
    - A 2 mi
    - C 4.5 mi
    - B 3 mi
    - D 6 mi

23. On Monday, Harvey received his weekly allowance. He spent \$3.25 on lunch each day at school. He bought two books for \$5.50 each. If Harvey has \$2.25 at the end of the school week, which expression can he use to find the amount of money he received on Monday? **G**
    - F $2(3.25) + 5(5.50) + 2.25$
    - H $2(3.25) + 5(5.50) - 2.25$
    - G $5(3.25) + 2(5.50) + 2.25$
    - J $5(3.25) + 2(5.50) - 2.25$

GO for Help

For Exercises	See Lesson
24–26	2-8

Write each number in standard form.

24. 2.02×10^5 **202,000**
25. 5.00×10^{-2} **0.05**
26. 9.606×10^{-6} **0.000009606**

Test Prep

Resources
For additional practice with a variety of test item formats:
- Test-Taking Strategies, p. 201
- Test Prep, p. 205
- Test-Taking Strategies with Transparencies

Alternative Assessment

Partners write down their heights and measure the lengths of their shadows. Each student finds the height of a building that casts a 100-ft shadow, using the ratio of his or her height to shadow length.

Test-Taking Strategies

Using a Variable

You can solve many problems by using a variable to represent an unknown quantity. Use the variable to write an equation.

EXAMPLE

You have a copy of your company logo that is 3.8 cm long and 2 cm wide. You need an enlarged copy of the logo that is 6 cm long. How wide must the enlarged copy be?

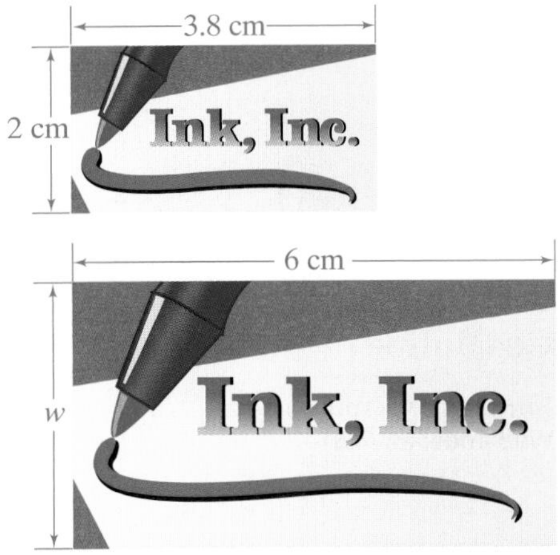

You can use the diagrams at the right to help visualize which side length you are trying to find.

Let w = the width of the enlargement.

Set up a proportion to find w.

$\frac{6}{w} = \frac{3.8}{2}$ ← **length** / ← **width**

$2 \cdot 6 = 3.8 \cdot w$ ← **Write the cross products.**

$12 = 3.8w$ ← **Multiply.**

$\frac{12}{3.8} = \frac{3.8w}{3.8}$ ← **Divide each side by 3.8.**

$3.2 \approx w$ ← **Simplify.**

The width of the enlargement should be about 3.2 cm.

Exercises

1. A family is on a 400-mi road trip. They have already driven 220 miles in 4 hours. If they continue driving at this rate, about how long will it take them to drive the entire 400 miles? **C**

(A) 2 h (B) 3 h (C) 7 h (D) 8 h

2. A map is 15.5 in. wide and 20 in. long. The map is enlarged so it is 32 in. long. Which proportion can you use to find the new width? **G**

(F) $\frac{15.5}{20} = \frac{32}{x}$ (H) $\frac{15.5}{32} = \frac{x}{20}$

(G) $\frac{15.5}{x} = \frac{20}{32}$ (J) $\frac{15.5}{x} = \frac{32}{20}$

3. A carpenter can build 3 tables in 5 hours. Which equation can he use to find how long it will take him to make 18 tables? **D**

(A) $t = 5 \cdot 18$ (C) $t = 3 \cdot 18$

(B) $t = 15 \cdot 18$ (D) $t = 5 \cdot 6$

Using a Variable

This feature shows students the advantages of using a variable to solve problems involving an unknown quantity.

Guided Instruction

Teaching Tip

Point out that any lower-case letter can be used to represent an unknown quantity. However, emphasize that selecting easy-to-recall letters, such as *h* for *height* or *w* for *width*, makes good sense.

Differentiated Instruction

Visual Learners

Encourage students to draw and label diagrams to help them keep track of corresponding quantities that are proportional to each other.

Resources

Test-Taking Strategies with Transparencies
- Transparency 11
- Practice sheet, p. 28

Test-Taking Strategies with Transparencies

Test-Taking Strategies: Using a Variable

You can solve many problems by using a variable to represent an unknown quantity.

Let the variable be the quantity that you are looking for.

Examples
Let x = the number of hours worked.
Let t = the amount of time spent.
Let A = the area of the backyard.

Then use the variable to write an equation.

You attend a cheerleading clinic with your team every Saturday morning. The clinic costs $6.50 per person. It costs $78 for your entire team to attend the clinic. How many cheerleaders are on your team?

Let c = the number of cheerleaders.

Write and solve an equation to find the number of cheerleaders.

$6.50c = 78$

$\frac{6.50}{6.50}c = \frac{78}{6.50}$ There are 12 cheerleaders on your team.

$c = 12$

Define a variable. Then, write and solve an equation for each problem.

1. An illustrator charges $75 per picture. Find the total number of pictures in a children's book if the illustrator earned $3,000.
2. There are 12 songs on a CD. The CD lasts 42 minutes. About how long is the average song on the CD?

Resources

Student Edition

Extra Skills and Word Problems Practice, Ch. 4, pp. 610–611
English/Spanish Glossary, p. 650
Formulas and Properties, p. 648
Tables, p. 643

All in One Teaching Resources

Vocabulary and Study Skills 4F

Differentiated Instruction

Spanish Vocabulary and Study Skills 4F — ELL
Interactive Textbook
- Audio Glossary

Online Vocabulary Quiz

Success Tracker™
Online at PHSchool.com

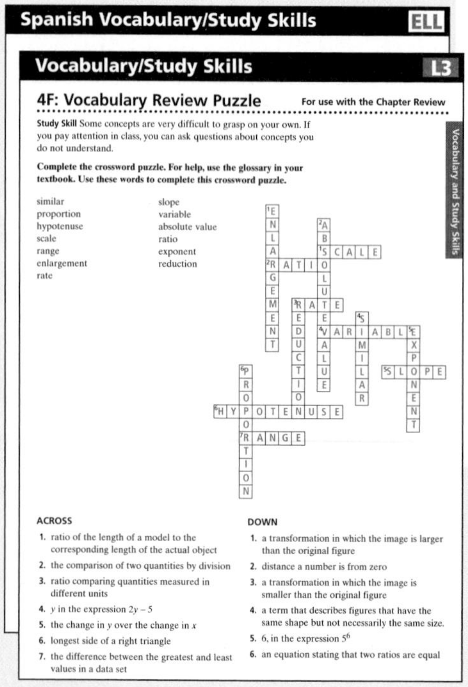
Spanish Vocabulary/Study Skills ELL

Vocabulary/Study Skills L3

4F: Vocabulary Review Puzzle — For use with the Chapter Review

Study Skill Some concepts are very difficult to grasp on your own. If you pay attention in class, you can ask questions about concepts you do not understand.

Complete the crossword puzzle. For help, use the glossary in your textbook. Use these words to complete this crossword puzzle.

similar, proportion, hypotenuse, scale, range, enlargement, rate, slope, variable, absolute value, ratio, exponent, reduction

ACROSS
1. ratio of the length of a model to the corresponding length of the actual object
2. the comparison of two quantities by division
3. ratio comparing quantities measured in different units
4. y in the expression $2y - 5$
5. the change in y over the change in x
6. longest side of a right triangle
7. the difference between the greatest and least values in a data set

DOWN
1. a transformation in which the image is larger than the original figure
2. distance a number is from zero
3. a transformation in which the image is smaller than the original figure
4. a term that describes figures that have the same shape but not necessarily the same size.
5. 6, in the expression 5^6
6. an equation stating that two ratios are equal

Chapter 4 Review

Vocabulary Review

congruent angles (p. 181)
conversion factor (p. 167)
cross products (p. 175)
dilation (p. 187)
enlargement (p. 188)
indirect measurement (p. 197)
proportion (p. 174)
rate (p. 161)
reduction (p. 188)
scale (p. 192)
scale factor (p. 187)
scale model (p. 192)
similar figures (p. 181)
similar polygons (p. 181)
unit rate (p. 161)

Go Online PHSchool.com
For: Online vocabulary quiz
Web Code: asj-0451

Choose the correct vocabulary term above to complete each sentence.

1. A speed of 30 mi/h is an example of a(n) __?__. unit rate
2. A(n) __?__ is an equation stating that two ratios are equal. proportion
3. A model of an office building may have a(n) __?__ of 1 : 200. scale factor
4. __?__ helps you to measure the height of very tall objects. indirect measurement
5. A(n) __?__ is a dilation with a scale factor less than one. reduction
6. You can use a(n) __?__ to convert 3.4 miles to feet. conversion factor

Skills and Concepts

Lessons 4-1, 4-2

- To write ratios and unit rates and to use rates to solve problems
- To convert units within and between the customary and metric systems

A **rate** is a ratio that compares quantities measured in different units. The rate for one unit of a given quantity is called the **unit rate.**

In both the metric and customary systems, it is important to choose appropriate units. Use **conversion factors** to convert units of measure.

Write each ratio in simplest form.

7. 6 s out of 48 s $\frac{1}{8}$
8. $\frac{10 \text{ m}}{300 \text{ cm}}$ $3\frac{1}{3}$
9. 1 ft : 1 yd $\frac{1}{3}$

Choose a Method **Use a calculator, paper and pencil, or mental math to find each unit rate.**

10. \$42 for 1.5 h \$28/h
11. 826 mi in 14 h 59 mi/h
12. 150 km per 24 L 6.25 km/L
13. A 36-oz container of ketchup costs \$2.52. A 24-oz container of ketchup costs \$1.69. Which container of ketchup is the better buy? Explain. Neither, the unit rate for each container is about \$.07.

Find an equivalent rate.

14. 33 m/h = ■ cm/h 3,300 cm/h
15. 16 lb/ft = ■ oz/ft 256 oz/ft
16. 1 L/min = ■ mL/s $16\frac{2}{3}$ mL/s
17. 3 mi/h = ■ ft/day 380,160 ft/day
18. ■ cm/min = 30 m/h 50 cm/min
19. \$.30/min = \$■/h \$18/h

Lesson 4-3
- To identify and solve proportions

To solve a **proportion,** you can write the **cross products** and then solve.

Solve each proportion.

20. $\frac{4}{5} = \frac{x}{20}$ 16 **21.** $\frac{6}{a} = \frac{18}{3}$ 1 **22.** $\frac{14}{6} = \frac{28}{t}$ 12 **23.** $\frac{b}{16} = \frac{9}{2}$ 72

24. Recently, the exchange rate for euros to U.S. dollars was 0.81 euros = \$1. How many euros would you receive for \$1,000? 810 euros

Lessons 4-4, 4-5
- To identify similar figures and to use proportions to find missing measurements in similar figures
- To graph dilations and to determine the scale factor of a dilation

Figures that have the same shape but not necessarily the same size are **similar figures.**

The image of a figure after a **dilation** is similar to the original figure. The **scale factor** of a dilation describes the size of the change from the original figure to its image.

In the figure, $\triangle ACE \sim \triangle BCD$. Find each unknown length.

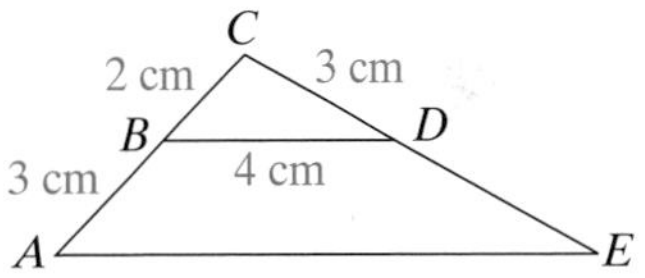

25. *AE* 10 cm **26.** *CE* 7.5 cm **27.** *DE* 4.5 cm

28. The blue figure is a dilation of the original figure. Find the scale factor and classify the dilation as an *enlargement* or a *reduction*. 4; enlargement

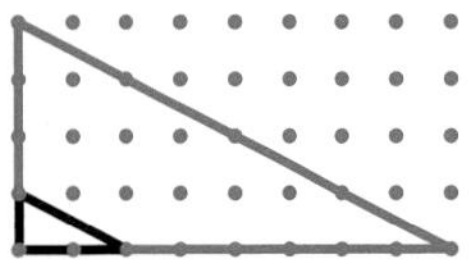

Lessons 4-6, 4-7
- To use proportions to solve problems involving scale
- To use proportions and similar figures to solve problems

Use proportions to solve **scale-model** and **indirect-measurement** problems.

The scale of a map is 1 in. : 7 mi. How many actual miles does each measurement on the map represent?

29. 6.2 in. 43.4 mi **30.** 9.5 in. 66.5 mi **31.** $4\frac{2}{3}$ in. 32.7 mi **32.** $8\frac{1}{5}$ in. 57.4 mi

33. **Plans** The scale of a plan is 1 in. : 8 ft. A room will be 18 ft long by 14 ft wide. Find the dimensions on the plan. $2\frac{1}{4}$ in. by $1\frac{3}{4}$ in.

The diagram at the right shows similar triangles.

34. Find *x*. 14.4 **35.** Find *AS*. 13.6

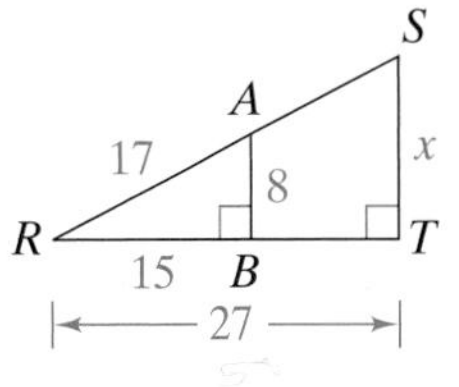

36. A person 5 ft 6 in. tall casts a 21-ft shadow. A nearby building casts a 45-ft shadow. How high is the building? 11 ft 9 in.

Alternative Assessment L4

Alternative Assessment **Form C**

Chapter 4

VACATION EXTRAVAGANZA

Congratulations! You have just won a free European vacation! You will visit Frankfurt, Stockholm, Rome, London, Madrid, and Paris.

The map below shows the exact location of each city; the chart shows approximate distances between the cities in kilometers.

	London	Madrid	Frankfurt	Stockholm	Paris
Madrid	1,250				
Frankfurt	1,000	1,400			
Stockholm	1,400	2,600	1,100		
Paris	350	1,000	500	1,500	
Rome	1,400	1,400	900	1,900	1,100

Show all of your work on a separate sheet of paper.

1. List the order in which you should visit these six cities in order to keep your total travel time to a minimum. You must visit each city once. Then show the approximate time it will take to travel from one city to the next, if you travel at an average speed of 100 km/h.

Chapter 4 Test

Go Online PHSchool.com **For:** Online chapter test **Web Code:** asa-0452

Write each ratio in simplest form.

1. 16 cm : 60 cm $\frac{4}{15}$
2. 3 ft to 9 in. 4
3. $\frac{100 \text{ min}}{8 \text{ h}}$ $\frac{5}{24}$
4. 6 yd to 36 ft $\frac{1}{2}$
5. 500 m : 2 km $\frac{1}{4}$
6. $\frac{54 \text{ c}}{6 \text{ oz}}$ 72

Choose a Method **Use a calculator, paper and pencil, or mental math to find each unit rate.**

7. 200 yd in 5 min 40 yd/min
8. 700 L in 24 h $29\frac{1}{6}$ L/h
9. 30 gal in 5 min 6 gal/min
10. \$2.50 for 10 oz \$.25/oz

Find an equivalent rate.

11. \$33/h = \$■/min 0.55
12. 3 ft/s = ■ yd/min 60

Solve each proportion.

13. $\frac{3}{7} = \frac{6}{n}$ 14
14. $\frac{25}{a} = \frac{100}{4}$ 1
15. $\frac{w}{5} = \frac{30}{13}$ $11\frac{7}{13}$

16. **Stocks** A stock investment of 160 shares paid a dividend of \$584. At this rate, what dividend would be paid on 270 shares of stock? \$985.50

17. $\triangle ABC$ has vertices $A(1, 2)$, $B(4, 3)$ and $C(-2, 5)$. Find the coordinates of the image of $\triangle ABC$ after a dilation with a scale factor of 3. $A'(3, 6)$, $B'(12, 9)$, $C'(-6, 15)$

$\triangle ABC \sim \triangle EDC$. Find each unknown length.

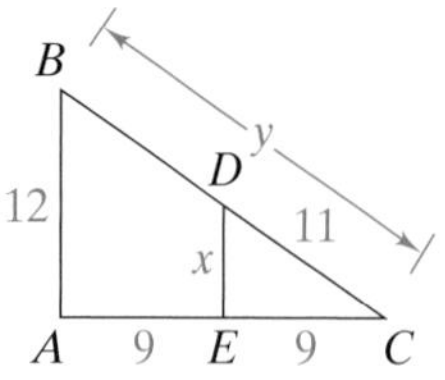

18. x 6
19. y 22

Convert each measure. If necessary, round to the nearest tenth.

20. 9 L = ■ qt 9.6
21. 4 kg = ■ lb 8.9
22. 28 lb = ■ kg 12.6
23. 25 in. = ■ cm 63.5

The scale of a map is 1 in. : 6 mi. How many inches does each distance occupy on the map? Round to the nearest tenth.

24. 23 mi 3.8 in.
25. 10 mi 1.7 in.
26. 45 mi 7.5 in.
27. 16 mi 2.7 in.

The scale of a map is 1 in. : 15 mi. How many actual miles does each measurement on the map represent?

28. 8.6 in. 129 mi
29. $10\frac{1}{3}$ in. 155 mi
30. $7\frac{3}{5}$ in. 114 mi
31. 11.2 in. 168 mi

32. **Writing in Math** Suppose you know the coordinates of the vertices of a triangle. Explain how you would find the coordinates of the vertices of its image after a dilation with a scale factor of r. See margin.

33. Copy $\triangle ABC$ below. Draw the image of $\triangle ABC$ after a dilation with a scale factor of 2. See margin.

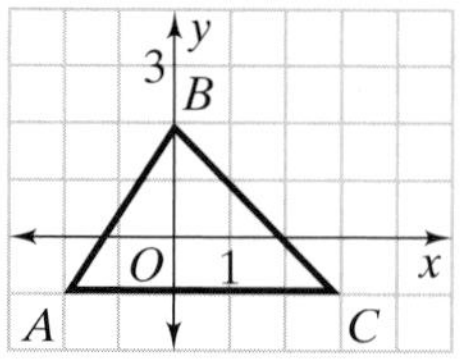

34. **Cranes** A student is 5 ft tall and casts a shadow 15 ft long. At the same time of day, a nearby crane casts a shadow 90 ft long. What is the height of the crane? 30 ft

35. In the figure below, $\triangle XBY$ is the image of $\triangle ABC$ after a dilation. What is the scale factor? $\frac{2}{3}$

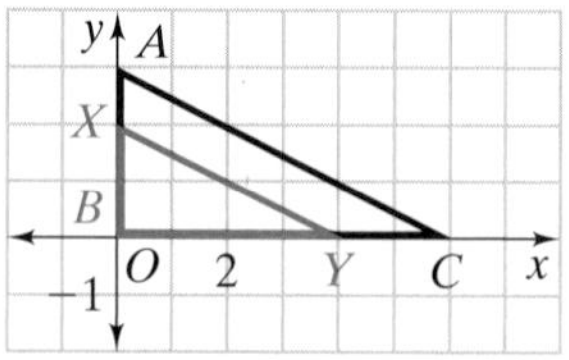

Chapter 4 Test

Resources

- ExamView Assessment Suite CD-ROM
  - Ch. 4 Ready-Made Test
  - Make your own Ch. 4 Test
- MindPoint Quiz Show CD-ROM
  - Chapter 4 Review

Differentiated Instruction

All in One Teaching Resources

- Below Level Chapter 4 Test L2
- Chapter 4 Test L3
- Chapter 4 Alternative Assessment L4

Spanish Assessment Resources ELL

- Below Level Chapter 4 test L2
- Chapter 4 test L3
- Chapter 4 Alternative Assessment L4

ExamView Assessment Suite CD-ROM

- Special Needs Test L1
- Special Needs Practice Bank L1

Online Chapter 4 Test at www.PHSchool.com L3

32. Answers may vary. Sample: If a vertex's coordinates were (x, y), the image coordinates would be $(r \cdot x, r \cdot y)$.

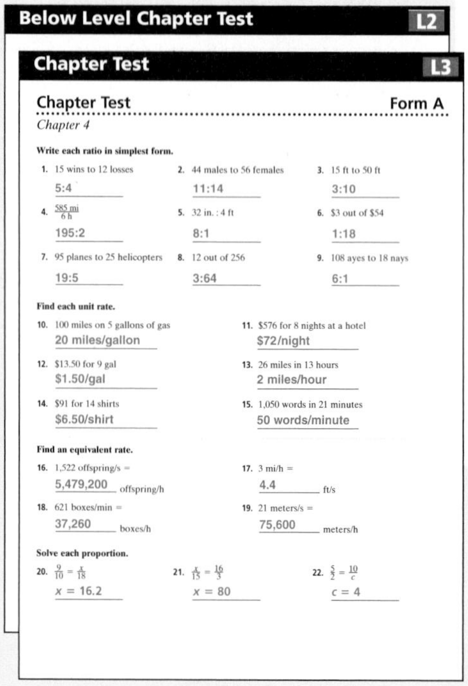

Below Level Chapter Test L2

Chapter Test L3

Chapter Test — Form A

Chapter 4

Write each ratio in simplest form.

1. 15 wins to 12 losses 5:4
2. 44 males to 56 females 11:14
3. 15 ft to 50 ft 3:10
4. $\frac{585 \text{ mi}}{6 \text{ h}}$ 195:2
5. 32 in. : 4 ft 8:1
6. \$3 out of \$54 1:18
7. 95 planes to 25 helicopters 19:5
8. 12 out of 256 3:64
9. 108 ayes to 18 nays 6:1

Find each unit rate.

10. 100 miles on 5 gallons of gas 20 miles/gallon
11. \$576 for 8 nights at a hotel \$72/night
12. \$13.50 for 9 gal \$1.50/gal
13. 26 miles in 13 hours 2 miles/hour
14. \$91 for 14 shirts \$6.50/shirt
15. 1,050 words in 21 minutes 50 words/minute

Find an equivalent rate.

16. 1,522 offspring/s = 5,479,200 offspring/h
17. 3 mi/h = 4.4 ft/s
18. 621 boxes/min = 37,260 boxes/h
19. 21 meters/s = 75,600 meters/h

Solve each proportion.

20. $\frac{9}{10} = \frac{x}{18}$ $x = 16.2$
21. $\frac{x}{15} = \frac{16}{3}$ $x = 80$
22. $\frac{5}{2} = \frac{10}{c}$ $c = 4$

33.

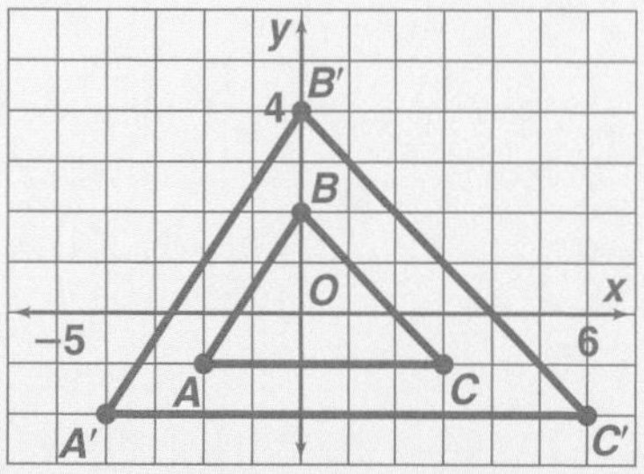

Reading Comprehension

Read the passage and answer the questions that follow.

> **Paper Money** U.S. paper money is 2.61 in. wide and 6.14 in. long. You probably know it is illegal to make an exact copy of money—that is counterfeiting! But did you know you can legally make a perfect copy as long as it is a different size? To be sure the copy does not fool anyone, it must be less than three fourths or more than one and a half times the length and width of the real bill.

1. How long is the diagonal (corner to opposite corner) of a real U.S. dollar bill? C
   - (A) 2.95 in.
   - (B) 4.34 in.
   - (C) 6.67 in.
   - (D) 8.75 in.

2. Would a 2 in.-by-4 in. copy of a $10 bill be a legal copy of a real $10 bill? G
   - (F) No, the copy would be too long.
   - (G) No, the copy would be too wide.
   - (H) No, the copy would be too long and too wide.
   - (J) Yes

3. A poster-sized copy of a $5 bill is 5.22 ft wide. What is the length of the poster if the copy has the same proportions as the real bill? D
   - (A) 12.28 in.
   - (B) 5.22 ft
   - (C) 6.14 ft
   - (D) 12.28 ft

4. What are the smallest dimensions (length and width) that would be legal for a larger-than-life copy of a $100 bill? G
   - (F) 4.60×1.95 in.
   - (G) 9.21×3.92 in.
   - (H) 6.45×2.74 in.
   - (J) 10.74×4.57 in.

> **Space Meal Math** Space shuttle astronauts can choose from a variety of foods. A dietician reviews the astronauts' menu selections to be sure that the foods are well balanced and that the meals provide the right amount of energy (Calories). Dieticians check the calorie needs with a formula.
>
> Part of the calculation depends on the astronaut's weight. For female astronauts, $E = 9.6 \times W$. For male astronauts, $E = 13.7 \times W$. In this formula, E is the daily food energy in Calories and W is the astronaut's weight in kilograms. (Other formulas consider height and age.)

5. A male and a female astronaut both weigh the same amount. According to the weight formula, what is the ratio of Calories the male will need compared to the female? A
   - (A) 13.7 : 9.6
   - (B) 9.6 : 13.7
   - (C) 9.6 : 23.3
   - (D) 13.7 : 23.3

6. A 70-kg male and a 50-kg female astronaut go on a two-week flight. What ratio of the total food supplies would belong to the female, according to the weight formula? J
   - (F) $\dfrac{50 \cdot 9.6}{70 \cdot 13.7}$
   - (G) $\dfrac{70 \cdot 13.7}{50 \cdot 9.6}$
   - (H) $\dfrac{9.6}{13.7}$
   - (J) $\dfrac{50 \cdot 9.6}{(50 \cdot 9.6 + 70 \cdot 13.7)}$

Test Prep

Resources

Test Prep Workbook

All in One **Teaching Resources**

- Cumulative Review L3

ExamView Assessment Suite CD-ROM

- Standardized Test Practice

Differentiated Instruction

Spanish Assessment Resources

- Spanish Cumulative Review ELL

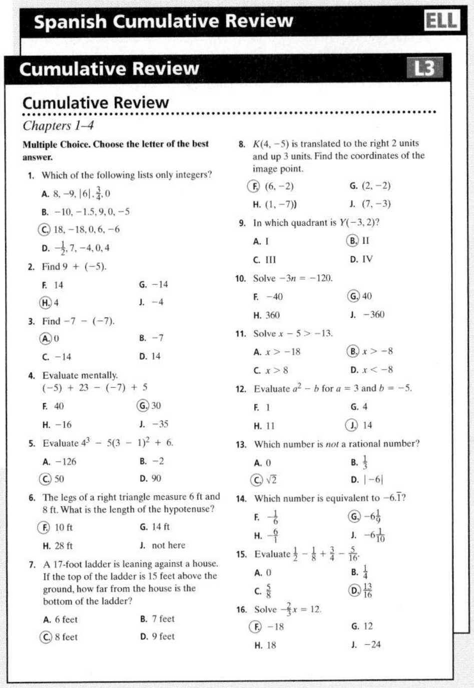

Spanish Cumulative Review ELL

Cumulative Review L3

Cumulative Review

Chapters 1–4

Multiple Choice. Choose the letter of the best answer.

1. Which of the following lists only integers?
   A. $8, -9, |6|, \frac{3}{4}, 0$
   B. $-10, -1.5, 9, 0, -5$
   (C.) $18, -18, 0, 6, -6$
   D. $-\frac{1}{2}, 7, -4, 0, 4$
2. Find $9 + (-5)$.
   F. 14 G. −14 (H.) 4 J. −4
3. Find $-7 - (-7)$.
   (A.) 0 B. −7 C. −14 D. 14
4. Evaluate mentally. $(-5) + 23 - (-7) + 5$
   F. 40 (G.) 30 H. −16 J. −35
5. Evaluate $4^3 - 5(3 - 1)^2 + 6$.
   A. −126 B. −2 (C.) 50 D. 90
6. The legs of a right triangle measure 6 ft and 8 ft. What is the length of the hypotenuse?
   (F.) 10 ft G. 14 ft H. 28 ft J. not here
7. A 17-foot ladder is leaning against a house. If the top of the ladder is 15 feet above the ground, how far from the house is the bottom of the ladder?
   A. 6 feet B. 7 feet (C.) 8 feet D. 9 feet
8. $K(4, -5)$ is translated to the right 2 units and up 3 units. Find the coordinates of the image point.
   (F.) (6, −2) G. (2, −2) H. (1, −7)) J. (7, −3)
9. In which quadrant is $Y(-3, 2)$?
   A. I (B.) II C. III D. IV
10. Solve $-3n = -120$.
   F. −40 (G.) 40 H. 360 J. −360
11. Solve $x - 5 > -13$.
   A. $x > -18$ (B.) $x > -8$ C. $x > 8$ D. $x < -8$
12. Evaluate $a^2 - b$ for $a = 3$ and $b = -5$.
   F. 1 G. 4 H. 11 (J.) 14
13. Which number is *not* a rational number?
   A. 0 B. $\frac{1}{3}$ (C.) $\sqrt{2}$ D. $|-6|$
14. Which number is equivalent to $-6.\overline{1}$?
   F. $-\frac{1}{6}$ (G.) $-6\frac{1}{9}$ H. $-\frac{6}{1}$ J. $-6\frac{1}{10}$
15. Evaluate $\frac{1}{2} - \frac{1}{8} + \frac{3}{4} - \frac{5}{16}$.
   A. 0 B. $\frac{1}{4}$ C. $\frac{5}{8}$ (D.) $\frac{13}{16}$
16. Solve $-\frac{2}{3}x = 12$.
   (F.) −18 G. 12 H. 18 J. −24

Problem Solving

Applying Proportions

Students will use data from these two pages to answer the questions posed here in Put It All Together.

Activating Prior Knowledge

Discuss students' understanding of Calories. Talk about the number of Calories they consume on a typical day and the Calories they burn doing a variety of physical activities. Refer students to the table of Calories burned on page 241.

Guided Instruction

History Connection
Tell students that human and animal pedaling has powered large machines for centuries. Invite interested students to learn more about the history of human-powered machines and to report on their findings.

Science Connection
Have students learn more about the Daedalus plane. Ask them to find out about the effort behind this achievement in flight and about advances in the field since that groundbreaking event in 1988.

Problem Solving Application

Applying Proportions

Food Power Food energy powers the human body, and the human body can power appliances. For example, you could connect a stationary bicycle to a generator and produce electricity when you pedal. Could this replace the power you get from your utility company?

What's a Calorie?
A calorie is the amount of energy needed to heat 1 g of water from 14.5°C to 15.5°C.

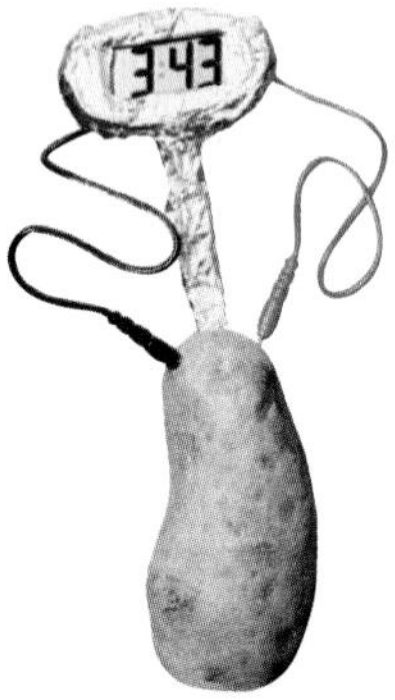

Organic Power
Juice in a fresh potato reacts with copper and zinc electrodes to power a digital clock.

Put It All Together

Data File Use the information on these two pages to answer these questions.

Energy Measurement Conversion Factors

1 food Calorie = 1,000 gram-calories (g-cal)
1 g-cal = 0.001162 watt-hours
1 watt-hour = 860.42 g-cal

1. a. A typical sandwich provides about 250 food Calories. How many watt-hours of energy does a sandwich provide?

b. Your body uses about $\frac{3}{4}$ of the chemical energy in food to maintain itself. The rest is available for activities like pedaling a bicycle. How much energy from the sandwich can you use for pedaling (in watt-hours)?

2. a. Use the energy formula to find how much energy you would need to light a 75-watt light bulb for 10 hours.

Energy Formula

energy to run device (watt-hours) = power used (watts) × time running (hours)

b. How many hours could you light a 75-watt bulb with a bicycle generator using the energy from one sandwich?

c. How long could you light a 30-watt light bulb? Give your answer in hours and minutes.

3. Suppose you eat about 2,500 food Calories per day.

a. Using your human-powered generator, how much electrical energy (in watt-hours) can you produce from these Calories?

b. Open-Ended Pick a device from the table and calculate how long you could run it with this energy.

Home Appliance Energy-Use Guide

Appliance	Watts Needed to Run
Computer	1,500
Digital clock	325
Hair dryer	1,200
Microwave	186
Refrigerator	50
Stereo system	30
Television	300
VCR	2

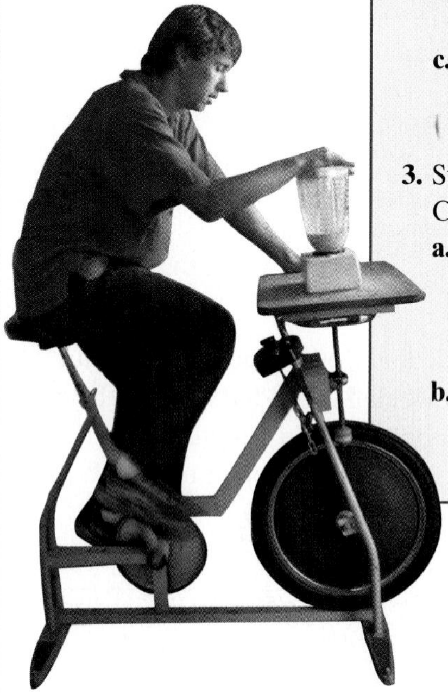

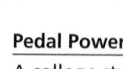

Pedal Power
A college student uses pedal power to operate a blender and make salad dressing.

206

1a. 290.5 watt-hours
b. 72.6 watt-hours
2a. 750 watt-hours
b. about 1 h or 58 min
c. 2 h and 25 min

3a. 726 watt-hours
b. Answers may vary. Sample: dryer, about 36 min

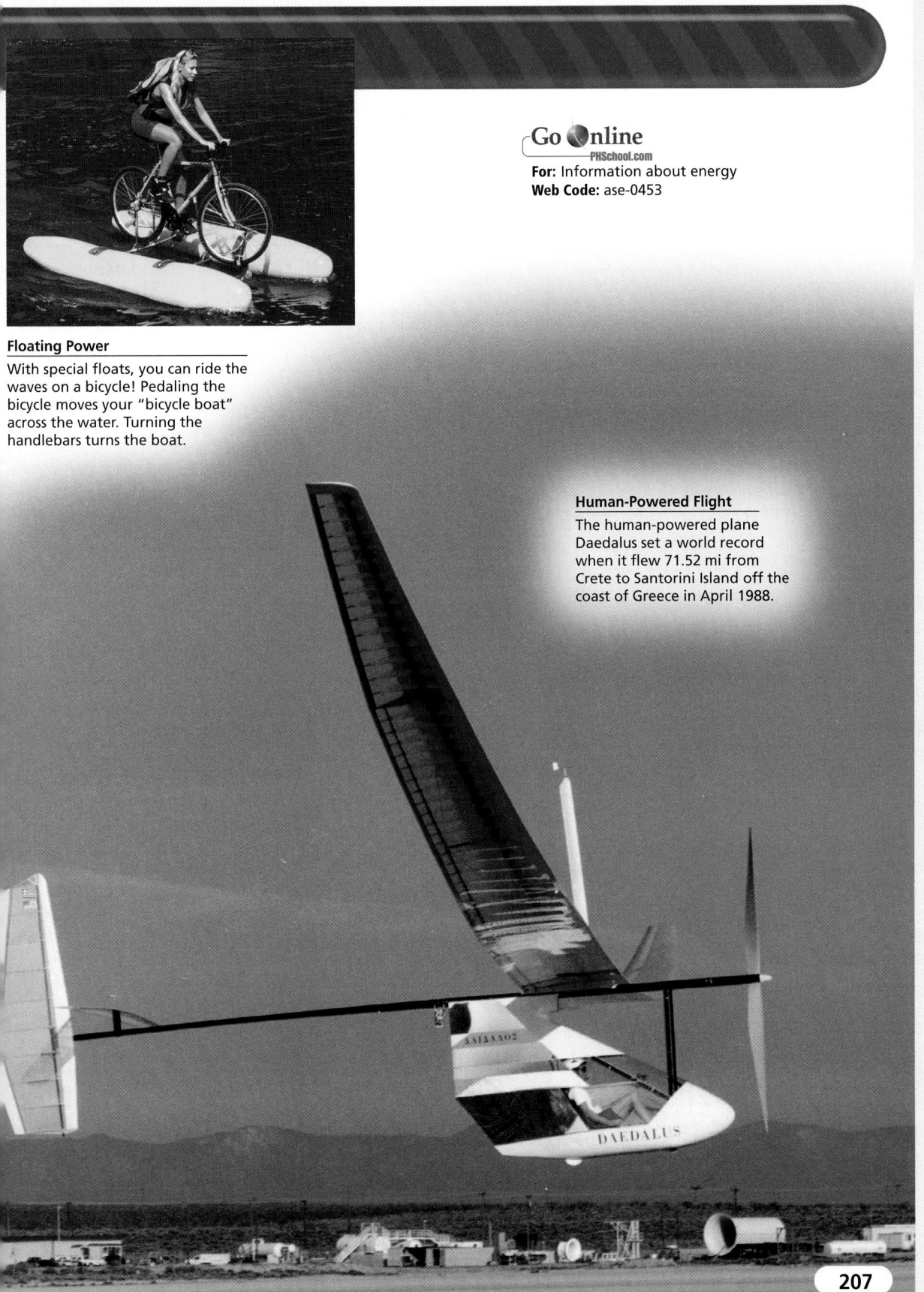

Floating Power

With special floats, you can ride the waves on a bicycle! Pedaling the bicycle moves your "bicycle boat" across the water. Turning the handlebars turns the boat.

Go Online
PHSchool.com
For: Information about energy
Web Code: ase-0453

Human-Powered Flight

The human-powered plane Daedalus set a world record when it flew 71.52 mi from Crete to Santorini Island off the coast of Greece in April 1988.

Put It All Together

Have students work in pairs or small groups to answer the questions. Guide them to work with calculators.

Exercise 3 Have students share their calculations and results for the device they run with human-powered energy.

Earth Science Connection
Invite interested students to investigate alternate source of energy, such as wind power, and report on their findings.

Language Arts Connection
Encourage interested students to write a persuasive essay on the advantages of using alternate sources of energy. You may wish to team with students' language arts teacher to review the key elements and style issues of an effective persuasive essay.

Differentiated Instruction

Special Needs L1
Help students understand and use the data in the Energy Measurement Conversion Factors table. Work through Exercise 1 together, step-by-step. Also help them understand and use the energy formula. As needed, work through and discuss a few examples using the formula.

English Language Learners ELL
Make sure students understand the terminology used in these pages: *energy, generator, watt, organic, power.* Guide them to refer to a dictionary or their science text for clarification.

5 Applications of Percent

Chapter at a Glance

Lesson Titles, Objectives, and Features	Assessment	NCTM Standards	Local Standards
5-1 Fractions, Decimals, and Percents • To convert between fractions, decimals, and percents and to order rational numbers	Lesson Quiz	1, 5, 6, 7, 8, 9, 10	
5-2 Estimating With Percents • To estimate percents using decimals and fractions	Lesson Quiz	1, 5, 6, 7, 8, 9, 10	
5-3 Percents and Proportions • To use proportions to find part of a whole, a whole amount, or a percent **5-3b Activity Lab, Data Analysis:** Percents and Graphs	Lesson Quiz	1, 3, 6, 7, 8, 9, 10	
5-4 Percents and Equations • To use equations to solve problems involving percent **Vocabulary Builder:** High-Use Academic Words	Lesson Quiz Checkpoint Quiz 1	1, 2, 5, 6, 7, 8, 9, 10	
5-5a Activity Lab: Describing Change **5-5 Percent of Change** • To find percent of change and to solve problems involving percent of increase and percent of decrease	Lesson Quiz	1, 2, 3, 6, 7, 8, 9, 10	
5-6 Markup and Discount • To use percent of change to find markup, discount, and selling price **5-6b Activity Lab, Hands On:** Using Percents **Guided Problem Solving:** Practice Solving Problems	Lesson Quiz	1, 5, 6, 7, 8, 9, 10	
5-7 Simple Interest • To find simple interest and account balances	Lesson Quiz Checkpoint Quiz 2	1, 2, 5, 6, 7, 8, 9, 10	
5-8a Activity Lab, Hands On: Exploring Probability **5-8 Ratios and Probability** • To find the probability and the sample space of an event	Lesson Quiz	1, 2, 3, 4, 5, 6, 7, 8, 9, 10	
Problem Solving Application: Applying Percents			

NCTM Standards 2000
1 Number and Operations
2 Algebra
3 Geometry
4 Measurement
5 Data Analysis and Probability
6 Problem Solving
7 Reasoning and Proof
8 Communication
9 Connections
10 Representation

Correlations to Standardized Tests

All content for these tests is contained in *Prentice Hall Math*, Course 3. This chart reflects coverage in this chapter only.

	5-1	5-2	5-3	5-4	5-5	5-6	5-7	5-8
Terra Nova CAT6 (Level 18)								
Number and Number Relations	✔		✔	✔	✔	✔	✔	✔
Computation and Numerical Estimation		✔						
Operation Concepts								
Measurement								
Geometry and Spatial Sense								
Data Analysis, Statistics, and Probability								✔
Patterns, Functions, Algebra			✔	✔	✔	✔		
Problem Solving and Reasoning	✔	✔	✔	✔	✔	✔	✔	✔
Communication	✔	✔	✔	✔	✔	✔	✔	✔
Decimals, Fractions, Integers, Percent								
Order of Operations								
Algebraic Operations								
Terra Nova CTBS (Level 18)								
Decimals, Fractions, Integers, Percents	✔	✔	✔	✔	✔	✔	✔	✔
Order of Operations, Numeration, Number Theory	✔	✔	✔	✔			✔	✔
Data Interpretation								✔
Measurement								
Geometry								
ITBS (Level 14)								
Number Properties and Operations	✔	✔	✔	✔	✔	✔	✔	✔
Algebra			✔	✔	✔	✔		
Geometry								
Measurement								
Probability and Statistics								✔
Estimation		✔						
SAT10 (Adv 1 Level)								
Number Sense and Operations	✔	✔	✔	✔	✔	✔	✔	✔
Patterns, Relationships, and Algebra			✔	✔	✔	✔		
Data, Statistics, and Probability								✔
Geometry and Measurement								
NAEP								
Number Sense, Properties, and Operations	✔	✔	✔	✔	✔	✔	✔	
Measurement								
Geometry and Spatial Sense								
Data Analysis, Statistics, and Probability								✔
Algebra and Functions								

CAT6 California Achievement Test, 6th Ed.
CTBS Comprehensive Test of Basic Skills
ITBS Iowa Test of Basic Skills, Form M
SAT10 Stanford Achievement Test, 10th Ed.
NAEP National Assessment of Educational Progress 2005 Mathematics Objectives

Skills Trace

BEFORE Chapter 5

Course 2 introduced solving of percent applications, such as markups and discounts.

DURING Chapter 5

Course 3 reviews and extends solving of percent applications to simple interest problems and probabilities.

AFTER Chapter 5

Throughout this course students use percents to solve real-world problems.

5-1 5-2 Fractions, Decimals, and Percents, and Estimating With Percents

Math Understandings

- A percent expresses parts per 100. The percent symbol, %, means "per 100" or "$\frac{}{100}$."
- Percents can be between 1% and 100%, less than 1%, and greater than 100%.
- Percent is relative to the size of the whole.
- The word "of" usually indicates multiplication in the statement of a problem.

A **percent** is a ratio that compares a number to 100. To write a percent as a fraction, you can write it as a fraction with a denominator of 100 and simplify. To write a percent as a decimal, move the decimal point two places to the left and remove the percent sign.

When estimating with percents, it is often helpful to know the fraction equivalents of common percents shown below.

Percent	10%	12.5%	25%	$33\frac{1}{3}$%	50%	$66\frac{2}{3}$%	75%
Fraction	$\frac{1}{10}$	$\frac{1}{8}$	$\frac{1}{4}$	$\frac{1}{3}$	$\frac{1}{2}$	$\frac{2}{3}$	$\frac{3}{4}$

Example: Estimate a 15% tip on \$21.82.
The bill is about \$22. First find 10% of \$22 (\$2.20). Then add half of that amount (\$1.10); which is 5%. A 15% tip for \$22 is \$2.20 + \$1.10, or \$3.30.

5-3 Percents and Proportions

Math Understandings

- Percent problems involve a part, a percent, and a whole.
- If you know two of the three quantities, you can find the missing one by using either a proportion or an equation.
- You can write a proportion in different but equivalent ways.
- When you find a percent that is greater than 100%, the part will be greater than the whole.

You can write and solve the proportion $\frac{\text{part}}{\text{whole}} = \frac{\text{percent}}{100}$ to find the missing part, percent, or whole.

Example: Find 300% of 180.

$\frac{n}{180} = \frac{300}{100}$

$100n = 300 \cdot 180$

$100n = 54{,}000$

$n = 540$

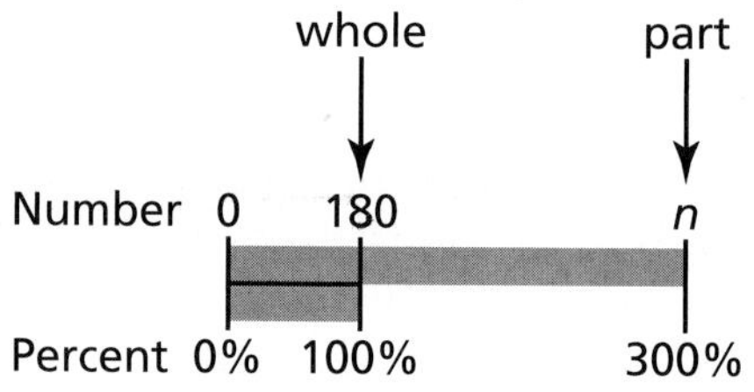

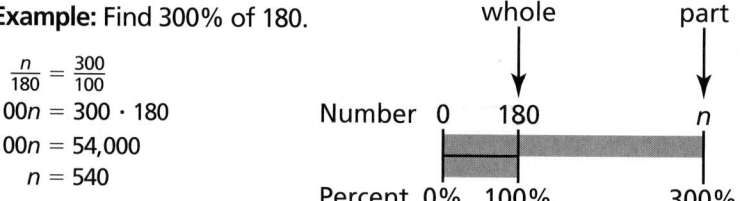

Percents and Proportions		
Finding the Part	**Finding the Whole**	**Finding the Percent**
What number is 20% of 25?	5 is 20% of what number?	5 is what percent of 25?
$\frac{n}{25} = \frac{20}{100}$	$\frac{5}{w} = \frac{20}{100}$	$\frac{5}{25} = \frac{p}{100}$

5-4 5-5 Percents and Equations, and Percent of Change

Math Understandings

- You can solve percent problems using equations.
- A percent of change may be an increase or a decrease.

Percents Equations		
Finding the Part	**Finding the Whole**	**Finding the Percent**
part = $P \cdot$ whole	part = $P \cdot$ whole	part = $P \cdot$ whole
What is 20% of 25?	5 is 20% of what?	5 is what percent of 25?
$n = 0.20 \cdot 25$	$5 = 0.20 \cdot w$	$5 = P \cdot 25$

The percent a quantity increases or decreases from its original amount is the **percent of change.**

$$\text{percent of change} = \frac{\text{amount of change}}{\text{original amount}}$$

5-6 Markup and Discount

Math Understandings

- A common percent decrease is a discount. The corresponding percent increase is a markup.

Markup is the amount of increase in price. Markup is added to a store's cost of an item to arrive at the **selling price**. The percent of increase in the price of an item is called the percent of markup. The amount by which the price of an item on sale is reduced is called the **discount**. The regular price of an item minus the discount equals the **sale price** of the item.

$$\text{percent of change} = \frac{\text{amount of change}}{\text{original amount}}$$

$$\text{percent of markup} = \frac{\text{markup}}{\text{store's cost}}$$

$$\text{percent of discount} = \frac{\text{discount}}{\text{regular price}}$$

5-7 Simple Interest

Math Understandings

- To calculate the amount of simple interest for an investment or a loan, you need to know the principal amount, the interest rate, and the time. The interest rate and the time must be expressed in the same units, usually years.

In return for depositing money in a savings account, the bank pays **interest** on money paid for the use of your money. **Simple interest** is interest calculated only on the principal.

The simple interest formula is $I = p \cdot r \cdot t$, where I is the interest, p is the principal, r is the interest rate per year, and t is the time in years.

5-8 Ratios and Probability

Math Understandings

- The laws of probability predict only what will happen when a very large number of events is surveyed.

An **outcome** is any of the possible results that can occur. The collection of all possible outcomes in an experiment is called the **sample space**. A collection of possible outcomes in a experiment is an **event**. The probability of an event E is given by this formula when outcomes are equally likely:

$$P(E) = \frac{\text{number of favorable outcomes}}{\text{total number of possible outcomes}}$$

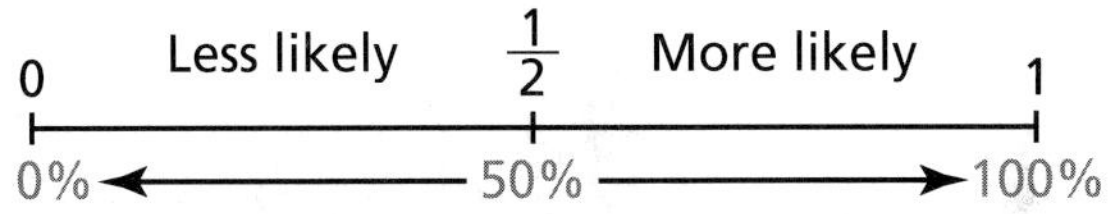

Example: A six-sided number cube is rolled. Express each probability as a fraction.

$P(6) = \frac{1}{6}$

$P\text{ (even)} = \frac{3}{6} = \frac{1}{2}$

$P\text{ (number less than 5)} = \frac{4}{6} = \frac{2}{3}$

Additional Professional Development Opportunities

Professional Development

Math Background Notes for Chapter 5: Every lesson has a Math Background in the PLAN section.

Research Overview, Mathematics Strands
Additional support for these topics and more is in the front of the Teacher's Edition.

LessonLab
LessonLab, a Pearson Education company, offers comprehensive, facilitated professional development designed to help teachers to improve student achievement. To learn more, please visit lessonlab.com.

Chapter 5 Resources

	5-1	5-2	5-3	5-4	5-5	5-6	5-7	5-8	For the Chapter
Print Resources									
L3 Practice	●	●	●	●	●	●	●	●	
L1 Adapted Practice	●	●	●	●	●	●	●	●	
L3 Guided Problem Solving	●	●	●	●	●	●	●	●	
L2 Reteaching	●	●	●	●	●	●	●	●	
L4 Enrichment	●	●	●	●	●	●	●	●	
L3 Daily Notetaking Guide	●	●	●	●	●	●	●	●	
L1 Adapted Daily Notetaking Guide	●	●	●	●	●	●	●	●	
L3 Vocabulary and Study Skills Worksheets	●		●	●		●		●	●
L3 Daily Puzzles	●	●	●	●	●	●	●	●	
L3 Activity Labs	●	●	●	●	●	●	●	●	
L3 Checkpoint Quiz				●			●		
L3 Chapter Project									●
L2 Below Level Chapter Test									●
L3 Chapter Test									●
L4 Alternative Assessment									●
L3 Cumulative Review									●
Spanish Resources ELL									
L3 Practice	●	●	●	●	●	●	●	●	●
L3 Vocabulary and Study Skills Worksheets	●		●	●		●		●	●
L3 Checkpoint Quiz				●			●		
L2 Below Level Chapter Test									●
L3 Chapter Test									●
L4 Alternative Assessment									●
L3 Cumulative Review									●
Transparencies									
Check Skills You'll Need	●	●	●	●	●	●	●	●	
Additional Examples	●	●	●	●	●	●	●	●	
Problem of the Day	●	●	●	●	●	●	●	●	
Classroom Aid	●		●	●	●		●		
Student Edition Answers	●	●	●	●	●	●	●	●	●
Lesson Quiz	●	●	●	●	●	●	●	●	
Test-Taking Strategies									●
Technology									
Interactive Textbook Online	●	●	●	●	●	●	●	●	●
StudentExpress™ CD-ROM	●	●	●	●	●	●	●	●	●
Success Tracker™ Online Intervention	●	●	●	●	●	●	●	●	●
TeacherExpress™ CD-ROM	●	●	●	●	●	●	●	●	●
PresentationExpress™ with QuickTake Presenter CD-ROM	●	●	●	●	●	●	●	●	●
ExamView® Assessment Suite CD-ROM	●	●	●	●	●	●	●	●	●
MindPoint® Quiz Show CD-ROM									●
Prentice Hall Web Site: PHSchool.com	●	●	●	●	●	●	●	●	●

Also available: **Prentice Hall Assessment System**
- Progress Monitoring Assessments
- Skills and Concepts Review
- Test Prep Workbook

Other Resources
Algebra Readiness Tests
All-in-One Student Workbook
All-in-One Student Workbook, Adapted Version
Multilingual Handbook
Solution Key
Math Notes Study Folder
Spanish Cumulative Assessment

Where You Can Use the Lesson Resources

Here is a suggestion, following the four-step teaching plan, for how you can incorporate Differentiated Instruction Resources into your teaching.

	Instructional Resources L3	Differentiated Instruction Resources
1. Plan		
Preparation Read the Math Background in the Teacher's Edition to connect this lesson with students' previous experience. **Starting Class** **Check Skills You'll Need** Assign these exercises to review prerequisite skills. **New Vocabulary** Help students pre-read the lesson by pointing out the new terms introduced in the lesson.	**Math Background** **Math Understandings** **Transparencies & PresentationExpress™ with QuickTake Presenter CD-ROM** Check Skills You'll Need Problem of the Day **Resources** Vocabulary and Study Skills	**Spanish Support** ELL Vocabulary and Study Skills
2. Teach		
L3 **Guided Instruction** Use the Activity Labs to build conceptual understanding. Teach each Example. Use the Teacher's Edition side column notes for specific teaching tips, including Error Prevention notes. Use the Additional Examples found in the side column (and on transparency and PowerPoint) as an alternative presentation for the content. After each Example, assign the Quick Check exercise for that Example to get an immediate assessment of student understanding. Use the Closure activity in the Teacher's Edition to help students attain mastery of lesson content.	**Student Edition** Activity Lab **Resources** Daily Notetaking Guide Activity Lab **Transparencies & PresentationExpress™ with QuickTake Presenter CD-ROM** Additional Examples Classroom Aids **ExamView® Assessment Suite CD-ROM**	**Teacher's Edition** Every lesson includes suggestions for working with students who need special attention. L1 Special Needs L2 Below Level L4 Advanced Learners ELL English Language Learners **Resources** L1 Adapted Daily Notetaking Guide **Multilingual Handbook**
3. Practice		
Assignment Guide **Check Your Understanding** Use these questions to check students' understanding before you assign homework. **Homework Exercises** Assign homework from these leveled exercises in the Assignment Guide. **A** Practice by Example **B** Apply Your Skills **C** Challenge Test Prep and Mixed Review **Homework Quick Check** Use these key exercises to quickly check students' homework.	**Transparencies & PresentationExpress™ with QuickTake Presenter CD-ROM** Student Answers **Resources** Practice Guided Problem Solving Vocabulary and Study Skills Activity Lab Daily Puzzles **ExamView® Assessment Suite CD-ROM**	**Spanish Support** ELL Practice ELL Vocabulary and Study Skills **Resources** L1 Adapted Practice L4 Enrichment
4. Assess & Reteach		
Lesson Quiz Assign the Lesson Quiz to assess students' mastery of the lesson content. **Checkpoint Quiz** Use the Checkpoint Quiz to assess student progress over several lessons.	**Transparencies & PresentationExpress™ with QuickTake Presenter CD-ROM** Lesson Quiz **Resources** Checkpoint Quiz	**Resources** L2 Reteaching ELL Checkpoint Quiz Success Tracker™ Online Intervention **ExamView® Assessment Suite CD-ROM**

KEY L1 Special Needs L2 Below Level L3 For All Students L4 Advanced, Gifted ELL English Language Learners

CHAPTER 5

Applications of Percent

Check Your Readiness

Answers for students are in the back of the textbook.

For intervention, direct students to:

Solving One-Step Equations
Lesson 1-7
Extra Skills and Word Problems Practice, Ch. 1

Equivalent Forms of Rational Numbers
Lesson 2-2
Extra Skills and Word Problems Practice, Ch. 2

Multiplying Rational Numbers
Lesson 2-5
Extra Skills and Word Problems Practice, Ch. 2

Solving Proportions
Lesson 4-3
Extra Skills and Word Problems Practice, Ch. 4

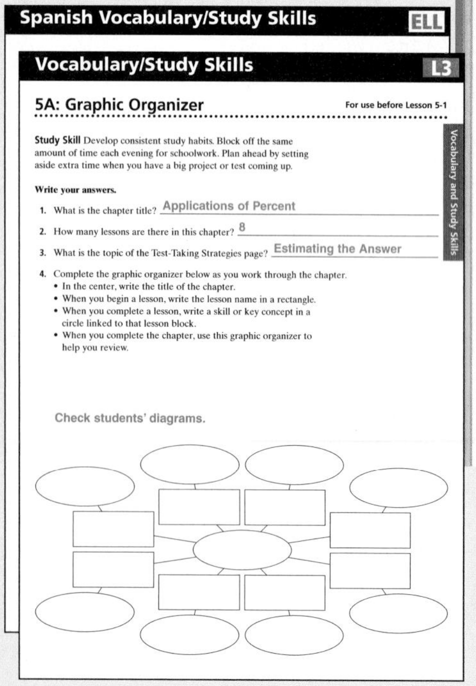
Spanish Vocabulary/Study Skills ELL

Vocabulary/Study Skills L3

5A: Graphic Organizer — For use before Lesson 5-1

Study Skill Develop consistent study habits. Block off the same amount of time each evening for schoolwork. Plan ahead by setting aside extra time when you have a big project or test coming up.

Write your answers.

1. What is the chapter title? Applications of Percent
2. How many lessons are there in this chapter? 8
3. What is the topic of the Test-Taking Strategies page? Estimating the Answer
4. Complete the graphic organizer below as you work through the chapter.
   - In the center, write the title of the chapter.
   - When you begin a lesson, write the lesson name in a rectangle.
   - When you complete a lesson, write a skill or key concept in a circle linked to that lesson block.
   - When you complete the chapter, use this graphic organizer to help you review.

Check students' diagrams.

Vocabulary and Study Skills

CHAPTER 5 Applications of Percent

What You've Learned

- In Chapter 2, you compared and ordered rational numbers.
- In Chapter 4, you wrote and used ratios and rates.
- You found solutions to problems involving proportional relationships.

Check Your Readiness

GO for Help

For Exercises	See Lessons
1–4	1-7
5–8	2-2
9–11	2-5
12–17	4-3

Solving One-Step Equations

Solve each equation.

1. $16 = 0.8p$ 20
2. $2m = 31.82$ 15.91
3. $0.32x = 76$ 237.5
4. $95v = 166.25$ 1.75

Equivalent Forms of Rational Numbers

Write each fraction in simplest form.

5. $\frac{50}{100}$ $\frac{1}{2}$
6. $\frac{25}{40}$ $\frac{5}{8}$
7. $\frac{6}{72}$ $\frac{1}{12}$
8. $\frac{36}{64}$ $\frac{9}{16}$

Multiplying Rational Numbers

Find each product. Write the answer in simplest form or as a mixed number.

9. $\frac{3}{10} \cdot 100$ 30
10. $15 \cdot \frac{17}{30}$ $8\frac{1}{2}$
11. $160 \cdot \frac{5}{8}$ 100

Solving Proportions

Solve each proportion.

12. $\frac{7}{12} = \frac{21}{n}$ 36
13. $\frac{k}{45} = \frac{10}{225}$ 2
14. $\frac{18}{t} = \frac{27}{48}$ 32
15. $\frac{1}{4} = \frac{25}{y}$ 100
16. $\frac{5}{3} = \frac{z}{11.4}$ 19
17. $\frac{h}{76} = \frac{9}{8}$ 85.5

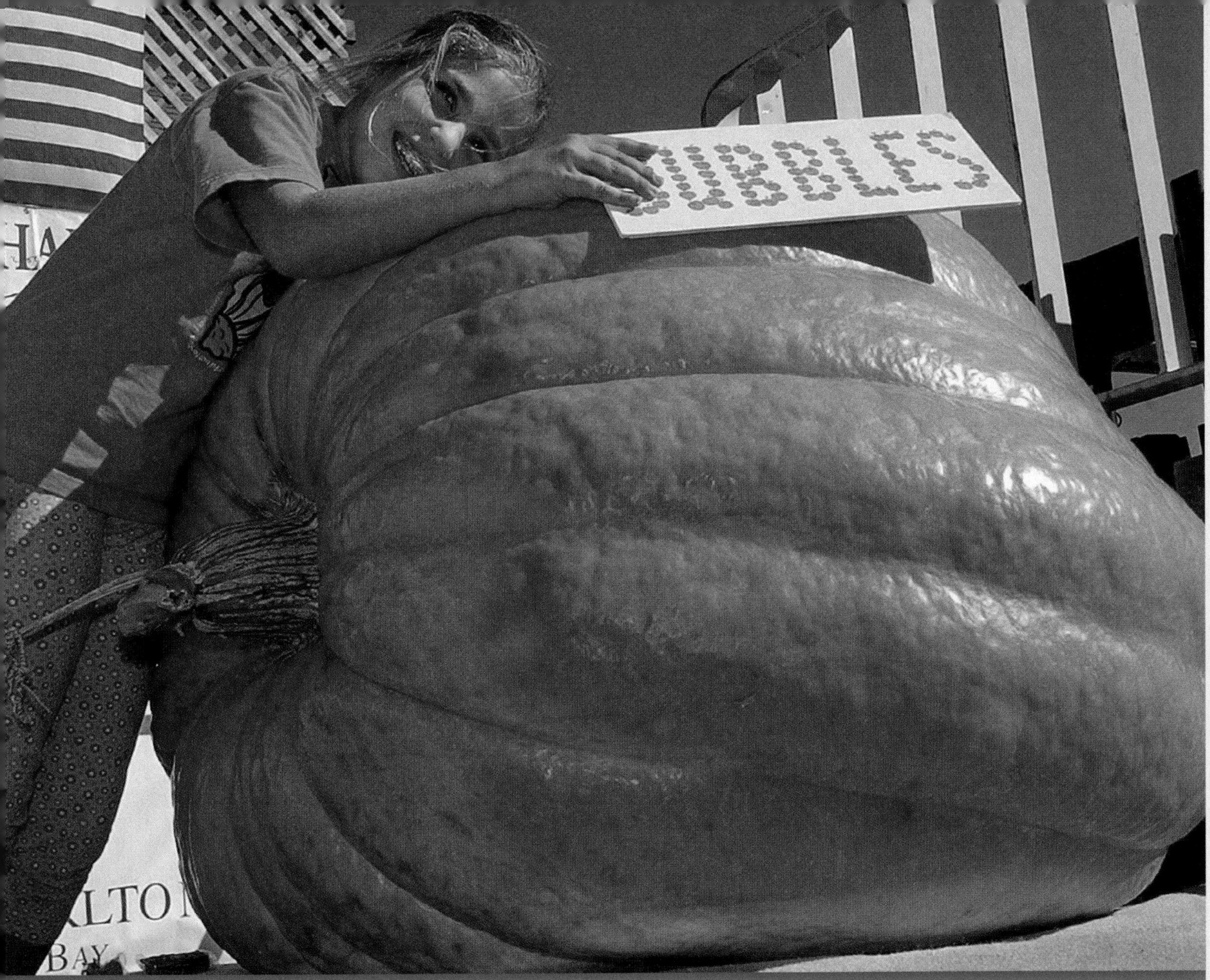

Chapter 5 Overview

In this chapter, students learn about percents; explore the relationships among fractions, decimals, and percents; and solve a variety of percent problems using different methods. They estimate percents and find percents using proportions and equations. They apply their understanding of percent to real-world situations as they find discounts and markups and work with simple interest. Lastly, they investigate probability.

Activating Prior Knowledge

In this chapter, as students work with percents, they build on their knowledge of ratios and rates, and of writing and solving proportions. They draw upon their prior understanding of the relationship between fractions and decimals. Ask questions such as:

- *A player has made 7 out of 10 free throw attempts. If she continues to shoot at that rate, how many free throws can she expect to make in 200 attempts?* 140 free throws
- *What is the value of x in the proportion* $\frac{4}{x} = \frac{88}{11}$? 0.5
- *Limes are 4 for $1 at the store. What would two dozen limes cost?* $6

What You'll Learn Next

- In this chapter, you will compare and order integers, percents, fractions, and decimals.
- You will use estimation, proportions, and equations to solve problems involving percents.
- You will use ratios to find probability.

Problem Solving Application On pages 256 and 257, you will work an extended activity on expenses.

Key Vocabulary

- balance (p. 243)
- discount (p. 235)
- event (p. 246)
- interest (p. 242)
- interest rate (p. 242)
- markup (p. 234)
- outcome (p. 246)
- percent (p. 210)
- percent of change (p. 230)
- principal (p. 242)
- probability of an event (p. 246)
- sale price (p. 235)
- sample space (p. 247)
- selling price (p. 234)
- simple interest (p. 242)

5-1

1. Plan

Objective

To convert between fractions, decimals, and percents and to order rational numbers

Examples

1 Writing a Fraction as a Percent
2 Writing a Decimal as a Percent
3 Writing a Percent as a Fraction
4 Ordering Rational Numbers

Math Understandings: p. 208C

Professional Development

Math Background

A *percent* is a ratio that compares a number to 100. When students understand percent as meaning parts per hundred, then they are more likely to translate easily and correctly between fractions, decimals, and percents.

More Math Background: p. 208C

Lesson Planning and Resources

See p. 208E for a list of the resources that support this lesson.

PowerPoint

Bell Ringer Practice

Check Skills You'll Need
Use student page, transparency, or PowerPoint. For intervention, direct students to:

Equivalent Forms of Rational Numbers
Lesson 2-2
Extra Skills and Word Problems Practice, Ch. 2

5-1 Fractions, Decimals, and Percents

Check Skills You'll Need

1. **Vocabulary Review** A *rational number* is a number that can be written in the form __?__. $\frac{a}{b}, b \neq 0$

Write each fraction in simplest form.

2. $\frac{90}{100}$ $\frac{9}{10}$
3. $\frac{80}{100}$ $\frac{4}{5}$
4. $\frac{35}{100}$ $\frac{7}{20}$
5. $\frac{25}{100}$ $\frac{1}{4}$

GO for Help
Lesson 2-2

What You'll Learn

To convert between fractions, decimals, and percents and to order rational numbers

New Vocabulary percent

Why Learn This?

Teachers can write grades in different forms. You may need to convert from one form to another in order to understand your grades better.

Suppose you correctly answer four fifths of the questions on a quiz. You can express this fraction as a percent. A **percent** is a ratio that compares a number to 100.

Sometimes you can use mental math to write percents.

GO Online

Video Tutor Help
Visit: PHSchool.com
Web Code: ase-0775

EXAMPLE Writing a Fraction as a Percent

1 Use mental math to write $\frac{4}{5}$ as a percent.

What you think

I can write $\frac{4}{5}$ as an equivalent fraction with a denominator of 100.

$$\frac{4}{5} \underset{\times 20}{\overset{\times 20}{=}} \frac{80}{100}$$

I can rewrite $\frac{80}{100}$ as 80%.

Why it works

$\frac{4}{5} = \frac{4 \cdot 20}{5 \cdot 20}$ ← **Multiply the numerator and denominator by 20.**

$= \frac{80}{100}$ ← **Simplify.**

$= 80\%$ ← **Write the fraction as a percent.**

Quick Check

1. Use mental math to write $\frac{11}{20}$ as a percent. 55%

Differentiated Instruction Solutions for All Learners

Special Needs L1
Students convert the rational numbers in Example 4 to something other than decimals if decimal-conversion proves too difficult. For example, they could convert each number to a fraction with a denominator of 100 and then compare the fractions.
learning style: visual

Below Level L2
Explain that a percent greater than 100 is like a decimal or fraction greater than 1. Make sure that students recognize that 1.1 is equivalent to 110% or $\frac{11}{10}$.
learning style: verbal

Percents can be between 1% and 100%, greater than 100%, or less than 1%.

EXAMPLE Writing a Decimal as a Percent

2 Write 1.2 as a percent.

$$1.2 = 1\frac{2}{10} = \frac{12}{10}$$ ← Write the decimal as a mixed number and then as a fraction.

$$= \frac{12 \cdot 10}{10 \cdot 10}$$ ← Multiply the numerator and denominator by 10.

$$= \frac{120}{100}$$ ← Write as an equivalent fraction with a denominator of 100.

$$= 120\%$$ ← Write the fraction as a percent.

Quick Check

2. Write 0.08 as a percent. 8%

You can also write percents as fractions.

EXAMPLE Writing a Percent as a Fraction

3 **Nutrition** A brand of daily vitamin supplies $2\frac{1}{2}\%$ of the Recommended Dietary Allowance (RDA) of potassium. Write this percent as a fraction.

$$2\frac{1}{2}\% = \frac{2\frac{1}{2}}{100}$$ ← Write the percent as a fraction with a denominator of 100.

$$= 2\frac{1}{2} \div 100$$ ← Rewrite the fraction as division.

$$= \frac{5}{2} \div 100$$ ← Write the mixed number as an improper fraction.

$$= \frac{\overset{1}{\cancel{5}}}{2} \cdot \frac{1}{\underset{20}{\cancel{100}}}$$ ← Multiply by the reciprocal of 100. Divide by the GCF.

$$= \frac{1}{40}$$ ← Simplify.

Quick Check

3. A vitamin has 150% of the RDA of vitamin C. Write this percent as a fraction. $\frac{3}{2}$

Another way to write a decimal as a percent is to multiply it by 100, or move the decimal point 2 places to the right. To write a percent as a decimal, divide it by 100, or move the decimal point 2 places to the left.

GO for Help

For help multiplying by powers of 10, go to Lesson 2-8, Example 1.

Online active math

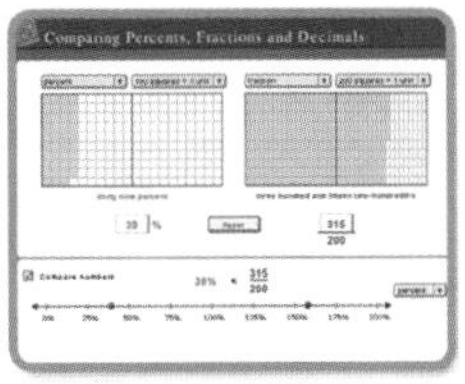

For: Comparing Numbers Activity
Use: Interactive Textbook, 5-1

2. Teach

Activity Lab

Use before the lesson.

All in One Teaching Resources

Activity Lab 5-1: Fractions, Decimals, and Percents

Guided Instruction

Example 2

Have students use nutrition labels to compare the percent of the RDA of vitamin C in different foods.

PowerPoint Additional Examples

1 Use mental math to write $\frac{3}{25}$ as a percent. 12%

2 Write each decimal as a percent.
a. 2.5 250% **b.** 0.003 0.3%

3 A brand of cereal supplied $7\frac{1}{2}\%$ of the RDA of sodium. Write this portion of the RDA as a fraction. $\frac{3}{40}$

4 Order 27%, 0.24, and $\frac{1}{5}$ from least to greatest. $\frac{1}{5} < 0.24 < 27\%$

All in One Teaching Resources

- Daily Notetaking Guide 5-1 L3
- Adapted Notetaking 5-1 L1

Closure

- *Explain how to write a percent as a fraction.* Sample: Remove the % symbol and use the resulting number as the numerator and 100 as the denominator of a fraction. Make sure the fraction is in simplest terms.
- *Explain how to write a fraction as a percent.* Sample: Write the fraction as an equivalent fraction with 100 as the denominator. The numerator will be the percent.
- *Explain how to write a decimal as a percent.* Sample: Write the decimal number as a fraction with 100 as the denominator.

Advanced Learners L4

Students research the origins, meaning, and usage of the word "percent" and the symbol "%." They share their findings with the class.

learning style: verbal

English Language Learners ELL

Explain the context of Example 3 to the students. State that the RDA stands for *recommended dietary allowance;* it is the amount of a certain nutrient in a person's diet recommended by the United States Department of Agriculture and the medical community.

learning style: verbal

3. Practice

Assignment Guide

Check Your Understanding

Go over Exercises 1–6 in class before assigning the Homework Exercises.

Homework Exercises

A Practice by Example	7–25
B Apply Your Skills	26–33
C Challenge	34
Test Prep and Mixed Review	35–39

Homework Quick Check

To check students' understanding of key skills and concepts, go over Exercises 19, 24, 26, 28, and 33.

Differentiated Instruction Resources

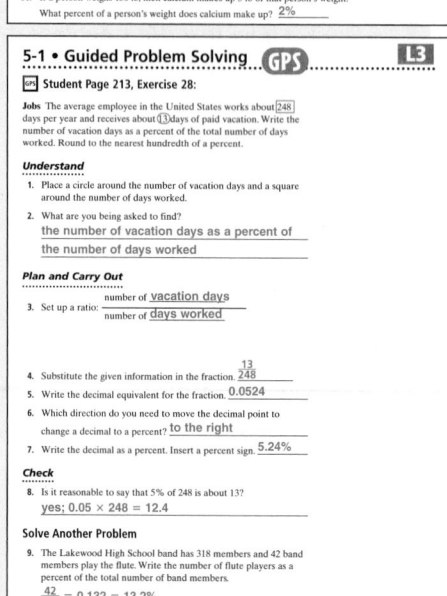

Adapted Practice 5-1 L1

Practice 5-1 Fractions, Decimals, and P… L3

Use mental math to write each decimal as a percent.

1. 0.95 95%
2. 0.06 6%
3. 0.004 0.4%
4. 0.63 63%
5. 0.005 0.5%
6. 1.4 140%

Write each fraction as a percent. Round to the nearest tenth of a percent.

7. $\frac{4}{5}$ 80%
8. $\frac{7}{10}$ 70%
9. $\frac{5}{6}$ 83.3%
10. $\frac{5}{8}$ 62.5%
11. $\frac{1}{15}$ 6.7%
12. $\frac{9}{25}$ 36%
13. $\frac{1}{6}$ 16.7%
14. $\frac{11}{12}$ 91.7%
15. $\frac{1}{20}$ 5%

Use mental math to write each percent as a decimal.

16. 70% 0.7
17. 10% 0.10
18. 800% 8.0
19. 2.6% 0.026
20. 234% 2.34
21. 9% 0.09

Write each percent as a fraction in simplest form.

22. 10% $\frac{1}{10}$
23. 47% $\frac{47}{100}$
24. $5\frac{1}{2}$% $\frac{11}{200}$
25. 15% $\frac{3}{20}$
26. 92% $\frac{23}{25}$
27. $3\frac{1}{4}$% $\frac{13}{400}$
28. 85% $\frac{17}{20}$
29. 42% $\frac{21}{50}$
30. 70% $\frac{7}{10}$

Order each set of numbers from least to greatest.

31. 12%, $\frac{1}{8}$, 1.2, $\frac{1}{12}$ — $\frac{1}{12}$; 12%; $\frac{1}{8}$; 1.2
32. 0.047, 0.5%, $\frac{1}{20}$, 1.5% — 0.6%; 1.5%; 0.047; $\frac{1}{20}$
33. $\frac{3}{7}$, 3.7%, 0.37, 0.073 — 3.7%; 0.073; 0.37; $\frac{3}{7}$
34. 0.001, $\frac{1}{100}$, 0.01%, $\frac{1}{10}$ — 0.01%; 0.001; $\frac{1}{100}$; $\frac{1}{10}$

Solve.

35. There are twelve pairs of cranial nerves connected to the brain. Ten of these pairs are related to sight, smell, taste, and sound. What percent of the pairs are related to sight, smell, taste, and sound? 83.3%
36. If a person weighs 150 lb, then calcium makes up 3 lb of that person's weight. What percent of a person's weight does calcium make up? 2%

5-1 • Guided Problem Solving GPS L3

GPS **Student Page 213, Exercise 28:**

Jobs The average employee in the United States works about 248 days per year and receives about 13 days of paid vacation. Write the number of vacation days as a percent of the total number of days worked. Round to the nearest hundredth of a percent.

Understand

1. Place a circle around the number of vacation days and a square around the number of days worked.
2. What are you being asked to find? the number of vacation days as a percent of the number of days worked

Plan and Carry Out

3. Set up a ratio: $\frac{\text{number of vacation days}}{\text{number of days worked}}$
4. Substitute the given information in the fraction. $\frac{13}{248}$
5. Write the decimal equivalent for the fraction. 0.0524
6. Which direction do you need to move the decimal point to change a decimal to a percent? to the right
7. Write the decimal as a percent. Insert a percent sign. 5.24%

Check

8. Is it reasonable to say that 5% of 248 is about 13? yes; $0.05 \times 248 = 12.4$

Solve Another Problem

9. The Lakewood High School band has 318 members and 42 band members play the flute. Write the number of flute players as a percent of the total number of band members. $\frac{42}{318} = 0.132 = 13.2\%$

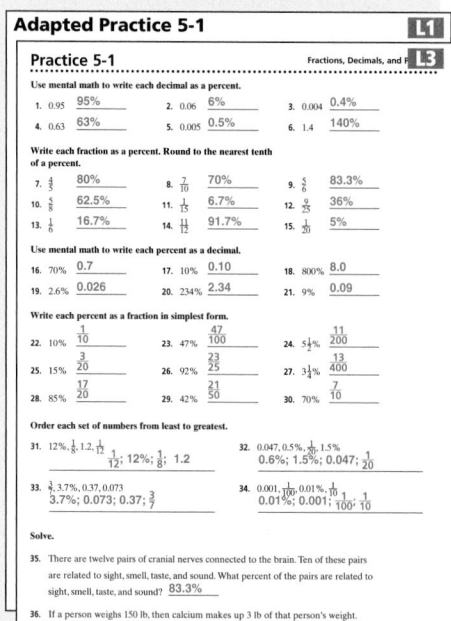

EXAMPLE Ordering Rational Numbers

4 Order 34%, 0.38, $\frac{1}{4}$, and 2 from least to greatest.

$34\% = 0.34 \qquad 0.38 = 0.38 \qquad \frac{1}{4} = 0.25$ ← **Change each number to a decimal.**

Since $0.25 < 0.34 < 0.38 < 2$, $\frac{1}{4} < 34\% < 0.38 < 2$.

Quick Check

4. Order 76%, 0.73, and $\frac{3}{4}$ from least to greatest. 0.73, $\frac{3}{4}$, 76%

Check Your Understanding

1. **Vocabulary** A percent compares a number to ■. 100

Match each fraction or decimal with a percent.

2. 1.0 D
3. $\frac{12}{200}$ B
4. 0.06 B
5. $\frac{14}{100}$ A
6. $\frac{10}{25}$ C

A. 14%
B. 6%
C. 40%
D. 100%

Homework Exercises

For more exercises, see Extra Skills and Word Problems.

GO for Help

For Exercises	See Examples
7–11	1
12–16	2
17–21	3
22–25	4

A **Mental Math** **Use mental math to write each fraction as a percent.**

7. $\frac{2}{5}$ 40%
8. $\frac{3}{4}$ 75%
9. $\frac{24}{25}$ 96%
10. $\frac{7}{20}$ 35%
11. $\frac{42}{50}$ 84%

Write each decimal as a percent.

12. 0.36 36%
13. 0.003 0.3%
14. 5.2 520%
15. 0.9 90%
16. 0.00007 0.007%

Write each percent as a fraction in simplest form.

17. 105% $\frac{21}{20}$
18. 220% $\frac{11}{5}$
19. $22\frac{2}{9}$% $\frac{2}{9}$
20. $66\frac{2}{3}$% $\frac{2}{3}$
21. On a math test, a student received a grade of 135 points out of 150 total points. Write the grade as a percent. 90%

Order each set of numbers from least to greatest.

22. $\frac{1}{3}$, 36%, 0.3, $\frac{3}{8}$ 0.3, $\frac{1}{3}$, 36%, $\frac{3}{8}$
23. 0.01, 0.09%, $\frac{1}{99}$, 1.01% 0.09%, 0.01, 1.01%, $\frac{1}{99}$
24. $\frac{2}{9}$, $\frac{1}{4}$, 0.2, 20.9% 0.2, 20.9%, $\frac{2}{9}$, $\frac{1}{4}$
25. 150%, 150, $\frac{9}{5}$, 1.5% 1.5%, 150%, $\frac{9}{5}$, 150

B GPS **26. Guided Problem Solving** The table below shows the results of a student survey about lunch. What percent of students did *not* choose tacos as their favorite food? Round to the nearest percent. 93%

Favorite Food	Hamburgers	Tacos	Sandwiches	Pizza
Number of Students	45	7	19	34

- How many students were surveyed?
- How many students *did* choose tacos as their favorite food?

27. Write the fraction, decimal, and percent that describe the shaded part of the figure. $\frac{5}{6}$, $0.8\overline{3}$, $83\frac{1}{3}\%$

28. Jobs The average employee in the United States works about 248 days per year and receives about 13 days of paid vacation. Write the number of vacation days as a percent of the total number of days worked. Round to the nearest hundredth of a percent. 5.24%

GPS

GO Online
Homework Video Tutor
Visit: PHSchool.com
Web Code: ase-0501

29. Jewelry 18-karat gold is 75% pure gold, and 14-karat gold is 58% pure gold. Write each percent as a fraction in simplest form. $\frac{3}{4}$, $\frac{29}{50}$

A bag contains 9 quarters, 4 dimes, and 12 nickels. Use this information for Exercises 30–32.

30. What percent of the coins are dimes? 16%

31. What percent of the coins are quarters and nickels? 84%

32. What percent of the coins are *not* nickels? 52%

33. Writing in Math Explain why 0.09 is different from 0.09%.

33. 0.09% is equal to 0.0009, which is not the same as 0.09.

C **34. Challenge** On average, about 60% of an adult's body weight is water. About how many pounds of a 135-lb person are water? about 81 lb

Test Prep and Mixed Review

Practice

Multiple Choice

35. Which list shows the numbers in order from least to greatest? D

(A) $0.63, \frac{25}{42}, 0.6, \frac{1}{2}, 62\frac{1}{2}\%$

(B) $\frac{1}{2}, 0.63, 0.6, 62\frac{1}{2}\%, \frac{25}{42}$

(C) $\frac{25}{42}, 0.6, 62\frac{1}{2}\%, 0.63, \frac{1}{2}$

(D) $\frac{1}{2}, \frac{25}{42}, 0.6, 62\frac{1}{2}\%, 0.63$

36. A scale model of a school is 7 inches high. If 2 inches on the model represents 9 feet on the actual building, how tall will the building be?

(F) 14 ft (G) 23.5 ft (H) 27 ft (J) 31.5 ft J

GO for Help

For Exercises	See Lesson
37–39	2-1

Find the GCF of each pair of numbers.

37. 15 and 39 3

38. 75 and 100 25

39. 18 and 54 18

Online lesson quiz, PHSchool.com, Web Code: asa-0501

Alternative Assessment

Students make a table showing how many hours in a typical day they spend eating, sleeping, doing chores, and doing schoolwork. Then they represent each category as a fraction, a decimal, and a percent.

Test Prep

Resources

For additional practice with a variety of test item formats:

- Test-Taking Strategies, p. 251
- Test Prep, p. 255
- Test-Taking Strategies with Transparencies

4. Assess & Reteach

PowerPoint

Lesson Quiz

1. A cereal supplies $1\frac{1}{4}\%$ of the RDA for calcium. Write $1\frac{1}{4}\%$ as a fraction. $\frac{1}{80}$
2. Write $\frac{7}{20}$ as a percent. 35%
3. Write 1.5 as a percent. 150%
4. Order 60%, 0.58, and $\frac{5}{8}$. $0.58 < 60\% < \frac{5}{8}$

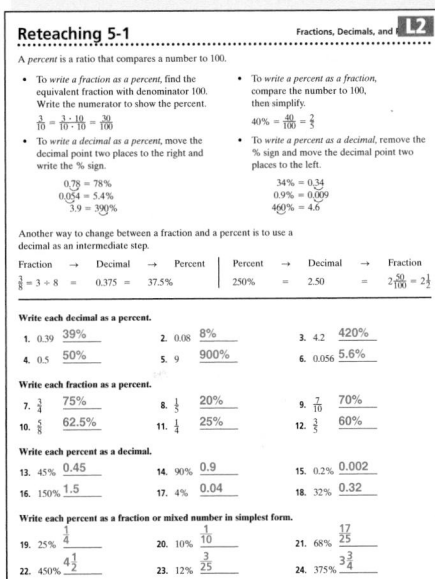

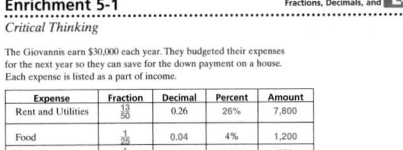

Reteaching 5-1 Fractions, Decimals, and P... L2

A *percent* is a ratio that compares a number to 100.

- To *write a fraction as a percent,* find the equivalent fraction with denominator 100. Write the numerator to show the percent.
  $\frac{3}{10} = \frac{3 \cdot 10}{10 \cdot 10} = \frac{30}{100}$
- To *write a percent as a fraction,* compare the number to 100, then simplify.
  $40\% = \frac{40}{100} = \frac{2}{5}$
- To *write a decimal as a percent,* move the decimal point two places to the right and write the % sign.
  0.78 = 78%
  0.054 = 5.4%
  3.9 = 390%
- To *write a percent as a decimal,* remove the % sign and move the decimal point two places to the left.
  34% = 0.34
  0.9% = 0.009
  460% = 4.6

Another way to change between a fraction and a percent is to use a decimal as an intermediate step.

Fraction	→	Decimal	→	Percent
$\frac{3}{8} = 3 \div 8$	=	0.375	=	37.5%

Percent	→	Decimal	→	Fraction
250%	=	2.50	=	$2\frac{50}{100} = 2\frac{1}{2}$

Write each decimal as a percent.

1. 0.39 39%
2. 0.08 8%
3. 4.2 420%
4. 0.5 50%
5. 9 900%
6. 0.056 5.6%

Write each fraction as a percent.

7. $\frac{3}{4}$ 75%
8. $\frac{1}{5}$ 20%
9. $\frac{7}{10}$ 70%
10. $\frac{5}{8}$ 62.5%
11. $\frac{1}{4}$ 25%
12. $\frac{3}{5}$ 60%

Write each percent as a decimal.

13. 45% 0.45
14. 90% 0.9
15. 0.2% 0.002
16. 150% 1.5
17. 4% 0.04
18. 32% 0.32

Write each percent as a fraction or mixed number in simplest form.

19. 25% $\frac{1}{4}$
20. 10% $\frac{1}{10}$
21. 68% $\frac{17}{25}$
22. 450% $4\frac{1}{2}$
23. 12% $\frac{3}{25}$
24. 375% $3\frac{3}{4}$

Enrichment 5-1 Fractions, Decimals, and L4

Critical Thinking

The Giovannis earn $30,000 each year. They budgeted their expenses for the next year so they can save for the down payment on a house. Each expense is listed as a part of income.

Expense	Fraction	Decimal	Percent	Amount
Rent and Utilities	$\frac{13}{50}$	0.26	26%	7,800
Food	$\frac{1}{25}$	0.04	4%	1,200
Entertainment	$\frac{1}{40}$	0.025	2.5%	750
Clothing	$\frac{3}{200}$	0.015	1.5%	450
Taxes	$\frac{1}{4}$	0.25	25%	7,500
Automobile	$\frac{3}{25}$	0.12	12%	3,600
Other	$\frac{2}{15}$	$0.1\overline{3}$	$13\frac{1}{3}\%$	4,000

1. Complete the table for each percent, fraction, and decimal. Then find the amount that is budgeted for each expense.
2. If the Giovannis follow this budget, how much money will they save? $4,700
3. What percent of income will be saved? $15\frac{2}{3}\%$
4. What percent of income is spent on clothing and entertainment? 4%
5. Which categories make up about the same amount of the budget as taxes and savings combined? Sample answer: Rent and Utilities (26%), Entertainment (2.5%), Automobile (12%)
6. Show the Giovannis' budget in the circle graph. Use your knowledge of the relative size of the fractions, decimals, and percents to determine the sections.

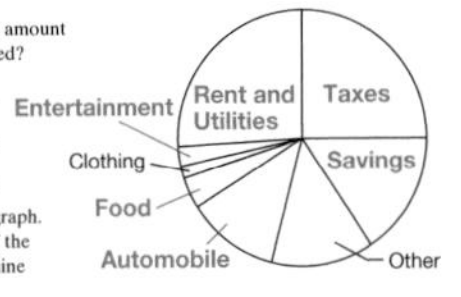

5-2

1. Plan

Objective
To estimate percents using decimals and fractions

Examples
1 Estimating Percents Using Decimals
2 Estimating Percents Using Fractions
3 Estimating Tips

Math Understandings: p. 208C

Professional Development

Math Background

Knowing how to express percents in decimal and fraction form makes it easy to select an appropriate method for finding the percent of a number. In real-life situations, it is sometimes useful to estimate the percent of a number by multiplying by the percent in decimal form. If the percent is close to a known common fraction, multiplying the fraction by a number works well. To estimate a 15% tip, using the sum of 10% and 5% is a helpful method.

More Math Background: p. 208C

Lesson Planning and Resources

See p. 208E for a list of the resources that support this lesson.

PowerPoint

Bell Ringer Practice

Check Skills You'll Need
Use student page, transparency, or PowerPoint. For intervention, direct students to:
Multiplying and Dividing Rational Numbers
Lesson 2-5
Extra Skills and Word Problems Practice, Ch. 2

5-2 Estimating With Percents

Check Skills You'll Need

1. **Vocabulary Review** The *multiplicative inverse* of $\frac{3}{7}$ is ■.
1–5. See below.

Find each product.

2. $36 \cdot \frac{3}{4}$ 3. $\frac{2}{3} \cdot 12$
4. $\frac{9}{10} \cdot 60$ 5. $81 \cdot \frac{5}{9}$

GO for Help
Lesson 2-5

What You'll Learn

To estimate percents using decimals and fractions

Why Learn This?

Estimation is a quick method for calculating numbers that do not need to be exact, such as a restaurant tip.

To find the percent of a number, multiply. You can estimate by using a decimal or fraction that is close to the percent. You can also use compatible numbers when estimating.

Vocabulary Tip
Compatible numbers are easy to compute mentally. The numbers 20 and 4 are compatible, but 37 and 8 are not.

Check Skills You'll Need
1. $\frac{7}{3}$
2. 27
3. 8
4. 54
5. 45

EXAMPLE 1 Estimating Percents Using Decimals

Use decimals to estimate 28% of 191.

$28\% \approx 0.3$ ← Use a decimal that is close to 28%.
$191 \approx 200$ ← Round 191 to a number that is compatible with 0.3.
$28\% \text{ of } 191 \approx 0.3 \text{ of } 200$
$= 0.3 \cdot 200$ ← Multiply to find 0.3 of 200.
$= 60$ ← Simplify.

28% of 191 is about 60.

Quick Check

1. Use decimals to estimate 18% of 107. about 20

To estimate, you should be familiar with common equivalent fractions.

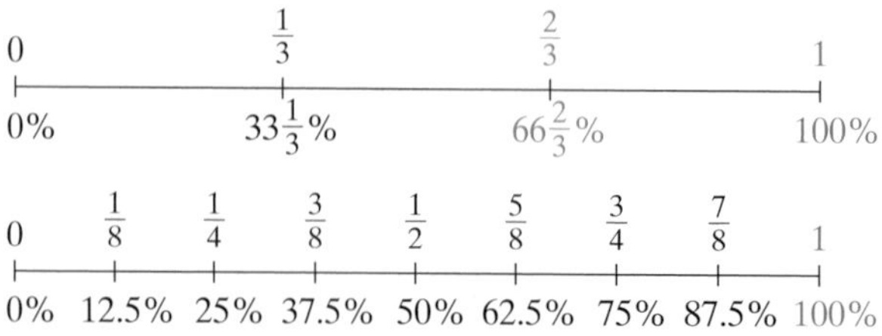

This model shows that $\frac{2}{3}$ is equal to $66\frac{2}{3}\%$.

Differentiated Instruction Solutions for All Learners

Special Needs L1	**Below Level** L2
Students practice estimating 10% of different decimal values, including money, mentally. Then they check their answers by writing their work down on paper. learning style: visual	Students find and say aloud quantities such as 25% of 8 (2), 50% of 48 (24), 75% of 100 (75), and so on. learning style: verbal

Careers Many disc jockeys start by working at small events, such as friends' parties.

EXAMPLE Estimating Percents Using Fractions

2 A disc jockey says that about 65% of his 238 CDs are pop albums. Using fractions, estimate the number of pop albums he has.

$65\% \approx \frac{2}{3}$ ← Use a fraction that is close to 65%.

$238 \approx 240$ ← Round to a number that is compatible with 3.

$65\% \text{ of } 238 \approx \frac{2}{3} \text{ of } 240$

$= \frac{2}{\cancel{3}_1} \cdot \frac{\cancel{240}^{80}}{1}$ ← Multiply to find $\frac{2}{3}$ of 240. Divide by the GCF.

$= 160$ ← Simplify.

About 160 CDs in the disc jockey's collection are pop albums.

Quick Check

2. A teacher says that about 35% of the 24 students in a class have blue eyes. Using fractions, estimate the number of blue-eyed students. about 8 students

You can also estimate percents by using multiples of 10%, which are easy to calculate mentally. This method is useful when computing tips in restaurants.

EXAMPLE Estimating Tips

3 You and a friend have a \$28.85 restaurant bill. Use mental math to estimate a 15% tip.

What you think

The bill is about \$30. I know 10% of 30 is $\frac{1}{10}$ of 30, or 3. Then 5% of 30 is half of 3, or 1.5. A 15% tip is about \$3.00 plus \$1.50, or \$4.50.

Why it works

$15\% \text{ of } 30 = 0.15 \cdot 30$ ← Rewrite 15% as 0.15.

$= (0.10 + 0.05)30$ ← Rewrite 0.15 as 0.10 + 0.05.

$= 0.10(30) + 0.05(30)$ ← Distributive Property

$= 3 + 1.50$ ← Multiply.

$= 4.50$ ← Add.

A 15% tip for a \$28.85 bill is about \$4.50.

Quick Check

3. **Mental Math** Estimate a 15% tip for a \$72.10 restaurant bill. about \$10.80

Advanced Learners L4
Students research and discuss uses of percents less than 1% in fields such as biology, computer science, and electronics.

learning style: verbal

English Language Learners ELL
Students talk through how 28% becomes a decimal close to 0.3 in Example 1. For instance, they rename the percent as $\frac{28}{100}$ and say "28 hundredths." Then students write it as a decimal so they can see it is close to 0.3.

learning style: verbal

2. Teach

Activity Lab

Use before the lesson.

All in One Teaching Resources

Activity Lab 5-2: Estimating with Percents

Guided Instruction

Error Prevention!

It is helpful to have students commit to memory the fractions for such common percents as $25\%\left(\frac{1}{4}\right)$, $33\frac{1}{3}\%\left(\frac{1}{3}\right)$, $50\%\left(\frac{1}{2}\right)$, $66\frac{2}{3}\%\left(\frac{2}{3}\right)$, and $75\%\left(\frac{3}{4}\right)$.

Alternative Method
Students may have different ideas about what numbers are easy to compute mentally. In Example 2, suggest that 65% might also be estimated as $\frac{6}{10}$.

PowerPoint

Additional Examples

1 Estimate 74% of 158 using decimals. about 120

2 A video store rented 297 videos. The customers returned 19% of the videos late. Estimate, using fractions, how many videos were returned late. about 60

3 Dion is saving for a coat that costs \$59.95. She has saved 45% of the cost. Estimate how much she has saved. about \$27

All in One Teaching Resources
- Daily Notetaking Guide 5-2 L3
- Adapted Notetaking 5-2 L1

Closure

- *How do compatible numbers help you estimate a percent using fractions or decimals?* Both the percent and the number it will be multiplied by can be rounded off to compatible values to make mental computation possible. It is also helpful to round off the percent to a familiar fraction or decimal that is close to the original percent.

3. Practice

Assignment Guide

Check Your Understanding

Go over Exercises 1–5 in class before assigning the Homework Exercises.

Homework Exercises

A	Practice by Example	6–22
B	Apply Your Skills	23–34
C	Challenge	35
	Test Prep and Mixed Review	36–40

Homework Quick Check

To check students' understanding of key skills and concepts, go over Exercises 12, 20, 28, 33, and 34.

Differentiated Instruction Resources

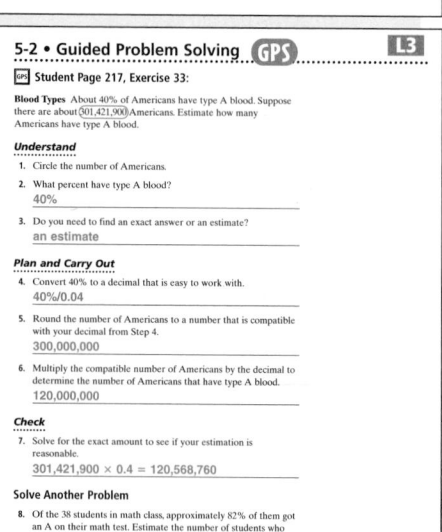

Adapted Practice 5-2 L1

Practice 5-2 Estimating Wit[...]s L3

Estimate each percent using decimals.

1. 6% of 140 — 8
2. 18.9% of 44 — 9
3. 61% of 180 — 108
4. 5.1% of 81 — 4
5. $16\frac{1}{2}$% of 36 — 6
6. 81% of 241 — 200
7. 67% of 300 — 200
8. 51% of 281 — 140
9. 62.9% of 400 — 250

Estimate each percent using fractions.

10. 76% of 600 — 450
11. 88% of 680 — 595
12. 37% of 481 — 180
13. 19.1% of 380 — 76
14. 41% of 321 — 128
15. 33% of 331 — 110
16. 83% of 453 — 360
17. 76.3% of 841 — 630
18. 67.1% of 486 — 320

Estimate.

19. Of the 307 species of mammals on the endangered list in 1992, 12.1% of them were found only in the United States. Estimate the number of mammal species in the United States that were on the endangered list. 38 species
20. In 1990, 19% of the people of Mali lived in urban settings. If the population that year was 9,200,000, estimate the number of people who lived in urban settings. 1,840,000 people
21. Of the 1,267 students at the school, 9.8% live within walking distance of school. Estimate the number of students within walking distance. 127 students

5-2 • Guided Problem Solving GPS L3

GPS Student Page 217, Exercise 33:

Blood Types About 40% of Americans have type A blood. Suppose there are about 301,421,900 Americans. Estimate how many Americans have type A blood.

Understand

1. Circle the number of Americans.
2. What percent have type A blood? 40%
3. Do you need to find an exact answer or an estimate? an estimate

Plan and Carry Out

4. Convert 40% to a decimal that is easy to work with. 40%/0.04
5. Round the number of Americans to a number that is compatible with your decimal from Step 4. 300,000,000
6. Multiply the compatible number of Americans by the decimal to determine the number of Americans that have type A blood. 120,000,000

Check

7. Solve for the exact amount to see if your estimation is reasonable. 301,421,900 × 0.4 = 120,568,760

Solve Another Problem

8. Of the 38 students in math class, approximately 82% of them got an A on their math test. Estimate the number of students who got an A. 40 × 0.80 = 32 students

Check Your Understanding

Estimate **Match each expression with the correct estimate.**

1. 15% of $38.90 B
2. 15% of $20.79 A
3. 15% of $398 C

A. $3
B. $6
C. $60

4. **Mental Math** Suppose you want to leave a 20% tip for a meal that costs $28. Use a multiple of 10% to calculate the tip. $5.60
5. **Number Sense** Use a decimal other than 0.3 to estimate 28% of 191. Answers may vary. Sample: 0.25 × 200 = 50

Homework Exercises

For more exercises, see Extra Skills and Word Problems.

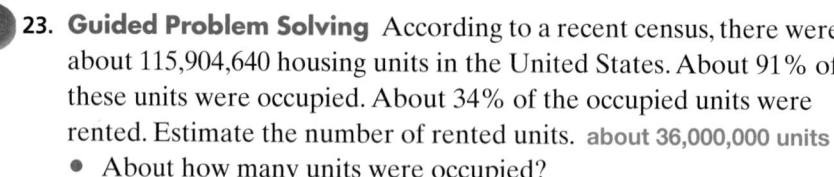

GO for Help

For Exercises	See Examples
6–11	1
12–15	2
16–22	3

A **Use decimals to estimate each percent.**

6. 9% of 9 about 1
7. 63% of 62 about 36
8. 15% of 78 about 12
9. 52% of 492 about 250
10. 38% of 81 about 32
11. 68% of 222 about 140

Use fractions to estimate each percent.

12. 27% of 39 about 10
13. 49.8% of 177 about 90
14. 74.5% of 31 about 24
15. **Student Government** In a recent student council election, 66% of the 310 students voted for the winning candidate. Use fractions to estimate how many students voted for the winner. about 200 students

Mental Math **Estimate a 15% tip for each restaurant bill.**

16. $9.85 about $1.50
17. $12.63 about $1.80
18. $18.20 about $3.00
19. $27.55 about $4.50
20. $31.49 about $4.50
21. $86.96 about $13.50
22. You decide to leave your waiter a 20% tip. Your dinner cost $47.51. Estimate the tip. about $10.00

B **GPS**

23. **Guided Problem Solving** According to a recent census, there were about 115,904,640 housing units in the United States. About 91% of these units were occupied. About 34% of the occupied units were rented. Estimate the number of rented units. about 36,000,000 units
    - About how many units were occupied?
    - Round 34% to a compatible number.
24. **Cities** About 41% of the 13 million people in Guatemala live in cities. Use decimals to estimate how many people live in cities. about 5 million people

GO Online
Homework Video Tutor
Visit: PHSchool.com
Web Code: ase-0502

34. Answers may vary. Sample: An estimate is a good way to check an answer.

Shopping The ad at the left shows the prices of several items on sale at a store. Estimate the discounted price of each item.

25. a pair of jeans about $23
26. a backpack about $21
27. a watch about $22.40

28. **Error Analysis** Your friend estimates that a 15% tip on a $41.28 bill is $2.50. Is this a reasonable estimate? Explain. No; 15% of $41.28 is about $4 + $2 = $6.

Number Sense Use <, >, or = to complete each statement.

29. $85\% \blacksquare \frac{5}{6}$ >
30. 15% of 24 ■ 20% of 18 =
31. 10% of 156 ■ 1% of 1,025 >
32. 9% of 57 ■ 5% of 47 >

33. **Blood Types** About 40% of Americans have type A blood. (GPS) Suppose there are about 301,421,900 Americans. Estimate how many Americans have type A blood. about 121,000,000 Americans

34. **Writing in Math** Explain why it is helpful to estimate with percents even when you are finding the exact answer. See margin.

(C) 35. **Challenge** The average person's daily caloric intake is about 2,000 Calories. You have eaten a blueberry muffin (135 Calories) and a banana (105 Calories) for breakfast, and a bag of pretzels for a snack. Suppose you have consumed 24% of your daily caloric intake. Estimate how many Calories were in the bag of pretzels. about 240 Calories

Test Prep and Mixed Review

Practice

Multiple Choice

36. In a recent city election, 66.7% of the registered voters in the city voted. If there were 717,449 registered voters in the city, about how many people voted in the election? C
    - (A) 47,853,848
    - (B) 1,195,987
    - (C) 478,538
    - (D) 238,911

37. Which equation can be represented by the line shown in the graph? H
    - (F) $y = -3x + 1$
    - (G) $y = x - \frac{1}{3}$
    - (H) $y = -\frac{1}{3}x + 1$
    - (J) $y = 3x + 1$

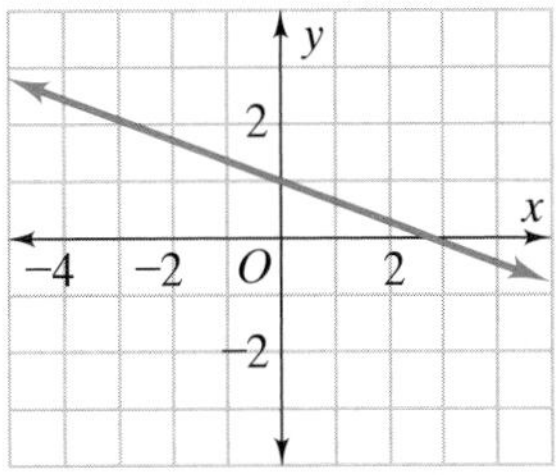

38. Ashley's class is using a microscope to study an insect. The insect is 8.2×10^{-4} meters long. What is this number in standard form? B
    - (A) 0.000082
    - (B) 0.00082
    - (C) 82,000
    - (D) 820,000

GO for Help

For Exercises	See Lesson
39–40	3-6

A point and its image are given. Write a rule to describe each translation.

39. $Q(-4, -3)$, $Q'(0, 2)$ $(x, y) \rightarrow (x + 4, y + 5)$
40. $R(6, -5)$, $R'(-7, 0)$ $(x, y) \rightarrow (x - 13, y + 5)$

Online lesson quiz, PHSchool.com, Web Code: asa-0502

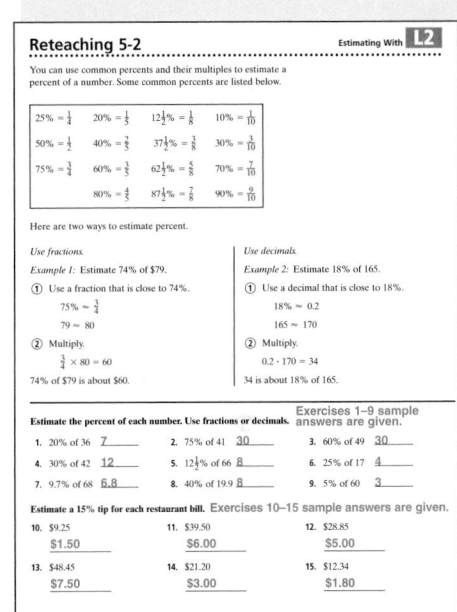

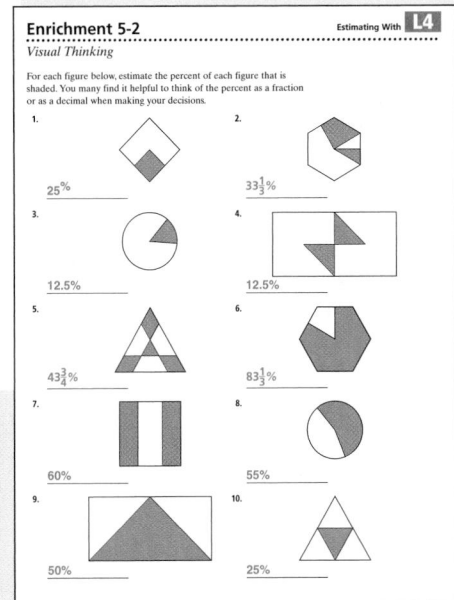

Alternative Assessment

Students estimate what percent of the class is male and what percent of the class is female.

Test Prep

Resources

For additional practice with a variety of test item formats:

- Test-Taking Strategies, p. 251
- Test Prep, p. 255
- Test-Taking Strategies with Transparencies

4. Assess & Reteach

PowerPoint

Lesson Quiz

Show the numbers you use to estimate. Numbers used may vary. Samples are given.

1. Use decimals to estimate 54% of 29. $0.5 \cdot 30 = 15$
2. Use fractions to estimate 74% of 38. $\frac{3}{4} \cdot 40 = 30$
3. Estimate a 15% tip on $8.15. $0.1(8) + 0.1(4) = 0.8 + 0.4 = \$1.20$
4. About 60% of 27 students are in the play. $\frac{3}{5}(30) = 18$ students or $0.6 \cdot 30 = 18$

Reteaching 5-2

Estimating With **L2**

You can use common percents and their multiples to estimate a percent of a number. Some common percents are listed below.

$25\% = \frac{1}{4}$	$20\% = \frac{1}{5}$	$12\frac{1}{2}\% = \frac{1}{8}$	$10\% = \frac{1}{10}$
$50\% = \frac{1}{2}$	$40\% = \frac{2}{5}$	$37\frac{1}{2}\% = \frac{3}{8}$	$30\% = \frac{3}{10}$
$75\% = \frac{3}{4}$	$60\% = \frac{3}{5}$	$62\frac{1}{2}\% = \frac{5}{8}$	$70\% = \frac{7}{10}$
	$80\% = \frac{4}{5}$	$87\frac{1}{2}\% = \frac{7}{8}$	$90\% = \frac{9}{10}$

Here are two ways to estimate percent.

Use fractions.

Example 1: Estimate 74% of $79.

① Use a fraction that is close to 74%.

$75\% \approx \frac{3}{4}$

$79 \approx 80$

② Multiply.

$\frac{3}{4} \times 80 = 60$

74% of $79 is about $60.

Use decimals.

Example 2: Estimate 18% of 165.

① Use a decimal that is close to 18%.

$18\% \approx 0.2$

$165 \approx 170$

② Multiply.

$0.2 \cdot 170 = 34$

34 is about 18% of 165.

Estimate the percent of each number. Use fractions or decimals. Exercises 1–9 sample answers are given.

1. 20% of 36 7
2. 75% of 41 30
3. 60% of 49 30
4. 30% of 42 12
5. $12\frac{1}{2}\%$ of 66 8
6. 25% of 17 4
7. 9.7% of 68 6.8
8. 40% of 19.9 8
9. 5% of 60 3

Estimate a 15% tip for each restaurant bill. Exercises 10–15 sample answers are given.

10. $9.25 $1.50
11. $39.50 $6.00
12. $28.85 $5.00
13. $48.45 $7.50
14. $21.20 $3.00
15. $12.34 $1.80

Enrichment 5-2

Estimating With **L4**

Visual Thinking

For each figure below, estimate the percent of each figure that is shaded. You many find it helpful to think of the percent as a fraction or as a decimal when making your decisions.

1.  25%
2. 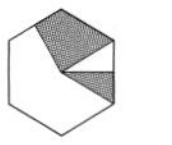 $33\frac{1}{3}\%$
3.  12.5%
4. 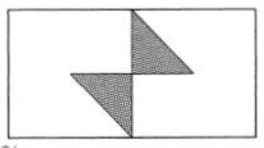 12.5%
5.  $43\frac{3}{4}\%$
6. 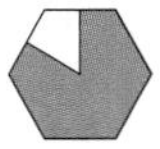 $83\frac{1}{3}\%$
7.  60%
8. 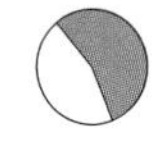 55%
9. 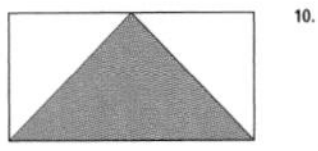 50%
10. 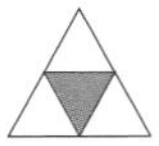 25%

5-3

1. Plan

Objective
To use proportions to find part of a whole, a whole amount, or a percent

Examples
1 Finding Part of a Whole
2 Finding Percents Greater Than 100%
3 Finding a Whole Amount
4 Finding a Percent

Math Understandings: p. 208C

Professional Development

Math Background

Finding the percent of a number means finding a portion of the number that is proportional to the percent. For example, calculating 45% of 16.8 involves solving the following proportion for x: $\frac{45}{100} = \frac{x}{16.8}$. The same is true for percents greater than 100: 245% of 16.8 equals x in the proportion $\frac{245}{100} = \frac{x}{16.8}$. If the portion and the percent of the whole that it represents are known, another proportion can be used to find the whole. For instance, if 3.1 is 67% of a number, the number can be found by solving for x in the following proportion: $\frac{67}{100} = \frac{3.1}{x}$.

More Math Background: p. 208C

Lesson Planning and Resources

See p. 208E for a list of the resources that support this lesson.

PowerPoint

Bell Ringer Practice

Check Skills You'll Need
Use student page, transparency, or PowerPoint. For intervention, direct students to:
Solving Proportions
Lesson 4-3
Extra Skills and Word Problems Practice, Ch. 4

Algebra

5-3 Percents and Proportions

Check Skills You'll Need

1. **Vocabulary Review** Two equal ratios form a ? . proportion

Solve each proportion.

2. $\frac{4}{b} = \frac{20}{100}$ 20
3. $\frac{8}{12} = \frac{e}{100}$ $66\frac{2}{3}$
4. $\frac{240}{n} = \frac{12}{5}$ 100
5. $\frac{s}{4} = \frac{75}{100}$ 3
6. $\frac{6}{y} = \frac{24}{100}$ 25

GO for Help Lesson 4-3

What You'll Learn
To use proportions to find part of a whole, a whole amount, or a percent

Why Learn This?
Large groups, such as an orchestra, are divided into sections. Percents and proportions can help you understand the relationship between the size of sections and the whole group.

When using percents, you can use a diagram to show the relationship between a part and the whole.

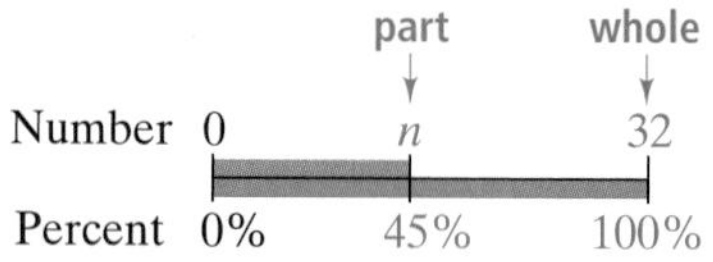

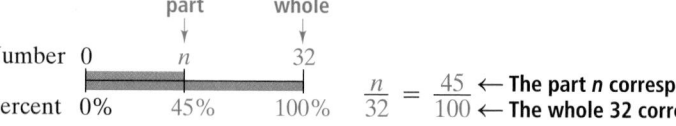

$\frac{n}{32} = \frac{45}{100}$ ← The part n corresponds to 45%. ← The whole 32 corresponds to 100%.

EXAMPLE Finding Part of a Whole

1 Find 45% of 32.

$\frac{n}{32} = \frac{45}{100}$ ← Write a proportion.
$100n = 45 \cdot 32$ ← Write the cross products.
$100n = 1{,}440$ ← Simplify.
$\frac{100n}{100} = \frac{1{,}440}{100}$ ← Divide each side by 100.
$n = 14.4$ ← Simplify.

45% of 32 is 14.4.

Calculator Tip
When using a calculator to solve the proportion $\frac{n}{32} = \frac{45}{100}$, use the calculator-ready form $n = \frac{45 \cdot 32}{100}$.

Quick Check

1. Use a proportion to find 74% of 95. 70.3

Some problems include percents that are greater than 100%. In these cases, the part is greater than the whole.

Differentiated Instruction Solutions for All Learners

Special Needs L1	Below Level L2
Many students frequently make errors setting up proportions. Students use a diagram, like those used in the Examples, to set up their proportions until they can set up the correct proportions without the diagram. **learning style: visual**	Students make a rough estimate of the answer first as an aid to catching errors in setting up a proportion. **learning style: verbal**

EXAMPLE Finding Percents Greater Than 100%

2 Bills This month's heating bill is 130% of last month's bill. Last month's bill was \$46. Find 130% of 46.

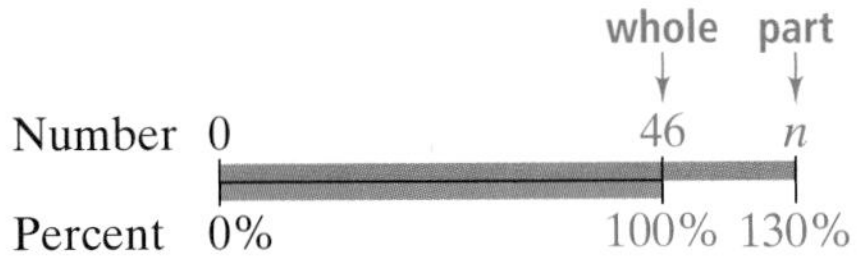

← A diagram can help you understand the problem.

$\frac{n}{46} = \frac{130}{100}$ ← Write a proportion.

$100n = 130 \cdot 46$ ← Write the cross products.

$100n = 5{,}980$ ← Simplify.

$\frac{100n}{100} = \frac{5{,}980}{100}$ ← Divide each side by 100.

$n = 59.8$ ← Simplify.

This month's bill is \$59.80.

Quick Check

2. Use a proportion to find 235% of 85. 199.75

Video Tutor Help
Visit: PHSchool.com
Web Code: ase-0775

If you know the percent a part represents, you can find the whole.

EXAMPLE Finding a Whole Amount

3 Orchestra About 35% of an orchestra's musicians, or 30 members, are violin players. Find the total number of musicians in the orchestra.

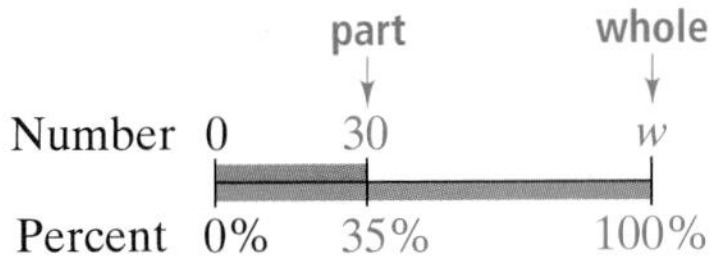

← A diagram can help you understand the problem.

$\frac{30}{w} = \frac{35}{100}$ ← Write a proportion.

$30 \cdot 100 = 35w$ ← Write the cross products.

$3{,}000 = 35w$ ← Simplify.

$\frac{3{,}000}{35} = \frac{35w}{35}$ ← Divide each side by 35.

$w = 85.71428571$ ← Use a calculator.

There are about 86 musicians in the orchestra.

Quick Check

3. About 40% of students in a school, or 110 students, are in an after-school program. How many students are in the school? 275 students

2. Teach

Activity Lab

Use before the lesson.

All in One Teaching Resources

Activity Lab 5-3: Percents and Proportions

Guided Instruction

Suggest that students say aloud to themselves, as they begin a problem, the basic proportion: *part divided by the whole equals percent divided by 100.* This strategy helps auditory learners and reminds all students that they need to identify the part, the whole, and the percent in each problem.

Example 2

Finding 200% of a number is the same as multiplying that number by 2. For example, to find 200% of 16.89, solve the proportion $\frac{x}{16.89} = \frac{200}{100}$ or $\frac{x}{16.89} = 2$. Then $x = 2 \times 16.89 = 33.78$. So another way students can find 235% of 85 is to calculate 35% of 85 and add this to 85×2.

PowerPoint

Additional Examples

1. Find 32% of 240. 76.8

2. Brenda saw a blender for \$24 in a bargain store. In a second store, the same blender was 160% of the cost of the blender in the bargain store. Find 160% of \$24. \$38.40

3. Suppose 11,550 elementary students make up 14% of a city's population. What is the population of the city? 82,500 people

Advanced Learners L4

Students calculate very large and small percents such as these:

What is 1,245% of 83? 1,033.35
What percent is 0.125 of 6.25? 2%
0.935 is 18.7% of what number? 5

learning style: verbal

English Language Learners ELL

Make sure students understand the difference between "cross products" and products of two fractions. Use an example to show that cross products can be found only when two fractions are **equal** to each other. Compare this with an example of two fractions multiplied.

learning style: verbal

Guided Instruction

Error Prevention!

Emphasize that the problem must be in the form of a proportion to cross multiply. Ask students to identify both examples (such as $\frac{4}{a} = \frac{b}{5}$) and counterexamples (such as $\frac{4}{a} + 1 = \frac{b}{5}$).

Also point out that, in the proportion, $\frac{\text{part}}{\text{whole}} = \frac{\text{percent}}{100}$, the percent is written, for example, as 30 and not as 30%. The % symbol has already been written by $\frac{\blacksquare}{100}$.

Alternative Method
Show students how to use four index cards to set up the proportion in Example 4. Write "105", "200", "*p*", and "100", each on one card. Arrange the cards to form the proportion. Then students can regroup the cards to show the cross-multiplication.

PowerPoint

Additional Examples

4 26 is what percent of 80?
32.5%

All in One Teaching Resources
- Daily Notetaking Guide 5-3 L3
- Adapted Notetaking 5-3 L1

Closure

- *State the proportion, in words, that you can use to solve percent problems.*
$\frac{\text{part}}{\text{whole}} = \frac{\text{percent}}{100}$; part divided by whole equals percent divided by 100

Test Prep Tip
Before solving a problem, check to make sure you set up the proportion correctly.

EXAMPLE Finding a Percent

4 105 is what percent of 200?

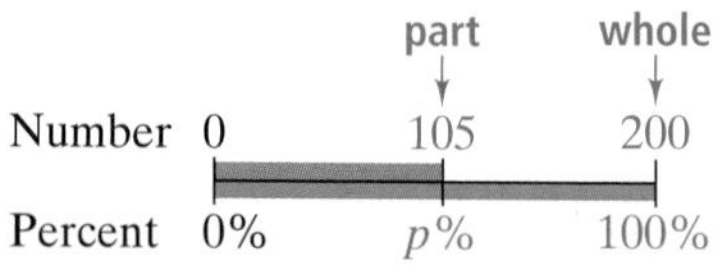

← **A diagram can help you understand the problem.**

$\frac{105}{200} = \frac{p}{100}$ ← **Write a proportion.**

$\frac{105 \div 2}{200 \div 2} = \frac{p}{100}$ ← **Use number sense to find a common divisor.**

$52.5\% = p$ ← **Divide 105 by 2 to find *p*.**

Check for Reasonableness 105 is about 100 and 100 is half of 200. Since $\frac{1}{2}$ is 50%, which is close to 52.5%, the answer is reasonable. ✔

Quick Check

4. 36 is what percent of 180? 20%

Online active math

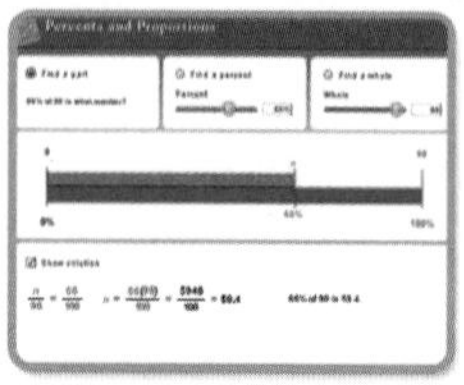

For: Percents and Proportions Activity
Use: Interactive Textbook, 5-3

You can use the following proportion to solve percent problems.

$$\frac{\text{part}}{\text{whole}} = \text{percent (written as a fraction)}$$

KEY CONCEPTS Percents and Proportions

Finding the Part	Finding the Whole	Finding the Percent
What number is 20% of 25?	5 is 20% of what number?	5 is what percent of 25?
$\frac{n}{25} = \frac{20}{100}$	$\frac{5}{w} = \frac{20}{100}$	$\frac{5}{25} = \frac{p}{100}$

Check Your Understanding

1.
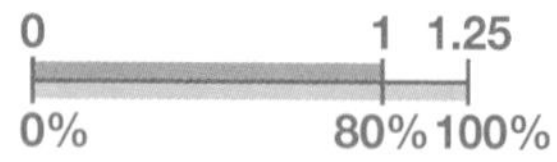

1. Draw a diagram to represent the percent of 1.25 that is 1.

Match each problem with the correct proportion.

2. 5 is 42% of what number? B

3. What number is 5% of 42? C

4. 5 is what percent of 42? A

A. $\frac{5}{42} = \frac{x}{100}$

B. $\frac{5}{y} = \frac{42}{100}$

C. $\frac{z}{42} = \frac{5}{100}$

Homework Exercises

For more exercises, see Extra Skills and Word Problems.

GO for Help

For Exercises	See Examples
5–17	1–2
18–24	3
25–30	4

A **Use a proportion to find the given percent of each number. A diagram may be helpful.**

5. 80% of 72 57.6
6. 3% of 48 1.44
7. 60% of 55 33
8. 38% of 50 19
9. 12% of 46 5.52
10. 26% of 65 16.9
11. 345% of 24 82.8
12. 200% of 24 48
13. 150% of 3 4.5
14. 275% of 60 165
15. 734% of 75 550.5
16. 195% of 66 128.7
17. **Shopping** Last month you spent \$87 on clothing. This month you spent 165% of what you spent last month. Find 165% of \$87. \$143.55

Use a proportion to solve each problem. A diagram may be helpful.

18. 6 is 80% of what number? 7.5
19. 3 is 60% of what number? 5
20. 74 is 32% of what number? 231.25
21. 38 is 4% of what number? 950
22. 120 is 48% of what number? 250
23. 150 is 25% of what number? 600
24. In one school, about 56% of the eighth-graders, or 140 students, have brown hair. How many students are in the eighth grade? 250 students

Use a proportion to solve each problem. A diagram may be helpful.

25. What percent of 25 is 16? 64%
26. 20 is what percent of 160? 12.5%
27. What percent of 300 is 12? 4%
28. 18 is what percent of 45? 40%
29. What percent of 64 is 24? 37.5%
30. What percent of 12 is 96? 800%

GPS **B**

31. **Guided Problem Solving** In an election with two candidates, the winner received about 72.2% of the 214,082 votes cast. By how many votes did the winning candidate win? 95,052 votes
    - Begin by finding the number of votes cast for the winner.

    Words: $\frac{\text{\% of winner's votes}}{\text{total \% of votes}} = \frac{\text{number of votes cast for winning candidate}}{\text{total number of votes cast}}$

    Proportion: $\frac{72.2}{100} = \frac{x}{\blacksquare}$

32. **Collections** The Library of Congress has more than 5 million maps. Maps make up just 3.75% of the library's entire collection of items. How many items does the Library of Congress have? about 133 million items
33. **Reasoning** Explain how a percent can be greater than 100. See above left.
34. **Number Sense** If x% of y is 15, then what is y% of x? 15
35. **Writing in Math** Explain why researchers often use percents to report their findings. See above left.

33. Answers may vary. Sample: A "whole" is an arbitrary number, and you can have a "part" that is more than that arbitrary number.

35. Answers may vary. Sample: Percents let you compare relative sizes.

GO Online
Homework Video Tutor
Visit: PHSchool.com
Web Code: ase-0503

Online lesson quiz, PHSchool.com, Web Code: asa-0503

3. Practice

Assignment Guide

Check Your Understanding

Go over Exercises 1–4 in class before assigning the Homework Exercises.

Homework Exercises

A	Practice by Example	5–30
B	Apply Your Skills	31–44
C	Challenge	45
	Test Prep and Mixed Review	46–51

Homework Quick Check

To check students' understanding of key skills and concepts, go over Exercises 18, 28, 35, 42, and 44.

Differentiated Instruction Resources

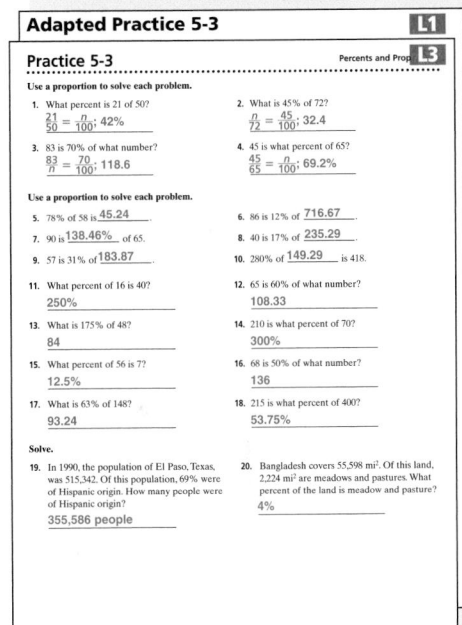

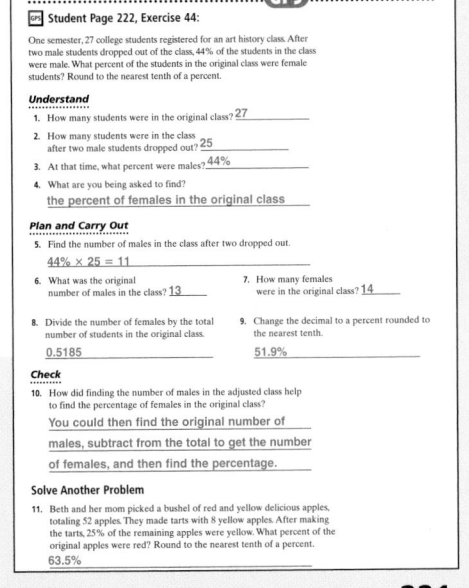

Adapted Practice 5-3 L1

Practice 5-3 Percents and Prop L3

Use a proportion to solve each problem.

1. What percent is 21 of 50? $\frac{21}{50} = \frac{n}{100}$; 42%
2. What is 45% of 72? $\frac{n}{72} = \frac{45}{100}$; 32.4
3. 83 is 70% of what number? $\frac{83}{n} = \frac{70}{100}$; 118.6
4. 45 is what percent of 65? $\frac{45}{65} = \frac{n}{100}$; 69.2%

Use a proportion to solve each problem.

5. 78% of 58 is 45.24.
6. 86 is 12% of 716.67.
7. 90 is 138.46% of 65.
8. 40 is 17% of 235.29.
9. 57 is 31% of 183.87.
10. 280% of 149.29 is 418.
11. What percent of 16 is 40? 250%
12. 65 is 60% of what number? 108.33
13. What is 175% of 48? 84
14. 210 is what percent of 70? 300%
15. What percent of 56 is 7? 12.5%
16. 68 is 50% of what number? 136
17. What is 63% of 148? 93.24
18. 215 is what percent of 400? 53.75%

Solve.

19. In 1990, the population of El Paso, Texas, was 515,342. Of this population, 69% were of Hispanic origin. How many people were of Hispanic origin? 355,586 people
20. Bangladesh covers 55,598 mi^2. Of this land, 2,224 mi^2 are meadows and pastures. What percent of the land is meadow and pasture? 4%

5-3 • Guided Problem Solving GPS L3

GPS **Student Page 222, Exercise 44:**

One semester, 27 college students registered for an art history class. After two male students dropped out of the class, 44% of the students in the class were male. What percent of the students in the original class were female students? Round to the nearest tenth of a percent.

Understand

1. How many students were in the original class? 27
2. How many students were in the class after two male students dropped out? 25
3. At that time, what percent were males? 44%
4. What are you being asked to find? the percent of females in the original class

Plan and Carry Out

5. Find the number of males in the class after two dropped out. 44% × 25 = 11
6. What was the original number of males in the class? 13
7. How many females were in the original class? 14
8. Divide the number of females by the total number of students in the original class. 0.5185
9. Change the decimal to a percent rounded to the nearest tenth. 51.9%

Check

10. How did finding the number of males in the adjusted class help to find the percentage of females in the original class? You could then find the original number of males, subtract from the total to get the number of females, and then find the percentage.

Solve Another Problem

11. Beth and her mom picked a bushel of red and yellow delicious apples, totaling 52 apples. They made tarts with 8 yellow apples. After making the tarts, 25% of the remaining apples were yellow. What percent of the original apples were red? Round to the nearest tenth of a percent. 63.5%

4. Assess & Reteach

PowerPoint

Lesson Quiz

1. Find 25% of 160. 40
2. The price of a music CD is \$12. If the store raises the price to 125% of its current price, what will be the new price of the CD? \$15
3. So far, the sixth grade class has sold 32 tickets to their play. The number represents 20% of the tickets that are available. How many tickets are available? 160
4. 98 is what percent of 56? 175%

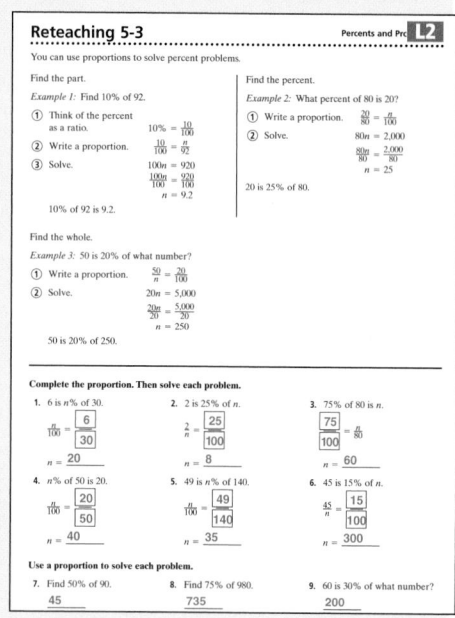

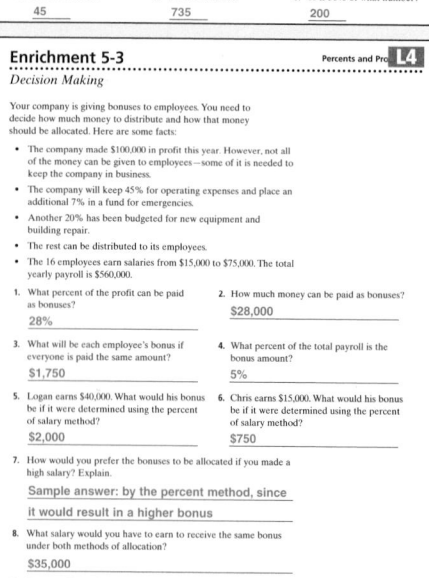

Reteaching 5-3

Percents and Pro L2

You can use proportions to solve percent problems.

Find the part.

Example 1: Find 10% of 92.

① Think of the percent as a ratio. $10\% = \frac{10}{100}$

② Write a proportion. $\frac{10}{100} = \frac{n}{92}$

③ Solve. $100n = 920$

$\frac{100n}{100} = \frac{920}{100}$

$n = 9.2$

10% of 92 is 9.2.

Find the percent.

Example 2: What percent of 80 is 20?

① Write a proportion. $\frac{20}{80} = \frac{n}{100}$

② Solve. $80n = 2{,}000$

$\frac{80n}{80} = \frac{2{,}000}{80}$

$n = 25$

20 is 25% of 80.

Find the whole.

Example 3: 50 is 20% of what number?

① Write a proportion. $\frac{50}{n} = \frac{20}{100}$

② Solve. $20n = 5{,}000$

$\frac{20n}{20} = \frac{5{,}000}{20}$

$n = 250$

50 is 20% of 250.

Complete the proportion. Then solve each problem.

1. 6 is n% of 30. $\frac{n}{100} = \frac{6}{30}$ $n =$ 20
2. 2 is 25% of n. $\frac{2}{n} = \frac{25}{100}$ $n =$ 8
3. 75% of 80 is n. $\frac{75}{100} = \frac{n}{80}$ $n =$ 60
4. n% of 50 is 20. $\frac{n}{100} = \frac{20}{50}$ $n =$ 40
5. 49 is n% of 140. $\frac{n}{100} = \frac{49}{140}$ $n =$ 35
6. 45 is 15% of n. $\frac{45}{n} = \frac{15}{100}$ $n =$ 300

Use a proportion to solve each problem.

7. Find 50% of 90. 45
8. Find 75% of 980. 735
9. 60 is 30% of what number? 200

Enrichment 5-3

Percents and Pro L4

Decision Making

Your company is giving bonuses to employees. You need to decide how much money to distribute and how that money should be allocated. Here are some facts:

- The company made \$100,000 in profit this year. However, not all of the money can be given to employees—some of it is needed to keep the company in business.
- The company will keep 45% for operating expenses and place an additional 7% in a fund for emergencies.
- Another 20% has been budgeted for new equipment and building repair.
- The rest can be distributed to its employees.
- The 16 employees earn salaries from \$15,000 to \$75,000. The total yearly payroll is \$560,000.

1. What percent of the profit can be paid as bonuses? 28%
2. How much money can be paid as bonuses? \$28,000
3. What will be each employee's bonus if everyone is paid the same amount? \$1,750
4. What percent of the total payroll is the bonus amount? 5%
5. Logan earns \$40,000. What would his bonus be if it were determined using the percent of salary method? \$2,000
6. Chris earns \$15,000. What would his bonus be if it were determined using the percent of salary method? \$750
7. How would you prefer the bonuses to be allocated if you made a high salary? Explain. Sample answer: by the percent method, since it would result in a higher bonus
8. What salary would you have to earn to receive the same bonus under both methods of allocation? \$35,000
9. How would you allocate the bonuses? Why did you choose that way? Sample answer: by the straight dollar amount, since it recognizes everyone's contribution equally.

Use a proportion to solve each problem.

36. Find 0.025% of 120. 0.03
37. Find 1,342% of 5,678. 76,198.76
38. 99.6 is 200% of what number? 49.8
39. 1.8 is 30% of what number? 6
40. Find 0.108% of 1,375. 1.485
41. Find 234% of 468. 1,095.12

42. **Geography** Rhode Island's area is 1,231 square miles. Indiana's area is about 2,958.6% of Rhode Island's area. Indiana's area is about 0.98% of the area of the United States. Find the area of the United States. about 3,716,363.9 mi^2
43. **Error Analysis** A student said that 40 percent of one number plus 30 percent of another number is the same as 70 percent of the sum of the two numbers. Do you agree? Explain. See margin.
44. GPS One semester, 27 college students registered for an art history class. After two male students dropped out of the class, 44% of the students in the class were male. What percent of the students in the original class were female? Round to the nearest tenth of a percent. 51.9%
45. C **Challenge** A meter is what percent of a centimeter? 10,000%

Test Prep and Mixed Review

Practice

Multiple Choice

46. A recent survey was done of the shopping habits of 500 households. The graph shows the day those surveyed did their major shopping. Based on the results, how many more households did their major shopping on Saturday than on Sunday? B

Days People Shop

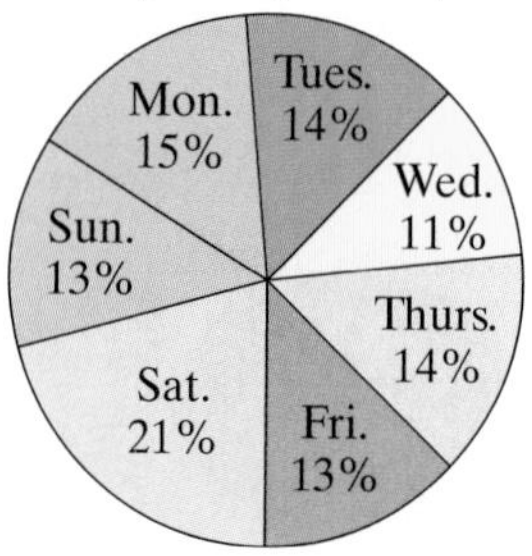

Ⓐ 10 Ⓑ 40 Ⓒ 100 Ⓓ 400

47. A quality-control inspector found that 3 out of every 45 radios produced on his assembly line were defective. About what percent of the radios were NOT defective? H

Ⓕ 7% Ⓖ 67% Ⓗ 93% Ⓙ 135%

48. Jada bought 12 bottles of water for \$2.99. Which expression can be used to find the cost of 60 bottles of water? A

Ⓐ 2.99 · 5 Ⓑ 2.99 · 12 Ⓒ 35.88 · 12 Ⓓ 35.88 · 60

GO for Help

For Exercises	See Lesson
49–51	4-2

Write each ratio in simplest form.

49. 10 cm : 25 m 1 cm : 250 cm
50. $\frac{16 \text{ in.}}{2 \text{ ft}}$ $\frac{2 \text{ in.}}{3 \text{ in.}}$
51. $\frac{35 \text{ oz}}{5 \text{ lb}}$ $\frac{7 \text{ oz}}{16 \text{ oz}}$

Test Prep

Resources

For additional practice with a variety of test item formats:

- Test-Taking Strategies, p. 251
- Test Prep, p. 255
- Test-Taking Strategies with Transparencies

Alternative Assessment

Each student in a pair writes a number. They each write their partner's number to find what percent their number is of their partner's number.

43. No; for example, if the two numbers are 100 and 200, then (40% of 100) + (30% of 200) = 40 + 60 = 100, but 70% of 300 = 210.

Percents and Graphs

Graphs and percents can be used to represent and compare information. When you analyze data, you have to be careful that the data are not misrepresented.

ACTIVITY

The bar graph at the right shows the results of a survey of what type of music students listen to. Notice that the horizontal scale does not start at 0.

What Music Do You Listen To?

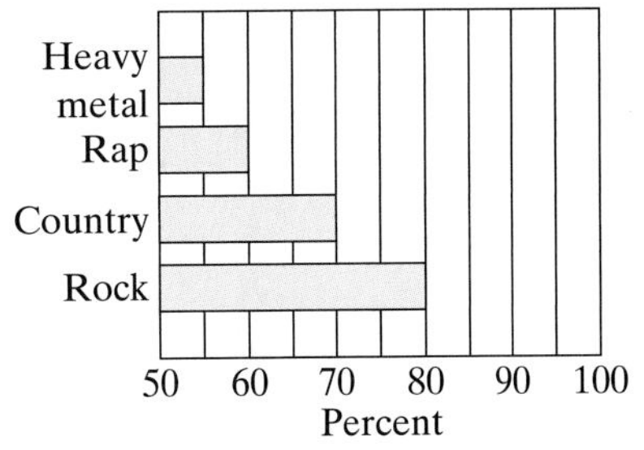

1. Redraw the graph. Use a vertical scale starting at 0. See margin.
2. Explain how the new graph represents the data more clearly. See right.

2. Answers may vary. Sample: The original graph made it appear that there were large differences in the data; the new graph shows that they're much closer.

The table below shows the results of a survey asking students whether they would attend a school barbecue.

Barbecue Survey Results

Answer	Number
Yes	62
Maybe	32
No	26

3. Calculate the percent of student responses for each answer category and use this information to make a bar graph. See margin.
4. Suppose 320 students were asked, but only 120 students responded to the survey. Draw a new graph based on the total number of students who were asked. See margin.
5. **Reasoning** How does knowing that 200 students didn't respond change your interpretation of the data? See margin.

The table at the right shows the number of free throws made by four members of a basketball team.

Free-Throw Results

Player	Shots	Baskets
Anna	50	35
Carla	20	12
Nikki	5	4
Raylene	40	30

6. Calculate the free-throw percentage for each student. Show the results in a bar graph. See margin.
7. According to your graph, which player has the best free-throw percentage? Nikki
8. **Writing in Math** Is this player necessarily the best free-throw shooter in the group? Explain. See margin.

Activity Lab

Percents and Graphs

Students analyze and use graphs and data tables to explore if and how data and data displays can be used to misrepresent information.

Guided Instruction

Activity

Call attention to the bar graph displaying musical preferences. Ask: *If you look only at the bars in the graph, about how much more popular does rock music appear to be than rap music?* Sample: about three times as popular *What is the actual difference in the percent popularity of rap and rock music?* 60% rap and 80% rock, a difference of 20% Elicit the fact from students that beginning a graph at zero, with no break, helps to put the data in perspective.

Teaching Tip

Have students find the percent of students who answer "yes" to attending a barbeque by first using the total number of students surveyed, $\frac{62}{320} \approx 19\%$. Then have them use the number who actually answered the survey, $\frac{62}{120} \approx 52\%$. Have them share how their interpretation of the data changes with how the data is presented.

Exercises

Remind students that the free-throw percentage is computed by dividing the number of free throws made (baskets) by the number of attempts (shots).

Resources

- graph paper

1. See back of book.
3. See back of book.
4.

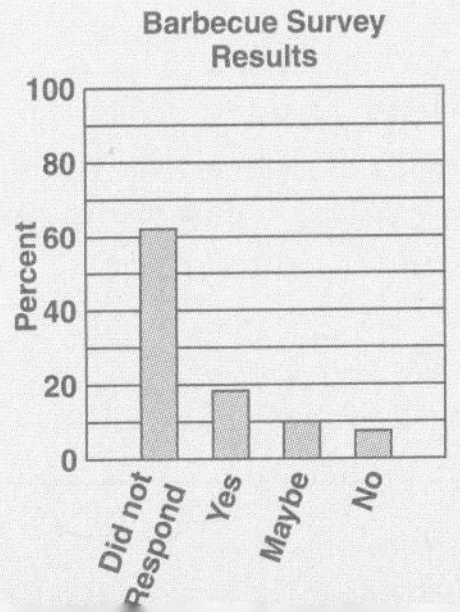

5. Answers may vary. Sample: Without knowing that 200 students did not respond, it seemed that most of the students said yes. Knowing that 200 students did not respond, you can see that very few of the students said yes.
6. See back of book.
8. No; she only shot 5 times, so there is not enough data to support the statement that she is the best.

5-4

1. Plan

Objective
To use equations to solve problems involving percent

Examples
1 Finding Part of a Whole
2 Finding a Whole Amount

Math Understandings: p. 208C

Professional Development

Math Background

The vocabulary associated with percents may be a source of some confusion. The part of the whole has sometimes been called the *percentage*. Use the words *part* and *whole* for clarity, but make sure students understand that in percent problems, the part may be greater than the whole.

More Math Background: p. 208C

Lesson Planning and Resources

See p. 208E for a list of the resources that support this lesson.

PowerPoint

Bell Ringer Practice

Check Skills You'll Need
Use student page, transparency, or PowerPoint. For intervention, direct students to:
Solving Equations by Multiplying and Dividing
Lesson 1-7
Extra Skills and Word Problems Practice, Ch. 1

Algebra

5-4 Percents and Equations

Check Skills You'll Need

1. **Vocabulary Review** Is $2 \cdot 8 = 16$ an *equation* or an *expression*? Explain. See below.

Solve each equation.

2. $0.25p = 10$ 40
3. $12.25 = 9.8x$ 1.25
4. $24 = 1.6s$ 15
5. $0.64k = 0.02$ 0.03125

GO for Help Lesson 1-7

Check Skills You'll Need

1. Equation; it contains an = sign.

What You'll Learn

To use equations to solve problems involving percents

Why Learn This?

The sales tax on an item is a percent of the item's cost. Understanding percents helps you calculate the total price of your purchases.

You can use the relationship between the part and the whole to solve various kinds of problems.

KEY CONCEPTS Percent Equations

Finding the Part	Finding the Whole	Finding the Percent
part = $P \cdot$ whole	part = $P \cdot$ whole	part = $P \cdot$ whole
What is 20% of 25?	5 is 20% of what?	5 is what percent of 25?
$n = 0.20 \cdot 25$	$5 = 0.20 \cdot w$	$5 = P \cdot 25$

EXAMPLE Finding Part of a Whole

1 **Sales Tax** A hair dryer costs \$22. The sales tax rate is 4.9%. Find the amount of sales tax.

Let t = the amount of sales tax.

part = $P \cdot$ whole ← Use the percent equation.
$t = 0.049 \cdot 22$ ← Substitute.
$t = 1.078 \approx 1.08$ ← Simplify. Round to the nearest cent.

The sales tax is about \$1.08.

Check for Reasonableness 4.9% of 22 ≈ 5% of 20. Since 5% of 20 is 1, which is close to 1.08, the answer is reasonable. ✔

Quick Check

1. A bike costs \$195.99 plus 6% for sales tax. Find the amount of tax. \$11.76

Differentiated Instruction Solutions for All Learners

Special Needs L1	Below Level L2
Students make sense of the answer to the *More than One Way* example: Since 100% is about 5 times 22.1%, the total trash should be about 5 times 372.3. If students multiply by 5, their total is a bit more than the answer 1,684 pounds. learning style: verbal	Students write three problems and the equation needed to solve them, one of each type: finding part, whole, and percent. learning style: verbal

Test Prep Tip

To write a percent as a decimal, divide the percent by 100, or move the decimal point two places to the left.

EXAMPLE Finding a Whole Amount

2 60 is 48% of what number?

$60 = 0.48 \cdot w$ ← **Write a percent equation.**

$\frac{60}{0.48} = \frac{0.48w}{0.48}$ ← **Divide each side by 0.48.**

$125 = w$ ← **Simplify.**

Quick Check

2. Using an equation, 18% of what number is 16.2? 90

More Than One Way

The average American recycles 372.3 lb, or 22.1%, of his or her trash per year. How much trash does the average American generate per year?

Tina's Method

I can use a percent equation. Let t = pounds of trash generated.

$372.3 = 0.221 \cdot t$ ← **Write a percent equation.**

$\frac{372.3}{0.221} = \frac{0.221t}{0.221}$ ← **Divide each side by 0.221.**

372.3 ÷ 0.221 = 1684.615385 ← **Use a calculator.**

The average American generates about 1,684.6 lb of trash each year.

Kevin's Method

I can use a proportion. Let t = pounds of trash generated.

$\frac{372.3}{t} = \frac{22.1}{100}$ ← **Write a proportion.**

$37{,}230 = 22.1t$ ← **Write the cross product.**

$\frac{37{,}230}{22.1} = \frac{22.1t}{22.1}$ ← **Divide each side.**

37,230 ÷ 22.1 = 1684.615385 ← **Use a calculator.**

Each year, the average American generates about 1,684.6 lb of trash.

Choose a Method

In a recent year, the population of Arkansas was about 2,675,000. This was 12% of the population of Texas. What was the approximate population of Texas that year? Explain why you chose the method you used. About 22, 291, 667 people; check students' work.

Advanced Learners L4

Which is a better deal, having a $5 discount applied before sales tax or after? Justify your answer. before is better: ($10 − $5) · 1.05 = $5.25; after: ($10 · 1.05) − $5 = $5.50

learning style: verbal

English Language Learners ELL

Explain that the amount of sales tax is added to the cost of an item. The total of the cost plus the sales tax is the purchase price.

learning style: verbal

2. Teach

Activity Lab

Use before the lesson.

All in One Teaching Resources

Activity Lab 5-4: Percents

Guided Instruction

Teaching Tip

Emphasize that the P stands for the percent expressed, for example, either as 20% or $\frac{1}{5}$ or 0.20.

Example 2

For tactile learners, provide a concrete model for 60, such as base 10 bars or 60 counters or pennies. Ask students to move the model to show a reasonable estimate for 48%.

Alternative Method

Emphasize that percent means "hundredths." Therefore, 48% means "48 hundredths" and can be written as the fraction $\frac{48}{100}$ or the decimal 0.48. Have students solve Example 2 using the fraction form of 48%. Compare with the use of the decimal form in the book.

PowerPoint

Additional Examples

1 Misha got 84% correct on a 25 problem test. How many did he answer correctly? 21

2 Use an equation. 12 is 8% of what number? 150

All in One Teaching Resources

- Daily Notetaking Guide 5-4 L3
- Adapted Notetaking 5-4 L1

Closure

- *What is the equation you use to find part of a whole amount?* part = P · whole
- *How can you rewrite this equation to find the whole?* whole = $\frac{\text{part}}{P}$
- *How can you rewrite this equation to find the percent?* $P = \frac{\text{part}}{\text{whole}}$

3. Practice

Assignment Guide

Check Your Understanding

Go over Exercises 1–6 in class before assigning the Homework Exercises.

Homework Exercises

A	Practice by Example	7–14
B	Apply Your Skills	15–24
C	Challenge	25
	Test Prep and Mixed Review	26–31

Homework Quick Check

To check students' understanding of key skills and concepts, go over Exercises 8, 13, 17, 18, and 24.

Differentiated Instruction Resources

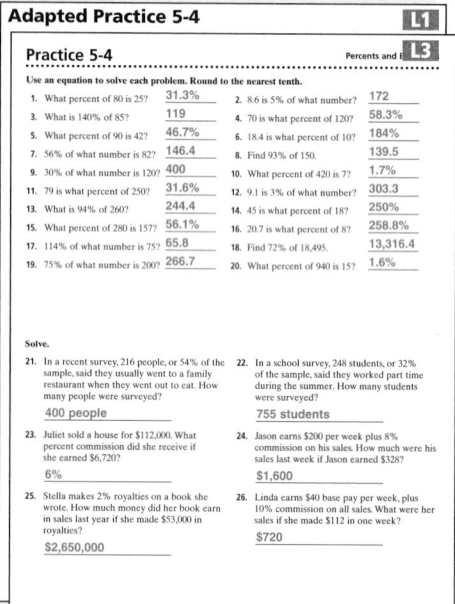

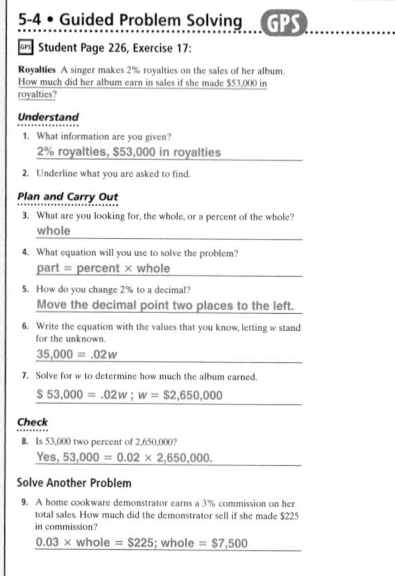

Adapted Practice 5-4 L1

Practice 5-4 Percents and E... L3

Use an equation to solve each problem. Round to the nearest tenth.

1. What percent of 80 is 25? 31.3%
2. 8.6 is 5% of what number? 172
3. What is 140% of 85? 119
4. 70 is what percent of 120? 58.3%
5. What percent of 90 is 42? 46.7%
6. 18.4 is what percent of 10? 184%
7. 56% of what number is 82? 146.4
8. Find 93% of 150. 139.5
9. 30% of what number is 120? 400
10. What percent of 420 is 7? 1.7%
11. 79 is what percent of 250? 31.6%
12. 9.1 is 3% of what number? 303.3
13. What is 94% of 260? 244.4
14. 45 is what percent of 18? 250%
15. What percent of 280 is 157? 56.1%
16. 20.7 is what percent of 8? 258.8%
17. 114% of what number is 75? 65.8
18. Find 72% of 18,495. 13,316.4
19. 75% of what number is 200? 266.7
20. What percent of 940 is 15? 1.6%

Solve.

21. In a recent survey, 216 people, or 54% of the sample, said they usually went to a family restaurant when they went out to eat. How many people were surveyed? 400 people
22. In a school survey, 248 students, or 32% of the sample, said they worked part time during the summer. How many students were surveyed? 755 students
23. Juliet sold a house for $112,000. What percent commission did she receive if she earned $6,720? 6%
24. Jason earns $200 per week plus 8% commission on his sales. How much were his sales last week if Jason earned $328? $1,600
25. Stella makes 2% royalties on a book she wrote. How much money did her book earn in sales last year if she made $53,000 in royalties? $2,650,000
26. Linda earns $40 base pay per week, plus 10% commission on all sales. What were her sales if she made $112 in one week? $720

5-4 • Guided Problem Solving GPS L3

GPS Student Page 226, Exercise 17:

Royalties A singer makes 2% royalties on the sales of her album. How much did her album earn in sales if she made $53,000 in royalties?

Understand

1. What information are you given?
   2% royalties, $53,000 in royalties
2. Underline what you are asked to find.

Plan and Carry Out

3. What are you looking for, the whole, or a percent of the whole?
   whole
4. What equation will you use to solve the problem?
   part = percent × whole
5. How do you change 2% to a decimal?
   Move the decimal point two places to the left.
6. Write the equation with the values that you know, letting *w* stand for the unknown.
   35,000 = .02*w*
7. Solve for *w* to determine how much the album earned.
   $ 53,000 = .02*w* ; *w* = $2,650,000

Check

8. Is 53,000 two percent of 2,650,000?
   Yes, 53,000 = 0.02 × 2,650,000.

Solve Another Problem

9. A home cookware demonstrator earns a 3% commission on her total sales. How much did the demonstrator sell if she made $225 in commission?
   0.03 × whole = $225; whole = $7,500

Check Your Understanding

1. **Mental Math** 12 is 50% of what number? 24

Use an equation to find each percent.

2. 31% of 82 25.42
3. 5% of 28 1.4
4. 27% of 16 4.32
5. A sales tax is 6 cents on the dollar. What is this tax as a percent? 6%
6. **Reasoning** Suppose that 36 is 20% of some number. Is the unknown number greater than or less than 36? Explain.

6. Greater; since 36 represents 20% of the whole, the whole must be greater.

Homework Exercises

For more exercises, see Extra Skills and Word Problems.

GO for Help

For Exercises	See Examples
7–8	1
9–14	2

A

7. **Cell Phones** In 2005, the Pennsylvania sales tax rate was 6%. Find the sales tax paid in Pennsylvania for a $39.99 cellular phone. $2.40
8. A college student buys a $19.95 poster for his dorm room. If the sales tax rate is 4.75%, how much sales tax does the student pay? $.95

Use an equation to solve each problem. Round to the nearest hundredth.

9. 2.8 is 4% of what number? 70
10. 6 is 92% of what number? 6.52
11. 356 is 80% of what number? 445
12. 0.777 is 7% of what number? 11.1
13. 58.5 is 15% of what number? 390
14. 174 is 25% of what number? 696

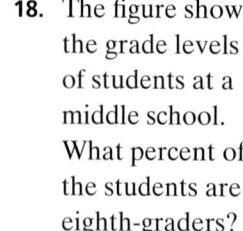

B GPS

15. **Guided Problem Solving** In a recent year, Mississippi's sales tax was 7%. Arizona's tax was 80% of Mississippi's tax. Find the tax on a $25.85 concert ticket in Arizona. $1.45
    - The equation (■)(0.07) = p represents Arizona's sales tax p.
    - Use (■)(25.85) = t to find the tax on the ticket in Arizona.
16. In 1980, about 17.7 million households had cable television. This was about 25.8% of the households that had cable in 2000. How many households had cable in 2000? 68.6 million
17. **Royalties** A singer makes 2% royalties on the sales of her album. GPS How much did her album earn in sales if she made $53,000 in royalties? $2,650,000
18. The figure shows the grade levels of students at a middle school. What percent of the students are eighth-graders?

18. 40.9%

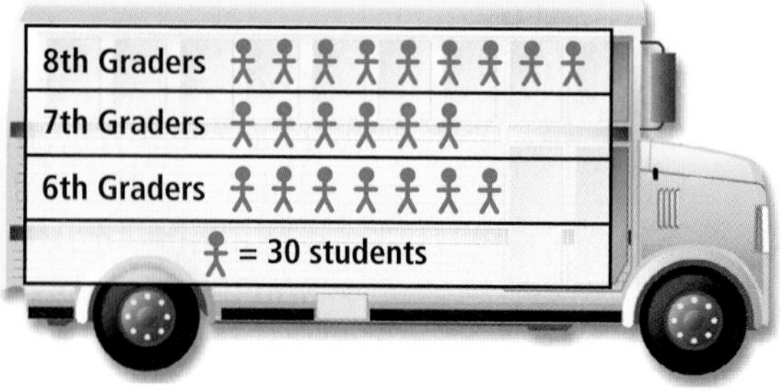

GO Online
Homework Video Tutor
Visit: PHSchool.com
Web Code: ase-0504

Electronics **Use the table below to find the total price (including sales tax) of an $899 television in each state.**

State	Sales-Tax Rate
Kansas	5.3%
North Carolina	4%
Virginia	5%

19. Kansas $946.65

20. North Carolina $934.96

21. Virginia $943.95

22. **Agriculture** About 12,457,350 tons of the oranges harvested in the United States in one year were used to make juice. If 13,113,000 tons of oranges were harvested, what percent were used to make juice? 95%

23. **Choose a Method** In 2000, the population of Hawaii was about 1,200,000 people. The population of Florida in 2000 was about 1,333% of the population of Hawaii. What was the approximate population of Florida in 2000? Explain why you chose the method you used. 15,996,000 people

24. **Writing in Math** Explain two ways you can find 13% of a number. See margin.

(C) 25. **Challenge** Your neighbor bought a remote-controlled car for 20% off the original price of x dollars. The sales tax rate was 6.5%. She later sold the car for 75% of what she paid for it (including the tax). Write an equation for the amount your neighbor received for the car. $0.75(0.8x)(1.065)$

Test Prep and Mixed Review

Practice

Multiple Choice

26. A local television station devotes about 15% of its prime-time programming to commercials. How many minutes of commercials air in each hour of prime-time programming? B

    (A) 4 min (B) 9 min (C) 12 min (D) 15 min

27. Gary bought a couch for $899.99 and a coffee table for $119.99, including tax. He is going to pay the total amount over a 2-year period. What is a reasonable amount for each monthly payment? F

    (F) $43.00 (G) $54.00 (H) $65.00 (J) $85.00

28. The triangles shown below are similar. Find x. A

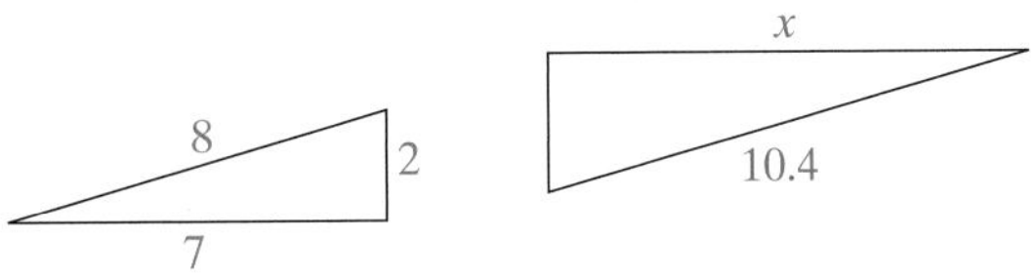

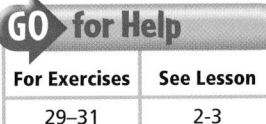

    (A) 9.1 (B) 9.4 (C) 11.4 (D) 11.9

GO for Help

For Exercises	See Lesson
29–31	2-3

Determine which number is greater.

29. $1.23, \frac{15}{12}$ $\frac{15}{12}$

30. $-45.78, -\frac{412}{9}$ $-\frac{412}{9}$

31. $\frac{1}{66}, 0.015$ $\frac{1}{66}$

Online lesson quiz, PHSchool.com, Web Code: asa-0504

Alternative Assessment

Have students write three different percent problems modeled after those on page 224, but with different numbers. Then have them trade papers with a partner and solve.

Test Prep

Resources

For additional practice with a variety of test item formats:

- Test-Taking Strategies, p. 251
- Test Prep, p. 255
- Test-Taking Strategies with Transparencies

4. Assess & Reteach

PowerPoint

Lesson Quiz

1. Find 81% of 110. 89.1
2. You buy a book for $17.80. Sales tax is 8%. What is the sales tax cost of the book? $1.42
3. 45 is 75% of what number? 60
4. Find what percent 68 is of 80. 85%

24. Answers may vary. Sample: Multiply the number by 0.13 or multiply the number by $\frac{13}{100}$.

Reteaching 5-4 Percents and E... **L2**

You can use an equation to solve percent problems.

Find the whole.

Example 1: 25% of what number is 20?

① Think of the percent as a decimal. $25\% = 0.25$

② Write an equation. $0.25n = 20$

③ Solve. $n = \frac{20}{0.25} = 80$

25% of 80 is 20.

Find the part.

Example 2: Find 12% of 48.

① Think of the percent as a decimal. $12\% = 0.12$

② Write an equation. $0.12 \times 48 = n$

③ Solve. $5.76 = n$

12% of 48 is 5.76.

Find the percent.

Example 3: What percent of 48 is 30?

① Write an equation. $n \times 48 = 30$

② Solve. $n = \frac{30}{48} = 0.625 = 62.5\%$

30 is 62.5% of 48.

Use an equation to solve each problem.

1. 30% of what number is 6? $0.30n = 6; n = 20$
2. 32 is 25% of what number? $0.25n = 32; n = 128$
3. What percent of 80 is 20? $n \times 80 = 20; n = 25\%$
4. What is 10% of 35? $0.10 \times 35 = n; n = 3.5$
5. Find 40% of 90. $0.40 \times 90 = n; n = 36$
6. What percent of 60 is 27? $n \times 60 = 27; n = 45\%$
7. What is 11% of 99? $0.11 \times 99 = n; n = 10.89$
8. 22 is 55% of what number? $0.55n = 22; n = 40$

Enrichment 5-4 Percents and E... **L4**

Critical Thinking

During the summer months the Center of Science and Industry Museum gives students a 15% discount off the regular admission price. Use the regular admission pricing to answer the following questions.

Admission Prices for the Center of Science and Industry Museum	
Under 2 years	Free
3 years to Preschool	$4.50
Kindergarten to 5th grade	$6.25
6th to 8th grade	$8.50
9th grade and up	$10.50

1. What is the admission price to the Center of Science and Industry Museum for an 8th grade student during the month of October? $8.50
2. Complete the equation to find what percent of the regular price is the summer student price.

   100% − 15 % = 85 %
3. Write an equation to find the price of a ticket for an 8th grader attending the Center of Science and Industry Museum during the month of July. $0.85 \times 8.50 = n$
4. What is the price of a ticket for an 8th grader attending the museum during the month of July? $7.23
5. About how much money do 10th graders save by using the summer discount at the museum? Write and solve an equation you would use to find the amount to the nearest cent. about $1.50; $10.5 \times 0.15 = n$; 10th grade students would save $1.58 during the summer.
6. Four 8th graders and two 9th graders went to the museum on August 1. What was the total cost of their admission? Write the equation you used to find the total cost. $46.75; $0.85(4 \times 8.50) + 0.85(2 \times 10.50) = C$

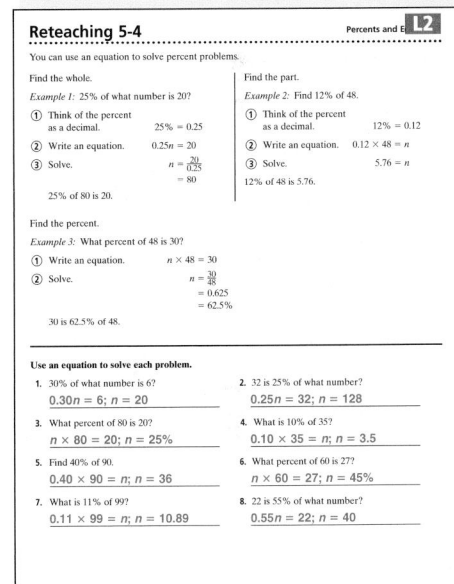

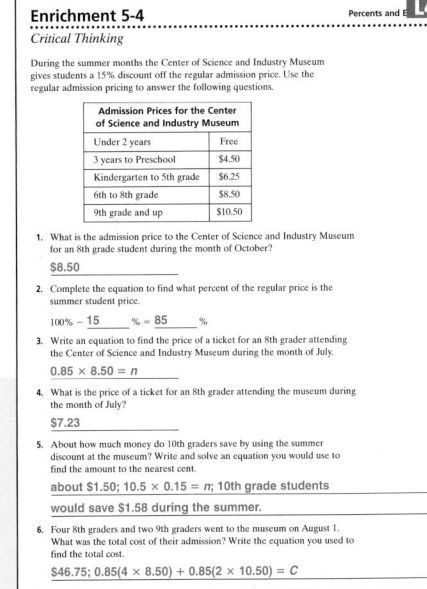

Vocabulary Builder

High-Use Academic Words

Students define and use three academic words: *estimate*, *calculate*, and *show*. These words are not exclusively mathematical terms, but they are commonly used in the study of mathematics.

Guided Instruction

Have students describe the meaning of each listed word in their own words. Brainstorm examples to illustrate their understanding of the words.

Differentiated Instruction

Visual Learners
After students complete the Exercises, draw a simple circle graph on the chalkboard. Divide the circle into 4 different-sized parts. Label the graph: "Students' Favorite Pets." Tell students the graph represents the results of a survey that shows the percents of students who chose cats, dogs, birds, or none of these as their favorite pet.
Ask: *What is wrong with this circle graph?* Sample: The parts are missing labels.
Have a volunteer write percents in the parts. Percents must total 100%. Let students decide which animal name to put in each section.

Resources

- Vocabulary and Study Skills Worksheet

Vocabulary Builder

High-Use Academic Words

High-use academic words are words that you will see often in textbooks and on tests. These words are not math vocabulary terms, but knowing them will help you to succeed in mathematics.

Direction Words

Some words tell what to do in a problem. I need to understand what these words are asking so that I give the correct answer.

Word	Meaning
Estimate	To find an approximate answer
Calculate	To find an exact answer by computing
Show	To explain or prove using logic or examples

Exercises

1. Estimate your age in days.
2. Calculate your age in days. 1–2. Check students' work.
3. Show that your birthday will never fall on the same day of the week in two consecutive years. See margin.
4. Estimate the total you pay if you leave a 15% tip for a restaurant bill of \$29.42. about \$34

Use the table at the right for Exercises 5–6.

5. Calculate the cost of a game plus sales tax at the rate of 8%. \$57.51
6. Show that \$200 is enough money to purchase a tax-free monitor if you have a coupon for 10% off the regular price. See margin.

Home Arcade

Equipment	Price (\$)
Controller	\$29.95
Game	\$53.25
Monitor	\$219.95

7. **Word Knowledge** Think about the word *label*.
   a. Choose the letter for how well you know the word. 7a–c. Check students' work.
      A. I know its meaning.
      B. I've seen it, but I don't know its meaning.
      C. I don't know it.
   b. **Research** Look up and write the definition of *label*.
   c. Use the word in a sentence involving mathematics.

3. $365 \div 7 = 52\frac{1}{7}$; since 7 is not a factor of 365, your birthday will never fall on the same day of the week in two consecutive years.

6. $219.95 - 0.1(219.95) =$ \$197.96; \$197.96 < \$200.

Checkpoint Quiz 1

Lessons 5-1 through 5-4

Write each fraction as a percent. Round to the nearest hundredth of a percent where necessary.

1. $\frac{2}{4}$ 50%
2. $\frac{1}{11}$ 9.09%
3. $\frac{3}{8}$ 37.5%
4. $\frac{15}{6}$ 250%
5. $\frac{10}{25}$ 40%

Estimate the given percent of each number.

6. 19% of 58 about 12
7. 0.66% of 36 about 0.24
8. 137% of 8 about 11
9. 1.9% of 2 about 0.04
10. **Population** In 2000, about 25% of the 5,130,632 people living in Arizona were Latino. Find how many Arizona residents were Latino. about 1,300,000 people

Use an equation to solve each problem.

11. 20.5 is 41% of what number? 50
12. What percent of 320 is 16? 5%
13. Find 3% of 26. 0.78
14. 0.08 is 32% of what number? 0.25

5-5a Activity Lab

Describing Change

City	1950 Population	2000 Population
Jacksonville, Florida	204,517	753,617
Virginia Beach, Virginia	5,390	425,257

SOURCE: U.S. Census Bureau. Go to **PHSchool.com** for an update. Web Code: asg-9041

Use the table above for Exercises 1–3.

1. Find the change in population for each city from 1950 to 2000. State whether the change is an increase or a decrease. Jacksonville: 549,100, increase; Virginia Beach: 419,867, increase
2. Write the ratio $\frac{\text{change in population}}{\text{1950 population}}$ for each city. Then write each ratio as a percent to the nearest tenth. This is the percent of change of the population for each city. Jacksonville: $\frac{549{,}100}{204{,}517} = 268.5\%$ Virginia Beach: $\frac{419{,}867}{5{,}390} = 7{,}789.7\%$
3. Does your answer to Exercise 1 or Exercise 2 better describe the population change for each city? Explain. See margin.

3. Answers may vary. Sample: The answer to Exercise 1 better describes which city's population changed by the greater number of people. The answer in Exercise 2 better describes which city's population changed by a greater percent of its original population.

Checkpoint Quiz

Use this Checkpoint Quiz to check students' understanding of the skills and concepts of Lessons 5-1 through 5-4.

Resources

- All in One Teaching Resources Checkpoint Quiz 1
- ExamView Assessment Suite CD-ROM
- Success Tracker Online Intervention

Activity Lab

Describing Change

Students extract information about change from a table. They are guided to describe the change in two different ways. Then they decide which way better describes the change. This activity explores and demonstrates the use of percent of change.

Guided Instruction

Teaching Tip
Have students describe what they can about change just by looking at the numbers in the table without performing any calculations. Tell them they will learn a way of describing change mathematically.

Error Prevention!

Emphasize that the comparison is made between the change and the original. Some students may confuse this with the ratio of the new to the old, which is *not* the percent of change.

Resources

Activity Lab 5-5: Percent Increase

5-5

1. Plan

Objective
To find percent of change and to solve problems involving percent of increase and percent of decrease

Examples
1 Finding Percent of Increase
2 Application: Sports
3 Finding Percent of Decrease

Math Understandings: p. 208C

Professional Development

Math Background

The equation for finding the percent of change (whether increase or decrease) is essentially the same as the percent equation. Point out to students that the numerator is the *part* which can be thought of as the *amount of change*. The denominator is the *whole* which can be thought of as the *original amount*.

More Math Background: p. 208C

Lesson Planning and Resources

See p. 208E for a list of the resources that support this lesson.

PowerPoint

Bell Ringer Practice

Check Skills You'll Need
Use student page, transparency, or PowerPoint. For intervention, direct students to:
Fractions, Decimals, and Percents
Lesson 5-1
Extra Skills and Word Problems Practice, Ch. 5

Algebra

5-5 Percent of Change

Check Skills You'll Need

1. **Vocabulary Review** A _?_ is a ratio that compares a number to 100. percent

Write each fraction as a percent. Round to the nearest tenth of a percent.

2. $\frac{9}{8}$ 112.5%
3. $\frac{6}{22}$ 27.3%
4. $\frac{4}{15}$ 26.7%
5. $\frac{11}{3}$ 366.7%

GO for Help Lesson 5-1

What You'll Learn

To find percent of change and to solve problems involving percent of increase and percent of decrease

New Vocabulary percent of change

Why Learn This?

The U.S. Census is taken every ten years. Percents can help you understand the changes from one census to another.

The percent a quantity increases or decreases from its original amount is the **percent of change.**

$$P = \frac{\text{amount of change}}{\text{original amount}}$$ ← **P is the percent of change.**

EXAMPLE Finding Percent of Increase

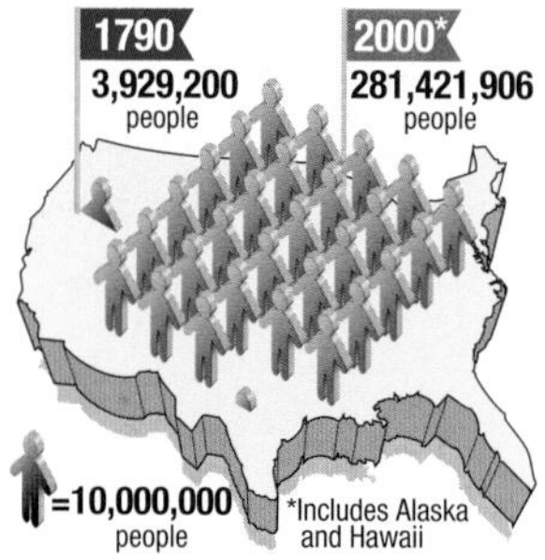

SOURCE: U.S. Census Bureau. Go to **PHSchool.com** for an update. Web Code: asg-9041

1 **Population** When the first U.S. Census was taken in 1790, the population was 3,929,200. In 2000, the population was 281,421,906. Find the percent of increase. Round to the nearest percent.

amount of change = 281,421,906 − 3,929,200 = 277,492,706

$$P = \frac{277{,}492{,}706}{3{,}929{,}200}$$ ← **amount of change** / ← **original amount**

277,492,706 ÷ 3,929,200 = 70.62320727 ← **Use a calculator to divide.**

≈ 7,062% ← **Write the decimal as a percent. Round to the nearest percent.**

The percent of increase in the population was about 7,062%.

Check for Reasonableness 7,062% of 3,929,200 is about 7,000% of 4,000,000. Since 7,000% of 4,000,000 is 280,000,000, which is close to 281,421,906, the answer is reasonable.

Quick Check

1. **Education** In 1995, about 3,748,000 students were enrolled in Texas public schools. In 2010, there will be about 4,475,000 students enrolled. Find the percent of increase to the nearest tenth. 19.4%

Differentiated Instruction Solutions for All Learners

Special Needs L1
Use data from Example 2. On a number line on the board, draw a line segment from zero to 20 ft 10 in., and another from 20 ft 10 in. to 28 ft 0.75 in. Students compare the length of the two line segments.

learning style: visual

Below Level L2
Students solve percent of increase problems such as these:

50 to 75 50%	50 to 90 80%
50 to 100 100%	50 to 125 150%

learning style: verbal

When working with different units of measure, convert all measures to the same units.

EXAMPLE **Application: Sports**

2 In the 1896 Olympic Games, Ellery Clark of the United States jumped 20 ft 10 in. to win the men's long jump. In a recent Olympic Games, an athlete jumped 28 ft 0.75 in. to win the men's long jump. Find the percent of increase in the length of the men's winning long jump.

GO for Help
For help converting units, see Lesson 4-2, Example 1.

20 ft 10 in. $= 20 \cdot 12 + 10 = 250$ in.
28 ft 0.75 in. $= 28 \cdot 12 + 0.75 = 336.75$ in.
← **Write measures in the same units.**

amount of change $= 336.75 - 250 = 86.75$

$P = \frac{86.75}{250}$ ← amount of change / ← original amount

$= 0.347$ ← **Simplify.**

$= 34.7\%$ ← **Write the decimal as a percent.**

The length of the winning long jump increased by 34.7%.

Quick Check

2. A girl was 4 ft 9 in. tall last year. This year she is 5 ft tall. Find the percent of increase in her height. Round to the nearest tenth. 5.3%

Percent of decrease is the percent a quantity decreases from its original amount.

EXAMPLE **Finding Percent of Decrease**

3 In 1967, there were 3,384 drive-in movie theaters in the United States. In 1997, there were 619 drive-in theaters. Find the percent of decrease in the number of theaters. Round to the nearest tenth.

amount of change $= 3{,}384 - 619 = 2{,}765$

$P = \frac{2{,}765}{3{,}384}$ ← amount of change / ← original amount

$= 0.817080378$ ← **Use a calculator.**

$\approx 81.7\%$ ← **Write the decimal as a percent. Round to the nearest tenth of a percent.**

The number of drive-in theaters decreased by about 81.7%.

Quick Check

3. In 1995, the average price of a personal computer was $2,100. In 2001, the average price was $899. Find the percent of decrease in the average price. Round to the nearest tenth. 57.2%

2. Teach

Activity Lab

Use before the lesson.
Student Edition Activity Lab 5-5a, Describing Change, p. 229

All in One Teaching Resources
Activity Lab 5-5: Percent Increase

Guided Instruction

Error Prevention!

Students might forget which amount is the *original amount* after finding the percent change. They then might divide by the wrong amount. Some students also think they should simply divide by the larger amount, even if it is not the original amount.

Example 3
Encourage students to make a note, when planning their solution, whether a change is an increase or decrease.

PowerPoint
Additional Examples

1 Ten years ago, Max's comic book was worth $2.50. Now it is worth $13. Find the percent of increase in value. 420%

2 Andre changed the height of his basketball hoop from 8 ft 4 in. to 9 ft 2 in. Find the percent of increase. 10%

3 In 1980, the population of a city was 557,927. In 1990, its population was 496,938. Find the percent of decrease. Round to the nearest tenth. 10.9%

All in One Teaching Resources
- Daily Notetaking Guide 5-5 L3
- Adapted Notetaking 5-5 L1

Closure

- *Explain the difference between percent of increase and percent of decrease.* Sample: Percent of increase shows a change in a quantity that is growing larger, while percent of decrease shows a change in a quantity that is growing smaller.

Advanced Learners L4	**English Language Learners** ELL
Students find sale ads in newspapers and determine the original price, percent of discount, and sale price of five items.	Elicit the fact that although decrease and increase are opposites, they both are changes in percent.
learning style: visual	**learning style: verbal**

3. Practice

Assignment Guide

Check Your Understanding

Go over Exercises 1–5 in class before assigning the Homework Exercises.

Homework Exercises

A Practice by Example	6–22
B Apply Your Skills	23–31
C Challenge	32
Test Prep and Mixed Review	33–38

Homework Quick Check

To check students' understanding of key skills and concepts, go over Exercises 13, 18, 23, 31, and 32.

Differentiated Instruction Resources

Adapted Practice 5-5 L1

Practice 5-5 Percent of Change L3

Find each percent of increase or decrease. Round your answer to the nearest tenth, if necessary.

1. 15 to 20 — 33.3% increase
2. 18 to 10 — 44.4% decrease
3. 10 to 7.5 — 25% decrease
4. 86 to 120 — 39.5% increase
5. 17 to 34 — 100% increase
6. 32 to 24 — 25% decrease
7. 27 to 38 — 40.7% increase
8. 40 to 10 — 75% decrease
9. 8 to 10 — 25% increase
10. 43 to 86 — 100% increase
11. 100 to 23 — 77% decrease
12. 846 to 240 — 71.6% decrease
13. 130 to 275 — 111.5% increase
14. 193 to 270 — 39.9% increase
15. 436 to 118 — 72.9% decrease
16. 457 to 318 — 30.4% decrease
17. 607 to 812 — 33.8% increase
18. 500 to 118 — 76.4% decrease

Solve.

19. In 1995, the price of a laser printer was $1,299. In 2002, the price of the same type of printer had dropped to $499. Find the percent of decrease. 61.6%
20. The amount won in harness racing in 1991 was $1.238 million. In 1992, the amount was $1.38 million. What was the percent of increase? 11.5%
21. In 1980, there were about 3 million people in Chicago. In 1990, the population was about 2.8 million people. Find the percent of decrease in the population of Chicago. 6.7%
22. Caryn was 58 in. tall last year. This year she is 61 in. tall. What is the percent of increase in her height? 5.2%

5-5 • Guided Problem Solving GPS L3

Student Page 233, Exercise 30:

Education A middle school increased the length of its school day from 6 h 10 min to 6 h 25 min. Find the percent of increase in the length of the school day. Round to the nearest tenth of a percent.

Understand

1. What is the original length of the school day? 6 h 10 min
2. What is the new length of the school day? 6 h 25 min
3. Was the length of the day increased or decreased? increased
4. What are you being asked to find? the percent of increase in the length of the school day

Plan and Carry Out

5. What is the original length of the school day in minutes? 370 minutes
6. What is the new length of the school day in minutes? 385 minutes
7. How many minutes has the school day changed? 15 minutes
8. What is the percent change equation? $P = \frac{\text{amount of change}}{\text{original amount}}$
9. Substitute the values in the equation. $P = \frac{15 \text{ min}}{370 \text{ min}}$
10. Solve to the nearest tenth of a percent. 4.1%

Check

11. Is your answer reasonable? Is 4.1% of 370 minutes approximately 15 minutes? yes; 370 × .041 = 15.17

Solve Another Problem

12. Albert is 3 ft 1 in. tall on his second birthday and grows to 6 ft 4 inches by his 20th birthday. Find the percent of increase in his height to the nearest tenth of a percent. $\frac{39}{37}$ = 105.4%

Check Your Understanding

1. **Vocabulary** The percent of change is the percent a quantity increases or decreases from its __?__ amount. original

2. **Shopping** Use the information at the right to find the percent of increase in online shopping sales from 2000 to 2003. Round to the nearest tenth. 48.0%

Find the percent of change.

3. from 12 to 15 25% increase
4. from 36 to 27 25% decrease
5. from 9 to 27 200% increase

Homework Exercises

For more exercises, see Extra Skills and Word Problems.

GO for Help

For Exercises	See Examples
6–12	1
13–15	2
16–22	3

A **Find each percent of increase. Round your answer to the nearest tenth, if necessary.**

6. 75 to 110 46.7%
7. 10 to 23 130%
8. 4 to 56 1,300%
9. 20 to 28 40%
10. 15 to 25 66.7%
11. 50 to 80 60%

12. **Money** In 1950, the minimum hourly wage for non-farm workers was $.75. In 2000, the minimum hourly wage was $5.15. Find the percent of increase. Round to the nearest tenth. 586.7%

Find each percent of increase. Round your answer to the nearest tenth, if necessary.

13. 36 ft 3 in. to 37 ft 6 in. 3.4%
14. 16 lb 4 oz to 20 lb 1 oz 23.5%

15. **Infants** A baby weighed 7 lb 3 oz at birth. Four months later, the baby weighed 13 lb 5 oz. Find the percent of increase. Round to the nearest tenth. 85.2%

Find each percent of decrease. Round your answer to the nearest tenth, if necessary.

16. 190 to 183 3.7%
17. 15 to 10 33.3%
18. 205 to 164 20%
19. 87 to 64 26.4%
20. 52 to 1 98.1%
21. 368 to 275 25.3%

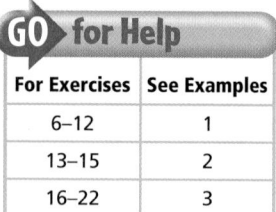

22. **Entertainment** In 1998, there were 824 "easy listening" radio stations. In 2001, there were 299 easy listening stations. Find the percent of decrease. Round to the nearest tenth. 63.7%

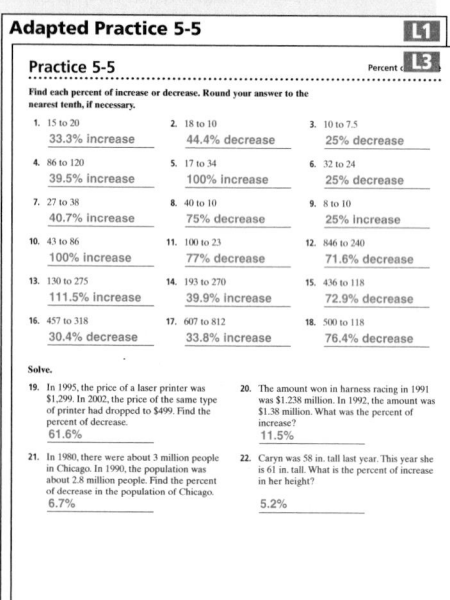

B GPS 23. **Guided Problem Solving** In 1990, Mexico and Central America had about 204,450,000 acres of forest. In 2000, the amount of forest had decreased by 18%. Find the number of acres of forest in 2000. 167,649,000 acres

- Find the decrease in the number of acres a by using the formula $a = (\blacksquare)(204{,}450{,}000)$.
- Find the number of acres of forest in 2000 by using the formula $204{,}450{,}000 - a = \blacksquare$.

Find each percent of change. Round to the nearest tenth. Label your answer *increase* or *decrease*.

24. 1.4 to 9.6 — 585.7% increase
25. 0.8 to 0.2 — 75% decrease
26. 8.7 to 99.9 — 1,048.3% increase
27. 5 to $1\frac{1}{4}$ — 75% decrease
28. $\frac{7}{5}$ to 130 — 9,185.7% increase
29. $610\frac{1}{3}$ to 81 — 86.7% decrease

GO Online
Homework Video Tutor
Visit: PHSchool.com
Web Code: ase-0505

30. **Education** GPS A middle school increased the length of its school day from 6 h 10 min to 6 h 25 min. Find the percent of increase in the length of the school day. Round to the nearest tenth of a percent. 4.1%

31. **Writing in Math** The number 100 is increased by 20%. The result is then decreased by 20%. Is 100 the final result? Explain. See margin.

C 32. **Challenge** Three weeks ago, a sunflower plant was 1 ft 3 in. tall. Since then, its height has increased by $213\frac{1}{3}$%. Find the current height of the sunflower in feet and inches. 47 in. or 3 ft 11 in.

Test Prep and Mixed Review

Practice

Multiple Choice

33. The population of Marisa's town increased by 3% from last year to this year. If 30,000 people lived in the town last year, how many people live there this year? C

Ⓐ 900 Ⓑ 9,000 Ⓒ 30,900 Ⓓ 39,000

34. If $\triangle PQR$ is reflected over the y-axis, what will be the coordinates of R'? J

Ⓕ (2, −3) Ⓗ (−2, 3)
Ⓖ (2, 3) Ⓙ (−2, −3)

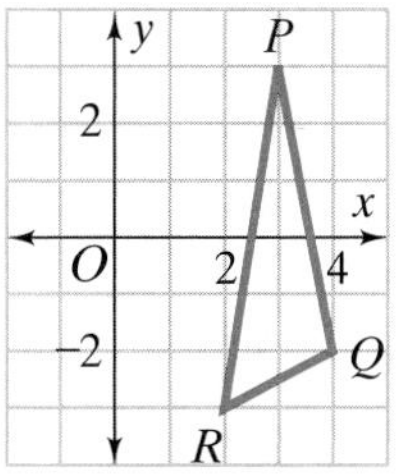

35. Luis uses the Pythagorean Theorem and finds that the distance across a fish pond is $\sqrt{7}$ meters. Which whole number is closest to $\sqrt{7}$? B

Ⓐ 2 Ⓑ 3 Ⓒ 4 Ⓓ 5

GO for Help

For Exercises	See Lesson
36–38	4-2

Convert each measure. Round to the nearest hundredth, if necessary.

36. 2.25 t = ■ lb — 4,500
37. 6 qt = ■ c — 24
38. 240 s = ■ h — 0.07

31. No; 20% of 100 is 20, so the result of a 20% increase from 100 is 120. Then 20% of 120 is 24, so the result of a 20% decrease from 120 is 96.

Test Prep

Resources

For additional practice with a variety of test item formats:

- Test-Taking Strategies, p. 251
- Test Prep, p. 255
- Test-Taking Strategies with Transparencies

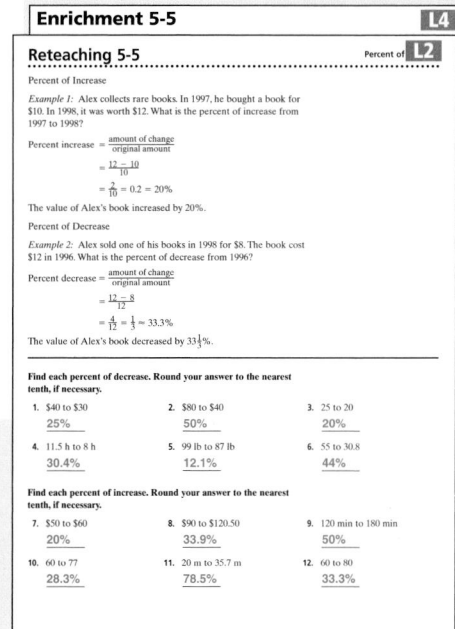

4. Assess & Reteach

PowerPoint

Lesson Quiz

Round to the nearest whole percent.

1. 81 people attended last year's annual picnic, and 93 people attended this year's picnic. What is the percent of increase? about 15%
2. The speed limit on a highway was 55 miles per hour last year. This year, the speed limit was increased to 65 miles per hour. What is the percent increase in the speed limit? 18%
3. The population in Arthur County, Nebraska, dropped from 462 in 1990 to 444 in 2000. What was the percent of decrease? about 4%

Alternative Assessment

One student in a pair chooses a number and the partner chooses another number. Then students work together to compute the corresponding percent of increase and the percent of decrease associated with these numbers.

Enrichment 5-5 L4

Reteaching 5-5 Percent of L2

Percent of Increase

Example 1: Alex collects rare books. In 1997, he bought a book for \$10. In 1998, it was worth \$12. What is the percent of increase from 1997 to 1998?

$$\text{Percent increase} = \frac{\text{amount of change}}{\text{original amount}} = \frac{12 - 10}{10} = \frac{2}{10} = 0.2 = 20\%$$

The value of Alex's book increased by 20%.

Percent of Decrease

Example 2: Alex sold one of his books in 1998 for \$8. The book cost \$12 in 1996. What is the percent of decrease from 1996?

$$\text{Percent decrease} = \frac{\text{amount of change}}{\text{original amount}} = \frac{12 - 8}{12} = \frac{4}{12} = \frac{1}{3} \approx 33.3\%$$

The value of Alex's book decreased by $33\frac{1}{3}$%.

Find each percent of decrease. Round your answer to the nearest tenth, if necessary.

1. \$40 to \$30 — 25%
2. \$80 to \$40 — 50%
3. 25 to 20 — 20%
4. 11.5 h to 8 h — 30.4%
5. 99 lb to 87 lb — 12.1%
6. 55 to 30.8 — 44%

Find each percent of increase. Round your answer to the nearest tenth, if necessary.

7. \$50 to \$60 — 20%
8. \$90 to \$120.50 — 33.9%
9. 120 min to 180 min — 50%
10. 60 to 77 — 28.3%
11. 20 m to 35.7 m — 78.5%
12. 60 to 80 — 33.3%

5-6

1. Plan

Objective
To use percent of change to find markup, discount, and selling price

Examples
1 Finding Percent of Markup
2 Finding Selling Price
3 Finding Sale Price
4 Finding Regular Price

Math Understandings: p. 208D

Professional Development

Math Background

With markups and discounts, the percent of markup or discount involves the same ratio as percent of change: amount of change to original amount. For markups, the original amount is the original cost the store had to pay.

More Math Background: p. 208D

Lesson Planning and Resources

See p. 208E for a list of the resources that support this lesson.

PowerPoint

Bell Ringer Practice

Check Skills You'll Need
Use student page, transparency, or PowerPoint. For intervention, direct students to:
Percents and Equations
Lesson 5-4
Extra Skills and Word Problems Practice, Ch. 5

Algebra

5-6 Markup and Discount

Check Skills You'll Need

1. **Vocabulary Review** A ? relates a part to the whole. percent

Use an equation to solve each problem.

2. What number is 16% of 25? 4
3. Find 80% of 250. 200
4. 33 is 3% of what number? 1,100
5. 0.55% of what number is 77? 14,000

GO for Help Lesson 5-4

What You'll Learn

To use percent of change to find markup, discount, and selling price

New Vocabulary markup, selling price, discount, sale price

Why Learn This?

Store owners use percents in many ways. Sales flyers advertise a percent of a price. Store owners calculate a percent increase over their cost to make a profit.

Markup is the amount of increase in price. Markup is added to the store's cost for the item to arrive at the **selling price,** the price the store charges.

The percent of increase in the price of an item is called the percent of markup. Use the percent of change equation to find percent of markup.

$$\text{percent of change} = \frac{\text{amount of change}}{\text{original amount}} \qquad \text{percent of markup} = \frac{\text{markup}}{\text{store's cost}}$$

EXAMPLE Finding Percent of Markup

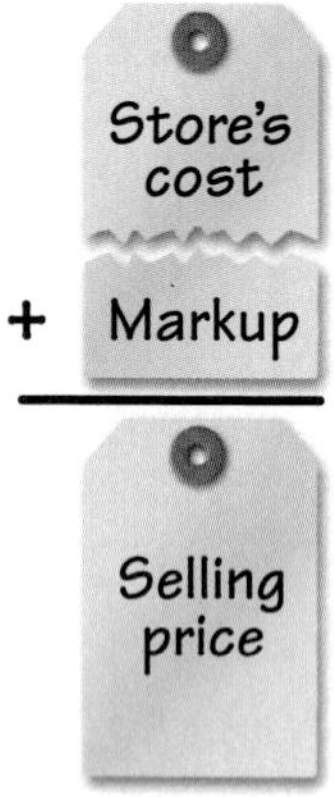

1 Clothing Find the percent of markup on a sweater that cost a store \$25 and has a selling price of \$45.

$$\begin{aligned} \text{markup} &= \text{selling price} - \text{store's cost} \\ &= \$45 - \$25 \quad \leftarrow \textbf{Substitute.} \\ &= \$20 \quad \leftarrow \textbf{Subtract.} \end{aligned}$$

$$\begin{aligned} \text{percent of markup} &= \frac{20}{25} \begin{array}{l}\leftarrow \text{markup} \\ \leftarrow \text{store's cost}\end{array} \\ &= 0.8 \quad \leftarrow \textbf{Write the fraction as a decimal.} \\ &= 80\% \quad \leftarrow \textbf{Write the decimal as a percent.} \end{aligned}$$

Quick Check

1. Find the percent of markup on an item that cost a store \$10 and has a selling price of \$19. 90%

Differentiated Instruction Solutions for All Learners

Special Needs L1	**Below Level** L2
To better understand Example 2, students draw a number line and label it from 0%–100%. They highlight the point 100% and label it "0.79." Then they extend the line to 200%, and mark the point where 165% would fall. **learning style: visual**	Students identify whether two dollar amounts indicate a markup or discount. \$45.99 to \$39.99 discount; \$16.88 to \$18.99 markup; \$2.35 to \$2.19 discount **learning style: verbal**

Managers use the store's cost for an item and percent of markup to calculate the item's selling price.

EXAMPLE Finding Selling Price

2 **Business** A school store sells pens. Each pen costs the store \$.79. The store then marks up the price 65%. What is the selling price of each pen?

Method 1 Find the markup first. Then find the selling price.

65% of \$.79 equals the markup.

$0.65 \cdot 0.79 = 0.5135$ ← **Multiply to find the markup.**

≈ 0.51 ← **Round to the nearest hundredth.**

$\$.79 + \$.51 = \$1.30$ ← **store's cost + markup = selling price**

The school store sells each pen for \$1.30.

Method 2 Find the selling price directly.

The selling price equals 100% of the store's cost plus a markup of 65% of the store's cost. The selling price of each pen is 100% + 65%, or 165%, of \$.79.

165% of \$.79 equals the selling price.

$1.65 \cdot 0.79 = 1.3035$ ← **Multiply to find the selling price.**

≈ 1.30 ← **Round to the nearest hundredth.**

The school store sells each pen for \$1.30.

Quick Check

2. An item costs a store \$89.89. The store then marks the price up 80%. What is the selling price of the item? **\$161.80**

Stores also use percents to calculate the prices of items on sale. The amount by which the price of an item on sale is reduced is called the **discount.** The regular price of an item minus the discount equals the **sale price** of the item.

The percent of decrease in the price of an item after a discount is called the percent of discount. Use the percent of change equation to find the percent of discount.

$$\text{percent of change} = \frac{\text{amount of change}}{\text{original amount}} \qquad \text{percent of discount} = \frac{\text{discount}}{\text{regular price}}$$

You can calculate the sale price of an item if you know the regular price and the percent of discount for the item. You can find the regular price of an item when you know the sale price and the percent of discount.

2. Teach

Activity Lab

Use before the lesson.

All in One Teaching Resources

Activity Lab 5-6: Discount

Guided Instruction

Teaching Tip
To make sure that students understand the vocabulary of sales, ask them to explain *cost, selling price,* and *markup* in their own words.

Career Note
Have students name careers where finding markups and discounts would be helpful. Suggest the list includes *you, the consumer.*

Error Prevention!

Students might confuse markup with discount. Emphasize that the storeowner uses the markup to find the *selling price,* the amount the store will charge for the item. The owner uses the discount to find the *sale price,* the amount a customer will pay after the regular price is reduced or discounted.

PowerPoint

Additional Examples

1 Find the percent of markup for a stapler costing the school store \$2.10 and selling for \$3.36. **60%**

2 A store sells a skirt that costs the store \$40 and marks up the price 25%. What is the selling price for this skirt? **\$50**

Advanced Learners L4
What is a store's profit on a gold necklace that cost \$226, is marked up 50%, and discounted 15%? **\$62.15**

learning style: verbal

English Language Learners ELL
Students write *markup = increase* and *discount = decrease* on index cards. They practice saying the words and connecting them so that they use them interchangeably when appropriate.

learning style: verbal

Guided Instruction

Example 4

Ask:

- *If you sharpen off two-fifths of a pencil, what part of the pencil is left?* three-fifths
- *If 40% of the price is taken off, what percent of the price will you pay?* 60%

PowerPoint

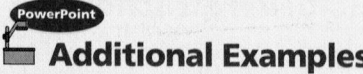

Additional Examples

3 A shoe store advertises a 35%-off sale. What is the sale price of shoes that regularly cost \$94.99? \$61.74

4 You buy a CD at the sale price of \$6. This is 25% off the regular price. Find the regular price of the CD. \$8

All in One Teaching Resources

- Daily Notetaking Guide 5-6 L3
- Adapted Notetaking 5-6 L1

Closure

- *Explain the difference between markup and discount.* Sample: Markup is added to the store's cost; discount is subtracted from the selling price for the customer.

EXAMPLE Finding Sale Price

3 **Furniture** A furniture store is having a 30%-off sale. What is the sale price of a table that regularly costs \$259.98?

Method 1 Find the discount first. Then subtract to find the sale price.

30% of \$259.98 equals the discount.

$0.3 \cdot 259.98 \approx 77.99$ ← **Multiply to find the discount. Round to the nearest hundredth.**

$259.98 - 77.99 = 181.99$ ← **regular price − discount = sale price**

The sale price is \$181.99.

Method 2 Find the sale price directly.

The sale price is 100% − 30%, or 70%, of \$259.98.

$0.7 \cdot 259.98 \approx 181.99$ ← **Multiply. Round to the nearest hundredth.**

The sale price is \$181.99.

Quick Check

3. An item that regularly sells for \$182.75 is on sale for 45% off. Find the sale price to the nearest cent. \$100.51

EXAMPLE Finding Regular Price

Test Prep Tip

Remember that when an item is discounted, the regular price is more than the sale price.

4 **Multiple Choice** You buy a pair of in-line skates on sale for \$54. This price is 40% off the regular price. Find the regular price.

Ⓐ \$21.60 Ⓑ \$32.40 Ⓒ \$75.60 Ⓓ \$90.00

regular price − 40% of regular price = sale price

Let r = the regular price.

$r - 0.4r = 54$ ← **Substitute. Write the percent as a decimal.**

$(1 - 0.4)r = 54$ ← **Distributive Property**

$0.6r = 54$ ← **Subtract.**

$\frac{0.6r}{0.6} = \frac{54}{0.6}$ ← **Divide each side by 0.6.**

$r = 90$ ← **Simplify.**

The regular price of the skates is \$90. The correct answer is choice D.

GO for Help

For help with the Distributive Property, go to Lesson 1-5, Example 4.

Quick Check

4. A stereo is on sale for \$99 at 15% off. Find the regular price. \$116.47

Check Your Understanding

Vocabulary **Match each term with its meaning.**

1. markup C
2. sale price A
3. selling price B

A. regular price of an item minus the discount
B. cost of the item plus the markup
C. amount of increase in price

4. **Reasoning** Explain why selling price after markup is always greater than selling price after a discount. Markup adds to the cost of an item, but discount reduces the cost.

Homework Exercises

For more exercises, see Extra Skills and Word Problems.

GO for Help

For Exercises	See Examples
5–8	1
9–11	2
12–14	3
15–17	4

A **Find each percent of markup.**

5. store's cost: $26
selling price: $39
50%

6. store's cost: $125
selling price: $168.75
35%

7. store's cost: $75
selling price: $90
20%

8. **Video Games** A video game costs a store $20. If the store sells the game for $33, what is the percent of markup? 65%

Find each selling price. Round to the nearest cent.

9. store's cost: $118.12
percent of markup: 60%
$188.99

10. store's cost: $22.05
percent of markup: 95%
$43.00

11. A soccer ball costs a store $29.50. What is the selling price of the ball after a 35% markup? Round to the nearest cent. $39.83

Find each sale price. Round to the nearest cent.

12. regular price: $16.99
percent of discount: 55%
$7.65

13. regular price: $77.00
percent of discount: 5%
$73.15

14. A nursery has a 25%-off sale. Find the sale price of a $200 tree. $150

Find each regular price. Round to the nearest cent.

15. sale price: $66.30
percent of discount: 65%
$189.43

16. sale price: $13
percent of discount: 20%
$16.25

17. Employees at a clothing store get a 15% discount. Find the regular price of jeans that cost an employee $24.65. $29

B **GPS** 18. **Guided Problem Solving** A store buys bags for $5.25 and marks them up 80%. Find the sale price of the bags after a 30% discount. $6.62
- What is 80% of $5.25?
- What is 30% of the selling price?

GO Online
Homework Video Tutor
Visit: PHSchool.com
Web Code: ase-0506

Online lesson quiz, PHSchool.com, Web Code: asa-0506

3. Practice

Assignment Guide

Check Your Understanding

Go over Exercises 1–4 in class before assigning the Homework Exercises.

Homework Exercises

A	Practice by Example	5–17
B	Apply Your Skills	18–23
C	Challenge	24
	Test Prep and Mixed Review	25–31

Homework Quick Check

To check students' understanding of key skills and concepts, go over Exercises 8, 14, 21, 22, and 23.

Differentiated Instruction Resources

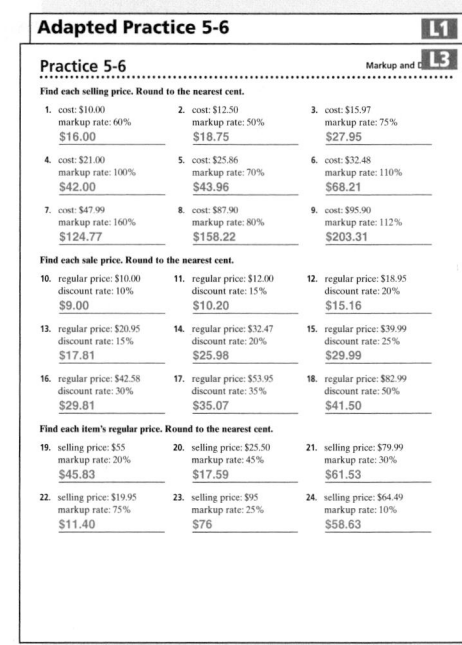

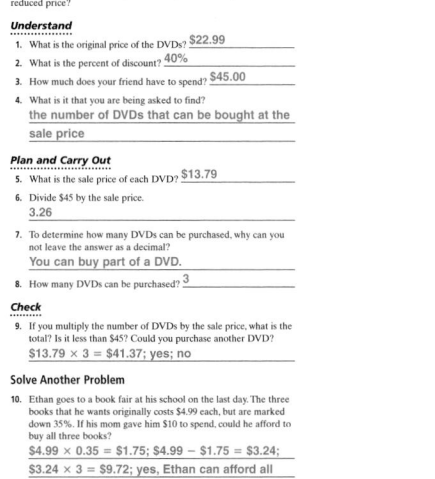

Adapted Practice 5-6 L1

Practice 5-6 Markup and D L3

Find each selling price. Round to the nearest cent.

1. cost: $10.00, markup rate: 60% — $16.00
2. cost: $12.50, markup rate: 50% — $18.75
3. cost: $15.97, markup rate: 75% — $27.95
4. cost: $21.00, markup rate: 100% — $42.00
5. cost: $25.86, markup rate: 70% — $43.96
6. cost: $32.48, markup rate: 110% — $68.21
7. cost: $47.99, markup rate: 160% — $124.77
8. cost: $87.90, markup rate: 80% — $158.22
9. cost: $95.90, markup rate: 112% — $203.31

Find each sale price. Round to the nearest cent.

10. regular price: $10.00, discount rate: 10% — $9.00
11. regular price: $12.00, discount rate: 15% — $10.20
12. regular price: $18.95, discount rate: 20% — $15.16
13. regular price: $20.95, discount rate: 15% — $17.81
14. regular price: $32.47, discount rate: 20% — $25.98
15. regular price: $39.99, discount rate: 25% — $29.99
16. regular price: $42.58, discount rate: 30% — $29.81
17. regular price: $53.95, discount rate: 35% — $35.07
18. regular price: $82.99, discount rate: 50% — $41.50

Find each item's regular price. Round to the nearest cent.

19. selling price: $55, markup rate: 20% — $45.83
20. selling price: $25.50, markup rate: 45% — $17.59
21. selling price: $79.99, markup rate: 30% — $61.53
22. selling price: $19.95, markup rate: 75% — $11.40
23. selling price: $95, markup rate: 25% — $76
24. selling price: $64.49, markup rate: 10% — $58.63

5-6 • Guided Problem Solving GPS L3

Student Page 238, Exercise 22:

DVDs are on sale for 40% off the regular price of $22.99. Your friend has $45 to spend. How many DVDs can your friend buy at the reduced price?

Understand

1. What is the original price of the DVDs? $22.99
2. What is the percent of discount? 40%
3. How much does your friend have to spend? $45.00
4. What is it that you are being asked to find? the number of DVDs that can be bought at the sale price

Plan and Carry Out

5. What is the sale price of each DVD? $13.79
6. Divide $45 by the sale price. 3.26
7. To determine how many DVDs can be purchased, why can you not leave the answer as a decimal? You can buy part of a DVD.
8. How many DVDs can be purchased? 3

Check

9. If you multiply the number of DVDs by the sale price, what is the total? Is it less than $45? Could you purchase another DVD? $13.79 × 3 = $41.37; yes; no

Solve Another Problem

10. Ethan goes to a book fair at his school on the last day. The three books that he wants originally costs $4.99 each, but are marked down 35%. If his mom gave him $10 to spend, could he afford to buy all three books? $4.99 × 0.35 = $1.75; $4.99 − $1.75 = $3.24; $3.24 × 3 = $9.72; yes, Ethan can afford all three books, because $9.72 is less than $10.00.

4. Assess & Reteach

PowerPoint

Lesson Quiz

1. A pair of shoes costs the store \$40. The store sells them for \$65. What is the percent markup? 62.5%
2. A school service club sells calendars. Each calendar costs the club \$5.50. The club marks up the price 80%. What is the selling price of each calendar? \$9.90
3. A sweater regularly sells for \$49. It is on sale for 20% off. What is the sale price? \$39.20
4. You buy a baseball cap for \$13. This price is 35% off the regular price. Find the regular price. \$20.00

Alternative Assessment

One student in a pair chooses a number and the partner chooses a percent. Then students work together to compute the corresponding selling price and sale price associated with these numbers.

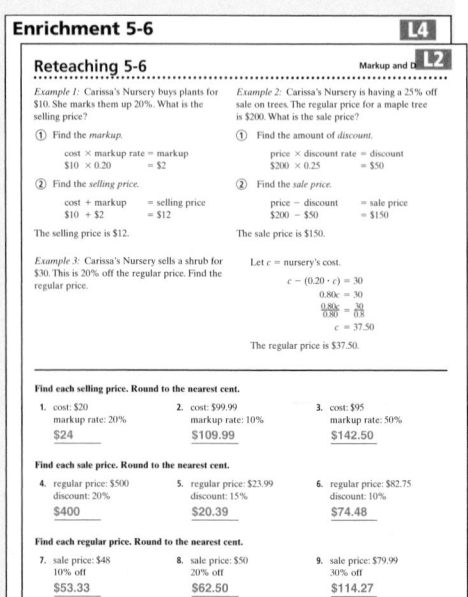

Enrichment 5-6 L4

Reteaching 5-6 Markup and D L2

Example 1: Carissa's Nursery buys plants for \$10. She marks them up 20%. What is the selling price?

① Find the *markup.*

cost × markup rate = markup
\$10 × 0.20 = \$2

② Find the *selling price.*

cost + markup = selling price
\$10 + \$2 = \$12

The selling price is \$12.

Example 2: Carissa's Nursery is having a 25% off sale on trees. The regular price for a maple tree is \$200. What is the sale price?

① Find the amount of *discount.*

price × discount rate = discount
\$200 × 0.25 = \$50

② Find the *sale price.*

price − discount = sale price
\$200 − \$50 = \$150

The sale price is \$150.

Example 3: Carissa's Nursery sells a shrub for \$30. This is 20% off the regular price. Find the regular price.

Let c = nursery's cost.

$$c - (0.20 \cdot c) = 30$$
$$0.80c = 30$$
$$\frac{0.80c}{0.80} = \frac{30}{0.8}$$
$$c = 37.50$$

The regular price is \$37.50.

Find each selling price. Round to the nearest cent.

1. cost: \$20 markup rate: 20% \$24
2. cost: \$99.99 markup rate: 10% \$109.99
3. cost: \$95 markup rate: 50% \$142.50

Find each sale price. Round to the nearest cent.

4. regular price: \$500 discount: 20% \$400
5. regular price: \$23.99 discount: 15% \$20.39
6. regular price: \$82.75 discount: 10% \$74.48

Find each regular price. Round to the nearest cent.

7. sale price: \$48 10% off \$53.33
8. sale price: \$50 20% off \$62.50
9. sale price: \$79.99 30% off \$114.27

Find each selling price. Round to the nearest cent.

19. store's price: \$71.99
percent of markup: $66\frac{2}{3}\%$ \$119.98

20. store's price: \$364.38
percent of markup: $37\frac{1}{2}\%$ \$501.02

21. **Reasoning** A travel agency offers the trip advertised at the left. There is a 10% service fee. Will you do better if the agency adds the service fee and then subtracts the discount, or if the agency subtracts the discount and then adds the service fee? Explain. See margin.
22. DVDs are on sale for 40% off the regular price of \$22.99. Your friend has \$45 to spend. How many DVDs can your friend buy at the reduced price? 3 DVDs
23. **Writing in Math** Write a general rule for finding a store's cost for an item if you know the selling price and the percent of markup. See margin.
24. **Challenge** There is a "buy two, get one free" sale on energy bars that regularly cost \$1.25 each. How much do four bars cost? \$3.75

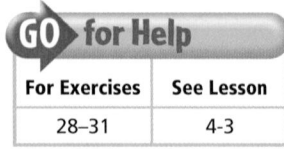

Test Prep and Mixed Review — Practice

Multiple Choice

25. Emily saw a dress she liked for \$60. The following week, the dress was on sale for \$45. By what percent was the dress marked down? B
   (A) 1.3% (B) 25% (C) 33% (D) 75%
26. Which graph contains all the points represented by the coordinate pairs in the table at the right? G

x	−1	$-\frac{1}{2}$	1
y	−3	−2	1

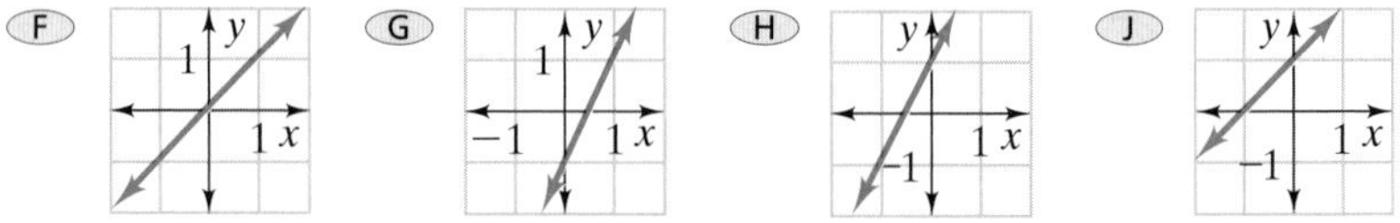

27. Jason bought a 10-pound box of Clementine oranges for \$3.99. If navel oranges sell for \$0.99 per pound, why did Jason believe that he made the better buy? C
   (A) Navel oranges are heavier than Clementine oranges.
   (B) The cost per pound of Clementine oranges is \$0.60 more than the cost per pound of navel oranges.
   (C) The cost per pound of Clementine oranges is \$0.60 less than the cost per pound of navel oranges.
   (D) The cost for all kinds of oranges in 10-pound boxes is the same.

GO for Help

For Exercises	See Lesson
28–31	4-3

Solve each proportion.

28. $\frac{3}{8} = \frac{t}{24}$ 9
29. $\frac{k}{234} = \frac{4}{5}$ 187.2
30. $\frac{16}{25} = \frac{9.6}{n}$ 15
31. $\frac{10}{f} = \frac{3.4}{8.5}$ 25

Test Prep

Resources

For additional practice with a variety of test item formats:

- Test-Taking Strategies, p. 251
- Test Prep, p. 255
- Test-Taking Strategies with Transparencies

21. No difference; the final cost is \$192.50 either way.
23. Answers may vary. Sample: Divide the selling price by 1 plus the percent of markup written in decimal form.

5-6b Activity Lab

Hands On

Using Percents

Suppose a restaurant meal costs $17 and you want to leave a 15% tip. What is your total cost? You could calculate the exact amount of the tip or you could use estimation and the model below.

ACTIVITY

Step 1 On graph paper, draw a horizontal axis and label it from 0% to 150%. At 100%, draw a vertical axis and label it from $0 to $60.

Step 2 Hold one end of a string at the 0% point on the horizontal axis.

Step 3 To find the total cost of the meal, pull the string tight and move it until it crosses the vertical axis at $17. Then find the point where the string crosses 115%, which represents the cost of the meal (100%) plus tip (15%). Estimate the amount at this point. The total is about $19.00.

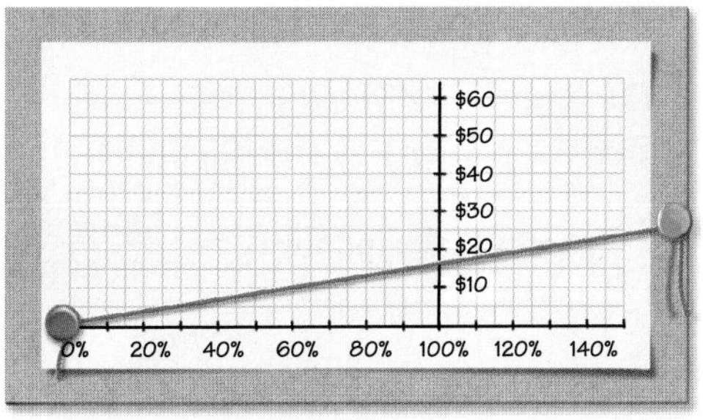

Exercises

Use your model to estimate a value for each exercise.

1. Your purchases cost $55. The sales tax rate is 6%. What is the total? $58.30
2. An item costs a store owner $28. She adds 35% to get the selling price. What is the selling price? $37.80
3. A CD costs $17 and you have a coupon for 25% off. What is your cost? $12.75
4. **Reasoning** The cost of a restaurant meal plus an 18% tip is $25. Explain how you can use your model to find the cost of the meal. See margin.

4. Answers may vary. Sample: Move the string until it crosses 118% on the horizontal axis and $25 on the vertical axis. Then find the dollar amount where the string crosses 100%.

Activity Lab

Using Percents

Students use a graph model to estimate percents of increase and decrease as applied to markups, discounts, and commissions. Percents from 0% to 150% are marked along the horizontal axis. Dollar values are marked on a vertical axis drawn at 100%. Then students move a string anchored at 0% to cross the dollar values at point required to solve each problem.

Guided Instruction

Activity

Help students create and label the graphs. Work through the activity with them. Then ask: *What other markup problems can you think of that can be solved by holding your string on 0% and crossing the vertical axis at $17?* Sample: If $17 is a price a store pays for something, you can estimate the cost of a 25% markup by looking at where the string aligns with 125%.

What discount problems? Sample: If an item had a regular price of $17, you could find the sale price if there is a 10% discount by looking at where the string aligns with 90%.

Exercises

For Exercise 2, remind students that they can find the selling price by multiplying $28 by 100% + 35% = 135%.

For Exercise 3, remind students that they can find the sale price by multiplying $17 by 100% − 25% = 75%.

Resources

- graph paper
- string or ruler

GPS Guided Problem Solving

Practice Solving Problems

Students must be able to extract important information from word problems in order to successfully solve the problems. This feature helps students analyze word problems and extract relevant information.

Guided Instruction

Have a volunteer read the introductory paragraph and question. Ask questions such as:

- *What is the question that must be answered?* Should the sweater be on the sale rack?
- *What specifically do you need to find out to answer the question?* if the sale price of the sweater is 40% or more off its original price

Teaching Tip

Have a volunteer read aloud the questions in the *What You Might Think* column. Have a second volunteer answer by reading the text in the *What You Write* column. Call attention to the fact that the answer is an explanation in the form of a complete sentence. Have students work through the problem, rather than just read it. Have them identify any steps they don't understand or that don't match their own work.

GPS Guided Problem Solving

Practice Solving Problems

A sign over a rack reads "40% or more off." A sweater on the rack shows a sale price of \$20 and a regular price of \$36. Should the sweater be on the sale rack? Explain.

What You Might Think	What You Might Write
What do I know? What do I want to find out?	I know the regular price of the sweater is \$36 and the sale price is \$20. I want to find the percent of discount.
How can I find the amount of the discount?	To find the amount of the discount, I subtract the sale price from the regular price. The amount of the discount is \$36 − \$20 = \$16.
How can I use the discount in an equation to find the percent of discount?	The discount divided by the regular price will give the percent of the discount.
Should the sweater be on the sale rack?	The sweater should be on the sale rack because 44.4% > 40%. The percent of discount on the sweater is greater than 40%.

$$\text{percent of discount} = \frac{\text{discount}}{\text{regular price}} = \frac{16}{36} = \frac{4}{9} = 0.44444\ldots \approx 44.4\%$$

Think It Through

1. **Reasoning** Could you have solved the problem by dividing the sale price by the regular price? Explain. See margin.
2. Does a 25% discount cancel a 25% markup? Explain. See margin.
3. Suppose the sweater was discounted by 20% and then discounted by another 20%. Should the sweater still be on the sale rack? no

1. Yes; $\frac{20}{36} = 0.5\overline{5}$, which means, if you buy the sweater for \$20, you are paying only 55.5% of the original price, or about 44.5% off the original price.
2. No; for example, a 25% markup on \$100 would give you a cost of \$125; if you subtract 25% of \$125, the price is only \$93.75.

Exercises

Solve each problem. For Exercises 4–5, answer the questions first.

4. Spending by federal, state, and local sources for K–12 public education in 2003 was $440.3 billion. This was a 4.9% increase from 2002. About how much was the total spending in 2002? $419.73 billion
   a. What percent of the spending for 2002 is $440.3 billion? 104.9%
   b. Write an equation, where x equals the spending in 2002. $1.049x = 440.3$

5. New Jersey spends y% more than the national average of $8,019 per student. Find y. 52.16

Per Pupil Spending

State	Amount
District of Columbia	$13,328
New Jersey	$12,202
New York	$12,140
Connecticut	$10,372
Vermont	$10,322
Massachusetts	$10,223

SOURCE: U.S. Census Bureau. Go to **PHSchool.com** for an update. Web Code: asg-9041

   a. How much more did New Jersey spend than the national average? $4,183
   b. Find the percent of increase for New Jersey. about 52%

For Exercises 6–7, use the table at the right.

6. By approximately what percent did the average price of a gallon of gasoline increase during the year? about 7%

7. Between what two months was the greatest percent of increase in the average price of a gallon of gasoline? May and June

8. During August, the price of a gallon of gasoline in Seattle was about 2.7% higher than in Boston. The price of gasoline in Boston was about 0.6% higher than in Cleveland. The price of gasoline in Cleveland was $2.59 per gallon. What was the price of a gallon of gasoline in Seattle? $2.68

U.S. Retail Prices for Regular Gasoline

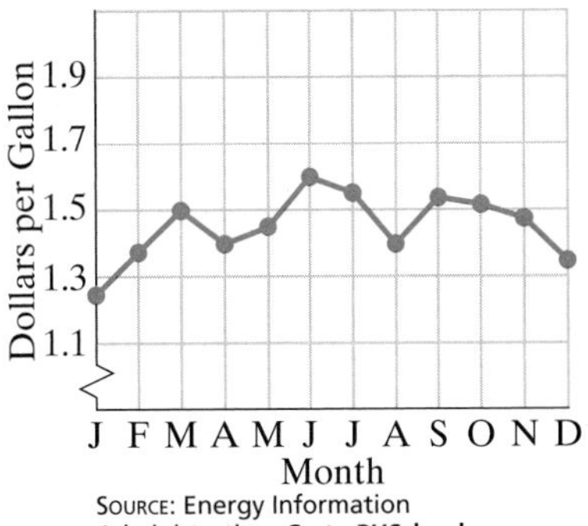

SOURCE: Energy Information Administration. Go to **PHSchool.com** for a data update. Web Code: asg-9041

Error Prevention!

Review the percent of discount equation by relating it to the percent of change.

percent of change = $\frac{\text{amount of change}}{\text{original amount}}$

percent of discount = $\frac{\text{discount}}{\text{regular price}}$

Exercises

Have students work in pairs to complete Exercises 1–3. Then have partners share with the class what they were thinking as they wrote each step. Elicit the fact that there is often more than one way to arrive at the solution of a problem.

Alternatively, have students work independently. Then have them form groups in which members share and evaluate their answers. Students should make adjustments in their work based on their group discussion.

Differentiated Instruction

Special Needs L1

Student may be unfamiliar with the word *billion*. Explain that a billion is equivalent to 1,000,000,000 (or a 1 with 9 zeros).

5-7

1. Plan

Objective
To find simple interest and account balances

Examples
1 Finding Simple Interest
2 Finding an Account Balance

Math Understandings: p. 208D

Professional Development

Math Background

More Math Background: p. 208D

Lesson Planning and Resources

See p. 208E for a list of the resources that support this lesson.

PowerPoint

Bell Ringer Practice

Check Skills You'll Need
Use student page, transparency, or PowerPoint. For intervention, direct students to:
Formulas
Lesson 2-6
Extra Skills and Word Problems Practice, Ch. 2

2. Teach

Activity Lab

Use before the lesson.

All in One Teaching Resources

Activity Lab 5-7: Simple Interest

Guided Instruction

Example 1
Provide students with a blank grid.

5-7 Simple Interest

Check Skills You'll Need

1. **Vocabulary Review** A __?__ is a rule that shows a relationship between quantities. formula

Solve each formula for the variable indicated in red. See below.

2. $V = \ell wh$
3. $d = rt$
4. $y = x + b$
5. $V = \frac{1}{3}Bh$

GO for Help Lesson 2-6

Check Skills You'll Need
2. $w = \frac{V}{\ell h}$
3. $r = \frac{d}{t}$
4. $b = y - x$
5. $B = \frac{3V}{h}$

What You'll Learn

To find simple interest and account balances

New Vocabulary interest, interest rate, principal, simple interest, balance

Why Learn This?

When you deposit money in a bank, the bank pays you for the use of your money. When you borrow money, the bank charges you for the use of its money.

Interest is the amount of money paid for the use of money. Interest is calculated at a certain percentage rate called the **interest rate. Principal** is the original amount deposited or borrowed. **Simple interest** is interest calculated only on the principal.

KEY CONCEPTS Simple Interest

$$I = p \cdot r \cdot t$$

where I is the interest, p is the principal, r is the interest rate per year, and t is the time in years.

EXAMPLE Finding Simple Interest

1 Gridded Response A student deposits \$200 in a bank account. The simple interest rate is $6\frac{1}{2}\%$ per year. Find the interest the account earns in 4 years.

$I = p \cdot r \cdot t$ ← simple interest formula
$= 200 \cdot 0.065 \cdot 4$ ← Substitute.
$= 52$ ← Multiply.

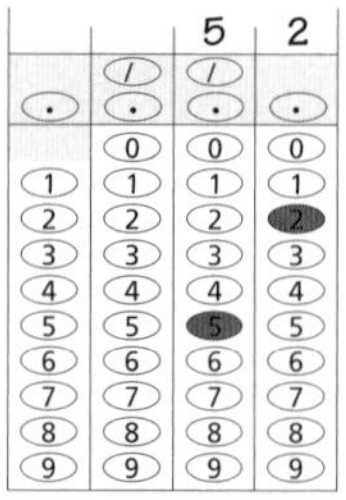

In 4 years, the interest earned is \$52.00.

Test Prep Tip
Check the placement of the decimal point in your answer for reasonableness.

Quick Check

1. Find the interest earned on \$3,600 invested at $3\frac{1}{2}\%$ simple interest for 5 years. \$630

Differentiated Instruction Solutions for All Learners

Special Needs L1
Students start by finding the interest earned in 1 year in Example 1. They find that the same amount of interest is earned every year. *Why?* Sample: Because every year the same percent of the same amount of money (the principal) is found.
learning style: verbal

Below Level L2
In Lessons 5-4 and 5-5, a capital *P* was used for percent as a decimal. Clarify that here *p* is used for principal and *r* is used for rate, or percent.
learning style: visual

Vocabulary Tip

The word *principal* means the money you deposit and the person in charge of a school.

The principal in an account plus the earned interest is the **balance.**

EXAMPLE Finding an Account Balance

2 **Savings** You deposit $120 in an account that earns 5% simple interest. Find the balance in the account after 3 years.

Step 1 Find the interest earned.

$I = p \cdot r \cdot t$

$= 120 \cdot 0.05 \cdot 3$ ← Substitute.

$= 18$ ← Multiply.

Step 2 Find the balance in the account.

principal + earned interest = balance

120 + 18 = 138 ← Substitute. Then add.

The final balance in the account is $138.

Quick Check

2. A teacher invests $205 in an account that earns 8% simple interest. Find the balance in the account after 10 years. $369

Check Your Understanding

Vocabulary **Match each term with the correct definition.**

1. simple interest C
2. interest B
3. interest rate A

A. percent on which savings earnings are based
B. money earned by a depositor or lender
C. money earned based only on the deposit

4. An account with $545 is invested at 5% simple interest for 6 years. What is the final balance in the account? $708.50

Homework Exercises

For more exercises, see Extra Skills and Word Problems.

GO for Help

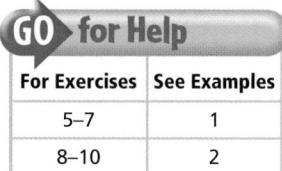

For Exercises	See Examples
5–7	1
8–10	2

A **Find the interest earned on each account.**

5. $970 at $4\frac{1}{4}$% simple interest for 2 years $82.45
6. $182 at 6% simple interest for 4 years $43.68
7. You deposit $3,500 in an account. Find the interest earned in 5 years at a simple interest rate of $7\frac{1}{2}$% per year. $1,312.50

Advanced Learners L4
Students research current interest rates offered and charged by a local bank.
learning style: verbal

English Language Learners ELL
Words such as *interest* and *principal* have entirely different meanings in mathematics than they do in everyday life. Students define these words in common English, and then give examples of their use in mathematics.
learning style: verbal

PowerPoint

Additional Examples

1 **2** A student deposits $150 into a bank that pays 6% simple interest. Find the interest earned in 4 years and the final balance after 5 years. $36, $195

All in One Teaching Resources
- Daily Notetaking Guide 5-7 L3
- Adapted Notetaking 5-7 L1

Closure

- *Explain how finding the simple interest and finding the account balance are different.* Sample: To find simple interest, multiply the principal times the rate times the time. To find the account balance, add the earned interest to the principal.

3. Practice

Assignment Guide

Check Your Understanding
Go over Exercises 1–4 in class before assigning the Homework Exercises.

Homework Exercises

A Practice by Example	5–10
B Apply Your Skills	11–13
C Challenge	14
Test Prep and Mixed Review	15–19

Homework Quick Check
To check students' understanding of key skills and concepts, go over Exercises 6, 9, 11, 12, and 13.

4. Assess & Reteach

PowerPoint

Lesson Quiz

1. You deposit $80 into an account that earns 6% simple interest. Find the amount of interest earned in 3 years. $14.40
2. You deposit $180 into an account that earns 6% simple interest. How much will be in the account after 3 years? $212.40

Differentiated Instruction Resources

Adapted Practice 5-7 (L1)

Practice 5-7 (L3)

Simp... t

Find the interest earned on each account. Round answers to nearest cent.

1. \$100 at 6% simple interest for 3 years — \$18.00
2. \$200 at 7% simple interest for 1 year — \$14.00
3. \$142 at $5\frac{1}{4}$% simple interest for 5 years — \$37.28
4. \$6,250 at 4% simple interest for 2 years — \$500.00
5. \$884 at 5% simple interest for 10 years — \$442.00
6. \$75 at $3\frac{1}{2}$% simple interest for 5 years — \$13.13
7. Bonnie deposited \$500 in an account with a simple interest rate of $6\frac{1}{4}$%. How much interest will she earn in 4 years? \$125.00
8. John invested \$100 in an account with 2% simple interest. Julie invested \$75 in an account with 3% simple interest. Who will earn more interest in 5 years? Julie will earn more.

Find the final balance in each account.

9. \$200 invested at 2% simple interest for 5 years — \$220.00
10. \$200 invested at $4\frac{1}{2}$% simple interest for 5 years — \$245.00
11. \$4,500 invested at 6% simple interest for 7 years — \$6,390.00
12. \$1,256 invested at 7% simple interest for 6 years — \$1,783.52
13. You deposit \$100 in an account with $7\frac{1}{2}$% simple interest. What is the account balance after 2 years? \$115.00
14. Simon invested \$3,200 in an account with $3\frac{1}{2}$% simple interest. After 3 years, he transferred his balance to an account with 6% simple interest. What is Simon's final balance after 6 years in the second account? \$4,808.96

5-7 • Guided Problem Solving GPS (L3)

Student Page 244, Exercise 12:

Investments A woman invests \$500 in a 36-month certificate of deposit (CD) with a simple interest rate of 5.36%. At the end of the 36 months, the woman redeposits the final balance of the CD into another 36-month CD with the same simple interest rate. Find the final balance of the CD.

Understand

1. How much money does the woman originally invest? \$500
2. What is the original length of time and interest rate? 36 months, or 3 years, and 5.36%
3. Underline what you are asked to do.

Plan and Carry Out

4. What is the formula for simple interest? $I = prt$
5. In the simple interest formula, is time represented in months or years? years
6. Find the interest of the first investment by using the simple interest formula. $I = \$500 \times 0.0536 \times 3 = \$80.40$
7. Find the new balance by adding the original investment and the interest earned. $\$500 + \$80.40 = \$580.40$
8. Using this as the amount of money redeposited, find the interest earned during the next 36-month period. $I = \$580.40 \times 0.0536 \times 3 = \$93.33$
9. Find the final balance by adding this interest to the amount that was redeposited. $\$580.40 + \$93.33 = \$673.73$

Check

10. Would your answer be the same if you added the time together as 6 years and found the balance? Why or why not? No; The reinvested amount already included accrued interest.

Solve Another Problem

11. Mrs. Smith and Mrs. Jones open bank accounts for their children, each depositing \$250.00. Mrs. Smith earns an interest rate of 4.2%. Mrs. Jones earns an interest rate of 7.2% but pays a \$1 monthly maintenance fee. Who will have a higher balance after 2 years? Mrs. Smith; \$3.00

Enrichment 5-7 (L4)

Reteaching 5-7 (L2)

Simple...

Example: Marcia deposits \$200 in an account with 4% simple interest for 3 years.

Finding earned interest	***Finding an account balance***
Interest = principal · rate · time in years	principal + earned interest = balance
$I = p \cdot r \cdot t$	200 + 24 = 224
$I = 200 \cdot 0.04 \cdot 3$	After 3 years, the account balance is \$224.
$I = 24$	
In 3 years, the interest earned is \$24.	

Find the interest earned in each account.

1. \$400 at 6% simple interest for 3 years — \$72.00
2. \$100 at 3% simple interest for 6 years — \$18.00
3. \$5,500 at 2% simple interest for 8 years — \$880.00
4. \$120 at $4\frac{1}{2}$% simple interest for 1 year — \$5.40
5. \$350 at $5\frac{1}{4}$% simple interest for 2 years — \$36.75
6. \$75 at 4% simple interest for 5 years — \$15.00

Find the final balance in each account.

7. \$100 at 2% simple interest for 6 years — \$112.00
8. \$100 at 7% simple interest for 6 years — \$142.00
9. \$260 at 4% simple interest for 1 year — \$270.40
10. \$35,000 at $6\frac{1}{4}$% simple interest for 3 years — \$41,562.50
11. Joshua invests \$85 in an account that earns 5% simple interest. Find the final balance in the account after 7 years. \$114.75
12. Lindsey deposits \$300 in a bank account with $2\frac{1}{4}$% simple interest. Find the final balance in the account after 2 years and after 5 years. \$313.50; \$333.75

Find the balance in each account.

8. \$198 invested at 4% simple interest for 13 years **\$300.96**
9. \$535 invested at 6% simple interest for 10 years **\$856**
10. An electrician deposits \$6,000 in a bank account with 7% simple interest. What is the balance after 4 years? **\$7,680**

B GPS 11. **Guided Problem Solving** You deposit \$100 into an account that pays 5% simple interest. After 3 years, you move the balance to an account that pays 5.5% simple interest. What is your balance after 4 years in the second account? **\$140.30**
- **Understand the Problem** For 3 years, \$100 earns 5% simple interest. For the next 4 years, it earns 5.5% simple interest.
- **Make a Plan** Find the balance in the first account after 3 years and in the second account after 4 years.

12. **Investments** A woman invests \$500 in a 36-month certificate of deposit (CD) with a simple interest rate of 5.36%. At the end of the 36 months, the woman redeposits her final balance into another 36-month CD with the same simple interest rate. Find the final balance. **\$673.73** (GPS)

GO Online
Homework Video Tutor
Visit: PHSchool.com
Web Code: ase-0507

13. **Writing in Math** There are two accounts being offered at your bank. One account pays 1.3% simple interest and has no monthly maintenance fees. The other account pays 2% simple interest but charges a \$1 monthly maintenance fee. Into which account would you prefer to deposit \$747 for one year? Explain. **See left.**

13. The account that pays 1.3% simple interest, because $747(1 + 0.013) = \$756.71$ and $747(1 + 0.02) - 12 = \$749.94$

C 14. **Challenge** You deposit \$1,000 into an account. At what simple interest rate will the balance be \$1,240 after 180 months? **1.6%**

Test Prep and Mixed Review — Practice

Gridded Response

15. Nick deposited \$2,500 in an account that earns 6% simple interest. How many dollars will be in the account after 7 years? **3,550**
16. The boxes shown at the right are similar. What is the value of x, to the nearest tenth? **11.3**

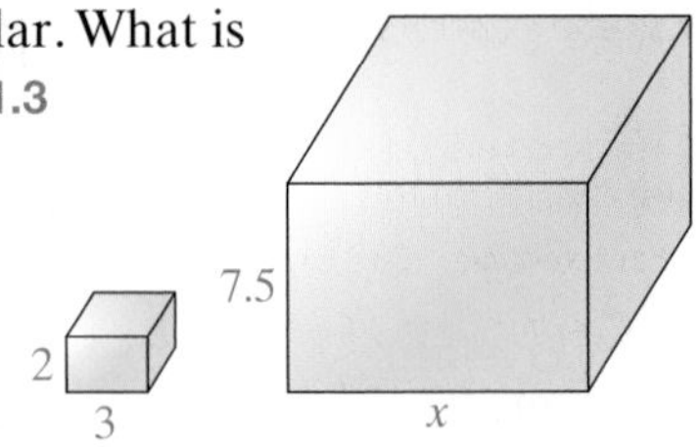

17. Mrs. Ramirez is sending three students from each homeroom in her school to a conference. If there are 36 homerooms, how many students will attend the conference? **108**

GO for Help

For Exercises	See Lesson
18–19	2-6

Find the area of each figure.

18. square: side = 3.6 cm **12.96 cm^2**
19. rectangle: 9 ft by 11.4 ft **102.6 ft^2**

Test Prep

Resources

For additional practice with a variety of test item formats:
- Test-Taking Strategies, p. 251
- Test Prep, p. 255
- Test-Taking Strategies with Transparencies

Alternative Assessment

Students work in pairs to solve the problem. *Which would earn you more money at the end of 2 years:*
- *You deposit \$100 in Account A at 6% interest or you deposit \$110 in Account B at 3% interest?*

Account B: Account A earns \$12 and account B earns \$6.60.

Checkpoint Quiz 2

Lessons 5-5 through 5-7

Find each percent of change. Round to the nearest tenth of a percent where necessary. Label your answer *increase* or *decrease*.

1. 14 to 154 1,000% increase
2. 427 to 420 1.6% decrease
3. 2 to 0.4 80% decrease
4. 123 to 456 270.7% increase
5. **Sports** At a track meet, a shot-putter's first throw was 36 ft 3 in. long. The shot-putter's second throw was 37 ft 6 in. long. Find the percent of increase in the length of the throws. Round to the nearest tenth of a percent. 3.4%
6. **Pets** A dog owner pays \$14.99 for a 20-lb bag of dog food at 35% off. Find the regular price for the dog food. Round to the nearest cent. \$23.06
7. **Shopping** Charlene buys a skirt on sale. The regular price is \$26.99, but she pays \$22.94. What is the percent of discount Charlene gets when she buys the skirt on sale? 15%

Find the simple interest earned on each account.

8. \$250 at $3\frac{1}{2}\%$ for 5 years \$43.75
9. \$95 at 6% for 3 years \$17.10

5-8a Activity Lab

Hands On

Exploring Probability

ACTIVITY

1–4. Check students' work.

1. Toss a coin. Record whether the coin lands heads or tails.
2. Repeat this process 20 times.
3. Copy and complete the table at the right. Did heads or tails occur more often?
4. Compare your results with those of your classmates. Did the entire class record the same results? Explain why or why not.

Result	Number of Occurrences
Heads	■
Tails	■

5. What results do you think you would get if you tossed the coin 100 times? Explain. See margin.

Activity Lab

5. In 100 tosses, you would get about 50 heads and 50 tails. In 200 tosses, you would get about 100 heads and 100 tails. The reason is that heads and tails are equally likely.

Checkpoint Quiz

Use this Checkpoint Quiz to check studentsÕunderstanding of the skills and concepts of Lessons 5-5 through 5-7.

Resources

- All in One Teaching Resources Checkpoint Quiz 2
- ExamView Assessment Suite CD-ROM
- Success Tracker Online Intervention

Activity Lab

Exploring Probability

Students perform a probability experiment. They tally the results, compare results with the rest of the class, and make a conjecture. This hands-on approach to probability helps students see the difference between experimental and theoretical probability.

Guided Instruction

Math Tip

The probability of an event is not a good predictor of what will happen in a single case or in a small number of cases. The laws of probability predict only what will happen in a very large number of events.

Activity

After each student compiles the results of 20 tosses, you may want to combine all the results into one. Help students see that as they add more tosses, the result is likely to show numbers that are about one-half heads and one-half tails.

Resources

- **Activity Lab 5-8:** Ratios and Probability
- coins

5-8

1. Plan

Objective
To find probability and the sample space of an event

Examples
1 Finding a Probability
2 Application: Surveys
3 Finding a Sample Space
4 Application: Biology

Math Understandings: p. 208D

Professional Development

Math Background

The probability of an event is always between 0 and 1 inclusive: 0 if the event is impossible, 1 if the event is certain. The more likely an event is to occur, the closer its probability is to 1.

More Math Background: p. 208D

Lesson Planning and Resources

See p. 208E for a list of the resources that support this lesson.

PowerPoint

Bell Ringer Practice

Check Skills You'll Need
Use student page, transparency, or PowerPoint. For intervention, direct students to:
Ratios and Rates
Lesson 4-1
Extra Skills and Word Problems Practice, Ch. 4

5-8 Ratios and Probability

Check Skills You'll Need

1. **Vocabulary Review** A _?_ is a comparison of two quantities by division. ratio

Write each ratio in simplest form.

2. 3 : 6 1 : 2
3. $\frac{8\text{ h}}{100\text{ h}}$ $\frac{2}{25}$
4. $\frac{90\text{ s}}{270\text{ s}}$ $\frac{1}{3}$
5. $\frac{20\text{ cm}}{36\text{ cm}}$ $\frac{5}{9}$
6. 17 to 68 1 to 4

GO for Help Lesson 4-1

What You'll Learn

To find probability and the sample space of an event

New Vocabulary outcome, event, probability of an event, sample space

Why Learn This?

Suppose you have six quarters like the ones shown, and you choose one at random. You can find the probability of choosing a quarter from a certain state.

An **outcome** is any of the possible results that can occur. A collection of possible outcomes in an experiment is an **event.** There are three possible events in this experiment: selecting an Indiana quarter, selecting a Tennessee quarter, and selecting an Ohio quarter.

The **probability of an event** E is given by the following formula when outcomes are equally likely.

$$P(E) = \frac{\text{number of favorable outcomes}}{\text{total number of possible outcomes}}$$

EXAMPLE Finding a Probability

1 Suppose you choose a ball at random from the balls in the bowl at the left. Find $P(\text{red})$.

$$P(\text{red}) = \frac{2}{8} \begin{array}{l}\leftarrow \text{2 favorable outcomes}\\ \leftarrow \text{8 possible outcomes}\end{array}$$

$$= \frac{1}{4} \quad \leftarrow \text{Simplify.}$$

The probability of choosing a red ball is $\frac{1}{4}$.

Quick Check

1. Find $P(\text{blue})$. $\frac{3}{8}$

Differentiated Instruction Solutions for All Learners

Special Needs L1
Students might have difficulty constructing a sample space on plain paper. Provide them with grid paper so that they can use the squares as guides for writing the sample space.

learning style: visual

Below Level L2
Use one number cube to make sure students understand the sample space for rolling one cube: 1, 2, 3, 4, 5, 6.

learning style: verbal

You can express probabilities as fractions or as percents.

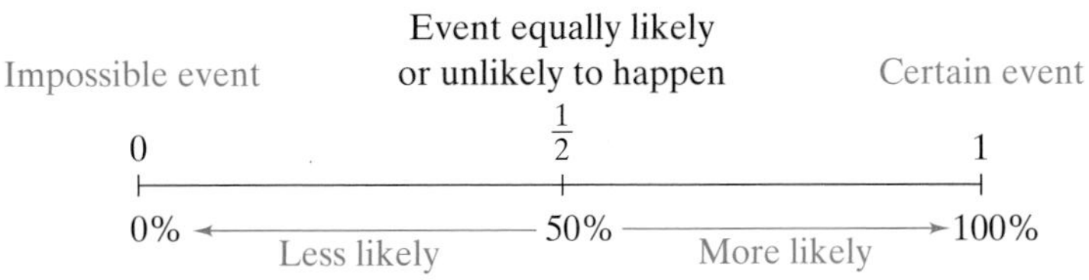

EXAMPLE Application: Surveys

2 **Multiple Choice** The circle graph shows the results of a survey of middle school students. Suppose you choose a student's name at random. Find the probability that the student's favorite music is pop or country.

Ⓐ 12% Ⓑ 32% Ⓒ 44% Ⓓ 63%

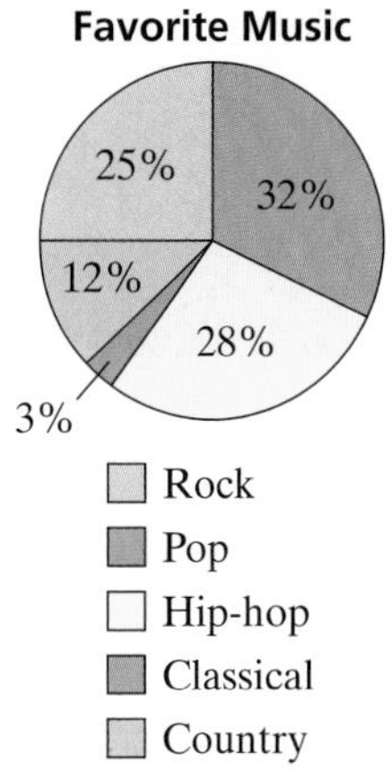

$P(\text{pop or country}) = P(\text{pop}) + P(\text{country})$

$= 32\% + 12\%$ ← **Substitute.**

$= 44\%$ ← **Simplify.**

Since the probability is 44%, the correct answer is choice C.

Test Prep Tip

The phrase "pop or country music" refers to anyone in either group. For this reason, you add the individual percents together.

Quick Check

2. Find P(classical or rock). 28%

The collection of all possible outcomes in an experiment is called the **sample space.** You can make a table to find the sample space.

EXAMPLE Finding a Sample Space

3 Construct the sample space for rolling two number cubes. Then find the probability that the two number cubes have a product of 12. Express the probability as a fraction and as a percent.

Of the 36 possible outcomes, four outcomes have a product of 12.

$P(\text{product of } 12) = \frac{4}{36}$, or $\frac{1}{9}$

The probability is $\frac{1}{9}$, or about 11.1%.

	1	2	3	4	5	6
1	(1, 1)	(2, 1)	(3, 1)	(4, 1)	(5, 1)	(6, 1)
2	(1, 2)	(2, 2)	(3, 2)	(4, 2)	(5, 2)	(6, 2)
3	(1, 3)	(2, 3)	(3, 3)	(4, 3)	(5, 3)	(6, 3)
4	(1, 4)	(2, 4)	(3, 4)	(4, 4)	(5, 4)	(6, 4)
5	(1, 5)	(2, 5)	(3, 5)	(4, 5)	(5, 5)	(6, 5)
6	(1, 6)	(2, 6)	(3, 6)	(4, 6)	(5, 6)	(6, 6)

Quick Check

3. Find P(sum is odd). Write the answer as a fraction. $\frac{1}{2}$

Advanced Learners L4
How many possible outcomes exist for rolling two number cubes and tossing a coin? 72 rolling two number cubes and tossing 2 coins? 144

learning style: verbal

English Language Learners ELL
Review with students what selecting "at random" means. Discuss selecting a ball from a group of balls that they can see (not at random), and then selecting a ball from a group they cannot see (at random).

learning style: verbal

2. Teach

Activity Lab

Use before the lesson.
Student Edition Hands-On Activity Lab 5-8a, Exploring Probability, p. 245

All in One Teaching Resources

Activity Lab 5-8: Ratios and Probability

Guided Instruction

Example 1
To compare the theoretical and experimental probabilities, use chips in a paper bag to represent the balls and have students choose a chip at random, replacing the chip each time and recording their results.

Example 2
Discuss the fact that the phrase "the student's favorite music is pop or country" in Example 2 includes any student who is in those two groups when they are put together. This is why the percents are added.

Error Prevention!

Some students may, in Example 3, find outcomes with a sum of 12. Ask them what operation the word "product" means.

PowerPoint

Additional Examples

1 There are 3 red, 2 green, 5 yellow, and 1 blue marker pens in a box. Suppose you choose one at random. Find these probabilities.

a. P(yellow) $\frac{5}{11}$ **b.** P(brown) 0

2 In a survey of the class, 13% of the students prefer vanilla, 27% prefer chocolate, 10% prefer strawberry, and the rest chose other flavors of ice cream. What is the probability that a student randomly selected from the class chose vanilla or chocolate? 40%

3 Express as a fraction the probability that the outcome for rolling two number cubes has a sum less than 7. $\frac{15}{36}$ or $\frac{5}{12}$

Guided Instruction

Connection to Biology
Example 4 assumes that the probabilities of a baby being a girl or a boy are each 50%. Actually, the probability of a boy is about 53%.

PowerPoint

Additional Examples

4 What is the probability of there being at least 1 male kitten in a litter of 4 kittens? Draw the sample space. Express the probability as a fraction. $\frac{15}{16}$

Sample space

MMMM	MMMF	MMFM
MMFF	MFMM	MFMF
MFFM	MFFF	FMMM
FMMF	FMFM	FMFF
FFFM	FFFF	FFMM
FFMF		

All in One Teaching Resources
- Daily Notetaking Guide 5-8 L3
- Adapted Notetaking 5-8 L1

Closure

- *What is meant by* P(E)? Sample: *P(E)* is the probability of an event, or the number of favorable outcomes divided by the total number of outcomes.
- *What is the sample space?* Sample: The sample space is the collection of all possible outcomes.

You can also use a tree diagram to construct a sample space.

EXAMPLE Application: Biology

4 A family has three children. Find the sample space showing the number of boys and girls in the family. Then find the probability that there are at least two girls, given that $P(B) = P(G)$. Express the probability as a fraction.

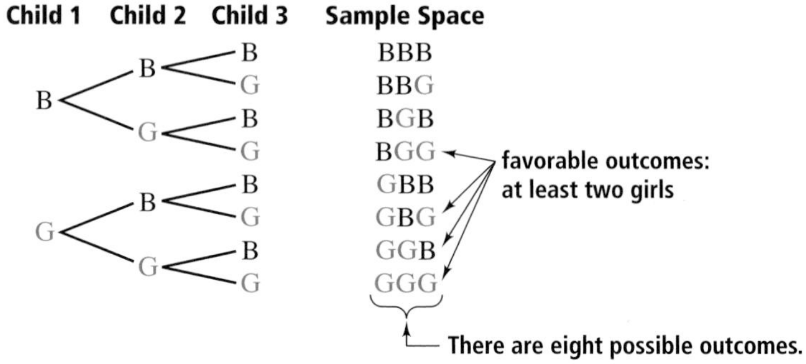

$$P(\text{at least two girls}) = \frac{\text{number of outcomes with at least two girls}}{\text{total number of outcomes}}$$

$$= \frac{4}{8} \quad \leftarrow \text{Substitute.}$$

$$= \frac{1}{2} \quad \leftarrow \text{Write the fraction in simplest form.}$$

Quick Check

4. Use the tree diagram from Example 4. Find the probability that a family with three children will have exactly two boys. Express the probability as a fraction. $\frac{3}{8}$

Check Your Understanding

1. Vocabulary Explain the difference between an outcome and an event. Can an outcome be an event? See margin.

2. Reasoning A jar contains only red, white, and blue marbles. Explain how you know that $P(\text{red, white, or blue}) = 1$.

2. If the jar has only red, white, and blue marbles, then you are certain to pick a red, white, or blue marble, so the probability is 100% or $P = 1$.

A dart lands at random within the circle on the game board shown at the right. Find each probability.

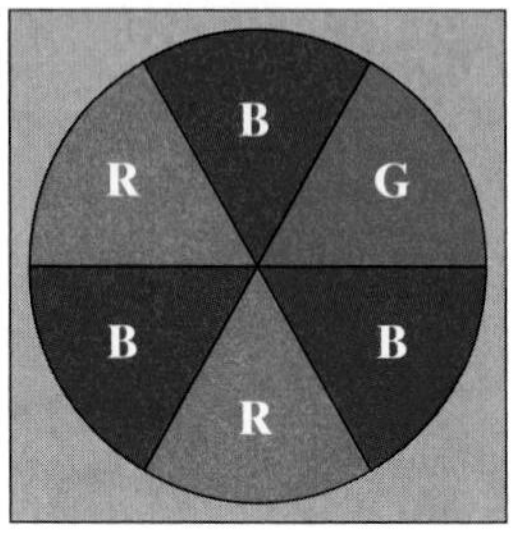

3. $P(\text{red})$ $\frac{1}{3}$

4. $P(\text{blue})$ $\frac{1}{2}$

5. $P(\text{green})$ $\frac{1}{6}$

1. Answers may vary. Sample: An outcome is any of the possible results that can occur. An event is the collection of possible outcomes in an experiment. An outcome can be an event if there is only one possible result of the experiment.

Homework Exercises

For more exercises, see Extra Skills and Word Problems.

GO for Help

For Exercises	See Examples
6–11	1
12–14	2
15–20	3
21–25	4

A **A spinner has eight equal sections labeled 1 through 8. You spin the spinner once. Write each probability as a fraction.**

6. $P(6)$ $\frac{1}{8}$
7. $P(3)$ $\frac{1}{8}$
8. $P(\text{even number})$ $\frac{1}{2}$
9. $P(\text{number less than } 4)$ $\frac{3}{8}$
10. $P(\text{number greater than } 8)$ 0
11. $P(\text{number less than } 10)$ 1

Using the graph at the right, find each probability.

12. $P(\text{music or silence})$ 83%
13. $P(\text{talk or ads})$ 10%
14. $P(\text{anything but silence})$ 78%

What We Prefer to Hear When on Hold

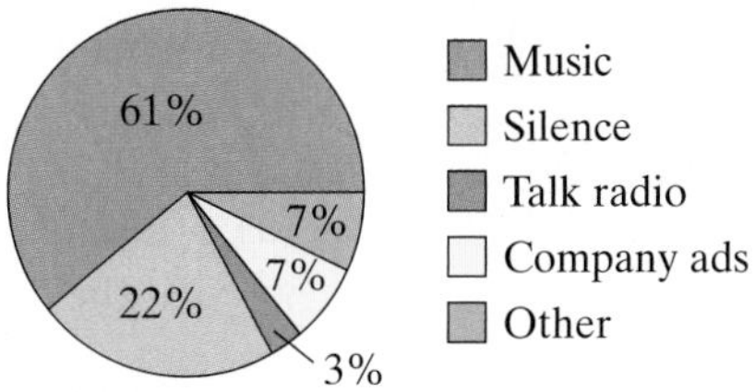

Two spinners have four sections of equal size labeled 1, 2, 3, and 4. Construct the sample space for spinning the two spinners. Write each probability as a fraction.

15. $P(\text{Product is } 4.)$ $\frac{3}{16}$
16. $P(\text{Sum is even.})$ $\frac{1}{2}$
17. $P(\text{Difference is } 2.)$ $\frac{1}{4}$
18. $P(\text{Sum is } 7.)$ $\frac{1}{8}$
19. $P(\text{Difference is odd.})$ $\frac{1}{2}$
20. $P(\text{Sum is } 5.)$ $\frac{1}{4}$

For Exercises 21–25, use three coins.

21. Draw a tree diagram to find the sample space. One possible outcome is heads–tails–tails. See margin.
22. Find $P(\text{no heads})$. $\frac{1}{8}$
23. Find $P(\text{exactly one head})$. $\frac{3}{8}$
24. Find $P(\text{exactly two heads})$. $\frac{3}{8}$
25. Find $P(\text{three heads})$. $\frac{1}{8}$

B GPS

26. **Guided Problem Solving** A vending machine contains 200 packages of granola bars and crackers. If you pick a package at random, $P(\text{crackers}) = 45\%$. How many packages are granola bars? 110 packages
    - **Make a Plan** Find the number of packages of crackers and subtract that from the total.
    - **Carry Out the Plan** The number of packages of crackers is ■. The number of packages of granola bars is $200 - ■$.

27. **Gardening** A package of wildflower seeds contains 50 daisy seeds, 80 sunflower seeds, 100 black-eyed Susan seeds, and 20 lupine seeds. Find the probability that a seed selected at random will be a daisy seed. $\frac{1}{5}$ (GPS)

GO Online
Homework Video Tutor
Visit: PHSchool.com
Web Code: ase-0508

21. Toss 1 Toss 2 Toss 3 Outcome

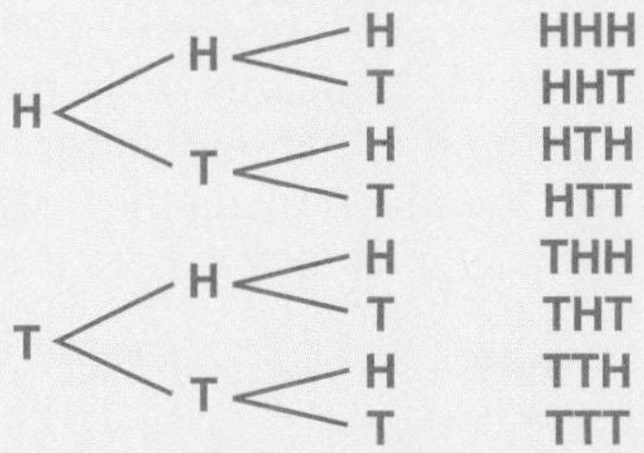

3. Practice

Assignment Guide

Check Your Understanding

Go over Exercises 1–5 in class before assigning the Homework Exercises.

Homework Exercises

A Practice by Example	6–25
B Apply Your Skills	26–32
C Challenge	33
Test Prep and Mixed Review	34–39

Homework Quick Check

To check students' understanding of key skills and concepts, go over Exercises 12, 21, 26, 28, and 32.

Differentiated Instruction Resources

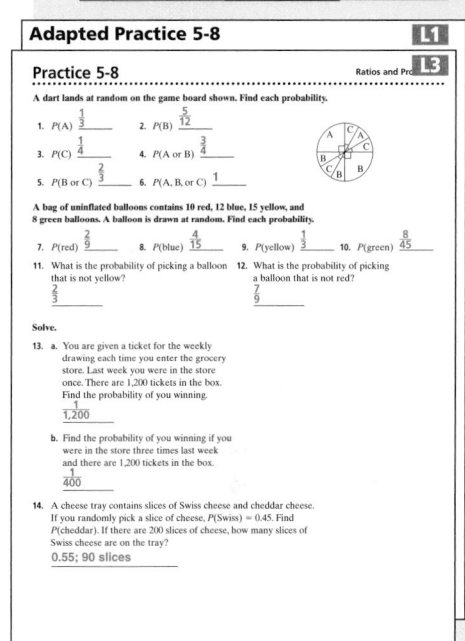

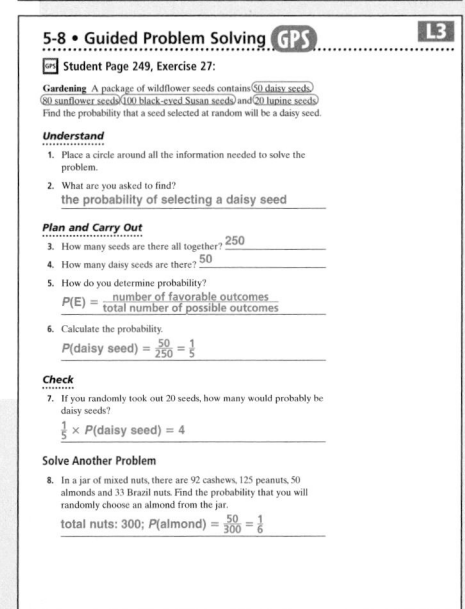

Adapted Practice 5-8 L1

Practice 5-8 Ratios and Pro... L3

A dart lands at random on the game board shown. Find each probability.

1. $P(A)$ $\frac{1}{3}$
2. $P(B)$ $\frac{5}{12}$
3. $P(C)$ $\frac{1}{4}$
4. $P(A \text{ or } B)$ $\frac{3}{4}$
5. $P(B \text{ or } C)$ $\frac{2}{3}$
6. $P(A, B, \text{or } C)$ 1

A bag of uninflated balloons contains 10 red, 12 blue, 15 yellow, and 8 green balloons. A balloon is drawn at random. Find each probability.

7. $P(\text{red})$ $\frac{2}{9}$
8. $P(\text{blue})$ $\frac{4}{15}$
9. $P(\text{yellow})$ $\frac{1}{3}$
10. $P(\text{green})$ $\frac{8}{45}$
11. What is the probability of picking a balloon that is not yellow? $\frac{2}{3}$
12. What is the probability of picking a balloon that is not red? $\frac{7}{9}$

Solve.

13. a. You are given a ticket for the weekly drawing each time you enter the grocery store. Last week you were in the store once. There are 1,200 tickets in the box. Find the probability of you winning. $\frac{1}{1{,}200}$
    b. Find the probability of you winning if you were in the store three times last week and there are 1,200 tickets in the box. $\frac{1}{400}$
14. A cheese tray contains slices of Swiss cheese and cheddar cheese. If you randomly pick a slice of cheese, $P(\text{Swiss}) = 0.45$. Find $P(\text{cheddar})$. If there are 200 slices of cheese, how many slices of Swiss cheese are on the tray? 0.55; 90 slices

5-8 • Guided Problem Solving GPS L3

Student Page 249, Exercise 27:

Gardening A package of wildflower seeds contains 50 daisy seeds, 80 sunflower seeds, 100 black-eyed Susan seeds and 20 lupine seeds. Find the probability that a seed selected at random will be a daisy seed.

Understand

1. Place a circle around all the information needed to solve the problem.
2. What are you asked to find? the probability of selecting a daisy seed

Plan and Carry Out

3. How many seeds are there all together? 250
4. How many daisy seeds are there? 50
5. How do you determine probability? $P(E) = \frac{\text{number of favorable outcomes}}{\text{total number of possible outcomes}}$
6. Calculate the probability. $P(\text{daisy seed}) = \frac{50}{250} = \frac{1}{5}$

Check

7. If you randomly took out 20 seeds, how many would probably be daisy seeds? $\frac{1}{5} \times P(\text{daisy seed}) = 4$

Solve Another Problem

8. In a jar of mixed nuts, there are 92 cashews, 125 peanuts, 50 almonds and 33 Brazil nuts. Find the probability that you will randomly choose an almond from the jar. total nuts: 300; $P(\text{almond}) = \frac{50}{300} = \frac{1}{6}$

4. Assess & Reteach

PowerPoint

Lesson Quiz

1. A 6-sided number cube has the numbers 1, 2, 3, 4, 5, and 6 on its faces. What is the probability of rolling a number less than 5? Write your answer as a fraction. $\frac{2}{3}$
2. A survey shows that 24% of people get their news from the Internet, 48% percent from TV, 22% from newspapers, and 6% from news magazines. If you interviewed at random one person who answered the survey, what is the probability that you would select someone who gets news from TV or the Internet? 72%
3. A spinner has two equal sections, one yellow and one green. You spin 3 times in a row. Make an organized list to show the sample space for spinning the spinner 3 times. What is the probability of spinning green at least twice in a row? Sample space: YYY YYG YGY YGG GYY GYG GGY GGG; $\frac{3}{8}$

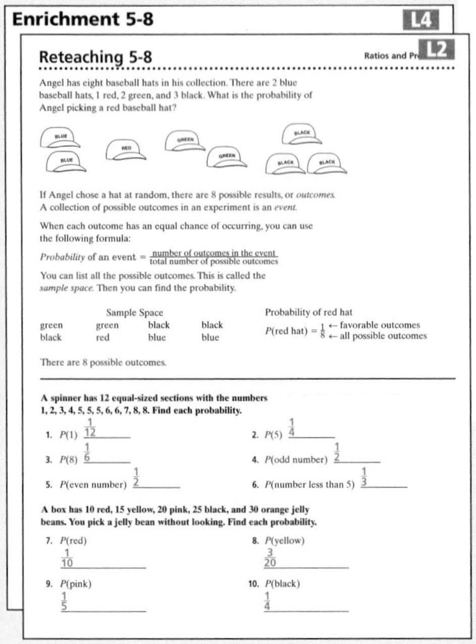

Enrichment 5-8 L4

Reteaching 5-8 Ratios and Pr... L2

Angel has eight baseball hats in his collection. There are 2 blue baseball hats, 1 red, 2 green, and 3 black. What is the probability of Angel picking a red baseball hat?

If Angel chose a hat at random, there are 8 possible results, or *outcomes*. A collection of possible outcomes in an experiment is an *event*.

When each outcome has an equal chance of occurring, you can use the following formula:

Probability of an event $= \frac{\text{number of outcomes in the event}}{\text{total number of possible outcomes}}$

You can list all the possible outcomes. This is called the *sample space*. Then you can find the probability.

Sample Space

green	green	black	black
black	red	blue	blue

Probability of red hat

$P(\text{red hat}) = \frac{1}{8}$ ← favorable outcomes / ← all possible outcomes

There are 8 possible outcomes.

A spinner has 12 equal-sized sections with the numbers 1, 2, 3, 4, 5, 5, 5, 6, 6, 7, 8, 8. Find each probability.

1. $P(1)$ $\frac{1}{12}$
2. $P(5)$ $\frac{1}{4}$
3. $P(8)$ $\frac{1}{6}$
4. $P(\text{odd number})$ $\frac{1}{2}$
5. $P(\text{even number})$ $\frac{1}{2}$
6. $P(\text{number less than 5})$ $\frac{1}{3}$

A box has 10 red, 15 yellow, 20 pink, 25 black, and 30 orange jelly beans. You pick a jelly bean without looking. Find each probability.

7. $P(\text{red})$ $\frac{1}{10}$
8. $P(\text{yellow})$ $\frac{3}{20}$
9. $P(\text{pink})$ $\frac{1}{5}$
10. $P(\text{black})$ $\frac{1}{4}$

32. Answers may vary. Sample: No; probability cannot be greater than 1.

28. Use the graph at the right to find the probability that a person chosen at random in 2065 will be under the age of 40. 51.3%

Projected 2065 U.S. Population by Age Group

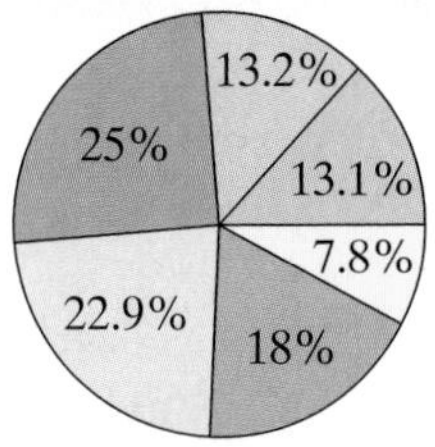

SOURCE: U.S. Census Bureau. Go to **PHSchool.com** for an update. Web Code: asg-9041

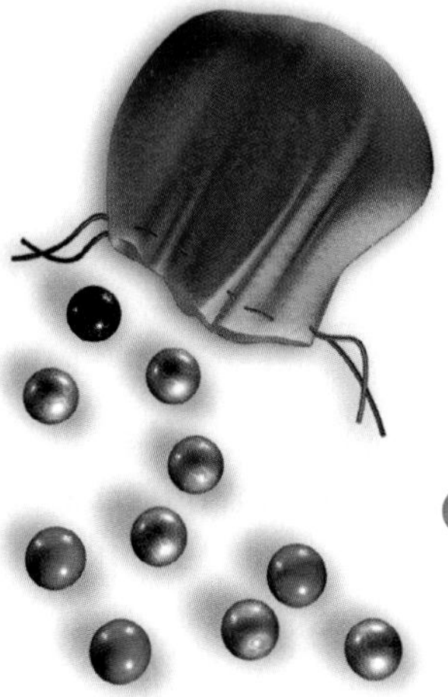

Marbles A bag contains 3 purple marbles, 2 orange marbles, 1 black marble, and 4 silver marbles. Find each probability when choosing at random.

29. $P(\text{orange})$ $\frac{1}{5}$ or 20%

30. $P(\text{silver})$ $\frac{2}{5}$ or 40%

31. Suppose you choose a silver marble, and you do not put it back in the bag. Find $P(\text{orange})$ if you choose a second marble. $\frac{2}{9}$ or about 22.2%

32. **Writing in Math** Can $\frac{5}{4}$ represent a probability? Explain. See above left.

Ⓒ 33. **Challenge** You flip a coin, toss a number cube, and then flip another coin. What is the probability that you will get heads on the first coin, a 3 or a 5 on the number cube, and heads on the second coin? $\frac{1}{12}$

Test Prep and Mixed Review — Practice

Multiple Choice

34. Rebecca is playing a game with a number cube. If she rolls a number greater than 4, she will win the game. What is the probability that Rebecca will win? B

Ⓐ $\frac{1}{6}$ Ⓑ $\frac{1}{3}$ Ⓒ $\frac{1}{2}$ Ⓓ $\frac{2}{3}$

35. Julio is drawing rectangle $ABCD$ on a coordinate grid. What will be the coordinates of point D? H

Ⓕ (2.5, 2.5) Ⓗ (2.5, −2.5)
Ⓖ (3.5, 3.5) Ⓙ (3.5, −3.5)

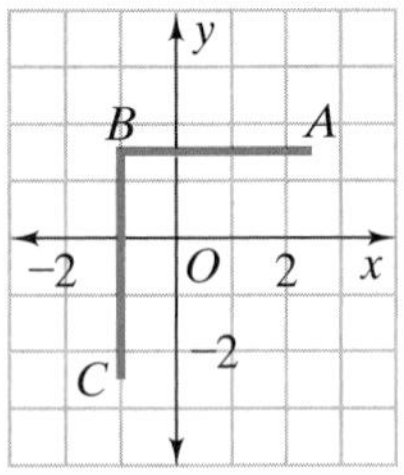

36. About 30% of the 126 students in Tanner's class play a musical instrument. Which proportion can be used to find n, the number of students who play an instrument? D

Ⓐ $\frac{n}{100} = \frac{30}{126}$ Ⓑ $\frac{126}{n} = \frac{30}{100}$ Ⓒ $\frac{126}{30} = \frac{100}{n}$ Ⓓ $\frac{n}{126} = \frac{30}{100}$

GO for Help

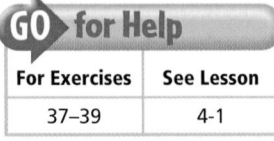

For Exercises	See Lesson
37–39	4-1

Write each ratio in simplest form.

37. 120 lb : 4 lb 30 lb : 1 lb

38. $\frac{74 \text{ mi}}{111 \text{ ft}}$ $\frac{3{,}520 \text{ ft}}{1 \text{ ft}}$

39. 9 h to 127 s $\frac{32{,}400 \text{ s}}{127 \text{ s}}$

Test Prep

Resources

For additional practice with a variety of test item formats:

- Test-Taking Strategies, p. 251
- Test Prep, p. 255
- Test-Taking Strategies with Transparencies

Alternative Assessment

Students write their first and last names on a paper. Then they suppose that each letter is on a separate card and find the probability of randomly selecting a vowel (a, e, i, o, u) or y from their names.

Estimating the Answer

Estimating answers may help you find answers, check an answer, or eliminate one or more answer choices.

EXAMPLES

1 A student collects baseball cards. The student bought one card in the collection for \$12.07. Five years later, the card was worth \$15.98. Find the percent of increase in the value of the baseball card.

(A) 3.91% (B) 24.5% (C) 32.4% (D) 39.1%

Since the beginning value is near \$12, and the ending value is near \$16, the amount of change is about \$4. Using the percent of change equation, you can estimate the percent of increase.

$P \approx \frac{4}{12} = \frac{1}{3} = 33\frac{1}{3}\%$

You can eliminate answer choices A, B, and D, which are not close to $33\frac{1}{3}\%$. The correct answer is choice C.

2 In an election, the winning candidate received 88% of the votes. If 558 students voted, how many voted for the winning candidate?

(A) 521 (B) 491 (C) 469 (D) 387

You can estimate the answer by finding 90% of 560. Since $0.9 \cdot 560$ is 504, the correct answer is choice B.

Exercises

Estimate to solve each problem.

1. A football kicker made 21 field goal attempts in one season and was successful about 73% of the time. How many goals did he make? B

   (A) 20 (B) 15 (C) 12 (D) 5

2. Which is closest to $\frac{78}{643}$? G

   (F) 10% (G) 12.5% (H) 20% (J) $33\frac{1}{3}\%$

3. During a tour, 44 of a rock band's 49 shows sold out. About what percent of the band's shows sold out? C

   (A) 85% (B) 87.5% (C) 90% (D) 95%

4. You and a friend have a \$23.04 restaurant bill. If you want to leave a 15% tip, about how much should you leave for a tip? H

   (F) \$2.50 (G) \$3 (H) \$3.50 (J) \$4

Test-Taking Strategies

Estimating the Answer

This strategy shows students how to estimate calculations involving percents.

Guided Instruction

Example 1

In this example, students round to find compatible numbers to estimate the correct answer. Watch for students who try to find what percent \$4 is of \$16, and not of \$12, the original price.

Exercises

Suggest to students that they can try different numbers as compatible numbers. There is more than one way to come to the correct answer. Remind students that if they have difficulty in a standardized multiple-choice test, they should eliminate the most obvious incorrect answers first.

Resources

Test-Taking Strategies with Transparecies
- Transparency 10
- Practice Sheet, p. 29

Test-Taking Strategies with Transparencies

Test-Taking Strategies: Estimating the Answer

Sometimes you can estimate to find the answer.

Example Find the sum: 0.75 + 8.23 + 5.5

A. 15.53 B. 14.48 C. 9.53 D. 21.23

Estimate: Round to the nearest whole number.

0.75 + 8.23 + 5.5

1 + 8 + 6 = 15

Both A and B are near 15, so round to the nearest tenth.

0.8 + 8.2 + 5.5 must be less than 15.

The answer is 14.48, or choice B.

Estimate to find the answer. Explain your reasoning.

1. The area of a square with side 2.7 cm is

   A. 5.4 cm^2. B. 7.29 cm^2. C. 54 cm^2. D. 72.9 cm^2.

2. Reese went grocery shopping to buy spaghetti sauce, spaghetti noodles, and a loaf of french bread. These items cost \$1.59, \$1.79, and \$1.89. About how much should Reese's grocery bill be?

   F. less than \$5 G. between \$5 and \$6
   H. between \$6 and \$7 J. more than \$7

Chapter 5 Review

Resources

Student Edition
Extra Skills and Word Problems Practice, Ch. 5, p. 612
English/Spanish Glossary, p. 650
Formulas and Properties, p. 648
Tables, p. 643

All in One Teaching Resources
- Vocabulary and Study Skills 5F L3

Differentiated Instruction

Spanish Vocabulary Workbook with Study Skills ELL
Interactive Textbook
- Audio Glossary

Online Vocabulary Quiz

Success Tracker™
Online at PHSchool.com

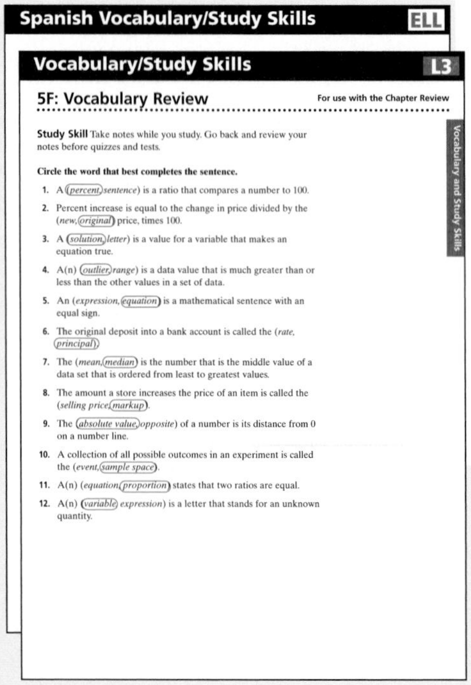
Spanish Vocabulary/Study Skills ELL

Vocabulary/Study Skills L3

5F: Vocabulary Review For use with the Chapter Review

Study Skill Take notes while you study. Go back and review your notes before quizzes and tests.

Circle the word that best completes the sentence.

1. A (*percent*, *sentence*) is a ratio that compares a number to 100.
2. Percent increase is equal to the change in price divided by the (*new*, *original*) price, times 100.
3. A (*solution*, *letter*) is a value for a variable that makes an equation true.
4. A(n) (*outlier*, *range*) is a data value that is much greater than or less than the other values in a set of data.
5. An (*expression*, *equation*) is a mathematical sentence with an equal sign.
6. The original deposit into a bank account is called the (*rate*, *principal*).
7. The (*mean*, *median*) is the number that is the middle value of a data set that is ordered from least to greatest values.
8. The amount a store increases the price of an item is called the (*selling price*, *markup*).
9. The (*absolute value*, *opposite*) of a number is its distance from 0 on a number line.
10. A collection of all possible outcomes in an experiment is called the (*event*, *sample space*).
11. A(n) (*equation*, *proportion*) states that two ratios are equal.
12. A(n) (*variable*, *expression*) is a letter that stands for an unknown quantity.

Vocabulary and Study Skills

Vocabulary Review

balance (p. 243)
discount (p. 235)
event (p. 246)
interest (p. 242)
interest rate (p. 242)
markup (p. 234)
outcome (p. 246)
percent (p. 210)
percent of change (p. 230)
principal (p. 242)
probability of an event (p. 246)
sale price (p. 235)
sample space (p. 247)
selling price (p. 234)
simple interest (p. 242)

Choose the correct vocabulary term to complete each sentence.

1. __?__ is the amount by which a store increases the price of an item. **markup**
2. The original deposit in a bank account is called the __?__. **principal**
3. A(n) __?__ is any of the possible results that can occur in an experiment. **outcome**
4. The amount by which the price of an item on sale is reduced is the __?__. **discount**
5. Interest calculated only on the principal of an account is __?__. **simple interest**

Go Online
PHSchool.com
For: Online Vocabulary Quiz
Web Code: asj-0551

Skills and Concepts

Lessons 5-1, 5-2
- To convert between fractions, decimals, and percents and to order rational numbers
- To estimate percents using decimals and fractions

A **percent** is a ratio that compares a number to 100. You can write fractions and decimals as percents. It is often helpful to estimate percents.

Write each fraction as a percent. Round to the nearest hundredth of a percent where necessary.

6. $\frac{7}{8}$ **87.5%** **7.** $\frac{13}{12}$ **108.33%** **8.** $\frac{5}{16}$ **31.25%** **9.** $\frac{27}{6}$ **450%**

Write each percent as a fraction or a mixed number in simplest form.

10. 36% $\frac{9}{25}$ **11.** $33\frac{1}{3}\%$ $\frac{1}{3}$ **12.** 124% $1\frac{6}{25}$ **13.** 27% $\frac{27}{100}$

Estimate each percent. **14–16. Answers may vary. Samples are given.**

14. 24% of 97 **about 25** **15.** 15% of \$35.07 **about \$5.25** **16.** 68% of 89 **about 63**

17. About 13% of the 23 students in a middle school class said that soccer was their favorite sport. Using fractions, estimate how many students said they liked soccer the best. **about 3 students**

Lessons 5-3, 5-4

- To use proportions to find part of a whole, a whole amount, or a percent
- To use equations to solve problems involving percents

You can solve a percent problem using a proportion or an equation.

$$\frac{\text{part}}{\text{whole}} = \frac{p}{100} \qquad \text{part} = P \cdot \text{whole}$$

Use a proportion or an equation to solve each problem.

18. 85% of what number is 170? 200

19. What percent of 2 is 0.8? 40%

20. Find 150% of 12. 18

21. 26% of what number is 39? 150

22. Tennis About 7.5% of the eighth-grade students in a middle school, or 12 students, are on the tennis team. How many students are in the eighth grade? 160 students

Lessons 5-5, 5-6

- To find percent of change and to solve problems involving percent of increase and percent of decrease
- To use percent of change to find markup, discount, and selling price

You can find the **percent of change** P expressed as a decimal.

$$P = \frac{\text{amount of change}}{\text{original amount}}$$

Markup is a type of percent of increase that stores use to calculate the **selling price** of an item. The amount stores reduce the price of an item to find the **sale price** is called the **discount.**

Find each percent of change. Round your answer to the nearest tenth of a percent where necessary. Label your answer *increase* or *decrease*.

23. 13 to 9 30.8% decrease

24. 2 to 88 4,300% increase

25. 154 to 155 0.6% increase

26. 18 to 3 83.3% decrease

27. Video Games A store is having a 20%-off sale. Find the sale price of a video game system that regularly costs $249.99. $199.99

Lesson 5-7

- To find simple interest and account balances

Simple interest is interest calculated only on the principal. To calculate simple interest, use the formula $I = p \cdot r \cdot t$.

Find the balance in each account.

28. $475 at 7% simple interest for 3 years $574.75

29. $710 at 2% simple interest for 7 years $809.40

30. $3,500 at 7% simple interest for 5 years $4,725

Lesson 5-8

- To find probability and the sample space of an event

An **event** is a collection of possible **outcomes** of an experiment. The collection of all possible outcomes is the **sample space.**

$$\textbf{probability of an event } E = P(E) = \frac{\text{number of favorable outcomes}}{\text{total number of possible outcomes}}$$

31. A swimmer wins 3 gold ribbons, 5 silver ribbons, and 1 bronze ribbon during a season. Suppose she chooses a ribbon from her collection at random. What is the probability that she will choose a silver ribbon? $\frac{5}{9}$

Alternative Assessment L4

Alternative Assessment Form C

Chapter 5

A SHOPPING SPREE

Imagine that a new shopping center had a raffle drawing and you have won $298! However, there are some restrictions on how you can spend the money. You must spend the money in 5 or more of the stores shown below, and you must spend at least 5% of the $298 in each store. You must also spend a different amount at each store.

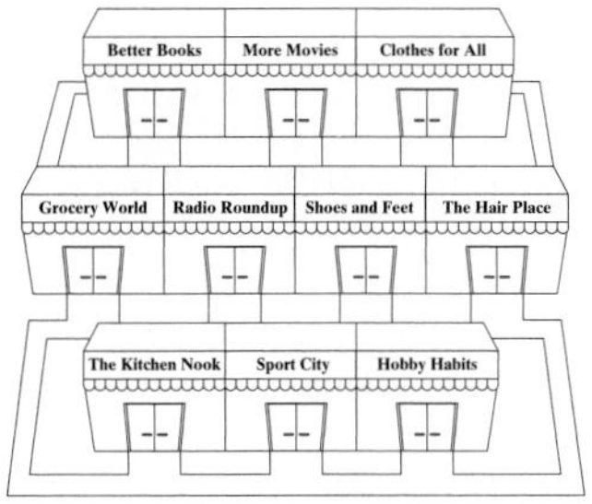

Show all of your work on a separate sheet of paper.

1. Select 5 or more stores and estimate the amount you would like to spend at each store. List the store names, the amount you will spend at each, and what you might be able to buy for that amount.
2. Using a protractor, create a circle graph showing what percent of the money you would spend at each store. Use the amounts from Exercise 1. Label each section of your graph with the name of the store and the percent of the $298 that you will spend at that store. Round appropriately.

Resources

- ExamView Assessment Suite CD-ROM
  - Chapter 5 Ready-Made test
  - Make your own Chapter 5 test
- MindPoint Quiz Show CD-ROM
  - Chapter 5 Review

Differentiated Instruction

All in One Teaching Resources
- Below Level Chapter 5 Test L2
- Chapter 5 Test L3
- Chapter 5 Alternative Assessment L4

Spanish Assessment Resources ELL
- Below Level Chapter 5 Test L2
- Chapter 5 Test L3
- Chapter 5 Alternative Assessment L4

ExamView Assessment Suite CD-ROM
- Special Needs Test L1
- Special Needs Practice Bank L1

Online Chapter 5 Test at www.PHSchool.com L3

Below Level Chapter Test L2

Chapter Test L3

Chapter Test — Form A

Chapter 5

Compare. Use >, <, or =.

1. $\frac{7}{8}$ = 0.875
2. 0.8% < 0.8
3. $\frac{2}{7}$ > 0.24

Write each fraction as a percent. Round to the nearest hundredth of a percent.

4. $\frac{9}{13}$ 69.23%
5. $\frac{34}{9}$ 377.78%
6. $\frac{1}{146}$ 0.68%

Estimate. Explain how you made your estimate and why.

7. 47% of 84 — 0.50 × 80 = 40
8. 30% of $34.78 — 0.30 × 30 = $9
9. A soccer goalie saved 85% of 315 goal attempts in one season. About how many saves did the goalie successfully make during the season? about 268

Use a proportion to solve each problem.

10. What is 42.3% of 168? 71.06
11. Find 0.6% of 9. 0.054
12. 79.8 is 5.32% of what number? 1,500
13. 420% of what number is 26,565? 6,325
14. At Brookpark Middle school, about 25% of the students have curly hair. If there are 643 students in the school, how many have curly hair? about 161 students

Use an equation to solve each problem.

15. What is 142% of 78? 110.76
16. Find 18% of 12. 2.16
17. 0.08% of what number is 0.204? 255
18. 130% of what number is 7.9? 6.07
19. How much sales tax would you pay on a $59.99 bicycle in a state that charges 6.5% sales tax? $3.90

Chapter 5 Test

Go Online PHSchool.com — For: Online chapter test Web Code: asa-0552

Compare. Use <, >, or =.

1. $\frac{5}{8}$ ■ 0.625 =
2. 0.6% ■ 0.6 <
3. $\frac{1}{3}$ ■ 0.34 <
4. $\frac{5}{6}$ ■ 85% <

Write each fraction as a percent. Round to the nearest hundredth of a percent.

5. $\frac{11}{13}$ 84.62%
6. $\frac{22}{9}$ 244.44%
7. $\frac{1}{205}$ 0.49%

Estimate each percent. Explain how you made your estimate and why. 8–11. Answers may vary. Samples are given.

8. 76% of 48 — about 36
9. 20% of $23.87 — about $4.80
10. 250% of 29 — about 75
11. 15% of $61.51 — about $9
12. **Athletics** More than 7 million high school students in the United States participate in a school sport. Suppose only 98,000 college students receive sports scholarships. Estimate what percent of high school athletes receive college sports scholarships. Round your answer to the nearest tenth of a percent. about 1.4%

Use a proportion to solve each problem.

13. Find 37% of 134. 49.58
14. Find 2% of 70. 1.4
15. 68 is 5% of what number? 1,360
16. 350% of what number is 21,000? 6,000
17. About 13% of a school's 782 students walk to school. How many students walk to school? 102 students

Use an equation to solve each problem.

18. Find 132% of 65. 85.8
19. Find 16% of 3. 0.48
20. 6% of what number is 105? 1,750
21. 120% of what number is 0.006? 0.005
22. How much sales tax would you pay on a skateboard priced at $49.95 in a state that charges 5.5% sales tax? $2.75

Find each percent of change. Round the answer to the nearest hundredth of a percent. Label your answer *increase* or *decrease*.

23. 99 to 163 — 64.65% increase
24. 13 to 1 — 92.31% decrease
25. 158 to 24 — 84.81% decrease
26. 613 to 655 — 6.85% increase
27. **Jobs** Last year, a student earned $6.00 per hour baby-sitting. This year he earns $6.75 per hour. Find the percent of increase. 12.5% increase

Find the final price after each markup or discount. Round to the nearest cent.

28. $90.00, 33% discount $60.30
29. $19.99, 15% markup $22.99
30. **Writing in Math** The Drama Club bought T-shirts for $4 and sold them for $5. A student claims that the markup rate is 20% because $1 is 20% of $5. Explain the student's error and give the correct markup rate. See margin.
31. **Savings** Miguel wants to save between 50% and 65% of his allowance to buy a new bike. He receives an allowance of $17 each week. What are the least and the greatest amounts of money he could save each week? between $8.50 and $11.05

Find the final balance in each account.

32. $250 at $4\frac{1}{2}$% simple interest for 3 years $283.75
33. $450 at 6% simple interest for 2 years $504
34. $800 at 6% simple interest for 3 years $944
35. Suppose you roll two cubes. Each cube has the numbers 1, 2, 3, 4, 5, and 6 on its faces.
    a. Use a table to find the sample space. See margin.
    b. Find *P*(sum greater than 8). $\frac{5}{18}$
    c. Find *P*(product even). $\frac{3}{4}$

30. Answers may vary. Sample: The student calculated the markup rate using the selling price instead of the store's cost. The correct markup rate is $\frac{1}{4}$ or 25%.

35a.

	1	2	3	4	5	6
1	(1, 1)	(1, 2)	(1, 3)	(1, 4)	(1, 5)	(1, 6)
2	(2, 1)	(2, 2)	(2, 3)	(2, 4)	(2, 5)	(2, 6)
3	(3, 1)	(3, 2)	(3, 3)	(3, 4)	(3, 5)	(3, 6)
4	(4, 1)	(4, 2)	(4, 3)	(4, 4)	(4, 5)	(4, 6)
5	(5, 1)	(5, 2)	(5, 3)	(5, 4)	(5, 5)	(5, 6)
6	(6, 1)	(6, 2)	(6, 3)	(6, 4)	(6, 5)	(6, 6)

Multiple Choice

Read each question. Then write the letter of the correct answer on your paper.

1. Which pair of numbers has a GCF of 21? C
   (A) 14 and 21 (C) 84 and 105
   (B) 630 and 126 (D) 42 and 84

2. An HO scale model railroad is $\frac{1}{87}$ scale, which means that 1 inch of an HO train is equal to 87 inches of a real train. Find the size of an HO boxcar if a real boxcar is 50 ft long. H
   (F) about 3.5 in. (H) about 7 in.
   (G) about 15 in. (J) about 7 ft

3. Subtract $4\frac{2}{3} - \left(-3\frac{3}{4}\right)$. D
   (A) $-1\frac{1}{7}$ (B) $\frac{11}{12}$ (C) $7\frac{11}{12}$ (D) $8\frac{5}{12}$

4. Fifteen is 12% of what number? J
   (F) 1.25 (G) 1.8 (H) 12.5 (J) 125

5. Find the length of the hypotenuse. B
   (A) 11
   (B) 13
   (C) 17
   (D) 26

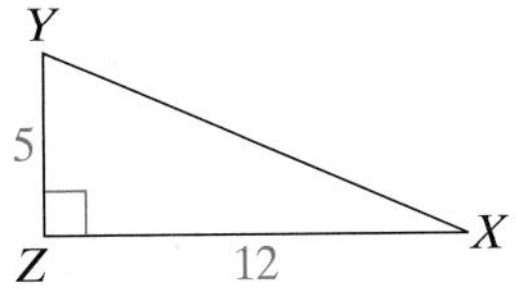

6. A jacket with a regular price of $79.99 is on sale for 35% off. Estimate the sale price of the jacket. G
   (F) $60 (G) $53 (H) $45 (J) $40

7. Which of these is NOT equal to 45%? C
   (A) 0.45 (B) $\frac{18}{40}$ (C) 4.5 (D) $\frac{27}{60}$

8. Solve $n - \frac{5}{6} = -\frac{1}{4}$. G
   (F) $-1\frac{1}{2}$ (G) $\frac{7}{12}$ (H) $\frac{3}{5}$ (J) $4\frac{1}{2}$

9. Solve $x + 7 = -11$. A
   (A) -18 (B) -3 (C) 3 (D) 18

10. Simplify $64 - 4^2 \div 8$. H
    (F) 6 (G) 7.5 (H) 62 (J) 450

11. When $\triangle ABC$ is reflected over the x-axis, what is the y-coordinate of the image of A? D

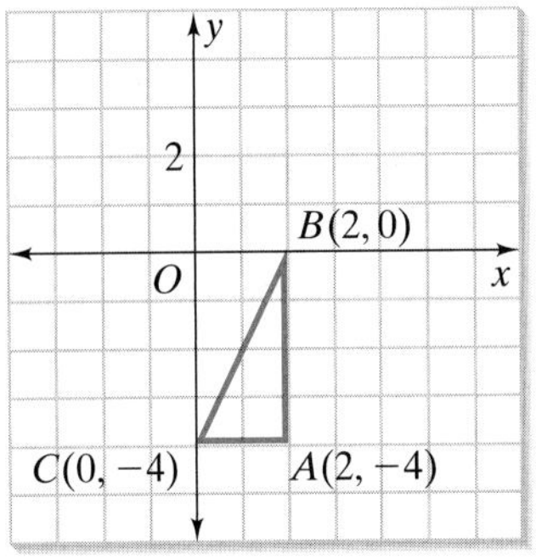

   (A) -4 (B) -2 (C) 2 (D) 4

Gridded Response

Record your answer in a grid.

12. Suppose you roll a number cube with numbers 1, 2, 3, 4, 5, and 6 on its faces. What is P(prime number)? $\frac{3}{6}$ or $\frac{1}{2}$

13. Add $2 + \frac{3}{4} + 7\frac{1}{8}$. $\frac{79}{8}$

Short Response 14–15. See margin.

14. On a sports team, the ratio of boys to girls is 3 to 2. Set up and solve a proportion to find how many boys are on a team with 8 girls.

15. Calculate the interest earned and the final balance in a savings account that has $150 and earns 5% simple interest over 4 years.

Extended Response

16. The table below contains coordinates of several points on a line. See margin.

x	−6	−2	2	6
y	3	1	−1	−3

   a. Write an equation to model the data in the table.
   b. Graph the data in the table. Draw a line through the points.

Test Prep

Resources

Test Prep Workbook

All in One Teaching Resources
- Cumulative Review L3

ExamView Assessment Suite CD-ROM
- Standardized Test Practice

Differentiated Instruction

Spanish Assessment Resources
- Spanish Cumulative Review ELL

14. $\frac{3}{2} = \frac{x}{8}$
    $2x = 24$
    $x = 12$; 12 boys

15. $I = 150(0.05)(4)$
    $= 30$; $30

16a. $y = -\frac{4}{3}x - \frac{7}{3}$

b.

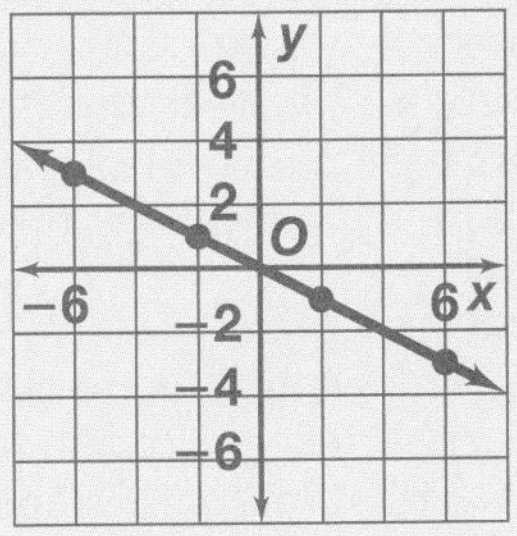

Item	1	2	3	4	5	6	7	8	9	10	11	12	13	14	15	16
Lesson	2-1	4-6	2-4	5-3	3-2	5-6	5-1	2-4	1-6	2-7	3-7	5-8	2-4	4-3	5-7	3-5

Problem Solving

Making Ends Meet

Students will use data from these two pages to answer the questions posed here in Put It All Together.

Activating Prior Knowledge

Have studens brainstorm a list of the many different utilities and estimate what they cost for an average month. Ask: *What do you think is the largest expense each month for an average family?* housing

Then ask students to share what they know about income taxes, property taxes, and sales tax. What services do their taxes pay for?

Guided Instruction

Follow up on students' discussions about jobs and costs of living by having groups look through a local newspaper to find out how much jobs pay and what housing costs are in their area. If possible show some monthly heat, electricity, or water bills for students to see.

Compensation Connection
What jobs rely heavily on tips? Ask students to find out about the pros and cons of working on commission. Have students brainstorm a list. Then invite them to interview restaurant servers, delivery people, taxi drivers, and others to find out about the pros and cons of working for tips.

Careers
Consider having students research a career of their choice and finding what math it involves. What might they need to know to be successful in such a career? What educational qualifications are expected?

Problem Solving Application

Applying Percents

Making Ends Meet Getting your first apartment is a big step! Suddenly you are responsible for taking care of yourself. You have to make enough money to cover your basic expenses for rent, food, and fun. When you start looking for a job, you'll want to think about what you like doing, as well as how much money you're going to make.

Paying Bills
People often pay bills monthly for heat, electricity, and water.

256

1a. $1,360/month
b. $1,813.33/month

2a. $1,413.33/month
b. $5,653.32/month
c. $94,222/month
d. 6 cars/month

3a. $1,413.33/month
b. about 377 people/month, or 94/week, or between 2 and 3/hour

4. Check students' work.

Job Fair

At a job fair, people who are looking for jobs meet with people who have jobs to fill. At a career day, students learn about different careers.

Go Online PHSchool.com
For: Information about careers
Web Code: ase-0553

Put It All Together

1. The list shows your projected monthly expenses.
  a. Find the total.
  b. 25% of your earnings go for taxes. How much will you need to make each month to cover your expenses?

Monthly Expenses

Expense	Cost
Rent	$1,000
Utilities	$60
Food	$150
Transportation	$50
Entertainment	$100
Total	■

2. One job you consider is selling cars. Your salary would be $400 a month plus a commission of 25% of the dealer's profit on each car you sell.
  a. How much must you make in commission each month?
  b. How much must the dealer's profit from your sales be each month?
  c. The dealer's profit is 6% of the selling price of each car. What will your total monthly sales have to be?
  d. The average selling price of a car is $18,000. How many cars will you have to sell each month?

3. Your second option is to wait tables. The job pays $2.50 per hour plus tips.
  a. If you work 40 hours per week, how much money must you earn in tips each month? (Assume there are four 40-hour working weeks in each month.)
  b. The average bill in this restaurant is $25 per person. Your tips average 15% of each bill. About how many customers will you need to serve in a month? In a week? In an hour?

4. **Writing in Math** Money is only one of the things you need to think about when choosing a job. Write a letter to yourself describing the pros and cons of each job.

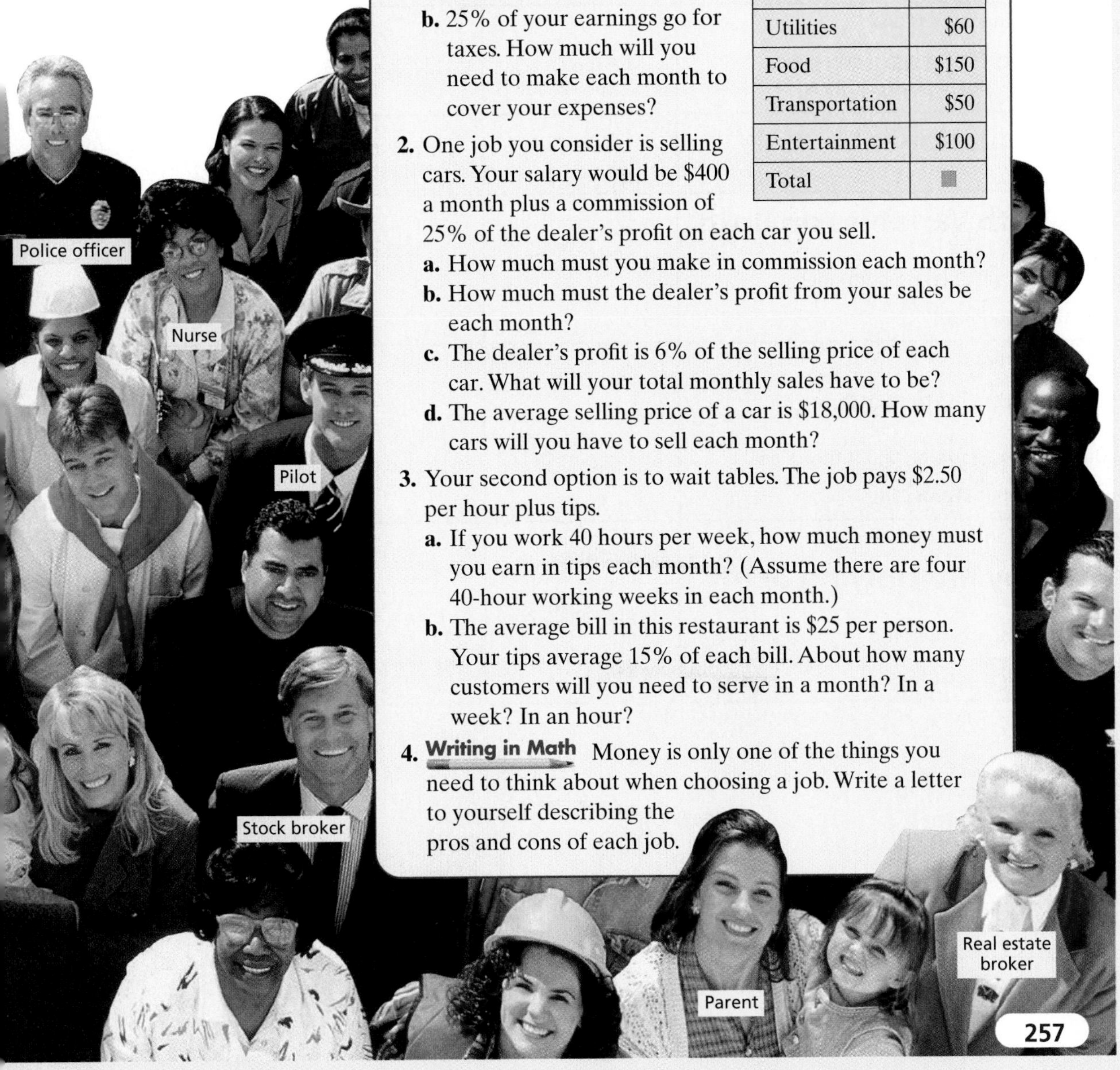

257

Put It All Together

Have students work in pairs to answer the questions.

Exercise 1b Have students write an equation to help them solve for the amount they need to earn each month. total expenses = 0.25(earnings) + earnings

Exercise 2 Elicit from students what kinds of jobs, other than those in car sales and real estate sales, pay salary plus commission. insurance salesperson, stock brokers, sports agents

Differentiated Instruction

Special Needs L1
As needed, review how to compute with percents to find commission and to find the total cost of meals, including tips.

English Language Learners ELL
Carefully discuss the meaning of the terms *earnings, expenses, commission* and *profit*. Provide concrete examples to help students better understand these words.

6 Equations and Inequalities

Chapter at a Glance

Lesson Titles, Objectives, and Features	Assessment	NCTM Standards	Local Standards
6-1a Activity Lab, Hands On: Modeling Multi-Step Equations **6-1 Solving Two-Step Equations** • To solve two-step equations and to use two-step equations to solve problems	Lesson Quiz	1, 2, 3, 6, 7, 8, 9, 10	
6-2a Activity Lab, Hands On: Modeling Expressions **6-2 Simplifying Algebraic Expressions** • To combine like terms and simplify algebraic expressions	Lesson Quiz Checkpoint Quiz 1	1, 2, 3, 6, 7, 8, 9, 10	
6-3 Solving Multi-Step Equations • To write and solve multi-step equations	Lesson Quiz	1, 2, 3, 6, 7, 8, 9, 10	
6-4 Solving Equations With Variables on Both Sides • To write and solve equations with variables on both sides **Guided Problem Solving:** Writing Equations	Lesson Quiz	1, 2, 3, 6, 7, 8, 9, 10	
6-5a Activity Lab: Graphing Inequalities **6-5 Solving Inequalities by Adding or Subtracting** • To write and solve inequalities using addition and subtraction **Vocabulary Builder:** High-Use Academic Words	Lesson Quiz Checkpoint Quiz 2	1, 2, 3, 6, 7, 8, 9, 10	
6-6a Activity Lab: Inequalities and Negative Numbers **6-6 Solving Inequalities by Multiplying or Dividing** • To write and solve inequalities using multiplication and division	Lesson Quiz	1, 2, 3, 6, 7, 8, 9, 10	
Problem Solving Application: Applying Equations			

NCTM Standards 2000
1 Number and Operations **2** Algebra **3** Geometry **4** Measurement **5** Data Analysis and Probability
6 Problem Solving **7** Reasoning and Proof **8** Communication **9** Connections **10** Representation

Correlations to Standardized Tests

All content for these tests is contained in *Prentice Hall Math,* Course 3. This chart reflects coverage in this chapter only.

	6-1	6-2	6-3	6-4	6-5	6-6
Terra Nova CAT6 (Level 18)						
Number and Number Relations						
Computation and Numerical Estimation	✔		✔	✔		
Operation Concepts		✔		✔		
Measurement						
Geometry and Spatial Sense						
Data Analysis, Statistics, and Probability						
Patterns, Functions, Algebra	✔	✔	✔	✔	✔	
Problem Solving and Reasoning	✔	✔	✔	✔	✔	✔
Communication	✔	✔	✔	✔	✔	✔
Decimals, Fractions, Integers, Percent						
Order of Operations	✔					
Algebraic Operations	✔	✔	✔	✔	✔	✔
Terra Nova CTBS (Level 18)						
Decimals, Fractions, Integers, Percents	✔	✔	✔	✔	✔	✔
Order of Operations, Numeration, Number Theory	✔					
Data Interpretation						
Measurement						
Geometry						
ITBS (Level 14)						
Number Properties and Operations	✔	✔	✔	✔	✔	✔
Algebra	✔	✔	✔	✔	✔	✔
Geometry						
Measurement						
Probability and Statistics						
Estimation	✔	✔	✔	✔		
SAT10 (Adv 1 Level)						
Number Sense and Operations	✔	✔	✔	✔	✔	✔
Patterns, Relationships, and Algebra	✔	✔	✔	✔	✔	✔
Data, Statistics, and Probability						
Geometry and Measurement						
NAEP						
Number Sense, Properties, and Operations	✔		✔	✔		✔
Measurement						
Geometry and Spatial Sense						
Data Analysis, Statistics, and Probability						
Algebra and Functions	✔	✔	✔	✔	✔	✔

CAT6 California Achievement Test, 6th Ed. **CTBS** Comprehensive Test of Basic Skills **ITBS** Iowa Test of Basic Skills, Form M
SAT10 Stanford Achievement Test, 10th Ed. **NAEP** National Assessment of Educational Progress 2005 Mathematics Objectives

Math Background

Professional Development

Skills Trace

BEFORE Chapter 6

Course 2 reviewed the solving of equations and of inequalities.

DURING Chapter 6

Course 3 reviews and extends the solving of equations and inequalities to include multi-step equations and one-step inequalities.

AFTER Chapter 6

Throughout this course students write and solve equations for real-world problems.

6-1 Solving Two-Step Equations

Math Understandings

Students have already solved one-step equations, using the following information:

- Addition and subtraction are inverse operations that undo each other. Multiplication and division are also inverse operations that undo each other.
- When you solve an equation, any operation that you do to one side you must also do to the other.

When you solve a two-step equation, it is often easier to begin by undoing the addition or subtraction, and then undoing the multiplication and division.

6-2 Simplifying Algebraic Expressions

Math Understandings

- The terms of an algebraic expression are separated by plus and minus signs.
- You can combine only like terms by addition or subtraction.
- There is an understood coefficient of 1 in front of a variable that does not have any numeric coefficient, so you can write b as $1b$ and $-c$ as $-1c$.

In an algebraic expression, a **term** is a number, a variable, or the product of a number and one or more variables. **Like terms** have exactly the same variable factors. The Distributive Property justifies combining like terms such as: $4a + 5a = (4 + 5)a$, or $9a$.

Example: $3ab - 2a + 4ab - ab$ has 4 terms while $14abc$ has 1 term. In the expression $3ab - 2a + 4ab - ab$, the terms $3ab$, $4ab$, and $-ab$ are like terms, and you can combine them so that the expression becomes $6ab - 2a$.

6-3 Solving Multi-Step Equations
6-4 Solving Equations With Variables on Both Sides

Math Understandings

- At every step in the process of solving an equation, the new equation must be equivalent to the original equation, that is, it has the same solution.
- When an equation has variables on both sides, you must bring all the variable terms to one side of the equation to solve it.
- When you solve an equation, before you apply inverse operations to each side of the equation, simplify as much as you can on both sides.

When you solve an equation to find the solution to a real-world problem, always make sure that the solution is a reasonable one.

6-5 Solving Inequalities by Adding or Subtracting

Math Understandings

- On a graph, an open dot means that the point is not a solution; a closed dot means that the point is a solution.
- You solve one-step inequalities involving addition or subtraction the same way you solve one-step equations involving addition or subtraction.
- Often you cannot check all the solutions to an inequality. Instead, you can check a sample point. Verify that the end point is correct (open or closed) and that the direction of the arrow is correct.

An **inequality** is a comparison of two expressions. The inequality symbols and their meanings are shown below.

$<$	is less than	$\leq$	is less than or equal to
$>$	is greater than	$\geq$	is greater than or equal to
$\neq$	is not equal to		

Addition and Subtraction Properties of Inequalities

If you add or subtract the same number on each side of an inequality, the relationship between the two sides does not change.

Arithmetic	Algebra
$8 < 12$, so $8 + 3 < 12 + 3$ and $8 - 4 < 12 - 4$.	If $a < b$, then $a + c < b + c$ and $a - c < b - c$.
$10 > 7$, so $10 + 5 > 7 + 5$ and $10 - 2 > 7 - 2$.	If $a > b$, then $a + c > b + c$ and $a - c > b - c$.

6-6 Solving Inequalities by Multiplying or Dividing

Math Understandings

- There is one very important difference between the operations you use to solve an equation and to solve an inequality: multiplying or dividing by a negative number reverses the sign of the inequality.

Multiplication and Division Properties of Inequalities

Using Positive Numbers to Multiply or Divide

When you multiply or divide an inequality by a positive number, the relationship between the two sides does not change.

		Multiplication		Division
Arithmetic	$6 > 5$	so $6(3) > 5(3)$	and	$\frac{6}{2} > \frac{5}{2}$
	$4 < 10$	so $4(5) < 10(5)$	and	$\frac{4}{2} < \frac{10}{2}$
Algebra		if a > b, and c > 0, then ac > bc	and	$\frac{a}{c} > \frac{b}{c}$
		if a < b, and c < 0, then ac < bc	and	$\frac{a}{c} < \frac{b}{c}$

Note these relationships are also true for $\leq$ and $\geq$.

Using Negative Numbers to Multiply or Divide

When you multiply or divide an inequality by a negative number, reverse the direction of the inequality sign.

		Multiplication		Division
Arithmetic	$6 > 5$,	so $6 \cdot (-3) < 5 \cdot (-3)$	and	$\frac{6}{-2} < \frac{5}{-2}$
	$4 < 10$	so $4 \cdot (-5) > 10 \cdot (-5)$	and	$\frac{4}{-2} > \frac{10}{-2}$
Algebra		if a > b, and c < 0, then ac < bc	and	$\frac{a}{c} < \frac{b}{c}$
		if a < b, and c < 0, then ac > bc	and	$\frac{a}{c} > \frac{b}{c}$

Note these relationships are also true for $\leq$ and $\geq$.

Example: Solve $2 < \frac{x}{-3}$. Graph the solution.

$(-3)(2) > (\frac{x}{-3})(-3)$

$-6 > x$

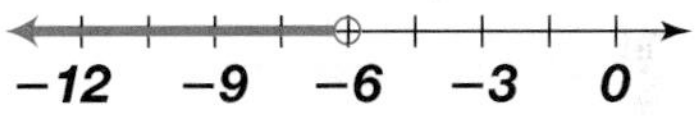

Additional Professional Development Opportunities

Professional Development

Math Background Notes for Chapter 6: Every lesson has a Math Background in the PLAN section.

Research Overview, Mathematics Strands
Additional support for these topics and more is in the front of the Teacher's Edition.

LessonLab
LessonLab, a Pearson Education company offers comprehensive, facilitated professional development designed to help teachers to improve student achievement. To learn more please visit lessonlab.com.

Chapter 6 Resources

	6-1	6-2	6-3	6-4	6-5	6-6	For the Chapter
Print Resources							
L3 Practice	●	●	●	●	●	●	
L1 Adapted Practice	●	●	●	●	●	●	
L3 Guided Problem Solving	●	●	●	●	●	●	
L2 Reteaching	●	●	●	●	●	●	
L4 Enrichment	●	●	●	●	●	●	
L3 Daily Notetaking Guide	●	●	●	●	●	●	
L1 Adapted Daily Notetaking Guide	●	●	●	●	●	●	
L3 Vocabulary and Study Skills Worksheets	●		●	●	●	●	●
L3 Daily Puzzles	●	●	●	●	●	●	
L3 Activity Labs	●	●	●	●	●	●	
L3 Checkpoint Quiz		●			●		
L3 Chapter Project							●
L2 Below Level Chapter Test							●
L3 Chapter Test							●
L4 Alternative Assessment							●
L3 Cumulative Review							●
Spanish Resources ELL							
L3 Practice	●	●	●	●	●	●	
L3 Vocabulary and Study Skills Worksheets	●		●	●	●	●	●
L3 Checkpoint Quiz		●			●		
L2 Below Level Chapter Test							●
L3 Chapter Test							●
L4 Alternative Assessment							●
L3 Cumulative Review							●
Transparencies							
Check Skills You'll Need	●	●	●	●	●	●	
Additional Examples	●	●	●	●	●	●	
Problem of the Day	●	●	●	●	●	●	
Classroom Aid	●	●	●		●	●	
Student Edition Answers	●	●	●	●	●	●	●
Lesson Quiz	●	●	●	●	●	●	
Test-Taking Strategies							●
Technology							
Interactive Textbook Online							
StudentExpress™ CD-ROM	●	●	●	●	●	●	●
Success Tracker™ Online Intervention	●	●	●	●	●	●	●
TeacherExpress™ CD-ROM	●	●	●	●	●	●	●
PresentationExpress™ with QuickTake Presenter CD-ROM	●	●	●	●	●	●	●
ExamView® Assessment Suite CD-ROM	●	●	●	●	●	●	●
MindPoint® Quiz Show CD-ROM							●
Prentice Hall Web Site: PHSchool.com	●	●	●	●	●	●	●

Also available:

Prentice Hall Assessment System
- Progress Monitoring Assessments
- Skills and Concepts Review
- Test Prep Workbook

Other Resources
Algebra Readiness Tests
All-in-One Student Workbook
All-in-One Student Workbook, Adapted Version
Multilingual Handbook
Solution Key
Math Notes Study Folder
Spanish Cumulative Assessment

Where You Can Use the Lesson Resources

Here is a suggestion, following the four-step teaching plan, for how you can incorporate Differentiated Instruction Resources into your teaching.

	Instructional Resources L3	Differentiated Instruction Resources
1. Plan		
Preparation Read the Math Background in the Teacher's Edition to connect this lesson with students' previous experience. **Starting Class** **Check Skills You'll Need** Assign these exercises to review prerequisite skills. **New Vocabulary** Help students pre-read the lesson by pointing out the new terms introduced in the lesson.	**Math Background** **Math Understandings** **Transparencies & PresentationExpress™ with QuickTake Presenter CD-ROM** Check Skills You'll Need Problem of the Day **Resources** Vocabulary and Study Skills	**Spanish Support** ELL Vocabulary and Study Skills
2. Teach		
L3 Guided Instruction Use the Activity Labs to build conceptual understanding. Teach each Example. Use the Teacher's Edition side column notes for specific teaching tips, including Error Prevention notes. Use the Additional Examples found in the side column (and on transparency and PowerPoint) as an alternative presentation for the content. After each Example, assign the Quick Check exercise for that Example to get an immediate assessment of student understanding. Use the Closure activity in the Teacher's Edition to help students attain mastery of lesson content.	**Student Edition** Activity Lab **Resources** Daily Notetaking Guide Activity Lab **Transparencies & PresentationExpress™ with QuickTake Presenter CD-ROM** Additional Examples Classroom Aids **ExamView® Assessment Suite CD-ROM**	**Teacher's Edition** Every lesson includes suggestions for working with students who need special attention. L1 Special Needs L2 Below Level L4 Advanced Learners ELL English Language Learners **Resources** L1 Adapted Daily Notetaking Guide **Multilingual Handbook**
3. Practice		
Assignment Guide **Check Your Understanding** Use these questions to check students' understanding before you assign homework. **Homework Exercises** Assign homework from these leveled exercises in the Assignment Guide. **A** Practice by Example **B** Apply Your Skills **C** Challenge Test Prep and Mixed Review **Homework Quick Check** Use these key exercises to quickly check students' homework.	**Transparencies & PresentationExpress™ with QuickTake Presenter CD-ROM** Student Answers **Resources** Practice Guided Problem Solving Vocabulary and Study Skills Activity Lab Daily Puzzles **ExamView® Assessment Suite CD-ROM**	**Spanish Support** ELL Practice ELL Vocabulary and Study Skills **Resources** L1 Adapted Practice L4 Enrichment
4. Assess & Reteach		
Lesson Quiz Assign the Lesson Quiz to assess students' mastery of the lesson content. **Checkpoint Quiz** Use the Checkpoint Quiz to assess student progress over several lessons.	**Transparencies & PresentationExpress™ with QuickTake Presenter CD-ROM** Lesson Quiz **Resources** Checkpoint Quiz	**Resources** L2 Reteaching ELL Checkpoint Quiz Success Tracker™ Online Intervention **ExamView® Assessment Suite CD-ROM**

KEY L1 Special Needs L2 Below Level L3 For All Students L4 Advanced, Gifted ELL English Language Learners

CHAPTER 6

Equation and Inequalities

Check Your Readiness

Answers for students are in the back of the textbook.

For intervention, direct students to:

Adding and Subtracting Integers
Lesson 1-3
Extra Skills and Word Problems Practice, Ch. 1

Multiplying and Dividing Integers
Lesson 1-4
Extra Skills and Word Problems Practice, Ch. 1

Using the Distributive Property
Lesson 1-5
Extra Skills and Word Problems Practice, Ch. 1

Spanish Vocabulary/Study Skills ELL

Vocabulary/Study Skills L3

6A: Graphic Organizer For use before Lesson 6-1

Study Skill It is important that you fully understand the basic concepts in each chapter before moving on to more complex material. Be sure to ask questions when you are not comfortable with the material you have learned.

Write your answers.

1. What is the chapter title? Equations and Inequalities
2. How many lessons are there in this chapter? 6
3. What is the topic of the Test-Taking Strategies page? Reading for Understanding
4. Complete the graphic organizer below as you work through the chapter.
   - In the center, write the title of the chapter.
   - When you begin a lesson, write the lesson name in a rectangle.
   - When you complete a lesson, write a skill or key concept in a circle linked to that lesson block.
   - When you complete the chapter, use this graphic organizer to help you review.

Check students' diagrams.

Vocabulary and Study Skills

Algebra

CHAPTER 6 Equations and Inequalities

What You've Learned

- In Chapter 1, you used integers and the order of operations to solve problems.
- In Chapter 3, you used tables, graphs, and algebraic equations to solve problems.
- In Chapter 4, you selected and used appropriate forms of rational numbers to solve problems.

Check Your Readiness

GO for Help

For Exercises	See Lessons
1–4	1-3
5–11	1-4
12–17	1-5

Adding and Subtracting Integers

Simplify each expression.

1. $8 + 15 + (-25)$ -2
2. $6 + 7 - 15$ -2
3. $14 - 8 + 8$ 14
4. $120 + (-6) + 9$ 123

Multiplying and Dividing Integers

Simplify each expression.

5. $-12 \div 3$ -4
6. $-3 \div (-1)$ 3
7. $3(-2 - 5) \div 7$ -3
8. $6 \cdot (-2) \div (-12)$ 1

Evaluate each expression when $a = 2$ and $b = -1$.

9. $\frac{ab}{2}$ -1
10. $\frac{a - 2b}{4}$ 1
11. $\frac{a - b}{a + b}$ 3

Using the Distributive Property

Find each product.

12. $5(c - 3)$ $5c - 15$
13. $-2(w + 8)$ $-2w - 16$
14. $-9(6 - t)$ $-54 + 9t$
15. $2(-5 + a)$ $-10 + 2a$
16. $11(4 - b)$ $44 - 11b$
17. $-1(x - 2)$ $-x + 2$

Chapter 6 Overview

In this chapter, students simplify algebraic expressions and write and solve both two-step equations and one-step inequalities. They also graph inequalities on a number line.

Activating Prior Knowledge

In this chapter, students draw on their knowledge of integers and computations with integers, on their understanding of the order of operations, and on their understanding of properties of numbers to write and solve equations and inequalities. Ask questions such as:

- *How do you find the product of −8 and −4?* **Multiply the absolute values of the digits; write a + sign for the answer because the product of two factors is positive when both factors have the same sign.**
- *How do you add −24 and +6?* **Since the signs of the two addends are different, find the difference of their absolute values. Write the sign of the number with the greater absolute value for the sum.**

What You'll Learn Next

- In this chapter, you will simplify algebraic expressions.
- You will solve problems by writing and solving multi-step equations.
- You will write, solve, and graph inequalities.

Key Vocabulary

- Addition Property of Inequality (p. 282)
- Division Property of Inequality (p. 288)
- inequality (p. 282)
- like terms (p. 266)
- Multiplication Property of Inequality (p. 288)
- Subtraction Property of Inequality (p. 282)
- term (p. 266)

Problem Solving Application On pages 298–299, you will work an extended activity about movies.

Activity Lab

Modeling Multi-Step Equations

By using manipulatives, such as algebra tiles, students can gain a concrete understanding of what an equation is and what it means to find its solution.

Guided Instruction

Error Prevention!

Remind students that the size of the *x*-bar has no relationship to its value (for example, some students might think the value of *x* is 3 because 3 unit squares fit into one *x*-bar). Help students resist the urge to simply bring the unit representing 1 to the other side. Remind them that each side is equivalent, and that what is done to one side must be done to the other side. Have students draw a vertical line on their papers to better visualize the idea of two sides of an equation.

Differentiated Instruction

Visual Learners
As you work through the solution to the equation, guide students to see that adding a negative unit tile to each side to create a zero pair is equivalent to subtracting positive 1 from each side. As needed, remind students that they use inverse operations to "undo" operations to solve equations, and that addition and subtraction are inverse operations.

Resources

- Activity Lab 6-1: Solving Two-Step Equations
- algebra tiles
- graph paper
- colored pencils

6-1a Activity Lab Hands On

Modeling Multi-Step Equations

You can use algebra tiles to model and solve multi-step equations.

To solve a multi-step equation, get the *x*-tiles alone on one side. Then divide each side into equal groups.

ACTIVITY

Use algebra tiles to solve $2x + 1 = -5$.

Model the equation. →

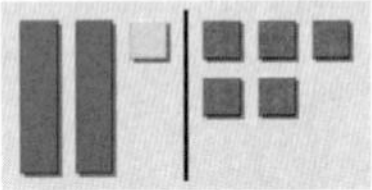

$2x + 1 = -5$

Add −1 to each side, creating a zero pair on the left side. →

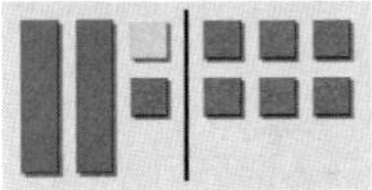

$2x + 1 + (-1) = -5 + (-1)$

Remove the zero pair. →

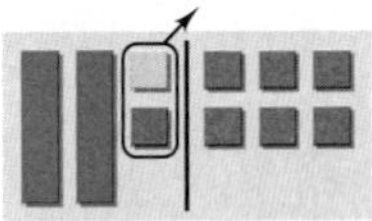

$2x = -6$

Divide each side into two equal groups. →

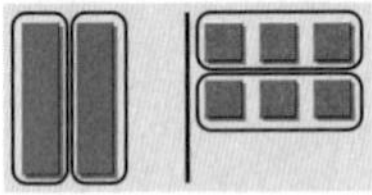

$\frac{2x}{2} = \frac{-6}{2}$

Remove one group from each side. →

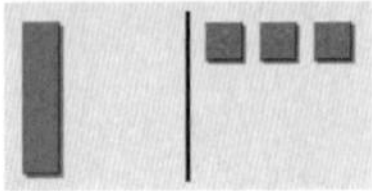

$x = -3$

Exercises

Use algebra tiles to solve each equation.

1. $-2x + 5 = 3$ 1 **2.** $3x + 2 = -7$ −3 **3.** $2x - 4 = -2$ 1

4. $2x - 7 = 5$ 6 **5.** $1 + 2x = 5$ 2 **6.** $3x - 5 = -11$ −2

7. $-15 - 8x = 25$ −5 **8.** $16x + 36 = 100$ 4 **9.** $46 - 12x = -62$ 9

10. Open-Ended Write two different equations that have the solution modeled at the right. Answers may vary. Sample: $-2x = -8$; $2x - 3 = 5$

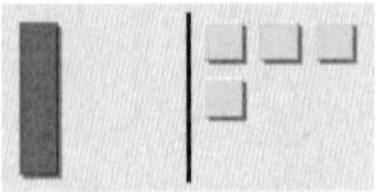

11. Use algebra tiles to model and solve $2x + 5 = x - 1$. Describe each step. See margin.

11. Answers may vary. Sample: Subtract 5 from each side; $2x + 5 - 5 = x - 1 - 5$. Remove the zero pair; $2x = x - 6$. Subtract x from each side; $2x - x = x - 6 - x$. Remove the zero pair; $x = -6$. The solution is −6.

Algebra

6-1 Solving Two-Step Equations

Check Skills You'll Need

1. **Vocabulary Review** What does it mean to *isolate* the variable? See below.

Solve each equation.

2. $x + 4 = -3$ -7
3. $c - 5 = 1$ 6
4. $5 + a = 35$ 30

GO for Help Lesson 1-6

What You'll Learn

To solve two-step equations and to use two-step equations to solve problems

Why Learn This?

Many real-world situations are modeled by equations with multiple steps.

Suppose you adopt a puppy from an animal shelter and buy 3 bags of dog food. The adoption fee is \$125 and you spend a total of \$154.97. How much does each bag of dog food cost?

Total cost \$154.97	
Adoption fee \$125	Bags $3b$

The model at the left shows that you can use the equation $125 + 3b = 154.97$ to represent the problem. This equation requires two steps to solve. Use the order of operations in reverse to choose the operation to undo first.

Check Skills You'll Need

1. to get the variable alone on one side of the equation

EXAMPLE Solving Using Subtraction and Division

1 Solve $125 + 3b = 154.97$.

$125 + 3b = 154.97$

$125 - 125 + 3b = 154.97 - 125$ ← Subtract 125 from each side.

$3b = 29.97$ ← Simplify.

$\frac{3b}{3} = \frac{29.97}{3}$ ← Divide each side by 3.

$b = 9.99$ ← Simplify.

Check $125 + 3b = 154.97$

$125 + 3(9.99) \stackrel{?}{=} 154.97$ ← Substitute 9.99 for b.

$154.97 = 154.97$ ✔ ← The solution checks.

Online active math

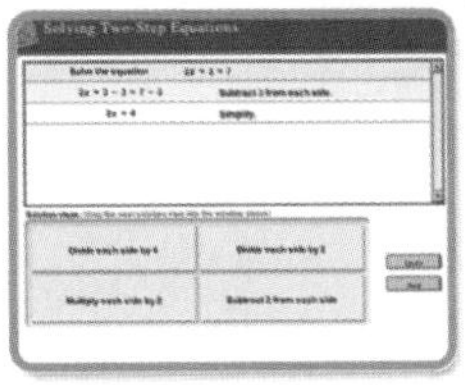

For: Two-Step Equations Activity
Use: Interactive Textbook, 6-1

Quick Check

1. Solve $4g + 11.6 = -23.2$. Check the solution. -8.7

Differentiated Instruction Solutions for All Learners

Special Needs L1
Students write the order of operations. Then they write the order of operations in reverse. Explain that they will follow the order of operations in reverse to isolate the variable.
learning style: verbal

Below Level L2
Students circle the variable in an equation they are solving and underline the operation they will undo first.
learning style: visual

6-1

1. Plan

Objective

1 To solve two-step equations and to use two-step equations to solve problems

Examples

1 Solving Using Subtraction and Division
2 Application: Sharing Costs

Math Understandings: p. 258C

Professional Development

Math Background

The variable in a two-step equation, such as $2x + 8 = 10$ has been multiplied by a number, and a number has also been added. These operations are usually *undone* (to solve by isolating the variable) in the *reverse* of the order of operations.

More Math Background: p. 258C

Lesson Planning and Resources

See p. 258E for a list of the resources that support this lesson.

PowerPoint

Bell Ringer Practice

Check Skills You'll Need
Use student page, transparency, or PowerPoint. For intervention, direct students to:
Solving Equations by Adding and Subtracting
Lesson 1-6
Extra Skills and Word Problems Practice, Ch. 1

2. Teach

Activity Lab

Use before the lesson.
Student Edition
Activity Lab, Hands On 6-1a, Modeling Multi-Step Equations, p. 260

All in One Teaching Resources

Activity Lab 6-1: Solving Two-Step Equations

Guided Instruction

Alternative Method
In Example 1, you may want to have students write the −125 below the 125 and the 154.97 as an algorithm. Some students find this stacked form easier.

$$\begin{array}{rcr} 125 + 3b & = & 154.97 \\ -\ 125 \quad & = & -\ 125 \\ \hline 3b & = & 29.97 \end{array}$$

Error Prevention!

Ask students to say aloud what each letter represents in the problem. Help them see how the English sentence lines up with the mathematical equation.

PowerPoint

Additional Examples

1. Solve $4p + 27 = 61.48$ 8.62

2. At a recent breakfast, four friends paid for their own drinks and shared the cost of a bag of doughnuts. Joe's drink was $1.75. He paid $3.20 total for breakfast. What equation can be used to find the cost of the doughnuts? How much did the bag of donuts cost? $\frac{d}{4} + 1.75 = 3.20$; $5.80

All in One Teaching Resources

- Daily Notetaking Guide 6-1 L3
- Adapted Notetaking 6-1 L1

Closure

- *What is the difference between the two steps involved in solving a two-step equation?* The first step undoes the addition or subtraction; the second undoes the multiplication or division.

EXAMPLE Application: Sharing Costs

2 **Multiple Choice** Suppose you buy a slice of pizza for $1.50. You also split the cost of renting a video with two friends. Your total cost is $2.75. Which equation can you use to find the cost of renting the video?

Ⓐ $1.50 + v = 2.75$
Ⓑ $1.50 + \frac{v}{2} = 2.75$
Ⓒ $1.50 + \frac{v}{3} = 2.75$
Ⓓ $\frac{1.50 + v}{3} = 2.75$

Test Prep Tip
You can represent the relationships in Example 2 with the model below.

Total amount paid $2.75	
Pizza $1.50	Video $\frac{v}{3}$

Words cost of pizza plus (cost of video ÷ 3) is $2.75

Let v = the cost of the video.

Equation $1.50 \quad + \quad \frac{v}{3} \quad = \quad 2.75$

The correct answer is C. You can solve the equation to find the cost.

$1.50 + \frac{v}{3} = 2.75$

$1.50 - 1.50 + \frac{v}{3} = 2.75 - 1.50$ ← **Subtract 1.50 from each side.**

$\frac{v}{3} = 1.25$ ← **Simplify.**

$(3)\frac{v}{3} = (3)1.25$ ← **Multiply each side by 3.**

$v = 3.75$ ← **Simplify.**

The cost of renting the video is $3.75.

Quick Check

2. **Telephone Bill** To make a long-distance call, it costs $.50 per call and $.85 per minute. You make a long-distance call that costs $3.90. Write and solve an equation to find the length of the call. $0.5 + 0.85c = 3.90$; 4 min

Check Your Understanding

Write an equation for each model.

1. 
$3x - 2 = 7$

2. 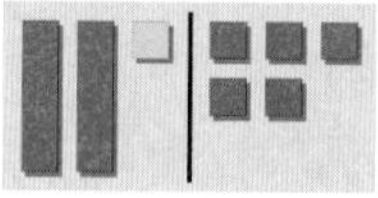
$-2x + 1 = -5$

Write the first step in solving each equation. 3–6. Answers may vary. Samples are given.

3. $\frac{t}{-2} - 8 = 10$ Add 8 to each side.
4. $-5 = \frac{x}{2} - 5$ Add 5 to each side.
5. $4m - 12 = 0$ Add 12 to each side.
6. $7q + 9 = 3$ Subtract 9 from each side.
7. **Estimation** Use estimation to solve $10.67 + \frac{x}{1.95} = 38.9$. about 56

Differentiated Instruction Solutions for All Learners

Advanced Learners L4
Students solve Example 1 by dividing first. Students write an equation that might be easier to solve by dividing first. Sample: $2x - 44 = 120$

learning style: verbal

English Language Learners ELL
Help students understand Example 1 by writing *What We Know* on the board. Below this, list *the price of the puppy* and *the total price of the puppy and dog food.* Then write *What We Want to Know*, and, below this, write *the price of one bag of food.*

learning style: visual

Homework Exercises

For more exercises, see Extra Skills and Word Problems.

GO for Help

For Exercises	See Examples
8–13	1
14–18	2

A **Solve each equation. Check the solution.**

8. $4x + 7 = 3$ −1
9. $1 + 2g = -7$ −4
10. $15 = 3y + 6$ 3
11. $-6b + 10 = -14$ 4
12. $23 + 8b = -4.2$ −3.4
13. $17 + 2.6b = 30$ 5
14. $7 + \frac{x}{4} = 3$ −16
15. $17 + \frac{b}{26} = 30$ 338
16. $15 = \frac{y}{3} + 6$ 27

Write and solve an equation to answer each question. You may find a model helpful.

17. Leo ordered 4 CDs by mail. Each CD cost the same amount. With a \$5 shipping charge, the total cost was \$68.96. How much did each CD cost? $4x + 5 = 68.96$; \$15.99

18. **School Supplies** Annamarie bought a notebook for \$1.19 and pencils for \$.39 each. The total cost was \$3.92. How many pencils did she buy? $0.39p + 1.19 = 3.92$; 7 pencils

B **GPS**

19. **Guided Problem Solving** A bag of rice costs \$1.99. You buy 1 bag of rice and 6 cans of black beans for a total cost of \$7.33. If you have \$8.25, can you buy another can of beans? Explain. See left.
    - What equation can you use to find *c*, the cost of a can of beans?
    - Knowing *c*, how can you determine whether you have enough money for another can of beans?

19. yes; one can of beans costs \$.89, so it will cost a total of \$8.22 to buy another can.

20. **Error Analysis** Which student's work is correct? Explain. See left.

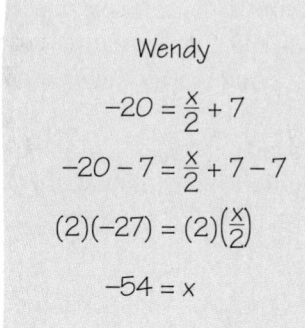

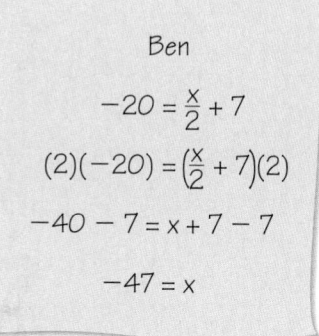

Wendy	Ben
$-20 = \frac{x}{2} + 7$	$-20 = \frac{x}{2} + 7$
$-20 - 7 = \frac{x}{2} + 7 - 7$	$(2)(-20) = (\frac{x}{2} + 7)(2)$
$(2)(-27) = (2)(\frac{x}{2})$	$-40 - 7 = x + 7 - 7$
$-54 = x$	$-47 = x$

20. Wendy's; Ben did not do the order of operations in reverse or use the Dist. Prop.

GO Online
Homework Video Tutor
Visit: PHSchool.com
Web Code: ase-0601

21. **Nutrition** (GPS) According to the Food and Drug Administration, the recommended daily intake of iron is 18 mg. This is 4 less than twice the recommended daily intake of zinc. What is the recommended daily intake of zinc? 11 mg

22. **Estimation** Use estimation to check whether 24.27 is a reasonable solution for $6p + 39.95 = 105.65$. Show your work. See margin.

23. Solve $7b + 3 = 24$. Justify your steps. See margin.

22. Round 39.95 to 40 and 105.65 to 100. Solve $6p + 40 = 100$. The solution is $p = 10$. 24.27 is not reasonable.

23. Check students' work.

$7b + 3 = 24$

$7b + 3 - 3 = 24 - 3$

Subtr. Prop. of Eq.

$\frac{7b}{7} = \frac{21}{7}$

Div. Prop. of Eq.

$b = 3$

3. Practice

Assignment Guide

Check Your Understanding

Go over Exercises 1–7 in class before assigning the Homework Exercises.

Homework Exercises

A Practice by Example	8–18
B Apply Your Skills	19–30
C Challenge	31
Test Prep and Mixed Review	32–35

Homework Quick Check

To check students' understanding of key skills and concepts, go over Exercises 14, 17, 20, 22, and 30.

Differentiated Instruction Resources

Adapted Practice 6-1 L1

Practice 6-1 Solving Two-Step Equ L3

Solve each equation.

1. $4r + 6 = 14$ $r = 2$
2. $9y - 11 = 7$ $y = 2$
3. $\frac{m}{4} + 6 = 3$ $m = -12$
4. $\frac{k}{-9} + 6 = -4$ $k = 90$
5. $-5b - 6 = -11$ $b = 1$
6. $\frac{v}{-7} + 8 = 19$ $v = -77$
7. $3.4t + 19.36 = -10.22$ $t = -8.7$
8. $\frac{n}{-1.6} + 7.9 = 8.4$ $n = -0.8$
9. $4.6b + 26.8 = 50.72$ $b = 5.2$
10. $\frac{a}{-8.06} + 7.02 = 18.4$ $a = -91.7228$
11. $-2.06d + 18 = -10.84$ $d = 14$
12. $\frac{e}{-95} + 6 = 4$ $e = 190$

Write and solve an equation to answer each question.

13. Hugo received \$100 for his birthday. He then saved \$20 per week until he had a total of \$460 to buy a printer. Use an equation to show how many weeks it took him to save the money. $100 + 20w = 460$; 18 wk

14. A health club charges a \$50 initial fee plus \$2 for each visit. Moselle has spent a total of \$144 at the health club this year. Use an equation to find how many visits she has made. $50 + 2v = 144$; 47 visits

Solve each equation to find the value of the variable. Write the answer in the puzzle. Do not include any negative signs or any decimals.

ACROSS
1. $6n - 12 = 2.4$
2. $\frac{n}{3} + 4.6 = 21.6$
4. $x - 3 = 51.29$
6. $2z + 2 = 7.6$

DOWN
1. $\frac{j}{5} - 14 = -9$
2. $3x - 2 = 169$
3. $\frac{x}{4} + 1 = 19$
4. $\frac{x}{3} + 4 = 22$
5. $2x - 2 = 182$

1. 2	4		2. 5	1
5			7	
		3. 7		
4. 5	4	2	5. 9	
4			6. 2	8

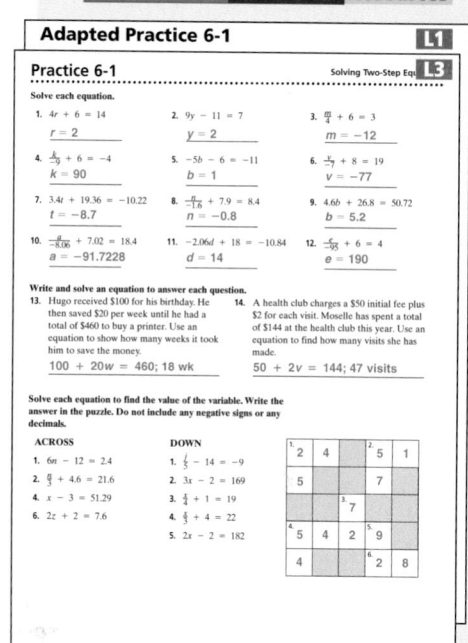

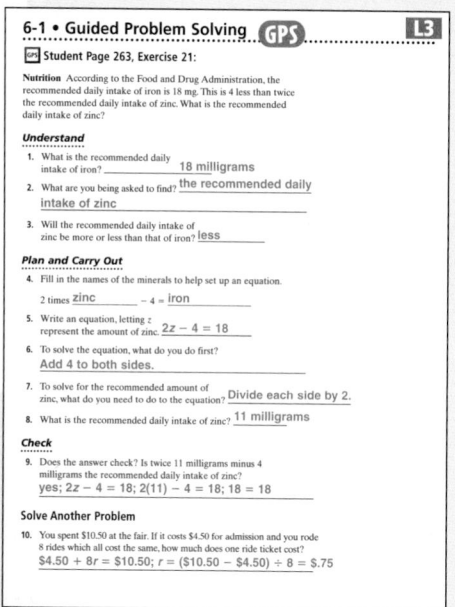

6-1 • Guided Problem Solving GPS L3

GPS Student Page 263, Exercise 21:

Nutrition According to the Food and Drug Administration, the recommended daily intake of iron is 18 mg. This is 4 less than twice the recommended daily intake of zinc. What is the recommended daily intake of zinc?

Understand

1. What is the recommended daily intake of iron? 18 milligrams
2. What are you being asked to find? the recommended daily intake of zinc
3. Will the recommended daily intake of zinc be more or less than that of iron? less

Plan and Carry Out

4. Fill in the names of the minerals to help set up an equation.
   2 times zinc − 4 = iron
5. Write an equation, letting *z* represent the amount of zinc. $2z - 4 = 18$
6. To solve the equation, what do you do first? Add 4 to both sides.
7. To solve for the recommended amount of zinc, what do you need to do to the equation? Divide each side by 2.
8. What is the recommended daily intake of zinc? 11 milligrams

Check

9. Does the answer check? Is twice 11 milligrams minus 4 milligrams the recommended daily intake of zinc? yes; $2z - 4 = 18$; $2(11) - 4 = 18$; $18 = 18$

Solve Another Problem

10. You spent \$10.50 at the fair. If it costs \$4.50 for admission and you rode 8 rides which all cost the same, how much does one ride ticket cost? $\$4.50 + 8r = \$10.50$; $r = (\$10.50 - \$4.50) \div 8 = \$.75$

4. Assess & Reteach

PowerPoint

Lesson Quiz

Solve each equation.

1. $\frac{n}{3} - 14 = 1$ **45**
2. $16 - 2x = 9$ **3.5**

Write and solve an equation.

3. Suppose you bought a \$2.75 sandwich and two drinks of equal price. You spend \$4.25 in all. How much does one drink cost? **$2d + 2.75 = 4.25$; \$.75**
4. Admission to a museum costs \$3.75 per person. A group of friends attend. They spend a total of \$30 on lunch. At the end of the day, they had spent a total of \$56.25. How many friends attended the museum? **7 friends**

Alternative Assessment

Each student picks a rational number, represented by w. They write the equation $4x - 6 = w$, then substitute their number for w. Partners trade papers, solve for x, and justify their solutions.

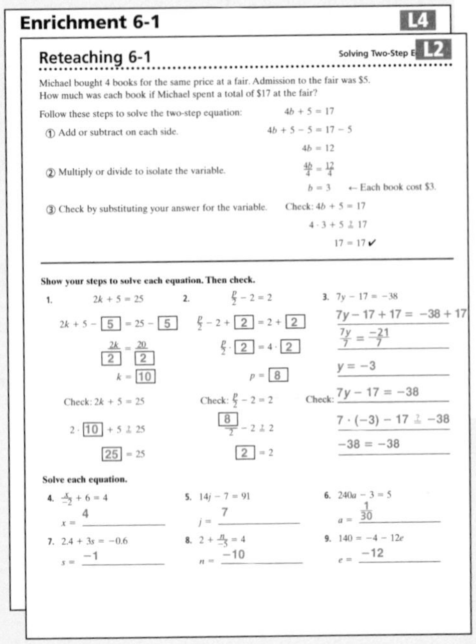
Enrichment 6-1 L4

Reteaching 6-1 Solving Two-Step E L2

Michael bought 4 books for the same price at a fair. Admission to the fair was \$5. How much was each book if Michael spent a total of \$17 at the fair?

Follow these steps to solve the two-step equation: $4b + 5 = 17$

① Add or subtract on each side. $4b + 5 - 5 = 17 - 5$; $4b = 12$

② Multiply or divide to isolate the variable. $\frac{4b}{4} = \frac{12}{4}$; $b = 3$ ← Each book cost \$3.

③ Check by substituting your answer for the variable. Check: $4b + 5 = 17$; $4 \cdot 3 + 5 \stackrel{?}{=} 17$; $17 = 17$ ✓

Show your steps to solve each equation. Then check.

1. $2k + 5 = 25$; $2k + 5 - \boxed{5} = 25 - \boxed{5}$; $\frac{2k}{\boxed{2}} = \frac{20}{\boxed{2}}$; $k = \boxed{10}$; Check: $2k + 5 = 25$; $2 \cdot \boxed{10} + 5 \stackrel{?}{=} 25$; $\boxed{25} = 25$
2. $\frac{p}{2} - 2 = 2$; $\frac{p}{2} - 2 + \boxed{2} = 2 + \boxed{2}$; $\frac{p}{2} \cdot \boxed{2} = 4 \cdot \boxed{2}$; $p = \boxed{8}$; Check: $\frac{p}{2} - 2 = 2$; $\frac{\boxed{8}}{2} - 2 \stackrel{?}{=} 2$; $\boxed{2} = 2$
3. $7y - 17 = -38$; $7y - 17 + 17 = -38 + 17$; $\frac{7y}{7} = \frac{-21}{7}$; $y = -3$; Check: $7y - 17 = -38$; $7 \cdot (-3) - 17 \stackrel{?}{=} -38$; $-38 = -38$

Solve each equation.

4. $\frac{x}{-2} + 6 = 4$ $x =$ 4
5. $14j - 7 = 91$ $j =$ 7
6. $240a - 3 = 5$ $a =$ $\frac{1}{30}$
7. $2.4 + 3s = -0.6$ $s =$ −1
8. $2 + \frac{n}{-5} = 4$ $n =$ −10
9. $140 = -4 - 12e$ $e =$ −12

Solve each equation.

24. $\frac{y}{3} - 9 = 30$ **117**
25. $\frac{n}{1.4} + 1 = 10$ **12.6**
26. $-8.2 + \frac{t}{-2} = 1.7$ **−19.8**
27. $12 = -6 - 3v$ **−6**
28. $1.2 = 3s - 1.8$ **1**
29. $10 = 3q - 2.6$ **4.2**

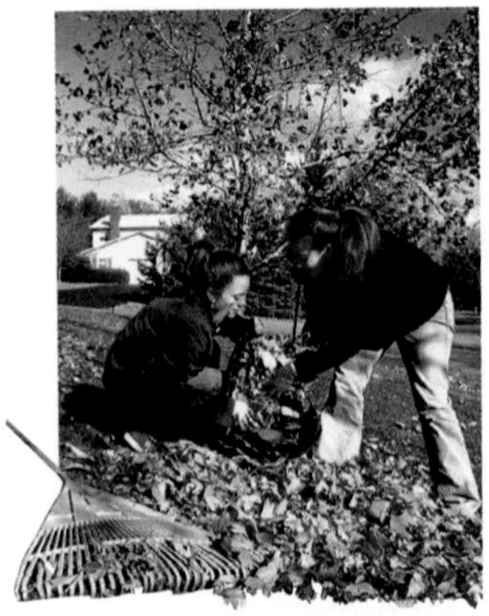

30. a. **Jobs** Two students want to save \$200 each. One student starts with \$60 and rakes leaves for \$6 per hour. The other student starts with nothing but earns \$9 per hour painting houses. Let x represent the number of hours worked. Write and solve two equations to find the number of hours each student will have to work. **30a–b. See margin.**
    b. **Writing in Math** Explain why one of the equations from part (a) is a one-step equation and the other is a two-step equation.

Ⓒ 31. **Challenge** Multiply each side of the equation $0.5x + 1.3 = 4.8$ by 10 and solve for x. How does this solution compare to the solution to the original equation? Explain why it is helpful to multiply by 10. **$x = 7$; It is the same. You could avoid working with decimals.**

Test Prep and Mixed Review — Practice

Multiple Choice

32. This year, 227 pets were adopted from a shelter. This is 35 fewer than twice the number that were adopted last year. Which equation can you use to find the number of pets adopted last year? **A**
    - Ⓐ $n = \frac{227 + 35}{2}$
    - Ⓑ $n = 2(227) - 35$
    - Ⓒ $n = \frac{227 - 35}{2}$
    - Ⓓ $n = 2(227) + 35$

33. A town's youth soccer teams play on fields as shown in the diagrams at the right. The two fields are similar. If the area of the field for players under 10 years old is 2,400 yd^2, what is the area of the field for players under 8 years old? **H**
    - Ⓕ 1,200 yd^2
    - Ⓖ 800 yd^2
    - Ⓗ 600 yd^2
    - Ⓙ 300 yd^2

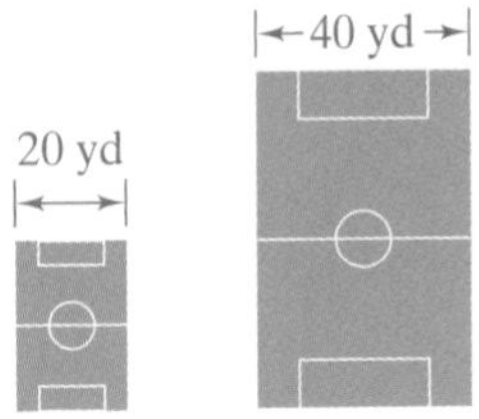

34. A recipe calls for $1\frac{3}{4}$ cups of flour. Sabrina is increasing the recipe by $2\frac{1}{2}$ times. She estimates that she'll need 5 cups of flour. Which of the following best describes her estimate? **B**
    - Ⓐ More than the actual amount since she rounded the cups down
    - Ⓑ More than the actual amount since she rounded the cups up
    - Ⓒ Less than the actual amount since she rounded the cups up
    - Ⓓ Less than the actual amount since she rounded the cups down

GO for Help

For Exercise	See Lesson
35	4-4

35. Rectangles $ABCD$ and $PQRS$ are similar. $ABCD$ is 4 m long and 9.5 m wide. The length of $PQRS$ is 9.6 m. How wide is $PQRS$? **22.8 m**

Test Prep

Resources

For additional practice with a variety of test item formats:
- Test-Taking Strategies, p. 293
- Test Prep, p. 297
- Test-Taking Strategies with Transparencies

30a. $60 + 6x = 200$, $23\frac{1}{3}$ h;
$9x = 200$, $22\frac{2}{9}$ h

b. In the first equation, you need to subtract 60 and then divide by 6. In the second equation, you need only to divide each side by 9.

Modeling Expressions

Two students from Garth School bicycled to a game. Three buses of students also went to the game. From Greenly School, four students on bicycles and two buses went to the game. Each bus carried the same number of students. You can model this situation with tiles.

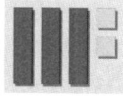

Let  represent *x*, the number of students on a bus.

Let  represent a student arriving by bicycle.

The tiles below model the total number of students at the game.

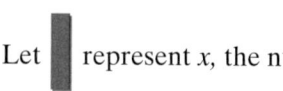

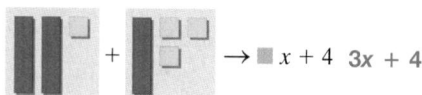

Garth School Greenly School

Exercises

1. Write two algebraic expressions, one for the number of students from Garth School who went to the game and one for the number of students from Greenly School who went to the game. $3x + 2$; $2x + 4$
2. **a.** How many buses were there in all at the game? 5 buses
   b. How many students rode bicycles to the game? 6 students
3. Use your answers to Exercise 2 to write an algebraic expression that represents the total number of students from the two schools who went to the game. $5x + 6$
4. **Reasoning** How are your algebraic expressions in Exercise 1 related to your algebraic expression in Exercise 3? The algebraic expression in Exercise 3 is the sum of the two expressions in Exercise 1.

Copy and complete the algebraic expression for each group of tiles.

5. 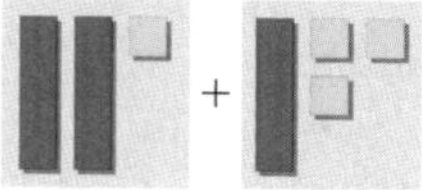 → ■$x + 4$ $3x + 4$

6. 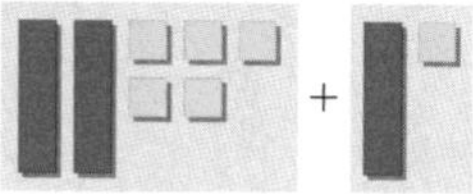 → ■x + ■ $3x + 6$

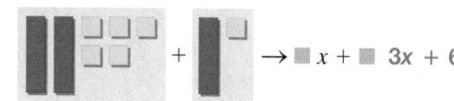

7. A student wrote the equation $3x + 2 + 5x + 1 = $ ■$x + 3$. What number should the student use to fill in the blank? Justify your reasoning. 8; the sum of $3x$ and $5x$ is $8x$.

Activity Lab

Modeling Expressions

Students use algebra tiles to model expressions that can be generated from real-world problems. This activity prepares students to simplify expressions and solve equations with more than one variable term.

Guided Instruction

Error Prevention!

Before beginning the activity, have students use tiles to convince themselves that the length of the *x*-tile is not an exact multiple of the unit tile. The *x*-tile is representing an unknown number rather than a specific length.

Connection to Algebra
Many students are not accustomed to expressing quantities symbolically because they are used to finding numerical answers. Explain that algebra provides a way of thinking about quantities and expressing the relationships between them even when we don't know their values.

Differentiated Instruction

Visual Learners
Have students make a chart with two columns wide enough to accommodate the tiles. Label the columns Garth School and Greenly School. Have students place corresponding tiles in each column. They could also write "x" and "1" underneath each tile to remind themselves what each tile represents.

Resources

- Activity Lab 6-2: Simplifying Expressions
- algebra tiles

6-2

1. Plan

Objective
1 To combine like terms and simplify algebraic expressions

Examples
1 Combining Like Terms
2 Application: Picnics
3 Distributing and Simplifying

Math Understandings: p. 258C

Professional Development

Math Background

The terms of an algebraic expression are separated by either + or − signs. Thus the entire expression $(6 + p)(32)$ consists of only one term, while the expression inside the first parentheses contains two terms.

More Math Background: p. 258C

Lesson Planning and Resources

See p. 258E for a list of the resources that support this lesson.

PowerPoint

Bell Ringer Practice

Check Skills You'll Need
Use student page, transparency, or PowerPoint. For intervention, direct students to:
Properties of Numbers
Lesson 1-5
Extra Skills and Word Problems Practice, Ch. 1

Algebra

6-2 Simplifying Algebraic Expressions

Check Skills You'll Need

1. **Vocabulary Review** Is the expression $5 + 3a - 15$ *simplified*? Explain. See below.

Simplify each expression.

2. $-8(r + 3)$ $-8r - 24$
3. $-7(s - 5)$ $-7s + 35$
4. $35(2 - t)$ $70 - 35t$

GO for Help Lesson 1-5

What You'll Learn

To combine like terms and to simplify algebraic expressions

New Vocabulary term, like terms

Why Learn This?

Some calculations, such as finding the cost of several items, involve more than one variable. Simplifying expressions first can make calculations easier.

An expression may have one or more terms. A **term** is a number, a variable, or the product of a number and one or more variables. **Like terms** are terms that have exactly the same variable factors.

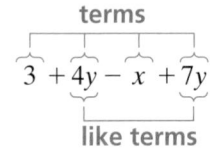

terms
$3 + 4y - x + 7y$
like terms

Like Terms	Not Like Terms
-5 and 8	$-5x$ and 8
$2x$ and $-3x$	$2x$ and $-3y$
$2x^2$ and $-3x^2$	$2x^2$ and $-3x$
$2xy$ and $-3xy$	$2x$ and $-3xy$

Vocabulary Tip
Expressions with only integers are always like terms.

Often a variable does not have a number in front of it. In this case, there is an *understood* "1" in front of the variable. For example, b is the same as $1b$ and $-a$ is the same as $-1a$.

When you add or subtract like terms, you are combining like terms.

Check Skills You'll Need
1. No; 15 can be subtracted from 5. The simplest form is $3a - 10$.

EXAMPLE Combining Like Terms

1 Combine like terms in the expression $5m + 9m + m$.

$5m + 9m + m = 5m + 9m + 1m$ ← Rewrite m as $1m$.
$= (5 + 9 + 1)m$ ← Distributive Property
$= 15m$ ← Combine like terms by adding.

Quick Check

1. Combine like terms in the expression $2t + t - 17t$. $-14t$

Differentiated Instruction Solutions for All Learners

Special Needs L1
Students get a copy of Examples 2 and 3. Before simplifying, students use a colored pencil or pen to circle the like terms in each expression.
learning style: visual

Below Level L2
Review the rules for multiplying signed numbers, especially the product of two negatives, as shown below.

$+ \cdot + = +$ $\quad - \cdot - = +$
$+ \cdot - = -$ $\quad - \cdot + = -$

learning style: visual

When defining variables, it is often helpful to choose letters that remind you of what the variables represent.

EXAMPLE Application: Picnics

2 Garrick buys 5 loaves of bread and 8 cans of tuna for a picnic. Tanya buys a loaf of bread and 2 cans of tuna. Define and use variables to represent the total cost.

Words Garrick: cost of 5 loaves plus cost of 8 cans

Let b = the cost of a loaf of bread.
Let t = the cost a can of tuna.

Expression $5b$ + $8t$

Words Tanya: cost of 1 loaf plus cost of 2 cans

Expression b + $2t$

Combined Expression $(5b + 8t) + (b + 2t)$

$(5b + 8t) + (b + 2t) = 5b + b + 8t + 2t$ ← **Commutative Property of Addition**

$= (5 + 1)b + (8 + 2)t$ ← **Distributive Property**

$= 6b + 10t$ ← **Simplify.**

Quick Check

2. In one trip to a hardware store, you buy 16 boards, 2 boxes of nails, and a hammer. On a second trip, you buy 10 more boards and a box of nails. Define and use variables to represent the total cost.
Let b = the cost of a board. Let n = the cost of a box of nails. Let h = the cost of a hammer. $26b + 3n + h$

When you use the Distributive Property with subtraction, remember to distribute the negative sign.

EXAMPLE Distributing and Simplifying

3 Simplify $8c - 3(c + 5)$.

$8c - 3(c + 5) = 8c + (-3)(c + 5)$ ← **Add the opposite of 3(c + 5).**

$= 8c + [-3c + (-15)]$ ← **Distributive Property**

$= 8c + (-3c) - 15$ ← **Simplify.**

$= [8 + (-3)]c - 15$ ← **Distributive Property**

$= 5c - 15$ ← **Simplify.**

Quick Check

3. Simplify the expression $11 - 2(3b + 1)$. **$9 - 6b$**

GO Online

Video Tutor Help
Visit: PHSchool.com
Web Code: ase-0775

2. Teach

Activity Lab

Use before the lesson.
Student Edition Activity Lab, Hands On 6-2a, Modeling Expressions, p. 265

All in One Teaching Resources

Activity Lab 6-2: Simplifying Expressions

Guided Instruction

Tactile Learners
In Example 2, use two different colored counters to model the addition of like terms. For example, use blue for b and red for t (5 blue + 8 red + 1 blue + 2 red = 6 blue + 10 red). After students understand the physical model, help them see how the abstract properties represent what they did with the counters.

Visual Learners
In Example 3, have students draw one arrow from the −3 to the c term and another arrow from the −3 to the 5 to emphasize that the multiplier is distributed to each term in the parentheses.

PowerPoint

Additional Examples

1 Combine like terms in the expression $8p + 13p + p$. **$22p$**

2 Carlos buys 6 tubes of paint and 3 pieces of fabric to make an art project. Shauna buys 8 tubes of paint and 1 piece of fabric. Define and use variables to represent the total cost.
$(6t + 3f) + (8t + f) = 14t + 4f$

3 Simplify the expression $7t - 2(t - 3)$ **$5t + 6$**

All in One Teaching Resources

- Daily Notetaking Guide 6-2 L3
- Adapted Notetaking 6-2 L1

Closure

- *When can you combine terms?* **when they are like terms**

Advanced Learners L4
Ask: *When is it possible to find a single value for the expression* $3x + 4y$*?* **when you have a value to substitute for both x and y**

learning style: verbal

English Language Learners ELL
Students read terms, such as 5b in Example 2, out loud to make sure they understand the meaning of the terms. For example, they should read this term as *5 times the cost of a loaf of bread,* **not** *5 loaves of bread.*

learning style: verbal

3. Practice

Assignment Guide

Check Your Understanding

Go over Exercises 1–6 in class before assigning the Homework Exercises.

Homework Exercises

A	Practice by Example	7–28
B	Apply Your Skills	29–42
C	Challenge	43
	Test Prep and Mixed Review	44–48

Homework Quick Check

To check students' understanding of key skills and concepts, go over Exercises 22, 25, 31, 40, and 42.

Differentiated Instruction Resources

Adapted Practice 6-2 L1

Practice 6-2 L3 Simplifying Algebraic Expressions

Combine like terms.

1. $9j + 34j$ $43j$
2. $23s - 12s$ $11s$
3. $5t - 12t + 17t$ $10t$
4. $6q + 14q - 8q$ $12q$
5. $7t - 12t + 4t$ $-t$
6. $16w + 7w - 5w$ $18w$
7. $y + 13y - 9y$ $5y$
8. $5z - 2z - 13z$ $-10z$
9. $4x + 21x - 6x$ $19x$

Simplify each expression.

10. $4a + 7 + 2a$ $6a + 7$
11. $8(k - 9)$ $8k - 72$
12. $(w + 3)7$ $7w + 21$
13. $5(b - 6) + 9$ $5b - 21$
14. $-4 + 3(6 + k)$ $14 + 3k$
15. $12j - (9j + 7)$ $3j$
16. $-9 + 8(x + 6)$ $8x + 39$
17. $4(m + 6) - 3$ $4m + 21$
18. $28k + 36(7 + k)$ $64k + 252$
19. $3.09(j + 4.6)$ $3.09j + 14.214$
20. $7.9y + 8.4 - 2.04y$ $5.86y + 8.4$
21. $4.3(5.6 + c)$ $4.3c + 24.08$
22. $9.8c + 8d - 4.6c + 2.9d$ $5.2c + 10.9d$
23. $18 + 27m - 29 + 36m$ $63m - 11$
24. $8(j + 12) + 4(k - 19)$ $8j + 4k + 20$
25. $4.2r + 8.1s + 1.09r + 6.32s$ $5.29r + 14.42s$

Solve.

26. Tyrone bought 15.3 gal of gasoline priced at g dollars per gallon, 2 qt of oil priced at q dollars per quart, and a wiper blade priced at \$3.79. Write an expression that represents the total cost of these items. $15.3g + 2q + 3.79$
27. Choose a number. Multiply by 2. Add 6 to the product. Divide by 2. Then subtract 3. What is the answer? Repeat this process using two different numbers. Explain. Let n be the number. $(2n + 6) \div 2 = n + 3$; $(n + 3) - 3 = n$. You get the number you started with.

6-2 • Guided Problem Solving GPS L3

GPS Student Page 269, Exercise 31:

On a shopping trip, Kelly buys 3 barrettes and a headband. Her sister buys 2 barrettes and 2 headbands. Define and use the variables to represent the total cost.

Understand

1. Place a circle around the number of barrettes purchased and a square around the number of headbands purchased.
2. How many headbands did Kelly buy? one
3. Underline what you are being asked to do.

Plan and Carry Out

4. Write an expression for the cost of the items Kelly bought on the shopping trip. Let b = cost of a barrette and h = cost of a headband. $3b + h$
5. Write an expression for the cost of the items Kelly's sister bought on the shopping trip. $2b + 2h$
6. Combine the like terms to represent the total cost of the items bought. $(3b + 1h) + (2b + 2h) = 5b + 3h$

Check

7. Add the numbers in each shape (circle and square) in the original problem to check your answer. $(3b + 2b) + (1h + 2h) = 5b + 3h$

Solve Another Problem

8. For a birthday party, you purchase 10 balloons, 8 party hats, and 5 game prizes. At the last minute you find that you will have a few extra guests. You pick up 3 more hats, 2 more balloons, and another game prize. Use variables where b = cost of a balloon, h = cost of a hat, and p = cost of a game prize to represent the total cost. $(2b + 10b) + (3h + 8h) + (1p + 5p) = 12b + 11h + 6p$

Check Your Understanding

1. No; the variable factors $x^2y^5z^{11}$ and $x^2z^5y^{11}$ are different.

1. **Vocabulary** Are $3x^2y^5z^{11}$ and $5x^2z^5y^{11}$ like terms? Explain.

Simplify each expression. The exercises have been started for you.

2. $-3r + 2r + r - 2$
 $= (-3 + 2 + 1)r - 2$
 -2
3. $4x - 2 + 6y + y - 4$
 $= 4x + 6y + y - 4 - 2$
 $4x + 7y - 6$
4. $9m + 2(2 + n)$
 $= 9m + 4 + 2n$
 $9m + 4 + 2n$
5. $3a + 5(3 + a)$
 $= 3a + 15 + 5a$
 $8a + 15$
6. **Mental Math** Combine like terms in the expression $1.3a + 2.4a$. $3.7a$

Homework Exercises

For more exercises, see Extra Skills and Word Problems.

GO for Help

For Exercises	See Examples
7–15	1
16–22	2
23–28	3

A Combine like terms.

7. $8b + 3b$ $11b$
8. $9r + 22r$ $31r$
9. $34x - 3x$ $31x$
10. $19z - 24z + 6z$ z
11. $-25t + 21t - 7t$ $-11t$
12. $-13b - 17b + 32b$ $2b$
13. $-6a + a + 28a$ $23a$
14. $19t - t + 6t$ $24t$
15. $j - 4j - 15j$ $-18j$

Simplify each expression.

16. $3a + 2 + a$ $4a + 2$
17. $2x + 1 + 3x$ $5x + 1$
18. $n + 4n - 3$ $5n - 3$
19. $5n - 6r + 4n + 3r$ $9n - 3r$
20. $2z - 3y - 8z + y$ $-6z - 2y$
21. $9 - 7t + 1 + 4t$ $10 - 3t$

22. **Clothing** For the summer, Tia buys 3 T-shirts and 2 pairs of shorts. Her brother buys 4 T-shirts and 1 pair of shorts. Define and use variables to represent the total cost. Let t = the cost of a T-shirt. Let s = the cost of a pair of shorts. $7t + 3s$

Simplify each expression.

23. $3 - 5(a - 4)$ $23 - 5a$
24. $7(t + 8.5) - 5t + 4$ $2t + 63.5$
25. $-8(m + 2) - 19m$ $-27m - 16$
26. $4.3(5.6 + c) + 9c$ $24.08 + 13.3c$
27. $-5b - 2(b - 1)$ $-7b + 2$
28. $16b - 4(c + 3) - 4b$ $12b - 4c - 12$

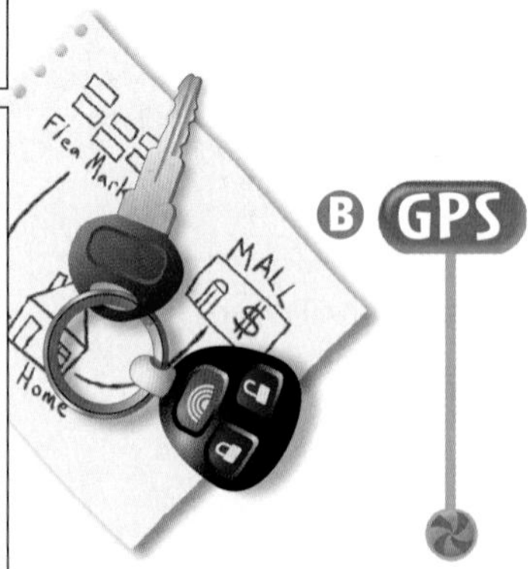

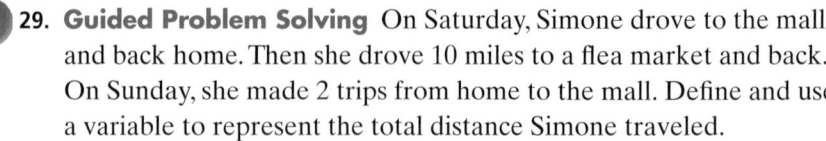

B GPS 29. **Guided Problem Solving** On Saturday, Simone drove to the mall and back home. Then she drove 10 miles to a flea market and back. On Sunday, she made 2 trips from home to the mall. Define and use a variable to represent the total distance Simone traveled.

- Draw a diagram showing the trips between the mall, the flea market, and home. Let d = distance to the mall. $6d + 20$.
- What quantity do you need to represent with a variable?

Go Online
Homework Video Tutor
Visit: PHSchool.com
Web Code: ase-0602

30. Let t = the cost of 1 lb of turkey. Let s = the cost of 1 lb of cole slaw. Let c = the cost of 1 lb of cheese. $10t + 5s + 7c$

30. **Party Planning** You buy 6 lb of sliced turkey, 3 lb of cole slaw, and 4 lb of cheese for a party. Then you invite more people to the party, so you buy another 4 lb of turkey, 2 lb of cole slaw, and 3 lb of cheese. Define and use variables to represent the total cost. See left.

31. On a shopping trip, Kelly buys 3 barrettes and a headband. Her sister buys 2 barrettes and 2 headbands. Define and use variables to represent the total cost. Let b = the cost of a barrette. Let h = the cost of a headband. $5b + 3h$

Simplify each expression.

32. $7b + 5 - 9b + c$ $-2b + c + 5$
33. $x + 2(x - y)$ $3x - 2y$
34. $-5u + 6 + u + 4u$ 6
35. $(5x + y) - (4x - 9)$ $x + y + 9$
36. $3(t - 14) - 5(t + 12)$ $-2t - 102$
37. $33.7y + 8.4 - 2.04y$ $31.66y + 8.4$
38. $9(a + 1.4b) + 8(b - 16a)$ $-119a + 20.6b$
39. $4.2x + 8.1x + 1.8x - 2.1x$ $12x$

40. **Writing in Math** One way to organize a CD collection is by categories of music. Explain how combining like terms is similar to organizing a CD collection by categories. See margin.

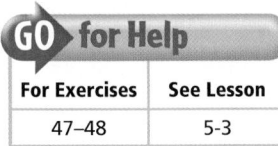

41. **Open-Ended** Write two different expressions that can be simplified to $3m + 8$. One expression should have three terms, and the other should have four terms. See margin.

42. **Reasoning** Does $5a + 5b = 10ab$? Explain. See margin.

43. **Challenge** Simplify the expression $2.5(2t - 8v) - 3(3v + 1.5t)$. $0.5t - 29v$

Test Prep and Mixed Review

Practice

Multiple Choice

44. The scale factor between two squares is 7. The area of the smaller square is 4 in.^{2}. What is the area of the larger square? C
   A 28 in.^{2}
   B 112 in.^{2}
   C 196 in.^{2}
   D 784 in.^{2}

45. Members of the Sylvester family are riding their bikes to a friend's house 20 miles away. If their average speed is 8 miles per hour, how long will they take to reach their destination? $[d = rt]$ G
   F 2 h
   G 2.5 h
   H 5 h
   J 10 h

46. A square has one vertex at (0, 3) on a coordinate grid. If the square is translated 3 units up and 2 units to the left, what are the new coordinates of this vertex? D
   A (5, 8)
   B (2, 6)
   C (−2, 0)
   D (−2, 6)

Go for Help

For Exercises	See Lesson
47–48	5-3

Use a proportion to solve each problem.

47. 16 is 80% of what number? 20
48. What percent of 250 is 160? 64%

4. Assess & Reteach

PowerPoint

Lesson Quiz

Simplify each expression.

1. $-13c + c$ $-12c$
2. $4y - 7 + 8y$ $12y - 7$
3. $1 - 6(b - 9)$ $-6b + 55$
4. Karen buys 4 boxes of cereal and 3 bags of almonds at the grocery store. Her brother, David, buys 2 boxes of cereal. Define and use variables to represent the total cost. Let c = the cost of a box of cereal and let a = the cost of a bag of almonds. Then $6c + 3a$ represents the total cost.

40. Similar categories of CDs are grouped together, and terms with similar variables are grouped together.

41. Answers may vary. Sample: $2m + m + 8$; $4m + 2 - m + 6$

42. Answers may vary. Sample: No; $5a$ and $5b$ are not like terms, because the variables are different.

Enrichment 6-2 L4

Reteaching 6-2 Simplifying Algebraic Exp L2

A *term* is a number, a variable, or the product of a number and variable(s). The two terms in $-2x + 4y$ are $-2x$ and $4y$.

Terms with exactly the same variable factor are called *like terms*. In $-3x + 4y + 5x$, $-3x$ and $5x$ are like terms.

One way to *combine like terms* is by addition or subtraction.

- Add to combine like terms in $4y + y$.
  $4y + y = (4 + 1)y = 5y$
- Subtract to combine like terms in $2m - 5m$.
  $2m - 5m = (2 - 5)m = -3m$

To *simplify* an expression, combine its like terms. Perform as many of its operations as possible.

Simplify: $3a + 5b - a + 2b$
$= (3a - a) + (5b + 2b)$
$= 2a + 7b$

Simplify: $2(x - 4)$
$= 2x - 2(4)$
$= 2x - 8$

Combine like terms.

1. $6x + 2x =$ $8x$
2. $4c - c =$ $3c$
3. $-h - h =$ $-2h$
4. $-3y + 4y =$ y
5. $m - 5m =$ $-4m$
6. $6n + n =$ $7n$
7. $2s - 6s =$ $-4s$
8. $-t - 2t =$ $-3t$
9. $3b - 9b =$ $-6b$

Simplify each expression.

10. $3(m + 4) - 5m =$ $-2m + 12$
11. $(v - 4)5 =$ $5v - 20$
12. $4a + 2 - 8a + 1 =$ $-4a + 3$
13. $6s + 5 - (s - 6) =$ $5s + 11$
14. $3(u + 4) - 5u =$ $-2u + 12$
15. $2x + y - (9 - 4x) =$ $6x + y - 9$
16. $-5x + 3(x - y) =$ $-2x - 3y$
17. $v + 6v - 2v =$ $5v$
18. $-2s + 6 - s - 4 =$ $-3s + 2$
19. $-x + 4(x - 2) =$ $3x - 8$
20. $3(k + j) - 4k - k =$ $3j - 2k$
21. $4a - 6 - a + 1 =$ $3a - 5$

Alternative Assessment

Write a term on the board such as $12z$. Several students take turns writing like terms under it. Then other students write unlike terms in a different place on the board.

Test Prep

Resources

For additional practice with a variety of test item formats:

- Test-Taking Strategies, p. 293
- Test Prep, p. 297
- Test-Taking Strategies with Transparencies

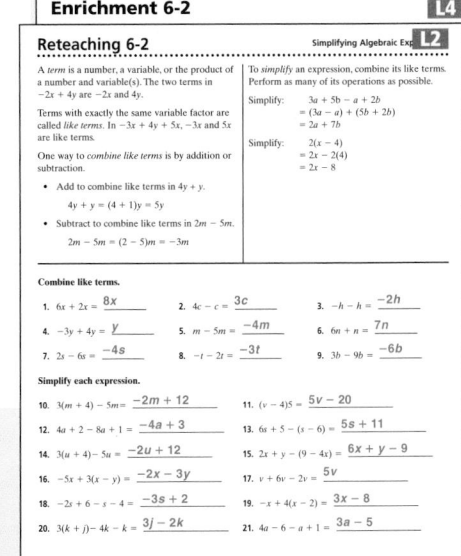

Checkpoint Quiz

Use this Checkpoint Quiz to check students' understanding of the skills and concepts of Lessons 6-1 through 6-2.

Resources

- All in One Teaching Resources Checkpoint Quiz 1
- ExamView Assessment Suite CD-ROM
- Success Tracker Online Intervention

MATH AT WORK

Research Scientist

Students learn about the work of a research scientist and the different areas in which scientists might conduct their research.

Guided Instruction

Discuss with students the meanings of the different categories of research science. Ask students to give examples of products and discoveries that have emerged from each category. Discuss the types of math, including topics from this chapter, that a scientist might use. Ask questions such as:

- *What kinds of inventions or discoveries have resulted from research? What are scientists currently researching that you have heard about in the news?*
- *What well-known scientists have you heard of?*
- *What well-known equations or expressions have you heard of?* **Samples: Einstein's $E = mc^2$, formulas for converting Fahrenheit to Celsius temperatures, chemical descriptions of molecular structure and reactions (such as H_2O the chemical formula for water)**

Checkpoint Quiz 1

Lessons 6-1 through 6-2

Solve each equation.

1. $-7 + 2q = 4$ **5.5**
2. $16 = -2v + 34$ **9**
3. $-9 = 3b - 12$ **1**
4. $2x + 5 = 11$ **3**
5. $49 = 5y - 26$ **15**
6. $\frac{m}{-2} + 7 = 21$ **−28**
7. $\frac{-3.4}{p} = -0.06$ **$56.\overline{6}$**
8. $-15 = \frac{z}{2.05} - 2$ **−26.65**
9. $-5 = 3a + 4$ **−3**
10. **Flowers** You buy 6 roses for \$2.45 each, 12 carnations for \$.99 each, and 9 tulips. Your total cost is \$40.08. How much does each tulip cost? **\$1.50**

Simplify each expression.

11. $-3m + 4 - 5m + p$ **$-8m + p + 4$**
12. $1.7(g - 0.5) - 6.4(-g + 2)$ **$8.1g - 13.65$**
13. $2h - 4(h - 5)$ **$-2h + 20$**
14. $-k - 11(-k - 0.01)$ **$10k + 0.11$**
15. $2.9(1.1j - 6.3) - 8j$ **$-4.81j - 18.27$**
16. $28 - 10(a - 14) + 7a$ **$168 - 3a$**
17. **Camping** You purchase 6 sleeping bags and 4 flashlights for a camping trip. Then you find out that more people are coming on the trip, so you buy 5 more sleeping bags and 3 more flashlights. Define and use variables to represent the total cost. **Let s = the cost of a sleeping bag. Let f = the cost of a flashlight. $11s + 7f$**

MATH AT WORK

Research Scientist

Research scientists work in many different areas, such as agriculture, biotechnology, chemical and nuclear technology, manufacturing, and forensic science. They make observations, calculate and record results, and interpret graphs and statistics.

Sometimes research scientists work outside the laboratory, researching plants and animals in their natural habitats. The research may lead to the development of new products and technologies.

Go Online PHSchool.com **For:** Information on Research Scientists **Web Code:** asb-2031

270

Algebra

6-3 Solving Multi-Step Equations

Check Skills You'll Need

1. **Vocabulary Review** Identify the *like terms* in $3x + 2x + 8 - x$. $3x, 2x, -x$

Simplify.

2. $5 - 3m + 7 - 23m$ $12 - 26m$
3. $4(7 - 3r)$ $28 - 12r$
4. $(q + 1)5 + 3q$ $8q + 5$

GO for Help Lesson 6-2

What You'll Learn

To write and solve multi-step equations

Why Learn This?

You can model many situations with one- and two-step equations. More complicated situations, such as finding the cost of multiple items, involve multiple steps.

You often need to simplify at least one side of an equation before solving it. To simplify, you combine like terms.

EXAMPLE Simplifying Before Solving an Equation

1 Solve $3n + 9 + 4n = 2$.

$3n + 9 + 4n = 2$

$3n + 4n + 9 = 2$ ← Commutative Property

$7n + 9 = 2$ ← Combine like terms.

$7n + 9 - 9 = 2 - 9$ ← Subtract 9 from each side.

$7n = -7$ ← Simplify.

$\frac{7n}{7} = \frac{-7}{7}$ ← Divide each side by 7.

$n = -1$ ← Simplify.

Check $3n + 9 + 4n = 2$

$3(-1) + 9 + 4(-1) \stackrel{?}{=} 2$ ← Substitute −1 for n.

$2 = 2$ ✔ ← The solution checks.

GO for Help

For help combining like terms, see Lesson 6-2, Example 1.

Quick Check

1. Solve $-15 = 5b + 12 - 2b + 6$. Check the solution. -11

You can use the Distributive Property to simplify an equation.

Differentiated Instruction Solutions for All Learners

Special Needs L1	Below Level L2
When working on More Than One Way, provide students who need it with a calculator for the division of −6.2 by 5. Also, providing a number line may help students subtract the decimal numbers 8.3 and 14.5 correctly. **learning style: visual**	Students, before writing any steps, say aloud what has been done to the variable and what operation will undo that. **learning style: verbal**

6-3

1. Plan

Objective

1 To write and solve multi-step equations

Examples

1 Simplifying Before Solving an Equation
2 Using the Distributive Property

Math Understandings: p. 258C

Professional Development

Math Background

Equations are made up of numbers, operations, and expressions with variables. Simplifying, by combining like terms and using the Distributive Property, can be part of the process of solving an equation.

More Math Background: p. 258C

Lesson Planning and Resources

See p. 258E for a list of the resources that support this lesson.

PowerPoint

Bell Ringer Practice

Check Skills You'll Need

Use student page, transparency, or PowerPoint. For intervention, direct students to:

Simplifying Algebraic Expressions
Lesson 6-2
Extra Skills and Word Problems Practice, Ch. 6

2. Teach

Activity Lab

Use before the lesson.

All in One Teaching Resources

Activity Lab 6-3: Solving Multi-Step Equations

Guided Instruction

Teaching Tip
Explain that students can save time and work if they form the habit of first examining the equation for terms that can be combined or simplified before using any further steps to isolate the variable.

Connection to Environmental Science
Suggest that students research and bring to the classroom data on the amount of paper and glass recycled in their community.

PowerPoint

Additional Examples

1. Solve $2c + 2 + 3c = 12$. $c = 2$

2. Eight cheerleaders set a goal of selling 424 boxes of cards to raise money. After two weeks, each cheerleader has sold 28 boxes. How many more boxes must each cheerleader sell? 25 boxes

All in One Teaching Resources
- Daily Notetaking Guide 6-3 L3
- Adapted Notetaking 6-3 L1

Closure

- *When can you simplify before solving an equation?* Sample: when you can combine like terms on either side of the equation or use the Distributive Property

Test Prep Tip
Be sure to answer the question asked. You need to find the number of bottles each student collects, not the total number.

EXAMPLE Using the Distributive Property

2 Multiple Choice Your class hopes to collect 1,200 returnable bottles to raise money for a class trip. During the first week, the 24 students in your class collect an average of 34 bottles each. How many more bottles per student should the class collect?

Ⓐ 11 bottles Ⓑ 16 bottles Ⓒ 49 bottles Ⓓ 384 bottles

Words 24 students · (34 bottles per student + additional bottles per student) = 1,200 bottles per student

Equation Let r = the number of additional bottles.

$24 \cdot (34 + r) = 1{,}200$

$$24(34 + r) = 1{,}200$$
$$816 + 24r = 1{,}200 \quad \leftarrow \text{Distributive Property}$$
$$816 - 816 + 24r = 1{,}200 - 816 \quad \leftarrow \text{Subtract 816 from each side.}$$
$$24r = 384 \quad \leftarrow \text{Simplify.}$$
$$\frac{24r}{24} = \frac{384}{24} \quad \leftarrow \text{Divide each side by 24.}$$
$$r = 16 \quad \leftarrow \text{Simplify.}$$

Each student should collect 16 more bottles. The correct answer is choice B.

Check for Reasonableness Round 24 to 20 and 34 to 40. The class collected about 20 · 40, or 800 bottles. They need to collect 400 more, or 20 bottles per student. 16 is close to 20. The answer is reasonable.

Quick Check

2. **Class Trips** Your class goes to an amusement park. Admission is \$10 for each student and \$15 for each chaperone. The total cost is \$380. There are 12 girls in your class and 6 chaperones on the trip. How many boys are in your class? 17 boys

You can also use division to simplify equations. The algebra tiles below model one way to simplify the equation $2(x + 1) = 12$. First, divide each side by 2, grouping the tiles into two equal groups. Then, remove one group from each side. The simplified equation is $x + 1 = 6$.

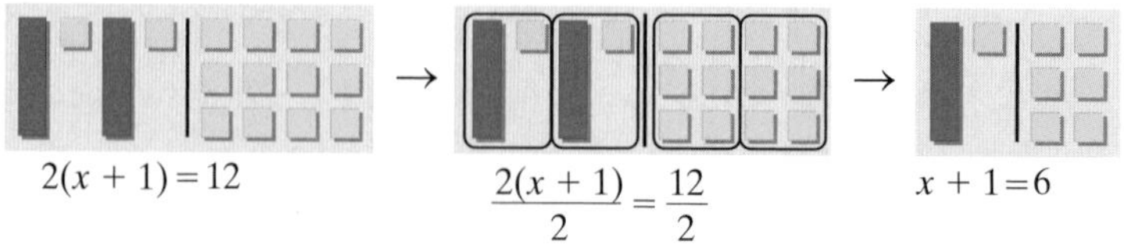

Differentiated Instruction Solutions for All Learners

Advanced Learners L4
Students write and solve a problem similar to Example 2. Sample: The yearbook printing costs were \$2,280. If 120 students paid an average of \$15, how much more per student must be collected? \$4

learning style: verbal

English Language Learners ELL
For Example 2, review the meaning of the word *average* and the words *per student*. Make sure students know they are finding the number of bottles *each* of the 24 students still has to collect, not the total number the class still has to collect.

learning style: verbal

More Than One Way

Solve the equation $5(2.9 + k) = 8.3$.

Eric's Method

I'll use the Distributive Property to eliminate the parentheses.

$$5(2.9 + k) = 8.3$$
$$5(2.9) + 5k = 8.3 \quad \leftarrow \text{Distributive Property}$$
$$14.5 + 5k = 8.3 \quad \leftarrow \text{Simplify.}$$
$$14.5 - 14.5 + 5k = 8.3 - 14.5 \quad \leftarrow \text{Subtract 14.5 from each side.}$$
$$5k = -6.2 \quad \leftarrow \text{Simplify.}$$
$$\frac{5k}{5} = \frac{-6.2}{5} \quad \leftarrow \text{Divide each side by 5.}$$
$$k = -1.24 \quad \leftarrow \text{Simplify.}$$

Jasmine's Method

I'll use division to eliminate the parentheses.

$$5(2.9 + k) = 8.3$$
$$\frac{5(2.9 - k)}{5} = \frac{8.3}{5} \quad \leftarrow \text{Divide each side by 5.}$$
$$2.9 + k = 1.66 \quad \leftarrow \text{Simplify.}$$
$$2.9 - 2.9 + k = 1.66 - 2.9 \quad \leftarrow \text{Subtract 2.9 from each side.}$$
$$k = -1.24 \quad \leftarrow \text{Simplify.}$$

Choose a Method

Solve $3(m - 6.5) = 27$. Explain why you chose the method you used.
15.5; Answers may vary.

Check Your Understanding

1. **Vocabulary** When you simplify an expression, you combine _?_ terms. like
2. Describe the first step in simplifying the expression $2h - 4(h - 5)$. Distribute −4.

Match each equation to the correct solution.

3. $-7 + x = 4$ C
4. $16 = -2x$ A
5. $-9 = x - 12$ B

A. -8
B. 3
C. 11

3. Practice

Assignment Guide

Check Your Understanding

Go over Exercises 1–5 in class before assigning the Homework Exercises.

Homework Exercises

A	Practice by Example	6–20
B	Apply Your Skills	21–33
C	Challenge	34
	Test Prep and Mixed Review	35–40

Homework Quick Check

To check students' understanding of key skills and concepts, go over Exercises 19, 20, 22, 26, and 32.

Differentiated Instruction Resources

Adapted Practice 6-3 L1

Practice 6-3 Solving Multi-Step Eq L3

Solve each equation. Check the solution.

1. $2(2.5b - 9) + 6b = -7$ $b = 1$
2. $0.7w + 16 + 4w = 27.28$ $w = 2.4$
3. $24 = -6(m + 1) + 18$ $m = -2$
4. $7k - 8 + 2(k + 12) = 52$ $k = 4$
5. $4(1.5c + 6) - 2c = -9$ $c = -8.25$
6. $0.5n + 17 + n = 20$ $n = 2$
7. $2x - 3 + 4x = 39$ $x = 7$
8. $3(3a + 3) + 6 = 81$ $a = 7.\overline{3}$
9. $20 = -4(f + 6) + 14$ $f = -7.5$
10. $9a - 4 + 3(a - 11) = 23$ $a = 5$
11. You want to join the tennis team. You go to the sporting goods store with $100. If the tennis racket you want costs $80 and the tennis balls cost $4 per can, how many cans of tennis balls can you buy? 5 cans
12. Johnny wants to ship a package to his friend. A shipping company charges $2.49 for the first pound and $1.24 for each additional pound. If it cost Johnny $11.17 to ship the package, how much did his package weigh? 8 pounds

6-3 • Guided Problem Solving GPS L3

GPS **Student Page 274, Exercise 22:**

Jobs An employee earns $7.00 an hour for the first 35 hours worked in a week and $10.50 for any hours over 35. One week's paycheck (before deductions) was for $308.00. How many hours did the employee work?

Understand

1. How much per hour does the employee make for the first 35 hours? $7.00
2. How much per hour does the employee make after 35 hours of work? $10.50
3. How much was the week's paycheck? $308.00
4. What is it you are asked to find? the number of hours the employee worked

Plan and Carry Out

5. Write an equation for this situation. Multiply the hourly rate by 35 hours. Add the overtime rate multiplied by an unknown, x. Set this sum equal to the total amount of the check. $7(35) + 10.50(x) = 308$; $308
6. Solve for x, the number of overtime hours the employee worked. 6 hours
7. What do you have to do to find the total hours worked? Add the overtime hours to 35 hours.
8. How many total hours did the employee work? 41 hours

Check

9. Does the answer check? Is 35 times $7 plus the overtime hours equal to the total check? Yes; $35(7) + (10.5)x = \$308$; $35(7) + (10.5)(6) = \$308$; $\$308 = \$308$

Solve Another Problem

10. A college student has a long-distance phone card. The phone-card rate for the first 100 minutes is 12 cents per minute and then goes to 15 cents per minute after that. If the student had a long distance charge of $21, how many total minutes did the student talk? $0.12(100) + 0.15t = 21$; $t = 60$ min; total time = 160 minutes

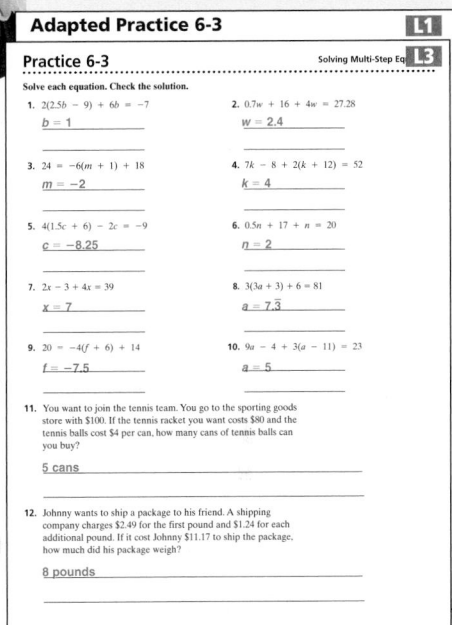

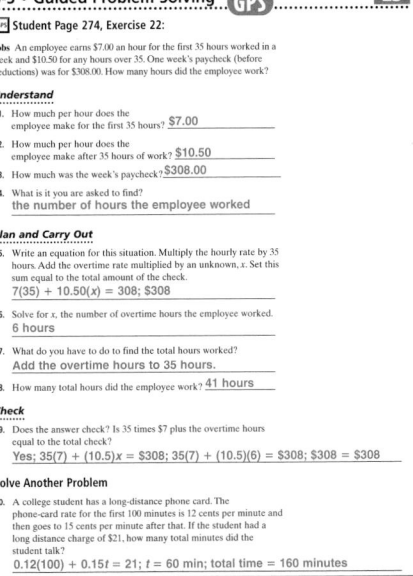

4. Assess & Reteach

PowerPoint

Lesson Quiz

Solve the following equations.

1. $2m + 4 - 8m = 28$ $m = -4$
2. $2(f - 1) + f = 37$ $f = 13$
3. $4.5(4x - 12) = 144$ $x = 11$
4. Jasmine earns a certain amount per hour for the first 40 hours worked in a week. Each hour she works over 40 in one week, she earns an additional \$4.50 per hour. If Jasmine works 46 hours one week, and earned \$383.50 that week, how much does she earn per hour for the first 40 hours? \$7.75 per hour

Alternative Assessment

Students write an expression that contains two like terms, with the variable n, and two numbers. Then they set their expression equal to 24 and solve the equation.

Homework Exercises

For more exercises, see Extra Skills and Word Problems.

GO for Help

For Exercises	See Examples
6–13	1
14–20	2

A Solve each equation. Check the solution.

6. $5h + 2 - h = 22$ 5
7. $-8 = z + 3z$ −2
8. $3b + b - 8 = 4$ 3
9. $3a + 12 - 6a = -9$ 7
10. $21 = 6 - x - 4x$ −3
11. $2m + 8 - 4m = 28$ −10
12. $-3y + 4 + 5y = -6$ −5
13. $78 = 3c + 12 - c + 4$ 31
14. $4(m + 3) = -32$ −11
15. $14 = 2(s + 5)$ 2
16. $40 = 5(d - 2)$ 10
17. $2(z - 1) = 16$ 9
18. $-2(x - 9) = -24$ 21
19. $7(4 - t) = -84$ 16

20. **Food** You want to buy 4 lb of Cortland apples and some Gala apples. Each variety of apple costs \$1.20/lb. You can spend \$7.20. How many pounds of Gala apples can you buy? 2 lb

B GPS

21. **Guided Problem Solving** You mailed 3 identical letters weighing more than 1 oz each. Mailing each letter cost \$.39 for the first ounce, plus \$.24 for each additional ounce. Each letter required \$1.59 postage. How much did each letter weigh, to the nearest ounce? 5 oz
    - **Make a Plan** Write and solve an equation to solve for x, the number of additional ounces.
    - **Check the Answer** Be sure you answer the question asked.

22. **Jobs** An employee earns \$7.00 an hour for the first 35 hours worked in a week and \$10.50 for any hours over 35. One week's paycheck (before deductions) was for \$308.00. How many hours did the employee work? 41 h

GPS

GO Online
Homework Video Tutor
Visit: PHSchool.com
Web Code: ase-0603

Use this information to write an equation for Exercises 23–25. When you count by ones from any integer, you are counting consecutive integers. Using variables, three consecutive integers are n, $n + 1$, and $n + 2$.

23. The sum of two consecutive integers is −45. What are they? $n + n + 1 = -45$; −23 and −22
24. The sum of three consecutive integers is 48. What are they? See left.
25. The sum of three consecutive integers is −255. What are they? $n + (n + 1) + (n + 2) = -255$; −86, −85, −84
26. **Writing in Math** To solve $5y - 2 - 3y = 8$, can you start by adding 2 to each side? Justify your reasoning. See left.

24. $n + (n + 1) + (n + 2) = 48$; 15, 16, and 17

26. Yes; as long as you do the same operation to each side, the order of the steps does not affect the solution.

Solve each equation.

27. $15 = -3(c - 1) + 9$ −1
28. $2(1.5n + 4) - 6n = -7$ 5
29. $2(z - 20) + 3z = 10$ 10
30. $5s - 2 + 3(s - 11) = 5$ 5

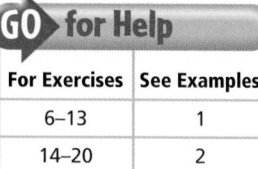

Write an equation for each diagram. Then find the unknown lengths.

31.

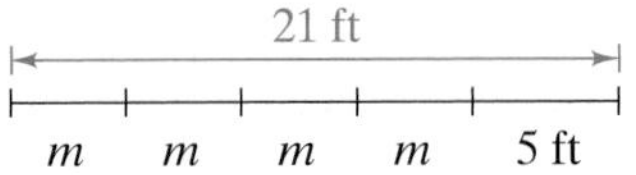

4m + 5 = 21; m = 4 ft

32.

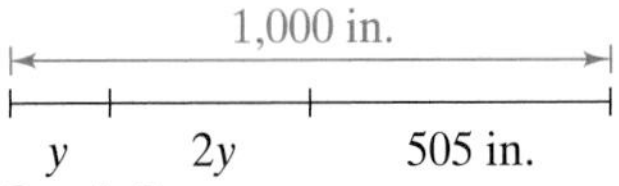

See left.

32. $3y + 505 = 1{,}000$; $y = 165$ in., $2y = 330$ in.

33. Choose a Method To make peanut butter and jelly sandwiches for her class, a teacher bought bread for \$2.79 per loaf, peanut butter for \$3.19 per jar, and jars of jelly. The total cost was \$14.56. If the teacher bought two of each item, what was the cost of one jar of jelly? Explain why you chose the method you used. See left.

33. \$1.30; answers may vary.

C **34. Challenge** Solve $1.5 - 0.25(a + 4) = 3 + 3(0.05 - 0.5a)$. 2.12

Test Prep and Mixed Review

Practice

Multiple Choice

35. Two classes went to the zoo for \$5 per person. The total cost was \$200. One class has 19 people. Solve the equation $5(n + 19) = 200$ to find n, the number of people in the other class. C

(A) 105 (B) 36 (C) 21 (D) 10

36. An interior designer researched prices and compiled the following data for a particular type of fabric. Which store's prices are based on a constant unit price? H

(F) **Materials Unlimited**

Yards	Total Price
2	\$10
4	\$18
6	\$27
8	\$32

(H) **The Fab Store**

Yards	Total Price
2	\$9
4	\$18
6	\$27
8	\$36

(G) **Haley's Fabric**

Yards	Total Price
2	\$8
4	\$18
6	\$28
8	\$38

(J) **We R Fabric**

Yards	Total Price
2	\$10
4	\$18
6	\$27
8	\$35

37. Based on her batting average, the probability that Maggie will get a hit in softball is 5 out of 12. Which of the following expresses this probability as a percent? C

(A) 2.4% (B) 29.4% (C) 41.7% (D) 70.6%

GO for Help

For Exercises	See Lesson
38–40	6-1

Algebra **Solve each equation.**

38. $\frac{n}{4} - 1 = 10$ 44 **39.** $\frac{x}{-5} - 7 = 8$ −75 **40.** $\frac{a}{8} + 12 = -4$ −128

Test Prep

Resources

For additional practice with a variety of test item formats:

- Test-Taking Strategies, p. 293
- Test Prep, p. 297
- Test-Taking Strategies with Transparencies

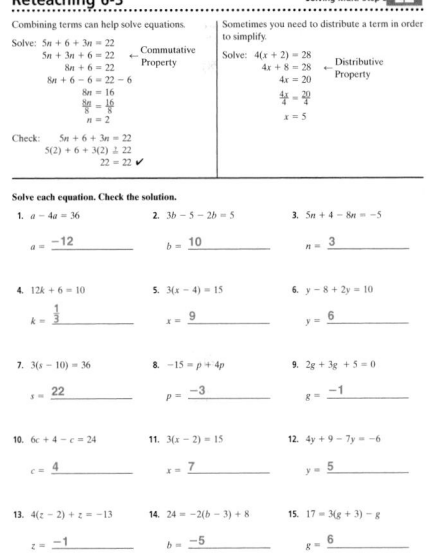

Reteaching 6-3

Solving Multi-Step E L2

Combining terms can help solve equations.

Solve: $5n + 6 + 3n = 22$
$5n + 3n + 6 = 22$ ← Commutative Property
$8n + 6 = 22$
$8n + 6 - 6 = 22 - 6$
$8n = 16$
$\frac{8n}{8} = \frac{16}{8}$
$n = 2$

Check: $5n + 6 + 3n = 22$
$5(2) + 6 + 3(2) \stackrel{?}{=} 22$
$22 = 22$ ✔

Sometimes you need to distribute a term in order to simplify.

Solve: $4(x + 2) = 28$
$4x + 8 = 28$ ← Distributive Property
$4x = 20$
$\frac{4x}{4} = \frac{20}{4}$
$x = 5$

Solve each equation. Check the solution.

1. $a - 4a = 36$ $a =$ −12
2. $3b - 5 - 2b = 5$ $b =$ 10
3. $5n + 4 - 8n = -5$ $n =$ 3
4. $12k + 6 = 10$ $k = \frac{1}{3}$
5. $3(x - 4) = 15$ $x =$ 9
6. $y - 8 + 2y = 10$ $y =$ 6
7. $3(s - 10) = 36$ $s =$ 22
8. $-15 = p + 4p$ $p =$ −3
9. $2g + 3g + 5 = 0$ $g =$ −1
10. $6c + 4 - c = 24$ $c =$ 4
11. $3(x - 2) = 15$ $x =$ 7
12. $4y + 9 - 7y = -6$ $y =$ 5
13. $4(z - 2) + z = -13$ $z =$ −1
14. $24 = -2(b - 3) + 8$ $b =$ −5
15. $17 = 3(g + 3) - g$ $g =$ 6

Enrichment 6-3

Solving Multi-Step E L4

Critical Thinking

Algebraic equations, as you have dealt with them here, are limited to a specific situation, like a word problem. Consider this simple word problem:

When Marissa baby-sits, she charges \$5 per hour for the first 4 hours, and then \$8 an hour for every additional hour. How many hours did she baby-sit if she earned \$44?

You should probably use the equation $4(5) + 8(x - 4) = 44$ to solve this problem, where 4(5) is the amount Marissa is paid for the first 4 hours, and $8(x - 4)$ is the amount she is paid for the time over 4 hours. This equation, however, will only work to calculate the hours Marissa baby-sat that particular time, when she earned \$44; $x = 7$.

1. How could you change this equation to make it useful for calculating the hours Marissa works each time she baby-sits, according to whatever amount she is paid?
$4(5) + 8(x - 4) = y$

2. Use the table to find x when y equals \$28, \$76, \$104, and \$150.

x	5	7	11	14.5	20.25
y	28	44	76	104	150

3. Graph the resulting coordinates and connect them with a line, which will represent Marissa's potential earnings for any amount of time she baby-sits over 4 hours.
Check the students' answers.

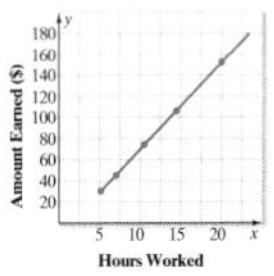

4. Marissa's little sister baby-sits too, but she only gets paid \$6.50 for every hour worked over 4. How can you change the equation above to describe Marissa's sister's pay?
$4(5) + 6.5(x - 4) = y$

5. Would the graph of this line look different? Explain.
Sample answer: Yes, it would be pointing the same way, but it would be less steep.

6-4

1. Plan

Objective
1 To write and solve equations with variables on both sides

Examples
1 Variables on Both Sides
2 Using the Distributive Property

Math Understandings: p. 258C

Professional Development

Math Background

More Math Background: p. 258C

Lesson Planning and Resources

See p. 258E for a list of the resources that support this lesson.

PowerPoint

Bell Ringer Practice

Check Skills You'll Need
Use student page, transparency, or PowerPoint. For intervention, direct students to:
Simplifying Algebraic Expressions
Lesson 6-2
Extra Skills and Word Problems Practice, Ch. 6

2. Teach

Activity Lab
Use before the lesson.

All-in-One Teaching Resources

Activity Lab 6-4: Solving Equations With Variables on Both Sides

Guided Instruction

Example 2
Provide students with a blank grid from **TAKS Strategies with Transparencies.**

Algebra

6-4 Solving Equations With Variables on Both Sides

Check Skills You'll Need

1. **Vocabulary Review** Operations that undo each other are called _?_. inverse operations

Simplify. 2–4. See below.

2. $9(t + 7) - 16$
3. $12 - 6(2r - 8)$
4. $2x - (5x + 7)$.

GO for Help Lesson 6-2

Check Skills You'll Need
2. $9t + 47$
3. $60 - 12r$
4. $-3x - 7$

What You'll Learn

To write and solve equations with variables on both sides

Why Learn This?

Equations can help you calculate your savings from part-time jobs. An equation shows that two expressions are equal. Because expressions can contain variables, some equations have variables on both sides of the equal sign.

To solve an equation with variables on both sides, bring all the variable terms to one side of the equation.

EXAMPLE Variables on Both Sides

1 Solve $7 + 3h = -1 - 5h$.

$7 + 3h = -1 - 5h$

$7 + 3h + 5h = -1 - 5h + 5h$ ← Add $5h$ to each side.

$7 + 8h = -1$ ← Combine like terms.

$7 - 7 + 8h = -1 - 7$ ← Subtract 7 from each side.

$8h = -8$ ← Simplify.

$\frac{8h}{8} = \frac{-8}{8}$ ← Divide each side by 8.

$h = -1$ ← Simplify.

Check $7 + 3h = -1 - 5h$

$7 + 3(-1) \stackrel{?}{=} -1 - 5(-1)$ ← Substitute −1 for h.

$4 = 4$ ✔ ← The solution checks.

Quick Check

1. Solve $7b - 2 = b + 10$. Check the solution. 2

Differentiated Instruction Solutions for All Learners

Special Needs L1
Provide students with copies of Examples 1 and 2 in this lesson. Students circle the terms with variables on both sides of each equation, and underline the constants. They then combine the like terms.

learning style: visual

Below Level L2
Give students the equation $3p - 2 = 4p + 9 + 7p$. Ask: *On which side of the equation do you want to isolate the variable? Why?* Sample answer: $3p$ is on the left, $4p$ and $7p$ are on the right; right side because $4p + 7p = 11p$ is greater than $3p$.

learning style: verbal

You may need to use the Distributive Property to simplify an equation before you can bring the variable terms to one side.

EXAMPLE Using the Distributive Property

2 **Gridded Response** Your science class is doing an experiment. You start with 2 plants. Plant A is 5 cm tall and Plant B is 8 cm tall. Plant A is fertilized and grows 2 cm per day. Plant B is not fertilized and grows 1.5 cm per day. Predict in how many days the plants will be the same height.

Words 5 + 2 cm · number of days = 8 + 1.5 cm · number of days

Let d = the number of days.

Equation $5 + 2 \cdot d = 8 + 1.5 \cdot d$

$$5 + 2d = 8 + 1.5d$$

$5 + 2d - 2d = 8 + 1.5d - 2d$ ← **Subtract 2*d* from each side.**

$5 = 8 - 0.5d$ ← **Simplify.**

$5 - 8 = 8 - 8 - 0.5d$ ← **Subtract 8 from each side.**

$-3 = -0.5d$ ← **Simplify.**

$\frac{-3}{-0.5} = \frac{-0.5d}{-0.5}$ ← **Divide each side by −0.5.**

$6 = d$ ← **Simplify.**

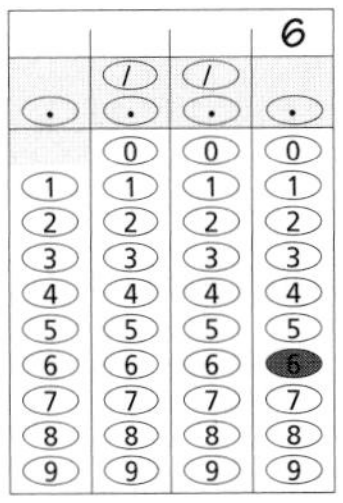

The plants will be the same height in 6 days.

Test Prep Tip

You can also solve the equation at the right by moving all of the variables to the left side.

Quick Check

2. One cell phone plan costs $29.94 per month plus $.10 for each text message sent. Another plan costs $32.99 per month plus $.05 for each text message sent. For what number of text messages will the monthly bill for both plans be the same? **61 text messages**

Check Your Understanding

Identify the like terms in each group of expressions.

1. $-\frac{7}{9}, -2.8, 3, 0$ **all of them**
2. xy, x, y, yx **xy and yx**
3. $11a, -4.1a^2, a, a^2$ **See left.**

3. $11a$ and a, $-4.1a^2$ and a^2

4. Is 7 a solution of the equation $3x + 8 - x = 5x - 4$? **No**
5. **Error Analysis** A student solved an equation as shown at the left. Explain the error the student made. Solve the equation correctly. **See back of book.**

$3x + 4 - x = 7 + x$
$3x + 4 = 7$
$3x = 3$
$x = 1$

6. **Mental Math** Is the solution of $2x = 3x - 12 - 5x$ a positive or a negative integer? Explain. **See back of book.**

Online lesson quiz, PHSchool.com, Web Code: asa-0604

Advanced Learners L4
Students solve equations with more than one variable term on each side, such as
$6n + 2 + 3n = 4(n - 1) + 4n$. $n = -6$
learning style: verbal

English Language Learners ELL
For a quick assessment of students' understanding, have them write examples of the following math concepts as you say them: *variable expression, constant, like terms, distributive property, inverse operations.*
learning style: verbal

PowerPoint

Additional Examples

1 Solve $9 + 2p = -3 - 4p$.
$p = -2$

2 Each week you set aside $18 for a stereo and put the remainder in a savings account. After 7 weeks, the amount you place in the savings account is 4.2 times your total weekly pay. How much do you make each week? $45

All in One Teaching Resources
- Daily Notetaking Guide 6-4 L3
- Adapted Notetaking 6-4 L1

3. Practice

Assignment Guide

Check Your Understanding
Go over Exercises 1–6 in class before assigning the Homework Exercises.

Homework Exercises

A Practice by Example	7–15
B Apply Your Skills	16–18
C Challenge	19
Test Prep and Mixed Review	20–24

Homework Quick Check
To check students' understanding of key skills and concepts, go over Exercises 14, 15, 16, 17, and 18.

4. Assess & Reteach

PowerPoint

Lesson Quiz

Solve each equation.

1. $4(3u - 1) = 20$ **2**
2. $5t - 4 = t - 8$ **−1**
3. $3(k - 8) = -k$ **$k = 6$**

Alternative Assessment

Have students write an expression involving the variable x. Then have them set it equal to $10x - 2$ and solve the equation.

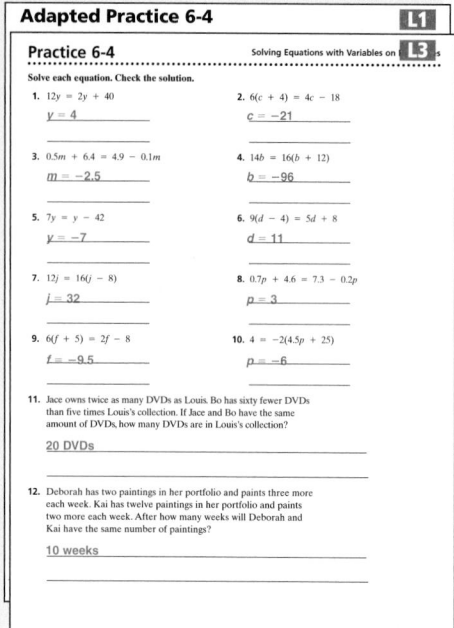

Adapted Practice 6-4 L1

Practice 6-4 — Solving Equations with Variables on Both Sides L3

Solve each equation. Check the solution.

1. $12y = 2y + 40$ $y = 4$
2. $6(c + 4) = 4c - 18$ $c = -21$
3. $0.5m + 6.4 = 4.9 - 0.1m$ $m = -2.5$
4. $14b = 16(b + 12)$ $b = -96$
5. $7y = y - 42$ $y = -7$
6. $9(d - 4) = 5d + 8$ $d = 11$
7. $12j = 16(j - 8)$ $j = 32$
8. $0.7p + 4.6 = 7.3 - 0.2p$ $p = 3$
9. $6(f + 5) = 2f - 8$ $f = -9.5$
10. $4 = -2(4.5p + 25)$ $p = -6$
11. Jace owns twice as many DVDs as Louis. Bo has sixty fewer DVDs than five times Louis's collection. If Jace and Bo have the same amount of DVDs, how many DVDs are in Louis's collection?
    20 DVDs
12. Deborah has two paintings in her portfolio and paints three more each week. Kai has twelve paintings in her portfolio and paints two more each week. After how many weeks will Deborah and Kai have the same number of paintings?
    10 weeks

6-4 • Guided Problem Solving GPS L3

Student Page 278, Exercise 17:

Efren leaves home at 9 A.M. and walks 4 miles per hour. His brother, Gregory, leaves half an hour later and runs 8.5 miles per hour in the same direction as Efren. At about what time will Gregory catch up to Efren?

Understand

1. What is the distance formula? $d = r \cdot t$
2. What can you say about the distance each boy will have traveled when Gregory catches up to Efren?
   The distance will be equal.

Plan and Carry Out

3. Write an expression for the distance Gregory travels per hour. Let h stand for time in hours. $8.5h$
4. Write an expression for the distance Efren travels per hour plus the distance he will have traveled when Gregory leaves the house. $4h + 2$
5. Write an equation setting the distance expressions in steps 3 and 4 equal. $8.5h = 4h + 2$
6. Solve for h. Use your answer to estimate the time at which Gregory will catch up to Efren. $8.5h = 4h + 2$; $4.5h = 2$; $h = \frac{2}{4.5}$; $h = 0.\overline{4}$; at about 10:00 A.M.

Check

7. Solve the expressions in steps 3 and 4 for your value of h. Are the distances equal? $8.5h = 8.5(0.\overline{4}) \approx 3.8$; $4h + 2 = 4(0.\overline{4}) + 2 \approx 1.8 + 2 = 3.8$

Solve Another Problem

10. Roshonda begins riding her bike home from school at 3:00 P.M., traveling 12 miles per hour. James leaves school in a bus a quarter of an hour later and travels 35 miles per hour in the same direction. At about what time will James catch up to Roshonda?
    $35h$; $12h + 3$; $35h = 12h + 3$; $23h = 3$; $h \approx 0.13$; $0.13 \times 60 = 7.8$; at about 3:23 P.M.

Enrichment 6-4 L4

Reteaching 6-4 — Solving Equations with Variables on Both Sides L2

When an equation has a variable on both sides, add or subtract to get the variable on one side.

Solve: $-6m + 45 = 3m$
$-6m + 6m + 45 = 3m + 6m$ ← Add 6m to each side.
$45 = 9m$
$\frac{45}{9} = \frac{9m}{9}$
$5 = m$

Check: $-6m + 45 = 3m$
$-6(5) + 45 \stackrel{?}{=} 3(5)$
$15 = 15$ ✔

Sometimes you need to distribute a term in order to simplify.

Solve: $5(x - 3) = 32 - 2$
$5x - 15 = 32 - 2$ ← Distributive Property
$5x - 15 = 30$
$5x = 45$
$\frac{5x}{5} = \frac{45}{5}$
$x = 9$

Solve each equation. Check the solution.

1. $9j + 35 = 4j$ $j = -7$
2. $13s = 2s - 66$ $s = -6$
3. $2(5t - 4) = 12t$ $t = -4$
4. $6q = 6(4q + 1)$ $q = -3$
5. $7(t - 2) - t = 4$ $t = 3$
6. $6w + 4 = 4w + 1$ $w = -1.5$
7. $2(2q + 1) = 3(q - 2)$ $q = -8$
8. $5z - 3 = 2(z - 3)$ $z = -1$
9. $4(x + 0) = 2x + 6$ $x = 3$
10. $5(k - 4) = 4 - 3k$ $k = 3$
11. $8 - m - 3m = 16$ $m = -2$
12. $6n + n + 14 = 0$ $n = -2$
13. $7(p + 1) = 9 - p$ $p = \frac{1}{4}$
14. $41 - q = 3(q - 5)$ $q = 14$
15. $25 + 2t = 5(t + 2)$ $t = 5$

Homework Exercises

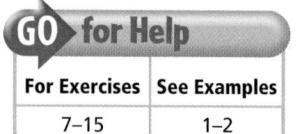

For more exercises, see Extra Skills and Word Problems.

GO for Help

For Exercises	See Examples
7–15	1–2

A Solve each equation. Check the solution.

7. $2 + 14z = -8 + 9z$ −2
8. $-8 - 5y = 12 - 9y$ 5
9. $22 + 2x = 37 + 6 + x$ 21
10. $6d + 1 = 15 - d$ 2
11. $-k = 9(k - 10)$ 9
12. $7m = 9(m + 4)$ −18
13. $8(4 - a) = 2a$ 3.2
14. $8 - 3(p - 4) = 2p$ 4
15. At Video Shack, movie rentals cost $3.99 each. The cost of renting three movies and one video game is $.11 less than the cost of renting five video games. How much does renting a video game cost? $3.02

B GPS 16. **Guided Problem Solving** A croquet ball weighs 460 grams. Together a golf ball and a croquet ball weigh the same as 11 golf balls. How much does one golf ball weigh? 46 g
- What quantity will you represent with a variable?
- Write and solve an equation.

17. Efren leaves home at 9 A.M. and walks 4 miles per hour. His brother, Gregory, leaves half an hour later and runs 8.5 miles per hour in the same direction as Efren. Predict the time at which Gregory will catch up to Efren. at about 9:57 A.M.

18. **Writing in Math** Explain how to solve an equation with the same variable on both sides. See margin.

GO Online
Homework Video Tutor
Visit: PHSchool.com
Web Code: ase-0604

C 19. **Challenge** Solve $0.75 + 2(x - 0.5) = 3x - 0.4$. 0.15

Test Prep and Mixed Review

Practice

Gridded Response

20. The side of a square is $2x + 8$ inches long. The perimeter of the square is $20x + 8$ inches. What is the side length of the square in inches? 12

21. The trapezoids shown at the right are similar. What scale factor was used to dilate trapezoid $FGHJ$ to trapezoid $LMNP$? 3

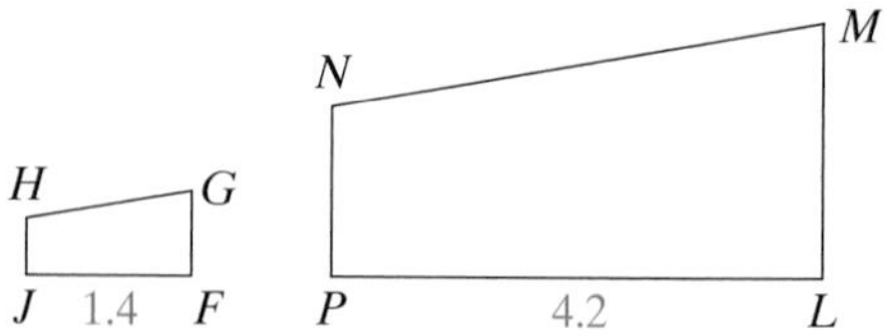

22. The federal minimum wage once rose from $4.25 to $4.75. To the nearest tenth of a percent, what was the percent of increase? 11.8

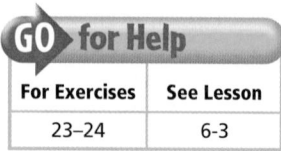

GO for Help

For Exercises	See Lesson
23–24	6-3

Algebra **Solve each equation.**

23. $6q + 3 - 4q = 9$ 3
24. $7(x + 1) - 1 = 34$ 4

Test Prep

Resources

For additional practice with a variety of test item formats:
- Test-Taking Strategies, p. 293
- Test Prep, p. 297
- Test-Taking Strategies with Transparencies

18. Use inverse operations to combine the variables and then isolate the variable on one side of the equation.

Writing Equations

Ticket Prices Mr. and Mrs. Smith have two children, ages 4 and 8. They are trying to decide whether to buy day passes or a yearly membership to an aquarium. With how many single-day visits would it be better for the Smiths to have a yearly membership?

What You Might Think	What You Might Write
What do I know? What do I want to find out?	I know single-day tickets are \$21.95 for adults and \$10.95 for children. Two adult tickets → 2 × \$21.95 = \$43.90. Two child tickets → 2 × \$10.95 = \$21.90. A yearly membership is \$175. I want to find when a yearly membership would be less expensive.
What equation can I write?	Let d = the number of visits. Then the total cost of d visits is $43.90d + 21.90d$.
When will the cost of single-day tickets equal the cost of a yearly membership?	$43.90d + 21.90d = 175$ $65.80d = 175$ $d \approx 2.66$ Since you cannot have 2.66 visits, round the answer up to 3. So for three or more visits it would be better to have the yearly membership.
Is the answer reasonable?	The cost for single-day tickets is about \$40 + \$20 or \$60. 3 × \$60 = \$180. So 3 visits is a reasonable answer.

GPS Guided Problem Solving

Writing Equations

Students read a guided real-world problem to develop problem-solving and reasoning skills. In the left column, they read questions they could ask themselves to make sense of the problem. In the right column, they read the steps for setting up and solving equations used to describe the situation.

Guided Instruction

Have students work through the problem, rather than just read it. Have them identify any steps they don't understand or that don't match their own work.

Error Prevention!

Students might tend to round 2.66 up to 3 by habit. Ask: *What does 2.66 represent?* value of d for which the cost of annual membership equals the cost of purchasing day passes *Why isn't 3 an exact answer?* Because 2.66 is the number of visits below which (1 or 2) it is better for the Smiths to purchase day passes, and above which (3 or more) it is better for them to purchase a yearly membership.

Alternative Method

Guide students toward writing the equation by having them start with a sentence. Sample: (2 adults)(Cost of adult ticket)(number of visits) + (2 children)(Cost of child ticket)(number of visits) = cost of yearly membership

Teaching Tip
Have students ask themselves the same or similar questions as in the example as they work through the Exercises.

Connection to Health and Nutrition
Discuss the food pyramid, including types of foods that are healthy between-meal snacks. Have students research nutrition information on these foods, such as suggested daily servings; vitamin, protein, sugar, or fat content; and ingredients.

Think It Through

1. **Reasoning** Can an answer to this problem be 2 visits? Explain. **No; if the family only visited on 2 days, the cost would be $131.60, which is cheaper than a yearly membership.**
2. Can you use the following equation to solve this problem? Explain. **Yes; 43.90 = 2 · 21.95 and 21.90 = 2 · 10.95. Multiplying 21.95 and 10.95 by 2 is the same as adding them to themselves.**
   $21.95d + 21.95d + 10.95d + 10.95d = 175$

Exercises

Solve each problem. For Exercises 3 and 4, answer parts (a) and (b) first.

3. The cost of a membership at a health club last year was 75% of the cost at the club this year. This year's membership costs $20 more than last year's membership. Find the cost of a membership last year and the cost of a membership this year. **$60; $80**
   a. Let x = the cost of last year's membership. Then $x + 20$ = the cost of this year's membership.
   b. Represent the cost of last year's membership as $0.75(x + 20)$. To find the value of x, solve $x = 0.75(x + 20)$.

4. A camp counselor buys granola bars and juice drinks for the campers. She decides to buy 3 times as many drinks as granola bars. Predict how many of each she can buy on a budget of $24. **10 granola bars; 30 drinks**

   a. Let x = the number of granola bars the counselor buys and let $3x$ = the number of juice drinks she buys. What is the cost of x granola bars? The cost of $3x$ juice drinks? **$.45x; $1.95x**
   b. Use your answers to part (a) to write and solve an equation to find how many of each the camp leader can buy. **$0.45x + 1.95x = 24$; $x = 10$**

5. In a random survey of adults and children, children were found to have 23% more snacks between meals each year than adults. Altogether, the adults and children in this survey had 3,000 snacks between meals in one year. About how many snacks did the children in this survey have in one year? (*Hint:* Let x = the number of between-meal snacks the adults in this survey had in one year.) **About 1,655 snacks**

6-5a Activity Lab

Graphing Inequalities

An *inequality* is a mathematical sentence that contains $<, >, \leq, \geq$, or $\neq$. The **graph of an inequality** shows all the solutions that satisfy the inequality.

Inequality	Graph	Word Sentence
$x < 3$		x is less than 3.
$x \leq 3$		x is less than or equal to 3.
$x > 3$	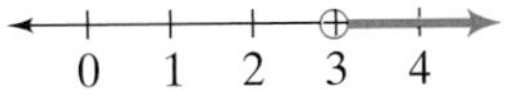	x is greater than 3.
$x \geq 3$	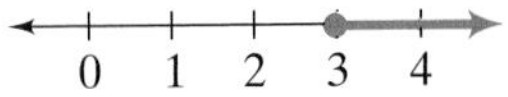	x is greater than or equal to 3.
$x \neq 3$	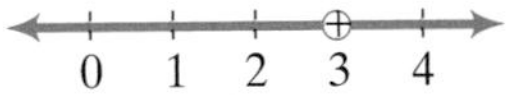	x is *not* equal to 3.

EXAMPLES Graphing Inequalities

1 Graph $x < 2$.

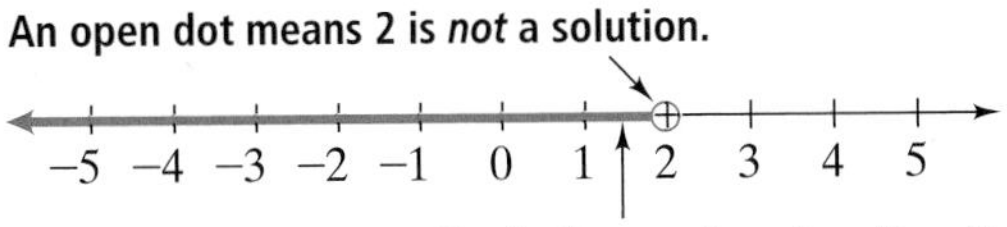

2 Graph $-3 \leq x$.

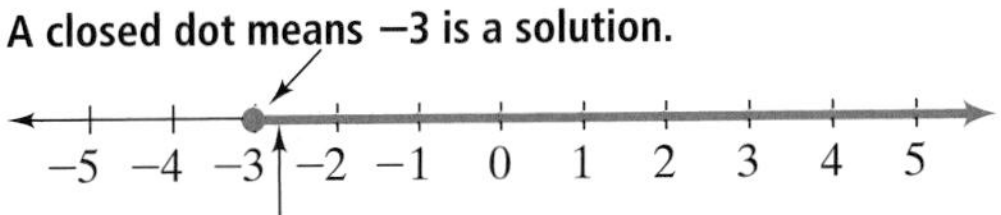

1. 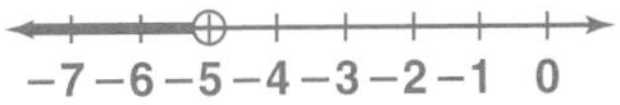

2. 

3. 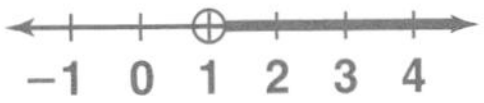

4. 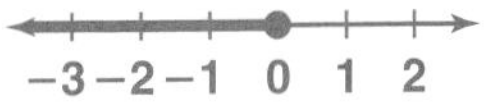

5. 

Exercises

Graph each inequality. 1–5. See above right.

1. $x < -5$
2. $-4 \leq x$
3. $x > 1$
4. $0 \geq x$
5. $x \neq 2$

Write an inequality for each word sentence.

6. y is less than −4. $y < -4$
7. p has a minimum of −5. $p \geq -5$
8. k is no more than 7. $k \leq 7$
9. **Reasoning** Is 6 a possible value for w in the word sentence "w is more than 6"? Explain. No; since 6 is equal to 6, it cannot also be more than 6.

Activity Lab

Graphing Inequalities

The equations students have solved so far in this chapter have a single solution. However, inequalities represent a range of solutions up to and sometimes including a particular value. In this activity, students write and graph inequalities.

Guided Instruction

Activity

Use plain language to discuss *x is greater than or equal to 3*. Make sure that students understand what *or* means mathematically. Ask:

- *Does 3 make the sentence true?* yes
- *Does 4 make the sentence true? Or 5.9? Or 106?* yes
- *Does 2 make the sentence true? Or −3? Or 2.7?* no

Teaching Tip
In Example 1, have students say the word sentence for $x < 2$. *x* is less than 2. Ask: *What is the word sentence for an equivalent inequality that has the variable on the right side?* Two is greater than *x*.

Error Prevention!

Remind students to consider the inequality symbol carefully when they are graphing. Graphs of inequalities that contain the symbol $\geq$ or $\leq$ include an endpoint. Graphs of inequalities that use the symbol $>$ or $<$ do not include an endpoint.

Resources

- Activity Lab 6–5: Solving Inequalities by Adding or Subtracting
- graph paper

6-5

1. Plan

Objective

1 To write and solve inequalities using addition and subtraction

Examples

1 Solving Inequalities by Adding
2 Solving Inequalities by Subtracting

Math Understandings: p. 258C

Professional Development

Math Background

The graph of $x = 3$ is one point. The graph of $x < 3$ is a set of points that contains infinitely many points. Notice that the graph of $x \neq 3$ is also a set of points that contains infinitely many points. The point $x = 3$ is one single point on a line, but there are infinitely many points *between* any two points on a line.

More Math Background: p. 258C

Lesson Planning and Resources

See p. 258E for a list of the resources that support this lesson.

PowerPoint

Bell Ringer Practice

Check Skills You'll Need
Use student page, transparency, or PowerPoint. For intervention, direct students to:

Solving Equations by Adding and Subtracting
Lesson 1-6
Extra Skills and Word Problems Practice, Ch. 1

Algebra

6-5 Solving Inequalities by Adding or Subtracting

Check Skills You'll Need

1. **Vocabulary Review** An _?_ is a mathematical sentence with an equal sign. equation

Solve each equation.

2. $x + 15 = -3$ -18
3. $y + 22 = 9$ -13
4. $a - 28 = -4$ 24

GO for Help
Lesson 1-6

What You'll Learn

To write and solve inequalities

New Vocabulary inequality, Addition Property of Inequality, Subtraction Property of Inequality

Why Learn This?

You can use inequalities to describe restrictions such as the maximum weight for luggage or the minimum height to ride a roller coaster.

An **inequality** is a mathematical sentence that contains $<, \leq, >, \geq$, or $\neq$.

Some inequalities, such as $x < 3$ and $x \geq 3$, contain a variable. You can graph inequalities on number lines.

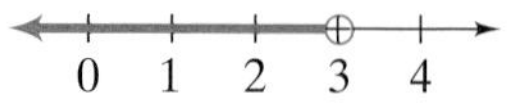

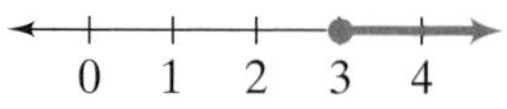

You can see from the number line below that if you add 2 to each side of the inequality $-5 \leq -1$, the resulting inequality, $-3 \leq 1$, is also true.

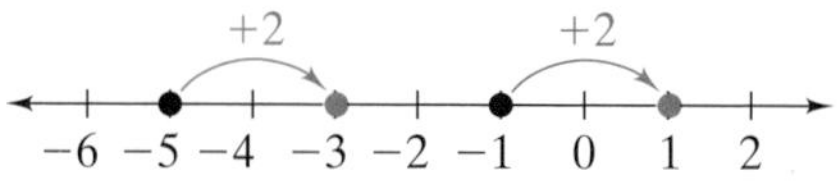

KEY CONCEPTS **Addition and Subtraction Properties of Inequalities**

If you add or subtract the same number on each side of an inequality, the relationship between the two sides does not change.

Arithmetic	Algebra
$8 < 12$, so $8 + 3 < 12 + 3$, and $8 - 4 < 12 - 4$.	If $a < b$, then $a + c < b + c$, and $a - c < b - c$.
$10 > 7$, so $10 + 5 > 7 + 5$, and $10 - 2 > 7 - 2$.	If $a > b$, then $a + c > b + c$, and $a - c > b - c$.

Vocabulary Tip

You can think of the $\geq$ symbol as $>$ and $=$ combined. You can think of the $\leq$ symbol as $<$ and $=$ combined.

You solve an inequality involving addition or subtraction by using inverse operations to isolate the variable. An inequality sometimes has an infinite number of solutions, making it impossible to check them all. Instead, check your computations and the direction of the inequality symbol.

Differentiated Instruction Solutions for All Learners

Special Needs L1	Below Level L2
Students *test out* their solutions to inequality statements with several numbers. This will help them understand that the solution to an inequality can represent more than one number. learning style: visual	After students solve an inequality, they change the inequality symbol to an equal sign and draw an open dot on a number line at the equation solution. They put back the inequality symbol and test a few points, and then darken the line and dot accordingly. learning style: visual

GO Online

Video Tutor Help
Visit: PHSchool.com
Web Code: ase-0775

EXAMPLE Solving Inequalities by Adding

1 Solve $q - 7 < -2$. Graph the solutions.

$$q - 7 < -2$$

$$q - 7 + 7 < -2 + 7$$ ← Isolate the variable. Use the Addition Property of Inequality.

$$q < 5$$ ← Simplify.

Check

Step 1 Check whether your answer is a solution to the related equation.

$q - 7 = -2$ ← Write the related equation.

$5 - 7 \stackrel{?}{=} -2$ ← Substitute 5 for *q*.

$-2 = -2$ ✔

Step 2 Check the inequality symbol by substituting into the inequality.

$q - 7 < -2$

$4 - 7 < -2$ ← Substitute a number less than 5 for *q*.

$-3 < -2$ ✔

Steps 1 and 2 both check, so $q < 5$ is the solution of $q - 7 < -2$.

Quick Check

1. Solve $1 \le u - 4$. Graph the solutions. See left.

1. $5 \le u$

EXAMPLE Solving Inequalities by Subtracting

2 **Luggage** An airline restricts checked baggage to 100 lb per person. You pack one 39-lb bag. How much can your second bag weigh?

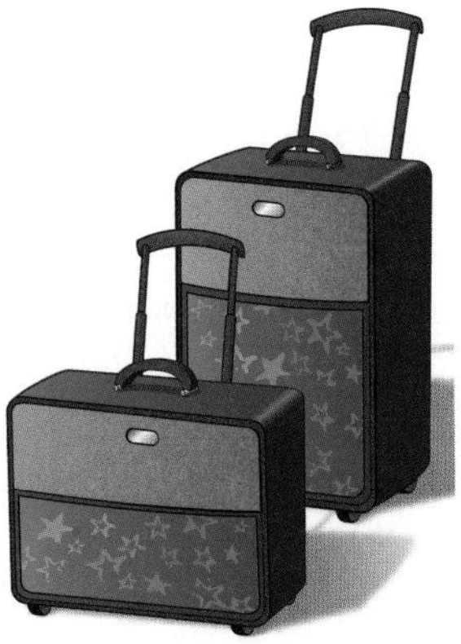

Words first bag plus second bag is at most 100 lb

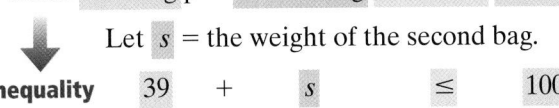

Let s = the weight of the second bag.

Inequality 39 + s ≤ 100

$$39 + s \le 100$$

$$39 + s - 39 \le 100 - 39$$ ← Isolate the variable. Use the Subtraction Property of Inequality.

$$s \le 61$$ ← Simplify.

Your second bag can weigh as much as 61 lb.

Quick Check

2. A school auditorium has 300 seats. If 89 people have tickets for the school play, how many more people can attend? See left.

2. At most, 211 more people can attend.

2. Teach

Activity Lab

Use before the lesson.
Student Edition Activity Lab 6-5a, Graphing Inequalities, p. 279

All in One Teaching Resources

Activity Labs 6-5: Solving Inequalities by Adding or Subtracting

Guided Instruction

Teaching Tip
In Example 1, have volunteers draw the graph on a number line of the solution, $q < 5$. Test several of the points that are shaded in the solution graph to see if they do make the inequality true. Then have them test several points that are not shaded to make sure that they do make the inequality false.

Error Prevention!

Emphasize that you must perform the *same* operation on both sides of an inequality in order to rewrite it as an equivalent inequality.

PowerPoint

Additional Examples

1 Solve $p - 3 < -5$. $p < -2$

2 After the hairdresser cut 3 in. from Rapunzel's hair, her hair was at least 15 in. long. How long was her hair before she had it cut? at least 18 in. long

All in One Teaching Resources

- Daily Notetaking Guide 6-5 L3
- Adapted Notetaking 6-5 L1

Closure

- *What is an inequality?* a comparison of two expressions that can be written using one of the following symbols: <, ≤, >, ≥, and ≠
- *Why is it not possible to check all the solutions of an inequality?* There are an infinite number of solutions.

Advanced Learners L4
Ask students to investigate whether the direction of the arrow on the graph always matches the direction of the inequality sign. only if the variable is on the left

learning style: verbal

English Language Learners ELL
Help students understand the difference between the solution to an equation and the solution to an inequality. For example, $q = 5$ can be read as q *is equal to the number 5;* while $q < 5$ is read as q *is all numbers less than 5*. Make sure students read their solutions.

learning style: verbal

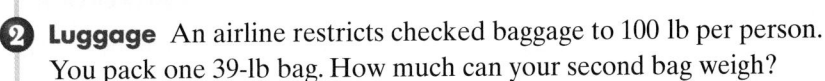

3. Practice

Assignment Guide

Check Your Understanding
Go over Exercises 1–7 in class before assigning the Homework Exercises.

Homework Exercises

A	Practice by Example	8–21
B	Apply Your Skills	22–31
C	Challenge	32
	Test Prep and Mixed Review	33–38

Homework Quick Check
To check students' understanding of key skills and concepts, go over Exercises 12, 21, 23, 26, and 27.

Differentiated Instruction Resources

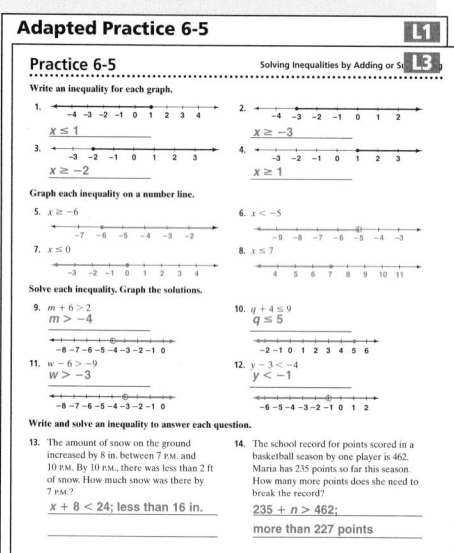

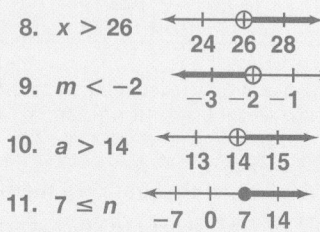

Adapted Practice 6-5 L1

Practice 6-5 Solving Inequalities by Adding or Su[btracting] L3

Write an inequality for each graph.

1. Number line −4 to 4, closed point at 1, shaded left. $x \le 1$
2. Number line −4 to 2, closed point at −3, shaded right. $x \ge -3$
3. Number line −3 to 3, closed point at −2, shaded right. $x \ge -2$
4. Number line −3 to 3, closed point at 1, shaded right. $x \ge 1$

Graph each inequality on a number line.

5. $x \ge -6$ (number line −7 to −2)
6. $x < -5$ (number line −9 to −3)
7. $x \le 0$ (number line −3 to 4)
8. $x \le 7$ (number line 4 to 11)

Solve each inequality. Graph the solutions.

9. $m + 6 > 2$ $m > -4$ (number line −8 to 0)
10. $q + 4 \le 9$ $q \le 5$ (number line −2 to 6)
11. $w - 6 > -9$ $w > -3$ (number line −8 to 0)
12. $y - 3 < -4$ $y < -1$ (number line −6 to 2)

Write and solve an inequality to answer each question.

13. The amount of snow on the ground increased by 8 in. between 7 P.M. and 10 P.M. By 10 P.M., there was less than 2 ft of snow. How much snow was there by 7 P.M.? $x + 8 < 24$; less than 16 in.
14. The school record for points scored in a basketball season by one player is 462. Maria has 235 points so far this season. How many more points does she need to break the record? $235 + n > 462$; more than 227 points

6-5 • Guided Problem Solving GPS L3

GPS Student Page 285, Exercise 26:

Banking A bank offers free checking for accounts with a balance greater than $500. You have a balance of $516.46 and you write a check for $26.47. Write an inequality to represent how much you would need to deposit to have free checking.

Understand

1. What does your balance have to be in order to get free checking? more than $500
2. Circle the information you need to know.
3. What do you need to find? The amount of deposit that will allow you to avoid a service fee.

Plan and Carry Out

4. Write an inequality to represent the given situation, where d represents the deposit. $\$516.46 - \$26.47 + d > \$500$
5. Simplify and solve the inequality. $489.99 + d > \$500$; $d > \$10.01$
6. How much should the deposit be? more than $10.01

Check

7. If you deposit $10.01, will you have free checking? Why? Yes, the balance has to be greater than, not equal to $500

Solve Another Problem

8. Most packages contain a nutritional analysis based on an average intake of 2,000 calories. You are trying to follow this guideline and have 580 calories for breakfast and 642 calories for lunch. What number of calories can you have for dinner? $c + 580 + 642 \le 2{,}000$; $c \le 778$ calories

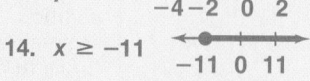

Check Your Understanding

1. **Vocabulary** What is the difference between an inequality and an equation? Explain.

1. An equation states that two expressions are equal; an inequality compares two expressions that are not usually equal.

Write an inequality for each word sentence.

2. n is at least −2. $n \ge -2$
3. 0.6 is no greater than x. $0.6 \le x$
4. y minus 4 is greater than −4. $y - 4 > -4$
5. $y - 4$ is a negative number. $y - 4 < 0$

Write an inequality to represent each situation.

6. The ages of people who pay children's admissions. $x < 12$
7. People at least 65 years old receive a senior citizen discount. $x \ge 65$

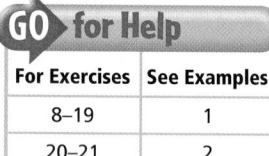

GENERAL ADMISSION	9.00
SENIOR CITIZENS	6.00
CHILDREN UNDER 12	6.00
BARGAIN MATINEE	6.00
GIFT CERTIFICATES	20.00

Homework Exercises

For more exercises, see Extra Skills and Word Problems.

GO for Help

For Exercises	See Examples
8–19	1
20–21	2

A **Solve each inequality. Graph the solutions.** 8–19. See margin.

8. $x - 8 > 18$
9. $m - 1 < -3$
10. $a - 13 > 1$
11. $2 \le n - 5$
12. $-11 > w - 1$
13. $p - 12 < -12$
14. $x + 12 \ge 1$
15. $3 + t \le 1$
16. $m + 1 \ge 22$
17. $w + 1 < 2$
18. $5 + b \ge 1$
19. $u + 10 < 0$

Write and solve an inequality to answer each question.

20. Eighteen is subtracted from a number. The result is at least 5. What numbers are solutions? $x - 18 \ge 5$; $x \ge 23$

21. **Electricity** You plug a microwave oven into a 20-ampere (amp) electrical circuit. The microwave uses as much as 12.5 amps. How many amps are available on this circuit for other appliances? $12.5 + x \le 20$; $x \le 7.5$ amps

B GPS 22. **Guided Problem Solving** During the summer months, a town restricts the water each family uses to 250 gallons of water per day. One day, a family uses 50 gallons for bathing, 27 gallons for laundry, and 25 gallons for cleaning. How many gallons can the family use to water the garden? 148 gallons

- How much water is used for bathing, laundry, and cleaning?
- Write and solve an inequality for the total water usage. Use a variable to represent the amount of water not used.

8. $x > 26$ (number line 24 26 28)
9. $m < -2$ (number line −3 −2 −1)
10. $a > 14$ (number line 13 14 15)
11. $7 \le n$ (number line −7 0 7 14)
12. $-10 > w$ (number line −11 −10 −9)
13. $p < 0$ (number line −4 −2 0 2)
14. $x \ge -11$ (number line −11 0 11)
15. $t \le -2$ (number line −4 −2 0)
16. $m \ge 21$ (number line 20 21 22)
17. $w < 1$ (number line 0 1 2)
18. $b \ge -4$ (number line −6 −4 −2 0)
19. $u < -10$ (number line −11 −10 −9)

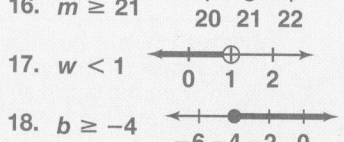

GO Online
Homework Video Tutor
Visit: PHSchool.com
Web Code: ase-0605

23. You can add or subtract the same number from each side of an equation or inequality without changing the value of the variable. They are different in that an equation usually has one solution, but an inequality has an infinite number of solutions.

24. $x > -1$

25. $x \le 0$

23. **Writing in Math** Describe how the solution of an inequality and the solution of an equation are alike. How are they different? See left.

Write an inequality for each graph. 24–25. See left.

24. 

25. 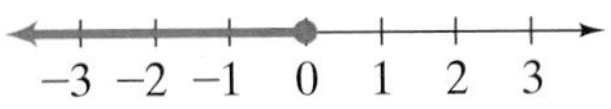

26. **Banking** A bank offers free checking for accounts with a balance greater than \$500. You have a balance of \$516.46 and you write a check for \$26.47. Write an inequality to represent how much you would need to deposit to have free checking. $x > \$10.01$

Reasoning Write > or < to make each statement true.

27. If $x > y$ and $y > z$, then x ■ z. >

28. If $a > b$, then b ■ a. <

Use the inequality $1.2 < x < 6.9$ to answer each question.

29. What is the greatest integer that is a solution of the inequality? 6

30. What is the least integer that is a solution of the inequality? 2

31. How many integers are solutions of the inequality? 5

Ⓒ 32. **Challenge** Solve the inequality $2(y + a) - y > a$ for y. $y > -a$

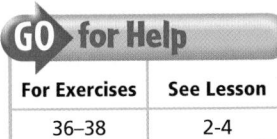

Test Prep and Mixed Review — Practice

Multiple Choice

33. Anita has \$15. She plans to save \$6 a week. Which equation can she use to find w, the number of weeks it will take her to save \$45? D

Ⓐ $6(w + 15) = 45$
Ⓑ $6w - 15 = 45$
Ⓒ $\frac{w}{6} + 15 = 45$
Ⓓ $6w + 15 = 45$

34. Five European countries and their land areas are shown in the table. Which country's land area is 97,066 km^2 more than Sweden's land area? F

Ⓕ France
Ⓖ Germany
Ⓗ Spain
Ⓙ Ukraine

Country	Area (km^2)
Ukraine	603,700
France	547,030
Spain	504,750
Sweden	449,964
Germany	357,021

35. In two more years, 5 times Solana's age will be the age of her grandfather, who will be 60. Which equation can be used to find n, Solana's age now? D

Ⓐ $5n - 2 = 60$
Ⓑ $5(n - 2) = 60$
Ⓒ $5n + 2 = 60$
Ⓓ $5(n + 2) = 60$

GO for Help

For Exercises	See Lesson
36–38	2-4

Find each sum or difference. Write your answer in simplest form.

36. $\frac{1}{5} + \frac{2}{9}$ $\frac{19}{45}$

37. $\frac{3}{4} - \frac{1}{3}$ $\frac{5}{12}$

38. $\frac{7}{11} + \frac{1}{2}$ $1\frac{3}{22}$

Online lesson quiz, PHSchool.com, Web Code: asa-0605

4. Assess & Reteach

PowerPoint

Lesson Quiz

1. Solve $r - 9 > 8$. $r > 17$
2. Solve and graph the inequality: $x + 6 \ge 4$. $x \ge -2$

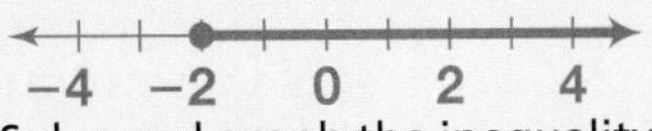

3. Solve and graph the inequality: $x - 14 < -13$. $x < 1$

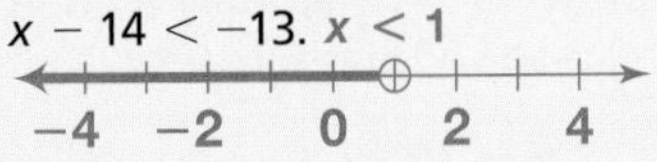

4. A lamp can use lightbulbs of up to 75 watts. The lamp is using a 45-watt bulb. At most, how many watts are available for brighter light? 30 watts

Reteaching 6-5 — Solving Inequalities by Adding and Su[btracting] L2

You can graph inequality solutions on a number line.

Inequality	Graph	How to Read the Graph
$x > 2$ *x is greater than 2*	(graph, −3 to 3)	An open dot at 2 shows that 2 is not included. All numbers greater than 2 are included.
$x < 2$ *x is less than 2*	(graph, −3 to 3)	An open dot at 2 shows that 2 is not included. All numbers less than 2 are included.
$x \ge 2$ *x is equal to or greater than 2*	(graph, −3 to 3)	A solid dot at 2 shows that 2 is included. All numbers greater than 2 are also included.
$x \le 2$ *x is equal to or less than 2*	(graph, −3 to 3)	A solid dot at 2 shows that 2 is included. All numbers less than 2 are also included.

To help solve an inequality, you can subtract the same number from or add the same number to each side.

Solve: $x + 5 > 8$.
$x + 5 > 8$
$x + 5 - 5 > 8 - 5$ ← Subtract 5 from each side.
$x > 3$ ← Simplify.
Graph the solution: (number line −2 to 4)

Solve: $y - 4 \le 1$.
$y - 4 \le 1$
$y - 4 + 4 \le 1 + 4$ ← Add 4 to each side.
$y \le 5$ ← Simplify.
Graph the solution: (number line −1 to 5)

Graph each inequality on a number line.

1. $x > -2$
2. $4 \ge a$

Solve each inequality. Graph the solution.

3. $9 + a > 11$ $a > 2$
4. $-4 + r < 0$ $r < 4$
5. $2 > n - 1$ $n < 3$
6. $1 + s \le 5$ $s \le 4$

Enrichment 6-5 — Solving Inequalities by Adding or Su[btracting] L4

Critical Thinking

To graph $|x| \ge 3$, you need to find all the points on the number line that are 3 or more units from 0 on the number line.

$|x| \ge 3$ means $x \le -3$ or $x \ge 3$.

To graph $|x| \le 3$, you need to find all the points on the number line that are 3 or less units from 0 on the number line.

$|x| \le 3$ means $x \ge -3$ and $x \le 3$. This solution can also be written as $-3 \le x \le 3$.

Graph each inequality.

1. $|x| < 2$
2. $|x| > 3$
3. $|x| < 5$
4. $|x - 1| \ge 2$
5. $|x + 2| \ge 3$
6. $|x - 3| < 2$

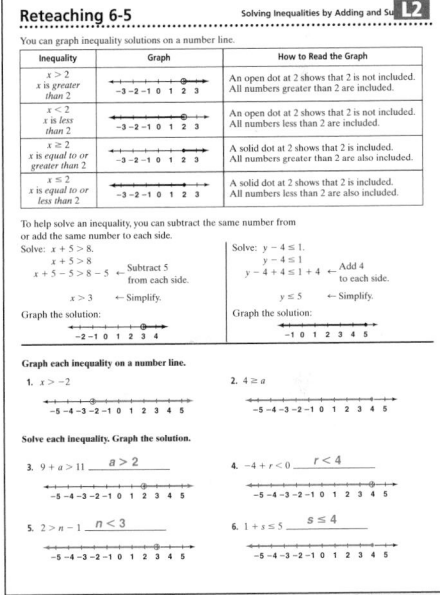

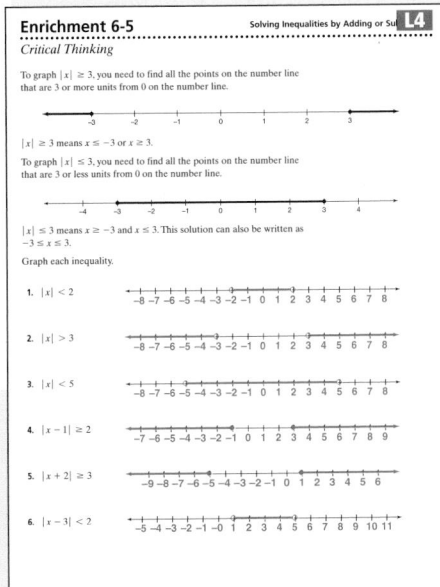

Alternative Assessment

Each student in a pair writes an inequality similar to those in Exercises 8–19 and challenges their partner to graph it.

Test Prep

Resources

For additional practice with a variety of test item formats:

- Test-Taking Strategies, p. 293
- Test Prep, p. 297
- Test-Taking Strategies with Transparencies

Vocabulary Builder

High-Use Academic Words

Students define and use three academic words: *define, solve,* and *combine.* These words are not exclusively mathematical terms, but they are commonly used in the study of mathematics.

Guided Instruction

Have students describe the meaning of each word in their own words. Have them give an example to illustrate their understanding of the words.

English Language Learners ELL
Have students list words that have specific meanings in math, but different meanings outside of math. Provide the words *term, expression,* and *product* as examples to get them started. Students may find it helpful to use the glossary to find additional examples. Have them give the mathematical and nonmathematical meaning of each word.

Connection to Language Arts
Have students identify related words with which they may also be familiar. Some examples are *solution* (for solve), *combination* (for combine), and, in Exercise 7, *infinity* or *infinitum*. Have them guess the meanings of *define, solve,* and *combine* based on their related words before looking them up in the dictionary.

Resources

- Vocabulary and Study Skills Worksheet

Vocabulary Builder

High-Use Academic Words

High-use academic words are words that you will see often in textbooks and on tests. These words are not math vocabulary terms, but knowing them will help you to succeed in mathematics.

Direction Words

Some words tell what to do in a problem. I need to understand what these words are asking so that I give the correct answer.

Word	Meaning
Define	To show that you understand what a term means by giving an accurate meaning of it
Solve	To work out a solution to a problem
Combine	To join things together

Exercises

1. Define "jigsaw puzzle." Check students' work.
2. Solve the puzzle at the right by drawing the missing piece. See margin.
3. Copy the jigsaw pieces below. Combine them to make a picture. See margin.

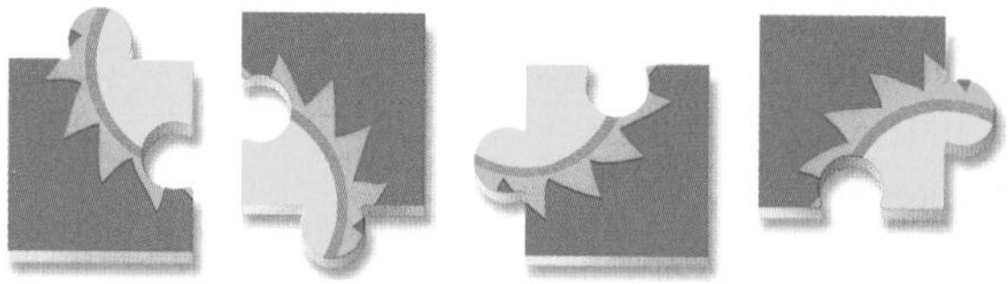

4. terms with exactly the same variable factors

4. Define "like terms." See above right.
5. Solve the equation $3x - 8 = 325$. 111
6. Combine like terms: $x + 2x + 3x + 4x + 5y - 4y + 3y - 2y$ $10x + 2y$
7. **Word Knowledge** Think about the word *infinite*. 7a–c. Check students' work.
   a. Choose the letter for how well you know the word.
      A. I know its meaning.
      B. I've seen it, but I don't know its meaning.
      C. I don't know it.
   b. **Research** Look up and write the definition of *infinite*.
   c. Use the word in a sentence involving mathematics.

2.

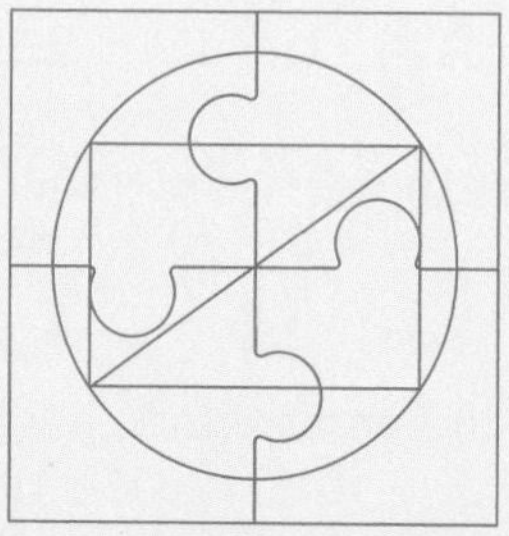

3.

Checkpoint Quiz 2

Lessons 6-3 through 6-5

Write an inequality for each graph.

1.  $x \geq -2$

2.  $x < 1$

Solve each equation or inequality.

3. $-3.5 - 4f = 10 - 2.5f$ -9
4. $-z - (z - 6) = 8$ -1
5. $\frac{m}{-2} + 7 = 21$ -28
6. $a + 3.4 \geq -2.6$ $a \geq -6$
7. $g + 1.5 \leq 2.5$ $g \leq 1$
8. $y - (-1) < -22$ $y < -23$

Write and solve an equation or inequality to answer each question. Round to the nearest hundredth, if necessary.

9. **Food** A pineapple costs \$4.99. Together one banana and one pineapple cost the same as 13 bananas. What does one banana cost?
Let b = the cost of a banana. $4.99 + b = 13b$; $b = \$.42$
10. A truck weighs 28,500 lb. The total weight limit for the truck is 64,000 lb. What is the maximum load weight the truck can carry?
Let x = the load weight. $28{,}500 + x = 64{,}000$; $x = 35{,}500$ lb

6-6a Activity Lab

Inequalities and Negative Numbers

ACTIVITY

1. **Mental Math** Simplify each side of each inequality at the right. Then replace each ■ with <, =, or >. See margin.
2. a. **Patterns** What happens to the direction of the inequality symbol as you multiply or divide each side by a positive number?
b. What happens as you multiply or divide each side by a negative number? 2a–b. See margin.
3. **Reasoning** Suppose a is larger than b. What is the relationship between $2a$ and $2b$? $-2a$ and $-2b$? $2a > 2b$; $-2a < -2b$

$6(3) < 12(3)$	$\frac{6}{3} < \frac{12}{3}$
$6(2)$ ■ $12(2)$	$\frac{6}{2}$ ■ $\frac{12}{2}$
$6(1)$ ■ $12(1)$	$\frac{6}{1}$ ■ $\frac{12}{1}$
$6(0)$ ■ $12(0)$	
$6(-1)$ ■ $12(-1)$	$\frac{6}{-1}$ ■ $\frac{12}{-1}$
$6(-2)$ ■ $12(-2)$	$\frac{6}{-2}$ ■ $\frac{12}{-2}$
$6(-3)$ ■ $12(-3)$	$\frac{6}{-3}$ ■ $\frac{12}{-3}$

1.

$6(3) < 12(3)$	$\frac{6}{3} < \frac{12}{3}$
$6(2) < 12(2)$	$\frac{6}{2} < \frac{12}{2}$
$6(1) < 12(1)$	$\frac{6}{1} < \frac{12}{1}$
$6(0) = 12(0)$	
$6(-1) > 12(-1)$	$\frac{6}{-1} > \frac{12}{-1}$
$6(-2) > 12(-2)$	$\frac{6}{-2} > \frac{12}{-2}$
$6(-3) > 12(-3)$	$\frac{6}{-3} > \frac{12}{-3}$

2a. It stays the same when you multiply or divide by a positive number.

b. It changes when you multiply or divide by a negative number.

Checkpoint Quiz

Use this Checkpoint Quiz to check students' understanding of the skills and concepts of Lessons 6-3 through 6-5.

Resources

- All-in-One Teaching Resources Checkpoint Quiz 2
- ExamView CD-ROM
- Success Tracker Online Intervention

Activity Lab

Inequalities and Negative Numbers

Students compare quantities and use inequality symbols to make true statements. They observe their results and begin to notice that multiplying or dividing by a negative number changes the direction of the inequality.

Guided Instruction

Visual Learners
To help students obtain accurate results, have them make a large number line with tick marks from −36 to 36. Ask students to find each pair of numbers on the number line to verify their comparisons.

Error Prevention!

For Exercise 3, have students who are not comfortable making a symbolic comparison reason about the same question using a few numerical examples. Then ask them to describe the pattern they notice, and make the transition to describing that pattern in terms of any two numbers a and b.

Resources

- Activity Lab 6–6: Solving Inequalities by Multiplying or Dividing

6-6

1. Plan

Objective

1 To write and solve inequalities using multiplication and division

Examples

1 Dividing by a Positive Number
2 Multiplying by a Negative Number
3 Dividing by a Negative Number

Math Understandings: p. 258D

Professional Development

Math Background

The steps involved in solving an equation and solving an inequality both end in isolating the variable on one side (either side). However, there is a key difference in the process of solving an inequality: multiplying or dividing each side of an inequality by a negative number reverses the direction of the inequality.

More Math Background: p. 258D

Lesson Planning and Resources

See p. 258E for a list of the resources that support this lesson.

PowerPoint

Bell Ringer Practice

Check Skills You'll Need
Use student page, transparency, or PowerPoint. For intervention, direct students to:

Solving Equations by Multiplying and Dividing
Lesson 1-7
Extra Skills and Word Problems Practice, Ch. 1

Algebra

6-6 Solving Inequalities by Multiplying or Dividing

Check Skills You'll Need

1. **Vocabulary Review** Is the definition "*Negative numbers* are numbers less than or equal to zero" correct? Explain. No; zero is not a negative number.

Solve each equation.

2. $4x = -16$ -4
3. $-8p = 808$ -101
4. $-2u = -12.4$ 6.2
5. $1 = \frac{t}{-8}$ -8

GO for Help Lesson 1-7

What You'll Learn

To write and solve inequalities using multiplication and division

New Vocabulary Multiplication Property of Inequality, Division Property of Inequality

Why Learn This?

Suppose you want to find the minimum number of people needed for a project or the maximum number of hours for a trip. To solve these problems, you can use the properties of inequalities.

The number line below shows the effect of multiplying the inequality $-1 < 2$ by a positive number, 3.

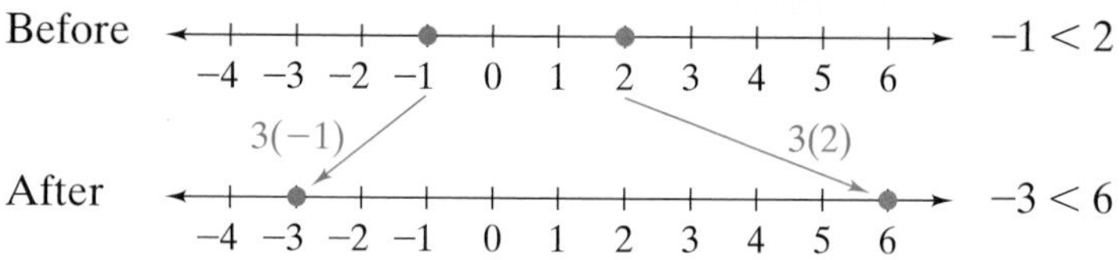

KEY CONCEPTS **Multiplication and Division Properties of Inequalities**

Using Positive Numbers to Multiply or Divide
When you multiply or divide each side of an inequality by a positive number, the relationship between the two sides does not change.

		Multiplication		Division
Arithmetic	$6 > 5,$	so $6(3) > 5(3)$	and	$\frac{6}{2} > \frac{5}{2}$
	$4 < 10,$	so $4(5) < 10(5)$	and	$\frac{4}{2} < \frac{10}{2}$
Algebra	If $a > b$ and $c > 0,$	then $ac > bc$	and	$\frac{a}{c} > \frac{b}{c}$
	If $a < b$ and $c > 0,$	then $ac < bc$	and	$\frac{a}{c} < \frac{b}{c}$

Note that these relationships are also true for $\leq$ and $\geq$.

Differentiated Instruction Solutions for All Learners

Special Needs L1
Students draw a picture for the Quick Check in Example 1. They draw people, labeling each person with the number 160, so they can picture the maximum number of people the elevator can hold.

learning style: visual

Below Level L2
Review the rules for multiplying signed numbers. Use the rules below to emphasize the division of signed number.

$\frac{+}{+} = +$ $\frac{-}{-} = +$ $\frac{+}{-} = -$ $\frac{-}{+} = -$

learning style: visual

EXAMPLE Dividing by a Positive Number

1 **Business** An Internet service provider is advertising the special offer below. The company's goal is to make at least an additional \$450,000. How many new customers must the company attract to meet its goal?

Words new customers times \$15 is at least \$450,000

Let n = the number of new customers.

Inequality $n \cdot 15 \geq 450{,}000$

$15n \geq 450{,}000$

$\frac{15n}{15} \geq \frac{450{,}000}{15}$ ← **Isolate the variable. Use the Division Property of Inequality.**

$n \geq 30{,}000$ ← **Simplify.**

The company must attract at least 30,000 new customers.

Check for Reasonableness The answer makes sense because $30{,}000 \cdot 15$ is 450,000, and any number over 30,000 multiplied by 15 is a number greater than 450,000.

Quick Check

1. A hotel elevator has a weight limit of 2,000 lb. Suppose the average weight of a passenger is 160 lb. How many passengers should the elevator safely hold? up to 12 passengers

The number line below shows the effect of multiplying an inequality by a negative number.

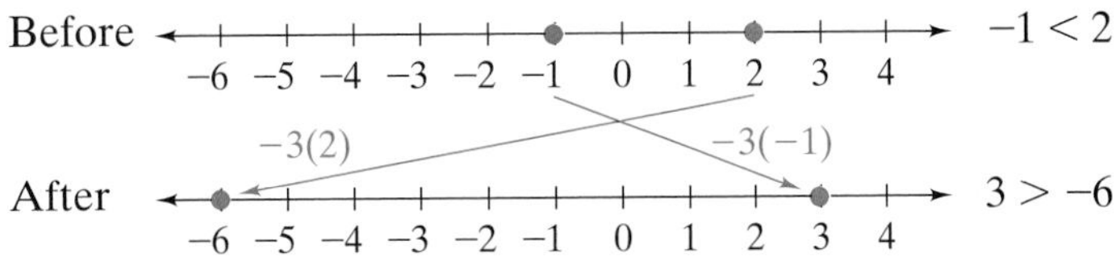

When the inequality $-1 < 2$ is multiplied by -3, the result is $3 > -6$. Notice that the direction of the inequality is reversed. The number lines suggest the following properties of inequalities.

2. Teach

Activity Lab

Use before the lesson.
Student Edition Activity Lab 6-6a, Inequalities and Negative Numbers, p. 287

All in One Teaching Resources

Activity Lab 6-6: Solving Inequalities by Multiplying or Dividing

Guided Instruction

Career Note
Discuss the services of an Internet-service provider (ISP). Brainstorm the education and training needed by people involved, such as programmers, customer representatives, and salespeople.

Teaching Tip
In preparation for Example 2 (multiplying by a negative number), ask students to verify that the inequality written in each step is equivalent to the inequality in the previous step, that is, it has exactly the same solution, even though the form has changed.

Error Prevention!

When solving an inequality that involves multiplying by a negative number, some students may write the negative multiplier in one step and fail to reverse the symbol until the second step. Ask students to check that each step they write as they solve an inequality expresses an equivalent inequality. This means that the *same* step that shows multiplying or dividing by a negative number must also show reversing the inequality.

Advanced Learners L4
Students write an informal explanation for a friend about why the inequality sign must be reversed when multiplying or dividing by a negative.

learning style: verbal

English Language Learners ELL
Read inequality statements and have students write them using math notation as you read them. Make sure they translate the words for *greater than, less than, greater than or equal to* and *less than or equal to* into the correct symbols.

learning style: verbal

Guided Instruction

Math Tip

Have students graph $x < 3$.

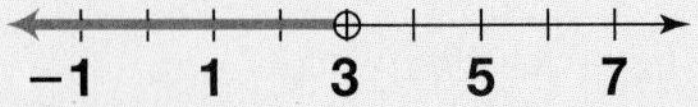

Then have them graph $-x < -3$ to convince them that these have two different solutions.

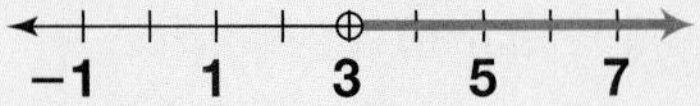

Then have them graph $-x > -3$. Elicit the fact that $-x > -3$ has the same solution set as $x < 3$.

Example 3

Ask:

- *Why is −3 divided by −3 equal to 1?* Any number divided by itself is one.
- *What is 1 times a?* *a*

PowerPoint

Additional Examples

1 A small business sells each CD of its game software for \$12. How many CDs must they sell to meet the goal of at least \$84,000? at least 7,000 CDs

Solve and graph the solution.

2 $\frac{y}{-4} > 3$ $y < -12$

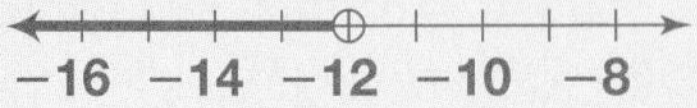

3 $-5b \le 15$ $b \ge -3$

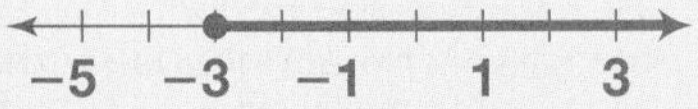

All in One Teaching Resources

- Daily Notetaking Guide 6-6 **L3**
- Adapted Notetaking 6-6 **L1**

Closure

- *What is the difference between multiplying or dividing an inequality by a number greater than zero and multiplying or dividing an inequality by a number less than zero?* Multiplying or dividing an inequality by a negative number reverses the direction of the inequality symbol.

Online active math

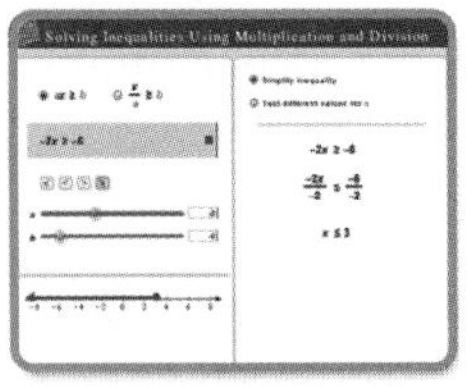

For: Solving Inequalities Activity
Use: Interactive Textbook, 6-6

KEY CONCEPTS **Multiplication and Division Properties of Inequalities**

Using Negative Numbers to Multiply or Divide

When you multiply or divide each side of an inequality by a negative number, *reverse* the direction of the inequality sign.

		Multiplication	Division
Arithmetic	$6 > 5$,	so $6 \cdot (-3) < 5 \cdot (-3)$	and $\frac{6}{-2} < \frac{5}{-2}$
	$4 < 10$,	so $4 \cdot (-5) > 10 \cdot (-5)$	and $\frac{4}{-2} > \frac{10}{-2}$
Algebra	If $a > b$ and $c < 0$,	then $ac < bc$	and $\frac{a}{c} < \frac{b}{c}$
	If $a < b$ and $c < 0$,	then $ac > bc$	and $\frac{a}{c} > \frac{b}{c}$

Note that these relationships are also true for $\le$ and $\ge$.

EXAMPLE Multiplying by a Negative Number

2 Solve $\frac{x}{-2} < 1$. Graph the solutions.

$\frac{x}{-2} < 1$

$-2 \cdot \left(\frac{x}{-2}\right) > -2 \cdot 1$ ← **Multiply each side by −2. Reverse the direction of the inequality.**

$x > -2$ ← **Simplify.**

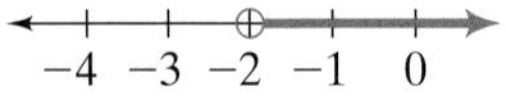

← **Graph.**

Quick Check

2. Solve the inequality $\frac{b}{-4} \ge 1$. Graph the solutions. See left.

2. $b \le -4$

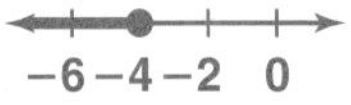

Vocabulary Tip

An open dot on a graph means the number *is not* included in the solution.

A closed dot on a graph means the number *is* included in the solution.

EXAMPLE Dividing by a Negative Number

3 Solve $-3a \le 12$. Graph the solutions.

$-3a \le 12$

$\frac{-3a}{-3} \ge \frac{12}{-3}$ ← **Divide each side by − 3. Reverse the direction of the inequality.**

$a \ge -4$ ← **Simplify.**

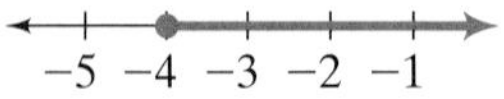

← **Graph.**

Quick Check

3. Solve the inequality $-2p \ge 34$. Graph the solutions. See left.

3. $p \le -17$

Check Your Understanding

1. When you multiply or divide each side of an inequality by a positive number, the relationship between the two sides does not change. When you multiply or divide by a negative number, the direction of the inequality sign reverses.

1. **Vocabulary** Explain how the Multiplication Property of Inequality differs for positive and negative numbers.

2. **Mental Math** Does the solution of $\frac{z}{-3} \geq 4$ include any positive numbers? Explain. No; it will only include numbers less than or equal to −12.

Solve each inequality. The exercises have been started for you.

3. $\frac{d}{3} > 4$
   $(3)\frac{d}{3} > 4(3)$
   $d > 12$

4. $2b < 8$
   $\frac{2b}{2} < \frac{8}{2}$
   $b < 4$

Homework Exercises

For more exercises, see Extra Skills and Word Problems.

GO for Help

For Exercises	See Examples
5–12	1
13–21	2–3

A **Solve each inequality.**

5. $\frac{y}{2} > 0$ $y > 0$
6. $-4 < \frac{r}{5}$ $-20 < r$
7. $5c < 10$ $c < 2$
8. $4y \leq -20$ $y \leq -5$
9. $6w \leq -54$ $w \leq -9$
10. $-18 \leq \frac{x}{2}$ $-36 \leq x$

Write and solve an inequality to answer each question.

11. The luncheon special at Little Jimmy's costs $4.89. The math club has $23.50 in its treasury. How many luncheon specials can the club buy? $4.89s \leq 23.50$; 4 specials

12. **Carpentry** A CD case is 0.375 in. thick. You are building a shelf 36 in. long. How many CD cases can you fit on the shelf? $0.375c \leq 36$; 96 CD cases

Solve each inequality. Graph the solutions. 13–21. See margin for graphs.

13. $\frac{r}{-2} \leq 3$ $r \geq -6$
14. $\frac{m}{-2} > 0$ $m < 0$
15. $\frac{z}{-12} \leq -8$ $z \geq 96$
16. $-20 \geq \frac{b}{-7}$ $140 \leq b$
17. $6 < \frac{x}{-2}$ $-12 > x$
18. $-6x \leq 24$ $x \geq -4$
19. $-2w < -14$ $w > 7$
20. $-15 > -3q$ $5 < q$
21. $27 \geq -0.9r$ $-30 \leq r$

B **GPS**

22. **Guided Problem Solving** There are 157 students and 8 teachers going on a field trip. Each bus can seat at most 48 passengers. How many buses should the school reserve? 4 buses
    - What is the total number of passengers going on the trip?
    - Write and solve an inequality to find x, the number of buses that should be reserved.

23. **Reasoning** What number is *not* a solution of $x < -3$ or $-x < 3$? −3

24. **Writing in Math** Explain how solving $5x < 20$ is different from solving $-5x < 20$. See above left.

24. In $5x < 20$, you must divide each side by a positive number to get $x < 4$. In $-5x < 20$, you must divide each side by a negative number, which changes the direction of the inequality. You will also get −4 on the right instead of 4. So $x > -4$.

GO Online
Homework Video Tutor
Visit: PHSchool.com
Web Code: ase-0606

Online lesson quiz, PHSchool.com, Web Code: asa-0606

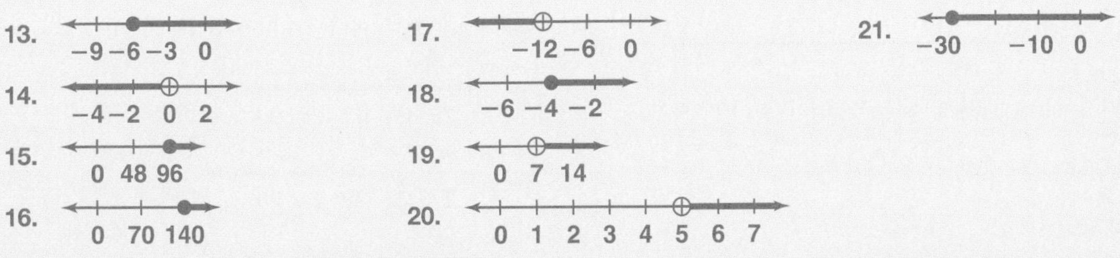

3. Practice

Assignment Guide

Check Your Understanding

Go over Exercises 1–4 in class before assigning the Homework Exercises.

Homework Exercises

A	Practice by Example	5–21
B	Apply Your Skills	22–30
C	Challenge	31
	Test Prep and Mixed Review	32–37

Homework Quick Check

To check students' understanding of key skills and concepts, go over Exercises 11, 17, 23, 24, and 30.

Differentiated Instruction Resources

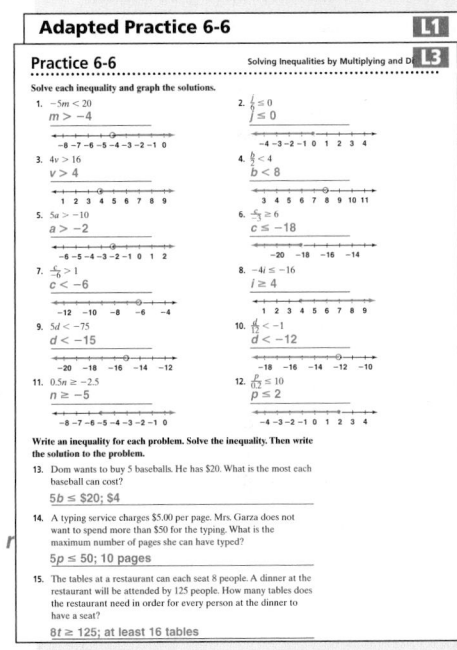

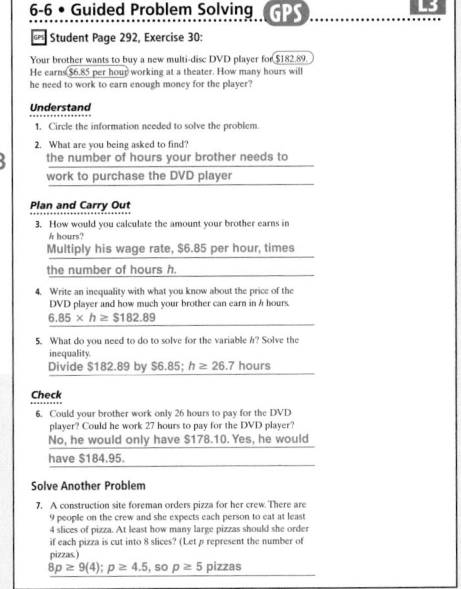

Adapted Practice 6-6 L1

Practice 6-6 Solving Inequalities by Multiplying and Di L3

Solve each inequality and graph the solutions.

1. $-5m < 20$ $m > -4$
2. $\frac{j}{6} \leq 0$ $j \leq 0$
3. $4v > 16$ $v > 4$
4. $\frac{b}{2} < 4$ $b < 8$
5. $5a > -10$ $a > -2$
6. $\frac{c}{-3} \geq 6$ $c \leq -18$
7. $\frac{c}{-6} > 1$ $c < -6$
8. $-4i \leq -16$ $i \geq 4$
9. $5d < -75$ $d < -15$
10. $\frac{d}{12} < -1$ $d < -12$
11. $0.5n \geq -2.5$ $n \geq -5$
12. $\frac{p}{0.2} \leq 10$ $p \leq 2$

Write an inequality for each problem. Solve the inequality. Then write the solution to the problem.

13. Dom wants to buy 5 baseballs. He has $20. What is the most each baseball can cost? $5b \leq \$20$; $4

14. A typing service charges $5.00 per page. Mrs. Garza does not want to spend more than $50 for the typing. What is the maximum number of pages she can have typed? $5p \leq 50$; 10 pages

15. The tables at a restaurant can each seat 8 people. A dinner at the restaurant will be attended by 125 people. How many tables does the restaurant need in order for every person at the dinner to have a seat? $8t \geq 125$; at least 16 tables

6-6 • Guided Problem Solving GPS L3

Student Page 292, Exercise 30:

Your brother wants to buy a new multi-disc DVD player for $182.89. He earns $6.85 per hour working at a theater. How many hours will he need to work to earn enough money for the player?

Understand

1. Circle the information needed to solve the problem.
2. What are you being asked to find? the number of hours your brother needs to work to purchase the DVD player

Plan and Carry Out

3. How would you calculate the amount your brother earns in h hours? Multiply his wage rate, $6.85 per hour, times the number of hours h.
4. Write an inequality with what you know about the price of the DVD player and how much your brother can earn in h hours. $6.85 \times h \geq \$182.89$
5. What do you need to do to solve for the variable h? Solve the inequality. Divide $182.89 by $6.85; $h \geq 26.7$ hours

Check

6. Could your brother work only 26 hours to pay for the DVD player? Could he work 27 hours to pay for the DVD player? No, he would only have $178.10. Yes, he would have $184.95.

Solve Another Problem

7. A construction site foreman orders pizza for her crew. There are 9 people on the crew and she expects each person to eat at least 4 slices of pizza. At least how many large pizzas should she order if each pizza is cut into 8 slices? (Let p represent the number of pizzas.) $8p \geq 9(4)$; $p \geq 4.5$, so $p \geq 5$ pizzas

4. Assess & Reteach

PowerPoint

Lesson Quiz

Solve each inequality.

1. $9c \le -36$ $c \le -4$
2. $-7r \ge 14$ $r \le -2$
3. $\frac{a}{-8} < -1$ $a > 8$
4. Leroy's class is having a cookie sale to raise money for a class trip. They will sell homemade cookies for \$1.50 each. If they earn at least \$200, a local business will match the amount they earn. At least how many cookies do they need to sell to get the local company to match their cookie-sale earnings? 134 cookies

Alternative Assessment

Each student in a pair writes a word problem similar to those in Exercises 29–30. Students then exchange problems and challenge each other to write an inequality for the problem and solve the inequality.

25. a and b must have opposite signs.

26. a and b must have opposite signs.

27. a can be positive or negative, but b must be positive.

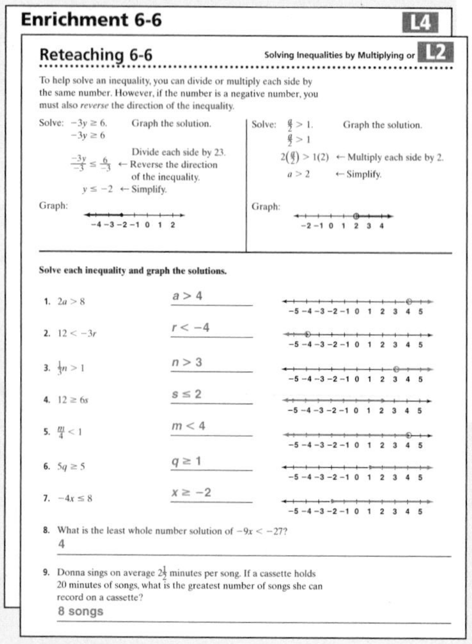

Enrichment 6-6 L4

Reteaching 6-6 Solving Inequalities by Multiplying or L2

To help solve an inequality, you can divide or multiply each side by the same number. However, if the number is a negative number, you must also *reverse* the direction of the inequality.

Solve: $-3y \ge 6$. Graph the solution.
$-3y \ge 6$
Divide each side by 23.
$\frac{-3y}{-3} \le \frac{6}{-3}$ ← Reverse the direction of the inequality.
$y \le -2$ ← Simplify.
Graph: −4 −3 −2 −1 0 1 2

Solve: $\frac{a}{2} > 1$. Graph the solution.
$\frac{a}{2} > 1$
$2(\frac{a}{2}) > 1(2)$ ← Multiply each side by 2.
$a > 2$ ← Simplify.
Graph: −2 −1 0 1 2 3 4

Solve each inequality and graph the solutions.

1. $2a > 8$ $a > 4$
2. $12 < -3r$ $r < -4$
3. $\frac{1}{3}n > 1$ $n > 3$
4. $12 \ge 6s$ $s \le 2$
5. $\frac{m}{4} < 1$ $m < 4$
6. $5q \ge 5$ $q \ge 1$
7. $-4x \le 8$ $x \ge -2$
8. What is the least whole number solution of $-9x < -27$? 4
9. Donna sings on average $2\frac{1}{2}$ minutes per song. If a cassette holds 20 minutes of songs, what is the greatest number of songs she can record on a cassette? 8 songs

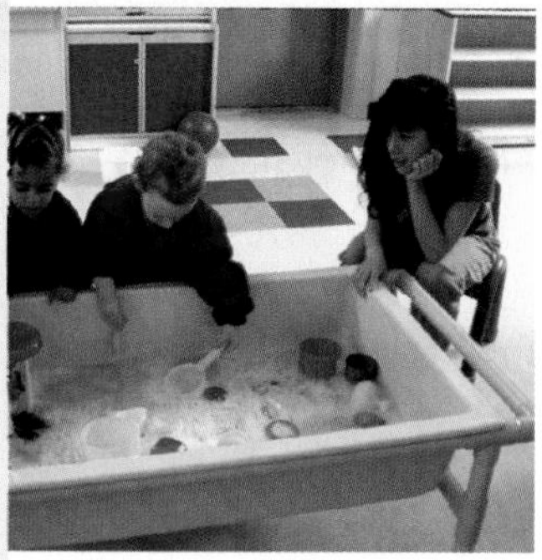

Careers Child-care workers perform a combination of basic care and teaching duties.

What values of a and b make each inequality true? 25–28. See margin.

25. $-ab > 0$ 26. $ab < 0$ 27. $a^2b > 0$ 28. $\frac{a}{b} > 0$

29. **Child Care** In Virginia, for every group of 5 two-year-olds in day care, there must be at least 1 teacher. If there are 19 two-year-olds in a class, how many teachers must the center have? 4 teachers

30. GPS Your brother wants to buy a new multi-disc DVD player for \$182.89. He earns \$6.85 per hour working at a theater. How many hours will he need to work to earn enough money for the player? 27 h

31. C **Challenge** A student solved $\frac{a}{b} > 2$ for a and got the solution $a > 2b$. Is the student's answer correct for all values of b? Explain. No; it is only true if b is positive. If $b = 0$, the problem is undefined. If b is negative, the inequality sign needs to change.

Test Prep and Mixed Review — Practice

Multiple Choice

32. At one store, a DVD is on sale for 25% off \$26.99. At another store, the same DVD is on sale for 30% off \$29.99. Why should Rueben buy the DVD at the first store? D
    - A 30% is more than 25%.
    - B \$26.99 is less than \$29.99.
    - C 25% of \$26.99 is less than 30% of \$29.99.
    - D 75% of \$26.99 is less than 70% of \$29.99.

33. A pattern of equations is shown below. Which statement best describes this pattern of equations? F

    64% of 25 = 16
    16% of 100 = 16
    4% of 400 = 16
    1% of 1600 = 16

    - F When the percent is divided by 4, and the other number is multiplied by 4, the answer is 16.
    - G When the percent is multiplied by 4, and the other number is divided by $\frac{1}{4}$, the answer is 16.
    - H When the percent is divided by 4, and the other number is divided by 4, the answer is 16.
    - J When the percent is multiplied by 4, and the other number is multiplied by 4, the answer is 16.

34. Two banners are similar. The height of the smaller banner is 24 inches, while the height of the larger banner is 60 inches. What scale factor was used to dilate the smaller banner to the larger one? D
    - A 0.4 B 0.6 C 1.4 D 2.5

GO for Help

For Exercises	See Lesson
35–37	6-5

Algebra **Solve each inequality. Graph the solutions.** 35–37. See margin for graphs.

35. $y + 3 \le 29$ $y \le 26$ 36. $a - 7 > 15$ $a > 22$ 37. $w - 6 \ge 9$ $w \ge 15$

Test Prep

Resources

For additional practice with a variety of test item formats:
- Test-Taking Strategies, p. 293
- Test Prep, p. 297
- Test-Taking with Transparencies

28. a and b must have the same sign, and a and $b \ne 0$.

35.

36.
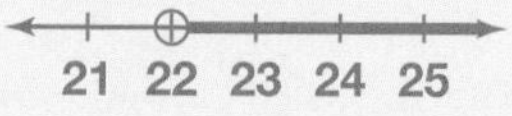

37.

Reading for Understanding

Reading-comprehension questions are based on a passage. Read the questions carefully *before* reading the passage. Then, as you read, look for the information you need to answer the questions.

EXAMPLE

Legislative Math

When a majority of the members of the Senate and a majority of the members of the House of Representatives vote in favor of a bill, the bill goes to the White House for the President's signature.

But the President can veto a bill to prevent it from becoming law. The President's veto outweighs the combined votes of the 100 members of the Senate and the 435 members of the House of Representatives.

Congress can override the veto, however. Two thirds of the members of the Senate and two thirds of the members of the House present at the vote must vote to override the veto. The bill then automatically becomes law.

If all senators are present at the vote, how many must vote in favor of an override of a presidential veto for the override to pass?

Two thirds of the members of the Senate present at the vote must vote to override a veto. There are 100 members of the Senate.

number of senators needed $= \frac{2}{3} \cdot 100 = 66.\overline{6}$

At least 67 senators must vote to override a presidential veto.

Exercises

Use the passage in the example for the following exercises.

1. If all members of the House of Representatives are present, how many votes are required to override a presidential veto? 290 votes
2. In 1845, President John Tyler's veto was overridden by Congress. There were 42 members of the Senate and 157 members of the House present at the vote. How many had to vote against the veto for it to be overridden? 28 members of the Senate; 105 members of the House
3. Can you find the total number of Senate and House members required for an override by adding the members of the Senate and the House and then taking two thirds of the total? Explain. No; an override requires $\frac{2}{3}$ of the Senate and $\frac{2}{3}$ of the House.

Reading for Understanding

Research shows that learning comprehension strategies helps students become purposeful, active readers who can gain control of their own reading comprehension. This feature provides students with a strategy they can use to answer questions about information presented in a passage of text.

Guided Instruction

Teaching Tip

Have students identify and discuss key phrases in the passage that might help them answer the question.

Resources

Test-Taking Strategies with Transparencies
- Transparency 5
- Practice sheet, p. 30

Test-Taking Strategies with Transparencies

Test-Taking Strategies: Reading for Understanding

Reading comprehension questions are based on a passage that gives information and facts.

To solve a problem use these steps:
- Read the directions and the passage.
- Read the questions carefully.
- Look for information that helps answer the questions.

EXAMPLE

Read the passage and answer the questions below.

Each year, more than 775,000 children and teenagers are treated in the emergency room for sports injuries. In a recent study, doctors found that 10 years ago, up to 70 percent of sports injuries in kids were acute injuries, such as a sprained ankle or a fracture. Over the past five years, however, overuse accounted for about half of all sports injuries among youngsters. Doctors are seeing a lot more elbow injuries from too much pitching and a lot more heel pain from tendinitis due to too much soccer.

This year about 25 athletes in your school will be injured. About how many of them will have injuries due to overuse?

What are you being asked?
How many of the 25 athletes will have injuries due to overuse?

What information helps you to solve the problem?
Over the past five years overuse accounted for about half of all sports injuries among youngsters.

Solve the problem: 50% of 25 students is about 13 students.

Resources

Student Edition
Extra Skills and Word Problems Practice, Ch. 6, p. 614
English/Spanish Glossary, p. 650
Formulas and Properties, p. 648
Tables, p. 643

All in One Teaching Resources
- Vocabulary and Study Skills 6F L3

Differentiated Instruction

Spanish Vocabulary Workbook with Study Skills ELL
Interactive Texbook
- Audio Glossary

Online Vocabulary Quiz

Success Tracker™
Online at PHSchool.com

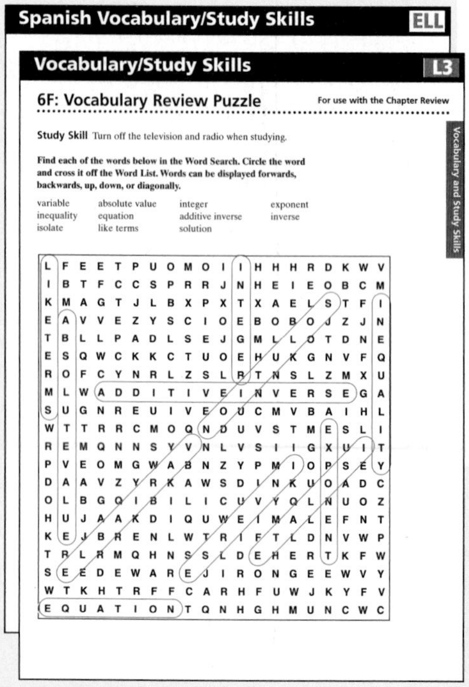
Spanish Vocabulary/Study Skills ELL
Vocabulary/Study Skills L3
6F: Vocabulary Review Puzzle — For use with the Chapter Review
Study Skill Turn off the television and radio when studying.
Find each of the words below in the Word Search. Circle the word and cross it off the Word List. Words can be displayed forwards, backwards, up, down, or diagonally.
variable, absolute value, integer, exponent, inequality, equation, additive inverse, inverse, isolate, like terms, solution

Chapter 6 Review

Vocabulary Review

Addition Property of Inequality (p. 282)
Division Property of Inequality (p. 288)
inequality (p. 282)
like terms (p. 266)
Multiplication Property of Inequality (p. 288)
Subtraction Property of Inequality (p. 282)
term (p. 266)

Go Online
PHSchool.com
For: Online Vocabulary Quiz
Web Code: asj-0651

Choose the correct term to complete each sentence.

1. (Terms, Like terms) have the same variables. like terms
2. An (equation, inequality) is a mathematical sentence that contains $<, >, \leq, \geq$, or $\neq$. inequality
3. A (solution, term) is a number, a variable, or the product of a number and a variable. term
4. When you use the (Addition Property of Inequality, Multiplication Property of Inequality), you may need to reverse the direction of the inequality sign. Mult. Prop. of Ineq.
5. To solve the inequality $x - 5 < 7$, use the (Addition Property of Inequality, Subtraction Property of Inequality). Add. Prop. of Ineq.

Skills and Concepts

Lesson 6-1
- To solve two-step equations and to use two-step equations to solve problems

To solve two-step equations, first undo the addition or subtraction. Then undo the multiplication or division.

Solve each equation. Check the solution.

6. $2n - 5 = 19$ 12
7. $4 + 3q = -7$ $-\frac{11}{3}$
8. $-1 = \frac{b}{5} + 2$ −15
9. $\frac{c}{-3} - 1 = 2$ −9
10. $12s + 2 = -8$ $-\frac{5}{6}$
11. $\frac{w}{4} + 10 = 20$ 40
12. You bought cat food for \$1.79 per can and a bag of rabbit food for \$6.59. The total cost was \$33.44. How many cans of cat food did you buy? 15 cans
13. At the mall, you spent a total of \$170.86. You bought 2 pairs of jeans for \$39.95 each, a jacket for \$45.99, and shirts for \$14.99 each. How many shirts did you buy? 3 shirts

Lesson 6-2

- To combine like terms and simplify algebraic expressions

The parts of an algebraic expression are **terms. Like terms** have exactly the same variable factors. You simplify an expression by combining like terms.

Simplify each expression.

14. $4 - 3(f - 1)$ $7 - 3f$

15. $3(a + 2) + 5$ $3a + 11$

16. $8x + 3(x - 4)$ $11x - 12$

Lessons 6-3, 6-4

- To write and solve multi-step equations
- To write and solve equations with variables on both sides

When simplifying an equation, combine like terms. If an equation has variables on each side, use the addition or subtraction property of equality to isolate the variable.

Solve each equation. Check the solution.

17. $4a + 3 - a = -7 + 2 + a$ -4

18. $2b - 8 = -b + 7$ 5

19. $18 = 2(3k + 1) - k$ $\frac{16}{5}$ or 3.2

20. $3(c + 4) - 7 = -10$ -5

21. Marsha buys 3 pounds of cheddar cheese and some Swiss cheese. Both cheeses cost $4.50 per pound. The total cost is $24.75. How many pounds of Swiss cheese did Marsha buy? 2.5 lb

Lesson 6-5

- To write and solve inequalities using addition and subtraction

An **inequality** is a mathematical sentence that contains $<, \leq, >, \geq$, or $\neq$. Any value of the variable that makes an inequality true is a solution. You can graph all the solutions of an inequality on a number line. You can solve an inequality using the addition and subtraction properties of inequality.

Solve each inequality. Graph the solutions. 22–24. See margin.

22. $g - 7 > 12$

23. $u + 3 \leq 5$

24. $4 + t \geq -7$

Write an inequality for each word sentence.

25. The jacket costs less than $75. $c < 75$

26. You must raise at least $150. $x \geq 150$

Lesson 6-6

- To write and solve inequalities using multiplication and division

When you multiply or divide an inequality by a positive number, the relationship between the two sides does not change. Multiplying or dividing an inequality by a negative number, however, reverses the direction of the inequality sign.

Solve each inequality. Graph the solutions. 27–32. See margin.

27. $4x < -12$

28. $-17y \geq 34$

29. $-6a > -42$

30. $\frac{w}{8} \leq 16$

31. $\frac{c}{-2} > 10$

32. $\frac{z}{-4} < -3$

22. $g > 19$

23. $u \leq 2$

24. $t \geq -11$

27. $x < -3$

28. $y \leq -2$

29. $a < 7$

30. $w \leq 128$

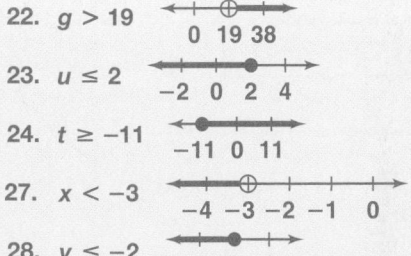

31. $c < -20$

32. $z > 12$

Alternative Assessment L4

Alternative Assessment Form C

Chapter 6

TIME TO TALK

Anthony wants his own telephone. His parents said he can have one if he pays for it himself. Use this chart to help Anthony decide whether he can afford his own phone.

Telephone Company Charges	
Installation:	$42
Deposit:	$50
Basic Monthly Charge:	$8

Show all of your work on a separate sheet of paper.

1. To earn money, Anthony mows lawns for $4 per hour. First, he wanted to find the least number of hours needed to pay for the installation and deposit. He wrote this inequality:

$$4h \geq 42 + 50$$

Describe what each term in this inequality represents. Then solve for h.

2. Next Anthony wanted to find the least number of hours he would have to work to pay his basic monthly charge. He wrote this inequality:

$$4h \geq 8$$

Describe what each term in this inequality represents and solve the inequality for h.

3. Anthony has two out-of-state friends whom he would like to call. He discovered the following about long-distance calls:

- The phone company charges one price for the first minute and then a lower price per minute for every minute thereafter.
- If a customer talks for any part of a minute, he or she is charged for the whole minute.
- Rates vary according to the time of day.

Anthony looked up the rates to the two cities where his friends live. He used this information to make the price chart shown on the next page. (n represents the number of minutes after the first minute.)

Spanish Quarter 2 Test—Forms A, B L3

Quarter 2 Test—Forms D, E L2

Quarter 2 Test—Forms A, B L3

Quarter 2 Test Form A

Chapters 4–6

1. Find the unit pay rate of $26.50 for 5 hours of work.

2. Find an equal rate.
44 ft/s = __?__ mi/h

3. Carol found she had a mystery-to-comedy videotape ratio of 8 to 3. If she has 36 comedy tapes in her collection, find the number of mystery tapes she has. Then find the total number of tapes.

4. Solve. $\frac{18}{q} = \frac{30}{65}$

5. Are the rectangles similar? Explain.

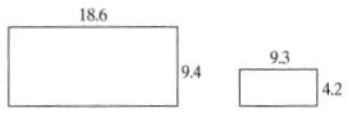

6. The two figures are similar. Find x.

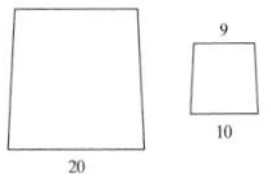

7. For a drawing that requires less detail, an architect has taken the drawing of a building and reduced it. Find the scale factor.

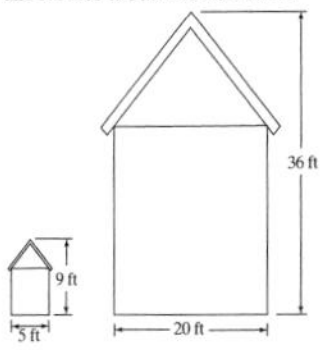

8. A map of the United States uses the scale 1 in. : 120 mi. On the map, Boston and Washington, D.C. are about 3.6 in. apart. What is the actual distance between these cities?

9. A 6 ft. tall man casts a shadow 20 ft. long. At the same time of day, a nearby tree casts a shadow 50 ft. long. What is the height of the tree?

10. Write $\frac{3}{8}$ as a decimal and as a percent.

11. Write 46% as a fraction in lowest terms.

12. Estimate 41% of 151.

13. What number is 30% of 180?

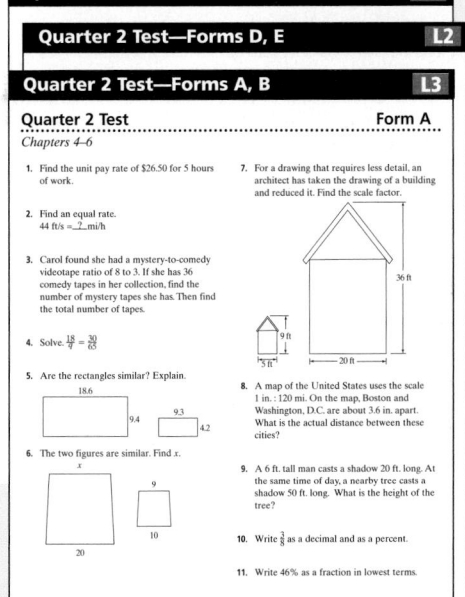

Chapter 6 Test

Go Online PHSchool.com For: Online chapter test Web Code: asa-0652

Resources

- ExamView Assessment Suite CD-ROM
  - Ch. 6 Ready-Made Test
  - Make your own Ch. 6 test
- MindPoint Quiz Show CD-ROM
  - Chapter 6 Review

Differentiated Instruction

All in One Teaching Resources

- Below Level Chapter 6 Test L2
- Chapter 6 Test L3
- Chapter 6 Alternative Assessment L4

Spanish Assessment Resources ELL

- Below Level Chapter 6 Test L2
- Chapter 6 Test L3
- Chapter 6 Alternative Assessment L4

ExamView CD-ROM

- Special Needs Test L1
- Special Needs Practice Bank L1

Online Chapter 6 Test at www.PHSchool.com L3

2. $5 - 4t$ 3. $6m - 4$ 4. $-36a - 5$

29. $-3x \geq 15$; $x \leq -5$; the greatest value is -5.

30. $11 + 0.40p \leq 15$; $p \leq 10$; 10 pens

31. $0.39 + 0.24w \leq 3.00$; $w \leq 10.875$; 10 oz

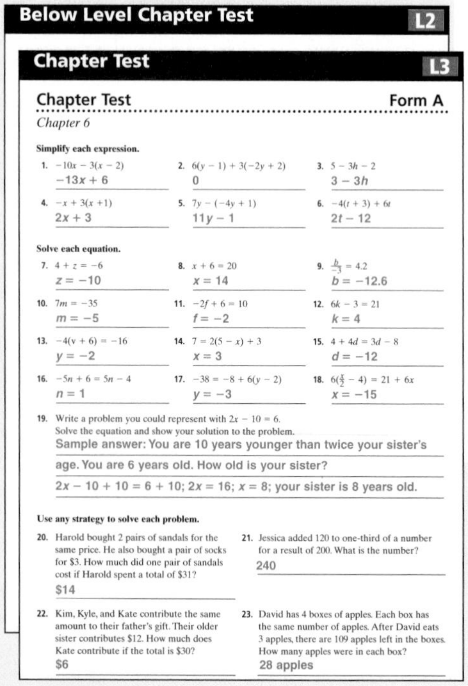

Below Level Chapter Test L2

Chapter Test L3

Chapter Test Form A

Chapter 6

Simplify each expression.

1. $-10x - 3(x - 2)$ $-13x + 6$
2. $6(y - 1) + 3(-2y + 2)$ 0
3. $5 - 3h - 2$ $3 - 3h$
4. $-x + 3(x + 1)$ $2x + 3$
5. $7y - (-4y + 1)$ $11y - 1$
6. $-4(t + 3) + 6t$ $2t - 12$

Solve each equation.

7. $4 + z = -6$ $z = -10$
8. $x + 6 = 20$ $x = 14$
9. $\frac{b}{-3} = 4.2$ $b = -12.6$
10. $7m = -35$ $m = -5$
11. $-2f + 6 = 10$ $f = -2$
12. $6k - 3 = 21$ $k = 4$
13. $-4(v + 6) = -16$ $y = -2$
14. $7 = 2(5 - x) + 3$ $x = 3$
15. $4 + 4d = 3d - 8$ $d = -12$
16. $-5n + 6 = 5n - 4$ $n = 1$
17. $-38 = -8 + 6(y - 2)$ $y = -3$
18. $6(\frac{x}{2} - 4) = 21 + 6x$ $x = -15$
19. Write a problem you could represent with $2x - 10 = 6$. Solve the equation and show your solution to the problem. Sample answer: You are 10 years younger than twice your sister's age. You are 6 years old. How old is your sister? $2x - 10 + 10 = 6 + 10$; $2x = 16$; $x = 8$; your sister is 8 years old.

Use any strategy to solve each problem.

20. Harold bought 2 pairs of sandals for the same price. He also bought a pair of socks for $3. How much did one pair of sandals cost if Harold spent a total of $31? $14
21. Jessica added 120 to one-third of a number for a result of 200. What is the number? 240
22. Kim, Kyle, and Kate contribute the same amount to their father's gift. Their older sister contributes $12. How much does Kate contribute if the total is $30? $6
23. David has 4 boxes of apples. Each box has the same number of apples. After David eats 3 apples, there are 109 apples left in the boxes. How many apples were in each box? 28 apples

Simplify each expression. 2–4. See margin.

1. $9 - 4r - 7$ $2 - 4r$
2. $5 + (-12t) + 8t$
3. $2(3m - 5) + 6$
4. $-4(7a + 2a) - 5$
5. $4v + 17 - 9v$ $-5v + 17$
6. $13s - (-6 - 4s)$ $17s + 6$

Solve each equation.

7. $x + 7 = 18 - 2x$ $\frac{11}{3}$
8. $2 + y = -7 + 2y$ 9
9. $\frac{6z}{7} = -30$ -35
10. $\frac{a}{-2} = 2.5 - 3a$ 1
11. $4m - 9 = 27$ 9
12. $-2c + 5 = 9$ -2
13. $-3(h + 7) = -18$ -1
14. $\frac{r}{-5} - 3 = 14$ -85
15. $6 + 2d = 3d - 4$ 10
16. $5 = 3(4 - b) + 2$ 3
17. $5t - 1 = 7t - 5$ 2
18. $2(c + 1) = c - 7$ -9
19. A quilter is making a quilt that will be 48 in. wide. The border will be 2 in. at each end. Each quilt block is 4 in. wide. How many quilt blocks does the quilter need across the width of the quilt? 11 blocks
20. **Groceries** You buy 15 apples and a $2.75 block of cheese. The bill is $6.20. How much does each apple cost? $.23
21. **Bowling** You and your friend go bowling. Your score is 6 more than twice your friend's score. If your score is 212, what is your friend's score? 103
22. A cricket bat weighs 42 oz. Together, two cricket balls and a cricket bat weigh the same as eight cricket balls plus 9 oz. How much does a cricket ball weigh? 5.5 oz
23. **Open-Ended** Write a problem you could represent with the equation $3k - 12 = 6$. Solve the equation and show your solution.
    23. Answers may vary. Sample: You save $3 each week for a number of weeks. Then you spend $12 on a poster, leaving you with $6 from the money you saved. How many weeks have passed? $k = 6$

Define a variable and write an inequality to describe each situation.

24. Each driver must be at least 16 years old. Let d = the age of driver; $d \geq 16$.
25. You can have no more than five passengers in a car. Let p = the number of passengers; $p \leq 5$.
26. There are fewer than three weeks until vacation. Let w = the number of weeks until vacation; $w < 3$.
27. There are at most 75 tickets to the play still available. Let t = the number of tickets available; $t \leq 75$.
28. Your essay must be at least four pages long. Let p = the number of essay pages; $p \geq 4$.

Write and solve an inequality to answer each question. 29–31. See margin.

29. When a number is multiplied by -3, the result is at least 15. What is the greatest value the number can have?
30. **Shopping** You have $15 to buy a sketch pad and some pens. The sketch pad you want costs $11, and pens cost $.40 each. How many pens can you buy?
31. **Postage** You want to send a package. First-class mail costs $.39 for the first ounce and $.24 for each additional ounce. You can spend at most $3.00 on postage. What is the maximum weight of your package? Round down to the nearest ounce.

Solve each inequality. Graph the solutions. 32–39. See margin for graphs.

32. $18 > w + 3$ $15 > w$
33. $y - 12 > -7$ $y > 5$
34. $\frac{z}{3} \leq 5$ $z \leq 15$
35. $-4s \geq 64$ $s \leq -16$
36. $3m < 12$ $m < 4$
37. $-2t \geq -3$ $t \leq 1.5$
38. $4b \leq 16$ $b \leq 4$
39. $-9c > 81$ $c < -9$
40. **Writing in Math** Describe how solving an inequality is like solving an equation. Describe how it is different. Include examples. See margin.

32. $15 > w$

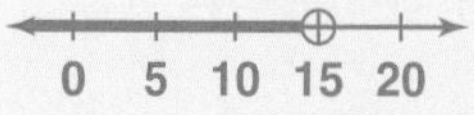

33. $y > 5$

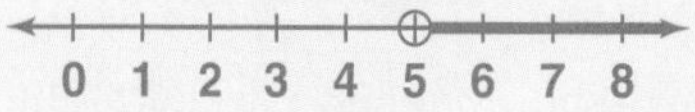

34. $z \leq 15$

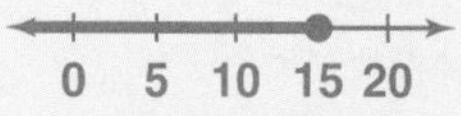

35. $s \leq -16$

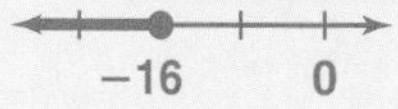

36. $m < 4$

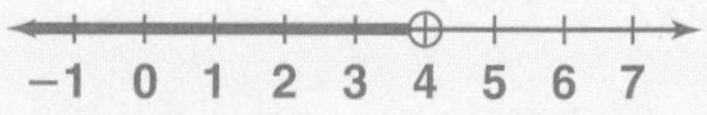

37. $t \leq 1.5$

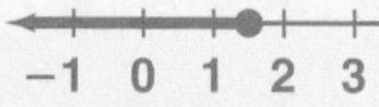

38. $b \leq 4$

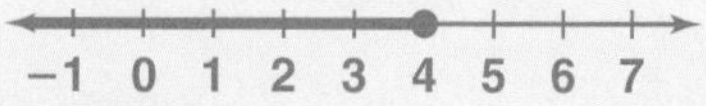

39. $c < -9$

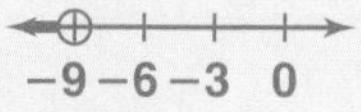

40. See back of book.

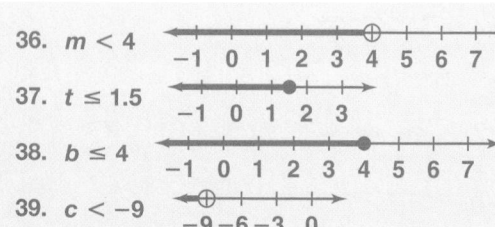

Multiple Choice

For Exercises 1–9, choose the correct letter.

1. Which graph shows the solution of $9y < 36$? A

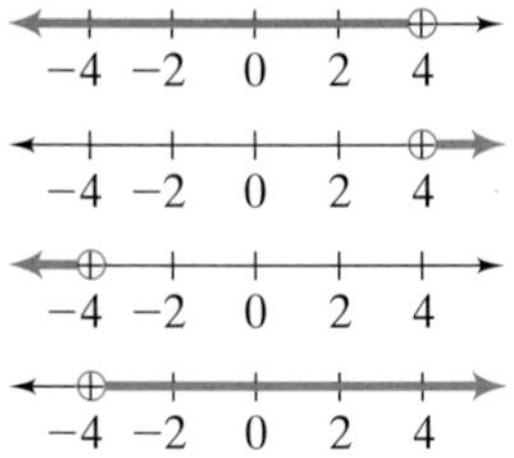

2. The perimeter of a rectangle is 28 cm. Its length is 10 cm more than its width (w). Which equation can be used to find the dimensions? G
   - F $w + (w + 10) = 28$
   - G $2w + 2(w + 10) = 28$
   - H $w(w + 10) = 28$
   - J $2w(2w + 20) = 28$

3. If $a - by = c$, then $y = \blacksquare$. A
   - A $\frac{a-c}{b}$ B $\frac{c-a}{b}$ C $\frac{c}{b} - a$ D $a - \frac{c}{b}$

4. Which numbers are all solutions of the inequality $x - 3 < -1$? F
   - F $-2, -1, 0$ H $0, 1, 2$
   - G $-1, 0, 2$ J $1, 2, 3$

5. Which variable expression is NOT equivalent to $2(y + 3)$? B
   - A $2(y) + 2(3)$ C $(y + 3) + (y + 3)$
   - B $2y + 3$ D $6 + 2y$

6. The solution of which inequality is represented by the graph below? F

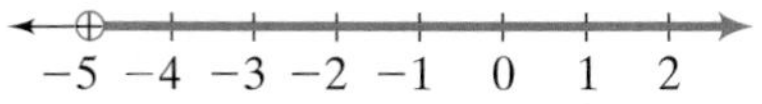

   - F $25 > -5w$ H $3x \geq -15$
   - G $-4y > -20$ J $2z < -10$

7. What can the expression $12k$ represent? B
   - A the cost (in cents) of a dozen cans of juice if each can costs 12 cents
   - B the cost (in cents) of k photocopies if each photocopy costs 12 cents
   - C the time it took Alana to run 1 mi if she ran 12 mi in k min
   - D Darrin's age, if Darrin is k years older than his 12-year-old brother

8. The variables x, y, and z represent integers other than zero. You know that $x > y$ and $y > z$. Which statement must be true? G
   - F $z > x$ G $z < x$ H $x \leq z$ J $\frac{x}{y} > \frac{y}{z}$

9. In professional ice hockey, a team earns 2 points for a win, 1 point for a tie, and 0 points for a loss. One season a team earned 31 points and had 10 losses and 7 ties. Which equation can be used to determine the number of wins (w) this team had? C
   - A $w + 7 = 31$ C $2w + 7 = 31$
   - B $10 + 7 + w = 31$ D $31 - 10 = 2w$

Gridded Response

10. You want a copy of a poster and copies of a flier. It costs \$6.00 for a poster and \$.08 for each copy of the flier. You have \$10.00. How many copies of the flier can you make? 50

Short Response

11. Define a variable and write an inequality to model the word sentence "There will be at most three tests this year." See margin.

Extended Response

12. Eli is on a diet and loses 2 lb a month. When he began his diet, he weighed 190 lb.
    a. Write an expression to model what Eli's weight will be after x months.
    b. How much will Eli weigh after 8 months? Show your work. a–b. See margin.

Item	1	2	3	4	5	6	7	8	9	10	11	12
Lesson	6-6	6-3	6-1	6-5	6-2	6-6	1-1	2-3	6-1	6-1	6-5	1-1

11. x = number of tests; $x \leq 3$

Resources

Test Prep Workbook

All in One Teaching Resources
- Cumulative Review L3

ExamView Assessment Suite
- Standardized Test Practice

Differentiated Instruction

Spanish Assessment Resources
- Spanish Cumulative Review ELL

12a. $190 - 2x$

b. 174 lb

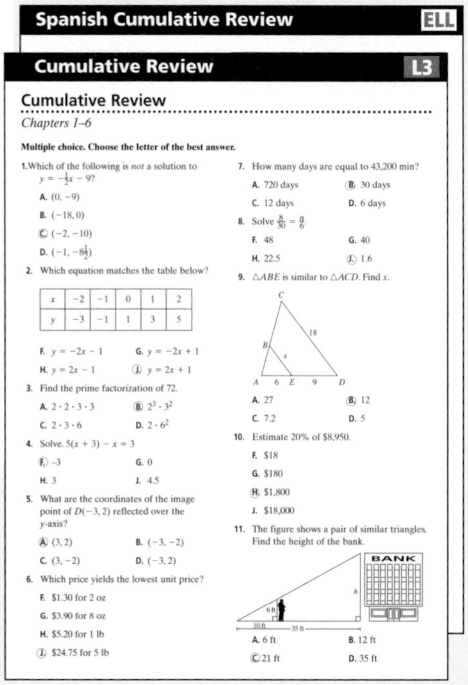

Spanish Cumulative Review ELL

Cumulative Review L3

Cumulative Review

Chapters 1–6

Multiple choice. Choose the letter of the best answer.

1. Which of the following is *not* a solution to $y = -\frac{1}{2}x - 9$?
   A. $(0, -9)$
   B. $(-18, 0)$
   C. $(-2, -10)$
   D. $(-1, -8\frac{1}{2})$
2. Which equation matches the table below?

x	−2	−1	0	1	2
y	−3	−1	1	3	5

   F. $y = -2x - 1$ G. $y = -2x + 1$
   H. $y = 2x - 1$ J. $y = 2x + 1$
3. Find the prime factorization of 72.
   A. $2 \cdot 2 \cdot 3 \cdot 3$ B. $2^3 \cdot 3^2$
   C. $2 \cdot 3 \cdot 6$ D. $2 \cdot 6^2$
4. Solve. $5(x + 3) - x = 3$
   F. −3 G. 0
   H. 3 J. 4.5
5. What are the coordinates of the image point of $D(-3, 2)$ reflected over the y-axis?
   A. $(3, 2)$ B. $(-3, -2)$
   C. $(3, -2)$ D. $(-3, 2)$
6. Which price yields the lowest unit price?
   F. \$1.30 for 2 oz
   G. \$3.90 for 8 oz
   H. \$5.20 for 1 lb
   J. \$24.75 for 5 lb
7. How many days are equal to 43,200 min?
   A. 720 days B. 30 days
   C. 12 days D. 6 days
8. Solve $\frac{8}{30} = \frac{n}{6}$.
   F. 48 G. 40
   H. 22.5 J. 1.6
9. $\triangle ABE$ is similar to $\triangle ACD$. Find x.
   A. 27 B. 12
   C. 7.2 D. 5
10. Estimate 20% of \$8,950.
   F. \$18
   G. \$180
   H. \$1,800
   J. \$18,000
11. The figure shows a pair of similar triangles. Find the height of the bank.
   A. 6 ft B. 12 ft
   C. 21 ft D. 35 ft

Problem Solving

Applying Equations

Students will use data from these two pages to answer the questions posed here in Put It All Together.

Activating Prior Knowledge

Have students share what they know about the roles that people, other than actors, fill in the process of making a movie. What do the director and the producer do? Have students discuss what they understand about what editors, set designers, cinematographers, screenwriters, and others do.

Guided Instruction

Have volunteers read aloud how movie makers use matte paintings to create backgrounds. Discuss *The Wizard of Oz* as an early example of movie-making wizardry. Then have students think of some of their favorite movies. Ask them to share what they know about how filmmakers make the fantastic visual effects many of today's movies feature.

History Connection
Tell students that Thomas Edison, although he did not invent movie-making, opened the world's first motion picture studio in 1893 and the first movie theater a year later.

Careers
What kinds of jobs are there, behind the scenes, in the movie business? Students need only look at movie credits to get an idea. What, for instance, does a gaffer do? What is a key grip? Have students put together an annotated list of job opportunities in the movie business.

Diversity
The United States is not the only country that supports a thriving movie-making business. Invite students to research and then report on filmmaking in other countries around the world.

Problem Solving Application

Applying Equations

Coming to Life Making movies is very expensive. It involves many people as well as many different stages. Some of the people who help make a movie are the producer, the director, the screenwriters, the animators, and many different types of artists.

Technical Wizardry
One of the first films to explore the possibilities of matte painting was *The Wizard of Oz* (1939).

Matte Paintings
Two-dimensional paintings on glass, or mattes, provide background detail when blended with live-action footage. Matte painting also saves time and money by eliminating travel to distant locations, expensive sets, and miniature models.

Before the Matte
The crew filmed the actors in *Jurassic Park III* on a simple set piece.

After the Matte
A digital matte painting makes a steep canyon blocking the characters' path.

1a. Answers may vary. Sample: *Bouncing Raisins from Planet 16*

b. Answers may vary. Sample: for $x = 7$; \$31,000,000

3a. Answers may vary. Sample: *Lion King* running time = 89 minutes; budget = \$79,300,000; cost per minute: about \$891,011.

b. Answers may vary. Sample: For the Lion King, 13,216,667 tickets, at a cost of \$6/ticket, would need to be sold to make a profit.

Put It All Together

Data File Use the information on these two pages and on page 647 to answer these questions.

Materials: 2 number cubes

1. Suppose you're a screenwriter with a movie idea that you're trying to sell to a Hollywood producer.
   a. Make up a title for your movie. It can be silly or serious.
   b. Your movie needs a budget. To determine the cost of your movie, roll two number cubes and let x = the sum of the two numbers. Find your movie's cost in dollars by evaluating the expression
   $$3{,}000{,}000x + 10{,}000{,}000.$$
2. You can use the following equation to model the profit from a movie.
   $$\text{profit} = \text{money from ticket sales} - \text{cost}$$
   a. Suppose a movie studio makes a \$4 profit on every ticket sold. Let t = the number of tickets to your movie that will be sold. Write an equation to calculate the profit.
   b. Use your equation to make a table showing how the profit depends on the number of tickets sold. Calculate the profit for every million tickets from 1 million to 15 million.
3. a. Choose a movie from the list on page 647. Calculate its cost per minute.
   b. Estimate the number of ticket sales needed before the movie can start making a profit.

Go Online
PHSchool.com
For: Information about movie-making
Web Code: ase-0653

Making the Matte

1. In the documentary *Manassas: End of Innocence*, about the Civil War, actors in period costumes walk by a church "acting" as a church in Washington, D.C.

2. A digital technician used wire-frame technology to build the church steeple and the Capitol in three dimensions. An artist painted the trees, the lamppost, and the nearby buildings in two dimensions.

3. The final composite shows a street scene in Washington, D.C. The Capitol dome was under construction in 1861.

Put It All Together

Have students work in pairs to do the activity and answer the questions. Guide them to record data as they accumulate it.

Discuss that in this activity, students will apply a formula to model how movie companies make a profit on the films they release.

Exercise 1b The purpose of using two number cubes is two-fold: to generate random numbers and to have students obtain different results. If you do not have number cubes, use a 1–6 spinner.

Exercise 2a Review the concept of *profit*, the amount of income remaining after all expenses have been deducted.

Exercise 2b Encourage students to record their profit results in a table.

2a. Answers may vary. Sample: profit = $4t - 31{,}000{,}000$

b. Answers may vary. Sample given.

Tickets Sold	Profit
1,000,000	−\$27,000,000
2,000,000	−\$23,000,000
3,000,000	−\$19,000,000
4,000,000	−\$15,000,000
5,000,000	−\$11,000,000
6,000,000	−\$ 7,000,000
7,000,000	−\$ 3,000,000
8,000,000	\$ 1,000,000
9,000,000	\$ 5,000,000
10,000,000	\$ 9,000,000
11,000,000	\$13,000,000
12,000,000	\$17,000,000
13,000,000	\$21,000,000
14,000,000	\$25,000,000
15,000,000	\$29,000,000

7 Geometry

Chapter at a Glance

Lesson Titles, Objectives, and Features	Assessment	NCTM Standards	Local Standards
7-1a Activity Lab, Hands On: Exploring Pairs of Angles **7-1 Pairs of Angles** • To identify types of angles and to find angle measures using the relationship between angles	Lesson Quiz	1, 2, 3, 4, 6, 7, 8, 9, 10	
7-2 Angles and Parallel Lines • To identify parallel lines and the angles formed by parallel lines **7-2b Activity Lab, Algebra Thinking:** Solving Angle Equations	Lesson Quiz	1, 2, 3, 4, 6, 7, 8, 9, 10	
7-3 Congruent Polygons • To identify congruent figures and use them to solve problems	Lesson Quiz Checkpoint Quiz 1	1, 2, 3, 4, 6, 7, 8, 9, 10	
7-4 Classifying Triangles and Quadrilaterals • To classify triangles and quadrilaterals **Vocabulary Builder:** Using Concept Maps	Lesson Quiz	1, 3, 6, 7, 8, 9, 10	
7-5a Activity Lab: Angle Sums **7-5 Angles and Polygons** • To find the angle measures of a polygon	Lesson Quiz	1, 2, 3, 4, 6, 7, 8, 9, 10	
7-6 Areas of Polygons • To find the areas of parallelograms, triangles, and trapezoids **Guided Problem Solving:** Geoboard Area	Lesson Quiz Checkpoint Quiz 2	1, 2, 3, 4, 6, 7, 8, 9, 10	
7-7a Activity Lab, Hands On: Estimating Area **7-7 Circumference and Area of a Circle** • To find the circumference and area of a circle and the area of irregular figures **Extension:** Arcs, Chords, and Semicircles	Lesson Quiz	1, 2, 3, 4, 5, 6, 7, 8, 9, 10	
7-8 Constructions • To construct congruent angles and parallel lines **7-8b Activity Lab, Technology:** Geometry Software and Constructions	Lesson Quiz	1, 3, 4, 6, 7, 8, 9, 10	
Problem Solving Application: Applying Geometry			

NCTM Standards 2000
1 Number and Operations
2 Algebra
3 Geometry
4 Measurement
5 Data Analysis and Probability
6 Problem Solving
7 Reasoning and Proof
8 Communication
9 Connections
10 Representation

Correlations to Standardized Tests

All content for these tests is contained in *Prentice Hall Math*, Course 3. This chart reflects coverage in this chapter only.

	7-1	7-2	7-3	7-4	7-5	7-6	7-7	7-8
Terra Nova CAT6 (Level 18)								
Number and Number Relations								
Computation and Numerical Estimation								
Operation Concepts								
Measurement						✔	✔	
Geometry and Spatial Sense	✔	✔	✔	✔	✔	✔	✔	✔
Data Analysis, Statistics, and Probability								
Patterns, Functions, and Algebra								
Problem Solving and Reasoning								
Communication								
Decimals, Fractions, Integers, Percent								
Order of Operations								
Algebraic Operations								
Terra Nova CTBS (Level 18)								
Decimals, Fractions, Integers, Percents								
Order of Operations, Numeration, Number Theory								
Data Interpretation								
Measurement						✔	✔	
Geometry	✔	✔	✔	✔	✔	✔	✔	✔
ITBS (Level 14)								
Number Properties and Operations								
Algebra								
Geometry	✔	✔	✔	✔	✔	✔	✔	✔
Measurement						✔	✔	
Probability and Statistics								
Estimation								
SAT10 (Adv 1 Level)								
Number Sense and Operations								
Patterns, Relationships, and Algebra								
Data, Statistics, and Probability								
Geometry and Measurement	✔	✔	✔	✔	✔	✔	✔	✔
NAEP								
Number Sense, Properties, and Operations								
Measurement						✔	✔	
Geometry and Spatial Sense	✔	✔	✔	✔	✔	✔	✔	✔
Data Analysis, Statistics, and Probability								
Algebra and Functions								

CAT6 California Achievement Test, 6th Ed. **CTBS** Comprehensive Test of Basic Skills **ITBS** Iowa Test of Basic Skills, Form M
SAT10 Stanford Achievement Test, 10th Ed. **NAEP** National Assessment of Educational Progress 2005 Mathematics Objectives

Math Background

Professional Development

Skills Trace

BEFORE Chapter 7

Course 2 introduced properties of geometric figures and finding areas of polygons.

DURING Chapter 7

Course 3 reviews and extends properties of two-dimensional figures, including basic constructions.

AFTER Chapter 7

Throughout this course students solve real-world problems using geometric figures.

7-1 Pairs of Angles

Math Understandings

- A pair of angles can be supplementary or complementary even though they are not adjacent, or even in the same figure.
- Two lines that intersect to form equal adjacent angles are perpendicular.

Adjacent angles (for example: ∠1 and ∠2; ∠2 and ∠3; ∠3 and ∠4; ∠1 and ∠4 in the figure below) have a common vertex and a common side, but no common interior points. **Vertical angles**, (for example: ∠1 and ∠3; ∠2 and ∠4 in the figure) are formed by two intersecting lines and are opposite each other. Vertical angles are congruent.

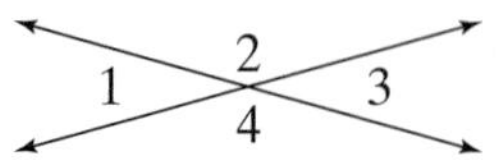

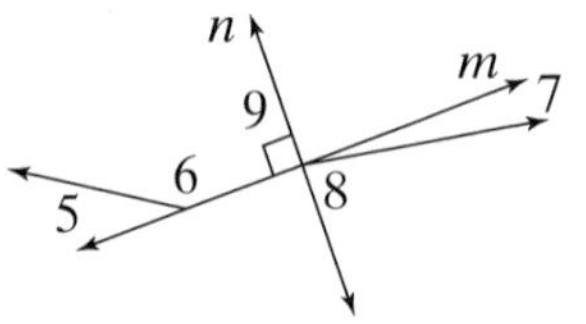

If the sum of the measures of two angles is 180°, the angles are **supplementary** (for example: ∠1 and ∠2; ∠2 and ∠3; ∠3 and ∠4; ∠1 and ∠4; ∠5 and ∠6 in the figure above). If the sum of the measures of two angles is 90°, the angles are **complementary** (for example: ∠7 and ∠8 in the figure above). **Perpendicular lines** (for example: lines *m* and *n* in the figure above) are two lines that intersect to form a right angle.

7-2 Angles and Parallel Lines

Math Understandings

- A transversal can intersect two lines that are, or are not, parallel to each other.
- If you know that corresponding angles or alternate interior angles are congruent, then you can be sure the lines intersected by the transversal are parallel.

A line that intersects two other lines at different points is a **transversal.** Corresponding angles lie on the same side of the transversal and in corresponding positions. *Alternate interior angles* lie within a pair of lines and on opposite sides of the transversal.

Transversals and Parallel Lines

When a transversal intersects two parallel lines,
- corresponding angles are congruent, and
- alternate interior angles are congruent.

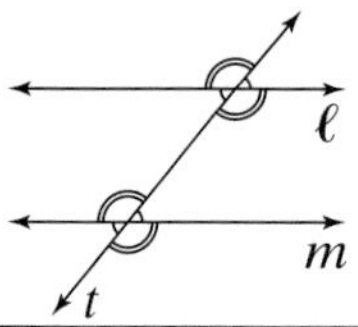

7-3 Congruent Polygons

Math Understandings

- When two polygons are congruent, you can slide, flip, or turn one so that it fits exactly on top of the other one.
- The matching angles and sides of congruent polygons are called corresponding parts. When you name congruent polygons, you always list the corresponding vertices in the same order.
- The order of the angles and sides is important in determining whether two triangles are congruent.

Congruent polygons are polygons with the same size and shape. The tick marks in a diagram identify congruent sides. The arcs identify congruent angles.

Showing Triangles Are Congruent

To demonstrate that two triangles are congruent, show that the following parts of one triangle are congruent to the corresponding parts of the other triangle.

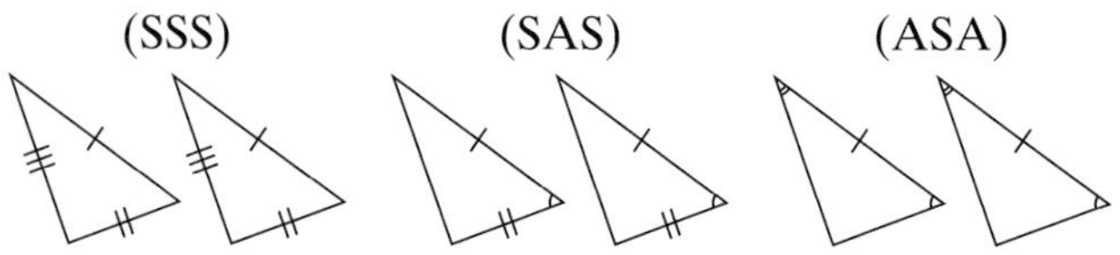

7-4 7-5 Classifying Triangles, Quadrilaterals, Angles and Polygons

Math Understandings

- You can classify triangles and quadrilaterals by their angle measures or by the number of congruent sides.

When a quadrilateral has more than one name, use the one that describes the quadrilateral most precisely.

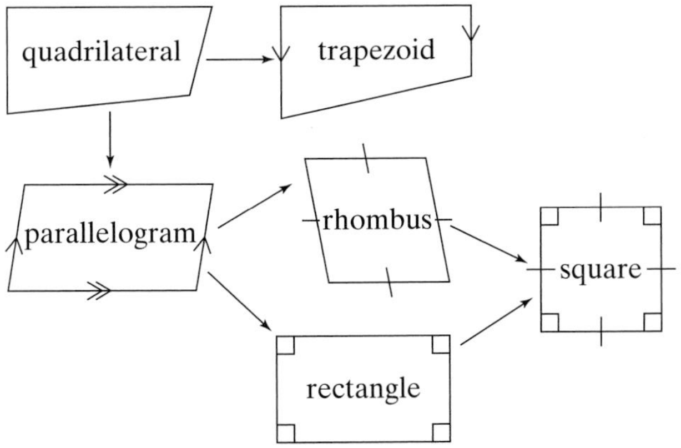

For a polygon with n sides, the **sum of the measures** of the interior angles is $(n - 2)180°$. A **regular polygon** is a polygon with all the sides congruent and all the angles congruent. You can find the measure of each angle of a regular polygon by dividing the sum of the angle measures by the number of angles.

7-6 7-7 Circumferences of Circles and Areas of Polygons and Circles

Math Understandings

- The area of a figure is the number of square units it encloses.
- The circumference of a circle is the distance around the circle, or its perimeter.

Areas of Polygons and Circles

Rectangle $A = bh$

Parallelogram $A = bh$

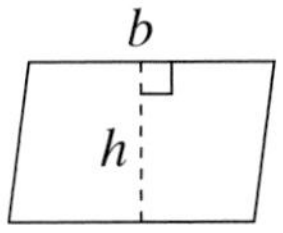

Triangle $A = \frac{1}{2}bh$

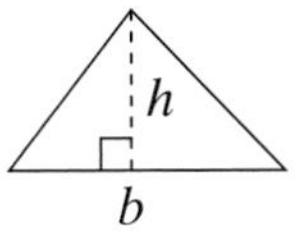

Trapezoid $A = \frac{1}{2}h(b_1 + b_2)$

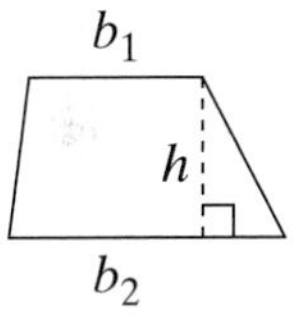

Circle $A = \pi r^2$
$C = \pi d$ or $C = 2\pi r$

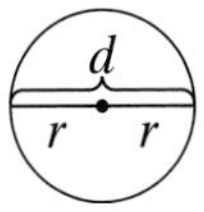

7-8 Constructions

Math Understandings

- Not all lines that bisect a line segment are perpendicular bisectors.

A **compass** is a tool used to draw circles and parts of circles called arcs. A straightedge, the only other tool used for classic geometric constructions, has no measurement markings.

Additional Professional Development Opportunities

Professional Development

Math Background Notes for Chapter 7: Every lesson has a Math Background in the PLAN section.

Research Overview, Mathematics Strands
Additional support for these topics and more is in the front of the Teacher's Edition.

LessonLab
LessonLab, a Pearson Education company, offers comprehensive, facilitated professional development designed to help teachers to improve student achievement. To learn more, please visit lessonlab.com.

Chapter 7 Resources

	7-1	7-2	7-3	7-4	7-5	7-6	7-7	7-8	For the Chapter
Print Resources									
L3 Practice	●	●	●	●	●	●	●	●	
L1 Adapted Practice	●	●	●	●	●	●	●	●	
L3 Guided Problem Solving	●	●	●	●	●	●	●	●	
L2 Reteaching	●	●	●	●	●	●	●	●	
L4 Enrichment	●	●	●	●	●	●	●	●	
L3 Daily Notetaking Guide	●	●	●	●	●	●	●	●	
L1 Adapted Daily Notetaking Guide	●	●	●	●	●	●	●	●	
L3 Vocabulary and Study Skills Worksheets	●		●	●		●		●	●
L3 Daily Puzzles	●	●	●	●	●	●	●	●	
L3 Activity Labs	●	●	●	●	●	●	●	●	
L3 Checkpoint Quiz			●			●			
L3 Chapter Project									●
L2 Below Level Chapter Test									●
L3 Chapter Test									●
L4 Alternative Assessment									●
L3 Cumulative Review									●
Spanish Resources ELL									
L3 Practice	●	●	●	●	●	●	●	●	●
L3 Vocabulary and Study Skills Worksheets	●		●	●		●		●	●
L3 Checkpoint Quiz			●			●			
L2 Below Level Chapter Test									●
L3 Chapter Test									●
L4 Alternative Assessment									●
L3 Cumulative Review									●
Transparencies									
Check Skills You'll Need	●	●	●	●	●	●	●	●	
Additional Examples	●	●	●	●	●	●	●	●	
Problem of the Day	●	●	●	●	●	●	●	●	
Classroom Aid	●		●	●	●		●		
Student Edition Answers	●	●	●	●	●	●	●	●	●
Lesson Quiz	●	●	●	●	●	●	●	●	
Test-Taking Strategies									●
Technology									
Interactive Textbook Online	●	●	●	●	●	●	●	●	●
StudentExpress™ CD-ROM	●	●	●	●	●	●	●	●	●
Success Tracker™ Online Intervention	●	●	●	●	●	●	●	●	●
TeacherExpress™ CD-ROM	●	●	●	●	●	●	●	●	●
PresentationExpress™ with QuickTake Presenter CD-ROM	●	●	●	●	●	●	●	●	●
ExamView® Assessment Suite CD-ROM	●	●	●	●	●	●	●	●	●
MindPoint® Quiz Show CD-ROM									●
Prentice Hall Web Site: PHSchool.com	●	●	●	●	●	●	●	●	●

Also available:

Prentice Hall Assessment System
- Progress Monitoring Assessments
- Skills and Concepts Review
- Test Prep Workbook

Other Resources
Algebra Readiness Tests
All-in-One Student Workbook
All-in-One Student Workbook, Adapted Version
Multilingual Handbook
Solution Key
Math Notes Study Folder
Spanish Cumulative Assessment

Where You Can Use the Lesson Resources

Here is a suggestion, following the four-step teaching plan, for how you can incorporate Differentiated Instruction Resources into your teaching.

	Instructional Resources L3	Differentiated Instruction Resources
1. Plan		
Preparation Read the Math Background in the Teacher's Edition to connect this lesson with students' previous experience. **Starting Class** **Check Skills You'll Need** Assign these exercises to review prerequisite skills. **New Vocabulary** Help students pre-read the lesson by pointing out the new terms introduced in the lesson.	**Math Background** **Math Understandings** **Transparencies & PresentationExpress™ with QuickTake Presenter CD-ROM** Check Skills You'll Need Problem of the Day **Resources** Vocabulary and Study Skills	**Spanish Support** ELL Vocabulary Masters with Study Skills
2. Teach		
L3 **Guided Instruction** Use the Activity Labs to build conceptual understanding. Teach each Example. Use the Teacher's Edition side column notes for specific teaching tips, including Error Prevention notes. Use the Additional Examples found in the side column (and on transparency and PowerPoint) as an alternative presentation for the content. After each Example, assign the Quick Check exercise for that Example to get an immediate assessment of student understanding. Use the Closure activity in the Teacher's Edition to help students attain mastery of lesson content.	**Student Edition** Activity Lab **Resources** Daily Notetaking Guide Activity Lab **Transparencies & PresentationExpress™ with QuickTake Presenter CD-ROM** Additional Examples Classroom Aids **ExamView® Assessment Suite CD-ROM**	**Teacher's Edition** Every lesson includes suggestions for working with students who need special attention. L1 Special Needs L2 Below Level L4 Advanced Learners ELL English Language Learners **Resources** L1 Adapted Daily Notetaking Guide **Multilingual Handbook**
3. Practice		
Assignment Guide **Check Your Understanding** Use these questions to check students' understanding before you assign homework. **Homework Exercises** Assign homework from these leveled exercises in the Assignment Guide. A Practice by Example B Apply Your Skills C Challenge Test Prep and Mixed Review **Homework Quick Check** Use these key exercises to quickly check students' homework.	**Transparencies & PresentationExpress™ with QuickTake Presenter CD-ROM** Student Answers **Resources** Practice Guided Problem Solving Vocabulary and Study Skills Activity Lab Daily Puzzles **ExamView® Assessment Suite CD-ROM**	**Spanish Support** ELL Practice ELL Vocabulary and Study Skills **Resources** L1 Adapted Practice L4 Enrichment
4. Assess & Reteach		
Lesson Quiz Assign the Lesson Quiz to assess students' mastery of the lesson content. **Checkpoint Quiz** Use the Checkpoint Quiz to assess student progress over several lessons.	**Transparencies & PresentationExpress™ with QuickTake Presenter CD-ROM** Lesson Quiz **Resources** Checkpoint Quiz	**Resources** L2 Reteaching ELL Checkpoint Quiz SuccessTracker™ Online Intervention **ExamView® Assessment Suite CD-ROM**

KEY L1 Special Needs L2 Below Level L3 For All Students L4 Advanced, Gifted ELL English Language Learners

CHAPTER 7

Geometry

Check Your Readiness

Answers for students are in the back of the textbook.

For intervention, direct students to:

Evaluating Expressions
Lesson 1-1
Extra Skills and Word Problems Practice, Ch. 1

Solving One-Step Equations
Lessons 1-6, 1-7
Extra Skills and Word Problems Practice, Ch. 1

Using Formulas to Solve Problems
Lesson 2-6
Extra Skills and Word Problems Practice, Ch. 2

4. 8
5. 43
6. −3
7. 32

Spanish Vocabulary/Study Skills ELL

Vocabulary/Study Skills L3

7A: Graphic Organizer — For use before Lesson 7-1

Study Skill As your teacher presents new material in the chapter, keep a paper and pencil handy to write down notes and questions. If you miss class, borrow a classmate's notes so you don't fall behind.

Write your answers.

1. What is the chapter title? Geometry
2. How many lessons are there in this chapter? 8
3. What is the topic of the Test-Taking Strategies page? Drawing a Diagram
4. Complete the graphic organizer below as you work through the chapter.
   - In the center, write the title of the chapter.
   - When you begin a lesson, write the lesson name in a rectangle.
   - When you complete a lesson, write a skill or key concept in a circle linked to that lesson block.
   - When you complete the chapter, use this graphic organizer to help you review.

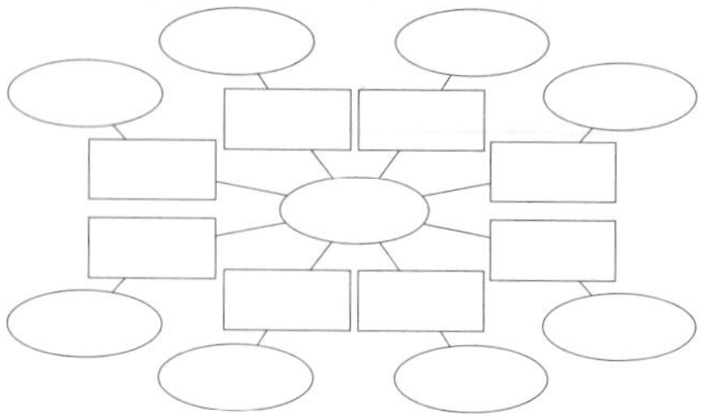

Vocabulary and Study Skills

CHAPTER 7 Geometry

What You've Learned

- In Chapter 2, you used formulas to solve problems.
- In Chapter 4, you used proportions to find missing measurements in triangles.
- In Chapter 6, you wrote and solved equations and inequalities.

Check Your Readiness

GO for Help

For Exercises	See Lessons
1–3	1-1
4–7	1-6
8–11	1-7
12–14	2-6

Evaluating Expressions

Evaluate each expression.

1. $\frac{1}{2}bh$ for $b = 9$ and $h = 8$ 36
2. $2(3.14)r$ for $r = 16$ 100.48
3. $\frac{1}{2}a(b + c)$ for $a = 4$, $b = 3$, and $c = 17$ 40

Solving One-Step Equations

Solve each equation. 4–7. See margin.

4. $25 = 17 + m$
5. $b + 13 = 56$
6. $44 + s = 41$
7. $10 = p - 22$
8. $4.2g = 63$ 15
9. $16 = 14k$ $1\frac{1}{7}$
10. $\frac{w}{3.5} = 24$ 84
11. $5.1 = \frac{c}{7}$ 35.7

Using Formulas to Solve Problems

Find the area of each figure.

12. 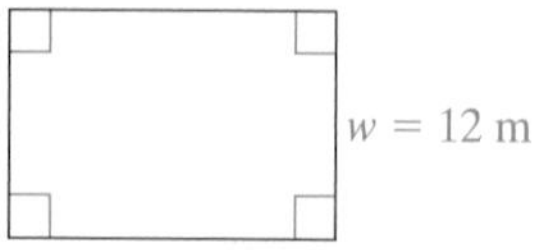

216 m²

13. 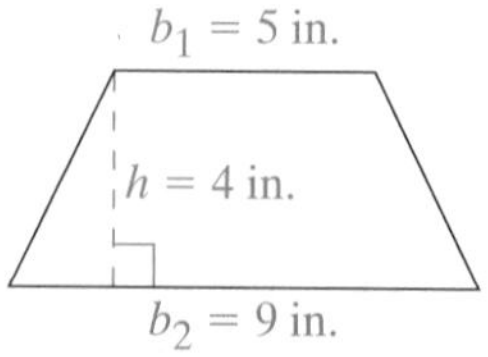

28 in.²

14. 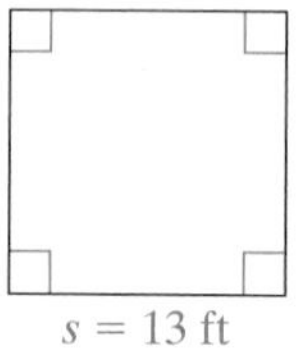

169 ft²

Chapter 7 Overview

In this chapter, students solve problems by learning and using the properties of pairs of angles, of parallel lines, and of polygons and circles. In addition, they find the areas of parallelograms, triangles, trapezoids, and circles. They also make constructions.

Activating Prior Knowledge

In this chapter, students build on their knowledge of geometric concepts and of applying formulas to solve problems. Ask questions such as:

- *An angle measures 28°. What kind of angle is it?* acute angle
- *What is the perimeter of the square 14 cm on a side?* 56 cm
- *What is the area of the square 14 cm on a side?* 196 cm^2

What You'll Learn Next

- In this chapter, you will use the properties of pairs of angles and parallel lines to find angle measures.
- You will find the areas of geometric figures, including parallelograms, triangles, trapezoids, and circles.
- You will construct congruent angles and parallel lines using a compass and straightedge.

Key Vocabulary

- alternate interior angles (p. 307)
- area (p. 328)
- compass (p. 341)
- complementary (p. 304)
- congruent polygons (p. 312)
- corresponding angles (p. 307)
- parallelogram (p. 319)
- perpendicular lines (p. 304)
- quadrilateral (p. 319)
- rectangle (p. 319)
- regular polygon (p. 325)
- rhombus (p. 319)
- right triangle (p. 318)
- square (p. 319)
- supplementary (p. 304)
- trapezoid (p. 319)

Problem Solving Application On pages 350 and 351, you will work an extended activity on sailing.

Activity Lab

Exploring Pairs of Angles

Students measure pairs of angles formed by intersecting lines. They make conjectures about relationships between pairs of angles.

Guided Instruction

Before beginning the activity, have students practice drawing intersecting lines and labeling all the resulting angles with arcs.

Ask: *Can you find two angles whose measures add up to 180°? What do they form?* **Accept all reasonable answers; a line**

Teaching Tip
Remind students that the notation $m\angle 1$ is read as "the measure of angle one." It is correct to say that $\angle 1$ is congruent to $\angle 3$, while $m\angle 1$ is equal to $m\angle 3$.

Error Prevention!

Remind students that to measure angles, they need a line of reference. Have them practice using both rays of an angle as a line of reference, making sure they get the same value, to reinforce the idea that they can use either ray as a line of reference. Encourage students to check the reasonableness of their measures. Ask: *What would an angle less than 90° look like? What would an angle greater than 90° look like?* **Sample: somewhere between 2 perpendicular lines, or an L-shape; wider than an L-shape**

Resources

- Activity Lab 7-1: Pairs of Angles
- protractors

7-1a Activity Lab

Hands On

Exploring Pairs of Angles

ACTIVITY

1–3. Check students' work.

1. Draw two intersecting lines. Number the angles as shown at the right.
2. Use a protractor. Measure the angles in your drawing. Record the results.
3. Draw three different pairs of intersecting lines.

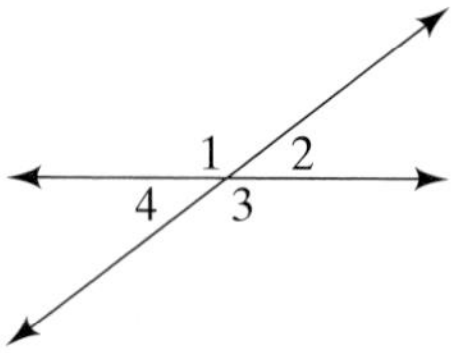

4. For each pair, compare $m\angle 1$ and $m\angle 3$. Then compare $m\angle 2$ and $m\angle 4$. **$m\angle 1 = m\angle 3$; $m\angle 2 = m\angle 4$**
5. **Patterns** Make a conjecture about these pairs of angles. **See margin.**
6. For each pair of lines, find the sum of $m\angle 1$ and $m\angle 2$. **180°**
7. For each pair of lines, find the sum of $m\angle 2$ and $m\angle 3$. **180°**
8. **Patterns** Make a conjecture about these pairs of angles. **Answers may vary. Sample: The sum of the measures of angles with a common side formed by the intersection of two lines is 180°.**

ACTIVITY

Navigation The pilot of a ship uses a navigational tool called a parallel rule to plot routes on charts. Recall that parallel lines lie in the same plane and do not intersect. In the diagram, *m* is parallel to *t*, and *r* is parallel to *s*.

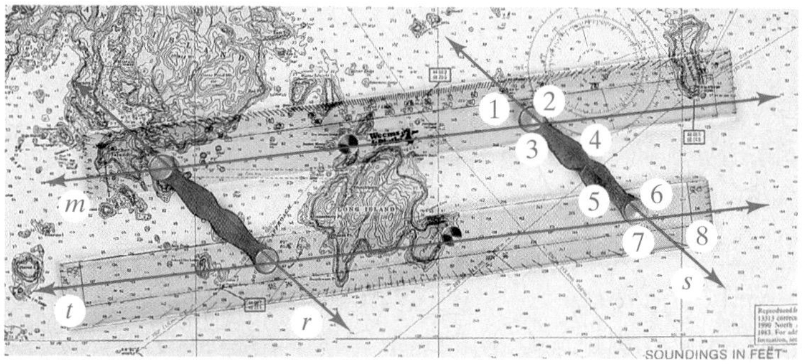

9. Use a protractor. Find the measures of the numbered angles. **9. $m\angle 1 = m\angle 4 = m\angle 5 = m\angle 8 = 50°$; $m\angle 2 = m\angle 3 = m\angle 6 = m\angle 7 = 130°$**
10. Identify all the congruent pairs of angles. **$\angle 1 \cong \angle 4 \cong \angle 5 \cong \angle 8$; $\angle 2 \cong \angle 3 \cong \angle 6 \cong \angle 7$**
11. Make a conjecture about the angles formed when a line intersects two parallel lines. **Answers may vary. Sample: Four angles will have the same measure, and the supplements of those angles will have the same measure.**
12. Check your conjecture by measuring other angles in the diagram. Is your conjecture correct? Explain. **Check students' work.**

5. **If two lines intersect each other, they form two pairs of angles with equal measures.**

7-1 Pairs of Angles

Check Skills You'll Need

1. **Vocabulary Review** What is the *inverse operation* of addition? subtraction

Solve each equation.

2. $a + 14 = 32$ 18
3. $b - 5 = 26$ 31
4. $10 + c = -31$ −41
5. $-48 = d - 19$ −29

GO for Help Lesson 1-6

What You'll Learn

To identify types of angles and to find angle measures using the relationship between angles

New Vocabulary vertical angles, adjacent angles, supplementary, complementary, perpendicular lines

Why Learn This?

City streets cross each other in certain ways. Understanding angles can help you read and draw maps.

Vertical angles are formed by two intersecting lines and are opposite each other. Vertical angles are congruent. They have the same measure.

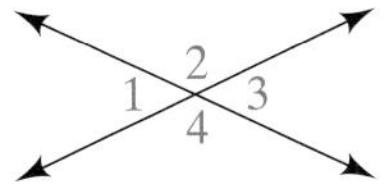

$\angle 1$ and $\angle 3$ are vertical angles; $m\angle 1 = m\angle 3$.
$\angle 2$ and $\angle 4$ are vertical angles; $m\angle 2 = m\angle 4$.

Adjacent angles have a common vertex and a common side, but no common interior points.

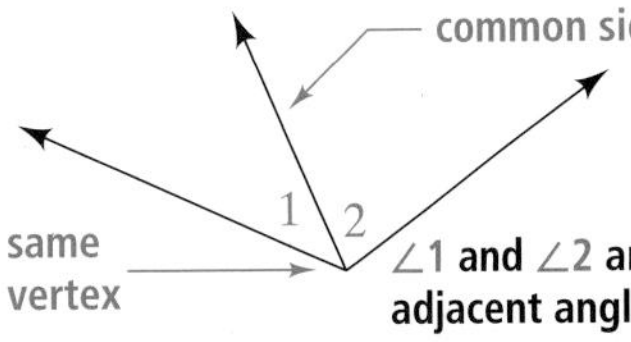

$\angle 1$ and $\angle 2$ are adjacent angles.

Vocabulary Tip

The *vertex* of an angle is the point of intersection of two sides of an angle or figure.

EXAMPLE Identifying Adjacent and Vertical Angles

1 City Planning Name a pair of adjacent angles and a pair of vertical angles in the photo at the right. Find $m\angle JBT$.

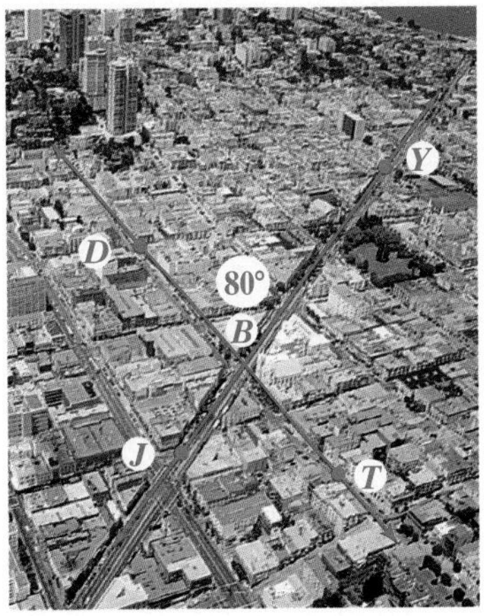

$\angle DBJ$ and $\angle JBT$ are adjacent angles.

$\angle DBY$ and $\angle JBT$ are vertical angles.

Vertical angles are congruent, so $m\angle JBT = m\angle DBY$. So $m\angle JBT$ is 80°.

Test Prep Tip

You can name the angle below in four ways.

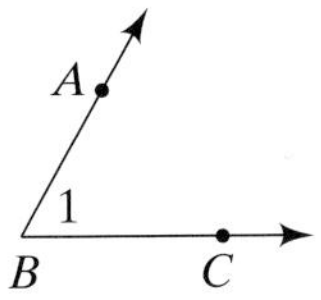

$\angle 1, \angle B, \angle ABC, \angle CBA$

Quick Check

1. Name another pair of vertical angles and another pair of adjacent angles in the photo. $\angle DBJ$ and $\angle YBT$; adjacent angles may vary. Sample: $\angle DBJ$ and $\angle DBY$

Differentiated Instruction Solutions for All Learners

Special Needs L1
Students sit in groups of four and suppose they are angles. One pair of adjacent angles stand up and then sit down. One pair of vertical angles stand up and sit down. Ask students to explain why they think they are adjacent angles or vertical angles.

learning style: tactile

Below Level L2
Students use protractors to review measuring and drawing angles including right angles and straight angles.

learning style: tactile

7-1

1. Plan

Objective

To identify types of angles and to find angle measures using the relationship between angles

Examples

1. Identifying Adjacent and Vertical Angles
2. Finding Supplementary Angles
3. Finding Angle Measures

Math Understandings: p. 300C

Professional Development

Math Background

When two straight lines intersect, both pairs of opposite angles (the pair marked $\angle 1$ and $\angle 2$, and the pair marked $\angle 3$ and $\angle 4$) are called *vertical angles,* and the two angles in each pair are congruent.

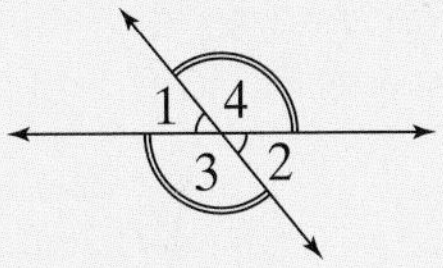

In the figure, $\angle 1$ and $\angle 4$ are *adjacent angles* because they share a vertex and a common side, and they are *supplementary angles* because their sum is a straight line, or 180°.

More Math Background: p. 300C

Lesson Planning and Resources

See p. 300E for a list of the resources that support this lesson.

PowerPoint

Bell Ringer Practice

Check Skills You'll Need
Use student page, transparency, or PowerPoint. For intervention, direct students to:

Solving Equations by Adding and Subtracting
Lesson 1-6
Extra Skills and Word Problems Practice, Ch. 1

2. Teach

Activity Lab

Use before the lesson.
Student Edition Activity Lab, Hands On 7-1a, Exploring Pairs of Angles, p. 302

All in One Teaching Resources

Activity Lab 7-1: Pairs of Angles

PowerPoint

Additional Examples

1 **2** Name a pair of adjacent angles and a pair of vertical angles in the figure below.

Find $m\angle HGK$. Find the measure of the supplement of $\angle IGJ$. 35°

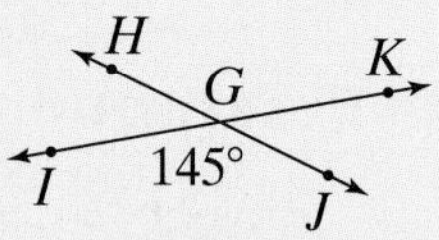

Sample: adjacent angles: $\angle HGK$ and $\angle KGJ$; vertical angles: $\angle HGK$ and $\angle JGI$. $m\angle HGK = 145°$

3 In this figure, if $m\angle DKH = 73°$, find the measures of $\angle GKJ$ and $\angle JKF$. 17°; 73°

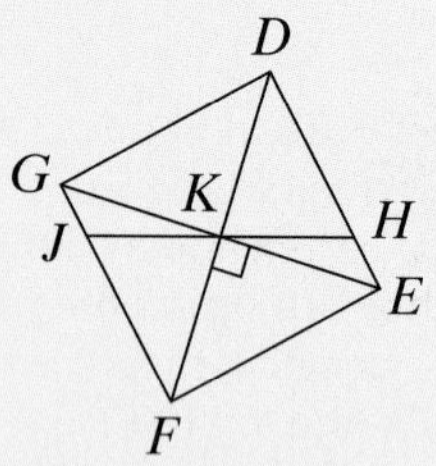

All in One Teaching Resources

- Daily Notetaking Guide 7-1 L3
- Adapted Notetaking 7-1 L1

Closure

- *What are vertical angles?* Sample: Vertical angles are a pair of non-adjacent angles formed by two intersecting lines.
- *What are supplementary angles and complementary angles?* Sample: Supplementary angles are two angles with measures that add to 180°, and complementary angles are two angles with measures that add to 90°.

If the sum of the measures of two angles is 180°, the angles are **supplementary.** If the sum of the measures of two angles is 90°, the angles are **complementary.**

In the diagram below, $\angle C$ and $\angle WYZ$ are both supplements of $\angle XYW$. $\angle C$ and $\angle VSR$ are both complements of $\angle VST$.

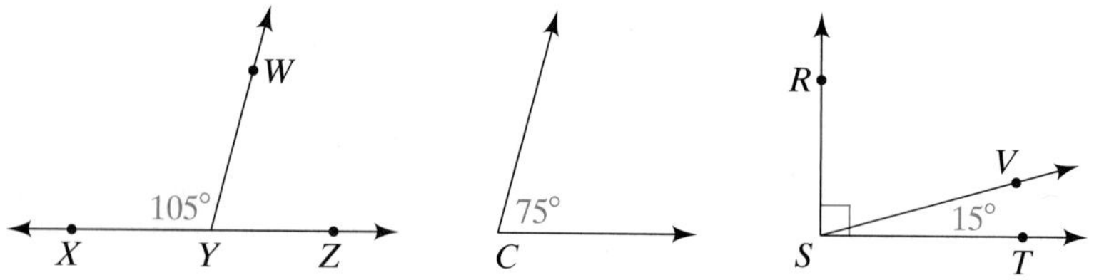

You can solve equations to find the measures of supplementary and complementary angles.

EXAMPLE Finding Supplementary Angles

2 **Algebra** Suppose $m\angle BCD = 121°$. Find the measure of its supplement.

Let $x°$ = the measure of the supplement of $\angle BCD$.

$x° + m\angle BCD = 180°$	← The sum of the measures of supplementary angles is 180°.
$x° + 121° = 180°$	← Substitute 121° for $m\angle BCD$.
$x° + 121° - 121° = 180° - 121°$	← Subtract 121° from each side.
$x° = 59°$	← Simplify.

The measure of the supplement of $\angle BCD$ is 59°.

Quick Check

2. An angle has a measure of 47°. Find the measure of its supplement. 133°

Perpendicular lines are two lines that intersect to form a right angle. Recall that a right angle has a measure of 90°.

EXAMPLE Finding Angle Measures

3 In the diagram at the right, $m\angle 5 = 58°$. Find the measures of $\angle 1$ and $\angle 2$.

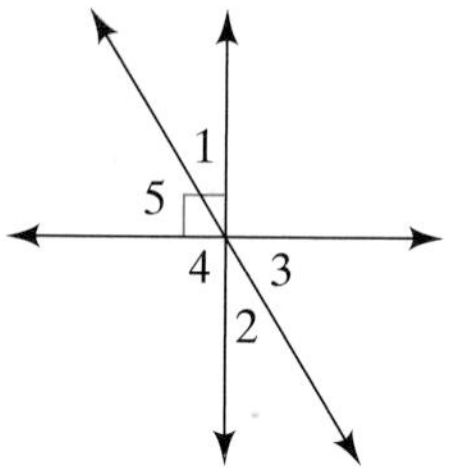

$m\angle 1 + 58° = 90°$	← $\angle 1$ and $\angle 5$ are complementary.
$m\angle 1 = 32°$	← Subtract 58° from each side.

Since $\angle 1$ and $\angle 2$ are vertical angles, $m\angle 2 = 32°$.

Quick Check

3. Find the measures of $\angle 3$ and $\angle 4$ in Example 3. 58°; 90°

Online active math

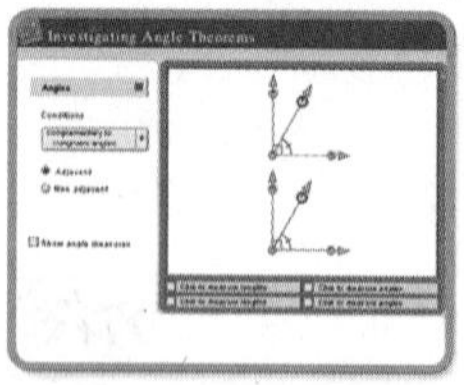

For: Investigating Angle Theorems Activity
Use: Interactive Textbook, 7-1

Differentiated Instruction Solutions for All Learners

Advanced Learners L4
Students explore to find the angles formed by the diagonals of a square or any parallelogram with four equal sides (rhombus). right angles

learning style: visual

English Language Learners ELL
Hand out copies of Example 1. Students highlight a pair of adjacent angles in one color and a pair of vertical angles in another color. Ask: *Why do some angles have more than one color?* Every angle is next to, and opposite, another angle.

learning style: visual

Check Your Understanding

1. No; they do not share a common side.
2. Yes; they share a common vertex and a common side, but no common interior points.
3. No; they do not share a common vertex.

Vocabulary Are ∠3 and ∠4 adjacent angles? Explain.

1. **2.** **3.**

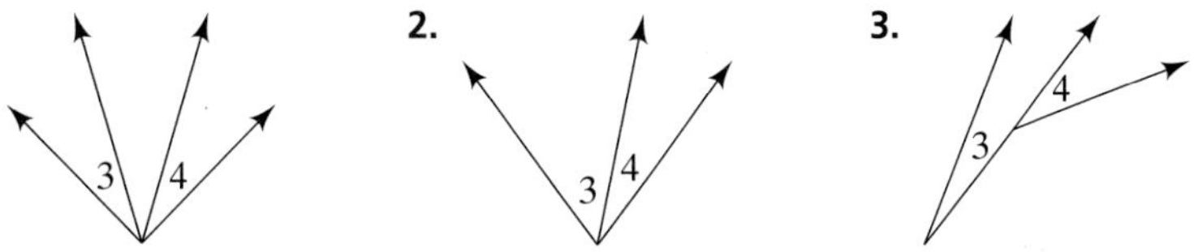

4. **Reasoning** Does every angle have a complement? Explain.
No; only angles with measures less than 90° have complements.

3. Practice

Assignment Guide

Check Your Understanding
Go over Exercises 1–4 in class before assigning the Homework Exercises.

Homework Exercises

A	Practice by Example	5–15
B	Apply Your Skills	16–31
C	Challenge	32
Test Prep and Mixed Review		33–35

Homework Quick Check
To check students' understanding of key skills and concepts, go over Exercises 7, 15, 26, 27, and 28.

Homework Exercises

For more exercises, see Extra Skills and Word Problems.

GO for Help

For Exercises	See Examples
5–7	1
8–12	2
13–15	3

A Name a pair of vertical and adjacent angles in each figure. Find $m\angle 1$.

5. **6.** **7.**

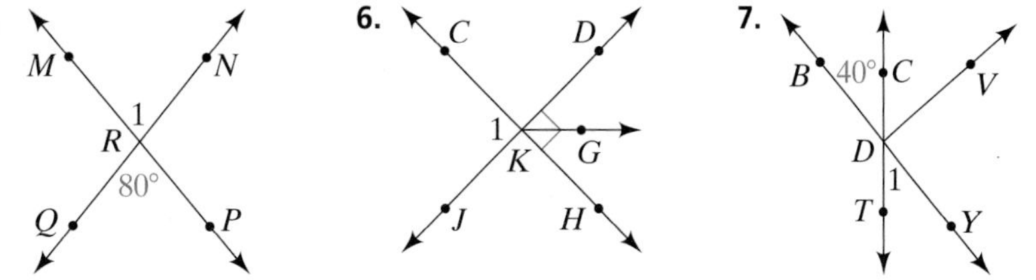

5–7. See margin.

Find the measure of the supplement of each angle.

8. 14° 166° **9.** 24° 156° **10.** 145° 35° **11.** 39° 141° **12.** 116° 64°

Find the measure of each numbered angle.

13. $m\angle 1 = 152°$; $m\angle 2 = 28°$; $m\angle 3 = 62°$; $m\angle 4 = 90°$
14. $m\angle 1 = 46°$; $m\angle 2 = 90°$; $m\angle 3 = 44°$; $m\angle 4 = 136°$
15. $m\angle 1 = 29°$; $m\angle 2 = 119°$; $m\angle 3 = 61°$; $m\angle 4 = 29°$; $m\angle 5 = 61°$

13. **14.** **15.**

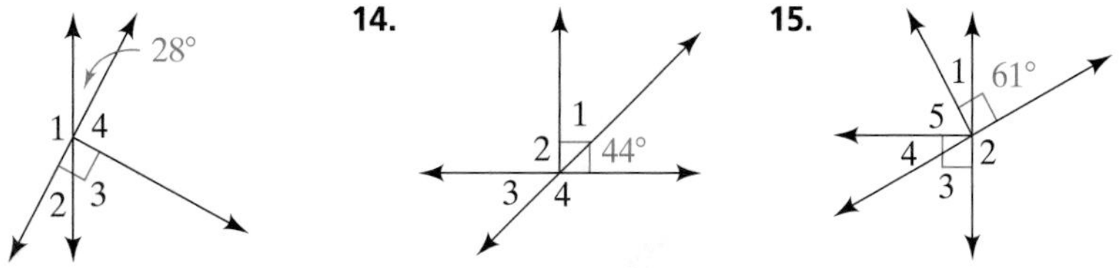

B **GPS** **16. Guided Problem Solving** Route 43 is perpendicular to Devon Avenue. Find the measure of the acute angle formed by Route 43 and Northwest Highway. 50°

- What kinds of angles do perpendicular lines form?
- What special pairs of angles do you see?

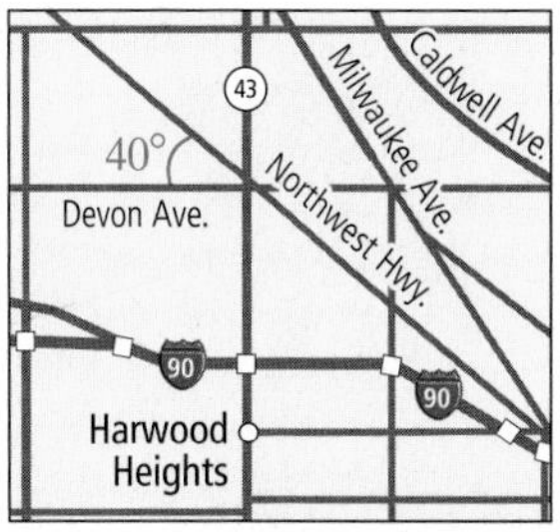

Find the measure of the complement and the supplement of each angle.
See above left.

17. 32° **18.** 77° **19.** 85.9° **20.** 42.3° **21.** 6.1°

17. 58°; 148°
18. 13°; 103°
19. 4.1°; 94.1°
20. 47.7°; 137.7°
21. 83.9°; 173.9°

Online lesson quiz, PHSchool.com, Web Code: asa-0701

5–7. Answers may vary. Samples are given.
5. ∠MRQ and ∠NRP; ∠NRP and ∠QRP; 80°
6. ∠CKJ and ∠DKH; ∠CKG and ∠GKH; 90°
7. ∠BDC and ∠TDY; ∠CDV and ∠VDY; 40°

Differentiated Instruction Resources

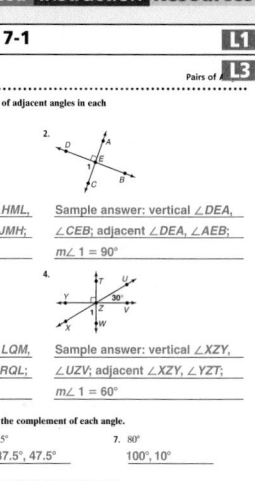

Adapted Practice 7-1 L1

Practice 7-1 Pairs of A... L3

Name a pair of vertical angles and a pair of adjacent angles in each figure. Find $m\angle 1$.

1. Sample answer: vertical ∠HML, ∠JMK; adjacent ∠HML, ∠JMH; $m\angle 1 = 62°$
2. Sample answer: vertical ∠DEA, ∠CEB; adjacent ∠DEA, ∠AEB; $m\angle 1 = 90°$
3. Sample answer: vertical ∠LQM, ∠PQN; adjacent ∠PQR, ∠RQL; $m\angle 1 = 45°$
4. Sample answer: vertical ∠XZY, ∠UZV; adjacent ∠XZY, ∠YZT; $m\angle 1 = 60°$

Find the measure of the supplement and the complement of each angle.

5. 10° 170°, 80°
6. 42.5° 137.5°, 47.5°
7. 80° 100°, 10°

Use the diagram at the right for Exercises 8–12. Decide whether each statement below is true or false.

8. ∠GAF and ∠BAC are vertical angles. false
9. ∠EAF and ∠EAD are adjacent angles. true
10. ∠CAD is a supplement of ∠DAF. true
11. ∠CAD is a complement of ∠EAF. true
12. $m\angle DAF = 109°$ true

7-1 • Guided Problem Solving GPS L3

Student Page 306, Exercises 28–31:

Use the diagram at the right for Exercises 28–31.

28. ∠LBD and ∠TBL are _?_ angles.
29. ∠RBT and ∠ _?_ are vertical angles.
30. $m\angle KBL$ = _?_
31. $m\angle DBK$ = _?_

Understand

1. What are you asked to do? identify angle types and measures of angles
2. What is true about the measures of two vertical angles? The measures of two vertical angles are the same.
3. What are adjacent angles? two angles with a common vertex and a common side but no common interior points

Plan and Carry Out

4. Do angles ∠LBD and ∠TBL share a side? If so what is it? Yes; they share side BL.
5. What type of angles are ∠LBD and ∠TBL? adjacent angles
6. What pairs of vertical angles are formed by the intersection of $\overleftrightarrow{TK}$ and $\overleftrightarrow{RL}$? ∠ RBT and ∠ KBL; ∠ TBL and ∠ RBK
7. What is the measure of angle KBL? 140°
8. $m\angle LBD + m\angle DBK$ = m∠ KBL or m∠ LBK
9. Which angle is adjacent to ∠LBD? ∠ KBD or ∠ LBT
10. Substitute what you know into the equation in step 8 and solve. 64 + x = 140; x = 76

Check

11. Explain how to check your answer in step 10. Sample answer: m∠ LBD + m∠ DBK = m∠ TBR; 64 + 76 = 140; 140 = 140

Solve Another Problem

12. Use the diagram at the right to solve.
a. ∠CFA and ∠DFE are _?_ angles. vertical
b. $m\angle BFC$ = _?_ ° 20°

4. Assess & Reteach

PowerPoint

Lesson Quiz

Use the diagram to answer Questions 1–3.

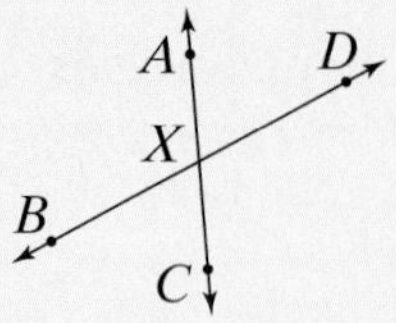

1. List all pairs of vertical angles. **∠AXD and ∠BXC; ∠AXB and ∠DXC**
2. List any angles adjacent to ∠CXD. **∠AXD and ∠BXC**
3. If m∠AXB = 110°, find m∠DXC. **110°**
4. An angle measures 57°. What is the measure of its supplement? **123°**

32. B; vertical angles are opposite each other, while adjacent angles share a common side.

Enrichment 7-1 L4

Reteaching 7-1 Pairs L2

- *Vertical angles* are pairs of opposite angles formed by two intersecting lines. They are congruent.

  Example 1: ∠1 and ∠3, ∠4 and ∠2

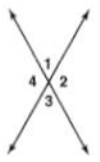

- *Adjacent angles* have a common vertex and a common side, but no common interior points.

  Example 2: ∠1 and ∠2, ∠1 and ∠4

- Two *supplementary angles* form a 180° angle.

  Example 3: ∠1 and ∠4 are supplementary angles. ∠3 is also a supplement of ∠4.

If you know the measure of one supplementary angle, you can find the measure of the other. → If m∠4 is 120°, then m∠1 is 180° − 120°, or 60°.

- Two *complementary angles* form a 90° angle.

  Example 4: ∠5 and ∠6 are complementary angles. ∠6 is a complement of ∠5.

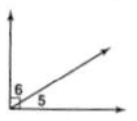

If you know the measure of one complementary angle, you can find the measure of the other. → If m∠5 is 30°, then m∠6 is 90° − 30°, or 60°.

Use the diagrams at the right for Exercises 1–5.

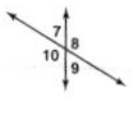

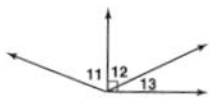

1. Vertical angles: ∠7 and ∠ 9
2. Adjacent angles: ∠10 and ∠ 7 or ∠ 9
3. Supplementary angles: ∠8 and ∠ 7 or ∠ 9
4. Complementary angles: ∠12 and ∠ 13
5. Vertical angles: ∠8 and ∠ 10

Find the measure of the supplement of each angle.

6. 38° 142°
7. 65° 115°
8. 120° 60°

Find the measure of the complement of each angle.

9. 25° 65°
10. 18° 72°
11. 40° 50°

GO Online
Homework Video Tutor
Visit: PHSchool.com
Web Code: ase-0701

22. No; they do not share a common side.
23. No; they are adjacent.
24–25. Answers may vary. Samples are given.
24. ∠1 and ∠2
25. ∠5 and ∠7
26. Yes; ∠5 is supplementary to ∠6. Since m∠1 = m∠6, ∠1 and ∠5 are supplementary angles.

Art **Use the stained glass window below for Exercise 22–26.** 22–26. See left.

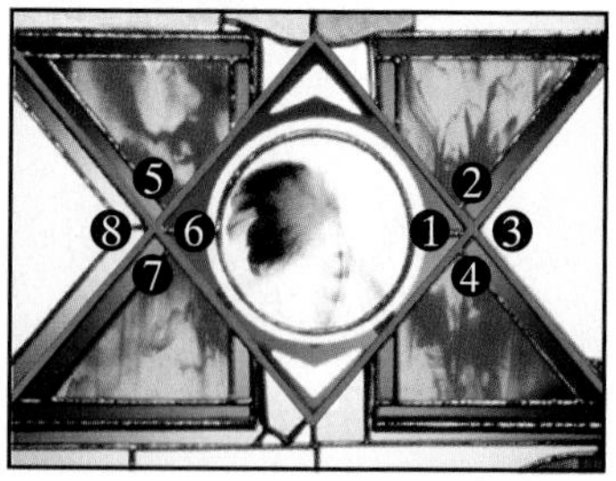

22. Are ∠1 and ∠7 adjacent? Explain.
23. Are ∠2 and ∠3 vertical? Explain.
24. Name a pair of adjacent angles.
25. Name a pair of vertical angles.
26. Suppose m∠1 = m∠6. Are ∠1 and ∠5 supplementary? Explain.
27. **Writing in Math** Can two supplementary angles have the same measure? Explain. **Yes; two right angles are supplementary and have measures of 90°.**

GPS **Use the diagram for Exercises 28–31.**

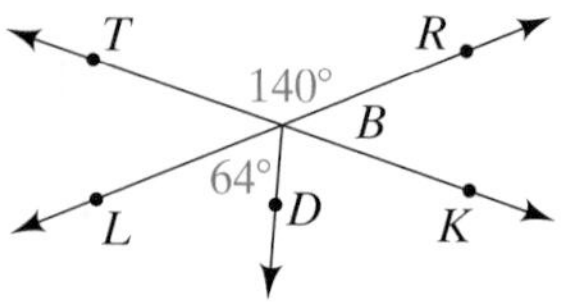

28. ∠LBD and ∠TBL are _?_ angles. **adjacent**
29. ∠RBT and ∠_?_ are vertical angles. **∠KBL**
30. m∠KBL = ■° **140°**
31. m∠DBK = ■° **76°**

C 32. **Challenge** Which pair of angles does NOT exist? Explain.
   - (A) adjacent supplementary
   - (B) vertical adjacent
   - (C) complementary vertical
   - (D) congruent complementary

   See margin.

Test Prep and Mixed Review

Practice

Multiple Choice

33. A truss is part of the roof of a house. What is the measure of ∠1 in the "fan" truss below? **A**

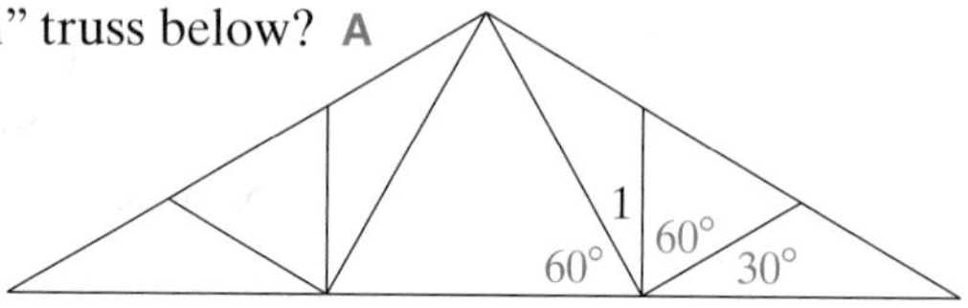

   - (A) 30°
   - (B) 45°
   - (C) 60°
   - (D) 90°

34. Which problem situation matches the equation 18 = 40*x*? **G**
   - (F) A credit card charges 18% interest on purchases. Debra bought a $40 item. What is *x*, the amount of interest charged?
   - (G) Isabella made 18 out of 40 paper snowflake decorations. What is *x*, the percent of the snowflakes Isabella made?
   - (H) Johannes gave the waitress an 18% tip. The cost of the meal was $40. What is *x*, the amount of the tip?
   - (J) Out of 40 free throw attempts, Rohit made 22 and missed 18. What is *x*, the percent of free throws he made?

GO for Help

For Exercise	See Lesson
35	5-6

35. **Shopping** A department store is having its annual 30%-off sale. A jacket is on sale for $63. What was the jacket's regular price? **$90**

Test Prep

Resources

For additional practice with a variety of test item formats:
- Test-Taking Strategies, p. 345
- Test Prep, p. 349
- Test-Taking Strategies with Transparencies

Alternative Assessment

Working in pairs, each student draws an angle. Then his or her partner measures that angle and finds its supplement.

7-2 Angles and Parallel Lines

Check Skills You'll Need

1. **Vocabulary Review** Which of the following pairs of angles are *supplementary*?
   50° and 40°,
   100° and 90°,
   120° and 60°,
   75° and 125°
   120° and 60°

Find the measure of the supplement of each angle.

2. 48° 3. 119°

4. 67° 5. 131°

2–5. See below.

GO for Help Lesson 7-1

Check Skills You'll Need

2. 132°
3. 61°
4. 113°
5. 49°

What You'll Learn

To identify parallel lines and the angles formed by parallel lines and transversals

Why Learn This?

Carpenters must know about angles and parallel lines in order to make correct measurements and cuts.

A line that intersects two other lines at different points is a **transversal.** In the diagrams below, line *t* is a transversal. Some pairs of angles formed by two lines and a transversal have special names.

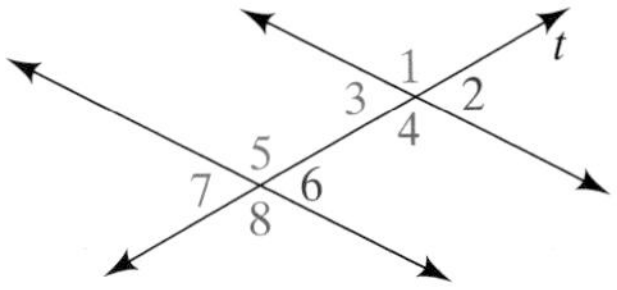

Corresponding angles lie on the same side of the transversal and in corresponding positions.

∠1 and ∠5 ∠2 and ∠6
∠3 and ∠7 ∠4 and ∠8

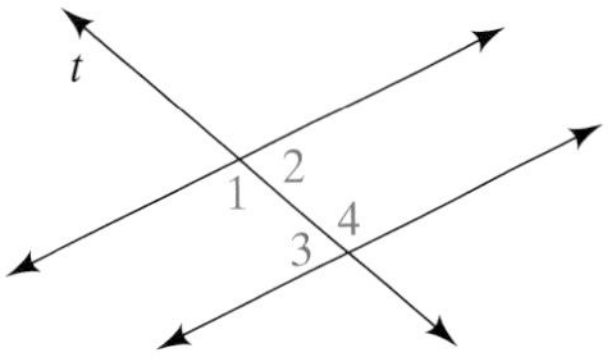

Alternate interior angles lie within a pair of lines and on opposite sides of the transversal.

∠1 and ∠4 ∠2 and ∠3

EXAMPLE 1 Identifying Angles

Identify a pair of corresponding angles and a pair of alternate interior angles.

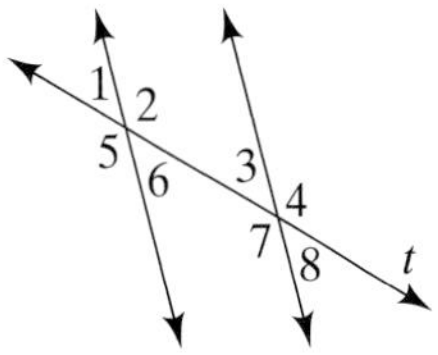

∠1 and ∠3 are corresponding angles.

∠2 and ∠7 are alternate interior angles.

Quick Check

1. Use the diagram in Example 1. Identify each pair of angles as *corresponding, alternate interior*, or *neither.* See left.
   a. ∠3, ∠6 b. ∠5, ∠7 c. ∠1, ∠8

1a. alternate interior
b. corresponding
c. neither

7-2

1. Plan

Objective
To identify parallel lines and the angle formed by parallel lines

Examples
1 Identifying Angles
2 Finding Angle Measures
3 Identifying Parallel Lines

Math Understandings: p. 300C

Professional Development

Math Background

A straight line (or *transversal*) that intersects two other straight lines forms angles. *Corresponding angles* lie on the same side of the transversal in matching positions. *Alternate interior angles* lie between the two lines but on opposite sides of the transversal. In the special case when the two lines intersected by a transversal are *parallel*, then the pairs of alternate interior angles are congruent, and the pairs of corresponding angles are congruent.

More Math Background: p. 300C

PowerPoint

Bell Ringer Practice

Check Skills You'll Need
Use student page, transparency, or PowerPoint. For intervention, direct students to:
Pairs of Angles
Lesson 7-1
Extra Skills and Word Problems Practice, Ch. 7

Lesson Planning and Resources

See p. 300E for a list of the resources that support this lesson.

Differentiated Instruction Solutions for All Learners

Special Needs L1
Provide each student with several copies of the diagrams used in Examples 1 and 2. Have the students use one sheet per question, highlighting a single pair of corresponding or alternate interior angles per sheet.

learning style: visual

Below Level L2
Students work in pairs to draw and identify parallel and non-parallel lines, right angles, acute angles, and obtuse angles.

learning style: visual

2. Teach

Activity Lab

Use before the lesson.

All in One Teaching Resources

Activity Lab 7-2: Angles and Parallel Lines

Guided Instruction

Example 2
Provide students with a blank grid

PowerPoint

Additional Examples

Use the diagram for Additional Examples 1 and 2.

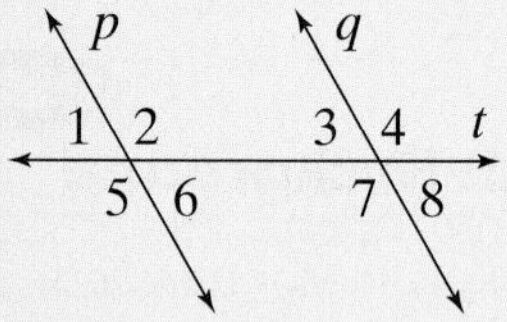

1. Identify each pair of corresponding angles and each pair of alternate interior angles. See back of book.

2. If p is parallel to q, and $m\angle 3 = 56°$, find $m\angle 6$. 56°

3. In the diagram below, $m\angle 5 = m\angle 6 = m\angle 7 = 80°$. Explain why p and q are parallel and why s and t are parallel. See back of book.

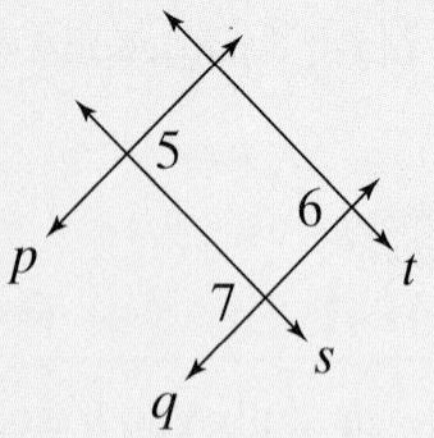

All in One Teaching Resources

- Daily Notetaking Guide 7-2 L3
- Adapted Notetaking 7-2 L1

Closure

- *What congruent angles are formed when a transversal intersects two parallel lines?* Sample: corresponding angles and alternate interior angles.

Vocabulary Tip

Recall that parallel lines lie in the same plane and do not intersect.

KEY CONCEPTS Transversals and Parallel Lines

When a transversal intersects two parallel lines,
- corresponding angles are congruent, and
- alternate interior angles are congruent.

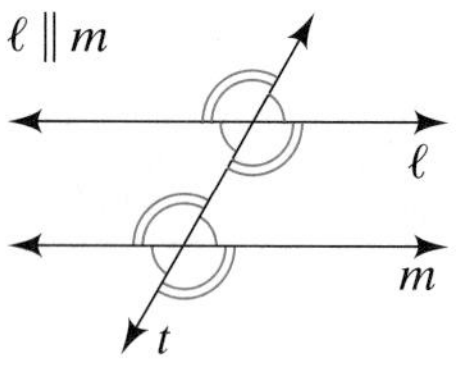

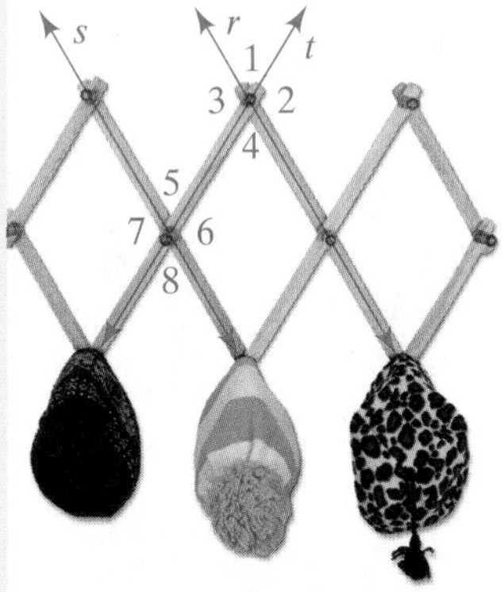

EXAMPLE Finding Angle Measures

2 **Gridded Response** A carpenter wants to make the hat rack at the left and needs to find all the angle measurements. She knows that line r is parallel to line s, and $m\angle 4 = 63°$. What is $m\angle 5$ measured in degrees?

$m\angle 5 = m\angle 4 = 63°$ ← **Alternate interior angles are congruent.**

The correct answer is 63 degrees.

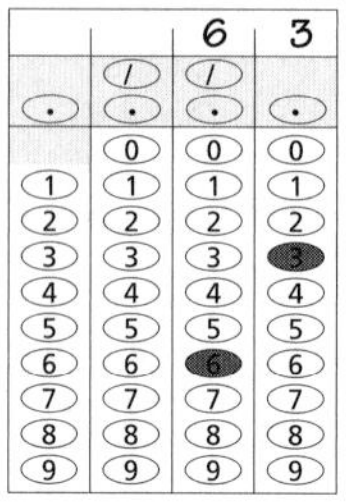

Quick Check

2. In Example 2, $m\angle 3 = 117°$. Find $m\angle 6$ and $m\angle 7$.
$m\angle 6 = m\angle 7 = 117°$

When a transversal intersects two parallel lines, some pairs of angles are congruent. The reverse is also true. If the corresponding angles or the alternate interior angles are congruent, the lines are parallel.

If $\overleftrightarrow{AB}$ is parallel to $\overleftrightarrow{CD}$, you write $\overleftrightarrow{AB} \parallel \overleftrightarrow{CD}$.

EXAMPLE Identifying Parallel Lines

3 In the diagram at the right, $m\angle 1 = 60°$, $m\angle 2 = 60°$, and $m\angle 3 = 60°$. Explain how you know $\overleftrightarrow{LP} \parallel \overleftrightarrow{MN}$ and $\overleftrightarrow{LM} \parallel \overleftrightarrow{PN}$.

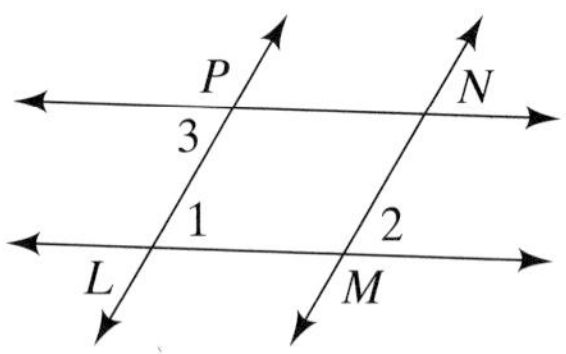

$\overleftrightarrow{LP} \parallel \overleftrightarrow{MN}$ because $\angle 1$ and $\angle 2$ are congruent corresponding angles. $\overleftrightarrow{LM} \parallel \overleftrightarrow{PN}$ because $\angle 1$ and $\angle 3$ are congruent alternate interior angles.

3. The measure of each angle formed by lines t and ℓ and lines t and m is 90°. Since pairs of corresponding angles are congruent, the lines are parallel.

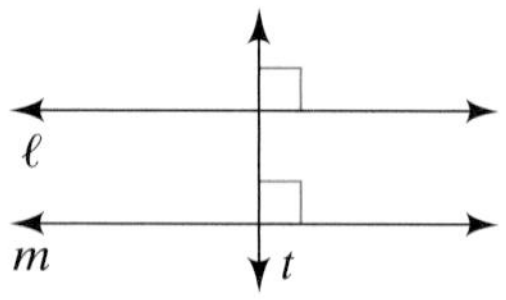

Quick Check

3. Transversal t at the left is perpendicular to lines ℓ and m. Explain how you know $\ell \parallel m$. See above left.

The reasoning used in Example 3 is called *deductive reasoning.* Deductive reasoning is the logical process of drawing conclusions from given facts.

Differentiated Instruction Solutions for All Learners

Advanced Learners L4
Students draw two perpendicular lines intersected by a transversal; then describe how the corresponding angles are related. In each corresponding pair, one angle is 90° larger than the other.

learning style: visual

English Language Learners ELL
Give students a drawing of two parallel lines intersected by a transversal. Have them label and identify the parallel lines, the transversal, and the alternate interior and corresponding angles. Then have them list all pairs of congruent angles.

learning style: visual

Check Your Understanding

1–2. Answers may vary. Samples are given.

1. ∠2 and ∠4

2. ∠2 and ∠6

5. False; corresponding angles lie on the same side of a transversal, but alternate interior angles do not.

In the diagram at the right, $\overleftrightarrow{PQ} \parallel \overleftrightarrow{ST}$.

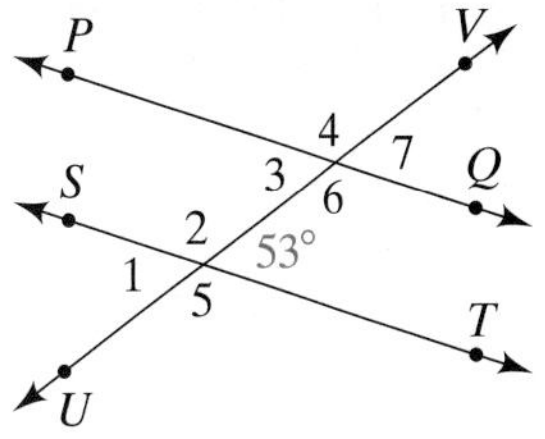

1. Name a pair of corresponding angles.
2. Name a pair of alternate interior angles.
3. Which line is the transversal? $\overleftrightarrow{UV}$
4. What other angles have measures of 53°? ∠1, ∠3, ∠7
5. **Reasoning** Is the following statement *true* or *false*? Corresponding angles can also be alternate interior angles. Explain. See left.

Homework Exercises

For more exercises, see Extra Skills and Word Problems.

GO for Help

For Exercises	See Examples
6–13	1
14–19	2
20–22	3

A **Identify the angles as *corresponding, alternate interior,* or *neither.***

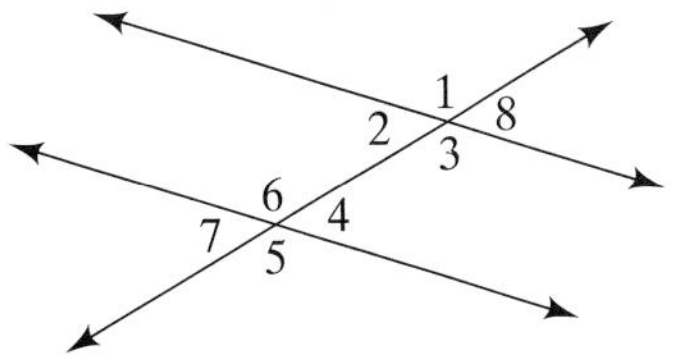

6. ∠6, ∠3
7. ∠8, ∠4
8. ∠2, ∠1
9. ∠2, ∠4
10. ∠1, ∠5
11. ∠2, ∠7
12. ∠3, ∠5
13. ∠4, ∠3

6–13. See margin.

In the diagram, ℓ ∥ m. If m∠3 = 122°, find the measure of each angle.

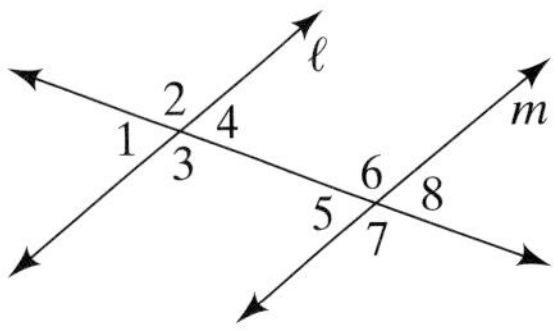

14. ∠4 58°
15. ∠2 122°
16. ∠6 122°
17. ∠7 122°
18. ∠8 58°
19. ∠5 58°

20. Corresponding angles are congruent.

21. Alternate interior angles are congruent.

22. Alternate interior angles are congruent.

For each diagram, explain how you know *a* ∥ *b*. 20–22. See above left.

20.

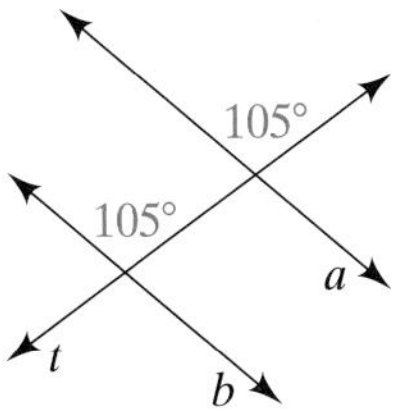

21.

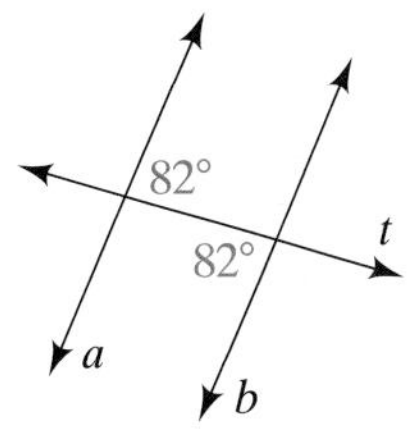

22.

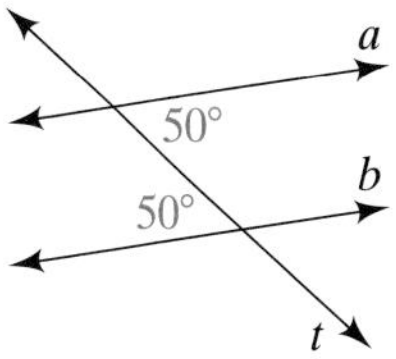

GO Online
Homework Video Tutor
Visit: PHSchool.com
Web Code: ase-0702

B **GPS**

23. no

23. **Guided Problem Solving** Two lines are cut by a transversal. The corresponding angles are not congruent. Are the two lines parallel?
   - **Understand the Problem** If a transversal cuts two parallel lines, corresponding angles are congruent. The question is, are two lines parallel if corresponding angles are not congruent?
   - **Make a Plan** Draw pictures of corresponding angles that are not congruent. Conclude whether or not the two lines are parallel.

6. alternate interior
7. corresponding
8. neither
9. alternate interior
10. neither
11. corresponding
12. corresponding
13. neither

3. Practice

Assignment Guide

Check Your Understanding
Go over Exercises 1–5 in class before assigning the Homework Exercises.

Homework Exercises

A Practice by Example	6–22
B Apply Your Skills	23–31
C Challenge	32
Test Prep and Mixed Review	33–39

Homework Quick Check
To check students' understanding of key skills and concepts, go over Exercises 15, 22, 28, 30, and 31.

Differentiated Instruction Resources

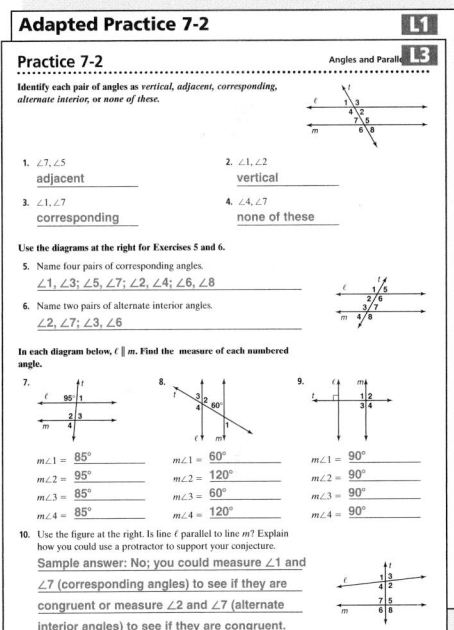

Adapted Practice 7-2 L1

Practice 7-2 Angles and Paralle[l Lines] L3

Identify each pair of angles as *vertical, adjacent, corresponding, alternate interior,* or *none of these.*

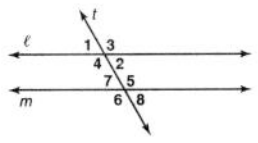

1. ∠7, ∠5 adjacent
2. ∠1, ∠2 vertical
3. ∠1, ∠7 corresponding
4. ∠4, ∠7 none of these

Use the diagrams at the right for Exercises 5 and 6.

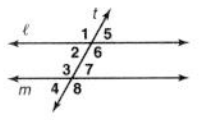

5. Name four pairs of corresponding angles.
∠1, ∠3; ∠5, ∠7; ∠2, ∠4; ∠6, ∠8
6. Name two pairs of alternate interior angles.
∠2, ∠7; ∠3, ∠6

In each diagram below, ℓ ∥ m. Find the measure of each numbered angle.

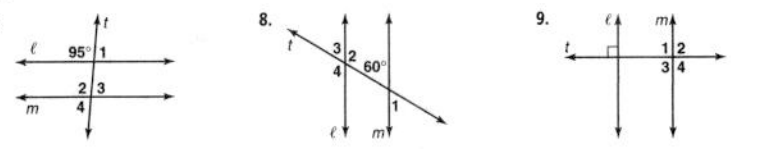

7. m∠1 = 85°; m∠2 = 95°; m∠3 = 85°; m∠4 = 85°
8. m∠1 = 60°; m∠2 = 120°; m∠3 = 60°; m∠4 = 120°
9. m∠1 = 90°; m∠2 = 90°; m∠3 = 90°; m∠4 = 90°

10. Use the figure at the right. Is line ℓ parallel to line m? Explain how you could use a protractor to support your conjecture.
Sample answer: No; you could measure ∠1 and ∠7 (corresponding angles) to see if they are congruent or measure ∠2 and ∠7 (alternate interior angles) to see if they are congruent.

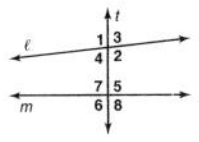

7-2 • Guided Problem Solving GPS L3

GPS Student Page 310, Exercise 31:

a. In the diagram at the right, $\overleftrightarrow{PQ} \parallel \overleftrightarrow{ST}$. Find the measure of each numbered angle.
b. What is the sum of the angle measures of the triangle?

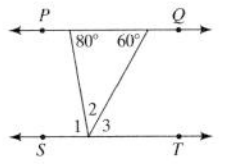

Understand

1. What are alternate interior angles?
Alternate interior angles lie within a pair of lines and on opposite sides of a transversal.
2. What are you asked to do?
Find the measure of each numbered angle.

Plan and Carry Out

3. Use angle 1 and angle 3 to name two pairs of alternate interior angles.
angle 1 and the 80° angle; angle 3 and the 60° angle
4. What is true of the measure of alternate interior angles?
The measures are the same.
5. What is the measure of angle 1?
80°
6. What is the measure of angle 3?
60°
7. What type of angle do angles 1, 2 and 3 form?
straight
8. How many degrees are in a straight angle?
180°
9. Use the information from steps 5 and 6 to help find the measure of angle 2.
180° − (80° + 60°) = 40°
10. What is the sum of the angle measures in the triangle?
180°

Check

11. Explain your answer from step 10.
m∠1 + m∠2 + m∠3 = 80° + 40° + 60° = 180°

Solve Another Problem

12. In the diagram, $\overleftrightarrow{AB} \parallel \overleftrightarrow{CD}$. Find the measure of each numbered angle.
m∠1 = 60°; m∠2 = 50°; m∠3 = 110°; m∠4 = 110°

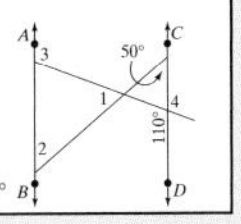

4. Assess & Reteach

PowerPoint

Lesson Quiz

Use the diagram to answer the questions.

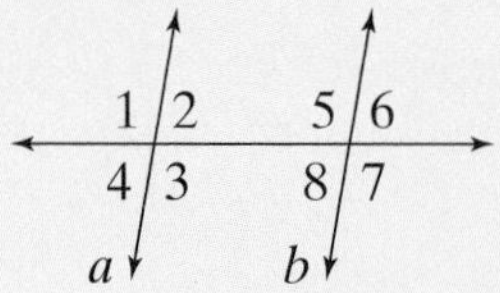

1. Classify ∠4 and ∠7 as *alternate interior angles, corresponding angles,* or *neither.* neither
2. Classify ∠2 and ∠8 as *alternate interior angles, corresponding angles,* or *neither.* alternate interior angles
3. If $a \parallel b$ and $m\angle 8 = 80°$, find $m\angle 4$. 80°
4. Suppose $m\angle 5 = 100°$ and $m\angle 3 = 100°$. What can you conclude about line a and line b? $a \parallel b$

25. No parallel lines; alternate interior angles are not congruent.
26. $y \parallel w$; corresponding angles are congruent.
27. $a \parallel b$; 70° and 110° are supplementary and adjacent. Corresponding angles are congruent and alternate interior angles are congruent.

Enrichment 7-2 L4

Reteaching 7-2 Angles and Para... L2

Look at the figure at the right.

- Line $\overleftrightarrow{AB}$ is parallel to line $\overleftrightarrow{CD}$ ($\overleftrightarrow{AB} \parallel \overleftrightarrow{CD}$)
- Line $\overleftrightarrow{EF}$ is a *transversal.*

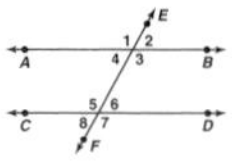

Alternate interior angles lie within a pair of lines and on opposite sides of the transversal.

Example 1: ∠3 and ∠5, ∠4 and ∠6

Alternate interior angles are congruent. If $m\angle 4$ is 60°, then $m\angle 6$ is also 60°.

Corresponding angles lie on the same side of the transversal and in corresponding positions.

Example 2: ∠1 and ∠5, ∠3 and ∠7

Corresponding angles are congruent. If $m\angle 1$ is 120°, then $m\angle 5$ is also 120°.

Use the diagram at the right to complete Exercises 1–2.

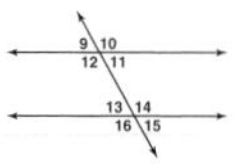

1. Name the alternate interior angles.
   a. ∠11 and ∠ ? 13
   b. ∠12 and ∠ ? 14
2. Name the corresponding angles.
   a. ∠16 and ∠ ? 12
   b. ∠14 and ∠ ? 10
   c. ∠9 and ∠ ? 13
   d. ∠11 and ∠ ? 15

In the diagram at the right, $\ell \parallel m$. Find the measure of each angle.

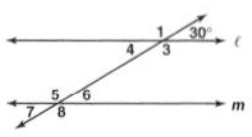

3. ∠1 150°
4. ∠3 150°
5. ∠6 30°
6. ∠5 150°

24. **Architecture** The railings in the photo at the left are parallel. If $m\angle 1 = 138°$, find $m\angle 2$ and $m\angle 3$. $m\angle 2 = 42°$; $m\angle 3 = 138°$

Which pairs of lines, if any, are parallel? Explain. 25–27. See margin.

25.

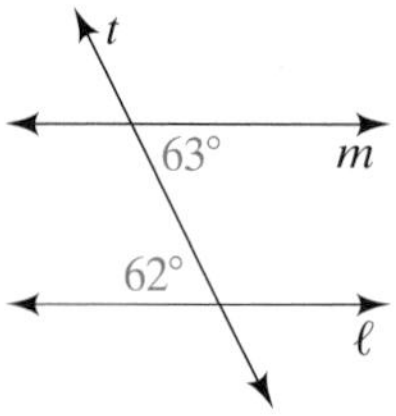

26.

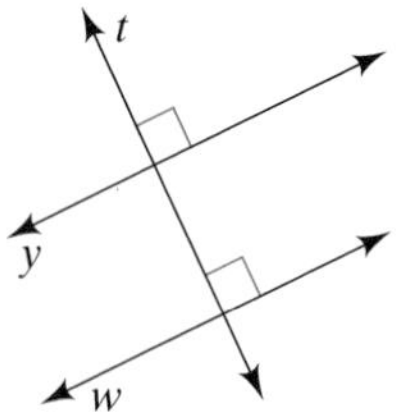

27.

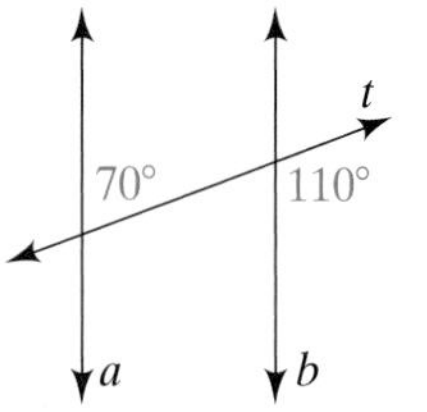

28. **Writing in Math** A transversal t cuts parallel lines m and n. If t is perpendicular to m, what is the relationship between t and n?

28. Answers may vary. Sample: Lines t and m are perpendicular, so they form a 90° angle. Since m is parallel to n, lines t and n must also form a 90° angle. So t is perpendicular to n.

Use the diagram at the right for Exercises 29–30. 29–30. See margin.

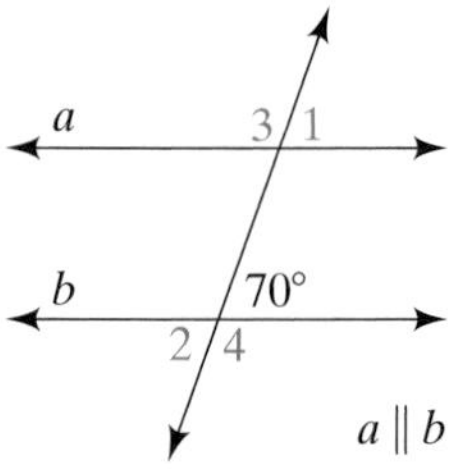

29. Find the measure of each numbered angle.
30. *Alternate exterior angles* lie outside a pair of lines and on opposite sides of a transversal. What do you notice about the measures of alternate exterior angles of parallel lines?

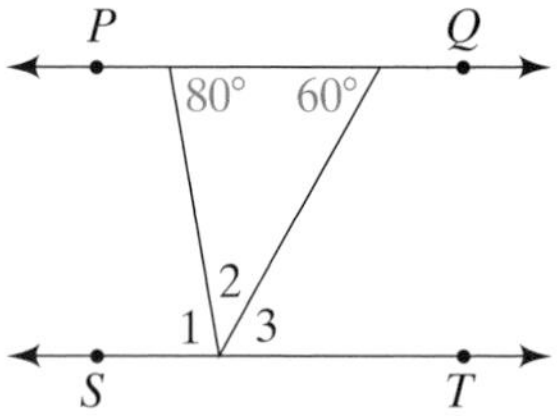

31. a. In the diagram at the left, $\overleftrightarrow{PQ} \parallel \overleftrightarrow{ST}$. Find the measure of each numbered angle. $m\angle 1 = 80°$; $m\angle 2 = 40°$; $m\angle 3 = 60°$
    GPS
    b. What is the sum of the angle measures of the triangle? 180°

32. **Challenge** Which pair of angles is always congruent? B
    Ⓐ alternate interior angles
    Ⓑ vertical angles
    Ⓒ corresponding angles
    Ⓓ alternate exterior angles

Test Prep and Mixed Review

Practice

Gridded Response

33. In the diagram at the right, triangle ABC is similar to triangle ADE. What scale factor was used to reduce triangle ABC to triangle ADE? 0.75

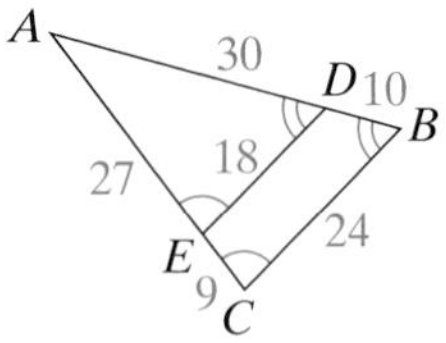

34. The equation $c = 17t + 5$ models the total cost c of a tomato garden, where t is the cost of each tomato plant. Find the total cost, in dollars, if each plant costs \$0.50. 13.50
35. A punch recipe calls for 3 quarts of pineapple juice, 2 quarts of orange juice, 3 cups of grapefruit juice, and 3 cups of cranberry juice. How many quarts of punch does the recipe make? 6.5

GO for Help

For Exercises	See Lesson
36–39	5-4

Use an equation to find each percent.

36. 23% of 55 12.65
37. 78% of 41 31.98
38. 14% of 36 5.04
39. 62% of 199 123.38

Test Prep

Resources

For additional practice with a variety of test item formats:

- Test-Taking Strategies, p. 345
- Test Prep, p. 349
- Test-Taking Strategies with Transparencies

Alternative Assessment

Students choose an exercise from Exercises 14–19. They explain how they reached their conclusions using the new vocabulary terms in this lesson.

29. $m\angle 1 = 70°$; $m\angle 2 = 70°$; $m\angle 3 = 110°$; $m\angle 4 = 110°$
30. They are congruent; they are vertical angles of congruent alternate interior angles.

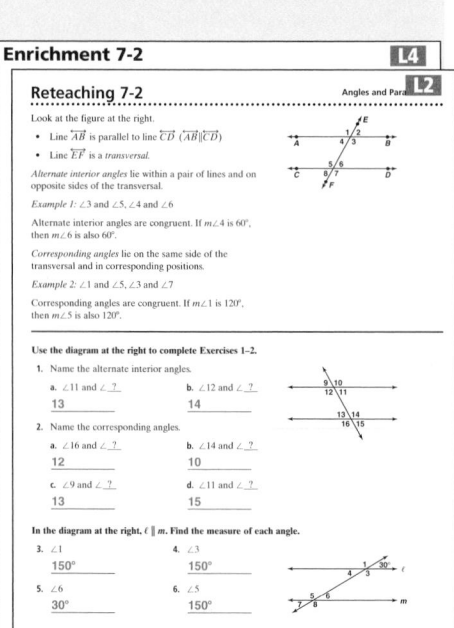

7-2b Activity Lab

Algebra Thinking

Solving Angle Equations

You can use what you know about solving equations to find angle measures.

EXAMPLE Solving Angle Equations

Find the measure of each angle in the diagram at the right.

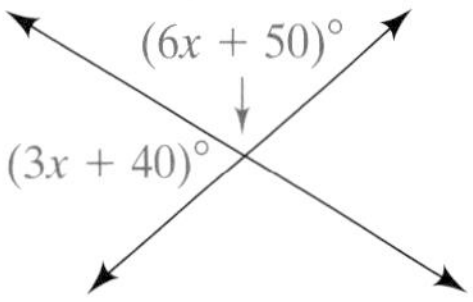

$$
\begin{aligned}
(3x + 40)^\circ + (6x + 50)^\circ &= 180^\circ && \leftarrow \text{adjacent supplementary angles}\\
9x + 90 &= 180 && \leftarrow \text{Combine like terms.}\\
9x + 90 - 90 &= 180 - 90 && \leftarrow \text{Subtract 90 from each side.}\\
9x &= 90 && \leftarrow \text{Simplify.}\\
\frac{9x}{9} &= \frac{90}{9} && \leftarrow \text{Divide each side by 9.}\\
x &= 10 && \leftarrow \text{Simplify.}
\end{aligned}
$$

To find the measure of each angle in the diagram, substitute 10 for x. $3(10) + 40 = 70$ and $6(10) + 50 = 110$. So the angle measures are 70° and 110°.

Exercises

Find the measures of the two angles in each diagram.

1.

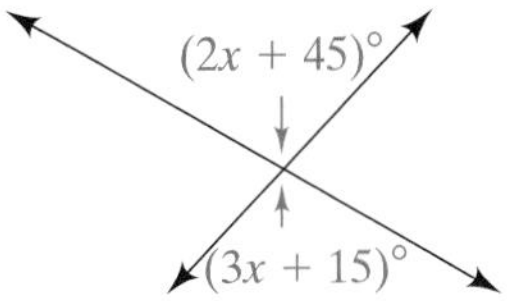

105°; 105°

2.

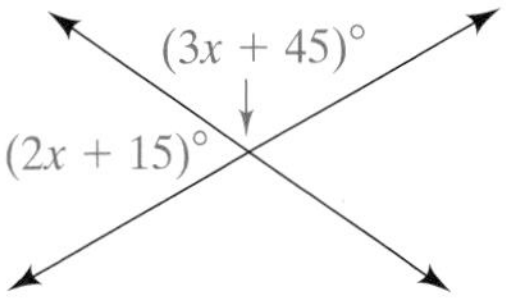

63°; 117°

3. Find the measure of ∠1 in the figure below.

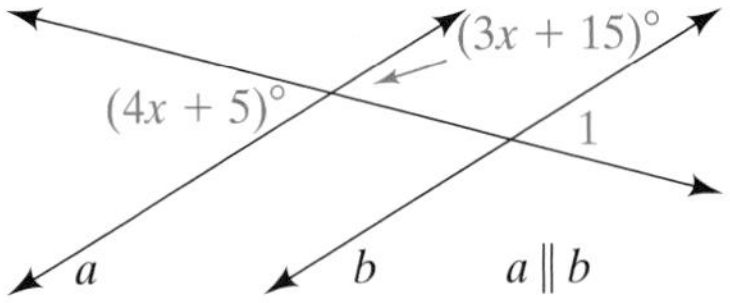

45°

Use the figure at the right.

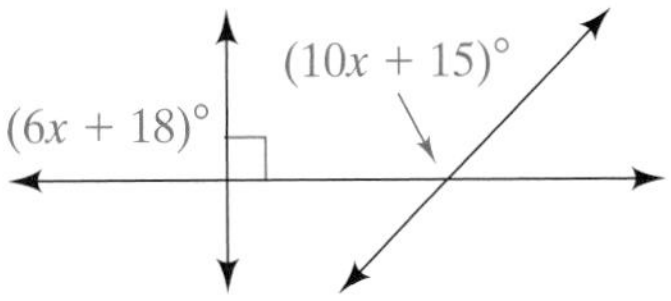

4. Find the measure of the obtuse angles. 135°

5. Find the measure of the acute angles. Then write an algebraic expression for that measure. 45°; Sample answer: $(165 - 10x)^\circ$

Activity Lab

Solving Angle Equations

Students apply their skills in solving equations to finding angle measures in diagrams. They use their knowledge of complementary and supplementary angles and angles formed by a transversal.

Guided Instruction

Before beginning the activity, review terms related to angles with students. Ask: *What are supplementary angles?* two angles whose measures add to 180° *If two angles add up to 90°, what are they called?* complementary *What is the difference between acute and obtuse angles?* acute angles measure less than 90°, obtuse angles measure greater than 90°

Error Prevention!

Once they have solved for *x*, students may forget that they're not yet done with the problem. Remind them to substitute the value of *x* in the expression that represents the angle measure they're finding.

Differentiated Instruction

Visual Learners
Provide each student with a copy of this page. Have students outline the rays that form each angle referred to in Exercises 1–5, and color the inside of each angle in corresponding colors.

Resources

- protractor

7-3

1. Plan

Objective
To identify congruent figures and use them to solve problems

Examples
1 Writing Congruence Statements
2 Congruent Triangles
3 Application: Surveying

Math Understandings: p. 300C

Professional Development

Math Background

Congruent polygons have exactly the same size and shape. Polygons are congruent if you can slide, turn, or flip them and make them coincide. This means that mirror images, or reflections, are congruent. The matching angles and sides of two polygons are called *corresponding parts.*

More Math Background: p. 300C

Lesson Planning and Resources

See p. 300E for a list of the resources that support this lesson.

PowerPoint

Bell Ringer Practice

Check Skills You'll Need
Use student page, transparency, or PowerPoint. For intervention, direct students to:
Similar Figures and Proportions
Lesson 4-4
Extra Skills and Word Problems Practice, Ch. 4

7-3 Congruent Polygons

Check Skills You'll Need

1. **Vocabulary Review** *Congruent angles* have __?__ measures. equal

Are the polygons similar? Explain.

2. 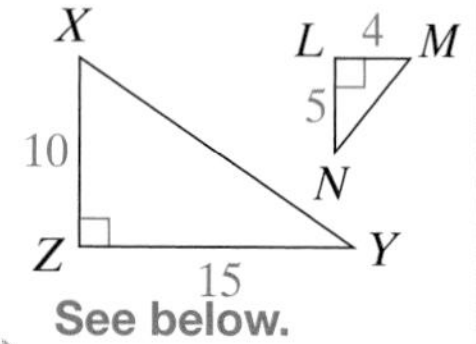

See below.

GO for Help Lesson 4-4

Check Skills You'll Need

2. Not similar; corresponding sides are not in proportion.

What You'll Learn

To identify congruent figures and use them to solve problems

New Vocabulary congruent polygons

Why Learn This?

Land surveyors measure angles and distances on land. To survey land, it is helpful to know about congruent polygons.

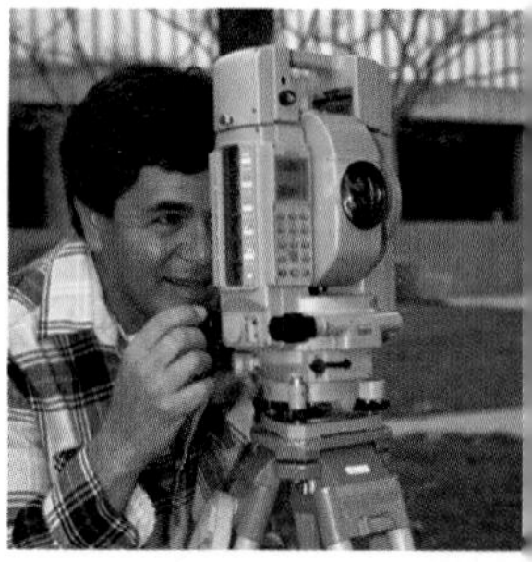

Congruent polygons are polygons that have the same size and shape. When two polygons are congruent, you can slide, flip, or turn one so that it fits exactly on top of the other one.

Corresponding angles and corresponding sides of congruent polygons are congruent. The two polygons below are congruent.

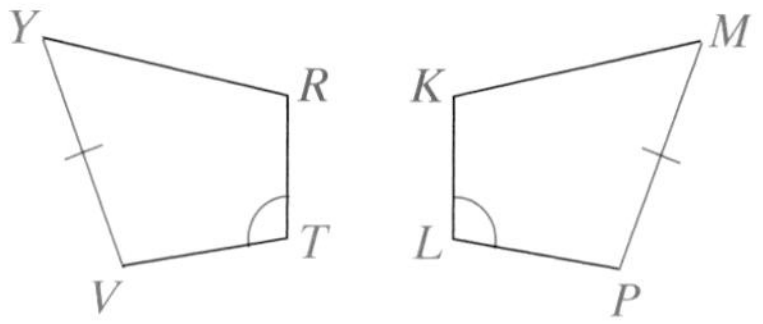

$\angle T$ corresponds to $\angle L$.

$\overline{YV}$ corresponds to $\overline{MP}$.

R corresponds to K.

You can write $VTRY \cong PLKM$.

The tick marks in the diagram tell you which sides are congruent. The arcs tell you which angles are congruent. When you name congruent polygons, you must list the corresponding vertices in the same order.

EXAMPLE **Writing Congruence Statements**

Test Prep Tip
Before you write congruence statements, copy the figures and mark the congruent corresponding parts.

1 Write a congruence statement for the congruent figures at the right.

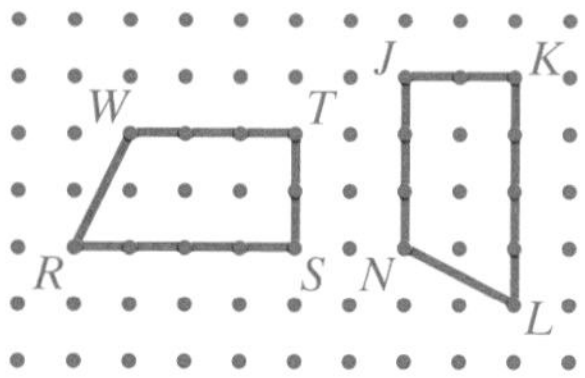

$\angle R \cong \angle L$, $\angle S \cong \angle K$, $\angle T \cong \angle J$, and $\angle W \cong \angle N$. So $RSTW \cong LKJN$.

Quick Check

1. Write a congruence statement for the congruent figures at the right. $\triangle TRS \cong \triangle KJL$

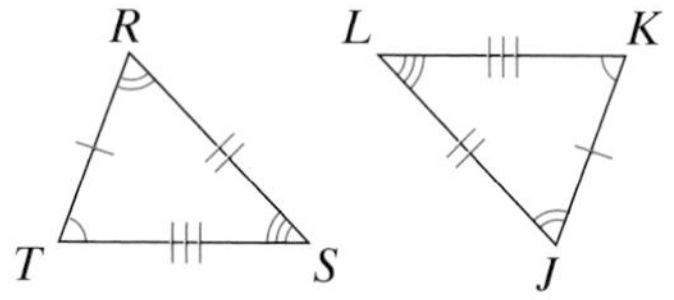

Differentiated Instruction Solutions for All Learners

Special Needs L1	**Below Level** L2
To help students better understand arcs and tic marks, have students cut out polygons of the same and different sizes. Then have them place one on top of another to "prove" or "disprove" the congruence of these two polygons. **learning style: tactile**	Students use cut corners from a sheet of paper to explore and demonstrate similar triangles of different sizes. **learning style: tactile**

You can use corresponding parts of triangles to show that two triangles are congruent. You do not need to know that *all* the corresponding parts are congruent to show congruent triangles. You can show congruence in several ways.

KEY CONCEPTS **Showing Triangles Are Congruent**

To demonstrate that two triangles are congruent, show that the following parts of one triangle are congruent to the corresponding parts of the other triangle.

Side-Side-Side (SSS)

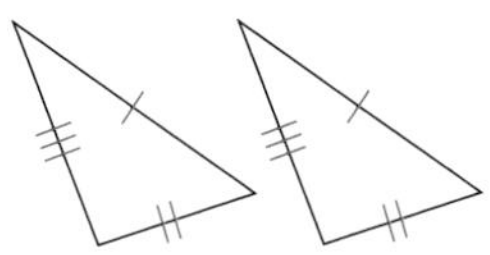

Side-Angle-Side (SAS)

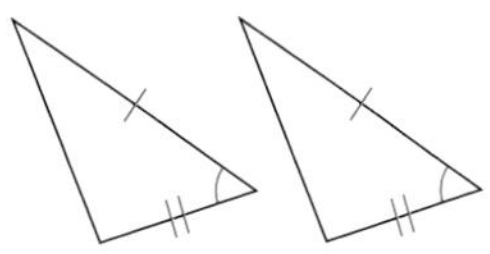

Angle-Side-Angle (ASA)

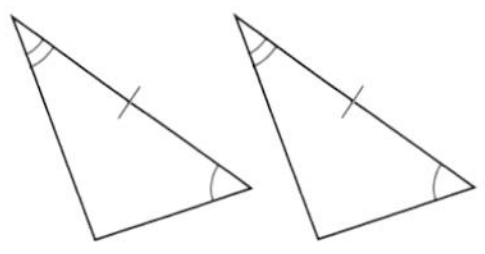

Vocabulary Tip

The abbreviations SSS, SAS, and ASA are easy ways to remember how to show triangles are congruent.

The order of the angles and sides is important in deciding whether two triangles are congruent.

EXAMPLE Congruent Triangles

2 Show that each pair of triangles is congruent.

a.

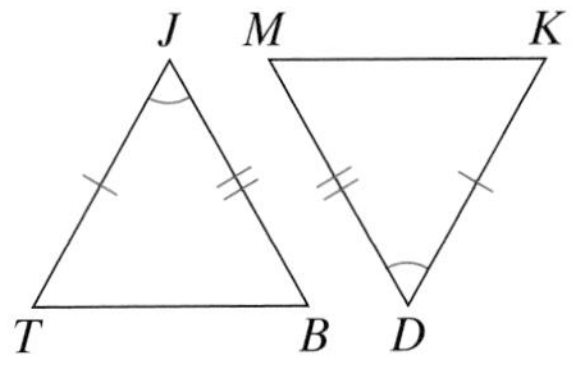

$\overline{TJ} \cong \overline{KD}$ **S**ide

$\angle J \cong \angle D$ **A**ngle

$\overline{BJ} \cong \overline{MD}$ **S**ide

$\triangle TJB \cong \triangle KDM$ by SAS.

b.

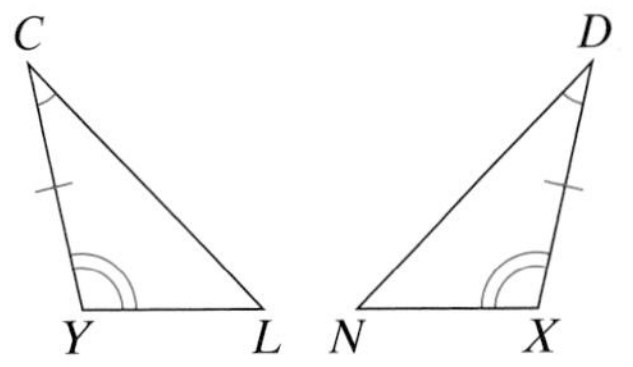

$\angle C \cong \angle D$ **A**ngle

$\overline{CY} \cong \overline{DX}$ **S**ide

$\angle Y \cong \angle X$ **A**ngle

$\triangle CYL \cong \triangle DXN$ by ASA

Quick Check

2. Show that each pair of triangles is congruent.

a.

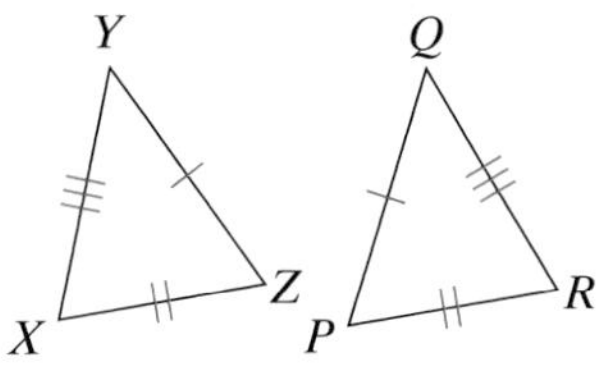

b.

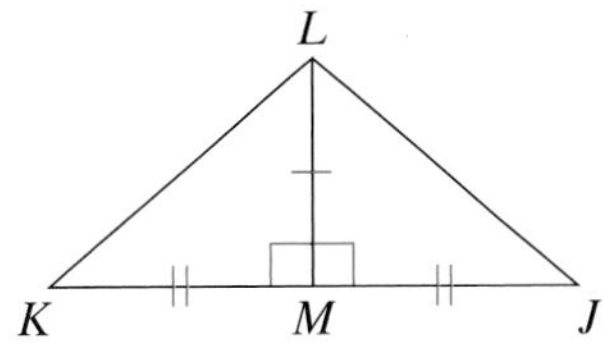

2a. $\triangle XYZ \cong \triangle RQP$ by SSS

b. $\triangle KLM \cong \triangle JLM$ by SAS

2. Teach

Activity Lab

Use before the lesson.

All in One Teaching Resources

Activity Lab 7-3: Congruent Polygons

Guided Instruction

Example 1

Have students draw the figures and use different colors to match the corresponding parts.

Teaching Tip

In Example 2, have students discuss how they can tell that the angle is included between the two sides or that the side is included between the two angles.

Error Prevention!

Watch for students who try to determine congruence by "eyeballing" a figure. Emphasize the importance of paying attention to the side and angle markings.

PowerPoint

Additional Examples

1 In the diagram below, list the congruent parts of the two figures. Then write a congruence statement.

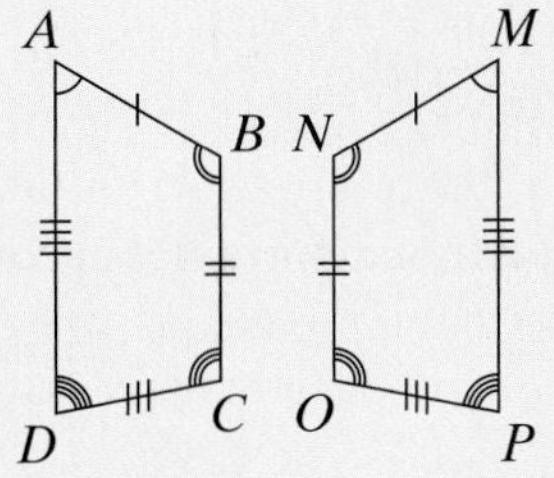

$\overline{AB} \cong \overline{MN}$; $\overline{BC} \cong \overline{NO}$; $\overline{CD} \cong \overline{OP}$; $\overline{DA} \cong \overline{PM}$; $\angle A \cong \angle M$; $\angle B \cong \angle N$; $\angle C \cong \angle O$; $\angle D \cong \angle P$; $ABCD \cong MNOP$

Advanced Learners L4

Students find and share congruent figures in pictures and in classroom objects.

learning style: visual

English Language Learners ELL

Make sure students can distinguish between the symbol for congruence (≅) and the symbol that means *about equal to* (≈). Make sure they know the symbol for congruence means *exactly* equal to or the same.

learning style: visual

PowerPoint

Additional Examples

2 Show that each pair of triangles is congruent.

a.

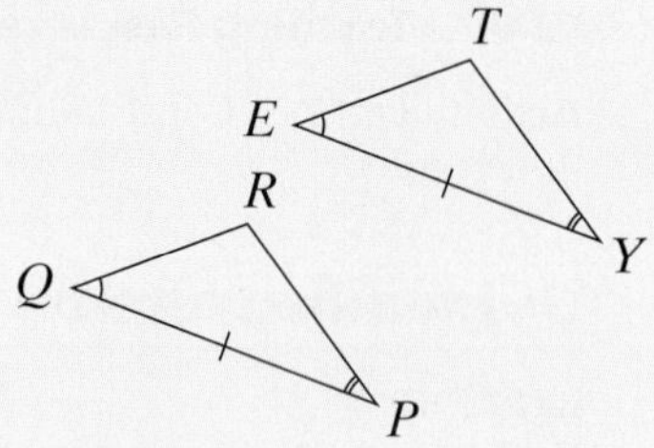

$\angle Q \cong \angle E$, $\overline{QP} \cong \overline{EY}$, $\angle P \cong \angle Y$; $\triangle QPR \cong \triangle EYT$;

Angle-Side-Angle

b.

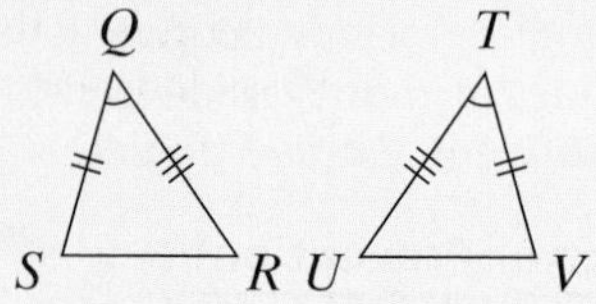

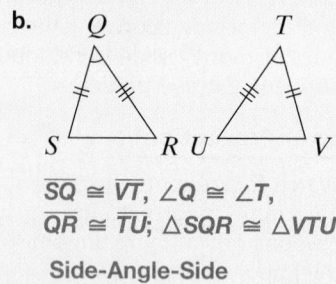

$\overline{SQ} \cong \overline{VT}$, $\angle Q \cong \angle T$, $\overline{QR} \cong \overline{TU}$; $\triangle SQR \cong \triangle VTU$;

Side-Angle-Side

3 A surveyor drew the picture below and found the distance from I to J across the canyon. Show that $\triangle GHI \cong \triangle KJI$. Then find JK. triangles are congruent by ASA; 36 ft

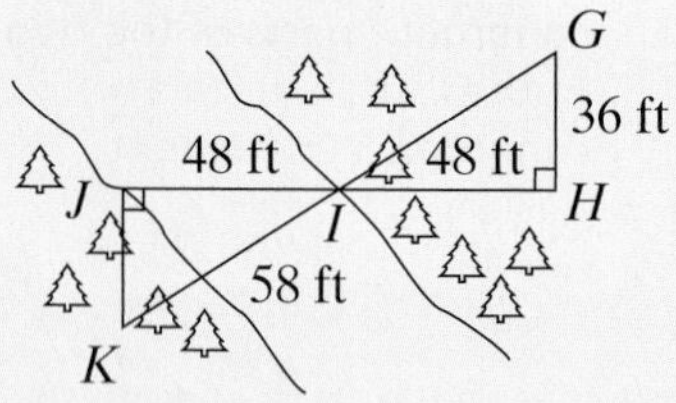

All in One Teaching Resources

- Daily Notetaking Guide 7-3 L3
- Adapted Notetaking 7-3 L1

Closure

- *Explain which parts of congruent figures are congruent to each other.* Sample: corresponding angles are congruent and corresponding sides are congruent
- *Name three ways you can demonstrate that two triangles are congruent.* Sample: SSS, SAS, and ASA

You can use corresponding parts of congruent figures to find distances.

EXAMPLE Application: Surveying

3 A surveyor drew the picture below. A bridge will be built across the river from point A to point B. Show that the two triangles are congruent. Then find AB.

$\angle B \cong \angle D$ ← **Both are right angles.**

$BC = DC$ ← **Both measure 70 yd.**

$\angle ACB \cong \angle ECD$ ← **They are vertical angles.**

So $\triangle ABC \cong \triangle EDC$ by ASA.

Corresponding parts of congruent triangles are congruent. $\overline{AB}$ corresponds to $\overline{ED}$, so AB is 82 yd.

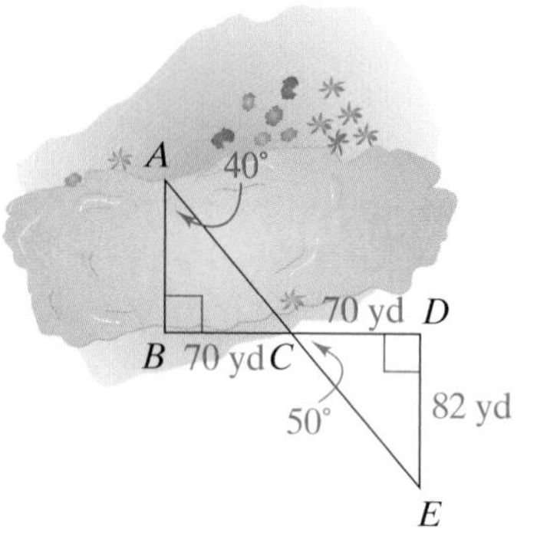

Quick Check

3. Use the diagram in Example 3 to find each measure.
   a. $m\angle E$ 40°
   b. $m\angle ACB$ 50°

Check Your Understanding

1. **Vocabulary** What two characteristics do congruent polygons have in common? size and shape
2. Is the following statement *true* or *false*? When two polygons are congruent, you can translate, reflect, or rotate one so that it fits on top of the other one. true

State whether each pair of triangles is congruent by SSS, SAS, or ASA.

3. 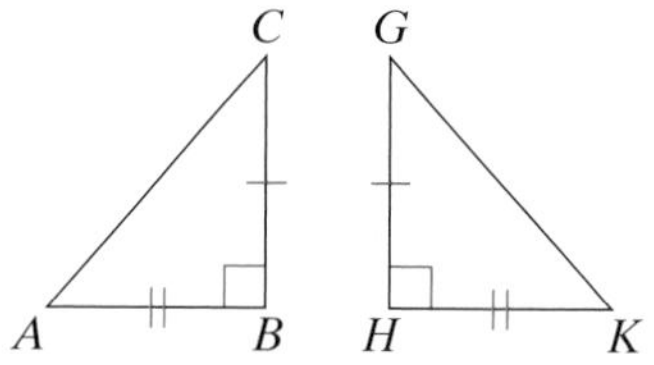

SAS

4. 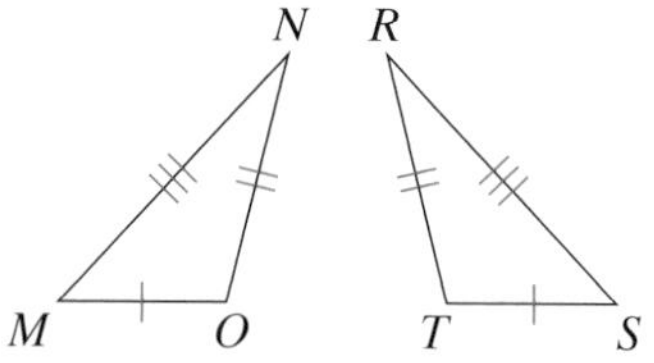

SSS

Use the two congruent triangles below for Exercises 5 and 6.

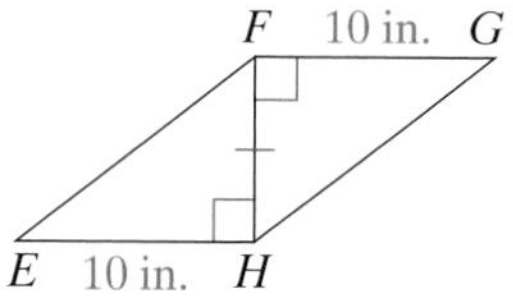

5. List the congruent corresponding angles and sides of the two triangles.
6. **Error Analysis** Vanessa writes $\triangle EFH \cong \triangle GFH$ by ASA. Michael writes $\triangle EFH \cong \triangle GHF$ by SAS. Who is correct?

5. $\overline{EH} \cong \overline{GF}$; $\angle EHF \cong \angle GFH$; $\overline{FH} \cong \overline{FH}$; $\angle FEH \cong \angle HGF$; $\overline{EF} \cong \overline{GH}$; $\angle EFH \cong \angle GHF$

6. Michael

Homework Exercises

For more exercises, see Extra Skills and Word Problems.

GO for Help

For Exercises	See Examples
7–8	1
9–10	2
11–18	3

A **Write a congruence statement for each pair of congruent figures.**

7.

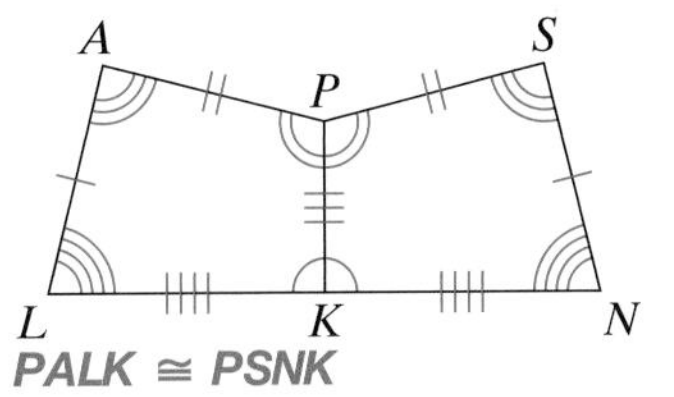

PALK ≅ PSNK

8.

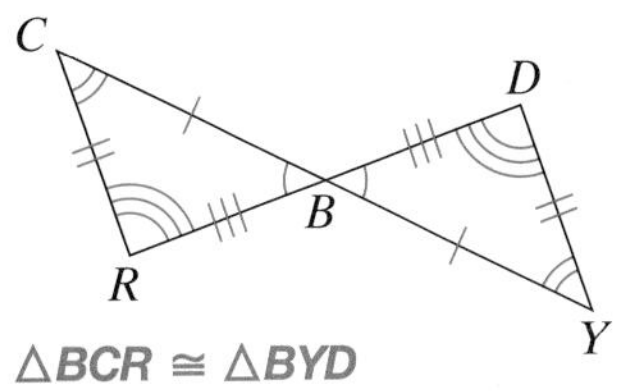

△BCR ≅ △BYD

Show that each pair of triangles is congruent.

9. SAS

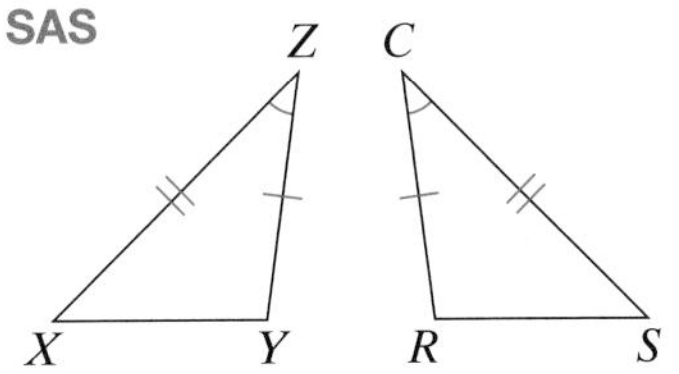

10. ASA

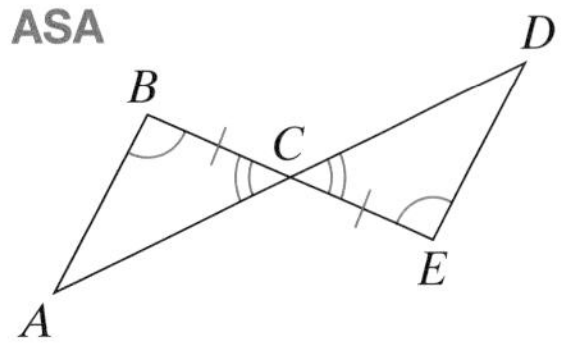

In the diagram below, *LMRC* ≅ *TXND*. Find each measure.

11. $m\angle N$ 104°

12. $m\angle T$ 86°

13. RM 0.9 cm

14. ND 1.6 cm

15. $m\angle C$ 62°

16. $m\angle M$ 108°

17. XT 1.4 cm

18. CL 1.7 cm

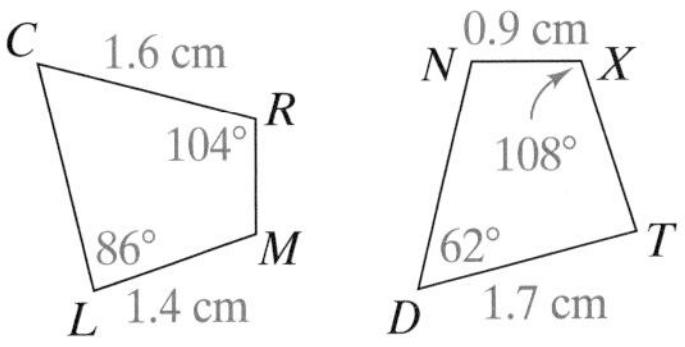

B **GPS**

19. Guided Problem Solving Use rotations and translations to find a point F such that $\triangle PQR \cong \triangle FGH$. (6, 1)

- Using the congruence statement, you know that $\overline{QR} \cong$ ■.
- $\triangle FGH$ is the exact image of $\triangle PQR$ after a rotation of ■° about point R followed by a translation ■ units to the right and ■ units up.

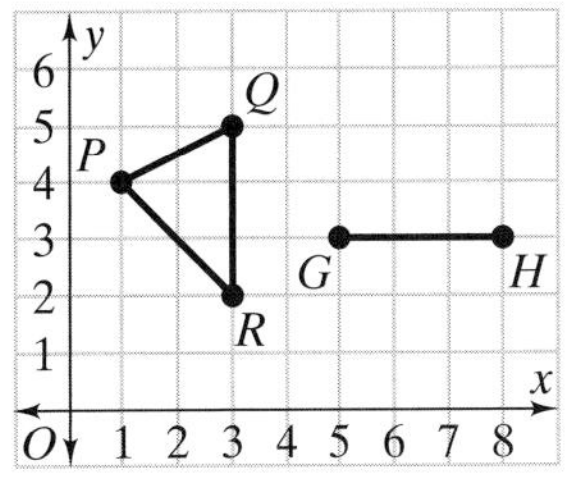

Is each pair of triangles congruent? Explain.

20.

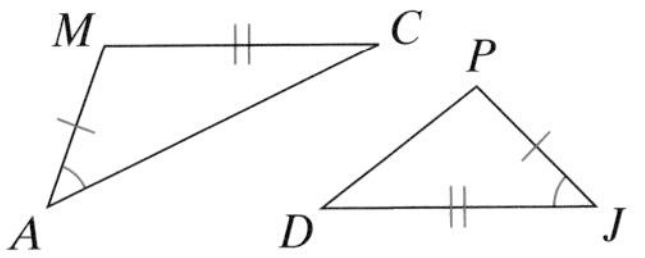

21.

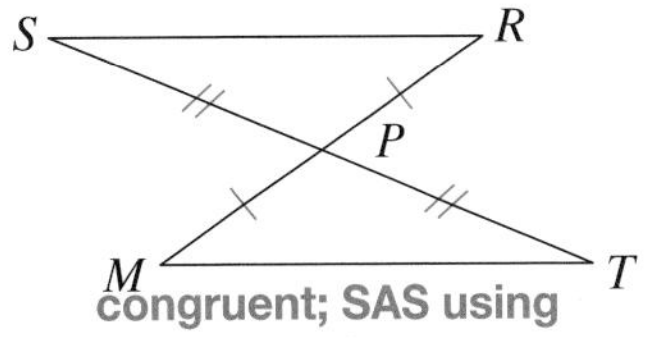

congruent; SAS using vertical angles

22. Writing in Math Explain the difference between similar triangles and congruent triangles.

23. Reasoning Can you show that two triangles are congruent by Angle-Angle-Angle? Draw figures to support your answer.
See margin.

20. Answers may vary. Sample: Not congruent; the triangles have two pairs of congruent sides and a pair of congruent angles, but the angles are not included between the two sides.

22. Answers may vary. Sample: Similar triangles have corresponding sides that are in proportion, while congruent triangles have corresponding sides that are congruent.

23. no; △ABC ≇ △DEF

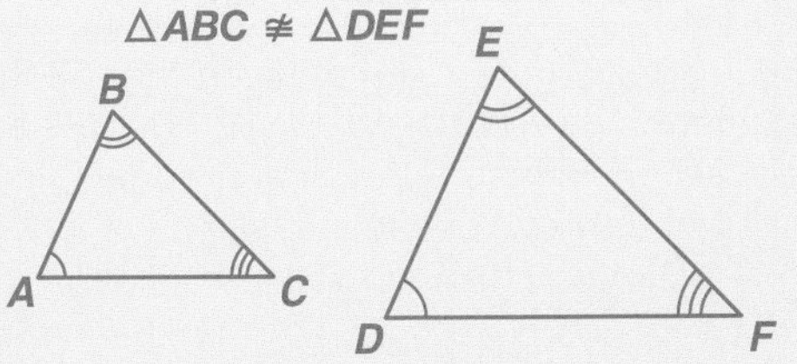

3. Practice

Assignment Guide

Check Your Understanding

Go over Exercises 1–6 in class before assigning the Homework Exercises.

Homework Exercises

A	Practice by Example	7–18
B	Apply Your Skills	19–27
C	Challenge	28
	Test Prep and Mixed Review	29–36

Homework Quick Check

To check students' understanding of key skills and concepts, go over Exercises 10, 15, 23, 24, and 26.

Differentiated Instruction Resources

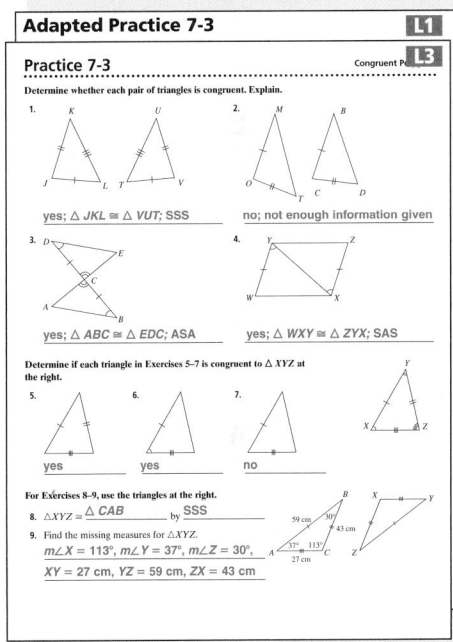

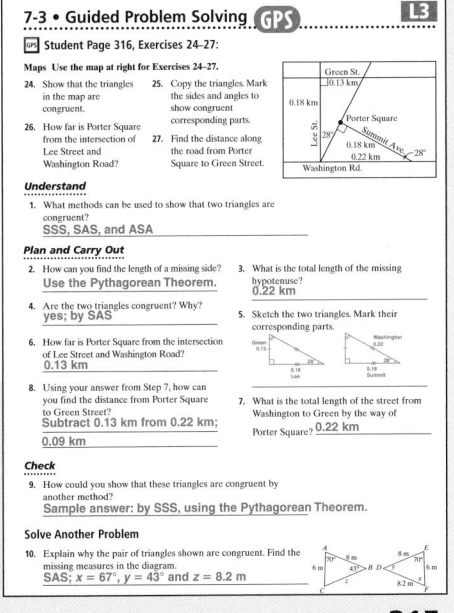

Adapted Practice 7-3 L1

Practice 7-3 Congruent P... L3

Determine whether each pair of triangles is congruent. Explain.

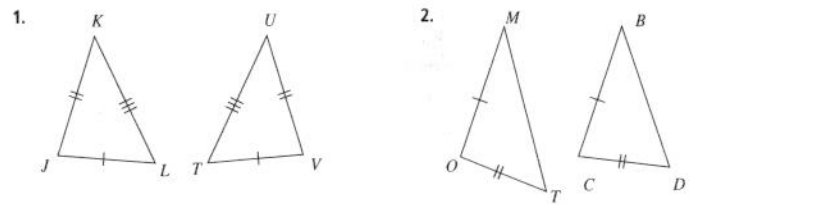

1. yes; △ JKL ≅ △ VUT; SSS
2. no; not enough information given

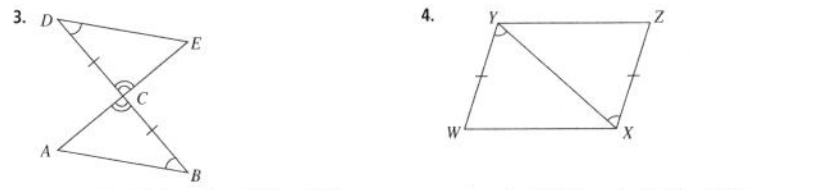

3. yes; △ ABC ≅ △ EDC; ASA
4. yes; △ WXY ≅ △ ZYX; SAS

Determine if each triangle in Exercises 5–7 is congruent to △ *XYZ* at the right.

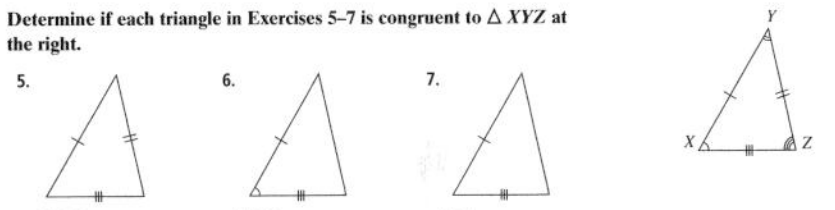

5. yes
6. yes
7. no

For Exercises 8–9, use the triangles at the right.

8. △XYZ ≅ △ CAB by SSS
9. Find the missing measures for △XYZ.
$m\angle X = 113°$, $m\angle Y = 37°$, $m\angle Z = 30°$,
$XY = 27$ cm, $YZ = 59$ cm, $ZX = 43$ cm

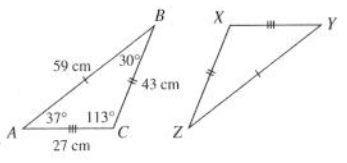

7-3 • Guided Problem Solving GPS L3

GPS Student Page 316, Exercises 24–27:

Maps Use the map at right for Exercises 24–27.

24. Show that the triangles in the map are congruent.
25. Copy the triangles. Mark the sides and angles to show congruent corresponding parts.
26. How far is Porter Square from the intersection of Lee Street and Washington Road?
27. Find the distance along the road from Porter Square to Green Street.

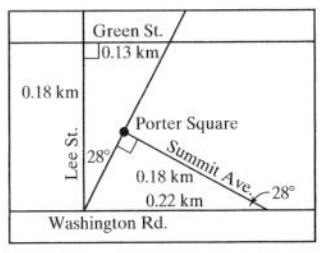

Understand

1. What methods can be used to show that two triangles are congruent?
SSS, SAS, and ASA

Plan and Carry Out

2. How can you find the length of a missing side?
Use the Pythagorean Theorem.
3. What is the total length of the missing hypotenuse?
0.22 km
4. Are the two triangles congruent? Why?
yes; by SAS
5. Sketch the two triangles. Mark their corresponding parts.

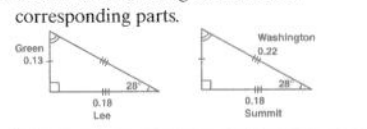

6. How far is Porter Square from the intersection of Lee Street and Washington Road?
0.13 km
7. What is the total length of the street from Washington to Green by the way of Porter Square? 0.22 km
8. Using your answer from Step 7, how can you find the distance from Porter Square to Green Street?
Subtract 0.13 km from 0.22 km; 0.09 km

Check

9. How could you show that these triangles are congruent by another method?
Sample answer: by SSS, using the Pythagorean Theorem.

Solve Another Problem

10. Explain why the pair of triangles shown are congruent. Find the missing measures in the diagram.
SAS; $x = 67°$, $y = 43°$ and $z = 8.2$ m

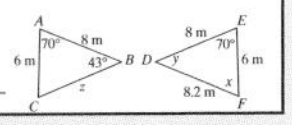

4. Assess & Reteach

PowerPoint

Lesson Quiz

Use $\triangle ABC$ and $\triangle XYZ$ to answer the questions.

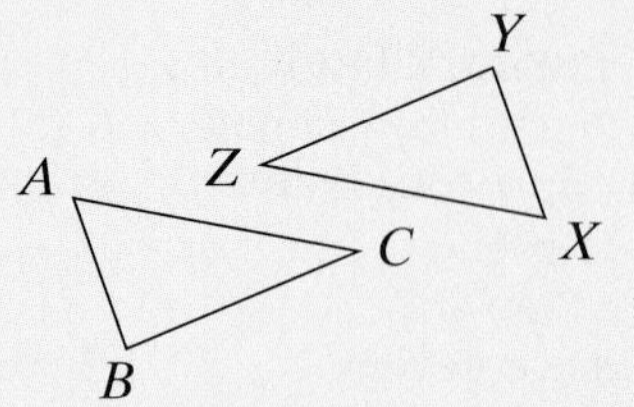

1. Suppose $AC = XZ$, $AB = XY$, and $BC = YZ$. Write a congruence statement for the figures. $\triangle ABC \cong \triangle XYZ$
2. Suppose $\triangle ABC$ and $\triangle XYZ$ are congruent. If $AB = 5$ cm, $BC = 8$ cm, and $AC = 10$ cm, find XZ. 10 cm
3. Suppose $\angle B \cong \angle Y$, $\angle A \cong \angle X$, and $\overline{AB} \cong \overline{XY}$. Why is $\triangle ABC \cong \triangle XYZ$? ASA
4. Let $AB = XY = 9$ inches; $BC = YZ = 24$ inches; and $m\angle B = 85°$, $m\angle Z = 35°$, and $m\angle Y = 85°$. Prove that the triangles are congruent and find $m\angle C$. $\triangle ABC \cong \triangle XYZ$ by SAS; $m\angle C = 35°$

32. 0.15 33. 0.0372
34. 1.8 35. 0.00015
36. 0.0049

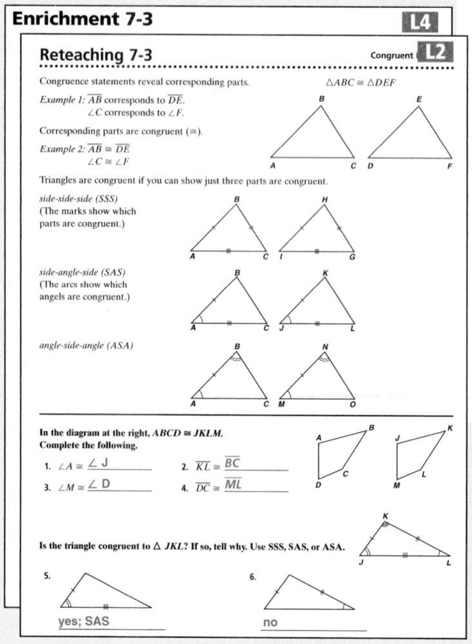

Enrichment 7-3 L4

Reteaching 7-3 Congruent L2

Congruence statements reveal corresponding parts. $\triangle ABC \cong \triangle DEF$

Example 1: $\overline{AB}$ corresponds to $\overline{DE}$. $\angle C$ corresponds to $\angle F$.

Corresponding parts are congruent (≅).

Example 2: $\overline{AB} \cong \overline{DE}$; $\angle C \cong \angle F$

Triangles are congruent if you can show just three parts are congruent.

side-side-side (SSS) (The marks show which parts are congruent.)

side-angle-side (SAS) (The arcs show which angles are congruent.)

angle-side-angle (ASA)

In the diagram at the right, ABCD ≅ JKLM. Complete the following.

1. $\angle A \cong$ ∠ J 2. $\overline{KL} \cong$ $\overline{BC}$
3. $\angle M \cong$ ∠ D 4. $\overline{DC} \cong$ $\overline{ML}$

Is the triangle congruent to △ JKL? If so, tell why. Use SSS, SAS, or ASA.

5. yes; SAS 6. no

GO Online
Homework Video Tutor
Visit: PHSchool.com
Web Code: ase-0703

25.

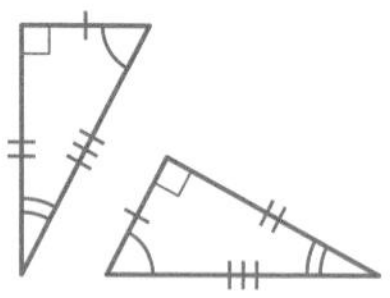

28. SAS or ASA; $m\angle E = 59°$; $DE = VX = 10$

GPS **Maps** **Use the map at the right for Exercises 24–27.**

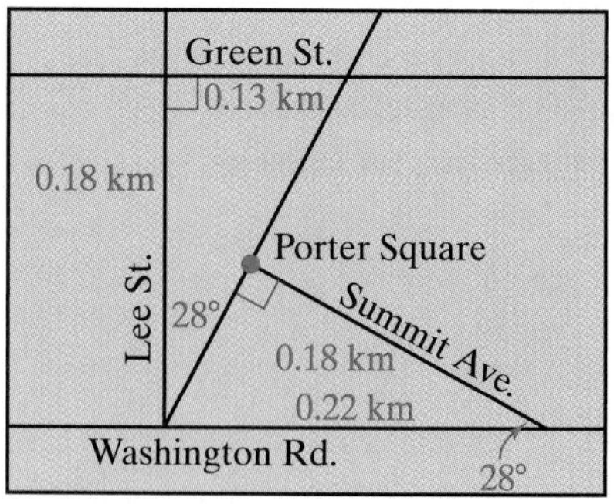

24. Show that the triangles in the map are congruent. ASA
25. Copy the triangles. Mark the sides and angles to show congruent corresponding parts.
26. How far is Porter Square from the intersection of Lee Street and Washington Road? 0.13 km
27. Find the distance along the road from Porter Square to Green Street. 0.09 km

C 28. **Challenge** Show that the two triangles at the right are congruent. Then find the missing measures.

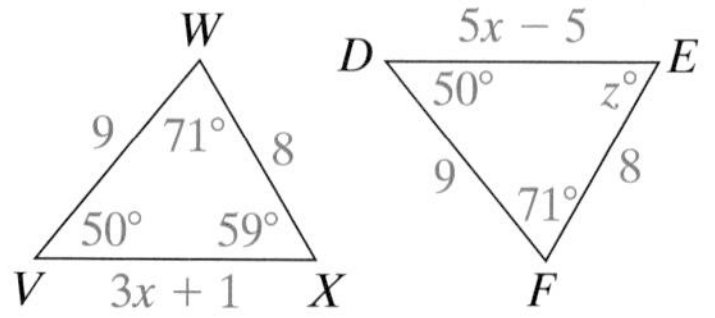

Test Prep and Mixed Review

Practice

Multiple Choice

29. James wants to buy a textbook. The price at University Bookstore is 12% off of \$24.50. Carson Books is selling the same book for 20% off of \$28. Why should James go to the University Bookstore? A
 - A The cost of the book after the discount was \$0.84 more at Carson Books.
 - B The cost of the book after the discount was \$0.84 more at University Bookstore.
 - C The price before the discount was less at University Bookstore.
 - D The percent of discount was more at Carson Books.

30. Which point on the graph at the right has the x-coordinate with the largest value? J
 - F P H R
 - G Q J S

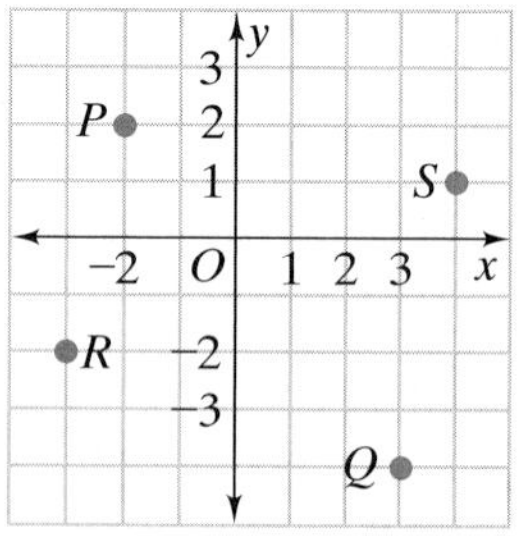

31. In 40 minutes, Alex can pick 3 quarts of berries. If 4 people work at that rate, how long will they take to pick 15 quarts? B
 - A 30 min B 50 min C 160 min D 200 min

GO for Help

For Exercises	See Lesson
32–36	5-1

Write each percent as a decimal. 32–36. See margin.

32. 15% 33. 3.72% 34. 180% 35. 0.015% 36. 0.49%

Test Prep

Resources

For additional practice with a variety of test item formats:
- Test-Taking Strategies, p. 345
- Test Prep, p. 349
- Test-Taking Strategies with Transparencies

Alternative Assessment

Students draw two triangles given the following information: In $\triangle FGH$ and $\triangle PQR$, $\overline{FH} \cong \overline{PR}$ and $\overline{GH} \cong \overline{QR}$. Students find what additional information is needed to prove $\triangle FGH \cong \triangle PQR$.
$\overline{FG} \cong \overline{PQ}$ or $\angle FHG \cong \angle PRQ$

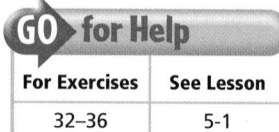

Checkpoint Quiz 1

Lessons 7-1 through 7-3

Identify each pair of angles as *adjacent, corresponding, alternate interior,* or *vertical.*

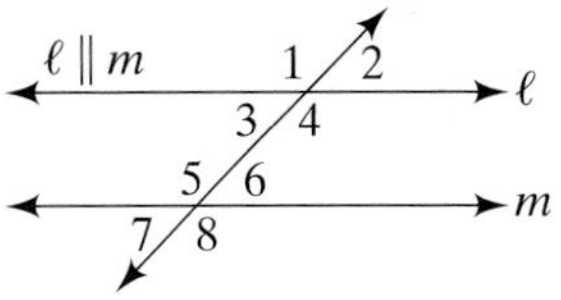

1. $\angle 6$, $\angle 7$ vertical
2. $\angle 4$, $\angle 5$ alternate interior
3. $\angle 2$, $\angle 6$ corresponding
4. $\angle 3$, $\angle 4$ adjacent
5. $\angle 1$, $\angle 5$ corresponding
6. $\angle 7$, $\angle 8$ adjacent
7. Show that the pair of triangles at the right is congruent. Answers may vary. Sample: SAS, ASA, or SSS; $\triangle JKD \cong \triangle WTB$.
8. Let $m\angle C = 67°$. Find the measures of the complement and the supplement. 23°; 113°

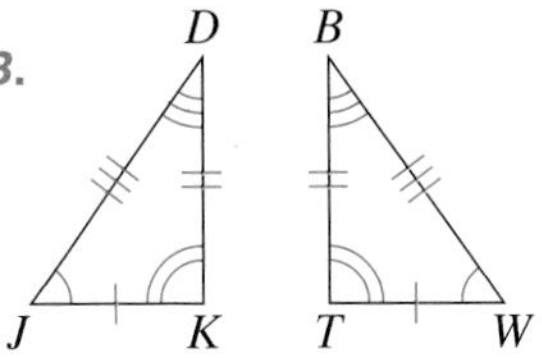

In the diagram below, *APKS* ≅ *OFND*. Find each measure.

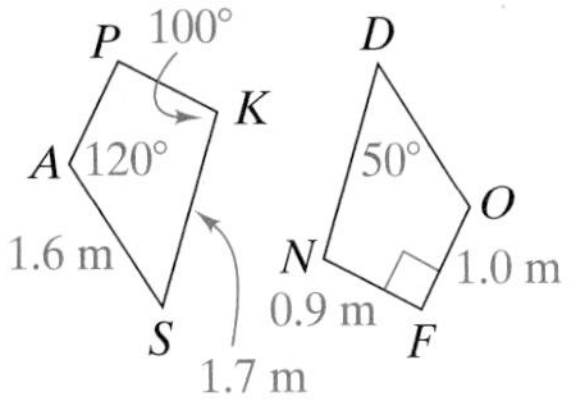

9. $m\angle N$ 100°
10. $m\angle P$ 90°
11. $m\angle O$ 120°
12. PK 0.9 m
13. DO 1.6 m
14. DN 1.7 m

MATH AT WORK

Dancers

Modern dance allows for freedom of movement and self-expression. Other types of dance include folk, classical ballet, ethnic, tap, and jazz.

You might wonder how math applies to dance. Dancers often perform as a group. The choreography, or arranged movements of the dance, often consists of repeated steps. Knowledge of patterns helps dancers memorize the steps and synchronize themselves with the other dancers.

Go Online PHSchool.com **For:** Information on Dancers **Web Code:** asb-2031

317

Checkpoint Quiz

Use this Checkpoint Quiz to check students' understanding of the skills and concepts of Lessons 7-1 through 7-3.

Resources

- All in One Teaching Resources Checkpoint Quiz 1
- ExamView Assessment Suite CD-ROM
- Success Tracker Online Intervention

MATH AT WORK

Dancers

This feature introduces students to a career that is not typically associated with mathematical skill. Students learn about what dancers do and how pattern recognition is important to their work.

Guided Instruction

Have students discuss where they might find examples of math, including topics from this chapter, in dance.

Ask questions such as:

- *What kinds of choreography have you seen? What types of dancing do you enjoy?* Sample: ballet, tap, hip-hop, ballroom
- *What types of dancers form angles with their bodies? How might congruent angles be important in synchronized dancing?* Sample: ballet dancers; dancers might need to make exactly the same movements and form the same angle measures for certain steps

7-4

1. Plan

Objective
To classify triangles and quadrilaterals

Examples
1 Classifying Triangles
2 Classifying Quadrilaterals

Math Understandings: p. 300D

Professional Development

Math Background

Triangles can be classified by their greatest angle: acute ($< 90°$), obtuse ($> 90°$), or right ($= 90°$). Triangles can also be classified by how many congruent sides they have: scalene (0), isosceles (2), or equilateral (3). Quadrilaterals are classified by their sides and angles and may have more than one name. For example, a square is also a rhombus, a rectangle, and a parallelogram, but it is not a trapezoid.

More Math Background: p. 300D

Lesson Planning and Resources

See p. 300E for a list of the resources that support this lesson.

PowerPoint

Bell Ringer Practice

Check Skills You'll Need
Use student page, transparency, or PowerPoint. For intervention, direct students to:
Classifying Angles
Skills Handbook, p. 640

7-4 Classifying Triangles and Quadrilaterals

Check Skills You'll Need

1. **Vocabulary Review** How many degrees does a *right angle* have? 90°

Classify each angle as *acute, right, obtuse,* or *straight.*

2.
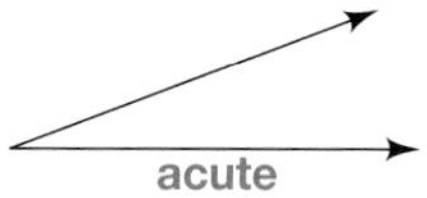
acute

3.
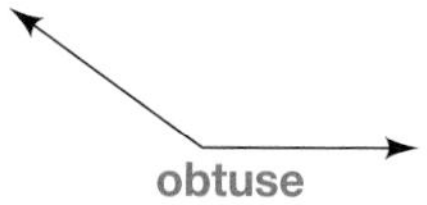
obtuse

GO for Help Skills Handbook page 640

What You'll Learn

To classify triangles and quadrilaterals

New Vocabulary acute triangle, obtuse triangle, right triangle, equilateral triangle, isosceles triangle, scalene triangle, quadrilateral, parallelogram, trapezoid, rhombus, rectangle, square

Why Learn This?

When you understand the properties of shapes, you can make designs such as quilt patterns.

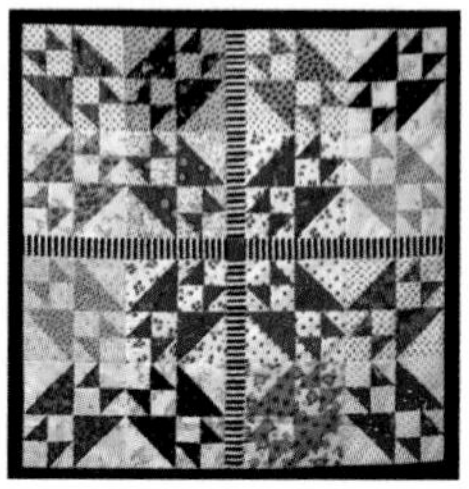

You can classify triangles by their angles and by their sides.

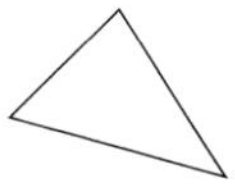
acute triangle
three acute angles

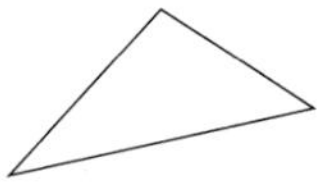
obtuse triangle
one obtuse angle

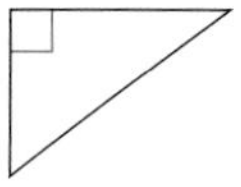
right triangle
one right angle

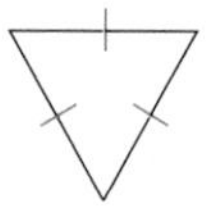
equilateral triangle
three congruent sides

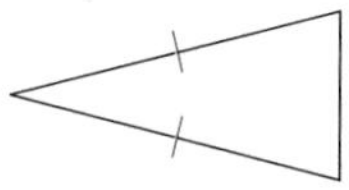
isosceles triangle
at least two congruent sides

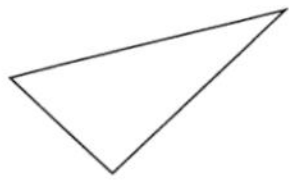
scalene triangle
no congruent sides

Vocabulary Tip
The prefix *equi-* means "equal." The word *equilateral* means "having equal sides."

EXAMPLE Classifying Triangles

1 **Signs** Classify the triangle in the sign at the right by its sides and its angles.

The triangle has three sides that are not congruent, and a right angle. It is a scalene right triangle.

Quick Check

1. Classify each triangle by its sides and its angles.

a.
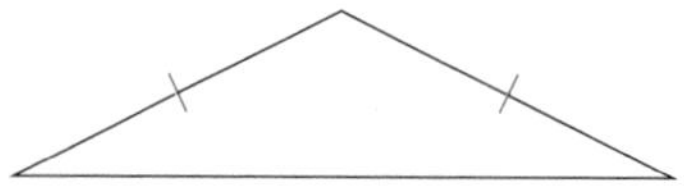
isosceles obtuse

b.

equilateral acute

Differentiated Instruction Solutions for All Learners

Special Needs L1	**Below Level** L2
For the vocabulary section, students who are able draw a couple of examples for each definition. Then students match the definitions to polygon names. learning style: visual	Students draw a rhombus that is not a square. learning style: visual

Vocabulary Tip

Quadrilateral comes from the Latin prefix *quad*, meaning "four," and the word *latus*, meaning "side."

You can classify quadrilaterals by their sides and angles. Arrowheads on the sides of quadrilaterals tell you which sides are parallel.

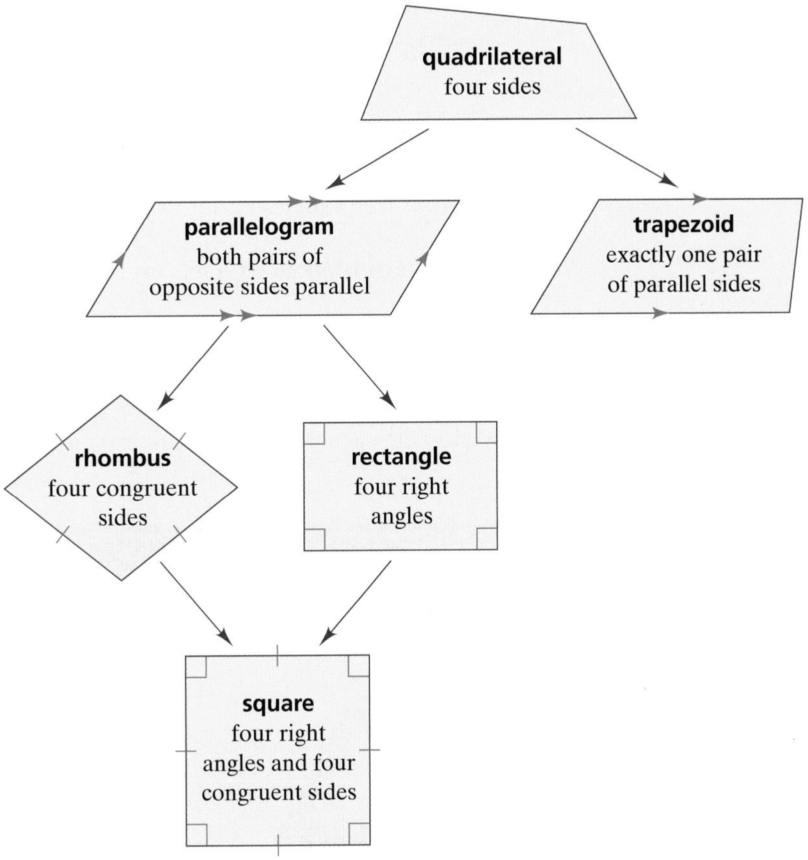

You name quadrilaterals by listing their vertices in consecutive order.

EXAMPLE Classifying Quadrilaterals

2 **Multiple Choice** What is the best name for parallelogram *DGHJ* at the right?

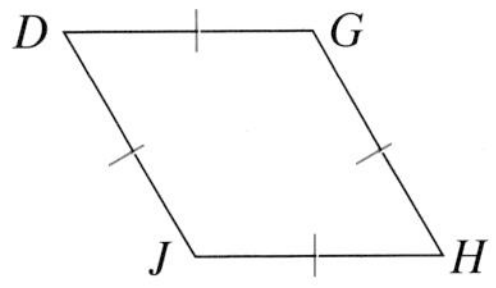

Ⓐ trapezoid Ⓒ rectangle
Ⓑ rhombus Ⓓ square

DGHJ has two pairs of opposite sides that are parallel, so it is a parallelogram. It has four congruent sides, so it is a rhombus. The best answer is choice B.

Test Prep Tip

A quadrilateral can have more than one name. If it does, use the name that describes it most precisely.

Quick Check

2. What is the best name for each quadrilateral? Explain.

a. 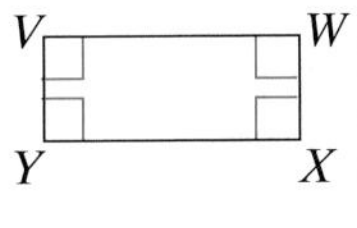

Rectangle; the quadrilateral has four right angles.

b. 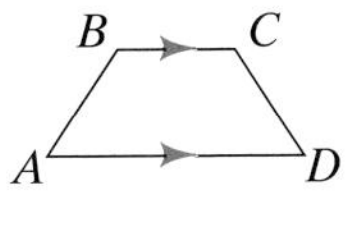

Trapezoid; the quadrilateral has exactly one pair of parallel sides.

2. Teach

Activity Lab

Use before the lesson.

All in One Teaching Resources

Activity Lab 7-4: Classifying Triangles and Quadrilaterals

Guided Instruction

Alternative Method
Have students use protractors and rulers to explore whether it is possible to draw an equilateral triangle that is not equiangular. **It is not possible.**

Connection to Geometry
Have students model each quadrilateral on geoboards and give the best name for each. Have them identify all the other possible names.

PowerPoint

Additional Examples

1 Classify △*LMN* by its sides and angles.

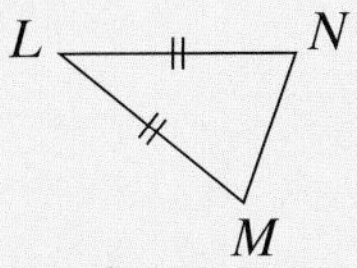

isosceles acute triangle

2 What is the best name for figure *WXYZ*? Explain your choice. **parallelogram; opposite sides are parallel but adjacent sides are not equal**

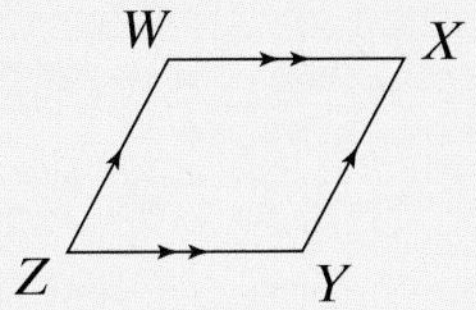

All in One Teaching Resources

- Daily Notetaking Guide 7-4 L3
- Adapted Notetaking 7-4 L1

Closure

- *How do you classify triangles and quadrilaterals?* **Sample: Triangles can be classified by angles or by congruent sides. Quadrilaterals are classified by sides and angles.**

Advanced Learners L4
Students explain how the angles formed by the diagonals of a rhombus differ from those of a rectangle that is not a rhombus. **diagonals of rhombus form 90° angles**

learning style: verbal

English Language Learners ELL
Students list the different types of triangles and quadrilaterals on a piece of paper. They draw triangles and quadrilaterals and identify each side length and angle measure. Then students match and label the drawings with the correct name.

learning style: visual

3. Practice

Assignment Guide

Check Your Understanding
Go over Exercises 1–7 in class before assigning the Homework Exercises.

Homework Exercises
A	Practice by Example	8–14
B	Apply Your Skills	15–25
C	Challenge	26
	Test Prep and Mixed Review	27–33

Homework Quick Check
To check students' understanding of key skills and concepts, go over Exercises 9, 12, 21, 22, and 25.

Differentiated Instruction Resources

Adapted Practice 7-4 L1

Practice 7-4 Classifying Triangles and Qua[drilateral]s L3

Determine the best name for each quadrilateral. Explain your choice.

1. parallelogram; opposite sides are parallel
2. rectangle; there are 4 right angles
3. square; there are 4 congruent sides and 4 right angles
4 rhombus; there are 4 congruent sides
5. rectangle; there are 4 right angles
6. $\triangle ABC \cong \triangle CDA$ parallelogram; since $\triangle ABC \approx \triangle CDA$, $\angle ABC \approx \angle CDA$ and $\angle BAC \approx \angle ACD$. So opposite sides are parallel using alt. int. angles

Classify each triangle by its sides and its angles. Explain your choice.

7. acute equilateral; all sides congruent
8. acute scalene; no sides congruent and all angles less than 90°
9. right scalene; right angle and no congruent sides

7-4 • Guided Problem Solving GPS L3

Student Page 321, Exercise 22:

The coordinates of three vertices of a parallelogram are (3, 5), (8, 5), and (1, −1). Find the coordinates of the fourth vertex.

Understand

1. Name the geometric figure in the problem. parallelogram
2. What do you know about the sides of this figure? Two pairs of opposite sides are parallel.
3. What do you know about the lengths of the opposite sides of this figure? The lengths of the opposite sides are equal.
4. What are you looking for? the coordinates of the fourth vertex

Plan and Carry Out

5. Plot the given points on the grid at right.
6. Must a parallelogram have right angles? no
7. Draw and measure the horizontal line segment. How long is it? 5 units
8. Keeping the length of the parallel lines the same, where should you place the point? (6, −1)

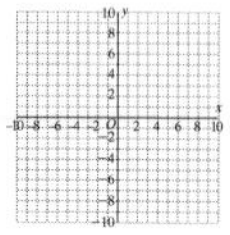

Check

9. Is every point plotted correctly to create a parallelogram? yes

Solve Another Problem

10. The coordinates of three vertices of a parallelogram are (2, 2), (4, 2), and (7, 5). What is the coordinate of the fourth vertex? (5, 5)

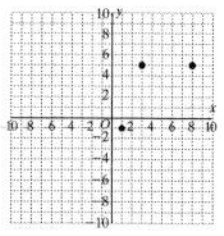

Check Your Understanding

Vocabulary **Match each definition to the figure it best describes.**

1. four right angles C
2. four congruent sides B
3. exactly one pair of parallel sides D
4. four right angles and four congruent sides A

A. square
B. rhombus
C. rectangle
D. trapezoid

Match each triangle with its correct name.

5. B 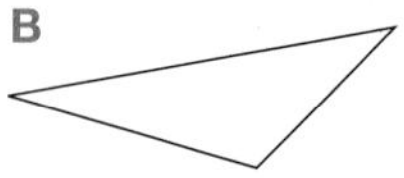
6. C 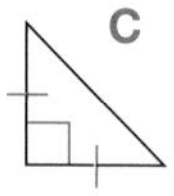
7. A 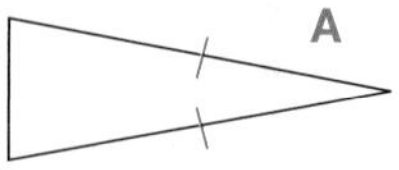

A. isosceles acute **B.** scalene obtuse **C.** isosceles right

Homework Exercises

For more exercises, see Extra Skills and Word Problems.

GO for Help

For Exercises	See Examples
8–10	1
11–14	2

A **Classify each triangle by its sides and its angles.**

8. 
equilateral acute

9. 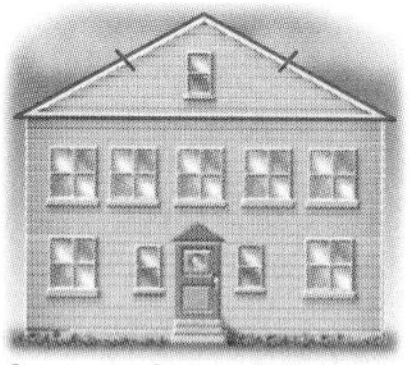
isosceles obtuse

10. 
scalene right

What is the best name for each quadrilateral? Explain.
11–14. Explanations may vary.

11. 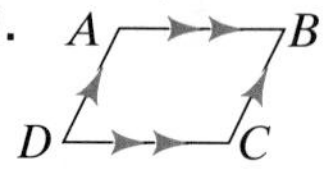

parallelogram

12. 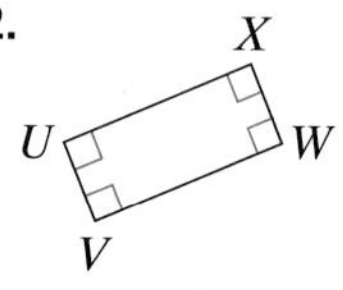

rectangle

13. 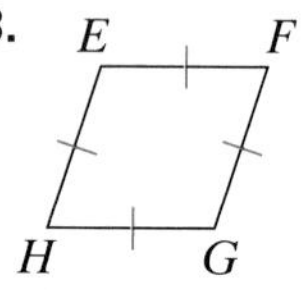

rhombus

14. 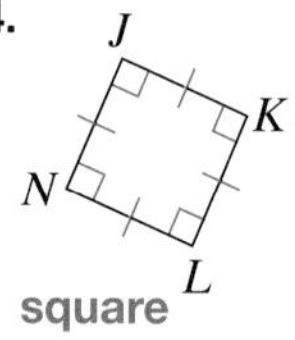

square

B GPS 15. **Guided Problem Solving** The perimeter of an equilateral triangle is 36 cm. You stick two equilateral triangles together to make a rhombus. Find the perimeter of the rhombus. 48 cm
- What do you know about the sides of an equilateral triangle?
- How many of these sides would make a rhombus?

Draw and label a figure to fit each description. 16–19. See margin.

16. isosceles right triangle
17. trapezoid with a right angle
18. rectangle with four congruent sides
19. trapezoid with two congruent sides

16–19. Answers may vary. Samples are given.

16. 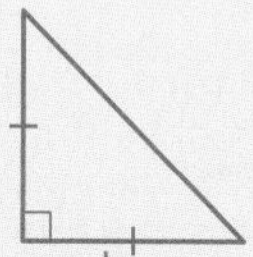

17. 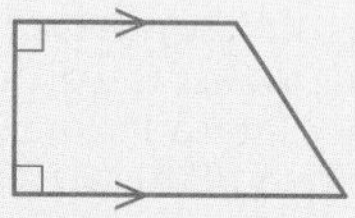

18. 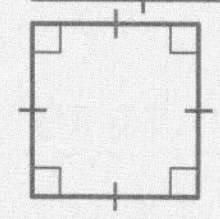

19. 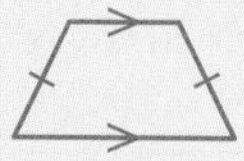

23. If a quadrilateral has two pairs of opposite sides that are parallel, then it is a parallelogram; true.

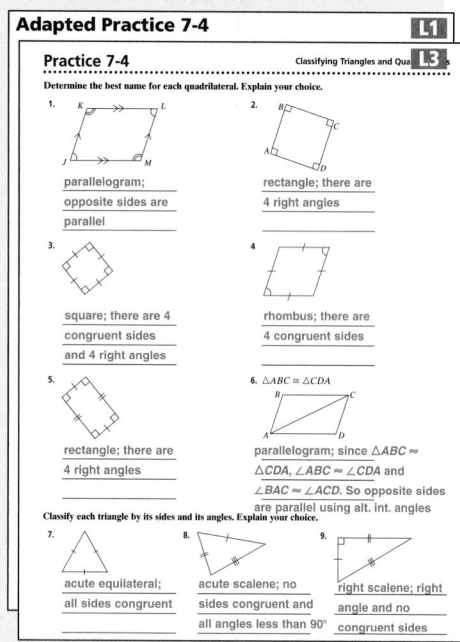

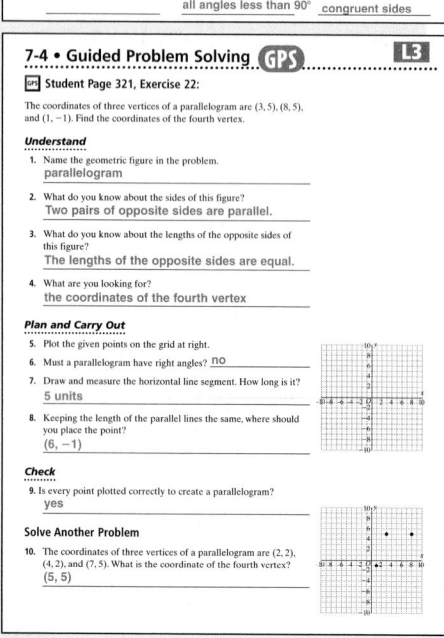

Go Online
Homework Video Tutor
Visit: PHSchool.com
Web Code: ase-0704

20. Sample answer: right isosceles triangle: $\triangle DCJ$; right scalene triangle: $\triangle TCR$; obtuse scalene triangle: $\triangle TKR$; acute scalene triangle: $\triangle ADJ$; quadrilateral: *ABRD*; parallelogram: *DRSJ*; rectangle: *ABGJ*; square: *CDGJ*; trapezoid: *TBDC*

21. A square has four right angles, like a rectangle, and four congruent sides, like a rhombus.

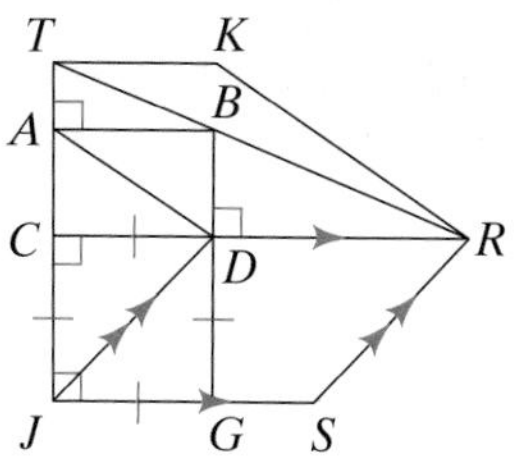

20. Give an example of each type of triangle or quadrilateral you see in the diagram at the right. See below left.

21. **Writing in Math** Why is a square both a rectangle and a rhombus? See left.

22. GPS The coordinates of three vertices of a parallelogram are $(3, 5)$, $(8, 5)$, and $(1, -1)$. Find the coordinates for the fourth vertex. $(6, -1)$

You can turn around "if-then" statements. Reverse each statement and decide whether the result is still a true statement.

SAMPLE If a quadrilateral is a rhombus, then it is a parallelogram.

If a quadrilateral is a parallelogram, then it is a rhombus. This statement is not true.

23–25. See margin.

23. If a quadrilateral is a parallelogram, then it has two pairs of opposite sides that are parallel.

24. If a rectangle has four congruent sides, then it is a square.

25. If a triangle is equilateral, then it is an isosceles triangle.

26a–c. Answers may vary. Samples are given.

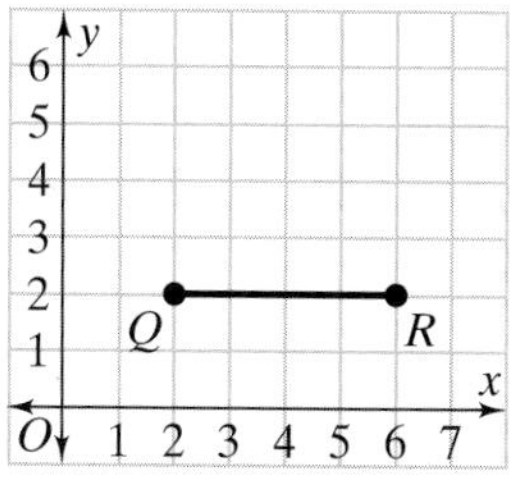

C 26. **Challenge** Name the coordinates of a point *P* in the graph at the left such that $\triangle PQR$ fits each description.

a. isosceles obtuse $(4, 3)$ **b.** scalene acute $(5, 5)$ **c.** isosceles right $(2, 6)$

Test Prep and Mixed Review

Practice

Multiple Choice

27. Which of the polygons listed CANNOT have four right angles? D
 A rectangle B rhombus C square D trapezoid

28. Two banners for advertising a new store are similar. The height of the letters on the smaller banner is 6 inches. The height of the letters on the larger banner is 15 inches. What scale factor was used to dilate the smaller banner to the larger one? J
 F 0.4 G 0.6 H 1.4 J 2.5

29. Which list shows the numbers $\frac{3}{5}$, $\frac{5}{8}$, 0.58, and 0.65 in order from least to greatest? A
 A $0.58, \frac{3}{5}, \frac{5}{8}, 0.65$
 B $0.58, 0.65, \frac{3}{5}, \frac{5}{8}$
 C $\frac{3}{5}, 0.58, \frac{5}{8}, 0.65$
 D $0.58, \frac{3}{5}, 0.65, \frac{5}{8}$

GO for Help

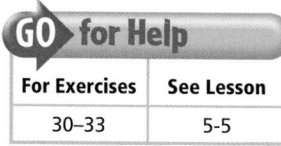

For Exercises	See Lesson
30–33	5-5

Find each percent of change. Round to the nearest tenth of a percent. Label your answer *increase* or *decrease*. 30–33. See margin.

30. 500 to 450 31. 11 to 18 32. 9.95 to 6.65 33. 12 to 13.52

Online lesson quiz, PHSchool.com, Web Code: asa-0704

Alternative Assessment

One student in a small group draws a quadrilateral or triangle but does not show it to anyone. Other students in the group take turns asking about its characteristics. The first student who guesses the correct name of the figure draws the next figure.

Test Prep

Resources
For additional practice with a variety of test item formats:
- Test-Taking Strategies, p. 345
- Test Prep, p. 349
- Test-Taking Strategies with Transparencies

4. Assess & Reteach

PowerPoint

Lesson Quiz

1. Classify the triangle according to its angles and sides.

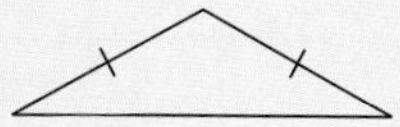

obtuse isosceles triangle

2. A triangle's sides are all congruent and its angles all measure 60°. Classify the triangle. equilateral, acute

3. Determine the best name for the quadrilateral. rhombus

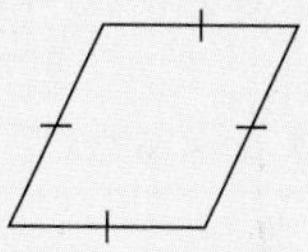

4. What is the best name for a figure that has four sides congruent, corresponding sides parallel, and all four angles congruent? square

24. If a rectangle is a square, then it has four congruent sides; true.

25. If a triangle is isosceles, then it is equilateral; not true.

30. 10% decrease

31. 63.6% increase

32. 33.2% decrease

33. 12.7% increase

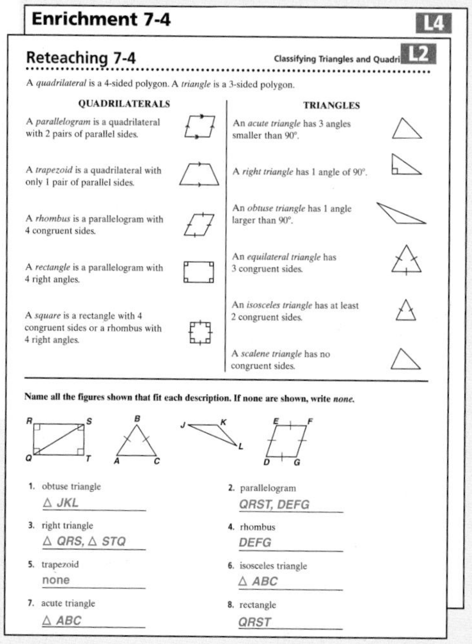
Enrichment 7-4 L4

Reteaching 7-4 Classifying Triangles and Quadri L2

A *quadrilateral* is a 4-sided polygon. A *triangle* is a 3-sided polygon.

QUADRILATERALS	TRIANGLES
A *parallelogram* is a quadrilateral with 2 pairs of parallel sides.	An *acute triangle* has 3 angles smaller than 90°.
A *trapezoid* is a quadrilateral with only 1 pair of parallel sides.	A *right triangle* has 1 angle of 90°.
A *rhombus* is a parallelogram with 4 congruent sides.	An *obtuse triangle* has 1 angle larger than 90°.
A *rectangle* is a parallelogram with 4 right angles.	An *equilateral triangle* has 3 congruent sides.
A *square* is a rectangle with 4 congruent sides or a rhombus with 4 right angles.	An *isosceles triangle* has at least 2 congruent sides.
	A *scalene triangle* has no congruent sides.

Name all the figures shown that fit each description. If none are shown, write *none*.

R S Q T B A C J K L E F D G

1. obtuse triangle $\triangle JKL$
2. parallelogram *QRST, DEFG*
3. right triangle $\triangle QRS$, $\triangle STQ$
4. rhombus *DEFG*
5. trapezoid none
6. isosceles triangle $\triangle ABC$
7. acute triangle $\triangle ABC$
8. rectangle *QRST*

Vocabulary Builder

Using Concept Maps

Graphic organizers provide visual representations of knowledge organized into patterns. They are valuable teaching tools that get students actively involved in their learning and help them to develop their critical-thinking skills. A concept map is a graphic organizer that shows the relationship between a main concept and supporting details. It is particularly useful for instruction in mathematics vocabulary, which is how it is used in the Example and in Exercise 2.

Guided Instruction

Discuss with students what a concept map is and how they can use one to help them focus on, understand, and remember math ideas. Then go over the sample concept map in the Example.

Teaching Tip
Check students' maps. Invite volunteers to display their maps and to explain the choices they made. Invite students to suggest other kinds of graphic organizers they could use for the same purpose.

Resources

- Vocabulary and Study Skills Worksheet.

2.

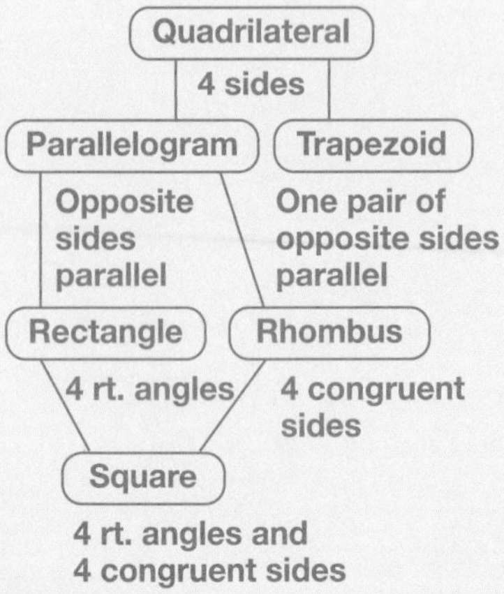

Vocabulary Builder

Using Concept Maps

Concept maps are visual tools that show how you can relate different ideas and terms you have used. Connecting new knowledge to existing knowledge is important in understanding mathematics.
To build a concept map, follow these steps:

- Place each concept or term inside a geometrical shape.
- Draw lines connecting the concepts or terms that are related.

EXAMPLE

In this chapter, you learned how different triangles can be classified by their angle measures or side lengths. You can show the relationships among these terms with the concept map below.

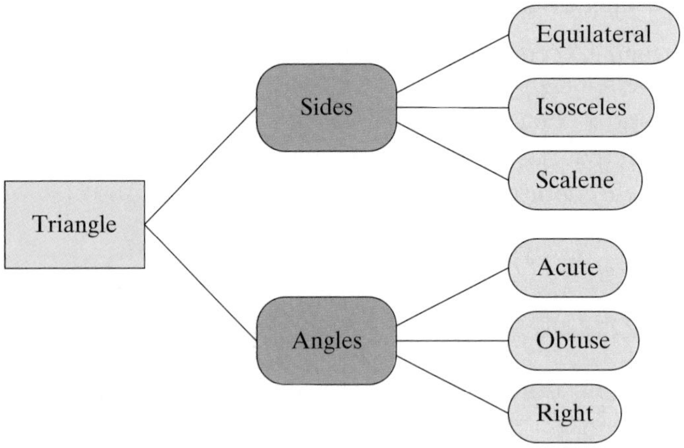

1.

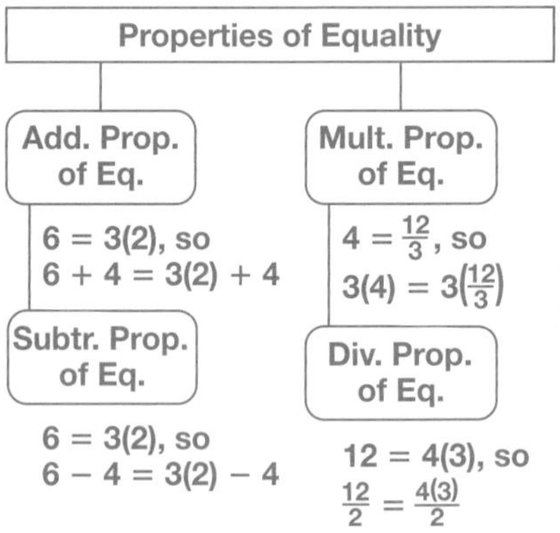

Exercises

1. Make a concept map for "Properties of Equality" using the following properties and examples from Chapter 1.
   - Addition Property of Equality
   - $12 = 4(3)$, so $\frac{12}{2} = \frac{4(3)}{2}$
   - $6 = 3(2)$, so $6 + 4 = (3)(2) + 4$
   - Multiplication Property of Equality
   - $6 = 3(2)$, so $6 - 4 = 3(2) - 4$
   - Subtraction Property of Equality
   - Division Property of Equality
   - $4 = \frac{12}{3}$, so $3(4) = 3\left(\frac{12}{3}\right)$
2. Use the terms from Lesson 7-4 that are related to quadrilaterals. Make a concept map showing the relationships among the terms. See margin.

Angle Sums

What is the sum of the measures of the angles of a figure such as a STOP sign? You can find the answer by drawing diagonals from one vertex to make triangles.

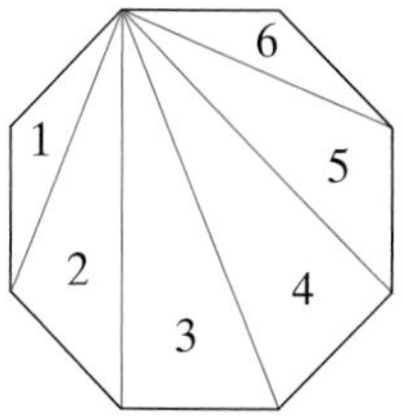

The diagonals form six triangles. The sum of the measures of all the angles of a triangle is 180°. The sum of the angles for a STOP sign is 6 × 180° = 1,080°.

ACTIVITY

You can develop a formula for finding the sum of the angles of a polygon.

1. Draw polygons with 4, 5, 6, and 7 sides. Draw all the diagonals from one vertex of each figure. Count the number of triangles formed. Check students' work.
2. Copy and complete the table below.

Number of Sides	Number of Triangles Formed	Sum of All Angle Measures
3	1	180°
■	■	■
■	■	■
■	■	■
■	■	■

Number of Sides	Number of Triangles Formed	Sum of All Angle Measures
3	1	180°
4	2	360°
5	3	540°
6	4	720°
7	5	900°

3. a. **Patterns** Describe how the sum of the angle measures changes as the number of sides of a polygon increases by 1. The sum increases by 180°.
   b. **Reasoning** What relationship do you notice between the number of sides of a polygon and the number of triangles formed? Explain. The number of triangles is two fewer than the number of sides.
4. a. An *exterior angle of a polygon* is an angle formed by a side and an extension of an adjacent side. ∠1, ∠2, ∠3, and ∠4 at the right are exterior angles of a polygon. Draw polygons with 3, 4, 5, and 6 sides. Draw and measure the exterior angles of each polygon.
   b. Find the sum of the measures of the exterior angles of each polygon. Record your information in a table.
   c. Make a conjecture about the sum of the exterior angles of a polygon. 4a–c. See margin.

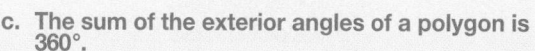

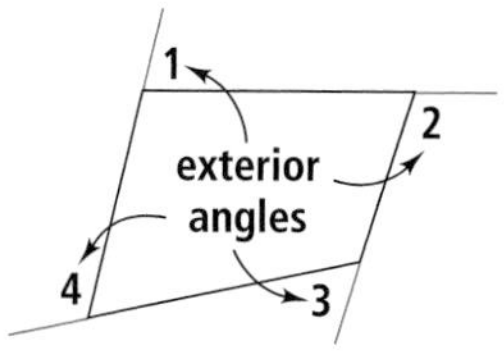

4a. Check students' work.

b.

Number of Sides	Sum of Angles
3	360°
4	360°
5	360°
6	360°

c. The sum of the exterior angles of a polygon is 360°.

Angle

In Lesson 7-5 … formula to f… measures of… develop tha… activity.

Guided Instruction

Before beginning the activity, review the names and attributes of polygons, from triangles through nonagons. Also review the meanings of *diagonal* and *vertex.*

Connection to Math
After students have completed their drawings and tables, ask:

- *How many diagonals can you draw from one vertex of any quadrilateral?* 1
- *Of any pentagon?* 2
- *Of any hexagon?* 3
- *How many diagonals can you draw from a vertex of a 10-sided figure?* 7
- *A 20-sided figure?* 17
- *An* n*-sided figure?* $n - 3$

Differentiated Instruction

Tactile Learners
Invite a volunteer to use a straightedge to draw a hexagon. Then use a protractor to find the sum of the measures of all six angles. Compare findings with those obtained using the formula.

Resources

- Activity Lab 7-5: Angles and Polygons
- rulers
- protractors

Plan

Objective
To find the angle measures of a polygon.

Examples
1 The Sum of Angle Measures of a Polygon
2 Angle Measures of a Polygon
3 Angle Measures of a Regular Polygon

Math Understandings: p. 300D

Professional Development

Math Background

A polygon has an interior angle at each vertex. The sum of the measures of all the interior angles of a polygon with n sides is $(n - 2)(180°)$. A *regular polygon* has all sides congruent and all angles congruent, so the measure of each of its angles is $\frac{(n-2)(180°)}{n}$.

More Math Background: p. 300D

Lesson Planning and Resources

See p. 300E for a list of the resources that support this lesson.

PowerPoint

Bell Ringer Practice

Check Skills You'll Need
Use student page, transparency, or PowerPoint. For intervention, direct students to:
Algebraic Expressions and Order of Operations
Lesson 1-1
Extra Skills and Word Problems Practice, Ch. 1

7-5 Angles and Polygons

Check Skills You'll Need

1. **Vocabulary Review** How do you *evaluate* an algebraic expression? See below.

Evaluate each expression for $a = 8$.

2. $3(a + 1)$ 27
3. $\frac{5a + 8}{a}$ 6
4. $(a - 2)6$ 36

GO for Help Lesson 1-1

What You'll Learn
To find the angle measures of a polygon

New Vocabulary regular polygon

Why Learn This?
Polygons often appear in art and architecture. In designing tile patterns, it helps to know about the angles of polygons.

Here is a list of common polygons.

Polygon Name	Number of Sides
Triangle	3
Quadrilateral	4
Pentagon	5
Hexagon	6
Heptagon	7

Polygon Name	Number of Sides
Octagon	8
Nonagon	9
Decagon	10
Dodecagon	12

Two consecutive sides of a polygon form one interior angle. The sum of the measures of the interior angles depends on the number of sides.

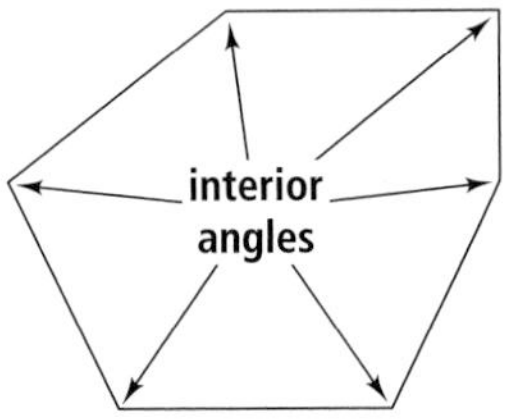

KEY CONCEPTS Polygon Angle Sum

For a polygon with n sides, the sum of the measures of the interior angles is $(n - 2)180°$.

EXAMPLE The Sum of Angle Measures of a Polygon

1 What is the sum of the measures of the interior angles of a nonagon?

$(n - 2)180° = (9 - 2)180°$ ← **A nonagon has nine sides. Substitute 9 for n.**
$= 1{,}260°$ ← **Simplify.**

The sum of the angle measures of a nonagon is $1{,}260°$.

Check Skills You'll Need

1. You replace each variable in the expression with a number and then simplify.

Quick Check

1. What is the sum of the measures of the interior angles of a heptagon? 900°

Differentiated Instruction Solutions for All Learners

Special Needs L1	Below Level L2
Students use a sheet with pictures of common polygons while working on the homework exercises. Feature regular polygons on a section of the page. learning style: visual	Students make posters that show and name polygons with various numbers of sides. learning style: visual

You can use the same formula to find angle measures in a polygon.

EXAMPLE Angle Measures of a Polygon

2 (Algebra) Find the missing angle measure in the pentagon at the right.

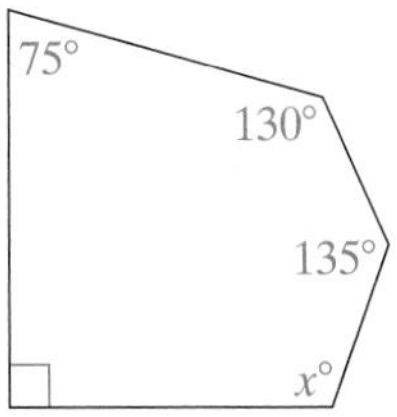

Step 1 Find the sum of the angle measures.

$(n - 2)180° = (5 - 2)180°$ ← **Substitute 5 for *n*.**

$= 540°$ ← **Simplify.**

Step 2 Write an equation. Let x = the missing angle measure.

$540° = 90° + 75° + 130° + 135° + x°$ ← **Write an equation.**

$540° = 430° + x°$ ← **Simplify.**

$110° = x°$ ← **Subtract 430° from each side.**

The missing angle measure is 110°.

Quick Check

2. A hexagon has five angles with measures of 142°, 84°, 123°, 130°, and 90°. What is the measure of the sixth angle? 151°

A **regular polygon** is a polygon with all sides congruent and all angles congruent. To find the measure of each angle of a regular polygon, divide the sum of the angle measures by the number of angles.

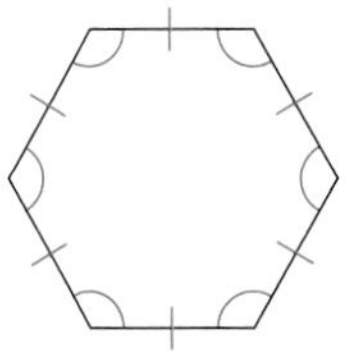

EXAMPLE Angle Measures of a Regular Polygon

3 **Multiple Choice** A carpenter wants to know the angle measures of the window at the right in order to cut out the correct space in a wall. If the window is a regular octagon, what is the measure of each angle?

(A) 85° (B) 135° (C) 142° (D) 156°

$(n - 2)180° = (8 - 2)180°$ ← **Substitute 8 for *n*.**

$= 1{,}080°$ ← **Simplify.**

$1{,}080° \div 8 = 135°$ ← **Divide the sum by the number of angles.**

Each angle of a regular octagon has a measure of 135°. The correct answer is choice B.

Quick Check

3. Find the measure of each angle of a regular polygon with 5 sides. 108°

Online active math

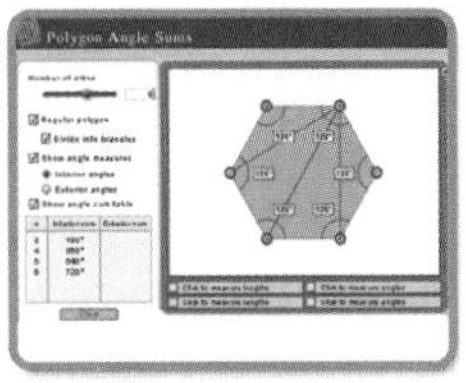

For: Polygon Angle Sums Activity
Use: Interactive Textbook, 7-5

Test Prep Tip

You can eliminate choice A because the angles of a regular octagon are obtuse.

2. Teach

Activity Lab

Use before the lesson.
Student Edition Activity Lab 7-5a, Angle Sums p. 323

All in One Teaching Resources
Activity Lab 7-5: Angles and Polygons

Guided Instruction

Teaching Tip
In Example 1, help students analyze the formula. Ask:
- *Is this formula the same if you write it as 180°(n − 2)?* Yes

Error Prevention!

In Example 3, ask students: *Why divide by n and not by n − 2?* **Sample: because there are *n* angles.**

PowerPoint

Additional Examples

1 Find the sum of the measures of the interior angles of an octagon. 1,080°

2 Find the missing angle measure in the hexagon. 122°

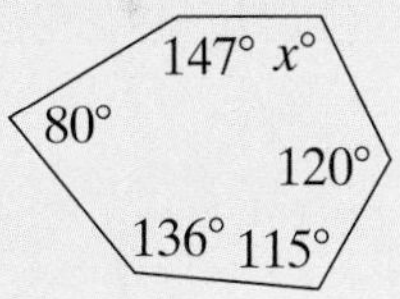

3 A design on a tile is in the shape of a regular nonagon. Find the measure of each angle. 140°

All in One Teaching Resources
- Daily Notetaking Guide 7-5 L3
- Adapted Notetaking 7-5 L1

Closure

- *How do you find the interior angle measures of a polygon?* **Sample: To find the sum for a polygon of *n* sides, use $(n - 2)180°$. To find each angle in a regular polygon of *n* sides, divide the sum by *n*.**

Advanced Learners L4	**English Language Learners** ELL
Students use a compass and straightedge to construct a regular hexagon within a circle. **learning style: tactile**	Students list the names of common polygons in a column. Next to each name, they draw the polygon. Next to each polygon, they write the number of sides, the number of angles, and the sum of the measures of its interior angles. Students read their lists to each other. **learning style: verbal**

3. Practice

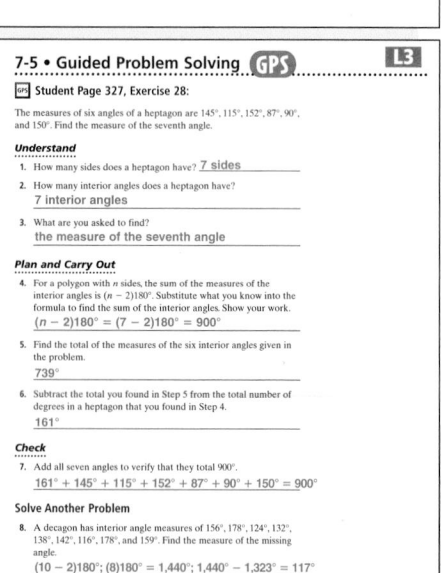

Assignment Guide

Check Your Understanding

Go over Exercises 1–6 in class before assigning the Homework Exercises.

Homework Exercises

A	Practice by Example	7–21
B	Apply Your Skills	22–29
C	Challenge	30
	Test Prep and Mixed Review	31–37

Homework Quick Check

To check students' understanding of key skills and concepts, go over Exercises 9, 17, 23, 27, and 28.

Differentiated Instruction Resources

Adapted Practice 7-5 L1

Practice 7-5 L3 Angles and ...s

Classify each polygon by its number of sides.

1. 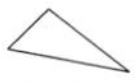 triangle
2.  hexagon
3.  heptagon
4. a polygon with 8 sides octagon
5. a polygon with 10 sides decagon
6. Find the measure of each angle of a regular hexagon. 120°
7. The measures of four angles of a pentagon are 143°, 118°, 56°, and 97°. Find the measure of the missing angle. 126°
8. Four of the angles of a hexagon measure 53°, 126°, 89°, and 117°. What is the sum of the measures of the other two angles? 335°
9. Four of the angles of a heptagon measure 109°, 158°, 117°, and 89°. What is the sum of the measures of the other three angles? 427°
10. Complete the chart for the total number of diagonals from all vertices in each polygon. The first three have been done for you.

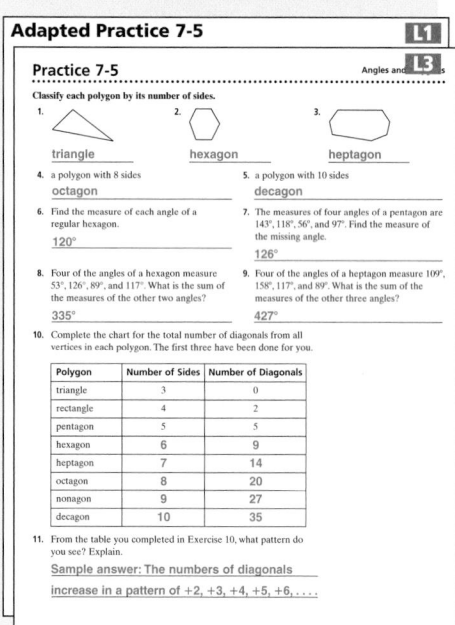

Polygon	Number of Sides	Number of Diagonals
triangle	3	0
rectangle	4	2
pentagon	5	5
hexagon	6	9
heptagon	7	14
octagon	8	20
nonagon	9	27
decagon	10	35

11. From the table you completed in Exercise 10, what pattern do you see? Explain.
Sample answer: The numbers of diagonals increase in a pattern of +2, +3, +4, +5, +6, ...

7-5 • Guided Problem Solving GPS L3

GPS **Student Page 327, Exercise 28:**

The measures of six angles of a heptagon are 145°, 115°, 152°, 87°, 90°, and 150°. Find the measure of the seventh angle.

Understand

1. How many sides does a heptagon have? 7 sides
2. How many interior angles does a heptagon have? 7 interior angles
3. What are you asked to find? the measure of the seventh angle

Plan and Carry Out

4. For a polygon with n sides, the sum of the measures of the interior angles is $(n-2)180°$. Substitute what you know into the formula to find the sum of the interior angles. Show your work.
$(n-2)180° = (7-2)180° = 900°$
5. Find the total of the measures of the six interior angles given in the problem. 739°
6. Subtract the total you found in Step 5 from the total number of degrees in a heptagon that you found in Step 4. 161°

Check

7. Add all seven angles to verify that they total 900°.
$161° + 145° + 115° + 152° + 87° + 90° + 150° = 900°$

Solve Another Problem

8. A decagon has interior angle measures of 156°, 178°, 124°, 132°, 138°, 142°, 116°, 178°, and 159°. Find the measure of the missing angle.
$(10-2)180°; (8)180° = 1{,}440°; 1{,}440° - 1{,}323° = 117°$

Check Your Understanding

1. A regular polygon is a polygon with all sides congruent and all angles congruent.

6. Miranda; the sum of the angle measures of a dodecagon is $(12-2)180°$, not $(6-2)180° \cdot 2$.

1. **Vocabulary** What is a regular polygon?

Classify each polygon by the number of its sides.

2. 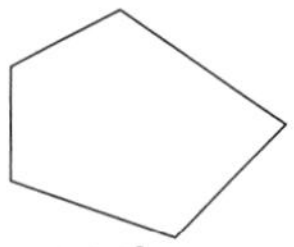 pentagon

3. 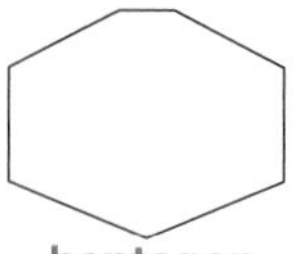 heptagon

4. 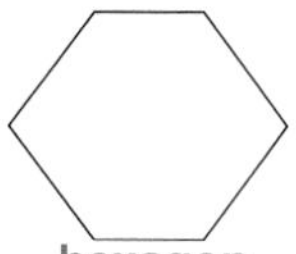 hexagon

5. 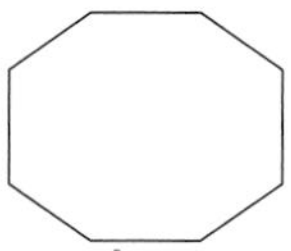 octagon

6. **Error Analysis** Jason knows the sum of the angle measures of a hexagon is 720°. To find the sum of the angle measures of a dodecagon, he multiplies 720° by 2 since $12 = 6 \cdot 2$. Miranda multiplies 180° by 10. Who is correct? Explain.

Homework Exercises

For more exercises, see Extra Skills and Word Problems.

GO for Help

For Exercises	See Examples
7–12	1
13–15	2
16–21	3

A **Find the sum of the measures of the interior angles of each polygon.**

7. pentagon 540°
8. octagon 1,080°
9. hexagon 720°
10. decagon 1,440°
11. triangle 180°
12. dodecagon 1,800°

Algebra **Find the missing angle measure in each figure.**

13. 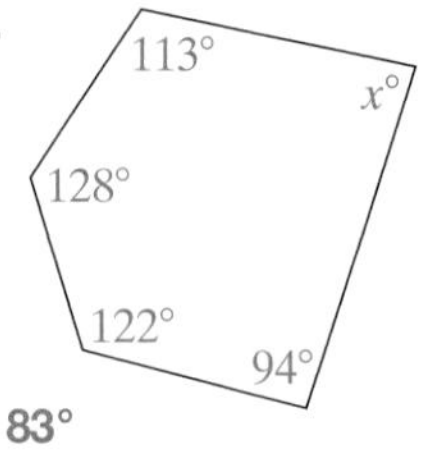

83°

14. 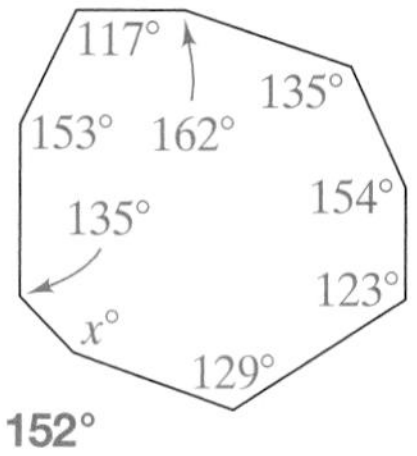

152°

15. 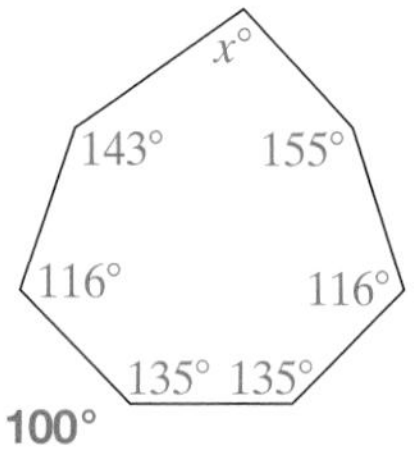

100°

16. **Coins** The Australian 50-cent coin at the left is a regular dodecagon. What is the measure of each interior angle of the coin? 150°

Find the measure of each angle of a regular polygon with the given number of sides. Round to the nearest tenth.

17. 7 128.6°
18. 10 144°
19. 14 154.3°
20. 15 156°
21. 18 160°

B GPS 22. **Guided Problem Solving** The measure of each interior angle of a regular polygon is 157.5°. How many sides n does the polygon have?
- What two expressions can you write for the sum of the measures of the interior angles of the polygon?
- What is the solution for n when you set the two expressions equal to each other? 16 sides

Online Homework Video Tutor
Visit: PHSchool.com
Web Code: ase-0705

23. **Reasoning** What is another name for a regular quadrilateral? square

Algebra **Find the missing angle measures in each figure.**

24. 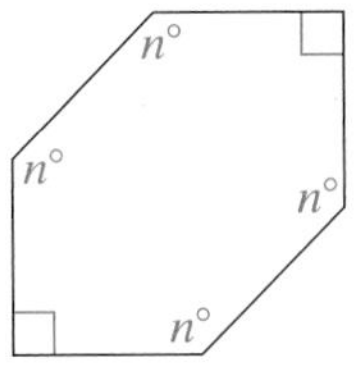

$n = 135°$

25. 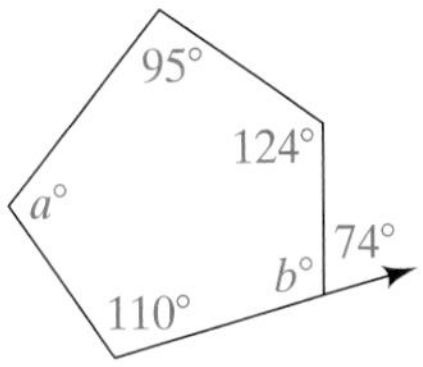

$a = 105°; b = 106°$

26. 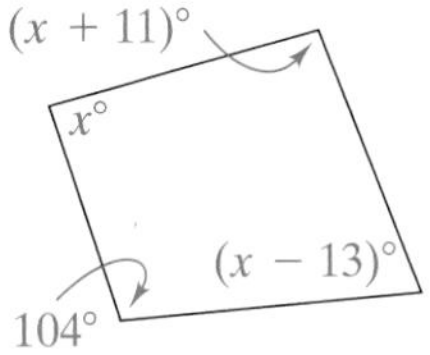

See margin.

27. **Writing in Math** An irregular polygon is a polygon that is *not* regular. Explain why you cannot find the measure of each angle in an irregular polygon by dividing the sum of the angle measures by the number of angles. See margin.

28. The measures of six angles of a heptagon are 145°, 115°, 152°, 87°, 90°, and 150°. Find the measure of the seventh angle. 161°

29. **Baseball** In the home plate at the left, $\angle 1 \cong \angle 2$. Find $m\angle 1$. 135°

30. **Challenge** A polygon is chosen at random from five regular polygons with 3, 4, 5, 6, and 8 sides. What is the probability that the measure of each angle of the polygon is a multiple of 30°? $\frac{3}{5}$, or 60%

Test Prep and Mixed Review

Practice

Multiple Choice

31. The following statements are true about $\triangle ABC$.
- $m\angle A$ is less than $m\angle B$.
- $m\angle B$ is less than $m\angle C$.
- $m\angle C$ is less than 90°.
- Each angle measure is divisible by 3.

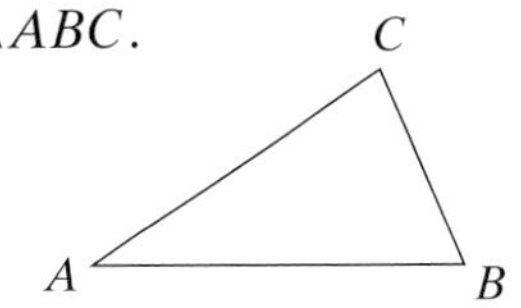

Which are possible measures of angles A, B, and C? B

A. $m\angle A = 33°, m\angle B = 66°, m\angle C = 99°$
B. $m\angle A = 33°, m\angle B = 66°, m\angle C = 81°$
C. $m\angle A = 81°, m\angle B = 66°, m\angle C = 33°$
D. $m\angle A = 30°, m\angle B = 60°, m\angle C = 90°$

32. The area of a square is 275 square feet. Which is closest to the side length of the square? J

F. 15.8 ft G. 16.1 ft H. 16.4 ft J. 16.6 ft

33. A distributor places a coupon for a free subscription inside 2 of 15,978 daily newspapers. What percent of the newspapers have a coupon? D

A. 12.5% B. 1.3% C. 0.125% D. 0.013%

GO for Help

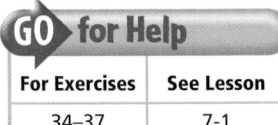

For Exercises	See Lesson
34–37	7-1

Find the measure of the supplement of each angle.

34. 65° 115° 35. 48° 132° 36. 127° 53° 37. 153° 27°

26. $x = 86°; (x + 11) = 97°; (x - 13) = 73°$
27. The angles in an irregular polygon are not all congruent.

Test Prep

Resources

For additional practice with a variety of test item formats:
- Test-Taking Strategies, p. 345
- Test Prep, p. 349
- Test-Taking Strategies with Transparencies

4. Assess & Reteach

PowerPoint

Lesson Quiz

1. Find the sum of the measures of the interior angles of a polygon having 17 sides. 2,700°
2. Five angles of a hexagon measure 128°, 190°, 112°, 154°, and 90°. Find the measure of the missing angle. 46°
3. Find the measure of each angle of a regular polygon having 24 sides. 165°
4. A regular figure has an interior angle measure of 135°. How many sides does it have? 8

Alternative Assessment

Pairs of students write down the following information: nine angles of a decagon measure 150°. They find the measure of the missing angle. 90°

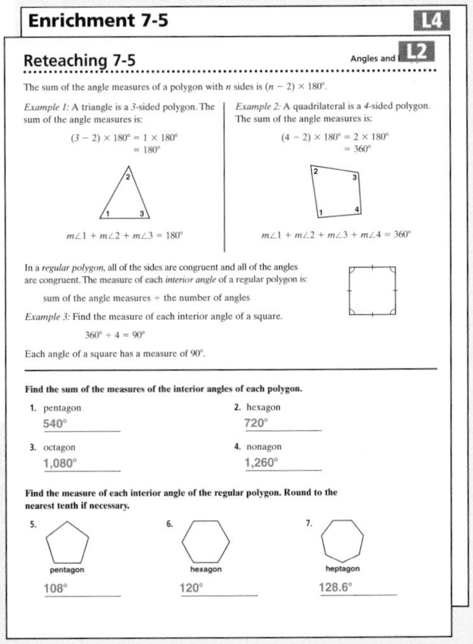
Enrichment 7-5 L4

Reteaching 7-5 Angles and L2

The sum of the angle measures of a polygon with n sides is $(n - 2) \times 180°$.

Example 1: A triangle is a 3-sided polygon. The sum of the angle measures is:

$(3 - 2) \times 180° = 1 \times 180° = 180°$

$m\angle 1 + m\angle 2 + m\angle 3 = 180°$

Example 2: A quadrilateral is a 4-sided polygon. The sum of the angle measures is:

$(4 - 2) \times 180° = 2 \times 180° = 360°$

$m\angle 1 + m\angle 2 + m\angle 3 + m\angle 4 = 360°$

In a *regular polygon*, all of the sides are congruent and all of the angles are congruent. The measure of each *interior angle* of a regular polygon is:

sum of the angle measures ÷ the number of angles

Example 3: Find the measure of each interior angle of a square.

$360° \div 4 = 90°$

Each angle of a square has a measure of 90°.

Find the sum of the measures of the interior angles of each polygon.

1. pentagon 540°
2. hexagon 720°
3. octagon 1,080°
4. nonagon 1,260°

Find the measure of each interior angle of the regular polygon. Round to the nearest tenth if necessary.

5. pentagon 108°
6. hexagon 120°
7. heptagon 128.6°

7-6

1. Plan

Objective
To find areas of parallelograms, triangles, and trapezoids

Examples
1 Finding the Area of a Triangle
2 Finding the Area of a Trapezoid

Math Understandings: p. 300D

Professional Development

Math Background

The area of a polygon is measured by finding the number of square units it encloses. For this reason, area is measured in square units, such as square inches (in.^{2}) or square meters (m^2).

To find the area of a rectangle or a parallelogram, use $A = bh$. For a triangle, use $A = \frac{1}{2}bh$. For a trapezoid, use $A = \frac{1}{2}h(b_1 + b_2)$.

More Math Background: p. 300D

Lesson Planning and Resources

See p. 300E for a list of the resources that support this lesson.

PowerPoint

Bell Ringer Practice

Check Skills You'll Need
Use student page, transparency, or PowerPoint. For intervention, direct students to:

Formulas
Lesson 2-6
Extra Skills and Word Problems Practice, Ch. 2

7-6 Areas of Polygons

Check Skills You'll Need

1. **Vocabulary Review** What is a *formula*? See below.

Find the area of each figure.

2. 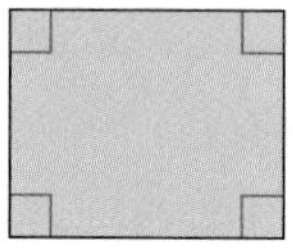

80 cm^2

3. 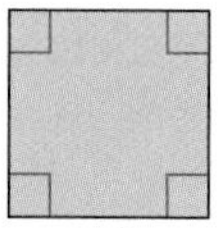

49 ft^2

GO for Help Lesson 2-6

What You'll Learn

To find the areas of parallelograms, triangles, and trapezoids

New Vocabulary area

Why Learn This?

People who work in fields such as construction and engineering must calculate area to find how much material they need for a job. The 15 square tiles at the right cover 15 square units of area.

The **area** of a figure is the number of square units the figure encloses.

The formula for the area of a parallelogram is $A = bh$, where b is the base, and h is the perpendicular distance between the bases.

KEY CONCEPTS **Area of a Parallelogram**

The area of a parallelogram equals the product of any base length b and the corresponding height h.

$$A = bh$$

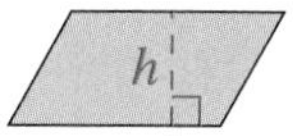

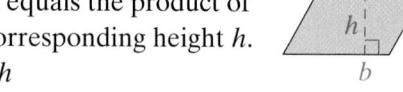

A diagonal divides a parallelogram into two congruent triangles. The area of each triangle is *half* the area of the parallelogram.

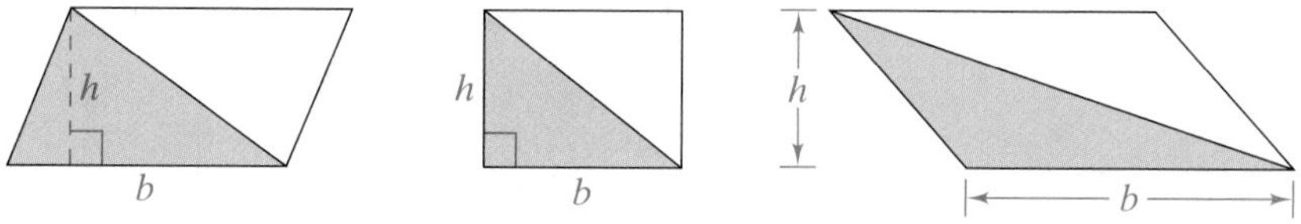

Any side of a triangle can be the base. The height of a triangle is the perpendicular distance between the base and the opposite vertex.

KEY CONCEPTS **Area of a Triangle**

The area of a triangle equals half the product of any base length b and the corresponding height h.

$$A = \frac{1}{2}bh$$

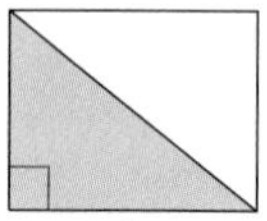

Check Skills You'll Need

1. A formula is a rule that shows the relationship between two or more quantities.

Differentiated Instruction Solutions for All Learners

Special Needs L1
For Example 1, students draw the triangle on grid paper, then add a congruent triangle to form a parallelogram. Show them that the parallelogram's area is *bh*. Show them that the triangle, which is half of the parallelogram's size, must have an area of $\frac{1}{2}bh$.
learning style: visual

Below Level L2
Students draw different parallelograms, triangles, and trapezoids. They draw a dotted line that represents the height in each of their diagrams. If the height is also a side of the polygon, they color it.
learning style: visual

EXAMPLE Finding the Area of a Triangle

1 **Architecture** An architect plans to cover the front triangular section of a townhouse with cedar shingles. Find the area of the triangle at the left.

$A = \frac{1}{2}bh$ ← **Use the formula for the area of a triangle.**

$= \frac{1}{2} \cdot 24 \cdot 16$ ← **Substitute 24 for *b* and 16 for *h*.**

$= 192$ ← **Multiply.**

The area is 192 ft^2.

Quick Check

1. Find the area of the triangle below. **10.5 cm^2**

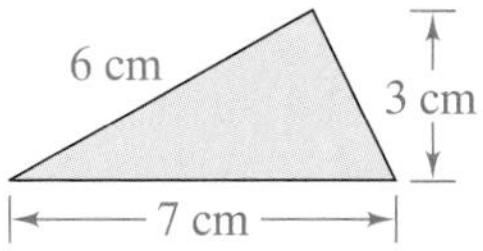

A trapezoid has two parallel sides, or bases, b_1 and b_2. The height h of a trapezoid is the perpendicular distance between the two bases.

You can use the diagram below to develop the formula for the area of a trapezoid. You can arrange two congruent trapezoids to form a parallelogram.

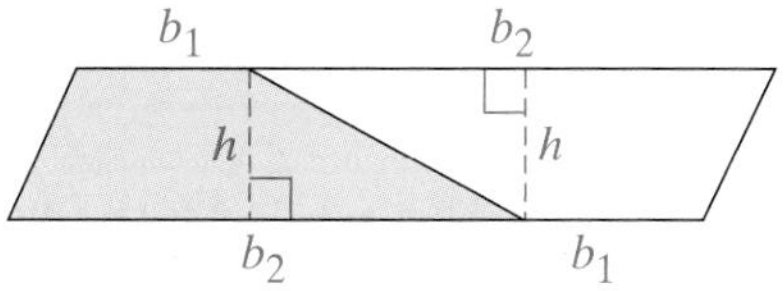

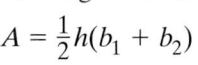

Area of parallelogram $= bh$ ← **Use the formula for the area of a parallelogram.**

$= (b_1 + b_2)h$ ← **Substitute for *b* and *h*. The base of the parallelogram is $b_1 + b_2$; the height is *h*.**

Area of trapezoid $= \frac{1}{2}(b_1 + b_2)h$ ← **The area of one of the trapezoids is half the area of the parallelogram.**

KEY CONCEPTS Area of a Trapezoid

The area of a trapezoid is one half the product of the height and the sum of the lengths of the bases.

$$A = \frac{1}{2}h(b_1 + b_2)$$

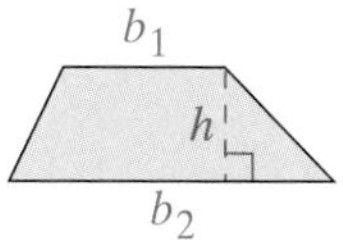

2. Teach

Activity Lab

Use before the lesson.

All in One Teaching Resources

Activity Lab 7-6: Areas of Polygons

Guided Instruction

Teaching Tip

Discuss the fact that every triangle has three heights, which may not be equal, but each specific height has a matching base. So no matter which pair of height, *h,* and matching base, *b,* you use, the area of a given triangle remains the same.

Example 2

Make sure that students understand the subscript, as in b_1 and b_2, names only two related variables and has no effect on the value of the variable. Contrast this to a superscript, as in b^2, which is an exponent and means $b \times b$.

Error Prevention!

Students might forget that height is defined as perpendicular to the base. Remind them not to use a slanted side of a figure as the height.

PowerPoint

Additional Examples

1 Find the area of the triangular part of the doghouse. **378 $in.^2$**

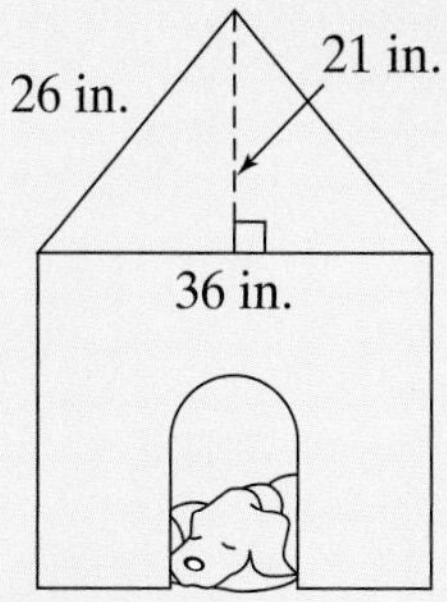

Advanced Learners L4

Students develop a special formula for using the legs of a right triangle to find its area. **Sample:**

$A = \frac{1}{2}(\text{leg}_1)(\text{leg}_2)$

learning style: verbal

English Language Learners ELL

Students write out the meaning of the letters used in the formulas. For example, A = area and b = base. They should practice reading the formulas using all the words necessary. For example, *the area of a trapezoid equals one-half the height times the sum of the base lengths.*

learning style: visual

PowerPoint

Additional Examples

2 Find the area of the trapezoid.
35.2 in.^{2}

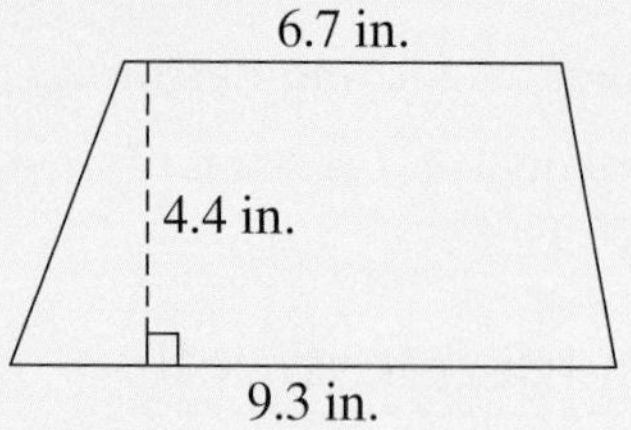

All in One Teaching Resources

- Daily Notetaking Guide 7-6 L3
- Adapted Notetaking 7-6 L1

Closure

- *What formulas do you use to find the areas of triangles and trapezoids?* Sample: for a triangle, $A = \frac{1}{2}bh$; for a trapezoid, $A = \frac{1}{2}h(b_1 + b_2)$

GO Online

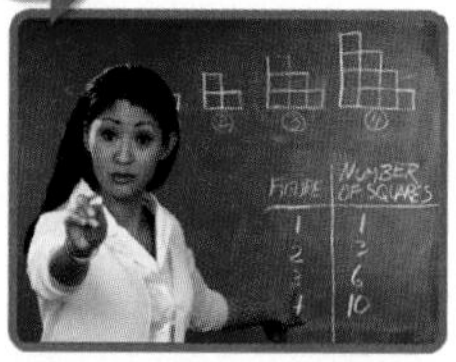

Video Tutor Help
Visit: PHSchool.com
Web Code: ase-0775

EXAMPLE Finding the Area of a Trapezoid

2 Find the area of the trapezoid at the right.

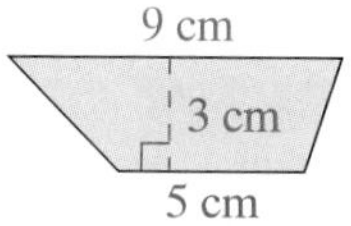

$A = \frac{1}{2}h(b_1 + b_2)$ ←Use the formula.

$= \frac{1}{2}(3)(9 + 5)$ ← Substitute 3 for h, 9 for b_1, and 5 for b_2.

$= 21$ ← Simplify.

The area of the trapezoid is 21 cm^2.

Quick Check

2. Find the area of the trapezoid at the right.
15 yd^2

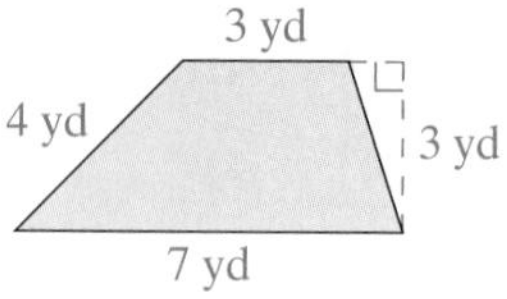

More Than One Way

Find the area of the picture frame at the left.

Nicole's Method

I will divide the frame into four rectangles. Then I will find the area of each rectangle and add the areas together.

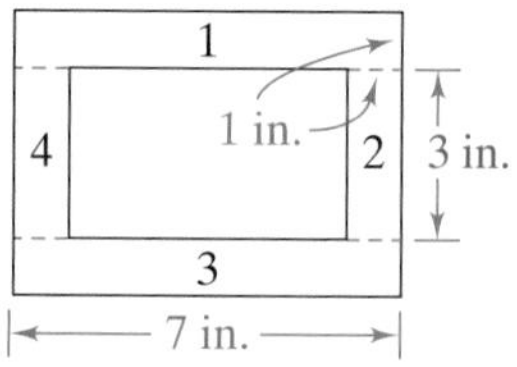

Rectangles 1 and 3
$A = bh$
$= (7)(1) = 7$

Rectangles 2 and 4
$A = bh$
$= (1)(3) = 3$

The area of the frame is $2(7) + 2(3)$, or 20 in.^{2}.

Roberto's Method

I will subtract the inner rectangle's area from the outer rectangle's area.

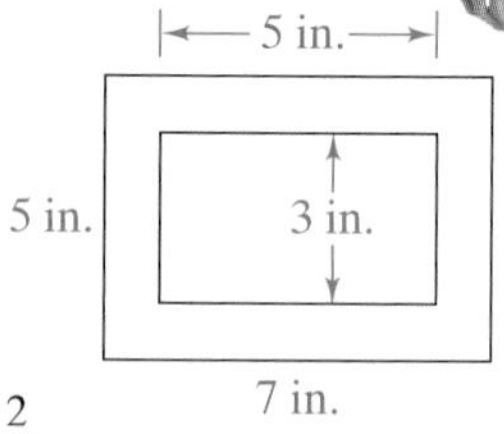

Outer Rectangle
$A = bh$
$= (7)(5) = 35$

Inner Rectangle
$A = bh$
$= (5)(3) = 15$

The area of the frame is $35 - 15$, or 20 in.^{2}.

Choose a Method

The four smaller triangles are congruent. Find the area of the shaded regions. Explain why you chose the method you used.

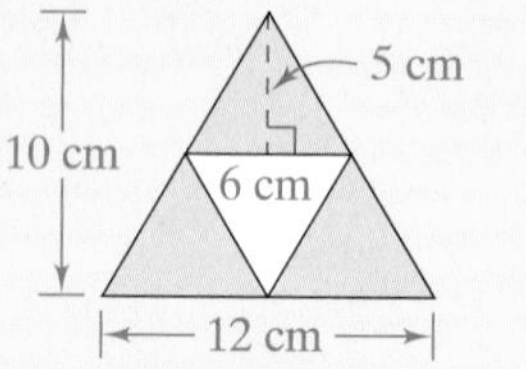

45 cm^2; methods and explanations may vary.

Check Your Understanding

1. **Vocabulary** Which unit *cannot* be used to express area? C
   - (A) square centimeters
   - (B) square inches
   - (C) feet
   - (D) square yards

Identify which polygon area each formula represents.

2. $A = bh$ parallelogram
3. $A = \frac{1}{2}bh$ triangle
4. $A = \frac{1}{2}h(b_1 + b_2)$ trapezoid

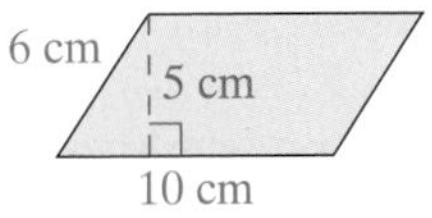

5. Find the area of the parallelogram at the left. 50 cm^2

Homework Exercises

For more exercises, see Extra Skills and Word Problems.

GO for Help

For Exercises	See Examples
6–8	1
9–11	2

A **Find the area of each triangle.**

6.
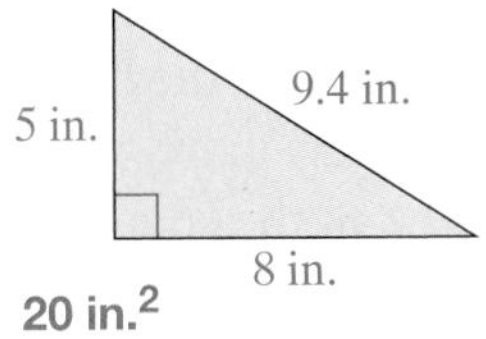

20 in.^{2}

7.
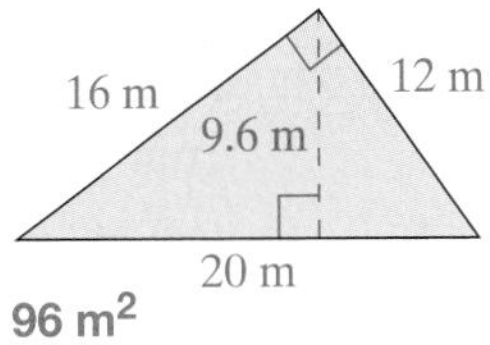

96 m^2

8.
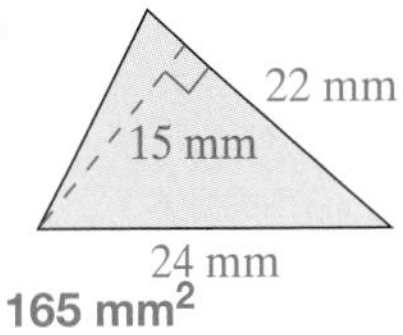

165 mm^2

Find the area of each trapezoid.

9.
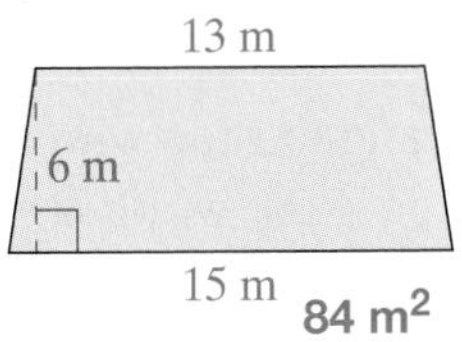

84 m^2

10.
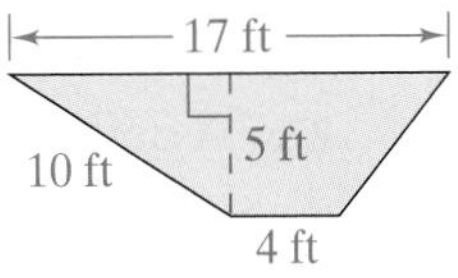

52.5 ft^2

11.
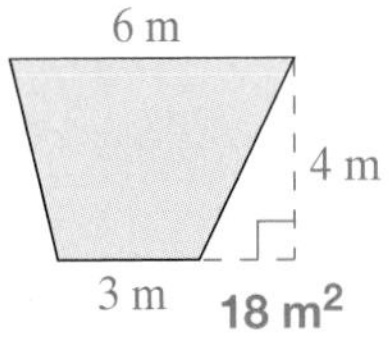

18 m^2

B **GPS** 12. **Guided Problem Solving** The perimeter of a rectangular garden is 54 yd. One side has a length of 15 yd. Find the area of the garden.
- What do you need to know to find the area of the garden?
- How can you use the perimeter and one side to find the area?
- What is the length of the other side of the garden? 180 yd^2

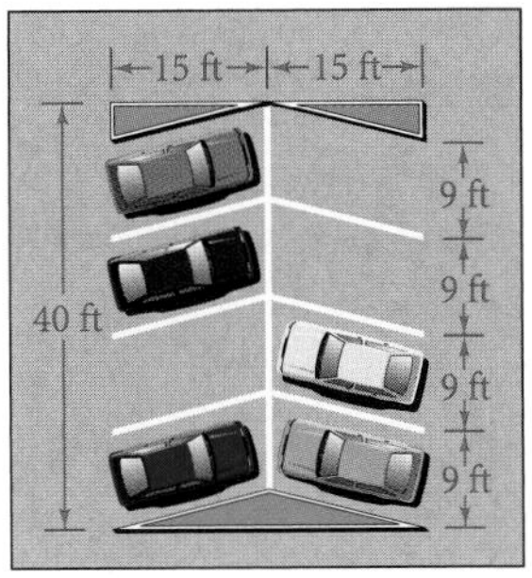

13. **Engineering** The plan for a new parking lot at the left uses parallelograms for parking spaces. Find the area of each parking space and the total area of the unpaved sections. Each area is 135 ft^2; 120 ft^2.

14. **Open-Ended** On graph paper, draw two different parallelograms with the same area. What are the lengths of their bases and heights? See margin.

Choose a Method **Find the area of each shaded region.**

15.
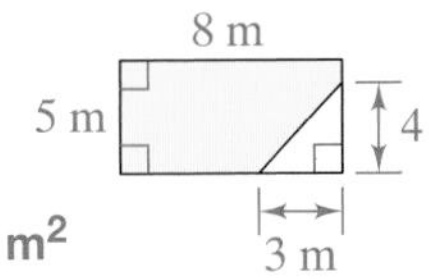

34 m^2

16.
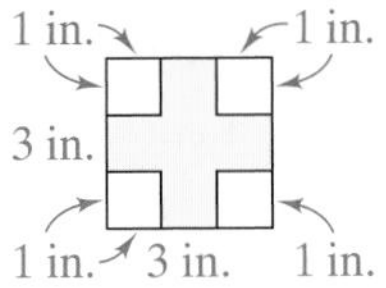

5 in.^{2}

17.
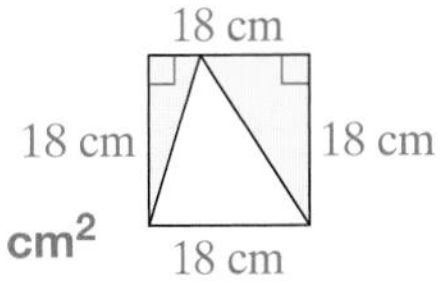

162 cm^2

14. Answers may vary. Sample:

3. Practice

Assignment Guide

Check Your Understanding
Go over Exercises 1–5 in class before assigning the Homework Exercises.

Homework Exercises

A Practice by Example	6–11
B Apply Your Skills	12–20
C Challenge	21
Test Prep and Mixed Review	22–27

Homework Quick Check
To check student's understanding of key skills and concepts, go over Exercises 7, 11, 15, 18, and 20.

Differentiated Instruction Resources

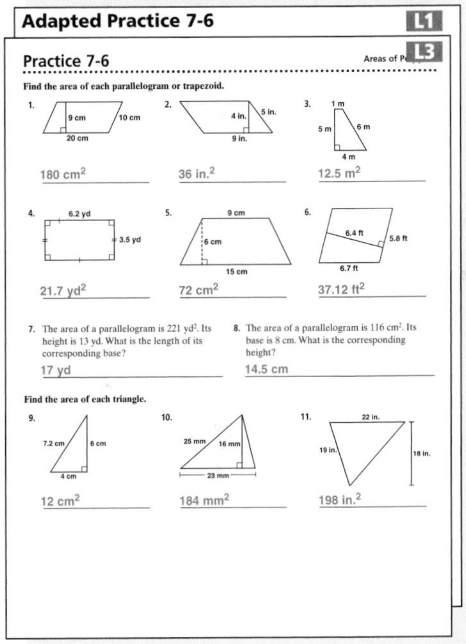
Adapted Practice 7-6 L1

Practice 7-6 Areas of Polygons L3

Find the area of each parallelogram or trapezoid.

1. 180 cm^2 2. 36 in.^{2} 3. 12.5 m^2
4. 21.7 yd^2 5. 72 cm^2 6. 37.12 ft^2

7. The area of a parallelogram is 221 yd^2. Its height is 13 yd. What is the length of its corresponding base? 17 yd

8. The area of a parallelogram is 116 cm^2. Its base is 8 cm. What is the corresponding height? 14.5 cm

Find the area of each triangle.

9. 12 cm^2 10. 184 mm^2 11. 198 in.^{2}

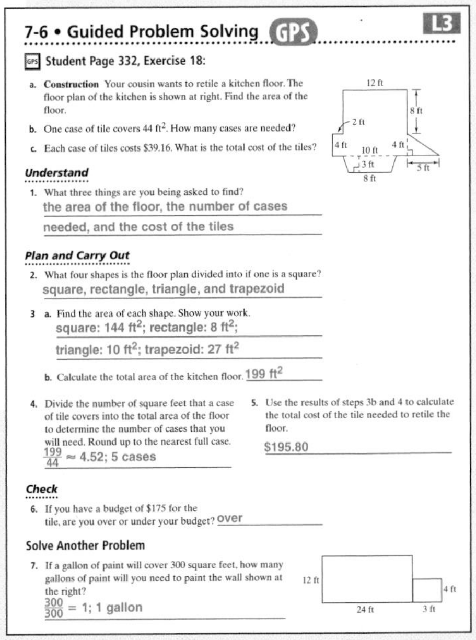
7-6 • Guided Problem Solving GPS L3

Student Page 332, Exercise 18:

a. Construction Your cousin wants to retile a kitchen floor. The floor plan of the kitchen is shown at right. Find the area of the floor.

b. One case of tile covers 44 ft^2. How many cases are needed?

c. Each case of tiles costs $39.16. What is the total cost of the tiles?

Understand

1. What three things are you being asked to find? the area of the floor, the number of cases needed, and the cost of the tiles

Plan and Carry Out

2. What four shapes is the floor plan divided into if one is a square? square, rectangle, triangle, and trapezoid

3. a. Find the area of each shape. Show your work. square: 144 ft^2; rectangle: 8 ft^2; triangle: 10 ft^2; trapezoid: 27 ft^2

b. Calculate the total area of the kitchen floor. 199 ft^2

4. Divide the number of square feet that a case of tile covers into the total area of the floor to determine the number of cases that you will need. Round up to the nearest full case. $\frac{199}{44} \approx 4.52$; 5 cases

5. Use the results of steps 3b and 4 to calculate the total cost of the tile needed to retile the floor. $195.80

Check

6. If you have a budget of $175 for the tile, are you over or under your budget? over

Solve Another Problem

7. If a gallon of paint will cover 300 square feet, how many gallons of paint will you need to paint the wall shown at the right? $\frac{300}{300} = 1$; 1 gallon

4. Assess & Reteach

PowerPoint

Lesson Quiz

1. Find the area. 14 cm^2

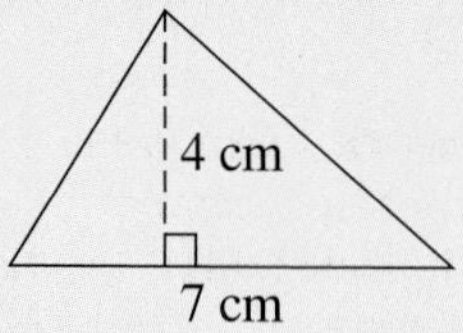

2. An architect is designing a restaurant with a triangular entrance. The base of the triangle is 10 ft wide. The entrance is 14 ft tall. Find the area of the triangle. 70 ft^2

3. Find the area. 56 ft^2

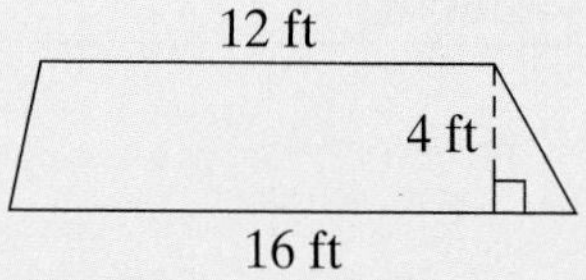

4. If both bases of the figure in part 3 are doubled, what is the new area of the trapezoid? 112 ft^2

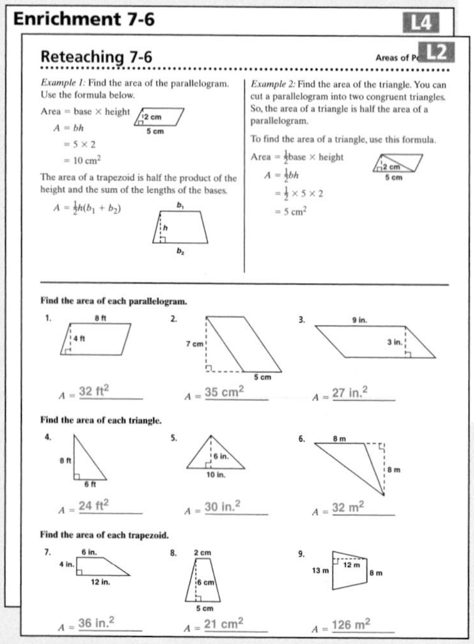
Enrichment 7-6 L4

Reteaching 7-6 Areas of P... L2

Example 1: Find the area of the parallelogram. Use the formula below.

Area = base × height

$A = bh$

$= 5 \times 2$

$= 10\ cm^2$

The area of a trapezoid is half the product of the height and the sum of the lengths of the bases.

$A = \frac{1}{2}h(b_1 + b_2)$

Example 2: Find the area of the triangle. You can cut a parallelogram into two congruent triangles. So, the area of a triangle is half the area of a parallelogram.

To find the area of a triangle, use this formula.

Area = $\frac{1}{2}$base × height

$A = \frac{1}{2}bh$

$= \frac{1}{2} \times 5 \times 2$

$= 5\ cm^2$

Find the area of each parallelogram.

1. A = 32 ft^2 2. A = 35 cm^2 3. A = 27 $in.^2$

Find the area of each triangle.

4. A = 24 ft^2 5. A = 30 $in.^2$ 6. A = 32 m^2

Find the area of each trapezoid.

7. A = 36 $in.^2$ 8. A = 21 cm^2 9. A = 126 m^2

GO Online
Homework Video Tutor
Visit: PHSchool.com
Web Code: ase-0706

18. a. **Construction** Your cousin wants to retile a kitchen floor. The floor plan of the kitchen is shown at the right. Find the area of the floor. 189 ft^2
GPS
b. One case of tiles covers 44 ft^2. How many cases are needed? 5 cases
c. Each case of tiles costs \$39.16. What is the total cost of the tiles? \$195.80

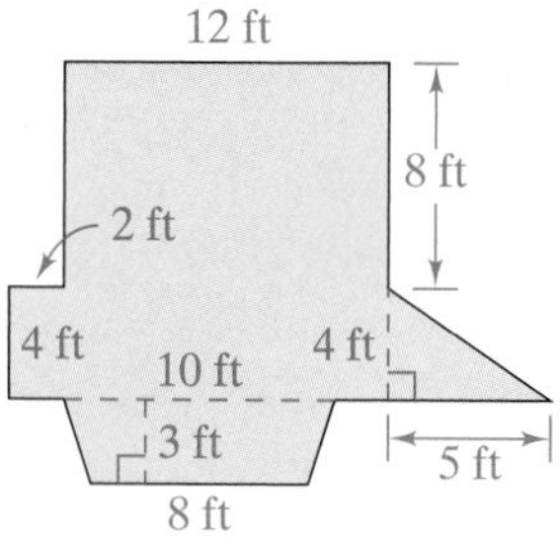

19. **Geography** Use the map at the left. Estimate the area of Virginia.

19. Answers may vary. Sample: about 81,000 km^2

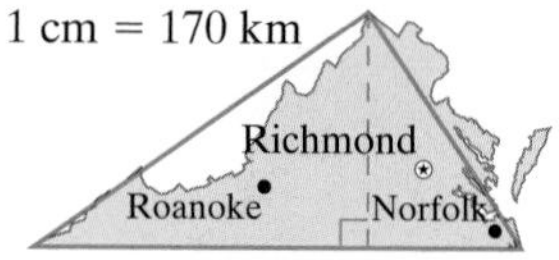

20. **Writing in Math** Use the diagram below to explain why the formulas for the area of a parallelogram and the area of a rectangle are the same.

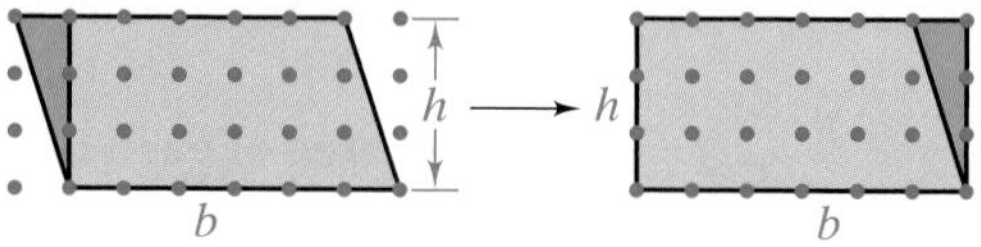

20. A parallelogram can be rearranged to form a rectangle, so both figures use the formula $A = bh$ for area.

C 21. **Challenge** The base and the height of a triangle are the same length as the side of a square. What is the ratio of the area of the triangle to the area of the square? 1 : 2

Test Prep and Mixed Review

Practice

Multiple Choice

22. A desk has a rectangular top with an area of 966 square inches. How long is the desktop if the width is 42 inches? A
(A) 23 in. (B) 42 in. (C) 882 in. (D) 924 in.

23. A soup recipe calls for these ingredients:

2 16-ounce cans of beans
32 ounces chicken broth
$3\frac{1}{2}$ cups cooked chicken
$\frac{1}{2}$ cup chopped carrots
5 cups cooked pasta

What is the smallest pan that will hold all the ingredients? G
(F) a 4-quart pan (H) a 6-quart pan
(G) a 5-quart pan (J) a 7-quart pan

GO for Help

For Exercises	See Lesson
24–27	7-5

Find the sum of the measures of the interior angles of a polygon with the given number of sides.

24. 3 sides 180° 25. 8 sides 1,080° 26. 16 sides 2,520° 27. 25 sides 4,140°

Test Prep

Resources
For additional practice with a variety of test item formats:
- Test-Taking Strategies, p. 345
- Test Prep, p. 349
- Test-Taking Strategies with Transparencies

Alternative Assessment

Each student in a pair draws and labels a triangle and a trapezoid on graph paper. Partners trade papers and find the areas of each other's polygons.

Geoboard Area

Louise designed a pendant on a geoboard for her math team, the X-Factors. She had the front of each pendant gold-plated at a cost of $1.25 per square inch. If the pegs on the geoboard are 1 in. apart, how much did it cost to gold-plate 8 pendants?

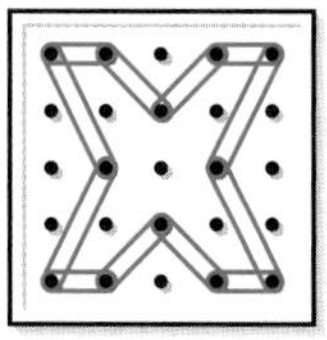

What You Might Think

What You Might Write

What do I know? What do I want to find out?
→ I know the cost per square inch. I need to find the area of the pendant, multiply the area by the cost, and then multiply the product by 8.

How do I find the area?
→ I can draw a square around the entire figure. I can remove two small triangles from the top and the bottom and two larger triangles from the left and right sides to find the area of the pendant.

What numerical expression represents the area *A*?
→ $A = \text{area of square} - 2 \times \text{area of small } \Delta - 2 \times \text{area of large } \Delta$

$= 16 - 2(\frac{1}{2})(2)(1) - 2(\frac{1}{2})(4)(1)$

$= 16 - 2 - 4$

$= 10$

What numerical expression represents the cost *C*?
→ $C = 8 \times 1.25 \times A$

$= 8 \times 1.25 \times 10$

$= 100$

What is the answer?
→ It cost $100 to gold-plate 8 pendants.

Think It Through

1. **Reasoning** Is there another way to find the area of the pendant by separating it into simpler figures? Explain.

1. You can separate the pendant into four right triangles and two trapezoids along the second, third, and fourth columns of pegs.

2. **Number Sense** Suppose the geoboard pegs were $\frac{1}{2}$ inch apart instead of 1 inch apart. Would the cost of gold-plating the pendants be half of $100? Explain.

2. No; the cost would be one fourth of $100.

Geoboard Area

Students read a guided real-world problem to develop problem solving and reasoning skills. In the left-hand column, they read questions they could ask themselves to make sense of the problem. In the right-hand column, they read the steps for setting up and solving equations used to describe the situation.

Guided Instruction

Have students work through the problem, rather than just read it. Have them identify any steps that are unclear or that don't match their own work.

Error Prevention!

Students might mistakenly multiply the cost to gold plate by the wrong area, such as the areas of the triangles. Have them focus first on understanding and finding the area of the pendant.

Math Tip
In Exercise 2, have students notice the relationship between $\frac{1}{2}$ inch and 1 inch. Ask them to first predict how halving lengths changes the area. Then have them calculate to confirm their predictions.

Teaching Tip
Have students ask themselves the same or similar questions as in the example as they work through the Exercises.

Exercises
The value of π can be approximated as 3.14. Remind students to keep track of units. Ask: *What is the difference between units of length and units of area?* length units are 1-dimensional, area units are squared

Differentiated Instruction

Tactile Learners
Have students design the pendant in the problem on a geoboard to get a better sense of the design and notice the triangles that are formed.

Exercises

Solve each problem. For Exercises 3 and 4, answer parts (a) and (b) first.

Aurora Gold-Plating Company Discounts

Area (in.^{2})	Discount
100–199	5%
200–399	10%
400–599	15%
600–900	20%

3. Aurora Gold-Plating Company offers discounts to customers based on the table at the right. How many 8-in.^{2} pendants would you have to plate to get a 5% discount? 13 pendants
   a. What do you know and what do you want to find out?
   b. What is the minimum number of square inches needed to get a 5% discount?

4. Sixth- and seventh-graders are in training for the X-Factors. They are called the Ys Team and the Z-Z-Z Team. The cost of silver-plating is about $\frac{3}{4}$ the cost of gold plating. The cost of copper-plating is about $\frac{1}{2}$ the cost of gold plating. How much would it cost to silver-plate 10 pendants for the Ys Team? How much would it cost to copper-plate 12 pendants for the Z-Z-Z Team? $56.25; $75

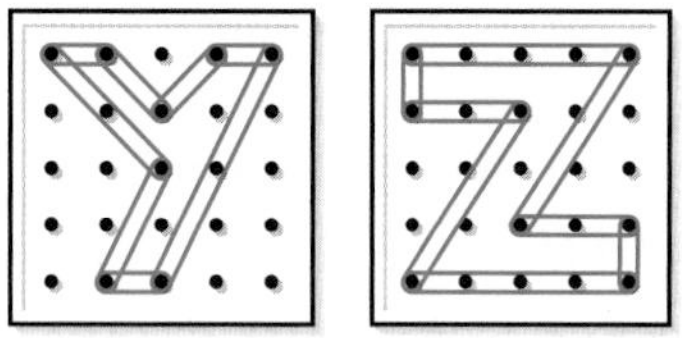

   a. What do you know and what do you want to find out?
   b. Find the cost to gold-plate each pin. Then find a fraction of each cost.

5. The formula for the area of a circle is $A = \pi r^2$. An approximate circle is shown on the geoboard below. Find the difference between the area of a circle with a radius of 2 in. and the area of the shape on the geoboard. How close is the approximation? about 1.4 in.^{2}

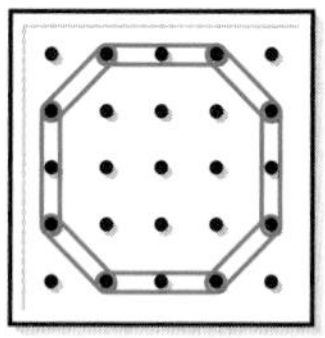

6. One pound of gold will make a thin wire about 900 mi long. A cubic mile of seawater contains about 25 tons of gold. The distance around the earth at the equator is about 25,000 mi. If the gold from a cubic mile of seawater were made into a thin wire, about how many times could the wire go around the equator of the earth? about 1,800 times

Resources

- geoboard and rubber bands

Checkpoint Quiz 2

Lessons 7-4 through 7-6

Determine the best name for each polygon. Then find the area.

1.

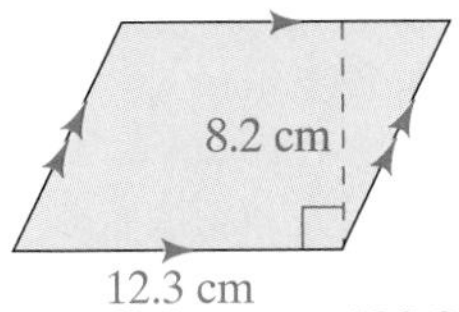

parallelogram; 100.86 cm^2

2.

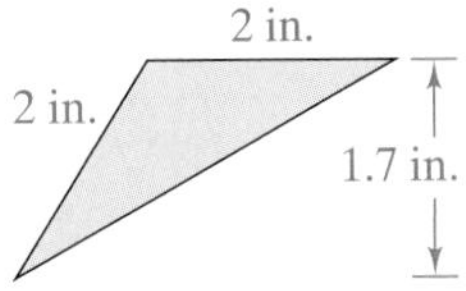

isosceles triangle; 1.7 in.^{2}

3.

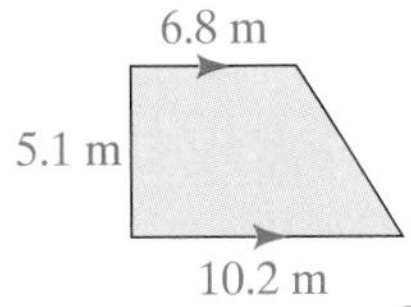

trapezoid; 43.35 m^2

4. Find the missing angle measure in the figure at the right. 133°

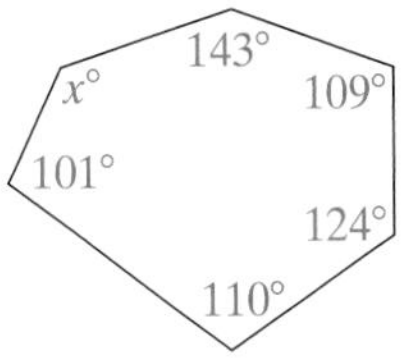

Draw and label a figure to fit each description. 5–6. See margin.

5. a scalene obtuse triangle

6. an equilateral triangle

7-7a Activity Lab

Hands On

Estimating Area

If you cut a pizza into equal pieces you can form a figure resembling a parallelogram.

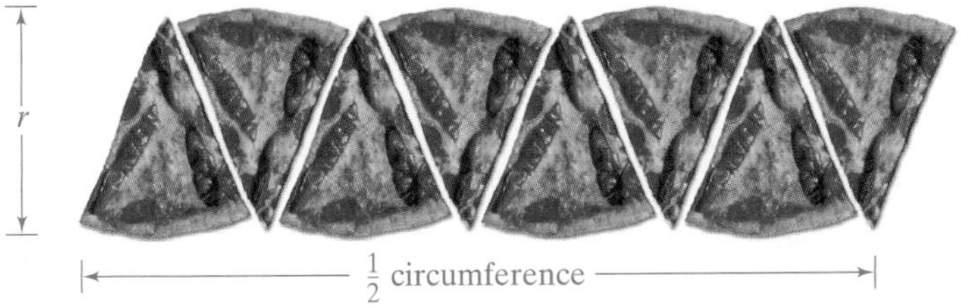

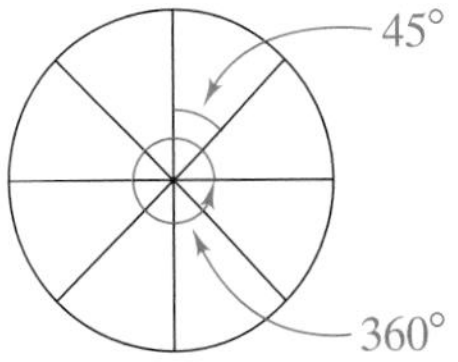

1. Use a compass and an inch ruler. Make a circle with a radius of 4 in. Use a protractor to divide your circle into eight equal sections with interior angles of 45°. Cut out the sections.

1–2. Check students' work.

2. Arrange the sections of your circle as in the pizza diagram above.

3. a. Estimation Measure the base and the height of the parallelogram you made. Use the formula $A = b \cdot h$ to estimate the area of the parallelogram. What does this area represent?

b. Algebra Write a formula to relate the radius of a circle to the area of a circle. Recall that $C = 2\pi r$.

3a–b. See margin.

5–6. Answers may vary. Samples are given.

5.

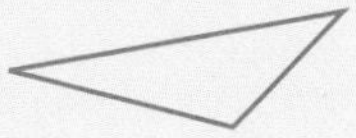

6.

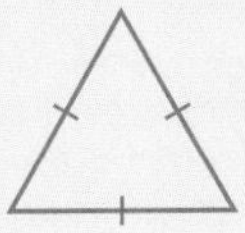

3a. Answers may vary. Sample: 50 in.^{2}; the area of a circle.

b. $A = \pi r^2$

Checkpoint Quiz

Use this Checkpoint Quiz to check students' understanding of the skills and concepts of Lessons 7-4 through 7-6.

Resources

- All in One Teaching Resources Checkpoint Quiz 2
- ExamView Assessment Suite CD-ROM
- Success Tracker Online Intervention

Activity Lab

Estimating Area

Students estimate the area of a circle by measuring it, cutting it into equal pieces, and rearranging it to form a parallelogram. They use the formula for the area of the parallelogram to write a formula for the area of a circle.

Guided Instruction

Error Prevention!

Remind students that the height of a parallelogram is perpendicular to its base; the height is not the length of a slanted side.

Teaching Tip

For Exercise 3a, ask:

- *To which length in a circle does the height of the parallelogram correspond?* radius
- *To which measurement in a circle does the base of the parallelogram correspond?* half of the circumference

Resources

- Activity Lab 7-7: Circumference and Area of a Circle
- compasses
- inch rulers
- protractors

7-7

1. Plan

Objective
To find the circumference and area of a circle and the area of irregular figures

Examples
1 Finding the Measures of a Circle
2 Finding the Area of an Irregular Figure

Math Understandings: p. 300D

Professional Development

Math Background

In every circle, the ratio of the distance around (circumference) to the distance across (diameter) is a constant value named π, pi. This ratio is an irrational number that can be approximated by rational numbers such as $\frac{22}{7}$ and 3.14.

The diameter of a circle is twice the radius. The circumference, or perimeter, of a circle is a linear measure given by $C = \pi d$. The area of a circle is measured in square units and given by $A = \pi r^2$.

More Math Background: p. 300D

Lesson Planning and Resources

See p. 300E for a list of the resources that support this lesson.

PowerPoint

Bell Ringer Practice

Check Skills You'll Need
Use student page, transparency, or PowerPoint. For intervention, direct students to:
Areas of Polygons
Lesson 7-6
Extra Skills and Word Problems Practice, Ch. 7

7-7 Circumference and Area of a Circle

Check Skills You'll Need

1. **Vocabulary Review** Explain the difference between *perimeter* and *area*. See below.
2. Find the area of the figure below. 45.5 ft²

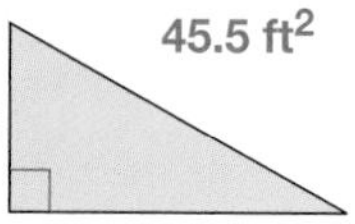

GO for Help Lesson 7-6

Check Skills You'll Need

1. Perimeter is the distance around a figure. Area is the number of square units a figure encloses.

What You'll Learn

To find the circumference and area of a circle and the area of irregular figures

Why Learn This?

When making sporting equipment, such as an archery target, knowing the circumference and area of circles is important.

Below are four terms related to a circle.

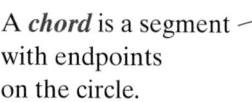

Circumference is the distance around the circle.

A *radius* is a segment that has one endpoint at the center and the other endpoint on the circle.

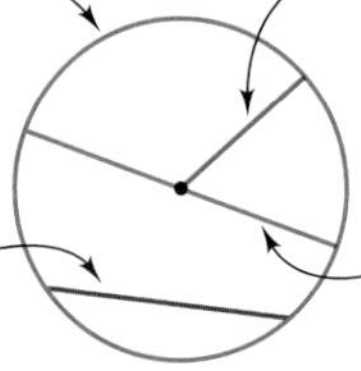

A *chord* is a segment with endpoints on the circle.

A *diameter* is a chord that passes through the center of the circle.

Pi (π) is the special name for the ratio of the circumference C of a circle to the diameter d of the circle.

$$\pi = \frac{C}{d}$$

If you solve this equation for C, you get $C = \pi d$, a formula for the circumference of a circle. The formula for the area of a circle is $A = \pi r^2$. Approximate values for π are $\frac{22}{7}$ and 3.14.

GO Online

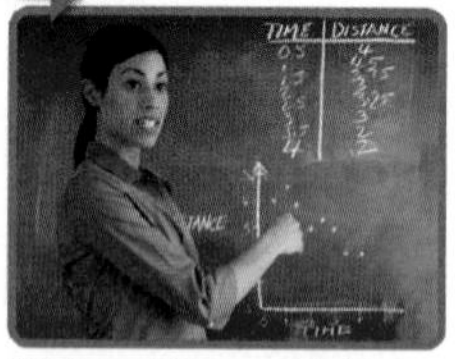

Video Tutor Help
Visit: PHSchool.com
Web Code: ase-0775

KEY CONCEPTS Circumference and Area of a Circle

The circumference of a circle is the product of π and the diameter d.

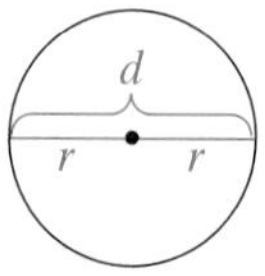

$$C = \pi d \text{ or } C = 2\pi r$$

The area of a circle is the product of π and the square of the radius r.

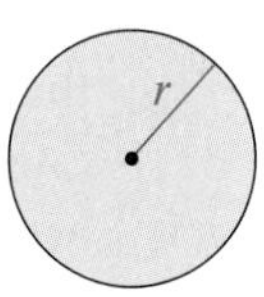

$$A = \pi r^2$$

Differentiated Instruction Solutions for All Learners

Special Needs L1	Below Level L2
For Example 2, students highlight the half circle with one color and the rectangle with another color. They can then see the different areas they are finding. **learning style: visual**	Review the meaning of *radius, diameter, circumference,* and *area.* Students use two fingers to "walk" around drawings of a rectangle and a circle. Ask them to compare their "walks" for each figure (relate the circumference of a circle to the perimeter of a rectangle). **learning style: tactile**

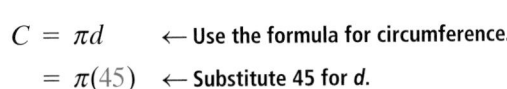

EXAMPLE Finding the Measures of a Circle

1 **Sports Equipment** Find the circumference and area of the basketball hoop at the right.

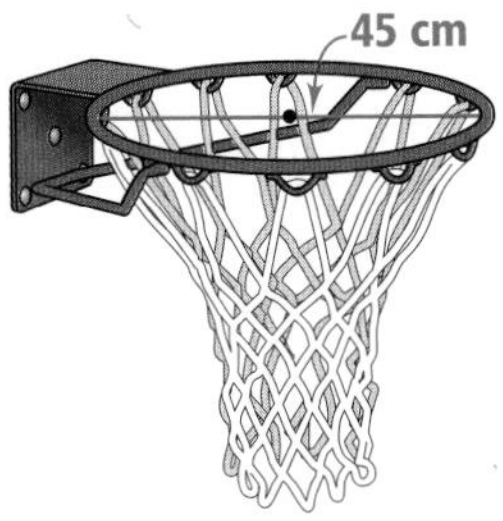

$C = \pi d$ ← Use the formula for circumference.

$= \pi(45)$ ← Substitute 45 for *d*.

[π] [×] 45 [=] 141.3716694 ← Use a calculator.

The circumference is about 141.4 cm.

$A = \pi r^2$ ← Use the formula for the area of a circle.

$= \pi(22.5)^2$ ← The radius is 45 ÷ 2, or 22.5. Substitute 22.5 for *r*.

[π] [×] 22.5 [x^2] [=] 1590.43128 ← Use a calculator.

The area is about 1,590 cm^2.

Calculator Tip

If you use 3.14 for π to find the circumference, the rounded result is 141.3, not 141.4. The calculator key [π] gives a more accurate value for π.

Quick Check

1. Find the circumference and area of the circle at the right. Round to the nearest tenth. 78.5 in.; 490.9 $in.^2$

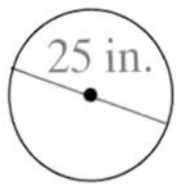

Sometimes you can separate an irregular figure into simpler figures.

EXAMPLE Finding the Area of an Irregular Figure

2 Find the area of the front of the mailbox.

Step 1 Find the area of the half circle.

$A = \frac{1}{2}\pi r^2$ ← Multiply the formula for the area of a circle by $\frac{1}{2}$.

$= \frac{1}{2}\pi(5)^2$ ← Substitute 5 for *r*.

≈ 39.3 ← Multiply. Round to the nearest tenth.

Step 2 Find the area of the rectangle.

$A = bh$ ← Use the formula for the area of a rectangle.

$= 10 \cdot 7 = 70$ ← Substitute 10 for *b* and 7 for *h*.

Step 3 Add the two areas: $39.3 + 70 = 109.3$.

The area of the front of the mailbox is about 109.3 $in.^2$.

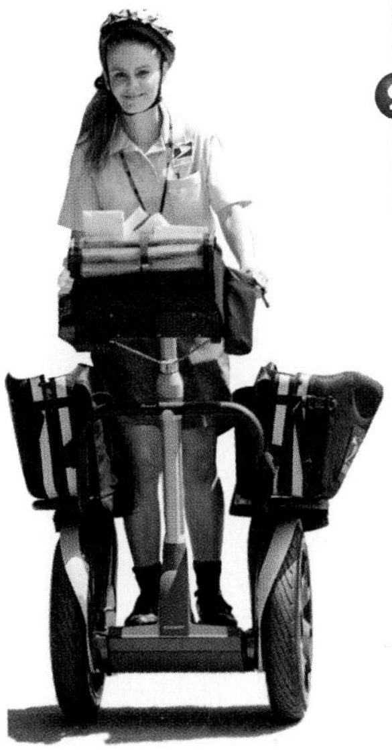

Careers The U.S. Postal Service hires over 300,000 mail carriers to collect, sort, and deliver the mail.

Quick Check

2. Find the area of the shaded region at the right. Round to the nearest tenth. 193.0 m^2

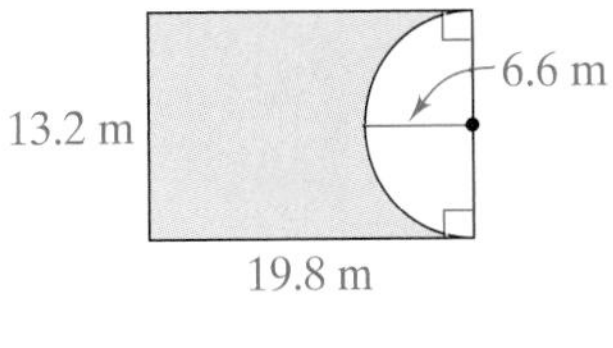

2. Teach

Activity Lab

Use before the lesson.
Student Edition Activity Lab, Hands On 7-7a, Estimating Area, p. 335

All in One Teaching Resources

Activity Lab 7-7: Circumference and Area of a Circle

Guided Instruction

Error Prevention!

Discuss the use of an approximate or rounded value for π. Help students see that calculated values using π will be "about" or an approximate value. If π is left as a symbol, the answer is exact.

PowerPoint

Additional Examples

1 The diameter of a tractor tire is 125 cm. Find its circumference and area. Round to the nearest tenth. 392.7 cm; 12,271.8 cm^2

2 Find the area of the unshaded region of the square tile with a circle inside of it, as shown below. Round to the nearest tenth. 30.9 cm^2

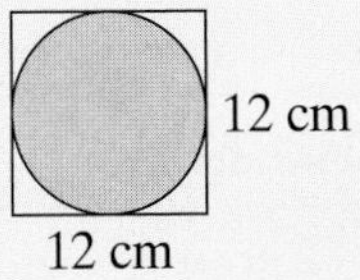

All in One Teaching Resources

- Daily Notetaking Guide 7-7 L3
- Adapted Notetaking 7-7 L1

Closure

- *Compare the formulas for finding the circumference and area of a circle.* Sample: The formula for the circumference, which is a linear measure, can use either the diameter, $C = \pi d$, or the radius, $C = \pi(2r)$. The area of a circle is measured in square units and the formula is $A = \pi r^2$. Both circumference and area use an approximate value for π in the calculations.

Advanced Learners L4
Students find the area of a circle whose circumference is 6π cm. $A = 9\pi$ cm^2

learning style: verbal

English Language Learners ELL
Students draw a circle and an arrow that curves around it. They label the arrow *circumference.* They shade the inside and label that *area.* They draw and label a *diameter* and a *radius.* They then write the formulas for *area* and *circumference.*

learning style: visual

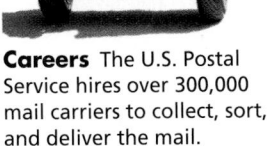

3. Practice

Assignment Guide

Check Your Understanding
Go over Exercises 1–7 in class before assigning the Homework Exercises.

Homework Exercises

A Practice by Example	8–22
B Apply Your Skills	23–33
C Challenge	34
Test Prep and Mixed Review	35–41

Homework Quick Check
To check students' understanding of key skills and concepts, go over Exercises 14, 20, 25, 30, and 32.

Appropriate Units
Remind students to use appropriate units in their answers. Circumference is expressed in linear units, and area is expressed in square units.

Differentiated Instruction Resources

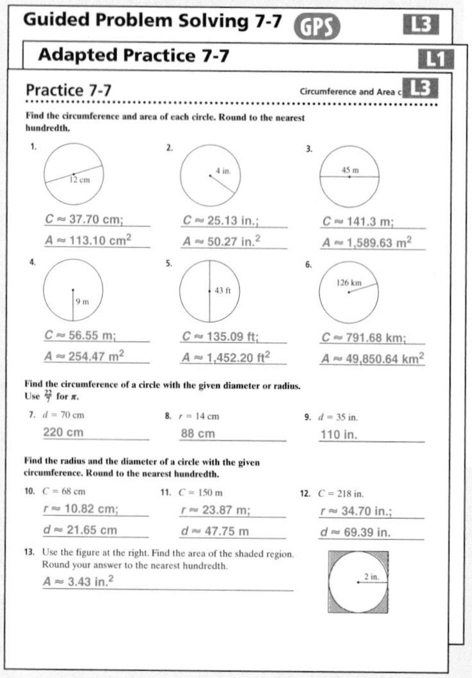

Guided Problem Solving 7-7 GPS L3

Adapted Practice 7-7 L1

Practice 7-7 Circumference and Area c L3

Find the circumference and area of each circle. Round to the nearest hundredth.

1. 12 cm — $C \approx 37.70$ cm; $A \approx 113.10$ cm^2
2. 4 in. — $C \approx 25.13$ in.; $A \approx 50.27$ in.^{2}
3. 45 m — $C \approx 141.3$ m; $A \approx 1,589.63$ m^2
4. 9 m — $C \approx 56.55$ m; $A \approx 254.47$ m^2
5. 43 ft — $C \approx 135.09$ ft; $A \approx 1,452.20$ ft^2
6. 126 km — $C \approx 791.68$ km; $A \approx 49,850.64$ km^2

Find the circumference of a circle with the given diameter or radius. Use $\frac{22}{7}$ for π.

7. $d = 70$ cm — 220 cm
8. $r = 14$ cm — 88 cm
9. $d = 35$ in. — 110 in.

Find the radius and the diameter of a circle with the given circumference. Round to the nearest hundredth.

10. $C = 68$ cm — $r \approx 10.82$ cm; $d \approx 21.65$ cm
11. $C = 150$ m — $r \approx 23.87$ m; $d \approx 47.75$ m
12. $C = 218$ in. — $r \approx 34.70$ in.; $d \approx 69.39$ in.
13. Use the figure at the right. Find the area of the shaded region. Round your answer to the nearest hundredth. 2 in. — $A \approx 3.43$ in.^{2}

Check Your Understanding

1. circumference
2. separate the figure into a rectangle and half a circle
3. $C = \pi d$
$= \pi(2r)$
$= 2\pi r$

1. **Vocabulary** What is the perimeter of a circle called?
2. How would you separate the figure at the right into simpler figures to find its area?

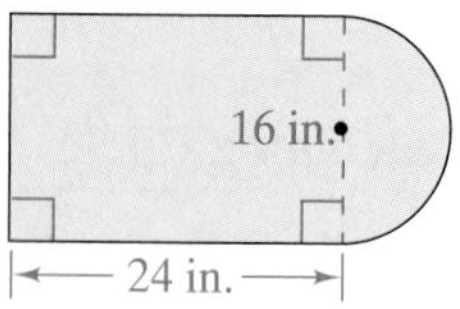

3. **Reasoning** Show that the two formulas for circumference, $C = \pi d$ and $C = 2\pi r$, are equivalent.

Mental Math **Find the circumference of a circle with the given radius or diameter. Use $\frac{22}{7}$ for π.**

4. $d = 21$ cm 66 cm
5. $r = 7$ km 44 km
6. $r = 3.5$ m 22 m
7. $d = 28$ in. 88 in.

Homework Exercises

For more exercises, see Extra Skills and Word Problems.

GO for Help

For Exercises	See Examples
8–16	1
17–22	2

8. 37.7 m; 113.1 m^2
9. 15.7 cm; 19.6 cm^2
10. 88.0 yd; 615.8 yd^2

GO for Help

For help with finding the area of a triangle, go to Lesson 7-6, Example 1.

11. 28.9 in.; 66.5 in.^{2}
12. 28.3 cm; 63.6 cm^2
13. 110.6 mm; 973.1 mm^2
14. 25.4 yd; 51.5 yd^2
15. 66.0 cm; 346.4 cm^2
16. 20.1 ft; 32.2 ft^2

A **Find the circumference and area of each circle with the given radius or diameter. Round to the nearest tenth.** 8–16. See left.

8. 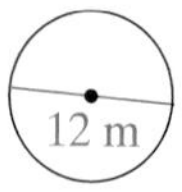

9. 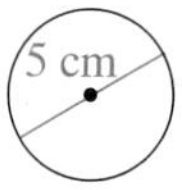

10. 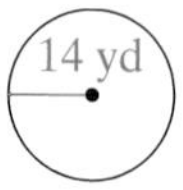

11. $d = 9.2$ in.
12. $r = 4.5$ cm
13. $r = 17.6$ mm
14. $d = 8.1$ yd
15. $r = 10.5$ cm
16. $d = 6.4$ ft

Find the area of each shaded region to the nearest tenth.

17. 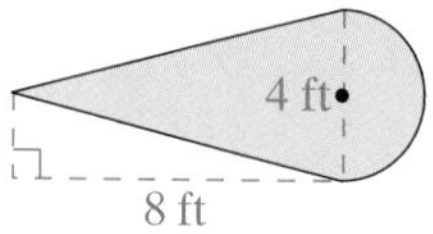

22.3 ft^2

18. 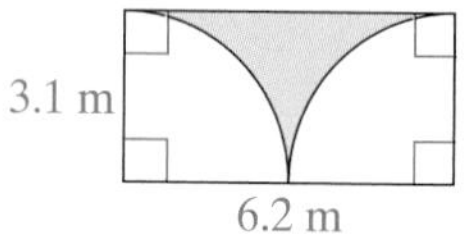

4.1 m^2

19. 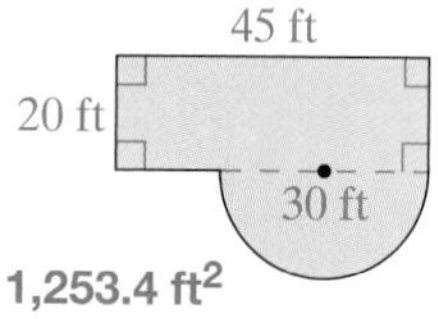

1,253.4 ft^2

20. 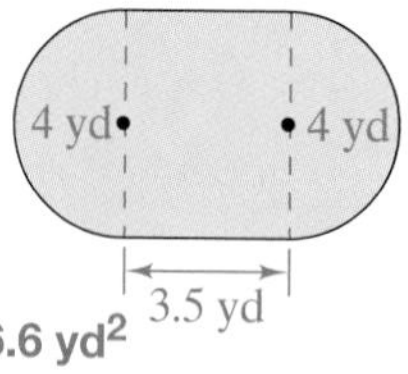

26.6 yd^2

21. 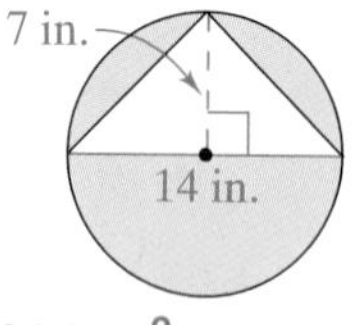

104.9 in.^{2}

22. 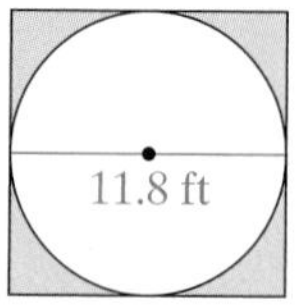

29.9 ft^2

B GPS 23. **Guided Problem Solving** Find the area of the shaded ring to the nearest square centimeter.

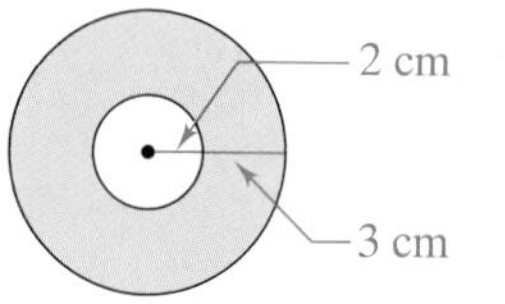

- **Make a Plan** Subtract the area of the smaller circle from the area of the larger circle.
- **Carry Out the Plan** The area of the larger circle is ▪. The area of the smaller circle is ▪. The difference between the two areas is ▪. 66 cm^2

GO Online
Homework Video Tutor
Visit: PHSchool.com
Web Code: ase-0707

25. A circle with a diameter of 2 in. has an area of 3.14 in.^{2}, while a square with a side length of 2 in. has an area of 4 in.^{2}.
26. 3.56 cm; 7.11 cm
27. 0.27 in.; 0.54 in.
28. 8.11 ft; 16.21 ft
29. 10.00 m; 20.00 m

24. **Basketball** A part of a basketball court is shown at the right. Find the area of the purple shaded region. 535.5 ft^2

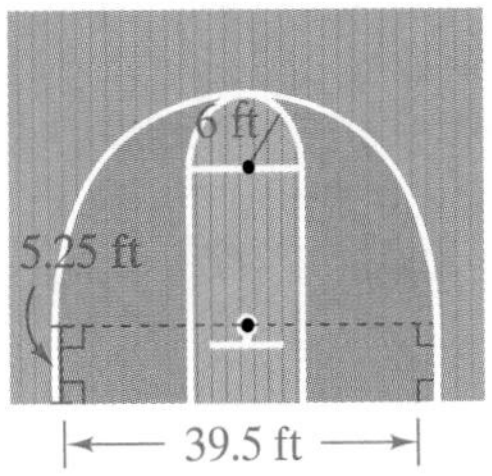

25. **Writing in Math** Compare the area of a circle with diameter 2 in. to the area of a square with side length 2 in. See left.

Find the radius and diameter of each circle with the given circumference. Round to the nearest hundredth. 26–29. See left.

26. 22.35 cm
27. 1.71 in.
28. 50.94 ft
29. 62.83 m

30. **Recreation** The circumference of a pool is about 63 ft. What is the area of the bottom of the pool? Round to the nearest tenth. 315.8 ft^2 (GPS)

31. **Food** A large pizza has a total diameter of 14 in. and a crust that is 1 in. wide. What is the area of the crust? Round to the nearest tenth. 40.8 in.^{2}

32. a. **Number Sense** The ratio of the radii of two circles is 3 : 1. What is the ratio of their areas? 9 : 1
b. **(Algebra)** The ratio of the radii of two circles is $a : b$. Write the ratio of their areas in terms of a and b. $a^2 : b^2$

33. The area of a circle is 432 ft^2. Estimate its radius. 12 ft

Ⓒ 34. **Challenge** The area of the shaded wedge at the right is about 64 cm^2. To the nearest tenth, what percent of the area of the circle is the wedge? 31.8%

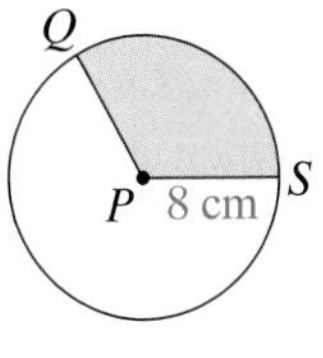

Test Prep and Mixed Review

Practice

Multiple Choice

35. Malcolm rode a Ferris wheel and traveled about 785 feet in one full rotation. What was the diameter of the wheel to the nearest foot? D
Ⓐ 63 ft Ⓑ 125 ft Ⓒ 225 ft Ⓓ 250 ft

36. Which procedure can be used to find the number of degrees in $\angle B$ at the right? J
Ⓕ Divide 180 by 3.
Ⓖ Divide 150 by 2.
Ⓗ Subtract the sum of 120 and 30 from 360.
Ⓙ Subtract the sum of 120 and 30 from 180.

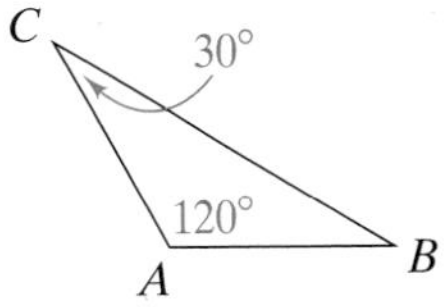

37. The temperature was 25°F at 6:00 P.M. and dropped 5°F each hour for the next 6 hours. What was the temperature at midnight? C
Ⓐ −30°F Ⓑ −25°F Ⓒ −5°F Ⓓ 5°F

GO for Help

For Exercises	See Lesson
38–41	5-2

Mental Math **Estimate a 15% tip for each restaurant bill.**

38. $28.55 $4.50
39. $64.82 $9.60
40. $13.97 $2.10
41. $108.16 $16.50

Online lesson quiz, PHSchool.com, Web Code: asa-0707

4. Assess & Reteach

PowerPoint

Lesson Quiz

1. Find the circumference and area of the circle. Round to the nearest tenth.

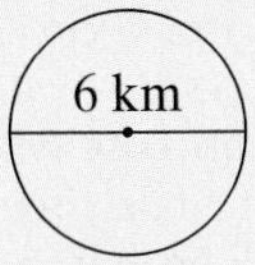

18.8 km; 28.3 km^2

2. The diameter of the lid of a can of soup is 5 cm. Find its circumference and area. Round to the nearest tenth. 15.7 cm; 19.6 cm^2

3. Find the area. Round to the nearest tenth. 273.0 in.^{2}

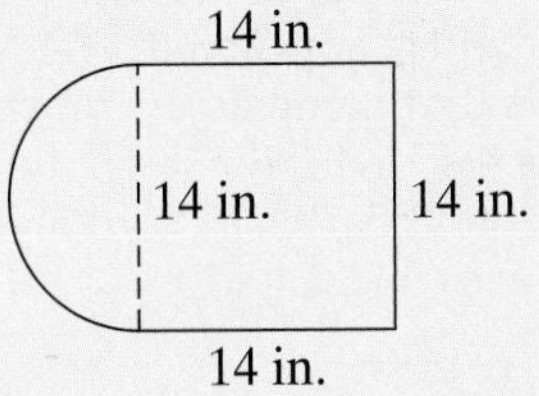

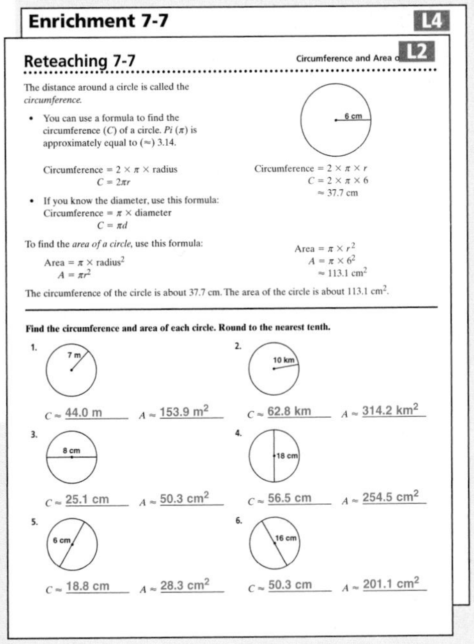
Enrichment 7-7 L4

Reteaching 7-7 Circumference and Area o L2

The distance around a circle is called the *circumference*.

- You can use a formula to find the circumference (C) of a circle. *Pi* (π) is approximately equal to ($\approx$) 3.14.

Circumference = 2 × π × radius
$C = 2\pi r$

Circumference = 2 × π × r
$C = 2 \times \pi \times 6$
≈ 37.7 cm

6 cm

- If you know the diameter, use this formula:
Circumference = π × diameter
$C = \pi d$

To find the *area of a circle*, use this formula:

Area = π × radius^2
$A = \pi r^2$

Area = $\pi \times r^2$
$A = \pi \times 6^2$
≈ 113.1 cm^2

The circumference of the circle is about 37.7 cm. The area of the circle is about 113.1 cm^2.

Find the circumference and area of each circle. Round to the nearest tenth.

1. 7 m $C \approx$ 44.0 m $A \approx$ 153.9 m^2
2. 10 km $C \approx$ 62.8 km $A \approx$ 314.2 km^2
3. 8 cm $C \approx$ 25.1 cm $A \approx$ 50.3 cm^2
4. 18 cm $C \approx$ 56.5 cm $A \approx$ 254.5 cm^2
5. 6 cm $C \approx$ 18.8 cm $A \approx$ 28.3 cm^2
6. 16 cm $C \approx$ 50.3 cm $A \approx$ 201.1 cm^2

Alternative Assessment

Students use rulers to measure the diameter of a circular classroom object, such as a coin or clock face. Then they use formulas to find its circumference and area.

Test Prep

Resources
For additional practice with a variety of test item formats:
- Test-Taking Strategies, p. 345
- Test Prep, p. 349
- Test-Taking Strategies with Transparencies

Extension

Parts of a Circle

Circles are named by their center points, but segments whose endpoints lie on the circle and portions of the circle itself are named differently. Students name chords and arcs in circles, describe lengths of arcs relative to semicircles, and use what they know about circle circumference to find the length of a semicircle.

Guided Instruction

Error Prevention!

Remind students that though a center point may name a circle itself, the center point does not appear when labeling an arc. Naming an arc is similar to naming a polygon, except that the "segments" are curved. The points that name an arc must all lie on the circle. Similarly, the points that define a chord must lie on the circle.

Differentiated Instruction

Visual Learners

Have students use a ruler to draw a dotted line through the diameter and extend it beyond the circle. They can use it as a line of reference, to decide which arcs are shorter, equal to, or longer than a semicircle. Have them color the portion of the circle circumference they are referring to.

Resources

- colored pencils or markers
- rulers

7. Yes; no; a diameter has both endpoints on a circle, whereas a radius has only one.

Extension For Use With Lesson 7-7

Arcs, Chords, and Semicircles

A **chord** is a segment that has both endpoints on the circle. In circle F, $\overline{AB}$ is a chord.

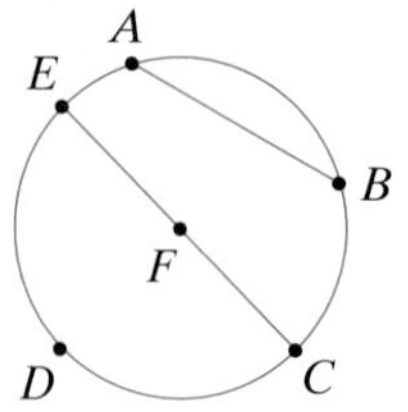

An **arc** is part of a circle. In circle F, $\widehat{CD}$ and $\widehat{DE}$ are arcs. An arc that is half the circumference of a circle is called a **semicircle.** $\widehat{CDE}$ is a semicircle. You use three letters to name a semicircle or an arc longer than a semicircle. Note that $\widehat{CDE}$ has the same endpoints as diameter $\overline{CE}$.

EXAMPLES

1 Name all the chords in circle O.

The chords are $\overline{PQ}$, $\overline{QR}$, $\overline{RS}$, $\overline{SP}$, and $\overline{QS}$.

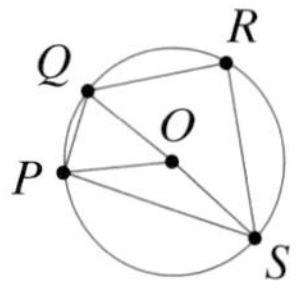

2 Name an arc that is shorter than, equal to, and longer than a semicircle in circle W.

$\widehat{XY}$ is shorter than a semicircle. $\overline{XZ}$ is a diameter, so $\widehat{XYZ}$ is a semicircle. $\widehat{XZY}$ is longer than a semicircle.

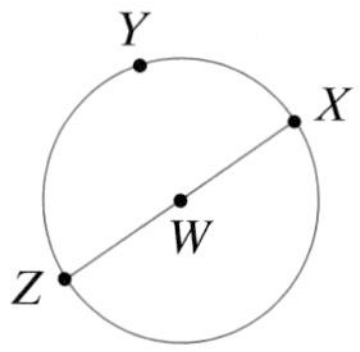

Exercises

Name all the chords in each circle.

1. 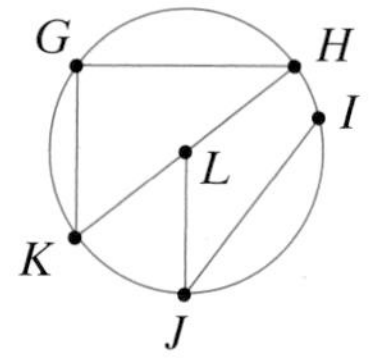

$\overline{GK}$, $\overline{GH}$, $\overline{KH}$, $\overline{IJ}$

2. 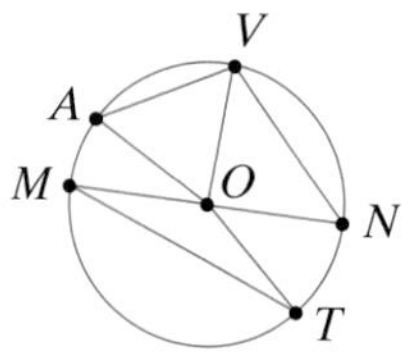

$\overline{AV}$, $\overline{VN}$, $\overline{MN}$, $\overline{MT}$

3. 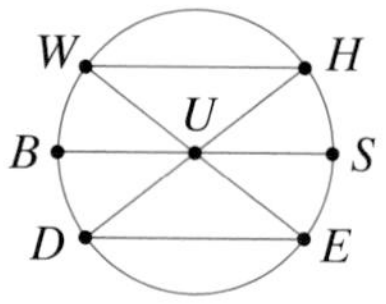

$\overline{WH}$, $\overline{BS}$, $\overline{DE}$, $\overline{WE}$, $\overline{HD}$

Use the circle at the right for Exercises 4–6.

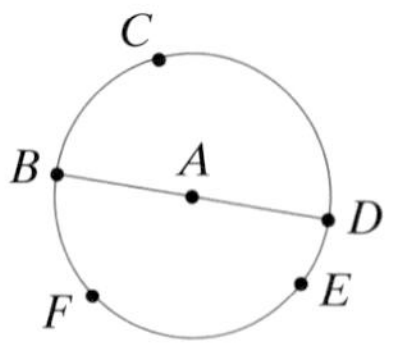

4. Name all the arcs shorter than a semicircle.
5. Name all the arcs equal to a semicircle.
6. Name all the arcs longer than a semicircle.
7. **Reasoning** Is a diameter a chord? Is a radius a chord? Explain. See margin.
8. What is the length of a semicircle of a circle with a diameter of 8 cm? Express your answer in terms of π. 4π

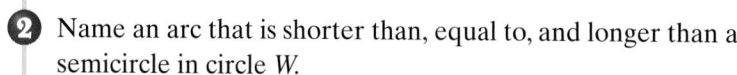

4. $\widehat{BC}$, $\widehat{CD}$, $\widehat{DE}$, $\widehat{EF}$, $\widehat{FB}$, $\widehat{CE}$, $\widehat{DF}$, $\widehat{EB}$, $\widehat{FC}$
5. $\widehat{BCD}$, $\widehat{BFD}$, or $\widehat{BED}$
6. $\widehat{BCE}$, $\widehat{BCF}$, $\widehat{CDF}$, $\widehat{CDB}$, $\widehat{DFC}$, $\widehat{EFC}$, $\widehat{EFD}$, $\widehat{FCD}$, $\widehat{FCE}$

7-8 Constructions

Check Skills You'll Need

1. Vocabulary Review How are *congruent polygons* the same?

1–3. See below.

List the congruent parts of each pair of congruent figures.

2. $\triangle PQR \cong \triangle TUV$

3. $ABCD \cong LMNO$

GO for Help Lesson 7-3

What You'll Learn

To construct congruent angles and parallel lines

New Vocabulary compass

Why Learn This?

Marine pilots use tools, such as compasses and rulers, to map the paths of ships. To navigate accurately, they construct angles and lines.

A **compass** is a tool used to draw circles and parts of circles called *arcs*. A straightedge is a ruler with no markings on it.

EXAMPLE Constructing Congruent Angles

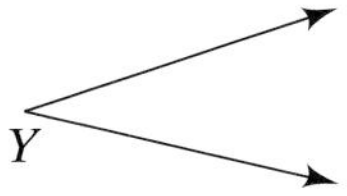

1 Construct $\angle S$ congruent to $\angle Y$ shown at the left.

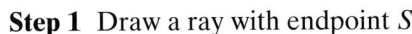

Step 1 Draw a ray with endpoint S.

Step 2 Put the compass tip at Y and draw an arc that intersects the sides of $\angle Y$. Label the points of intersection X and Z.

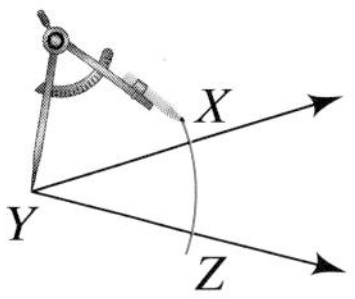

Step 3 Keep the compass open to the same width. Put the compass tip at S. Draw an arc that intersects the ray at a point T.

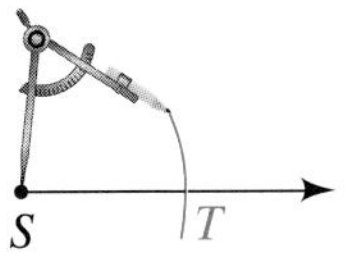

Step 4 Adjust the compass so that the tip is at Z and the pencil is at X. Using this compass opening, put the tip at T. Draw an arc to determine point R. Draw $\overrightarrow{SR}$.

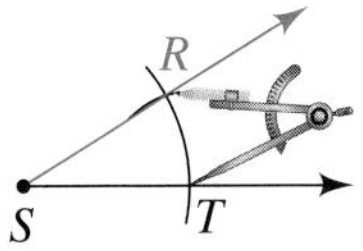

$\angle S$ is congruent to $\angle Y$.

Quick Check

See back of book.

1. Draw an obtuse angle, $\angle F$. Construct $\angle N$ congruent to $\angle F$.

Check Skills You'll Need

1. Congruent polygons have the same size and shape.

2. $\angle P \cong \angle T$; $\angle Q \cong \angle U$; $\angle R \cong \angle V$; $\overline{PQ} \cong \overline{TU}$; $\overline{QR} \cong \overline{UV}$; $\overline{RP} \cong \overline{VT}$

3. $\angle A \cong \angle L$; $\angle B \cong \angle M$; $\angle C \cong \angle N$; $\angle D \cong \angle O$; $\overline{AB} \cong \overline{LM}$; $\overline{BC} \cong \overline{MN}$; $\overline{CD} \cong \overline{NO}$; $\overline{DA} \cong \overline{OL}$

7-8

1. Plan

Objective

To construct congruent angles and parallel lines

Examples

1 Constructing Congruent Angles
2 Constructing Parallel Lines

Math Understandings: p. 300D

Professional Development

Math Background

Euclid, the "father" of geometry, stated, in about 300 B.C., that formal geometric constructions be made with only an unmarked straightedge and a compass.

More Math Background: p. 300D

Lesson Planning and Resources

See p. 300E for a list of the resources that support this lesson.

PowerPoint

Bell Ringer Practice

Check Skills You'll Need
Use student page, transparency, or PowerPoint. For intervention, direct students to:
Congruent Polygons
Lesson 7-3
Extra Skills and Word Problems Practice, Ch. 7

2. Teach

Activity Lab

Use before the lesson.

All in One Teaching Resources

- Activity Labs 7-8: Constructions

Use before the lesson.

Student Edition Activity Lab 7-8b Technology: Geometry Software and Constructions, p. 342

Guided Instruction

Teaching Tip
Have students use the compass by drawing circles and arcs.

Differentiated Instruction Solutions for All Learners

Special Needs L1
Some students may have difficulty handling a compass. If so, have them help label the parts of the construction while their partner does the drawing with the compass.

learning style: visual

Below Level L2
Students say and review the meaning of *line, line segment, ray, angle,* and *parallel.* They write the mathematical symbols for each.

learning style: verbal

Additional Examples

1 Use a protractor to draw a 40° angle and label it $\angle B$. Construct $\angle N$ congruent to $\angle B$. **Accept all reasonable answers. See back of book.**

2 Draw a line *f*. Construct a line parallel to line *f*. **Accept all reasonable answers. See back of book.**

All in One Teaching Resources

- Daily Notetaking Guide 7-8 L3
- Adapted Notetaking 7-8 L1

Closure

- *What tools can you use to make a geometric construction?* **an unmarked straightedge and a compass**

3. Practice

Assignment Guide

Check Your Understanding
Go over Exercises 1–4 in class before assigning the Homework Exercises.

Homework Exercises

A	Practice by Example	5–8
B	Apply Your Skills	9–11
C	Challenge	12
	Test Prep and Mixed Review	13–18

Homework Quick Check
To check students' understanding of key skills and concepts, go over Exercises 6, 8, 10, 11, and 12.

4. Assess & Reteach

Lesson Quiz

For Exercises 1–2, use the diagram below.

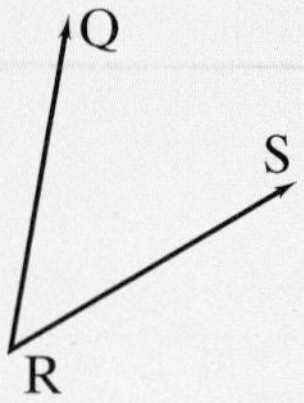

You can construct congruent angles to help construct parallel lines.

EXAMPLE Constructing Parallel Lines

2 Construct a line parallel to line *n* at the right.

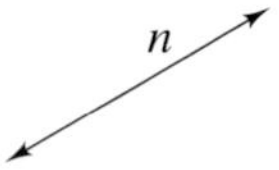

Step 1 Draw line *m* that intersects line *n* at *A*. Label the angle formed $\angle 1$. Then label point *B* on line *m*.

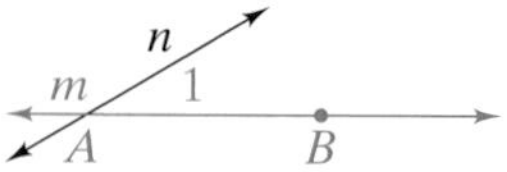

Step 2 Construct an angle at *B* that is congruent to $\angle 1$.

$\overleftrightarrow{BF}$ is parallel to line *n*.

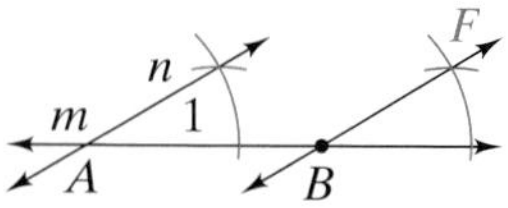

Quick Check

2. Draw a line *d*. Construct a line *e* parallel to line *d*. **See back of book.**

Check Your Understanding

1. **Vocabary** A compass is a tool used to draw __?__. **circles and arcs**
2. **Reasoning** Do you need to know the measure of an angle to construct a congruent angle? Explain.
3. Describe the step in constructing congruent angles that is shown at the right.

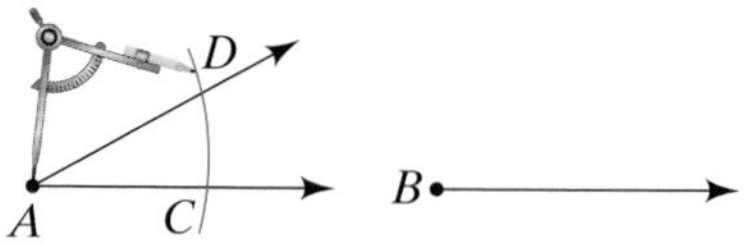

4. **Multiple Choice** To construct parallel lines, which pair of angles do you construct? **B**
   - (A) alternate interior
   - (B) corresponding
   - (C) supplementary
   - (D) vertical

2. No; the construction copies the angle without measuring it.

3. Place the compass tip at *A* and draw an arc that intersects the sides of $\angle A$. Label the points of intersection *C* and *D*.

Homework Exercises

For more exercises, see Extra Skills and Word Problems.

GO for Help

For Exercises	See Examples
5–6	1
7–8	2

A **Copy each angle. Then construct a congruent angle.** **5–6. See back of book.**

5.

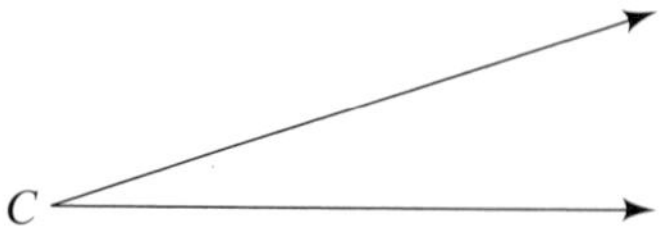

6.

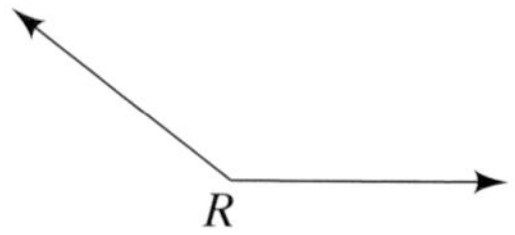

Draw each line. Then construct a line parallel to it. **7–8. See back of book.**

7. a horizontal line
8. a vertical line

Differentiated Instruction Solutions for All Learners

Advanced Learners L4
Students construct a parallelogram and verify that the opposite angles have equal measure.

learning style: visual

English Language Learners ELL
For both examples, students copy the written steps and the constructions. They read their own papers out loud, and use this page to draw the constructions in the homework exercises.

learning style: visual

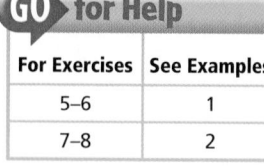

B **GPS** 9. **Guided Problem Solving** Use a compass and straightedge to construct a parallelogram. See below left.

- **Make a Plan** Draw a line a. Draw a line b that intersects line a. Construct line c parallel to line a. To draw the fourth side, connect the points where the arcs intersect lines a and c.
- **Check the Answer** Check that opposite sides and opposite angles are congruent.

9. 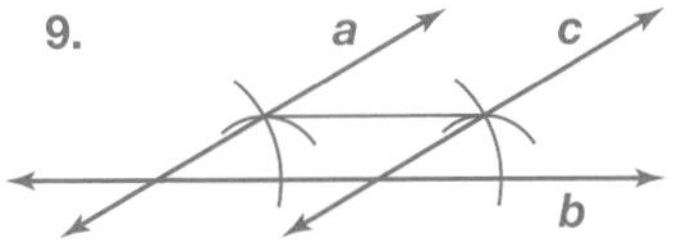

10. **Multiple Choice** Which is *not* a step in constructing $\angle E$ congruent to $\angle A$? D

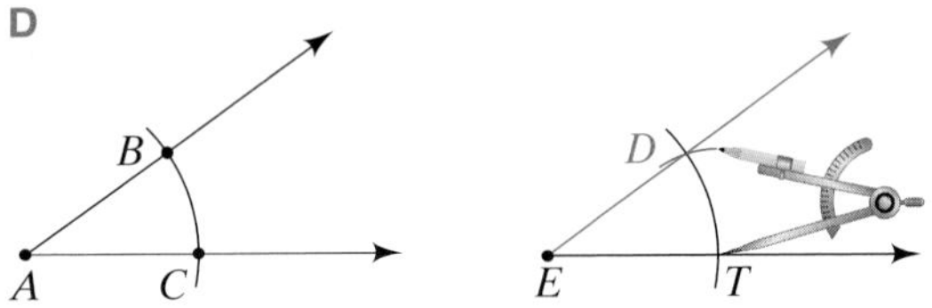

Ⓐ Adjust the compass width to the distance between B and C.
Ⓑ Draw a ray with endpoint E.
Ⓒ Draw an arc that intersects both sides of $\angle A$.
Ⓓ Adjust the compass width to the distance between A and B.

GO Online
Homework Video Tutor
Visit: PHSchool.com
Web Code: ase-0708

11. **Writing in Math** How could you construct a trapezoid?

11. First construct two parallel lines. Then connect the parallel lines with two segments that are *not* parallel.

C 12. **Challenge** Draw a triangle $\triangle ABC$. Construct a triangle with the same angle measures as $\triangle ABC$. Check students' work.

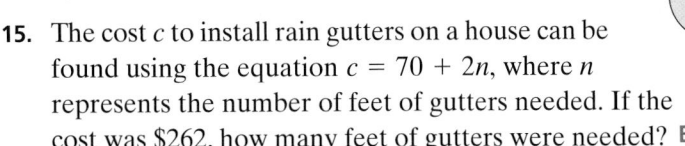

Test Prep and Mixed Review — Practice

Multiple Choice

13. A triangular traffic sign has an area of 390 square inches. If the height of the triangle is 26 inches, what is the length of its base? C
Ⓐ 14 in. Ⓑ 15 in. Ⓒ 30 in. Ⓓ 52 in.

14. Which of the following is an expression for the area in square meters of the figure at the right? J
Ⓕ $4(4\pi) + 4$ Ⓗ $4 + 4\pi$
Ⓖ 8π Ⓙ $2\pi + 2(2)$

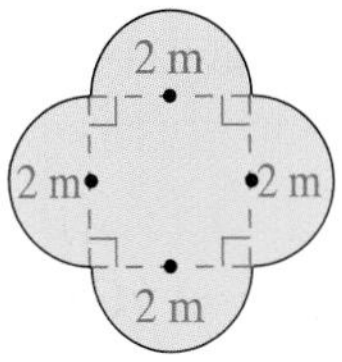

15. The cost c to install rain gutters on a house can be found using the equation $c = 70 + 2n$, where n represents the number of feet of gutters needed. If the cost was \$262, how many feet of gutters were needed? B
Ⓐ 61 ft Ⓑ 96 ft Ⓒ 166 ft Ⓓ 594 ft

Probability **Find each probability if you spin the spinner once.** A spinner has 26 sections of equal size. Each section is labeled with a different letter of the alphabet. Express each probability as a fraction.

16. P(M, A, T, or H) 17. P(a letter before I) 18. P(a letter after Q)
16–18. See margin.

GO for Help

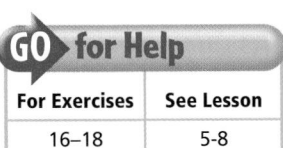

For Exercises	See Lesson
16–18	5-8

Online lesson quiz, PHSchool.com, Web Code: asa-0708

Lesson Quiz

PowerPoint

1. Construct an angle that is congruent to $\angle R$. Accept all reasonable answers. See back of book.
2. Construct a line parallel to $\overrightarrow{RS}$. Accept all reasonable answers. See back of book.

Differentiated Instruction Resources

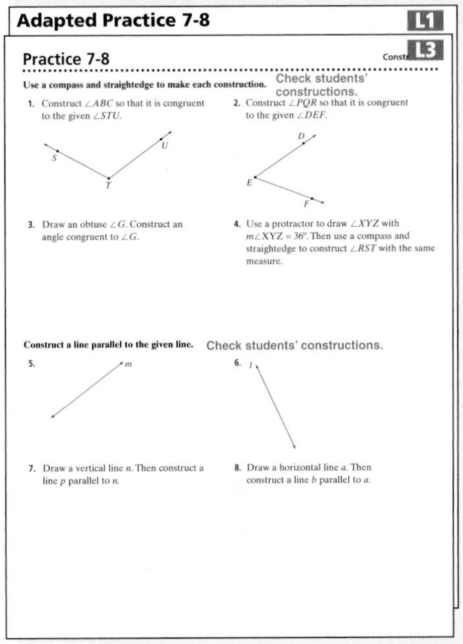
Adapted Practice 7-8 L1
Practice 7-8 L3
Use a compass and straightedge to make each construction. Check students' constructions.
1. Construct ∠ABC so that it is congruent to the given ∠STU.
2. Construct ∠PQR so that it is congruent to the given ∠DEF.
3. Draw an obtuse ∠G. Construct an angle congruent to ∠G.
4. Use a protractor to draw ∠XYZ with m∠XYZ = 36°. Then use a compass and straightedge to construct ∠RST with the same measure.
Construct a line parallel to the given line. Check students' constructions.
5.
6.
7. Draw a vertical line n. Then construct a line p parallel to n.
8. Draw a horizontal line a. Then construct a line b parallel to a.

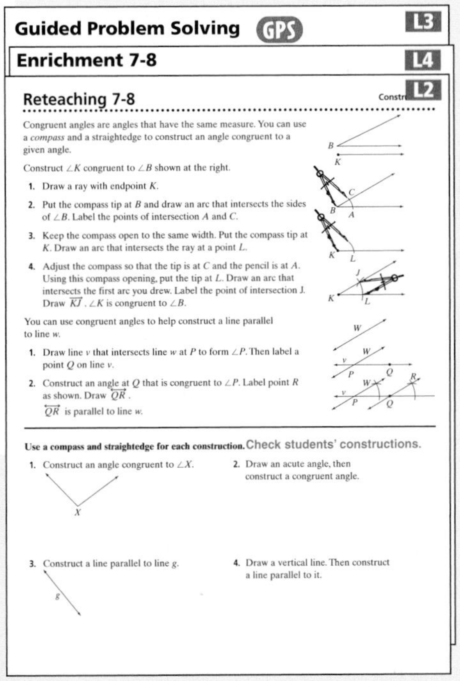
Guided Problem Solving GPS L3
Enrichment 7-8 L4
Reteaching 7-8 L2
Congruent angles are angles that have the same measure. You can use a compass and a straightedge to construct an angle congruent to a given angle.
Construct ∠K congruent to ∠B shown at the right.
1. Draw a ray with endpoint K.
2. Put the compass tip at B and draw an arc that intersects the sides of ∠B. Label the points of intersection A and C.
3. Keep the compass open to the same width. Put the compass tip at K. Draw an arc that intersects the ray at a point L.
4. Adjust the compass so that the tip is at C and the pencil is at A. Using this compass opening, put the tip at L. Draw an arc that intersects the first arc you drew. Label the point of intersection J. Draw KJ. ∠K is congruent to ∠B.
You can use congruent angles to help construct a line parallel to line w.
1. Draw line v that intersects line w at P to form ∠P. Then label a point Q on line v.
2. Construct an angle at Q that is congruent to ∠P. Label point R as shown. Draw QR. QR is parallel to line w.
Use a compass and straightedge for each construction. Check students' constructions.
1. Construct an angle congruent to ∠X.
2. Draw an acute angle, then construct a congruent angle.
3. Construct a line parallel to line g.
4. Draw a vertical line. Then construct a line parallel to it.

Alternative Assessment

Each student in a pair draws an angle. Partners construct a congruent angle and then a line that is parallel to one of the rays of the angle.

16. $\frac{2}{13}$ 17. $\frac{4}{13}$ 18. $\frac{9}{26}$

Test Prep

Resources
For additional practice with a variety of test item formats:
- Test-Taking Strategies, p. 345
- Test Prep, p. 349
- Test-Taking Strategies with Transparencies

Geometry Software and Constructions

Learning about constructions in a computer-based environment can expand students' understanding of important geometric properties and procedures. In this activity, students learn how to bisect angles and construct perpendicular bisectors using geometry software.

Guided Instruction

Activity

Have students share their constructions, methods, and conclusions. Ask groups to prepare a written comparison that highlights the similarities and differences in the process of making constructions with and without a computer.

Teaching Tip

Review, using sketches as needed, the meanings of the terms *perpendicular, bisector, midpoint, ray, angle, intersections, vertex,* and *reflection.*

Error Prevention!

In Exercise 3b, remind students not to assume that segments are congruent simply by looking at them. Have them verify, drawing on the meanings of bisectors, that their classification is correct.

Resources

- any dynamic geometry software application that can perform constructions and transformations

Geometry Software and Constructions

A **segment bisector** is a line, segment, or ray that goes through the midpoint of a segment. A **perpendicular bisector** is a line, segment, or ray that is perpendicular to a segment at its midpoint. An **angle bisector** is a ray that divides an angle into two angles of equal measure.

You can use the Construct menu in geometry software to make perpendicular bisectors and angle bisectors.

ACTIVITY

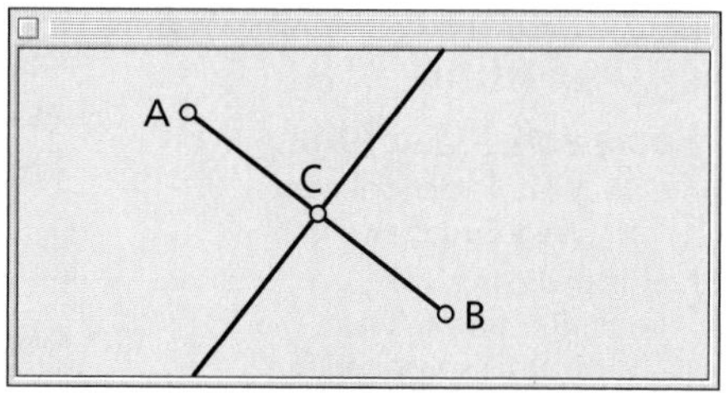

1. a. Draw $\overline{AB}$. Highlight $\overline{AB}$ and use the Construct menu to construct the midpoint of $\overline{AB}$. Label this point *C*.
   b. Highlight $\overline{AB}$ and *C* and use the Construct menu to construct a perpendicular line through $\overline{AB}$ at *C*.

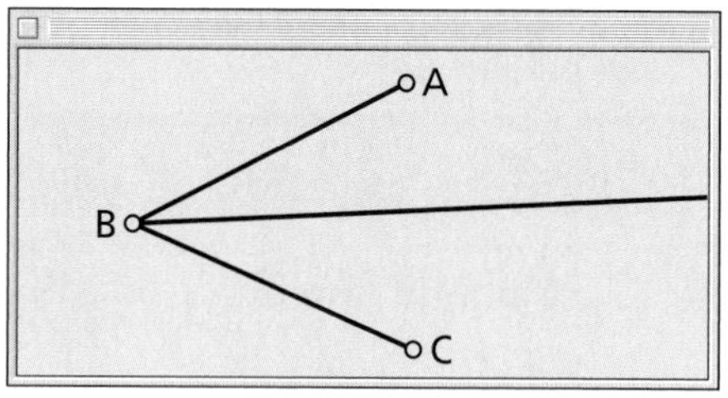

2. a. Draw $\angle ABC$. Highlight all three points of $\angle ABC$, making sure that *B* is the second point highlighted.
   b. Use the Construct menu to construct the angle bisector of $\angle ABC$.

Exercises

1. Draw $\angle ABC$ and use the Construct menu to construct an angle whose measure is $\frac{1}{4}$ of $m\angle ABC$. **Check students' work.**
2. a. Draw $\overline{AB}$ and construct its perpendicular bisector. Construct a point *C* on the perpendicular bisector. Draw $\overline{AC}$ and $\overline{BC}$. **Check students' work.**
   b. What type of triangle is $\triangle ABC$? **isosceles**

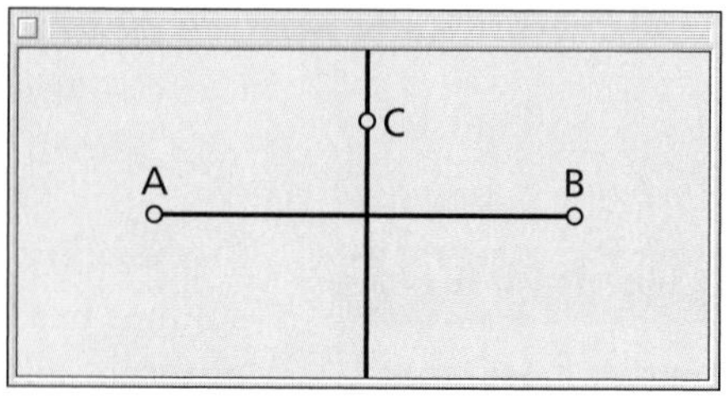

3. a. Draw $\overline{AB}$ and construct its perpendicular bisector as in the diagram at the right. Construct point *C* on this perpendicular bisector and use the Transform menu to reflect *C* over $\overline{AB}$. Label this point *D*. Draw segments connecting points *A, C, B,* and *D*.
   b. What type of quadrilateral is *ACBD*?

3a. Check students' work.

b. rhombus

Drawing a Picture

The problem-solving strategy *Draw a Picture* may help you answer test questions using given information.

EXAMPLE

Three cars, A, B, and C, are parked in that order in the same row of a parking lot as shown at the right. The distance between B and C is twice the distance between A and B. The distance between A and C is 3 meters more than the distance between B and C. Find the distance between B and C.

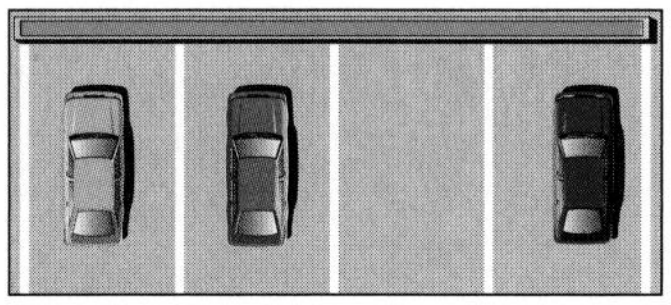

Ⓐ 3 m Ⓑ 5 m Ⓒ 6 m Ⓓ 9 m

You can draw a picture to model the situation. Let points A, B, and C represent the cars. Let x be the distance between A and B.

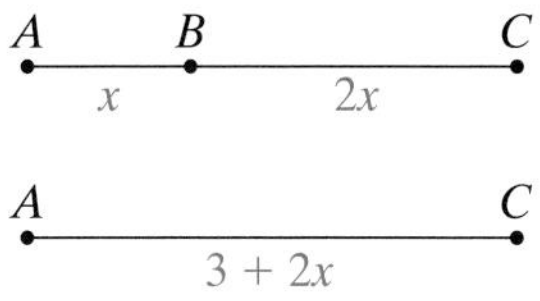

$2x + x = 3 + 2x$ ← **Use the picture to write an equation.**

$3x = 3 + 2x$ ← **Combine like terms.**

$3x - 2x = 3 + 2x - 2x$ ← **Subtract 2x from each side.**

$x = 3$ ← **Simplify.**

So $AB = 3$ m and $BC = 2(3\text{ m}) = 6$ m. The answer is C.

Exercises

1. Joe's house (J), Kate's house (K), and Lin's house (L) are located along a straight road in that order. The distance from K to L is 4 times the distance from J to K. The distance from J to L is 36 yards more than 3 times the distance from J to K. What is the distance from J to K? **B**
   Ⓐ 24 yd Ⓑ 18 yd Ⓒ 12 yd Ⓓ 4.5 yd

2. Points $F(7, 1)$, $G(2, 1)$, and $H(2, 6)$ are vertices of rectangle $FGHI$. Find the coordinates of I' if $FGHI$ is reflected over the x-axis. **J**
   Ⓕ (6, 2) Ⓖ (−2, 7) Ⓗ (7, 6) Ⓙ (7, −6)

3. Logan and Julie climbed different hills. Julie climbed 28 yards less than twice the height Logan climbed. They climbed a total of 95 yards. How far did Logan and Julie climb? **A**
   Ⓐ Logan climbed 41 yards and Julie climbed 54 yards.
   Ⓑ Logan climbed 54 yards and Julie climbed 41 yards.
   Ⓒ Logan climbed $22\frac{1}{3}$ yards and Julie climbed $72\frac{2}{3}$ yards.
   Ⓓ Logan climbed 28 yards and Julie climbed 56 yards.

Drawing a Picture

The problem-solving strategy of drawing a picture is also an effective test-taking strategy.

Guided Instruction

For Exercise 2, review reflections with students. Ask: *Does a reflection change the size, shape, or location of a figure?* location

How do you find the image of a point that is reflected about a line of symmetry? image is exactly the same distance away from the line of symmetry as original point; a line segment connecting the point and its image would be perpendicular to the line of symmetry

Error Prevention!

Stress the importance of making a picture that accurately represents the data provided. Guide students to reread the text after they have drawn their picture to make sure that they have presented the identical information.

Resources

Test-Taking Strategies with Transparencies
- Transparency 9
- Practice sheet, p. 31

Test-Taking Strategies with Transparencies

Test-Taking Strategies: Drawing a Picture

A diagram can help you see how to solve a problem.

Example A square quilt has 6 in. by 6 in. fabric squares. The outside perimeter is 144 in. How many squares are on the quilt perimeter?

A. 144 B. 36 C. 24 D. 20

Each side must be 144 ÷ 4 = 36 in.

Let one unit on graph paper represent 6 in.

There must be 36 ÷ 6 = 6 squares on each side.

Draw a diagram, and count the perimeter squares.

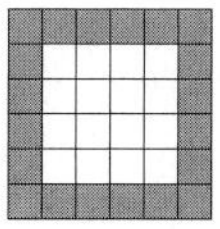

The answer is 20, or choice D.

Use a diagram to find the answer. Explain your reasoning.

1. Tess wants to fence in her garden, which is 5 ft long and 4 ft wide. She will put a post at each corner and at every foot. How many fence posts will she need?
   A. 14 B. 20 C. 18 D. 19
2. What is the area of the shaded square in the figure?
   F. 50 cm^2
   G. 100 cm^2
   H. 200 cm^2
   J. 400 cm^2

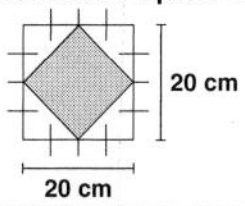

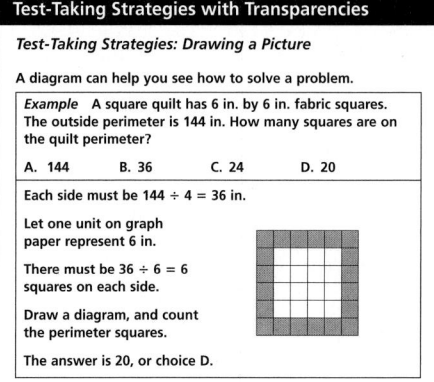

Resources

Student Edition
Extra Skills and Word Problems Practice, Ch. 7, p. 616
English/Spanish Glossary, p. 650
Formulas and Properties, p. 648
Tables, p. 643

All in One Teaching Resources
- Vocabulary and Study Skills 7F L3

Differentiated Instruction
Spanish Vocabulary Workbook with Study Skills ELL
Interactive Textbook
- Audio Glossary

Online Vocabulary Quiz

Success Tracker™
Online at PHSchool.com

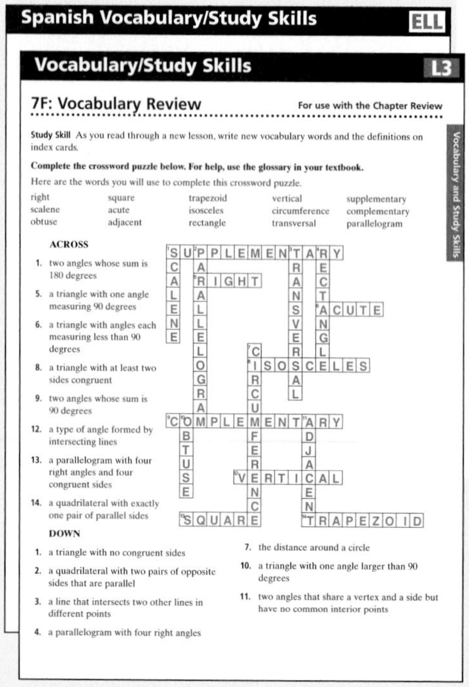
Spanish Vocabulary/Study Skills ELL

Vocabulary/Study Skills L3

7F: Vocabulary Review — For use with the Chapter Review

Study Skill As you read through a new lesson, write new vocabulary words and the definitions on index cards.

Complete the crossword puzzle below. For help, use the glossary in your textbook.

Here are the words you will use to complete this crossword puzzle.

right	square	trapezoid	vertical	supplementary
scalene	acute	isosceles	circumference	complementary
obtuse	adjacent	rectangle	transversal	parallelogram

ACROSS
1. two angles whose sum is 180 degrees
5. a triangle with one angle measuring 90 degrees
6. a triangle with angles each measuring less than 90 degrees
8. a triangle with at least two sides congruent
9. two angles whose sum is 90 degrees
12. a type of angle formed by intersecting lines
13. a parallelogram with four right angles and four congruent sides
14. a quadrilateral with exactly one pair of parallel sides

DOWN
1. a triangle with no congruent sides
2. a quadrilateral with two pairs of opposite sides that are parallel
3. a line that intersects two other lines in different points
4. a parallelogram with four right angles
7. the distance around a circle
10. a triangle with one angle larger than 90 degrees
11. two angles that share a vertex and a side but have no common interior points

Chapter 7 Review

Vocabulary Review

- **acute triangle** (p. 318)
- **adjacent angles** (p. 303)
- **alternate interior angles** (p. 307)
- **area** (p. 328)
- **compass** (p. 341)
- **complementary** (p. 304)
- **congruent polygons** (p. 312)
- **corresponding angles** (p. 307)
- **equilateral triangle** (p. 318)
- **isosceles triangle** (p. 318)
- **obtuse triangle** (p. 318)
- **parallelogram** (p. 319)
- **perpendicular lines** (p. 304)
- **quadrilateral** (p. 319)
- **rectangle** (p. 319)
- **regular polygon** (p. 325)
- **rhombus** (p. 319)
- **right triangle** (p. 318)
- **scalene triangle** (p. 318)
- **square** (p. 319)
- **supplementary** (p. 304)
- **transversal** (p. 307)
- **trapezoid** (p. 319)
- **vertical angles** (p. 303)

Go Online
PHSchool.com
For: Online Vocabulary Quiz
Web Code: asj-0751

Choose the correct vocabulary term to complete each sentence.

1. A (transversal, compass) intersects two lines at different points. transversal
2. A triangle with no congruent sides is (isosceles, scalene). scalene
3. The measures of (complementary, supplementary) angles add up to 180°. supplementary
4. A (rhombus, trapezoid) has four congruent sides. rhombus
5. All the sides and angles of a (congruent polygon, regular polygon) are congruent. regular polygon

Skills and Concepts

Lessons 7-1, 7-2

- To identify types of angles and to find angle measures using the relationship between angles
- To identify parallel lines and the angles formed by parallel lines and transversals

Vertical angles are congruent. The sum of the measures of a pair of **supplementary** angles is 180°. The sum of the measures of a pair of **complementary** angles is 90°.

If two parallel lines are cut by a **transversal,** the **corresponding angles** are congruent, and the **alternate interior angles** are congruent.

Find the measures of $\angle 1$ and $\angle 2$ in each diagram.

6. 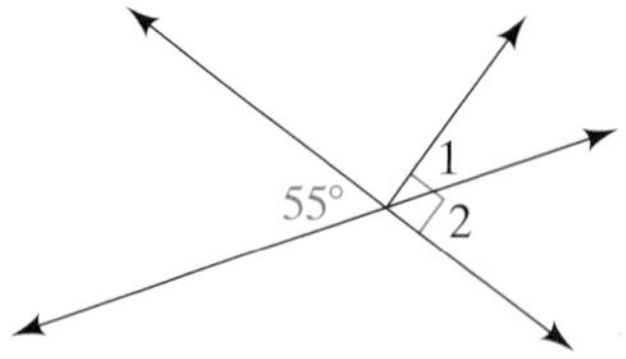

35°; 55°

7. 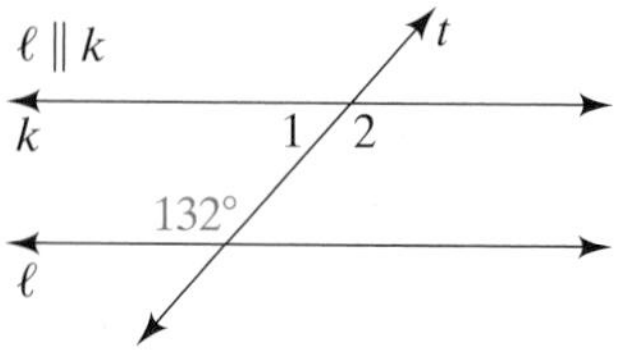

48°; 132°

Alternative Assessment L4

Alternative Assessment
Chapter 7

PIZZA PRICING

Ira is the restaurant reporter for his school newspaper. He decided to write his next article on pizza. He surveyed four pizza restaurants and recorded the largest and smallest pizza each offered in this table.

Restaurant	Pizza Choice	Diameter (in.)	Price
A	Tops Titan	12	\$ 8.00
	Tiny Tot	4	\$ 1.50
B	Colossal Caper	14	\$ 8.50
	Peewee Pie	6	\$ 3.50
C	Giant Pie	16	\$ 9.20
	Small Pie	8	\$ 4.00
D	Massive Monster	20	\$11.00
	Prince-o-Pie	10	\$ 5.00

Show all your work on a separate sheet of paper. You may use a calculator. Use 3.14 for π.

1. Which is the least expensive pizza? Which pizza is the least expensive per square inch? Explain how you found your answer.
2. What happens to the amount of pizza when its diameter is doubled? How should the price change? Explain.
3. For take-out pizza, boxes are required. What size square box would you recommend for each pizza? Explain. Could all four restaurants use boxes with a base that is 20 inches by 20 inches?
4. Part of Ira's article will be devoted to common pizza toppings: pepperoni, peppers, onions, and mushrooms. How many different pizzas can be formed by the four restaurants using just one of these four toppings? Explain how you found your answer.

Lessons 7-3, 7-4
- To identify congruent figures and use them to solve problems
- To classify triangles and quadrilaterals

Congruent polygons have exactly the same size and shape. You can use SAS, ASA, or SSS to decide whether two triangles are congruent. You can classify triangles by angle measures or by the number of congruent sides. You can classify quadrilaterals by their sides and angles.

Classify each triangle by its sides and its angles.

8. 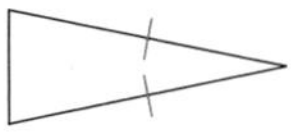
isosceles, acute

9. 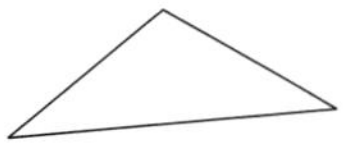
scalene, obtuse

10. 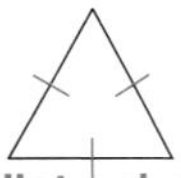
equilateral, acute

Write a congruence statement and show that the triangles are congruent.

11. 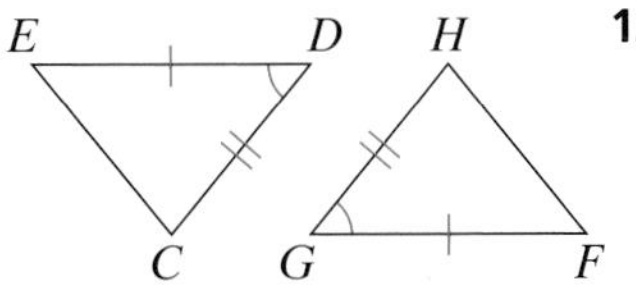

$\triangle CDE \cong \triangle HGF$; SAS

12. 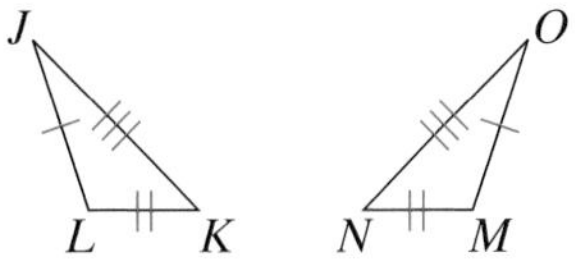

$\triangle JLK \cong \triangle OMN$; SSS

Lesson 7-5
- To find the angle measures of a polygon

For a polygon with n sides, the sum of the measures of the interior angles is $(n - 2)180°$. The measure of each angle of a **regular polygon** equals the sum of the angle measures divided by the number of angles.

Find the measure of each angle of a regular polygon with the given number of sides.

13. 6 120° **14.** 8 135° **15.** 12 150° **16.** 18 160°

Lessons 7-6, 7-7
- To find the areas of parallelograms, triangles, and trapezoids
- To find the circumference and area of a circle and the area of irregular figures

Area formulas: **parallelogram** $A = bh$ **triangle** $A = \frac{1}{2}bh$

trapezoid $A = \frac{1}{2}h(b_1 + b_2)$ **circle** $A = \pi r^2$

The distance around a circle is the **circumference** of the circle.

$C = \pi d$ or $C = 2\pi r$

Find the area of each figure. If necessary, round to the nearest tenth.

17. 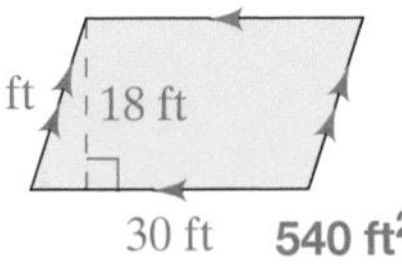

540 ft²

18. 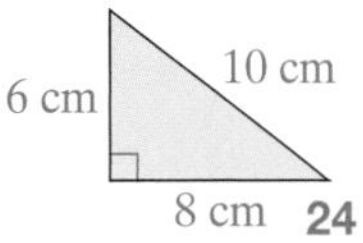

24 cm²

19. 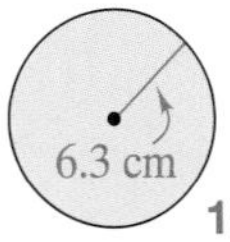

124.7 cm²

Lesson 7-8
- To construct congruent angles and parallel lines

You can construct congruent angles and parallel lines using a **compass.**

20. Draw an acute $\angle P$. Then construct $\angle T$ congruent to $\angle P$.
20–21. See margin.

21. Draw a vertical line a. Construct a line b parallel to a.

Page 348

13. Scalene obtuse triangle; there are no congruent sides and there is one obtuse angle.

14. Rhombus; the four sides are congruent but there are no right angles.

20. 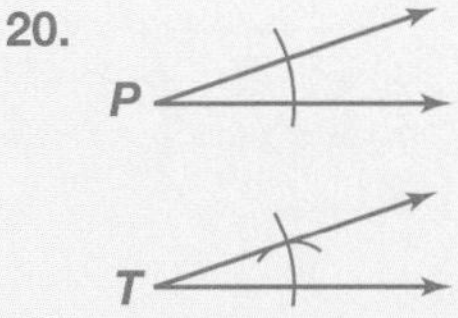

21. 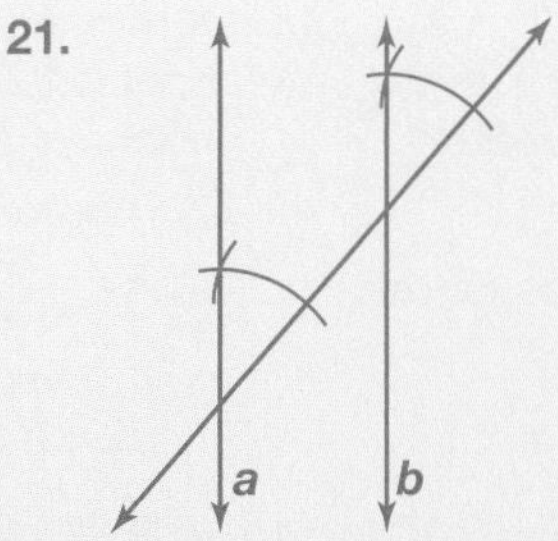

Chapter 7 Test

Resources

- ExamView Assessment Suite CD-ROM
  - Chapter 7 Ready-Made Test
  - Make your own Ch. 7 test
- MindPoint Quiz Show CD-ROM
  - Chapter 7 Review

Differentiated Instruction

All in One Teaching Resources
- Below Level Chapter 7 Test L2
- Chapter 7 Test L3
- Chapter 7 Alternative Assessment L4

Spanish Assessment Resources ELL
- Below Level Chapter 7 Test L2
- Chapter 7 Test L3
- Chapter 7 Alternative Assessment L4

ExamView Assessment Suite CD-ROM
- Special Needs Test L1
- Special Needs Practice Bank L1

Online Chapter 1 Test at www.PHSchool.com

1. alternate interior
2. none of these
3. corresponding
4. adjacent
5. none of these
6. vertical
7. $m\angle 1 = 150°$; $m\angle 2 = 30°$; $m\angle 3 = 150°$; $m\angle 4 = 30°$; $m\angle 5 = 150°$

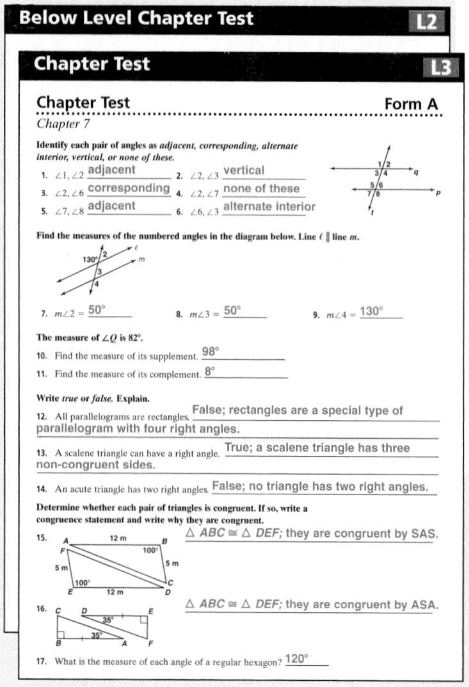
Below Level Chapter Test L2

Chapter Test L3

Chapter Test Form A

Chapter 7

Identify each pair of angles as *adjacent, corresponding, alternate interior, vertical, or none of these.*

1. ∠1, ∠2 adjacent
2. ∠2, ∠3 vertical
3. ∠2, ∠6 corresponding
4. ∠2, ∠7 none of these
5. ∠7, ∠8 adjacent
6. ∠6, ∠3 alternate interior

Find the measures of the numbered angles in the diagram below. Line ℓ ∥ line *m*.

7. $m\angle 2 =$ 50°
8. $m\angle 3 =$ 50°
9. $m\angle 4 =$ 130°

The measure of ∠Q is 82°.

10. Find the measure of its supplement. 98°
11. Find the measure of its complement. 8°

Write *true* or *false*. Explain.

12. All parallelograms are rectangles. False; rectangles are a special type of parallelogram with four right angles.
13. A scalene triangle can have a right angle. True; a scalene triangle has three non-congruent sides.
14. An acute triangle has two right angles. False; no triangle has two right angles.

Determine whether each pair of triangles is congruent. If so, write a congruence statement and write why they are congruent.

15. △ ABC ≅ △ DEF; they are congruent by SAS.
16. △ ABC ≅ △ DEF; they are congruent by ASA.
17. What is the measure of each angle of a regular hexagon? 120°

Chapter 7 Test

Go Online PHSchool.com For: Online chapter test Web Code: asa-0752

Identify each pair of angles in the diagram below as *adjacent, corresponding, alternate interior, vertical,* or *none of these.* 1–6. See margin.

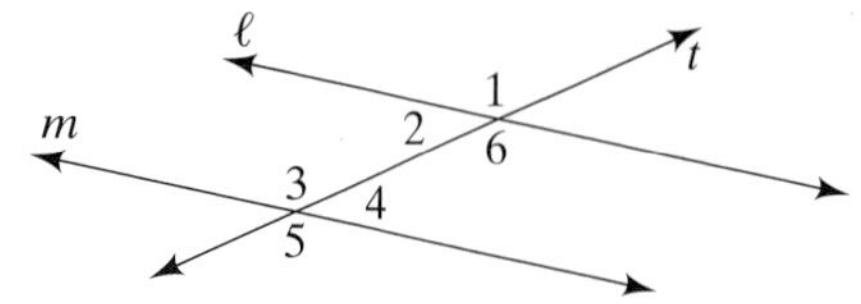

1. ∠2, ∠4
2. ∠1, ∠5
3. ∠1, ∠3
4. ∠3, ∠4
5. ∠4, ∠6
6. ∠3, ∠5

7. Find the measures of the numbered angles in the diagram below. See margin.

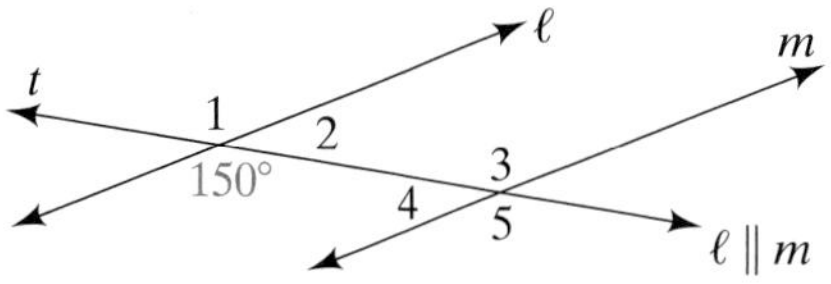

The measure of ∠D is 68°.

8. Find the measure of its supplement. 112°
9. Find the measure of its complement. 22°

Reasoning Write *true* or *false*. Explain. 10–12. See margin.

10. An obtuse triangle can be a right triangle.
11. A scalene triangle can be an acute triangle.
12. A rhombus can have four right angles.

Determine the best name for each figure. Explain. See p. 347 margin for explanations.

13. 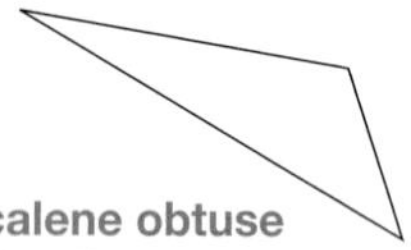
scalene obtuse triangle

14. 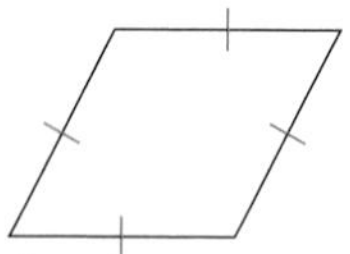
rhombus

15. **Writing in Math** Explain the difference between a rectangle and a parallelogram. See margin.

16. What is the measure of each interior angle of a regular pentagon? 108°

Determine whether each pair of triangles is congruent. If so, write a congruence statement and explain how you know the triangles are congruent.

17. 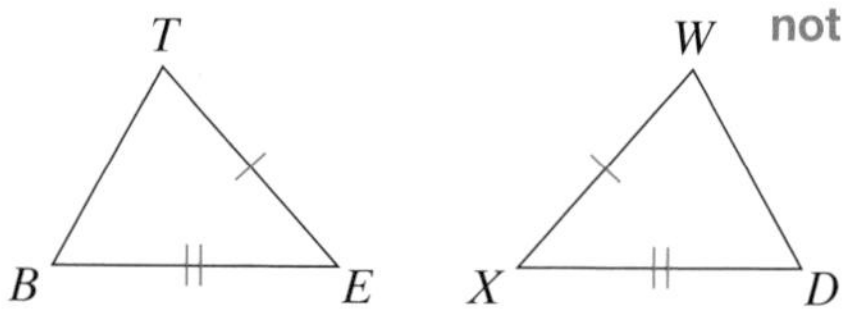

not congruent

18. 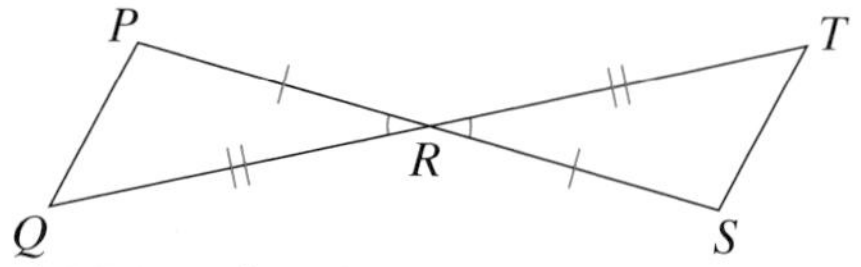

$\triangle PRQ \cong \triangle SRT$ by SAS

Draw and label a figure to fit each description. 19–22. See margin.

19. a scalene right triangle
20. an equilateral triangle
21. a parallelogram that is not a rectangle
22. a rectangle that is a rhombus

Find the sum of the measures of the interior angles of a polygon with the given number of sides.

23. 4 sides 360°
24. 7 sides 900°
25. 15 sides 2,340°

Find the area of each figure.

26. 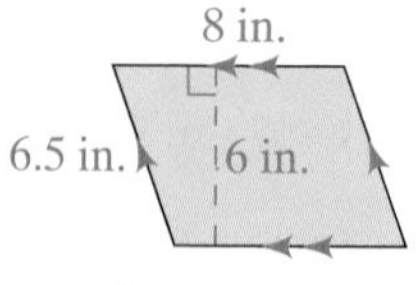

48 in.²

27. 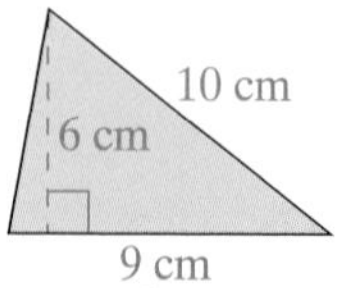

27 cm²

28. **Food** Find the circumference and the area of a pancake with a diameter of 15 cm. Round your answers to the nearest tenth. 47.1 cm; 176.7 cm²
29. Draw an obtuse angle and label it ∠G. Construct ∠H congruent to ∠G. See margin.

10. False; the sum of the measures of an obtuse angle and a right angle is greater than 180°.
11. True; a scalene triangle can be acute, right, or obtuse.
12. True; a square is a rhombus with four right angles.
15. A rectangle has four right angles. A parallelogram need not have four right angles.

19–22. Answers may vary. Samples are given.

19. 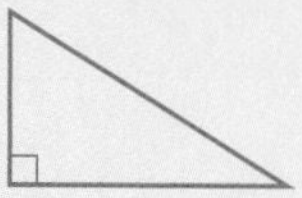

20. 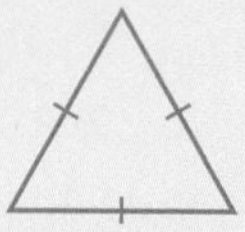

21. 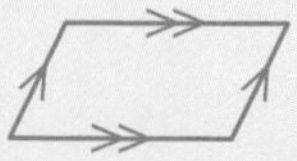

22. 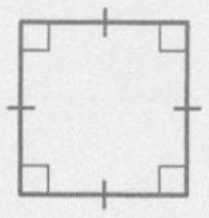

29. See back of book.

Multiple Choice

For Exercises 1–10, choose the correct letter.

1. Which square root lies between the whole numbers 11 and 12? C
   A $\sqrt{101}$ B $\sqrt{120}$ C $\sqrt{135}$ D $\sqrt{144}$

2. Aleisha can read four pages in 12 min. Which proportion can she use to figure out how long it will take her to read an 18-page chapter? G
   F $\frac{4}{12} = \frac{x}{18}$ H $\frac{4}{18} = \frac{12}{x}$
   G $\frac{12}{18} = \frac{4}{x}$ J $\frac{4}{x} = \frac{18}{12}$

3. Write $3\frac{1}{2}\%$ as a fraction in simplest form. C
   A $\frac{7}{2}$ B $\frac{7}{20}$ C $\frac{7}{200}$ D $\frac{3.5}{100}$

4. What is the circumference of a circle with an area of 36π in.^{2}? G
   F 6π in. H 18π in.
   G 12π in. J 36π in.

5. Which power is equivalent to $5^3 \cdot 5^2$? A
   A 5^5 B 5^6 C 25^5 D 25^6

6. Which is a pair of corresponding angles? J

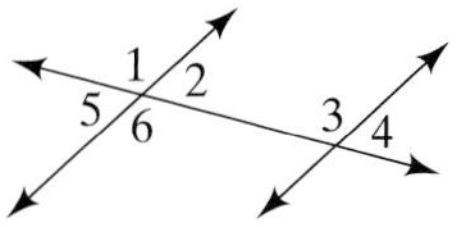

   F ∠1 and ∠6 H ∠3 and ∠6
   G ∠1 and ∠4 J ∠2 and ∠4

7. A job pays $160 for 25 hours. At this rate, what would it pay for 40 hours? B
   A $216 C $640
   B $256 D $1,000

8. Which algebraic expression is NOT equivalent to $2(x + 5)$? J
   F $2(x) + 2(5)$ H $(x + 5) + (x + 5)$
   G $2(5 + x)$ J $5 + 2x$

9. $S'(-3, -2)$ is the image after a translation of 6 units to the left and 2 units up. What are the coordinates of the original point? D
   A $(9, -2)$ C $(1, 2)$
   B $(3, 2)$ D $(3, -4)$

10. Choose the step you should complete first to construct ∠*E* congruent to ∠*M*. G
   F Put the compass tip at *M*.
   G Draw a ray with endpoint *E*.
   H Draw an arc that intersects the sides of ∠*M*.
   J Put the compass tip at *E*.

Gridded Response

Record your answer in a grid.

11. A painter needs 15 gallons of violet paint. The formula for mixing violet paint is 3 parts blue to 2 parts red. How many gallons of blue paint does the painter need? 9

Short Response

12. Farmer Hoyle usually takes the shortcut across his rectangular field. How much distance does he save by taking the shortcut instead of walking along two sides of the field? Justify your answer. See margin.

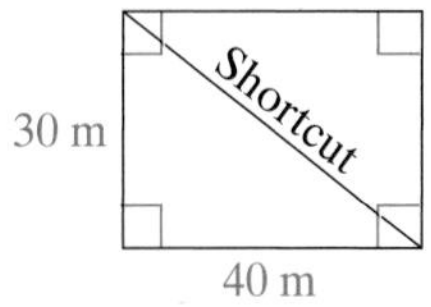

Extended Response

13. On the first day of gym class, students do 6 push-ups. The number of push-ups the students do will increase by 2 each time they come to class.
   a. Write an equation that represents the number of push-ups *p* the class does after *c* classes. 13a–b. See margin.
   b. How many push-ups will the class do on the ninth day of class? Justify your answer.

Item	1	2	3	4	5	6	7	8	9	10	11	12	13
Lesson	3-1	4-3	5-1	7-7	2-7	7-1	4-1	6-2	3-6	7-8	4-3	3-2	1-1

Test Prep

Resources

Test Prep Workbook

All in One Teaching Resources
- Cumulative Review L3
- ExamView Assessment Suite CD-ROM
- Standardized Test Practice

Differentiated Instruction

Spanish Assessment Resources
- Spanish Cumulative Review ELL

12. walking along sides:
$30 + 40 = 70$
shortcut: $30^2 + 40^2 = s^2$
$900 + 1{,}600 = s^2$
$2{,}500 = s^2$
$50 = s^2$
$70\text{ m} - 50\text{ m} = 20\text{ m}$

13. [4] a. $p = 6 + 2(c - 1)$
b. $p = 6 + 2(9 - 1)$
$= 6 + 2(8)$
$= 6 + 16$
$= 22$
[3] one minor computational error
[2] two minor computational errors
[1] correct answers without work shown

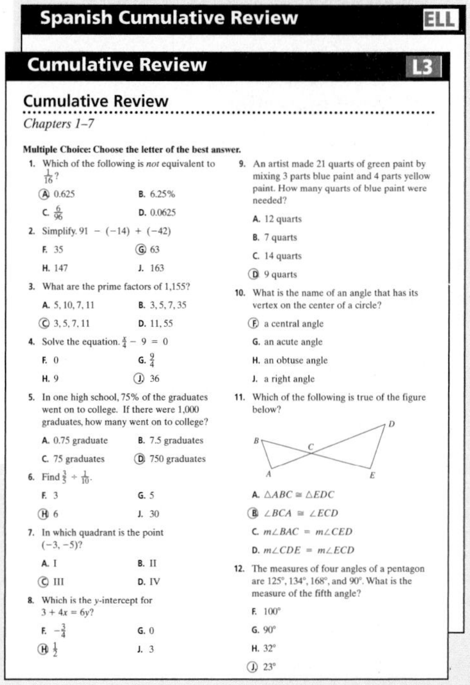

Spanish Cumulative Review ELL

Cumulative Review L3

Cumulative Review

Chapters 1–7

Multiple Choice: Choose the letter of the best answer.

1. Which of the following is *not* equivalent to $\frac{1}{16}$?
   (A) 0.625 B. 6.25%
   C. $\frac{6}{96}$ D. 0.0625
2. Simplify. $91 - (-14) + (-42)$
   F. 35 (G) 63
   H. 147 J. 163
3. What are the prime factors of 1,155?
   A. 5, 10, 7, 11 B. 3, 5, 7, 35
   (C) 3, 5, 7, 11 D. 11, 55
4. Solve the equation. $\frac{x}{4} - 9 = 0$
   F. 0 G. $\frac{9}{4}$
   H. 9 (J) 36
5. In one high school, 75% of the graduates went on to college. If there were 1,000 graduates, how many went on to college?
   A. 0.75 graduate B. 7.5 graduates
   C. 75 graduates (D) 750 graduates
6. Find $\frac{3}{5} \div \frac{1}{10}$.
   F. 3 G. 5
   (H) 6 J. 30
7. In which quadrant is the point $(-3, -5)$?
   A. I B. II
   (C) III D. IV
8. Which is the *y*-intercept for $3 + 4x = 6y$?
   F. $-\frac{3}{4}$ G. 0
   (H) $\frac{1}{2}$ J. 3
9. An artist made 21 quarts of green paint by mixing 3 parts blue paint and 4 parts yellow paint. How many quarts of blue paint were needed?
   A. 12 quarts
   B. 7 quarts
   C. 14 quarts
   (D) 9 quarts
10. What is the name of an angle that has its vertex on the center of a circle?
   (F) a central angle
   G. an acute angle
   H. an obtuse angle
   J. a right angle
11. Which of the following is true of the figure below?
   B, C, D, A, E
   A. $\triangle ABC \cong \triangle EDC$
   (B) $\angle BCA \cong \angle ECD$
   C. $m\angle BAC = m\angle CED$
   D. $m\angle CDE = m\angle ECD$
12. The measures of four angles of a pentagon are 125°, 134°, 168°, and 90°. What is the measure of the fifth angle?
   F. 100°
   G. 90°
   H. 32°
   (J) 23°

Problem Solving

Applying Geometry

Students will use data from these two pages to answer the questions posed here in Put It All Together.

Activating Prior Knowledge

Have students share any experiences they have had sailing, either as passengers or as members of a crew. Ask them to explain why they think some people become very attached to sailing, despite all its rigors and dangers.

Guided Instruction

Have a student read aloud the opening paragraph about how sailboats must tack to travel into the direction of the wind.

Language Arts Connection
Tell students that sailing, both as a means of travel or commerce, and as a sport or recreational activity, comes with its own specialized vocabulary. Have interested students or groups of students prepare a sailing glossary. Invite them to include pictures to accompany the definitions, or even to make fully labeled drawings of sailboats to clarify some of these nautical terms.

History Connection
Invite interested students to learn about the history of sailing, from the earliest small craft to the sleek and swift vessels that ruled the seas before the age of steam.

Sports Connection
Any sailor worth his or her salt knows about the importance and many uses of knots, such as the tucked double overhand hitch knot shown on page 351. Invite curious students to learn about other kinds of knots sailors use. Challenge students to learn how to tie a few of these knots, and demonstrate their skills for classmates.

Problem Solving Application

Applying Geometry

You Can't Get There From Here For a sailboat, the shortest distance between two points is not always a straight line. Sailboats cannot travel directly into the wind (upwind). They can head about 45° from the direction of the wind, but not closer. To get to a specific point upwind, the sailboat has to follow a zigzag course, as shown below. This is called tacking.

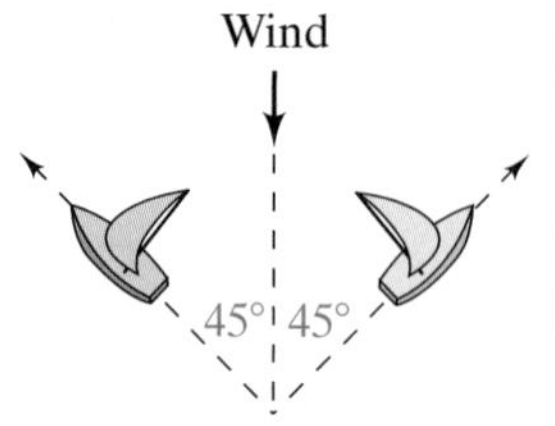

Sailing Upwind

Safe-Water Buoy
Buoys are floating aids that mark channels and warn sailors of obstructions in the water.

Put It All Together

Materials ruler, protractor

Three sailboats are racing upwind toward the finish line, 3 mi away. One crew tacks twice, another tacks three times, and the third crew tacks four times. Their courses create isosceles right triangles where they intersect the dashed lines.

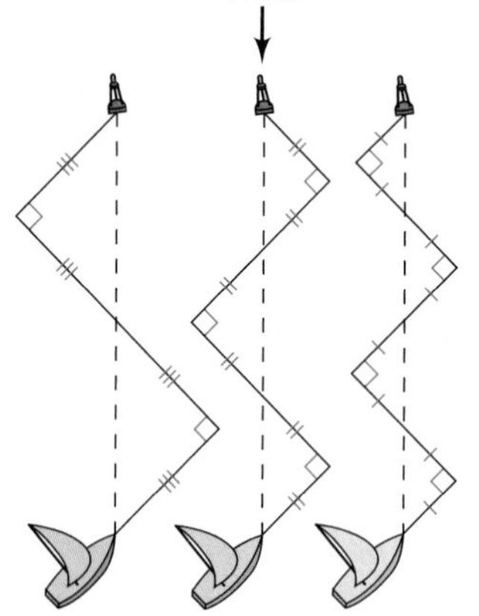

Tacking Toward the Mark

1. Copy the sailing diagram. For each course, find the length of the hypotenuse of each triangle.
2. **Writing in Math** In the triangle diagram below, point D is the midpoint of $\overline{BC}$, so $\overline{BD} \cong \overline{DC}$. Explain how you know that $\triangle ADC \cong \triangle ADB$.
3. **a.** Find the measures of the angles in $\triangle ABC$, $\triangle ADC$, and $\triangle ADB$. What do you notice?
   b. What are the measures of the three angles of an isosceles right triangle? Explain.
4. **a.** Suppose $DC = 100$ yd. How long is $\overline{AD}$? Explain.
   b. Reasoning Suppose the hypotenuse of $\triangle ABC$ measures 10 mi. How long is $\overline{AC}$? Explain.
5. **a.** Find the course length for each boat. Which boat follows the shortest course?
   b. Patterns If a boat tacks ten times, what will its course length be?
6. **Reasoning** Why might the skipper of a sailboat crew decide to tack more times? Fewer times?

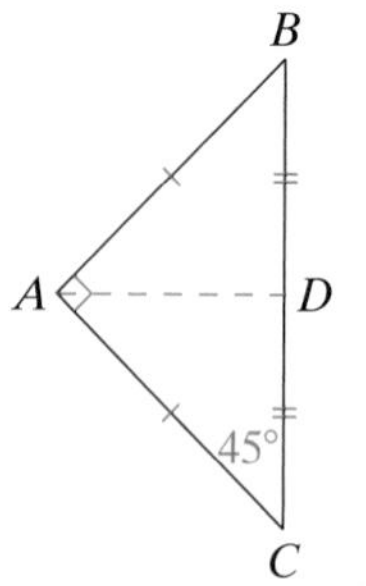

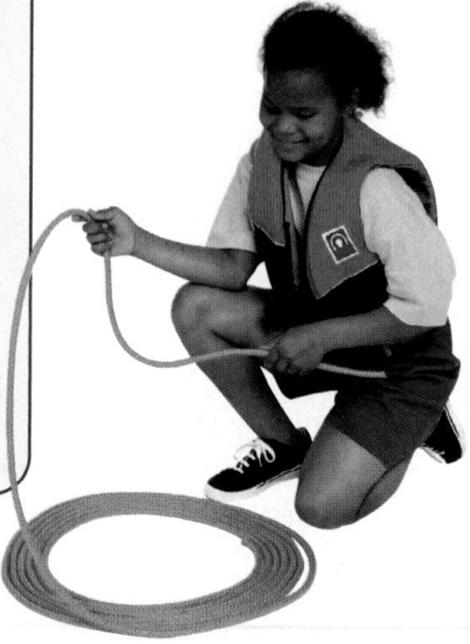

1. green: 1.5 miles; red: 1 miles: blue: 0.75 mile
2. by SSS, because $\overline{AD}$ is congruent to itself

3a. All three triangles have angle measures of 45°, 45°, and 90°.

b. 45°, 45°, and 90°; when two legs of a right triangle are congruent, the vertex of the two congruent sides must be the 90° angle. The remaining angle are congruent, meaning each one must be half of (180 – 90°), or 45°.

Learning to Sail

Knotting ropes is one of the most important parts of sailing. A good knot is easy to fasten and unfasten but doesn't slip.

Tucked double overhand hitch knot

Trimming the Sails

Trimming the sails means adjusting them so that they receive the wind properly, so the boat moves easily and quickly across the water.

Go Online PHSchool.com
For: Information about sailing
Web Code: ase-0753

Put It All Together

Have students work in pairs to answer the questions. Guide them to record data as they measure and accumulate it.

Discuss what a right isosceles triangle is. Emphasize that every right triangle with 45° angles is an isosceles triangle. Make sure students understand how the diagram shows the different tackings the three crews make.

Exercises 5–6 Discuss with students that each time a boat tacks, it loses speed.

Differentiated Instruction

Special Needs L1
As needed, review the properties of and terminology associated with right triangles. Review the symbols for triangle, congruence, and line segment.

4a. 100 yd; $\triangle CAD$ is an isosceles right triangle, so $DC = AD$. if $DC = 100$, then $AD = 100$.

b. approximately 7.07 mi; if $BC = 10$ miles, then $DC = 5$ miles and $AD = 5$ miles. Using the Pythagorean theorem, $AC = \sqrt{50} \approx 7.07$ miles.

5a. about 4.24 miles for all three courses

b. about 4.24 miles

6. Answers may vary. Sample: Sailors may tack to avoid obstacles and other boats, but might otherwise want to tack less because they lose some speed with each turn.

8 Measurement

Chapter at a Glance

Lesson Titles, Objectives, and Features	Assessment	NCTM Standards	Local Standards
8-1 Solids • To identify solids, parts of solids, and skew line segments	Lesson Quiz	1, 2, 3, 4, 6, 7, 8, 9, 10	
8-2 Drawing Views of Three-Dimensional Figures • To draw views of three-dimensional figures, including base plans and isometric views **8-2b Activity Lab:** Sketching Solids	Lesson Quiz	1, 2, 3, 4, 6, 7, 8, 9, 10	
8-3a Activity Lab, Hands On: Making Solids From Nets **8-3 Nets and Three-Dimensional Figures** • To identify nets of solids	Lesson Quiz	1, 2, 3, 4, 6, 7, 8, 9, 10	
8-4a Activity Lab, Hands On: Modeling Surface Area **8-4 Surface Areas of Prisms and Cylinders** • To find surface areas of prisms and cylinders using nets and formulas	Lesson Quiz Checkpoint Quiz 1	1, 3, 6, 7, 8, 9, 10	
8-5a Activity Lab, Hands On: Surface Area of a Pyramid **8-5 Surface Areas of Pyramids and Cones** • To find surface areas of pyramids and cones using nets and formulas	Lesson Quiz	1, 2, 3, 4, 6, 7, 8, 9, 10	
8-6a Activity Lab, Hands On: Modeling Volume **8-6 Volumes of Prisms and Cylinders** • To find the volumes of prisms and cylinders **Guided Problem Solving:** Using Formulas	Lesson Quiz	1, 2, 3, 4, 6, 7, 8, 9, 10	
8-7a Activity Lab, Hands On: Finding Volume Using Models **8-7 Volumes of Pyramids and Cones** • To find the volumes of pyramids and cones	Lesson Quiz Checkpoint Quiz 2	1, 2, 3, 4, 6, 7, 8, 9, 10	
8-8 Spheres • To find the surface area and volume of a sphere	Lesson Quiz	1, 2, 3, 4, 6, 7, 8, 9, 10	
8-9a Activity Lab: Changing Dimensions **8-9 Exploring Similar Solids** • To use proportions to find missing measurements of similar solids, including surface area and volume **8-9b Activity Lab, Data Analysis:** Precision and Significant Digits	Lesson Quiz	1, 2, 3, 4, 6, 7, 8, 9, 10	
Problem Solving Application: Applying Measurement			

NCTM Standards 2000
1 Number and Operations **2** Algebra **3** Geometry **4** Measurement **5** Data Analysis and Probability
6 Problem Solving **7** Reasoning and Proof **8** Communication **9** Connections **10** Representation

Correlations to Standardized Tests

All content for these tests is contained in *Prentice Hall Math*, Course 3. This chart reflects coverage in this chapter only.

	8-1	8-2	8-3	8-4	8-5	8-6	8-7	8-8	8-9
Terra Nova CAT6 (Level 18)									
Number and Number Relations									
Computation and Numerical Estimation									
Operation Concepts									
Measurement				✔	✔	✔	✔	✔	✔
Geometry and Spatial Sense	✔	✔	✔	✔	✔	✔	✔	✔	✔
Data Analysis, Statistics, and Probability									
Patterns, Functions, Algebra									
Problem Solving and Reasoning	✔	✔	✔	✔	✔	✔	✔	✔	✔
Communication	✔	✔	✔	✔	✔	✔	✔	✔	✔
Decimals, Fractions, Integers, Percent									
Order of Operations									
Algebraic Operations				✔	✔	✔	✔	✔	✔
Terra Nova CTBS (Level 18)									
Decimals, Fractions, Integers, Percents									
Order of Operations, Numeration, Number Theory									
Data Interpretation									
Measurement				✔	✔	✔	✔	✔	✔
Geometry	✔	✔	✔	✔	✔	✔	✔	✔	✔
ITBS (Level 14)									
Number Properties and Operations									
Algebra				✔	✔	✔	✔	✔	✔
Geometry	✔	✔	✔	✔	✔	✔	✔	✔	✔
Measurement				✔	✔	✔	✔	✔	✔
Probability and Statistics									
Estimation									
SAT10 (Adv 1 Level)									
Number Sense and Operations									
Patterns, Relationships, and Algebra				✔	✔	✔	✔	✔	✔
Data, Statistics, and Probability									
Geometry and Measurement	✔	✔	✔	✔	✔	✔	✔	✔	✔
NAEP									
Number Sense, Properties, and Operations									
Measurement				✔	✔	✔	✔	✔	
Geometry and Spatial Sense	✔	✔	✔	✔	✔	✔	✔	✔	✔
Data Analysis, Statistics, and Probability									
Algebra and Functions									

CAT6 California Achievement Test, 6th Ed.
CTBS Comprehensive Test of Basic Skills
ITBS Iowa Test of Basic Skills, Form M
SAT10 Stanford Achievement Test, 10th Ed.
NAEP National Assessment of Educational Progress 2005 Mathematics Objectives

Math Background

Professional Development

Skills Trace

BEFORE Chapter 8

Course 2 introduced basic three-dimensional figures.

DURING Chapter 8

Course 3 reviews and extends the study of three-dimensional figures to pyramids, cones, and similar solids.

AFTER Chapter 8

Throughout this course students solve problems that involve geometric reasoning.

8-1 Solids

Math Understandings

- Two-dimensional figures lie in a plane; three-dimensional figures lie in space, having length, width, and height.
- Prisms and pyramids have polygons, which are plane figures, for each face, and are polyhedrons; cylinders and cones have curved surfaces not in a plane and are not polyhedrons.

Solids, or three-dimensional figures, are objects that do not lie in a plane. A **polyhedron** is a solid with a polygon for each face.

Figure	Base(s)	Lateral face(s)
Prism	two parallel congruent polygons	parallelograms
Pyramid	exactly one polygon base	triangles
Cylinder	two parallel congruent circles	curved rectangle
Cone	exactly one circle, one vertex	curved surface

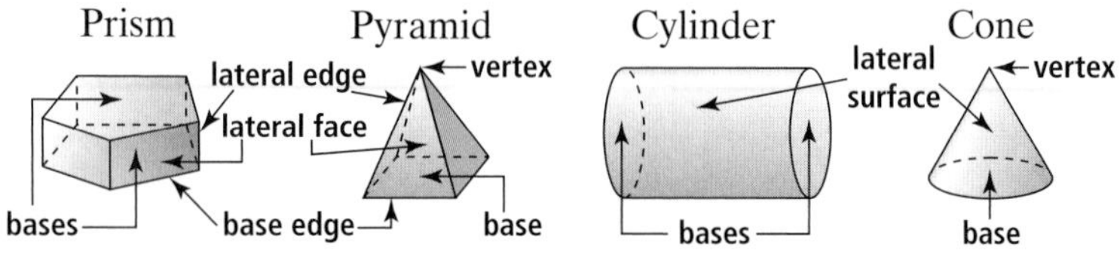

Skew lines are lines that do not intersect and are not parallel. Unlike a pair of parallel lines or a pair of intersecting lines, skew lines do not lie in the same plane.

8-2 Drawing Views of Three-Dimensional Figures

Math Understandings

- Drawings in a plane can specify the exact shape of a solid by using drawings from different perspectives.
- An isometric view allows you to see the top, front, and right side of an object in the same drawing.

A **base plan** shows the shape of the base and indicates the height of each part of a solid. An **isometric view** is a corner view of a solid, usually drawn on isometric dot paper.

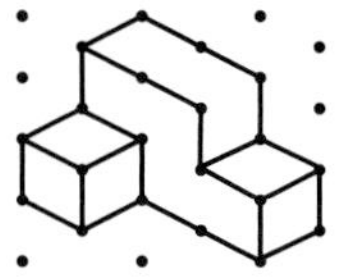

8-3 Nets and Three-Dimensional Figures

Math Understandings

- Nets for the same figure may be drawn in different configurations.

The **net** is a pattern that can be folded to form a solid. A net of a figure shows all the surfaces of that figure in one view.

8-4 8-5 Surface Areas of Prisms, Cylinders, Pyramids, and Cones

Math Understandings

- The surface area of a solid is the area of its net.
- The height of a pyramid is different from the height of its lateral faces.

The **surface area** of a solid is the sum of the areas of its surfaces. The lateral area is the portion of the surface area that is not the base(s). **Lateral area** is the sum of the areas of the lateral surfaces of a solid.

The height of a pyramid's lateral face is called the **slant height** and is indicated by the symbol ℓ. The four triangular faces of a square pyramid are congruent isosceles triangles.

Lateral Area and Surface Area	
Prism 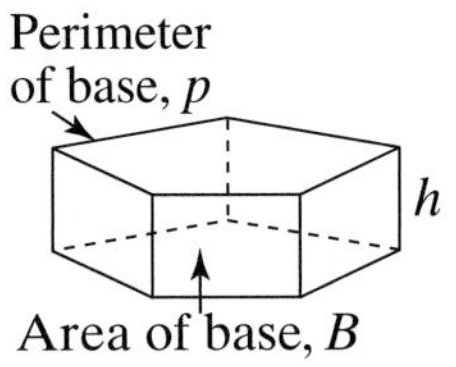 Lateral area L.A. $= ph$ Surface area S.A. $=$ L.A. $+ 2B$	**Square Pyramid** 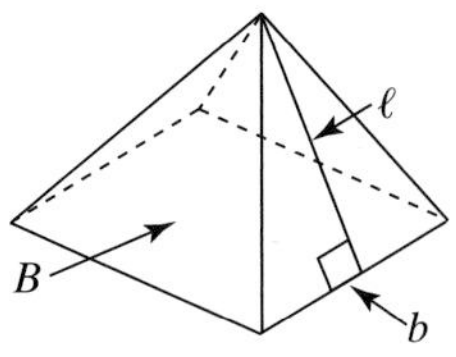 Lateral area L.A. $= 4 \cdot \left(\frac{1}{2}b\ell\right) = 2b\ell$ Surface area S.A. $=$ L.A. $+ B$
Cylinder 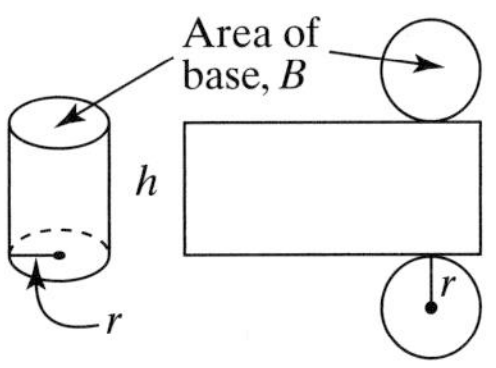 Lateral area L.A. $= 2\pi rh$ Surface area S.A. $=$ L.A. $+ 2B$	**Cone** 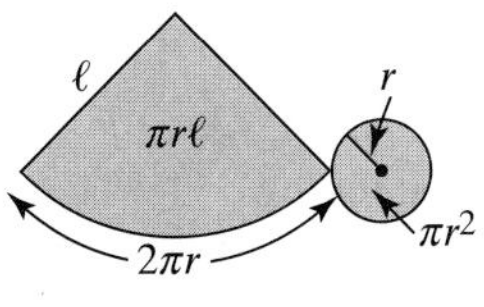 Lateral area L.A. $= \frac{1}{2}(2\pi r)\ell = \pi r\ell$ Surface area S.A. $=$ L.A. $+ B$

Volume	
Prism or Cylinder The volume V of a prism or a cylinder is the product of the base area B and the height h. $V = Bh$ 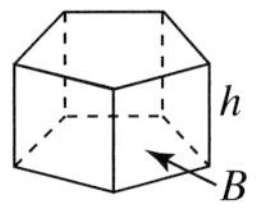 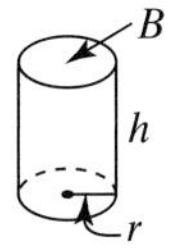	**Square Pyramid or Cone** The volume V of a pyramid or cone is one third the product of the base area B and the height h. $V = \frac{1}{3}Bh$ 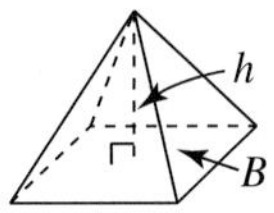 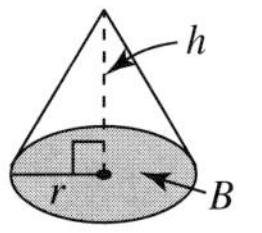

8-6 8-7 Volumes of Prisms, Cylinders, Pyramids, and Cones

Math Understandings

- Volume is an amount of three-dimensional space. You can also think of it as a measure of capacity.
- When you find the volume of a solid, the height is measured as perpendicular to the base.

Volume is the number of unit cubes, or cubic units, needed to fill a solid.

8-8 Spheres

A sphere is the set of all points in a space that are the same distance from a center point.

8-9 Exploring Similar Solids

Math Understandings

- If you change each dimension of a solid by a given amount, the surface area changes by that amount squared, and the volume changes by that amount cubed.

Two solids are **similar solids** if they have the same shape and if all of their corresponding lengths are proportional. If the ratios of the corresponding dimensions of similar solids is $\frac{a}{b}$, then the ratio of their surface areas is $\frac{a^2}{b^2}$ and the ratio of their volumes is $\frac{a^3}{b^3}$.

Additional Professional Development Opportunities

Professional Development

Math Background Notes for Chapter 8: Every lesson has a Math Background in the PLAN section.

Research Overview, Mathematics Strands
Additional support for these topics and more is in the front of the Teacher's Edition.

LessonLab
LessonLab, a Pearson Education company, offers comprehensive, facilitated professional development designed to help teachers to improve student achievement. To learn more, please visit lessonlab.com.

Chapter 8 Resources

	8-1	8-2	8-3	8-4	8-5	8-6	8-7	8-8	8-9	For the Chapter
Print Resources										
L3 Practice	●	●	●	●	●	●	●	●	●	
L1 Adapted Practice	●	●	●	●	●	●	●	●	●	
L3 Guided Problem Solving	●	●	●	●	●	●	●	●	●	
L2 Reteaching	●	●	●	●	●	●	●	●	●	
L4 Enrichment	●	●	●	●	●	●	●	●	●	
L3 Daily Notetaking Guide	●	●	●	●	●	●	●	●	●	
L1 Adapted Daily Notetaking Guide	●	●	●	●	●	●	●	●	●	
L3 Vocabulary and Study Skills Worksheets	●		●		●		●		●	●
L3 Daily Puzzles	●	●	●	●	●	●	●	●	●	
L3 Activity Labs	●	●	●	●	●	●	●	●	●	●
L3 Checkpoint Quiz				●			●			
L3 Chapter Project										●
L2 Below Level Chapter Test										●
L3 Chapter Test										●
L4 Alternative Assessment										●
L3 Cumulative Review										●
Spanish Resources ELL										
L3 Practice	●	●	●	●	●	●	●	●	●	
L3 Vocabulary and Study Skills Worksheets	●		●		●		●		●	●
L3 Checkpoint Quiz				●			●			
L2 Below Level Chapter Test										●
L3 Chapter Test										●
L4 Alternative Assessment										●
L3 Cumulative Review										●
Transparencies										
Check Skills You'll Need	●	●	●	●	●	●	●	●	●	
Additional Examples	●	●	●	●	●	●	●	●	●	
Problem of the Day	●	●	●	●	●	●	●	●	●	
Classroom Aid		●	●	●	●		●	●	●	
Student Edition Answers	●	●	●	●	●	●	●	●	●	●
Lesson Quiz	●	●	●	●	●	●	●	●	●	
Test-Taking Strategies										●
Technology										
Interactive Textbook Online	●	●	●	●	●	●	●	●	●	●
StudentExpress™ CD-ROM	●	●	●	●	●	●	●	●	●	●
Success Tracker™ Online Intervention	●	●	●	●	●	●	●	●	●	●
TeacherExpress™ CD-ROM	●	●	●	●	●	●	●	●	●	●
PresentationExpress™ with QuickTake Presenter CD-ROM	●	●	●	●	●	●	●	●	●	●
ExamView® Assessment Suite CD-ROM	●	●	●	●	●	●	●	●	●	●
MindPoint® Quiz Show CD-ROM										●
Prentice Hall Web Site: PHSchool.com	●	●	●	●	●	●	●	●	●	●

Also available: **Prentice Hall Assessment System**

- Progress Monitoring Assessments
- Skills and Concepts Review
- Test Prep Workbook

Other Resources
Algebra Readiness Tests
All-in-One Student Workbook
All-in-One Student Workbook, Adapted Version
Multilingual Handbook
Solution Key
Math Notes Study Folder
Spanish Cumulative Assessment

Where You Can Use the Lesson Resources

Here is a suggestion, following the four-step teaching plan, for how you can incorporate Differentiated Instruction Resources into your teaching.

	Instructional Resources L3	**Differentiated Instruction Resources**
1. Plan		
Preparation Read the Math Background in the Teacher's Edition to connect this lesson with students' previous experience. **Starting Class** **Check Skills You'll Need** Assign these exercises to review prerequisite skills. **New Vocabulary** Help students pre-read the lesson by pointing out the new terms introduced in the lesson.	**Math Understandings** **Transparencies & PresentationExpress™ with QuickTake Presenter CD-ROM** Check Skills You'll Need Problem of the Day **Resources** Vocabulary and Study Skills	**Spanish Support** ELL Vocabulary and Study Skills
2. Teach		
L3 **Guided Instruction** Use the Activity Labs to build conceptual understanding. Teach each Example. Use the Teacher's Edition side column notes for specific teaching tips, including Error Prevention notes. Use the Additional Examples found in the side column (and on transparency and PowerPoint) as an alternative presentation for the content. After each Example, assign the Quick Check exercise for that Example to get an immediate assessment of student understanding. Use the Closure activity in the Teacher's Edition to help students attain mastery of lesson content.	**Student Edition** Activity Lab **Resources** Daily Notetaking Guide Activity Lab **Transparencies & PresentationExpress™ with QuickTake Presenter CD-ROM** Additional Examples Classroom Aids **ExamView® Assessment Suite CD-ROM**	**Teacher's Edition** Every lesson includes suggestions for working with students who need special attention. L1 Special Needs L2 Below Level L4 Advanced Learners ELL English Language Learners **Resources** L1 Adapted Daily Notetaking Guide **Multilingual Handbook**
3. Practice		
Assignment Guide **Check Your Understanding** Use these questions to check students' understanding before you assign homework. **Homework Exercises** Assign homework from these leveled exercises in the Assignment Guide. **A** Practice by Example **B** Apply Your Skills **C** Challenge Test Prep and Mixed Review **Homework Quick Check** Use these key exercises to quickly check students' homework.	**Transparencies & Presentation Express™ with QuickTake Presenter CD-ROM** Student Answers **Resources** Practice Guided Problem Solving Vocabulary and Study Skills Activity Lab Daily Puzzles **ExamView® Assessment Suite CD-ROM**	**Spanish Support** ELL Practice ELL Vocabulary and Study Skills **Resources** L1 Adapted Practice L4 Enrichment
4. Assess & Reteach		
Lesson Quiz Assign the Lesson Quiz to assess students' mastery of the lesson content. **Checkpoint Quiz** Use the Checkpoint Quiz to assess student progress over several lessons.	**Transparencies & PresentationExpress™ with QuickTake Presenter CD-ROM** Lesson Quiz **Resources** Checkpoint Quiz	**Resources** L2 Reteaching ELL Checkpoint Quiz Success Tracker™ Online Intervention **ExamView® Assessment Suite CD-ROM**

KEY L1 Special Needs L2 Below Level L3 For All Students L4 Advanced, Gifted ELL English Language Learners

CHAPTER 8

Measurement

Check Your Readiness

Answers for students are in the back of the textbook.

For intervention, direct students to:

Finding Area
Lessons 7-6, 7-7
Extra Skills and Word Problems Practice, Ch. 7

Solving Proportions
Lesson 4-3
Extra Skills and Word Problems Practice, Ch. 4

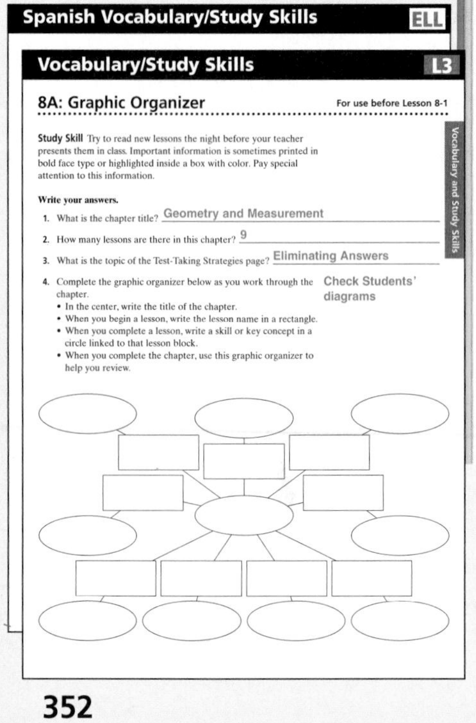
Spanish Vocabulary/Study Skills ELL

Vocabulary/Study Skills L3

8A: Graphic Organizer — For use before Lesson 8-1

Study Skill Try to read new lessons the night before your teacher presents them in class. Important information is sometimes printed in bold face type or highlighted inside a box with color. Pay special attention to this information.

Write your answers.

1. What is the chapter title? Geometry and Measurement
2. How many lessons are there in this chapter? 9
3. What is the topic of the Test-Taking Strategies page? Eliminating Answers
4. Complete the graphic organizer below as you work through the chapter. Check Students' diagrams
   - In the center, write the title of the chapter.
   - When you begin a lesson, write the lesson name in a rectangle.
   - When you complete a lesson, write a skill or key concept in a circle linked to that lesson block.
   - When you complete the chapter, use this graphic organizer to help you review.

Vocabulary and Study Skills

CHAPTER 8 Measurement

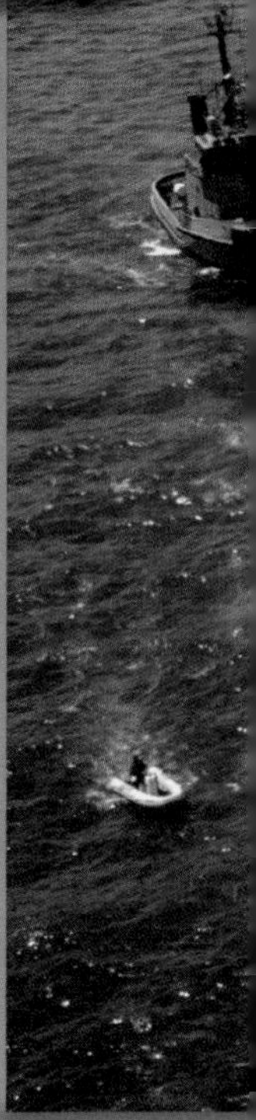

What You've Learned

- In Chapter 4, you used proportions and similar figures for indirect measurement.
- In Chapter 7, you found the areas of parallelograms, triangles, trapezoids, and circles.
- You classified two-dimensional figures based on their properties.

Check Your Readiness

GO for Help

For Exercises	See Lesson
1–2	7-7
3–6	7-6
7–10	4-3

Finding Area

Find the area of each figure. Round to the nearest square unit.

1. 7 ft²
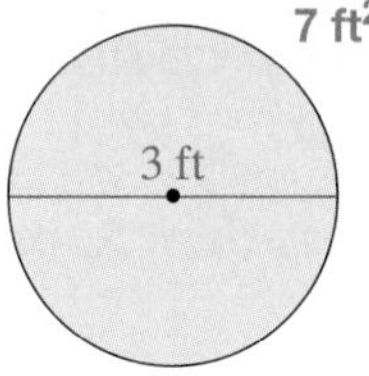

2.
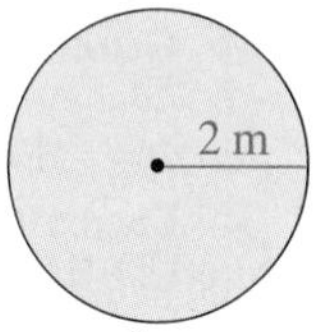

13 m²

3.
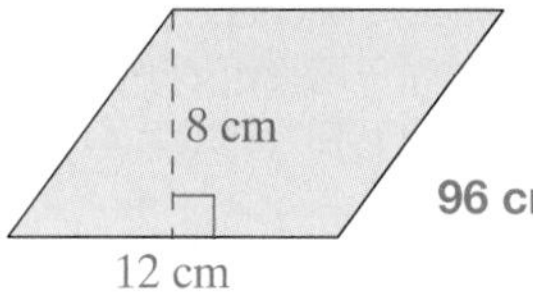

96 cm²

4.
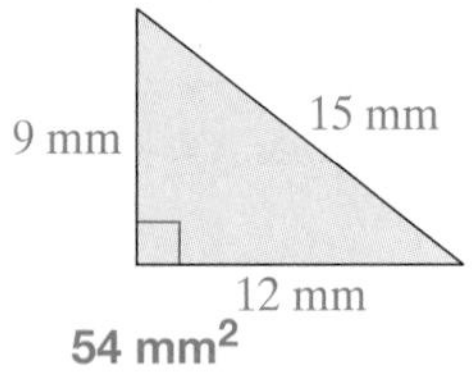

54 mm²

5.
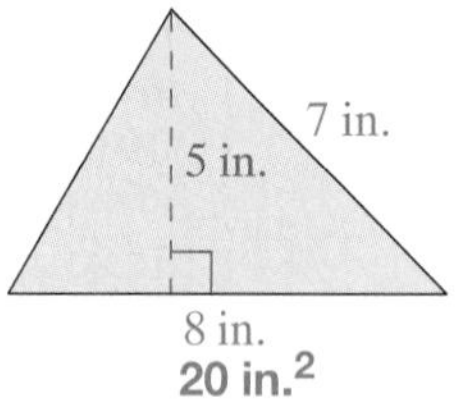

20 in.²

6.
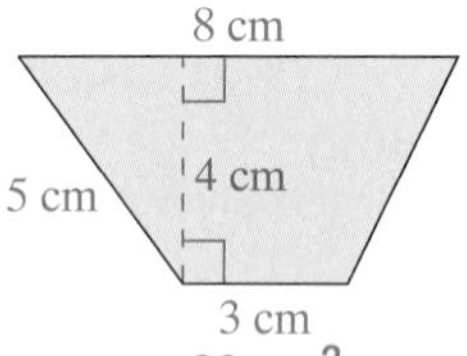

22 cm²

Solving Proportions

Solve each proportion.

7. $\frac{x}{4} = \frac{15}{20}$ 3
8. $\frac{a}{9} = \frac{21}{27}$ 7
9. $\frac{26}{5} = \frac{13}{b}$ 2.5
10. $\frac{10}{h} = \frac{30}{36}$ 12

What You'll Learn Next

- In this chapter, you will classify and draw three-dimensional figures.
- You will find the surface areas and volumes of prisms, cylinders, pyramids, cones, and spheres.
- You will use proportions to find missing measurements in similar solids.

Key Vocabulary

- base plan (p. 358)
- cone (p. 354)
- cylinder (p. 354)
- isometric view (p. 359)
- lateral area (p. 369)
- net (p. 364)
- polyhedron (p. 354)
- prism (p. 354)
- pyramid (p. 354)
- similar solids (p. 398)
- skew lines (p. 355)
- slant height (p. 374)
- solids (p. 354)
- sphere (p. 393)
- surface area (p. 368)
- volume (p. 380)

Problem Solving Application On pages 408 and 409, you will work an extended activity on wingspans.

Chapter 8 Overview

In this chapter, students continue their study of geometric concepts as they identify and draw different solid figures. They apply formulas to find the surface area and volume of prisms, pyramids, cylinders, cones, and spheres.

Activating Prior Knowledge

In this chapter, students build on their knowledge of the properties of polygons and of how to use formulas to find the areas of parallelograms, triangles, trapezoids, and circles. They also draw upon their understanding of similarity and congruence when they explore similar solids. Ask questions such as:

- *What is the area of a trapezoid with bases of 10 in. and 12 in. and a height of 15 in.?* 165 in.^{2}
- *A right triangle has sides 3 m, 4 m, and 5 m. A triangle similar to it has a hypotenuse of 15 m. What are the lengths of its remaining sides?* 9 m and 12 m

8-1

1. Plan

Objective
To identify solids, parts of solids, and skew line segments

Examples
1 Naming Solids and Their Parts
2 Recognizing Solids
3 Identifying Skew Line Segments

Math Understandings: p. 352C

Professional Development

Math Background

Solids are three-dimensional objects that do not lie in a plane. A polyhedron is a solid with a polygon for each face. Prisms and pyramids are polyhedrons. Cylinders and cones are not polyhedrons because they have at least one circular base. In this lesson, a cylinder is assumed to be a right circular cylinder; a prism is assumed to be a right prism. In general, the height is perpendicular to the base. Skew lines are lines that do not intersect and are not parallel.

More Math Background: p. 352C

Lesson Planning and Resources

See p. 352E for a list of the resources that support this lesson.

PowerPoint

Bell Ringer Practice

Check Skills You'll Need
Use student page, transparency, or PowerPoint. For intervention, direct students to:
Classifying Triangles and Quadrilaterals
Lesson 7-4
Extra Skills and Word Problems Practice, Ch. 7

8-1 Solids

Check Skills You'll Need

1. **Vocabulary Review** What does it mean to say that two triangles are *congruent*? 1–3. See below.

Determine the best name for each figure.

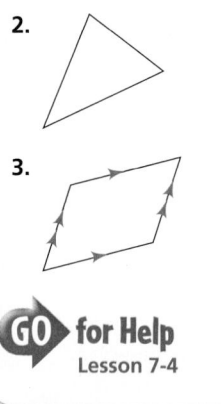

2. 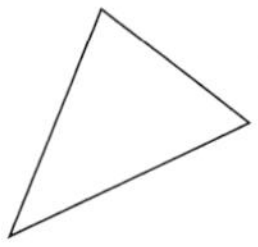

3. 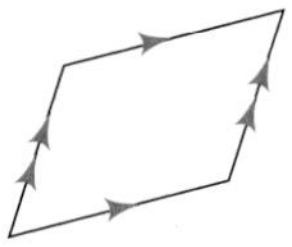

GO for Help Lesson 7-4

What You'll Learn

To identify solids, parts of solids, and skew line segments

New Vocabulary solids, prism, pyramid, cylinder, cone, polyhedron, skew lines

Why Learn This?

Our world is made up of largely three-dimensional figures, or solids. Artists use three-dimensional figures in sculptures.

Solids are objects that do not lie in a plane. They have length, width, and height. Below are some common solids.

A **prism** is a solid with two parallel bases that are congruent polygons. The lateral faces are parallelograms.

A **pyramid** is a solid with exactly one base, which is a polygon. The lateral faces are triangles.

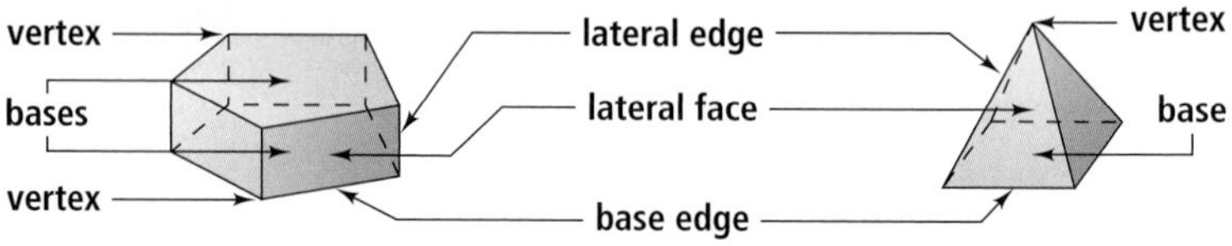

A prism is named for the shape of its bases. The prism above is a pentagonal prism.

A pyramid is named for the shape of its base. The pyramid above is a square pyramid.

A **cylinder** is a solid with two bases that are parallel, congruent circles.

A **cone** is a solid with exactly one circular base and one vertex.

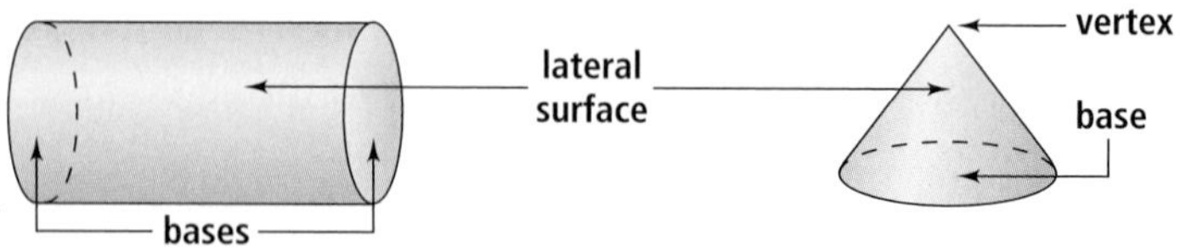

A **polyhedron** is a solid whose faces are polygons. Of the solids above, only prisms and pyramids are polyhedrons.

Check Skills You'll Need

1. Congruent triangles have the same shape and size.
2. scalene triangle
3. parallelogram

Vocabulary Tip
Polyhedron means "many surfaces."

Differentiated Instruction Solutions for All Learners

Special Needs L1
Students review polygon names and the number of sides each has. For example, *tri* means "3" and *penta* means "5." Then they trace the number of sides of each prism and pyramid base with their fingers, counting as they trace.
learning style: tactile

Below Level L2
Students identify and describe as geometric solids a soup can, a cereal or tissue box, a cone-shaped paper cup, and other examples in the classroom.
learning style: visual

EXAMPLE Naming Solids and Their Parts

1 Refer to the figure at the right. Describe the base, name the figure, and name $\overline{RL}$.

The only base is a circle. The figure is a cone. $\overline{RL}$ is a diameter.

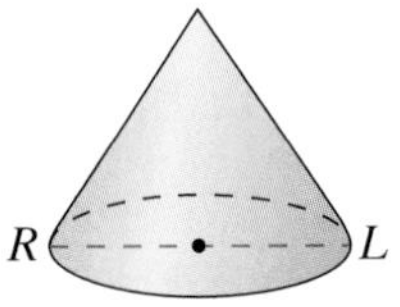

1. The figure is a pentagonal prism. $\overline{JK}$ is a lateral edge. Points J and K are vertices of the prism.

Quick Check

1. Refer to the figure at the right. Name the figure, $\overline{JK}$, and the points J and K. See left.

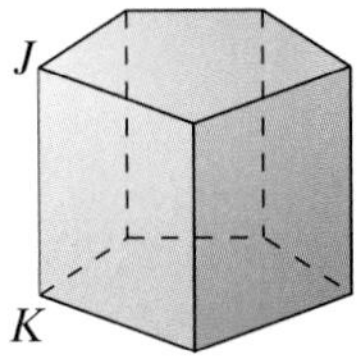

Common solids are everywhere. Often, solids form complex structures.

EXAMPLE Recognizing Solids

2 **Set Design** A stage crew for the school play constructed the ramp shown. Name the three solids used to construct the ramp.

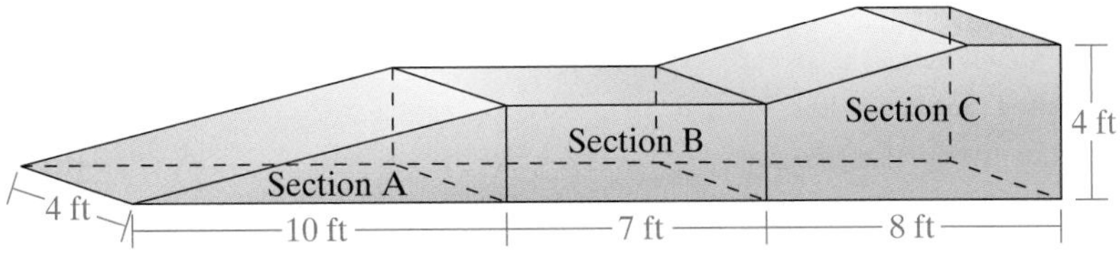

Section A is a triangular prism. Section B is a rectangular prism. Section C is a pentagonal prism.

In this staircase, $\overline{AB}$ and $\overline{CD}$ are skew line segments.

Quick Check

2. Name two solids that can be used to make up Section C. a trapezoidal prism; a rectangular prism

Skew lines are lines that do not intersect and are not parallel. Unlike parallel or intersecting lines, skew lines do not lie in the same plane.

EXAMPLE Identifying Skew Line Segments

3 Name a pair of skew line segments and a pair of parallel line segments in the figure at the right.

$\overline{AF}$ and $\overline{ED}$ are skew. $\overline{BC}$ and $\overline{FG}$ are parallel.

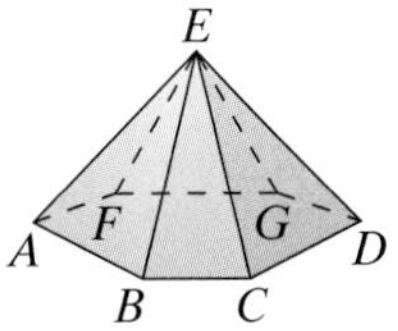

Quick Check

3. **Open-Ended** Name a pair of intersecting line segments in the figure above. Are they skew line segments? Answers may vary. Sample: $\overline{AB}$ and $\overline{BC}$ are intersecting line segments; no.

Advanced Learners L4

Students draw a plane intersecting a cone and discuss what plane figures the intersection might form. circle, ellipse, point, intersecting lines

learning style: tactile

English Language Learners ELL

Students discuss what it means to *lie in a plane* and *not lie in a plane.* They use the geometry and measurement words they know to explain what each idea means. Then they draw examples of a shape lying in a plane and not lying in a plane.

learning style: verbal

2. Teach

Activity Lab

Use before the lesson.

All in One Teaching Resources

Activity Lab 8-1: Solids

Guided Instruction

Connection to Sports

To help students connect *lateral* with "side", have a volunteer explain a lateral pass in football.

PowerPoint

Additional Examples

1 In the figure below, describe the base, name the figure, and name the part labeled $\overline{CD}$. rectangle, rectangular pyramid; base edge

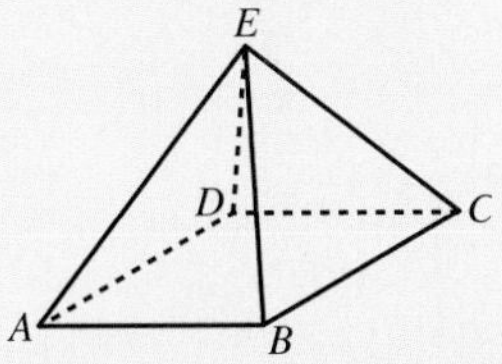

2 Which common solids make up this toy? rectangular prism, spheres, cone

3 Name a pair of skew line segments and a pair of parallel line segments in the figure below. Sample: $\overline{BC}$ and $\overline{DE}$ are skew; $\overline{AB}$ and $\overline{DE}$ are parallel

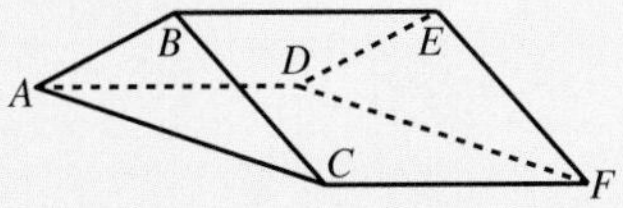

All in One Teaching Resources

- Daily Notetaking Guide 8-1 L3
- Adapted Notetaking 8-1 L1

Closure

- Explain how you can tell when two lines are skew. Sample: They do not lie in the same plane, they do not intersect, and they are not parallel.

3. Practice

Assignment Guide

Check Your Understanding
Go over Exercises 1–5 in class before assigning the Homework Exercises.

Homework Exercises

A Practice by Example	6–12
B Apply Your Skills	13–19
C Challenge	20
Test Prep and Mixed Review	21–26

Homework Quick Check
To check students' understanding of key skills and concepts, go over Exercises 7, 12, 14, 16, and 18.

Differentiated Instruction Resources

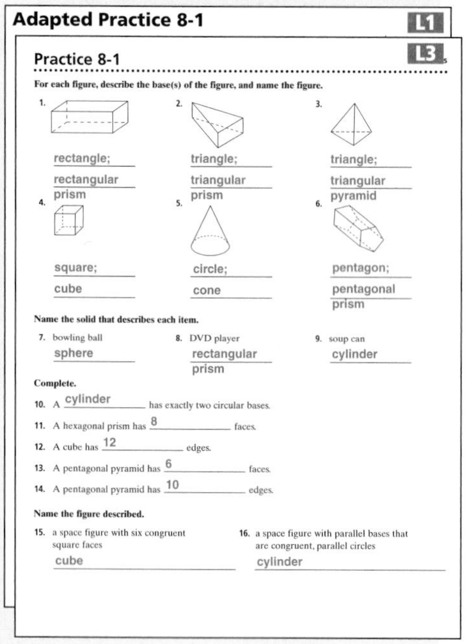
Adapted Practice 8-1 L1

Practice 8-1 L3

For each figure, describe the base(s) of the figure, and name the figure.

1. rectangle; rectangular prism
2. triangle; triangular prism
3. triangle; triangular pyramid
4. square; cube
5. circle; cone
6. pentagon; pentagonal prism

Name the solid that describes each item.

7. bowling ball sphere
8. DVD player rectangular prism
9. soup can cylinder

Complete.

10. A cylinder has exactly two circular bases.
11. A hexagonal prism has 8 faces.
12. A cube has 12 edges.
13. A pentagonal pyramid has 6 faces.
14. A pentagonal pyramid has 10 edges.

Name the figure described.

15. a space figure with six congruent square faces cube
16. a space figure with parallel bases that are congruent, parallel circles cylinder

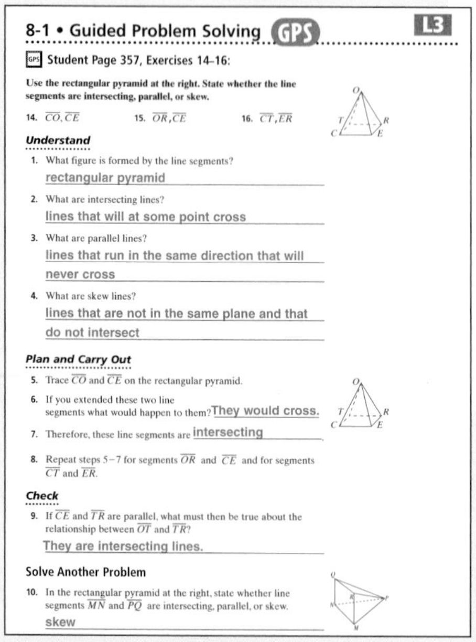
8-1 • Guided Problem Solving GPS L3

GPS Student Page 357, Exercises 14–16:

Use the rectangular pyramid at the right. State whether the line segments are intersecting, parallel, or skew.

14. $\overline{CO}, \overline{CE}$ 15. $\overline{OR}, \overline{CE}$ 16. $\overline{CT}, \overline{ER}$

Understand

1. What figure is formed by the line segments? rectangular pyramid
2. What are intersecting lines? lines that will at some point cross
3. What are parallel lines? lines that run in the same direction that will never cross
4. What are skew lines? lines that are not in the same plane and that do not intersect

Plan and Carry Out

5. Trace $\overline{CO}$ and $\overline{CE}$ on the rectangular pyramid.
6. If you extended these two line segments what would happen to them? They would cross.
7. Therefore, these line segments are intersecting.
8. Repeat steps 5–7 for segments $\overline{OR}$ and $\overline{CE}$ and for segments $\overline{CT}$ and $\overline{ER}$.

Check

9. If $\overline{CE}$ and $\overline{TR}$ are parallel, what must then be true about the relationship between $\overline{OT}$ and $\overline{TR}$? They are intersecting lines.

Solve Another Problem

10. In the rectangular pyramid at the right, state whether line segments $\overline{MN}$ and $\overline{PQ}$ are intersecting, parallel, or skew. skew

Check Your Understanding

1. **Vocabulary** What is the difference between parallel lines and skew lines? Parallel lines lie in the same plane; skew lines do not.

Use the figure at the right for Exercises 2–4.

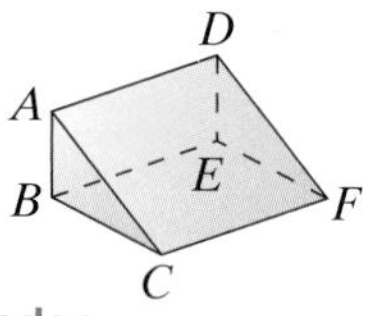

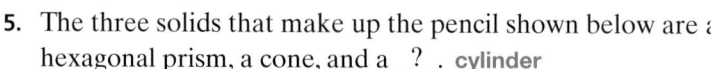

2. The bases are two _?_. triangles
3. The figure is a _?_ prism. triangular
4. $\overline{CF}$ is a (lateral face, lateral edge). lateral edge
5. The three solids that make up the pencil shown below are a hexagonal prism, a cone, and a _?_. cylinder

Homework Exercises

For more exercises, see Extra Skills and Word Problems.

GO for Help

For Exercises	See Examples
6–8	1
9	2
10–12	3

A For each figure, describe the base, name the figure, and name $\overline{PQ}$.

6. 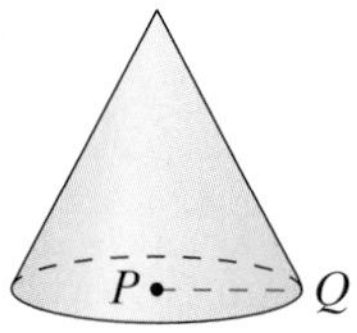

7. 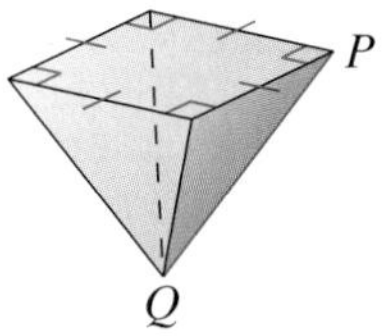

8. 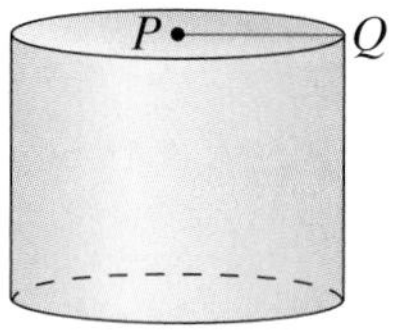

6–8. See margin.

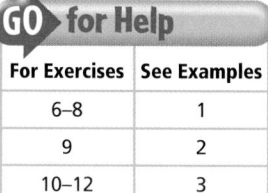

9. **Models** For an art project, you are building a model like the one at the right out of balsa wood. What solids will you use to construct your model? See left.

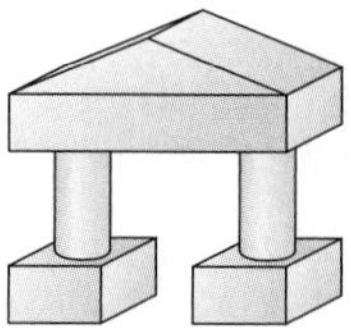

9. 3 rectangular prisms, 2 cylinders, and a triangular prism

For each figure, name a pair of skew line segments and a pair of parallel line segments. 10–12. Answers may vary. See left for samples.

10. 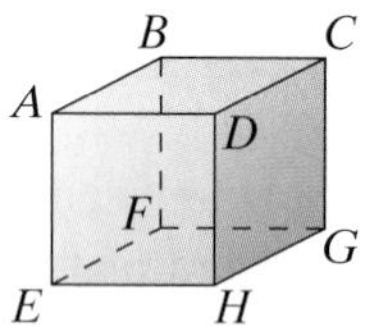

11. 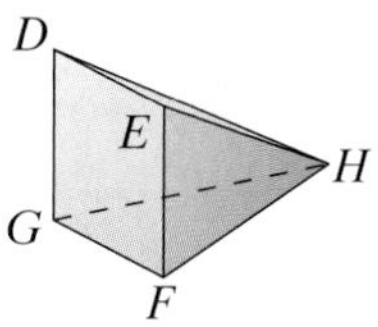

12. 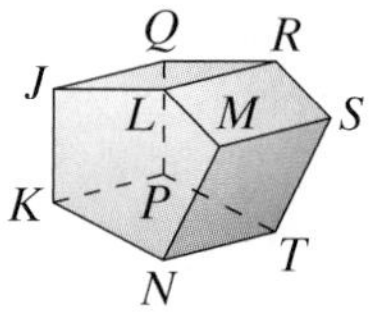

10. $\overline{AD}$ and $\overline{CG}$, $\overline{DC}$ and $\overline{HG}$
11. $\overline{DE}$ and $\overline{FH}$, $\overline{GD}$ and $\overline{EF}$
12. $\overline{JL}$ and $\overline{ST}$, $\overline{LR}$ and $\overline{KP}$

B GPS 13. **Guided Problem Solving** A figure has exactly four lateral faces that are triangles. What name best describes this solid?
- Use the strategy *Draw a Picture*. Experiment with different drawings. Do you have a figure with four triangular lateral faces?
- What is the name of your solid? rectangular pyramid

6. The base is a circle. The figure is a cone. $\overline{PQ}$ is the radius of the base.
7. The base is a square. The figure is a square pyramid. $\overline{PQ}$ is a lateral edge.
8. The base is a circle. The figure is a cylinder. $\overline{PQ}$ is a radius.

18. Yes; Kenji is right in that there are 2 parallel, congruent trapezoidal bases, and the lateral faces are parallelograms. Esther is also right in that a vertical cut could separate the figure into a rectangular prism and a triangular prism.

GO Online
Homework Video Tutor
Visit: PHSchool.com
Web Code: ase-0801

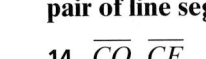

GPS **Use the rectangular pyramid at the right. State whether each pair of line segments is *intersecting, parallel,* or *skew.***

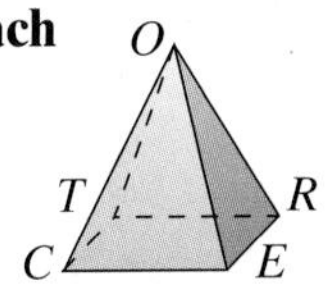

14. $\overline{CO}$, $\overline{CE}$ intersecting

15. $\overline{OR}$, $\overline{CE}$ skew

16. $\overline{CT}$, $\overline{ER}$ parallel

17. Design You are asked to help design the skating terrain for a local skate park. Explain which common solids you would choose to make the terrain challenging and fun for all skaters. Check students' work.

18. Writing in Math Kenji says the figure at the right is a trapezoidal prism. Esther says it is a triangular prism and rectangular prism combined. Are they both correct? Explain. See margin.

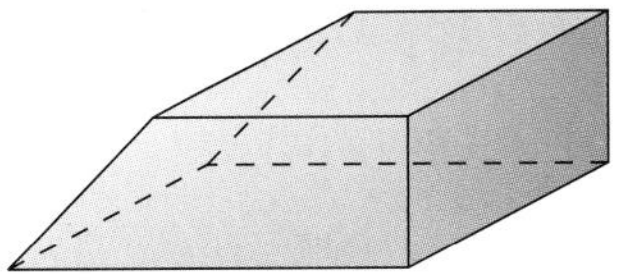

19. A figure has three lateral faces that are rectangles. Name the figure. triangular prism

C **20. Challenge** Describe one way the solid below can be made from three different types of prisms. Answers may vary. Sample: The solid could be broken down into one triangular prism, one rectangular prism, and one trapezoidal prism.

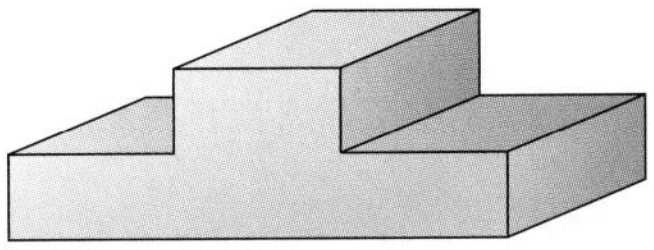

Test Prep and Mixed Review

Practice

Multiple Choice

21. The area of a swimming pool is 336 square feet. What is the length of the pool if the width is 28 feet? A

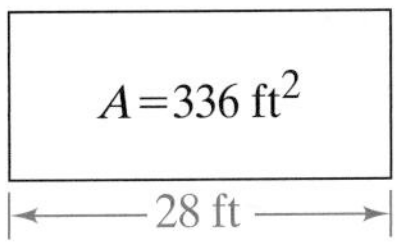

Ⓐ 12 ft
Ⓑ 56 ft
Ⓒ 14 ft
Ⓓ 84 ft

22. The three leading consumers of oil in millions of barrels per day are the United States with $20\frac{1}{2}$, China with $6\frac{1}{2}$, and Japan with $5\frac{2}{5}$. How many more million barrels does the United States consume than China and Japan combined? J

Ⓕ $10\frac{2}{5}$
Ⓖ 10
Ⓗ $9\frac{2}{5}$
Ⓙ $8\frac{3}{5}$

23. A parallelogram has four congruent sides but no right angles. Which statement about the figure is true? B

Ⓐ The figure could be a trapezoid.
Ⓑ The formula for the area of the figure is $A = bh$.
Ⓒ The measures of the interior angles are the same.
Ⓓ A diagonal of the figure divides the shape into two rhombuses.

GO for Help

For Exercises	See Lesson
24–26	5-2

Estimate each product.

24. 15% of 506 75

25. 60% of 38 24

26. 94% of 440 about 418

Online lesson quiz, PHSchool.com, Web Code: asa-0801

4. Assess & Reteach

PowerPoint

Lesson Quiz

Use this figure to answer questions 1–3.

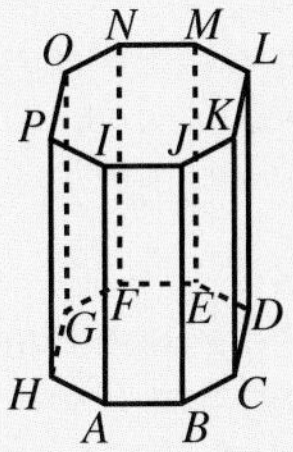

1. Describe the base(s), name the figure, and name the part labeled $\overline{BJ}$. octagons; octagonal prism; lateral edge

Describe whether the following pairs of line segments are parallel, intersecting, or skew.

2. $\overline{IJ}$, $\overline{ME}$ skew
3. $\overline{OG}$, $\overline{IA}$ parallel

4. Name the common solids that make up the structure. cylinder, cone, rectangular prism, triangular prism

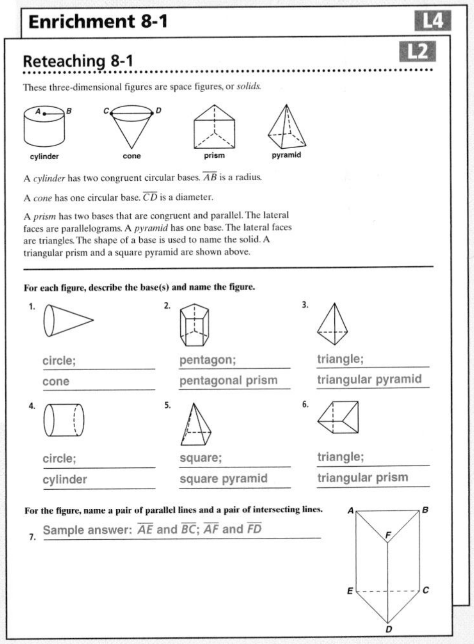

Enrichment 8-1 L4

Reteaching 8-1 L2

These three-dimensional figures are space figures, or *solids.*

cylinder cone prism pyramid

A *cylinder* has two congruent circular bases. $\overline{AB}$ is a radius.

A *cone* has one circular base. $\overline{CD}$ is a diameter.

A *prism* has two bases that are congruent and parallel. The lateral faces are parallelograms. A *pyramid* has one base. The lateral faces are triangles. The shape of a base is used to name the solid. A triangular prism and a square pyramid are shown above.

For each figure, describe the base(s) and name the figure.

1. circle; cone
2. pentagon; pentagonal prism
3. triangle; triangular pyramid
4. circle; cylinder
5. square; square pyramid
6. triangle; triangular prism

For the figure, name a pair of parallel lines and a pair of intersecting lines.

7. Sample answer: $\overline{AE}$ and $\overline{BC}$; $\overline{AF}$ and $\overline{FD}$

Alternative Assessment

Students sketch a bird house and name all the solids contained in it. They then identify a pair of edges that are skew.

Test Prep

Resources

For additional practice with a variety of test item formats:

- Test-Taking Strategies, p. 403
- Test Prep, p. 407
- Test-Taking Strategies with Transparencies

8-2

1. Plan

Objective
To draw views of three-dimensional figures, including base plans and isometric views

Examples
1 Drawing a Base Plan
2 Drawing Top, Front, and Right Views
3 Application: Gardening

Math Understandings: p. 352C

Professional Development

Math Background

You can sketch a solid geometric figure by drawing the bases and connecting them with straight lines. When a solid is drawn as connected rectangular prisms at different heights, a base plan shows the "footprint" of the base and indicates the height of each part. Isometric dot paper is useful for drawing isometric, or corner, views in order to see the top, front, and right sides of an object at the same time.

More Math Background: p. 352C

Lesson Planning and Resources

See p. 352E for a list of the resources that support this lesson.

PowerPoint

Bell Ringer Practice

Check Skills You'll Need
Use student page, transparency, or PowerPoint. For intervention, direct students to:
Solids
Lesson 8-1
Extra Skills and Word Problems Practice, Ch. 8

8-2 Drawing Views of Three-Dimensional Figures

Check Skills You'll Need

1. **Vocabulary Review** The *lateral faces* of a prism are (parallelograms, triangles). parallelograms
2. Name the common shapes that make up the structure below. rectangular prisms

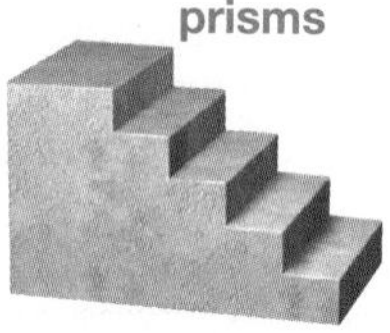

GO for Help Lesson 8-1

What You'll Learn

To draw views of three-dimensional figures, including base plans and isometric views

New Vocabulary base plan, isometric view

Why Learn This?

Engineers and architects design solids, such as houses, cars, and furniture, by using drawings from different perspectives.

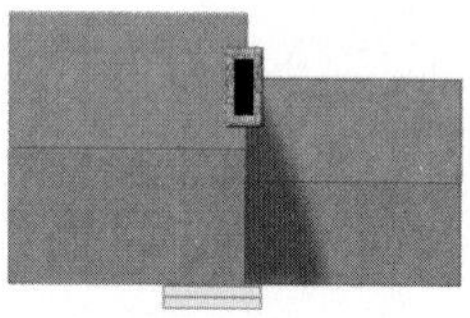
Top view

Front view

Right view

A **base plan** is a drawing that shows the shape of the base and indicates the height of each part of a solid. Base plans are particularly useful for representing structures with rectangular faces.

EXAMPLE Drawing a Base Plan

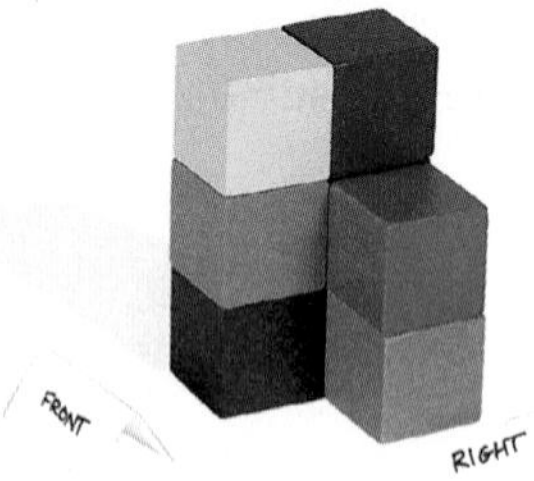

1 Draw the base plan for the stacked cubes pictured at the left.

Draw a square for each stack as seen from above.

Write the number of cubes in the stack inside each square.

Label the front and right sides.

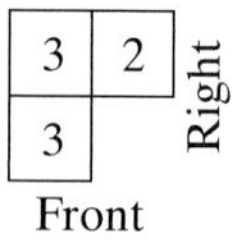

Quick Check

1. Draw a base plan for the stacked cubes pictured at the right. See left.

1.
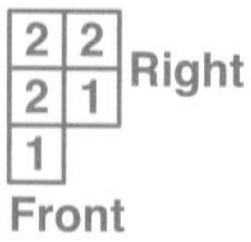

Differentiated Instruction Solutions for All Learners

Special Needs L1
Some students may have difficulty drawing the views of the solids. They work with a partner who can do the drawings, while they verify that the view or perspective in the drawing is correct.

learning style: visual

Below Level L2
On an overhead projector, place various objects without letting students see them. Students name the objects.

learning style: visual

An **isometric view** is a corner view of a solid. It is usually drawn on isometric dot paper. An isometric view allows you to see the top, front, and right side of an object in the same drawing.

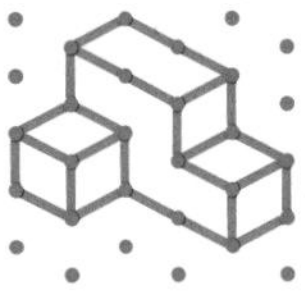

Drawing separate top, front, and right views helps you visualize and understand three-dimensional figures.

EXAMPLE Drawing Top, Front, and Right Views

2 Draw the top, front, and right views of the figure at the right. Assume there are no holes.

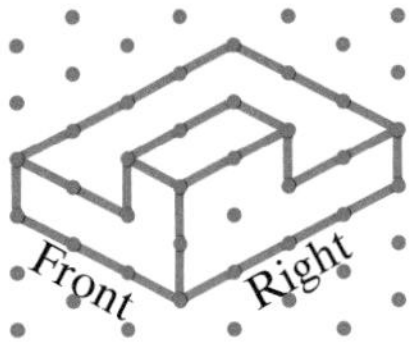

Treat each face as a two-dimensional figure.

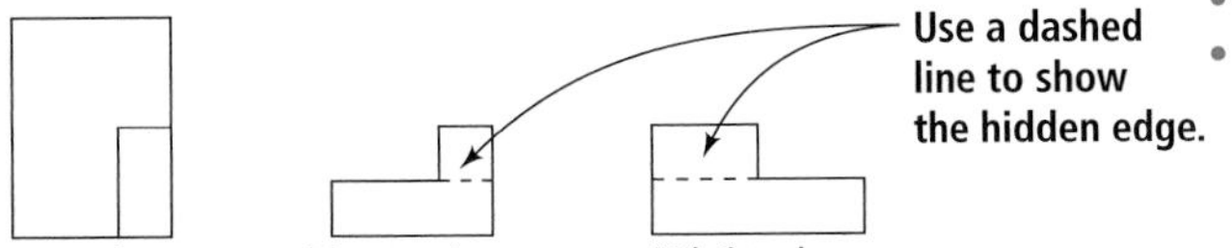

Top view   Front view   Right view

Quick Check

2. Draw the top, front, and right views of the figure at the right. Assume no blocks are hidden from view. See back of book.

Online active math

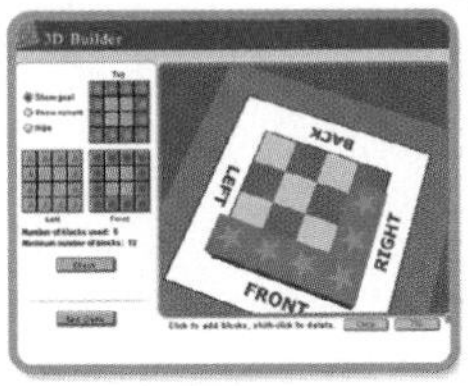

For: 3-D Builder Activity
Use: Interactive Textbook, 8-2

EXAMPLE Application: Gardening

3 **Multiple Choice** Which drawing best represents the top view of the garden at the right?

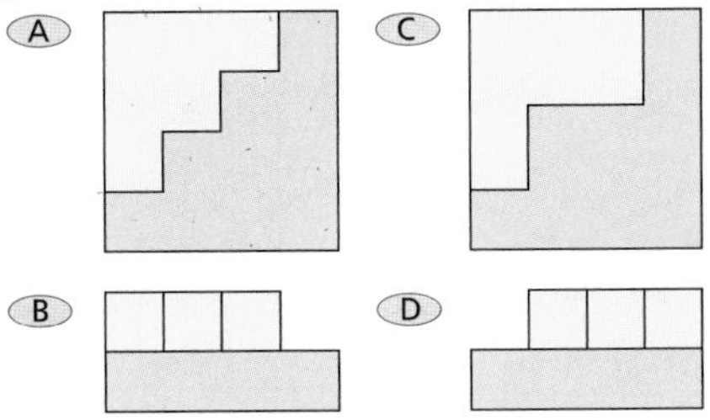

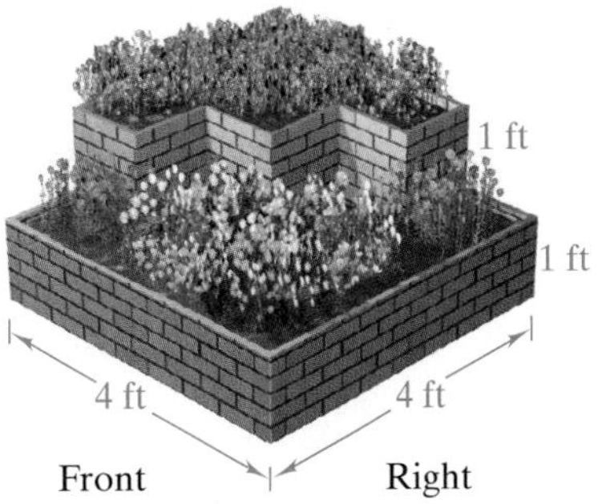

From the top, the garden is a four-by-four square with a second level of six squares at the top left corner. The correct answer is choice A.

Test Prep Tip

Sketch the shape of the bottom level first. Then add the details for the top level.

Quick Check

3. A landscaper wants to build a third level on the garden above by adding a single square to the left rear corner. Draw the top, front, and right views of the three-level garden. See back of book.

2. Teach

Activity Lab

Use before the lesson.

All in One Teaching Resources

Activity Lab 8-2: Views of 3-D Figures

Guided Instruction

Error Prevention!

Give students plastic or wooden cubes and have them model the solids shown in the figures in the Examples.

PowerPoint Additional Examples

1 Draw the base plan for the stacked cubes.

See back of book.

2 **3** Draw the top, front, and right view of the figure. Assume no blocks are hidden from view.

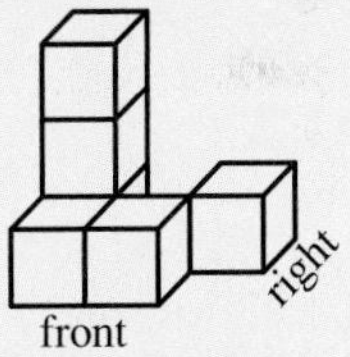

See back of book.

All in One Teaching Resources

- Daily Notetaking Guide 8-2 L3
- Adapted Notetaking 8-2 L1

Closure

- *What is shown in a base plan for a solid figure?* Sample: The plan shows the shape of the base and indicates the height. The front and right side are labeled.
- *What is shown in an isometric view of a solid?* Sample: This view shows the top, front, and right sides of a solid in the same drawing.

Advanced Learners L4	**English Language Learners** ELL
Students use isometric dot paper to draw a view of the school or an object in the classroom. **learning style: visual**	Place a cube on each student's desk. Students stand and look down at the cube. Say: *This is a top view. You are looking at the top.* Have students draw this view. Students do the same with a corner view. **learning style: visual**

3. Practice

Assignment Guide

Check Your Understanding
Go over Exercises 1–4 in class before assigning the Homework Exercises.

Homework Exercises

A	Practice by Example	5–10
B	Apply Your Skills	11–18
C	Challenge	19
	Test Prep and Mixed Review	20–24

Homework Quick Check
To check students' understanding of key skills and concepts, go over Exercises 6, 9, 11, 13, and 16.

Differentiated Instruction Resources

Adapted Practice 8-2 L1

Practice 8-2 L3 Drawing Views of Three-Dimensional Figures

Draw a base plan for each set of stacked cubes.

1. 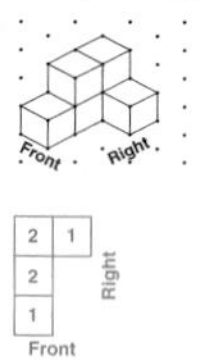

2. 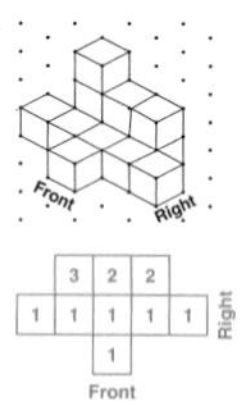

Draw the top, front, and right views of each figure.

3. 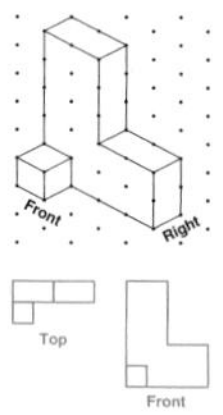

4. 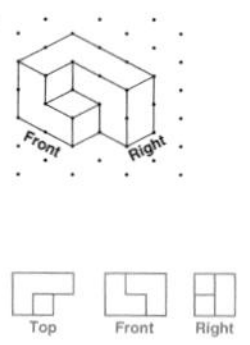

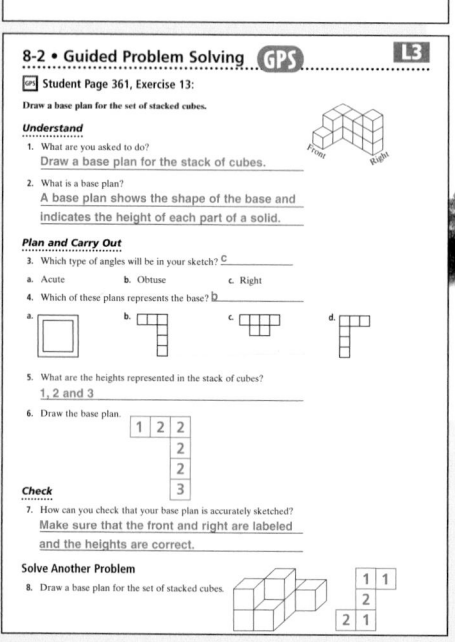

8-2 • Guided Problem Solving GPS L3

GPS Student Page 361, Exercise 13:

Draw a base plan for the set of stacked cubes.

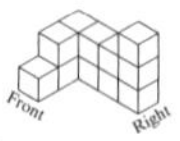

Understand

1. What are you asked to do?
Draw a base plan for the stack of cubes.
2. What is a base plan?
A base plan shows the shape of the base and indicates the height of each part of a solid.

Plan and Carry Out

3. Which type of angles will be in your sketch? c
a. Acute b. Obtuse c. Right
4. Which of these plans represents the base? b

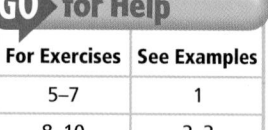

5. What are the heights represented in the stack of cubes?
1, 2 and 3
6. Draw the base plan.

Check

7. How can you check that your base plan is accurately sketched?
Make sure that the front and right are labeled and the heights are correct.

Solve Another Problem

8. Draw a base plan for the set of stacked cubes.

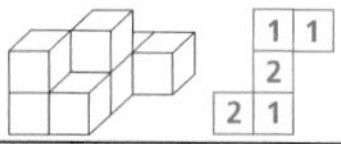

Check Your Understanding

1. **Vocabulary** A(n) (base plan, isometric view) allows you to see the top, front, and right sides of an object. isometric view

Use the figure at the right for Exercises 2–4.

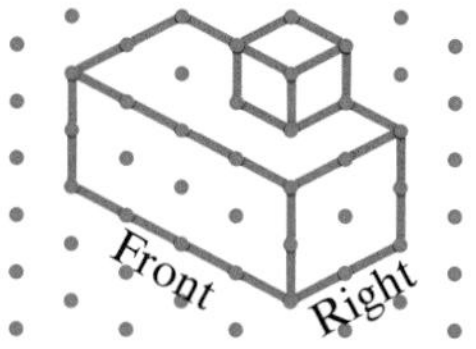

2. How many squares will a base plan of the figure require? 8
3. The bottom layer of the solid is a (rectangle, square). rectangle
4. The top view and front view of the figure are below. Draw the right view. See left.

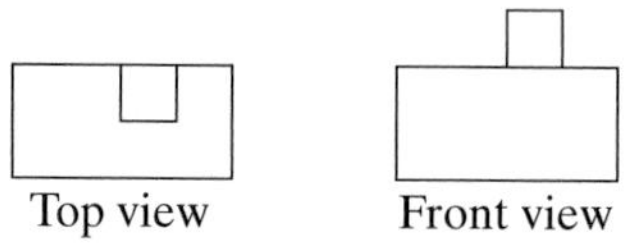

4. 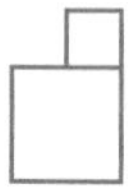

Homework Exercises

For more exercises, see Extra Skills and Word Problems.

GO for Help

For Exercises	See Examples
5–7	1
8–10	2–3

A **Draw a base plan for each set of stacked cubes.** 5–7. See margin.

5. 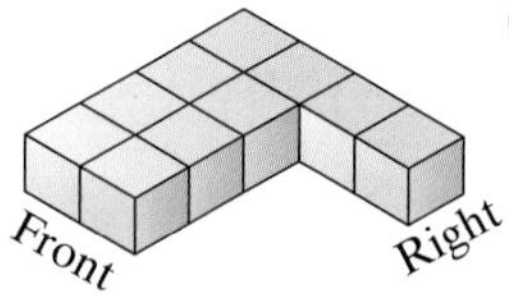

6. 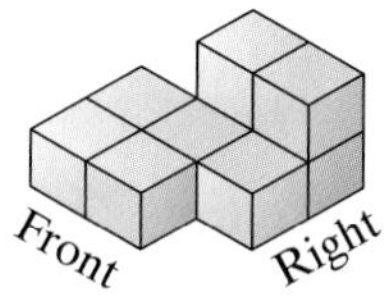

7. 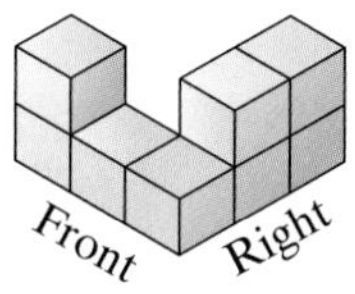

Draw the top, front, and right views of each figure. 8–10. See margin.

8. 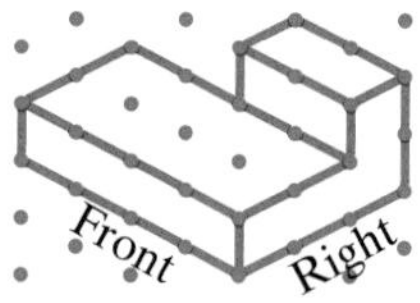

9. 

10. 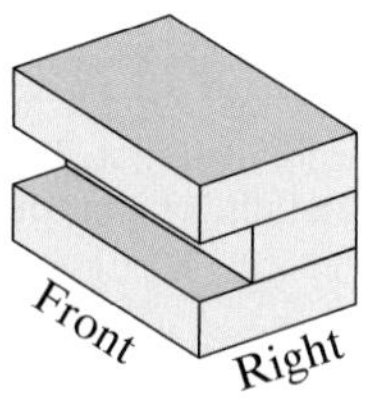

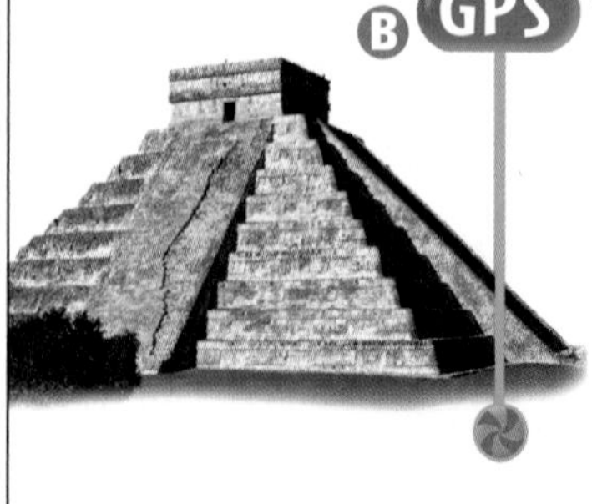

B GPS 11. **Guided Problem Solving** The Pyramid of Kukúlcan, shown at the left, is a stepped square pyramid in the ancient Mayan city of Chichen Itza. Draw a base plan for the Pyramid of Kukúlcan.
- Use the strategy *Work a Simpler Problem*.
- Complete the plan at the right for a two-level stepped square pyramid.
- Then *Look for a Pattern* to draw the complete base plan for the pyramid.

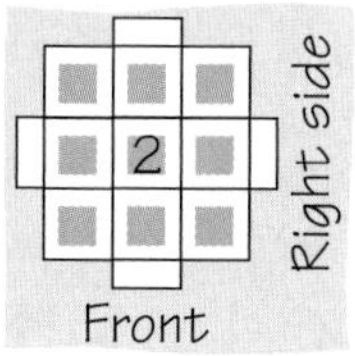

Check students' work.

5. 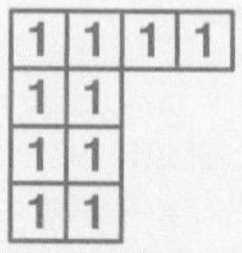

6. 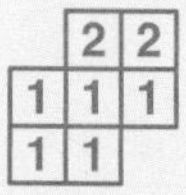

7. 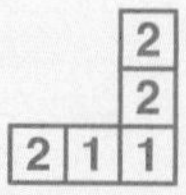

8. 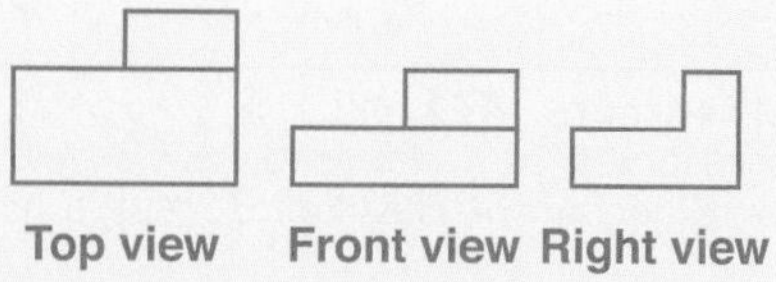

9–10. See back of book.

12–16. See back of book.

GO Online Homework Video Tutor
Visit: PHSchool.com
Web Code: ase-0802

Draw a base plan for each set of stacked cubes. 12–14. See margin.

12.
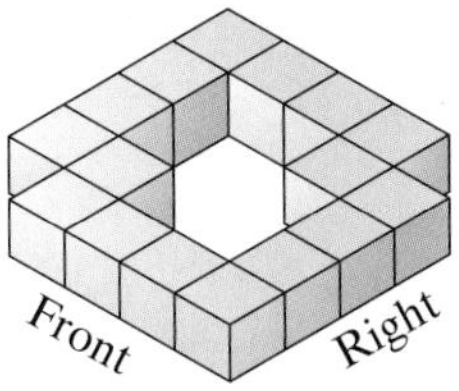

13. GPS
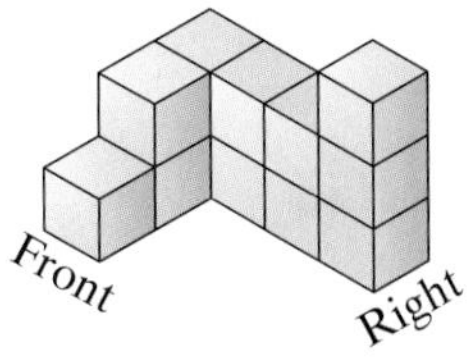

14.
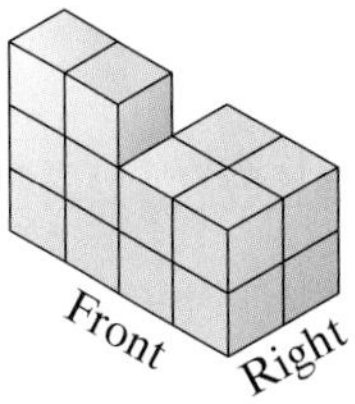

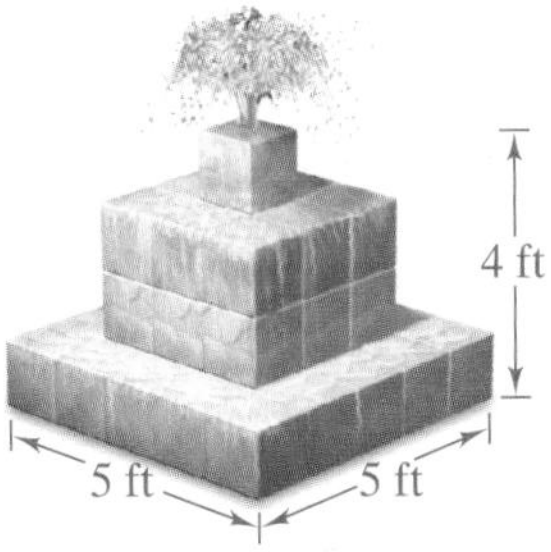

15. **Sculpture** Draw the top and front views of the fountain at the left. See margin.

16. **Writing in Math** Which two-dimensional shape(s) (circle, rectangle, or triangle) can a plane passing through the cylinder at the right make? Explain. See margin.

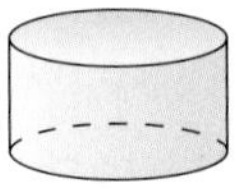

Act It Out Cut out each shape from a blank piece of paper. Rotate the shape 360° around the line of rotation shown. What three-dimensional figure is formed as you rotate the shape?

17.
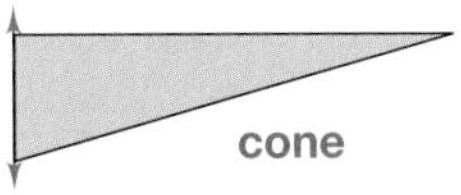
cone

18.
 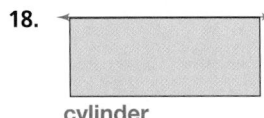
cylinder

Ⓒ 19. **Challenge** One cube has six faces. A stack of two cubes together still has only six faces. What are the different number of faces possible with an arrangement of three cubes? With four cubes? 6, 8; 6, 8, 10

Test Prep and Mixed Review

Practice

Multiple Choice

20. The top and right views of a solid figure built with cubes are shown. Which drawing shows a three-dimensional view of the solid figure? A

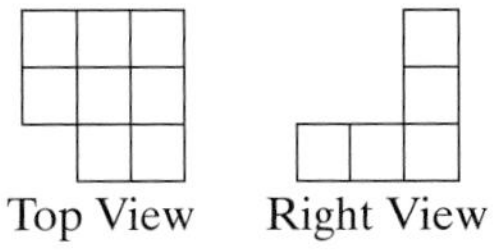

Ⓐ
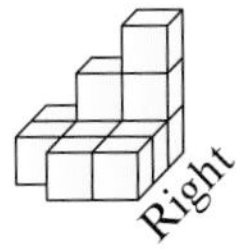

Ⓑ
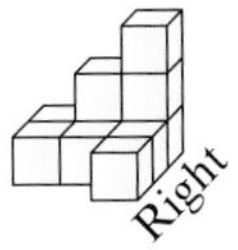

Ⓒ

Ⓓ

21. The area of House A is 2,200 ft^2. It sells for \$187,000. House B has an area of 1,800 ft^2 and sells for \$144,000. Which of the following is true? F

- Ⓕ House A sells for \$5 per square foot more than House B.
- Ⓖ House A sells for \$38 per square foot more than House B.
- Ⓗ House A sells for \$85 per square foot more than House B.
- Ⓙ Both houses sell for the same price per square foot.

GO for Help

For Exercises	See Lesson
22–24	7-7

Find the area of a circle with the given radius or diameter.

22. $r = 6.4$ m 128.7 m^2 23. $d = 3.9$ in. 11.9 $in.^2$ 24. $d = 167$ cm 24. 21,904.0 cm^2

Online lesson quiz, PHSchool.com, Web Code: asa-0802

4. Assess & Reteach

PowerPoint

Lesson Quiz

Use this figure of stacked cubes to answer questions 1–2.

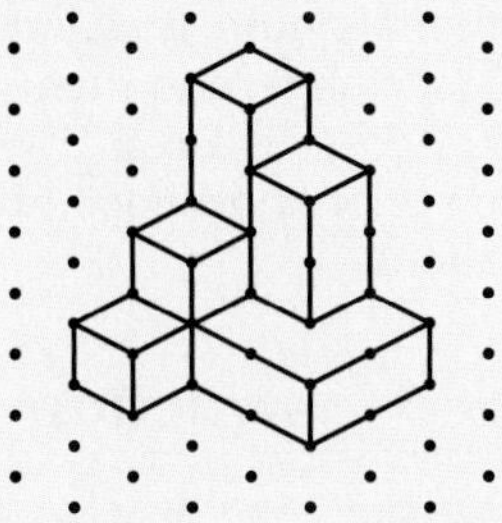

1. Draw a base plan for the stacked cubes.
2. Draw the top, front, and right views of the figure.

Use the picture to answer questions 3–4.

3. The pattern shown was designed with blocks. Draw a base plan for the pattern.
4. Draw the top, front, and right views of the block pattern.

1–4. See back of book.

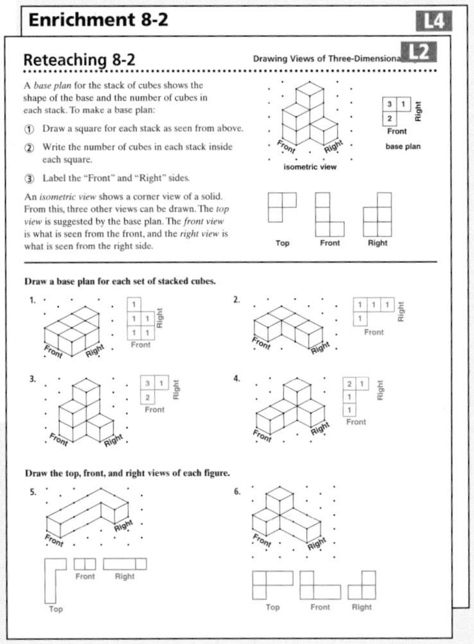
Enrichment 8-2 L4

Reteaching 8-2 Drawing Views of Three-Dimensional Figures L2

A *base plan* for the stack of cubes shows the shape of the base and the number of cubes in each stack. To make a base plan:

① Draw a square for each stack as seen from above.
② Write the number of cubes in each stack inside each square.
③ Label the "Front" and "Right" sides.

An *isometric view* shows a corner view of a solid. From this, three other views can be drawn. The *top view* is suggested by the base plan. The *front view* is what is seen from the front, and the *right view* is what is seen from the right side.

Draw a base plan for each set of stacked cubes.

1. 2. 3. 4.

Draw the top, front, and right views of each figure.

5. 6.

Alternative Assessment

Students in pairs take turns drawing a base plan and having their partner draw the top, front, and right views of the figure.

Test Prep

Resources

For additional practice with a variety of test item formats:

- Test-Taking Strategies, p. 403
- Test Prep, p. 407
- Test-Taking Strategies with Transparencies

8-2b Activity Lab

Sketching Solids

When you do not have dot paper, you can use translations to sketch some three-dimensional figures.

EXAMPLES

1 Sketch a rectangular solid.

- Draw a rectangle.
- Translate it, and connect the four corresponding corners.
- Draw the hidden lines as dashed lines.

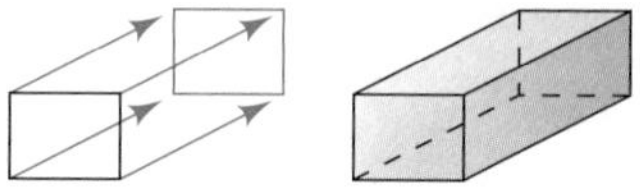

2 Sketch a cylinder.

- Draw a circle.
- Translate it, and connect the circles at corresponding points.
- Draw the hidden curves as dashed curves.

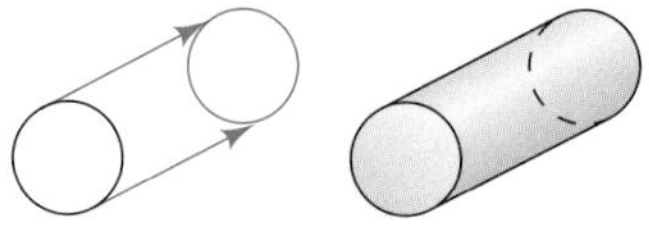

Exercises

Copy each diagram. Use it to draw a three-dimensional figure. 1–4. See margin.

1. 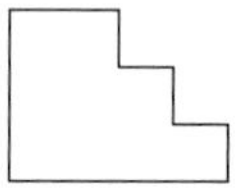

2. 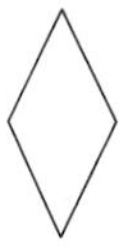

3. 

4. 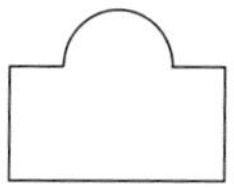

5. **Open-Ended** Pick an object in the room. Draw a three-dimensional figure of the object. Then see if a friend can tell what the object is. Check students' work.

Draw a three-dimensional figure for each object. (*Hint*: You may not be able to use translations to draw all figures.) 6–11. See margin.

6. square pyramid
7. triangular prism
8. cone
9. cylindrical water tower
10. bird house
11. rectangular building

Activity Lab

Sketching Solids

Students draw three-dimensional solids starting with a two-dimensional figure, drawing its translated image, and then connecting the vertices. They build on prior knowledge of translations.

Guided Instruction

Before beginning the activity, review translations. Ask: *When you translate a figure, what changes and what doesn't?* location changes, shape and size remain the same

Visual Learners
To help students visualize the translations, have them do the steps for drawing the solids on graph paper.

Error Prevention!

For Exercise 10, have students think about which *two* three-dimensional solids make up a birdhouse.

Differentiated Instruction

Tactile Learners
Have students "trace" the translation on three-dimensional solids in the classroom. They can use a finger to outline the original face or base, its image (opposite the original), and the edge that forms the connection between each corner.

Resources

- graph paper

1. 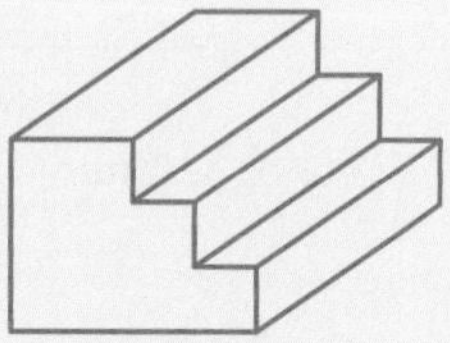

2. 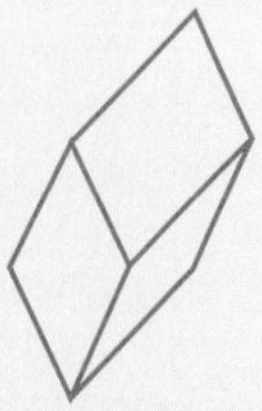

3. 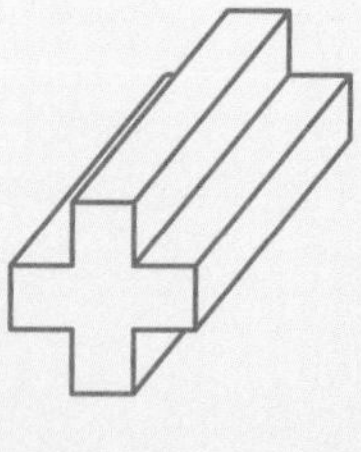

4. 

6–11. See back of book.

8-3a Activity Lab

Hands On

Making Solids From Nets

A *net* is a pattern that can be folded to form a solid.

ACTIVITY

Start with a piece of graph paper.

Step 1 Copy the pattern at the right onto the graph paper.

Step 2 Use scissors to cut out the pattern. Then fold the pattern along each black segment.

Step 3 Tape the edges together to form a solid.

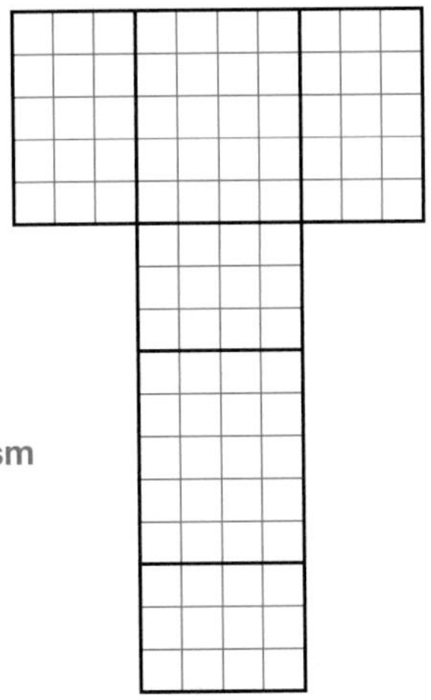

1. What solid does this pattern form? rectangular prism
2. What shapes make up its lateral faces and bases? rectangles

Exercises

Copy and fold each pattern to form a solid. Identify the solid formed.

1. 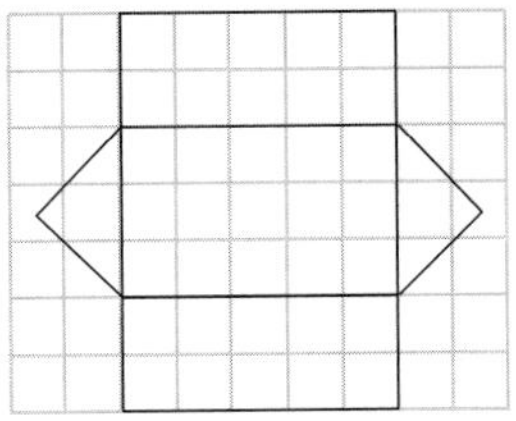

   triangular prism

2. 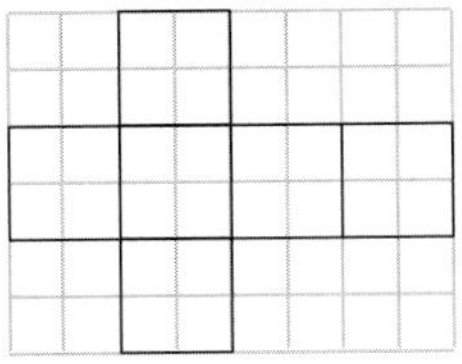

   cube

3. 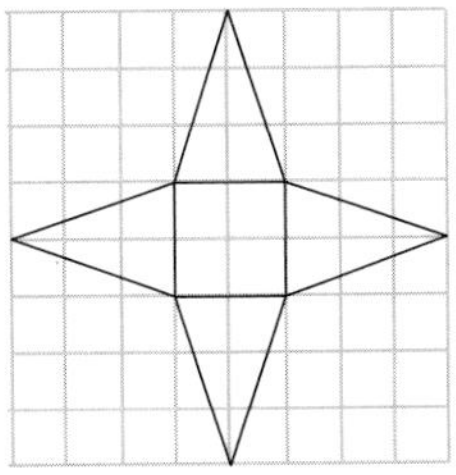

   square pyramid

Use a compass to draw the pattern at the right.

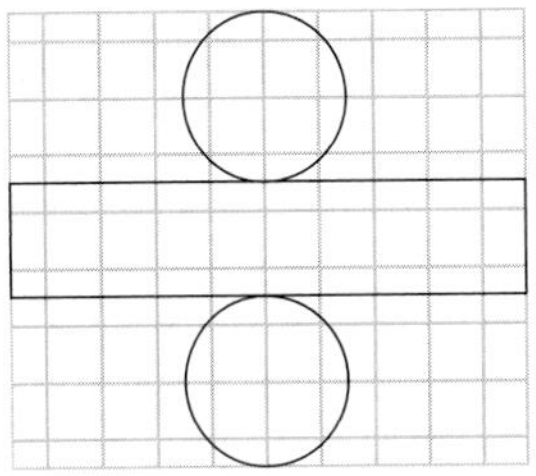

4. Follow the steps above to form a solid with the pattern. Check students' work.
5. What solid does this pattern form? cylinder
6. What shape makes up its entire lateral surface? rectangle

Look at the solid at the right below.

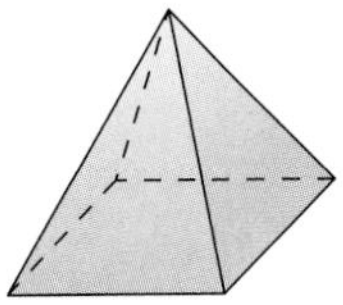

7. Describe the shapes that make up its faces. triangles
8. Describe the process of making the solid using a net. Then use scissors and paper to cut out a pattern that can be folded without any overlaps to form this figure. Check students' work.

Activity Lab

Making Solids From Nets

Students cut out patterns and fold them together to form solids, and identify the shapes of the faces. This hands-on activity prepares students to visualize the nets of three-dimensional figures and visualize the three-dimensional figures formed by nets.

Guided Instruction

Activity

Make sure students understand that the black segments on the nets represent fold lines. Before they make the figure, ask them to predict what type of figure it is.

Teaching Tip
Students may have difficulty visualizing how the sections of the net correspond to the completed solid. Have them picture placing the solid on a flat surface. Then have them picture unfolding the surfaces, starting at some point (as in the pyramid in Exercises 7–8) or edge (as in a rectangular prism).

Differentiated Instruction

Tactile Learners
Have students dismantle common objects, such as cereal or shoeboxes or paper towel tubes, and observe the shapes that make up the objects and their relative sizes. Have them reassemble the solids.

Resources

- Activity Lab 8-3: Nets
- graph paper
- scissors
- compasses

8-3

1. Plan

Objective
To identify nets of solids

Examples
1 Recognizing Nets of Solids
2 Identifying Solids From Nets

Math Understandings: p. 352C

Professional Development

Math Background

A *net* is a pattern, showing all the faces of a solid in one view. A given solid may have several different associated nets.

More Math Background: p. 352C

Lesson Planning and Resources

See p. 352E for a list of the resources that support this lesson.

PowerPoint

Bell Ringer Practice

Check Skills You'll Need
Use student page, transparency, or PowerPoint. For intervention, direct students to:
Drawing Views of Three-Dimensional Figures
Lesson 8-2
Extra Skills and Word Problems Practice, Ch. 8

2. Teach

Activity Lab

Use before the lesson.
Student Edition Activity Lab, Hands On 8-3a, Making Solids From Nets, page 363

All in One **Teaching Resources**

Activity Lab 8-3: Nets

8-3 Nets and Three-Dimensional Figures

Check Skills You'll Need

1. **Vocabulary Review** A corner view of a solid is called a(n) __?__ view. isometric
2. Draw a top view of the figure below. See back of book.

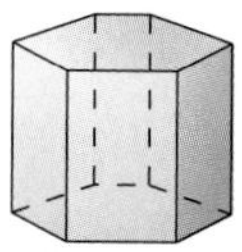

GO for Help Lesson 8-2

What You'll Learn

To identify nets of solids

New Vocabulary net

Why Learn This?

Many common packages and boxes are made by folding flat cardboard into three-dimensional figures.

A **net** is a pattern that can be folded to form a solid. A net of a figure shows all the surfaces of that figure in one view.

EXAMPLE Recognizing Nets of Solids

1 Packaging Match each package with its net.

a.

b.

I.

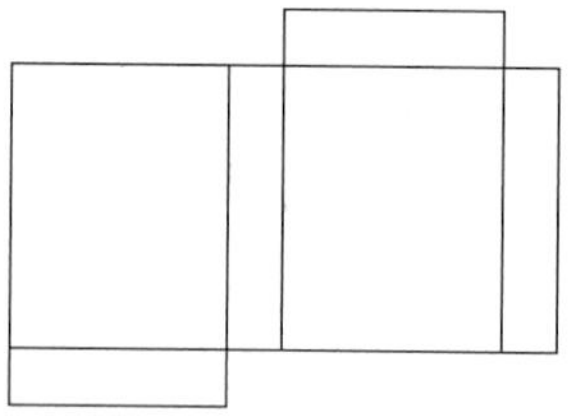

II.

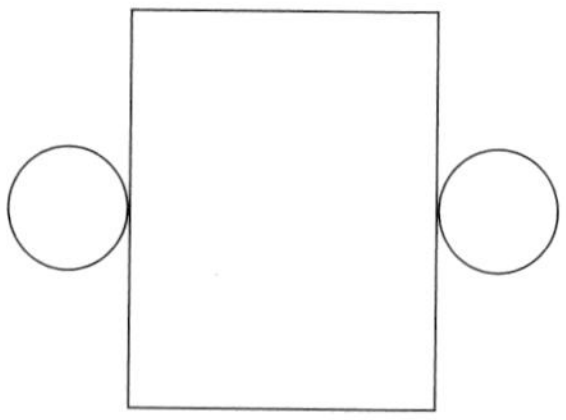

The oatmeal container is a cylinder, which has two circular bases. Figure II shows a net with two circles. The rice box is a rectangular prism, which has six rectangular faces. Figure I shows a net with six rectangles.

Quick Check

1. Describe the net of a standard number cube. six congruent squares

Differentiated Instruction Solutions for All Learners

Special Needs L1	**Below Level** L2
Show students an unassembled, flattened box that has no overlapping edges and have them draw the net on paper. Then a pair of students assembles the box, taping the edges together. Say: *It was a net; now it is a prism.*	Students draw and label a square, a circle, a pyramid, a prism, and a cone.
learning style: visual	learning style: visual

Examining the different shapes in a net can help you determine which solid the net will form.

EXAMPLE Identifying Solids From Nets

2 Identify the solid that each net forms.

a.

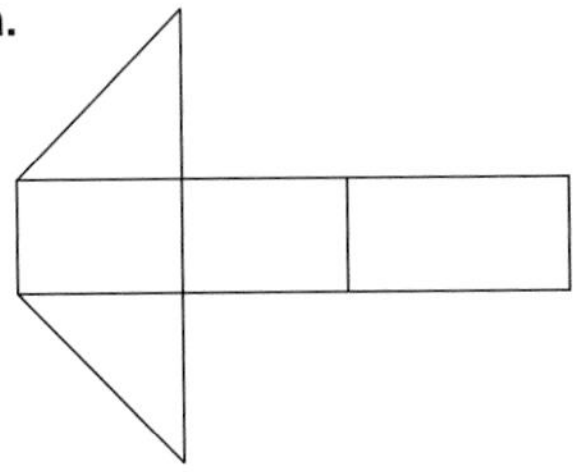

Two congruent triangles form the base of a triangular prism.

b.

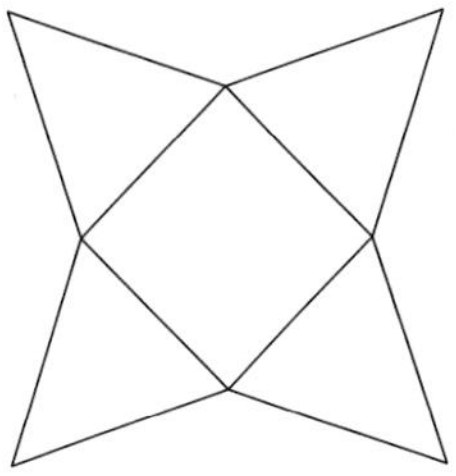

The square forms the base of a square pyramid.

Quick Check

2. A net consists of one regular pentagon and five congruent triangles. What solid will it form? pentagonal pyramid

PowerPoint Additional Examples

1 2 Match each shape with its net.

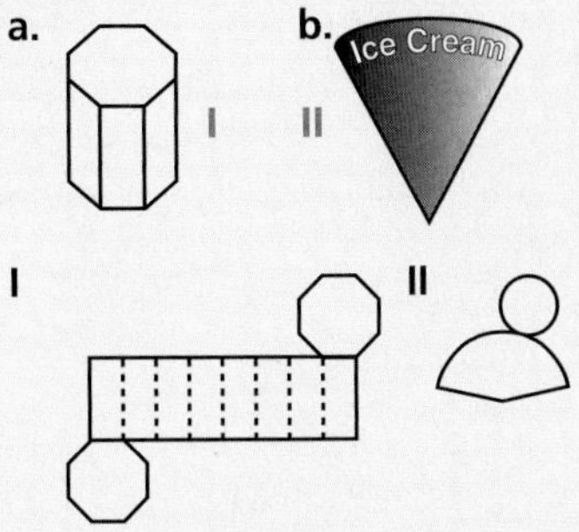

All in One Teaching Resources

- Daily Notetaking Guide 8-3 L3
- Adapted Notetaking 8-3 L1

Check Your Understanding

1. A net is a two-dimensional pattern; a prism is a three-dimensional solid.

1. **Vocabulary** What is the difference between a net and a prism?
2. List the shapes that make up the net for the figure. Then write the number of times each shape is used. 2 trapezoids, 4 rectangles

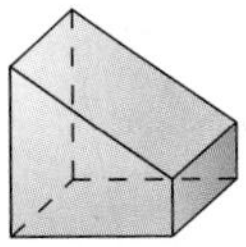

3. The net of a cylinder will always include two __?__. circles

3. Practice

Assignment Guide

Check Your Understanding
Go over Exercises 1–3 in class before assigning the Homework Exercises.

Homework Exercises

A	Practice by Example	4–9
B	Apply Your Skills	10–13
C	Challenge	14
Test Prep and Mixed Review		15–20

Homework Quick Check
To check students' understanding of key skills and concepts, go over Exercises 4, 8, 11, 12, and 13.

Homework Exercises

For more exercises, see Extra Skills and Word Problems.

GO for Help

For Exercises	See Examples
4–6	1
7–9	2

A Match each solid with its net.

4. 

B

5. 

C

6. 

A

A. 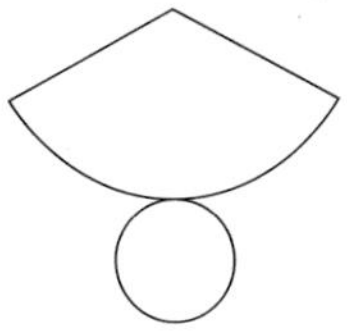

B. 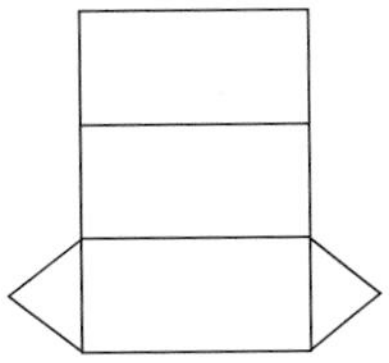

C. 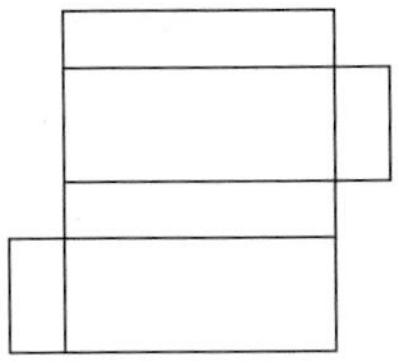

4. Assess & Reteach

PowerPoint Lesson Quiz

1. Identify the solid this net forms. cube

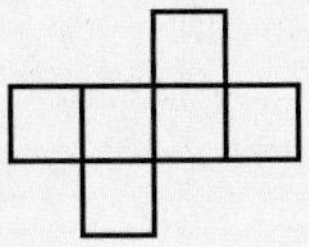

2. Draw a net for this solid.

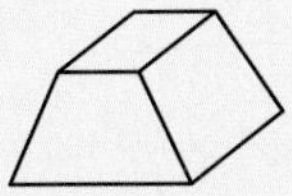

See back of book.

Advanced Learners L4
Students work with a partner to draw as many different nets for a cube as they can.

learning style: visual

English Language Learners ELL
For the **Vocabulary** question in *Check Your Understanding,* students discuss their ideas with a partner. Then they write their explanations, using drawings if necessary, if they do not know the words. Students attach a label to their drawings.

learning style: visual

Differentiated Instruction Resources

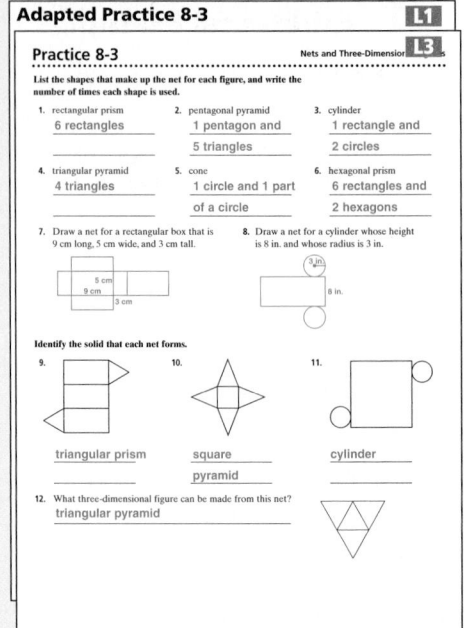

Adapted Practice 8-3 L1

Practice 8-3 — Nets and Three-Dimensional Figures L3

List the shapes that make up the net for each figure, and write the number of times each shape is used.

1. rectangular prism — 6 rectangles
2. pentagonal pyramid — 1 pentagon and 5 triangles
3. cylinder — 1 rectangle and 2 circles
4. triangular pyramid — 4 triangles
5. cone — 1 circle and 1 part of a circle
6. hexagonal prism — 6 rectangles and 2 hexagons
7. Draw a net for a rectangular box that is 9 cm long, 5 cm wide, and 3 cm tall.
8. Draw a net for a cylinder whose height is 8 in. and whose radius is 3 in.

Identify the solid that each net forms.

9. 10. 11.

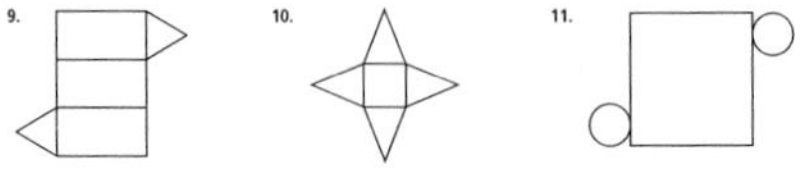

triangular prism — square pyramid — cylinder

12. What three-dimensional figure can be made from this net? triangular pyramid

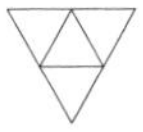

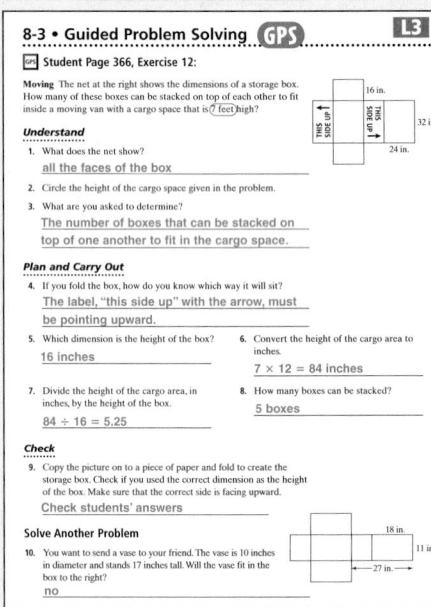

8-3 • Guided Problem Solving GPS L3

Student Page 366, Exercise 12:

Moving The net at the right shows the dimensions of a storage box. How many of these boxes can be stacked on top of each other to fit inside a moving van with a cargo space that is 7 feet high?

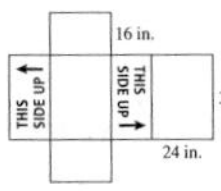

Understand

1. What does the net show? all the faces of the box
2. Circle the height of the cargo space given in the problem.
3. What are you asked to determine? The number of boxes that can be stacked on top of one another to fit in the cargo space.

Plan and Carry Out

4. If you fold the box, how do you know which way it will sit? The label, "this side up" with the arrow, must be pointing upward.
5. Which dimension is the height of the box? 16 inches
6. Convert the height of the cargo area to inches. 7 × 12 = 84 inches
7. Divide the height of the cargo area, in inches, by the height of the box. 84 ÷ 16 = 5.25
8. How many boxes can be stacked? 5 boxes

Check

9. Copy the picture on to a piece of paper and fold to create the storage box. Check if you used the correct dimension as the height of the box. Make sure that the correct side is facing upward. Check students' answers

Solve Another Problem

10. You want to send a vase to your friend. The vase is 10 inches in diameter and stands 17 inches tall. Will the vase fit in the box to the right? no

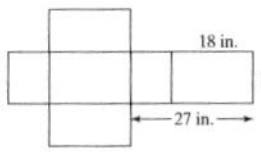

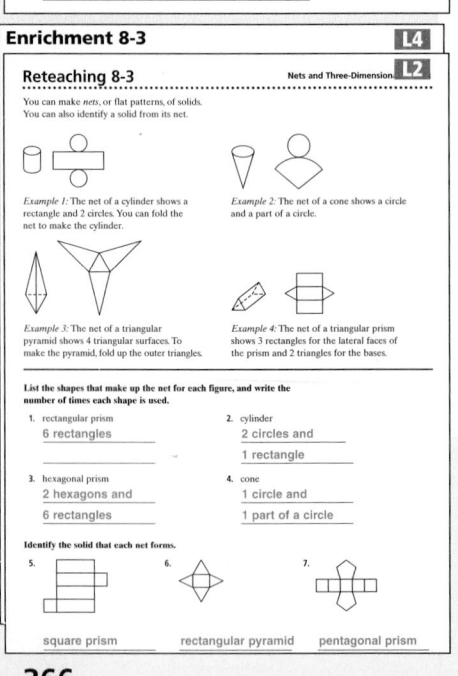

Enrichment 8-3 L4

Reteaching 8-3 — Nets and Three-Dimension L2

You can make *nets*, or flat patterns, of solids. You can also identify a solid from its net.

Example 1: The net of a cylinder shows a rectangle and 2 circles. You can fold the net to make the cylinder.

Example 2: The net of a cone shows a circle and a part of a circle.

Example 3: The net of a triangular pyramid shows 4 triangular surfaces. To make the pyramid, fold up the outer triangles.

Example 4: The net of a triangular prism shows 3 rectangles for the lateral faces of the prism and 2 triangles for the bases.

List the shapes that make up the net for each figure, and write the number of times each shape is used.

1. rectangular prism — 6 rectangles
2. cylinder — 2 circles and 1 rectangle
3. hexagonal prism — 2 hexagons and 6 rectangles
4. cone — 1 circle and 1 part of a circle

Identify the solid that each net forms.

5. 6. 7.

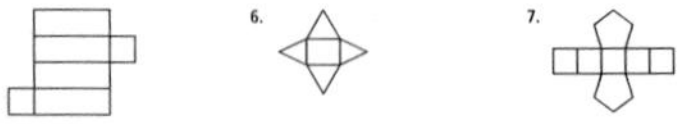

square prism — rectangular pyramid — pentagonal prism

Identify the solid that each net forms.

7.

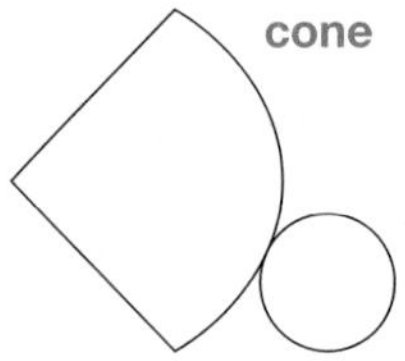

8.

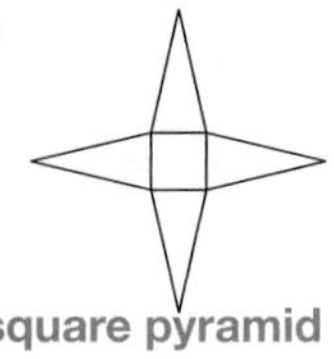

9.

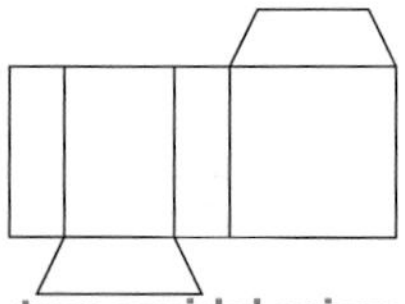

B GPS **10. Guided Problem Solving** Draw a net to represent the package at the right. See margin.

- What type of prism is shown?
- What best describes its faces?
- How many shapes are in the net?

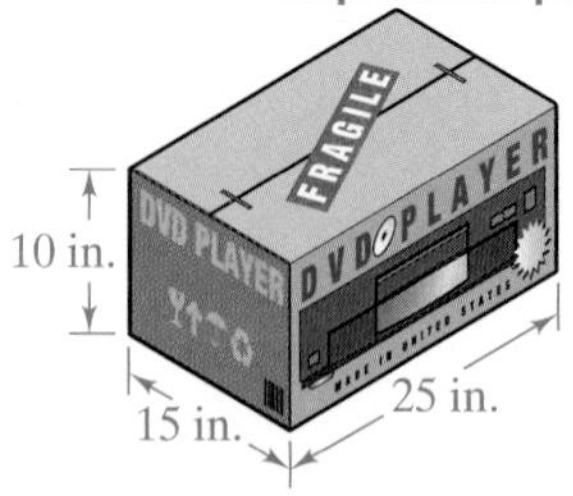

11. **Writing in Math** Explain how you can tell the difference between a net for a triangular pyramid and a net for a triangular prism. See margin.

12. **Moving** The net at the right shows the dimensions of a storage box. How many of these boxes can be stacked on top of each other to fit inside a moving van with a cargo space that is 7 feet high? 5 boxes

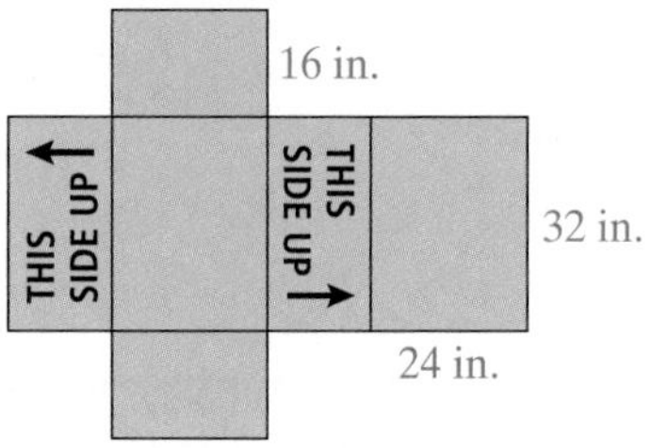

GO Online
Homework Video Tutor
Visit: PHSchool.com
Web Code: ase-0803

13. Draw a net for a cylinder with a height of 8 cm and a radius of 4 cm. See margin.

C 14. **Challenge** A gift box is 9 in. by 7 in. by 12 in. Would a sheet of wrapping paper that is 1 yard on each side cover the gift? Explain. Yes; the box can be represented by a net 32 in. by 30 in., so the 36 in.-by-36 in. wrapping paper will cover it.

Test Prep and Mixed Review — Practice

Multiple Choice

15. A hula hoop travels about 132 inches in one full rotation. What is the diameter of the hoop, to the nearest inch? C
    - (A) 16 in.
    - (B) 21 in.
    - (C) 42 in.
    - (D) 66 in.

16. A group of students went to the zoo. Tickets cost $3 per student. The zoo charged a $20 fee for the group to have a tour guide. The total cost was $68. How many students went to the zoo? H
    - (F) 3
    - (G) 8
    - (H) 16
    - (J) 31

GO for Help

For Exercises	See Lesson
17–20	7-5

Find the measure of each angle of a regular polygon with the given number of sides.

17. 3 sides 60°
18. 5 sides 108°
19. 8 sides 135°
20. 14 sides 154.3°

Test Prep

Resources

For additional practice with a variety of test item formats:

- Test-Taking Strategies, p. 403
- Test Prep, p. 407
- Test-Taking Strategies with Transparencies

Alternative Assessment

Students in pairs take turns drawing a net and having the partner identify the solid.

Modeling Surface Area

A cereal box has six surfaces. You can think of it as modeling a prism. The sum of the areas of the four lateral, or side, surfaces equals the lateral area of the prism. The total surface area of the prism is equal to the lateral area plus the area of the bases.

ACTIVITY

1–3. Check students' work.

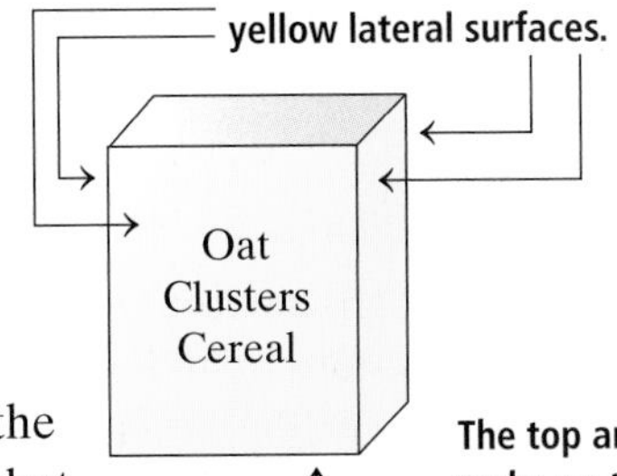
Lateral means "on the side." This box has four yellow lateral surfaces.
Oat Clusters Cereal
The top and bottom of the box make up the other two surfaces of the prism.

1. Use a centimeter ruler to measure the edges of a cereal box from top to bottom.
2. Find the area of each lateral surface. Use the values to find the lateral area of the cereal box.

Remove the bases (the top and the bottom) from the cereal box with scissors. Then cut along one edge that joins two lateral surfaces.

Unfold the four lateral surfaces to form one rectangle.

3. Measure the length and width of the flattened rectangle and find its area. Compare this value to the lateral area you calculated in Question 2.
4. **Writing in Math** Explain how you can calculate the lateral area of the cereal box using its height and the perimeter of one of its bases. Answers may vary. Sample: Lateral area is the perimeter of the base times the height.

ACTIVITY

Remove the label of a soup can by making a single cut along the height of the label.

Lateral area wraps around a cylinder, just like the label on a can of soup wraps around the can.
Vegetable Soup
The top and bottom of the can are the two bases of the cylinder.

5. Calculate the lateral area of the soup can. Check students' work.
6. Write a formula for calculating the lateral surface area of a cylinder using its circumference and height. L.A. = $C \cdot h$
7. Measure the diameter of the soup can. Find the total surface area of the soup can. Check students' work.
8. **Reasoning** Write a formula for calculating the surface area of a soup can using its height and the radius of its base. S.A. = $2\pi r^2 + 2\pi rh$

Activity Lab

Modeling Surface Area

In the previous lesson, students identified the nets of solids. Here students use this knowledge to identify and measure the lateral surface area of a cereal box (a rectangular prism), as well as the total surface area of a soup can (a cylinder). They then describe how to find or write formulas for each surface area.

Guided Instruction

Math Tip
As students find the lateral area of the cereal box or the surface area of the can, help them recognize that the areas of pairs of opposite sides are the same.

Teaching Tip
Have students include the top and bottom of the cereal box to find total surface area.

Resources

- Activity Lab 8-4: Surface Area of Prisms and Cylinders
- cereal boxes
- cylindrical cans
- centimeter ruler

Exercises, p. 366

10. See back of book.
11. A triangular prism will have two triangular faces and three rectangular faces, whereas a pyramid will have four triangular faces.
13. See back of book.

8-4

1. Plan

Objective
To find surface areas of prisms and cylinders using nets and formulas

Examples
1 Using a Net to Find Surface Area
2 Using the Prism Surface Area Formula
3 Finding Surface Area of a Cylinder

Math Understandings: p. 352C

Professional Development

Math Background

The sum of the areas of the surfaces of a solid is called the *surface area* (S.A.). The sum of the area of the lateral surfaces, excluding the bases, is called the *lateral area* (L.A.).

Prism: L.A. = ph
S.A. = L.A. + $2B$

Cylinder: L.A. = $2\pi rh$
S.A. = L.A. + $2B$

More Math Background: p. 352C

Lesson Planning and Resources

See p. 352E for a list of the resources that support this lesson.

PowerPoint

Bell Ringer Practice

Check Skills You'll Need
Use student page, transparency, or PowerPoint. For intervention, direct students to:
Circumference and Area of a Circle
Lesson 7-7
Extra Skills and Word Problems Practice, Ch. 7

8-4 Surface Areas of Prisms and Cylinders

Check Skills You'll Need

1. **Vocabulary Review** Explain how to find the *area* of a rectangle. See below.

Find each area to the nearest tenth.

2. a rectangle that is 5.5 cm by 3 cm 16.5 cm^2
3. a circle with a radius of 2 ft 12.6 ft^2

GO for Help Lesson 7-7

What You'll Learn

To find surface areas of prisms and cylinders using nets and formulas

New Vocabulary surface area, lateral area

Why Learn This?

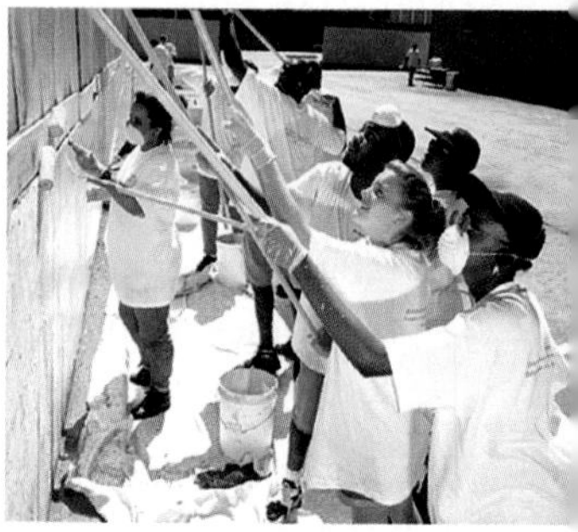

Knowing how to find surface area helps you in situations such as painting. If you know the area of the space to be painted, you can figure out how much paint to buy.

The **surface area** of a solid is the sum of the areas of all its surfaces. The surface area of a solid is the total area of its net.

EXAMPLE 1 Using a Net to Find Surface Area

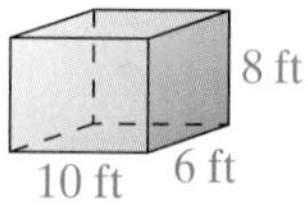

Check Skills You'll Need

1. Multiply the length times the width.

Use a net to find the surface area of the prism at the left.

Draw a net of the prism. Find the area of each rectangle in the net.

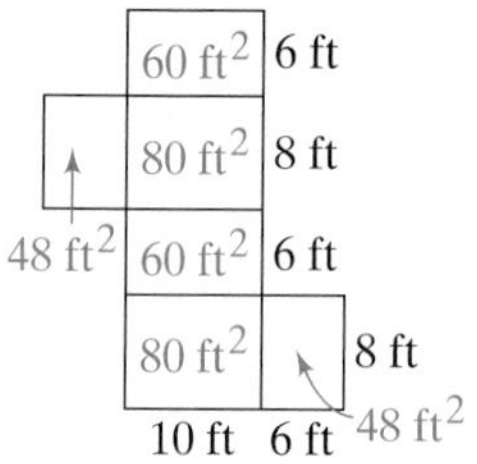

Let S.A. stand for surface area. Add the areas.

S.A. = 60 + 80 + 60 + 80 + 48 + 48

S.A. = 376

The surface area of the prism is 376 ft^2.

Quick Check

1. Use a net to find the surface area of the prism at the right. 936 cm^2

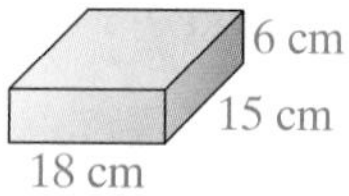

Vocabulary Tip
Lateral means "on the side."

You can also use a formula to find the surface area of a figure. First you must know how to find the lateral area.

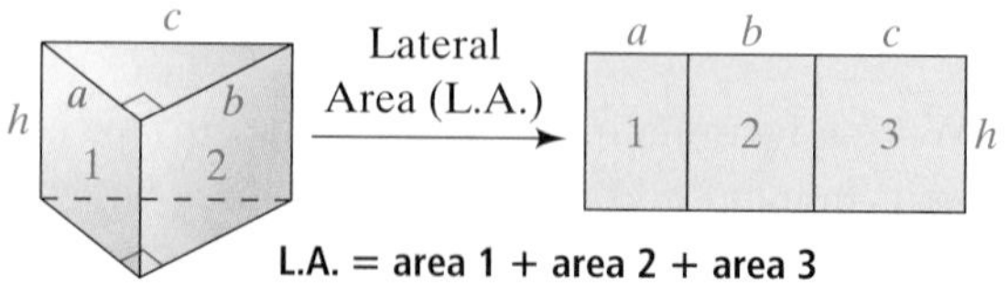

L.A. = area 1 + area 2 + area 3

Differentiated Instruction Solutions for All Learners

Special Needs L1
For Example 2, provide each student with wrapping paper and a box. Students cut pieces of wrapping paper to fit each side, then measure and calculate the area of each piece. Students total these areas, then compare their work to the prism surface area formula.
learning style: tactile

Below Level L2
Students look at diagrams of a cube and an octagonal prism. They point to and count the number of lateral faces and the total number of faces for each solid.
Cube 4; 6 Octagonal prism 8; 10
learning style: visual

Lateral area is the sum of the areas of the lateral surfaces of a solid.

KEY CONCEPTS Lateral Area and Surface Area of a Prism

The lateral area L.A. of a prism is the product of the perimeter of the base and the height.

$$\text{L.A.} = ph$$

The surface area S.A. of a prism is the sum of the lateral area and the area of its two bases.

$$\text{S.A.} = \text{L.A.} + 2B$$

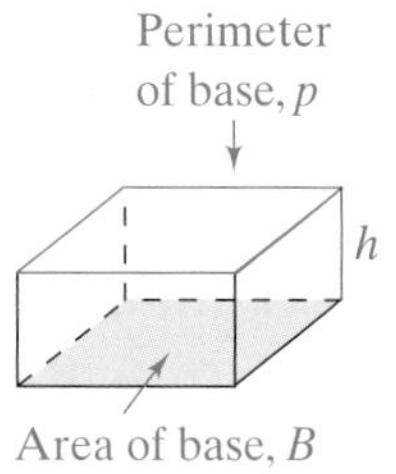

EXAMPLE Using the Prism Surface Area Formula

2 **Multiple Choice** A gift box has the shape of the prism at the right. Which of the following is closest to the amount of wrapping paper you need to cover the box completely without any overlap?

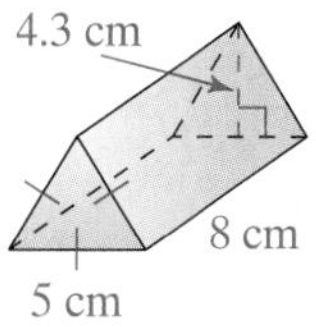

Ⓐ 120 cm^2 Ⓑ 142 cm^2 Ⓒ 163 cm^2 Ⓓ 172 cm^2

$\text{S.A.} = \text{L.A.} + 2B$	← surface area formula
$= ph + 2B$	← Use ph for L.A.
$= (3 \cdot 5)8 + 2B$	← The perimeter of the base is $3 \cdot 5$ cm. The height of the prism is 8 cm.
$= 120 + 2B$	← Use the order of operations.
$= 120 + 2\left(\frac{1}{2} \cdot 5 \cdot 4.3\right)$	← Find the area of the bases.
$= 141.5$	← Add.

The surface area of the prism is about 142 cm^2. The correct answer is B.

Test Prep Tip

The mathematics chart uses *S* to represent lateral or total surface area. Be sure to choose the correct formula.

Quick Check

2. **Packaging** The base of a decorative box for dolls is 8 in. by 5 in. Its height is 12 in. Estimate the surface area of the box. about 392 in.^2

The rectangular label on a can covers the lateral area of the can.

The height of the rectangle is the height of the can.

The base length of the rectangle is the circumference of the can.

2. Teach

Activity Lab

Use before the lesson.
Student Edition Activity Lab, Hands On 8-4a, Modeling Surface Area, p. 367

All in One Teaching Resources

Activity Lab 8-4: Surface Area of Prisms and Cylinders

Guided Instruction

Diversity
Discuss various ways of wrapping and presenting gifts in different cultures. For example, gifts in Japan are often wrapped in cloth.

Concrete Models
Have students build prisms with unit cubes. Have them count the exposed faces of the cubes to find lateral and total surface area.

Error Prevention!

Make sure students understand that surface area includes *all* the faces, including both bases and sides. To illustrate the surface area of a prism, tie a string around the edges of one base. Roll the string along the prism surface to the other base. Suggest that they think of the lateral area of the prism as the amount of surface area touched by the string.

PowerPoint

Additional Examples

1 Use a net to find the surface area of this prism.

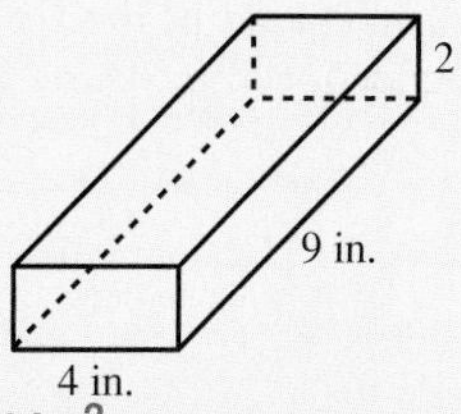

124 in.^2

2 Suppose you are wrapping a portable CD player in a rectangular box. The box is 24 in. long, 6 in. wide, and 8.2 in. tall. How much wrapping paper do you need to completely cover the box? Round to the nearest square inch. 780 in.^2

Advanced Learners L4	**English Language Learners** ELL
Students work in pairs to draw prisms of 5, 6, 8, and 9 sides. They mark the dimensions on their drawings. Then, they calculate the surface area of each prism. learning style: visual	Students describe, orally and in writing, the difference between lateral area and surface area. learning style: verbal

Guided Instruction

Concrete Models
To reinforce the concept of lateral area, have students use cardboard tubes to model cylinders. They then cut and measure tubes to find lateral area.

Have students find total surface of objects such as soup cans by measuring or covering objects with paper.

Alternative Method
In Example 3, students may realize that they can apply the Distributive Property to first add rh and r^2, and then multiply the sum by 2π.

PowerPoint

Additional Examples

3 Find the surface area of a cylindrical can with a height of 7.2 cm and a diameter of 3.96 cm. Give the answer to the nearest whole unit.
114 cm^2

All in One Teaching Resources
- Daily Notetaking Guide 8-4 L3
- Adapted Notetaking 8-4 L1

Closure

- *How do you find the surface area of a prism?* Sample: Find the Lateral Area by multiplying the perimeter of the base by the height. Add the L.A. to the area of the two bases to find the S.A.
- *How do you find the surface area of a cylinder?* Sample: Find the Lateral Area by multiplying the circumference of the base ($2\pi r$) by the height. Add the L.A. to the area of the two bases to find the S.A.

GO for Help
For help with the area and circumference of a circle, go to Lesson 7-7, Example 1.

KEY CONCEPTS **Lateral Area and Surface Area of a Cylinder**

The lateral area L.A. of a cylinder is the product of the circumference of the base and the height of the cylinder.

$$\text{L.A.} = 2\pi rh$$

The surface area S.A. of a cylinder is the sum of the lateral area and the area of the bases.

$$\text{S.A.} = \text{L.A.} + 2B$$

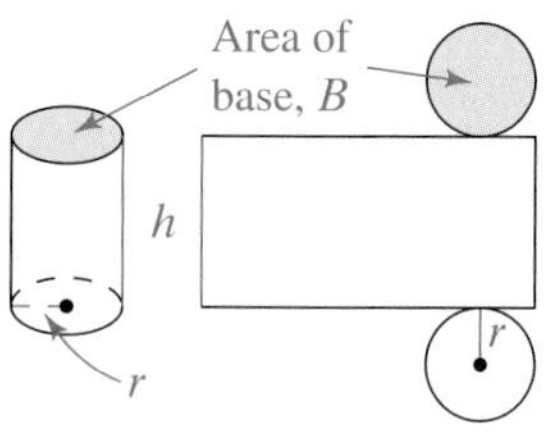

EXAMPLE Finding Surface Area of a Cylinder

3 Find the surface area of the can at the right to the nearest square centimeter.

Estimate Use 3 for π, 4 cm for the radius, and 11 cm for the height.

$$\text{L.A.} \approx 2(3)(4)(11) = 264$$

$B \approx 3(4)^2 = 48$

$B \approx 3(4)^2 = 48$

S.A. $\approx$ 48 + 264 + 48. The surface area is about 360 cm^2.

The radius is 7 cm $\div$ 2, or 3.5 cm. Use the cylinder surface area formula.

$\text{S.A.} = \text{L.A.} + 2B$	← surface area formula
$= 2\pi rh + 2(\pi r^2)$	← Use $2\pi rh$ for L.A. and πr^2 for B.
$= 2\pi(3.5)(11.5) + 2\pi(3.5)^2$	← Substitute 3.5 for r and 11.5 for h.
$= 105\pi$	← Simplify.
$\approx$ 329.8672286	← Use a calculator.

The surface area of the can is about 330 cm^2.

Check for Reasonableness The answer 330 cm^2 is close to the estimate of 360 cm^2. The answer is reasonable.

Test Prep Tip
You can estimate to find whole-number approximations of expressions that use π.

Quick Check

3. Find the surface area of the cylinder at the right to the nearest square meter. 151 m^2

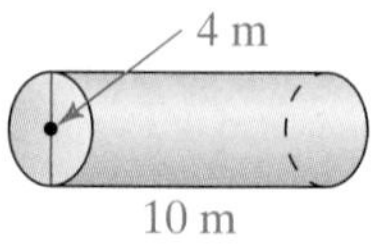

Check Your Understanding

1. The lateral area of a prism is the sum of the areas of the lateral faces. The surface area includes the lateral area plus the area of the two bases.
2. 768 in.^{2}

1. **Vocabulary** What is the difference between the lateral area of a prism and the surface area of a prism?

The net for a rectangular prism is shown at the right. Find each area.

2. front face
3. right face 384 in.^{2}
4. top face 512 in.^{2}
5. lateral area 2,304 in.^{2}

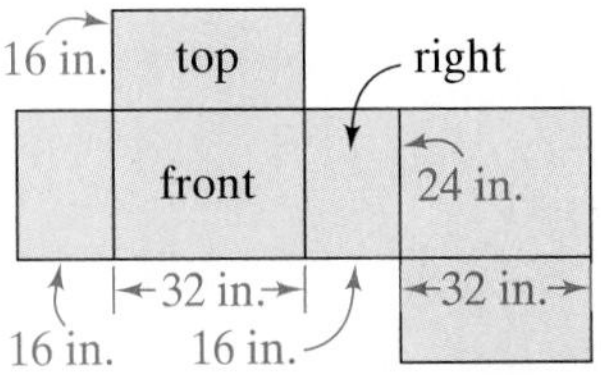

Homework Exercises

For more exercises, see Extra Skills and Word Problems.

GO for Help

For Exercises	See Examples
6–7	1
8–11	2
12–13	3

A **Use a net to find the surface area of each prism.**

6. 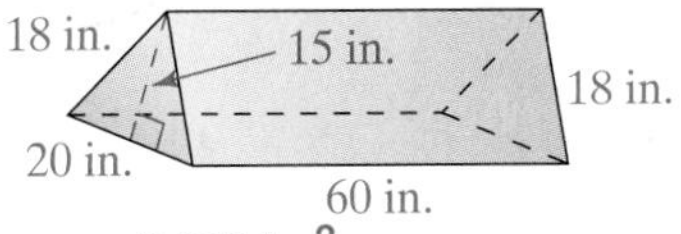

3,660 in.^{2}

7. 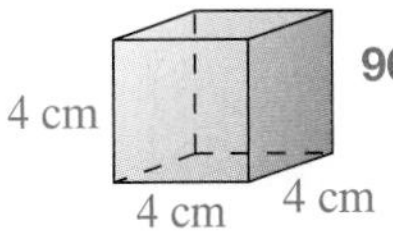

96 cm^2

8. The shed at the right needs to be painted. Find the lateral area of the shed including the door and windows. 440 ft^2

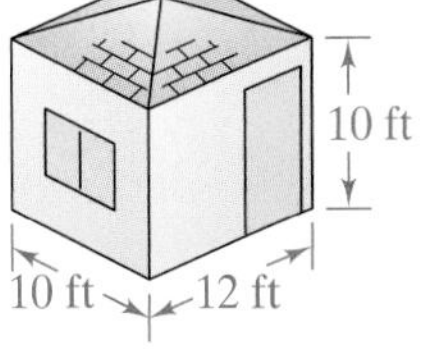

Use a formula to find the surface area of each figure.

9. 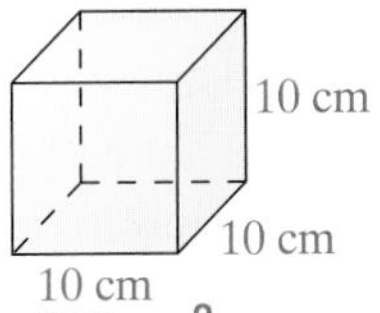

600 cm^2

10. 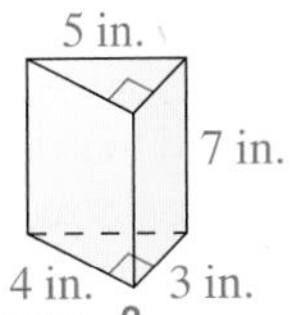

96 in.^{2}

11. 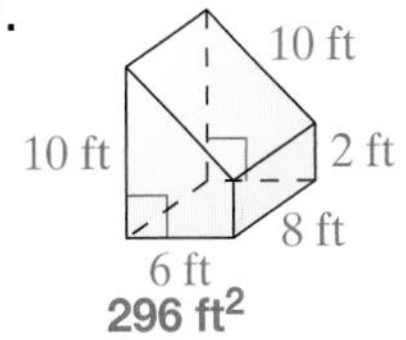

296 ft^2

Find the surface area of each cylinder. Round to the nearest square unit.

12. radius: 4 in., height: 6 in. 251 in.^{2}

13. diameter: 7 cm, height: 9 cm 275 cm^2

B **GPS** 14. **Guided Problem Solving** A cleaning company is hired to clean the windows of the building shown. Estimate the area that needs to be cleaned. 20,790 ft^2

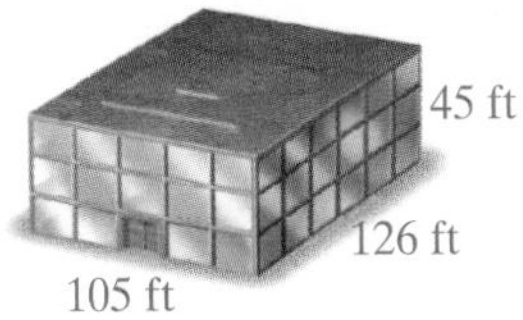

- **Understand the Problem** The windows are on the four sides of the building. To estimate the area that needs to be cleaned, find the __?__ area of a __?__.
- **Carry Out the Plan** What is the perimeter p of the base? What is the height h? Find $p \times h$ to determine the area.

3. Practice

Assignment Guide

Check Your Understanding

Go over Exercises 1–5 in class before assigning the Homework Exercises.

Homework Exercises

A	Practice by Example	6–13
B	Apply Your Skills	14–20
C	Challenge	21
	Test Prep and Mixed Review	22–26

Homework Quick Check

To check students' understanding of key skills and concepts, go over Exercises 11, 13, 15, 16, and 17.

Exercises

For Exercises 12–13, to reinforce surface area, have students draw nets for each cylinder. Have them use the nets to find lateral and total surface area.

Differentiated Instruction Resources

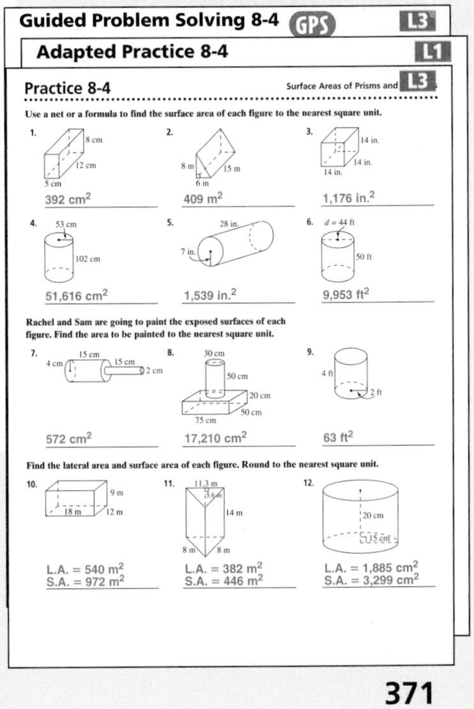
Guided Problem Solving 8-4 GPS L3

Adapted Practice 8-4 L1

Practice 8-4 Surface Areas of Prisms and L3

Use a net or a formula to find the surface area of each figure to the nearest square unit.

1. 392 cm^2
2. 409 m^2
3. 1,176 in.^{2}
4. 51,616 cm^2
5. 1,539 in.^{2}
6. 9,953 ft^2

Rachel and Sam are going to paint the exposed surfaces of each figure. Find the area to be painted to the nearest square unit.

7. 572 cm^2
8. 17,210 cm^2
9. 63 ft^2

Find the lateral area and surface area of each figure. Round to the nearest square unit.

10. L.A. = 540 m^2 S.A. = 972 m^2
11. L.A. = 382 m^2 S.A. = 446 m^2
12. L.A. = 1,885 cm^2 S.A. = 3,299 cm^2

4. Assess & Reteach

PowerPoint

Lesson Quiz

1. Use a net to find the surface area of the prism. 192 ft^2

Find each surface area.

2.

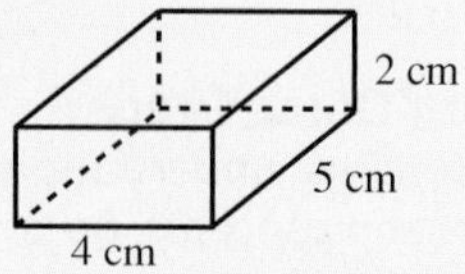

76 cm^2

3.

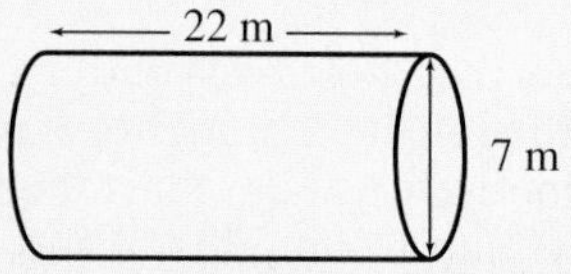

about 561 m^2

4. How much paint is needed to cover the lateral surface of a cylindrical-shaped telescope that is 18.2 cm high with bases that have a radius of 5 cm? Round to the nearest square centimeter. about 572 cm^2

15. The 9 cm-by-5.5 cm-by-11.75 cm box will require more cardboard because it has a greater surface area.

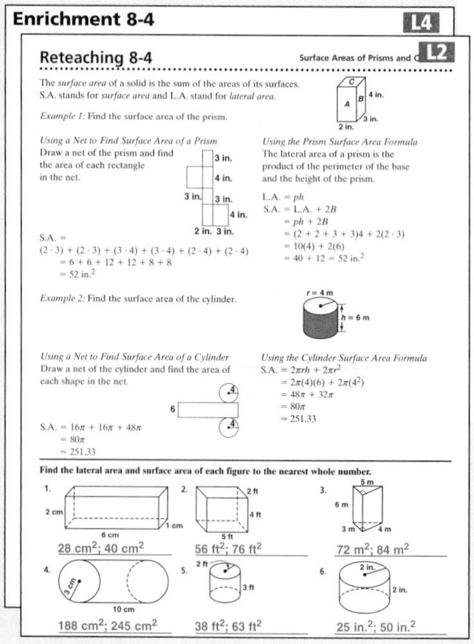

Enrichment 8-4 L4

Reteaching 8-4 — Surface Areas of Prisms and C... L2

The *surface area* of a solid is the sum of the areas of its surfaces. S.A. stands for *surface area* and L.A. stand for *lateral area*.

Example 1: Find the surface area of the prism.

Using a Net to Find Surface Area of a Prism
Draw a net of the prism and find the area of each rectangle in the net.

S.A. =
$(2 \cdot 3) + (2 \cdot 3) + (3 \cdot 4) + (3 \cdot 4) + (2 \cdot 4) + (2 \cdot 4)$
$= 6 + 6 + 12 + 12 + 8 + 8$
$= 52$ in.^{2}

Using the Prism Surface Area Formula
The lateral area of a prism is the product of the perimeter of the base and the height of the prism.

L.A. $= ph$
S.A. $=$ L.A. $+ 2B$
$= ph + 2B$
$= (2 + 2 + 3 + 3)4 + 2(2 \cdot 3)$
$= 10(4) + 2(6)$
$= 40 + 12 = 52$ in.^{2}

Example 2: Find the surface area of the cylinder.

Using a Net to Find Surface Area of a Cylinder
Draw a net of the cylinder and find the area of each shape in the net.

S.A. $= 16\pi + 16\pi + 48\pi$
$= 80\pi$
≈ 251.33

Using the Cylinder Surface Area Formula
S.A. $= 2\pi rh + 2\pi r^2$
$= 2\pi(4)(6) + 2\pi(4^2)$
$= 48\pi + 32\pi$
$= 80\pi$
≈ 251.33

Find the lateral area and surface area of each figure to the nearest whole number.

1. 28 cm^2; 40 cm^2
2. 56 ft^2; 76 ft^2
3. 72 m^2; 84 m^2
4. 188 cm^2; 245 cm^2
5. 38 ft^2; 63 ft^2
6. 25 in.^{2}; 50 in.^{2}

GO Online
Homework Video Tutor
Visit: PHSchool.com
Web Code: ase-0804

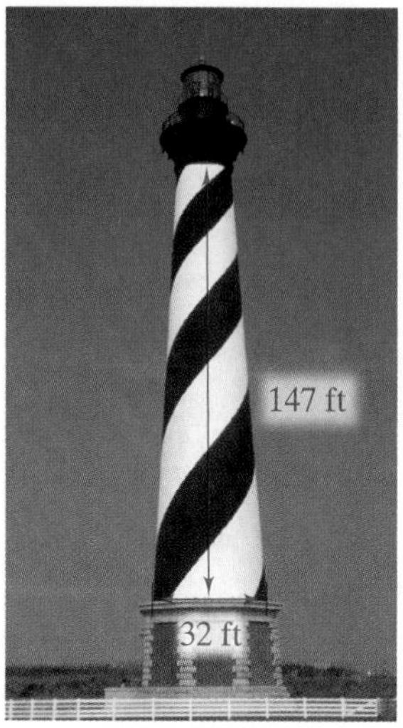

15. Which will require more cardboard to make: a box 9 cm by 5.5 cm by 11.75 cm, or a box 8 cm by 6.25 cm by 10.5 cm? Explain. See margin.

16. **Writing in Math** You can draw a net or use a formula to find the surface area of a solid. Which way do you prefer? Explain. Check students' work.

17. a. **Lighthouses** Explain how you can estimate the lateral area of Cape Hatteras Lighthouse, shown at the left. 17a–b. See margin.
    b. **Estimation** One gallon of paint covers 350 square feet. Estimate the number of gallons of black paint and the number of gallons of white paint necessary to repaint the lighthouse.

Find the lateral and surface areas of each figure to the nearest square unit. 19–20. See margin.

18.

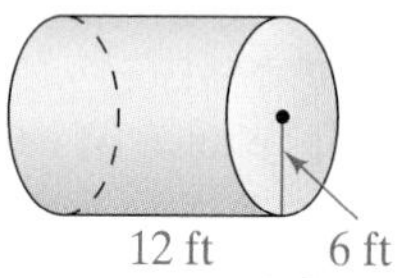

L.A. = 452 ft^2;
S.A. = 679 ft^2

19.

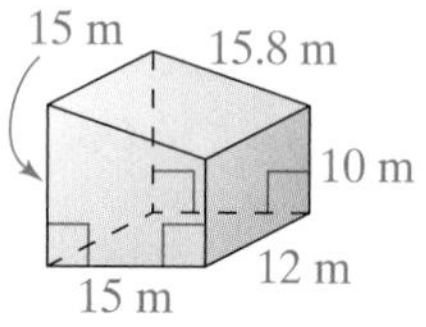

20.

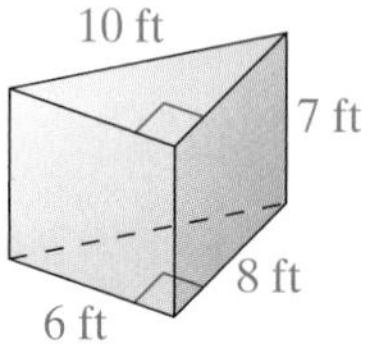

21. **Challenge** In the drawing, the surface area of cube A was 150 cm^2 before cube B was removed. The surface area of cube B is 24 cm^2. What effect did removing cube B have on the surface area of cube A? Explain.
None; the area of the three new surfaces of figure A is exactly the same as the area of three surfaces of cube B.

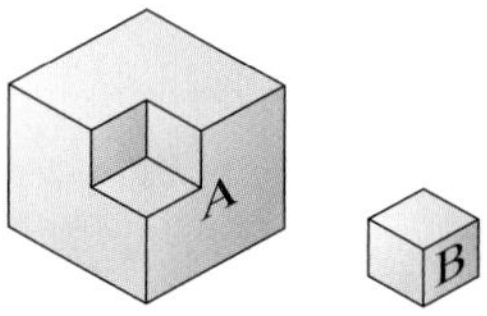

Test Prep and Mixed Review

Practice

Multiple Choice

22. A painter uses the roller shown. To the nearest square inch, what is the area covered by one complete revolution of the roller? D
    A 28 in.^{2} C 57 in.^{2}
    B 38 in.^{2} D 75 in.^{2}

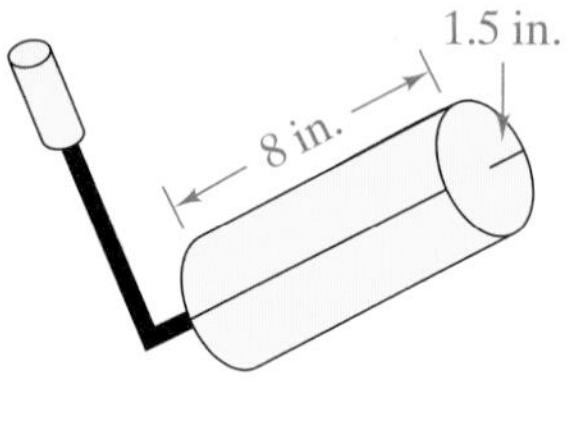

23. The average cost of gasoline increased \$0.34 per gallon, or 16%. What was the original average cost per gallon? G
    F \$2.41 G \$2.13 H \$1.99 J \$1.83

24. What is the width x of the kite at the right to the nearest inch? C
    A 12 in. C 21 in.
    B 17 in. D 30 in.

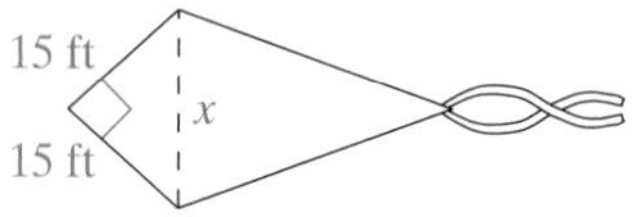

GO for Help

For Exercises	See Lesson
25–26	7-1

Find the measure of each angle.

25. the supplement of 62° 118°

26. the complement of 78° 12°

Test Prep

Resources
For additional practice with a variety of test item formats:
- Test-Taking Strategies, p. 403
- Test Prep, p. 407
- Test-Taking Strategies with Transparencies

Alternative Assessment

Students compare surface areas of a cylinder whose radius and height are 10 cm, with that of a cube whose sides are 10 cm. 1,257 cm^2 > 600 cm^2

17a–b. See back of book.

19. L.A. = 675 m^2;
S.A. = 1,045 m^2

20. L.A. = 168 ft^2;
S.A. = 216 ft^2

Checkpoint Quiz 1

Lessons 8-1 through 8-4

Use the figure at the right for Exercises 1 and 2.

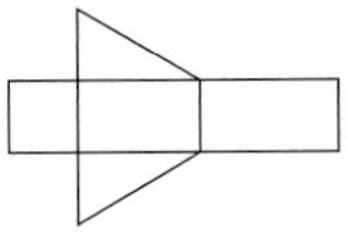

1. What three-dimensional figure will this net form? triangular prism
2. Name the shapes that make up the lateral faces of this figure. rectangles

Use the figure at the right for Exercises 3 and 4. 3–4. See margin.

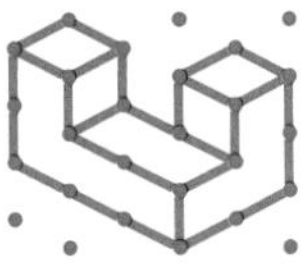

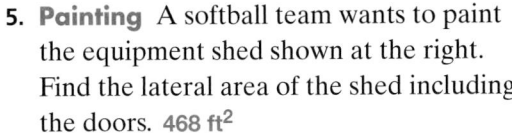

3. Draw a base plan for the figure.
4. Draw the top, front, and right views for the figure.
5. **Painting** A softball team wants to paint the equipment shed shown at the right. Find the lateral area of the shed including the doors. $468\ ft^2$

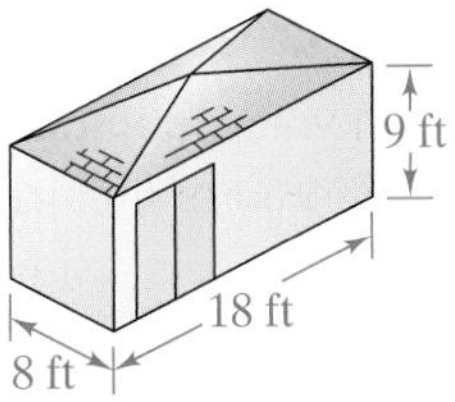

8-5a Activity Lab

Hands On

Surface Area of a Pyramid

Step 1 Draw an isosceles triangle on a piece of cardboard.

Step 2 Duplicate your triangle three times. Each triangle should share one side with another triangle, as in the diagram at the right.

Step 3 Cut out your pattern along its outside edge. Fold the pattern along the long sides of the triangles. Tape it together.

Step 4 Cut a square to be the base of the pyramid. Tape it in place.

Pyramid Pattern

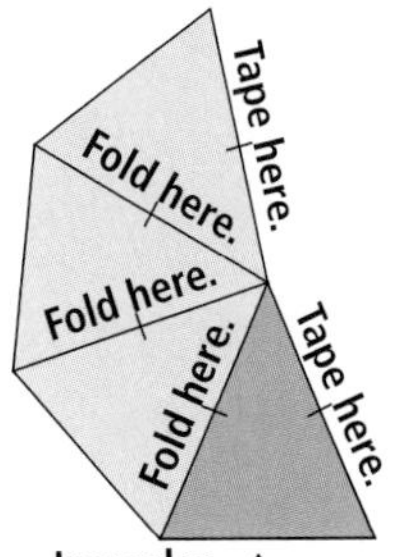

1. Measure the height and base of one of the triangles. Calculate the area of the triangle. 1–4. Check students' work.
2. The lateral area of the square pyramid is the sum of the areas of the four lateral triangular surfaces. Calculate the lateral area.
3. Find the area of the base of the pyramid. Calculate the total surface area of the pyramid.
4. **Reasoning** Write a formula to find the surface area of a pyramid.

Checkpoint Quiz 1

3.

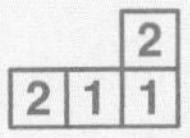

4.

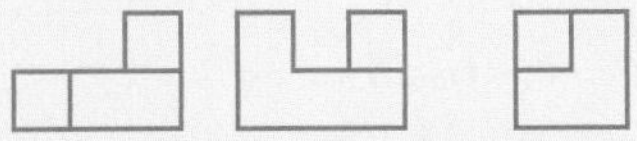

Top view Front view Right view

Checkpoint Quiz

Use this Checkpoint Quiz to check students' understanding of the skills and concepts of Lessons 8-1 through 8-4.

Resources

- All in One Teaching Resources Checkpoint Quiz 1
- ExamView Assessment Suite CD-ROM
- Success Tracker Online Intervention

Activity Lab

Surface Area of a Pyramid

Students draw and cut out a net of the lateral surface area of a pyramid using isosceles triangles. They measure the height and base of one of the triangular sides, and they calculate the pyramid's surface area. Then they use this work to write a formula for a pyramid's surface area.

Guided Instruction

Error Prevention!

Some students may confuse the height of a triangular face with the height of the pyramid. Demonstrate the triangle height by holding the ruler against one triangular face of the pyramid, along the triangle's height. (In the next lesson, they'll learn this is called the *slant height.*)

Resources

- Activity Lab 8-5: Comparing Cones
- card board
- tape
- ruler

8-5

1. Plan

Objective
To find surface areas of pyramids and cones using nets and formulas

Examples
1 Using a Net to Find Surface Area
2 Finding Lateral and Surface Area
3 Using the Cone Surface Area Formula

Math Understandings: p. 352C

Professional Development

Math Background

The height of one of a pyramid's lateral faces is called the *slant height,* or ℓ. For a square pyramid, each of the four faces is an isosceles triangle and the L.A. $= 4\left(\frac{1}{2}b\ell\right)$ or $2b\ell$ and the S.A. = L.A. + B, where B is the area of the base. For a cone, the L.A. $= \frac{1}{2}(2\pi r)\ell$ or $\pi r\ell$ and the S.A. = L.A. + B.

More Math Background: p. 352C

Lesson Planning and Resources

See p. 352E for a list of the resources that support this lesson.

PowerPoint

Bell Ringer Practice

Check Skills You'll Need
Use student page, transparency, or PowerPoint. For intervention, direct students to:
Areas of Polygons
Lesson 7-6
Extra Skills and Word Problems Practice, Ch. 7

8-5 Surface Areas of Pyramids and Cones

Check Skills You'll Need

1. **Vocabulary Review** The longest side of a right triangle is the ? . hypotenuse
2. Find the area of the figure below to the nearest whole unit.

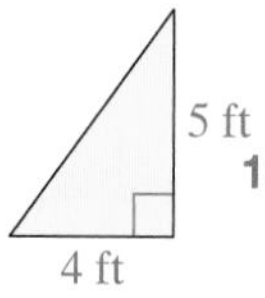

10 ft²

GO for Help Lesson 7-6

What You'll Learn

To find surface areas of pyramids and cones using nets and formulas

New Vocabulary slant height

Why Learn This?

When you can find the surface area of pyramids and cones, you can find the amount of materials you need for projects as large as roofing a house or as small as making a funnel.

The height of a pyramid is different from the height of its lateral faces. For this reason, the height of a pyramid's lateral faces is called the **slant height** and is indicated by the symbol ℓ.

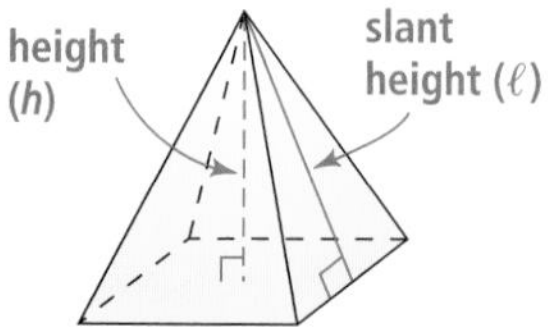

You can draw a net to find the surface area of a square pyramid. The four triangular faces are congruent isosceles triangles.

EXAMPLE 1 Using a Net to Find Surface Area

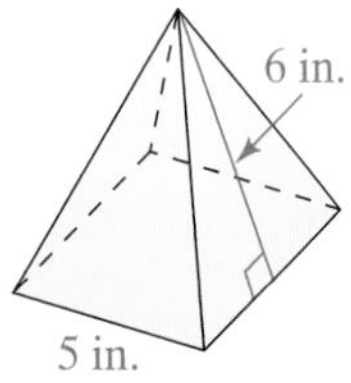

Find the surface area of the square pyramid at the left.

Step 1 Draw a net of the pyramid.

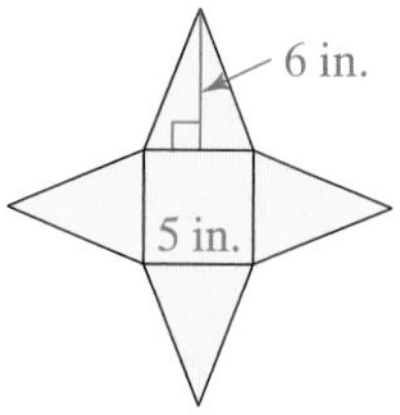

Step 2 Find the area of the faces and the base.

S.A. = area of triangles + area of square

$= 4 \cdot \frac{1}{2}bh + s^2$

$= 4 \cdot \frac{1}{2}(5 \cdot 6) + 5^2$ ← **Substitute 5 for *b*, 6 for *h*, and 5 for *s*.**

$= 60 + 25$ ← **Simplify.**

$= 85$ ← **Add.**

The surface area is 85 in.².

GO for Help For help with nets, go to Lesson 8-3, Examples 1 and 2.

Quick Check

1. Draw a net of the square pyramid at the right. Then find its surface area. See back of book.

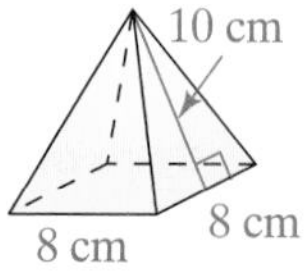

Differentiated Instruction Solutions for All Learners

Special Needs L1
If students have difficulty using the formulas for lateral area and surface area, let them use nets until they are comfortable making the transition. Students solve an example using both nets and formulas to help them see the connection between the two methods.
learning style: visual

Below Level L2
Students sketch a square pyramid and a cone and identify the bases, the lateral faces, the slant height, and the perimeter (or circumference) of the bases.
learning style: visual

You can also use a formula to find the surface area of a square pyramid.

KEY CONCEPTS **Lateral Area and Surface Area of a Square Pyramid**

The lateral area L.A. of a square pyramid is four times the area of one of the lateral faces.

$$\text{L.A.} = 4 \cdot \left(\tfrac{1}{2}b\ell\right) = 2b\ell$$

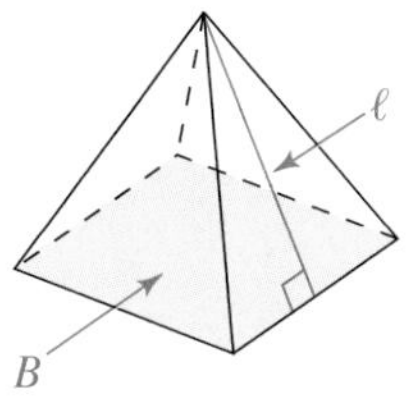

The surface area S.A. of a square pyramid is the sum of the lateral area and the area of the base.

$$\text{S.A.} = \text{L.A.} + B$$

EXAMPLES Finding Lateral and Surface Area

2 **Architecture** The photo at the right shows the Pyramid Arena in Tennessee. Find the lateral area to determine the amount of siding material it needs.

L.A. $= 2b\ell$ ← **lateral area formula**

$= 2(450)(367)$ ← **Substitute 450 for b and 367 for ℓ.**

$= 330{,}300$ ← **Simplify.**

The lateral area of the Pyramid Arena is 330,300 ft^2.

3 Find the surface area of the Pyramid Arena.

S.A. $=$ L.A. $+ B$ ← **surface area formula**

$= 2b\ell + b^2$ ← **Use $2b\ell$ for L.A. and b^2 for B.**

$= 2(450)(367) + 450^2$ ← **Substitute 450 for b and 367 for ℓ.**

$= 330{,}300 + 202{,}500$ ← **Simplify.**

$= 532{,}800$ ← **Add.**

The surface area is 532,800 ft^2.

Quick Check 2–3. See left.

2. 922,610 ft^2
3. 1,492,635 ft^2

2. Find the lateral area of the Great Pyramid of Khufu, shown at the right.
3. Find the surface area of the Great Pyramid of Khufu.

2. Teach

Activity Lab

Use before the lesson.
Student Edition Activity Lab, Hands On 8-5a, Surface Area of a Pyramid, p. 373

All in One Teaching Resources

Activity Lab 8-5: Comparing Cones

Guided Instruction

Tactile Learners
For students who have difficulty visualizing solids from a drawing, provide models or have students build models. Have them write the measurements on pieces of tape to mark dimensions on the model and then calculate lateral and total surface area.

Teaching Tip
To reinforce the formula, have students draw a net for the Pyramid arena and use it to find lateral and total surface areas.

PowerPoint

Additional Examples

1 Find the surface area of this square pyramid. 161 cm^2

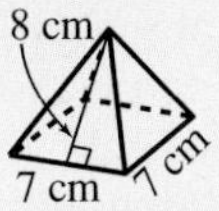

2 Find the lateral area of the roof of the playhouse to determine the amount of roofing material needed. 42 ft^2

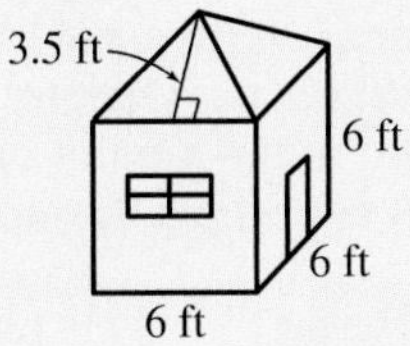

3 Find the surface area of the square pyramid. 495 cm^2

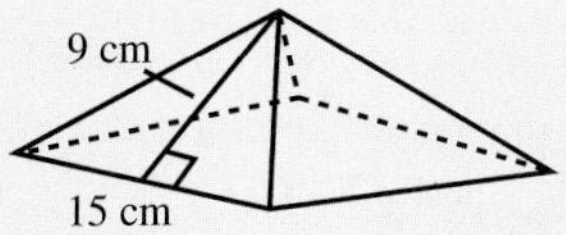

Advanced Learners L4
Students make cones of various dimensions. For each cone, they compare the height (perpendicular from vertex to base), slant height, and radius to verify that $\ell > h$, $\ell > r$, and $\ell^2 = h^2 + r^2$.

learning style: tactile

English Language Learners ELL
Students write and label the two formulas in this chapter. They write a description of each symbol in the formulas. Next to each formula, they draw the figure and label its parts.

learning style: visual

Guided Instruction

Technology Tip
On many calculators, π is a second function, so you will press the key marked 2nd before pressing the key marked π.

Example 4
Have students cut a cone-shaped paper drinking cup along a slant height. Then have them flatten it out to see the shape of the part of the net that represents the lateral area of a cone.

PowerPoint

Additional Examples

4 Find the surface area of the cone to the nearest whole unit. 2,111 yd^2

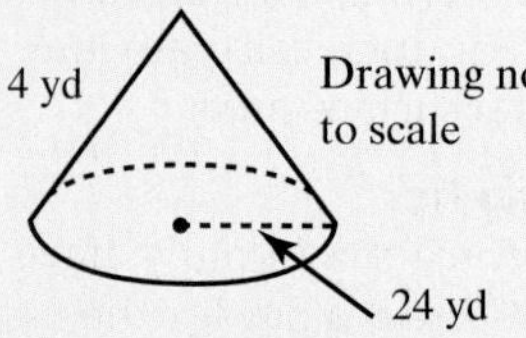

All in One Teaching Resources

- Daily Notetaking Guide 8-5 L3
- Adapted Notetaking 8-5 L1

Closure

- *How do you find the surface area of a square pyramid?* Sample: Find the Lateral Area by multiplying four times the area of one of the lateral faces. Add the L.A. to the area of the base (s^2) to find the Surface Area.
- *How do you find the surface area of a cone?* Sample: Find the Lateral Area by multiplying one-half times the circumference of the base ($2\pi r$) times the slant height. Add the L.A. to the area of the base (πr^2) to find the Surface Area.

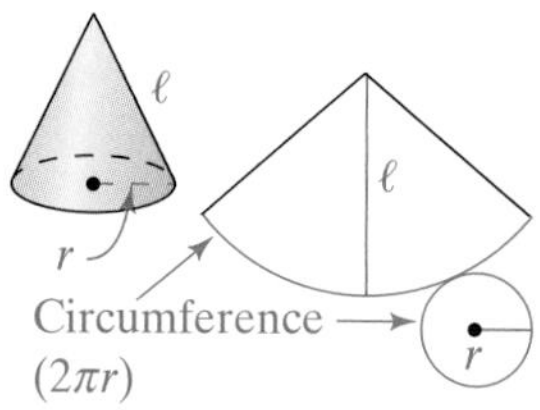

The curved surface of a cone is its lateral surface. In the net at the left, the cone's lateral surface may remind you of a triangle.

The height of the lateral surface is the slant height ℓ. The length of the base of the surface is the circumference of the circular base, $2\pi r$.

You can substitute ℓ and $2\pi r$ in the formula for area of a triangle to find the lateral area of a cone.

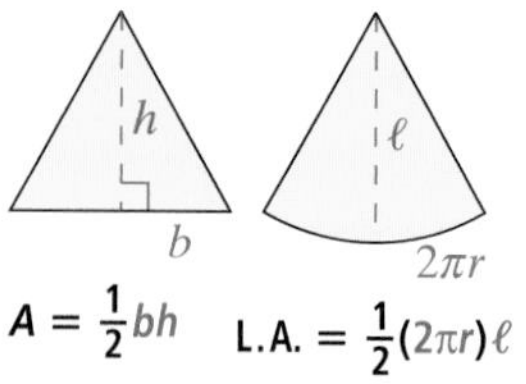

L.A. $= \frac{1}{2}bh$ ← **area of a triangle**

$= \frac{1}{2}(2\pi r)\ell$ ← **Substitute $2\pi r$ for b and ℓ for h.**

$= \pi r\ell$ ← **Simplify.**

KEY CONCEPTS **Lateral Area and Surface Area of a Cone**

The lateral area L.A. of a cone is one half the product of the circumference of the base and the slant height.

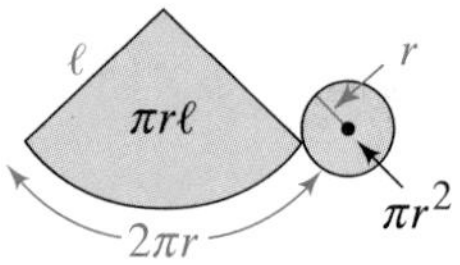

$$\text{L.A.} = \frac{1}{2}(2\pi r)\ell = \pi r\ell$$

The surface area S.A. of a cone is the sum of the lateral area and the area of the base.

$$\text{S.A.} = \text{L.A.} + B$$

EXAMPLE Using the Cone Surface Area Formula

4 Find the surface area of the cone at the right to the nearest square meter.

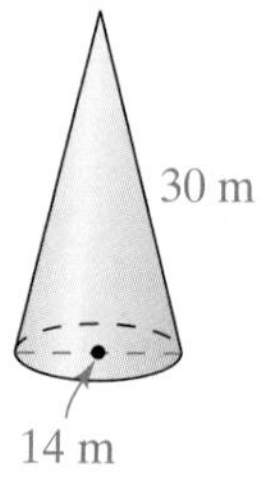

S.A. $=$ L.A. $+ B$ ← **surface area formula**

$= \pi r\ell + \pi r^2$ ← **Use $\pi r\ell$ for L.A. and πr^2 for B.**

$= \pi(7)(30) + \pi(7^2)$ ← **Substitute 7 for r and 30 for ℓ.**

$= 210\pi + 49\pi$ ← **Use the order of operations.**

$= 259\pi$ ← **Simplify.**

≈ 813.6724973 ← **Use a calculator.**

The surface area of the cone is about 814 m^2.

Test Prep Tip
Be sure that you understand each variable in a formula so you can substitute in the formula correctly.

Quick Check

4. Find the surface area of the cone at the right to the nearest square yard. 113 yd^2

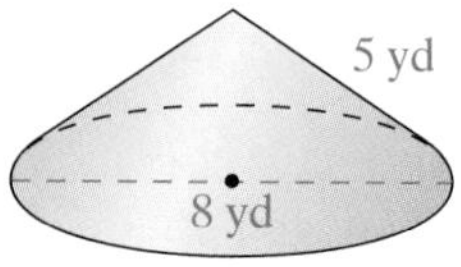

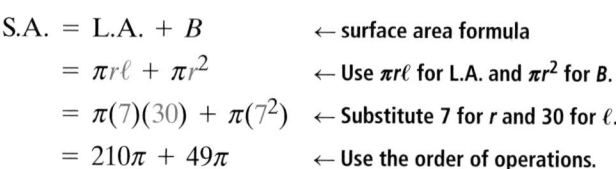

Check Your Understanding

1. Lateral area is less than surface area because it does not include the area of the square base.

1. **Vocabulary** Describe the difference between the lateral area of a square pyramid and the surface area of a square pyramid.
2. **Mental Math** A square pyramid has a lateral area of 10.25 m^2 and a base area B of 5.3 m^2. Find its surface area. 15.55 m^2

Use the cone at the right.

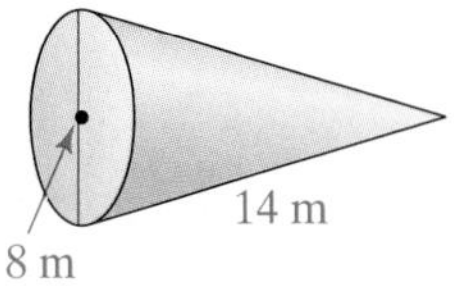

3. The slant height ℓ is ■ m. 14
4. Write an expression for lateral area using π.
5. Write an expression you can simplify to find the surface area. S.A. = $56\pi + 16\pi = 72\pi$

4. L.A. = $(4\pi)(14) = 56\pi$

Homework Exercises

For more exercises, see Extra Skills and Word Problems.

GO for Help

For Exercises	See Examples
6–8	1
9–11	2–3
12–14	4

A **Use a net to find the surface area of each pyramid.**

6. 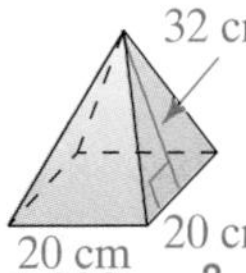

1,680 cm^2

7. 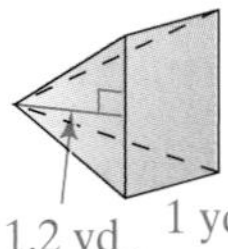

3.4 yd^2

8. 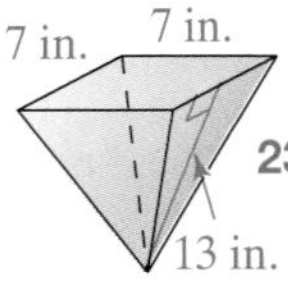

231 $in.^2$

Use formulas to find the lateral and surface areas of each pyramid. 9–11. See left.

9. 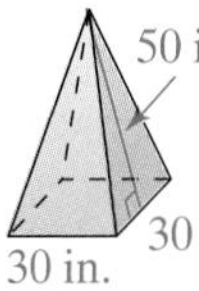

10. 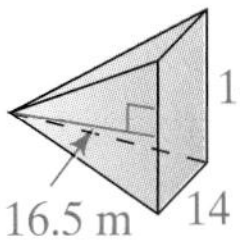

11. 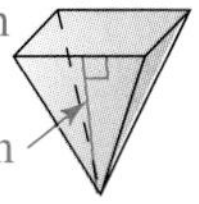

9. L.A. = 3,000 $in.^2$; S.A. = 3,900 $in.^2$
10. L.A. = 462 m^2; S.A. = 658 m^2
11. L.A. = 24 cm^2; S.A. = 33 cm^2

Find the surface area of each cone to the nearest square unit.

12. 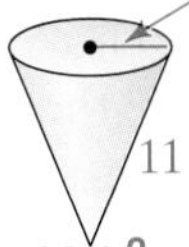

188 ft^2

13. 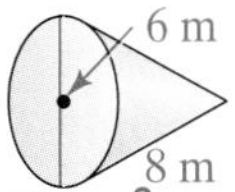

104 m^2

14. 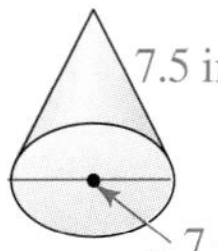

121 $in.^2$

B **GPS** 15. **Guided Problem Solving** The roof of the doghouse at the right is a square pyramid. If shingles cost \$1.25 to cover one square foot, how much would it cost to put new shingles on the roof of the doghouse? \$50
- What is the lateral area of the roof?
- What operation would you use to find the cost?

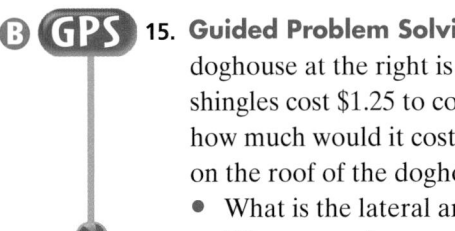

Online lesson quiz, PHSchool.com, Web Code: asa-0805.

3. Practice

Assignment Guide

Check Your Understanding

Go over Exercises 1–5 in class before assigning the Homework Exercises.

Homework Exercises

A	Practice by Example	6–14
B	Apply Your Skills	15–23
C	Challenge	24
	Test Prep and Mixed Review	25–27

Homework Quick Check

To check students' understanding of key skills and concepts, go over Exercises 10, 14, 16, 21, and 22.

Differentiated Instruction Resources

Adapted Practice 8-5 L1

Practice 8-5 Surface Areas of Pyramids an L3

Use a net to find the surface area of each square pyramid to the nearest square unit.

1. 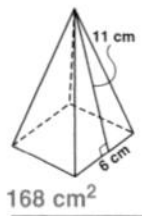

168 cm^2

2. 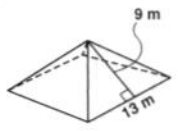

403 m^2

3. 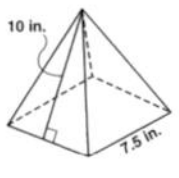

206 $in.^2$

Find the lateral area of each pyramid to the nearest whole square unit.

4. 

56 m^2

5. 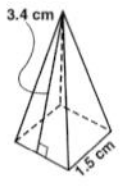

10 cm^2

Find the surface area of each cone to the nearest square unit.

6. 

553 ft^2

7. 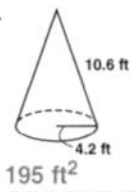

195 ft^2

Find the lateral area of each cone to the nearest square unit.

8. 

662 m^2

9. 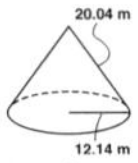

764 m^2

8-5 • Guided Problem Solving GPS L3

GPS Student Page 378, Exercise 16:

Error Analysis A student tried to find the lateral area of the cone below. Explain the mistake. Then find the correct solution.

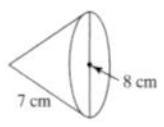

L.A. = πrl
= $\pi(8)(7)$
= 56π
≈ 175.93
≈ 176 cm^2

Understand

1. Is the answer given correct? no
2. What are you asked to find? the student's mistake and the correct solution

Plan and Carry Out

3. Look at the first step of the student's solution. What is the mistake? The diameter is used instead of the radius.
4. What value should he have used? 4 cm
5. Solve the problem using the correct dimensions. Show your work. L.A. = $\pi rl = \pi(4)(7) = 28\pi \approx 87.92 \approx 88$ cm^2

Check

6. How can you estimate to see if your answer is reasonable? Multiply the radius by the slant height by 3 (as an approximation for π). (3)(4)(7) = 84; 88 cm^2 is reasonable since it is close to the estimate of 84 cm^2.

Solve Another Problem

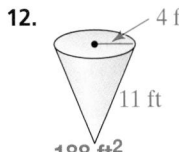

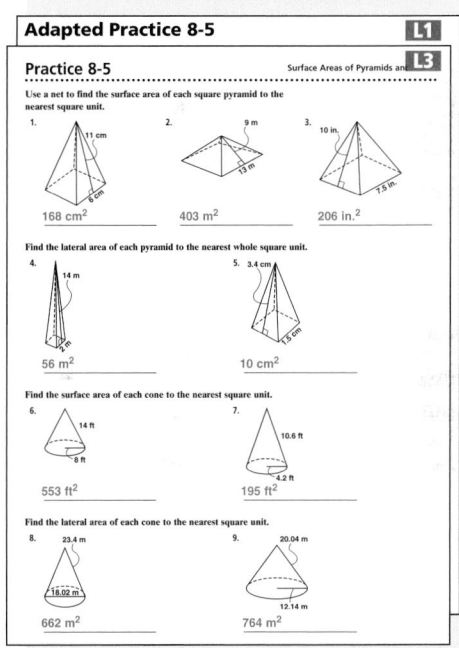

7. Find the lateral area of a cone with a diameter of 6 inches and slant height of 8 inches. L.A. = $\pi(3)(8) = 24\pi \approx 75$ cm^2

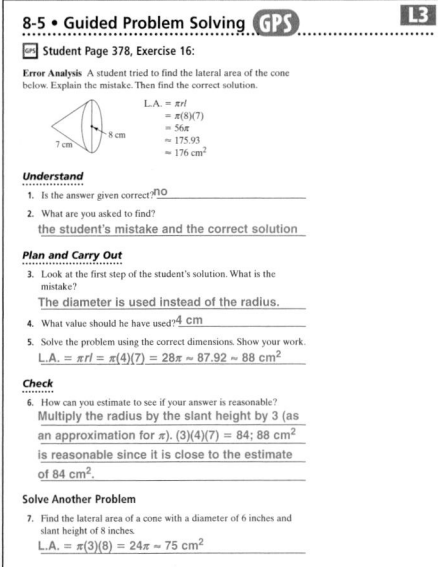

4. Assess & Reteach

PowerPoint

Lesson Quiz

Find each surface area to the nearest whole unit.

1. 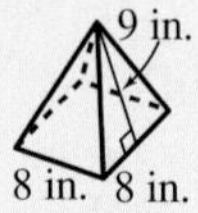

208 in.^{2}

2. 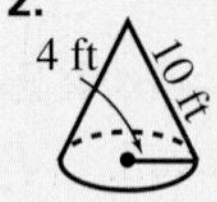

176 ft^2

3. In order to buy paint to cover the inside of the roof and the floor of this playhouse, use the formula for S.A. of a square pyramid to find the area. 78 ft^2

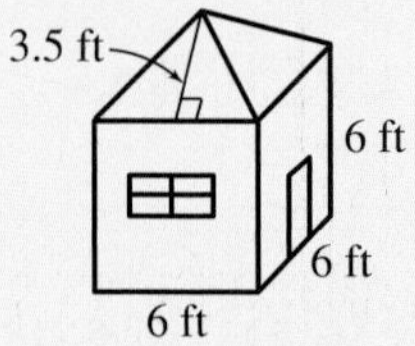

4. Find the surface area of a cone with a radius of 9 ft and a slant height of 15 ft to the nearest whole unit. 679 ft^2

16. The student used 8 for the radius, rather than 4; the correct solution is about 88 cm^2.

21. yes, because it is equivalent to $\pi r^2 + \pi r\ell$

24. See back of book.

27. See back of book.

Enrichment 8-5 L4

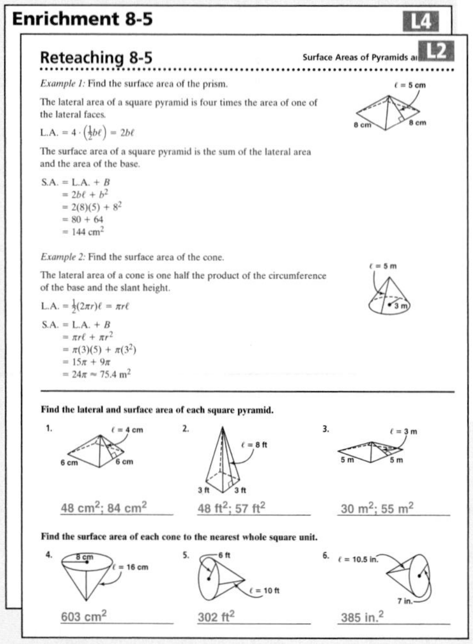
Reteaching 8-5 — Surface Areas of Pyramids a[nd Cones] L2

Example 1: Find the surface area of the prism.

The lateral area of a square pyramid is four times the area of one of the lateral faces.

L.A. $= 4 \cdot \left(\frac{1}{2}b\ell\right) = 2b\ell$

The surface area of a square pyramid is the sum of the lateral area and the area of the base.

S.A. $=$ L.A. $+ B$
$= 2b\ell + b^2$
$= 2(8)(5) + 8^2$
$= 80 + 64$
$= 144$ cm^2

($\ell = 5$ cm; 8 cm; 8 cm)

Example 2: Find the surface area of the cone.

The lateral area of a cone is one half the product of the circumference of the base and the slant height.

L.A. $= \frac{1}{2}(2\pi r)\ell = \pi r\ell$

S.A. $=$ L.A. $+ B$
$= \pi r\ell + \pi r^2$
$= \pi(3)(5) + \pi(3^2)$
$= 15\pi + 9\pi$
$= 24\pi \approx 75.4$ m^2

($\ell = 5$ m; 3 m)

Find the lateral and surface area of each square pyramid.

1. $\ell = 4$ cm; 6 cm; 6 cm — 48 cm^2; 84 cm^2
2. $\ell = 8$ ft; 3 ft; 3 ft — 48 ft^2; 57 ft^2
3. $\ell = 3$ m; 5 m; 5 m — 30 m^2; 55 m^2

Find the surface area of each cone to the nearest whole square unit.

4. 8 cm; $\ell = 16$ cm — 603 cm^2
5. 6 ft; $\ell = 10$ ft — 302 ft^2
6. $\ell = 10.5$ in.; 7 in. — 385 in.^{2}

GO Online
Homework Video Tutor
Visit: PHSchool.com
Web Code: ase-0805

The Transamerica Building in San Francisco is roughly a square pyramid with height of 853 ft and base-edge length of 145 ft.

22. Yes, because $\pi r\ell = \pi(2r)\left(\frac{\ell}{2}\right)$.

23. Answers may vary. Sample: 270 m^2; 268 m^2

16. **Error Analysis** A student tried to find the lateral area of the cone at the right. Explain the student's mistake. Then find the correct solution. See margin.
GPS

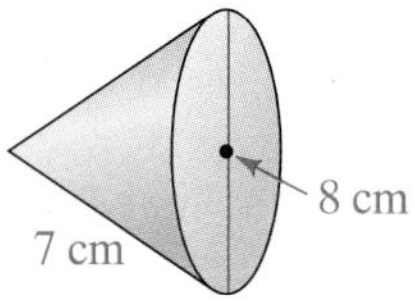

L.A. $= \pi r\ell$
$= \pi(8)(7)$
$= 56\pi$
≈ 175.93
L.A. ≈ 176 cm^2

17. **Buildings** Use the photo caption at the left.
   a. Find the slant height of the Transamerica Building. 856 ft
   b. Find the lateral area of the Transamerica Building. 248,240 ft^2

Find the lateral area of each cone to the nearest square unit.

18. 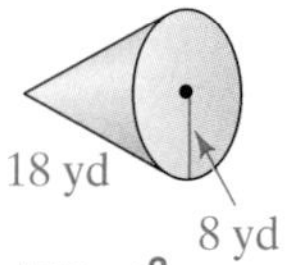

452 yd^2

19. 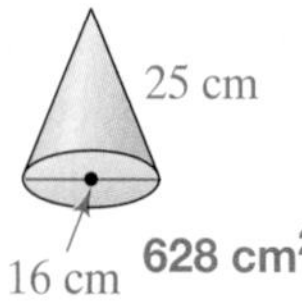

628 cm^2

20. 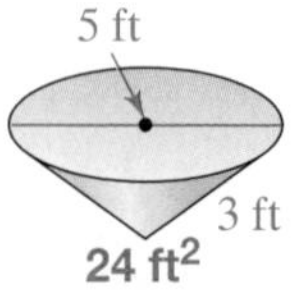

24 ft^2

21. **Algebra** Corey uses the formula S.A. $= \pi r(r + \ell)$ to find the surface area of a cone. Will this always work? Explain. See margin.

22. **Writing in Math** You double the radius of a cone and divide the slant height by 2. Does the lateral area stay the same? Explain. See left.

23. **Estimation** Estimate the lateral area of the square pyramid at the right. Then find the actual lateral area to the nearest square meter. See left.

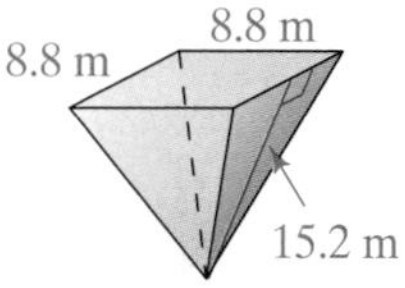

C 24. **Challenge** A cone and a pyramid have the same slant height. The areas of both bases are the same. Which has the larger surface area? Explain. See margin.

Test Prep and Mixed Review

Practice

Multiple Choice

25. The net for a square pyramid is at the right. Use a centimeter ruler to measure the dimensions. Which of the following is closest to the surface area of the pyramid? D

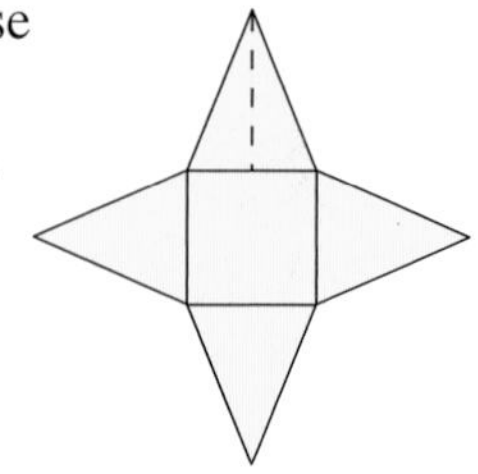

   A 9 cm^2
   B 8 cm^2
   C 5 cm^2
   D 3 cm^2

26. Jamal plans to attend a college with a current tuition rate of \$5,500 per year. Jamal plans for a 10% increase in tuition before he starts. He wins scholarships for 30% of his tuition. About how much will Jamal pay for 4 years of college? H
   F \$27,000
   G \$18,000
   H \$17,000
   J \$12,000

GO for Help

For Exercise	See Lesson
27	7-8

27. Draw an obtuse $\angle K$. Construct $\angle L$ congruent to $\angle K$. See margin.

Test Prep

Resources

For additional practice with a variety of test item formats:
- Test-Taking Strategies, p. 403
- Test Prep, p. 407
- Test-Taking Strategies with Transparencies

Alternative Assessment

Each student in a pair draws and labels measures for a cone and a square pyramid. Partners trade papers and find the surface area for each of their partner's figures.

8-6a Activity Lab

Hands On

Modeling Volume

The volume of a rectangular prism depends on its height and its base area. You can use this relationship to find the volume of nonrectangular prisms.

ACTIVITY

1. Use cubes to build each prism below. Copy and complete the table. **See margin.**

Prism	Height	Base Area	Volume (total number of cubes)
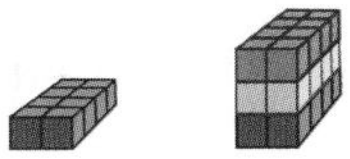 base	■	■	■
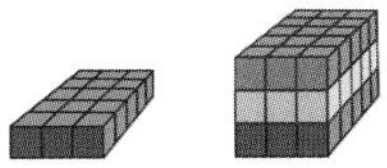 base	■	■	■

2. **Writing in Math** Explain how you can find the volume of a prism using its height and the area of its base. **Answers may vary. Sample: The volume is the base area times the height.**
3. Use the figures in the table below. Copy and complete the table. **See margin.**

Figure	Height	Base area	Volume (total number of cubes)
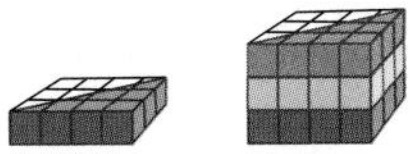 base	■	■	■
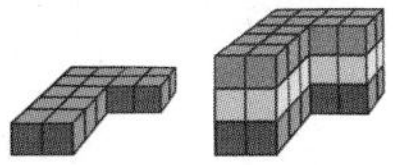 base	■	■	■
 base	■	■	■

4. (Algebra) Write a formula to find the volume of a cylinder using its height and the radius of its base. $V = \pi r^2 h$

1.

Base dimensions	Height	Base area	Volume of prism
2 × 4	3	8	24
3 × 5	3	15	45

3. See back of book.

Activity Lab

Modeling Volume

In prior lessons, students have found the surface area of objects. Now students explore volume. They use cubes to build rectangular prisms, and they describe the relationship between a prism's base area, height, and volume. Then they find a formula for volume, using pictures of regular, irregular, and circular shapes made from cubes.

Guided Instruction

Alternative Method
Have students find the total volume of the first prism pictured in this activity by adding the number of cubes in each layer: 8 cubic units + 8 cubic units + 8 cubic units = 24 cubic units. (This will include adding cubes hidden behind other cubes in the picture.) Then elicit the fact that they could write this more efficiently using multiplication: 8 cubic units × 3 = 24 cubic units. *Ask: What are we multiplying by?* the number of layers Finally, have students verify with cubes that when the 2 × 4 base layer (containing 8 cubes) is multiplied by 3, the result is 24 cubes: the entire base area, not just a row or column, is multiplied by 3.

Error Prevention!

Volume is measured in cubic units. In this activity, each cube equals 1 cubic unit. Therefore, in the product 8 cubic units × 3 = 24 cubic units, 3 has no units.

Resources

- Activity Lab 8-6: Volume of Prisms and Cylinders
- cubes

8-6

1. Plan

Objective
To find the volumes of prisms and cylinders

Examples
1 Finding Volume of a Triangular Prism
2 Finding Volume of a Cylinder

Math Understandings: p. 352C

Professional Development

Math Background

The volume V of a prism is the product of the base area B and the height h, $V = Bh$. For a rectangular prism, this formula can also be written as $V = lwh$.

The volume of a cylinder is also the product of the base area B and the height h, $V = Bh$. The area of the circular base is given by $B = \pi r^2$, so the formula for the volume of a cylinder can also be written as $V = \pi r^2 h$.

More Math Background: p. 352D

Lesson Planning and Resources

See p. 352E for a list of the resources that support this lesson.

PowerPoint

Bell Ringer Practice

Check Skills You'll Need
Use student page, transparency, or PowerPoint. For intervention, direct students to:
Surface Areas of Prisms and Cylinders
Lesson 8-4
Extra Skills and Word Problems Practice, Ch. 8

8-6 Volumes of Prisms and Cylinders

Check Skills You'll Need

1. **Vocabulary Review** Is a *cylinder* also a *prism*? Explain. See below.

Find the surface area of each figure to the nearest square unit.

2. 105 ft²

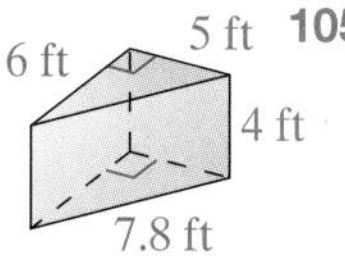

3. 207 m²

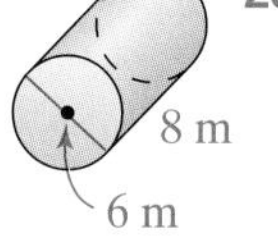

GO for Help
Lesson 8-4

What You'll Learn

To find the volumes of prisms and cylinders

New Vocabulary volume

Why Learn This?

When you pack a bag or load a car, you must consider the amount of space, or volume, each object occupies.

Volume is the number of unit cubes, or cubic units, needed to fill a solid. In the prism above, each layer has 2×4, or 8, cubes. The prism has 3 layers, so its volume is 8×3, or 24, cubic units.

KEY CONCEPTS Volume of a Prism

The volume V of a prism is the product of the base area B and the height h.

$$V = Bh$$

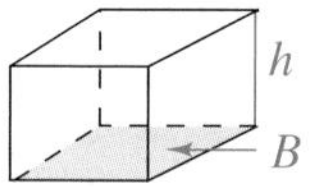

Check Skills You'll Need

1. No; the base of a cylinder is a circle, not a polygon.

EXAMPLE Finding Volume of a Triangular Prism

1 **Camping** The tent at the left approximates a triangular prism. Find its volume.

Step 1 Find the area B of the base.

$B = \frac{1}{2}bh$ ← area of a triangle

$= \frac{1}{2} \cdot 5 \cdot 4$ ← Substitute.

$= 10$ ← Multiply.

Step 2 Use the base area to find the volume.

$V = Bh$ ← volume of a prism

$= 10 \cdot 7.5$ ← Substitute.

$= 75$ ← Multiply.

The volume of the tent is 75 ft³.

Quick Check

1. Find the volume of the prism at the right. 52.5 ft³

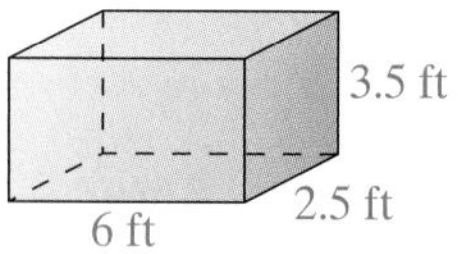

Differentiated Instruction Solutions for All Learners

Special Needs L1	Below Level L2
Provide students with unit cubes and with small boxes that can be completely filled with these cubes. Students fill these boxes with cubes and then count the number of cubes used. learning style: tactile	Students explain volume in their own words. They point out examples in the classroom, such as the volume of a waste basket, a book, or a backpack. learning style: verbal

GO Online

Video Tutor Help
Visit: PHSchool.com
Web Code: ase-0775

You can think of a cylinder with height h as having h layers of circles stacked on top of each other. Then the volume of the cylinder is the product of its base area and its height.

Since the bases of cylinders are circles, you can use the formula for the area of a circle to find a cylinder's base area.

KEY CONCEPTS **Volume of a Cylinder**

The volume V of a cylinder is the product of the base area B and the height h.

$$V = Bh$$

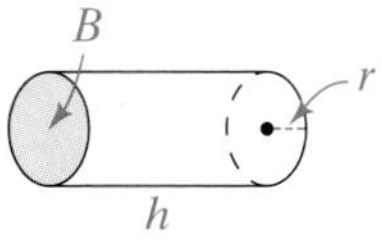

EXAMPLE Finding Volume of a Cylinder

2 Find the volume of the cylinder below to the nearest cubic centimeter.

Estimate Use 3 for π. The area of the base is about 3×5^2 cm^2, or 75 cm^2. The volume is about 75×80 cm^3, or 6,000 cm^3.

Step 1 Find the area of the base.

$B = \pi r^2$ ← area of a circle
$= \pi(5^2)$ ← Substitute.
$= 25\pi$ ← Simplify.

Step 2 Use the base area to find the volume.

$V = Bh$ ← volume of a cylinder
$= 25\pi \cdot 80$ ← Substitute 25π for B and 80 for h.
$= 2{,}000\pi$ ← Simplify.
≈ 6283.185307 ← Use a calculator.

The volume of the cylinder is about 6,283 cm^3.

Check for Reasonableness The answer 6,283 cm^3 is close to the estimate of 6,000 cm^3. The answer is reasonable.

The AquaDom in Berlin is the world's largest cylindrical aquarium. It is over 52 ft high and has a diameter of 36 ft.

Quick Check

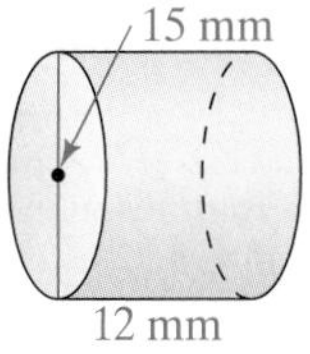

2. a. **Estimation** Estimate the volume of the cylinder at the right. Use 3 for π. about 2,025 mm^3
   b. Find the volume of the cylinder to the nearest cubic millimeter. 2,120 mm^3

2. Teach

Activity Lab

Use before the lesson.
Student Edition Activity Lab, Hands On 8-6a, Modeling Volume, p. 379

All in One Teaching Resources

Activity Lab 8-6: Volume of Prisms and Cylinders

Guided Instruction

Error Prevention!

Some students may think that the base of a prism must be the face that is resting on a plane surface. Remind them that a prism has two bases that are in parallel planes, regardless of how the solid itself is turned or placed. This means that for the tent in Example 1, the face with the entrance is one of the bases.

Diversity
Have students who have used tents tell how the height and the area of the base affect the users.

PowerPoint

Additional Examples

1 Find the volume of this prism. 14 cm^3

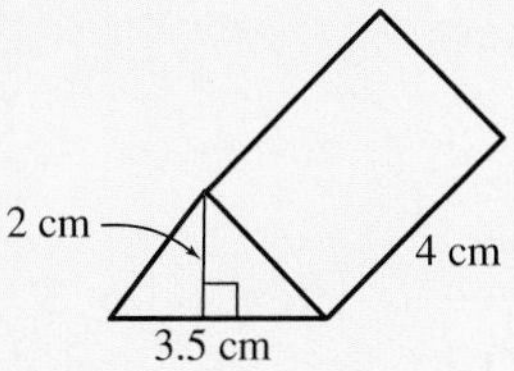

2 Find the volume of the cylinder to the nearest whole unit. 15,080 m^3

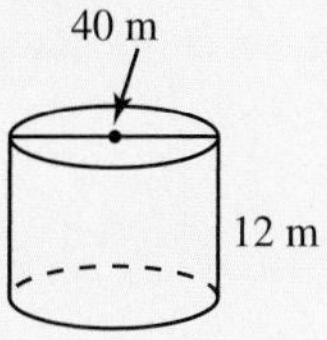

All in One Teaching Resources
- Daily Notetaking Guide 8-6 L3
- Adapted Notetaking 8-6 L1

Advanced Learners L4
Students decide whether they can make more different rectangular prisms with 12 or 15 unit cubes, and why. You can make more with 12, because 12 has more factors.
learning style: visual

English Language Learners ELL
Students may confuse the symbols B (base area) and b (base length). Students read the formulas out loud using words rather than just symbols. For example, the formula $B = \frac{1}{2}bh$ could be read as *the base area is one half the base length times the base height.*
learning style: verbal

Guided Instruction

Teaching Tip

Have students use circular chips to build cylinders. Discuss the fact that the total volume is the volume of one chip multiplied by how many chips high the cylinder is.

Error Prevention!

Remind students that volume is measured in cubic units (unlike area, which is measured in square units). Also remind students that if the diameter of a cylinder is given, they need to use the radius to find the cylinder volume.

Closure

- *What is similar about finding the volume of prisms and the volume of cylinders?* Sample: For both, the volume is the product of the area of the base and the height, $V = Bh$.
- *What is different in the formulas for finding the volume of prisms and the volume of cylinders?* Sample: The area of the base of a cylinder is always πr^2 while the area of the base of a prism may use the formula for the area of a triangle, a rectangle, or other polygon.

More Than One Way

Find the volume of a cylinder with a radius of 3 m and a height of 8 m.

Jasmine's Method

I can first find base area B. Then I can multiply by the height h.

$B = \pi r^2$ ← area of a circle

$= \pi(3^2)$ ← Substitute.

$= 9\pi$ ← Simplify.

$V = Bh$ ← volume of a prism

$= 9\pi \cdot 8$ ← Substitute 9π for B and 8 for h.

$= 72\pi$ ← Multiply.

≈ 226.1946711 ← Use a calculator.

The volume is about 226 m^3.

Kevin's Method

I can find the volume by combining formulas first.

$V = Bh$ ← volume of a prism

$= \pi r^2 h$ ← Use πr^2 for B.

$= \pi(3^2)(8)$ ← Substitute 3 for r and 8 for h.

$= 72\pi$ ← Simplify.

≈ 226.1946711 ← Use a calculator.

The volume is about 226 m^3.

Choose a Method

Find the volume of the cylinder with a radius of 12 ft and a height of 4.5 ft. Explain why you chose the method you used.
Check students' methods; about 2,036 ft^3.

Check Your Understanding

Online active math

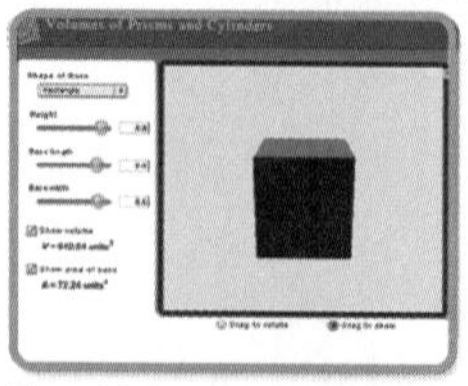

For: Volumes Activity
Use: Interactive Textbook, 8-6

1. **Vocabulary** Give three examples of cubic units. Answers may vary. Sample: ft^3, $in.^3$, cm^3
2. **Estimation** Estimate the volume of a cylinder with a base area of 2.7 $in.^2$ and a height of 2.3 in. about 6 $in.^3$

Mental Math **Match the volume with the solid.**

3. a cube with each edge 10 ft long B
4. a rectangular prism with a square base 7 ft on each side and a height of 10 ft A
5. a cylinder with a base area of 100 ft^2 and a height of 8 ft C

A. 490 ft^3
B. 1,000 ft^3
C. 800 ft^3

Homework Exercises

For more exercises, see Extra Skills and Word Problems.

GO for Help

For Exercises	See Examples
6–12	1
13–15	2

A **Find the volume of each prism.**

6.
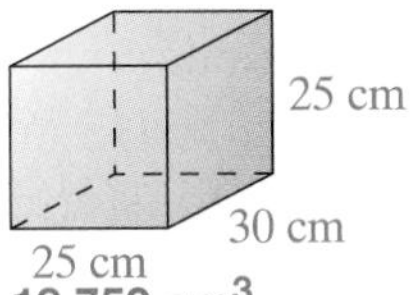

18,750 cm^3

7.
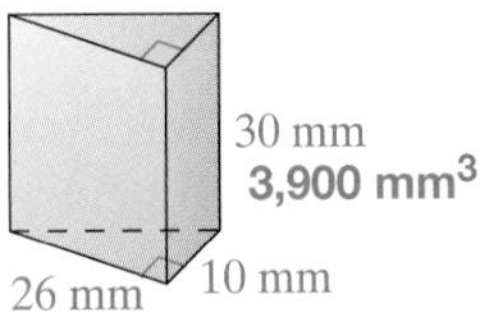

3,900 mm^3

8.
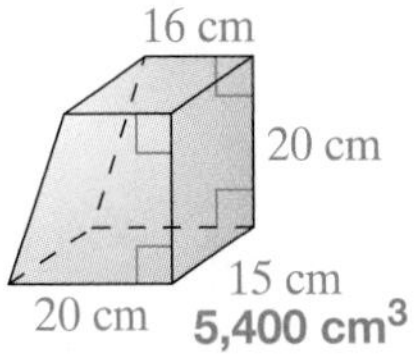

5,400 cm^3

9.
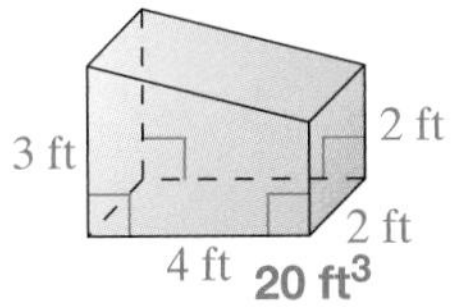

20 ft^3

10.
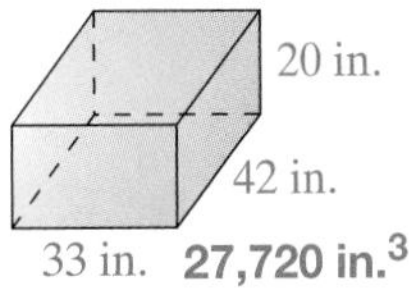

27,720 $in.^3$

11.
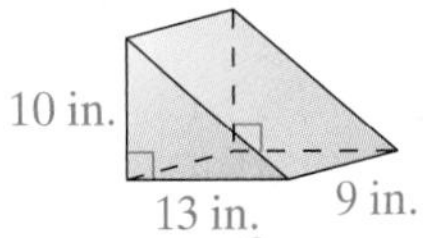

585 $in.^3$

12. **Landscaping** A goldfish pond in the shape of a triangular prism sits in the center of a mall. Use the diagram at the right to find the volume of the pond. 784 ft^3

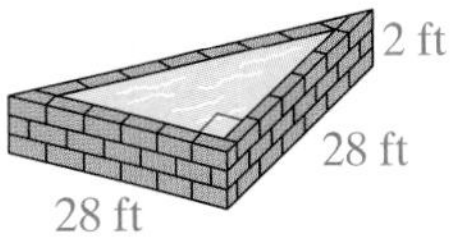

Find the volume of each cylinder to the nearest whole cubic unit.

13.
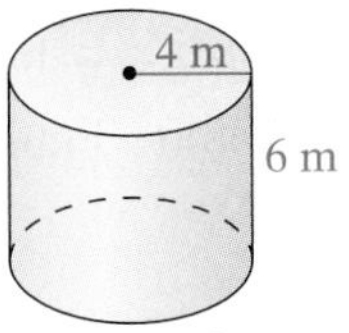

302 m^3

14.
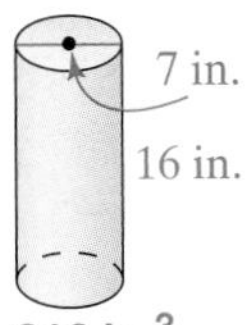

616 $in.^3$

15.
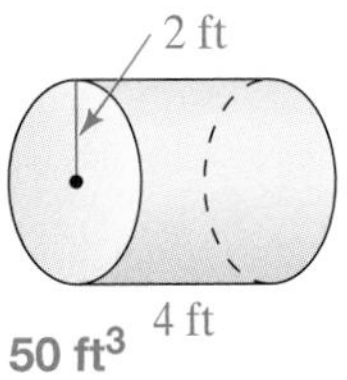

50 ft^3

B **GPS** 16. **Guided Problem Solving** Below are the top, front, and right views of a pool. Find the volume of the pool. 3,808 ft^3

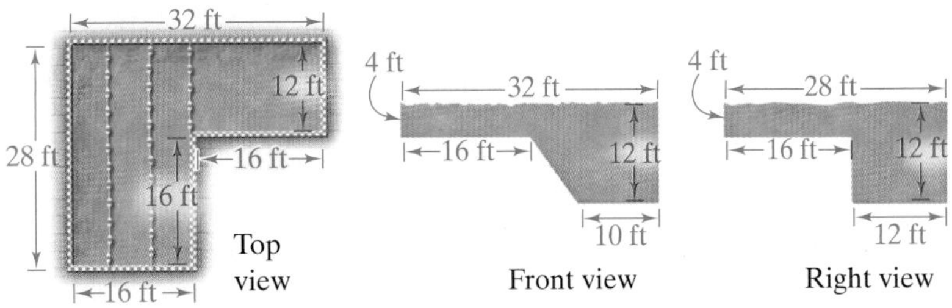

- You can use the strategy *Draw a Picture*. The isometric view will help you see the solids that make up the pool.
- What prisms make up the pool?

17. **Choose a Method** Find the volume of a cylinder with diameter 11 ft and height 6.2 ft. Explain why you chose the method you used. See left.

18. **Algebra** A rectangular prism with a volume of 48 $units^3$ has edge lengths that are whole units. One edge length is 4 units. What are the possible combinations of lengths of the other two edges? See left.

17. 589 ft^3; check students' work.

18. 1 and 12, 2 and 6, 3 and 4

GO Online
Homework Video Tutor
Visit: PHSchool.com
Web Code: ase-0806

3. Practice

Assignment Guide

Check Your Understanding

Go over Exercises 1–5 in class before assigning the Homework Exercises.

Homework Exercises

A Practice by Example	6–15
B Apply Your Skills	16–24
C Challenge	25
Test Prep and Mixed Review	26–31

Homework Quick Check

To check students' understanding of key skills and concepts, go over Exercises 12, 15, 16, 20, and 23.

Differentiated Instruction Resources

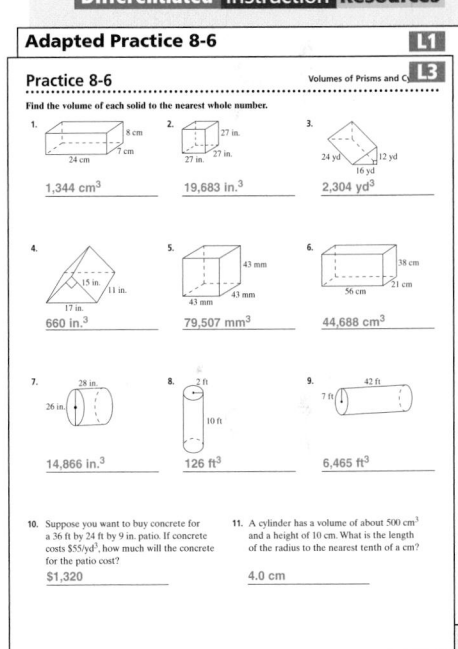

Adapted Practice 8-6 L1

Practice 8-6 Volumes of Prisms and Cy L3

Find the volume of each solid to the nearest whole number.

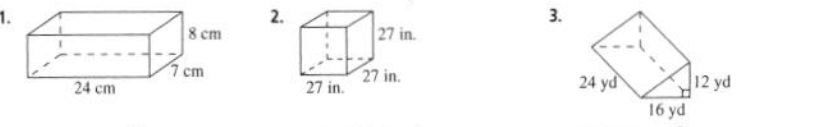

1. 1,344 cm^3
2. 19,683 $in.^3$
3. 2,304 yd^3

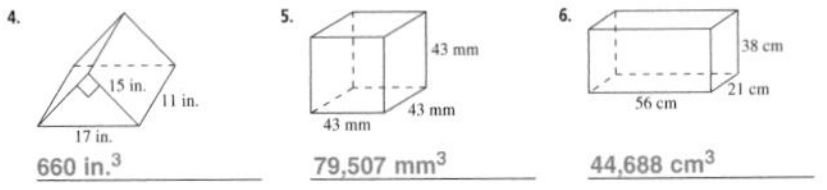

4. 660 $in.^3$
5. 79,507 mm^3
6. 44,688 cm^3

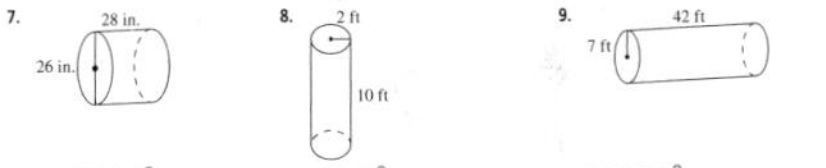

7. 14,866 $in.^3$
8. 126 ft^3
9. 6,465 ft^3

10. Suppose you want to buy concrete for a 36 ft by 24 ft by 9 in. patio. If concrete costs $55/$yd^3$, how much will the concrete for the patio cost? $1,320

11. A cylinder has a volume of about 500 cm^3 and a height of 10 cm. What is the length of the radius to the nearest tenth of a cm? 4.0 cm

8-6 • Guided Problem Solving GPS L3

GPS **Student Page 384, Exercise 20:**

A store keeps roughly 240 boxes of crayons in its inventory.

a. If each box measures 6 in. by 2.5 in. by 4 in., how many cubic inches of storage space does the store need for the boxes of crayons?

b. One cubic foot is equal to $(12 \text{ in.})^3$, or 1,728 $in.^3$ Find the number of cubic feet necessary for storing 240 boxes of crayons.

Understand

1. Circle the measures of the crayon boxes.
2. Underline how many boxes the art supply store has for inventory.

Plan and Carry Out

3. What formula will you use to find the volume of one box of crayons? $V = lwh$ or $V = Bh$
4. What is the volume of one box of crayons? $6 \times 2.5 \times 4 = 60$ $in.^3$
5. What operation will you use to find the volume of 240 boxes? multiplication
6. What is the volume of 240 boxes of crayons? $240 \times 60 = 14{,}400$ $in.^3$
7. How many cubic inches are in one cubic foot? 1,728 $in.^3$
8. How can you change cubic inches to cubic feet? Divide the total number of cubic inches by 1,728.
9. How many cubic feet are necessary for storing 240 boxes of crayons? 8.333 ft^3

Check

10. What is a way to check the problem? Use compatible numbers, to estimate.

Solve Another Problem

11. A video store keeps approximately 350 boxes of storage cases in its inventory.

a. If each storage case measures 1 in. by 5.5 in. by 8.75 in., how many cubic inches of storage space does the store need for the boxes of storage cases? $1 \times 5.5 \times 8.75 = 48.125$ $in.^3$

b. Find the number of cubic feet necessary for storing 350 boxes of cases. $\frac{48.125 \times 350}{1{,}728} \approx 9.74$ ft^3

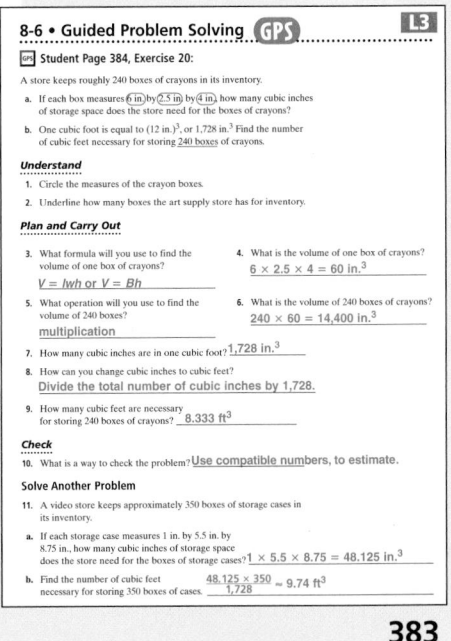

4. Assess & Reteach

PowerPoint

Lesson Quiz

Find the volume. The figures are not drawn to scale.

1.

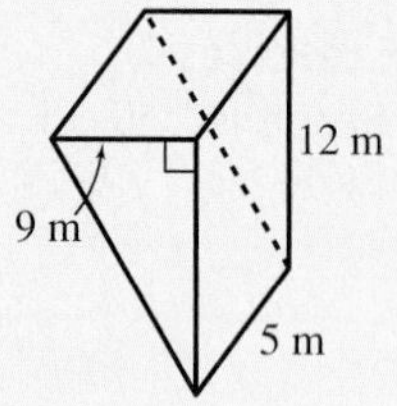

270 m^3

2.

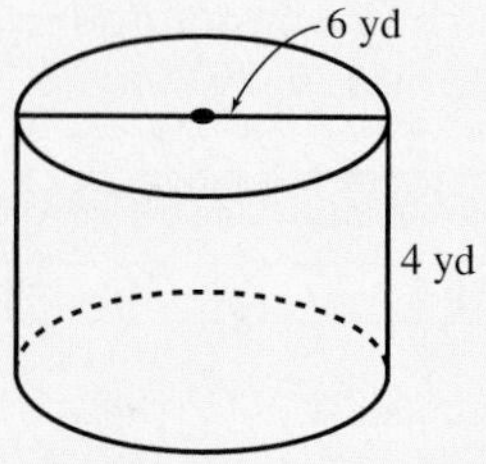

113 yd^3

3. Find the volume of a cylindrical cake that is 5 in. tall with a diameter of 15 in. Give your answer to the nearest whole unit. 884 in.^{3}

4. A triangular container is designed to hold pizza slices. The base of the lid is 7 in. long and its height is 11 in. The container is 3 in. deep. What is the volume of the container, to the nearest cubic inch? 116 in.^{3}

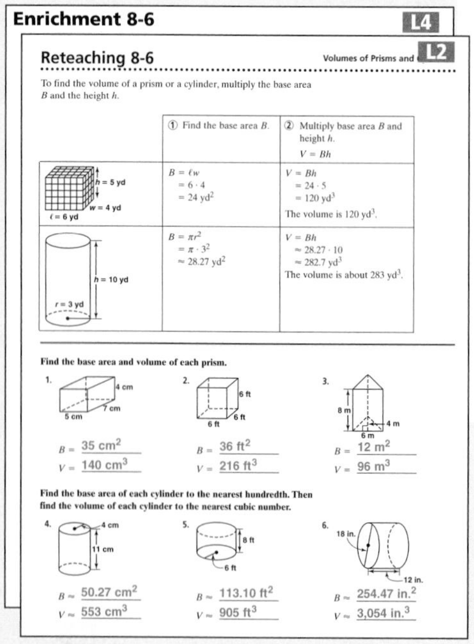

Enrichment 8-6 L4

Reteaching 8-6 Volumes of Prisms and Cylinders L2

To find the volume of a prism or a cylinder, multiply the base area B and the height h.

	① Find the base area B.	② Multiply base area B and height h. $V = Bh$
h = 5 yd, w = 4 yd, ℓ = 6 yd	$B = \ell w$ $= 6 \cdot 4$ $= 24$ yd^2	$V = Bh$ $= 24 \cdot 5$ $= 120$ yd^3 The volume is 120 yd^3.
h = 10 yd, r = 3 yd	$B = \pi r^2$ $= \pi \cdot 3^2$ ≈ 28.27 yd^2	$V = Bh$ $\approx 28.27 \cdot 10$ ≈ 282.7 yd^3 The volume is about 283 yd^3.

Find the base area and volume of each prism.

1. (4 cm, 7 cm, 5 cm) B = 35 cm^2 V = 140 cm^3
2. (6 ft, 6 ft, 6 ft) B = 36 ft^2 V = 216 ft^3
3. (8 m, 4 m, 6 m) B = 12 m^2 V = 96 m^3

Find the base area of each cylinder to the nearest hundredth. Then find the volume of each cylinder to the nearest cubic number.

4. (4 cm, 11 cm) $B \approx$ 50.27 cm^2 $V \approx$ 553 cm^3
5. (8 ft, 6 ft) $B \approx$ 113.10 ft^2 $V \approx$ 905 ft^3
6. (18 in., 12 in.) $B \approx$ 254.47 in.^{2} $V \approx$ 3,054 in.^{3}

23. Answers may vary. Sample: Start with the equation $\pi r^2 h = 565.5$. Divide each side by 20π, which results in $r^2 = 9.0002$. Take the square root of each side to find the radius. $r \approx 3$ in.

19. **Number Sense** Which has a greater effect on the volume of a cylinder, doubling the radius or doubling the height? Explain. See margin.

20. A store keeps about 240 boxes of crayons in its inventory.
 GPS a. If each box measures 6 in. by 2.5 in. by 4 in., how many cubic inches of storage space does the store need for the crayons?
 b. One cubic foot is equal to (12 in.)^3, or 1,728 in.^{3}. Find the number of cubic feet necessary for storing 240 boxes of crayons.
 20a. 14,400 in.^{3} 20b. 8.3 ft^3

Find the volume of each prism.

21.

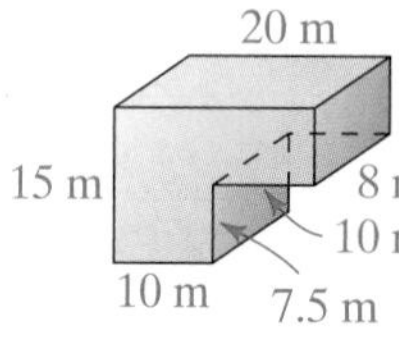

1,800 m^3

22.

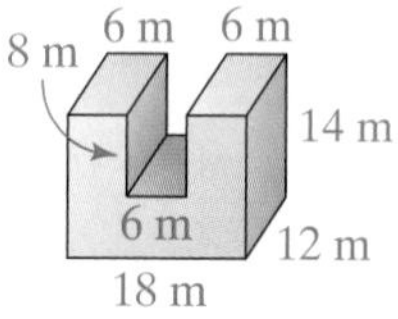

2,448 m^3

23. **Writing in Math** Explain how you would find the radius of a cylinder with a height of 20 in. and a volume of 565.5 in.^{3}. See left.

24. **Food** You cut a 3-in. circle in the center of a 3-in.-high cake and served the outer ring. The cake had a diameter of 12 in. How much cake did you serve? about 318 in.^{3}

C 25. **Challenge** A rectangular prism has square bases and a height of 11 ft. Its lateral area is 308 ft^2. Find its volume. 539 ft^3

Test Prep and Mixed Review — Practice

Multiple Choice

26. A refrigerator is 30 inches wide, 30 inches deep, and 5 feet 6 inches tall. Which is closest to the volume of the refrigerator in cubic feet? B
 A 10.5 ft^3 B 34 ft^3 C 55 ft^3 D 75 ft^3

27. A cylindrical paperweight has the net shown at the right. Which is the closest to the lateral surface area of the paperweight? G
 F 9 in.^{2} H 23 in.^{2}
 G 27 in.^{2} J 50 in.^{2}

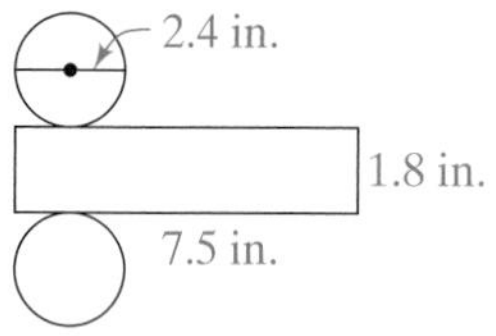

28. A pair of jeans is on sale for 20% off the original price. A student buys the jeans on sale and saves \$12. What was the regular price of the jeans? C
 A \$14.40 C \$60.00
 B \$48.00 D \$240.00

GO for Help

For Exercises	See Lesson
29–31	5-5

Find each percent of decrease. Round to the nearest tenth of a percent.

29. 34 to 22 35.3% 30. 456 to 92 79.8% 31. 100 to 86 14.0%

Test Prep

Resources
For additional practice with a variety of test item formats:
- Test-Taking Strategies, p. 403
- Test Prep, p. 407
- Test-Taking Strategies with Transparencies

Alternative Assessment

Students find the volume of a triangular prism. The base of the triangle is 3 in. with a height of 4 in., and the height of the prism is 6 in. 36 in.^{3} Students then find the height of a cylinder with the same volume and a radius of 2 in. $\frac{9}{\pi}$ in. or about 2.9 in.

Using Formulas

The surface area of an adult's skin is about 2,500 in.^{2}. The adult is 5 ft 5 in. tall. Consider the person a cylinder with no top or bottom. What is the diameter of a cylinder with this surface area?

What You Might Think / What You Might Write

What do I know? What do I want to find out? → The adult's height is 5 ft 5 in., or 65 in. The formula for the lateral area of a cylinder is $2\pi rh$. I need to solve $2{,}500 = 2\pi rh$ for r and then double r to get the diameter.

How can I estimate the answer? → I will use 3 for π and compatible numbers.

$$2{,}500 = 2\pi rh$$
$$2{,}500 \approx 2(3)r(65)$$
$$2{,}500 \approx 390r$$
$$2{,}400 \approx 400r$$
$$6 \approx r$$

I estimate a 6-in. radius or 12-in. diameter.

How can I find the answer? → I will substitute exact values in the formula.

$$2{,}500 = 2\pi rh$$
$$2{,}500 = 2\pi r(65)$$
$$2{,}500 = 130\pi r$$
$$6.121343965 \approx r$$

The diameter is about 2 × 6.12 in., or 12.24 in.

Is the answer reasonable? → Since 12.24 in. is close to 12 in., the answer is reasonable.

Think It Through

1. **Reasoning** Justify each step in solving $2{,}500 = 2\pi rh$ for r. **Check students' work.**
2. **Estimation** What compatible numbers were used in the estimate? **The numbers 2,500 and 390 were changed to 2,400 and 400.**

Exercises, p. 384

19. **doubling the radius, since the radius is squared in calculating the volume**

Using Formulas

Students analyze a real-world problem to develop problem solving and reasoning skills. Building on their knowledge of formulas for volume of three-dimensional figures, they consider irregular figures and use estimation to determine the reasonableness of their answers.

Guided Instruction

Have students work through the problem, rather than just read it. Have them identify any steps that are unclear or that don't match their own work.

Error Prevention!

Some students may begin to add the area of two circular bases into the formula for the surface area of a middle-school student's skin. Remind students that the example excludes the circular bases. Therefore, 2,500 in.^{2} equals only the lateral area of a cylinder ($2\pi rh$).

Alternative Method
Have students write the general formula for the surface area of a cylinder first. Then have them consider which surfaces of the cylinder are being used, and which surfaces are not, to describe the skin area. Ask: *How would you find the surface area of only the cylindrical tube?* **Find the lateral area of the cylinder: multiply 2π by the cylinder's radius and height, or, multiply the cylinder's circumference by its height.**

Connection to Math
Review compatible numbers. Ask: *Which compatible number could be used to estimate π?* **3** *When might you prefer to estimate your answers?* **Possible answers: when an exact answer is not required; when you want to check the reasonableness of an exact answer**

Teaching Tip
Have students ask themselves the same or similar questions as in the example as they work through the Exercises.

Exercises
Have students recall the type of units used to measure volume (cubed), as compared to surface area (squared). Ask: *Why is the measure of volume a cubed unit?* Sample: The product of two linear units (lengths) is an area. So, area is a squared unit. This area is multiplied by another linear unit (length) to get volume. So volume is a cubed unit. Another answer: Volume is measured by unit cubes, and each of these equals one cubed unit.

Differentiated Instruction

Tactile Learners
Provide each student with a cardboard tube. Have students draw a straight line, indicating the height of the cylinder, from one end to the other. Have them cut the roll along the line, then ask: *What is the shape of the flattened surface area?* a rectangle

Resources

- graph paper
- scissors
- cardboard tubes which can be easily cut, such as paper towel rolls

Exercises

Solve each problem. For Exercises 3 and 4, answer parts (a) and (b) first.

3. Alexa was curious about her lung capacity. She took a deep breath and blew up a balloon. The balloon had an approximate shape of a cylinder with a diameter of 16 cm and a length of 11 cm. What is Alexa's lung capacity? Round to the nearest whole unit. about 2,212 cm^3
   a. What is the formula for the volume of a cylinder? $V = \pi r^2 h$
   b. What values do you substitute for each variable in the formula? $h = 11$, $r = 8$

4. Four students found the volume of their cupped hands. They used a bottle that held 354 mL of water. The bottle filled Sara's hands 5 times, Jan's hands 4 times, Bill's hands $4\frac{1}{2}$ times, and Juanita's hands $3\frac{1}{2}$ times. What is the capacity of each person's cupped hands? Round to the nearest milliliter. See margin.
   a. Draw and label a diagram like the one at the right for each person.
   b. How do the diagrams help you find each person's cupped hand capacity?

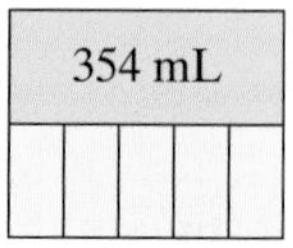

Sara

5. The table below shows the trash thrown away by 296 million Americans in one year. About how many pounds of trash did the average American throw away? about 1,212 lb

Trash in America

Trash Type	Percentage	Tonnage (million tons)
Paper	40.4	71.6
Yard trimmings	17.6	31.6
Metals	8.5	15.3
Plastics	8.0	14.4
Food scraps	7.4	13.2
Glass	7.0	12.5
Other	11.6	20.8

SOURCE: *Consumer Handbook for Reducing Solid Waste*

6. Suppose the square region on the geoboard at the right represents solid silver and is worth $1,000. How much money is the region outlined by the geoband worth? $625

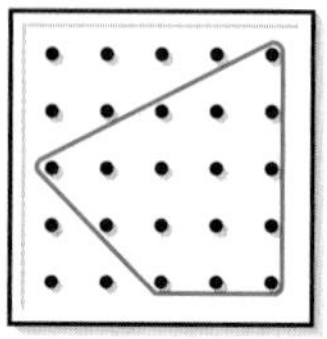

4. Sara's capacity is about 71 mL, Jan's capacity is about 89 mL, Bill's capacity is about 79 mL, and Juanita's capacity is about 101 mL.

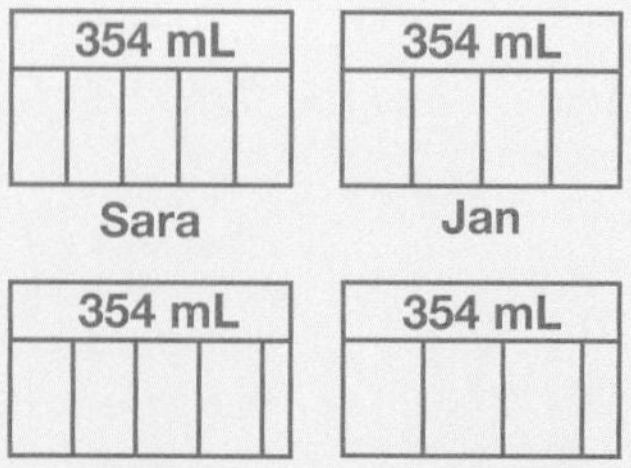

8-7a Activity Lab

Hands On

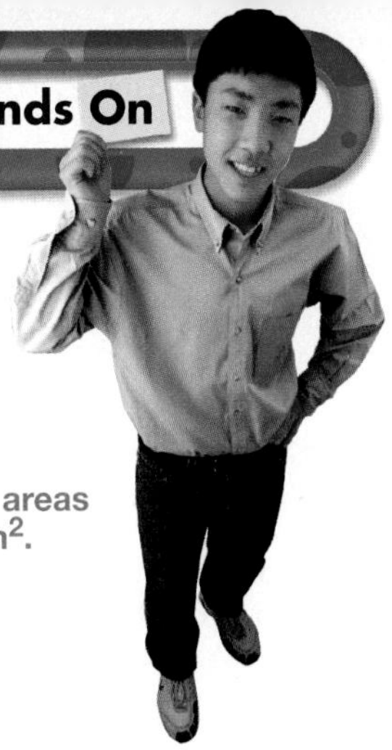

Finding Volume Using Models

ACTIVITY

Draw and cut out the nets at the right. Fold them to make a cube and a square pyramid. Each model will have one open base.

1. Both base areas are 100 cm^2.

1. What are the base areas of the pyramid and the cube?
2. What are the heights of the pyramid and the cube? See margin.
3. Fill the pyramid with sand. Then pour the sand from the pyramid into the cube. How many pyramids full of sand does the cube hold? 3
4. What fractional part of the volume of the cube is the volume of the pyramid? $\frac{1}{3}$
5. Make a conjecture about the formula for the volume of a pyramid. Check students' work.

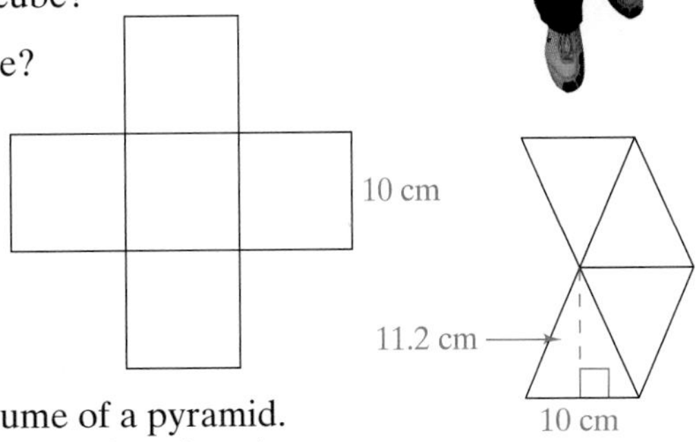

ACTIVITY

Draw and cut out the nets below. Fold them to make a cylinder and a cone. Each model will have one open base.

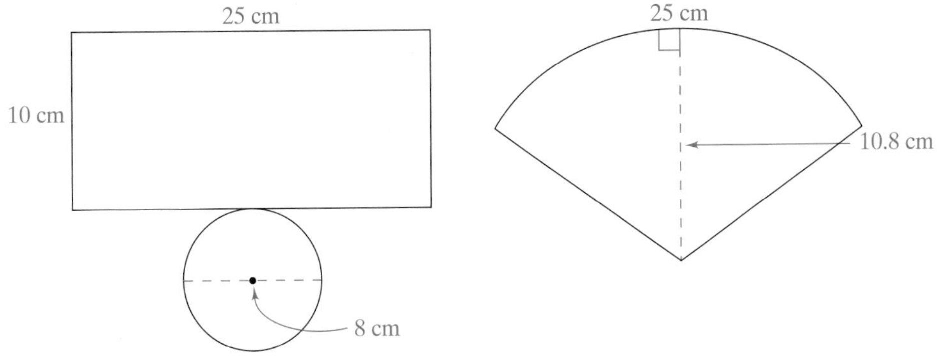

6. What are the base areas of the cylinder and the cone? Both base areas are about 50 cm^2.
7. What are the heights of the cone and the cylinder? The height of the cone is 10 cm, and the height of the cylinder is also about 10 cm.
8. Fill the cone with sand. Then pour the sand from the cone into the cylinder. How many cones full of sand does the cylinder hold? 3
9. What fractional part of the volume of the cylinder is the volume of the cone? $\frac{1}{3}$
10. Make a conjecture about the formula for the volume of a cone. Check students' work.

2. The height of the cube is 10 cm. The height of the square pyramid is also about 10 cm.

Activity Lab

Finding Volume Using Models

The volume of square pyramids and cubes are related, as are the volumes of cylinders and cones. Students cut out paper models and fill them with sand to make conjectures about the relationships between the volumes.

Guided Instruction

Before beginning the activity, review the formulas for the area of squares and circles. Have students draw, or identify from drawings, these three-dimensional figures: square pyramids, cubes, cones, and cylinders. Ask: *What does volume measure?* Sample: the amount of space inside a solid

Activity
Before pouring sand, have students predict what fraction of the cube the square pyramid will take up. Have them predict what fraction of the cylinder the cone will take up. They can check their predictions visually.

Differentiated Instruction

Tactile Learners
If students have difficulty estimating how much of a solid is filled with sand, they can pour the sand into a measuring cup and record the volume for each solid. They can then compare the volumes and conjecture about the volume formulas for prisms and cylinders.

Resources

- Activity Lab 8-7: Volumes of Pyramids and Cones
- cardstock paper, construction paper, or plain white paper
- scissors
- sand
- measuring cups (optional)

8-7

1. Plan

Objective
To find the volumes of pyramids and cones

Examples
1 Finding Volume of a Square Pyramid
2 Using the Volume Formula

Math Understandings: p. 352C

Professional Development

Math Background

When a prism and a pyramid have congruent bases and the same height, the volume of the prism will be three times the volume of the matching pyramid. Similarly, when a cylinder and a cone have congruent bases and the same height, the volume of the cylinder will be three times the volume of the matching cone. For a pyramid, $V = \frac{1}{3}Bh$. If the base of the pyramid is square, this becomes $V = \frac{1}{3}s^2h$. For a cone, $V = \frac{1}{3}Bh$. Since the base of a cone is a circle, this becomes $V = \frac{1}{3}\pi r^2h$.

More Math Background: p. 352D

Lesson Planning and Resources

See p. 352E for a list of the resources that support this lesson.

PowerPoint

Bell Ringer Practice

Check Skills You'll Need
Use student page, transparency, or PowerPoint. For intervention, direct students to:
Surface Area of Pyramids and Cones
Lesson 8-5
Extra Skills and Word Problems Practice, Ch. 8

8-7 Volumes of Pyramids and Cones

Check Skills You'll Need

1. **Vocabulary Review** How are the shapes of *pyramids* and *cones* different? See below.
2. Find the surface area of the figure below to the nearest square inch. 429 in.^{2}

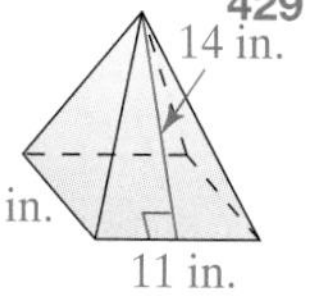

GO for Help Lesson 8-5

Check Skills You'll Need

1. The base of a pyramid is a polygon, whereas the base of a cone is a circle.

What You'll Learn

To find the volumes of pyramids and cones

Why Learn This?

When you fill an ice cream cone or use a funnel, you must consider volume. The volumes of pyramids and cones are related to the volumes of prisms and cylinders.

The contents you need to fill a prism with base area B will fill exactly three pyramids with the same base area and height as the prism.

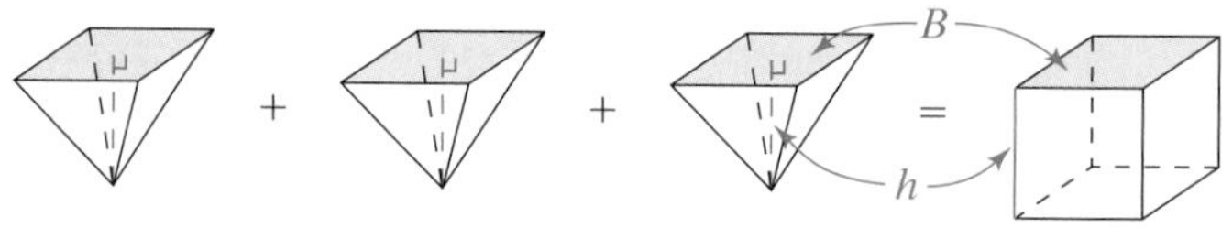

KEY CONCEPTS **Volume of a Pyramid**

The volume V of a pyramid is one third the product of the base area B and the height h.

$$V = \frac{1}{3}Bh$$

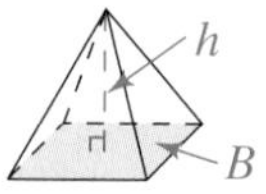

EXAMPLE **Finding Volume of a Square Pyramid**

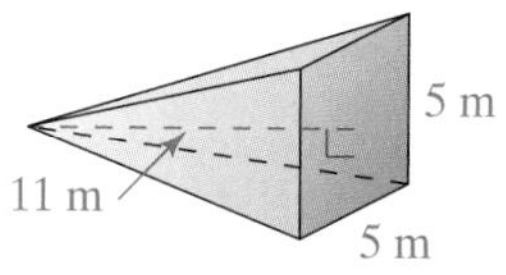

1 Find the volume of the pyramid at the left to the nearest cubic meter.

Step 1 Find the area of the base.

$B = s^2$ ← area of a square
$= 5^2$ ← Substitute.
$= 25$ ← Simplify.

Step 2 Find the volume.

$V = \frac{1}{3}Bh$ ← volume of a pyramid
$= \frac{1}{3}(25)11$ ← Substitute 25 for B and 11 for h.
$= 91.\overline{6}$ ← Multiply.

The volume of the pyramid is about 92 m.^{3}.

Quick Check

1. Find the volume of a square pyramid with a base-edge length of 30 in. and a height of 64 in. to the nearest cubic inch. 19,200 in.^{3}

Differentiated Instruction Solutions for All Learners

Special Needs L1
Students are given hollow models of rectangular pyramids and prisms with the same base area and height. Using rice or beans, or foam pieces, they show which has the greater volume.

learning style: tactile

Below Level L2
Show students models or pictures of a pyramid, a prism, a cone, and a cylinder: Ask: *Which of these figures have two bases?* prism and cylinder *Which have at least one circular base?* cone and cylinder

learning style: visual

The contents of three cones fill a cylinder with the same dimensions.

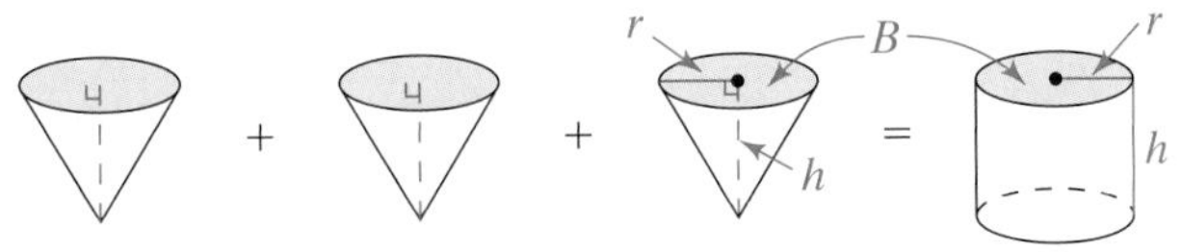

KEY CONCEPTS **Volume of a Cone**

The volume V of a cone is one third the product of base area B and height h.

$$V = \frac{1}{3}Bh$$

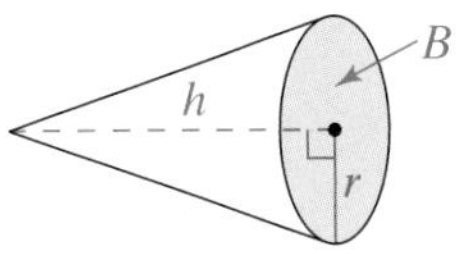

You can use the formula to find the volume or missing dimensions.

EXAMPLES Using the Volume Formula

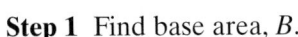

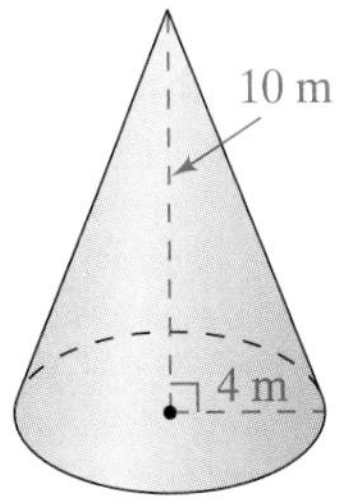

2 Find the volume of the cone at the left to the nearest cubic meter.

Step 1 Find base area, B.

$B = \pi r^2$ ← area of a circle

$= \pi(4^2)$ ← Substitute.

$= 16\pi$ ← Simplify.

Step 2 Find the volume.

$V = \frac{1}{3}Bh$ ← volume of a cone

$= \frac{1}{3}(16\pi)10$ ← Substitute 16π for B and 10 for h.

≈ 168 ← Simplify.

The volume of the cone is about 168 m^3.

3 **Food** An ice cream shop owner designs a new ice cream cone. He wants the volume to be about 240 cm^3. The cone is 14 cm tall. What is its radius?

$240 = \frac{1}{3}(\pi r^2)(14)$ ← Substitute 240 for V, πr^2 for B, and 14 for h in the formula for the volume of a cone.

$240 = \frac{14\pi}{3}r^2$ ← Simplify.

$\frac{3}{14\pi} \cdot 240 = \frac{3}{14\pi} \cdot \frac{14\pi}{3}r^2$ ← Multiply each side by the reciprocal of $\frac{14\pi}{3}$.

$\frac{3(240)}{14\pi} = r^2$ ← Simplify.

$\sqrt{\frac{3(240)}{14\pi}} = \sqrt{r^2}$ ← Find the positive square root of each side.

$4.046013188 \approx r$ ← Use a calculator.

The radius of the cone is about 4 cm.

GO Online

Video Tutor Help
Visit: PHSchool.com
Web Code: ase-0775

Quick Check

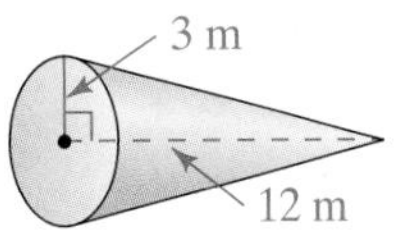

2. Find the volume of the cone at the right. Round to the nearest cubic meter. **113 m^3**
3. Find the radius of a cone with a volume of 360 cm^3 and a height of 9 cm. **$r \approx 6.2$ cm**

2. Teach

Activity Lab

Use before the lesson.
Student Edition Activity Lab, Hands On 8-7a, Finding Volume Using Models, p. 387

All in One Teaching Resources

Activity Lab 8-7: Volumes of Pyramids and Cones

PowerPoint

Additional Examples

1 Find the volume of the pyramid to the nearest cubic foot. **213 ft^3**

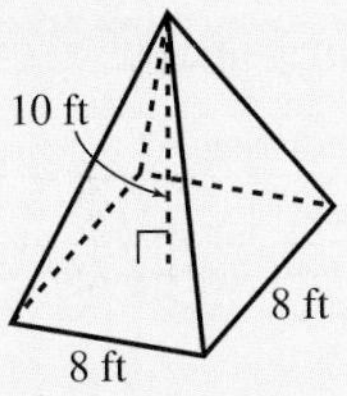

2 Find the volume of this cone to the nearest cubic centimeter. **105 cm^3**

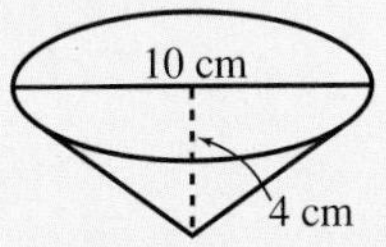

3 At an amusement park, the person whose cone-shaped top spins the longest wins a prize. The volume of the top is about 14 $in.^3$. If the height of the top is 4 in., what is its radius to the nearest inch? **2 in.**

All in One Teaching Resources
- Daily Notetaking Guide 8-7 L3
- Adapted Notetaking 8-7 L1

Closure

- *How are the volumes of a prism and a pyramid related?*
- *How are the volumes of a cylinder and a cone related?* **See back of book.**

Advanced Learners L4	**English Language Learners** ELL
Ask: *What effect does doubling the height have on the volume of a cone? doubling the radius?* **increases the volume by 2; increases the volume by 4**	Show students a rectangular pyramid and a rectangular prism with the same base area and height. Ask: *Which will have the greater volume?* **Prism** *How do you know?* **There's more space inside.** Repeat for a cylinder and cone.
learning style: verbal	**learning style: visual**

3. Practice

Assignment Guide

Check Your Understanding
Go over Exercises 1–4 in class before assigning the Homework Exercises.

Homework Exercises

A Practice by Example	5–11
B Apply Your Skills	12–19
C Challenge	20
Test Prep and Mixed Review	21–24

Homework Quick Check
To check students' understanding of key skills and concepts, go over Exercises 6, 8, 16, 17, and 19.

Differentiated Instruction Resources

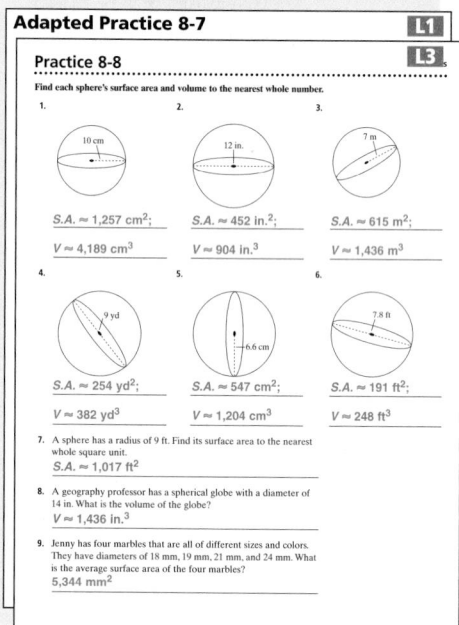

Adapted Practice 8-7 L1

Practice 8-8 L3

Find each sphere's surface area and volume to the nearest whole number.

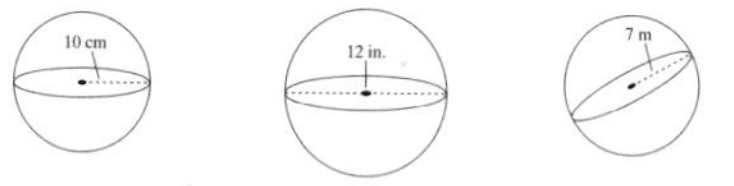

1. S.A. ≈ 1,257 cm^2; V ≈ 4,189 cm^3
2. S.A. ≈ 452 in.^{2}; V ≈ 904 in.^{3}
3. S.A. ≈ 615 m^2; V ≈ 1,436 m^3

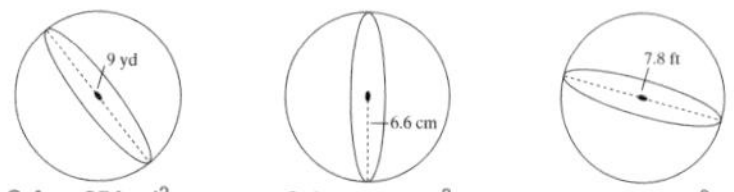

4. S.A. ≈ 254 yd^2; V ≈ 382 yd^3
5. S.A. ≈ 547 cm^2; V ≈ 1,204 cm^3
6. S.A. ≈ 191 ft^2; V ≈ 248 ft^3

7. A sphere has a radius of 9 ft. Find its surface area to the nearest whole square unit.
S.A. ≈ 1,017 ft^2
8. A geography professor has a spherical globe with a diameter of 14 in. What is the volume of the globe?
V ≈ 1,436 in.^{3}
9. Jenny has four marbles that are all of different sizes and colors. They have diameters of 18 mm, 19 mm, 21 mm, and 24 mm. What is the average surface area of the four marbles?
5,344 mm^2

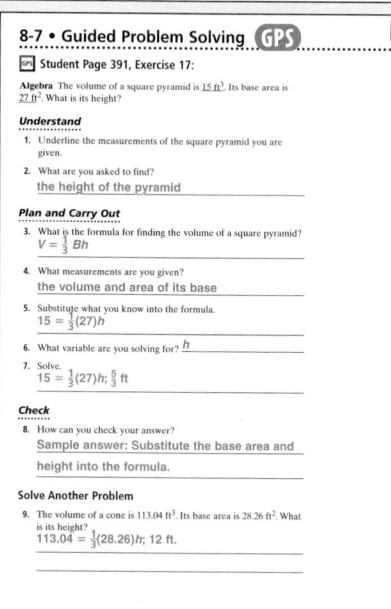

8-7 • Guided Problem Solving GPS L3

GPS Student Page 391, Exercise 17:

Algebra The volume of a square pyramid is 15 ft^3. Its base area is 27 ft^2. What is its height?

Understand
1. Underline the measurements of the square pyramid you are given.
2. What are you asked to find?
the height of the pyramid

Plan and Carry Out
3. What is the formula for finding the volume of a square pyramid?
$V = \frac{1}{3}Bh$
4. What measurements are you given?
the volume and area of its base
5. Substitute what you know into the formula.
$15 = \frac{1}{3}(27)h$
6. What variable are you solving for? h
7. Solve.
$15 = \frac{1}{3}(27)h$; $\frac{5}{3}$ ft

Check
8. How can you check your answer?
Sample answer: Substitute the base area and height into the formula.

Solve Another Problem
9. The volume of a cone is 113.04 ft^3. Its base area is 28.26 ft^2. What is its height?
$113.04 = \frac{1}{3}(28.26)h$; 12 ft.

Check Your Understanding

1. **Mental Math** A square pyramid has a base area of 9 m^2. Its height is 5 m. The volume of the pyramid is (15 m^3, 45 m^3). 15 m^3

Match each pyramid or cone with the expression you can use to find the area of its base.

2. 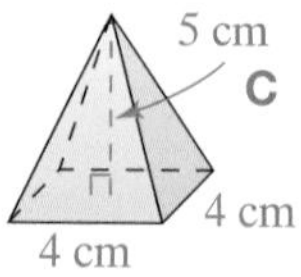

C

3. 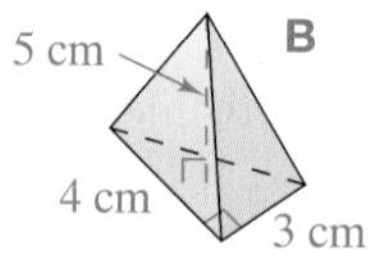

B

4. 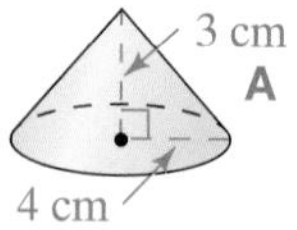

A

A. $B = \pi(4^2)$ B. $B = \frac{1}{2}(4)(3)$ C. $B = 4^2$

Homework Exercises

For more exercises, see Extra Skills and Word Problems.

GO for Help

For Exercises	See Examples
5–7	1
8–10	2
11	3

A **Find the volume of each pyramid to the nearest whole cubic unit.**

5. 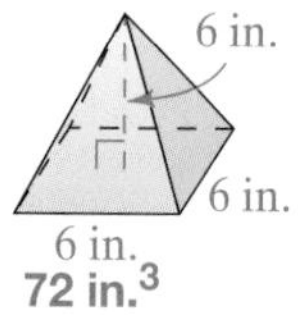

72 in.^{3}

6. 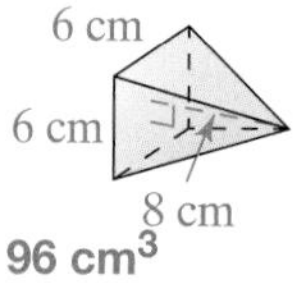

96 cm^3

7. 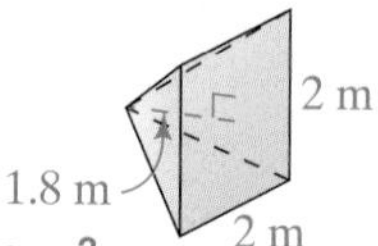

2 m^3

Find the volume of each cone to the nearest whole cubic unit.

8. 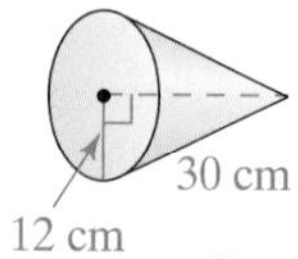

4,524 cm^3

9. 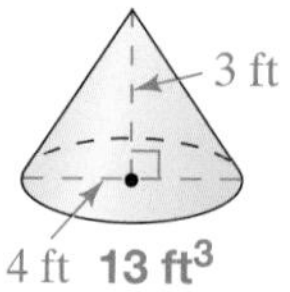

13 ft^3

10. 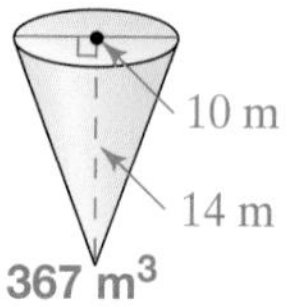

367 m^3

11. A party hat has the shape of a cone. The volume of the hat is about 419 cm^3. If the hat has a height of 16 cm, what is its radius? 5 cm

B GPS 12. **Guided Problem Solving** The funnel shown at the right can hold 500 cm^3 of fluid. Its height (without the stem) is 12 cm. Find the diameter of the cone part of the funnel. about 13 cm

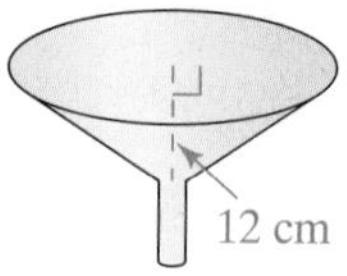

- **Estimation** You can use the strategy *Systematic Guess and Check* to estimate the radius. Select radius values for the formula $V = \frac{1}{3}\pi r^2 h$ until you calculate a volume of about 500 cm^3. Then estimate the diameter.
- Use the formula for the volume of a cone to solve the problem. Use your estimation to check that your answer is reasonable.

15. no; because the radius is squared in the formula, and the height is not

18. Suppose the original volume is $\frac{1}{3}b^2h$. If the dimensions are doubled, the new volume is $\frac{1}{3}(2b)^2(2h)$, which simplifies to $\frac{8}{3}b^2h$. The new volume is 8 times the original.

19. See back of book.

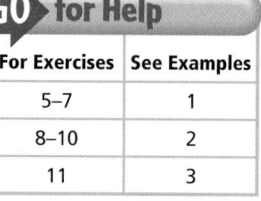

Online Homework Video Tutor
Visit: PHSchool.com
Web Code: ase-0807

Find the volume of the following solids to the nearest whole cubic unit.

13. 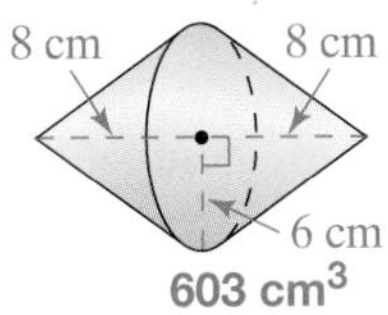

603 cm^3

14. 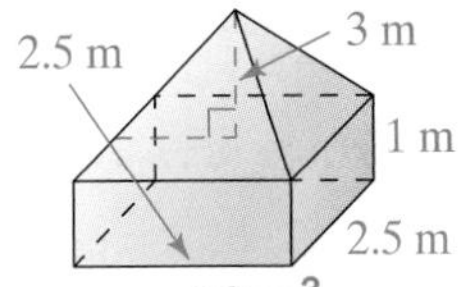

13 m^3

15. **Reasoning** Does the volume of a cone stay the same if you add 1 unit to the radius and subtract 1 unit from the height? Explain. See margin.

16. A glassblower decides to make an hourglass that will hold about 47 in.^{3} in each cone. If the radius of each cone is 3 in., what is the height of each cone h? 5 in.

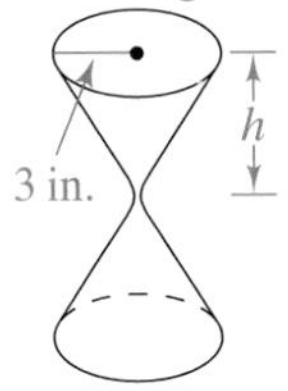

17. **Algebra** GPS The volume of a square pyramid is 15 ft^3. Its base area is 27 ft^2. What is its height? 1.67 ft

18. **Error Analysis** Lian says that if you double the dimensions of a square pyramid, you double its volume. What is her error? See margin.

19. **Writing in Math** Explain how you might use the area formulas for rectangles, triangles, and circles to help you remember volume formulas for pyramids, cones, prisms, and cylinders. See margin.

Ⓒ 20. **Challenge** Find the volume of a cone with a slant height of 7.5 in. and a lateral area of about 106 in.^{2}. about 127 in.^{3}

Test Prep and Mixed Review

Practice

Multiple Choice

21. Which is closest to the volume of the pyramid at the right? A

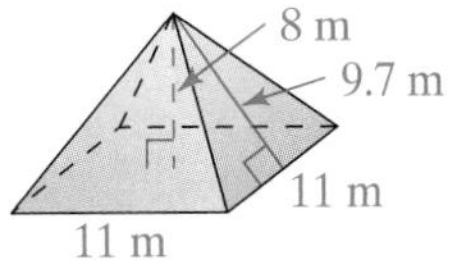

Ⓐ 323 m^3 Ⓒ 88 m^3
Ⓑ 121 m^3 Ⓓ 16 m^3

22. Steel cylinders 18 inches in diameter and 30 inches long powered a steam locomotive. What was the lateral area of steel needed for one of the cylinders, to the nearest square inch? H

Ⓕ 540 in.^{2} Ⓖ 848 in.^{2} Ⓗ 1,696 in.^{2} Ⓙ 2,205 in.^{2}

23. Dennis earned \$25 mowing lawns. If he pays the \$8 he owes his mother and spends \$6 on a movie, which procedure can he use to find the amount of money he will have left? A

Ⓐ Add −8 and 25 and then subtract 6 from the result.
Ⓑ Add −8 and 25 and then add 6 to the result.
Ⓒ Subtract −8 from 25 and then subtract 6 from the result.
Ⓓ Subtract 25 from −8 and then add 6 to the result.

GO for Help

For Exercise	See Lesson
24	8-4

24. Find the surface area of a cylinder with a diameter of 24 ft and a height of 24 ft. Round to the nearest square foot. 2,714 ft^2

4. Assess & Reteach

PowerPoint

Lesson Quiz

1. Find the volume of a pyramid with a base of 7 m by 7 m and height of 12 m. 196 m^3
2. Find the volume of a cone with radius 4 cm and height 8 cm to the nearest cubic centimeter. 134 cm^3
3. Find the height of a cone with a volume of 150.8 cm^3 and a radius of 6 cm. 4 cm
4. A glass ornament has the shape of a double cone with a radius of 2 in. The double cone has a volume of 240 in.^{3}. What is the height of each of the two cones to the nearest tenth? about 28.6 in.

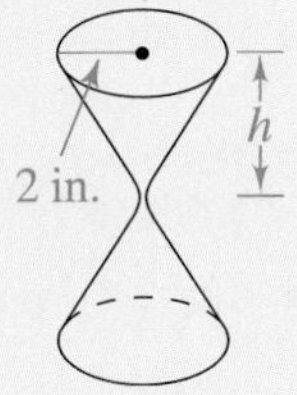

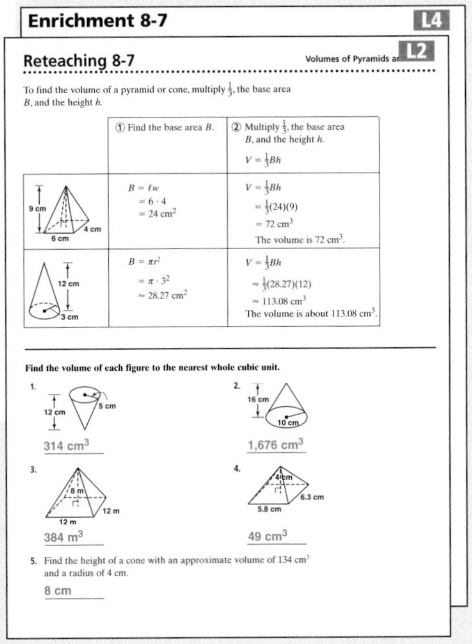

Enrichment 8-7 L4

Reteaching 8-7 Volumes of Pyramids a… L2

To find the volume of a pyramid or cone, multiply $\frac{1}{3}$, the base area B, and the height h.

	① Find the base area B.	② Multiply $\frac{1}{3}$, the base area B, and the height h. $V = \frac{1}{3}Bh$
9 cm, 4 cm, 6 cm	$B = \ell w$ $= 6 \cdot 4$ $= 24$ cm^2	$V = \frac{1}{3}Bh$ $= \frac{1}{3}(24)(9)$ $= 72$ cm^3 The volume is 72 cm^3.
12 cm, 3 cm	$B = \pi r^2$ $= \pi \cdot 3^2$ ≈ 28.27 cm^2	$V = \frac{1}{3}Bh$ $\approx \frac{1}{3}(28.27)(12)$ ≈ 113.08 cm^3 The volume is about 113.08 cm^3.

Find the volume of each figure to the nearest whole cubic unit.

1. 12 cm, 5 cm — 314 cm^3
2. 16 cm, 10 cm — 1,676 cm^3
3. 8 m, 12 m, 12 m — 384 m^3
4. 4 cm, 6.3 cm, 5.8 cm — 49 cm^3
5. Find the height of a cone with an approximate volume of 134 cm^3 and a radius of 4 cm. 8 cm

Alternative Assessment

Students are given the following description: A cone with a 15-m diameter has a volume equal to that of a square pyramid having 15-m sides and height. Students draw and label the cone and the square pyramid and then find the height of the cone to the nearest tenth. 19.1 m

Test Prep

Resources

For additional practice with a variety of test formats:

- Test-Taking Strategies, p. 403
- Test Prep, p. 407
- Test-Taking Strategies with Transparencies

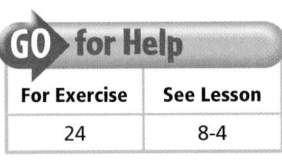

Checkpoint Quiz

Use this Checkpoint Quiz to check students' understanding of the skills and concepts of Lessons 8-5 through 8-7.

Resources

- All in One Teaching Resources Checkpoint Quiz 2
- ExamView Assessment Suite CD-ROM
- Success Tracker Online Intervention

MATH AT WORK

Landscape Architect

Students learn that landscape architects use geometry skills to plan, design, and prepare models of proposed sites.

Guided Instruction

Have students discuss landscapes where they might find examples of the three-dimensional figures they have studied in this chapter. Share an example of a landscape architect's blueprint, if possible.

Checkpoint Quiz 2

Lessons 8-5 through 8-7

Find the surface area and volume of each figure to the nearest whole number.

1.

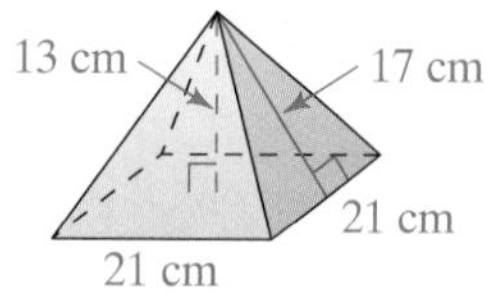

1,155 cm^2; 1,911 cm^3

2.

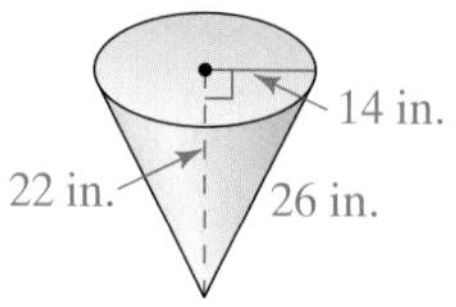

1,759 $in.^2$; 4,516 $in.^3$

3.

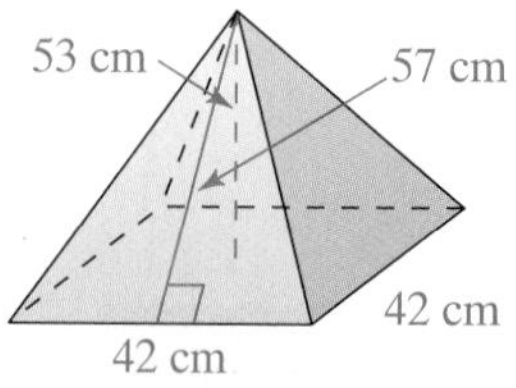

6,552 cm^2; 31,164 cm^3

Find the volume of each figure to the nearest cubic unit.

4.

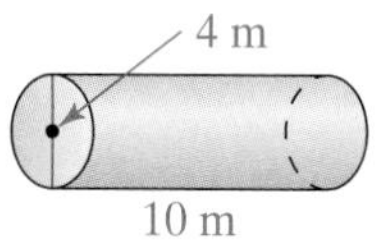

126 m^3

5.

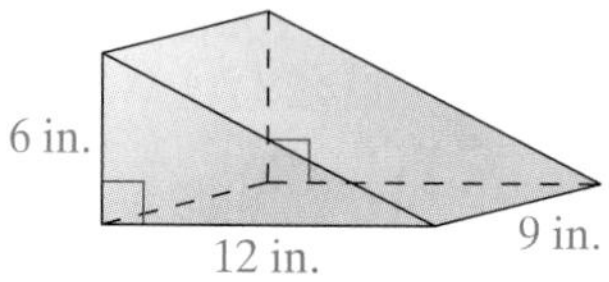

324 $in.^3$

6.

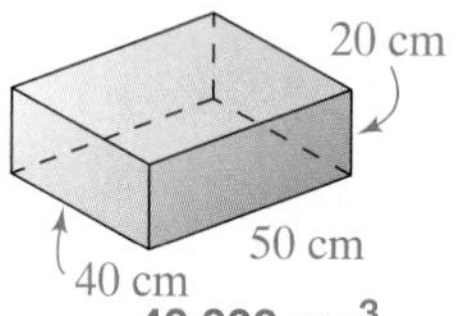

40,000 cm^3

7. Find the radius of a cone with an approximate volume of 22 ft^3 and a height of 21 ft. about 1 ft

8. **Art** Jacques is making ice sculptures for an upcoming party. He starts with a cube of ice that measures 5 ft on an edge. What is the volume of the largest pyramid he can sculpt? about 42 ft^3

MATH AT WORK

Landscape Architect

Landscape architects are involved in planning and designing residential areas, parks, shopping centers, golf courses, and college campuses. Landscape architects make detailed plans that include the location of buildings, roads, and walkways, and the arrangement of shrubs, trees, and flowers. A knowledge of geometry helps them prepare sketches and models of proposed sites. They also use their mathematical skills to estimate the costs of their projects.

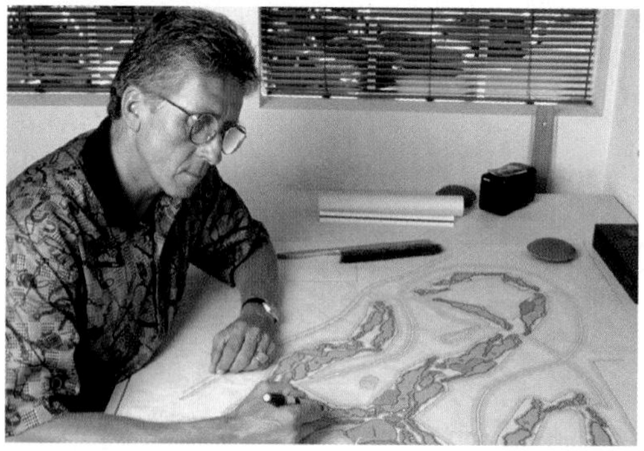

Go Online PHSchool.com **For:** Information on landscape architects **Web Code:** asb-2031

8-8 Spheres

Check Skills You'll Need

1. Vocabulary Review How is a circle's *radius* related to its *diameter*?
1–5. See below.

Estimate the area of each circle with the given radius or diameter. Use 3 for π.

2. $r = 4$ cm

3. $d = 12$ m

4. $r = 3.2$ ft

5. $d = 17$ in.

GO for Help Lesson 7-7

Check Skills You'll Need

1. The radius is half the diameter.
2. about 48 cm^2
3. about 108 m^2
4. about 27 ft^2
5. about 217 $in.^2$

Test Prep Tip

Simplify the product of whole numbers before you multiply by the decimal values.

What You'll Learn

To find the surface area and volume of a sphere

New Vocabulary sphere

Why Learn This?

Many objects have the shape of a sphere, including toys. To make these objects, it is helpful to know about the surface area and volume of spheres.

A **sphere** is the set of all points in space that are the same distance from a center point.

KEY CONCEPTS **Surface Area of a Sphere**

The surface area of a sphere is four times the product of π and the square of the radius r.

$$\text{S.A.} = 4\pi r^2$$

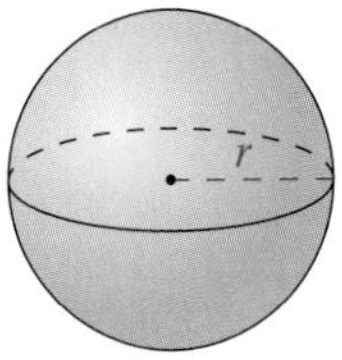

EXAMPLE Finding the Surface Area of a Sphere

1 Find the surface area of the sphere at the right to the nearest square centimeter.

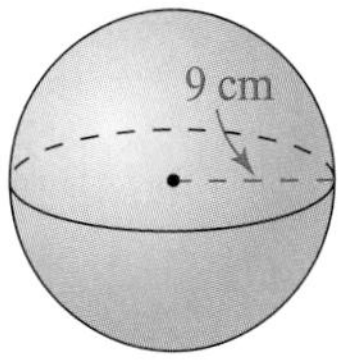

$\text{S.A.} = 4\pi r^2$ ← surface area of a sphere

$= 4\pi(9^2)$ ← Substitute.

$= 324\pi$ ← Simplify.

≈ 1017.87602 ← Use a calculator.

The surface area of the sphere is about 1,018 cm^2.

Quick Check

1. A sphere has a radius of 7 ft. Find its surface area to the nearest square foot. 616 ft^2

Differentiated Instruction Solutions for All Learners

Special Needs L1	Below Level L2
Partners help each other enter numbers into their calculators as needed. learning style: tactile	Students cut a spherical object, such as a foam ball, in half. Students point to and measure the radius with a ruler. They find the surface area and volume of these objects using the formulas. learning style: tactile

8-8

1. Plan

Objective
To find the surface area and volume of a sphere

Examples
1 Finding the Surface Area of a Sphere
2 Finding the Volume of a Sphere

Math Understandings: p. 352D

Professional Development

Math Background

A circle is one of the conic sections. When you cut through the center of a sphere with a plane, the intersection of the plane and the sphere is a circle (called the *great circle*). The diameter and radius of the sphere are the same as the diameter and radius, respectively, of that circle. The surface area of the sphere depends on the radius of that circle, and is given by the formula S.A. $= 4\pi r^2$. The formula for the volume of the sphere is $V = \frac{4}{3}\pi r^3$.

More Math Background: p. 352D

Lesson Planning and Resources

See p. 352E for a list of the resources that support this lesson.

PowerPoint

Bell Ringer Practice

Check Skills You'll Need
Use student page, transparency, or PowerPoint. For intervention, direct students to:

Circumference and Area of a Circle
Lesson 7-7
Extra Skills and Word Problems Practice, Ch. 7

2. Teach

Activity Lab

Use before the lesson.

All in One Teaching Resources

Activity Lab 8-8: Spheres

Guided Instruction

Connection to History
Archimedes, who lived during the third century B.C., discovered that the volume of a sphere with radius *r* is $\frac{2}{3}$ the volume of a cylinder with radius *r* and height 2*r*. The same relationship exists between the surface area of this sphere and this cylinder.

Error Prevention!

Remind students that surface area is measured in square units and volume is measured in cubic units. Also remind them to use the radius when they are given the diameter.

Example 2
Provide students with a blank grid.

PowerPoint

Additional Examples

1 Find the surface area of the sphere to the nearest whole unit. 804 m^2

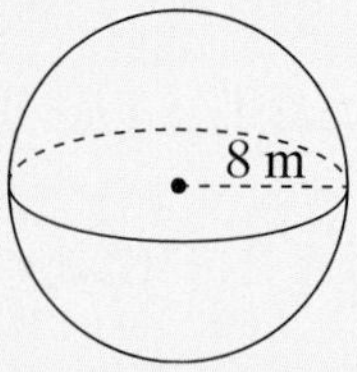

2 A streetlight uses a bulb shaped like a sphere. The bulb has a radius of 8 in. What is the volume of the bulb to the nearest cubic inch? 2,145 $in.^3$

All in One Teaching Resources

- Daily Notetaking Guide 8-8 L3
- Adapted Notetaking 8-8 L1

Closure

- *How are the formulas for surface area of a sphere and volume of a sphere different?* See back of book.

Consider a sphere with radius *r* inside a cylinder with radius *r* and height 2*r*. You know how to find the volume of the cylinder.

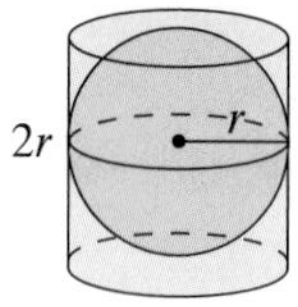

$V = Bh$		← volume of a cylinder
$= (\pi r^2)(2r)$		← Substitute πr^2 for *B* and 2*r* for *h*.
$= 2\pi r^3$		← Simplify.

The volume of the sphere is two thirds of the volume of the cylinder.

KEY CONCEPTS **Volume of a Sphere**

The volume of a sphere is four thirds of the product of π and the radius *r* cubed.

$$V = \frac{4}{3}\pi r^3$$

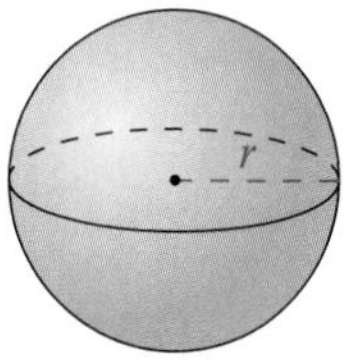

EXAMPLE **Finding the Volume of a Sphere**

2 **Gridded Response** The diameter of a sphere in a water fountain is 4 ft. What is the volume of the sphere to the nearest cubic foot?

Estimate Use 3 for π. The radius of the sphere is 2 ft. The volume of the sphere is about $\frac{4}{3}(3)(2)^3 = 32$ ft^3.

$V = \frac{4}{3}\pi r^3$	← volume of a sphere
$= \frac{4}{3}\pi(2^3)$	← Substitute 2 for *r*.
$= \frac{32}{3}\pi$	← Simplify.
$\approx$ 33.51032164	← Use a calculator.

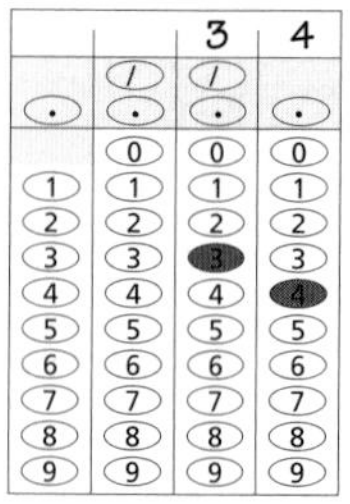

The volume of the sphere is about 34 ft^3.

Check for Reasonableness The answer 34 ft^3 is close to the estimate of 32 ft^3. The answer is reasonable.

Quick Check

2. **Globes** A globe in a brass stand has a diameter of 40 in. What is the volume of the globe to the nearest cubic inch? 33,510 $in.^3$

Differentiated Instruction Solutions for All Learners

Advanced Learners L4
Students are asked how increasing or decreasing the radius by a factor of 4 changes the surface area and volume of a sphere. When increased, the volume is multiplied by 4^3 or 64; surface area is multiplied by 4^2 or 16. When decreased, the volume is divided by 64 and surface area is divided by 16. **learning style: verbal**

English Language Learners ELL
Students practice the terms they have learned in this chapter by explaining why the surface area of a sphere is expressed in square units. Then have them explain why volume is in cubic units.
learning style: verbal

Check Your Understanding

Vocabulary **Match each solid's definition with the correct term.**

1. exactly one circular base and one vertex C
2. two bases that are parallel, congruent circles A
3. set of all points in space that are the same distance from a center point B

A. cylinder
B. sphere
C. cone

Use the sphere at the right for Exercises 4–6.

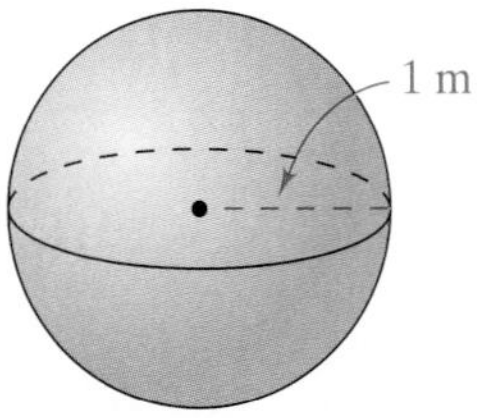

4. Which is the correct expression for the surface area of the sphere: $\frac{4}{3}(3.14)(1)^3$ or $4(3.14)(1)^2$? $4(3.14)(1)^2$
5. What is the surface area of the sphere? $12.6\ m^2$
6. What is the volume of the sphere? $4.2\ m^3$

Homework Exercises

For more exercises, see Extra Skills and Word Problems.

GO for Help

For Exercises	See Examples
7–13	1 and 2

A **Find each sphere's surface area and volume to the nearest whole number.** 7–9. See left.

7. 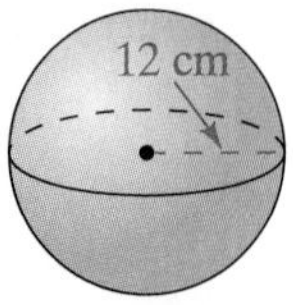

8. 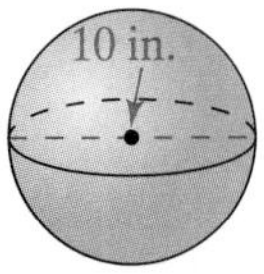

9. 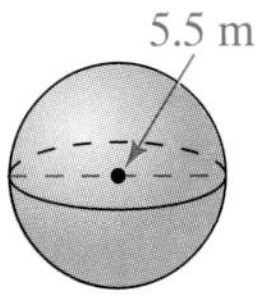

7. $1{,}810\ cm^2$; $7{,}238\ cm^3$
8. $314\ in.^2$; $524\ in.^3$
9. $95\ m^2$; $87\ m^3$

10. 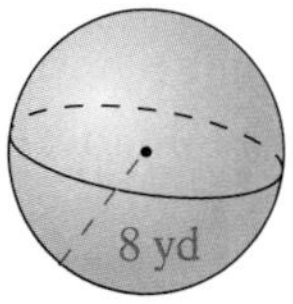

$804\ yd^2$; $2{,}145\ yd^3$

11. 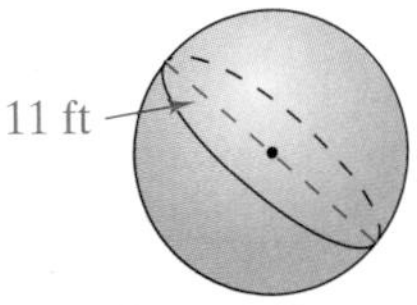

$380\ ft^2$; $697\ ft^3$

12. 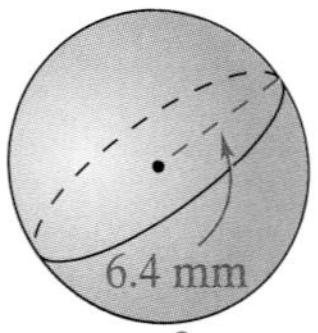

$515\ mm^2$; $1{,}098\ mm^3$

13. **Mental Math** A model of the moon has a radius of about 3 cm. Find the volume of the model to the nearest cubic centimeter. about $110\ cm^3$

B **GPS**

14. **Guided Problem Solving** Water covers approximately 70% of Earth's surface. The diameter of Earth is about 13,000 km. Find the approximate area of Earth that is covered by water.
    - What is the formula for the surface area of a sphere?
    - What is the surface area of Earth?
    - What is 70% of Earth's surface area?

14. about $3.7165 \times 10^8\ km^2$

GO Online
Homework Video Tutor
Visit: PHSchool.com
Web Code: ase-0808

15. **Baseball** Balls used in major league baseball have diameters that range from 2.86 in. to 2.94 in. What is the difference in surface area between the largest and the smallest baseball? about $1.5\ in.^2$

Online lesson quiz, PHSchool.com, Web Code: asa-0808

3. Practice

Assignment Guide

Check Your Understanding

Go over Exercises 1–6 in class before assigning the Homework Exercises.

Homework Exercises

A	Practice by Example	7–13
B	Apply Your Skills	14–24
C	Challenge	25
	Test Prep and Mixed Review	26–31

Homework Quick Check

To check students' understanding of key skills and concepts, go over Exercises 11, 13, 16, 17, and 24.

Differentiated Instruction Resources

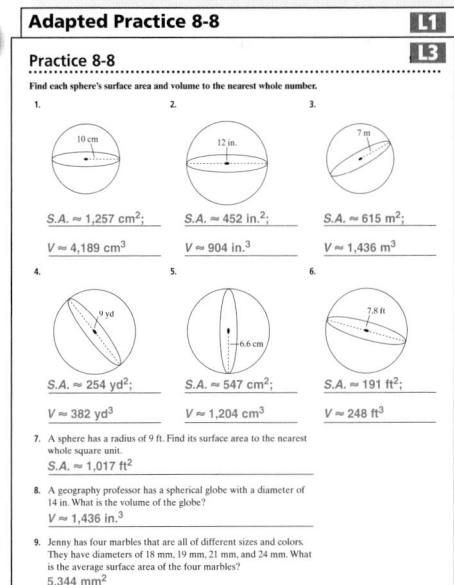

Adapted Practice 8-8 L1

Practice 8-8 L3

Find each sphere's surface area and volume to the nearest whole number.

1. 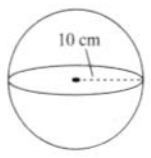

S.A. ≈ $1{,}257\ cm^2$; V ≈ $4{,}189\ cm^3$

2. 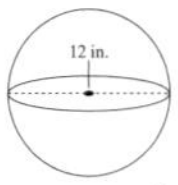

S.A. ≈ $452\ in.^2$; V ≈ $904\ in.^3$

3. 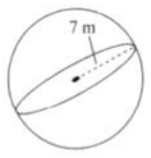

S.A. ≈ $615\ m^2$; V ≈ $1{,}436\ m^3$

4. 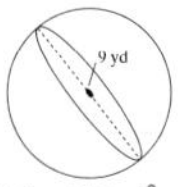

S.A. ≈ $254\ yd^2$; V ≈ $382\ yd^3$

5. 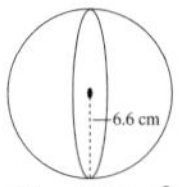

S.A. ≈ $547\ cm^2$; V ≈ $1{,}204\ cm^3$

6. 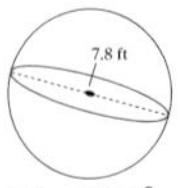

S.A. ≈ $191\ ft^2$; V ≈ $248\ ft^3$

7. A sphere has a radius of 9 ft. Find its surface area to the nearest whole square unit.
S.A. ≈ $1{,}017\ ft^2$

8. A geography professor has a spherical globe with a diameter of 14 in. What is the volume of the globe?
V ≈ $1{,}436\ in.^3$

9. Jenny has four marbles that are all of different sizes and colors. They have diameters of 18 mm, 19 mm, 21 mm, and 24 mm. What is the average surface area of the four marbles?
$5{,}344\ mm^2$

8-8 • Guided Problem Solving GPS L3

GPS Student Page 396, Exercise 16:

The circumference of a glass terrarium in the shape of a sphere is about 12.5 in. What is the surface area of the tank to the nearest square inch?

Understand

1. What is the given measurement? 12.5 in. circumference
2. What formula do you use to find circumference? $C = 2\pi r$
3. What are you being asked to find? surface area of the tank

Plan and Carry Out

4. How can you use the circumference to find the surface area? Solve the circumference formula for the radius. Substitute the result into the surface are formula.
5. What is the radius of the terrarium? about 2 inches
6. How will you find the surface area of the terrarium? $SA = 4\pi r^2 = 4\pi 2^2$
7. What is the surface area of the terrarium to the nearest square inch? $50\ in.^2$

Check

8. Does your answer check? Is your answer consistent with the circumference given in the question? yes, yes

Solve Another Problem

9. The volume of a weather balloon is about $33.5\ ft^3$. What is the surface area of the weather balloon? Round your answer to the nearest whole square unit. $99\ ft^2$

4. Assess & Reteach

PowerPoint

Lesson Quiz

Use the diagram to answer items 1 and 2.

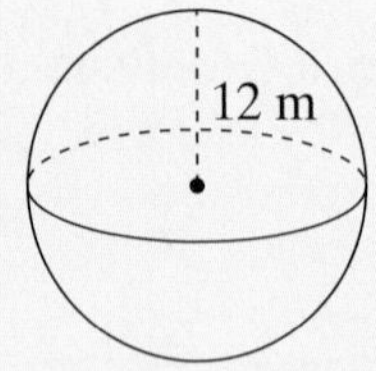

1. Find the surface area of the sphere to the nearest whole unit. 1,810 m^2
2. Find the volume of the sphere to the nearest whole unit. 7,238 m^3
3. The diameter of a beach ball is 14 in. To the nearest in.^{2}, how much plastic forms the surface of the ball when it is fully inflated? 616 in.^{2}
4. How much air is needed to fully inflate the beach ball (in item 3) to the nearest cubic inch? 1,437 in.^{3}

24. Since S.A. = $4\pi r^2$, you can solve for r by dividing $\frac{S.A.}{4\pi}$ and taking the square root. Therefore, $r = \sqrt{\frac{S.A.}{4\pi}}$. Then you can substitute into $\frac{4}{3}\pi r^3$ to get the volume of the sphere.

Enrichment 8-8 L4

Reteaching 8-8 L2

Find the surface area and volume of a beach ball with a radius of 8 inches.

The *surface area* of a sphere is four times the product of π and the square of the radius r.

$$
\begin{aligned}
S.A. &= 4\pi r^2 && \leftarrow \text{Surface area of a sphere} \\
&= 4\pi(8^2) && \leftarrow \text{Substitute.} \\
&= 256\pi && \leftarrow \text{Simplify.} \\
&\approx 804 && \leftarrow \text{Use a calculator.}
\end{aligned}
$$

The surface area of the beach ball is about 804 in.^{2}.

The *volume* of a sphere is four-thirds of the product of π and the radius r cubed.

$$
\begin{aligned}
V &= \tfrac{4}{3}\pi r^3 && \leftarrow \text{Volume of a sphere} \\
&= \tfrac{4}{3}\pi(8^3) && \leftarrow \text{Substitute.} \\
&= \tfrac{2{,}048}{3}\pi && \leftarrow \text{Simplify.} \\
&\approx 2{,}145 && \leftarrow \text{Use a calculator.}
\end{aligned}
$$

The volume of the beach ball is about 2.145 in.^{3}.

A glass blower sells opalescent glass spheres. Find the surface area and volume of each sphere to the nearest whole number.

1. blue: $r = 2$ in.
   S.A. ≈ 50 in.^{2}
   V ≈ 34 in.^{3}
2. green: $d = 9$ cm
   S.A. ≈ 254 cm^2
   V ≈ 382 cm^3
3. yellow: $d = 6$ in.
   S.A. ≈ 113 in.^{2}
   V ≈ 113 in.^{3}
4. multicolored: $r = 3.5$ in.
   S.A. ≈ 154 in.^{2}
   V ≈ 180 in.^{3}
5. clear: $r = 6.3$ cm
   S.A. ≈ 499 cm^2
   V ≈ 1,047 cm^3
6. opaque: $d = 8.5$ in.
   S.A. ≈ 227 in.^{2}
   V ≈ 321 in.^{3}

18. 113 cm^2; 113 cm^3
19. 5,027 mm^2; 33,510 mm^3
20. 50 mm^2; 34 mm^3
21. 5 cm^2; 1 cm^3

23. 83 in.^{2}; 64 in.^{3}

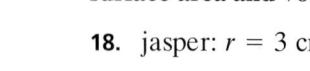

16. The circumference of a glass terrarium in the shape of a sphere is (GPS) about 12.5 in. What is the surface area of the terrarium to the nearest square inch? 50 in.^{2}

17. **Error Analysis** Your classmate found the volume of a sphere with a radius of 5 ft to be 500π ft^3. What error did your classmate make? She forgot to divide by 3.

Gemstones A jeweler sells spherical gemstones for pendants. Find the surface area and volume of each gemstone to the nearest whole number. 18–21. See left.

18. jasper: $r = 3$ cm
19. rose quartz: $d = 40$ mm
20. topaz: $d = 4$ mm
21. pearl: $r = 0.6$ cm

22. **Tennis** Tennis balls have a diameter of 2.5 in. A can holds three balls and has the shape of a cylinder. 22a. 25 in.^{3} 22b. 37 in.^{3}
    a. Find the total volume of the balls to the nearest whole cubic unit.
    b. Find the volume of the can to the nearest whole cubic unit. Assume the balls touch the can on the sides, top, and bottom.

23. Find the surface area and volume of the figure at the right. Round to the nearest whole number. See left.

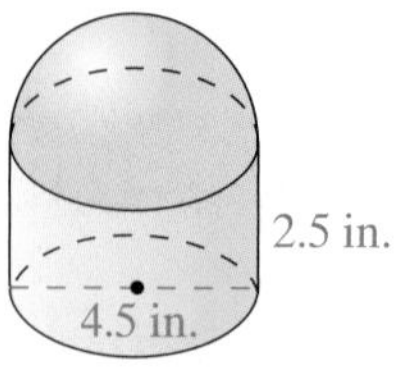

24. **Writing in Math** Suppose you know the surface area of a sphere. Explain how you would find the volume of the sphere. See margin.

25. **Challenge** (C) The volume of Mars is about 1.642×10^{11} km^3. What is the radius of Mars to the nearest kilometer? about 3,397 km

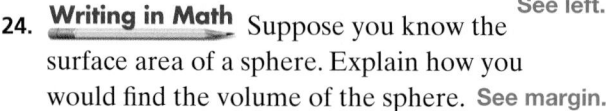

Test Prep and Mixed Review

Practice

Gridded Response

26. A bowling ball is required to have a radius of no more than 4.3 inches and a weight of no more than 16 pounds. To the nearest cubic inch, what is the volume of a ball with radius 4.3 inches? 333

27. A cylinder has a height of 19 feet and a diameter of 10 feet. What is the surface area of the cylinder to the nearest square foot? 754

28. The field and running track at the right are made up of one rectangle and two semicircles. What is the outer perimeter of the track to the nearest meter? 412

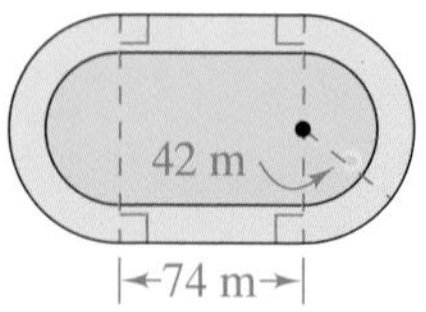

Find the volume of each figure to the nearest cubic unit.

29. 14 in.^{3}

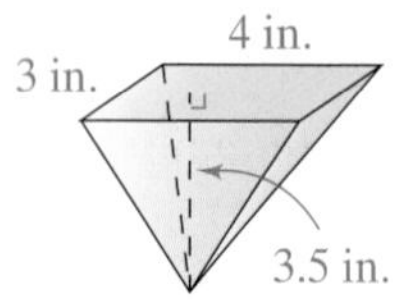

30. 134 cm^3

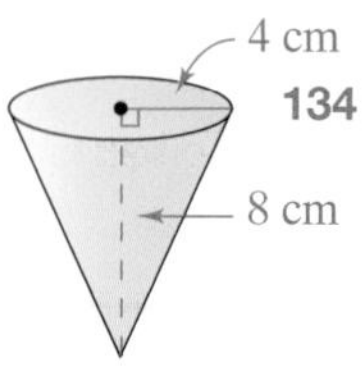

31. 112 ft^3

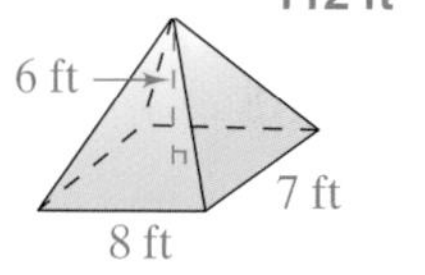

GO for Help

For Exercises	See Lesson
29–31	8-7

Test Prep

Resources

- For additional practice with a variety of test item formats:
- Test-Taking Strategies, p. 403
- Test Prep, p. 407
- Test-Taking Strategies with Transparencies

Alternative Assessment

Students in pairs draw and label the dimensions of a sphere. Partners find the surface area and volume of each other's diagram.

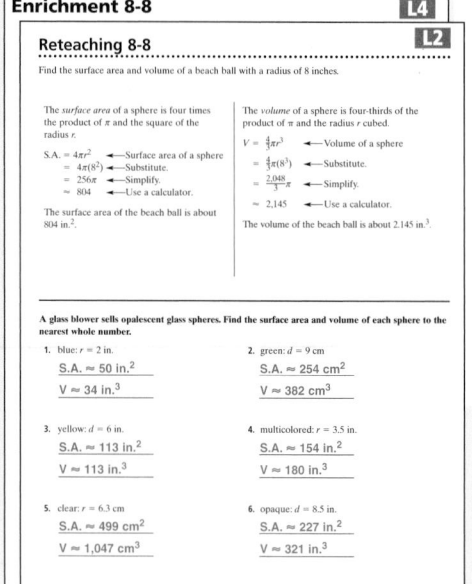

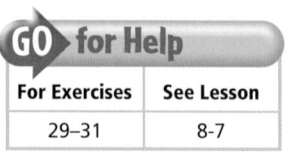

8-9a Activity Lab

Changing Dimensions

ACTIVITY

1. What is the surface area of a block with dimensions 1 × 1 × 1? 6 sq. units

2. What is the volume of the block? 1 cubic unit

One colored block, cube A, has dimensions 1 × 1 × 1. The dimensions of cube B are double the dimensions of cube A. The dimensions of cube C are triple the dimensions of cube A.

3. Copy and complete the table below. See margin.

Cube	Dimensions	Surface Area	Volume
A	1 × 1 × 1	■	■
B	2 × 2 × 2	■	■
C	■ × ■ × ■	■	■

4. Use the data in the table above. Copy and complete the table below. See margin.

Cubes	Ratio of Side Lengths	Ratio of Surface Areas	Ratio of Volumes
A : B	■ : ■	■ : ■	■ : ■
B : C	■ : ■	■ : ■	■ : ■
C : A	■ : ■	■ : ■	■ : ■

5. The ratios of surface areas are equal to the ratios of sides squared and the ratios of volumes are equal to the ratios of sides cubed.

5. **Patterns** What patterns do you notice in your table?

6. Predict the next row of data in both tables for a 4 × 4 × 4 cube.
96, 64; (D : A) 4 : 1, 16 : 1, 64 : 1

7. **Multiple Choice** Which of the prisms below contains about half as much water as the prism at the right? D

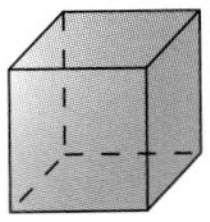

I.
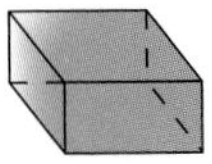

II.
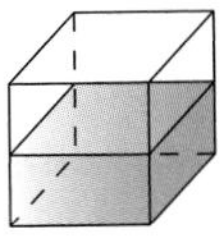

III.
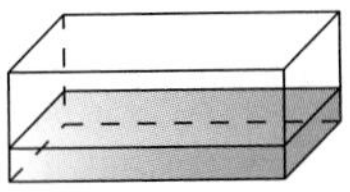

Ⓐ I only

Ⓑ I and II only

Ⓒ I and III only

Ⓓ I, II, and III

Activity Lab

Changing Dimensions

Students compare three cubes, each with dimensions that are multiples of the first. They compare and predict side lengths, surface areas, and volumes to understand how changing dimensions affects these measurements.

Guided Instruction

Activity

Ask:

- *For a square with a side of 3, what are the factors of the area?* 3 × 3
- *For a cube with a side of 3, what are the factors of the volume?* 3 × 3 × 3
- *How many times is the side used as a factor for the area?* twice *for the volume?* three times

Error Prevention!

Guide students to find ratios by comparing corresponding values. They can set up their comparisons as fractions, and simplify. For example, the ratio of surface areas for cubes A : B is the fraction $\frac{6}{24}$. Simplified, this fraction is $\frac{1}{4}$, or the ratio 1 : 4.

Differentiated Instruction

Tactile Learners
Have students use wooden or plastic cubes to model the problem and record measurements.

Resources

- Activity Lab 8-9: Exploring Similar Solids
- wooden or plastic cubes (optional)

3.

Cube	Dimensions	Surface Area	Volume
A	1 × 1 × 1	6	1
B	2 × 2 × 2	24	8
C	3 × 3 × 3	54	27

4.

Cubes	Ratio of Side Lengths	Ratio of Surface Areas	Ratio of Volumes
A : B	1 : 2	1 : 4	1 : 8
B : C	2 : 3	4 : 9	8 : 27
C : A	3 : 1	9 : 1	27 : 1

8-9

1. Plan

Objective
To use proportions to find missing measurements of similar solids, including surface area and volume

Examples
1 Finding Dimensions of a Similar Solid
2 Surface Area and Volume of Similar Solids

Math Understandings: p. 352D

Professional Development

Math Background

Similar solids have the same shape and proportional corresponding measurements. The idea that doubling linear dimensions does not simply double the area and the volume is counter-intuitive for most people. Experiments with models and actual measurements help make the effects of changing dimensions seem more reasonable.

More Math Background: p. 352D

Lesson Planning and Resources

See p. 352E for a list of the resources that support this lesson.

PowerPoint

Bell Ringer Practice

Check Skills You'll Need
Use student page, transparency, or PowerPoint. For intervention, direct students to:
Solving Proportions
Lesson 4-3
Extra Skills and Word Problems Practice, Ch. 4

8-9 Exploring Similar Solids

Check Skills You'll Need

1. **Vocabulary Review** What is a *proportion*? See below.

Solve each proportion.

2. $\frac{x}{4} = \frac{7}{16}$ 1.75
3. $\frac{9}{5} = \frac{m}{24}$ 43.2
4. $\frac{3}{k} = \frac{9}{27}$ 9

GO for Help Lesson 4-3

What You'll Learn

To use proportions to find missing measurements of similar solids, including surface area and volume

New Vocabulary similar solids

Why Learn This?

The dolls in the photo at the right have proportional heights and diameters. These and other art objects are examples of similar solids.

Two solids are **similar solids** if they have the same shape and if all of their corresponding dimensions are proportional.

You can use a proportion to find the missing dimensions of similar solids.

Check Skills You'll Need

1. A proportion is an equation stating that two ratios are equal.

GO for Help

For help with proportions and similar figures, go to Lesson 4-4, Example 2.

EXAMPLE Finding Dimensions of a Similar Solid

1 The two pyramids below are similar. Find the value of x.

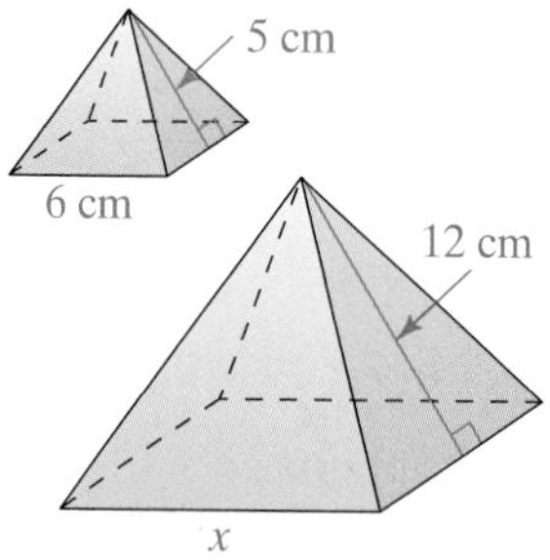

Use corresponding parts to write a proportion.

$$\frac{x}{6} = \frac{12}{5}$$ ← dimensions of large pyramid / ← dimensions of small pyramid

$$6 \cdot \frac{x}{6} = \frac{12}{5} \cdot 6$$ ← Multiply each side by 6.

$$x = \frac{72}{5}$$ ← Simplify.

$$= 14.4$$

The base-edge length x is 14.4 cm.

Quick Check

1. Two cylinders are similar. The small cylinder has a diameter of 4 m and a height of h. The large cylinder has a diameter of 5 m and a height of 11 m. What is the value of h? 8.8 m

Differentiated Instruction Solutions for All Learners

Special Needs L1	Below Level L2
Students are given nets of similar rectangular prisms drawn on grid paper. They then build the solids. Students count the units along the length of the sides of each to verify that corresponding side lengths are proportional. learning style: visual	Students explain why the ratio of the surface areas of similar solids equals the ratio of the squares of the linear measurements. Students describe the difference between one-, two-, and three-dimensional measures. learning style: verbal

KEY CONCEPTS Surface Area and Volume of Similar Solids

If the ratio of the corresponding dimensions of similar solids is $\frac{a}{b}$, then

- the ratio of surface areas is $\frac{a^2}{b^2}$ and
- the ratio of volumes is $\frac{a^3}{b^3}$.

You can use ratios of corresponding dimensions to find the surface area and volume of similar solids.

EXAMPLE Surface Area and Volume of Similar Solids

Careers Some potters make ceramic pieces by shaping wet clay as it spins on a potter's wheel.

2 **Pottery** The surface area of the cylindrical pitcher below is about 90 in.^{2}. Its volume is about 157 in.^{3}. The pitcher and creamer are similar. Find the surface area and volume of the creamer.

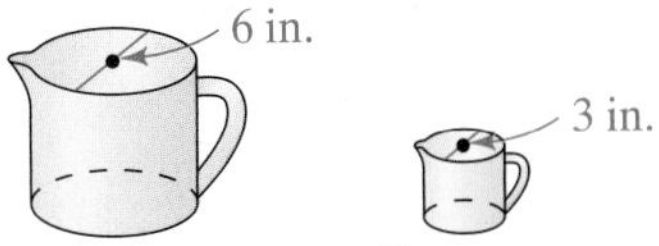

The ratio of the diameters is $\frac{3}{6}$, or $\frac{1}{2}$. So the ratio of the surface areas is $\frac{1^2}{2^2}$, or $\frac{1}{4}$.

$\frac{\text{surface area of creamer}}{\text{surface area of pitcher}} = \frac{1}{4}$ ← **Write a proportion.**

$\frac{S}{90} = \frac{1}{4}$ ← **Substitute the surface area of the pitcher.**

$4 \cdot S = 1 \cdot 90$ ← **Write the cross products.**

$S = 22.5$ ← **Simplify.**

The surface area of the creamer is about 22.5 in.^{2}.

If the ratio of the diameters is $\frac{1}{2}$, the ratio of the volumes is $\frac{1^3}{2^3}$, or $\frac{1}{8}$.

$\frac{\text{volume of creamer}}{\text{volume of pitcher}} = \frac{1}{8}$ ← **Write a proportion.**

$\frac{V}{157} = \frac{1}{8}$ ← **Substitute the volume of the pitcher.**

$8 \cdot V = 1 \cdot 157$ ← **Write the cross products.**

$V = 19.625$ ← **Simplify.**

The volume of the creamer is about 20 in.^{3}.

Quick Check

See left.

2. A box has a surface area of about 54 in.^{2} and a volume of about 27 in.^{3}. The edge lengths of the box are about $\frac{1}{3}$ of the edge lengths of a larger box. Find the surface area and volume of the larger box.

2. 486 in.^{2}; 729 in.^{3}

2. Teach

Activity Lab

Use before the lesson.
Student Edition Activity Lab 8-9a, Changing Dimensions, p. 397

All in One Teaching Resources

Activity Lab 8-9: Exploring Similar Solids

Guided Instruction

Concrete Models
Have students construct similar figures, including prisms, pyramids, and cylinders, out of cardboard. Have them calculate lateral and total surface area by measuring or covering the models with paper.

PowerPoint

Additional Examples

1 The two triangular pyramids are similar. Find the value of x. **9 in.**

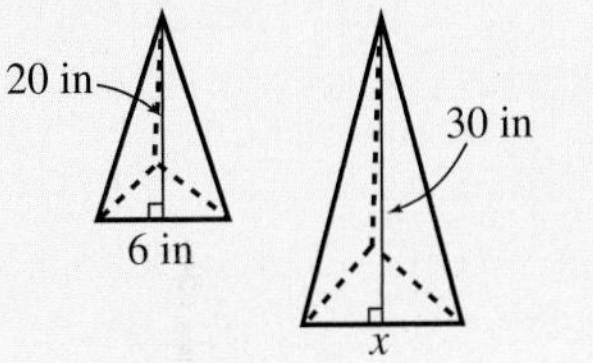

2 The surface area of a cylindrical vase is about 1,470 in.^{2} and its volume is about 490 in.^{3}. The vase is similar to a drinking glass. The diameter of the vase is 6 in. and that of the drinking glass is 3 in. Find the surface area and volume of the drinking glass. **about 368 in.^{2}; about 61 in.^{3}**

All in One Teaching Resources

- Daily Notetaking Guide 8-9 L3
- Adapted Notetaking 8-9 L1

Closure

- *How do you find the dimensions of similar solids using proportions?*
- *How do you find surface areas and volumes of similar solids?*
See back of book.

Advanced Learners L4	**English Language Learners** ELL
Students design a triangular prism and a square prism that will have the same volume; draw and mark the dimensions on each. Get a partner to check the volumes. **learning style: visual**	Students review the meaning of *double* (two times as much), *triple* (three times as much), and *quadruple* (four times as much). They compare the prefixes to numbers in their own and other languages, such as Latin, Spanish, and French. **learning style: verbal**

3. Practice

Assignment Guide

Check Your Understanding

Go over Exercises 1–4 in class before assigning the Homework Exercises.

Homework Exercises

A Practice by Example	5–9
B Apply Your Skills	10–16
C Challenge	17
Test Prep and Mixed Review	18–23

Homework Quick Check

To check students' understanding of key skills and concepts, go over Exercises 6, 9, 10, 14, and 15.

Differentiated Instruction Resources

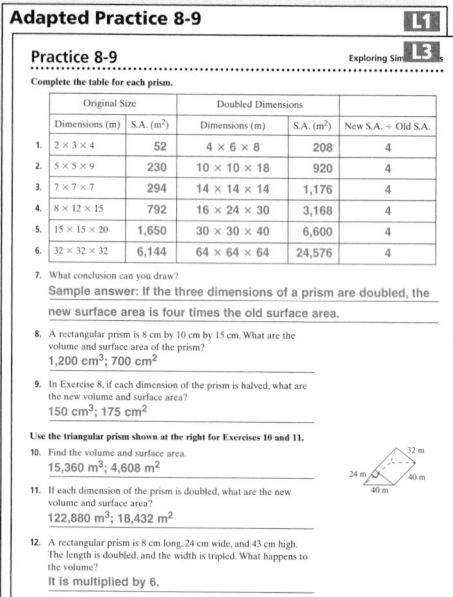

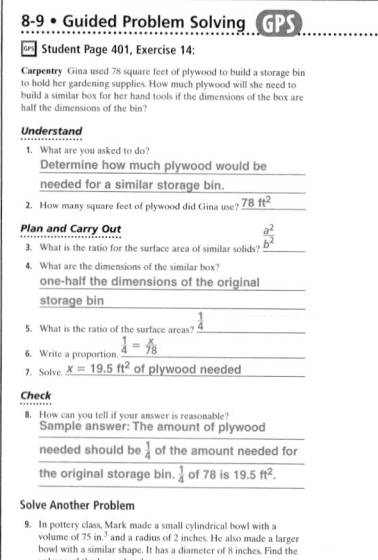

Adapted Practice 8-9 L1

Practice 8-9 Exploring Sim[...]s L3

Complete the table for each prism.

	Original Size		Doubled Dimensions		
	Dimensions (m)	S.A. (m^2)	Dimensions (m)	S.A. (m^2)	New S.A. ÷ Old S.A.
1.	2 × 3 × 4	52	4 × 6 × 8	208	4
2.	5 × 5 × 9	230	10 × 10 × 18	920	4
3.	7 × 7 × 7	294	14 × 14 × 14	1,176	4
4.	8 × 12 × 15	792	16 × 24 × 30	3,168	4
5.	15 × 15 × 20	1,650	30 × 30 × 40	6,600	4
6.	32 × 32 × 32	6,144	64 × 64 × 64	24,576	4

7. What conclusion can you draw?
Sample answer: If the three dimensions of a prism are doubled, the new surface area is four times the old surface area.

8. A rectangular prism is 8 cm by 10 cm by 15 cm. What are the volume and surface area of the prism?
1,200 cm^3; 700 cm^2

9. In Exercise 8, if each dimension of the prism is halved, what are the new volume and surface area?
150 cm^3; 175 cm^2

Use the triangular prism shown at the right for Exercises 10 and 11.

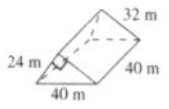

10. Find the volume and surface area.
15,360 m^3; 4,608 m^2

11. If each dimension of the prism is doubled, what are the new volume and surface area?
122,880 m^3; 18,432 m^2

12. A rectangular prism is 8 cm long, 24 cm wide, and 43 cm high. The length is doubled, and the width is tripled. What happens to the volume?
It is multiplied by 6.

8-9 • Guided Problem Solving GPS L3

GPS Student Page 401, Exercise 14:

Carpentry Gina used 78 square feet of plywood to build a storage bin to hold her gardening supplies. How much plywood will she need to build a similar box for her hand tools if the dimensions of the box are half the dimensions of the bin?

Understand

1. What are you asked to do?
Determine how much plywood would be needed for a similar storage bin.
2. How many square feet of plywood did Gina use? 78 ft^2

Plan and Carry Out

3. What is the ratio for the surface area of similar solids? $\frac{a^2}{b^2}$
4. What are the dimensions of the similar box?
one-half the dimensions of the original storage bin
5. What is the ratio of the surface areas? $\frac{1}{4}$
6. Write a proportion. $\frac{1}{4} = \frac{x}{78}$
7. Solve. $x = 19.5$ ft^2 of plywood needed

Check

8. How can you tell if your answer is reasonable?
Sample answer: The amount of plywood needed should be $\frac{1}{4}$ of the amount needed for the original storage bin. $\frac{1}{4}$ of 78 is 19.5 ft^2.

Solve Another Problem

9. In pottery class, Mark made a small cylindrical bowl with a volume of 75 in.^{3} and a radius of 2 inches. He also made a larger bowl with a similar shape. It has a diameter of 8 inches. Find the volume of the larger bowl.
$\frac{1}{8} = \frac{75}{x}$; $x = 600$; 600 in.^{3}

Check Your Understanding

1. **Vocabulary** What does it mean to say that two rectangular solids are similar? Two solids are similar if they have the same shape and all their corresponding lengths are proportional.

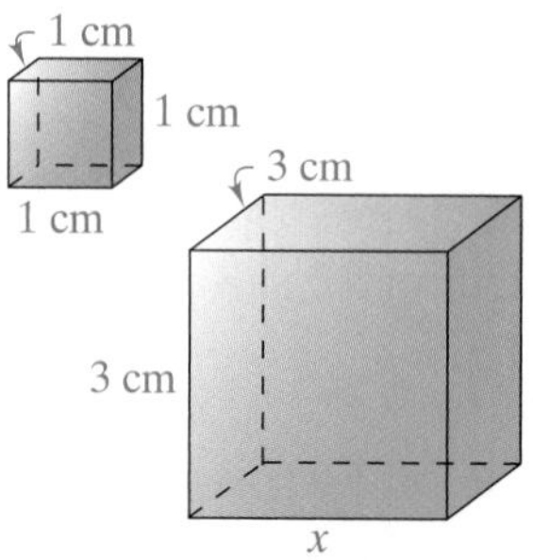

Use the similar solids at the left for Exercises 2–4.

2. What proportion would you write to find x? $\frac{1}{3} = \frac{1}{x}$
3. The surface area of the smaller cube is 6 cm^2. What is the surface area of the larger cube? 54 cm^2
4. **Mental Math** The volume of the smaller cube is 1 cm^3. What is the volume of the larger cube? 27 cm^3

Homework Exercises

For more exercises, see Extra Skills and Word Problems.

GO for Help

For Exercises	See Examples
5–6	1
7–9	2

A For each pair of similar solids, find the value of the variable.

5.

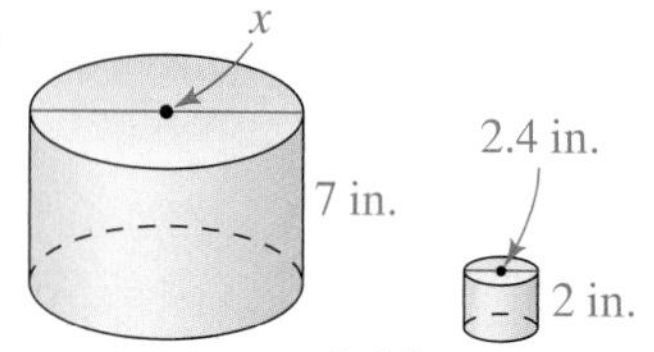

8.4 in.

6.

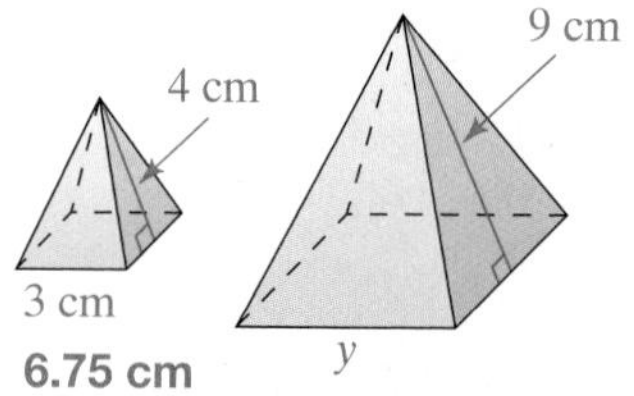

6.75 cm

Find the surface area and volume of each smaller similar solid.

7. S.A. = 1,575 m^2 1,008 m^2; 2,074 m^3
$V = 4{,}050$ m^3

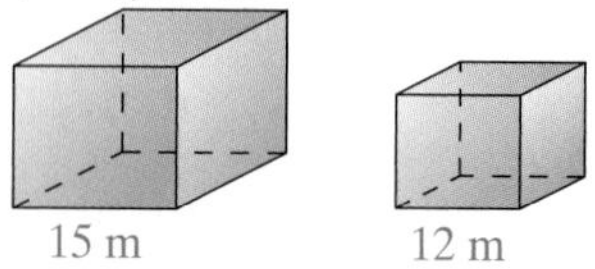

8.

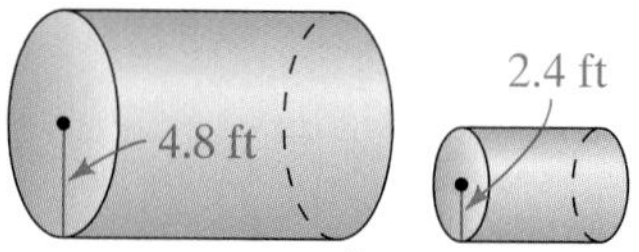

S.A. = 356 ft^2
$V = 507$ ft^3 89 ft^2; 63 ft^3

9. 3,484 in.^{2}; 804 in.^{3}

9. **Vases** Two similar cylindrical vases have diameters of 6 in. and 8 in. The smaller vase has a surface area of 1,960 in.^{2} and a volume of 339 in.^{3}. Find the surface area and volume of the larger vase. See left.

B GPS 10. **Guided Problem Solving** A glass cube has edges that are $\frac{3}{4}$ of the length of the edges of a larger cube. The larger cube has a surface area of 6,000 cm^2. What is the surface area of the smaller cube?
- The ratio of the surface areas is ■. 3,375 cm^2
- How can you use the ratio of the surface areas in a proportion to find the surface area of the smaller cube?

11. Two prisms are similar. The larger prism has a height of 18 m and a base-edge length of 20 m. The smaller prism has a height of 4.5 m. What is the base-edge length of the smaller prism? 5 m

12. Answers may vary. Sample: about 20 times as great.
$\frac{2.5^3}{1^3} = \frac{V}{1}$, $V \approx 16$
$\frac{3^3}{1^3} = \frac{V}{1}$, $V \approx 27$
So the volume would be between 16 and 27 times as great.

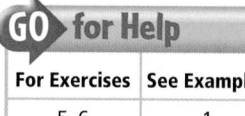

GO Online
Homework Video Tutor
Visit: PHSchool.com
Web Code: ase-0809

12. **Number Sense** Amelia sees two cubic sculptures. She estimates the edge length of the larger sculpture is between 2.5 and 3 times the edge length of the smaller one. How much greater should she estimate the volume of the larger sculpture to be? Explain. See margin.

13. A second figure with a height of 19 ft is similar to the figure at the right. Find the surface area and volume of the second figure. $1{,}274\text{ ft}^2$; $2{,}382\text{ ft}^3$

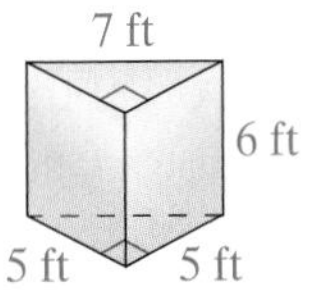

14. **Carpentry** Gina used 78 square feet of plywood to build a storage (GPS) bin to hold her gardening supplies. How much plywood will she need to build a similar box for her hand tools if the dimensions of the box are half the dimensions of the bin? 19.5 ft^2

15. **Writing in Math** Explain how to determine whether two cones are similar. If the ratio of their heights is the same as the ratio of their radii, they are similar.

16. **Algebra** Two prisms are similar. The surface area of one is four times the surface area of the other. What is the ratio of the corresponding dimensions? $\frac{2}{1}$

(C) 17. **Challenge** How long is the edge of a cube whose volume is twice that of the cube at the right? Round to the nearest tenth. 10.1 cm

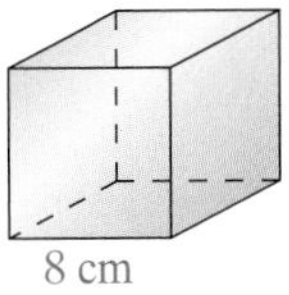

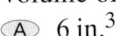

Test Prep and Mixed Review — Practice

Multiple Choice

18. The volume of the larger cube at the right is 216 cubic inches. What is the volume of the smaller cube? B
    - (A) 6 in.^3
    - (B) 8 in.^3
    - (C) 24 in.^3
    - (D) 72 in.^3

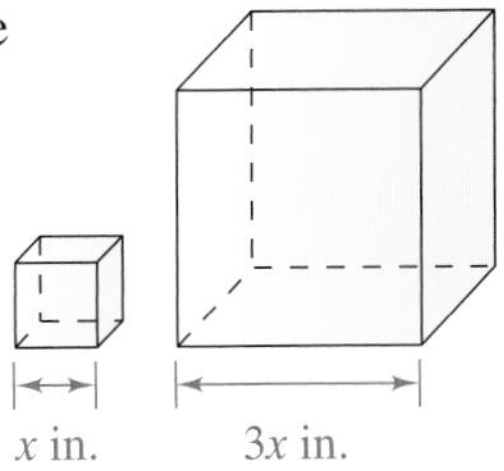

19. Mr. Coffey has 300 yd of fencing for a rectangular garden. A river borders one side. He uses whole-number lengths of fencing for the remaining three sides. What is the greatest area he can enclose? H
    - (F) $5{,}625\text{ yd}^2$ (G) $10{,}000\text{ yd}^2$ (H) $11{,}250\text{ yd}^2$ (J) $22{,}500\text{ yd}^2$

20. There are 5.256×10^5 minutes in a year. A teenager's heart beats about 80 times per minute. How many times does it beat in a year? C
    - (A) 6.57×10^7 (C) 4.205×10^7
    - (B) 6.57×10^3 (D) 4.205×10^3

GO for Help

For Exercises	See Lesson
21–23	2-8

Write each number in scientific notation.

21. 75,000 7.5×10^4
22. 0.00194 1.94×10^{-3}
23. 0.000083 8.3×10^{-5}

Online lesson quiz, PHSchool.com, Web Code: asa-0809

4. Assess & Reteach

PowerPoint

Lesson Quiz

Use these similar square pyramids to answer items 1-4.

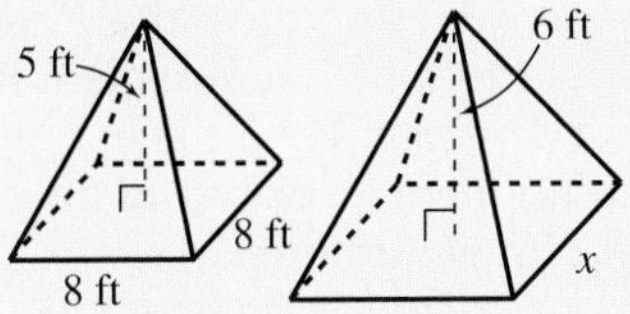

1. Find the ratio of the corresponding dimensions of the smaller pyramid to the larger pyramid. 5 : 6
2. The surface area of the larger pyramid is 239.7 ft^2. Find the surface area of the smaller pyramid. about 166.5 ft^2
3. Find the volume of the larger pyramid to the nearest cubic foot. 184 ft^3
4. Find the value of x. 9.6 ft

Alternative Assessment

Students make a rectangular solid from a graph-paper net. They then count squares to find its surface area. Students then double and halve the dimensions to create two other rectangular solids. Then they compare their surface areas.

Test Prep

Resources

- For additional practice with a variety of test item formats:
- Test-Taking Strategies, p. 403
- Test Prep, p. 407
- Test-Taking Strategies with Transparencies

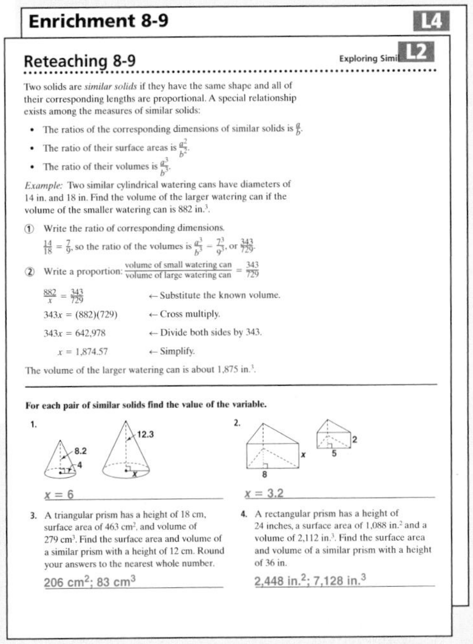

Enrichment 8-9 L4

Reteaching 8-9 Exploring Simil L2

Two solids are *similar solids* if they have the same shape and all of their corresponding lengths are proportional. A special relationship exists among the measures of similar solids:

- The ratios of the corresponding dimensions of similar solids is $\frac{a}{b}$.
- The ratio of their surface areas is $\frac{a^2}{b^2}$.
- The ratio of their volumes is $\frac{a^3}{b^3}$.

Example: Two similar cylindrical watering cans have diameters of 14 in. and 18 in. Find the volume of the larger watering can if the volume of the smaller watering can is 882 in.^3.

① Write the ratio of corresponding dimensions.
$\frac{14}{18} = \frac{7}{9}$, so the ratio of the volumes is $\frac{a^3}{b^3} = \frac{7^3}{9^3}$, or $\frac{343}{729}$.

② Write a proportion: $\frac{\text{volume of small watering can}}{\text{volume of large watering can}} = \frac{343}{729}$

$\frac{882}{x} = \frac{343}{729}$ ← Substitute the known volume.
$343x = (882)(729)$ ← Cross multiply.
$343x = 642{,}978$ ← Divide both sides by 343.
$x = 1{,}874.57$ ← Simplify.

The volume of the larger watering can is about $1{,}875\text{ in.}^3$.

For each pair of similar solids find the value of the variable.

1. 8.2, 4, 12.3, x — $x = 6$
2. x, 8, 2, 5 — $x = 3.2$
3. A triangular prism has a height of 18 cm, surface area of 463 cm^2, and volume of 279 cm^3. Find the surface area and volume of a similar prism with a height of 12 cm. Round your answers to the nearest whole number. 206 cm^2; 83 cm^3
4. A rectangular prism has a height of 24 inches, a surface area of $1{,}088\text{ in.}^2$ and a volume of $2{,}112\text{ in.}^3$. Find the surface area and volume of a similar prism with a height of 36 in. $2{,}448\text{ in.}^2$; $7{,}128\text{ in.}^3$

Activity Lab

Precision and Significant Digits

This activity introduces the concept that no measurement is exact. The precision of any measurement is related to the unit of measure used. A measurement can be no more precise than the accuracy of the instrument making the measurement. The use of significant digits is also introduced.

Guided Instruction

Discuss with students that when adding or subtracting numbers, the answer must be rounded off to match the precision of the less precise number. As an example, 2.3 + 4 = 6 while 2.3 + 4.0 = 6.3.

Emphasize that when multiplying or dividing numbers, the result must be rounded off to match the measurement with the least number of significant digits. Give an example of significant digits: 22 has two significant digits while 22.4 has three. Then go over the information in the chart. Have students provide additional examples for each of the cases presented. Emphasize the fact that significant digits are counted only when multiplying or dividing.

Error Prevention!

Tell students that zeros placed *between* other digits are *always* significant: 0.046 has two significant digits, whereas 4009 has four. This explains why the zero preceding the 4 in 0.006040 for the first case in the chart is significant.

8-9b Activity Lab — Data Analysis

Precision and Significant Digits

When you add or subtract measurements, your results can be only as precise as the least precise measurement. The measurement with the smaller units is more precise.

When you multiply or divide measurements, you use significant digits to determine how precise your result should be. Round your answer to match the measurement with the fewest significant digits.

Type of Number	Which Zeros Are Significant	Example
Decimal numbers between 0 and 1	Zeros to the left of *all* the nonzero digits are not significant. All other zeros are significant.	Significant digits: 6040; 0.006040; Not significant digits: 0.00
Positive integers	Zeros to the right of *all* the nonzero digits are not significant. Zeros between nonzero digits are significant.	Significant digits: 2034; 203,400; Not significant digits: 00
Noninteger decimal numbers greater than 1	All zeros are significant.	Significant digits: 350,070.50

EXAMPLES Calculating With Measurements

1 Add 20.08 km + 5.2 km.

20.08 km + 5.2 km = 25.28 km ← **Add.**

≈ 25.3 km ← **Since 5.2 is less precise than 20.08, round to the nearest tenth.**

2 Find the area of a plot of land that is 115.6 ft by 81.2 ft.

115.6 · 81.2 = 9,386.72 ← **Multiply.**

115.6: **4 significant digits**; 81.2: **3 significant digits**

Since the least number of significant digits in the measurement is 3, round the answer to 3 significant digits. The area is about 9,390 ft^2.

Exercises

Compute.

1. 34 ft + 16.9 ft 51 ft
2. 1.1 cm + 1.01 cm 2.1 cm
3. 60 in. − 22.80 in. 40 in.
4. 42.00 m^2 − 21.0 m^2 21.0 m^2
5. 372 mi × 278 mi 103,000 mi^2
6. 189.9 km × 5.40 km 1,030 km^2
7. 6 yd ÷ 0.0569 yd 100
8. 124.6 m ÷ 8.101 m 15.38

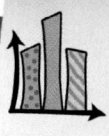

Eliminating Answers

Before solving a multiple-choice problem, you can usually eliminate some answer choices. This can save you time and help you to make an "educated" guess if you do not actually know how to find the answer.

EXAMPLE

Find the volume of the square pyramid below.

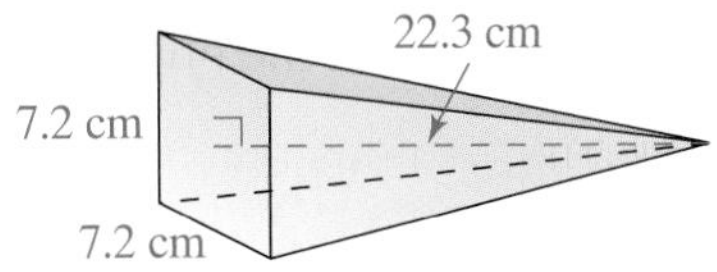

Ⓐ $36.528\ \text{cm}^3$ Ⓒ $320.724\ \text{cm}^3$
Ⓑ $385.344\ \text{cm}^3$ Ⓓ $3{,}187.367\ \text{cm}^3$

Underestimate and overestimate the answer using compatible numbers.

Underestimate

$V = \frac{1}{3}Bh \approx \frac{1}{3}(48)(20) = 320$

Overestimate

$V = \frac{1}{3}Bh \approx \frac{1}{3}(50)(24) = 400$

The correct answer is between 320 and 400. Since choices A and D are not between 320 and 400, you can eliminate them. Choice C is very close to the underestimate, so you can make an educated guess that choice B is the most likely answer.

Exercises

1. To the nearest square meter, what is the surface area of a cone with a radius of 3 m and a slant height of 4 m? **B**
   Ⓐ $21\ \text{m}^2$ Ⓑ $66\ \text{m}^2$ Ⓒ $83\ \text{m}^2$ Ⓓ $120\ \text{m}^2$
2. A cell measures 1.3×10^{-5} mm in length. Which number represents this measurement in standard form? **J**
   Ⓕ 130,000 Ⓖ 13 Ⓗ 0.013 Ⓙ 0.000013
3. A gift box is 24 inches long, 8 inches wide, and 6 inches high. Which is closest to the volume of the box in cubic feet? **A**
   Ⓐ $\frac{1}{2}\ \text{ft}^3$ Ⓑ $2\frac{1}{2}\ \text{ft}^3$ Ⓒ $3\ \text{ft}^3$ Ⓓ $6\ \text{ft}^3$

Eliminating Answers

Students can increase their chances of success on multiple choice standardized tests by eliminating answer choices in multiple-choice questions.

Guided Instruction

Error Prevention!

Many students are more comfortable with calculating solutions than considering their reasonableness. Encourage students to think about which answers are either too high or too low to be valid. Underestimating and overestimating the answer using compatible numbers can help identify these values.

Differentiated Instruction

Visual Learners
To help students maintain focus, have them cross out choices as they are eliminated.

Resources

Test-Taking Strategies with Transparencies
- Transparency 6
- Practice sheet, p. 32

Test-Taking Strategies with Transparencies

Test-Taking Strategies: Eliminating Answers

When solving a multiple choice problem, first try to eliminate some of the answer choices.

Be sure to cross out answers you eliminate in the test booklet—*not* on the answer sheet.

Example The original price of a coat was \$65. It was discounted 20% the day you bought it. How much money did you save?
A. \$78 B. \$52 C. \$13 D. \$5

Since \$78 is more than the original amount, you can immediately eliminate choice A.

By estimating you can determine that \$60 times 0.20 is greater than \$5, so you can eliminate choice D.

Since the question is asking for how much you saved, you can eliminate choice B because you know by estimating that you did not save more than 50% of the original price.

The answer is choice C.

Identify two answer choices you can immediately eliminate. Then solve the problem.

1. There are 32 students in Wyatt's class. At least 75% of the students have been vaccinated against chicken pox. About how many students have not had this vaccination?
   A. 40 students B. 28 students
   C. 16 students D. 8 students

Eliminate choice A: There are only 32 students in the class. Eliminate choice B: By estimating you know that less than half the class has not had the vaccination. The answer is choice D.

Chapter 8 Review

Resources

Student Edition
Extra Skills and Word Problems Practice, Ch. 8, p. 618
English/Spanish Glossary, p. 650
Formulas and Properties, p. 648
Tables, p. 643

All in One Teaching Resources
- Vocabulary and Study Skills 8F L3

Differentiated Instruction
Spanish Vocabulary Workbook with Study Skills ELL
Interactive Textbook
- Audio Glossary

Online Vocabulary Quiz

Success Tracker™
Online at PHSchool.com

Spanish Vocabulary/Study Skills ELL

Vocabulary/Study Skills L3

8F: Vocabulary Review For use with the Chapter Review

Vocabulary and Study Skills

Study Skill Take a few minutes to relax before and after studying. Your mind will absorb and retain more information if you alternate studying with brief rest intervals.

Find and circle each of the words below in the puzzle. Words can be displayed forwards, backwards, up, down, or diagonally.

prism	pyramid	cylinder	cone
skew	polyhedron	space figures	obtuse
precision	isometric view	base plan	slant height
scale factor	parallelogram	square	rectangle
rhombus	acute	straight	

Q	D	R	S	N	O	U	T	A	L	L	E	S	S	E	T	H	M
O	R	H	V	A	W	I	X	L	R	R	U	P	M	R	E	N	B
N	U	O	Q	Z	E	J	J	E	A	S	Y	A	P	C	W	U	G
O	C	M	O	J	I	I	J	E	N	R	F	P	R	I	S	M	X
R	Y	B	W	R	V	X	N	E	A	O	F	B	H	S	R	Y	M
D	L	U	R	L	C	V	O	M	F	S	C	A	Z	Q	V	A	R
E	I	S	E	E	I	Y	I	B	Z	W	K	S	A	U	S	Z	G
H	N	U	C	S	R	D	E	K	F	F	S	E	K	A	L	N	Y
Y	D	R	T	U	T	J	G	B	B	Z	T	P	W	R	A	O	Y
L	E	P	A	T	E	S	T	O	H	V	R	L	D	E	N	I	B
O	R	B	N	B	M	T	K	F	E	S	A	A	O	D	T	S	O
P	U	R	G	O	O	F	A	Q	R	H	I	N	N	G	H	I	O
I	C	J	L	F	S	Z	H	K	Z	X	G	B	S	U	E	C	P
C	J	X	E	J	I	C	N	P	H	J	H	U	Y	O	I	E	V
N	F	I	S	X	X	N	X	L	V	E	T	U	C	A	G	R	I
P	A	R	A	L	L	E	L	O	G	R	A	M	E	N	H	P	V
X	O	N	F	S	C	A	L	E	F	A	C	T	O	R	T	Y	R
A	X	J	S	E	R	U	G	I	F	E	C	A	P	S	J	I	K

404

Chapter 8 Review

Vocabulary Review

base plan (p. 358)	**polyhedron** (p. 354)	**slant height** (p. 374)
cone (p. 354)	**prism** (p. 354)	**solids** (p. 354)
cylinder (p. 354)	**pyramid** (p. 354)	**sphere** (p. 393)
isometric view (p. 359)	**similar solids** (p. 398)	**surface area** (p. 368)
lateral area (p. 369)	**skew lines** (p. 355)	**volume** (p. 380)
net (p. 364)		

Go Online
PHSchool.com
For: Online vocabulary quiz
Web Code: asj-0851

Choose the correct vocabulary term above to complete each sentence.

1. The _?_ of an object is the number of cubic units in the object. volume
2. A(n) _?_ has one base and one vertex, but it is not a polyhedron. cone
3. Both _?_ area and _?_ area are measured in square units. lateral, surface
4. Both a(n) _?_ and a(n) _?_ have two parallel, congruent bases. cylinder, prism
5. A(n) _?_ shows all the surfaces of a solid in one view. isometric view

Skills and Concepts

Lesson 8-1
- To identify solids, parts of solids, and skew line segments

Solids are any objects that have a length, a width, and a height. If all the faces of a solid are polygons, the figure is a **polyhedron. Prisms** and **pyramids** are polyhedrons. **Cylinders** and **cones** are not polyhedrons.

For each solid, describe the shape of the base(s) and the lateral surface(s).

6. rectangular prism
rectangle, parallelograms
7. square pyramid
square, triangles
8. cylinder
circle, curved surface

Lessons 8-2, 8-3
- To draw views of three-dimensional figures, including base plans and isometric views
- To identify nets of solids

A **base plan** shows the shape of the base and the height of each part of a solid. Top, front, and right views show a solid from three different perspectives. A **net** is a pattern that can be folded to form a solid.

Draw a base plan and top, front, and right views of each figure.

9. 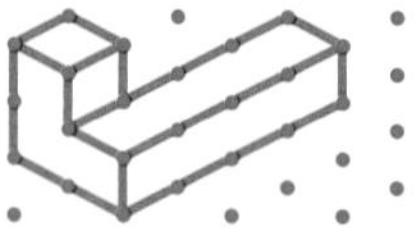

10. 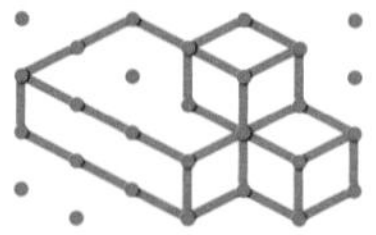

11. 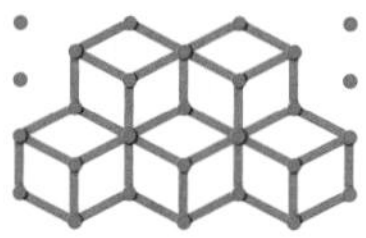

9–11. See margin.

Identify the solid formed by each net.

12. 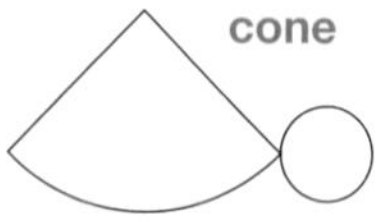
cone

13. 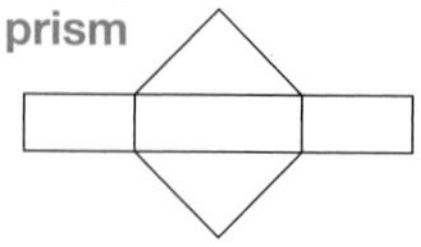
triangular prism

14. 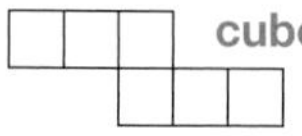
cube

9. 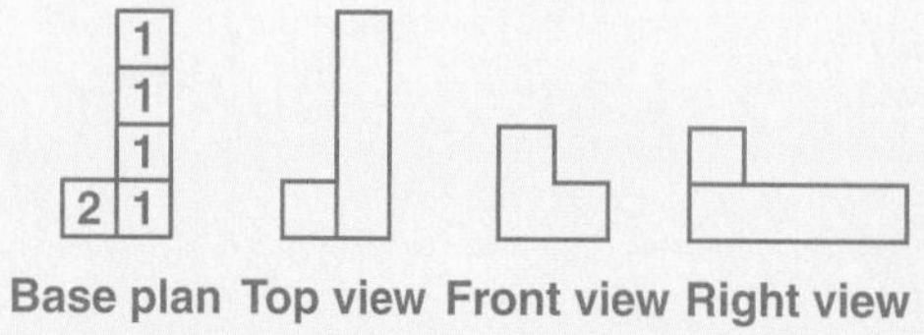

10. 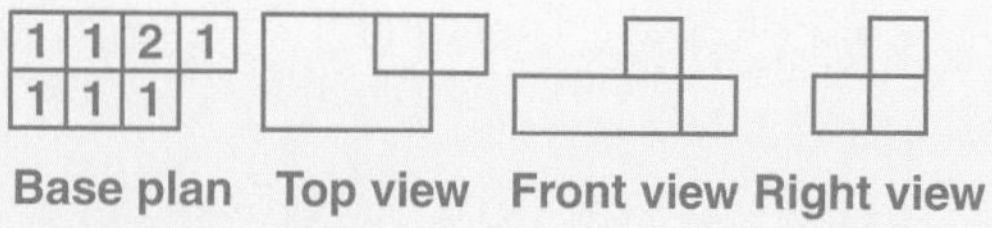

11. 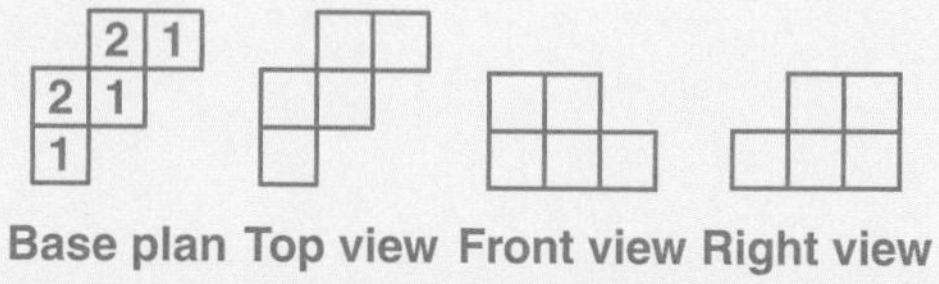

Lessons 8-4, 8-6

- To find surface areas of prisms and cylinders using nets and formulas
- To find the volumes of prisms and cylinders

Lateral area L.A. is the sum of the areas of all of a solid's surfaces except the base(s). **Surface area** S.A. is the sum of the areas of all of the surfaces of a solid. **Volume** V is the number of cubic units in a solid.

Formulas for prisms	Formulas for cylinders	Volume formula for prisms and cylinders
L.A. $= ph$	L.A. $= 2\pi rh$	$V = Bh$
S.A. $=$ L.A. $+ 2B$	S.A. $=$ L.A. $+ 2B$	

Find the surface area and volume to the nearest whole number.

15. 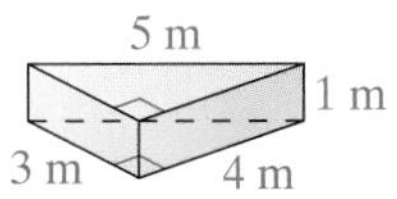

16. 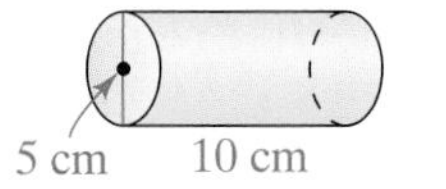

17. 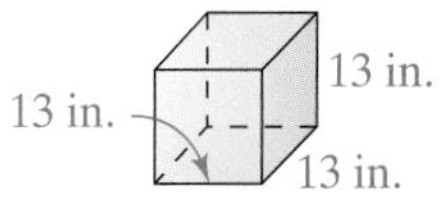

15–17. See margin.

Lessons 8-5, 8-7

- To find surface areas of pyramids and cones using nets and formulas
- To find the volumes of pyramids and cones

The **slant height** ℓ of a pyramid or a cone is the distance from the figure's vertex to its base edge b. It is used to find the lateral area or surface area.

Formulas for pyramids	Formulas for cones	Volume formula for pyramids and cones
L.A. $= 2b\ell$	L.A. $= \pi r\ell$	$V = \frac{1}{3}Bh$
S.A. $=$ L.A. $+ B$	S.A. $=$ L.A. $+ B$	

Find the surface area and volume to the nearest whole number.

18. 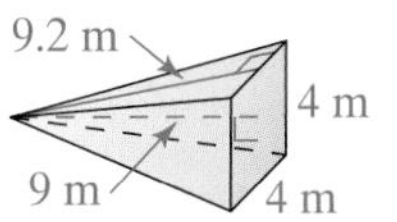

19. 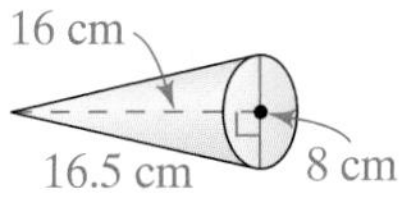

20. 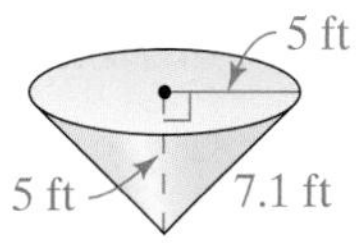

18–20. See margin.

Lesson 8-8

- To find the surface area and volume of a sphere

A **sphere** is the set of all points in space that are the same distance from a center point. The formula for the surface area of a sphere is S.A. $= 4\pi r^2$. The formula for volume is $V = \frac{4}{3}\pi r^3$.

21. The earth has a diameter of about 13,000 km. Estimate the earth's surface area and volume. 5.3×10^8 km^2; 1.15×10^{12} km^3

Lesson 8-9

- To use proportions to find missing measurements of similar solids, including surface area and volume

Similar solids have the same shape and proportional corresponding dimensions. If the ratio of their corresponding dimensions is $\frac{a}{b}$, the ratio of their surface areas is $\frac{a^2}{b^2}$, and the ratio of their volumes is $\frac{a^3}{b^3}$.

For each solid, find the surface area and volume of a similar solid whose dimensions are $\frac{4}{5}$ of those given. Round to the nearest whole number. 22–24. See margin.

22. 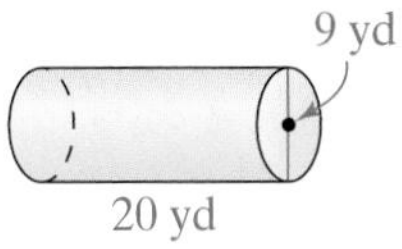

23. 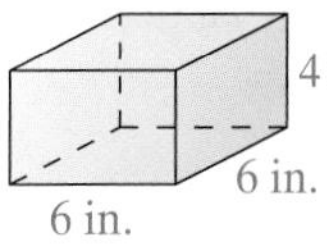

24. 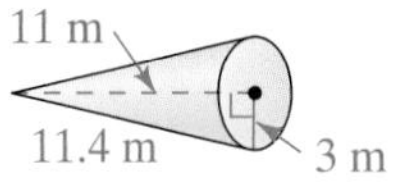

Alternative Assessment L4

Alternative Assessment

Chapter 8

WHO ATE THE CAKE?

Mr. Lee made a three-layer cake with icing on the top and sides. He left it on a paper plate in the kitchen. Each of his five children came in one at a time and had a piece of cake. The cuts left lines on the paper plate just like those shown here.

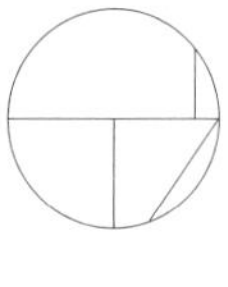

Mr. Lee thought the lines looked so peculiar that he wanted to know who ate each piece. He called the children into the kitchen to hear their explanations.

Joan said she cut the first piece, without making a central angle. Then Kyle made a cut almost the length of the diameter of the cake. He ate the smaller of the two pieces he created. Then Mark made one cut, which started at the center of the cake and was perpendicular to a cut Kyle had made. Nedra said she came after Mark. Nedra made a cut so that her piece would have a very large ratio of icing to cake. Chris ate the last piece.

Show all of your work on a separate sheet of paper.

1. Trace the outline of the cake slices on your paper. Write each person's name on the portion of the plate that outlines that person's piece of cake.
2. Mr. Lee used three pans for his cake, one pan for each layer, each with an eight-inch diameter. Each of the three layers is about 1 in. tall. About how many cubic inches was the volume of the cake? Use an approximation for π.
3. Estimate the number of cubic inches each child ate. Show or describe how you arrive at each estimate.

15. 24 m^2; 6 m^3
16. 196 cm^2; 196 cm^3
17. 1,014 in.^{2}; 2,197 in.^{3}
18. 90 m^2; 48 m^3
19. 258 cm^2; 268 cm^3
20. 190 ft^2; 131 ft^3

22. 443 yd^2; 651 yd^3
23. 108 in.^{2}; 74 in.^{3}
24. 87 m^2; 53 m^3

Resources

- ExamView Assessment Suite CD-ROM
  - Chapter 8 Ready-Made Test
  - Make your own Chapter 8 test
- MindPoint Quiz Show CD-ROM
  - Chapter 8 Review

Differentiated Instruction

All in One Teaching Resources
- Below Level Chapter 8 Test L2
- Chapter 8 Test L3
- Chapter 8 Alternative Assessment L4

Spanish Assessment Resources ELL
- Below Level Chapter 8 Test L2
- Chapter 8 Test L3
- Chapter 8 Alternative Assessment L4

ExamView Assessment Suite CD-ROM
- Special Needs Test L1
- Special Needs Practice Bank L1

Online Chapter 8 Test at www.PHSchool.com L3

7.
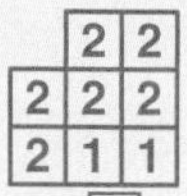

8.
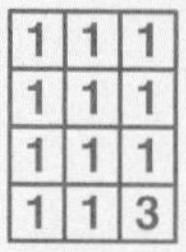

9.
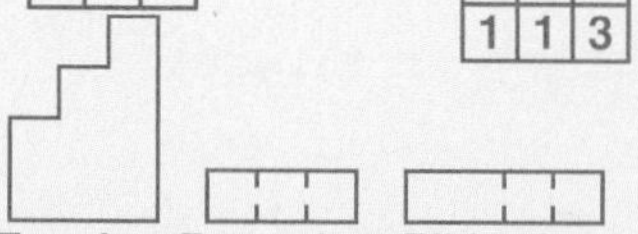

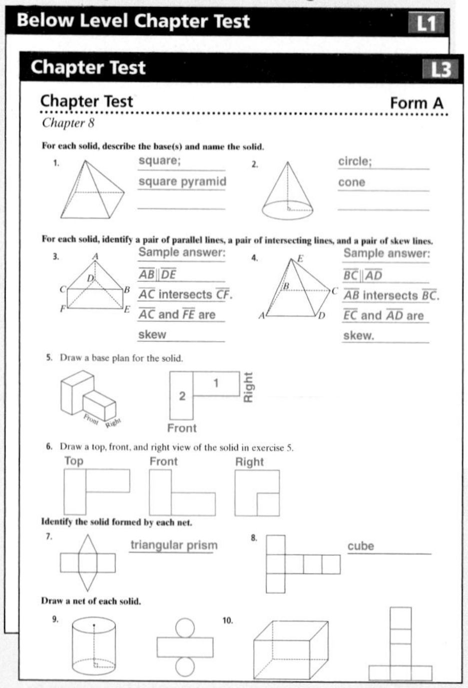
Below Level Chapter Test L1

Chapter Test L3

Chapter Test Form A

Chapter 8

For each solid, describe the base(s) and name the solid.

1. square; square pyramid
2. circle; cone

For each solid, identify a pair of parallel lines, a pair of intersecting lines, and a pair of skew lines.

3. Sample answer: $\overline{AB} \parallel \overline{DE}$; $\overline{AC}$ intersects $\overline{CF}$. $\overline{AC}$ and $\overline{FE}$ are skew
4. Sample answer: $\overline{BC} \parallel \overline{AD}$; $\overline{AB}$ intersects $\overline{BC}$. $\overline{EC}$ and $\overline{AD}$ are skew.

5. Draw a base plan for the solid.

6. Draw a top, front, and right view of the solid in exercise 5.

Top Front Right

Identify the solid formed by each net.

7. triangular prism
8. cube

Draw a net of each solid.

9.
10.

Chapter 8 Test

Go Online PHSchool.com For: Online chapter test Web Code: asa-0852

Name each solid and describe its base(s).

1. 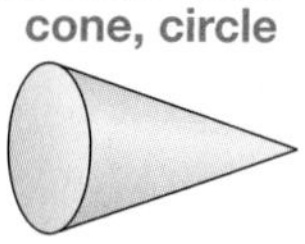 cone, circle
2. 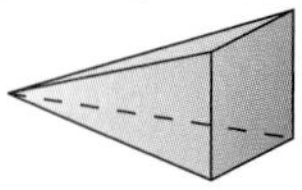 pyramid, rectangle
3. 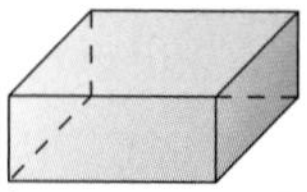 prism, rectangles
4. 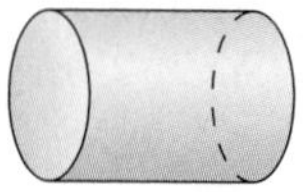 cylinder, circles

For each figure, name a pair of skew line segments and a pair of parallel line segments. 5–6. Answers may vary. Samples are given.

5. 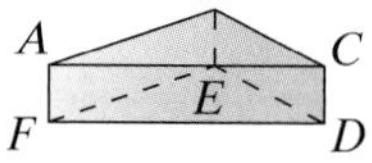

$\overline{AB}, \overline{CD}$; $\overline{BC}, \overline{ED}$

6. 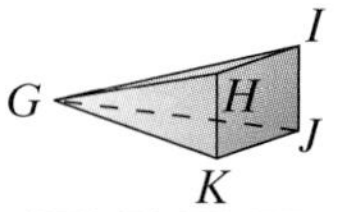

$\overline{GH}, \overline{IJ}$; $\overline{HI}, \overline{JK}$

Draw a base plan for each solid. 7–8. See margin.

7. 
8. 

Draw a top, front, and side view of each solid.

9. 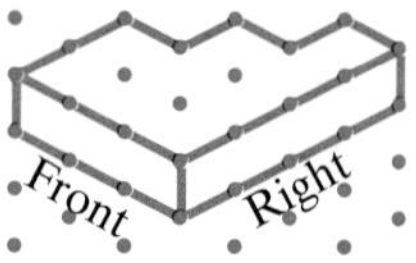

10. 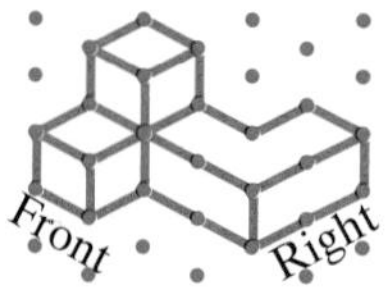

9–10. See margin.

Identify the solid formed by each net.

11. 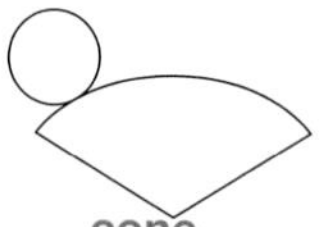 cone
12. 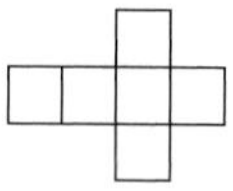 cube

Draw a net of each solid. 13–14. See margin.

13. 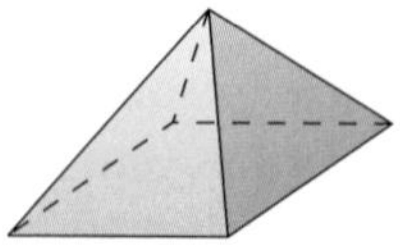
14. 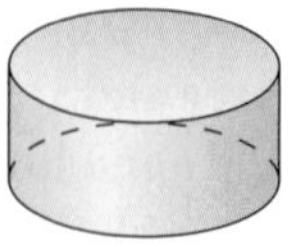

Find the lateral area and surface area of each solid to the nearest square unit. 248 m^2; 329 m^2

15. 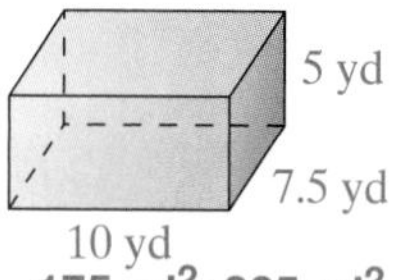

175 yd^2; 325 yd^2

16. 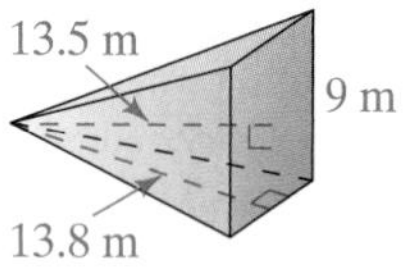

17. 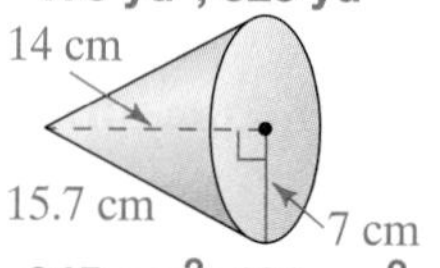

345 cm^2; 499 cm^2

18. 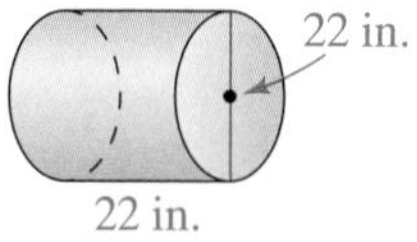

1,521 $in.^2$; 2,281 $in.^2$

Find the volume of each solid. When using π, round to the nearest cubic unit.

19. 0.25 ft^3 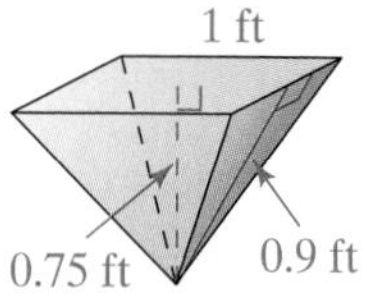

20. 2,262 $in.^3$ 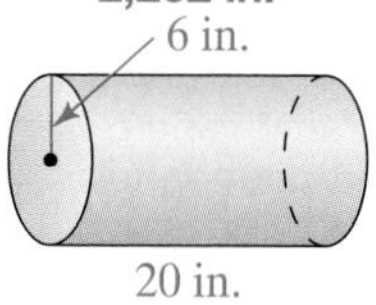

21. 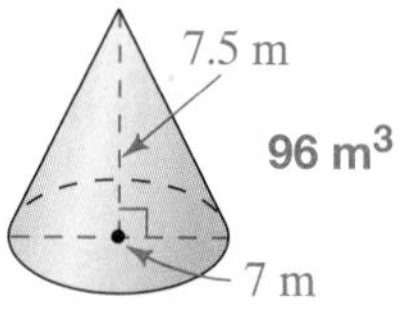

96 m^3

22. 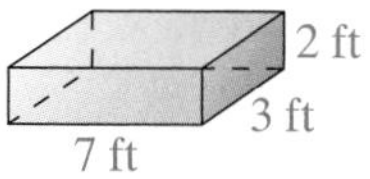

42 ft^3

23. **Writing in Math** The formulas for surface area and volume of a cylinder involve $\pi r^2 h$ and $2\pi rh + 2\pi r^2$. Explain how to tell which expression goes with which formula. See margin.

24. The figures below are similar solids. Find the measures of all missing lengths. See margin

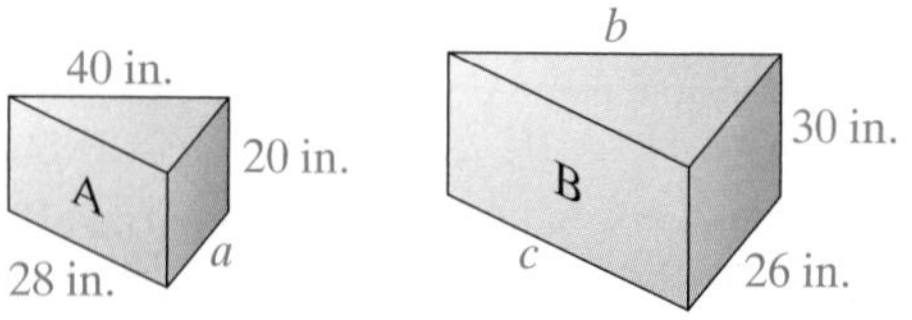

Find the surface area and volume of a sphere with the given radius or diameter to the nearest whole number. 25–28. See margin.

25. $r = 2$ in.
26. $r = 5$ ft
27. $d = 6$ m
28. $d = 8$ cm

10.
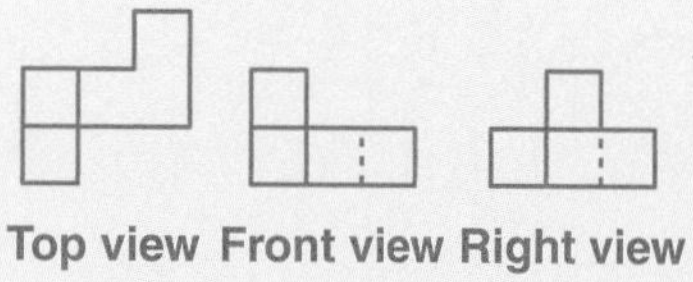

13.

14.
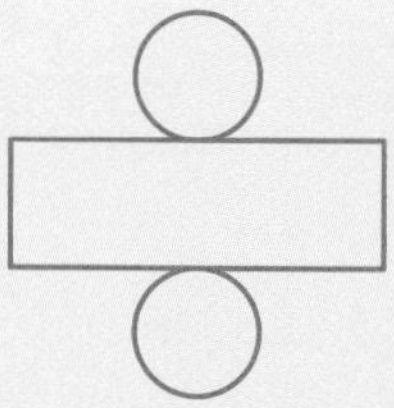

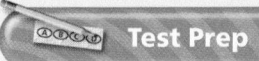

Test Prep Practice

Reading Comprehension

Read each passage and answer the questions that follow.

CD Players Compact disc players read the data on CDs as the discs spin, moving from the center to the outer edge of the disc. Some CD players spin at a steady rate. They read a different amount of data because the data circle gets larger with each revolution. Other CD players read data at a constant rate. Their discs spin at a variable rate, changing the speed as the circumference of the data circle changes.

1. How does the amount of data read per second change for a CD player that spins at a steady rate? C
   - (A) less data per second as the circles grow
   - (B) less data per second as the circles shrink
   - (C) more data per second as the circles grow
   - (D) more data per second as the circles shrink

2. For a disc of radius r, which expression gives the length of a data circle located halfway from the center to the disc's outer edge? G
   - (F) $\frac{1}{2}\pi r^2$
   - (G) $\frac{1}{2}\pi r$
   - (H) πr
   - (J) $2\pi r$

3. How does the rate of spin change for a CD player that reads a constant amount of data per second? C
   - (A) spins faster as the data circles grow
   - (B) spins faster as the data circles shrink
   - (C) spins slower as the data circles grow
   - (D) spins slower as the data circles shrink

4. For a variable-speed CD player, the speed halfway to the outer edge is what percent of the speed at the outer edge? J
   - (F) 25%
   - (G) 50%
   - (H) 100%
   - (J) 200%

Airplanes Why do wings work? The top of a typical wing is curved. The underside is relatively flat. As a plane flies, air molecules sliding over a wing have as much as 15% farther to travel to reach the wing's trailing edge than molecules passing under the wing. Even so, molecules passing over the wing reach the trailing edge first. The wing shape speeds up air flowing over the wing and forces it downward. In turn, the air reacts by pushing upward on the wing, resulting in the lift needed to keep the plane aloft.

5. Which inequality is reasonable for the speed of molecule a passing above the wing and the speed of molecule u passing under it? D
   - (A) $a < u + 0.15a$
   - (B) $a < 0.15u$
   - (C) $0.15a > u$
   - (D) $a > 1.15u$

6. If the surface area of the top of a wing is $16\ m^2$, what might the surface area of the bottom of the wing be? G
   - (F) $8\ m^2$
   - (G) $14\ m^2$
   - (H) $16\ m^2$
   - (J) $19\ m^2$

23. Since $\pi r^2 h$ multiplies three linear measures together, the result will be in cubic units, which is appropriate for volume.

24. $a = 17\frac{1}{3}$ in.
    $b = 60$ in.
    $c = 42$ in.

25. 50 in.^{2}; 34 in.^{3}

26. 314 ft^2; 524 ft^3

27. 113 m^2; 113 m^3

28. 201 cm^2; 268 cm^3

Test Prep

Resources

Test Prep Workbook

All in One Teaching Resources
- Cumulative Review L3

ExamView Assessment Suite CD-ROM
- Standardized Test Practice

Differentiated Instruction

Spanish Assessment Resources
- Spanish Cumulative Review ELL

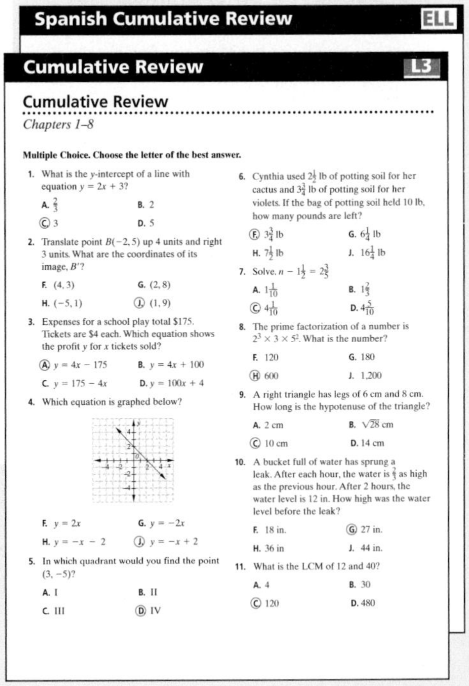
Spanish Cumulative Review ELL

Cumulative Review L3

Cumulative Review

Chapters 1–8

Multiple Choice. Choose the letter of the best answer.

1. What is the y-intercept of a line with equation $y = 2x + 3$?
   A. $\frac{2}{3}$ B. 2 (C) 3 D. 5
2. Translate point $B(-2, 5)$ up 4 units and right 3 units. What are the coordinates of its image, B'?
   F. (4, 3) G. (2, 8) H. (−5, 1) (J) (1, 9)
3. Expenses for a school play total $175. Tickets are $4 each. Which equation shows the profit y for x tickets sold?
   (A) $y = 4x - 175$ B. $y = 4x + 100$ C. $y = 175 - 4x$ D. $y = 100x + 4$
4. Which equation is graphed below?
   F. $y = 2x$ G. $y = -2x$ H. $y = -x - 2$ (J) $y = -x + 2$
5. In which quadrant would you find the point (3, −5)?
   A. I B. II C. III (D) IV
6. Cynthia used $2\frac{1}{2}$ lb of potting soil for her cactus and $3\frac{3}{4}$ lb of potting soil for her violets. If the bag of potting soil held 10 lb, how many pounds are left?
   (F) $3\frac{3}{4}$ lb G. $6\frac{1}{4}$ lb H. $7\frac{1}{2}$ lb J. $16\frac{1}{4}$ lb
7. Solve. $n - 1\frac{1}{2} = 2\frac{3}{5}$
   A. $1\frac{1}{10}$ B. $1\frac{2}{3}$ (C) $4\frac{1}{10}$ D. $4\frac{5}{10}$
8. The prime factorization of a number is $2^3 \times 3 \times 5^2$. What is the number?
   F. 120 G. 180 (H) 600 J. 1,200
9. A right triangle has legs of 6 cm and 8 cm. How long is the hypotenuse of the triangle?
   A. 2 cm B. $\sqrt{28}$ cm (C) 10 cm D. 14 cm
10. A bucket full of water has sprung a leak. After each hour, the water is $\frac{2}{3}$ as high as the previous hour. After 2 hours, the water level is 12 in. How high was the water level before the leak?
    F. 18 in. (G) 27 in. H. 36 in J. 44 in.
11. What is the LCM of 12 and 40?
    A. 4 B. 30 (C) 120 D. 480

Problem Solving

Applying Measurement

Students will use data from these two pages to answer the questions posed and make the models in Put It All Together.

Activating Prior Knowledge

Some animals can fly while others cannot. Certain airplane designs are better suited than others for different kinds of flight. Have students share their understanding of what it takes for an animal or a machine to lift off the ground and then stay up in the air.

Guided Instruction

Have a volunteer read the opening paragraph about flightless birds. Discuss with students that in the Put It All Together activity they will make models to investigate the relationship between a bird's weight and wingspan and its ability to fly.

History Connection
Refer students to the picture and information about dodos on page 529. Point out that dodos are not the only animals that have become extinct. Invite students to learn about (a) other animals that have suffered the fate of the dodos, or (b) why the dodo is no longer with us.

Careers
Invite interested students to find out about opportunities in the field of aeronautics. Alternatively, students can look into the requirements for becoming a commercial pilot.

Problem Solving Application

Applying Measurement

For The Birds Did you know that not all birds can fly? Although people usually think of birds as airborne, there are more than 40 species of flightless birds. The Australian emu, New Zealand kiwi, African ostrich, and South American rhea are all birds that cannot fly. Although some birds are simply too large or heavy to get off the ground, they have learned other skills—ostriches can run up to 40 mi/h, and penguins spend most of their lives in the ocean and use their wings as flippers.

Ostriches
At 5.7 to 9 ft tall, the ostrich is the largest living bird. Its normal walking pace is 2.5 mi/h, but it can run at speeds of up to 45 mi/h.

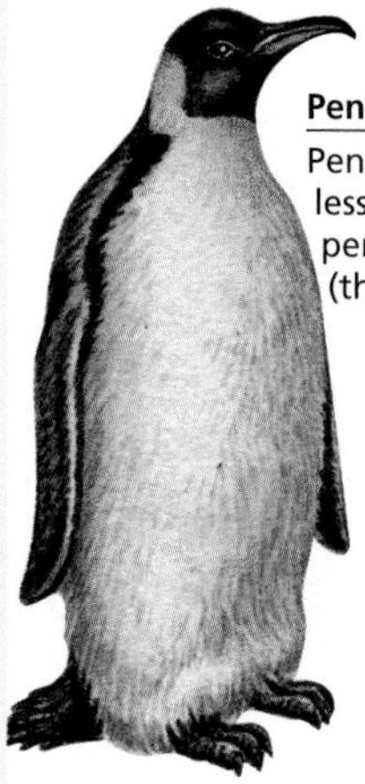

Penguins
Penguins range in size from less than 18 in. tall (the little penguin) to nearly 4 ft tall (the emperor penguin).

Kiwis
The kiwi, the national bird of New Zealand, is about the size of a chicken and weighs between 2.6 and 8.6 lb. Kiwi eggs are large and can weigh up to a pound!

Go Online
PHSchool.com
For: Information about birds
Web Code: ase-0853

1. Check students' work
2.

Size of Bird	Volume	Wing Area	Ratio $\frac{\text{volume}}{\text{wing area}}$
Small	96 cm^3	96 cm^2	$\frac{96}{96} = \frac{1}{1}$
Large	768 cm^3	384 cm^2	$\frac{768}{384} = \frac{2}{1}$

3. 8 times
4. 4 times

Put It All Together

Use the information on these two pages and on page 647 to answer these questions.

Materials construction paper, ruler or straightedge, tape

Copy and cut out the patterns in Figures 1 and 2 for a bird body and two bird wings. Assemble your bird.

1. Examine your bird. Think about what would happen to your bird's body and wings if it grew. Sketch a larger bird by doubling all the dimensions of the original pattern.
2. Copy and complete the table.

Size of Bird	Volume	Wing Area	Ratio $\frac{\text{volume}}{\text{wing area}}$
Small	■	■	■
Large	■	■	■

3. The upward force that keeps birds (and planes) in the air is called lift. The amount of lift needed to get off the ground is proportional to the weight of the bird. Using volume as an estimate for weight, how many times more lift will the larger bird require than the smaller bird?
4. The amount of lift from a bird's wings is proportional to the area of the wings. How many times more lift will the larger bird's wings provide than the smaller bird's?
5. **Writing in Math** Use your answers to Questions 3 and 4 to explain why the larger bird will have a harder time getting off the ground than the smaller bird.
6. **Open-Ended** Choose a bird from the table on page 647. Compare it to the two birds in the activity. How does it compare in terms of weight (volume)? How does it compare in terms of lift?

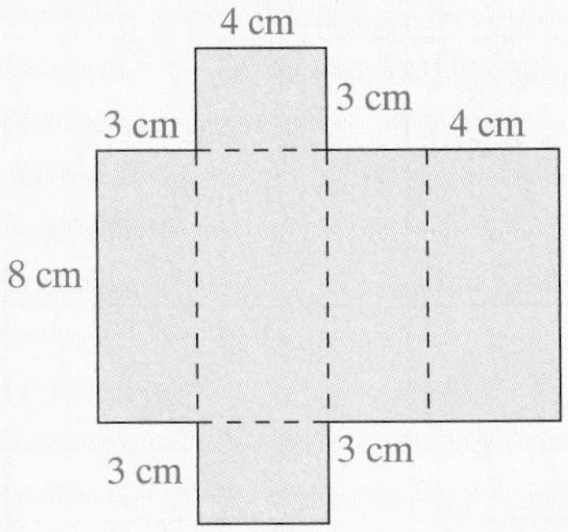

Figure 1

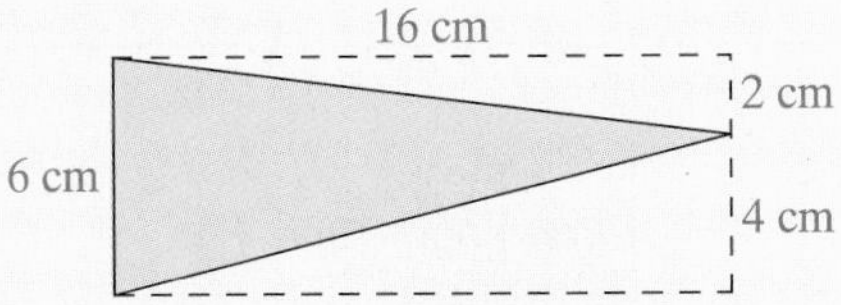

Figure 2

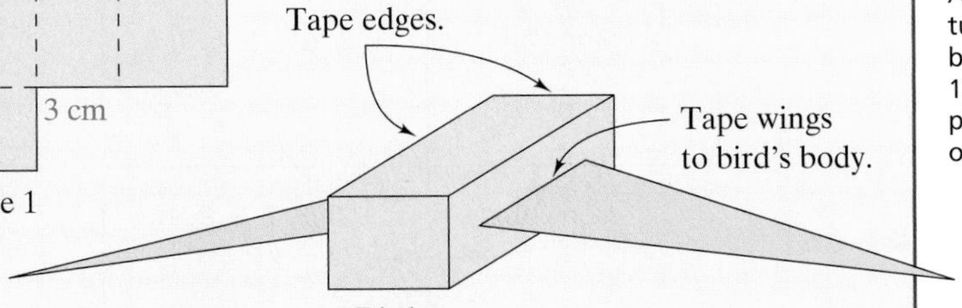

Bird

Rheas

Male rheas sit on their nests and incubate the eggs laid by females. The average clutch, or group of eggs, is about 25.

Dodos

About the size of turkeys, dodos have been extinct since the 1700s, so there are no photographs of them, only illustrations.

Put It All Together

Have students work in pairs to answer the questions and make the models. Guide them to record data as they measure and accumulate it. Then distribute the materials students need to make their model birds.

Exercise 6 The connection between volume and weight is left for students to make. They can realize that doubling the volume also doubles the weight (in the context of this problem).

To extend the activity, have students sketch a smaller bird by halving the original dimensions. They can then expand the table to include the new data.

Differentiated Instruction

Special Needs L1

Guide students to measure and cut carefully. Remind them of the carpenter's maxim: measure twice, cut once. You may wish to have students sketch and cut out their models using centimeter graph paper.

5. Answers may vary. Sample: The larger bird requires eight times as much lift, but its wings provide only four times as much lift. For the larger bird to fly, its wings would have to be able to carry twice as much bird volume per square centimeter of wing.
6. Check students' work

409

9 Using Graphs to Analyze Data

Chapter at a Glance

Lesson Titles, Objectives, and Features	Assessment	NCTM Standards	Local Standards
9-1 Finding Mean, Median, and Mode • To describe data using mean, median, mode and range and to choose an appropriate measure of central tendency **9-1b Activity Lab, Data Collection:** Comparing Mean and Median	Lesson Quiz	1, 5, 6, 7, 8, 9, 10	
9-2 Displaying Frequency • To use line plots, frequency tables, and histograms to represent data **9-2b Activity Lab, Technology:** Making Histograms	Lesson Quiz	1, 5, 6, 7, 8, 9, 10	
9-3 Venn Diagrams • To use Venn diagrams to represent relationships between data	Lesson Quiz	1, 3, 6, 7, 8, 9, 10	
9-4a Activity Lab, Data Analysis: Reading Graphical Displays **9-4 Reading Graphs Critically** • To recognize misleading graphs and to choose appropriate scales **9-4b Activity Lab, Data Analysis:** Making Graphs to Tell A Story	Lesson Quiz Checkpoint Quiz 1	1, 2, 5, 6, 7, 8, 9, 10	
9-5 Stem-and-Leaf Plots • To represent and interpret data using stem-and-leaf plots	Lesson Quiz	1, 2, 3, 6, 7, 8, 9, 10	
9-6 Box-and-Whisker Plots • To represent and interpret data using box-and-whisker plots **9-6b Activity Lab, Technology:** Making Box-and-Whisker Plots	Lesson Quiz	1, 5, 6, 7, 8, 9, 10	
9-7a Activity Lab, Data Collection: Scatter Plots **9-7 Making Predictions from Scatter Plots** • To make scatter plots and to use trends to make predictions **9-7b Activity Lab, Algebra Thinking:** Plotting a Strategy	Lesson Quiz Checkpoint Quiz 2	1, 2, 5, 6, 7, 8, 9, 10	
9-8 Circle Graphs • To represent and interpret data using circle graphs **Guided Problem Solving:** Equations and Graphs	Lesson Quiz	1, 2, 3, 4, 5, 6, 7, 8, 9, 10	
9-9 Choosing an Appropriate Graph • To choose appropriate graphs to represent different data **9-9b Activity Lab, Technology:** Graphing Data Using Spreadsheets	Lesson Quiz	1, 5, 6, 7, 8, 9, 10	
Problem Solving Application: Applying Data Analysis			

NCTM Standards 2000

1 Number and Operations; 2 Algebra; 3 Geometry; 4 Measurement; 5 Data Analysis and Probability
6 Problem Solving; 7 Reasoning and Proof; 8 Communication; 9 Connections; 10 Representation

Correlations to Standardized Tests

All content for these tests is contained in *Prentice Hall Math*, Course 3. This chart reflects coverage in this chapter only.

	9-1	9-2	9-3	9-4	9-5	9-6	9-7	9-8	9-9
Terra Nova CAT6 (Level 18)									
Number and Number Relations	✔	✔			✔	✔			
Computation and Numerical Estimation									
Operation Concepts									
Measurement									
Geometry and Spatial Sense									
Data Analysis, Statistics, and Probability	✔	✔	✔	✔	✔	✔	✔	✔	✔
Patterns, Functions, Algebra									
Problem Solving and Reasoning	✔	✔	✔	✔	✔	✔	✔	✔	✔
Communication	✔	✔	✔	✔	✔	✔	✔	✔	✔
Decimals, Fractions, Integers, Percent	✔	✔			✔	✔		✔	
Order of Operations									
Algebraic Operations									
Terra Nova CTBS (Level 18)									
Decimals, Fractions, Integers, Percents	✔				✔	✔		✔	
Order of Operations, Numeration, Number Theory									
Data Interpretation	✔	✔	✔	✔	✔	✔	✔	✔	✔
Measurement									
Geometry									
ITBS (Level 14)									
Number Properties and Operations	✔	✔			✔				
Algebra									
Geometry									
Measurement									
Probability and Statistics	✔	✔	✔	✔	✔	✔	✔	✔	✔
Estimation									
SAT10 (Adv 1 Level)									
Number Sense and Operations	✔	✔			✔	✔			
Patterns, Relationships, and Algebra									
Data, Statistics, and Probability	✔	✔	✔	✔	✔	✔	✔	✔	✔
Geometry and Measurement									
NAEP									
Number Sense, Properties, and Operations								✔	
Measurement									
Geometry and Spatial Sense									
Data Analysis, Statistics, and Probability	✔	✔	✔	✔	✔	✔	✔	✔	✔
Algebra and Functions									

CAT6 California Achievement Test, 6th Ed. **CTBS** Comprehensive Test of Basic Skills **ITBS** Iowa Test of Basic Skills, Form M
SAT10 Stanford Achievement Test, 10th Ed. **NAEP** National Assessment of Educational Progress 2005 Mathematics Objectives

Math Background

Professional Development

Skills Trace

BEFORE Chapter 9

Course 2 introduced making and interpreting various types of graphical displays.

DURING Chapter 9

Course 3 extends the critical reading and making of various graphs to include selecting an appropriate graph for a given set of data.

AFTER Chapter 9

Throughout this course students make and interpret a wide variety of graphs.

9-1 Finding the Mean, Median, and Mode

Math Understandings

- Outliers do not greatly affect the mode or the median, but they may make the mean a less effective way to represent the central tendency of a particular set of data.
- Use the mode to represent a data set when the data are not numerical. Use the mean when there are no outliers and the values are fairly close together.

A **measure of central tendency** is a single central value that summarizes a set of data. The **mean** is the sum of data values divided by the number of data items. The **median** is the middle value, or the mean of two middle values, when you arrange the data in numerical order. The **mode** is the item with the greatest frequency. A data set may have no mode, one mode, or more than one mode. **Range** is the difference between the greatest and least values in a data set. If one data item is much higher or lower than the other data items, it is an **outlier**.

9-2 Displaying Frequency

Math Understandings

- The number of times a data item occurs is the **frequency** of the item.
- A **frequency table** lists the frequency of each item in a set of data.
- A **line plot** displays data values with an ✗ mark above each data value on a number line.
- Both frequency tables and line plots show the distribution or shape of a set of data.

Temp. (°F)	100	101	102	103	104
Tally	I	卌	IIII	I	I
Frequency	1	5	4	1	1

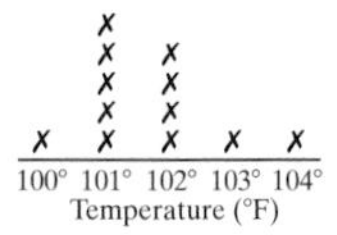

When there are too many values to display separately, you can use a grouped-frequency table to organize data into intervals of equal size that do not overlap. A **histogram** is a special type of bar graph with no spaces between the bars. The height of each bar shows the frequency of data within that interval.

9-3 Venn Diagrams

Venn diagrams show how sets of objects are related. Each set is represented by a shape, such as a circle or oval. Items belonging to more than one set appear in the overlaps.

9-4 Reading Graphs Critically

Bar graphs and line graphs can give a misleading visual impression of the data being displayed. This can happen when scales start at some value other than zero, or breaks in the scale are not clearly marked.

9-5 Stem-and-Leaf Plots

Math Understandings

- A stem-and-leaf plot can quickly show the distribution of a data set and retains each data value.
- Each stem-and-leaf plot must include a key that shows what the stems and leaves represent for a particular plot.

A **stem-and-leaf plot** shows numeric data arranged in order. Each data item is broken into a stem and a leaf.

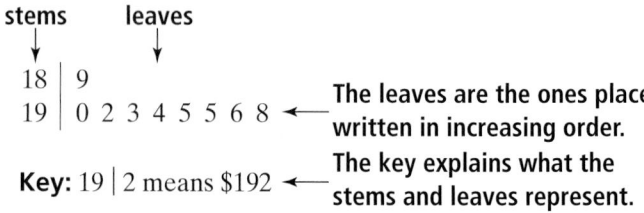

stems	leaves
18	9
19	0 2 3 4 5 5 6 8

← **The leaves are the ones place written in increasing order.**

Key: 19 | 2 means $192 ← **The key explains what the stems and leaves represent.**

9-6 Box-and-Whisker Plots

Math Understandings

- Box-and-whisker plots do not include every data value.
- By comparing the lengths of the box and whiskers, you can easily see where data values are more spread out.
- Box-and-whisker plots are useful with very large data sets or for making comparisons between data sets.

A **box-and-whisker plot** uses five summary values to show the distribution of a data set along a number line. **Quartiles** are numbers that divide the data set into four equal parts.

Box-and-Whisker Plot

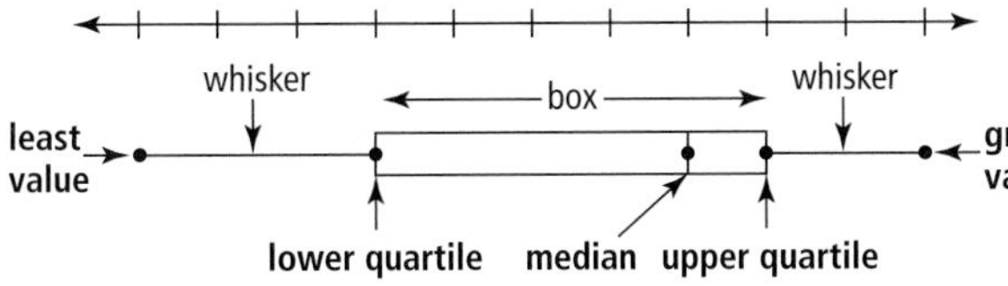

9-7 Making Predictions From Scatter Plots

Math Understandings

- You can use a scatter plot to help decide whether one set of data relates to another. Note that such a mathematical correlation does not mean that one causes the other.
- You can use trend lines to make predictions about data values that do not appear on a scatter plot.

A **scatter plot** is a graph that displays two sets of data as ordered pairs. A **trend line** is a line you draw on a graph to approximate the relationship between the two sets of data. When a scatter plot shows a **positive trend**, one set of values increases as the other set tends to increase. When a scatter plot shows a **negative trend**, one set of values increases as the other tends to decrease. When the points in a scatter plot do not cluster along a trend line, the points show no relationship and **no trend**.

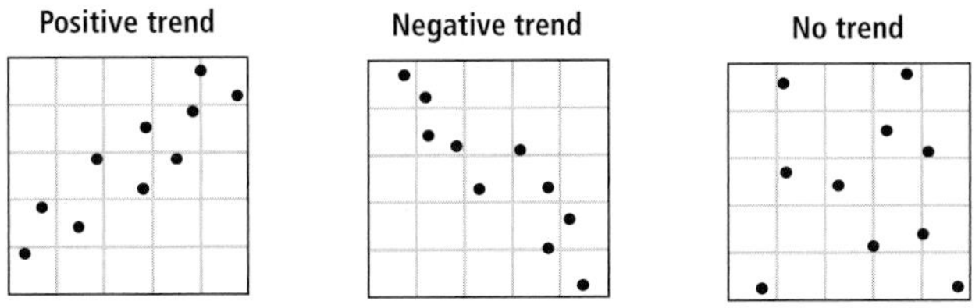

9-8 Circle Graphs

Math Understandings

- Because each sector of a **circle graph** represents a part of the whole, the total of the data represented by the sectors must equal 100%, or 1.
- In a circle graph, the total of the central angles of the sectors is a complete circle, or 360°.

To draw the sectors of a circle graph, you must find the measure of each central angle. A **central angle** is an angle whose vertex is the center of the circle.

Ages of College Students

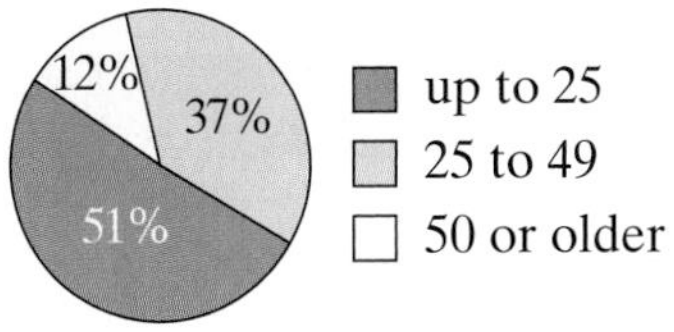

9-9 Choosing an Appropriate Graph

Math Understandings

- When you present data, the type of data and your presentation purpose influence the type of graph you choose.

A *circle graph* shows parts of a whole. Its use becomes less effective when too many parts are shown. A *line graph* can show changes over time. There are three distinct changes: an increase, a decrease, or no change. You can illustrate data divided into equal intervals that show frequency with a *histogram*.

Additional Professional Development Opportunities

Professional Development

Math Background Notes for Chapter 9: Every lesson has a Math Background in the PLAN section.

Research Overview, Mathematics Strands
Additional support for these topics and more is in the front of the Teacher's Edition.

LessonLab
LessonLab, a Pearson Education company, offers comprehensive, facilitated professional development designed to help teachers to improve student achievement. To learn more, please visit lessonlab.com.

Chapter 9 Resources

	9-1	9-2	9-3	9-4	9-5	9-6	9-7	9-8	9-9	For the Chapter
Print Resources										
L3 Practice	●	●	●	●	●	●	●	●	●	
L1 Adapted Practice	●	●	●	●	●	●	●	●	●	
L3 Guided Problem Solving	●	●	●	●	●	●	●	●	●	
L2 Reteaching	●	●	●	●	●	●	●	●	●	
L4 Enrichment	●	●	●	●	●	●	●	●	●	
L3 Daily Notetaking Guide	●	●	●	●	●	●	●	●	●	
L1 Adapted Daily Notetaking Guide	●	●	●	●	●	●	●	●	●	
L3 Vocabulary and Study Skills Worksheets	●		●		●		●		●	●
L3 Daily Puzzles	●	●	●	●	●	●	●	●	●	
L3 Activity Labs	●	●	●	●	●	●	●	●	●	
L3 Checkpoint Quiz				●			●			
L3 Chapter Project										●
L2 Below Level Chapter Test										●
L3 Chapter Test										●
L4 Alternative Assessment										●
L3 Cumulative Review										●
Spanish Resources ELL										
L3 Practice	●	●	●	●	●	●	●	●	●	
L3 Vocabulary and Study Skills Worksheets	●		●		●		●		●	●
L3 Checkpoint Quiz				●			●			
L2 Below Level Chapter Test										●
L3 Chapter Test										●
L4 Alternative Assessment										●
L3 Cumulative Review										●
Transparencies										
Check Skills You'll Need	●	●	●	●	●	●	●	●	●	
Additional Examples	●	●	●	●	●	●	●	●	●	
Problem of the Day	●	●	●	●	●	●	●	●	●	
Classroom Aid		●	●	●	●	●	●	●	●	
Student Edition Answers	●	●	●	●	●	●	●	●	●	●
Lesson Quiz	●	●	●	●	●	●	●	●	●	
Test-Taking Strategies										●
Technology										
Interactive Textbook Online	●	●	●	●	●	●	●	●	●	●
StudentExpress™ CD-ROM	●	●	●	●	●	●	●	●	●	●
Success Tracker™ Intervention Online	●	●	●	●	●	●	●	●	●	●
TeacherExpress™ CD-ROM	●	●	●	●	●	●	●	●	●	●
PresentationExpress™ with QuickTake Presenter CD-ROM	●	●	●	●	●	●	●	●	●	●
ExamView® Assessment Suite CD-ROM	●	●	●	●	●	●	●	●	●	●
MindPoint® Quiz Show CD-ROM										●
Prentice Hall Web Site: PHSchool.com	●	●	●	●	●	●	●	●	●	●

Also available: **Prentice Hall Assessment System**
- Progress Monitoring Assessments
- Skills and Concepts Review
- Test Prep Workbook

Other Resources
Algebra Readiness Tests
All-in-One Student Workbook
All-in-One Student Workbook, Adapted Version
Multilingual Handbook
Solution Key
Math Notes Study Folder
Spanish Cumulative Assessment

Where You Can Use the Lesson Resources

Here is a suggestion, following the four-step teaching plan, for how you can incorporate Differentiated Instruction Resources into your teaching.

	Instructional Resources L3	Differentiated Instruction Resources
1. Plan		
Preparation Read the Math Background in the Teacher's Edition to connect this lesson with students' previous experience. **Starting Class** **Check Skills You'll Need** Assign these exercises to review prerequisite skills. **New Vocabulary** Help students pre-read the lesson by pointing out the new terms introduced in the lesson.	**Math Background** **Math Understandings** **Transparencies & PresentationExpress™ with QuickTake Presenter CD-ROM** Check Skills You'll Need Problem of the Day **Resources** Vocabulary and Study Skills	**Spanish Support** ELL Vocabulary and Study Skills
2. Teach		
L3 **Guided Instruction** Use the Activity Labs to build conceptual understanding. Teach each Example. Use the Teacher's Edition side column notes for specific teaching tips, including Error Prevention notes. Use the Additional Examples found in the side column (and on transparency and PowerPoint) as an alternative presentation for the content. After each Example, assign the Quick Check exercise for that Example to get an immediate assessment of student understanding. Use the Closure activity in the Teacher's Edition to help students attain mastery of lesson content.	**Student Edition** Activity Lab **Resources** Daily Notetaking Guide Activity Lab **Transparencies & PresentationExpress™ with QuickTake Presenter CD-ROM** Additional Examples Classroom Aids **ExamView® Assessment Suite CD-ROM**	**Teacher's Edition** Every lesson includes suggestions for working with students who need special attention. L1 Special Needs L2 Below Level L4 Advanced Learners ELL English Language Learners **Resources** L1 Adapted Daily NoteTaking Guide **Multilingual Handbook**
3. Practice		
Assignment Guide **Check Your Understanding** Use these questions to check students' understanding before you assign homework. **Homework Exercises** Assign homework from these leveled exercises in the Assignment Guide. A Practice by Example B Apply Your Skills C Challenge Test Prep and Mixed Review **Homework Quick Check** Use these key exercises to quickly check students' homework.	**Transparencies & PresentationExpress™ with QuickTake Presenter CD-ROM** Student Answers **Resources** Practice Guided Problem Solving Vocabulary and Study Skills Activity Lab Daily Puzzles **ExamView® Assessment Suite CD-ROM**	**Spanish Support** ELL Practice ELL Vocabulary and Study Skills **Resources** L1 Adapted Practice L4 Enrichment
4. Assess & Reteach		
Lesson Quiz Assign the Lesson Quiz to assess students' mastery of the lesson content. **Checkpoint Quiz** Use the Checkpoint Quiz to assess student progress over several lessons.	**Transparencies & PresentationExpress™ with QuickTake Presenter CD-ROM** Lesson Quiz **Resources** Checkpoint Quiz	**Resources** L2 Reteaching ELL Checkpoint Quiz Success Tracker™ Online Intervention **ExamView® Assessment Suite CD-ROM**

KEY L1 Special Needs L2 Below Level L3 For All Students L4 Advanced, Gifted ELL English Language Learners

CHAPTER 9

Using Graphs to Analyze Data

Check Your Readiness

Answers for students are in the back of the textbook.

For intervention, direct students to:

Graphing Points
Lesson 3-4
Extra Skills and Word Problems Practice, Ch. 3

Solving Proportions
Lesson 4-3
Extra Skills and Word Problems Practice, Ch. 4

Fractions, Decimals, and Percents
Lesson 5-1
Extra Skills and Word Problems Practice, Ch. 5

Spanish Vocabulary/Study Skills ELL

Vocabulary/Study Skills L3

9A: Graphic Organizer — For use before Lesson 9-1

Study Skill Pay attention in class and concentrate when reading assignments so information does not slip out of your "short-term" memory.

Write your answers.

1. What is the chapter title? Using Graphs to Analyze Data
2. How many lessons are there in this chapter? 8
3. What is the topic of the Test-Taking Strategies page? Finding Multiple Correct Answers
4. Complete the graphic organizer below as you work through the chapter. Check students' diagrams
   - In the center, write the title of the chapter.
   - When you begin a lesson, write the lesson name in a rectangle.
   - When you complete a lesson, write a skill or key concept in a circle linked to that lesson block.
   - When you complete the chapter, use this graphic organizer to help you review.

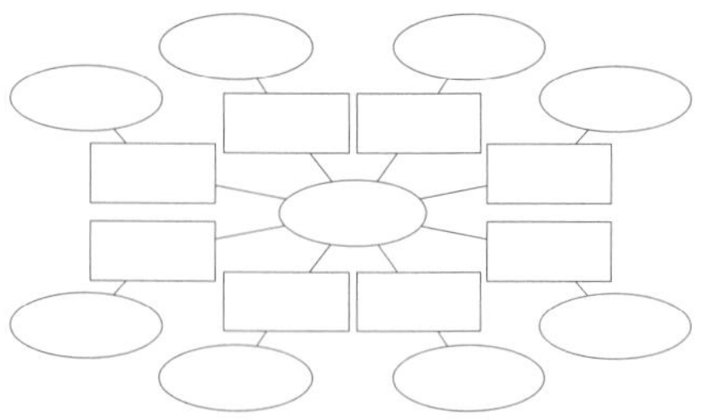

Vocabulary and Study Skills

CHAPTER 9 Using Graphs to Analyze Data

What You've Learned

- In Chapter 3, you located and named points on a coordinate plane using ordered pairs of rational numbers.
- You also used tables, graphs, and equations to solve problems.

Check Your Readiness

GO for Help

For Exercises	See Lessons
1–9	3-4
10–13	4-3
14–22	5-1

Graphing Points 1–9. See margin.

Graph each point on the same coordinate plane.

1. $(2, 5)$ **2.** $(8, 0)$ **3.** $(-5, 4)$

4. $(3, -1)$ **5.** $(-6, -8)$ **6.** $(-4, 0)$

7. $(3, 7)$ **8.** $(-3, -6)$ **9.** $(0, 4)$

Solving Proportions

Solve each proportion.

10. $\frac{8}{9} = \frac{16}{x}$ 18 **11.** $\frac{a}{24} = \frac{14}{12}$ 28

12. $\frac{6}{3} = \frac{s}{12}$ 24 **13.** $\frac{3}{m} = \frac{75}{125}$ 5

Fractions, Decimals, and Percents

Write each percent as a fraction in simplest form.

14. 26% $\frac{13}{50}$ **15.** 48% $\frac{12}{25}$ **16.** 13% $\frac{13}{100}$

17. 72% $\frac{18}{25}$ **18.** 20% $\frac{1}{5}$ **19.** 47% $\frac{47}{100}$

20. 50% $\frac{1}{2}$ **21.** 10% $\frac{1}{10}$ **22.** 5% $\frac{1}{20}$

1–9. See back of book.

What You'll Learn Next

- In this chapter, you will use different types of graphs to represent and analyze data.
- You will make predictions using trends in scatter plots.
- You will read graphs critically and choose an appropriate graph to display a set of data.

Problem Solving Application On pages 466 and 467, you will work an extended activity on food production.

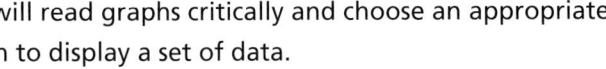

Key Vocabulary

- box-and-whisker plot (p. 438)
- circle graph (p. 450)
- frequency (p. 418)
- histogram (p. 419)
- line plot (p. 418)
- mean (p. 412)
- measure of central tendency (p. 412)
- median (p. 412)
- mode (p. 412)
- outlier (p. 413)
- quartiles (p. 438)
- range (p. 413)
- scatter plot (p. 444)
- stem-and-leaf plot (p. 433)
- trend line (p. 445)
- Venn diagram (p. 424)

Chapter 9 Overview

In this chapter, students learn to find the mean, median, and mode of data. Students learn to read graphs critically and to make various kinds of graphs. They work with line plots, histograms, Venn diagrams, stem-and-leaf plots, box-and-whisker plots, scatter plots, and circle graphs. They draw upon their understandings to choose the appropriate graph for a given set of data.

Activating Prior Knowledge

In this chapter, students build on their knowledge of bar graphs, pictographs, and line graphs. They use graphs to solve problems. They also draw upon their understanding of how to solve proportions. Ask questions such as:

- *A bar graph shows the following numbers of cellphones sold in each of four weeks at an electronics store: 25, 32, 38, 41. What is the mean of this data?* 34
- *Solve:* $A < B$ $n = 15$

9-1

1. Plan

Objective
To describe data using mean, median, mode, and range and to choose an appropriate measure of central tendency

Examples
1 Finding Mean, Median, and Mode
2 Finding Range
3 Outliers
4 Choosing a Measure of Central Tendency

Math Understandings: p. 410C

Professional Development

Math Background

Often one single number is used to represent a collection of numbers, or data items. This representative number shows a typical value, or central tendency, for the collection. A set of numbers can have only one mean and only one median, but a set may have more than one mode.

More Math Background: p. 410C

Lesson Planning and Resources

See p. 410E for a list of the resources that support this lesson.

PowerPoint

Bell Ringer Practice

Check Skills You'll Need
Use student page, transparency, or PowerPoint. For intervention, direct students to:

Solving Equations by Adding and Subtracting
Lesson 1-6
Extra Skills and Word Problems Practice, Ch. 1

9-1 Finding Mean, Median, and Mode

Check Skills You'll Need

1. **Vocabulary Review** What is the *inverse operation* of addition? subtraction

Solve each equation.

2. $a + 14 = 32$ 18
3. $b - 5 = 26$ 31
4. $10 + c = -31$ −41
5. $-48 = d - 19$ −29

GO for Help Lesson 1-6

What You'll Learn

To describe data using mean, median, mode, and range and to choose an appropriate measure of central tendency

New Vocabulary measure of central tendency, mean, median, mode, range, outlier

Why Learn This?

Statistics like the mean are used to calculate scores and averages in sports.

A **measure of central tendency** is a single value that summarizes how a set of data is centered. Mean, median, and mode are measures of central tendency.

The **mean** is the sum of the data values divided by the number of data items.

The **median** is the middle value when the data values are arranged in numerical order. For an even number of data values, the median is the mean of the two middle items.

The **mode** is the item with the greatest frequency. A data set may have no mode, one mode, or more than one mode.

Vocabulary Tip
In math, the word *average* usually refers to the mean.

EXAMPLE Finding Mean, Median, and Mode

1 **Golf** Players in a tournament have scores −4, −3, −5, −5, +2, −5, −4, −2, −2, and −2. Find the mean, median, and mode of the scores.

Mean:

$$\frac{(-4)+(-3)+(-5)+(-5)+2+(-5)+(-4)+(-2)+(-2)+(-2)}{10} = \frac{-30}{10} = -3$$

← **Add.** ← **Divide.**

Median:

$-5\ \ -5\ \ -5\ \ -4\ \ -4\ \ -3\ \ -2\ \ -2\ \ -2\ \ 2$ ← **Order the data.**

$\frac{-4 + (-3)}{2} = -3.5$ ← **Find the mean of the middle two numbers.**

Mode: There are two modes, −5 and −2.

Quick Check

1. Find the mean, median, and mode of 11, 19, 11, 15, 16, 18, and 8. 14; 15; 11

Differentiated Instruction Solutions for All Learners

Special Needs L1
On lined paper, students rewrite data values in numerical order, first in a horizontal line, then in a vertical line. Encourage them to use whichever presentation helps them to keep track of each value and to add them more easily.
learning style: visual

Below Level L2
Students line up their writing instruments (pens, pencils) in order from shortest to longest. Visually illustrate the mode and median length of the pens and pencils.
learning style: tactile

Online active math

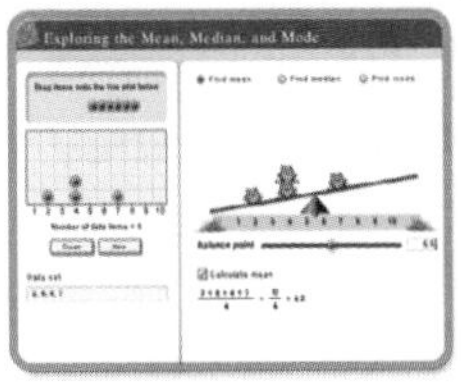

For: Data Set Activity
Use: Interactive Textbook, 9-1

The **range** of a set of data is the difference between the greatest and least values in the set. Range is a measure of how spread out the data in a set are.

EXAMPLE Finding Range

2 Find the range of the data: 4.2, 8.1, −2.7, 6, −3.9, 7.2, 5.1, 8.3, −2.5.

The greatest value is 8.3. The least value is −3.9.

$8.3 - (-3.9) = 12.2$ ← **Subtract.**

The range is 12.2.

Quick Check

2. Find the range of the data: −24.9, −26.5, −33.1, −24.2, −31.4, −32.1, −28.4, −30. **8.9**

If one data item is much higher or lower than the other data items, it is an **outlier.** Outliers can have a great effect on the mean of a set of data. They usually have very little effect on the median and mode.

EXAMPLE Outliers

3 **Wages** A juice stand hires students for the summer. The students' hourly wages are listed below, in dollars. How does the outlier affect the mean?

7.25 7.25 7.25 7.25 7.25 8.00 8.00
8.00 8.25 9.00 9.00 9.00 15.00

15 is an outlier. It is 15 − 9, or 6, away from the closest data value.

To find the mean with the outlier, find the sum of all data values and divide by the number of data values, 13.

$\frac{110.5}{13} = 8.5$ ← **Find the mean with the outlier.**

To find the mean without the outlier, find the sum of the data values excluding the outlier. Then divide by 12, the number of data values not including the outlier.

$\frac{95.5}{12} \approx 7.96$ ← **Find the mean without the outlier.**

The outlier raises the mean about $8.5 - 7.96 = 0.54$, or \$.54.

Quick Check

3. Find an outlier in each data set and tell how it affects the mean.
- **a.** 11, 14, 9, 1, 12, 15, 12, 13 **1; it lowers the mean about 1.4.**
- **b.** −5, −3, 0, 2, −1, −18, −6, 3, −2 **−18; it lowers the mean about 1.8.**

Test Prep Tip
To save time in your calculations, you can drop zeros after decimal points when they are not followed by any other numbers.

2. Teach

Activity Lab

Use before the lesson.

All in One Teaching Resources
Activity Lab 9-1: Finding Mean, Median, and Mode

Guided Instruction

Alternative Method
Point out to students that, if they have ever "averaged their grades," they have found the mean.

Example 2
Ask:
- *What information does the range give you about a data set?* **The range shows how spread out or close the data items are to one another.**
- *How is this information different from what the mean provides?* **The mean describes a central value for the data set.**

Technology Tip
Calculators often have statistics keys that make it possible to enter the data values and then calculate the mean in one step.

PowerPoint
Additional Examples

1 Find the mean, the median, and the mode for the values in a set of coins with 4 pennies, 2 nickels, 3 dimes, and a quarter. **mean: 6.9¢; median: 5¢; mode: 1¢**

2 Find the range for: 5, −3.2, 1.5, 4.1, −7.3, 2.8, −5.6, 9.8, and 1.7. **17.1**

3 The prices of new books bought for the library are in dollars below. How does the outlier affect the mean? 7.95, 5, 12.05, 10, 6.25, 8, 56, 8.75, 9, 7 **The outlier, 56, raises the mean by about \$4.80.**

Advanced Learners L4	**English Language Learners** ELL
Students explain, with their own examples or reasoning, why outliers affect only the mean, but not the median or mode. **learning style: verbal**	Students may remember the definitions for *mean, median,* and *mode* by associating them with similar words or everyday concepts. For example, the *mode* is the number that appears *most often* in a set of data. The *median* strip marks the *middle* of the road. **learning style: verbal**

Additional Examples

4 A pet store asked 12 people the number of dogs in their household. The responses were 2, 1, 0, 5, 2, 3, 1, 1, 7, 1, 1, and 1. Which measure of central tendency would make the number of dogs per family seem highest? mean

Teaching Resources

- Daily Notetaking Guide 9-1 L3
- Adapted Notetaking 9-1 L1

Closure

- *How do you find the mean, median, and mode of a set of values?* mean: the sum of data values divided by the number of data items; median: the middle value or mean of the 2 middle values (when the data is arranged in numerical order); mode: the data value or values that occur most often
- *How do you choose which measure of central tendency to use?* mode: when data is not numerical; mean: when no outliers; median: when outliers are likely

For the same set of data, the values of the mean, median, and mode can vary significantly. Before you choose which statistic to report, ask yourself what you want to show about the data.

EXAMPLE Choosing a Measure of Central Tendency

4 **Multiple Choice** A meteorologist recorded the temperature at a local airport at 5:00 P.M. every day last week. The temperatures in degrees Fahrenheit (°F) were 45, 78, 75, 80, 78, 61, and 58. Which measure would make the temperature seem most warm?

Ⓐ Mode Ⓑ Median Ⓒ Mean Ⓓ Range

GO for Help For help with ordering integers, go to Lesson 1-2, Example 2.

45 58 61 75 78 78 80 ← **Order the data.**

The mode is 78.

The median is 75.

The mean is $(45 + 78 + 75 + 80 + 78 + 61 + 58) \div 7 \approx 67.9$.

The range is $80 - 45 = 35$.

The greatest measure is the mode, so the correct answer is choice A.

Quick Check

4. Your scores on the last six math tests were 82, 84, 88, 72, 91, and 72. Which measure of data would make your scores seem greatest—mean, median, mode, or range? median

Check Your Understanding

1. **Vocabulary** Does the following set of data have a mode? Explain.
   1 3 7 5 9 8 6 4 2 10

   1. No; because none of the data values are repeated, there is no mode.

Use the table below for Exercises 2–6.

2. What is the sum of the temperatures? 31
3. How many data values are in the set? 12
4. Use your answers to Questions 2 and 3. Find the mean of the data. 2.58

Minimum Daily Temperatures (°F)

Date	Temperature	Date	Temperature
12/20	−3	12/26	1
12/21	−2	12/27	15
12/22	−9	12/28	6
12/23	−8	12/29	11
12/24	2	12/30	7
12/25	0	12/31	11

5. List the data in order from least to greatest. Find the median and the mode.

   5. −9, −8, −3, −2, 0, 1, 2, 6, 7, 11, 11, 15; median: 1.5; mode: 11

6. Find the greatest and least values. 15; −9

Homework Exercises

For more exercises, see Extra Skills and Word Problems.

GO for Help

For Exercises	See Examples
7–12	1–2
13–15	3
16	4

A **Find the mean, median, mode, and range of each data set.**

7. hits per game:
0 0 0 0 1 1 2 2 3
1; 1; 0; 3

8. test scores:
70 80 84 90 92 100
86; 87; no mode; 30

9. hours of sleep:
7 8 8 9 9 9 9 10 10
$8.\overline{7}$; 9; 9; 3

10. number of movies seen
0 1 1 2 2 3 3 3 4 6
2.5; 2.5; 3; 6

11. **Change in Numbers of Endangered U.S. Bird Species**

Year	Change
1997	2
1998	0
1999	−2
2000	4
2001	0
2002	0
2003	0
2004	−1

SOURCE: U.S. Fish and Wildlife Service. Go to **PHSchool.com** for a data update. Web Code: asg–9041.
0.375; 0; 0; 6

12. **Minimum Daily Temperatures**

Date	Temperature (°F)
1/23	−1
1/24	16
1/25	7
1/26	8
1/27	7
1/28	14
1/29	8
1/30	−3
1/31	−9

$5.\overline{2}$; 7; 7 and 8; 25

Whooping cranes are an endangered species.

For Exercises 13–15, find an outlier and tell how it affects the mean.

13. 1, 0, 3, 10, 0, 2, 4, 1
10; it raises the mean about 1.05.

14. 28, 12, 37, 36, 30, 32, 35
12; it lowers the mean 3.

15. **Wages** A park hires students for the summer. The students' hourly wages are $8.00, $7.50, $8.00, $8.00, $8.00, and $20.50.
$20.50; it raises the mean $2.10.

16. **Jobs** A company reports the following salaries for its employees: $20,000; $22,000; $34,000; $42,000; $43,000; $50,000; and $80,000. Which measure of central tendency would make you most want to apply for a job with this company? median

B **GPS** **17.** **Guided Problem Solving** A data set has nine values. The mean of the set is 5. When a tenth value is added, the mean becomes 6. What is the tenth value? 15

- What is the sum of the original 9 data values?
- **Make a Plan** Write and solve an equation to find the tenth value.

18. **Homework** The number of hours that Olivia spent on homework in the last five days was 2.75, 1.75, 1.25, 3.00, and 2.75. Which measure of central tendency could Olivia use to most impress her parents? median or mode

3. Practice

Assignment Guide

Check Your Understanding

Go over Exercises 1–6 in class before assigning the Homework Exercises.

Homework Exercises

A Practice by Example	7–16
B Apply Your Skills	17–24
C Challenge	25
Test Prep and Mixed Review	26–32

Homework Quick Check

To check students' understanding of key skills and concepts, go over Exercises 12, 14, 22, 23, and 24.

Differentiated Instruction Resources

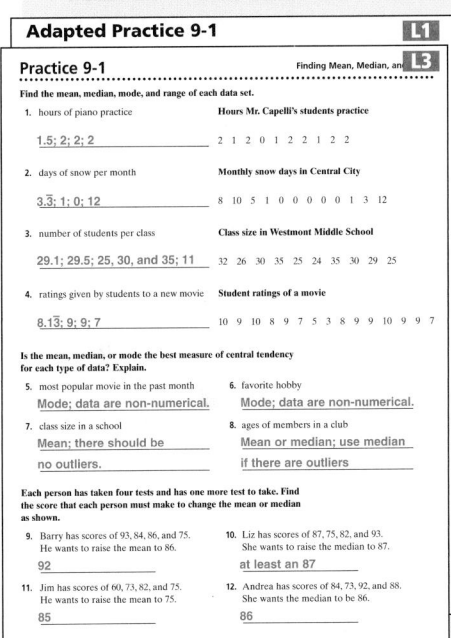

Adapted Practice 9-1 L1

Practice 9-1 Finding Mean, Median, an[d Mode] L3

Find the mean, median, mode, and range of each data set.

1. hours of piano practice — **Hours Mr. Capelli's students practice**
   2 1 2 0 1 2 2 1 2 2
   1.5; 2; 2; 2
2. days of snow per month — **Monthly snow days in Central City**
   8 10 5 1 0 0 0 0 0 1 3 12
   $3.\overline{3}$; 1; 0; 12
3. number of students per class — **Class size in Westmont Middle School**
   32 26 30 35 25 24 35 30 29 25
   29.1; 29.5; 25, 30, and 35; 11
4. ratings given by students to a new movie — **Student ratings of a movie**
   10 9 10 8 9 7 5 3 8 9 9 10 9 9 7
   $8.1\overline{3}$; 9; 9; 7

Is the mean, median, or mode the best measure of central tendency for each type of data? Explain.

5. most popular movie in the past month
   Mode; data are non-numerical.
6. favorite hobby
   Mode; data are non-numerical.
7. class size in a school
   Mean; there should be no outliers.
8. ages of members in a club
   Mean or median; use median if there are outliers

Each person has taken four tests and has one more test to take. Find the score that each person must make to change the mean or median as shown.

9. Barry has scores of 93, 84, 86, and 75. He wants to raise the mean to 86.
   92
10. Liz has scores of 87, 75, 82, and 93. She wants to raise the median to 87.
    at least an 87
11. Jim has scores of 60, 73, 82, and 75. He wants to raise the mean to 75.
    85
12. Andrea has scores of 84, 73, 92, and 88. She wants the median to be 86.
    86

9-1 • Guided Problem Solving GPS L3

Student Page 416, Exercise 24:

Reasoning You have one more math test to take. The scores you have are 89, 92, 78, 83, and 83.

a. What score must you get to raise the mean to 87?
b. What score must you get to raise the median by 2 points?

Understand

1. How many tests have been taken? 5 tests
2. How many more tests are to be taken? 1 test
3. What two measures of central tendency will be used? mean and median

Plan and Carry Out

4. How do you find the mean? Add the scores and divide by the total number of scores.
5. How many points do you have so far? 425 points
6. How many tests will you have taken? 6 tests
7. How many total points do you need to have so that when you divide the total by 6, you get an answer of 87? 522 points
8. How many points do you need on the last math test so that you can get that total number of points? 97 points
9. List your current tests scores in order from least to greatest. 78, 83, 83, 89, 92
10. How do you find the median if there are an even number of scores? Average the two middle scores.
11. What do the two middle scores have to total to average 85? 170
12. One middle score is 83. What does the other have to be? 87

Check

13. Do your answers check? Yes

Solve Another Problem

14. Your bowling scores for two games are 134 and 142. What score must you get on the last game to raise your mean to 141 and raise the median by 4 points? 147

4. Assess & Reteach

PowerPoint

Lesson Quiz

Use the data set below for problems 1–5.

0, −2, 3, 9, 1, −2, −1, 3, −2

1. Find the mean. 1
2. Find the median. 0
3. Find the mode. −2
4. Find the range. 11
5. Find the outlier. 9
6. A dance teacher advertises individual attention and small class sizes. He is currently teaching classes of 16, 18, 22, 25, 22, and 23 students. Which measure of central tendency would make the class size look smallest? mean

Alternative Assessment

Assign small groups. Each student in a group rolls a number cube. Together the members find the mean, median, mode, and range of the set of numbers rolled.

Enrichment 9-1 L4

Reteaching 9-1 Finding Mean, Median, a L2

- The *median* of this set of data is the middle value when the scores are ordered.

  23 25 25 26 26 **26** **26** 26 27 27 28 29

  Since there are two middle scores, add them and divide by 2.

  $\frac{26 + 26}{2} = 26$

Number of Pages Read by Members of the Science Fiction Book Club

25	26	28	25
26	27	27	26
26	29	26	23

- The *mean* is the sum of the scores divided by the number of scores.

  25 + 26 + 28 + 25 + 26 + 27 + 27 + 26 + 26 + 29 + 26 + 23 = 314

  $\frac{314}{12} = 26.166\ldots$ or about 26.2 pages

- The *mode* is the score that occurs the most. The mode is 26 pages.

Find the mean, median, and mode of each set of data.

1. movies seen: 3 3 1 4 0 4 2 5 7 4 1 2
   mean: 3; median: 3; mode: 4
2. yards earned: 0 0 −8 4 15 −9 1 −1 6 7 −10 2
   mean: 0.58; median: 0.5; mode: 0
3. cost of tickets:
   $3.25 $2.50 $4.00 $4.00 $3.50 $2.00 $4.00 $3.00 $2.50 $3.00 $4.00
   mean: $3.25; median: $3.25; mode: $4

Which would you report to your parents—mean, median, or mode? Give your reason.

4. test scores: 89 84 79 80 81 55
   Median; there is no mode and the median is greater than the mean.
5. friends' allowances: $10 $15 $12 $15 $8
   Mode; both the median and the mean are less than the mode.

GO Online
Homework Video Tutor
Visit: PHSchool.com
Web Code: ase-0901

Complete each data set so that the mean is 8.

19. 11, 5, 11, 5, ■ 8 **20.** 7, 7, 7, 7, ■ 12 **21.** 18, 0, 18, 6, ■ −2

Use the data at the right.

Average Number of Vacation Days per Year

Country	Days
Italy	42
France	37
Germany	35
Brazil	34
Canada	26
Korea	25
Japan	25
United States	13

22. Find the mean, median, and mode. 29.625; 30; 25

23. **Writing in Math** Is the data value for the United States an outlier? Explain.

23. Yes; the United States brings the mean down more than 2 days.

24. **Reasoning** You have one more test to take. The scores you have already received are 89, 92, 78, 83, and 83. (GPS)

a. What score must you get to raise the mean to 87? 97

b. What score must you get to raise the median by 2 points? 87

C 25. **Challenge** The median of three numbers is 7. The range is 14. The mean is 11. What are the three numbers? 6, 7, 20

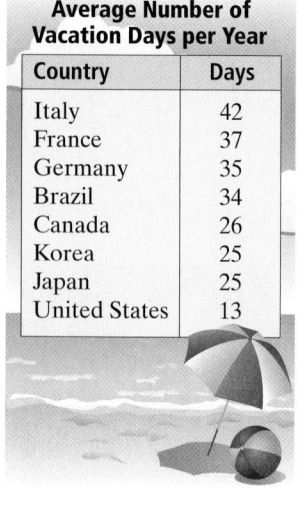

Test Prep and Mixed Review

Practice

Multiple Choice

26. The bar graph shows the number of rainy days in Cleveland. Which measure of data makes the weather in Cleveland appear the least rainy? A

Ⓐ Mean Ⓒ Mode
Ⓑ Median Ⓓ Range

SOURCE: National Oceanic and Atmospheric Administration. Go to **PHSchool.com** for a data update. Web Code: asg-9041.

27. A cube has a surface area of 337.5 ft^2. What is the length of any one side? F

Ⓕ 7.5 ft Ⓗ 28 ft
Ⓖ 18 ft Ⓙ 56 ft

28. An interior designer saved $29 on a pair of window blinds. If the sale price was 20% off the regular price, what was the regular price of the blinds? B

Ⓐ $345 Ⓑ $145 Ⓒ $69 Ⓓ $36

GO for Help

For Exercises	See Lesson
29–32	1-4

Simplify each expression.

29. $15(-20)$ −300 **30.** $-7(-11)$ 77 **31.** $\frac{-120}{-6}$ 20 **32.** $\frac{60}{-4}$ −15

Test Prep

Resources

For additional practice with a variety of test item formats:

- Test-Taking Strategies, p. 461
- Test Prep, p. 465
- Test-Taking Strategies with Transparencies

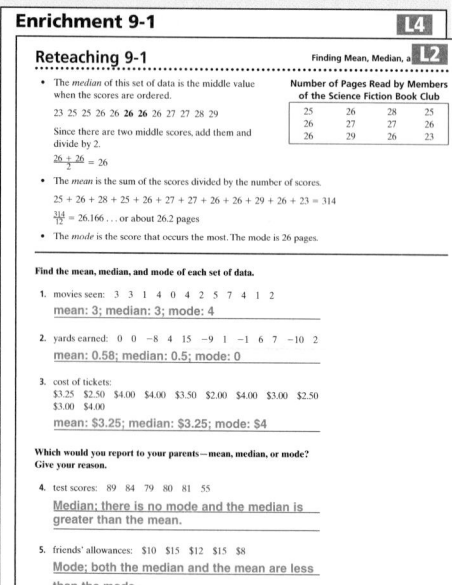

Comparing Mean and Median

When you use a measure of central tendency, you choose one number to represent an entire set of data. This is like choosing one adjective to describe your pet, so choose carefully! The characteristics of a data set can help you choose an appropriate measure.

ACTIVITY

Work in a group. 1–2. Check students' work.

1. Write each group member's height in inches. Calculate the group's mean and median height.
2. Suppose a person whose height is 7 ft 2 in. joins your group. Calculate the new mean and median height for the group.
3. Which measure, the mean or the median, was more affected by the new data? Explain why this happened. Mean; 7 ft 2 in. is an outlier that raises the mean.
4. Which measure of central tendency, mean or median, better describes the height of your group with the additional person? Give reasons for your choice. 4. Median; the mean is affected by the outlier, and the mode may be too high or too low.

ACTIVITY

5. Calculate the mean body length for the rodent species in the table at the right. 19 in.
6. Write the range of the data. Explain why the range tells you more about the data than the mean does. 45 in.; the data are very spread out, and the mean does not indicate this.

Body Length of Some Rodents

Rodent	Body Length (in.)
Capybara	48
Flying squirrel	9
Gray squirrel	10
Harvest mouse	3
Porcupine	26
Woodchuck	18

Exercises

Collect group data for each question. Then calculate the mean, median, and range for each data set. Choose either the mean or the median as the best measure of central tendency for each set of data. Explain your choice.

1. How long (in seconds) can you stand on one leg?
2. How many states in the United States have you visited?
3. How many pets have you had?
4. What is the length of your hair? 1–4. Check students' work.

Activity Lab

Data Collection: Comparing Mean and Median

Working in groups, students collect data, calculate the mean, median, and range for the data, and compare the measures of central tendency. They explore which measures most accurately describe the data and how extreme values affect the measures of central tendency.

Guided Instruction

You may wish to tape yardsticks to the wall, or have a wall chart with feet and inches marked for each group so students can easily measure each other's heights.

Activity

When students complete Items 5 and 6, have them compare their conclusions for each set of data. Ask: *Why does the range better describe the body length of the rodents but not the height of your group of students?* Sample: There is a greater range in the rodents' sizes than there is for students' heights. The range gives that information. If you saw just the mean of each set of data, you would not be able to tell that the rodents' lengths varied so widely, whereas the students' heights were much closer together.

Resources

- tools that students can use to measure each other's heights, such as measuring tapes or a wall chart with feet and inches marked

9-2

1. Plan

Objective
To use line plots, frequency tables, and histograms to represent data

Examples
1 Making a Line Plot
2 Using a Line Plot
3 Making a Histogram

Math Understandings: p. 410C

Professional Development

Math Background

Data items in a list are often difficult to interpret or to use as information. One way of organizing data so that their meaning is easier to see is by making a *frequency table* that shows how often repeated data items occur. A *line plot* stacks ✗ marks for repeated data items on a number line. Data can be grouped into intervals and displayed on a frequency table or a histogram. A *histogram* is a type of bar graph that shows data grouped in intervals and represented by bars that have no spaces between them.

More Math Background: p. 410C

Lesson Planning and Resources

See p. 410E for a list of the resources that support this lesson.

PowerPoint

Bell Ringer Practice

Check Skills You'll Need
Use student page, transparency, or PowerPoint. For intervention, direct students to:
Finding Mean Median and Mode
Lesson 9-1
Extra Skills and Word Problems Practice, Ch. 9

9-2 Displaying Frequency

Check Skills You'll Need

1. **Vocabulary Review** Which is *not* a *measure of central tendency*—mean, median, or range? range

Find the mean, median, mode, and range.

2. hours driving: 6 6.5 7 7 8 8 9 9.5 10
3. low temperatures: 4 −2 0 −1 2 −4 5 3

2–3. See below.

GO for Help Lesson 9-1

Check Skills You'll Need
2. 7.9; 8; 7 and 8; 4
3. 0.875; 1; no mode; 9

What You'll Learn

To use line plots, frequency tables, and histograms to represent data

New Vocabulary frequency, line plot, frequency table, histogram

Why Learn This?

You can use a frequency table or line plot to display data such as body temperatures of cats. Line plots are useful for comparing amounts, finding the most common value in a data set quickly, or identifying outliers.

Body Temperatures of Cats (°F)
101, 102, 101, 100, 102, 103
102, 101, 101
104, 101, 102

The number of times a data item occurs is the **frequency** of the item. You can display frequency in a line plot. A **line plot** displays data with ✗ marks above each data value on a number line.

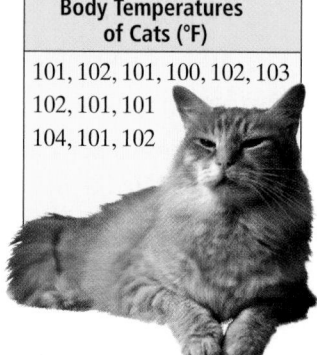

EXAMPLE Making a Line Plot

1 **Biology** The table above shows the body temperatures of some cats. Use the data to make a line plot.

Body Temperatures of Cats

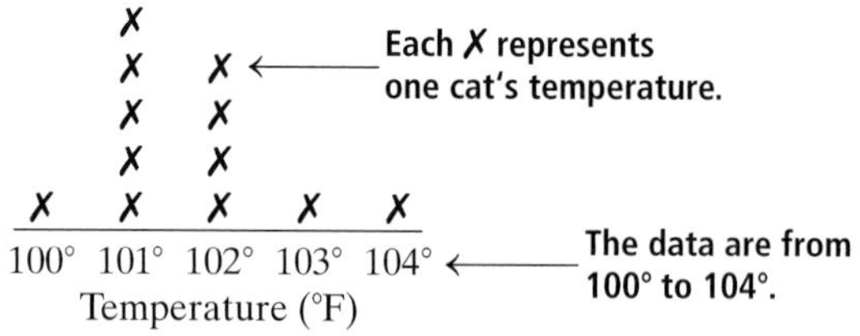

Quick Check

1. Make a line plot for these human body temperatures (°F): 98, 98, 99, 97, 98, 96, 99, 98, 97, 100, 99, 98, 99. See back of book.

Online active math

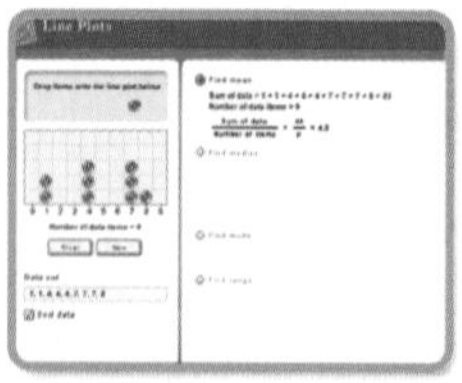

For: Line Plots Activity
Use: Interactive Textbook, 9-2

You can find the mean, median, and mode of a set of data using a line plot. Use the frequency of each data item to find the sum of the items and the total number of items.

Differentiated Instruction Solutions for All Learners

Special Needs L1	Below Level L2
Students who have difficulty drawing graphs work with a partner. The partner can draw the line plots, while the student can check that all the data values have been accurately plotted. learning style: tactile	Discuss tally marks and have students make a tally chart for items such as the number of chairs, desks, and tables in the room. learning style: verbal

To find the mean of data in a frequency table or line plot, first multiply each data value by its frequency.

EXAMPLE Using a Line Plot

2 Find the mean of the data in the line plot in Example 1.

Multiply each data value by its frequency.

$$\frac{(1 \cdot 100) + (5 \cdot 101) + (4 \cdot 102) + (1 \cdot 103) + (1 \cdot 104)}{1 + 5 + 4 + 1 + 1}$$

Add the frequency of each item to find the total number of items.

$\frac{1{,}220}{12} \approx 101.7$ ← **Simplify. Then round to the nearest tenth.**

Quick Check

2. Use the line plot in Example 1. Find the median and mode. **101.5°; 101°**

Vocabulary Tip

An interval of 8–12 includes the numbers 8, 9, 10, 11, and 12.

A **frequency table** lists the frequency of each item in a set of data. To display the data visually, make a histogram. A **histogram** is a special type of bar graph with no spaces between bars. The height of each bar shows the frequency of data within that interval. The intervals of a histogram are of equal size and do not overlap.

EXAMPLE Making a Histogram

3 **Energy** Some brands of batteries last longer than others. Make a frequency table and histogram for the data on hours of battery life: 12, 9, 10, 14, 10, 11, 10, 18, 21, 10, 14, 22.

Make a frequency table. The data range from 9 to 22. Use equal-sized intervals that begin with multiples of 5. Then make a histogram.

Battery Life

Hours	Tally	Frequency
0–4		0
5–9	/	1
10–14	卌 ///	8
15–19	/	1
20–24	//	2

Battery Life

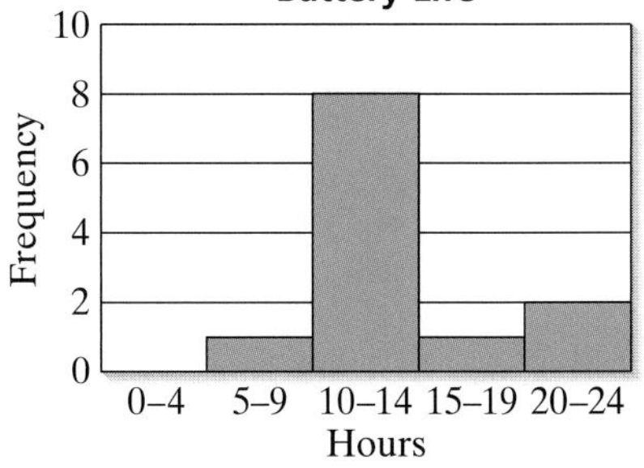

Online active math

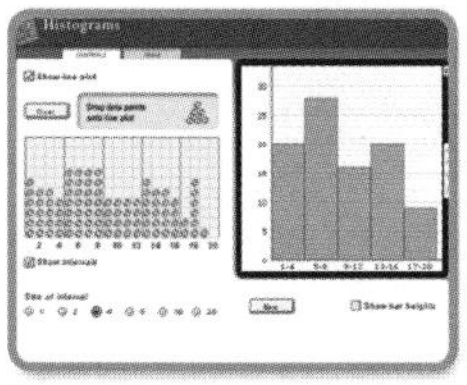

For: Histogram Activity
Use: Interactive Textbook, 9-2

Quick Check

3. Make a frequency table and histogram for the data on the cost of a movie: \$5.00, \$6.00, \$8.50, \$9.00, \$5.50, \$7.00, \$7.00, \$7.50, \$6.00, \$7.50, \$4.00, \$9.00, \$8.00, \$5.50. See back of book.

2. Teach

Activity Lab

Use before the lesson.

All in One Teaching Resources

Activity Lab 9-2: Displaying Frequency

Guided Instruction

After reviewing Examples 1 and 2, ask:

- *How is a line plot similar to a frequency table?* **Sample: Both show the number of times a data value occurs.**
- *How does a line plot differ from a frequency table?* **Sample: A line plot stacks ✗s above repeated data values on a number line while the table uses tally marks.**

Technology Tip

Have students use the first Online Active Math in Interactive Textbook Lesson 9-2 to make line plots and find mean, median, and mode.

Have students use the second Online Active Math feature to make line plots and histograms. Have them compare the types of data displays.

PowerPoint

Additional Examples

1 Make a line plot for the number of songs on a collection of CDs: 10, 11, 13, 8, 12, 11, 9, 15, 12, 11, 13, 15, and 14. See back of book.

2 Find the mean, median, and mode of the data in the line plot in Question 1. **mean: 11.8; median: 12; mode: 11**

3 The number of goals a soccer team scored in each game of the season is shown. Make a frequency table and a histogram for the data.
0 3 0 0 7 2 1 0 4 1 0 3 6 0 1
See back of book.

Advanced Learners L4

Students make a histogram for Example 3 with unequal intervals. They explain how these intervals could be misleading.

learning style: verbal

English Language Learners ELL

As partners, students write what is similar and what is different about line plots and histograms. Then each pair shares its ideas with the class. From their ideas, create a list that you can post in the classroom.

learning style: verbal

All in One Teaching Resources
- Daily Notetaking Guide 9-2 L3
- Adapted Notetaking 9-2 L1

Closure

- *Why are frequency tables and line plots useful?* Sample: They quickly organize and display raw data by the number of times each item occurs.
- *When is a frequency table with intervals or a histogram useful?* Sample: when there are a large number of data values

Exercises

For Exercises 9-10, have students use the Online Active Math for Interactive Textbook Lesson 9-2 to make histograms and line plots with different intervals.

4. Hours Spent on Homework

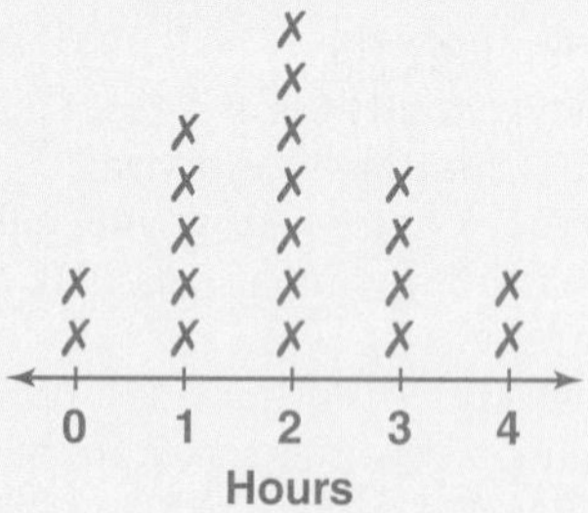

5. Hard-Drive Size

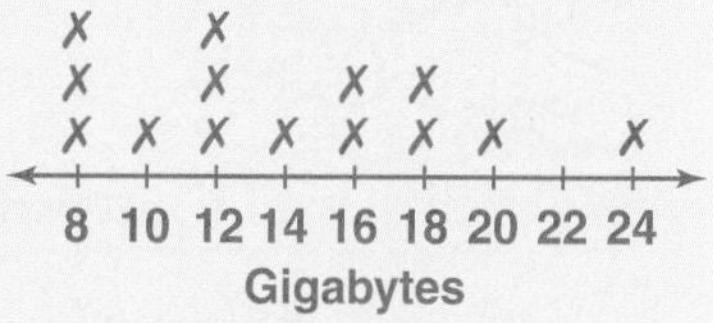

8. Answers may vary. Sample:

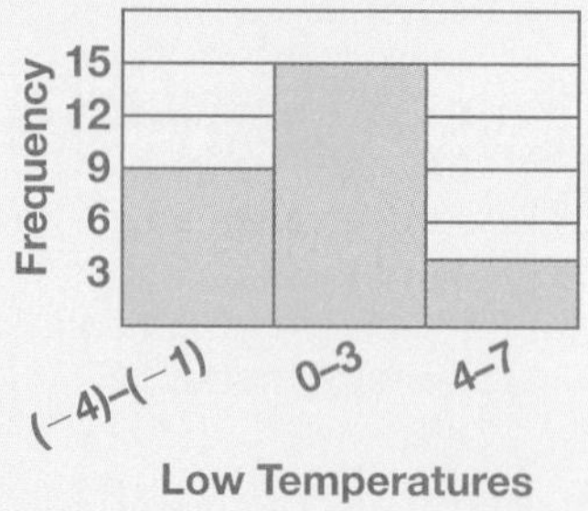

9. Answers may vary. Sample:

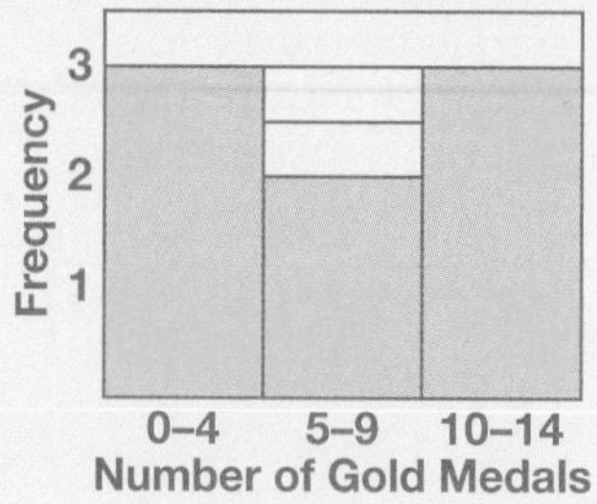

Check Your Understanding

1. A histogram is a bar graph with no spaces between the bars.

2. There are no values less than 25 in the data.

1. **Vocabulary** How is a histogram different from a bar graph?

Use the line plot below for Exercises 2 and 3.

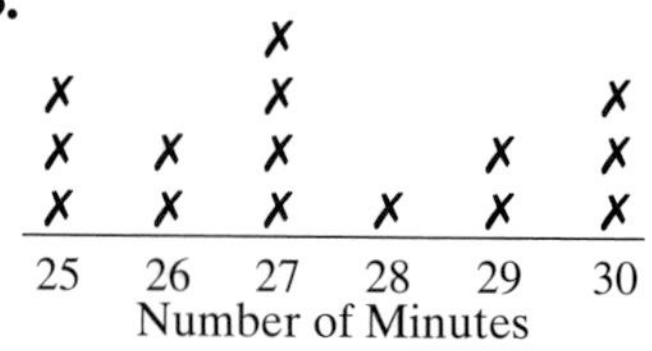

2. **Reasoning** Explain why the number line for the line plot at the right starts at 25 instead of 0.
3. Find the mean of the data set. 27.4

Homework Exercises

For more exercises, see Extra Skills and Word Problems.

GO for Help

For Exercises	See Examples
4–5	1
6–7	2
8	3

A **Make a line plot for each set of data.** 4–5. See margin.

4. hours spent on homework:
2 2 3 1 1 2 0 3 2 0
4 2 1 3 1 3 1 4 2 2

5. hard-drive sizes (gigabytes):
8 10 8 12 16 20 18 16
12 14 18 24 12 8

Find the mean, median, and mode of the data to the nearest tenth.

6.

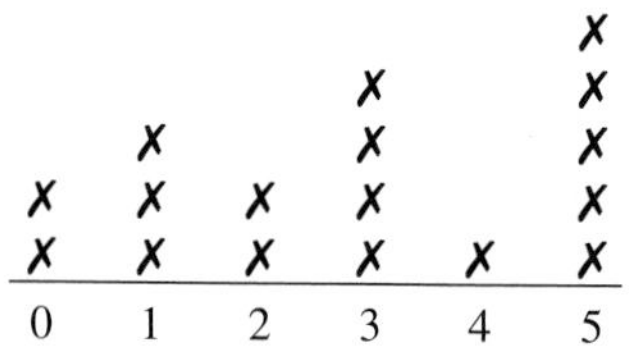

2.8; 3; 5

7.

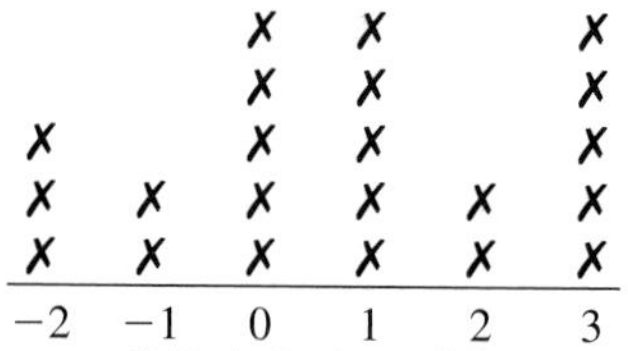

0.7; 1; 0, 1, and 3

8. Make a histogram for the data.
Low temperatures in February (°F):
−2 −1 0 −2 −1 −4 2 3 0 −1 2 −3
−1 0 1 2 3 2 −2 3 4 2 1 5 6 4 3 1
See margin.

B **GPS**

9. **Guided Problem Solving** Use the table at the right. Make a histogram for the data.
   - What intervals will you use?
   - Using those intervals, how will you organize the data? See margin.

10. Use a line plot to display the frequency of medals won at the 2002 Winter Olympics. See margin.

Distribution of Gold Medals at the 2002 Winter Olympics

Country	Medals
Germany	12
Norway	11
United States	10
Canada	6
Russian Federation	6
Finland	4
France	4
Italy	4

SOURCE: *The World Almanac*

Write the intervals described in each statement.

11. intervals that are multiples of 10 for data that range from 58 to 100
12. intervals that are multiples of 20 for data that range from 305 to 458

11–12. Answers may vary. Samples are given.

11. 50–59, 60–69, 70–79, 80–89, 90–99, 100–109

12. 300–319, 320–339, 340–359, 360–379, 380–399, 400–419, 420–439, 440–459

10.

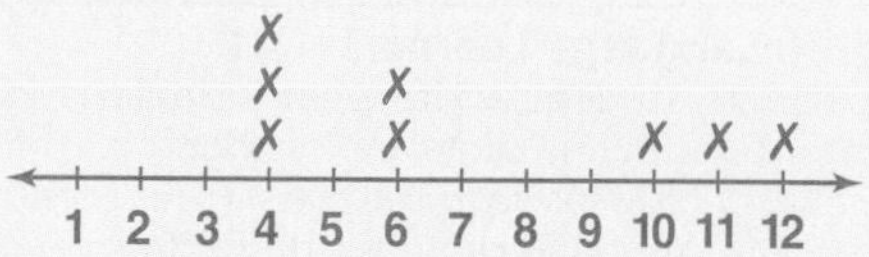

13. Cars Sold Per Month

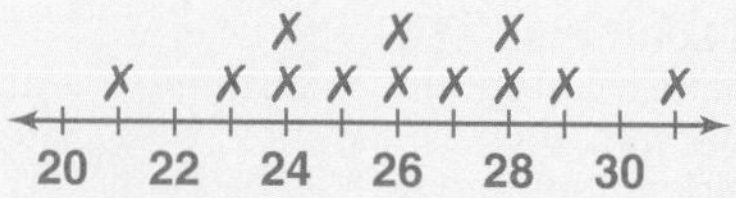

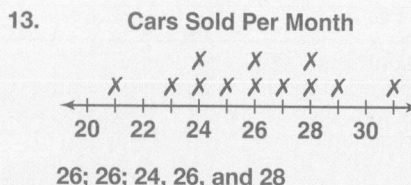

26; 26; 24, 26, and 28

GO Online
Homework Video Tutor
Visit: PHSchool.com
Web Code: ase-0902

15. Keystrokes in Computer Passwords

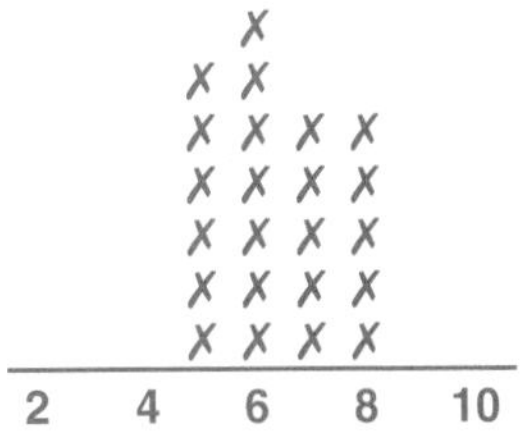

6.39; 6; 6

Make a line plot for each data set. Then find the mean, median, and mode of the data. 13–14. See margin.

13. cars sold per month:
24 25 23 26 28 29 21 27 31 28 26 24

14. ages of members of the Seniors Hiking Club (years):
62 73 78 66 67 67 60 73 76 62 78 78 60 67 75 62

15. keystrokes in computer passwords:
8 7 8 6 6 5 6 7 7 8 8 8 6 5 5 6 5 6 7 7 6 5 5
See left.

Make a frequency table and histogram for each data set. Use intervals of equal sizes to group the data. 16–17. See margin.

16. televisions sold at a store each day:
7 8 9 13 14 18 5 9 11 16 5 6 14 12 10 9 7 9 2 21

17. golf scores:
0 −2 −1 0 3 −1 0 2 1 −2 3 0 1 −5 4 3
4 5 −2 0 −1 4 0 −2 3 2 3 1 4 0 −2 1

18. monthly car payments (dollars):
205 190 305 346 452 325 140 376 289 368 512 337 254 398
See back of book.

19. **Writing in Math** How does the appearance of a histogram change when you use many small intervals instead of a few large intervals? The bars will not be as high when using small intervals.

GO Online

Video Tutor Help
Visit: PHSchool.com
Web Code: ase-0775

Families Use the line plots below for Exercises 20–22. The Bakers and the Smiths are each having a family reunion. The line plots below show the number of children attending from each family.

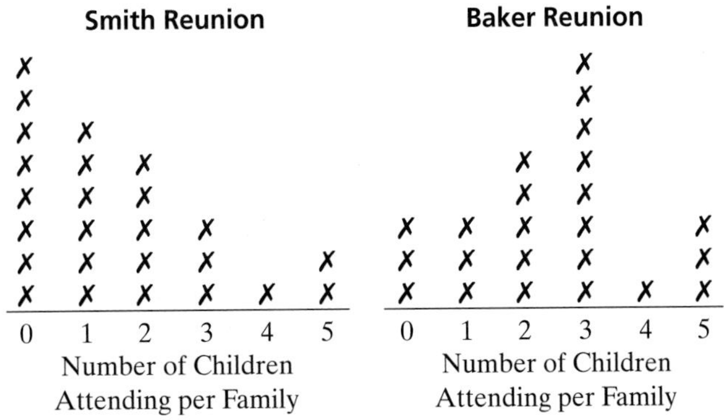

20. Which reunion, the Bakers or the Smiths, has more families without children? the Smiths

21. Which reunion, the Bakers or the Smiths, has more large families attending? the Bakers

22. Find the mean, median, and mode for each line plot. Round to the nearest tenth.

22. Smith: 1.6; 1; 0
Baker: 2.4; 3; 3

Online lesson quiz, **PHSchool.com, Web Code:** asa-0902

14. Ages of Members of the Seniors Hiking Club

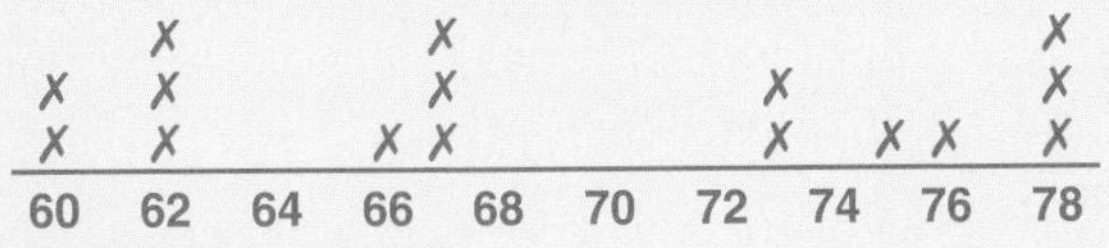

69; 67; 62, 67 and 78

16–17. See back of book.

3. Practice

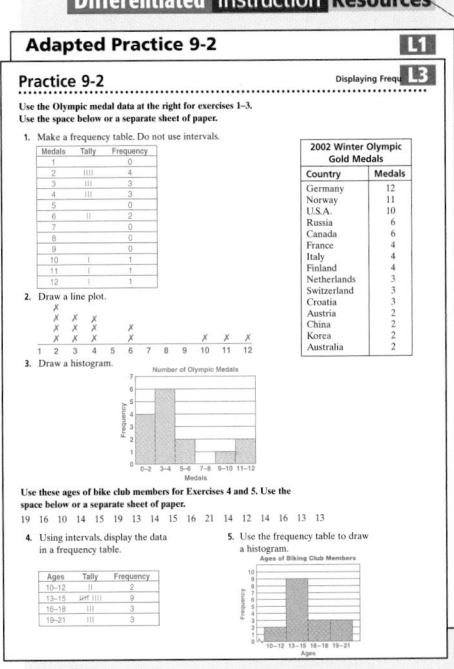

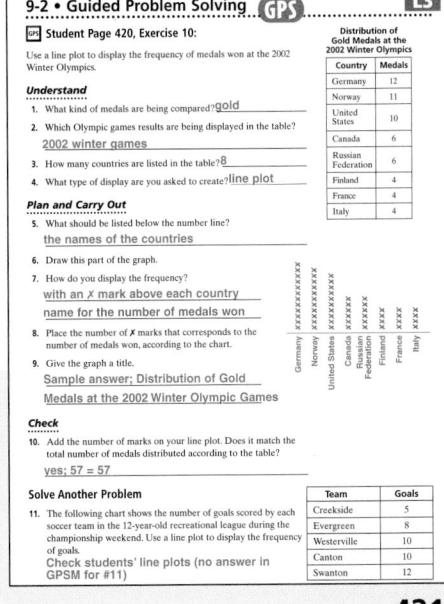

Assignment Guide

Check Your Understanding

Go over Exercises 1–3 in class before assigning the Homework Exercises.

Homework Exercises

A	Practice by Example	4–8
B	Apply Your Skills	9–22
C	Challenge	23
	Test Prep and Mixed Review	24–28

Homework Quick Check

To check students' understanding of key skills and concepts, go over Exercises 4, 8, 10, 19, and 22.

Differentiated Instruction Resources

Adapted Practice 9-2 L1

Practice 9-2 Displaying Frequ L3

Use the Olympic medal data at the right for exercises 1–3. Use the space below or a separate sheet of paper.

1. Make a frequency table. Do not use intervals.

Medals	Tally	Frequency
1		0
2	IIII	4
3	III	3
4	III	3
5		0
6	II	2
7		0
8		0
9		0
10	I	1
11	I	1
12	I	1

2002 Winter Olympic Gold Medals

Country	Medals
Germany	12
Norway	11
U.S.A.	10
Russia	6
Canada	6
France	4
Italy	4
Finland	4
Netherlands	3
Switzerland	3
Croatia	3
Austria	2
China	2
Korea	2
Australia	2

2. Draw a line plot.

3. Draw a histogram.

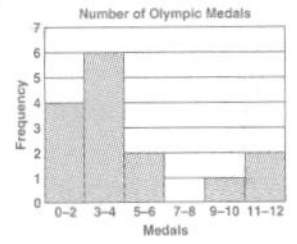

Use these ages of bike club members for Exercises 4 and 5. Use the space below or a separate sheet of paper.

19 16 10 14 15 19 13 14 15 16 21 14 12 14 16 13 13

4. Using intervals, display the data in a frequency table.

Ages	Tally	Frequency
10–12	II	2
13–15	~~IIII~~ IIII	9
16–18	III	3
19–21	III	3

5. Use the frequency table to draw a histogram.

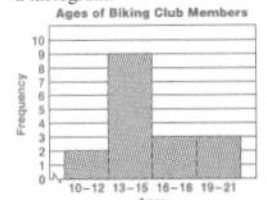

9-2 • Guided Problem Solving GPS L3

GPS **Student Page 420, Exercise 10:**

Use a line plot to display the frequency of medals won at the 2002 Winter Olympics.

Distribution of Gold Medals at the 2002 Winter Olympics

Country	Medals
Germany	12
Norway	11
United States	10
Canada	6
Russian Federation	6
Finland	4
France	4
Italy	4

Understand

1. What kind of medals are being compared? gold
2. Which Olympic games results are being displayed in the table? 2002 winter games
3. How many countries are listed in the table? 8
4. What type of display are you asked to create? line plot

Plan and Carry Out

5. What should be listed below the number line? the names of the countries
6. Draw this part of the graph.
7. How do you display the frequency? with an ✗ mark above each country name for the number of medals won
8. Place the number of ✗ marks that corresponds to the number of medals won, according to the chart.
9. Give the graph a title. Sample answer; Distribution of Gold Medals at the 2002 Winter Olympic Games

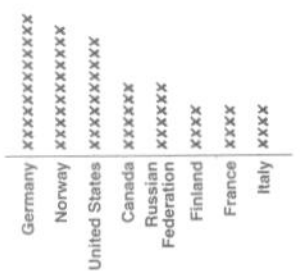

Check

10. Add the number of marks on your line plot. Does it match the total number of medals distributed according to the table? yes; 57 = 57

Solve Another Problem

11. The following chart shows the number of goals scored by each soccer team in the 12-year-old recreational league during the championship weekend. Use a line plot to display the frequency of goals. Check students' line plots (no answer in GPSM for #11)

Team	Goals
Creekside	5
Evergreen	8
Westerville	10
Canton	10
Swanton	12

4. Assess & Reteach

PowerPoint

Lesson Quiz

1. Make a line plot for the number of school spirit ribbons purchased. 1 3 11 2 2 10 9 1 7 6 4 3 1 1

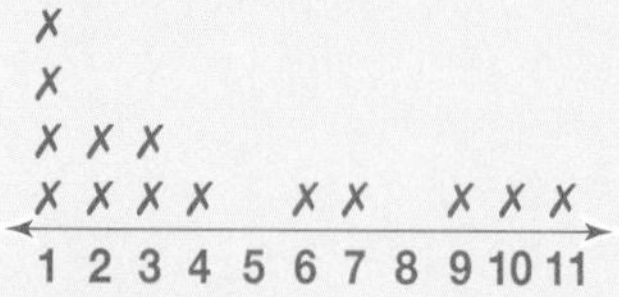

2. Find the mean of the data in the line plot in Item 1. 4.4

3. Make a frequency table with intervals for data in Item 1. Sample:

Ribbons	Tally	Freq.
0-2	~~||||~~ |	6
3-5	|||	3
6-8	||	2
9-11	|||	3

4. Make a histogram for the data in Item 1.

Spirit Ribbons Purchased

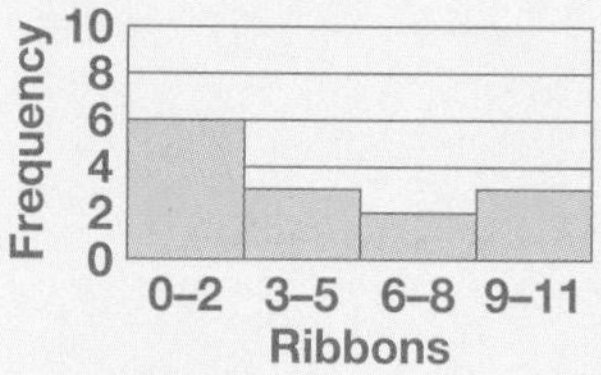

Enrichment 9-2 L4

Reteaching 9-2

Displaying Fr L2

The *frequency* of a data item is the number of times it appears. A *frequency table* provides intervals, then tallies each data item in its interval.

The last four digits of 24 phone numbers were chosen from a phone book.

Make a frequency table for the data.

① Choose an appropriate interval. All intervals must be the same size.

② Mark tallies and write totals for the data.

Telephone Numbers (Last Four Digits)

9782	8609	7880	9012	5620	1190	2324	2568
9877	4085	6856	7367	3642	6784	8015	7761
9001	4227	7452	9811	4326	6433	4228	8111

Telephone Numbers

Last Four Digits	Tally	Frequency
1000–1999	|	1
2000–2999	||	2
3000–3999	|	1
4000–4999	||||	4
5000–5999	|	1
6000–6999	|||	3
7000–7999	||||	4
8000–8999	|||	3
9000–9999	~~||||~~	5

You can use a frequency table to make a *histogram*.

In a histogram, there is no space between the bars.

Digits in Phone Numbers

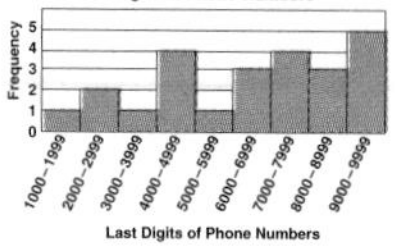

Use the following data for Exercises 1 and 2.

Raisins in a small box: 33 32 30 40 29 35 36 33 42 28 41 39 30 29 35 40 33 34 31 28

1. Make a frequency table for the data.
2. Use your frequency table to make a histogram.

Number of Raisins	Tally	Frequency
25–29	||||	4
30–34	|||| |||	8
35–39	||||	4
40–44	||||	4

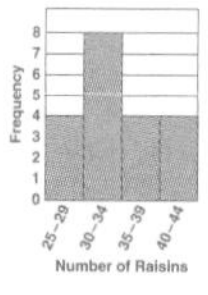

23. Answers may vary. Sample:

Cars	Frequency
0–9	1
10–19	1
20–29	0
30–39	2
40–49	3
50–59	1

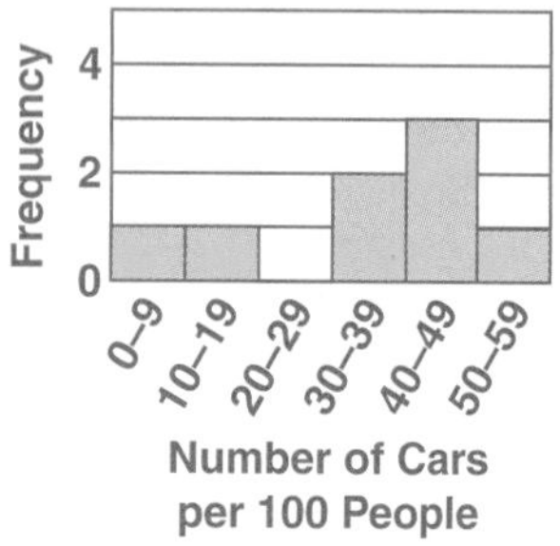

Ⓒ **23. Challenge** Use equal intervals to make a frequency table and histogram of the number of cars per 100 people.

Who's on the Road?

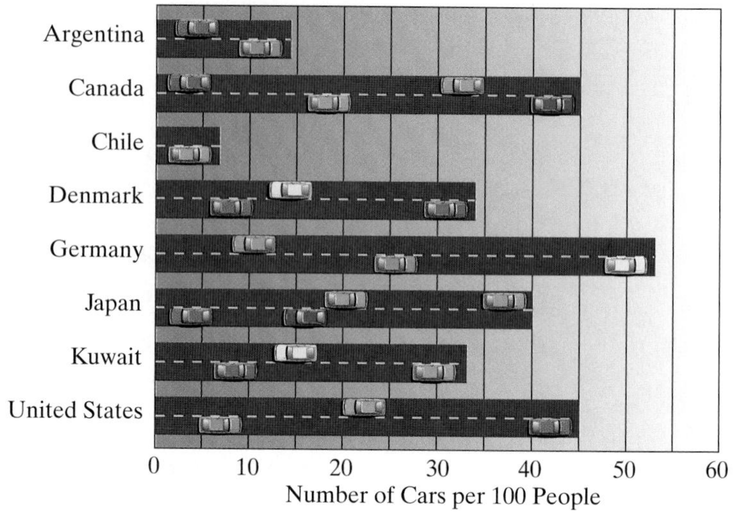

SOURCE: *Ward's Motor Vehicle Facts & Figures*

Test Prep and Mixed Review

Practice

Multiple Choice

24. Which line plot best represents the following data? B
2 1 5 4 1 3 7 8 2 2 3 4 1 6
8 9 1 1 2 4 5 4 3 5 4 3 2 1

Ⓐ
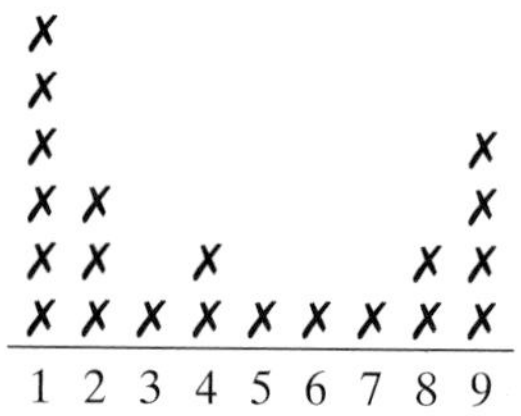

Ⓒ
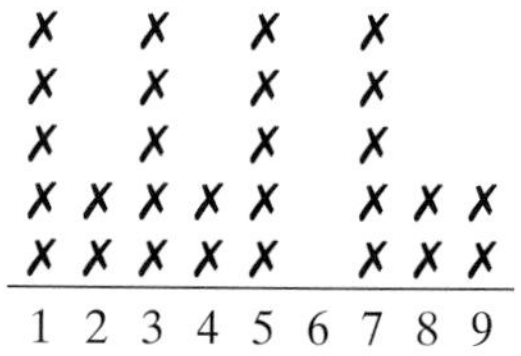

Ⓑ
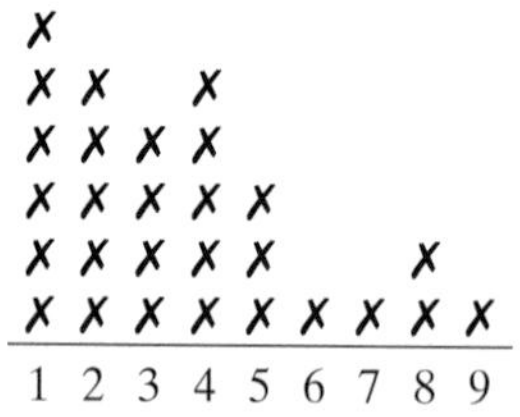

Ⓓ
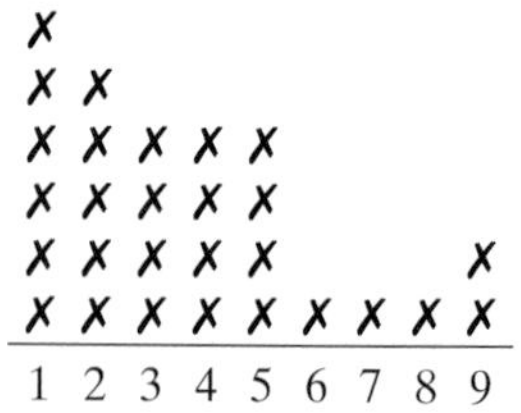

25. Sixteen percent of the executives in a company are women. What fraction of executives are women? F

Ⓕ $\frac{4}{25}$ Ⓖ $\frac{16}{25}$ Ⓗ $\frac{8}{5}$ Ⓙ $\frac{25}{4}$

GO for Help

For Exercises	See Lesson
26–28	5-1

Write each percent as a fraction in simplest form.

26. 20% $\frac{1}{5}$ **27.** $33\frac{1}{3}\%$ $\frac{1}{3}$ **28.** 1.75% $\frac{7}{400}$

Test Prep

Resources

For additional practice with a variety of test item formats:

- Test-Taking Strategies, p. 461
- Test Prep, p. 465
- Test-Taking Strategies with Transparencies

Alternative Assessment

Students toss two number cubes. They record the sums in a frequency table and make a line plot and a histogram with intervals.

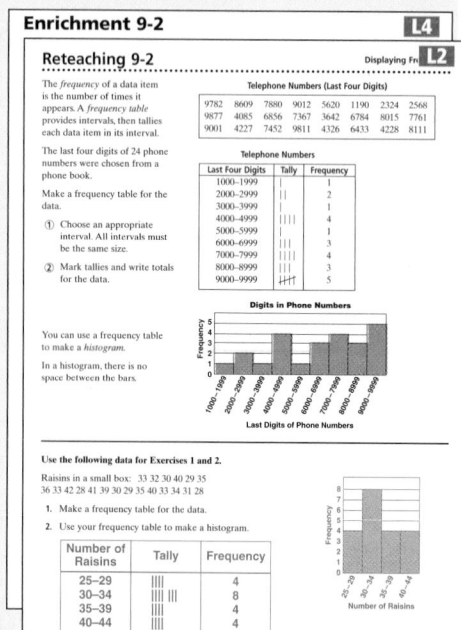

9-2b Activity Lab Technology

Making Histograms

A graphing calculator can help you make histograms.

ACTIVITY

Off the coast of Hawaii, a researcher recorded the following wave heights (in feet): 6.0, 6.5, 6.6, 6.3, 6.7, 7.4, 7.2, 7.4, 7.0, 7.2, 7.2, 7.3, 6.8, 7.3, 7.7, 7.8, 7.5, 7.2, 7.6, 7.3, 7.3, 7.1, 7.5, 6.9, and 6.8. Make a histogram of these data.

Step 1 Press LIST. Enter the 25 data values into L_1.

Step 2 Use the PLOT feature. Select the first plot. Select **On**. Select the type of graph that looks like a histogram. Set Xlist = L_1.

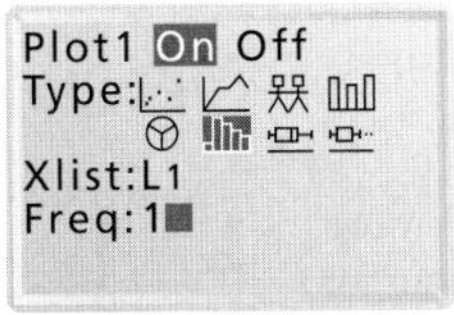

Step 3 Press ZOOM. Select ZoomStat.

Step 4 Press WINDOW. To make the intervals on the horizontal axis 0.1, set Xscl = 0.1.

Step 5 Press GRAPH to see the histogram.

Step 6 Press TRACE and move the cursor across the histogram to see the frequency of each interval.

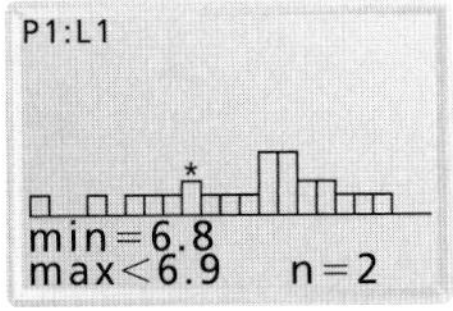

Step 7 Sketch a histogram of the data values.

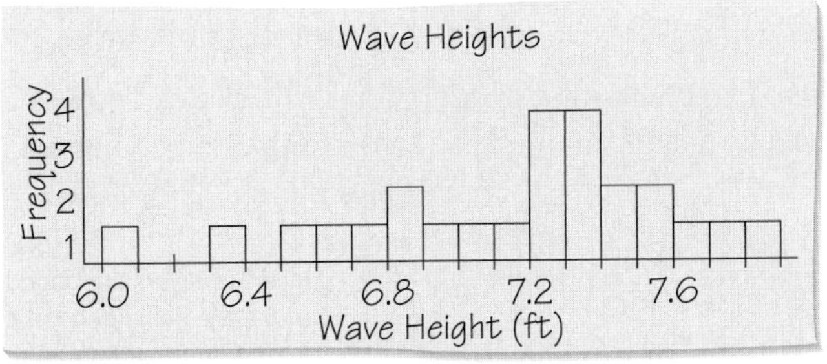

Exercises

Graph a histogram for each data set using a graphing calculator. Then sketch the histogram. 1–2. See margin.

1. 9, 12, 11, 14, 12, 11, 13, 14, 13, 11, 14, 14, 15, 11, 14, 16, 12, 12, 13, 11
2. 100, 120, 140, 160, 120, 180, 180, 280, 260, 240, 220, 220, 200, 200, 260, 240, 240, 120, 140, 160, 160

Activity Lab

Making Histograms

In Lesson 9-2, students drew histograms to display frequency data. In this activity, they use a graphing calculator to make a histogram of wave-height data, then sketch the histogram.

Guided Instruction

Exercises

Working in pairs, one student enters the data from the first exercise into the calculator and enters the keystrokes, then the other sketches the histogram. For the second problem, students switch tasks.

Resources

- any graphing calculator

1.

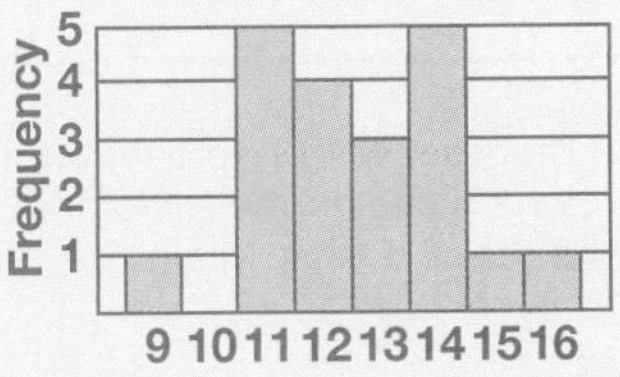

2.

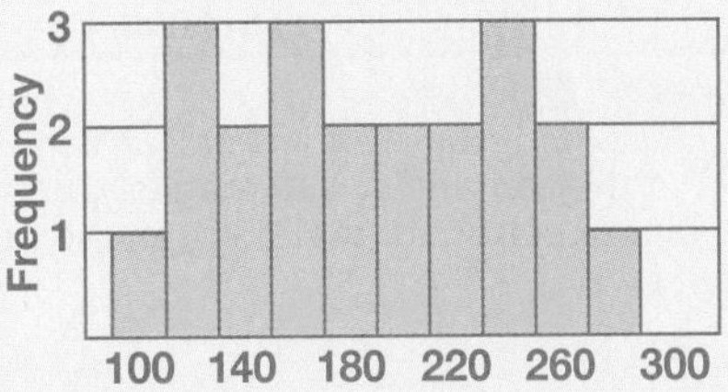

9-3

1. Plan

Objective
To use Venn diagrams to represent relationships between data

Example
1 Using a Venn Diagram

Math Understandings: p. 410C

Professional Development

Math Background

More Math Background: p. 410C

Lesson Planning and Resources

See p. 410E for a list of the resources that support this lesson.

PowerPoint

Bell Ringer Practice

Check Skills You'll Need
Use student page, transparency, or PowerPoint. For intervention, direct students to:
Adding and Subtracting Integers
Lesson 1-3
Extra Skills and Word Problems Practice, Ch. 1

2. Teach

Activity Lab

Use before the lesson.

All in One Teaching Resources
Activity Lab 9-3: Venn Diagrams

Technology Tip
Have students use a drawing program to generate Venn diagrams. They may want to draw pictures for individual items in each circle.

9-3 Venn Diagrams

Check Skills You'll Need

1. **Vocabulary Review** Two numbers whose sum is 0 are _?_. additive inverses

Simplify.

2. 10 − (−6) 16
3. −4 + 3 −1
4. 16 + (−9) 7

GO for Help Lesson 1-3

What You'll Learn

To use Venn diagrams to represent relationships between data

New Vocabulary Venn diagram

Why Learn This?

You can use Venn diagrams to describe the skills of the players on a sports team.

A **Venn diagram** is a diagram that uses regions, usually circles, to show how sets of numbers or objects are related.

EXAMPLE Using a Venn Diagram

1 A soccer coach is working on the lineup for the next game. The team has 15 players. Ten players on the team are good at offense. Six of those players are equally good at offense and defense. Eleven players are good at defense. Draw a Venn diagram for this situation.

First draw two circles that overlap. Label the circles Offense and Defense. Use the given information to complete the diagram.

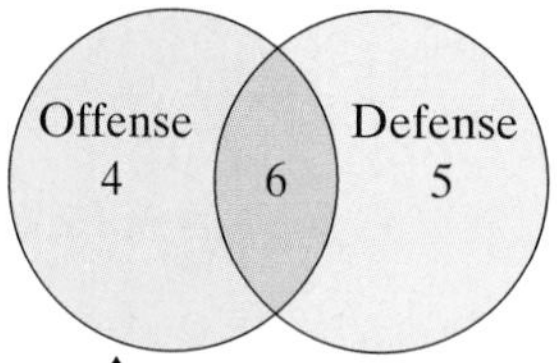

Since 11 players are good at defense but 6 are equally good at offense, 11−6 or 5 are good at only defense.

Since 10 players are good at offense but 6 are equally good at defense, 10−6 or 4 players are good at only offense.

1.
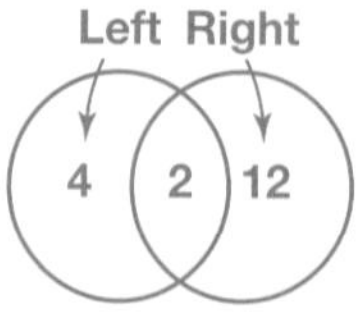

Quick Check

1. A softball team has 18 players. Fourteen players bat right-handed. Two players can bat left- or right-handed. Four players bat only left-handed. Draw a Venn diagram for this situation. See left.

Differentiated Instruction Solutions for All Learners

Special Needs L1	Below Level L2
Provide students with copies of pre-drawn Venn diagrams that they can fill in. Alternatively, provide them with cans or plastic lids that they can use to trace the circles. learning style: tactile	Students draw a Venn diagram with two overlapping circles. They draw vertical stripes in one circle and horizontal stripes in the other. They explain the meaning of the stripes in each area. learning style: visual

Check Your Understanding

1. **Vocabulary** In a Venn diagram, what does the region of the overlapping circles represent? **objects or people that fall into both categories**

2. Use the Venn diagram at the right. How many dogs are brown and have a long tail? **1 dog**

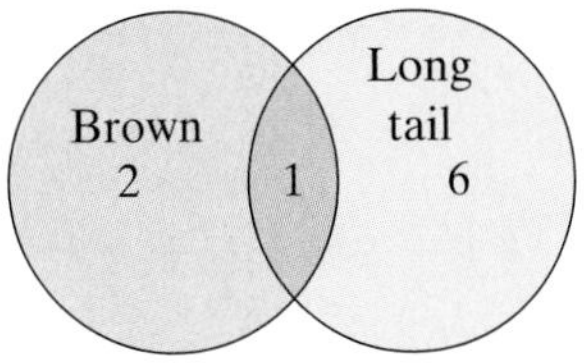

3. Of 120 students surveyed, 72 listen to pop music, 45 listen to country music, and 12 listen to both. How many students listen to only pop music? **60 students**

Homework Exercises

For more exercises, see Extra Skills and Word Problems.

GO for Help

For Exercises	See Examples
4–6	1

A **Draw a Venn diagram for each situation.** **4–6. See margin.**

4. 18 students play a sport.
   15 students are in the band.
   11 do both activities.

5. 12 red shapes
   12 triangles
   8 non-red triangles

6. 75 people are downhill skiers.
   51 people are cross-country skiers.
   26 ski both downhill and cross-country.

6.
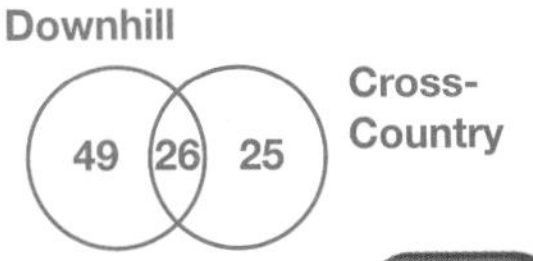

B **GPS**

7. **Guided Problem Solving** At a summer camp, 20 campers try canoeing or climbing. Suppose 13 campers try canoeing and 15 try climbing. Of those 15 campers, 7 try only climbing. How many campers try only canoeing? **5 campers**
   - Place the information in a Venn diagram. Use two circles.
   - How many students try both activities?

Solve each problem by drawing a Venn diagram.

8. What is the greatest common factor of 30 and 40? **10**

9. (GPS) Between 1 and 20, there are 10 odd numbers and 8 prime numbers. Three odd numbers are not prime. How many prime numbers are *not* odd? **1 number**

10. **School** Of 15 students in summer school, 11 take math and 9 take English. Of the students taking English, 5 also take math. What is the probability that a randomly-selected student takes only math? $\frac{6}{15}$

11. **Reasoning** A Venn diagram has two circles that do not overlap. What conclusion can you draw about the categories of data? **Nothing falls in both categories.**

GO Online
Homework Video Tutor
Visit: PHSchool.com
Web Code: ase-0903

PowerPoint Additional Examples

1 Twenty children made drawings with red or blue crayons. Thirteen children used red crayons to color. Of those using red crayons, 4 children used only red to color. Twelve children used blue crayons to color. Draw a Venn diagram to represent the situation. How many children used both red and blue crayons? **See back of book.**

All in One Teaching Resources
- Daily Notetaking Guide 9-3 L3
- Adapted Notetaking 9-3 L1

3. Practice

Assignment Guide

Check Your Understanding
Go over Exercises 1–3 in class.

Homework Exercises

A	Practice by Example	4–6
B	Apply Your Skills	7–12
C	Challenge	13
	Test Prep and Mixed Review	14–18

Homework Quick Check
To check students' understanding of key skills and concepts, go over Exercises 4, 6, 8, 9, and 11.

PowerPoint Lesson Quiz

1. Forty-two students took summer school classes. Twenty-seven students took math, 28 took science, and 1 took math only. Draw a Venn diagram. How many students took both math and science? **See back of book.**

4.
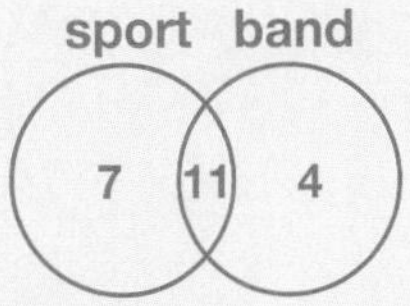

5.
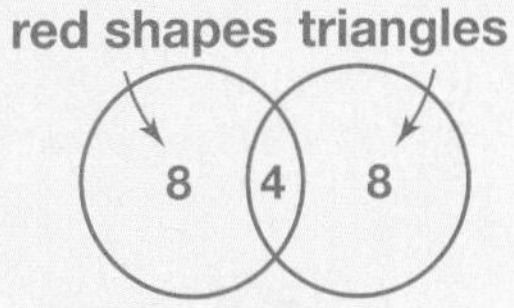

6. See above left

Advanced Learners L4
Students write a problem that can be solved by making a Venn diagram with three overlapping regions. They can challenge classmates to solve their problems.

learning style: verbal

English Language Learners ELL
Given a phrase, such as *4 of those people play only offense*, elicit the fact that *of those people* means from a larger group, and *only* indicates that they will not be included in the overlapping part of the Venn diagram.

learning style: verbal

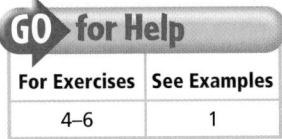

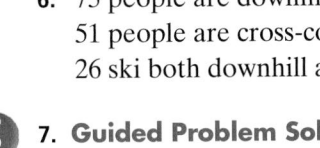

Activity

Have students find statistics in newspapers or magazines that can be represented by Venn diagrams. Use technology to generate a media report including the diagram.

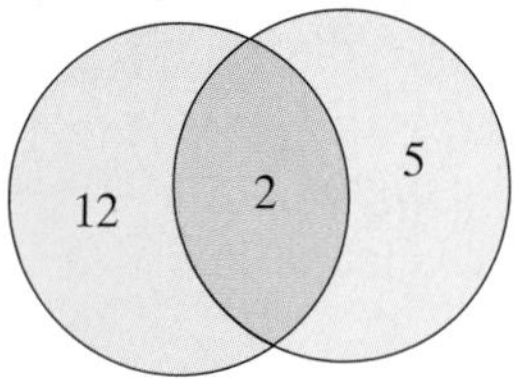

12. **Writing in Math** Write a problem that you could solve using the Venn diagram at the left. **Check students' work.**

Ⓒ 13. **Challenge** The Venn diagram below shows the results of a survey of the types of pets in 580 households. The area within the rectangle but outside the circles represents households that do not have a dog or a cat. Find the probability that a household chosen at random has neither a cat nor a dog. **$\frac{105}{580}$ or 0.181 or 18.1%**

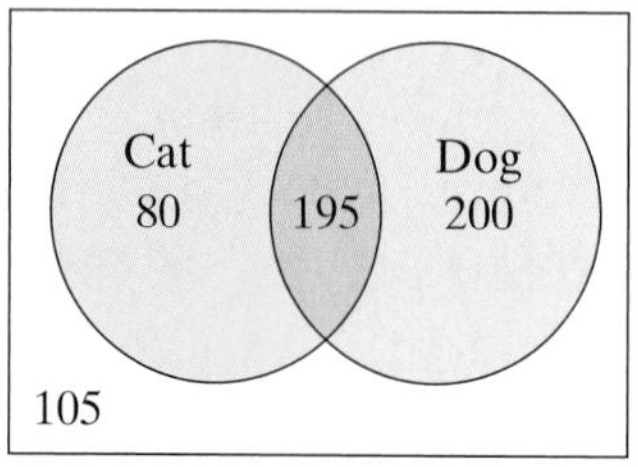

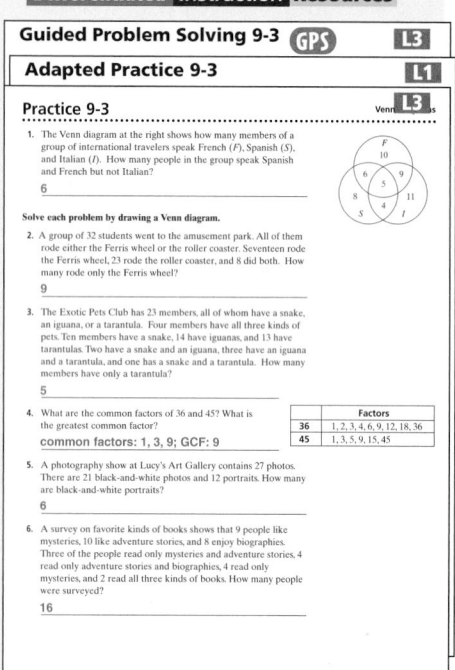

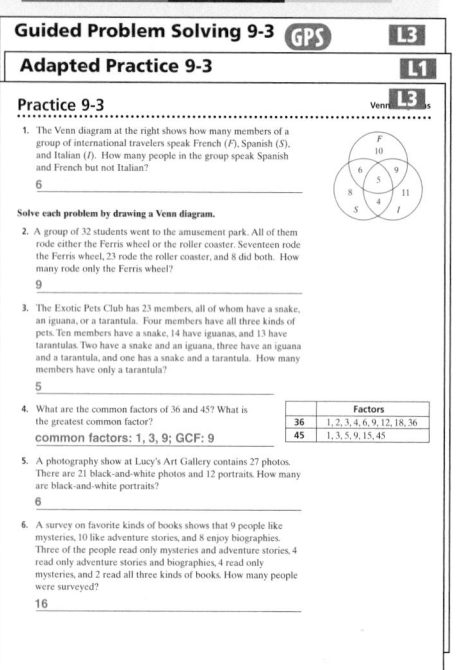

Test Prep and Mixed Review

Practice

Multiple Choice

14. Use the Venn diagram at the right. How many more employees work in the stock room than at the register? **D**
    - Ⓐ 3
    - Ⓑ 4
    - Ⓒ 5
    - Ⓓ 6

Store Employees

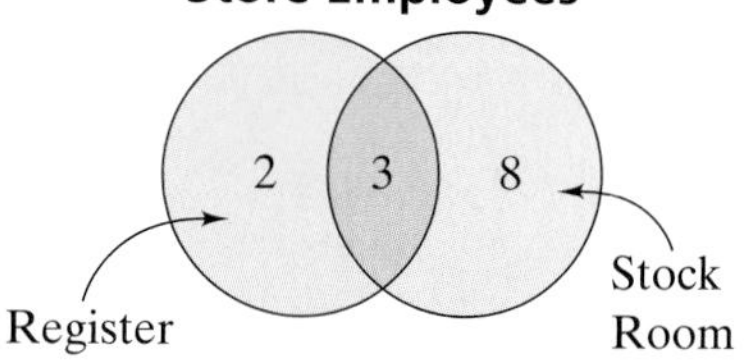

15. A circular fountain has a radius of 5 feet. The circular center of the fountain does not hold water and has a diameter of 3 feet. The outer part of the fountain that holds water is 2.5 feet deep. About how much water does the outer part hold? **H**
    - Ⓕ 18 ft^3
    - Ⓖ 125 ft^3
    - Ⓗ 178 ft^3
    - Ⓙ 196 ft^3

16. Manuella is planning a garden 80 feet wide and 125 feet long. The garden will have a square fountain, 8 feet on a side. It will also have 2,500 square feet of paths. The rest of the garden is reserved for plants. What is the area of the garden that is reserved for plants? **A**
    - Ⓐ 7,436 ft^2
    - Ⓑ 7,484 ft^2
    - Ⓒ 7,492 ft^2
    - Ⓓ 10,000 ft^2

Make a frequency table and a histogram for each data set. Use intervals of equal size to group the data. **17–18. See margin.**

GO for Help

For Exercises	See Lesson
17–18	9-2

17. lengths of wood (cm):
    23 26 25 26 23 25 25 24 21 21 22 23

18. weekly earnings (dollars):
    260 270 260 300 290 300 250 270 320 260

Differentiated Instruction Resources

Guided Problem Solving 9-3 GPS L3

Adapted Practice 9-3 L1

Practice 9-3 Venn L3

1. The Venn diagram at the right shows how many members of a group of international travelers speak French (F), Spanish (S), and Italian (I). How many people in the group speak Spanish and French but not Italian?
   6

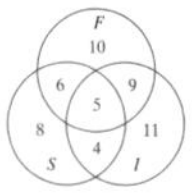

Solve each problem by drawing a Venn diagram.

2. A group of 32 students went to the amusement park. All of them rode either the Ferris wheel or the roller coaster. Seventeen rode the Ferris wheel, 23 rode the roller coaster, and 8 did both. How many rode only the Ferris wheel?
   9
3. The Exotic Pets Club has 23 members, all of whom have a snake, an iguana, or a tarantula. Four members have all three kinds of pets. Ten members have a snake, 14 have iguanas, and 13 have tarantulas. Two have a snake and an iguana, three have an iguana and a tarantula, and one has a snake and a tarantula. How many members have only a tarantula?
   5
4. What are the common factors of 36 and 45? What is the greatest common factor?
   common factors: 1, 3, 9; GCF: 9

	Factors
36	1, 2, 3, 4, 6, 9, 12, 18, 36
45	1, 3, 5, 9, 15, 45

5. A photography show at Lucy's Art Gallery contains 27 photos. There are 21 black-and-white photos and 12 portraits. How many are black-and-white portraits?
   6
6. A survey on favorite kinds of books shows that 9 people like mysteries, 10 like adventure stories, and 8 enjoy biographies. Three of the people read only mysteries and adventure stories, 4 read only adventure stories and biographies, 4 read only mysteries, and 2 read all three kinds of books. How many people were surveyed?
   16

Enrichment 9-3 L4

Reteaching 9-3 Venn L2

A *Venn diagram* shows relationships between sets of items. Each circle represents one set. Items that belong to both sets are contained in the overlap between the circles.

Example 1: Carlos has classes in English, algebra, chemistry, track, and history. Otis has classes in English, history, tennis, and computer science. Which classes do both students attend?

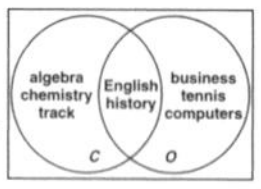

To draw a Venn diagram, draw a rectangle. Inside it, draw circle C for Carlos's classes, circle O for Otis's classes. The overlap shows the classes both boys attend: English and History.

Example 2: Carlos asks 25 math/science students whether they are taking math or science. Every student takes at least one of these classes. Twenty-two of the students take science and 15 take math. Twelve students take both classes. Use a Venn diagram to find out how many students take only math.

The number 12 is in the overlap between the two circles. Circle S contains the 22 students taking science: 12 who take both math and science, and 10 who take only science. Circle M contains the 15 math students: 12 take both classes, so 3 take only math.

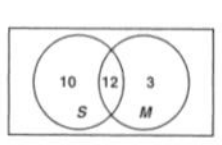

Solve each problem by using a Venn diagram.

1. Alice likes potatoes, sandwiches, fish, crackers, and steak. Rosie likes vegetables, rice, steak, chicken, and crackers. Which foods do both Alice and Rosie like?
   steak and crackers
2. What are the common factors of 18 and 24? What is the greatest common factor?
   common factors: 1, 2, 3, 6; GCF 6

	Factors
18	1, 2, 3, 6, 9, 18
24	1, 2, 3, 4, 6, 8, 12, 24

3. Barbara asks 18 friends who love to read whether they read fiction or nonfiction. Twelve of her friends read fiction. Eleven of her friends read nonfiction. Five read both fiction and nonfiction. How many friends read only fiction?
   7 friends

Test Prep

Resources

For additional practice with a variety of test item formats:
- Test-Taking Strategies, p. 461
- Test Prep, p. 465
- Test-Taking Strategies with Transparencies

Alternative Assessment

Working in pairs, each student writes and solves a problem similar to the Example. Partners exchange problems and confirm solutions.

17–18. See back of book.

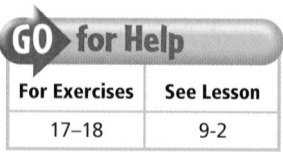

Reading Graphical Displays

The manager of a store made the graphs below as part of a report to the corporate office. At first glance, things seem to be going well. Sales went up from January to September, and expenses increased only a small amount.

ACTIVITY

1. Use the Monthly Sales Record graph at the right. Calculate the increase in sales from January to September. What percent of the January sales is this increase? **$2,500; 2.5% increase**

Monthly Sales

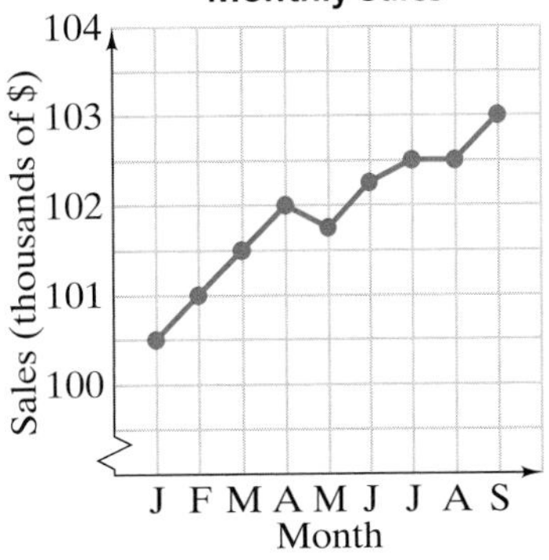

2. **Reasoning** Explain how the manager drew the Monthly Sales graph to make the increase in sales seem to be greater than it is. **See margin.**
3. Use the graph below to calculate the percent of increase in operating expenses from January to September. **100%**

Operating Expenses

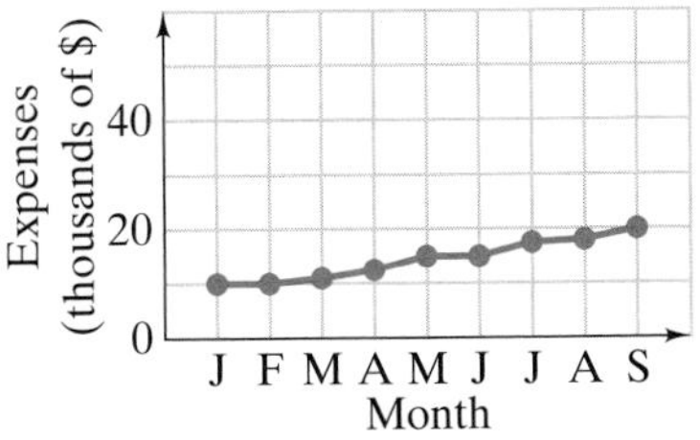

4. **Reasoning** Explain how the manager drew the Operating Expenses graph to make the increase in operating expenses seem to be less than it is.
5. **Writing in Math** Write a report that better describes the store's sales and operating expenses. Include the percent changes you calculated in Questions 1 and 3. Include new graphs that remove the distortions you described in Questions 2 and 4. **See margin.**

4. The manager used a vertical scale with large increments that went much higher than the data.

Exercises

1–2. Check students' work.

1. Find a graph in a newspaper or magazine that you think misrepresents or distorts the numerical data it was meant to represent. Explain why the data are not represented fairly.
2. Make a new graph that shows the data more fairly.

2. The manager started the vertical scale at 100 instead of 0 and made the increments very small.

5. See back of book.

Activity Lab

Data Analysis: Reading Graphical Displays

Just because students can read a written passage does not ensure that they can read a graph. Therefore, students need instruction and practice in reading information that appears in graphs. They also need to be able to identify graphs that misrepresent or distort data. This activity introduces students to a few ways that data can be misrepresented in graphs.

Guided Instruction

Error Prevention!

Stress that using intervals that are too large, too small—as in the Operating Expense graph—or not equal can distort data presented in a graph. Discuss why the break is used. Point out that it, too, can be used to distort changes in data—as in the Monthly Sales Record graph. Remind students to make note of the scale, scale intervals, and any breaks used when viewing a graph.

Technology Tip
Have students use a spreadsheet program to draw the graphs with different intervals.

Resources

- Activity Lab 9-4: Decision Making
- newspapers or magazines
- graph paper
- ruler

9-4

1. Plan

Objective
To recognize misleading graphs and to choose appropriate scale

Examples
1 Recognizing Misleading Graphs
2 Selecting an Appropriate Scale

Math Understandings: p. 410C

Professional Development

Math Background

An appropriate scale for a graph must include the least and the greatest values, with the interval between these divided into equal increments. A break symbol can be used on either axis to show that some increments have been omitted. A scale that does not begin at zero may be misleading.

More Math Background: p. 410C

Lesson Planning and Resources

See p. 410E for a list of the resources that support this lesson.

PowerPoint

Bell Ringer Practice

Check Skills You'll Need
Use student page, transparency, or PowerPoint. For intervention, direct students to:
Bar Graphs
Skills Handbook, p. 641

9-4 Reading Graphs Critically

Check Skills You'll Need
1–2. See below.

1. **Vocabulary Review** What does a *bar graph* show?
2. The following data show the number of students in a class who prefer each primary color. Red: 12; Yellow: 3; Blue: 10. Make a bar graph of this data.

GO for Help
Skills Handbook p. 641

What You'll Learn

To recognize misleading graphs and to choose appropriate scales

Why Learn This?

You can analyze graphs of real-world data to compare passenger activity at various airports.

The same set of data may be graphed in several different ways. Sometimes, however, a graph can give a misleading visual impression.

EXAMPLE Recognizing Misleading Graphs

Test Prep Tip
When deciding how a graph is misleading, consider how each choice would affect the graph.

1 **Multiple Choice** The graph gives the impression that Chicago O'Hare Airport is four times as busy as Los Angeles International Airport. Which statement explains why?

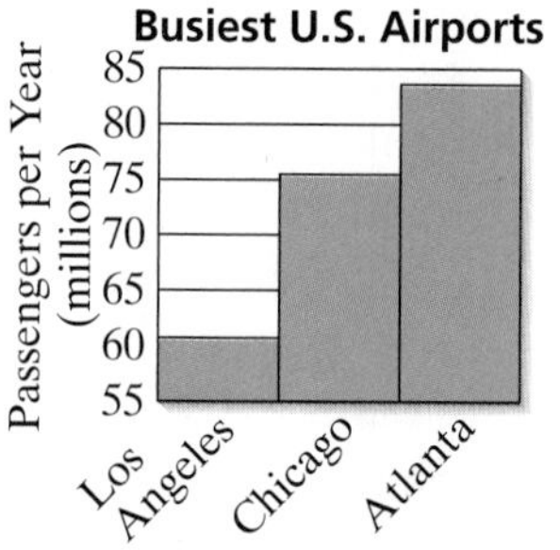

Ⓐ The graph should be a line graph.
Ⓑ The intervals are not equal.
Ⓒ The intervals on the vertical axis are too small.
Ⓓ The scale on the vertical axis does not start at 0.

The bar for Chicago appears to be four times as long as the bar for Los Angeles because the scale on the vertical axis does not start at 0. The correct answer is choice D.

Check Skills You'll Need
1. A bar graph compares amounts.
2. See back of book.

Quick Check

1. Explain why the graph at the right is more clear than the graph in Example 1. See back of book.

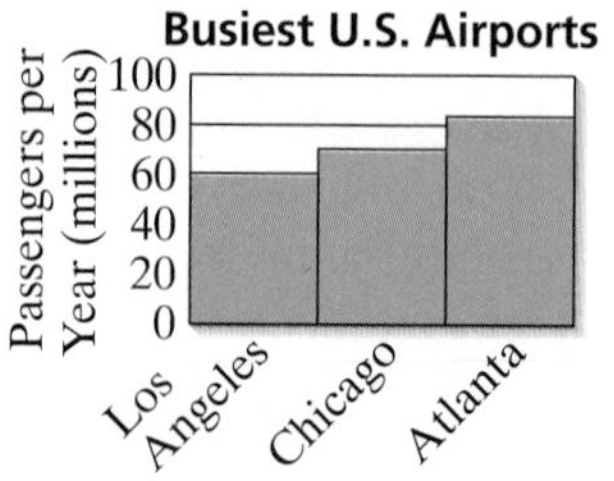

Differentiated Instruction Solutions for All Learners

Special Needs L1	Below Level L2
Students graph Exercise 3 starting at zero, with no break in the data. Then they compare this to the Example 1 graph. Discuss the impressions given by each graph. learning style: visual	Students review key terms: *axes, title, label, scale, key,* and *legend.* learning style: verbal

When some of the values on an axis of a graph have been left out, the graph should have a break symbol, ⩽, to alert the reader.

Projected U.S. College Enrollment

Year	Students (millions)
2007	17.0
2008	17.2
2009	17.4
2010	17.5
2011	17.7
2012	17.9
2013	18.2

SOURCE: U.S. National Center for Educational Statistics

EXAMPLE Selecting an Appropriate Scale

2 **Education** Using different scales, make two line graphs for the data at the left. Use a break symbol in only one of the graphs.

The highest projected college enrollment is 18.2 million. Label the vertical axis with multiples of 5 from 0 to 20.

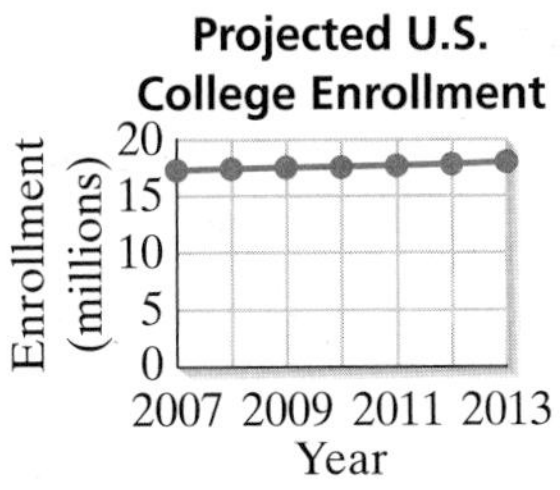

The data start at 17 million. Label the vertical axis with multiples of 0.5, beginning with 16. Use a break symbol.

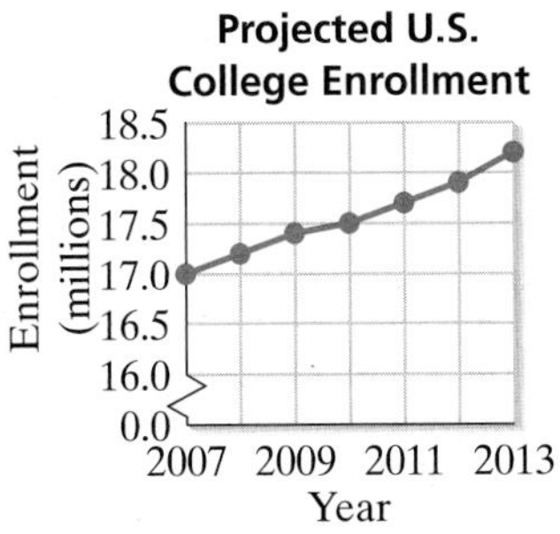

Quick Check

2. Which graph above shows the data more clearly? Explain.

2. The second graph with the break symbol shows the data more clearly because the scale is more spread out.

Check Your Understanding

1. **Vocabulary** What features can make a graph misleading?

1. Answers may vary. Sample: not starting at zero on the vertical scale; using intervals that are too small, too large, or unequal

Use the graph at the right.

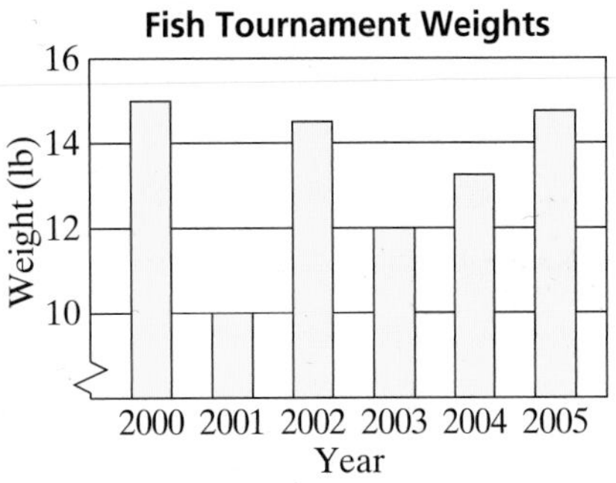

2. In which year does it appear that the winning fish weighed twice as much as the 2001 winning fish? 2003

3. Do you think the graph represents the data fairly? Explain.

3. No; the break in the scale makes the differences appear greater than they are.

Advanced Learners L4
Students find misleading graphs in advertisements, share them, and explain why they are misleading.

learning style: verbal

English Language Learners ELL
The choices in Example 1 require a strong English reading and comprehension ability. Students work with a partner to read and analyze the meaning of each choice. Make sure students know what terms such as *intervals* and *vertical axis* mean.

learning style: verbal

2. Teach

Activity Lab

Use before the lesson.
Student Edition Data Analysis Activity Lab 9-4a, Reading Graphical Displays, p. 427

All in One Teaching Resources

- **Activity Lab 9-4:** Decision Making

Guided Instruction

Error Prevention!

For Example 1, point out the difference between comparing the areas of the bars and the values where the bars stop.

PowerPoint

Additional Examples

1

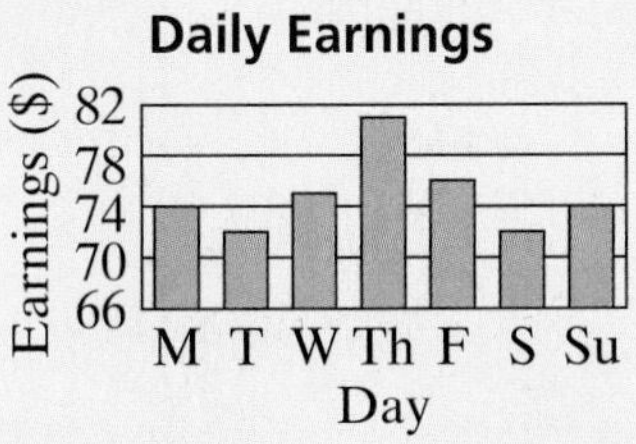

The graph makes it appear that almost twice as much is earned on Thursday as on Monday. Explain. The vertical scale begins at 66 instead of 0.

2 Using different scales, make two bar graphs for the data. Use a break symbol in only one of the graphs.

Quarter Mile Records

Car	Time (s)
Indy car	8
Sprint car	9
NASCAR stock car	10
Stock Bonneville	17

See back of book.

All in One Teaching Resources

- Daily Notetaking Guide 9-4 L3
- Adapted Notetaking 9-4 L1

Closure

- *Explain what you would look for in a graph to see if the scale is an appropriate one.* Sample: See where each scale starts and if breaks in the data are indicated.

3. Practice

Assignment Guide

Check Your Understanding
Go over Exercises 1–3 in class before assigning the Homework Exercises.

Homework Exercises
A	Practice by Example	4–7
B	Apply Your Skills	8–16
C	Challenge	17
	Test Prep and Mixed Review	18–23

Homework Quick Check
To check students' understanding of key skills and concepts, go over Exercises 6, 7, 9, 11, 13, and 14.

Technology Tip
Have students use graphing calculators or spreadsheet programs to quickly redraw line and bar graphs.

Homework Exercises

For more exercises, see Extra Skills and Word Problems.

GO for Help

For Exercises	See Examples
4–6	1
7	2

A Publishing **Use the graph below for Exercises 4–7.**

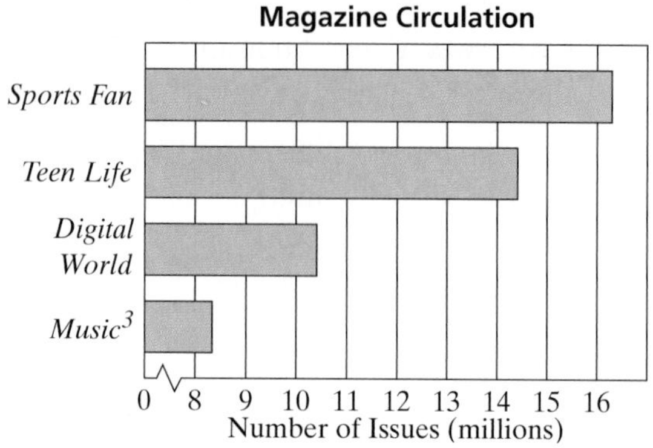

4. Which magazine appears to have about twice the circulation of *Music*³? *Digital World*
5. Which magazine actually has about twice the circulation of *Music*³? *Sports Fan*
6. Explain why the graph gives a misleading impression of the data.

   6. The horizontal scale does not start at 0, so the differences are exaggerated.
7. Redraw the graph so it gives a less misleading impression of the data. See margin.

B GPS

8. **Guided Problem Solving** The table at the right shows the winning times for men and women runners in the Boston Marathon for several years. Draw a graph that gives the impression that the winning times for women have decreased to less than one third of what they were in 1970. See margin.
   - Write the minutes as fractions of an hour.
   - Decide what vertical scale to use.

Boston Marathon Winning Times

Year	Men	Women
1970	2:10:30	3:05:07
1975	2:09:55	2:42:24
1980	2:12:11	2:34:28
1985	2:14:05	2:35:06
1990	2:08:09	2:25:23
1995	2:09:22	2:25:11
2000	2:09:47	2:26:11
2005	2:11:45	2:25:13

Jean Driscoll won the women's wheelchair division of the Boston Marathon a record eight times.

Using different scales, make either two line graphs or two bar graphs for each set of data. Use a break symbol in only one of the graphs. Explain which graph shows the data more clearly. 9–10. See margin.

9. **Top Films**

Film	Total (millions)
Titanic	$601
Star Wars	$461
Shrek 2	$436.7
E.T., The Extra-Terrestrial	$435

SOURCE: *Variety*

10. **Population Density**

Year	Population/mi^2
1	50.6
2	57.4
3	64.0
4	70.3
5	79.6

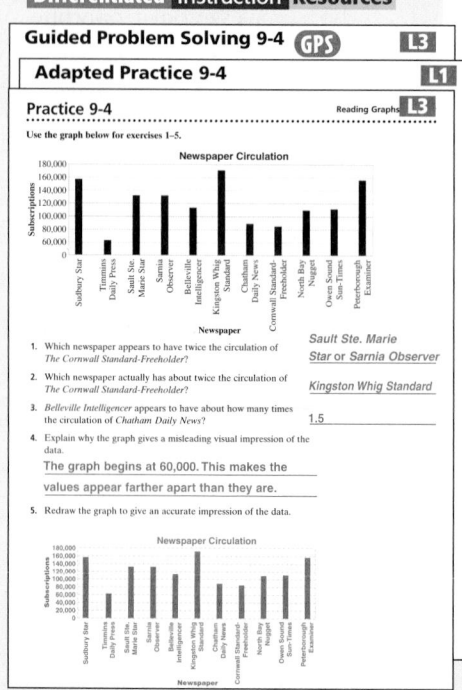

Differentiated Instruction Resources

Guided Problem Solving 9-4 GPS L3

Adapted Practice 9-4 L1

Practice 9-4 Reading Graphs L3

Use the graph below for exercises 1–5.

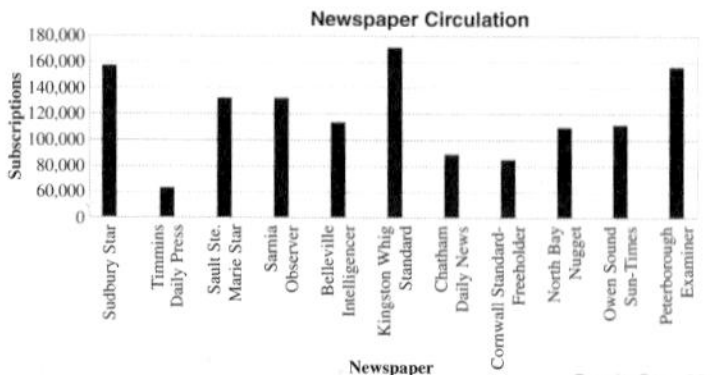

1. Which newspaper appears to have twice the circulation of *The Cornwall Standard-Freeholder*? *Sault Ste. Marie Star* or *Sarnia Observer*
2. Which newspaper actually has about twice the circulation of *The Cornwall Standard-Freeholder*? *Kingston Whig Standard*
3. *Belleville Intelligencer* appears to have about how many times the circulation of *Chatham Daily News*? 1.5
4. Explain why the graph gives a misleading visual impression of the data.
   The graph begins at 60,000. This makes the values appear farther apart than they are.
5. Redraw the graph to give an accurate impression of the data.

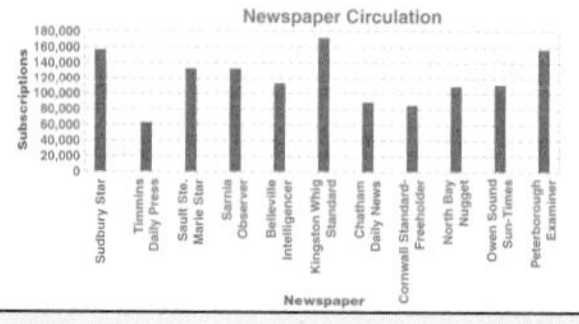

7–12, 14–17. See back of book.

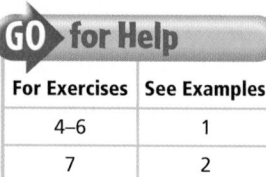

Go Online
Homework Video Tutor
Visit: PHSchool.com
Web Code: ase-0904

13. In the first graph, starting the vertical scale at 0 minimizes the appearance of change. In the second graph, the differences are exaggerated.

Public School Enrollment in the United States

Year	Enrollment (thousands)
1970	52,322
1975	53,654
1980	50,335
1985	48,901
1990	52,061
1995	55,933
2000	58,976
2005	61,090

SOURCE: U.S. Census Bureau. Go to **PHSchool.com** for a data update. Web Code: asg-9041

Recycling **Use the table below for Exercises 11–13.**

Recycling of Drink Containers

Year	Percent
1998	62.8%
1999	62.5%
2000	62.1%
2001	55.4%
2002	53.4%
2003	50.0%
2004	51.2%

11. GPS Make a line graph to show that the recycling rate of drink containers stayed about the same. See margin.

12. Make a line graph to show that the recycling rate has varied. See margin.

13. **Writing in Math** Explain how the scale you chose for each graph gives the visual impression you want to create. See left.

Use the table at the left for Exercises 14–16.

14. You want to encourage the school board to approve the hiring of more teachers. Graph the data in a way that would show a big change in school enrollment. See margin.

15. Graph the data to show very little change in the school enrollment over the years. See margin.

16. **Reasoning** Which of the graphs you drew more fairly presents the data? Explain. See margin.

C 17. **Challenge** A graph uses the following labels at equal intervals along the horizontal axis: 1940, 1945, 1955, 1975, 2015.
a. What are the intervals being used?
b. Is this an appropriate scale? Explain.
c. **Patterns** Is there a pattern in the scale? Explain.
17a–c. See margin.

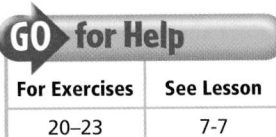

Test Prep and Mixed Review

Practice

Multiple Choice

18. The stated size of computer monitors is based on the measurement of the diagonal of the screen. If the height of a screen is 9.75 inches and the width is 12.75 inches, what is the best estimate of the stated size of the monitor? C
(A) 8.5 in. (B) 15 in. (C) 16 in. (D) 22 in.

19. Rachel is making three aprons for a school play. Each apron uses $2\frac{1}{4}$ yards of fabric. If Rachel has $7\frac{1}{2}$ yards of fabric, how much will be left after she makes the aprons? G
(F) $\frac{1}{4}$ yd (G) $\frac{3}{4}$ yd (H) $5\frac{1}{4}$ yd (J) $6\frac{3}{4}$ yd

Go for Help

For Exercises	See Lesson
20–23	7-7

Geometry **Find the area of a circle with the given radius. Round to the nearest tenth.**

20. $r = 8$ cm 201.1 cm^2
21. $r = 14$ in. 615.8 $in.^2$
22. $r = 9.6$ m 289.5 m^2
23. $r = 1.2$ ft 4.5 ft^2

Online lesson quiz, PHSchool.com, Web Code: asa-0904

4. Assess & Reteach

PowerPoint

Lesson Quiz

Use the graph for Questions 1–2.

Favorite Juice

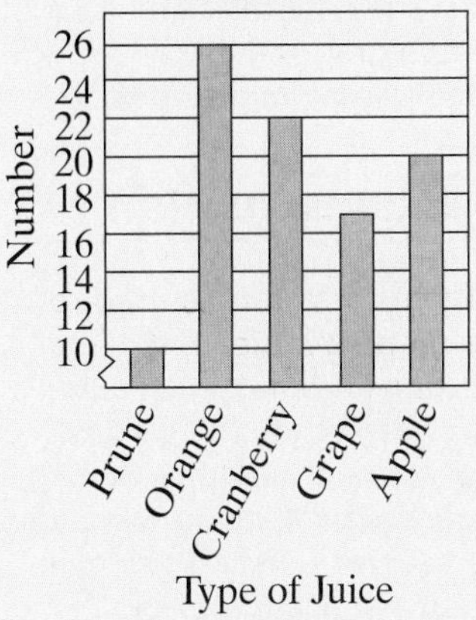

1. The graph makes it appear that about 6 times as many people prefer apple juice to prune juice. Why? The vertical scale has a break in it and it begins at 10.

2. How would you redraw the graph in Question 1 to more accurately portray the data? Sketch the graph. See back of book.

Alternative Assessment

Students find in newspapers and magazines examples of bar or line graphs with a broken axis. Students explain whether the published graph is misleading and redraw the graph if it is.

Test Prep

Resources
For additional practice with a variety of test item formats:
- Test-Taking Strategies, p. 461
- Test Prep, p. 465
- Test-Taking Strategies with Transparencies

Enrichment 9-4 L4

Reteaching 9-4 Reading Graphs L2

Two important factors in determining whether a graph gives a correct impression of data are:
- how the scale is chosen and
- whether the entire scale is shown.

The data at the right can be shown in a bar graph.

Countries with Most Universities (2000)	
India	7,513
United States	3,559

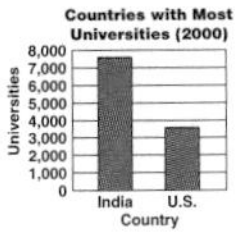

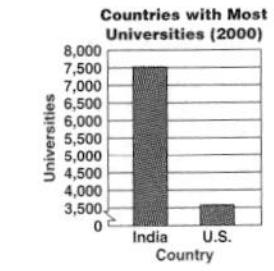

In the first graph, the scale is in multiples of 1,000. The entire scale from 0 through 8,000 is shown. The graph accurately compares the numbers of universities in the two countries.

In the second graph, the scale is in multiples of 500. There is a break in the vertical scale. The graph gives a misleading comparison between the two countries.

Use the bar graphs above for exercises 1–4.

1. From which graph is it easier to tell that India has about twice the number of universities as the United States? the first graph

2. In the second graph, about how many times the number of U.S. universities does India *appear* to have? about 9 times

3. Which graph makes it easier to estimate the number of universities in each country? Why? The second graph; since the scale is smaller, the bars can be read more accurately.

4. Why does the second graph give a misleading impression of the data? By using the break, most of the bar for the United States has been left out.

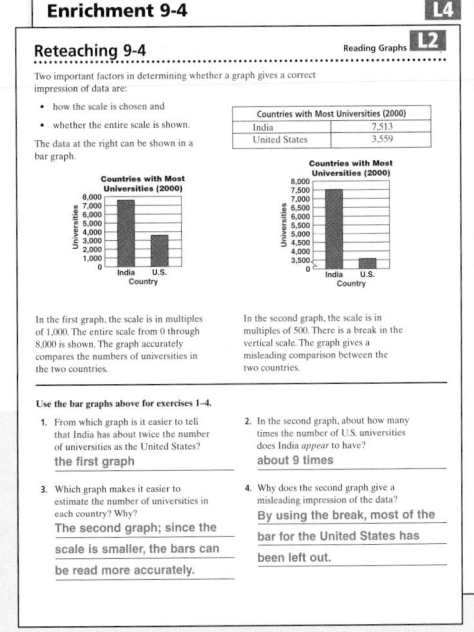

Activity Lab

Making Graphs to Tell a Story

Students use what they know about representing data in graphs. They use the same data to draw two graphs that give different visual impressions.

Guided Instruction

Ask: *What tricks can be used to give a graph a misleading visual impression?* A break in an axis scale or beginning the vertical axis at some value other than zero can be misleading. Also, the scale interval selected can give different visual impressions.

Activity

Have volunteers share their two graphs with the class. Discuss the similarities and differences in their graphs.

Resources

- graph paper

Checkpoint Quiz

Use this Checkpoint Quiz to check students' understanding of the skills and concepts of Lessons 9-1 through 9-4.

Resources

- All in One Teaching Resources Checkpoint Quiz 1
- ExamView Assessment Suite CD-ROM
- Success Tracker Online Intervention

9-4b Activity Lab — Data Analysis

Making Graphs to Tell a Story

Visitors to National Parks

Year	1998	1999	2000	2001	2002	2003	2004
Number of Visitors (millions)	435.7	436.3	429.9	424.3	421.3	413.9	427.7

SOURCE: National Park Service. Go to **PHSchool.com** for a data update. Web Code: asg-9041

1. Make a graph that gives the visual impression of a sizeable annual change in the number of visitors. See margin.
2. Make a second graph that gives the visual impression of a modest annual change in the number of visitors. See margin.
3. Compare your graphs. Which graph do you think more fairly represents the data in the table? Explain. See right.

3. The second graph; the first graph visually exaggerates the change in visitors.

Checkpoint Quiz 1

Lesson 9-1 through 9-4

For Exercises 1–4, use these temperatures for 11 days in July:
80 83 88 88 90 106 100 101 110 109 85

1. Find the mean. 94.5
2. Find the median. 90
3. Find the mode. 88
4. Find the range. 30

For Exercises 5–7, use these math test scores:
93 75 87 83 99 75 80 90 72 77 95 98 82 87 100 91 68

5. Make a frequency table. Use intervals of equal size.
6. Make a line plot. See margin.
7. Use the frequency table from Exercise 5 to make a histogram. See margin.
8. Make two bar graphs for the set of data at the right. In one of the graphs, use a break symbol. Explain which graph shows the data more clearly. See margin.

5.

Scores	Frequency
61–70	1
71–80	5
81–90	5
91–100	6

Average Number of Students per Computer

High School	10.5
Middle School	12.75
Elementary School	13.25

Activity Lab
1–2. See back of book.

Checkpoint Quiz 1
6–8. See back of book.

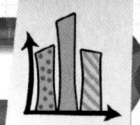

9-5 Stem-and-Leaf Plots

What You'll Learn

To represent and interpret data using stem-and-leaf plots

New Vocabulary stem-and-leaf plot

Why Learn This?

A stem-and-leaf plot is an efficient way to compare prices of digital music players.

Prices of Digital Music Players (dollars)
189, 214, 200, 195,
190, 192, 193, 211,
201, 196, 195, 194,
205, 198, 208, 201

A **stem-and-leaf plot** is a graph that shows numerical data arranged in order. Each data item is broken into a stem and a leaf.

The stem is the digit or digits on the left and the leaf is the digit or digits on the right.

1 | 0 ← leaf (↑ stem)   5. | 52 ← leaf (↑ stem)   5.5 | 2 ← leaf (↑ stem)

EXAMPLE Making Stem-and-Leaf Plots

1 Make a stem-and-leaf plot for the data in the table above.

Step 1 Choose the stems. The least value is 189; the greatest value is 214. For this data use the first two digits as the stems. The stems in this case are 18, 19, 20, and 21.

Step 2 Draw the stem-and-leaf plot. Include a key.

stems	leaves
18	9
19	0 2 3 4 5 5 6 8
20	0 1 1 5 8
21	1 4

← The leaves are the ones place written in increasing order.

Key: 19 | 2 means $192 ← The key explains what the stems and leaves represent.

Quick Check

See back of book.

1. At the left are the monthly high temperatures for Death Valley, California. Make a stem-and-leaf plot for the data.

High Temperatures (°F) Death Valley, California
87 91 101 111 120
125 134 126 120
113 97 86

Check Skills You'll Need

1. **Vocabulary Review** What does a *line plot* display? See below.

Use the line plot for Exercises 2–4.

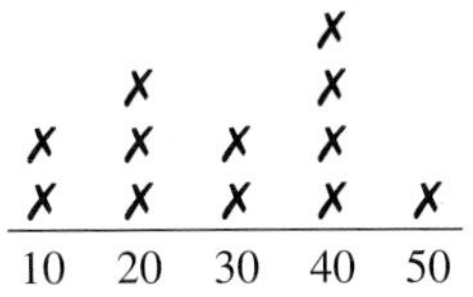

2. Find the mean. 29.2
3. Find the median. 30
4. Find the mode. 40

GO for Help Lesson 9-2

Check Skills You'll Need

1. the frequency of each data value

9-5

1. Plan

Objective

To represent and interpret data using stem-and-leaf plots

Example

1 Making Stem-and-Leaf Plots

Math Understandings: p. 410C

Professional Development

Math Background

A stem-and-leaf plot groups data as leaves coming off the side(s) of each stem. The last digit, or leaf, is recorded alongside the preceding digit(s), written just once as the stem. The plot has a number of stems, each with many or no leaves. A key explains how to read the numbers in the plot.

More Math Background: p. 410C

Lesson Planning and Resources

See p. 410E for a list of the resources that support this lesson.

PowerPoint

Bell Ringer Practice

Check Skills You'll Need

Use student page, transparency, or PowerPoint. For intervention, direct students to:

Displaying Frequency
Lesson 9-2
Extra Skills and Word Problems Practice, Ch. 9

Differentiated Instruction Solutions for All Learners

Special Needs L1
Pair students who have a hard time drawing stem-and-leaf plots with a partner. The student can label the drawing, and make a key, after the partner does the drawing.

learning style: visual

Below Level L2
Students review the definitions for mean, mode, and median. For each definition, they give an example.

learning style: verbal

2. Teach

Activity Lab

Use before the lesson.

All in One Teaching Resources

Activity Lab 9-5: Stem-and-Leaf Plots

Guided Instruction

After students review both methods for finding median and mode, discuss with them which method they prefer and why.

Error Prevention!

Remind students to include a key for each stem-and-leaf plot they make.

PowerPoint

Additional Examples

1. Make a stem-and-leaf plot for the data: 51, 56, 67, 44, 50, 63, 65, 58, 49, 51, 66, 59, 63, 47.

4	4 7 9
5	0 1 1 6 8 9
6	3 3 5 6 7

Key: 4 | 4 means 44

Because stem-and-leaf plots display data items in numerical order, they are useful tools for finding median and mode.

More Than One Way

The table shows the annual percent change in the United States Consumer Price Index. The Consumer Price Index measures the average change in how much you pay for things. Find the median and mode.

United States Consumer Price Index

Year	Percent Change
1993	3.0
1994	2.6
1995	2.8
1996	3.0
1997	2.3
1998	1.6
1999	2.2
2000	3.4
2001	2.8
2002	1.6
2003	2.3
2004	2.7

SOURCE: Bureau of Labor Statistics. Go to **PHSchool.com** for a data update. Web Code: asg-9041

Michelle's Method

A stem-and-leaf plot is an appropriate way to organize the data to find the median and mode.

1	6 6
2	2 3 3 6 7 8 8
3	0 0 4

Key: 3 | 0 means 3.0%

$\frac{2.6 + 2.7}{2} = 2.65$ ← **There are 12 leaves in the stem-and-leaf plot. So the median is the mean of the sixth and seventh leaves.**

The median change in the United States Consumer Price Index is 2.65%. The modes are 1.6%, 2.3%, 2.8%, and 3.0%.

Eric's Method

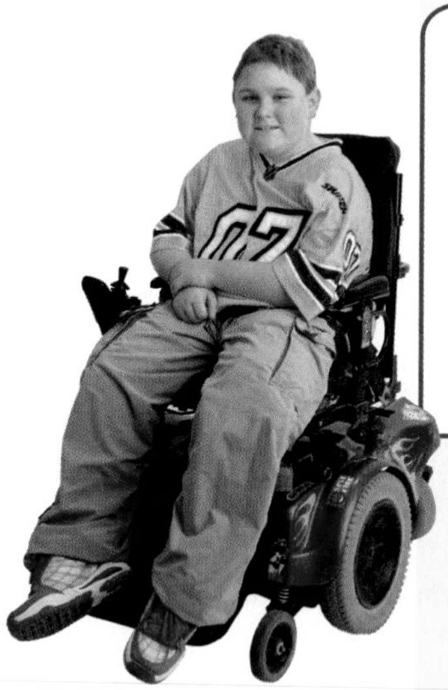

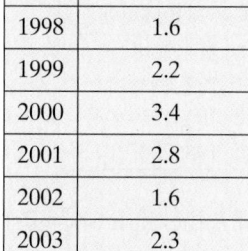

To find the median and mode, I need to put the data items in order.

1.6 1.6 2.2 2.3 2.3 2.6 2.7 2.8 2.8 3.0 3.0 3.4

The median is the mean of the sixth and seventh items, which is 2.65.

The median change in the United States Consumer Price Index is 2.65%. The modes are 1.6%, 2.3%, 2.8%, and 3.0%.

Choose a Method

The table shows the average amount of time drivers in different cities spend in traffic annually. Find the median and mode of the data. Explain why you chose the method you used.

City	Hours	City	Hours
Los Angeles	56	Denver	45
Phoenix	31	Houston	50
Seattle	53	New York	34
Las Vegas	21	Miami	42
Chicago	34	Detroit	41

SOURCE: *Time Almanac*

Median: 41.5; mode: 34; check students' work.

Differentiated Instruction Solutions for All Learners

Advanced Learners L4

Students find suitable data from newspapers or magazines and make their own stem-and-leaf plot.

learning style: visual

English Language Learners ELL

Help students read the back-to-back stem-and-leaf plot comparing gas mileage in Example 2. Ask them to identify what they are reading. For example, 8 | 1 | represents a stem of 10 and a leaf of 8—18 miles/gallon—in the city.

learning style: verbal

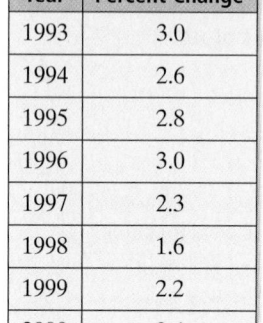

Test Prep Tip

When dealing with large sets of data, first make a list of the data. Then cross off each data item as you use it.

When you compare two sets of the same type of data, use back-to-back stem-and-leaf plots.

EXAMPLE Application: Gas Mileage

2 The back-to-back stem-and-leaf plot below shows the city mileage and the highway mileage of seven new cars. Compare the city mileage to the highway mileage by using the mode of each data set.

New Car Mileage (mi/gal)

City		Highway
9 8 8	1	
7 4 2	2	4 5 7 8
0	3	3 3
	4	0

Key: means 27 ← 7 | 2 | 8 → means 28

The mode for city mileage is 18 mi/gal. The mode for highway mileage is 33 mi/gal. This measure of central tendency gives the impression that the highway mileage of the new cars is higher than the city mileage.

Quick Check

2. Compare city mileage to highway mileage using the mean and the median.

2. The mean and median for the city mileage are 22.6 mi/gal and 22 mi/gal, respectively. The mean and median for the highway mileage are 30 mi/gal and 28 mi/gal, respectively. Both the mean and median give the impression that the highway mileage of the new cars is higher than the city mileage.

Check Your Understanding

1. **Vocabulary** Identify the stem and the leaf in the number 6.7. 6 is the stem; 7 is the leaf.

Use the stem-and-leaf plot below for Exercises 2–5.

2. What numbers make up the stems? 6, 7, 8, 9
3. What are the leaves for the first stem? 8, 8
4. How many data items are shown in the stem-and-leaf plot? 24
5. Find the median and mode of the data. median: 84% mode: 78%

Test Scores

6	8 8
7	8 8 8 8 9
8	1 2 2 4 4 4 5 5 6 7 7
9	2 2 5 5 5 8

Key: 7 | 8 means 78%

6. GPS Make a stem-and-leaf plot for the data below. Find the median and the mode. See margin.
18 19 27 8 19 20 19 6 18 27 16 13 12 7
8 18 19 11 10 19 18 18 8 17 16 12

Online active math

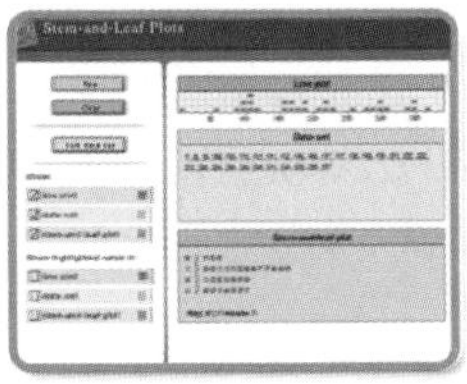

For: Stem-and-Leaf Plot Activity
Use: Interactive Textbook, 9-5

Guided Instruction

Example 2

Elicit an explanation of why this plot is called a back-to-back stem-and-leaf plot. Sample: The leaves extend to either side of the stem.

Technology Tip

Have students use the Online Active Math for Interactive Textbook Lesson 9-5 to generate line plots and stem-and-leaf plots. Ask them to compare and contrast displays.

PowerPoint

Additional Examples

2 Compare the number of basketball and baseball cards using the mode of each data set.

Basketball and Baseball Cards

Basketball		Baseball
9 9 8	1	
4 2 1 0	2	8 9
	3	1 2 2 3 4

Key: means 24 ← 4 | 2 | 9 → means 29

basketball: 19; baseball: 32; no. of baseball cards appears greater than the no. of basketball cards

All in One Teaching Resources

- Daily Notetaking Guide 9-5 L3
- Adapted Notetaking 9-5 L1

Closure

- Describe how to read a stem-and-leaf plot. Answers should include how stems and leaves are related and how to read the key.

6.

0	6 7 8 8 8
1	0 1 2 2 3 6 6 7 8 8 8 8 8 9 9 9 9 9
2	0 7 7

Key: 0 | 6 means 6

3. Practice

Assignment Guide

Check Your Understanding

Go over Exercises 1–6 in class before assigning the Homework Exercises.

Homework Exercises

A Practice by Example	7–11
B Apply Your Skills	12–15
C Challenge	16
Test Prep and Mixed Review	17–20

Homework Quick Check

To check students' understanding of key skills and concepts, go over Exercises 7, 10, 13, 14, and 15.

Exercises

For Exercise 10, have students discuss and evaluate the following conclusion. A study uses the data to conclude that an average man will have a blood pressure between 89 and 92.

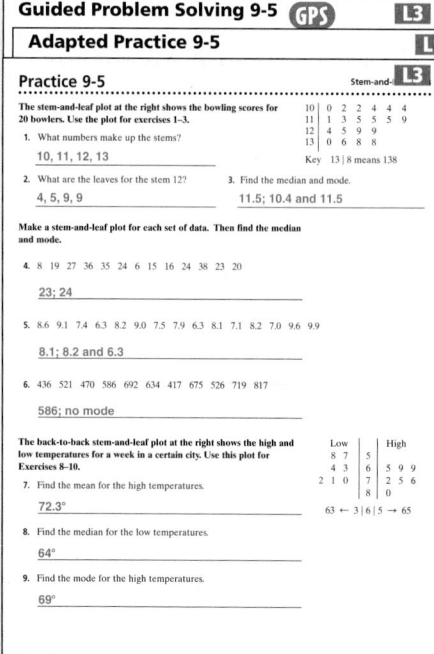

Differentiated Instruction Resources

Guided Problem Solving 9-5 GPS L3

Adapted Practice 9-5 L1

Practice 9-5 Stem-and- L3

The stem-and-leaf plot at the right shows the bowling scores for 20 bowlers. Use the plot for exercises 1–3.

10	0 2 2 4 4 4
11	1 3 5 5 5 9
12	4 5 9 9
13	0 6 8 8

Key 13 | 8 means 138

1. What numbers make up the stems? 10, 11, 12, 13
2. What are the leaves for the stem 12? 4, 5, 9, 9
3. Find the median and mode. 11.5; 10.4 and 11.5

Make a stem-and-leaf plot for each set of data. Then find the median and mode.

4. 8 19 27 36 35 24 6 15 16 24 38 23 20 — 23; 24
5. 8.6 9.1 7.4 6.3 8.2 9.0 7.5 7.9 6.3 8.1 7.1 8.2 7.0 9.6 9.9 — 8.1; 8.2 and 6.3
6. 436 521 470 586 692 634 417 675 526 719 817 — 586; no mode

The back-to-back stem-and-leaf plot at the right shows the high and low temperatures for a week in a certain city. Use this plot for Exercises 8–10.

Low		High
8 7	5	
4 3	6	5 9 9
2 1 0	7	2 5 6
	8	0

63 ← 3 | 6 | 5 → 65

7. Find the mean for the high temperatures. 72.3°
8. Find the median for the low temperatures. 64°
9. Find the mode for the high temperatures. 69°

Homework Exercises

For more exercises, see Extra Skills and Word Problems.

GO for Help

For Exercises	See Examples
7–9	1
10–11	2

A **Make a stem-and-leaf plot for each set of data.** 7–9. See margin.

7. 54 48 52 53 67 61 68 49 40 50 69 73 74 76 78

8. 124 129 131 116 138 107 105 116 122 137 138 134

9. 3.7 5.0 6.9 3.2 4.5 6.3 6.7 5.8 5.2 6.9 5.0 4.3 4.1

Use the stem-and-leaf plot below for Exercises 10 and 11.

Vocabulary Tip

In a stem-and-leaf plot of two sets of data, 8 | 6 | 5 means that both 8 and 5 are leaves of the stem 6.

10. **Health** The plot at the right shows the blood pressure of 40 men and women of the same age. Find the mean and median of each data set. See margin.

Blood Pressure

Men		Women
8	6	5 5 6 8
9 7 7 6	7	0 1 1 2 5 6 8 8 9
9 9 8 7 4 4 1	8	0 0 3 5 6
8 5 4 2 0 0	9	0 1
2 0	10	

Key: means 94 ← 4 | 9 | 1 → means 91

11. **Reasoning** What conclusions can you draw about men's blood pressure compared to women's blood pressure? Explain. See left.

11. Both measures of central tendency indicate that the women's blood pressure in the survey was considerably less than the men's blood pressure.

B GPS 12. **Guided Problem Solving** Make a back-to-back stem-and-leaf plot for the data sets below. Then find the median and mode. See margin.

Length of Wood Boards (in.)

Saw A	Saw B
64 58 63 57 54 61 52 54	72 63 52 57 64 49 45 43

- For Saw B, make a stem-and-leaf plot.
- For Saw A, add any missing stems to the existing list of stems. Draw a vertical line to the left of the stems. Write each leaf for Saw A to the left of its stem.

13. **Golf** In golf, a player's score is based on the total number of strokes needed to get the ball into the holes. The player with the lowest score is the winner. Use the mean, median, and mode of each set of data below to compare men's scores to women's scores in a four-round tournament. See margin.

U.S. Open 1983–2004

Men's Scores		Women's Scores
9 9 9 9 8 8 8 7 7 6 6 6 6 2 2 2	27	2 2 3 4 4 6 7 7 8 8
5 2 0 0 0 0	28	0 0 0 2 3 3 4 5 7
	29	0 0 0

Key: means 276 ← 6 | 27 | 2 → means 272

SOURCE: *Sports Illustrated 2005 Almanac*

GO Online
Homework Video Tutor
Visit: PHSchool.com
Web Code: ase-0905

7.

4	0 8 9
5	0 2 3 4
6	1 7 8 9
7	3 4 6 8

Key: 4 | 8 means 48

8.

10	5 7
11	6 6
12	2 4 9
13	1 4 7 8 8

Key: 13 | 1 means 131

9.

3	2 7
4	1 3 5
5	0 0 2 8
6	3 7 9 9

Key: 3 | 2 means 3.2

10, 12–14. See back of book

14. a. **Animals** Use the data below on the life spans of different animals (in years) to make a stem-and-leaf plot. **See margin.**

1 10 3 10 4 12 13 15 15 20 40 6 7 10 15 18 22 20 25 7 12 5 15 20 25 20 15

b. **Number Sense** If you add the data values 13.2, 14.5, 13.5, 15.6, 18.2, 19.7, 21.3, 35.6, 40.2, 13.7, and 12.8, why might you choose different stems in your stem-and-leaf plot? **See margin.**

15. **Writing in Math** A set of data contains numbers in the 30s, 40s and 60s only. Is it necessary to put a 5 on the stem of a stem-and-leaf plot? Justify your answer. **It is not necessary, but it would help show the range of data.**

Ⓒ 16. **Challenge** The data sets below have the same mean, median, mode, and range. Copy and complete the back-to-back stem-and-leaf plot. **See margin.**

7 6 ■	3	1 2 3
6 5 4 3 1	4	2 ■ ■ 6
■ 0	5	0 0 1

Key: means 3■ ← ■ | 3 | 1 → means 31

Test Prep and Mixed Review

Practice

Multiple Choice

17. Which stem-and-leaf plot has a median of 3.2? **B**

Ⓐ

1	2
2	4
3	2 2 6
4	0 1 7

1 | 2 means 1.2

Ⓑ

1	6
2	8 9
3	1 3 6
4	2 5

1 | 2 means 1.2

Ⓒ

1	8
2	0 0 2
3	2
4	7 8 9

1 | 2 means 1.2

Ⓓ

1	4 7
2	9
3	0 1 2 2 2
4	

1 | 2 means 1.2

18. Students recorded the number of hours of sleep they got Monday night. Which list shows the data in order from least to greatest? **F**

Ⓕ $9.25, 9\frac{1}{3}, 9\frac{5}{6}, 10, 10\frac{1}{6}$

Ⓗ $10, 9.25, 9\frac{1}{3}, 10\frac{1}{6}, 9\frac{5}{6}$

Ⓖ $9.25, 9\frac{1}{3}, 9\frac{5}{6}, 10\frac{1}{6}, 10$

Ⓙ $9\frac{1}{3}, 9.25, 9\frac{5}{6}, 10, 10\frac{1}{6}$

GO for Help

For Exercises	See Lesson
19–20	9-1

Find the mean, median, mode, and range of each set of data.

19. 178 179 180 182 177 183 185 180 180 179 **180.3; 180; 180; 8**

20. 4 2 4 8 10 12 10 6 4 8 4 6 8 4 6 8 10 **6.7; 6; 4; 10**

4. Assess & Reteach

PowerPoint

Lesson Quiz

1. Make a stem-and-leaf plot for the data.
21 39 20 22 22 31 40 33
See back of book.
2. Use your stem-and-leaf plot from Question 1 to find the median and mode.
median: 26.5; mode: 22
3. The back-to-back stem-and leaf plot shows the scores 16 students earned on their last math quiz. Compare each class's grades using the median for each group.

Ms. Perezís Class		Mr. Harmon's Class
2	1	2 2
	2	6
	3	5
2	4	5
3	5	0 0 7
9 7	6	
	7	
7	8	
0	9	6

Key:42 ← means 2 | 4 | 5 means → 45

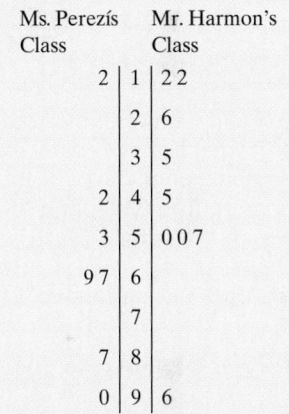

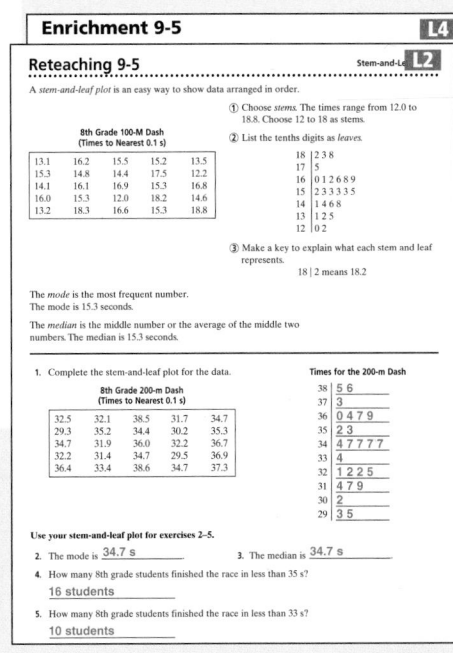

See back of book.

Enrichment 9-5 L4

Reteaching 9-5 Stem-and-Le… L2

A *stem-and-leaf plot* is an easy way to show data arranged in order.

8th Grade 100-M Dash
(Times to Nearest 0.1 s)

13.1	16.2	15.5	15.2	13.5
15.3	14.8	14.4	17.5	12.2
14.1	16.1	16.9	15.3	16.8
16.0	15.3	12.0	18.2	14.6
13.2	18.3	16.6	15.3	18.8

① Choose *stems.* The times range from 12.0 to 18.8. Choose 12 to 18 as stems.

② List the tenths digits as *leaves.*

18	2 3 8
17	5
16	0 1 2 6 8 9
15	2 3 3 3 3 5
14	1 4 6 8
13	1 2 5
12	0 2

③ Make a key to explain what each stem and leaf represents.
18 | 2 means 18.2

The *mode* is the most frequent number.
The mode is 15.3 seconds.

The *median* is the middle number or the average of the middle two numbers. The median is 15.3 seconds.

1. Complete the stem-and-leaf plot for the data.

8th Grade 200-m Dash
(Times to Nearest 0.1 s)

32.5	32.1	38.5	31.7	34.7
29.3	35.2	34.4	30.2	35.3
34.7	31.9	36.0	32.2	36.7
32.2	31.4	34.7	29.5	36.9
36.4	33.4	38.6	34.7	37.3

Times for the 200-m Dash

38	5 6
37	3
36	0 4 7 9
35	2 3
34	4 7 7 7 7
33	4
32	1 2 2 5
31	4 7 9
30	2
29	3 5

Use your stem-and-leaf plot for exercises 2–5.

2. The mode is 34.7 s.
3. The median is 34.7 s.
4. How many 8th grade students finished the race in less than 35 s?
16 students
5. How many 8th grade students finished the race in less than 33 s?
10 students

Alternative Assessment

Students in small groups find appropriate data and make a stem-and-leaf plot. Groups exchange plots and find the median and the mode of the data.

16.

7 6 0	3	1 2 3
6 5 4 3 1	4	2 3 4 6
0 0	5	0 0 1

Key: means 30 ← 0 | 3 | 1 → means 31

Test Prep

Resources
For additional practice with a variety of test item formats:

- Test-Taking Strategies, p. 461
- Test Prep, p. 465
- Test-Taking Strategies with Transparencies

9-6

1. Plan

Objective
To represent and interpret data using box-and-whisker plots

Examples
1 Comparing Two Sets of Data
2 Making Box-and-Whisker Plots

Math Understandings: p. 410D

Professional Development

Math Background

A box-and-whisker plot groups data into quartiles, separated by the median of all the data and the medians of the upper and lower halves of the data.

More Math Background: p. 410D

Lesson Planning and Resources

See p. 410E for a list of the resources that support this lesson.

PowerPoint

Bell Ringer Practice

Check Skills You'll Need
Use student page, transparency, or PowerPoint. For intervention, direct students to:

Finding Mean, Median, and Mode
Lesson 9-1
Extra Skills and Word Problems Practice, Ch. 9

9-6 Box-and-Whisker Plots

Check Skills You'll Need

1. **Vocabulary Review** Which *measure of central tendency* is the middle value of a data set? median

Find the median.

2. 23 32 24 22 25 24 35 24
3. 6 2 9 3 5 4 2 9 4 2 3 4
4. 90 95 92 91 95 96 97 98 96 95

GO for Help Lesson 9-1

What You'll Learn

To represent and interpret data using box-and-whisker plots

New Vocabulary box-and-whisker plot, quartiles

Why Learn This?

You can use box-and-whisker plots to organize very large data sets or to make comparisons between data sets.

A **box-and-whisker plot** is a graph that summarizes a data set along a number line. To make a box-and-whisker plot, you use values called quartiles. **Quartiles** divide data into four equally-sized groups.

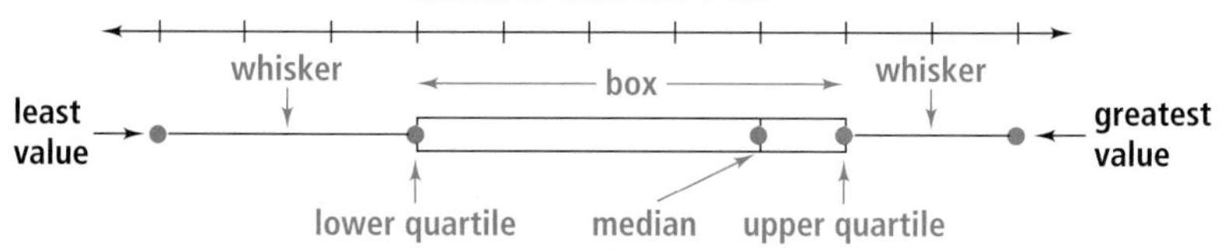

EXAMPLE Comparing Two Sets of Data

1 Shopping The two box-and-whisker plots show the prices for clothing at two stores. Write a paragraph comparing the data.

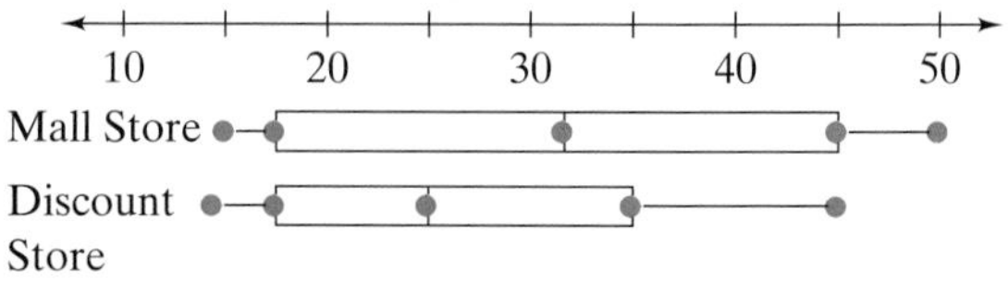

The mall store's prices vary more than the discount store's. The discount store's shorter box means that its prices are less spread out.

Quick Check

1. Write a paragraph comparing the data below.

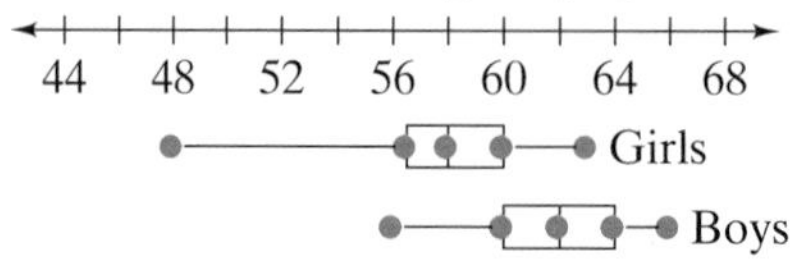

1. Answers may vary. Sample: The range for the girls' heights is greater than the boys'. Overall, the boys tend to be taller than the girls. The girls' upper quartile is equal to the boys' lower quartile.

Differentiated Instruction Solutions for All Learners

Special Needs L1	Below Level L2
Students rewrite data sets as lists in a column. A vertical instead of a horizontal format may help them keep track of the number of data values in any given set.	Students review median by finding the median of these sets of data. 5, 10, 8, 12, 3 8; 19, 23, 15, 21, 17, 14 18
learning style: visual	learning style: verbal

Online active math

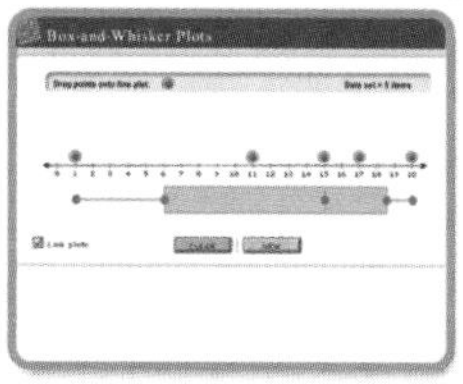

For: Box-and-Whisker Activity
Use: Interactive Textbook, 9-6

Test Prep Tip

When a data set has two middle values, the median is the average of the two.

Before you draw a box-and-whisker plot, you need to find the quartiles of the data.

The lower quartile is the median of the lower half of data. The middle quartile is the median of the entire data set. The upper quartile is the median of the upper half of data.

EXAMPLE Making Box-and-Whisker Plots

2 Travel Make a box-and-whisker plot for the data below.

Average Amount Spent by Visitors to the United States (per person)

Country	Amount	Country	Amount
Canada	$483	France	$2,688
Mexico	$562	Brazil	$3,389
Japan	$2,341	Italy	$2,726
United Kingdom	$2,142	South Korea	$3,405
Germany	$2,466	Australia	$3,618

SOURCE: *The World Almanac*

Step 1 Arrange the data from least to greatest. Find the median.

483 562 2,142 2,341 2,466 2,688 2,726 3,389 3,405 3,618

The median is $\frac{2{,}466 + 2{,}688}{2}$, or 2,577.

Step 2 Find the lower quartile and the upper quartile.

483 562 **2,142** 2,341 2,466 2,688 2,726 **3,389** 3,405 3,618

The lower quartile is 2,142, and the upper quartile is 3,389.

Step 3 Draw a number line that spans all of the data values. Mark points below the number line at the least and greatest values, at the median, and at the lower and upper quartiles.

Use the lower and upper quartiles to form a box. Mark the median. Then draw whiskers from the box to the least and greatest values.

Amount Spent by Visitors to the United States (dollars per person)

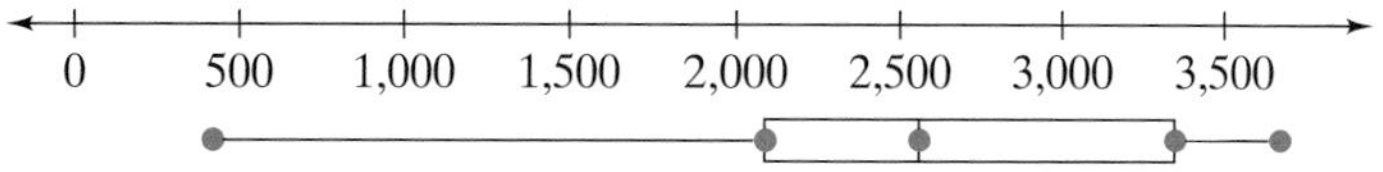

Quick Check

2. Make a box-and-whisker plot for the data below. See back of book.
10 16 24 11 35 26 29 31 4 53 47 12 21 24 25 26

2. Teach

Activity Lab

Use before the lesson.

All in One Teaching Resources

Activity Lab 9-6: Box-and-Whisker Plots

Guided Instruction

Technology Tip
Have students use the Online Active Math in Interactive Textbook Lesson 9-6 to make box-and-whisker plots.

PowerPoint

Additional Examples

1 Write a paragraph to compare the data shown in these plots.

Game Attendance in Hundreds

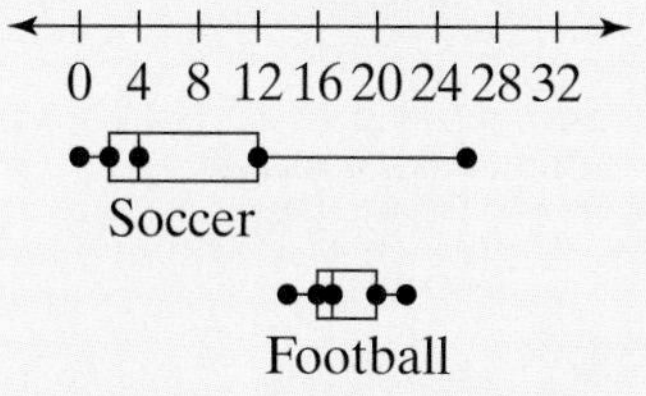

Answers will vary but should include: soccer: median 400, range 2,600, has a larger range; football: median 1,650, range 900, attendance clusters around the median

2 Make a box-and-whisker plot for this data on study hours per week: 10, 13, 16, 17, 20, 22, 23, 24, 26, 30, 31.

Study Hours per Week

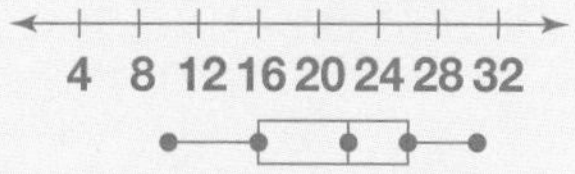

All in One Teaching Resources

- Daily Notetaking Guide 9-6 L3
- Adapted Notetaking 9-6 L1

Closure

- Explain how to make a box-and-whisker plot. Answers should include ordering data, finding quartiles, and drawing the box and the whiskers.

Advanced Learners L4	**English Language Learners** ELL
Students find appropriate data and make a double box-and-whisker plot. learning style: visual	Students remember the meaning of *quartile* by being asked to name words related to *four* in several languages, such *quarter, quatre* (French), and *cuatro* (Spanish). learning style: verbal

3. Practice

Assignment Guide

Check Your Understanding

Go over Exercises 1–4 in class before assigning the Homework Exercises.

Homework Exercises

A	Practice by Example	5–8
B	Apply Your Skills	9–15
C	Challenge	16
	Test Prep and Mixed Review	17–20

Homework Quick Check

To check students' understanding of key skills and concepts, go over Exercises 6, 8, 9, 12, and 13.

Differentiated Instruction Resources

Adapted Practice L1

Practice 9-6 Box-and-Wh… L3

Use the box-and-whisker plot to find each value.

Height in Inches

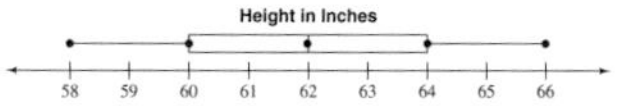

1. the median height 62
2. the lower quartile 60
3. the upper quartile 64
4. the greatest height 66
5. the shortest height 58
6. the range of heights 8

Make a box-and-whisker plot for each set of data.

7. 8 10 11 7 12 6 10 5 9 7 10

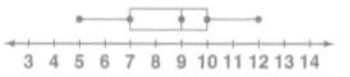

8. 20 21 25 18 25 15 27 26 24 23 20 20

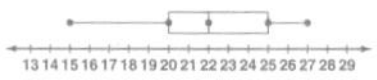

9.

Cargo Airlines in the U.S. (1991)	
Airline	Freight ton-miles (1,000,000s)
Federal Express	3,622
Northwest	1,684
United	1,214
American	884
Delta	668
Continental	564
Pan American	377
Trans World	369
United Parcel Service	210

10.

Immigration to the U.S. (1981–1990)	
Country	Number (1,000s)
Mexico	1,656
Philippines	549
China	347
Korea	334
Vietnam	281
Dominican Republic	252
India	251
El Salvador	214
Jamaica	208
United Kingdom	159

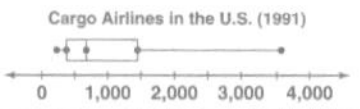

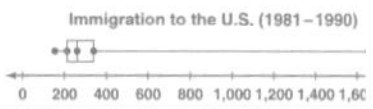

9-6 • Guided Problem Solving GPS L3

Student Page 441, Exercise 14:

Racing Make a box-and-whisker plot for the data.

Average Speed of Daytona 500 Winners								
Year	1998	1999	2000	2001	2002	2003	2004	2005
Speed (mi/h)	173	162	156	162	143	134	156	135

Understand

1. What three values will you need to make the box? lower quartile, median, upper quartile
2. What two values will you need to make the whiskers? least and greatest

Plan and Carry Out

3. Order the speeds from least to greatest and find the median. 134, 135, 143, 146, 156, 162, 162, 173; median, 155
4. Find the upper and lower quartiles by finding the medians of the upper and lower halves. lower, 139; upper, 162
5. Use the number line at right. Use the median and the lower and upper quartiles to draw the box. Draw the whiskers from the box to the least and greatest values.

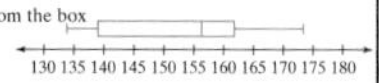

Check

6. Are all of the data displayed or it is it summarized? summarized

Solve Another Problem

7. A biology class consists of sophomores and a few freshmen. Make a box-and-whisker plot from the grades in the table.

Test Scores								
Freshmen	89	78	91	87	92	89		
Sophomores	72	95	86	87	98	76	85	93

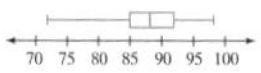

Check Your Understanding

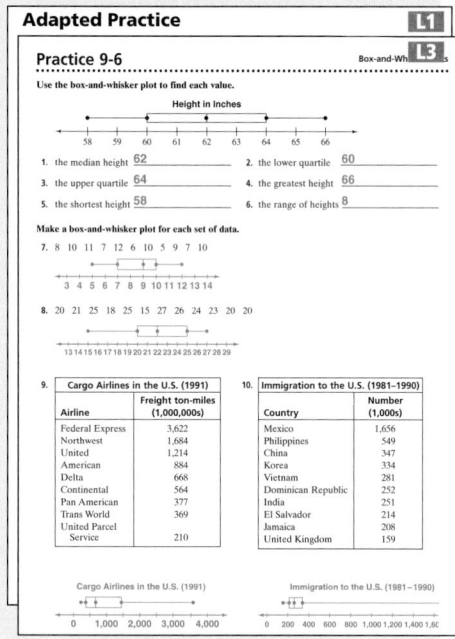

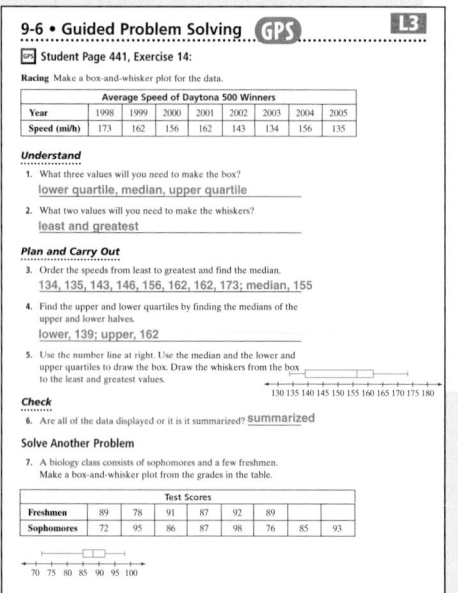

1. **Vocabulary** The _?_ is the middle quartile of a data set. median

Match each term with the correct point *A, B, C, D,* or *E*.

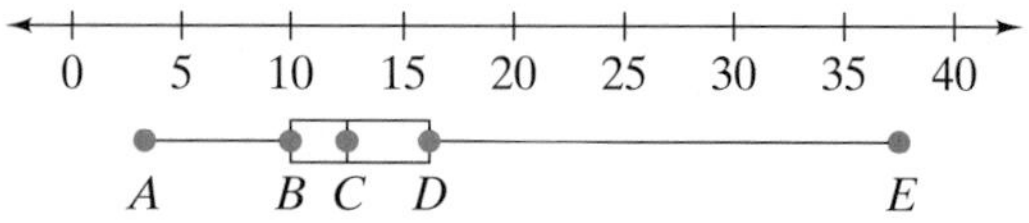

2. median C
3. greatest value E
4. lower quartile B

Homework Exercises

For more exercises, see Extra Skills and Word Problems.

GO for Help

For Exercises	See Examples
5–6	1
7–8	2

A For each box-and-whisker plot, write a paragraph to compare the data.

5. **On-Time Flight Arrivals and Departures in 2004 (percent per day)**

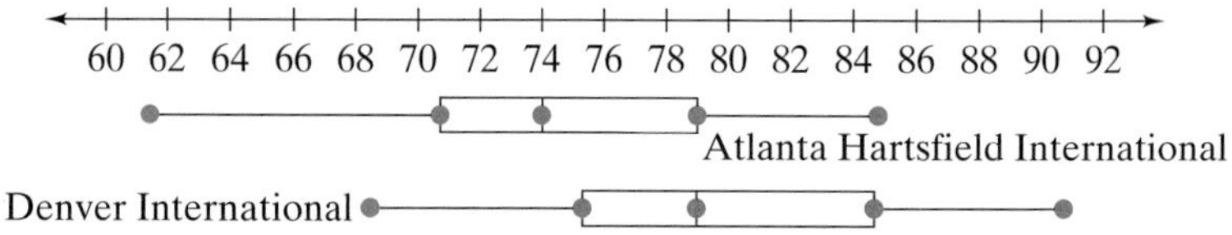

SOURCE: U.S. Census Bureau. Go to **PHSchool.com** for a data update. Web Code: asg-9041

6. **Median Income for Men and Women 1984 to 2003 (thousands of dollars)**

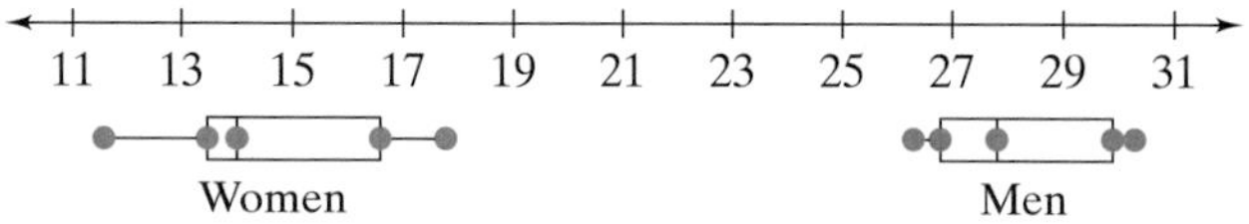

SOURCE: U.S. Census Bureau. Go to **PHSchool.com** for a data update. Web Code: asg-9041

5. Answers may vary. Sample: the range of percents of on-time arrivals is about the same for Atlanta and Denver. Overall, Denver had a greater percent of on-time arrivals per day in 2004 than Atlanta. The median for Denver is about the same as the upper quartile for Atlanta.

6. Answers may vary. Sample: the median income for men exceeded that of women. The range for women's incomes was greater than men's. The men's incomes were more consistent than the women's.

Make a box-and-whisker plot for each set of data. 7–8. See margin.

7. lengths of snakes at a zoo (ft):

2 9 5 6 8 5 4 6 13 5 8 11 6 14 10 9 13 8 5 7 6 18 9 12

8. bowling scores:

229 152 161 267 193 184 271 199 161 273 221 180

B GPS

9. **Guided Problem Solving** Which league in the table below had the greater range in number of home runs hit by league leaders? See margin.

Home Runs Hit by League Leaders (2004 Season)

American League	43	41	41	39	38	36	36	34	32
National League	48	46	46	45	42	42	39	38	37

SOURCE: *Sports Illustrated 2005 Almanac*

- Draw box-and-whisker plots on the same number line.
- How can you use the plots to compare the ranges?

7.

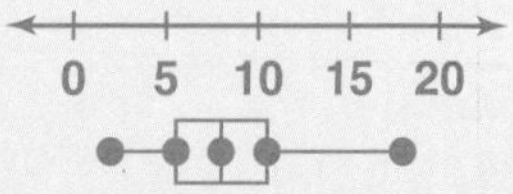

8.

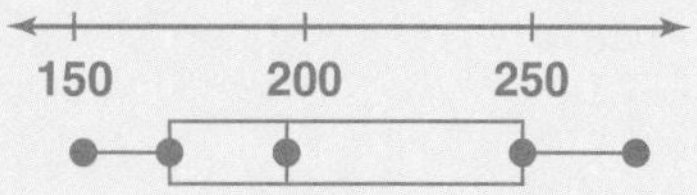

9.

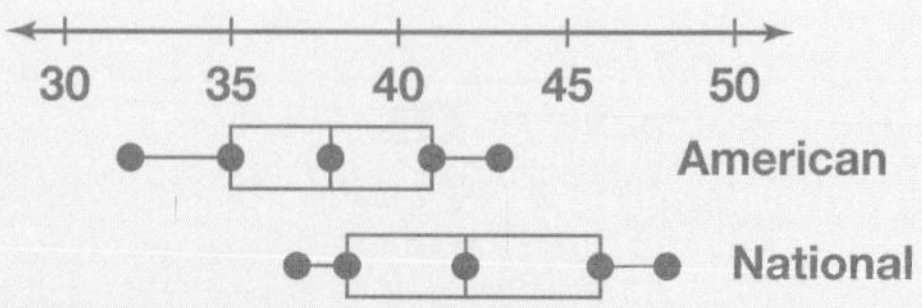

They had the same range.

Go Online
Homework Video Tutor
Visit: PHSchool.com
Web Code: ase-0906

Use the box-and-whisker plot below to find each value.

Test Scores

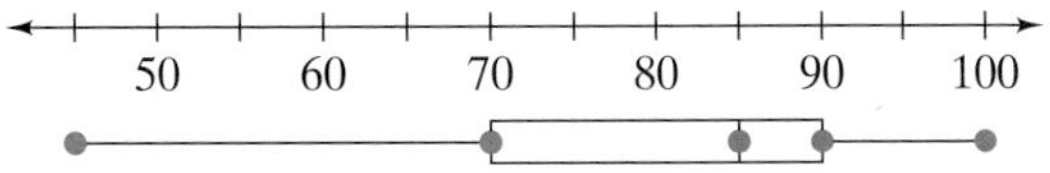

10. the median 85
11. the lower quartile 70
12. the range 55

13. **Writing in Math** Describe what it means when the median is not exactly in the middle of the box in a box-and-whisker plot. See left.

13. The data are skewed. The two middle quartiles of the data are not evenly spread out.

Racing Use the table below for Exercises 14 and 15.

Average Speed of Daytona 500 Winners

Year	1998	1999	2000	2001	2002	2003	2004	2005
Speed (mi/h)	173	162	156	162	143	134	156	135

SOURCE: NASCAR

14. Make a box-and-whisker plot for the data. See margin.

GPS 15. **Number Sense** Would the size of the box in your plot change if the average speed were 192 mi/h in 2003? Explain. See margin.

C 16. **Challenge** A scientist has 10 pieces of data in order. The median is 60.5. The sixth piece of data is 71. What is the fifth piece of data? 50

Test Prep and Mixed Review — Practice

Multiple Choice

17. What is the median in the box-and-whisker plot at the right? C

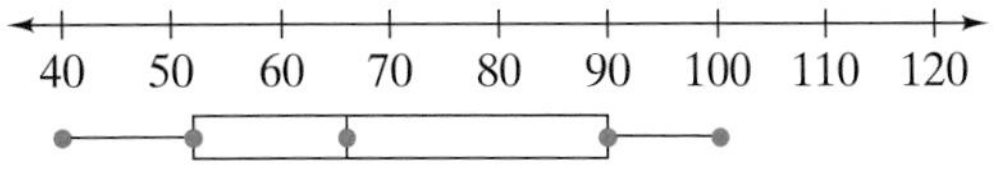

Ⓐ 100 Ⓑ 90 Ⓒ 67 Ⓓ 51

18. The base of an isosceles triangle is 3 centimeters longer than its leg. If the perimeter is 18 centimeters, you can use the equation $18 - 2n = n + 3$ to find the length n of each leg. What is the length of each leg? J

Ⓕ 15 cm Ⓖ 7.5 cm Ⓗ 7 cm Ⓙ 5 cm

19. Tasha rolled out dough to make a pie. Which of the following is closest to the area her rolling pin at the right will cover in one complete rotation? C

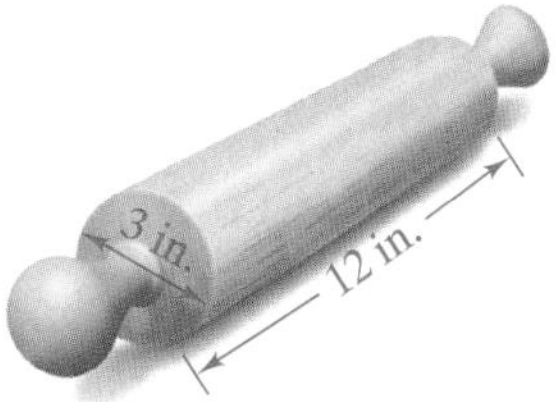

Ⓐ 36 in.^{2} Ⓒ 113 in.^{2}
Ⓑ 57 in.^{2} Ⓓ 226 in.^{2}

GO for Help

For Exercise	See Lesson
20	9-5

20. Make a stem-and-leaf plot for the following set of data: See margin.
120 123 125 130 124 125 126 123 119 131 126 127 132 118

4. Assess & Reteach

PowerPoint

Lesson Quiz

1. Write a paragraph to describe the data in the following box-and-whisker plot.

Miles Run by Track Club Members

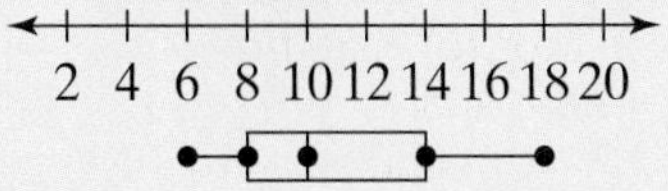

1–3. See back of book.

2. Make box-and-whisker plots on a single number line to compare the individual points scored by boys and girls.
Girls: 14, 15, 18, 20, 21, 21, 24, 24, 25, 27, 29
Boys: 8, 8, 9, 10, 14, 18, 25, 25, 28, 28, 30

3. Write a paragraph to compare the data in Question 2.

14.

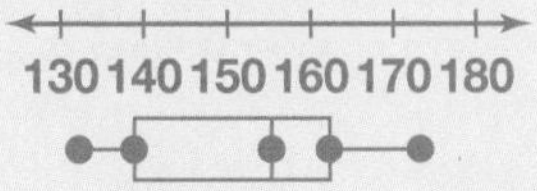

15. Yes; it would move the upper quartile from 162 to 167.5, and the lower quartile would move from 139 to 149.5.

20.
11 | 8 9
12 | 0 3 3 4 5 5 6 6 7
13 | 0 1 2
Key: 13 | 0 means 130

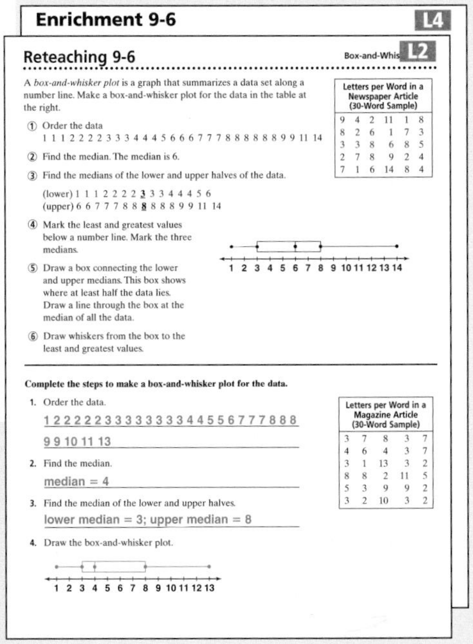
Enrichment 9-6 L4

Reteaching 9-6 Box-and-Whis L2

A *box-and-whisker plot* is a graph that summarizes a data set along a number line. Make a box-and-whisker plot for the data in the table at the right.

Letters per Word in a Newspaper Article (30-Word Sample)					
9	4	2	11	1	8
8	2	6	1	7	3
3	3	8	6	8	5
2	7	8	9	2	4
7	1	6	14	8	4

① Order the data
1 1 1 2 2 2 2 3 3 3 4 4 4 5 6 6 6 7 7 7 8 8 8 8 8 8 9 9 11 14

② Find the median. The median is 6.

③ Find the medians of the lower and upper halves of the data.
(lower) 1 1 1 2 2 2 2 3 3 3 4 4 4 5 6
(upper) 6 6 7 7 7 8 8 8 8 8 8 9 9 11 14

④ Mark the least and greatest values below a number line. Mark the three medians.

1 2 3 4 5 6 7 8 9 10 11 12 13 14

⑤ Draw a box connecting the lower and upper medians. This box shows where at least half the data lies. Draw a line through the box at the median of all the data.

⑥ Draw whiskers from the box to the least and greatest values.

Complete the steps to make a box-and-whisker plot for the data.

Letters per Word in a Magazine Article (30-Word Sample)				
3	7	8	3	7
4	6	4	3	7
3	1	13	3	2
8	8	2	11	5
5	3	9	9	2
3	2	10	3	2

1. Order the data.
1 2 2 2 2 2 3 3 3 3 3 3 3 4 4 5 5 6 7 7 7 8 8 8
9 9 10 11 13

2. Find the median.
median = 4

3. Find the median of the lower and upper halves.
lower median = 3; upper median = 8

4. Draw the box-and-whisker plot.

1 2 3 4 5 6 7 8 9 10 11 12 13

Alternative Assessment

Each student draws a general diagram of a box-and-whisker plot and labels the five key points in their plot. Students then write a paragraph that explains what each whisker shows and what each part of the box represents.

Test Prep

Resources
For additional practice with a variety of test item formats:
- Test-Taking Strategies, p. 461
- Test Prep, p. 465
- Test-Taking Strategies with Transparencies

Activity Lab

Making Box-and-Whisker Plots

In Lesson 9-6, students drew box-and-whisker plots to display large data sets. In this activity, they learn how to use a graphing calculator to make box-and-whisker plots.

Guided Instruction

Exercises
Working in pairs, one student enters the data from the first exercise into the calculator and enters the keystrokes, then the other sketches the box-and-whisker plot. For the second problem, students switch tasks.

After finishing the exercises, have students work on one of the exercises a second time, replacing one data value with an outlier. Have them compare the resulting box-and-whisker plot with the original.

Technology Tip
Have students use the Online Active Math in Interactive Textbook Lesson 9-5 to make a stem-and-leaf plot for the data in Exercise 2. Have them compare the effectiveness of the representations.

Resources

- any graphing calculator

9-6b Activity Lab — Technology

Making Box-and-Whisker Plots

A graphing calculator can help you make box-and-whisker plots.

ACTIVITY

The heights of the twenty largest giant sequoia trees in feet are 275, 255, 268, 241, 256, 243, 269, 253, 223, 270, 248, 255, 251, 248, 244, 244, 273, 236, 246, and 286. Make a box-and-whisker plot of these data values

Step 1 Press LIST. Enter the 20 values into L_1.

Step 2 Use the PLOT feature. Select the first plot. Select **On**. Select the type of graph that looks like a box-and-whisker plot. Set Xlist = L_1.

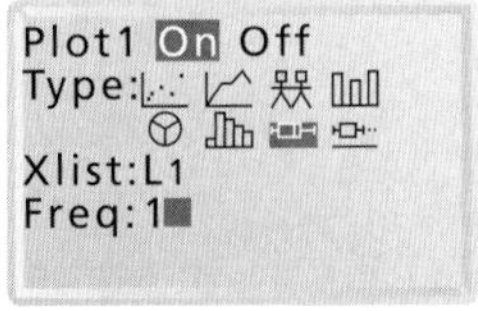

Step 3 Press ZOOM. Select ZoomStat.

Step 4 Press WINDOW. Set Xscl = 1.

Step 5 Press GRAPH to see the box-and-whisker plot.

Step 6 Press TRACE. Move the cursor to see the minimum, first quartile, median, third quartile, and maximum values.

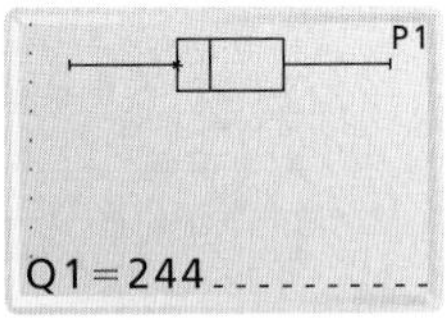

Step 7 Sketch a box-and-whisker plot of the data.

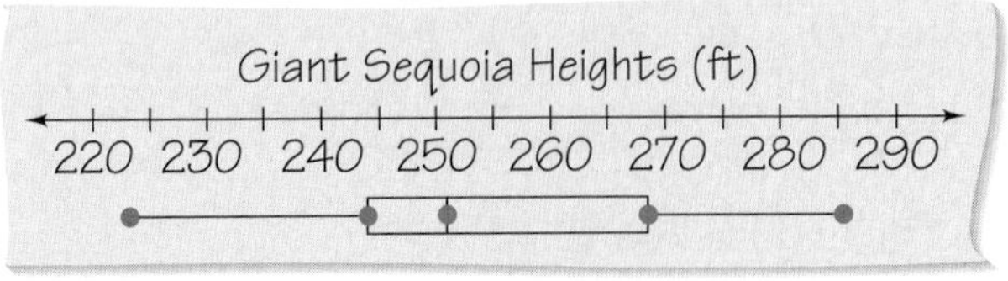

Exercises

Graph a box-and-whisker plot for each set of data using a graphing calculator. Then sketch the box-and-whisker plot.

1. 46, 45, 36, 36, 52, 35, 38, 44, 53, 50, 44, 35, 37, 37
2. 7, 2, 5, 12, 13, 10, 6, 3, 4, 11, 12, 13, 10, 5, 8, 8, 9, 3, 4, 6

1. 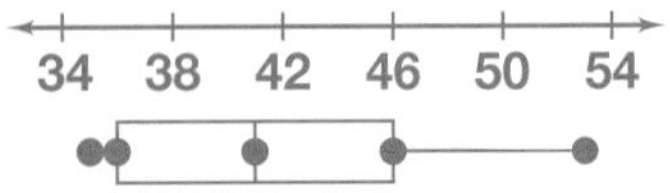

2. 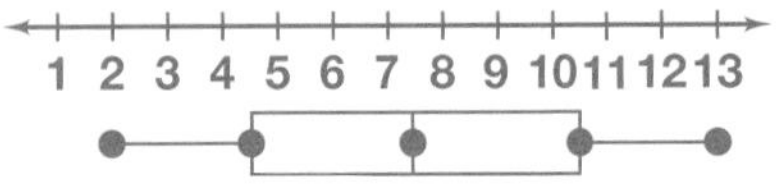

Scatter Plots

Is the length of your arm span (from fingertip to fingertip) related to your height? Graphing data in a scatter plot can help you decide whether one thing is related to another.

ACTIVITY 1–10. Check students' work.

1. Have a classmate measure and record your height in centimeters.
2. Arm span is the greatest possible distance between the tips of your index fingers when your arms are stretched outward. To measure your arm span, hold one end of a tape measure in one hand and stretch your arms outward as the other hand slides along the tape measure. Measure your arm span in centimeters.
3. Write your data as an ordered pair: (height, arm span).
4. Exchange ordered pairs with your classmates. Record the ordered pairs in a table like the one below.

Height (cm)	■	■	■	■
Arm span (cm)	■	■	■	■

5. Make a graph of the ordered pairs. Label the horizontal axis Height (cm) and the vertical axis Arm Span (cm). Choose an appropriate scale.
6. **Writing in Math** What do you notice about the graph? Can you predict a person's arm span based on the person's height? Explain.
7. Suppose a person 176 cm tall joins your class. About how long would you expect his or her arm span to be? Explain.
8. Plot a few points on your graph where height and arm span are equal. Draw a line through these points.
9. Look at the points that lie above the line you drew. Describe the relationship between height and arm span for these points.
10. Look at the points that lie below the line. Describe the relationship between height and arm span for these points.

Activity Lab

Data Collection: Scatter Plots

Students explore whether there is a relationship between height and arm span. Working together, they measure their height and arm span, write the values as an ordered pair, and then graph the resulting pairs on a coordinate grid. Their graph will be a scatter plot from which they will draw conclusions and make predictions.

Guided Instruction

Have students make conjectures about whether arm span and height are related before they begin. Be sensitive that some students may feel uncomfortable taking these measurements.

Evaluating Predictions
Have students discuss the reasoning behind their predictions and evaluate the reasonableness of their predictions.

Differentiated Instruction

Special Needs L1
Review graphing on a coordinate plane. Elicit the fact that a point's distance from the origin along horizontal axis, or *x*-axis, is represented by the first coordinate in an ordered pair. A point's distance from the origin along the vertical axis, or *y*-axis, is represented by the second number in an ordered pair. Help them label the graph correctly.

Resources

- Activity Lab 9-7: Making Predictions from Scatter Plots
- grid paper
- measuring tape, yardstick, or meter stick

9-7

1. Plan

Objective
To make scatter plots and to use trends to make predictions

Examples
1 Making Scatter Plots
2 Drawing Trend Lines

Math Understandings: p. 410D

Professional Development

Math Background

One way to examine a possible relationship between two measured quantities is to make a scatter plot of the values, one value plotted along the *x*-axis and the other value on the *y*-axis. When the plotted points appear to lie approximately along a line, called a *trend line*, it is reasonable to conjecture that there is some relationship between the two measurements plotted. A trend can be used to predict other values for similar data.

More Math Background: p. 410D

Lesson Planning and Resources

See p. 410E for a list of the resources that support this lesson.

PowerPoint

Bell Ringer Practice

Check Skills You'll Need
Use student page, transparency, or PowerPoint. For intervention, direct students to:
Graphing in the Coordinate Plane
Lesson 3-4
Extra Skills and Word Problems Practice, Ch. 3

9-7 Making Predictions From Scatter Plots

Check Skills You'll Need

1. **Vocabulary Review** What is an *ordered pair*? 1–3. See below.

Graph each point on a coordinate plane.

2. $A(1, -2)$
3. $B(-3, 5)$

GO for Help Lesson 3-4

Check Skills You'll Need
1. It identifies the location of a point.
2–3. See back of book.

What You'll Learn

To make scatter plots and to use trends to make predictions

New Vocabulary scatter plot, positive trend, negative trend, no trend, trend line

Why Learn This?

You can use a scatter plot to determine whether the age of a car is related to what the car is worth.

A **scatter plot** is a graph that displays two sets of data as ordered pairs. It can help you decide whether two sets of data are related.

EXAMPLE Making Scatter Plots

1 **Cars** Make a scatter plot for the data in the table below.

What's a Car Worth? Average Value of a Midsize Sedan (dollars)

Age (yr)	Value	Age (yr)	Value
3	11,000	1	15,000
2	12,000	4	8,000
7	3,000	5	7,000
8	1,000	3	6,000
2	10,000	6	6,000

Step 1 Use the horizontal scale to represent the age of the car. Use the vertical scale to represent the car's value.

Step 2 Plot each data pair. (3, 11,000) represents a data pair.

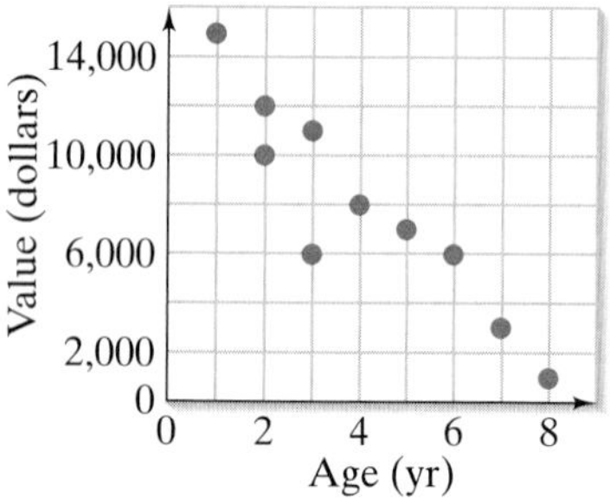

Quick Check

1. Make a scatter plot for the data below. See back of book.

Age (yr):	1	15	6	19	12	3	5	13	20	6
Sleep Time (h):	15	8.5	9.5	7	9.25	12	11	9	7	9.75

Differentiated Instruction Solutions for All Learners

Special Needs L1
Students show, with their forearm, what a trend line with a negative trend looks like. They do the same for a positive trend. They brainstorm examples of data that would display a negative trend.
learning style: tactile

Below Level L2
Students review the meaning of an ordered pair, such as $(-3, 2)$, and describe how it relates to the position of a point on the coordinate plane.
learning style: verbal

Vocabulary Tip

A trend can also be a current style, as in fashion.

The three scatter plots below show the types of relationships, or trends, two sets of data may have.

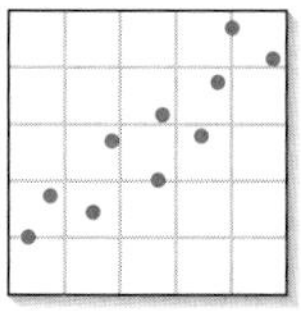

Positive trend
As one set of values increases, the other set tends to increase.

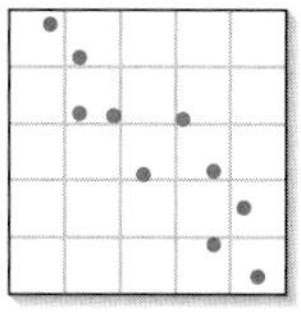

Negative trend
As one set of values increases, the other set tends to decrease.

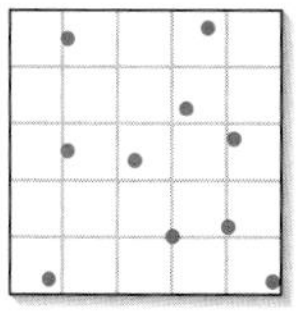

No trend
The points show no relationship.

A **trend line** is a line you draw on a graph to approximate the relationship between the data sets. If there is no trend to the data, you cannot draw a trend line.

You can use trend lines to make predictions about data values that do not appear on a scatter plot.

EXAMPLE Drawing Trend Lines

2 **Gridded Response** The table below shows the circumference and height of a variety of trees. Use a scatter plot to predict the height of a tree that has a circumference of 175 in.

Tree Height and Circumference

Height (ft)	19	32	57	43	75	97	110
Circumference (in.)	10	63	72	111	150	185	214

Step 1 Plot each data pair.

Step 2 The plotted points go up from left to right. This scatter plot shows a positive trend.

Step 3 Draw a line with positive slope. Make sure there are about as many points above the line as there are below it.

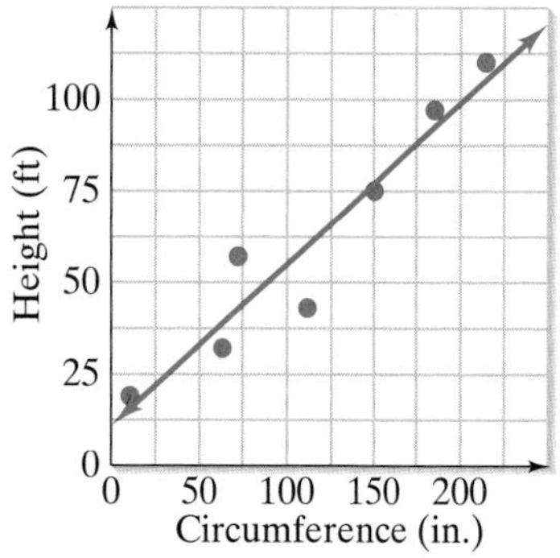

Step 4 Find 175 on the horizontal axis. Move up to the trend line. Then move left to the vertical axis.

A tree with a circumference of 175 in. should have a height of about 88 ft.

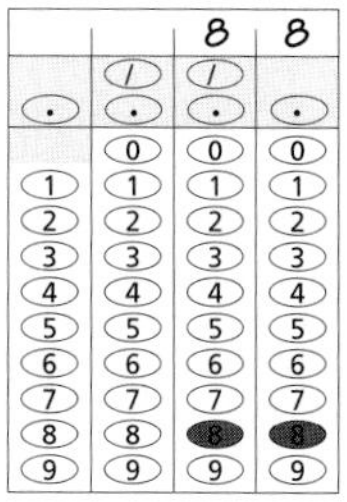

Quick Check

2. Copy the scatter plot from Example 1 and draw a trend line.
See back of book.

Advanced Learners L4	**English Language Learners** ELL
Students discuss examples of two events which may occur simultaneously, but one does not cause the other. Sample: Tuesday and winning a game	Students describe to a partner a relationship that shows a positive trend, such as the relationship between car gasoline usage and miles driven. They do the same regarding a negative trend.
learning style: verbal	learning style: verbal

2. Teach

Activity Lab

Use before the lesson.
Student Edition Data Collection Activity Lab 9-7a, Scatter Plots, p. 443

All in One Teaching Resources

- **Activity Lab 9-7:** Making Predictions from Scatter Plots

Guided Instruction

Example 2
Provide students with a blank grid from **TAKS Strategies with Transparencies.**

PowerPoint

Additional Examples

1 Make a scatter plot for the data.

Miles Traveled and Gas Used

Gas (gal)	Miles
5	150
4	112
7	217
3	87
8	216
5	155

1–2. See back of book.

2 Describe the trend of the data in the scatter plot in Question 1 and draw a trend line. Then predict the miles for 6 gallons of gas.

All in One Teaching Resources

- Daily Notetaking Guide 9-7 L3
- Adapted Notetaking 9-7 L1

Closure

- Explain how to make a scatter plot and how to use it to find a trend. Answers should include plotting data pairs, looking for a trend line, and deciding whether the plot shows a positive trend, a negative trend, or no trend.

3. Practice

Assignment Guide

Check Your Understanding
Go over Exercises 1–4 in class before assigning the Homework Exercises.

Homework Exercises
A	Practice by Example	5–8
B	Apply Your Skills	9–13
C	Challenge	14
	Test Prep and Mixed Review	15–18

Homework Quick Check
To check students' understanding of key skills and concepts, go over Exercises 5, 8, 9, 12, and 13.

Differentiated Instruction Resources

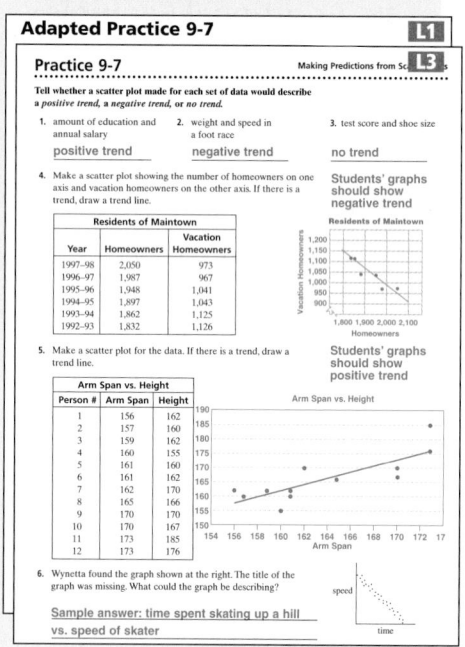

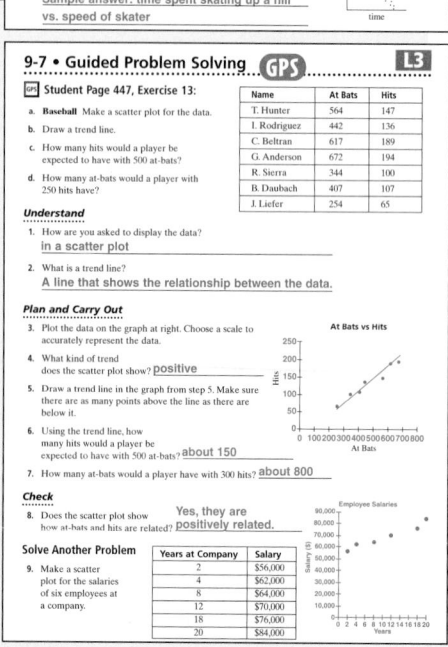

Adapted Practice 9-7 L1

Practice 9-7 — Making Predictions from Sc[atter Plot]s L3

Tell whether a scatter plot made for each set of data would describe a *positive trend*, a *negative trend*, or *no trend*.

1. amount of education and annual salary — positive trend
2. weight and speed in a foot race — negative trend
3. test score and shoe size — no trend
4. Make a scatter plot showing the number of homeowners on one axis and vacation homeowners on the other axis. If there is a trend, draw a trend line. — Students' graphs should show negative trend

Residents of Maintown		
Year	Homeowners	Vacation Homeowners
1997–98	2,050	973
1996–97	1,987	967
1995–96	1,948	1,041
1994–95	1,897	1,043
1993–94	1,862	1,125
1992–93	1,832	1,126

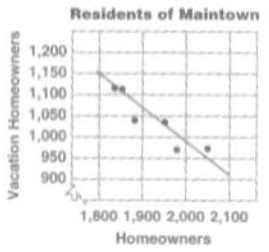

5. Make a scatter plot for the data. If there is a trend, draw a trend line. — Students' graphs should show positive trend

Arm Span vs. Height		
Person #	Arm Span	Height
1	156	162
2	157	160
3	159	162
4	160	155
5	161	160
6	161	162
7	162	170
8	165	166
9	170	170
10	170	167
11	173	185
12	173	176

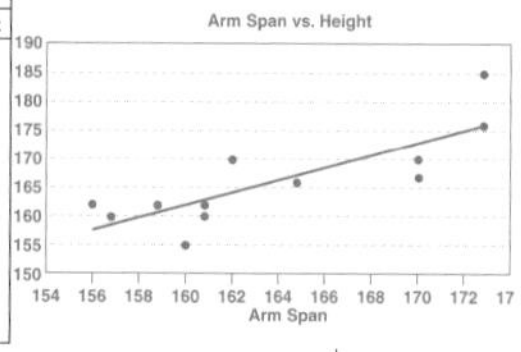

6. Wynetta found the graph shown at the right. The title of the graph was missing. What could the graph be describing?

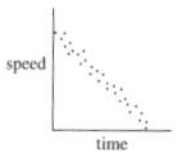

Sample answer: time spent skating up a hill vs. speed of skater

9-7 • Guided Problem Solving GPS L3

GPS **Student Page 447, Exercise 13:**

a. **Baseball** Make a scatter plot for the data.
b. Draw a trend line.
c. How many hits would a player be expected to have with 500 at-bats?
d. How many at-bats would a player with 250 hits have?

Name	At Bats	Hits
T. Hunter	564	147
I. Rodriguez	442	136
C. Beltran	617	189
G. Anderson	672	194
R. Sierra	344	100
B. Daubach	407	107
J. Liefer	254	65

Understand

1. How are you asked to display the data? in a scatter plot
2. What is a trend line? A line that shows the relationship between the data.

Plan and Carry Out

3. Plot the data on the graph at right. Choose a scale to accurately represent the data.
4. What kind of trend does the scatter plot show? positive
5. Draw a trend line in the graph from step 5. Make sure there are as many points above the line as there are below it.
6. Using the trend line, how many hits would a player be expected to have with 500 at-bats? about 150
7. How many at-bats would a player have with 300 hits? about 800

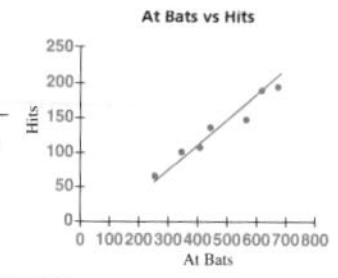

Check

8. Does the scatter plot show how at-bats and hits are related? Yes, they are positively related.

Solve Another Problem

9. Make a scatter plot for the salaries of six employees at a company.

Years at Company	Salary
2	$56,000
4	$62,000
8	$64,000
12	$70,000
18	$76,000
20	$84,000

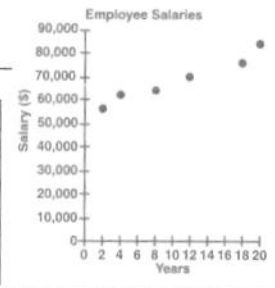

Check Your Understanding

1. **Vocabulary** Which type of graph is used to compare two sets of data—a line plot or a scatter plot? scatter plot

Match each scatter plot with a trend: *positive, negative,* or *no trend.*

2. 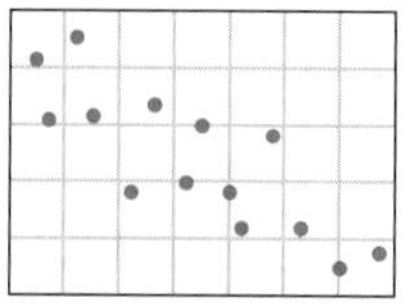
negative

3. 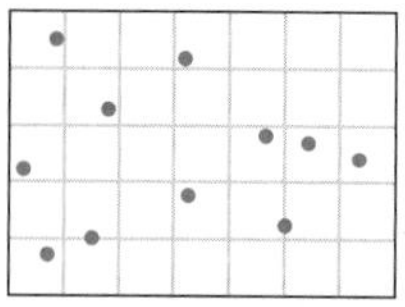
no trend

4. 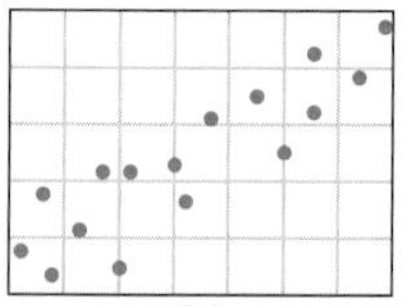
positive

Homework Exercises

For more exercises, see Extra Skills and Word Problems.

GO for Help

For Exercises	See Examples
5–6	1
7–8	2

A **Make a scatter plot for each set of data.** 5–6. See margin.

5. roommates: 3 2 3 2 4
   Rent (per person): $400 $900 $500 $700 $300

6. Hits: 7 8 4 11 8 2 5 9 1 4
   Runs: 3 2 2 7 4 2 1 3 0 1

Make a scatter plot for each set of data. If possible, draw a trend line and describe the trend. 7–8. See margin.

7. **Life Expectancy**

Current Age (yr)	10	15	20	25	30	35	40	45
Life Expectancy (yr)	67.4	62.5	57.7	53.0	48.2	43.5	38.8	34.3

SOURCE: U.S. Census Bureau. Go to **PHSchool.com** for a data update. Web Code: asg-9041

8. **Farm Sizes in the United States**

Number of Farms (millions)	6.30	6.10	5.39	3.96	2.95	2.44	2.15	2.17
Average Size (acres)	157	175	216	297	373	426	460	434

SOURCE: U.S. National Agricultural Statistics. Go to **PHSchool.com** for a data update. Web Code: asg-9041

B GPS

9. **Guided Problem Solving** Estimate the world production of oil when the United States produced 12% of the world's oil.
   - Draw a scatter plot and a trend line.
   - Find 12% on the vertical axis. Move horizontally to the trend line. Then move down to the horizontal axis.

   about 62 billion barrels

Oil Production 1960–2000 (billion barrels)

World Oil Production	U.S. Percent of World Oil Production
45.9	21
52.8	16
59.9	13
68.3	9
72.5	7

SOURCE: U.S. Energy Information Administration

5–8. See back of book.

13a–b.

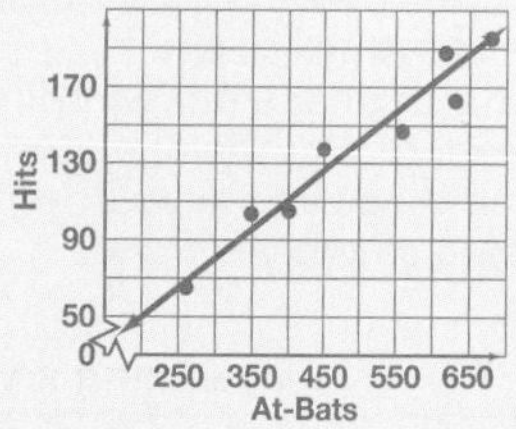

18.

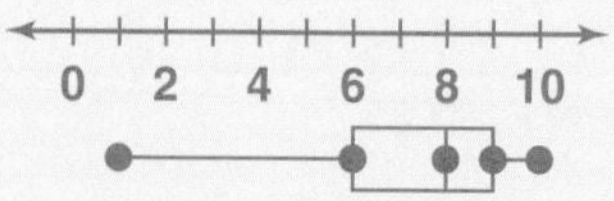

Online
Homework Video Tutor
Visit: PHSchool.com
Web Code: ase-0907

10. No trend; people of all ages own varying numbers of pets.

11. Negative trend; as the temperature increases, you wear fewer layers of clothing.

12. No; it depends on how close the points are on the line; also, the farther your prediction point is from the last point used to create the trend line, the less accurate your predictions will be.

14. No; there is no relationship between these two variables—one did not cause the other.

For each topic, decide which type of trend a scatter plot of the data would likely show. Explain your choice. 10–11. See left.

10. age of owner and number of pets currently owned

11. outdoor temperature and layers of clothing

12. **Writing in Math** Do you think predictions made from a trend line will always be accurate? Explain. See left.

13. a. **Baseball** Make a scatter plot for the data at the right. See margin.
GPS
b. Draw a trend line.
c. How many hits would a player be expected to have with 500 at-bats? about 140
d. How many at-bats would a player with 250 hits have? about 800

Name	At-Bats	Hits
T. Hunter	564	147
I. Rodriguez	442	136
C. Beltran	617	189
G. Anderson	672	194
R. Sierra	344	100
B. Daubach	407	107
J. Liefer	254	65

SOURCE: Major League Baseball Association

C 14. **Challenge** As the number of women holding jobs increased, the record time in the women's 200-m run decreased. Does this negative trend mean that one set of data *caused* the other to occur? Explain.

Test Prep and Mixed Review

Practice

Gridded Response

15. Use the scatter plot below to predict the cost in dollars for five people to dine out. 45

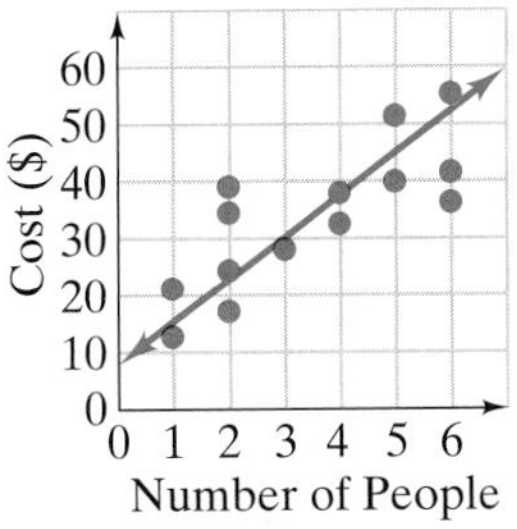

16. Find the median of the following data. 69
67 72 69 75 81 69 66 85 57

17. An astronomical unit, or AU, is the average distance from Earth to the sun. One AU is 149,597,870.691 kilometers. In scientific notation, this number is about 1.496×10^x. What is the value of x? 8

18. Make a box-and-whisker plot for the following data.
number of questions answered correctly on a 10-question pop quiz: See margin.
9 8 1 8 7 6 3 7 9 8 6 4 7 8 9 10 10

GO for Help

For Exercise	See Lesson
18	9-6

4. Assess & Reteach

PowerPoint

Lesson Quiz

The following data give the high temperatures for the first week in June. Use this data to answer the questions. (1, 68), (2, 70), (3, 65), (4, 67), (5, 71), (6, 75), (7, 74)

1. Make a scatter plot for the data. 1–2. See back of book.

2. Draw a trend line for the data in the scatter plot in Question 1. Describe the trend of the data.

3. Predict what will happen to the high temperature in June if the trend continues. Sample: High temperatures will continue to rise.

Alternative Assessment

Students copy the graph for Example 1. They sketch a trend line. They are asked what happens to the trend line when (6, 6,000), (7, 7,000), (1, 12,000), and (2, 8,000) are added to the data. The slope becomes less steep.

Test Prep

Resources
For additional practice with a variety of test item formats:
- Test-Taking Strategies, p. 461
- Test Prep, p. 465
- Test-Taking Strategies with Transparencies

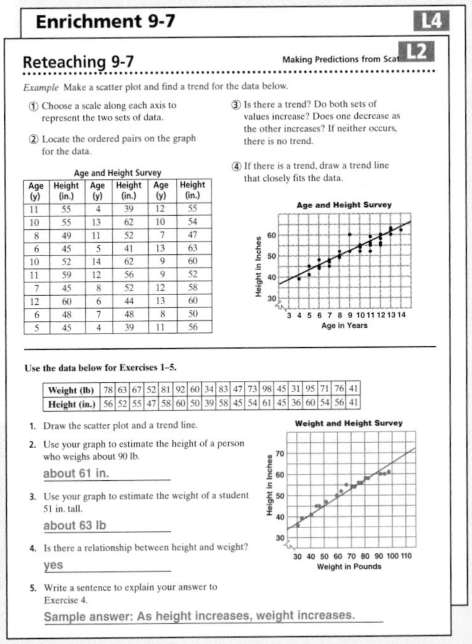

Enrichment 9-7 L4

Reteaching 9-7 Making Predictions from Scat L2

Example Make a scatter plot and find a trend for the data below.

① Choose a scale along each axis to represent the two sets of data.

② Locate the ordered pairs on the graph for the data.

③ Is there a trend? Do both sets of values increase? Does one decrease as the other increases? If neither occurs, there is no trend.

④ If there is a trend, draw a trend line that closely fits the data.

Age and Height Survey

Age (y)	Height (in.)	Age (y)	Height (in.)	Age (y)	Height (in.)
11	55	4	39	12	55
10	55	13	62	10	54
8	49	11	52	7	47
6	45	5	41	13	63
10	52	14	62	9	60
11	59	12	56	9	52
7	45	8	52	12	58
12	60	6	44	13	60
6	48	7	48	8	50
5	45	4	39	11	56

Use the data below for Exercises 1–5.

Weight (lb)	78	63	67	52	81	92	60	34	83	47	73	98	45	31	95	71	76	41
Height (in.)	56	52	55	47	58	60	50	39	58	45	54	61	45	36	60	54	56	41

1. Draw the scatter plot and a trend line.
2. Use your graph to estimate the height of a person who weighs about 90 lb. about 61 in.
3. Use your graph to estimate the weight of a student 51 in. tall. about 63 lb
4. Is there a relationship between height and weight? yes
5. Write a sentence to explain your answer to Exercise 4. Sample answer: As height increases, weight increases.

Algebra Thinking: Plotting a Strategy

In this activity, students study points on a scatter plot and read clues. Each written clue corresponds to a point in the scatter plot. Using logic and their knowledge of scatter plots, students answer the activity questions.

Guided Instruction

Read over the clues to the first Activity with students. Have students identify what each axis represents. Then ask: *Which point on the scatter plot can you identify immediately? Explain.* **Sample: Point (10, 8) represents Tom's family. Tom's family has more phones than anyone and 8 is the highest *y*-value in any of the pairs.**

Encourage students to use the clues in any order. You may want to do the first activity together, having volunteers explain their strategy.

Differentiated Instruction

Visual Learners
Have students copy each graph onto grid paper. Have them label each point that they identify.

Resources

- grid paper

Plotting a Strategy

In scatter plots, the relationship between the variables is important. Analyze the clues to solve each problem.

ACTIVITY

The scatter plot at the right shows the number of cellular telephones in each of five families.

- DeWayne's family has three times as many members as cellular phones.
- Tom's family has more cellular phones than any other family.
- Each person in Rita's family has a cellular phone.
- Jack's family has six people in it.
- Manny's family has one extra cellular phone.

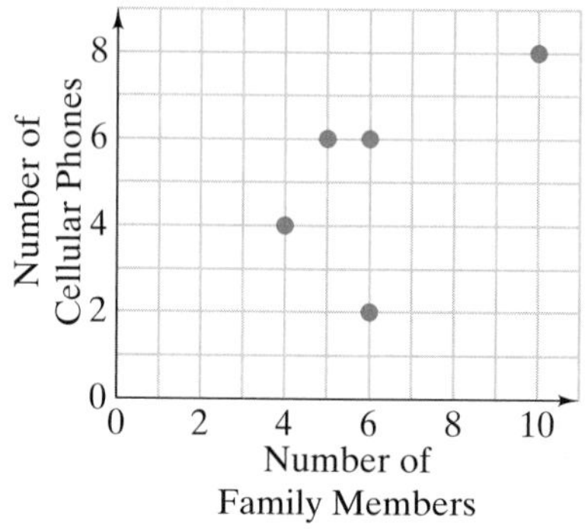

1. How many cellular phones does each person's family own? **DeWayne: 2; Tom: 8; Rita: 4; Jack: 6; Manny: 6**

ACTIVITY

The scatter plot at the right shows the grades of five students on the last English test and the length of their hair.

- Art's grade is his hair length times a multiple of 10.
- Sam shaved his head for the football game the day before the test.
- DeeDee got her usual perfect score.
- Barb's score was almost as good as Sam's.
- Wilma didn't pay attention to the directions for the test.

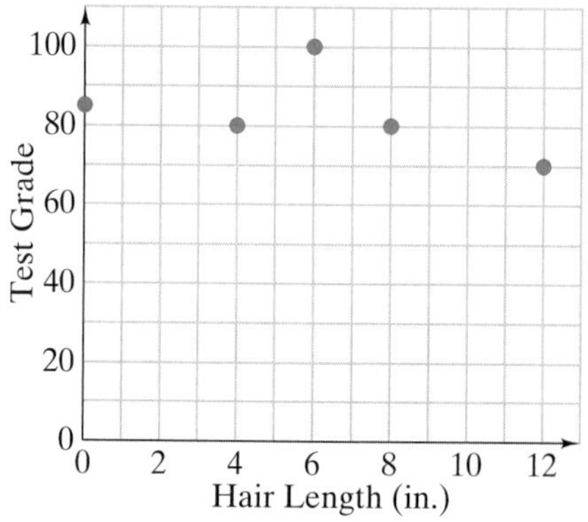

2. What was each student's test score? **Art: 80%; Sam: 85%; Dee Dee: 100%; Barb: 80%; Wilma: 70%**

ACTIVITY

3–4. Check students' work.

3. Write five clues to describe how much time five friends spent doing homework last night. Draw a scatter plot to go with your clues.
4. Exchange problems with someone in your class and solve each other's problems.

Checkpoint Quiz 2

Lessons 9-5 through 9-7

Make a stem-and-leaf plot for each set of data. 1–2. See margin.

1. test scores:
68 98 91 100 87 75 82 95 77 93 72 90 80 75 99 83 87

2. current ages of World War II veterans:
83 86 91 91 75 76 73 88 89 92 95 95 79 80 73 74 87

3. Make a box-and-whisker plot for the following set of data.
number of hours spent practicing a musical instrument per week:
1 2 8 5 9 12 4 7 5 8 11 13 8 9 2 7 6 12 11

3.

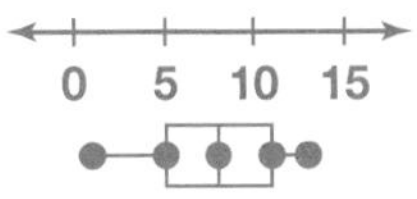

4. Make a scatter plot for the data in the table below. Describe the type of trend: *positive, negative,* or *no trend.* Draw a trend line. See margin.

Electoral Vote Data

State	CA	FL	AZ	TX	DE	AL	PA
Population (millions)	33.9	16.0	5.1	20.9	0.8	4.4	12.3
Electoral Votes	55	27	10	34	3	9	21

SOURCE: *The World Almanac*

MATH GAMES

Frequent Spinner

What You'll Need

- 2 spinners, each with three equal sections numbered 1, 2, and 3
- a copy of the number line at the right.

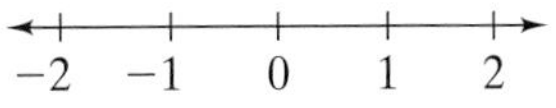

How to Play

- Player A chooses a number between −2 and 2. Player B chooses a different number.
- Each player spins a spinner. Subtract Player B's result from Player A's result. Record the difference on the number line with an ✘.
- Repeat until the ✘ marks for one player's chosen number reach a frequency of 6. That player wins the game.
- Repeat the game with Player B choosing the first number.

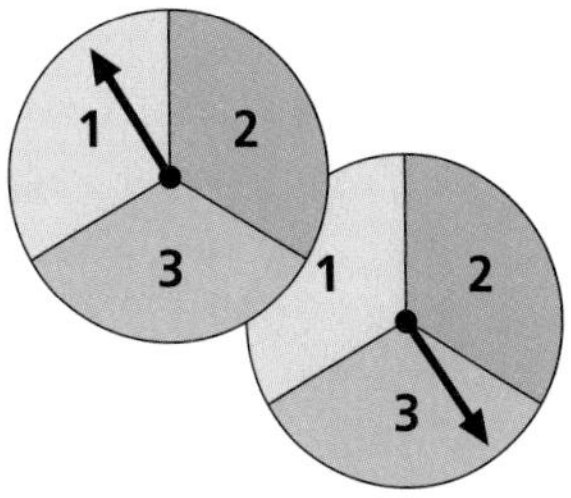

1. **Grades**

6	8
7	2 5 5 7
8	0 2 3 7 7
9	0 1 3 5 8 9
10	0

Key: 6 | 8 means 68%

2. **Ages of WWII Veterans**

7	3 3 4 5 6 9
8	0 3 6 7 8 9
9	1 1 2 5 5

Key: 7 | 3 means 73 yrs.

Checkpoint Quiz

Use this Checkpoint Quiz to check students' understanding of the skills and concepts of Lessons 9-5 through 9-7.

Resources

- All in One Teaching Resources Checkpoint Quiz 2
- ExamView Assessment Suite CD-ROM
- Success Tracker Online Intervention

MATH GAMES

Frequent Spinner

In this game, students practice subtracting integers.

For each turn, two players each spin a spinner marked with the numbers 1, 2, and 3. The results are subtracted to yield a number from −2 to +2. The resulting numbers are recorded with x's on a number line. The first player to accumulate 6 x's wins.

Guided Instruction

Students play in pairs. Have students read through the instructions before they begin to play. You may want to have a volunteer read the instructions aloud to assist English learners.

Resources

- 2 spinners, each with 3 equal sections numbered 1, 2, and 3
- copies of a number line

4. positive trend

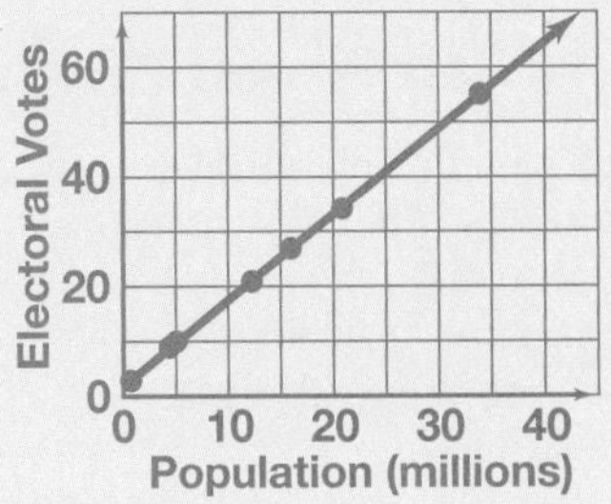

9-8

1. Plan

Objective
To represent and interpret data using circle graphs

Examples
1 Reading Circle Graphs
2 Making Circle Graphs

Math Understandings: p. 410D

Professional Development

Math Background

When the data values add to a whole, or 100%, and when there are only a few categories, a circle graph is often an effective way to present the data so that the categories can be easily compared.

More Math Background: p. 410D

Lesson Planning and Resources

See p. 410E for a list of the resources that support this lesson.

PowerPoint

Bell Ringer Practice

Check Skills You'll Need
Use student page, transparency, or PowerPoint. For intervention, direct students to:
Solving Proportions
Lesson 4-3
Extra Skills and Word Problems Practice, Ch. 4

9-8 Circle Graphs

Check Skills You'll Need

1. **Vocabulary Review** How are *ratios* and *proportions* related? See below.

Solve each proportion.

2. $\frac{2}{3} = \frac{16}{y}$ 24
3. $\frac{s}{12} = \frac{5}{2}$ 30
4. $\frac{7}{3} = \frac{r}{12}$ 28
5. $\frac{25}{p} = \frac{75}{125}$ $41\frac{2}{3}$

GO for Help Lesson 4–3

Check Skills You'll Need

1. A proportion is an equation stating that two ratios are equal.

What You'll Learn

To represent and interpret data using circle graphs

New Vocabulary circle graph, central angle

Why Learn This?

You can use a circle graph to display the ages of people who use food pantries. A circle graph shows how parts of a data set relate to the whole.

A **circle graph** is a graph of data in which an entire circle represents a whole. Each wedge, or sector, in the circle represents part of the whole. The total of the data must equal 100%, or 1.

EXAMPLE Reading Circle Graphs

1 **Food Pantries** About 21.3 million people in the United States use food pantries each year. The circle graph below shows their ages. How many people who use food pantries are 17 or younger?

Ages of People Using Food Pantries

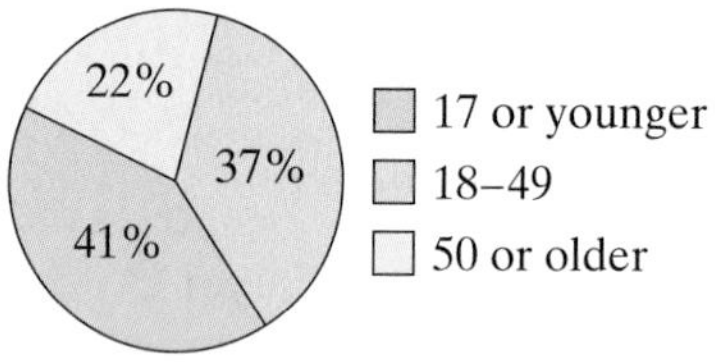

SOURCE: America's Second Harvest

Step 1 Use the key. Pink represents people 17 or younger. This means 41% of the people who use food pantries are 17 or younger.

Step 2 21,300,000 · 41% = 21,300,000 × 0.41 ENTER 8733000

About 8,733,000 people 17 or younger use food pantries.

Quick Check

1. How many people who use food pantries are 50 or older? about 4,686,000 people

Differentiated Instruction Solutions for All Learners

Special Needs L1	Below Level L2
Assist students who have a difficult time using a protractor or a compass as needed, or pair them up with a student who can do the constructions. Have someone hold the protractor so that the student who has difficulty drawing can check the angle measures. learning style: tactile	Students use drawings to review the number of degrees in a circle, 360 the degrees in a right angle, 90 and the definition of a central angle. vertex at the center of the circle learning style: verbal

To make a circle graph, you must find the measure of each central angle. A **central angle** is an angle whose vertex is the center of a circle. The sum of the measures of the central angles of a circle is 360°. Use this total to set up proportions for finding the measure of each central angle.

EXAMPLE Making Circle Graphs

Endangered Species

Group	Number of Species
Mammals	342
Birds	273
Fish	126
Reptiles	115
Clams	72
Insects	48
Other	94

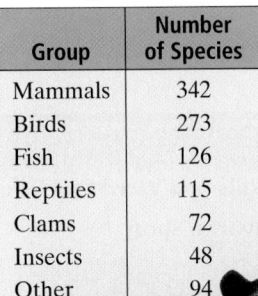

SOURCE: U.S. Fish and Wildlife Service. Go to **PHSchool.com** for a data update. Web Code: asg-9041

2 **Environment** Make a circle graph for the data in the table at the left.

Step 1 Find the total number of species.

$$342 + 273 + 126 + 115 + 72 + 48 + 94 = 1{,}070 \quad \leftarrow \textbf{Add.}$$

Step 2 Use proportions to find the measures of the central angles.

$\frac{342}{1{,}070} = \frac{m}{360°}$, so $m \approx 115°$ $\quad$ $\frac{273}{1{,}070} = \frac{b}{360°}$, so $b \approx 92°$

$\frac{126}{1{,}070} = \frac{f}{360°}$, so $f \approx 42°$ $\quad$ $\frac{115}{1{,}070} = \frac{r}{360°}$, so $r \approx 39°$

$\frac{72}{1{,}070} = \frac{c}{360°}$, so $c \approx 24°$ $\quad$ $\frac{48}{1{,}070} = \frac{i}{360°}$, so $i \approx 16°$

$\frac{94}{1{,}070} = \frac{o}{360°}$, so $o \approx 32°$

Step 3 Use a compass to draw a circle. Mark the center of the circle and draw a radius. Construct the central angles with a protractor.

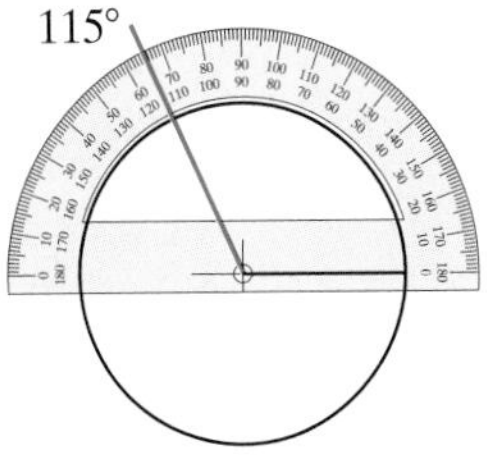

Step 4 Calculate the percents of each group by dividing the number of species by the total number, 1,070.

Step 5 Label each sector and title your graph. Set up a key to make the graph easier to read.

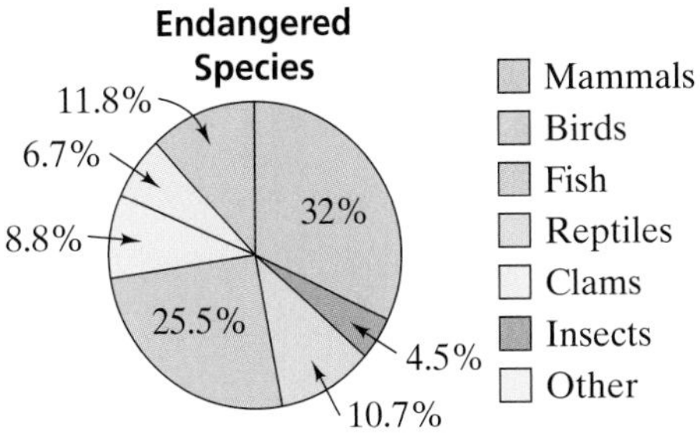

Quick Check

2. Make a circle graph for the data below. See back of book.

Fuel Used by Types of Vehicles (billions of gallons)

Cars	Vans, Pickups, SUVs	Trucks	Other
75	55	37	1

SOURCE: U.S. Census Bureau. Go to **PHSchool.com** for a data update. Web Code: asg-9041

2. Teach

Activity Lab

Use before the lesson.

All in One Teaching Resources

Activity Lab 9-8: Circle Graphs

Guided Instruction

Technology Tip

Students can use graphing calculators to make bar and circle graphs of the data in Example 2. Have them discuss the effectiveness of each representation.

PowerPoint Additional Examples

1 Use this circle graph for a school with a total enrollment of 1,308 students. How many students are there in the eighth grade? 476

Central Middle School Enrollment (by Grade)

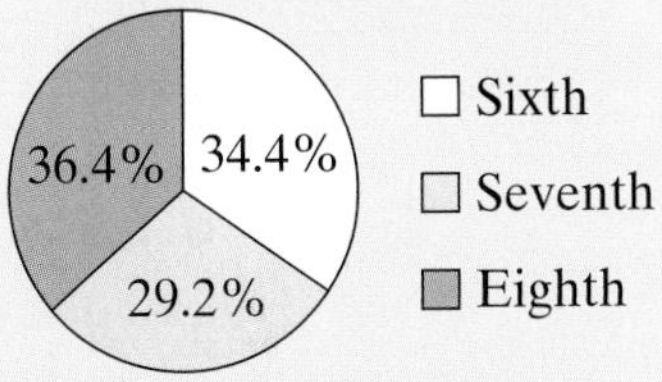

2 Make a circle graph for the results of a survey of students' favorite season.

Favorite Season	Number
Spring	20
Summer	53
Fall	28
Winter	19

See back of book for graph.

All in One Teaching Resources

- Daily Notetaking Guide 9-8 L3
- Adapted Notetaking 9-8 L1

Closure

- Explain how a circle graph represents data. Circles represent a whole and each sector is a part of the whole.

Advanced Learners L4

Students make a chart showing the degrees in the central angle for 10%, 25%, 30%, 50%, and 75%. 36°, 90°, 108°, 180°, 270°

learning style: visual

English Language Learners ELL

Help students make sense of the proportions for finding the measures of central angles. Ask: *Why are we using* $\frac{m}{360°}$? The sum of the measures of the central angles equals 360° and the measure of each central angle m is a portion of 360°.

learning style: verbal

3. Practice

Assignment Guide

Check Your Understanding
Go over Exercises 1–3 in class before assigning the Homework Exercises.

Homework Exercises

A	Practice by Example	4–9
B	Apply Your Skills	10–13
C	Challenge	14
	Test Prep and Mixed Review	15–17

Homework Quick Check
To check students' understanding of key skills and concepts, go over Exercises 4, 8, 11, 12, and 13.

Differentiated Instruction Resources

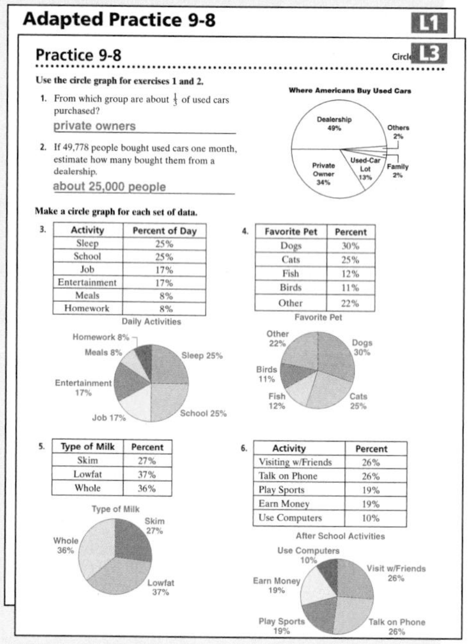
Adapted Practice 9-8 L1

Practice 9-8 Circle L3

Use the circle graph for exercises 1 and 2.

1. From which group are about $\frac{1}{3}$ of used cars purchased? private owners
2. If 49,778 people bought used cars one month, estimate how many bought them from a dealership. about 25,000 people

Make a circle graph for each set of data.

3.

Activity	Percent of Day
Sleep	25%
School	25%
Job	17%
Entertainment	17%
Meals	8%
Homework	8%

4.

Favorite Pet	Percent
Dogs	30%
Cats	25%
Fish	12%
Birds	11%
Other	22%

5.

Type of Milk	Percent
Skim	27%
Lowfat	37%
Whole	36%

6.

Activity	Percent
Visiting w/Friends	26%
Talk on Phone	26%
Play Sports	19%
Earn Money	19%
Use Computers	10%

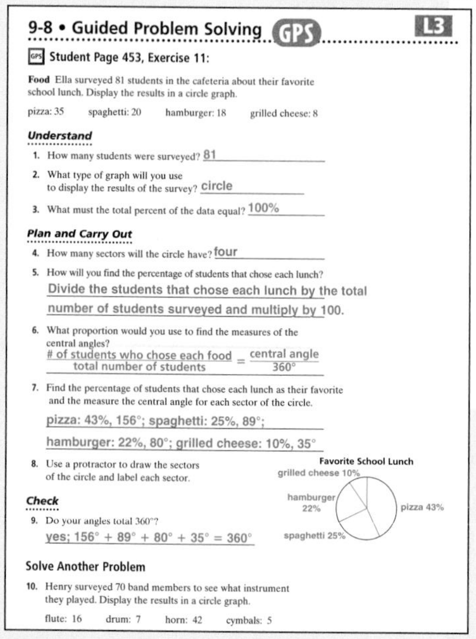
9-8 • Guided Problem Solving GPS L3

Student Page 453, Exercise 11:

Food Ella surveyed 81 students in the cafeteria about their favorite school lunch. Display the results in a circle graph.

pizza: 35 spaghetti: 20 hamburger: 18 grilled cheese: 8

Understand

1. How many students were surveyed? 81
2. What type of graph will you use to display the results of the survey? circle
3. What must the total percent of the data equal? 100%

Plan and Carry Out

4. How many sectors will the circle have? four
5. How will you find the percentage of students that chose each lunch? Divide the students that chose each lunch by the total number of students surveyed and multiply by 100.
6. What proportion would you use to find the measures of the central angles? $\frac{\text{\# of students who chose each food}}{\text{total number of students}} = \frac{\text{central angle}}{360^\circ}$
7. Find the percentage of students that chose each lunch as their favorite and the measure the central angle for each sector of the circle. pizza: 43%, 156°; spaghetti: 25%, 89°; hamburger: 22%, 80°; grilled cheese: 10%, 35°
8. Use a protractor to draw the sectors of the circle and label each sector.

Check

9. Do your angles total 360°? yes; 156° + 89° + 80° + 35° = 360°

Solve Another Problem

10. Henry surveyed 70 band members to see what instrument they played. Display the results in a circle graph.

flute: 16 drum: 7 horn: 42 cymbals: 5

Check Your Understanding

1. **Vocabulary** What is the sum of the measures of the central angles of a circle? 360°
2. Use the circle graph. How much money does the graph allow for lunch? $10.84
3. **Reasoning** Explain why the key on a circle graph is important. It identifies each sector.

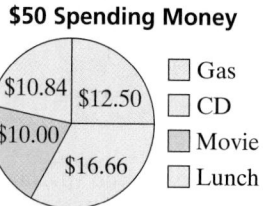

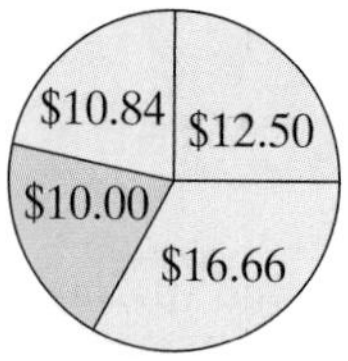

Homework Exercises

For more exercises, see Extra Skills and Word Problems.

GO for Help

For Exercises	See Examples
4–7	1
8–9	2

A **Survey A survey asked 200 students about their favorite sport. The circle graph shows the results.**

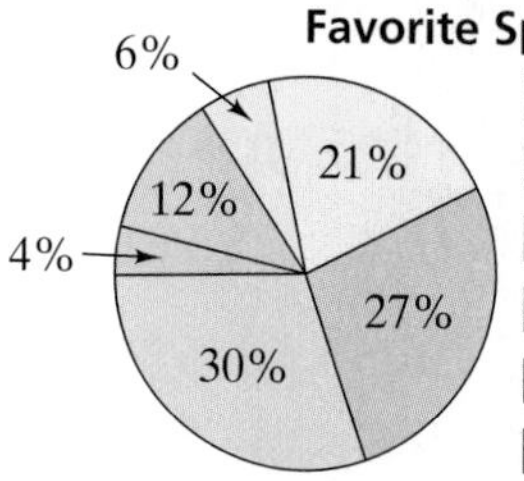

4. Which sport was chosen by the most students? football
5. How many students chose each sport? football: 60; baseball: 54; soccer: 42; basketball: 24; swimming: 12; tennis: 8
6. Suppose 90 of the students said their favorite sport was football. How many students in all would have been surveyed? 300 students
7. **Reasoning** If the percents were not written on the graph, could you still find the sport that had the least percent of votes? Explain. Yes; it would be the smallest sector.

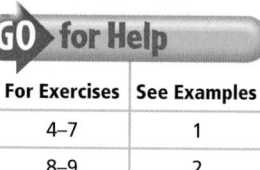

Test Prep Tip
When the data are in percents, set up a proportion.

$$\frac{\text{percent}}{100} = \frac{\text{central angle}}{360^\circ}$$

Make a circle graph for each set of data. 8–9. See margin.

8. **Favorite Books**

Book Type	People
Adventure	82
Romance	86
Horror	22
Science Fiction	10

9. **Vehicles Owned**

Vehicle Type	Percent
Small	28
Mid-size	48
Large	7
Luxury	17

B **GPS** 10. **Guided Problem Solving** A doctor surveyed patients who ran a mile or more each day. Display the data in a circle graph. See margin.

Miles	More than 6	6	5	4	3	Less than 3
Number of Patients	34	29	41	73	65	98

- Find the total number of patients.
- Use proportions to find the measures of the six central angles.

8.
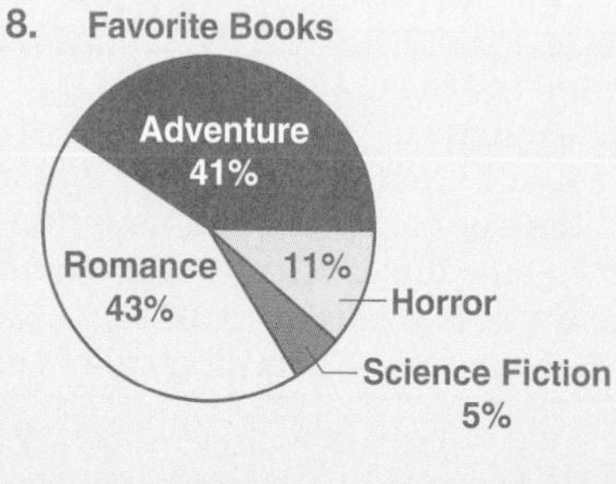

9.
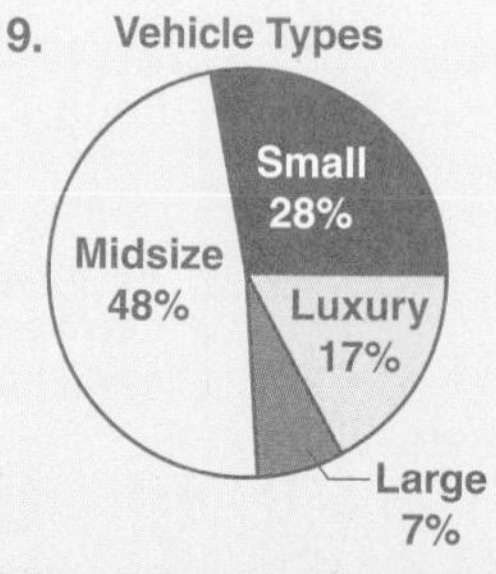

10.
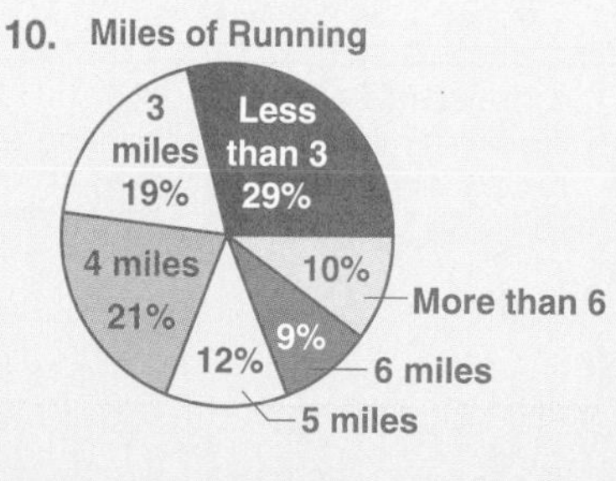

GO Online
Homework Video Tutor
Visit: PHSchool.com
Web Code: ase-0908

11. Food Ella surveyed 81 students in the cafeteria about their favorite school lunch. Display the results in a circle graph. See margin.

pizza: 35 spaghetti: 20 hamburger: 18 grilled cheese: 8

12. Writing in Math If the data for a budget is given in percents rather than dollars, would you make a circle graph or a bar graph of the data? Explain your choice. Circle graph; it allows you to show all the parts as a whole.

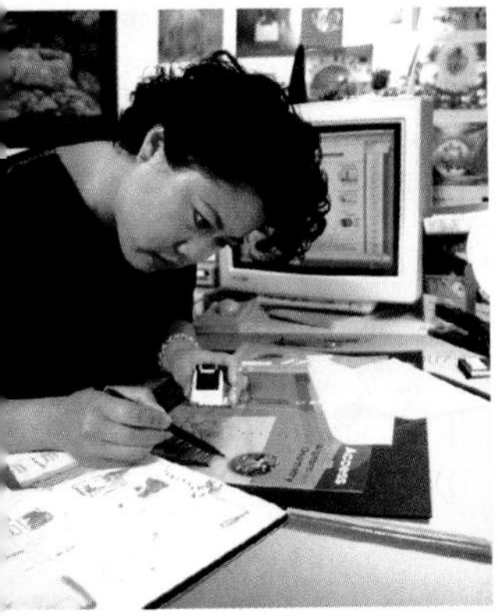

Careers Graphic artists paste up layouts and photos to get magazines ready to be printed.

13. Publishing A magazine conducted a survey about the kinds of images women prefer to see on magazine covers. Out of 400 women surveyed, 17.7% preferred images of models, 37.4% preferred images of athletes, and 44.9% preferred images of other celebrities.

a. Display the results in a circle graph. 13a–c. See margin.

b. About how many women surveyed preferred images of athletes?

c. How many women did *not* prefer images of other celebrities?

14. Challenge The bar graph shows the results of a survey that asked, "What color is your cell phone cover?" Display the data in a circle graph. Which graph do you think is a more appropriate display of the data? Explain. See margin.

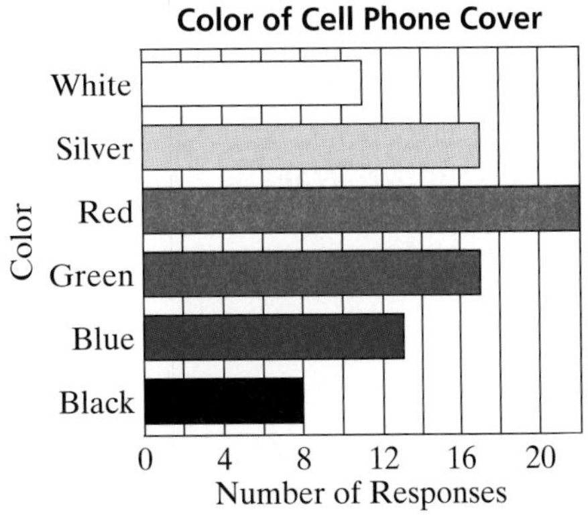

Test Prep and Mixed Review

Practice

Multiple Choice

15. The table shows a budget. Which graph best represents the data? B

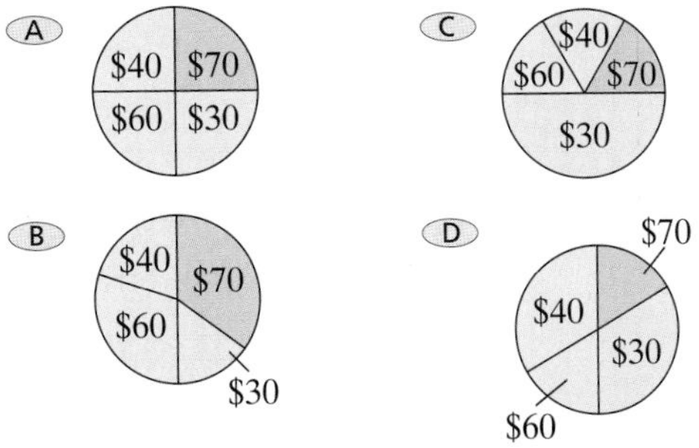

Weekly Budget

Item	Amount
Meals	$70
Recreation	$30
Bills	$60
Savings	$40

16. What type of trend would you expect to see in a scatter plot comparing mosquito population and the sale of insect repellent? F

(F) positive (G) negative (H) none (J) opposite

17. Make a scatter plot of the data set. If possible, draw a trend line. See margin.

height (in.): 56 52 55 47 58 60 50 39 58 45 54 61 45 34

weight (lb): 78 63 67 52 81 92 60 34 83 47 73 98 45 31

GO for Help

For Exercise	See Lesson
17	9-7

Online lesson quiz, PHSchool.com, Web Code: asa-0908

4. Assess & Reteach

PowerPoint

Lesson Quiz

The circle graph shows the survey results of 400 students.

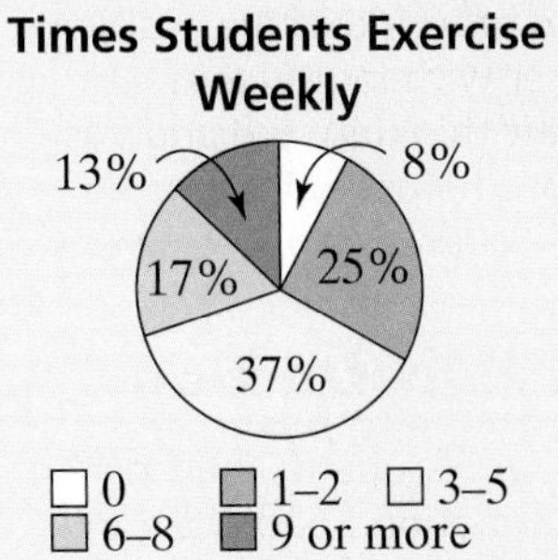

1. What percent exercise 3–5 times each week? 37%
2. How many exercise 6–8 times each week? 68 students
3. A fruit seller has the following amounts of fruit at his stand. Make a circle graph using this data.

Favorite Fruit

Fruit	Number
Mango	80
Banana	90
Pear	40
Papaya	30

See back of book.

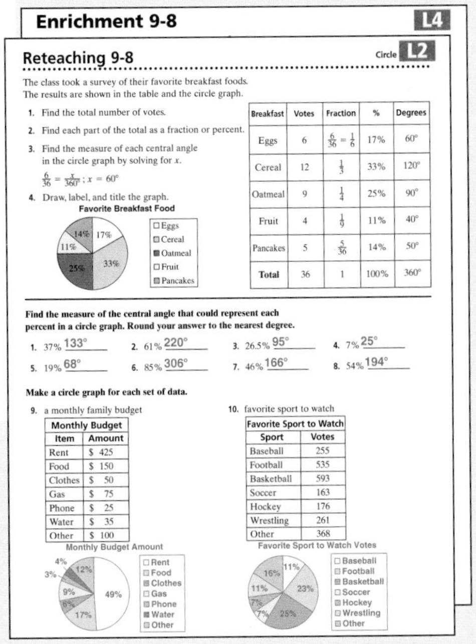

Enrichment 9-8 L4

Reteaching 9-8 Circle L2

The class took a survey of their favorite breakfast foods. The results are shown in the table and the circle graph.

1. Find the total number of votes.
2. Find each part of the total as a fraction or percent.
3. Find the measure of each central angle in the circle graph by solving for x. $\frac{6}{36} = \frac{x}{360°}$; $x = 60°$
4. Draw, label, and title the graph.

Favorite Breakfast Food: Eggs 17%, Cereal 33%, Oatmeal 25%, Fruit 11%, Pancakes 14%

Breakfast	Votes	Fraction	%	Degrees
Eggs	6	$\frac{6}{36} = \frac{1}{6}$	17%	60°
Cereal	12	$\frac{1}{3}$	33%	120°
Oatmeal	9	$\frac{1}{4}$	25%	90°
Fruit	4	$\frac{1}{9}$	11%	40°
Pancakes	5	$\frac{5}{36}$	14%	50°
Total	36	1	100%	360°

Find the measure of the central angle that could represent each percent in a circle graph. Round your answer to the nearest degree.

1. 37% 133°
2. 61% 220°
3. 26.5% 95°
4. 7% 25°
5. 19% 68°
6. 85% 306°
7. 46% 166°
8. 54% 194°

Make a circle graph for each set of data.

9. a monthly family budget

Monthly Budget	
Item	Amount
Rent	$ 425
Food	$ 150
Clothes	$ 50
Gas	$ 75
Phone	$ 25
Water	$ 35
Other	$ 100

Monthly Budget Amount: Rent 49%, Food 17%, Clothes 6%, Gas 9%, Phone 3%, Water 4%, Other 12%

10. favorite sport to watch

Favorite Sport to Watch	
Sport	Votes
Baseball	255
Football	535
Basketball	593
Soccer	163
Hockey	176
Wrestling	261
Other	368

Favorite Sport to Watch Votes: Baseball 11%, Football 23%, Basketball 25%, Soccer 7%, Hockey 7%, Wrestling 11%, Other 16%

Alternative Assessment

Students are asked their favorite type of pet. They make a circle graph of the data.

11, 13–14, 17. See back of book.

Test Prep

Resources

For additional practice with a variety of test item formats:

- Test-Taking Strategies, p. 461
- Test Prep, p. 465
- Test-Taking Strategies with Transparencies

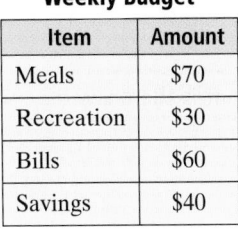

GPS Guided Problem Solving

Equations and Graphs

It is important for students to use their understanding of different types of graphs to solve problems. Together with logical and algebraic thinking, the analysis of graphs helps students solve problems in real-world contexts.

Guided Instruction

Discuss with students that some of the information needed to solve problems comes from written information and other information may come from graphical information.

Work through the solution strategy. Have students identify what they know and what they want to find out. Ask:

- *What does the use of a circle graph tell you about the total percents in this problem?* **The percents add up to 100%.**
- *How do you know to make the variable x represent the uphill percent?* **Sample: The problem information describes the downhill percent and the flat percent in terms of the uphill percent.**

Have students articulate that when they add the three variable expressions, the sum should be 100 percent: $x + 5x + \frac{2}{3}x = 100$.

Error Prevention!

Remind students that x is understood to mean $1x$. Explain aloud for the benefit of auditory learners: *Add the coefficients of* x: *1*x *plus 5*x *plus* $\frac{2}{3}$x adds up to $6\frac{2}{3}$x.

GPS Guided Problem Solving

Equations and Graphs

Sports The percent of mountain bike accidents that happen on downhill slopes is 5 times the percent that happen on uphill slopes. The percent that happen on flat areas is two thirds of the percent that happen on uphill slopes. What percent should you use for each part of a circle graph representing this data?

Location of Mountain Bike Accidents

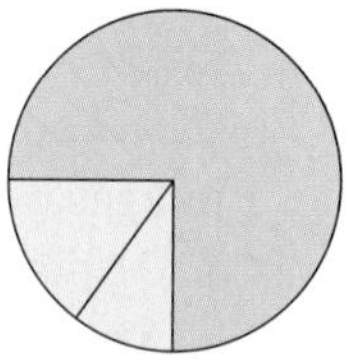

What You Might Think	What You Might Write
What do I know? What do I want to find out?	The downhill percent is 5 times the uphill percent. The flat percent is $\frac{2}{3}$ of the uphill percent. The total for a circle graph is 100%. I need to find the percents for each part of the graph.
What equation can I write?	Let x = uphill percent. Then, 5x = downhill percent and $\frac{2}{3}$x = flat percent. uphill + downhill + flat = 100 percent $x + 5x + \frac{2}{3}x = 100$ $6\frac{2}{3}x = 100$ $x = 15$
What is the answer?	The percents for the circle graph are: uphill: 15% downhill: 5 × 15% = 75% flat: $\frac{2}{3}$ × 15% = 10%.
Is the answer reasonable?	The sum of the percents is 15 + 75 + 10 = 100. The numbers make sense for the size of the sections of the graph. The answer is reasonable.

Think It Through

1. How was 15 found in the work shown? Like terms were combined to get $6\frac{2}{3}x = 100$, and each side was divided by $6\frac{2}{3}$.
2. **Reasoning** What does it mean to say that the numbers make sense for the size of the sections in the graph? The biggest section looks like $\frac{3}{4}$ of the circle, so 75% makes sense. The other two sections look like about 25% of the circle with one being slightly less than the other.

Exercises

3. **Fishing** The percent of fish in a lake that are smallmouth bass is twice the percent that are white perch. The percent of fish that are sunfish is one third the percent that are white perch. What percent should you use for each part of a circle graph representing this data? small mouth bass: 60%; white perch: 30%; sunfish: 10%

Types of Fish

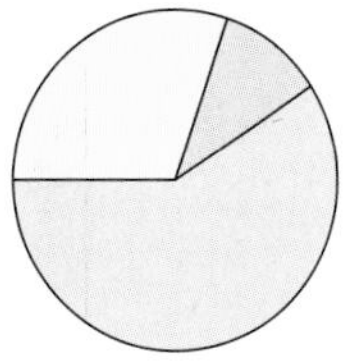

Use the table below for Exercises 4–6.

Available Drink Sizes at a Convenience Store

Year	Sizes Available (oz)
1973	12, 20
1976	12, 16, 20
1978	12, 16, 20, 32
1983	12, 16, 20, 32, 44
1988	12, 16, 20, 32, 44, 64
2003	12, 20, 32, 44, 64
2005	20, 32, 44, 64

4. Make a scatter plot of the data. Use the year on the horizontal scale and the number of ounces on the vertical scale. See margin.
5. Describe the trend in the data. positive
6. **Writing in Math** Predict the largest available drink size in the year 2010. Is this a realistic drink size? Explain.
7. The data below show the largest major earthquakes around the world over a ten-year period, measured on the Richter Scale.

   7.1 7.8 7.3 7.2 6.8 6.9 8.1 7.3 6.5 7.3

   Make a box-and-whisker plot. About how many data values fall between the lower and upper quartiles? See margin.

6. Answers may vary. Sample: 70 oz; no, because the largest drink size probably will not continue to increase as quickly now that the largest size is so big.

Exercises

For Exercise 3, have students check their work by using a graphing calculator or spreadsheet program to make the circle graph for a lake with 240 total fish.

For Exercise 7, have students use a graphing calculator to make the box-and- whisker plot.

Differentiated Instruction

Special Needs L1

Review the differences between a circle graph, line graph, scatter plot, and box-and whisker plot. Have students identify each type of graph and have them explain the type of information each type contains. Have students name graphs or data displays they have studied in this chapter that are not shown on these two pages. Sample: bar graph, histogram, Venn diagram, stem-and-leaf plot

4.

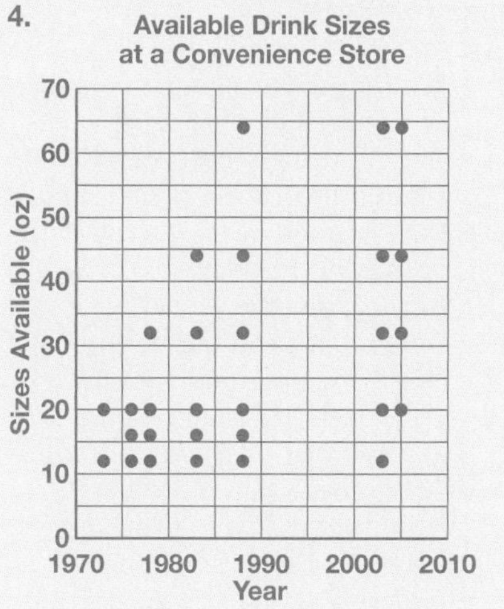

7.

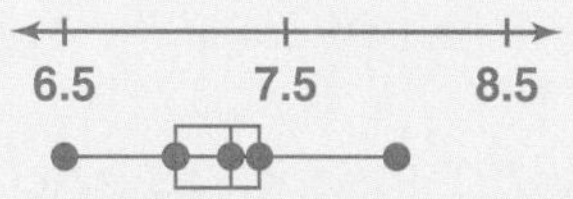

about half of the data values

Resources

- graph paper

9-9

1. Plan

Objective
To choose appropriate graphs to represent different data

Examples
1 Choosing an Appropriate Graph
2 Application: Weather

Math Understandings: p. 410D

Professional Development

Math Background

Data are usually suited to a particular kind of graph:

- Data showing change over time: *line graph;*
- Data that show parts of a whole that add to 100%: *circle graph;*
- Data divided into intervals and describing frequency: *histogram;*
- Data in large amounts, where clustering and medians are important but exact numbers are not: *box-and-whisker plot;*
- Data where values are fairly close together, and exact values are important: *stem-and-leaf plot.*

More Math Background: p. 410D

Lesson Planning and Resources

See p. 410E for a list of the resources that support this lesson.

PowerPoint

Bell Ringer Practice

Check Skills You'll Need
Use student page, transparency, or PowerPoint. For intervention, direct students to:

Displaying Frequency
Lesson 9-2
Extra Skills and Word Problems Practice, Ch. 9

9-9 Choosing an Appropriate Graph

Check Skills You'll Need

1. **Vocabulary Review** What do you call the number of times a data item occurs? frequency
2. Make a frequency table for the data set: 2, 0, 8, 3, 4, 1, 2.5, 0, 3, 1.5, 4, 8, 7, 2, 0, 3.5, 6.5. See below.

GO for Help Lesson 9-2

Check Skills You'll Need

2.

Values	Frequency
0–1.9	5
2–3.9	6
4–5.9	2
6–7.9	2
8–9.9	2

What You'll Learn

To choose appropriate graphs to represent different data

Why Learn This?

You can use graphs to describe the population in a city and how it changes over time. To do this effectively, you must be able to choose the appropriate graph.

EXAMPLE Choosing an Appropriate Graph

1 You want to graph data on the percent of city dwellers in the United States every decade since 1900. Which is more appropriate for displaying the data, a line graph or a circle graph? Explain your choice.

A circle graph shows percents, but it does not show change over time. A line graph shows change over time.

Since the percent of city dwellers in the United States changes over time, a line graph is more appropriate than a circle graph.

Quick Check

1. Choose the appropriate graph to display each set of data. Explain your choice. See left.
   a. life spans of selected animals: bar graph or scatter plot?
   b. average household income and number of cars: histogram or scatter plot?
   c. price of a gallon of gas over a twelve-month period: line graph or circle graph?

1a. Bar graph; scatter plots need to be numerical; bar graphs represent categorical data.
b. Scatter plot; you are looking to see if there is a trend or a relationship.
c. Line graph; it shows change over time.

When presenting data, the idea you want to express influences the type of graph you choose.

Differentiated Instruction Solutions for All Learners

Special Needs L1
Students who have difficulty drawing circle graphs or plotting points on a graph can still have some tasks assigned to them. For example, they may draw and label the axes on a line graph or decide the intervals for line graphs and histograms.
learning style: visual

Below Level L2
Sketch a line graph, circle graph, histogram, box-and-whisker plot, and stem-and-leaf plot (without specific numbers or data). Students are asked to name each type.
learning style: verbal

EXAMPLE Application: Weather

Meteorologists use graphs to analyze atmospheric data.

2 The table shows the number of hurricanes that have struck the mainland of the United States in past decades. Decide which type of graph would be most appropriate to illustrate the frequency of these hurricanes over time. Explain your choice. Then draw the graph.

Hurricanes in the United States

Decade	1900s	1910s	1920s	1930s	1940s	1950s	1960s	1970s	1980s	1990s
Number of Hurricanes	15	20	15	17	23	18	15	12	16	14

SOURCE: *The Weather Almanac*

The table divides the data into intervals. It also describes the frequency of hurricanes. A histogram is the most appropriate graph.

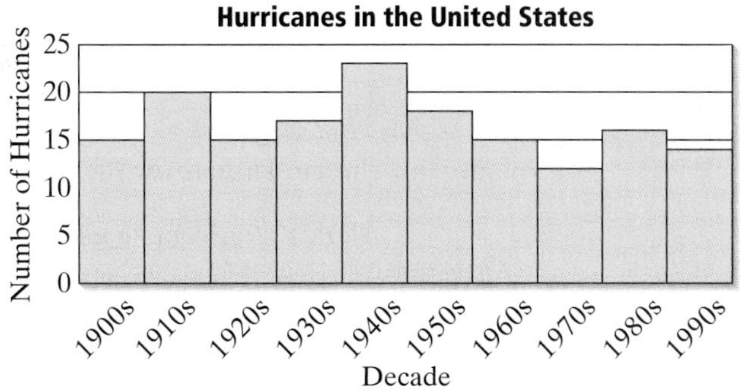

GO for Help

For help making histograms, go to Lesson 9-2, Example 3.

Quick Check

2. Decide which type of graph would be most appropriate for the data in the table. Explain your choice. Then draw the graph. See back of book.

Weekly Budget

Budget Item	Lunch	Recreation	Clothes	Savings
Amount	$27.00	$13.50	$31.50	$18.00

Check Your Understanding

1–3. Check students' work.

Vocabulary **Summarize the types of graphs by following these steps.**

1. Make a three-column table. In the first column, list the types of graphs you have studied in this chapter.
2. In the second column, sketch an example of each type of graph.
3. In the third column, list the different purposes for which you can use each graph. These may include showing frequency, comparing sets of data, showing changes over time, and showing parts of a whole.

Advanced Learners L4

Students find graphed data in print or on the Internet. They graph the data in another form or explain why one form is more appropriate.

learning style: verbal

English Language Learners ELL

Students work in pairs to create a list of types of data and which types of data displays are best suited for the data. They share their ideas with the class and create a list to post in the classroom.

learning style: verbal

2. Teach

Activity Lab

Use before the lesson.

All in One Teaching Resources

Activity Lab 9-9: Choosing an Appropriate Graph

Guided Instruction

Technology Tip

Have students use a graphing calculator to generate box-and-whisker plots for the data in the stem-and-leaf plot in Exercise 13 on page 436. Have them discuss the effectiveness of the different representations.

PowerPoint

Additional Examples

1 Choose the appropriate graph to display the data about a survey of students' favorite type of music. Explain your choice. 1–2. See back of book.

2 This table shows membership in the Computer Club over several years. Decide which type of graph would be most appropriate. Explain your choice and draw the graph.

Year	Number of Members
1999	11
2000	15
2001	21
2002	22
2003	25

All in One Teaching Resources

- Daily Notetaking Guide 9-9 L3
- Adapted Notetaking 9-9 L1

Closure

- *What factors go into your decision about what kind of graph is appropriate for a given set of data?* Sample: the amount of data and whether the data show a change over time or are parts of a whole or occur in intervals

3. Practice

Assignment Guide

Check Your Understanding
Go over Exercises 1–3 in class before assigning the Homework Exercises.

Homework Exercises

A	Practice by Example	4–10
B	Apply Your Skills	11–16
C	Challenge	17
	Test Prep and Mixed Review	18–24

Homework Quick Check
To check students' understanding of key skills and concepts, go over Exercises 5, 8, 11, 15, and 16.

Technology Tip
Have students use graphing calculators or computer software to generate several representations for Exercises 8–11. Have them compare how each representation displays the data.

Differentiated Instruction Resources

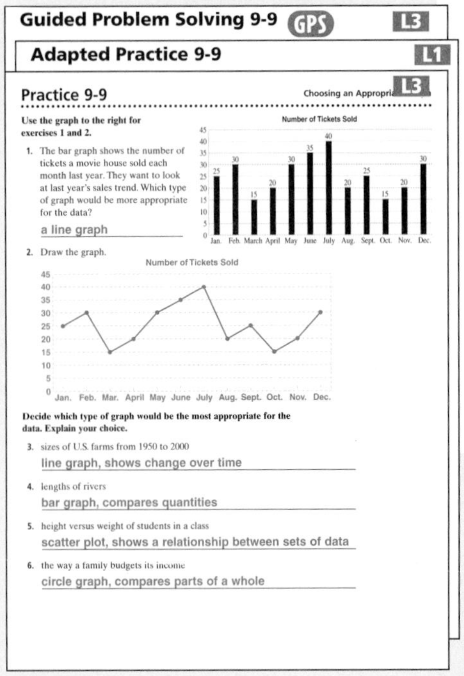
Guided Problem Solving 9-9 GPS L3
Adapted Practice 9-9 L1
Practice 9-9 Choosing an Appropri... L3

Use the graph to the right for exercises 1 and 2.

1. The bar graph shows the number of tickets a movie house sold each month last year. They want to look at last year's sales trend. Which type of graph would be more appropriate for the data? a line graph

2. Draw the graph.

Decide which type of graph would be the most appropriate for the data. Explain your choice.

3. sizes of U.S. farms from 1950 to 2000 — line graph, shows change over time
4. lengths of rivers — bar graph, compares quantities
5. height versus weight of students in a class — scatter plot, shows a relationship between sets of data
6. the way a family budgets its income — circle graph, compares parts of a whole

Homework Exercises

For more exercises, see Extra Skills and Word Problems.

GO for Help

For Exercises	See Examples
4–7	1
8–10	2

A **Choose the appropriate graph for each data set. Explain your choice.**

4. inches of rain and the temperature each day for a given city: histogram or scatter plot?

4. Scatter plot; if there are two sets of data, you can see if there is a relationship.

5. **Percent of Total Music Sales Made Up by Country Music**

Year	1997	1998	1999	2000	2001	2002	2003
Percent	14.4	14.7	10.8	10.7	10.5	10.7	10.4

SOURCE: Recording Industry Association of America

line graph or scatter plot?

5. Line graph; this graph is better for showing data over time.

6. number of boys and number of girls who use a park each day: box-and-whisker plot or double bar graph?

6. Double bar graph; this graph can show a comparison of the two groups.

7. 40 people's choices of the five best cities to visit: stem-and-leaf plot or circle graph?

7. Circle graph; a circle graph is a good way to compare parts of a whole.

Decide which type of graph would be most appropriate for the data. Explain your choice. Then draw the graph. 8–9. See margin.

8. **Florida's Resident Population (thousands)**

Year	1999	2000	2001	2002	2003	2004
Population	15,111	16,049	16,354	16,681	16,999	17,397

SOURCE: U.S. Census Bureau. Go to **PHSchool.com** for a data update. Web Code: asg-9041

9. height (in.) of students in an eighth-grade class:
63 60 58 56 52 53 57 57 56 55 56 57 56 67 56 58 57 61

10. ages of 15 corporate executives: See left.
31 62 51 44 61 47 49 50 40 52 60 51 67 47 63

10. Stem-and-leaf plot; it shows a data set arranged in order.

3	1
4	0 4 7 7 9
5	0 1 1 2
6	0 1 2 3 7

Key: 6 | 0 means 60

B GPS

11. **Guided Problem Solving** The table shows the number of hourly workers in the United States who earn less than or more than \$10 per hour. Draw a graph for the data. See margin.
- List the types of graphs you can use to compare two data sets.
- Choose one of these types, and draw the graph.

Number of Workers Paid Hourly Rates in the United States (millions)

Age	Less Than \$10	\$10 or More
16 to 24	12.1	4.2
25 to 34	5.8	10.0
35 to 44	5.0	12.2
45 to 54	3.9	9.9
55 to 64	2.3	4.3
65 and older	1.1	0.9

SOURCE: *The World Almanac*

GO Online
Homework Video Tutor
Visit: PHSchool.com
Web Code: ase-0909

For each graph listed, describe a set of data that would be appropriate.
12–14. Check students' work.

12. scatter plot
13. circle graph
14. line plot

8. See back of book.

11, 15, 17. See back of book.

9. Box-and-whisker plot; it gives a good summary of data, including high and low, median, and upper and lower quartiles.

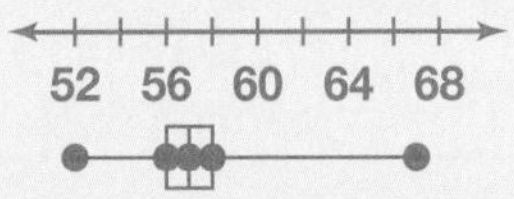

Percent of Homes in the United States With Personal Computers

Year	Percent
1994	33
1996	40
1998	44
2000	56
2002	61
2004	68

SOURCE: Consumer Electronics Association

16. Any data that represent part of a whole can be represented with a circle graph or a bar graph.

15. GPS The table at the left and the circle graph at the right show the percent of homes in the United States with personal computers in various years. 15a–b. See margin.

a. **Error Analysis** Explain why using a circle graph for this set of data is not appropriate.

b. Choose an appropriate graph for the data and then draw the graph. Explain your choice.

Percent of Homes in the United States With Personal Computers

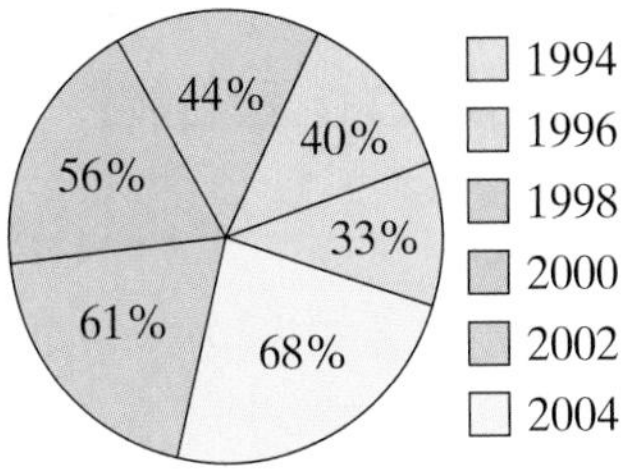

16. **Writing in Math** Describe data you can collect and display in both a bar graph and a circle graph. See left.

17. **Challenge** Which type of graph might you choose when you have too large a set of data to graph each item? Explain. See margin.

Test Prep and Mixed Review

Practice

Multiple Choice

18. The data below show the average lengths, to the nearest quarter inch, of some species of beetles. Which type of graph is most appropriate to represent the data? D

0.5 1.5 3.25 2.5 1.25 3.0 6.0 2.75 2.0 0.25 1.5 1.0
0.5 1.0 1.5 0.75 0.25 1.75 1.25 0.25 0.75 0.25

Ⓐ Line graph
Ⓑ Bar graph
Ⓒ Circle graph
Ⓓ Box-and-whisker plot

19. The graph below shows the results of a read-a-thon. Which conclusion best reflects the data in the histogram? J

Ⓕ Almost half of the participants read between 6 and 11 books.
Ⓖ Participants between the ages of 9 and 11 read the most books.
Ⓗ Most of the participants read between 9 and 11 books.
Ⓙ About one-third of the participants read between 9 and 11 books.

Read-A-Thon Participation

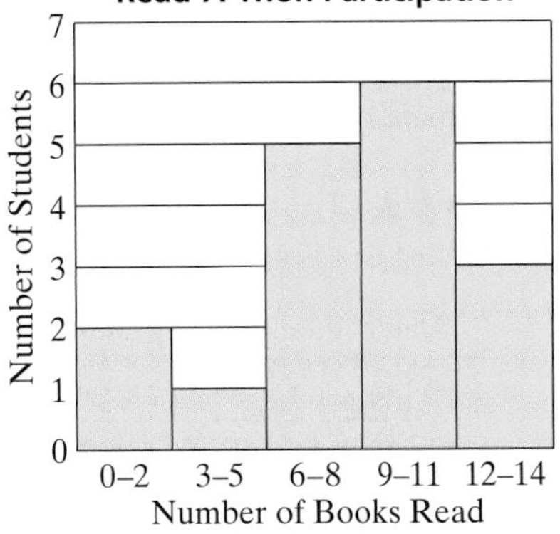

GO for Help

For Exercises	See Lesson
20–24	7-1

Find the measure of the supplement of each angle.

20. 37° 143° **21.** 95° 85° **22.** 42° 138° **23.** 170° 10° **24.** 64° 116°

4. Assess & Reteach

PowerPoint

Lesson Quiz

1. Which type of graph would be appropriate to show the daily high temperatures for May? Explain your choice. Sample: a line graph shows changes during the month

2. Five students in a sixth-grade class are surveyed about the number of hours they watched television and the number of hours they worked on homework one Sunday.

Sunday: Television vs. Homework		
Name	**Hours of television**	**Hours of homework**
Andre	2	5
Brianna	4	2
Olivia	1	4
Carter	5	1
Juan	6	3

Decide which type of graph would be most appropriate. Explain your choice.
2–3. See back of book.

3. Draw the graph of the data in Item 2.

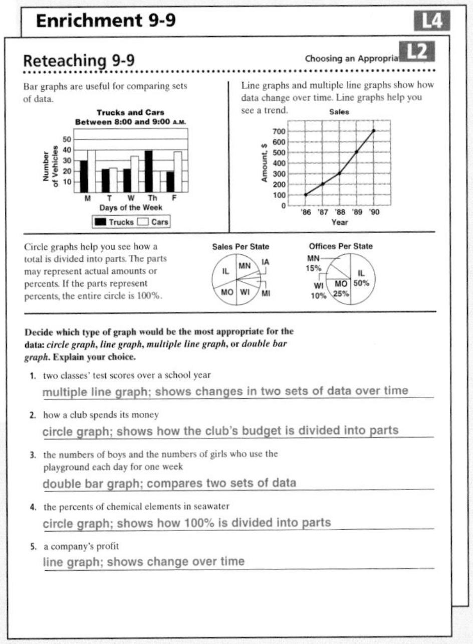
Enrichment 9-9 L4

Reteaching 9-9 Choosing an Appropria L2

Bar graphs are useful for comparing sets of data.

Line graphs and multiple line graphs show how data change over time. Line graphs help you see a trend.

Circle graphs help you see how a total is divided into parts. The parts may represent actual amounts or percents. If the parts represent percents, the entire circle is 100%.

Decide which type of graph would be the most appropriate for the data: *circle graph, line graph, multiple line graph,* or *double bar graph.* Explain your choice.

1. two classes' test scores over a school year
multiple line graph; shows changes in two sets of data over time
2. how a club spends its money
circle graph; shows how the club's budget is divided into parts
3. the numbers of boys and the numbers of girls who use the playground each day for one week
double bar graph; compares two sets of data
4. the percents of chemical elements in seawater
circle graph; shows how 100% is divided into parts
5. a company's profit
line graph; shows change over time

Alternative Assessment

Students make a table for their activities in a 24-hour school day. Have them include sleeping, attending school, eating, playing, studying, and other activities. Then have them represent the data on an appropriate graph and explain why they chose the particular graph.

Test Prep

Resources

For additional practice with a variety of test item formats:

- Test-Taking Strategies, p. 461
- Test Prep, p. 465
- Test-Taking Strategies with Transparencies

Activity Lab

Technology: Graphing Data Using Spreadsheets

Students learn how to use spreadsheet software to create an appropriate graph for a given set of data.

Guided Instruction

Technology Tip
Review how formulas instruct the computer to repeat math operations using different numbers.

Have students generate several different representations for each situation, including bar graphs, circle graphs, and line graphs. Students can also use graphing calculators to make graphs.

Exercises
Have students work in pairs on the exercises. Have each pair justify their graph choices by asking questions such as:

- *Why would a histogram be an appropriate graph to use to display the data in Exercise 1?* **Intervals of data are given; histograms show the frequencies of intervals of data.**
- *What must be true about the graph you choose for the data in Exercise 2?* **It must be able to show how parts are related to a whole or total.**

Differentiated Instruction

Special Needs L1
Review, as needed, the uses and characteristics of the different graphs covered in the chapter.

Resources

- any spreadsheet software

9-9b Activity Lab — Technology

Graphing Data Using Spreadsheets

You can use a spreadsheet program to make many types of graphs.

ACTIVITY

The data at the right show the lengths and masses of different birds' eggs.

Step 1 Enter the data into the spreadsheet.

Step 2 Choose an appropriate type of graph from the spreadsheet program. Since you are comparing two related sets of data, a scatter plot is appropriate.

	A	B
1	Length (cm)	Mass (g)
2	2.5	3.6
3	3.1	9
4	3.6	14
5	3.9	20.7
6	4.0	19

A spreadsheet has no title.

Row 1 contains the type of data being compared.

Each row represents the size of one egg. Column A is the egg's length. Column B is the egg's mass.

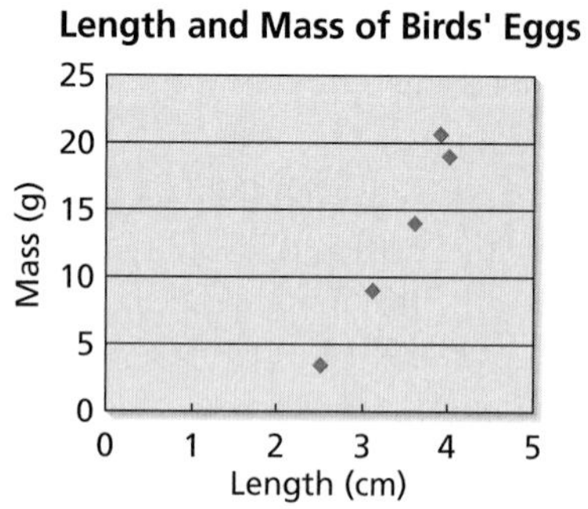

Exercises

Enter each set of data into a spreadsheet. Choose an appropriate type of graph and use the program to make each graph. 1–2. Check students' work.

1. **Annual Spending per Child by Middle Income Families in 2004**

Age (yr)	0–2	3–5	6–8	9–11	12–14	15–17
Dollars Spent	9,840	10,120	10,030	9,910	10,640	10,900

SOURCE: U.S. Department of Agriculture. Go to **PHSchool.com** for a data update. Web Code: asg-9041

2. **Bedrooms in New One-Family Houses**

Number of Bedrooms	Two or Fewer	Three	Four or More
Percent of Homes	11	51	37

SOURCE: U.S. Census Bureau. Go to **PHSchool.com** for a data update. Web Code: asg-9041

Measuring to Solve

Some test questions ask you to measure with a centimeter ruler before solving the problem.

EXAMPLE

The net at the right forms a cylinder. Measure its dimensions in centimeters. Which is closest to the surface area of the cylinder?

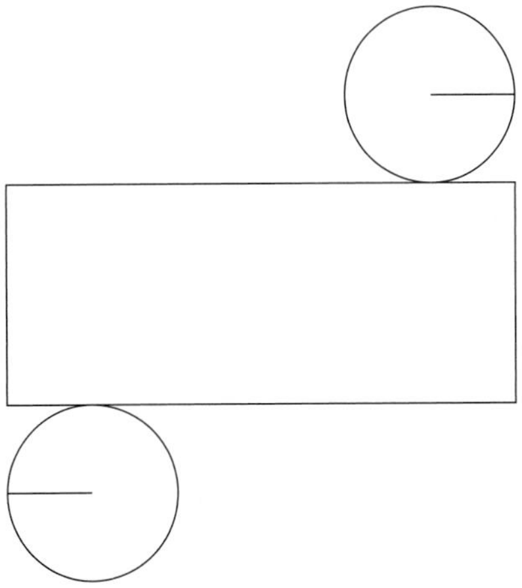

Ⓐ 6 cm^2 Ⓒ 16 cm^2
Ⓑ 11 cm^2 Ⓓ 22 cm^2

Use a centimeter ruler to measure the width of the rectangle and the radius of one of the circles. To find the surface area, use the formula for surface area of a cylinder. Use 3.14 for π.

$$\begin{aligned} \text{S.A.} &= 2\pi rh + 2\pi r^2 \\ &= 2(3.14)(1)(2.5) + 2(3.14)(1)^2 \\ &= 21.98 \end{aligned}$$

The surface area of the cylinder is about 22 cm^2.
The correct answer is choice D.

Exercises

1. A square bead has the net shown at the right. Measure the dimensions of the net. Which is closest to the lateral surface area of the bead? **B**

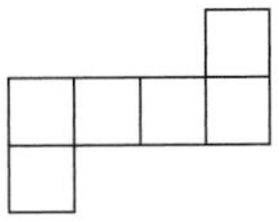

Ⓐ 0.5 cm^2 Ⓑ 1 cm^2 Ⓒ 1.5 cm^2 Ⓓ 2 cm^2

2. Measure the net of the square pyramid below.

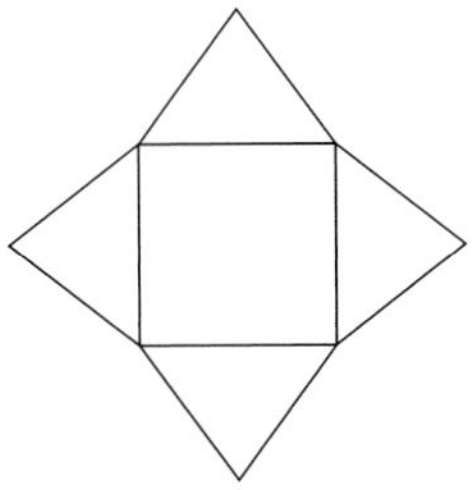

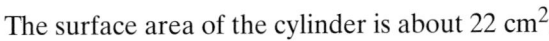

Which is closest to the total surface area of the pyramid? **H**

Ⓕ 2.5 cm^2 Ⓖ 3.75 cm^2 Ⓗ 5.25 cm^2 Ⓙ 5.5 cm^2

Measuring to Solve

Since some standardized tests ask students to measure lengths and use the measurements to solve problems, this activity provides students with practice using a centimeter ruler for measuring.

Guided Instruction

Provide centimeter rulers for pairs of students. Before doing the activity, have students identify the centimeter markings.

Differentiated Instruction

Special Needs L1
Review with students the formulas for surface area and volume and write them on the chalkboard. Have volunteers read each formula aloud.

Resources

Test-Taking Strategies with Transparencies
- Transparency 13
- Practice sheet, p. 33

Test-Taking Strategies with Transparencies

Test-Taking Strategies: Measuring to Solve

Some questions ask you to measure with a protractor or ruler to solve a problem.

Example What is the area of the circle below, to the nearest square centimeter?

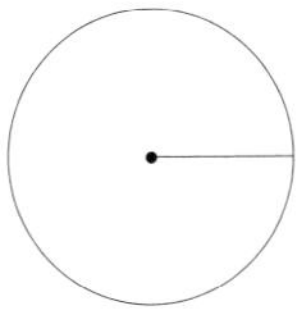

A. 9 cm^2 B. 19 cm^2
C. 28 cm^2 D. 113 cm^2

Use a centimeter ruler to measure the radius of the circle. To find the area of the circle, use the formula for the area of a circle.

$A = \pi r^2$

$A = \pi(3)^2 = \pi \times 9 \approx 28.27$

The area of the circle is about 28 cm^2. The answer is choice C.

Example Find the measure of angle *S* in the polygon below.

F. 83° G. 87° H. 93° J. 97°

The side of the angle falls between the 85° and 90° marks on the same scale that side SW crosses at its zero point. The measure of the angle is about 87°. The answer is choice G.

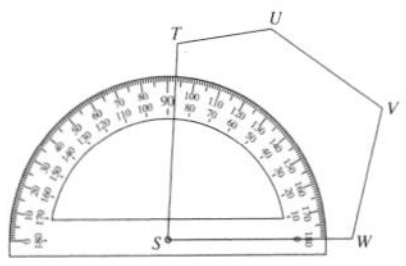

Chapter 9 Review

Chapter 9 Review

Resources

Student Edition
Extra Skills and Word Problems Practice, Ch. 9, p. 620
English/Spanish Glossary, p. 650
Formulas and Properties, p. 648
Tables, p. 643

All in One Teaching Resources
- Vocabulary and Study Skills 9F **L3**

Differentiated Instruction
Spanish Vocabulary Workbook with Study Skills **ELL**
Interactive Textbook
- Audio Glossary

Online Vocabulary Quiz

Success Tracker™
Online at PHSchool.com

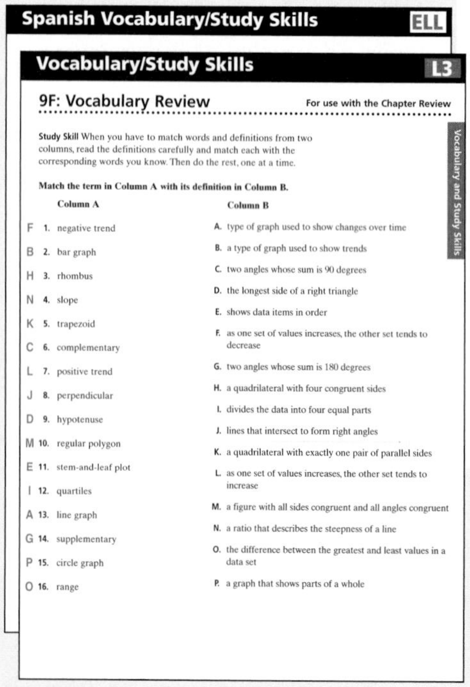
Spanish Vocabulary/Study Skills ELL

Vocabulary/Study Skills L3

9F: Vocabulary Review — For use with the Chapter Review

Study Skill When you have to match words and definitions from two columns, read the definitions carefully and match each with the corresponding words you know. Then do the rest, one at a time.

Match the term in Column A with its definition in Column B.

	Column A	Column B
F	1. negative trend	A. type of graph used to show changes over time
B	2. bar graph	B. a type of graph used to show trends
H	3. rhombus	C. two angles whose sum is 90 degrees
N	4. slope	D. the longest side of a right triangle
K	5. trapezoid	E. shows data items in order
C	6. complementary	F. as one set of values increases, the other set tends to decrease
L	7. positive trend	G. two angles whose sum is 180 degrees
J	8. perpendicular	H. a quadrilateral with four congruent sides
D	9. hypotenuse	I. divides the data into four equal parts
M	10. regular polygon	J. lines that intersect to form right angles
E	11. stem-and-leaf plot	K. a quadrilateral with exactly one pair of parallel sides
I	12. quartiles	L. as one set of values increases, the other set tends to increase
A	13. line graph	M. a figure with all sides congruent and all angles congruent
G	14. supplementary	N. a ratio that describes the steepness of a line
P	15. circle graph	O. the difference between the greatest and least values in a data set
O	16. range	P. a graph that shows parts of a whole

Vocabulary and Study Skills

Vocabulary Review

- box-and-whisker plot (p. 438)
- central angle (p. 451)
- circle graph (p. 450)
- frequency (p. 418)
- frequency table (p. 419)
- histogram (p. 419)
- line plot (p. 418)
- mean (p. 412)
- measure of central tendency (p. 412)
- median (p. 412)
- mode (p. 412)
- negative trend (p. 445)
- no trend (p. 445)
- outlier (p. 413)
- positive trend (p. 445)
- quartiles (p. 438)
- range (p. 413)
- scatter plot (p. 444)
- stem-and-leaf plot (p. 433)
- trend line (p. 445)
- Venn diagram (p. 424)

Go Online
PHSchool.com
For: Online Vocabulary Quiz
Web Code: asj-0951

Choose the correct vocabulary term to complete each sentence.

1. _?_ divide a data set into four equal parts. quartiles
2. A _?_ displays two sets of data as ordered pairs. scatter plot
3. An angle whose vertex is the center of the circle is a _?_. central angle
4. A display that shows numeric data in order is a _?_. stem-and-leaf plot

Skills and Concepts

Lessons 9-1, 9-2

- To describe data using mean, median, mode, and range and to choose an appropriate measure of central tendency
- To use line plots, frequency tables, and histograms to represent data

The **mean** of a set of numbers is the sum of the numbers divided by the number of data items. The **median** is the middle value in a set of numbers in numerical order. The **mode** is the data item that occurs most often. The **range** is the difference between the greatest and least values. An **outlier** is a value that is much higher or much lower than the other values in a set.

A **frequency table** lists the frequency of each item in a set of data. A **histogram** is a special type of bar graph used to show the frequency of data.

Find the mean, median, mode, and range of each set of data. Round to the nearest hundredth where necessary.

5. 15, 12, 10, 16, 24, 16, 12, 15, 18, 14, 15 15.18; 15; 15; 14
6. 9.1, 10.2, 9.5, 10.3, 10.5, 9.1, 9.0, 9.8, 9.9, 9.4, 10.7, 10.3
9.82; 9.85; 9.1 and 10.3; 1.7
7. Make a frequency table and a histogram for the data set below. Use intervals of equal size to group the data. See margin.
53 57 78 64 68 72 77 58 60 78 80 81 55 70 52 63 65 79

7. Answers may vary. Sample:

Number	Frequency
50–54	2
55–59	3
60–64	3
65–69	2
70–74	2
75–79	4
80–84	2

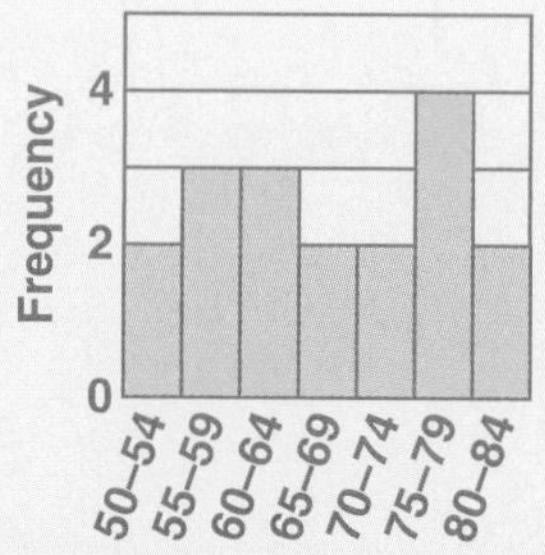

Lessons 9-3, 9-4

- To use Venn diagrams to represent relationships between data
- To recognize misleading graphs and to choose appropriate scales

Sometimes a graph can give a misleading visual impression.

8. Art Out of 25 artists, 22 are painters and 8 are sculptors. How many artists are both painters and sculptors? 5 artists

9. Make two line graphs for the set of data. In one of the graphs, use a break. Explain which graph shows the data more clearly. See margin.

School Chorus Members

Year	1	2	3	4	5
Girls	35	32	35	34	32
Boys	41	40	43	37	39

Lessons 9-5, 9-6

- To represent and interpret data using stem-and-leaf plots and box-and-whisker plots

A **stem-and-leaf plot** shows numeric data arranged in order. A **box-and-whisker plot** shows the distribution of data along a number line.

The data listed show different juice prices (in cents) at various stores.

89 79 85 79 85 67 75 99 79 63 90 72 78 65 78

10–11. See margin.

10. Make a stem-and-leaf plot. Then find the mode and median.

11. Find the quartiles. Then make a box-and-whisker plot.

Lesson 9-7

- To make scatter plots and to use trends to make predictions

A **scatter plot** is a graph that displays two sets of data as ordered pairs. It shows any relationship, or trend, that may exist between the sets of data. To show a trend, draw a trend line. A **trend line** is a line you draw on a graph to approximate the data.

12. Rivers Make a scatter plot and draw a trend line for the data at the right. See margin.

Length (mi) and Water Flow ($1{,}000\ ft^3/s$) of Rivers

Length	Flow	Length	Flow
2,540	76	1,040	57
1,980	225	886	68
1,460	41	774	67
1,420	58	724	67
1,290	56	659	41

Lessons 9-8, 9-9

- To represent and interpret data using circle graphs
- To choose appropriate graphs to represent different data

A **circle graph** is a graph of data in which the entire circle represents the whole. Each section in the circle represents part of the whole. When choosing a graph, consider the data and the idea you want to convey.

Decide which type of graph would be the most appropriate for the data. Explain your choice and then draw the graph. 13–14. See margin.

13.

Students Wearing Jackets

Temperature (°F)	55	57	63	68	70	73	80
Number of Students	10	11	8	5	4	2	0

14. hours a student worked each week at a summer job:
29 23 21 20 17 16 15 33 30

9. See back of book.

10.
6 | 3 5 7
7 | 2 5 8 8 9 9 9
8 | 5 5 9
9 | 0 9
Key: 9 | 0 means 90
79; 79

11.

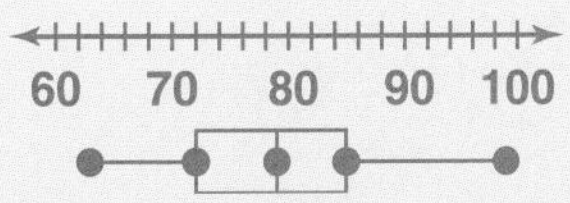

72; 85

12–13. See back of book.

14. Stem-and-leaf plot; it shows numerical data arranged in order.
1 | 5 6 7
2 | 0 1 3 9
3 | 0 3
Key: 3 | 0 means 30

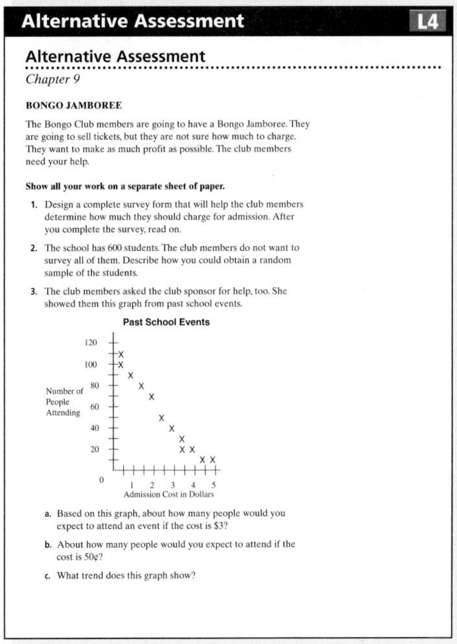

Alternative Assessment L4

Alternative Assessment
Chapter 9

BONGO JAMBOREE

The Bongo Club members are going to have a Bongo Jamboree. They are going to sell tickets, but they are not sure how much to charge. They want to make as much profit as possible. The club members need your help.

Show all your work on a separate sheet of paper.

1. Design a complete survey form that will help the club members determine how much they should charge for admission. After you complete the survey, read on.
2. The school has 600 students. The club members do not want to survey all of them. Describe how you could obtain a random sample of the students.
3. The club members asked the club sponsor for help, too. She showed them this graph from past school events.

Past School Events
Number of People Attending: 0, 20, 40, 60, 80, 100, 120
Admission Cost in Dollars: 1, 2, 3, 4, 5

a. Based on this graph, about how many people would you expect to attend an event if the cost is $3?
b. About how many people would you expect to attend if the cost is 50¢?
c. What trend does this graph show?

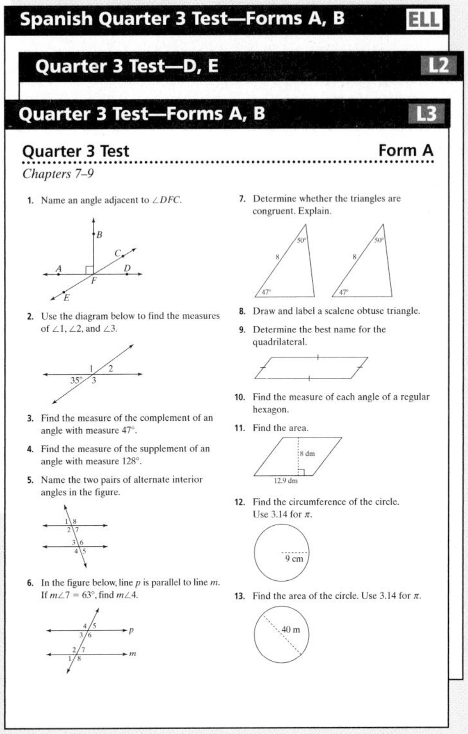

Spanish Quarter 3 Test—Forms A, B ELL

Quarter 3 Test—D, E L2

Quarter 3 Test—Forms A, B L3

Quarter 3 Test **Form A**
Chapters 7–9

1. Name an angle adjacent to $\angle DFC$.
2. Use the diagram below to find the measures of $\angle 1$, $\angle 2$, and $\angle 3$.
3. Find the measure of the complement of an angle with measure 47°.
4. Find the measure of the supplement of an angle with measure 128°.
5. Name the two pairs of alternate interior angles in the figure.
6. In the figure below, line p is parallel to line m. If $m\angle 7 = 63°$, find $m\angle 4$.
7. Determine whether the triangles are congruent. Explain.
8. Draw and label a scalene obtuse triangle.
9. Determine the best name for the quadrilateral.
10. Find the measure of each angle of a regular hexagon.
11. Find the area.
12. Find the circumference of the circle. Use 3.14 for π.
13. Find the area of the circle. Use 3.14 for π.

Resources

- ExamView Assessment Suite CD-ROM
  - Ch. 9 Ready-Made Test
  - Make your own Ch. 9 test
- MindPoint Quiz Show CD-ROM
  - Chapter 9 Review

Differentiated Instruction

All in One Teaching Resources
- Below Level Chapter 9 Test L2
- Chapter 9 Test L3
- Chapter 9 Alternative Assessment L4

Spanish Assessment Resources ELL
- Below Level Chapter 9 Test L2
- Chapter 9 Test L3
- Chapter 9 Alternative Assessment L4

ExamView Assessment Suite CD-ROM
- Special Needs Test L1
- Special Needs Practice Bank L1

Online Chapter 9 Test at www.PHSchool.com L3

4.

Movies	Frequency
0	3
1	4
2	6
3	3
4	2
5	1
6	0
7	1

5.

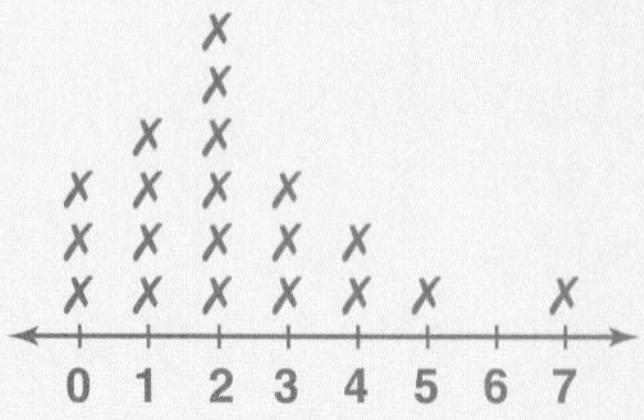

7–8. See back of book.

12.
81 | 0 0 3 3 8 8 9
82 | 1 5
83 | 3
Key: 83 | 3 means 83.3

Chapter 9 Test

Go Online PHSchool.com For: Online chapter test Web Code: asa-0952

Find the mean, median, mode, and range of each data set. Round to the nearest hundredth where necessary.

1. −1 9 −2 3 −1 5 −3 7 2.13; 1; −1; 12
2. 5.8 5.9 6.3 6.5 5.7 6.2 6.4 6.0 6.3 6.12; 6.2; 6.3; 0.8
3. Tell how the outlier affects the mean: 12, 10, 14, 18, 2, 15, 12, 12, 16. It lowers the mean by about 1.3.

Movies In a survey, twenty students were asked how many movies they saw in a month. The results are 2 3 2 2 1 0 1 2 5 7 2 1 0 3 4 4 3 0 1 2.

4. Make a frequency table.
5. Make a line plot. 4–5. See margin.
6. Find the mean, median, and mode. 2.25; 2; 2

Make a frequency table and a histogram for each data set. Use intervals of equal size to group the data. 7–8. See margin.

7. hours of sleep per night:
5 7 8 8 9 8 9 10 11 7 6 5 8 9 8 7 7
8. monthly salaries (in dollars) at local store:
600 780 750 1,200 1,500 1,000 1,100 850 900 425 832 700 900 1,000

Jobs Six hundred high school students were surveyed about the types of jobs they hold. Use the graph for Exercises 9–11.

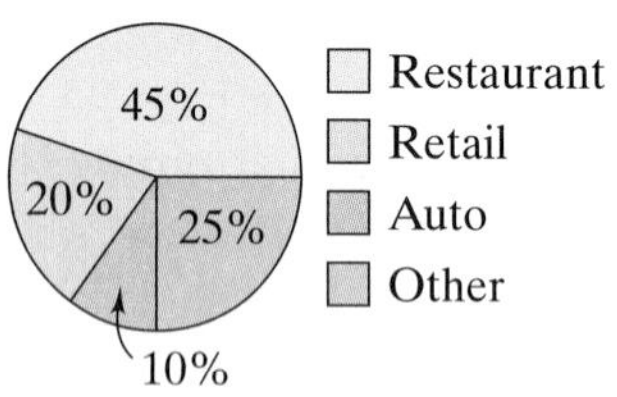

9. How many students work in a restaurant? 270 students
10. How many students work in retail sales? 120 students
11. What percent of the students do not work at a restaurant? How many students is that? 55%; 330 students

12. **Television** Make a stem-and-leaf plot for the number of subscribers (in millions) of ten cable television networks: 81.8, 81.3, 81.3, 81.0, 82.5, 83.3, 82.1, 81.9, 81.8, 81.0. See margin.
13. a. **Golf** The data below show the career earnings in millions of dollars of the top male and female golfers. Use a single number line to make a box-and-whisker plot for each set of data. See margin.

    Male: 21.9 18.0 17.8 15.3 14.6 14.5 14.7
    Female: 10.2 8.5 7.6 7.3 6.9 6.7 6.3

    b. **Writing in Math** Write a paragraph comparing the sets of data. See margin.

Decide which type of graph would be most appropriate for each set of data below. Explain your choice and then draw the graph. 14–16. See margin.

14. **Leading U.S. Clothing Businesses**

Company	Earnings (billions of dollars)
Nike	10.7
VF	5.2
Jones Apparel Group	4.4
Liz Claiborne	4.2
Reebok International	3.5

SOURCE: *The World Almanac*

15. **Percent of Music Sold on CDs**

Year	1999	2000	2001	2002	2003	2004
Percent	83.2	89.3	89.2	90.5	87.8	90.3

SOURCE: Recording Industry Association of America

16. per capita freshwater use (gallons per day): Florida, 509; California, 1,130; Ohio, 944; Kentucky, 1,150; Oregon, 2,520; Alaska, 350
17. In a recent survey of 100 mothers, 67 said they had a daughter. If 23 mothers said they had both a son and a daughter, how many mothers had only a son? 33 mothers

13a.

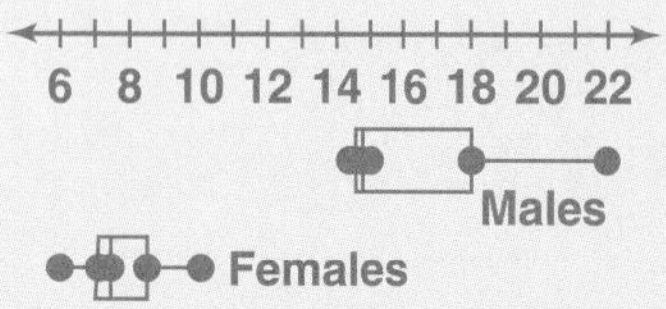

b. The earnings of top male golfers range from $14.5 million to $21.9 million, with half of them earning more than $15.3 million. The top female golfers earn from $6.3 million to $10.2 million, with half earning more than $7.3 million. Each of the top male golfers makes more than the top female golfer.

14–16. See back of book.

Multiple Choice

Read each question. Then write the letter of the correct answer on your paper.

1. Find the median and the mode of the data in the line plot. B
   - A 7 and 8
   - B 7.5 and 7
   - C 7.5 and 8
   - D 8 and 9

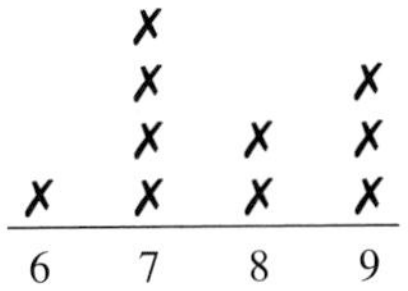

2. Which measure of central tendency would you use to describe the data on your classmates' favorite brand of sneakers? F
   - F mode
   - H median
   - G range
   - J mean

3. At a middle school gymnastics competition, the scores for the floor exercises were 5.1, 5.6, 5.3, 5.1, 4.8, 4.6, and 5.2. Find the mean (to the nearest tenth) and the median. B
   - A 5.1 and 5.3
   - C 5.2 and 5.1
   - B 5.1 and 5.1
   - D 5.2 and 5.2

4. Which object is not an example of a prism? J
   - F a shoe box
   - H a domino
   - G a file cabinet
   - J a soup can

5. Describe the trend in the scatter plot at the right. B

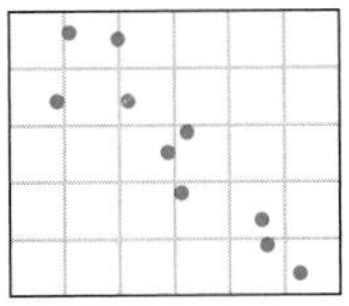

   - A positive trend
   - B negative trend
   - C no trend
   - D positive and negative trend

6. Which type of graph shows how a category changes over time? J
   - F histogram
   - H line plot
   - G circle
   - J line graph

7. At the Armstrong School, the student-to-teacher ratio is 12 : 1. There are 30 teachers in the school. How many students are there? D
   - A 42
   - C 300
   - B 250
   - D 360

8. The sum of three consecutive integers is 42. What is the value of the least integer? H
   - F 25
   - G 18
   - H 13
   - J 9

9. What are the missing numbers in the pattern? B

   −2, −3, −5, −8, −12, ■, −23, ■, . . .
   - A −18 and −28
   - C −15 and −26
   - B −17 and −30
   - D −19 and −26

10. A rectangular skateboard park has 7 curbs and 4 ramps. The width of the park is $2x$ and the length is $3x$, where x equals 48 meters. What are the dimensions of the park? G
    - F 48 m and 72 m
    - G 96 m and 144 m
    - H 100 m and 4 m
    - J 65 m and 35 m

Gridded Response

Record your answer in a grid.

11. Round 3.0481 to the nearest hundredth. 3.05

12. A cubit was a measure used in ancient times. There are about 2 cubits in a yard. How many inches are in a cubit? 18

Short Response

13. Leana had $50.00 before she went shopping. She bought three books that all cost the same price, and a hat for $18.99, including tax. After shopping, she had $7.04 left. How much was each book? Show your work. See margin.

Extended Response

14. The ages of the players on a basketball team are below. Find the lower quartile, median, and upper quartile for their ages. Use a box-and-whisker plot to display the data. Show your work.

    23 25 34 25 19 24 25 25 26 40 33
    21 27 29 31 26 33 See margin.

Item	1	2	3	4	5	6	7	8	9	10	11	12	13	14
Lesson	9-2	9-1	9-1	8-1	9-7	9-9	4-3	6-3	Problem Solving Handbook	1-1	p. 630	4-1	Problem Solving Handbook	9-6

Test Prep

Resources

Test Prep Workbook

All in One Teaching Resources
- Cumulative Review L3

ExamView Assessment Suite CD-ROM
- Standardized Test Practice

Differentiated Instruction

Spanish Assessment Resources
- Spanish Cumulative Review ELL

13. $7.99; $50.00 − $7.04 = $42.96. She spent a total of $42.96 on the shopping trip. $42.96 − $18.99 = $23.97. She spent $23.97 on the three books. $\frac{\$23.97}{3} = \$7.99$.

14. 19 21 23 24 25 25 25 25 26 26 27 29 31 33 33 34 40
    $n = 17$
    median: 26
    lower quartile: 24.5
    $\frac{24 + 25}{2} = 24.5$
    upper quartile: 32
    $\frac{31 + 33}{2} = 32$

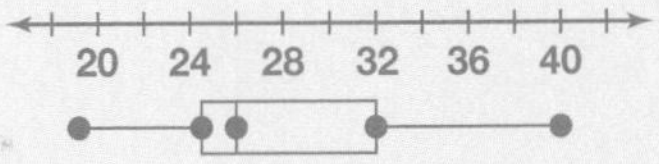

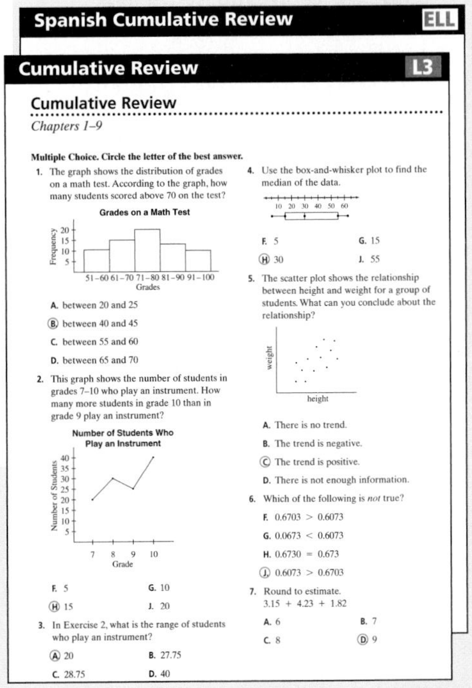

Spanish Cumulative Review ELL

Cumulative Review L3

Cumulative Review

Chapters 1–9

Multiple Choice. Circle the letter of the best answer.

1. The graph shows the distribution of grades on a math test. According to the graph, how many students scored above 70 on the test?

   Grades on a Math Test (Frequency; Grades 51–60, 61–70, 71–80, 81–90, 91–100)

   A. between 20 and 25
   Ⓑ between 40 and 45
   C. between 55 and 60
   D. between 65 and 70

2. This graph shows the number of students in grades 7–10 who play an instrument. How many more students in grade 10 than in grade 9 play an instrument?

   Number of Students Who Play an Instrument (Number of Students; Grade 7, 8, 9, 10)

   F. 5 G. 10
   Ⓗ 15 J. 20

3. In Exercise 2, what is the range of students who play an instrument?

   Ⓐ 20 B. 27.75
   C. 28.75 D. 40

4. Use the box-and-whisker plot to find the median of the data.

   F. 5 G. 15
   Ⓗ 30 J. 55

5. The scatter plot shows the relationship between height and weight for a group of students. What can you conclude about the relationship?

   A. There is no trend.
   B. The trend is negative.
   Ⓒ The trend is positive.
   D. There is not enough information.

6. Which of the following is *not* true?

   F. 0.6703 > 0.6073
   G. 0.0673 < 0.6073
   H. 0.6730 = 0.673
   Ⓙ 0.6073 > 0.6703

7. Round to estimate.
   3.15 + 4.23 + 1.82

   A. 6 B. 7
   C. 8 Ⓓ 9

Problem Solving

Applying Data Analysis

Students will use data from these two pages to answer the questions posed here in Put It All Together.

Activating Prior Knowledge

Tell students that people eat 35,000 tons of pineapples every day. Have them use this data as a benchmark. Then list some of the foods mentioned in this feature, but provide no consumption data about them. Ask students first to try to place the foods in order of most consumed to least consumed. Then challenge them to estimate how much of each food is eaten world-wide each day.

Guided Instruction

Have students examine the cones and information about food consumption on these pages. Discuss with students how visual images make great numbers less abstract.

History Connection
Have students research the history of some of these foods. Where were they first grown and in what conditions do they thrive? Invite students to investigate the link between the availability of certain foods in a region and the rise of civilization there. Have students look into the relationship between planting crops and the growth of towns and cities.

Careers
Invite interested students to find out more about the field of graphic design. Have them learn what jobs are available and what training, skills, and talents are required. Students can start their inquiry by talking with the art teacher.

Problem Solving Application

Applying Data Analysis

Conic Cuisine Graphic designers often use pictures to present data. You can read that people eat 35,000 tons of pineapples every day, but seeing a pile of pineapples drawn to the size of a large hotel gives you a better sense of how many pineapples this is. The drawings on these pages show the volumes of various crops that the people of the world eat or produce each day.

Potatoes
We dig up 801,000 tons of potatoes every day.

Put It All Together

Materials scale or balance, ruler, food sample

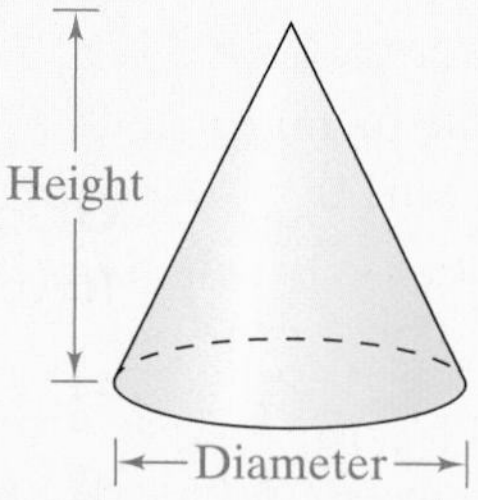

Height
Diameter

1. Weigh a serving of one of the foods shown on these pages. Remember to subtract the weight of the container if there is one. Use the conversion tables in the back of the book to convert the weight to pounds.
2. Estimate the volume of your food sample in cubic inches.
3. How many tons of your food does the world eat or produce each day? Convert this amount to pounds. Write your answer in scientific notation.
4. Suppose you piled the amount of the food eaten or produced each day into a cone. Find the volume of the cone. (*Hint:* 1,728 in.^{3} = 1 ft^3)
5. Suppose the diameter and the height of the cone are equal.
   a. Use the formula $V = \frac{2}{3}\pi r^3$ and *systematic guess and check* to estimate the radius of the cone.
   b. Calculate the diameter and the height of the cone in feet.
6. **Reasoning** What would the cone of food weigh? Explain.

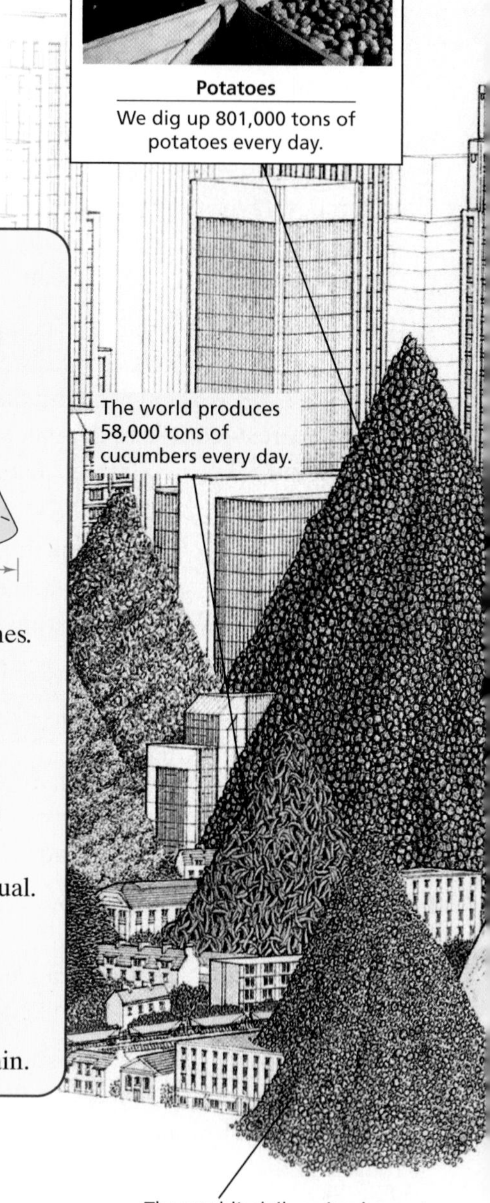

The world produces 58,000 tons of cucumbers every day.

The world's daily onion harvest weighs 98,000 tons, as much as the ocean liner *Queen Elizabeth*.

Go Online PHSchool.com
For: Information about food
Web Code: ase-0953

1–5. Answers may vary. Samples are given for wheat.

1. 4.9 oz = 0.306 lb
2. 13.9 in.^{3}
3. 1.6 million tons = 3.2×10^9 lb
4. about 1.45×10^{11} in.^{3}

5a. about 4,110 in. or 342.5 ft

b. both are about 685 ft

6. 1.6 million tons, or 3.2×10^9 lb; this is the amount of wheat the world eats per day.

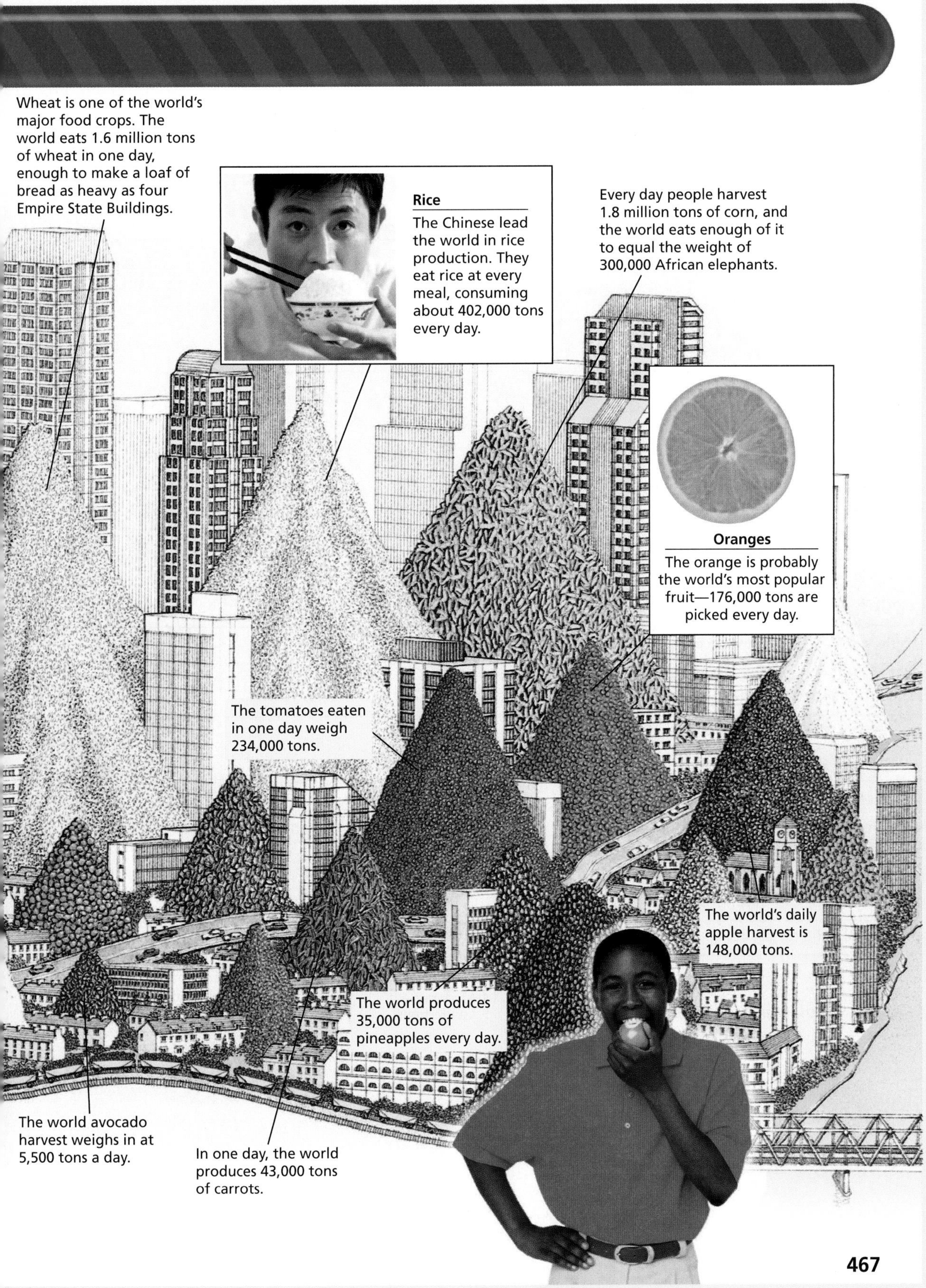
Wheat is one of the world's major food crops. The world eats 1.6 million tons of wheat in one day, enough to make a loaf of bread as heavy as four Empire State Buildings.
Rice
The Chinese lead the world in rice production. They eat rice at every meal, consuming about 402,000 tons every day.
Every day people harvest 1.8 million tons of corn, and the world eats enough of it to equal the weight of 300,000 African elephants.
Oranges
The orange is probably the world's most popular fruit—176,000 tons are picked every day.
The tomatoes eaten in one day weigh 234,000 tons.
The world's daily apple harvest is 148,000 tons.
The world produces 35,000 tons of pineapples every day.
The world avocado harvest weighs in at 5,500 tons a day.
In one day, the world produces 43,000 tons of carrots.
467

Put It All Together

Have students work in pairs to answer the questions. Guide them to record data as they measure and accumulate it.

Discuss that in this activity, students will weigh and estimate the size of food samples.

Exercise 4 Elicit from students that when they compute volume, they measure it in cubic units—cubic feet or cubic inches in this case. Guide students to understand that $1{,}728 = 12 \times 12 \times 12$, or 12^3.

Challenge students to pick a food from the activity and estimate the height of a cone that shows how much of that food is consumed in one year. Ask: *Why is the height not 365 times the height of a 1-day cone?* **The cone expands in three directions, not just upwards.**

Differentiated Instruction

Special Needs L1

As needed, review what a cone is and the formula for finding its volume $\left(V = \frac{1}{3}Bh\right)$. Compare finding its volume to finding the volume of a cylinder ($V = Bh$). Also review how to use scientific notation to express very large quantities.

10 Probability

Chapter at a Glance

Lesson Titles, Objectives, and Features	Assessment	NCTM Standards	Local Standards
10-1 Theoretical and Experimental Probability • To find theoretical probability, experimental probability, and odds	Lesson Quiz	1, 2, 5, 6, 7, 8, 9, 10	
10-2a Activity Lab, Hands On: Fair Games **10-2 Making Predictions** • To make predictions based on theoretical and experimental probabilities **Extension:** Complements and Probability	Lesson Quiz Checkpoint Quiz 1	1, 2, 3, 4, 5, 6, 7, 8, 9, 10	
10-3 Conducting a Survey • To identify random samples and biased questions and to judge conclusions based on survey results **10-3b Activity Lab, Technology:** Simulations With Random Numbers	Lesson Quiz	1, 2, 3, 6, 7, 8, 9, 10	
10-4a Activity Lab, Hands On: Comparing Types of Events **10-4 Independent and Dependent Events** • To find the probabilities of independent and dependent events	Lesson Quiz Checkpoint Quiz 2	1, 2, 3, 4, 6, 7, 8, 9, 10	
10-5 Permutations • To find the number of permutations of a set of objects	Lesson Quiz	1, 2, 6, 7, 8, 9, 10	
10-6 Combinations • To find the number of combinations of a set of objects using lists and combination notation **Vocabulary Builder:** Understanding Vocabulary **Guided Problem Solving:** Permutations, Combinations, and Probability	Lesson Quiz	1, 2, 3, 6, 7, 8, 9, 10	
Problem Solving Application: Applying Probability			

NCTM Standards 2000
1 Number and Operations
2 Algebra
3 Geometry
4 Measurement
5 Data Analysis and Probability
6 Problem Solving
7 Reasoning and Proof
8 Communication
9 Connections
10 Representation

Correlations to Standardized Tests

All content for these tests is contained in *Prentice Hall Math*, Course 3. This chart reflects coverage in this chapter only.

	10-1	10-2	10-3	10-4	10-5	10-6
Terra Nova CAT6 (Level 18)						
Number and Number Relations					✔	✔
Computation and Numerical Estimation					✔	✔
Operation Concepts						
Measurement						
Geometry and Spatial Sense						
Data Analysis, Statistics, and Probability	✔	✔	✔	✔	✔	✔
Patterns, Functions, Algebra		✔				
Problem Solving and Reasoning	✔	✔	✔	✔	✔	✔
Communication	✔	✔	✔	✔	✔	✔
Decimals, Fractions, Integers, Percent	✔	✔		✔		
Order of Operations						
Algebraic Operations		✔				
Terra Nova CTBS (Level 18)						
Decimals, Fractions, Integers, Percents	✔	✔		✔		
Order of Operations, Numeration, Number Theory						
Data Interpretation						
Measurement						
Geometry						
ITBS (Level 14)						
Number Properties and Operations	✔	✔		✔	✔	✔
Algebra		✔				
Geometry						
Measurement						
Probability and Statistics	✔	✔	✔	✔	✔	✔
Estimation						
SAT10 (Adv 1 Level)						
Number Sense and Operations					✔	✔
Patterns, Relationships, and Algebra		✔				
Data, Statistics, and Probability	✔	✔	✔	✔	✔	✔
Geometry and Measurement						
NAEP						
Number Sense, Properties, and Operations						
Measurement						
Geometry and Spatial Sense						
Data Analysis, Statistics, and Probability	✔	✔	✔	✔	✔	✔
Algebra and Functions						

CAT6 California Achievement Test, 6th Ed. **CTBS** Comprehensive Test of Basic Skills **ITBS** Iowa Test of Basic Skills, Form M
SAT10 Stanford Achievement Test, 10th Ed. **NAEP** National Assessment of Educational Progress 2005 Mathematics Objectives

Math Background

Professional Development

Skills Trace

BEFORE Chapter 10

Course 2 introduced theoretical probability, experimental probability, and compound probability.

DURING Chapter 10

Course 3 reviews and extends probability with independent events, dependent events, and sampling techniques.

AFTER Chapter 10

Throughout this course students use ratios, proportions, percents, fractions, and decimals to build a foundation for probability.

10-1 Theoretical and Experimental Probability

Math Understandings

- Probability is expressed as a number from 0 (impossible) to 1 (certain) that tells how often an event will occur.
- Experimental probability is based on the results of an actual experiment.
- Theoretical probability is based on the assumption that certain outcomes are equally likely.

Probability based on experimental data is called experimental probability. You can find the experimental and theoretical probability of an event using the following formulas.

experimental probability $= P(\text{event}) = \frac{\text{number of times an event occurs}}{\text{total number of trials}}$

theoretical probability $= P(\text{event}) = \frac{\text{number of favorable outcomes}}{\text{total number of possible outcomes}}$

Odds
odds in favor of an event = the ratio of the number of favorable outcomes to the number of unfavorable outcomes
odds against an event = the ratio of the number of unfavorable outcomes to the number of favorable outcomes

10-2 Making Predictions

Math Understandings

Predictions about event outcomes can be made using theoretical probability. The actual event outcome may differ from the prediction. The probability may be provided to you, or you may determine it using survey results, for example.

The **complement of an event** is the opposite of that event. For any event A, its complement is *not A,* and $P(A) + P(\text{not A}) = 1$. To find the probability of a complement, use $P(\text{not } A) = 1 - P(A)$.

10-3 Conducting a Survey

Math Understandings

- You can select a random sample to accurately represent the entire population.
- A survey question should not influence responses by making one answer appear more attractive.
- Poor sampling or poor questions can lead to invalid conclusions.

Any group of objects or people in a survey is called a **population**. A **sample** is a part of the population. In a **random sample**, each object in the population has an equal chance of being selected. In a **systematic sample**, the members of a survey population are selected using a system of selection that depends on a random number. In a **stratified sample**, members of the survey population are separated into groups to ensure a balanced sample. Then a random sample is selected from each group. Unfair questions in a survey are **biased** questions.

10-4 Independent and Dependent Events

Math Understandings

- Two events are independent if one event does not affect the sample space of the other event.
- Two events are dependent if one event affects the sample space of the other event.

For **independent events**, the outcome of one event does not affect the outcome of a second event. For **dependent events**, the outcome of one event affects the outcome of a second event.

Independent Events	Dependent Events
If *A* and *B* are independent events, then *P(A, then B)* = *P(A)* · *P(B)*.	If A and B are dependent events, then *P(A, then B)* = *P(A)* · *P(B* after *A)*.

10-5 10-6 Permutations and Combinations

Math Understandings

- In permutations, order makes a difference.
- In combinations, order does not matter.

A **permutation** is an arrangement of a set of objects in a particular order. You can use a diagram to find the number of permutations. This diagram shows that there are six permutations, or ways, that Ryan, Emily, and Justin can line up.

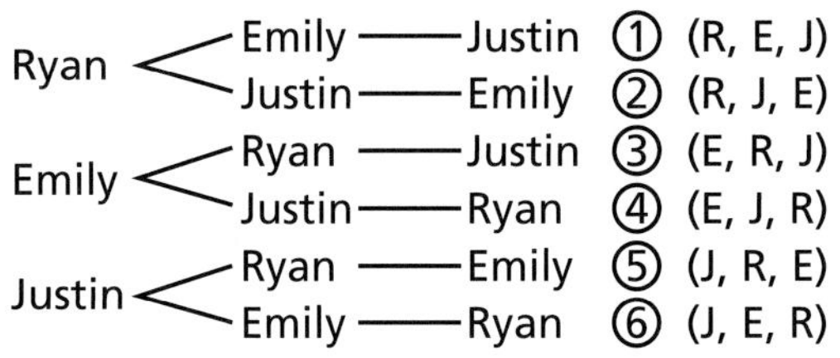

You can also use the counting principle to find the number of possible outcomes.

The Counting Principle
Suppose there are *m* ways of making one choice and *n* ways of making a second choice. Then there are $m \cdot n$ ways to make the first choice followed by the second choice

Example: The number of ways that Ryan, Emily, and Justin can line up is $3 \times 2 \times 1$ or 6.

The product of all positive integers less than or equal to a number is a **factorial**. For example, $3! = 3 \times 2 \times 1$, or 6. The number of permutations of *n* items, using all *n* in each arrangement, is $n!$, which you read as "*n* factorial." The number of permutations of *n* items, chosen *r* at a time, is $n!$ divided by $(n - r)!$.

Permutation Notation
The expression $_nP_r$ represents the number of permutations of *n* objects chosen *r* at a time.

Example: Simplify $_{25}P_2$. $_{25}P_2 = 25 \cdot 24 = 600$

A **combination** is a group of items in which the order of the items is *not* considered. The number of combinations of *n* items, chosen *r* at a time, is the number of permutations of *n* items taken *r* at a time divided by $r!$.

Combination Notation
The expression $_nC_r$ represents the number of combinations of *n* objects chosen *r* at a time. $_nC_r = \frac{_nP_r}{r!}$

Example: Simplify $_{12}C_3$.

$$_{12}C_3 = \frac{_{12}P_3}{3!} = \frac{12 \cdot 11 \cdot 10}{3 \cdot 2 \cdot 1} = \frac{1{,}320}{6} = 220$$

Additional Professional Development Opportunities

Professional Development

Math Background Notes for Chapter 10: Every lesson has a Math Background in the PLAN section.

Research Overview, Mathematics Strands
Additional support for these topics and more is in the front of the Teacher's Edition.

LessonLab
LessonLab, a Pearson Education company, offers comprehensive, facilitated professional development designed to help teachers to improve student achievement. To learn more, please visit lessonlab.com.

Chapter 10 Resources

	10-1	10-2	10-3	10-4	10-5	10-6	For the Chapter
Print Resources							
L3 Practice	●	●	●	●	●	●	
L1 Adapted Practice	●	●	●	●	●	●	
L3 Guided Problem Solving	●	●	●	●	●	●	
L2 Reteaching	●	●	●	●	●	●	
L4 Enrichment	●	●	●	●	●	●	
L3 Daily Notetaking Guide	●	●	●	●	●	●	
L1 Adapted Daily Notetaking Guide	●	●	●	●	●	●	
L3 Vocabulary and Study Skills Worksheets	●		●	●	●	●	●
L3 Daily Puzzles	●	●	●	●	●	●	
L3 Activity Labs	●	●	●	●	●	●	
L3 Checkpoint Quiz		●		●			
L3 Chapter Project							●
L2 Below Level Chapter Test							●
L3 Chapter Test							●
L4 Alternative Assessment							●
L3 Cumulative Review							●
Spanish Resources ELL							
L3 Practice	●	●	●	●	●	●	
L3 Vocabulary and Study Skills Worksheets	●		●	●	●	●	●
L3 Checkpoint Quiz		●		●			
L2 Below Level Chapter Test							●
L3 Chapter Test							●
L4 Alternative Assessment							●
L3 Cumulative Review							●
Transparencies							
Check Skills You'll Need	●	●	●	●	●	●	
Additional Examples	●	●	●	●	●	●	
Problem of the Day	●	●	●	●	●	●	
Classroom Aid					●	●	
Student Edition Answers	●	●	●	●	●	●	●
Lesson Quiz	●	●	●	●	●	●	
Test-Taking Strategies							●
Technology							
Interactive Textbook Online	●	●	●	●	●	●	●
StudentExpress™ CD-ROM	●	●	●	●	●	●	●
Success Tracker™ Intervention Online	●	●	●	●	●	●	●
TeacherExpress™ CD-ROM	●	●	●	●	●	●	●
PresentationExpress™ with QuickTake Presenter CD-ROM	●	●	●	●	●	●	●
ExamView® Assessement Suite CD-ROM	●	●	●	●	●	●	●
MindPoint® Quiz Show CD-ROM							●
Prentice Hall Web Site: PHSchool.com	●	●	●	●	●	●	●

Also available: **Prentice Hall Assessment System**
- Progress Monitoring Assessments
- Skills and Concepts Review
- Test Prep Workbook

Other Resources
Algebra Readiness Tests
All-in-One Student Workbook
All-in-One Student Workbook, Adapted Version
Multilingual Handbook
Solution Key
Math Notes Study Folder
Spanish Cumulative Assessment

Where You Can Use the Lesson Resources

Here is a suggestion, following the four-step teaching plan, for how you can incorporate Differentiated Instruction Resources into your teaching.

	Instructional Resources L3	Differentiated Instruction Resources
1. Plan		
Preparation Read the Math Background in the Teacher's Edition to connect this lesson with students' previous experience. **Starting Class** **Check Skills You'll Need** Assign these exercises to review prerequisite skills. **New Vocabulary** Help students pre-read the lesson by pointing out the new terms introduced in the lesson.	**Math Background** **Math Understandings** **Transparencies & PresentationExpress™ with QuickTake Presenter CD-ROM** Check Skills You'll Need Problem of the Day **Resources** Vocabulary and Study Skills	**Spanish Support** ELL Vocabulary and Study Skills
2. Teach		
L3 **Guided Instruction** Use the Activity Labs to build conceptual understanding. Teach each Example. Use the Teacher's Edition side column notes for specific teaching tips, including Error Prevention notes. Use the Additional Examples found in the side column (and on transparency and PowerPoint) as an alternative presentation for the content. After each Example, assign the Quick Check exercise for that Example to get an immediate assessment of student understanding. Use the Closure activity in the Teacher's Edition to help students attain mastery of lesson content.	**Student Edition** Activity Lab **Resources** Daily Notetaking Guide Activity Lab **Transparencies & PresentationExpress™ with QuickTake Presenter CD-ROM** Additional Examples Classroom Aids **ExamView® Assessment Suite CD-ROM**	**Teacher's Edition** Every lesson includes suggestions for working with students who need special attention. L1 Special Needs L2 Below Level L4 Advanced Learners ELL English Language Learners **Resources** L1 Adapted Daily Notetaking Guide **Multilingual Handbook**
3. Practice		
Assignment Guide **Check Your Understanding** Use these questions to check students' understanding before you assign homework. **Homework Exercises** Assign homework from these leveled exercises in the Assignment Guide. A Practice by Example B Apply Your Skills C Challenge Test Prep and Mixed Review **Homework Quick Check** Use these key exercises to quickly check students' homework.	**Transparencies & PresentationExpress™ with QuickTake Presenter CD-ROM** Student Answers **Resources** Practice Guided Problem Solving Vocabulary and Study Skills Activity Lab Daily Puzzles **ExamView® Assessment Suite CD-ROM**	**Spanish Support** ELL Practice ELL Vocabulary and Study Skills **Resources** L1 Adapted Practice L4 Enrichment
4. Assess & Reteach		
Lesson Quiz Assign the Lesson Quiz to assess students' mastery of the lesson content. **Checkpoint Quiz** Use the Checkpoint Quiz to assess student progress over several lessons.	**Transparencies & PresentationExpress™ with QuickTake Presenter CD-ROM** Lesson Quiz **Resources** Checkpoint Quiz	**Resources** L2 Reteaching ELL Checkpoint Quiz Success Tracker™ Online Intervention **ExamView® Assessment Suite CD-ROM**

KEY L1 Special Needs L2 Below Level L3 For All Students L4 Advanced, Gifted ELL English Language Learners

CHAPTER 10

Probability

Check Your Readiness

Answers for students are in the back of the textbook.

For intervention, direct students to:

Multiplying Rational Numbers
Lesson 2-5
Extra Skills and Word Problems Practice, Ch. 2

Writing Ratios
Lesson 4-1
Extra Skills and Word Problems Practice, Ch. 4

Finding Probabilities
Lesson 5-8
Extra Skills and Word Problems Practice, Ch. 5

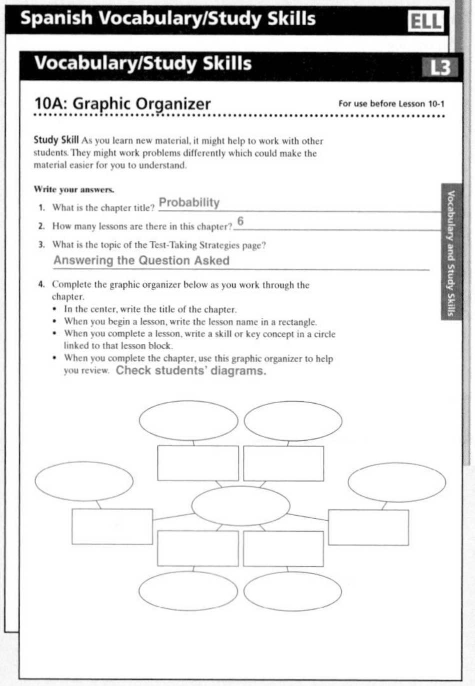
Spanish Vocabulary/Study Skills ELL

Vocabulary/Study Skills L3

10A: Graphic Organizer — For use before Lesson 10-1

Study Skill As you learn new material, it might help to work with other students. They might work problems differently which could make the material easier for you to understand.

Write your answers.

1. What is the chapter title? Probability
2. How many lessons are there in this chapter? 6
3. What is the topic of the Test-Taking Strategies page? Answering the Question Asked
4. Complete the graphic organizer below as you work through the chapter.
   - In the center, write the title of the chapter.
   - When you begin a lesson, write the lesson name in a rectangle.
   - When you complete a lesson, write a skill or key concept in a circle linked to that lesson block.
   - When you complete the chapter, use this graphic organizer to help you review. Check students' diagrams.

Vocabulary and Study Skills

CHAPTER 10

Probability

What You've Learned

- In Chapter 4, you used ratios to solve problems.
- In Chapter 5, you used ratios and percents to describe probabilities.
- In Chapter 9, you used scatter plots to make predictions.

Check Your Readiness

GO for Help

For Exercises	See Lessons
1–6	2-5
7–8	4-1
9–14	5-8

Multiplying Rational Numbers

Find each product.

1. $\frac{3}{7} \cdot \frac{1}{2}$ $\frac{3}{14}$
2. $\frac{1}{6} \cdot \frac{24}{25}$ $\frac{4}{25}$
3. $\frac{9}{14} \cdot \frac{7}{12}$ $\frac{3}{8}$
4. $\frac{8}{9} \cdot \frac{12}{32}$ $\frac{1}{3}$
5. $\frac{27}{34} \cdot \frac{2}{3}$ $\frac{9}{17}$
6. $\frac{10}{17} \cdot \frac{1}{5}$ $\frac{2}{17}$

Writing Ratios

Write three ratios that each diagram can represent.
Answers may vary. Samples are given.

7. 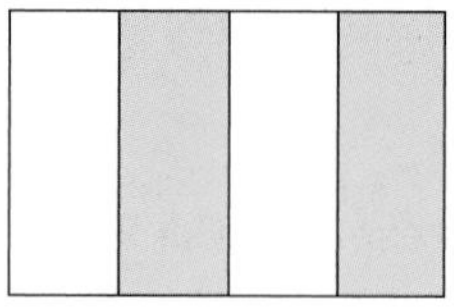 $\frac{2}{4}, \frac{4}{2}, \frac{2}{2}$

8. 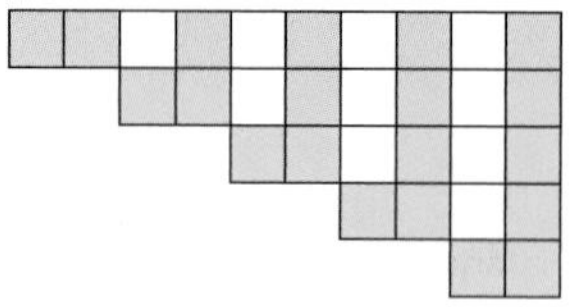 $\frac{20}{30}, \frac{10}{30}, \frac{10}{20}$

Finding Probabilities

Suppose you spin the spinner once. Find each probability. Express each probability as a fraction.

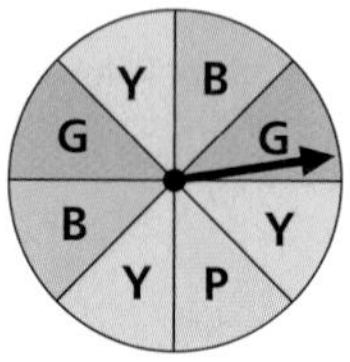

9. $P(\text{yellow})$ $\frac{3}{8}$
10. $P(\text{green})$ $\frac{1}{4}$
11. $P(\text{purple})$ $\frac{1}{8}$
12. $P(\text{green or blue})$ $\frac{1}{2}$
13. $P(\text{blue or yellow})$ $\frac{5}{8}$
14. $P(\text{green or purple})$ $\frac{3}{8}$

Chapter 10 Overview

In this chapter, students learn about theoretical and experimental probability. They explore the distinction between independent and dependent events. They also consider outcomes by investigating the concepts of permutations and combinations.

Activating Prior Knowledge

In this chapter, students build on their knowledge of ratios and rates and of applications of proportions. They draw upon their understanding of the concept of probability and of how to find the probability of certain events. Ask questions such as:

- *How would you express the ratio 4 : 20 in simplest form?* 1 : 5
- *You roll a 1–6 number cube. What is the probability you will roll an even number?* $\frac{1}{2}$
- *You make 7 of 10 free throws. If you continue to shoot with that rate of success, how many free throws can you expect to make if you shoot 50 of them?* 35

What You'll Learn Next

- In this chapter, you will use theoretical and experimental probabilities to make predictions and decisions.
- You will use permutations and combinations to count outcomes.
- You will evaluate methods of sampling and identify biased and unbiased survey questions.

Key Vocabulary

- biased questions (p. 481)
- combination (p. 496)
- counting principle (p. 492)
- dependent events (p. 487)
- experimental probability (p. 470)
- factorial (p. 492)
- independent events (p. 486)
- odds in favor (p. 471)
- odds against (p. 471)
- permutation (p. 491)
- population (p. 480)
- random sample (p. 480)
- sample (p. 480)
- theoretical probability (p. 471)

Problem Solving Application On pages 508 and 509, you will work an extended activity on animal population.

10-1

1. Plan

Objective
To find the theoretical probability, experimental probability, and odds

Examples
1 Finding Experimental Probability
2 Identifying the Type of Probability
3 Determining Odds

Math Understandings: p. 468C

Professional Development

Math Background

Probability based on experimental data is called *experimental probability*. The *theoretical probability* of an event, written as $P(E)$, is the number of favorable outcomes divided by the total number of possible outcomes. For ten trials of tossing a fair coin, the theoretical $P(\text{heads}) = \frac{5}{10}$, or $\frac{1}{2}$. The experimental probability can vary from $\frac{0}{10}$ to $\frac{10}{10}$.

More Math Background: p. 468C

Lesson Planning and Resources

See p. 468E for a list of the resources that support this lesson.

PowerPoint

Bell Ringer Practice

Check Skills You'll Need
Use student page, transparency, or PowerPoint. For intervention, direct students to:
Ratios and Probability
Lesson 5-8
Extra Skills and Word Problems Practice, Ch. 5

10-1 Theoretical and Experimental Probability

Check Skills You'll Need

1. **Vocabulary Review** A collection of all the possible outcomes in an experiment is a(n) __?__. sample space

Suppose you roll a number cube.

2. What are the possible outcomes? 1, 2, 3, 4, 5, 6
3. Find $P(4)$. $\frac{1}{6}$
4. Find $P(\text{even number})$. $\frac{1}{2}$
5. Find $P(3 \text{ or } 4)$. $\frac{1}{3}$

GO for Help Lesson 5-8

What You'll Learn

To find theoretical probability, experimental probability, and odds

New Vocabulary experimental probability, theoretical probability, odds in favor, odds against

Why Learn This?

You can use probabilities to estimate the likelihood of events. For example, you can estimate the probability of having homework on a Friday.

Probability based on experimental data is called **experimental probability.** You find the experimental probability of an event by using the results of an experiment, or trial, repeated many times.

KEY CONCEPTS **Experimental Probability**

$$P(\text{event}) = \frac{\text{number of times event occurs}}{\text{total number of trials}}$$

EXAMPLE **Finding Experimental Probability**

1 **Science** The scientist Gregor Mendel crossbred green-seed plants and yellow-seed plants. Out of 8,023 crosses, 6,022 plants had yellow seeds and 2,001 had green seeds. Find the probability that a plant had green seeds.

$$P(\text{green}) = \frac{\text{number of plants with green seeds}}{\text{total number of crossbred plants}} \quad \leftarrow \text{Write the probability ratio.}$$

$$= \frac{2{,}001}{8{,}023} \quad \leftarrow \text{Substitute.}$$

$$\approx 0.249 \quad \leftarrow \text{Divide.}$$

The probability that a plant had green seeds is about 0.249.

Quick Check

Heads	𝍸 III
Tails	𝍸 𝍸 II

1. Use the table at the left. Find the experimental probability of getting heads. 0.4

Differentiated Instruction Solutions for All Learners

Special Needs L1
Students make predictions about the outcomes of spinning spinners and flipping coins. They test their predictions by conducting "trials" to find the experimental probabilities of these events.
learning style: tactile

Below Level L2
Students review writing commonly used fractions as percents, and percents as fractions. For example, $\frac{1}{4} = 0.25 = 25\%$; $15\% = \frac{15}{100} = \frac{3}{20}$.
learning style: visual

GO Online

Video Tutor Help
Visit: PHSchool.com
Web Code: ase-0775

You can toss a coin to find the experimental probability of getting heads. You can find the theoretical probability without using trials because both possible outcomes (heads or tails) are equally likely. To find the theoretical probability, use the formula from Chapter 5.

$$\text{theoretical probability} = \frac{\text{number of favorable outcomes}}{\text{total number of possible outcomes}}$$

The experimental probability of getting a heads is likely to get closer to the theoretical probability the more times you toss the coin.

EXAMPLE Identifying the Type of Probability

2 **Voting** The table shows the results of a survey. Does 55% represent *experimental* or *theoretical* probability?

Survey of Town Voters

Number of People Surveyed	Number of People in Favor	Probability of Voting in Favor
200	110	55%

The survey records actual responses from town voters. 55% represents experimental probability.

Quick Check

2. A bag contains two red cubes and three white cubes. Does $P(\text{red}) = \frac{2}{5}$ represent *experimental* or *theoretical* probability? Theoretical; the result is based on the number of possible outcomes.

Sometimes probabilities are expressed in the form of a ratio called odds. The statement "There's a 2 to 1 chance of rain" uses odds.

KEY CONCEPTS Odds

- **Odds in favor** of an event is the ratio number of favorable outcomes : number of unfavorable outcomes.
- **Odds against** an event is the ratio number of unfavorable outcomes : number of favorable outcomes.

EXAMPLE Determining Odds

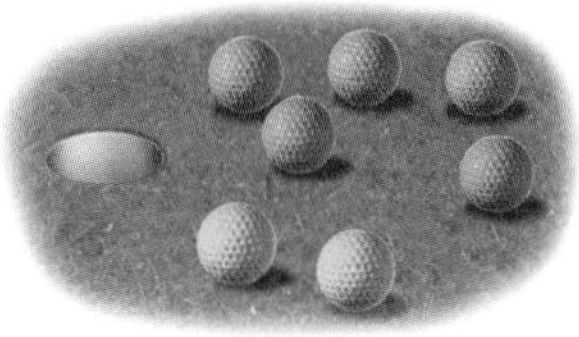

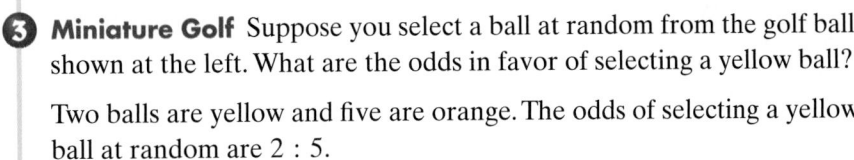

3 **Miniature Golf** Suppose you select a ball at random from the golf balls shown at the left. What are the odds in favor of selecting a yellow ball?

Two balls are yellow and five are orange. The odds of selecting a yellow ball at random are 2 : 5.

Quick Check

3. What are the odds against selecting a yellow ball at random? 5 : 2

2. Teach

Activity Lab

Use before the lesson.

All in One Teaching Resources

Activity Lab 10-1: Theoretical and Experimental Probability

Guided Instruction

Error Prevention!

In Example 2, ask students to find the sum of the percent *in favor* and the percent *not in favor.* 100

PowerPoint

Additional Examples

1 A gardener plants 250 sunflower seeds and 210 germinate. Find the experimental probability that a sunflower seed will germinate. 84%

2 The probability of tossing one six-sided number cube and getting a 5 is $\frac{1}{6}$, or about 17%. Is this experimental or theoretical probability? theoretical

3 Suppose you select a pen at random from 3 red ones and 4 blue ones. What are the odds in favor of selecting a red pen? 3 : 4

All in One Teaching Resources

- Daily Notetaking Guide 10-1 L3
- Adapted Notetaking 10-1 L1

Closure

- *How does experimental probability differ from theoretical probability?* Sample: Experimental probability is based on experimental data.
- *What is the relationship between the odds in favor of an event and the odds against an event?* Sample: The odds in favor is the inverse ratio of the odds against.

Advanced Learners L4
Students find the theoretical and experimental probabilities of getting an even number when tossing a number cube 50 times. 50%; Experimental probability will vary.

learning style: visual

English Language Learners ELL
Students relate the words *in favor* to *favorable*, and *against* to *unfavorable* (*not favorable*). Odds in favor show the number of favorable outcomes first, but odds against show the number of unfavorable outcomes first.

learning style: verbal

3. Practice

Assignment Guide

Check Your Understanding

Go over Exercises 1–4 in class before assigning the Homework Exercises.

Homework Exercises

A	Practice by Example	5–10
B	Apply Your Skills	11–19
C	Challenge	20
	Test Prep and Mixed Review	21–27

Homework Quick Check

To check students' understanding of key skills and concepts, go over Exercises 7, 10, 11, 13, and 19.

Differentiated Instruction Resources

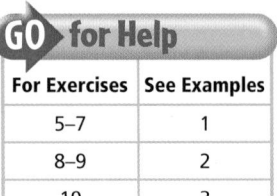

Adapted Practice 10-1 L1

Practice 10-1 Theoretical and Experimental P L3

A dart is thrown at the game board shown. Notice that the diameters are at right angles and that some of the slices are congruent. Find each probability.

1. $P(A)$ $\frac{1}{3}$ 2. $P(B)$ $\frac{5}{12}$ 3. $P(C)$ $\frac{1}{4}$
4. $P(\text{not } A)$ $\frac{2}{3}$ 5. $P(\text{not } B)$ $\frac{7}{12}$ 6. $P(\text{not } C)$ $\frac{3}{4}$

The odds in favor of winning a game are 5 to 9.

7. Find the probability of winning the game. $\frac{5}{14}$
8. Find the probability of *not* winning the game. $\frac{9}{14}$

A box of marbles contains 10 red, 12 blue, 15 yellow, and 8 green marbles. A marble is drawn at random. Find each probability.

9. $P(\text{red})$ $\frac{2}{9}$ 10. $P(\text{blue})$ $\frac{4}{15}$
11. What are the odds in favor of picking a blue marble? 4 to 11
12. What are the odds in favor of picking a green marble? 8 to 37
13. What is the probability of picking a marble that is not yellow? $\frac{2}{3}$
14. What is the probability of picking a marble that is not red? $\frac{7}{9}$

Solve.

15. a. You buy a ticket for the weekly drawing by a community charity. Last week you bought one ticket. Find the probability and odds of winning if 1,200 tickets were bought that week. $\frac{1}{1,200}$; 1 to 1,199
    b. Find the probability and odds of you winning if you bought three tickets and there were 1,200 tickets bought that week. $\frac{1}{400}$; 1 to 399
16. A cheese tray contains slices of Swiss cheese and cheddar cheese. If you randomly pick a slice of cheese, $P(\text{Swiss}) = 0.45$. Find $P(\text{cheddar})$. If there are 200 slices of cheese, how many slices of Swiss cheese are on the cheese tray? 0.55; 90 slices

10-1 • Guided Problem Solving GPS L3

GPS Student Page 472, Exercise 12:

The probability of an event is $\frac{1}{4}$. What are the odds in favor of the event occurring?

Understand

1. What does the probability of an event being $\frac{1}{4}$ mean? Sample answer: There is one favorable event out of four possible outcomes.
2. What are you being asked to determine? the odds in favor of the event occurring

Plan and Carry Out

3. How many outcomes are there? four
4. What does the first number of a ratio mean when finding the odds in favor of an event? the number of favorable outcomes
5. What does the second number of a ratio mean when finding the odds in favor of an event? the number of unfavorable outcomes
6. Write the odds in favor of the event occurring. 1 : 3

Check

7. How can you determine the probability when given the odds? Write the first number in the odds over the sum of both numbers $\frac{1}{1+3}$ or $\frac{1}{4}$.

Solve Another Problem

8. The probability of an event is $\frac{3}{8}$. What are the odds in favor of the event occurring? $\frac{3}{8} = \frac{3}{5+3}$, so the odds in favor are 3 : 5

Check Your Understanding

1. **Vocabulary** Suppose you conduct trials to gather data. Are you finding experimental probability or theoretical probability? experimental

Using the data shown in the table, find each probability.

Cereals in a Food Store

Type	Number of Brands
With nuts	16
With fruit	40
With whole grains	24
Total	**80**

2. $P(\text{cereal with nuts})$ $\frac{1}{5}$
3. $P(\text{cereal with whole grains})$ $\frac{3}{10}$
4. A baseball team has a record of 63 wins and 42 losses. Sam says the odds of winning the next game are 3 to 2. Explain his reasoning. The odds of winning are $\frac{63}{42} = \frac{3}{2}$.

Homework Exercises

For more exercises, see Extra Skills and Word Problems.

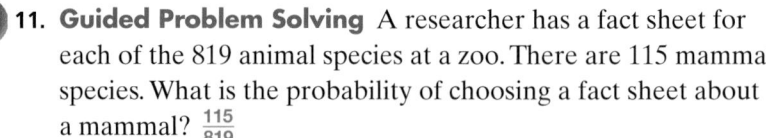

GO for Help

For Exercises	See Examples
5–7	1
8–9	2
10	3

A **Find each experimental probability.** You planted 250 seeds from a bag. All the seeds grew, and there were 68 marigolds, 94 alyssum, 8 poppies. The rest were zinnias.

5. $P(\text{marigold})$ 0.272 6. $P(\text{alyssum})$ 0.376 7. $P(\text{zinnia})$ 0.32

Decide whether each probability is experimental or theoretical.

8. You toss two pennies 20 times. $P(2 \text{ heads})$ is $\frac{3}{20}$. experimental
9. A spinner is divided into six equal sections. Three sections are green and three sections are blue. $P(\text{green})$ is $\frac{1}{2}$. theoretical
10. A 12-sided solid has faces numbered 1 to 12. The probability of any side facing upward when the solid is rolled is the same. What are the odds in favor of rolling a 7? 1 : 11

B GPS 11. **Guided Problem Solving** A researcher has a fact sheet for each of the 819 animal species at a zoo. There are 115 mammal species. What is the probability of choosing a fact sheet about a mammal? $\frac{115}{819}$
- How many outcomes are possible?
- How many outcomes are favorable?

12. The probability of an event is $\frac{1}{4}$. What are the odds in favor of the event occurring? 1 : 3 (GPS)
13. **Writing in Math** The odds in favor of an event are 2 : 3. Does this mean the probability of the event occuring is $\frac{2}{3}$? Explain. No, since the odds in favor are 2 : 3, the probability would be $\frac{2}{3+2} = \frac{2}{5}$.

Go Online Homework Video Tutor
Visit: PHSchool.com
Web Code: ase-1001

Data Analysis **In a survey, 171 children were asked what time they go to bed. The results are shown below. Find the experimental probability that a randomly selected child goes to bed at a certain time.**

Bedtimes of Children

Time (P.M.)	7:30	8:00	8:30	9:00	9:30
Number	24	31	38	42	36

14. $P(9{:}30)$ $\frac{36}{171}$ **15.** $P(8{:}30)$ $\frac{38}{171}$ **16.** $P(7{:}30\text{–}8{:}30)$ $\frac{93}{171}$

17. $P(\text{not } 9{:}00)$ $\frac{129}{171}$ **18.** $P(\text{after } 8{:}30)$ $\frac{78}{171}$ **19.** $P(\text{before } 9{:}30)$ $\frac{135}{171}$

C **20.** **Challenge** To win a game, you have to toss a coin that lands in the green area of the game board at the right. Suppose the center of the coin lands on the board. What is the theoretical probability that the center of the coin will land in the green area? $\frac{1}{9}$

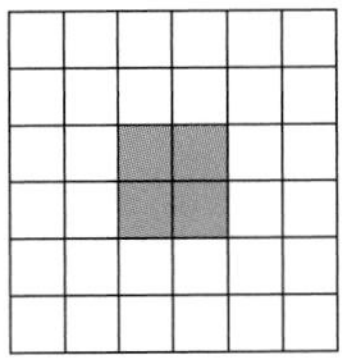

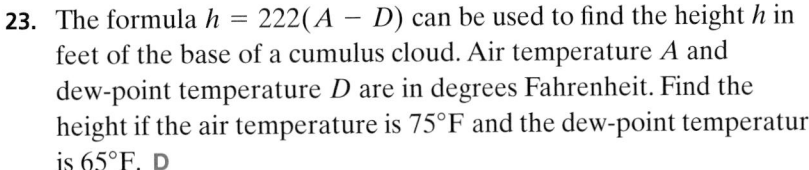

Test Prep and Mixed Review

Practice

Multiple Choice

21. Tammy selected a marble from a bag, recorded the color, and returned the marble to the bag. She did this several times. She got a green marble 8 times and a blue marble 7 times. There are 20 marbles in the bag. Predict the number of green marbles. B

Ⓐ 41 Ⓑ 11 Ⓒ 8 Ⓓ 6

22. The net for an eraser is shown at the right. Measure the dimensions of the net in inches. Which of the following is closest to the total surface area of the eraser? J

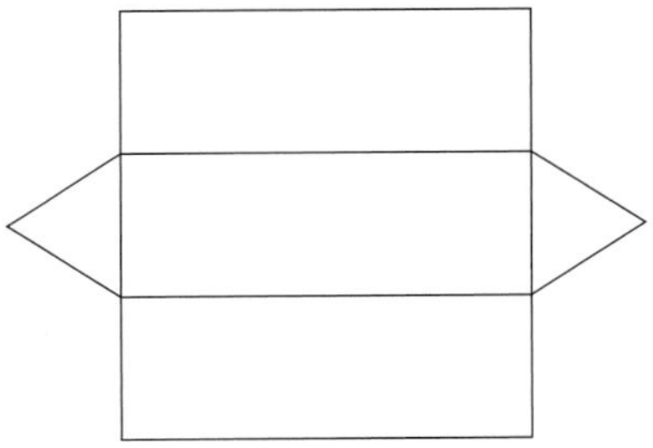

Ⓕ 0.25 in.^{2} Ⓗ 2.00 in.^{2}
Ⓖ 0.75 in.^{2} Ⓙ 2.5 in.^{2}

23. The formula $h = 222(A - D)$ can be used to find the height h in feet of the base of a cumulus cloud. Air temperature A and dew-point temperature D are in degrees Fahrenheit. Find the height if the air temperature is 75°F and the dew-point temperature is 65°F. D

Ⓐ 212 ft Ⓑ 232 ft Ⓒ 1,110 ft Ⓓ 2,220 ft

GO for Help

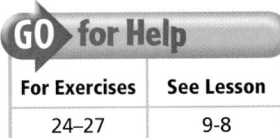

For Exercises	See Lesson
24–27	9-8

Find the measure of the central angle that could represent each percent in a circle graph.

24. 25% 90° **25.** 10% 36° **26.** 20% 72° **27.** 15% 54°

Test Prep

Resources

For additional practice with a variety of test item formats:

- Test-Taking Strategies, p. 503
- Test Prep, p. 507
- Test-Taking Strategies with Transparencies

4. Assess & Reteach

PowerPoint

Lesson Quiz

Use this information to solve the problems: You toss two nickels 50 times. You get one head and one tail 38 times, and two heads 8 times.

1. Find the probability of getting one head and one tail. 76%
2. Find the probability of getting two heads. 16%
3. What kind of probability do your answers to 1 and 2 represent? experimental
4. What are the odds in favor of getting exactly one head and one tail? 38 : 12 or 19 : 6

Alternative Assessment

Students consider this statement: *The probability of rain tomorrow is 45%.* Is this a theoretical or experimental probability? experimental What are the odds in favor of the event? 45 : 55 or 9 : 11

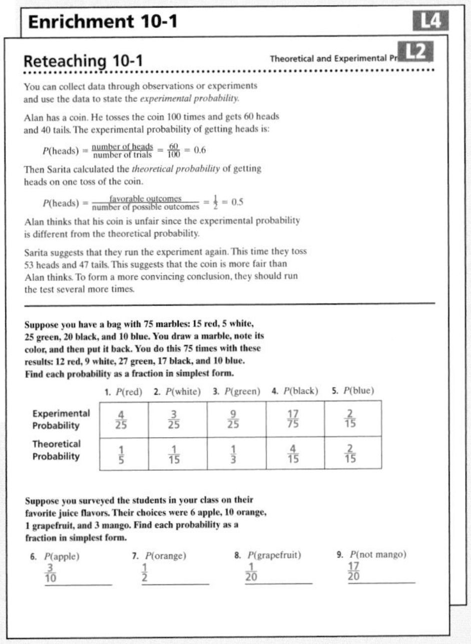

Enrichment 10-1 L4

Reteaching 10-1 Theoretical and Experimental Pr L2

You can collect data through observations or experiments and use the data to state the *experimental probability.*

Alan has a coin. He tosses the coin 100 times and gets 60 heads and 40 tails. The experimental probability of getting heads is:

$$P(\text{heads}) = \frac{\text{number of heads}}{\text{number of trials}} = \frac{60}{100} = 0.6$$

Then Sarita calculated the *theoretical probability* of getting heads on one toss of the coin.

$$P(\text{heads}) = \frac{\text{favorable outcomes}}{\text{number of possible outcomes}} = \frac{1}{2} = 0.5$$

Alan thinks that his coin is unfair since the experimental probability is different from the theoretical probability.

Sarita suggests that they run the experiment again. This time they toss 53 heads and 47 tails. This suggests that the coin is more fair than Alan thinks. To form a more convincing conclusion, they should run the test several more times.

Suppose you have a bag with 75 marbles: 15 red, 5 white, 25 green, 20 black, and 10 blue. You draw a marble, note its color, and then put it back. You do this 75 times with these results: 12 red, 9 white, 27 green, 17 black, and 10 blue. Find each probability as a fraction in simplest form.

	1. $P(\text{red})$	2. $P(\text{white})$	3. $P(\text{green})$	4. $P(\text{black})$	5. $P(\text{blue})$
Experimental Probability	$\frac{4}{25}$	$\frac{3}{25}$	$\frac{9}{25}$	$\frac{17}{75}$	$\frac{2}{15}$
Theoretical Probability	$\frac{1}{5}$	$\frac{1}{15}$	$\frac{1}{3}$	$\frac{4}{15}$	$\frac{2}{15}$

Suppose you surveyed the students in your class on their favorite juice flavors. Their choices were 6 apple, 10 orange, 1 grapefruit, and 3 mango. Find each probability as a fraction in simplest form.

6. $P(\text{apple})$ $\frac{3}{10}$
7. $P(\text{orange})$ $\frac{1}{2}$
8. $P(\text{grapefruit})$ $\frac{1}{20}$
9. $P(\text{not mango})$ $\frac{17}{20}$

Fair Games

Students simulate a real-world situation about World Series baseball. They use mathematical reasoning to consider possible outcomes and probabilities of winning the series.

Guided Instruction

Error Prevention!

Remind students that performing one coin toss does not represent a simulation. Students must toss a coin until a team wins 4 games to complete one simulation. Students then repeat the simulation 40 times.

Teaching Tip
Have students use tables to record and compare the results of their simulations for Team H and Team T. After students complete the activity, have them write the ratio of series wins for Team H to series wins for Team T after 10 simulations. Have them compare this to the ratio after 40 simulations. Ask: *What is the advantage of simulating the situation 40 times compared to 10 times?* results (experimental probability) will be closer to the theoretical probability *How reliable do you think the results would be if we tried 80 times?* even closer to the theoretical probability

Connection to Sports
Ask students of different cultural backgrounds to share how other final sports competitions are arranged (e.g., World Cup, French Open).

Resources

- Activity Lab 10-2: Making Predictions
- coins

Fair Games

In the World Series, two baseball teams play as many as 7 games. The series ends when a team wins 4 games.

Your friend's favorite team is ahead of your favorite team in the World Series, 3 games to 1. Since his team has won three times as many games as yours, he offers you this deal: If his team wins, you will do his chores for a week. If your team wins, he will do your chores for *three* weeks.

ACTIVITY

Assume that the two teams are evenly matched. You can toss a coin to simulate the outcome of each game. 1–3. Check students' work.

victory for Team H, your friendís team

victory for Team T, your team

1. Simulate the remaining games of the World Series by tossing a coin until one team has won a total of 4 games.
2. Repeat the simulation 40 times. Record the number of series wins for each team.
3. Write the ratio of series wins for Team H to series wins for Team T. Compare this to the deal your friend offered.
4. Explain why the only possible outcomes of a simulation for the end of the series are H, T-H, T-T-H, and T-T-T. See margin.
5. Complete the tree diagram below to show all the possible outcomes of three consecutive games. See margin.

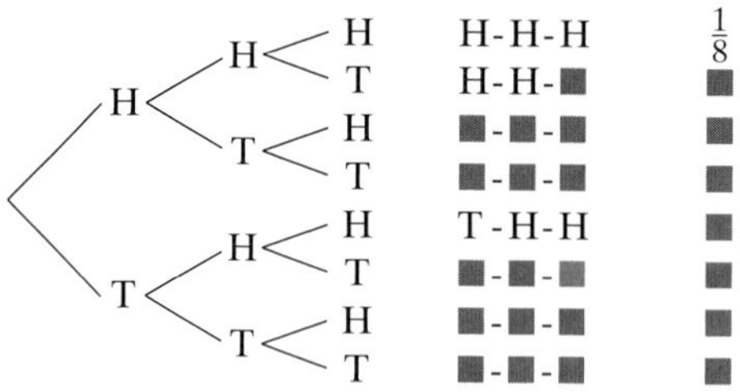

6. Use the completed tree diagram to find P(Team H wins the series) and P(Team T wins the series). $\frac{7}{8}$; $\frac{1}{8}$
7. Should you accept your friend's deal? If not, for how many weeks should he be willing to do your chores if your team wins? Justify your answer. No; he should be willing to do your chores for 7 weeks since his team is 7 times more likely to win.

4. The series ends when a team wins 4 games, so Team H needs to win one more game or Team T needs to win all 3 remaining games.

5. See back of book.

10-2 Making Predictions

Check Skills You'll Need

1. **Vocabulary Review** To solve a proportion, you can first write the __?__ *products.* cross

Solve each proportion.

2. $\frac{9}{14} = \frac{x}{210}$ 135

3. $\frac{5}{8} = \frac{85}{x}$ 136

4. $\frac{x}{6} = \frac{21}{28}$ 4.5

GO for Help Lesson 4-3

What You'll Learn

To make predictions based on theoretical and experimental probabilities

Why Learn This?

If you know the probability that it will rain, you can decide whether to wear rain gear. In a similar way, business people make predictions and decisions about how to market their products by relying on both surveys and theoretical probability.

When you use probability to make predictions, the actual outcome may differ from your prediction. The prediction only indicates what is *likely* to happen.

EXAMPLE Using Probability

1 According to game rules, the probability that a bottled-water cap can be redeemed for a prize is $\frac{1}{24}$. If a store stocks 500 bottles of water, about how many winning caps are likely?

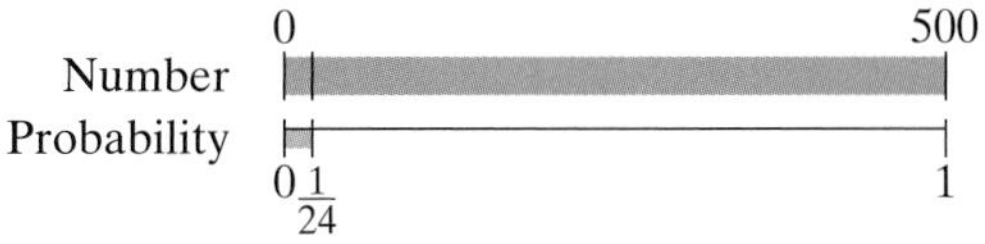

A diagram can help you understand the problem.

$$\frac{1}{24} \cdot 500 = \frac{1}{24} \cdot \frac{500}{1}$$ ← Find $\frac{1}{24}$ of 500.

$$= \frac{1}{\cancel{24}_6} \cdot \frac{\cancel{500}^{125}}{1}$$ ← Divide the numerator and denominator by the GCF, 4.

$$= \frac{125}{6}$$ ← Simplify.

$$= 20\frac{5}{6}$$ ← Write the fraction as a mixed number.

About 21 winning caps are likely.

Quick Check

1. Suppose the probability that a bottle has a prize-winning cap is only 1 out of 40. How many winning caps are likely among 500 bottles? about 13 winning caps

10-2

1. Plan

Objective

To make predictions based on theoretical and experimental probabilities

Examples

1 Using Probability
2 Using Survey Results

Math Understandings: p. 468C

Professional Development

Math Background

Predicting the probability of an outcome can be based on theoretical or experimental probability. If the probability is expressed as a decimal or ratio, then it can be used to determine how often an event may occur out of any size sample space. For example, out of 60 flips of a coin, the expected number of heads would be about 30 since $60 \times \frac{1}{2} = 30$, where $\frac{1}{2}$ is the theoretical probability of getting heads. Predictions based upon either type of probability may differ from the actual outcomes.

More Math Background: p. 468C

Lesson Planning and Resources

See p. 468E for a list of the resources that support this lesson.

PowerPoint

Bell Ringer Practice

Check Skills You'll Need

Use student page, transparency, or PowerPoint. For intervention, direct students to:

Solving Proportions
Lesson 4-3
Extra Skills and Word Problems Practice, Ch. 4

Differentiated Instruction Solutions for All Learners

Special Needs L1
Students use Method 2 from Example 2 in these types of examples. Using Method 2 will minimize errors because it has fewer steps. Method 2 calls for students to calculate the probability first, then apply it.

learning style: visual

Below Level L2
Students write proportions using the units. For example, there are 4 playgrounds in 6 neighborhoods. About how many playgrounds are there in 48 neighborhoods? $\frac{\text{playgrounds}}{\text{neighborhoods}} = \frac{4}{6} = \frac{x}{48}$

learning style: visual

2. Teach

Activity Lab

Use before the lesson.
Student Edition Activity Lab, Hands On 10-2a, Fair Games, p. 474

All in One Teaching Resources

Activity Lab 10-2: Making Predictions

Guided Instruction

Example 2
Provide students with a blank grid.

Error Prevention!

Remind students that in a proportion, where fractions are equal to each other, values diagonally across from each other are multiplied. When fractions are multiplied, values aligned horizontally are multiplied.

PowerPoint

Additional Examples

1. A restaurant promotion offers $\frac{1}{48}$ chance of winning a free dessert with a meal. Out of 570 meals served, how many winners are likely? about 12

2. In a random survey at a school, 16 out of 25 students prefer reading books for leisure. If there are 400 students in the school, predict how many students prefer reading books. There are likely to be 256 students who prefer reading books for leisure.

All in One Teaching Resources

- Daily Notetaking Guide 10-2 L3
- Adtapted Notetaking 10-2 L1

Closure

- *When can you use a proportion to solve a probability problem?* when a probability or survey result is given and you want to find or predict results for a larger or smaller group

EXAMPLE Using Survey Results

2 Gridded Response In a random survey of town voters, 36 out of 60 people say they plan to vote for Mrs. Islas for mayor. If 1,200 people vote in the election, about how many votes will Mrs. Islas receive?

Test Prep Tip
You could solve the proportion using cross products. Use number sense to make calculations easier.

Method 1 Write a proportion.

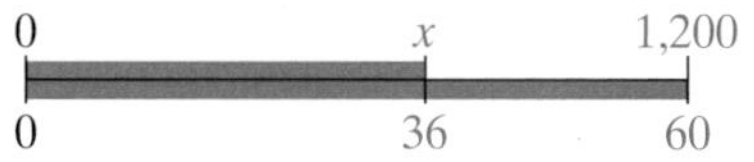

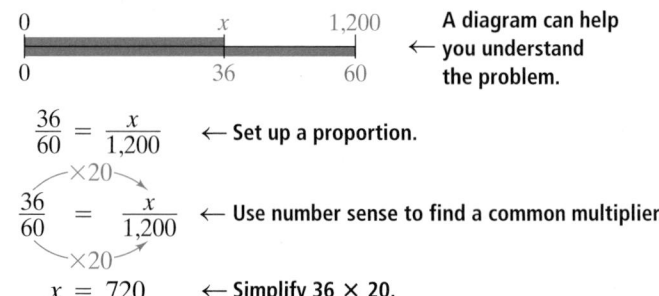

← A diagram can help you understand the problem.

$\frac{36}{60} = \frac{x}{1{,}200}$ ← Set up a proportion.

$\frac{36}{60} = \frac{x}{1{,}200}$ (×20 on numerator and denominator) ← Use number sense to find a common multiplier.

$x = 720$ ← Simplify 36 × 20.

Mrs. Islas is likely to receive 720 votes.

Method 2 From the survey, find the probability that a voter will vote for Mrs. Islas. Apply this probability to all the voters.

$\frac{36}{60} = \frac{6}{10}$, or 60% ← The event "vote for Mrs. Islas" occurred in 36 out of 60 trials.

Find 60% of 1,200.

$60\% \text{ of } 1{,}200 = 0.6 \times 1{,}200$ ← Find 60% of 1,200.

$= 720$ ← Simplify.

Mrs. Islas is likely to receive 720 votes.

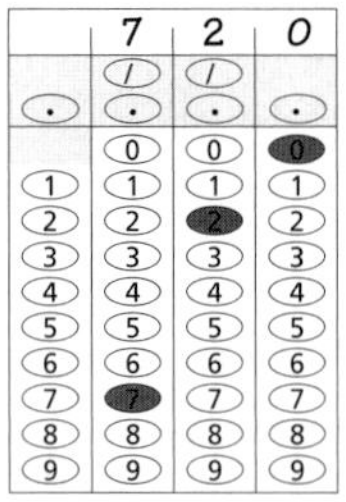

Quick Check

2. In the same survey, 19 out of 60 people said they would vote for Mr. Chiu. Predict how many votes Mr. Chiu will receive in the election. 380 votes

Check Your Understanding

1. At an auto factory, $\frac{3}{100}$ of the cars produced have a minor defect. If the factory produces 600 cars, about how many are likely to have a defect? 18 cars

Use theoretical probability to predict the number of heads when a fair coin is tossed each number of times.

2. 10 5
3. 60 30
4. 300 150
5. 599 300

Differentiated Instruction Solutions for All Learners

Advanced Learners L4
The probability of being a middle-school student is $\frac{1}{8}$ and the probability of a middle-schooler wearing glasses is $\frac{2}{5}$. Students predict how many middle-schoolers who wear glasses are in a town of 800 people. about 40
learning style: verbal

English Language Learners ELL
Students frequently misinterpret probability as a guarantee that something will happen. In Example 1, point out that the result is "about" 21 prizes because there can be more, or fewer, than 21. This number (21) is what is *likely* based on probability.
learning style: verbal

Homework Exercises

For more exercises, see Extra Skills and Word Problems.

GO for Help

For Exercises	See Examples
6–11	1
12–17	2

A **Predict how many times the given outcome will occur for each number of spins.** A spinner has sections labeled A, B, C, D, E, F, and 0. The probability the spinner lands on each letter is $\frac{3}{20}$ and the probability it lands on 0 is $\frac{1}{10}$.

6. outcome D; 60 spins 9
7. outcome D; 600 spins 90
8. outcome B; 12,000 spins 1,800
9. outcome F; 54 spins 8
10. outcome 0; 80 spins 8
11. outcome A; 95 spins 14

Use the table below. A hot dog company surveyed 100 people in a town of 12,000 to find their favorite grilled foods. Predict how many people in the town prefer each grilled food.

Favorite Grilled Foods

Type	Number of Responses
Hot dogs	22
Hamburgers	20
Steak	19
Chicken	17
Fish	12
Other	10

12. hot dogs 2,640 people
13. hamburgers 2,400 people
14. steak 2,280 people
15. fish 1,440 people
16. chicken 2,040 people
17. other 1,200 people

B GPS 18. **Guided Problem Solving** From past experience, Marguerite knows that 1 out of 4 beans that she plants will not grow. How many beans should she plant in order for it to be likely that at least 24 bean plants will grow? 32 beans
- What is the probability that a planted bean *will* grow?
- Do 24 plants represent favorable outcomes or all outcomes?
- Write a proportion using probability and predicted outcomes.

19. The probability of a wooden baseball bat being defective is $\frac{1}{250}$. In a shipment of 1,400 bats, how many are likely to be defective? about 6 bats

20. **Transportation** The probability that a flight on a certain airline will be on time is $\frac{4}{5}$. At an airport, the airline has 125 flights leaving each day. Predict how many of these flights will be on time. 100 flights
GPS

Online lesson quiz, PHSchool.com, Web Code: asa-1002

3. Practice

Assignment Guide

Check Your Understanding
Go over Exercises 1–5 in class before assigning the Homework Exercises.

Homework Exercises

A Practice by Example	6–17
B Apply Your Skills	18–28
C Challenge	29
Test Prep and Mixed Review	30–33

Homework Quick Check
To check students' understanding of key skills and concepts, go over Exercises 10, 14, 20, 22, and 24.

Exercises
For Exercises 12–17, have students discuss the following: For the town fair, a party planner predicts that 2,000 hot dogs and 2,400 hamburgers will be eaten. Is the prediction valid?

Activity
Have students ask classmates to identify 1 or 2 preferred foods from steak, chicken, or fish. Have them display their data using Venn diagrams with and without technology.

Differentiated Instruction Resources

Guided Problem Solving 10-2 GPS L3

Adapted Practice 10-2 L1

Practice 10-2 Making Pre L3

A cube has 3 green sides, 2 red sides, and 1 orange side. Find the probability of each toss result.

1. P(green) $\frac{1}{2}$
2. P(red) $\frac{1}{3}$
3. P(orange) $\frac{1}{6}$

Using the probability data from exercises 1–3, predict how many times the given outcome will occur for each number of tosses.

4. 600 tosses; red 200
5. 144 tosses; green 72
6. 86 tosses; orange 14
7. 45 tosses; red 15

Suppose 300 students were surveyed to find which method of transportation they most frequently use to get to school. Based on the data at the right, predict how many students in a school of 800 frequently use each method of transportation.

Most Frequent StudentTransportation

Transportation to School	Number of Students
Bus	160
Automobile or Motorcycle	80
Bicycle	20
Walk	40

8. bus 427
9. automobile or motorcycle 213
10. bicycle 53
11. walk 107
12. A certain shoe manufacturer examined 250 pairs of shoes and found 41 pairs with defects. In a shipment of 6,000 pairs of shoes, how many are likely to have defects?
984
13. A store owner notes that 1 out of 4 customers do not make a purchase. How many customers need to come into the store in order for the owner to make 70 sales?
280
14. A large jar contains pennies, nickels, dimes, and quarters. If you pick a coin at random $P(\text{quarter}) = 0.28$. If there are 500 coins in the jar, how many quarters are in the jar?
140

4. Assess & Reteach

PowerPoint

Lesson Quiz

1. The probability that a train leaving Central Station will arrive at its destination on time is $\frac{5}{6}$. The station has 58 trains leaving each day. Predict how many trains will arrive on time. about 48 trains
2. A random survey of 24 buses leaving Central Station one day showed that 15 buses arrived at their destinations on time. Each day, 146 buses leave Central Station. Predict how many of these buses will arrive on time. about 91 buses
3. A spinner is divided into different colored sections. The probability of the spinner landing on the purple section is $\frac{2}{7}$. Predict how many times the spinner lands on the purple section if it spins 98 times. about 28 times
4. In a random survey of voters in a small town, 52% of the people plan to vote for Mrs. Teller for state representative. If 1,500 people vote, predict the number of votes Mrs. Teller will receive. about 780

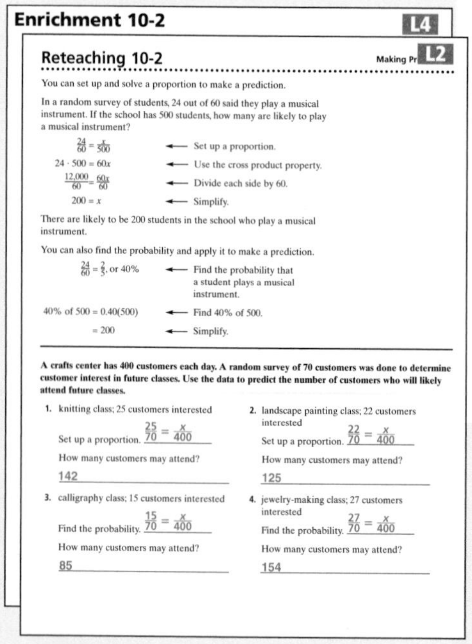
Enrichment 10-2 L4

Reteaching 10-2 Making Pr L2

You can set up and solve a proportion to make a prediction.

In a random survey of students, 24 out of 60 said they play a musical instrument. If the school has 500 students, how many are likely to play a musical instrument?

$\frac{24}{60} = \frac{x}{500}$ ← Set up a proportion.
$24 \cdot 500 = 60x$ ← Use the cross product property.
$\frac{12{,}000}{60} = \frac{60x}{60}$ ← Divide each side by 60.
$200 = x$ ← Simplify.

There are likely to be 200 students in the school who play a musical instrument.

You can also find the probability and apply it to make a prediction.

$\frac{24}{60} = \frac{2}{5}$, or 40% ← Find the probability that a student plays a musical instrument.
40% of 500 = 0.40(500) ← Find 40% of 500.
= 200 ← Simplify.

A crafts center has 400 customers each day. A random survey of 70 customers was done to determine customer interest in future classes. Use the data to predict the number of customers who will likely attend future classes.

1. knitting class; 25 customers interested
   Set up a proportion. $\frac{25}{70} = \frac{x}{400}$
   How many customers may attend? 142
2. landscape painting class; 22 customers interested
   Set up a proportion. $\frac{22}{70} = \frac{x}{400}$
   How many customers may attend? 125
3. calligraphy class; 15 customers interested
   Find the probability. $\frac{15}{70} = \frac{x}{400}$
   How many customers may attend? 85
4. jewelry-making class; 27 customers interested
   Find the probability. $\frac{27}{70} = \frac{x}{400}$
   How many customers may attend? 154

GO Online
Homework Video Tutor
Visit: PHSchool.com
Web Code: ase-1002

For Exercises 21–24, use the table at the right. Suppose 9,000 people vote in the election. Predict the number of votes each candidate will receive.

Election Poll

Candidate	Number of Votes
Araujo	50
Beech	15
Ciardi	58
Undecided	27
Total	**150**

21. Araujo 3,000 votes
22. Beech 900 votes
23. Ciardi 3,480 votes
24. **Writing in Math** On the day of the election, Araujo received the most votes. Explain why your prediction may have been incorrect. See left.

24. Answers may vary. Sample: Experimental results are not necessarily the same as the actual results. For example, the survey results could have been based on a small percentage of the people voting.

The probability that a randomly selected student fits a description is given. Use the probability to predict the number of students in a school of 600 who will be in that category.

25. The probability a student wears contact lenses is 16%. 96 students
26. The probability a student has a brother is 45%. 270 students
27. The probability a student has a sister is 48%. 288 students
28. The probability a student has a brother and a sister is 23%. 138 students

C 29. **Challenge** Suppose the probability of being an eighth-grader at Sunrise Middle School is $\frac{1}{3}$. The probability of an eighth-grader being in Mr. Shelton's math class is $\frac{2}{7}$. Predict how many of the school's 630 students are in Mr. Shelton's eighth-grade math class. 60 students

Test Prep and Mixed Review

Practice

Gridded Response

30. The probability that an adult in America is lactose intolerant is $\frac{1}{4}$. About how many people would be lactose intolerant in a group of 450 adult Americans? 113
31. The two triangles below are similar. Find the length of FD. 6

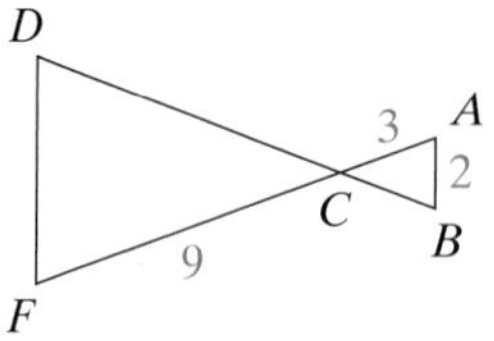

GO for Help

For Exercises	See Lesson
32–33	8-5

Find the lateral area of each figure to the nearest square unit.

32.

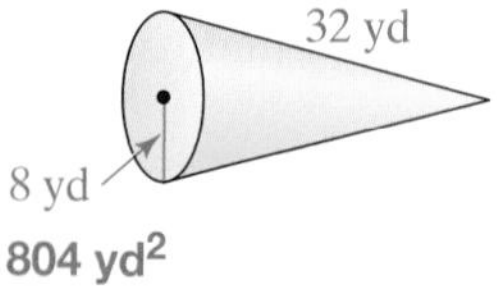

804 yd²

33.

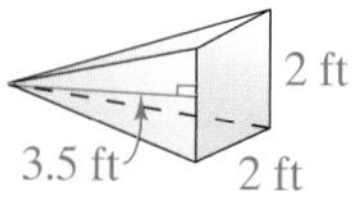

14 ft²

Test Prep

Resources

For additional practice with a variety of test item formats:

- Test-Taking Strategies, p. 503
- Test Prep, p. 507
- Test-Taking Strategies with Transparencies

Alternative Assessment

Students in pairs describe an election result. Each student writes a ratio to represent the probability of voting for a candidate and decides on the number of people who vote. Partners switch papers and predict the number of people who vote for their partner's candidate.

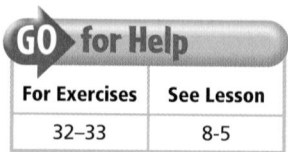

Extension

For Use With Lesson 10-2

Complements and Probability

The **complement** of an event is the opposite of that event. For example, in a coin toss, heads is the complement of tails. The sum of the probabilities of an event and its complement is 1.

EXAMPLE

Find the probability of *not* rolling a 5 with a number cube.

Since *not rolling a 5* and *rolling a 5* are complements, first find $P(5)$.

$P(5) = \frac{1}{6}$ ← Rolling a 5 is one of six equally likely outcomes.

$1 - \frac{1}{6} = \frac{5}{6}$ ← $P(\text{not } 5)$ is the complement of $P(5)$, so $P(\text{not } 5) + P(5) = 1$. Subtract $P(5)$ from 1.

The probability of *not* rolling a 5 is $\frac{5}{6}$.

Exercises

A spinner is divided into 12 equal sections numbered from 1 to 12. You spin the spinner once. Find each probability. Write it as a fraction.

1. $P(\text{complement of } 2)$ $\frac{11}{12}$
2. $P(\text{not odd})$ $\frac{1}{2}$
3. $P(\text{not } 3, 5, \text{or } 10)$ $\frac{3}{4}$

Checkpoint Quiz 1

Lessons 10-1 through 10-2

Use the table at the right for Exercises 1–3. Find the probability that a randomly selected student ate each meal.

1. $P(\text{dinner})$ 0.95
2. $P(\text{lunch})$ 0.94
3. $P(\text{breakfast})$ 0.77
4. Do your answers to Exercises 1–3 represent theoretical or experimental probability? Explain. See margin.
5. The probability that a fair coin lands on heads is 50%. Predict the number of heads you will toss in 20 trials. 10 heads
6. The probability that a toy is defective is $\frac{1}{630}$. Predict how many defective toys will be in a shipment of 5,670 toys. 9 toys

Meals Eaten by 1,493 Students

Meals	Number of Students
Breakfast	1,150
Lunch	1,403
Dinner	1,413
Snack	1,329

Checkpoint Quiz 1

4. Experimental; the results are based on a survey.

Extension

Complements and Probability

Probabilities refer to the chances that an event may or may not happen. Students consider the probability of an event occurring, as well as its *complement*—the probability that the same event will not occur.

Guided Instruction

Before beginning the feature, review the difference between experimental and theoretical probability. Discuss possible outcomes of tossing a coin once. Ask:

- *What is the theoretical probability, when you toss a coin, of getting heads?* $\frac{1}{2}$
- *What is the theoretical probability of getting tails?* $\frac{1}{2}$
- *Is there any other possible result?* No
- *What is the sum of these two probabilities?* 1

Differentiated Instruction

Special Needs L1

Help students remember the correct spelling for the *complement* of an event by relating it to *complete*. A *compliment*, or approving remark, has a different spelling.

Checkpoint Quiz

Use this Checkpoint Quiz to check students' understanding of the skills and concepts of Lessons 10-1 through 10-2.

Resources

- All in One Teaching Resources Checkpoint Quiz 1
- ExamView Assessment Suite CD-ROM
- Success Tracker Online Intervention

10-3

1. Plan

Objective
To identify random samples and biased questions and to judge conclusions based on survey results

Examples
1 Determining Random Samples
2 Identifying Bias in Questions
3 Judging Valid Conclusions

Math Understandings: p. 468C

Professional Development

Math Background

A survey collects information about a group of people or objects called a *population*. A *sample* is a part of the population. In a *random sample*, each member of the population has the same chance of being selected as every other member. A *biased* survey question is unfair because it makes one answer seem better than another and can affect survey conclusion.

More Math Background: p. 468C

Lesson Planning and Resources

See p. 468E for a list of the resources that support this lesson.

PowerPoint

Bell Ringer Practice

Check Skills You'll Need
Use student page, transparency, or PowerPoint. For intervention, direct students to:
Experimental and Theoretical Probability
Lesson 10-1
Extra Skills and Word Problems Practice, Ch. 10

10-3 Conducting a Survey

Check Skills You'll Need

1. **Vocabulary Review** How do *theoretical* and *experimental* probability differ? See back of book.

There are 9 blue, 5 red, and 4 green pencils in a bag. Find the probability of randomly selecting each color.

2. $P(\text{blue})$ $\frac{1}{2}$
3. $P(\text{green})$ $\frac{2}{9}$
4. $P(\text{red})$ $\frac{5}{18}$

GO for Help Lesson 10-1

What You'll Learn

To identify random samples and biased questions and to judge conclusions based on survey results

New Vocabulary population, sample, random sample, biased questions

Why Learn This?

Television program ratings are based on a sample of households from across the United States. You can use random samples to make conjectures about larger groups.

Statisticians use surveys to collect information about specific groups. Any group of objects or people in a survey is called a **population.**

Sometimes a population includes too many objects or people to survey. You can use a sample of the population to find the characteristics of the population. A **sample** is a part of the population.

In a **random sample,** each object or person in the population has the same chance of being selected.

EXAMPLE Determining Random Samples

1 Determine whether each survey uses a random sample. Describe the population of the sample.

a. **Game Shows** At a game show, five people in the audience are selected to play by drawing seat numbers.

This is a random sample. The population is the audience.

b. **Surveys** A student interviews several people in his art class to determine the movie star most admired by the students at school.

This is not a random sample. The students in the art class may not represent the views of all the students at school. The population is the students at school.

Quick Check

1. To find out the type of music people in a city prefer, you survey people from 18 to 30 years old. Is the sample random? Explain. See back of book.

Differentiated Instruction Solutions for All Learners

Special Needs L1	**Below Level** L2
Students write questions for a survey about ice cream. They ask questions such as, *"Would it make sense if I stood in front of an ice-cream shop and asked only its customers if they liked ice-cream?"* No, this is not random. learning style: verbal	Students write a biased and unbiased question on a topic of their own choosing. They discuss why each question is biased or unbiased. Students rewrite each biased question as an unbiased question. learning style: verbal

Unfair questions in a survey are **biased questions.** They make assumptions that may not be true. Biased questions can also make one answer seem better than another.

EXAMPLE Identifying Bias in Questions

2 Look at the clipboard at the right. Determine whether the first two questions are biased.

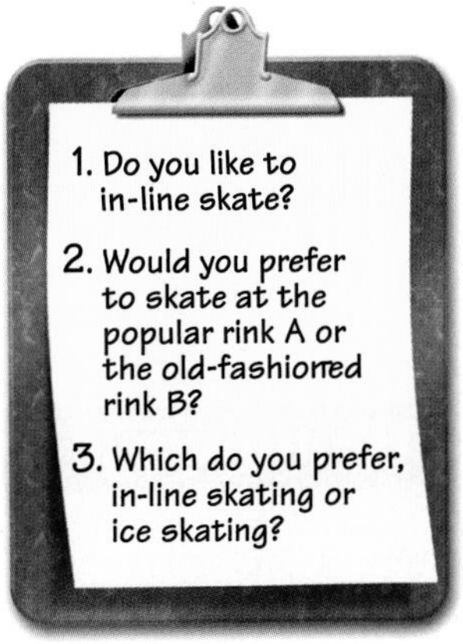

1. Do you like to in-line skate?
2. Would you prefer to skate at the popular rink A or the old-fashioned rink B?
3. Which do you prefer, in-line skating or ice skating?

Question 1 is unbiased. It does not try to persuade you one way or the other.

Question 2 is biased. It makes rink A seem more appealing than rink B.

Quick Check

2. What bias is there in Question 3? Revise the question to be unbiased.
   See back of book.

Using biased questions or poor sampling techniques leads to invalid conclusions.

EXAMPLE Judging Valid Conclusions

3 **Multiple Choice** Julie conducted a survey of people entering a women's clothing store.

Favorite Shopping Trip

Type	Number of Responses
Music	9
Clothing	26
Groceries	3
Books	2
Cars	1
Other	9
Total	**50**

From the results at the right, she concluded that shopping for clothes was the favorite shopping trip for people in her town. Which of the following best describes the reason her conclusion may not be valid?

(A) The survey should have been done on several days.
(B) The survey should have included more choices.
(C) The survey should have included people in a variety of stores.
(D) The survey should have included only women.

Julie surveyed only people entering a clothing store. She did not get a random sample of all shoppers. The correct answer is choice C.

Quick Check

3. Suppose Julie had surveyed only women. Would her conclusion be more valid? Explain why or why not.
   No; she would not get a random sample of all shoppers.

Test Prep Tip

Consider all the answer choices before choosing one. Think about how each change to the survey could affect the results.

2. Teach

Activity Lab

Use before the lesson.

All-in-One Teaching Resources

Activity Lab 10-3: Conducting a Survey

PowerPoint

Additional Examples

1 Tell whether the survey uses a random sample. Describe the population of the sample.

To find out how often students in your school go to movies, you select names at random from the school directory to interview.
Random; the population is the students in your school.

2 Determine whether the question is biased or not. Explain your answer.

Do you enjoy modern songs or old songs? Biased; "modern" and "old" are not neutral terms.

3 Malka asked three classmates from each table in the cafeteria:

What's your favorite shopping trip?	
Music	27
Clothing	26
Groceries	2
Household Items	3
Total	58

She concluded that shopping for music was the favorite activity of people in her town. Describe a reason why her conclusion may be invalid.
Malka should have asked shoppers of all ages.

All-in-One Teaching Resources

- Daily Notetaking Guide 10-3 L3
- Adapted Notetaking 10-3 L1

Advanced Learners L4
Students design a survey that includes a random sample and unbiased questions. They explain the validity of their conclusions.

learning style: verbal

English Language Learners ELL
Students identify bias in questions. They can use product advertisements or political questionnaires as examples. Volunteers read different questions out loud, and students identify words that indicate neutrality vs. words that lead a person to think in a particular way.

learning style: verbal

3. Practice

Assignment Guide

Check Your Understanding

Go over Exercises 1–4 in class before assigning the Homework Exercises.

Homework Exercises

A	Practice by Example	5–12
B	Apply Your Skills	13–17
C	Challenge	18
	Test Prep and Mixed Review	19–22

Homework Quick Check

To check students' understanding of key skills and concepts, go over Exercises 7, 12, 13, 14, and 15.

Differentiated Instruction Resources

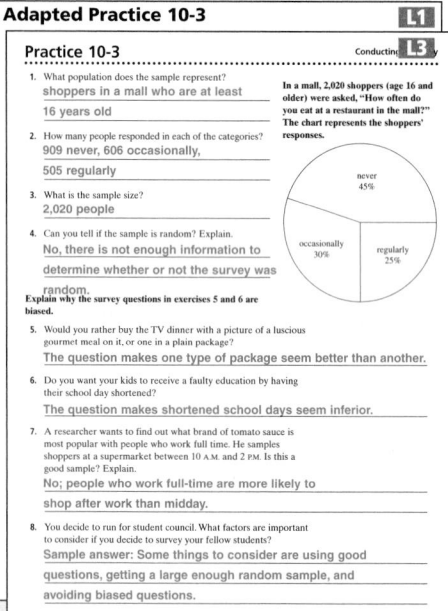

Adapted Practice 10-3 L1

Practice 10-3 Conducting ... L3

In a mall, 2,020 shoppers (age 16 and older) were asked, "How often do you eat at a restaurant in the mall?" The chart represents the shoppers' responses.

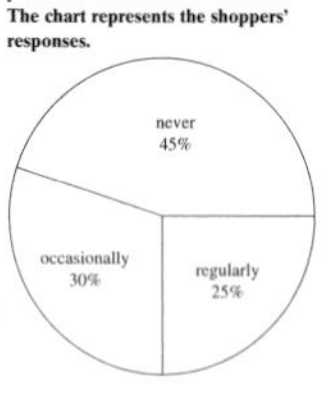

1. What population does the sample represent? shoppers in a mall who are at least 16 years old
2. How many people responded in each of the categories? 909 never, 606 occasionally, 505 regularly
3. What is the sample size? 2,020 people
4. Can you tell if the sample is random? Explain. No, there is not enough information to determine whether or not the survey was random.

Explain why the survey questions in exercises 5 and 6 are biased.

5. Would you rather buy the TV dinner with a picture of a luscious gourmet meal on it, or one in a plain package? The question makes one type of package seem better than another.
6. Do you want your kids to receive a faulty education by having their school day shortened? The question makes shortened school days seem inferior.
7. A researcher wants to find out what brand of tomato sauce is most popular with people who work full time. He samples shoppers at a supermarket between 10 A.M. and 2 P.M. Is this a good sample? Explain. No; people who work full-time are more likely to shop after work than midday.
8. You decide to run for student council. What factors are important to consider if you decide to survey your fellow students? Sample answer: Some things to consider are using good questions, getting a large enough random sample, and avoiding biased questions.

10-3 • Guided Problem Solving GPS L3

GPS Student Page 483, Exercise 15:

Market Research A market research company interviews randomly selected people who register a car during the year to recommend a fair purchase price of cars at a local dealership.

a. What is the population used in the survey?

b. **Probability** Find the experimental probability of a customer choosing the \$20,000–\$24,999 range.

Price Range	Frequency
\$10,000–\$14,999	15
\$15,000–\$19,999	8
\$20,000–\$24,999	12
\$25,000–\$29,999	6

Understand

1. What does *population* refer to in part (a)? the group of people that are surveyed.
2. What are you asked to find in part (b)? the experimental probability of a customer choosing the \$20,000–\$24,000 range

Plan and Carry Out

3. Who is interviewed? randomly selected people who registered a car during the year
4. What is the population used for the survey? randomly selected people who registered a car during the year
5. What is the ratio for experimental probability? $P(\text{event}) = \frac{\text{number of times event occurs}}{\text{total number of trials}}$
6. Use the frequencies from the chart to find the experimental probability. $P(\text{event}) = \frac{12}{41}$

Check

7. For a sample to be random, each item has an equal opportunity to be picked. Did this market research use a random sample? Explain. Yes; the people were randomly selected.

Solve Another Problem

8. Jane conducts a survey of women's fitness club members aged 35–44. What is the population used for her survey? female fitness club members aged 35–44

Check Your Understanding

1. **Vocabulary** Why do researchers use samples?
   1. Researchers use samples because there are usually too many objects or people in a population to survey.
2. Explain why this sample is not random: To find how much time students spend traveling to school, you interview students as they get off one school bus. Students from one bus do not represent all students traveling to school.
3. Rewrite this question to be unbiased: Do you like entertaining reality television or boring homework?
   3. Answers may vary. Sample: Do you like reality television or homework, or neither?
4. Why should you avoid using biased questions in a survey? Answers may vary. Sample: Biased questions may lead to invalid conclusions.

Homework Exercises

For more exercises, see Extra Skills and Word Problems.

GO for Help

For Exercises	See Examples
5–8	1
9–11	2
12	3

A **Determine whether each survey uses a random sample. Describe the population of the sample.** 5–8. See margin.

5. Your teacher puts the names of the students in your class into a box. He selects class representatives by drawing names out of the box.
6. You survey 25 friends about student support of school sports teams.
7. You want to know how often middle school students buy clothes. You survey every tenth student who arrives at a middle school.
8. Your principal wants to find out what foods to serve at school. The principal interviews 30 students in the eighth grade.

Determine whether each question is biased. Explain your answer.

9. Do you like putrid carnations or sweet-smelling roses? Biased; it makes roses sound more appealing than carnations.
10. Do you prefer the green chair or the blue chair? Not biased; it does not try to influence your answer.
11. What types of movies have you seen? Not biased; it does not try to influence your answer.
12. A local market surveys every twentieth customer to determine whether customers think the store's cashiers are friendly and helpful. Is this a good sample? Explain. Yes; you are using a random sample.

B **GPS**

13. **Guided Problem Solving** Suppose you survey people walking on the street in a city. Of those surveyed, 60% think the city is a wonderful place to visit. Should you conclude that there is a high probability that a visitor will enjoy the city? Explain. See left.
    - What is the population you are trying to survey?
    - What population did you actually survey?

    13. No; not everyone walking on the street is a visitor.
14. **Writing in Math** How do biased surveys affect probability and statistics? Answers may vary. Sample: biased surveys may lead to misleading probability values and statistics.

GO Online
Homework Video Tutor
Visit: PHSchool.com
Web Code: ase-1003

5. This is a random sample; the population is the students in the class.
6. This is not a random sample; 25 friends may not be representative of all of the students in the school.
7. This is not a random sample; students at one middle school may not represent all middle school students.
8. This is not a random sample; students in the eighth grade are not representative of all the students in the school.
17. Answers may vary. Sample: Do you prefer to swim in a pool or in the ocean, or neither?

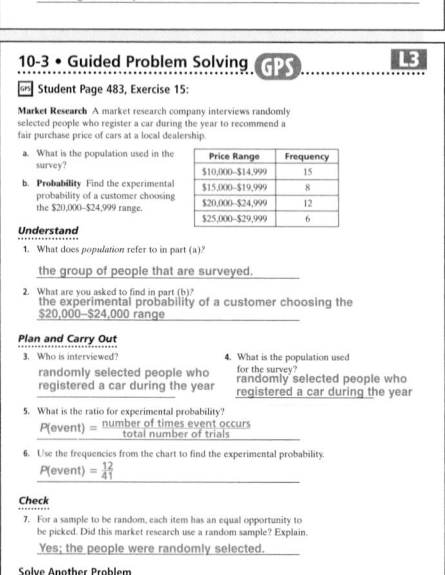

Careers Market researchers analyze data to make recommendations and predictions to companies about their products.

15. **Market Research** A market research company interviews randomly selected people who register a car during the year to recommend fair purchase prices of cars at a local dealership. (GPS)
    a. What is the population used in the survey? people who register a car
    b. Find the experimental probability of a customer choosing the \$20,000–\$24,999 range. $\frac{12}{41}$

Recommended Purchase Price

Price Range	Frequency
\$10,000–\$14,999	15
\$15,000–\$19,999	8
\$20,000–\$24,999	12
\$25,000–\$29,999	6

Open-Ended **Rewrite each biased question as an unbiased question.**

16. Would you rather watch a long baseball game or an exciting figure skating competition? Answers may vary. Sample: Do you prefer to watch baseball or figure skating, or neither?
17. Do you prefer swimming in a closed-in area, such as a pool, or a more open and challenging area, such as a lake or an ocean? See margin.

(C) 18. **Challenge** Explain why this question is biased: How do you like your eggs cooked? It assumes you like eggs.

Test Prep and Mixed Review

Practice

Multiple Choice

19. One Tuesday, Kristy asked every fifth person who entered the local pool whether he or she prefers swimming in a pool or the ocean. She concluded that most people prefer swimming in a pool. Which is the best explanation for why her conclusion might NOT be valid? C
    (A) The survey should have been done on a Saturday.
    (B) The survey should have been done with children only.
    (C) The sample only represents people who swim at the pool.
    (D) The pool is only open during the summer.
20. Katie has read 19 books this year and plans to read two books each week for the rest of the year. Which procedure can she use to find how many books she will have read after six more weeks? J
    (F) Multiply 19 by 2 and subtract 6.
    (G) Multiply 19 by 2 and add 6.
    (H) Multiply 6 by 2 and subtract 19.
    (J) Multiply 6 by 2 and add 19.
21. Kim has \$30. School lunch costs \$2 each day. Which equation can she use to find y, the money she has left after x days of buying school lunches? B
    (A) $y = 30 + 2x$
    (B) $y = 30 - 2x$
    (C) $y = 2 + 30x$
    (D) $y = 2 - 30x$
22. You roll a number cube. Find the odds in favor of rolling a number less than 5. 2 : 1

GO for Help

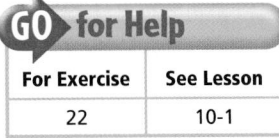

For Exercise	See Lesson
22	10-1

Online lesson quiz, PHSchool.com, Web Code: asa-1003

4. Assess & Reteach

PowerPoint

Lesson Quiz

For items 1–3, use this situation: You want to find out how many people plan to attend the school pep rally.

1. You survey all students in your science class. Explain why this is not a good sample. See back of book.
2. Explain why this is a biased question: Wouldn't you rather stay home the night of the pep rally? See back of book.
3. You survey the members of the football team. Explain how your conclusions will be affected. See back of book.
4. The owner of a fitness center wants to increase the number of members. She mails a questionnaire to current members, asking them to indicate their satisfaction with the center. Is this a good sample? Explain. See back of book.

Enrichment 10-3 L4

Reteaching 10-3 Conducting L2

In a survey, the entire group is called the *population*.
A *sample* is a small part of the population.

For a sample to be fair, it should be *random*. In a random sample, each member of the population has an equal chance of being selected.

- Survey questions should be fair, not *biased*. They should not make one answer appear better than another.

  Biased question: Did you hate that movie as much as I did?

  Fair question: What did you think of that movie?

Suppose you want to find out how students feel about new school colors. Tell whether each survey plan describes a good sample. Justify your answer.

1. You interview students while they are in art class. No; the sample includes only students interested in art, not the whole population.
2. You randomly select students from each homeroom in the school. Yes; every student has an equal chance of being selected.

Rewrite each question so that it is fair.

3. Do you prefer salad or a nice, juicy steak for dinner? Do you prefer a salad or steak for dinner?
4. Isn't purple your favorite T-shirt color? What is your favorite T-shirt color?

Explain why each question is biased.

5. Don't you agree that Mrs. Meredith expects too much of her students? Questioner is giving away his or her own feelings.
6. Were you able to follow that boring movie? Question assumes that the movie was boring.

Alternative Assessment

Students in pairs make up a biased survey question and suggest a sample that may produce invalid conclusions. Partners trade papers, suggest a more valid sample, and rewrite the survey question without bias.

Test Prep

Resources

For additional practice with a variety of test item formats:

- Test-Taking Strategies, p. 503
- Test Prep, p. 507
- Test-Taking Strategies with Transparencies

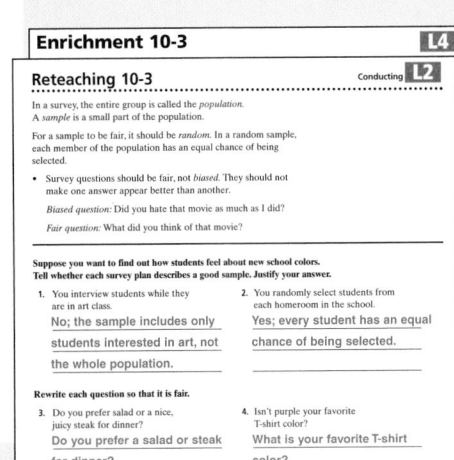

Activity Lab

Simulations With Random Numbers

Students may be familiar with how to use spreadsheet software to generate random digits in order to simulate a situation. This activity shows them how to use a graphing calculator to generate the random digits for a simulation.

Guided Instruction

Elicit from students what the advantages are of using a simulation to do a probability experiment. Guide them to appreciate that calculators can generate random digits rapidly.

Error Prevention!

Remind students that even though they are using a calculator to simulate a situation, the simulation is still only a model, much like the probability experiments with coins and spinners they completed previously. Emphasize, therefore, that the graphing calculator, with its ability to quickly generate random digits, may provide results other than those they would expect, given their prior knowledge of the theoretical probability of outcomes.

Resources

- graphing calculators

10-3b Activity Lab Technology

Simulations With Random Numbers

You can generate random numbers with a graphing calculator or a computer to simulate some situations.

To generate a group of ten digits on a graphing calculator, select the **rand** option from the PRB menu. Each time you press ENTER you will get a different random number. If a random number contains nine digits, use 0 for the tenth digit. When reordering random numbers, ignore the decimal point.

rand	.606334928
rand	.9518983326
rand	.2209784733
rand	.5972865589

EXAMPLE

Blood Types About 10% of people in the United States have type-B blood. Find the experimental probability that exactly one of the next two donors at a hospital will have type-B blood.

Since 10% of the people have type-B blood, let 10%, or one out of ten digits, represent this group of people. Let 0 represent type-B blood and the remaining nine digits represent the other blood types.

Group the digits of a random number into pairs to represent two donors.

60	63	34	92	80
95	18	98	33	26
22	09	78	47	33
59	72	86	55	89

Any pair with exactly one 0 represents one of two people with type-B blood. There are three such pairs in this list.

Based on 20 trials, the experimental probability is $\frac{3}{20}$, or 15%.

Exercises

Generate random numbers to simulate each problem. 1–2. Check students' work.

1. **Blood Types** About 40% of people in the United States have type-A blood. Find the experimental probability that exactly one of the next two donors at a blood drive will have type-A blood.

2. Choose *coin, number cube, spinner,* or *calculator* to simulate each probability. Justify your choice.
   a. 30% chance of rain
   b. random date is Saturday
   c. 1 in 3 chance of winning

10-4a Activity Lab

Hands On

Comparing Types of Events

You can conduct an experiment with more than one event. Sometimes the outcome of the second event does not depend on the outcome of the first event. In other cases the first event affects the probability of the second event.

ACTIVITY

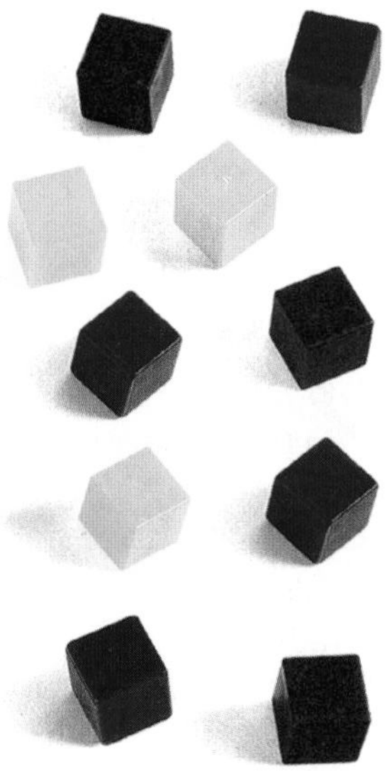

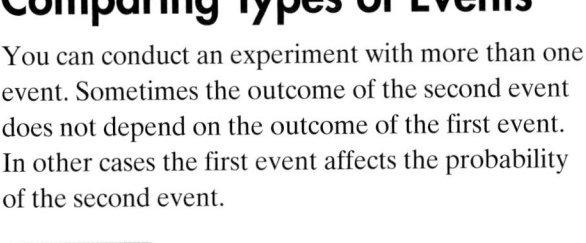

1. Place three blue cubes, four green cubes, and three yellow cubes in a bag. **Check students' work.**
2. Find the theoretical probability of drawing a green cube. $\frac{2}{5}$
3. Suppose you draw a green cube and replace it. What is the theoretical probability of drawing a green cube on a second draw? $\frac{2}{5}$
4. Suppose you draw a green cube and do *not* replace it. What is the theoretical probability of drawing a green cube on the second draw? $\frac{1}{3}$
5. **Number Sense** Is the probability of drawing a green cube on the second draw with replacement *greater than, less than,* or *equal to* the probability without replacement? **greater than**
6. Copy and extend the table below for 20 trials. For each trial, draw a cube from the bag, record the color, return the cube to the bag, and draw a second cube. Then return the second cube to the bag.

Trial	First Draw	Second Draw
1	?	?
2	?	?

6–10. Check students' work.

7. Use your results to find the experimental probability of drawing two green cubes when the first cube is drawn and replaced.
8. Complete another table for 20 trials. For each trial, draw a cube from the bag, record the color, do not return the cube to the bag, and draw a second cube. Then return both cubes to the bag.
9. Use your results to find the experimental probability of drawing two green cubes when the first cube drawn is not replaced.
10. **Writing in Math** Compare your answers for Exercises 7 and 9.
11. **Reasoning** You draw two cubes from a bag of 20 cubes of varying colors, including yellow. Will P(both yellow) be greater *with* or *without* replacement? Justify your answer.

11. The probability of selecting two yellow cubes will be greater with replacement since you will have more yellow cubes to choose from.

Activity Lab

Comparing Types of Events

Students pick colored cubes at random to examine the difference between events that depend on each other, *dependent events*, and those events that occur separately from one another, *independent events*.

Guided Instruction

Have students use a set of colored cubes (or tiles) and a bag. Make sure that students record their results after drawing each cube.

Teaching Tip
Review the difference between *theoretical probability* and *experimental probability*. **Theoretical probability is the expected likelihood that an event will occur; experimental probability is the likelihood of an event based on a number of experimental trials.**

Error Prevention!

Remind students to pay close attention to whether they are returning or not returning a cube to the bag.

Exercises
For exercise 9 ask: *Does drawing two cubes of the same color seem more or less likely than drawing one cube of that color?* **less likely** *How about drawing three cubes of the same color?* **even less likely**

Resources

- Activity Lab 10-4: Independent and Dependent Events
- colored cubes or tiles

10-4

1. Plan

Objective
To find the probabilities of independent and dependent events

Examples
1 Probability of Independent Events
2 Probability of Dependent Events
3 Dependent or Independent Events?

Math Understandings: p. 468C

Professional Development

Math Background

Compound events are two or more related events. If the outcome of the first event does not affect the outcome of the second, the events are *independent*. If the outcome of the first event affects the outcome of the second, the events are *dependent*.

More Math Background: p. 468C

Lesson Planning and Resources

See p. 468E for a list of the resources that support this lesson.

PowerPoint

Bell Ringer Practice

Check Skills You'll Need
Use student page, transparency, or PowerPoint. For intervention, direct students to:
Making Predictions
Lesson 10-2
Extra Skills and Word Problems Practice, Ch. 10

10-4 Independent and Dependent Events

Check Skills You'll Need

1. **Vocabulary Review** How can you use *theoretical probability* to make predictions? See below.

You roll a number cube 50 times. Predict how many times the given outcome will occur.

2. 2 about 8	**3.** 5 about 8
4. 8 0	**5.** odd about 25

GO for Help Lesson 10-2

Check Skills You'll Need

1. You can set up a proportion to solve, or you can multiply the theoretical probability by the population size.

What You'll Learn

To find the probabilities of independent and dependent events

New Vocabulary independent events, dependent events

Why Learn This?

As people buy different items, a store's stock changes. The chances of finding your favorite team's jersey will change if the store does not replace its stock.

Compound events are two or more related events. Two events are **independent events** if the occurrence of one event does not affect the probability of the occurrence of the other.

KEY CONCEPTS **Independent Events**

If A and B are independent events, then $P(A, \text{ then } B) = P(A) \cdot P(B)$.

EXAMPLE **Probability of Independent Events**

1 **Inventory** The table shows colors for 20 shirts. A clerk selects one shirt from a rack at random, puts a price tag on it, replaces it, and selects again. Find the probability that the first shirt is blue and the second is red.

Color	Number of Shirts
Blue	6
Red	4
Black	3
Orange	7

Because the first shirt is replaced, these are independent events.

$$P(\text{blue, then red}) = P(\text{blue}) \cdot P(\text{red})$$
$$= \frac{6}{20} \cdot \frac{4}{20} \quad \leftarrow \text{Substitute.}$$
$$= \frac{24}{400} = \frac{3}{50} \quad \leftarrow \text{Multiply and simplify.}$$

The probability of choosing a blue and then a red shirt is $\frac{3}{50}$.

Online active math

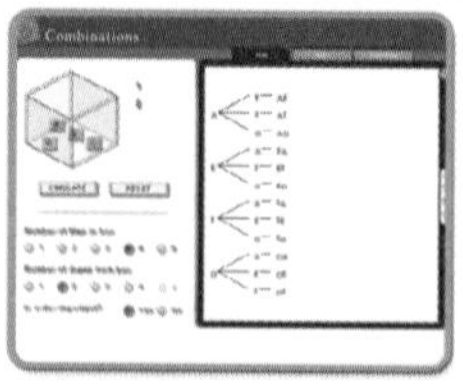

For: Compound Events Activity
Use: Interactive Textbook, 10-4

Quick Check

1. Use the data in Example 1 to find $P(\text{orange, then black})$. $\frac{21}{400}$ or 0.0525

Differentiated Instruction Solutions for All Learners

Special Needs L1
Students find the probability of independent and dependent events using colored marbles or counters. They discuss what makes each set of events independent or dependent.
learning style: tactile

Below Level L2
Review multiplying and simplifying fractions. Students can use a different color for each set of common factors.
$\frac{3}{20} \cdot \frac{10}{21} = \frac{3}{2 \times 2 \times 5} \cdot \frac{2 \times 5}{3 \times 7} = \frac{\cancel{3}}{\cancel{2} \times 2 \times \cancel{5}} \cdot \frac{\cancel{2} \times \cancel{5}}{\cancel{3} \times 7} = \frac{1}{14}$
learning style: visual

When the outcome of one event does affect the outcome of a second event, the events are **dependent events.**

KEY CONCEPTS **Dependent Events**

If A and B are dependent events, $P(A, \text{ then } B) = P(A) \cdot P(B \text{ after } A)$.

EXAMPLE Probability of Dependent Events

2 **Multiple Choice** Two girls and three boys volunteer to speak at a school assembly. One student is selected at random to speak. Then another student is selected. What is the probability of selecting two girls?

Ⓐ $\frac{2}{5}$ Ⓑ $\frac{1}{5}$ Ⓒ $\frac{1}{10}$ Ⓓ $\frac{1}{25}$

First student $P(\text{girl}) = \frac{2}{5}$ ← **Two of the five volunteers are girls.**

Second student $P(\text{girl after girl}) = \frac{1}{4}$ ← **One girl is left of four volunteers.**

$P(\text{girl, then girl}) = P(\text{girl}) \cdot P(\text{girl after girl})$ ← **Use the formula for dependent events.**

$= \frac{2}{5} \cdot \frac{1}{4}$ ← **Substitute.**

$= \frac{2}{20} = \frac{1}{10}$ ← **Multiply and simplify.**

The probability of selecting two girls is $\frac{1}{10}$. The correct answer is choice C.

Quick Check

2. Find the probability that first a boy and then a girl are selected. $\frac{3}{10}$

EXAMPLE Dependent or Independent Events?

State whether the events are dependent or independent. Explain.

3 **a.** Select a croquet ball. Do not replace it. Then select another ball.

After the first ball is chosen, the collection of remaining items has changed. These are dependent events.

b. Roll a number cube. Then roll the number cube again.

The result of the first roll will have no effect on how the number cube rolls the second time. These are independent events.

Quick Check 3a–b. See above left.

3. Are the events dependent or independent? Explain.
   a. Flip a coin and then flip it again.
   b. Pick a name from a hat. Without replacing it, pick another.

Test Prep Tip

When answering probability questions, first decide whether the events are independent or dependent.

3a. Independent; the outcome of the first coin flip does not affect the outcome of the second coin flip.

b. Dependent; since you do not replace the name after you pick it, the outcome of the first pick affects the outcome of the second pick.

2. Teach

Activity Lab

Use before the lesson.
Student Edition Activity Lab, Hands On 10-4a, Comparing Types of Events, p. 485

All in One Teaching Resources

Activity Lab 10-4: Independent and Dependent Events

Guided Instruction

Example 2
Have students write names on five index cards and experiment with drawing the names and recording the results.

PowerPoint

Additional Examples

1 A box contains 3 red marbles and 7 blue ones. You draw a marble at random, replace it, and draw another. Find P(blue and blue). $\frac{49}{100}$

2 From a class of 12 girls and 14 boys, you select two students at random. What is the probability that both students are boys? $\frac{7}{25}$

3 State whether the event is a dependent or independent event.

A piggy bank is filled with dimes, nickels, and pennies. You draw a coin at random, and get a penny, which you keep. You draw at random again, and get a dime. dependent

All in One Teaching Resources

- Daily Notetaking Guide 10-4 L3
- Adapted Notetaking 10-4 L1

Closure

- Contrast the formulas for finding the probability of independent and dependent events. Sample: For independent events, you multiply *P(A)* times *P(B)*; for dependent events, you multiply *P(A)* times *P(B after A)*.

Advanced Learners L4	**English Language Learners** ELL
In Example 2, students find the probability of selecting a boy and then another boy. $\frac{3}{10}$ or 0.3 **learning style: verbal**	Make sure to include the terms *with replacement* and *without replacement* when reviewing the vocabulary for this lesson. Students should know that putting something back (a marble, for example) after taking it means the item has been *replaced*. **learning style: verbal**

3. Practice

Assignment Guide

Check Your Understanding

Go over Exercises 1–5 in class before assigning the Homework Exercises.

Homework Exercises

A	Practice by Example	6–16
B	Apply Your Skills	17–24
C	Challenge	25
	Test Prep and Mixed Review	26–30

Homework Quick Check

To check students' understanding of key skills and concepts, go over Exercises 9, 12, 21, 23, and 24.

Differentiated Instruction Resources

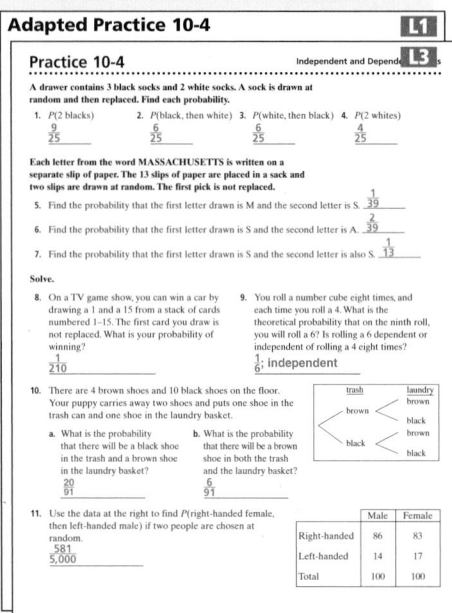

Adapted Practice 10-4 L1

Practice 10-4 L3 Independent and Dependent Events

A drawer contains 3 black socks and 2 white socks. A sock is drawn at random and then replaced. Find each probability.

1. *P*(2 blacks) $\frac{9}{25}$
2. *P*(black, then white) $\frac{6}{25}$
3. *P*(white, then black) $\frac{6}{25}$
4. *P*(2 whites) $\frac{4}{25}$

Each letter from the word MASSACHUSETTS is written on a separate slip of paper. The 13 slips of paper are placed in a sack and two slips are drawn at random. The first pick is not replaced.

5. Find the probability that the first letter drawn is M and the second letter is S. $\frac{1}{39}$
6. Find the probability that the first letter drawn is S and the second letter is A. $\frac{2}{39}$
7. Find the probability that the first letter drawn is S and the second letter is also S. $\frac{1}{13}$

Solve.

8. On a TV game show, you can win a car by drawing a 1 and a 15 from a stack of cards numbered 1–15. The first card you draw is not replaced. What is your probability of winning? $\frac{1}{210}$
9. You roll a number cube eight times, and each time you roll a 4. What is the theoretical probability that on the ninth roll, you will roll a 6? Is rolling a 6 dependent or independent of rolling a 4 eight times? $\frac{1}{6}$; independent
10. There are 4 brown shoes and 10 black shoes on the floor. Your puppy carries away two shoes and puts one shoe in the trash can and one shoe in the laundry basket.

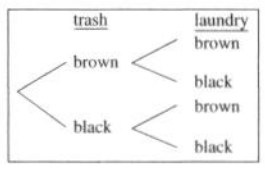

   a. What is the probability that there will be a black shoe in the trash and a brown shoe in the laundry basket? $\frac{20}{91}$
   b. What is the probability that there will be a brown shoe in both the trash and the laundry basket? $\frac{6}{91}$
11. Use the data at the right to find *P*(right-handed female, then left-handed male) if two people are chosen at random. $\frac{581}{5,000}$

	Male	Female
Right-handed	86	83
Left-handed	14	17
Total	100	100

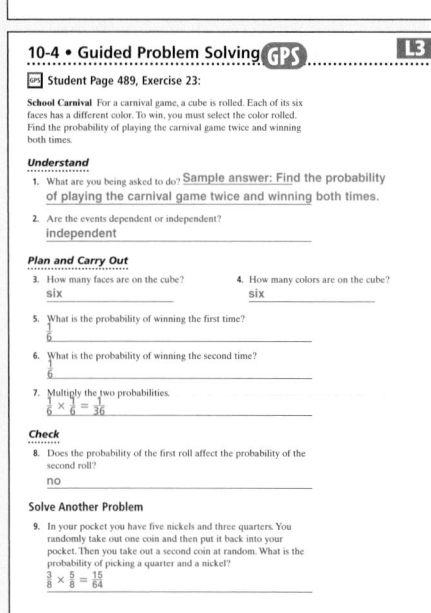

10-4 • Guided Problem Solving GPS L3

GPS Student Page 489, Exercise 23:

School Carnival For a carnival game, a cube is rolled. Each of its six faces has a different color. To win, you must select the color rolled. Find the probability of playing the carnival game twice and winning both times.

Understand

1. What are you being asked to do? Sample answer: Find the probability of playing the carnival game twice and winning both times.
2. Are the events dependent or independent? independent

Plan and Carry Out

3. How many faces are on the cube? six
4. How many colors are on the cube? six
5. What is the probability of winning the first time? $\frac{1}{6}$
6. What is the probability of winning the second time? $\frac{1}{6}$
7. Multiply the two probabilities. $\frac{1}{6} \times \frac{1}{6} = \frac{1}{36}$

Check

8. Does the probability of the first roll affect the probability of the second roll? no

Solve Another Problem

9. In your pocket you have five nickels and three quarters. You randomly take out one coin and then put it back into your pocket. Then you take out a second coin at random. What is the probability of picking a quarter and a nickel? $\frac{3}{8} \times \frac{5}{8} = \frac{15}{64}$

Check Your Understanding

1. **Vocabulary** How can you distinguish between independent and dependent events? See margin.

Are the events dependent or independent? Explain.

2. Toss a coin. Then roll a number cube. Independent; the outcome of the coin toss will have no effect on the roll.
3. Select a card. Do not replace it. Then select another card.

3. Dependent; after the first card is chosen, the remaining collection of cards has changed.

4. You choose an apple from two green apples and three red apples and eat it. Then you choose and eat another apple. Find *P*(green, then red). $\frac{3}{10}$
5. You roll a number cube and then roll it again. Find *P*(3, then 4). $\frac{1}{36}$

Homework Exercises

For more exercises, see Extra Skills and Word Problems.

GO for Help

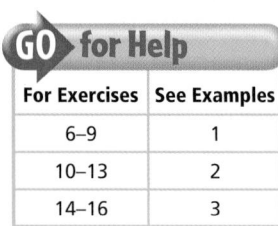

For Exercises	See Examples
6–9	1
10–13	2
14–16	3

A **Find each probability.** A different letter of the alphabet appears on each of 26 cards. You choose a card at random and then replace it. Then you choose a second card. Vowels are A, E, I, O, and U.

6. *P*(A, then B) $\frac{1}{676}$
7. *P*(C, then X) $\frac{1}{676}$
8. *P*(I, then a vowel) $\frac{5}{676}$
9. *P*(vowel, then a vowel) $\frac{25}{676}$

Find each probability. A bag contains the following marbles: 6 red, 4 orange, 3 yellow, 2 blue, and 5 green. You choose a marble at random and do not replace it. Then you select another marble.

10. *P*(red, then blue) $\frac{3}{95}$
11. *P*(red, then yellow) $\frac{9}{190}$
12. *P*(orange, then blue) $\frac{2}{95}$
13. *P*(red, then red) $\frac{3}{38}$

Are the events dependent or independent? Explain.

14. Select a card. Replace it. Then select another card. See left.

14. Independent; the outcome of the second draw is not dependent on the first draw.

15. Spin a spinner once. Then spin it again. Independent; the first spin does not affect the second spin.
16. Select a marble from a bag. Put it aside. Then select another marble. Dependent; the second selection is affected by the first selection.

B GPS 17. **Guided Problem Solving** Your family plans to visit two amusement parks. You have three favorite parks. Your sister has two different favorites. You write the name of each of the five parks on slips of paper. Then you select two parks at random. Find the probability that both parks selected are among your favorites. $\frac{3}{10}$
- How does the problem indicate replacement or not? Explain.
- Find the probability for each of the two drawings. Then multiply.

1. If the outcome of the first event affects the outcome of the second event, the events are dependent. If the outcome of the first event has no effect on the outcome of the second event, the events are independent.

28.

Stem	Leaves
0	9
1	0 0 1 3 4 4 4 4 6 7 9
2	0 2 5

Key: 1 | 0 means 10

24. See back of book.

GO Online
Homework Video Tutor
Visit: PHSchool.com
Web Code: ase-1004

Find each probability. Suppose you roll a number cube and spin the spinner at the right. Express your answer as a fraction in simplest form.

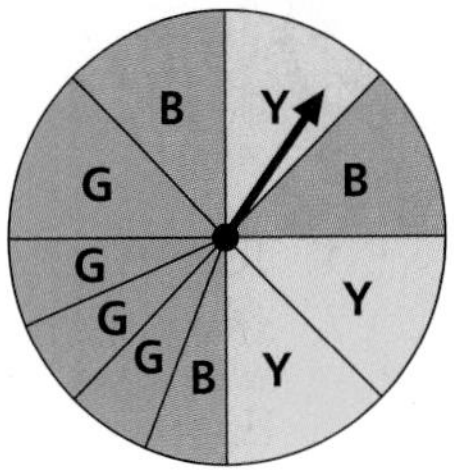

18. $P(3, \text{then green})$ $\frac{5}{96}$
19. $P(\text{prime, then blue})$ $\frac{5}{32}$
20. $P(5, \text{then yellow})$
21. $P(8, \text{then yellow})$ 0
22. $P(\text{an even number, then green})$ $\frac{5}{32}$

20. $\frac{1}{16}$

23. **School Carnival** GPS For a carnival game, a cube is rolled. Each of its six faces has a different color. To win, you must select the color rolled. You play the game twice. Find the probability of winning both times. $\frac{1}{36}$
24. **Writing in Math** What is the difference between independent and dependent events? Explain. See margin.
25. **Challenge** Suppose two events, A and B, are dependent. You know that $P(A, \text{then } B) = \frac{2}{15}$ and $P(B \text{ after } A) = \frac{1}{3}$. Find $P(A)$. $\frac{2}{5}$

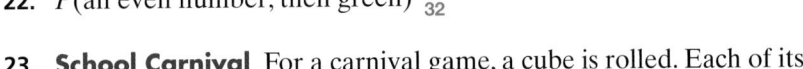

Test Prep and Mixed Review — Practice

Multiple Choice

26. A study indicates that the probability of a man being colorblind is $\frac{1}{20}$ and the probability of a woman being colorblind is $\frac{1}{200}$. What is the probability that two women chosen at random are colorblind? B
 - (A) $\frac{1}{400{,}000}$
 - (B) $\frac{1}{40{,}000}$
 - (C) $\frac{1}{400}$
 - (D) $\frac{11}{200}$
27. The figures shown below have a repeating pattern.

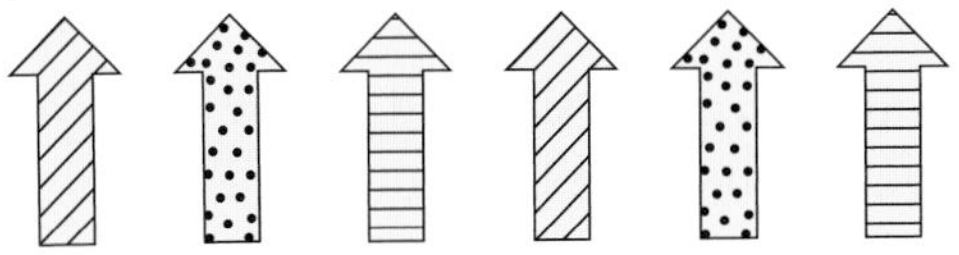

Which of the following is a 270° rotation of the ninth figure? J

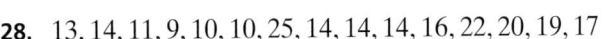

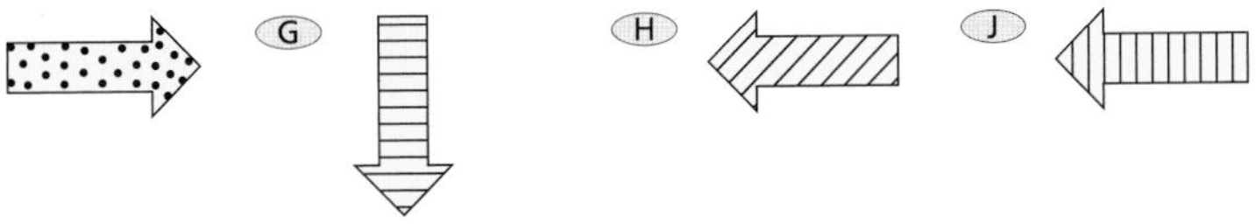

Make a stem-and-leaf plot for each set of data. 28–29. See margin.

28. 13, 14, 11, 9, 10, 10, 25, 14, 14, 14, 16, 22, 20, 19, 17
29. 6.4, 5.0, 6.5, 5.5, 5.5, 5.7, 6.8, 5.2, 6.1, 6.1, 5.7, 5.6, 7.0
30. 122, 125, 136, 100, 102, 105, 151, 144, 129, 128, 133, 156, 100, 100 See left.

30.

Stem	Leaf
10	0 0 0 2 5
11	
12	2 5 8 9
13	3 6
14	4
15	1 6

Key: 12 | 2 means 122

GO for Help

For Exercises	See Lesson
28–30	9-5

4. Assess & Reteach

PowerPoint

Lesson Quiz

A bag of marbles contains 2 red, 3 green, and 1 ivory marble. Use this information to solve Questions 1 and 2.

1. You randomly choose one marble, replace it, and then choose a second marble. Find the probability that both are green. $\frac{1}{4}$
2. You randomly choose one marble and then, without replacing the first marble, you choose a second marble. Find the probability that the first is ivory and the second is green. $\frac{1}{10}$
3. What kind of event is described in Question 1? independent
4. What kind of event is described in Question 2? dependent

28.

Stem	Leaf
0	9
1	0 0 1 3 4 4 4 4 6 7 9
2	0 2 5

Key: 1 | 0 means 10

29.

Stem	Leaf
5	0 2 5 5 6 7 7
6	1 1 4 5 8
7	0

Key: 5 | 0 means 5.0

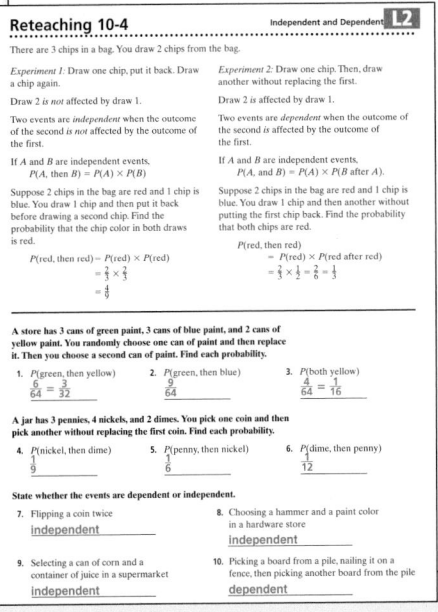

Enrichment 10-4 L4

Reteaching 10-4 Independent and Dependent L2

There are 3 chips in a bag. You draw 2 chips from the bag.

Experiment 1: Draw one chip, put it back. Draw a chip again.

Draw 2 *is not* affected by draw 1.

Two events are *independent* when the outcome of the second *is not* affected by the outcome of the first.

If A and B are independent events,
$P(A, \text{then } B) = P(A) \times P(B)$

Suppose 2 chips in the bag are red and 1 chip is blue. You draw 1 chip and then put it back before drawing a second chip. Find the probability that the chip color in both draws is red.

$P(\text{red, then red}) = P(\text{red}) \times P(\text{red}) = \frac{2}{3} \times \frac{2}{3} = \frac{4}{9}$

Experiment 2: Draw one chip. Then, draw another without replacing the first.

Draw 2 *is* affected by draw 1.

Two events are *dependent* when the outcome of the second *is* affected by the outcome of the first.

If A and B are independent events,
$P(A, \text{and } B) = P(A) \times P(B \text{ after } A)$.

Suppose 2 chips in the bag are red and 1 chip is blue. You draw 1 chip and then another without putting the first chip back. Find the probability that both chips are red.

$P(\text{red, then red}) = P(\text{red}) \times P(\text{red after red}) = \frac{2}{3} \times \frac{1}{2} = \frac{2}{6} = \frac{1}{3}$

A store has 3 cans of green paint, 3 cans of blue paint, and 2 cans of yellow paint. You randomly choose one can of paint and then replace it. Then you choose a second can of paint. Find each probability.

1. $P(\text{green, then yellow})$ $\frac{6}{64} = \frac{3}{32}$
2. $P(\text{green, then blue})$ $\frac{9}{64}$
3. $P(\text{both yellow})$ $\frac{4}{64} = \frac{1}{16}$

A jar has 3 pennies, 4 nickels, and 2 dimes. You pick one coin and then pick another without replacing the first coin. Find each probability.

4. $P(\text{nickel, then dime})$ $\frac{1}{9}$
5. $P(\text{penny, then nickel})$ $\frac{1}{6}$
6. $P(\text{dime, then penny})$ $\frac{1}{12}$

State whether the events are dependent or independent.

7. Flipping a coin twice — independent
8. Choosing a hammer and a paint color in a hardware store — independent
9. Selecting a can of corn and a container of juice in a supermarket — independent
10. Picking a board from a pile, nailing it on a fence, then picking another board from the pile — dependent

Alternative Assessment

Each student in a pair writes one problem that involves independent events and one problem that involves dependent events. Partners trade papers and solve each other's problems.

Test Prep

Resources
For additional practice with a variety of test item formats:
- Test-Taking Strategies, p. 503
- Test Prep, p. 507
- Test-Taking Strategies with Transparencies

Checkpoint Quiz

Use this Checkpoint Quiz to check students' understanding of the skills and concepts of Lessons 10-3 through 10-4.

Resources

- All in One Teaching Resources Checkpoint Quiz 2
- ExamView Assessment Suite CD-ROM
- Success Tracker Online Intervention

MATH GAMES

Yellow Up

Students toss 4 two-colored chips. They gain or lose points based on the outcome of the color(s) facing up. The first student to reach 20 points wins.

Guided Instruction

Alternative Method
Students may use coins or any object with two different faces.

Teaching Tip
Students could also make predictions before tossing. Have students explain why they made the predictions they did. Once they have tried the game a few times, ask students to describe any strategies they used to increase the accuracy of their predictions.

Resources

- two-colored chips, one side yellow and the other side red

Checkpoint Quiz 2

Lessons 10-3 through 10-4

1. To find out the types of books young readers prefer, you survey people at random at a local music store. Is this a good sample? Explain.
No; people at the music store are not representative of all the people who read.
2. Explain whether the question "Do you prefer watching an exciting movie or reading a dull book?" is biased.
Yes; it makes watching a movie seem more appealing than reading a book.

Find each probability. You place 10 cards marked with the letters of the word SIMULATION in a box and select one card at random. You return the card and select again.

3. P(I, then N) $\frac{1}{50}$
4. P(I, then vowel) $\frac{1}{10}$
5. P(N, then vowel) $\frac{1}{20}$
6. P(A, then not U) $\frac{9}{100}$

Find each probability. You place 14 cards marked with the numbers 0–13 in a box and select one card at random. You put the card aside and select again.

7. P(3, then 0) $\frac{1}{182}$
8. P(3, then even) $\frac{1}{26}$
9. P(5, then odd) $\frac{3}{91}$
10. P(2, then not 11) $\frac{6}{91}$

MATH GAMES

Yellow Up

What You'll Need

- a set of four chips, with red on one side and yellow on the other side of each chip, as shown at the right

How to Play

- Decide who is Player A and who is Player B.
- Each player tosses the chips once. If all four chips are the same color, Player A scores a point. If not, Player B scores a point.
- The first player to reach 20 points is the winner.

Do you think this game is fair? Explain.

You can evaluate the fairness of the game. Make an organized list of all possible outcomes. Which is more likely: exactly 1, exactly 2, exactly 3, or exactly 4 red sides up?

Does this change your decision about the fairness of the game? Explain.

490

10-5 Permutations

Check Skills You'll Need

1. **Vocabulary Review** What is a *sample space*? See below.

Find the number of possible outcomes in each situation.

2. Roll a number cube and toss a coin. 12
3. Roll two number cubes. 36
4. Toss two coins. 4

GO for Help Lesson 5-8

Check Skills You'll Need

1. a collection of all possible outcomes

What You'll Learn

To find the number of permutations of a set of objects

New Vocabulary permutation, counting principle, factorial

Why Learn This?

In a track meet, six runners compete in the 200-meter dash. The order in which the runners finish matters because it affects the scoring of the meet.

Sometimes, the order of objects in an arrangement is important. A **permutation** is an arrangement of a set of objects in a particular order. You can use a tree diagram to find the number of permutations of objects.

EXAMPLE Permutations Using a Diagram

1 In how many ways can Ryan, Emily, and Justin line up in gym class?

Ryan	Emily	Justin	①	(R, E, J)
	Justin	Emily	②	(R, J, E)
Emily	Ryan	Justin	③	(E, R, J)
	Justin	Ryan	④	(E, J, R)
Justin	Ryan	Emily	⑤	(J, R, E)
	Emily	Ryan	⑥	(J, E, R)

← **Draw a tree diagram.**

Ryan, Emily, and Justin can line up in six different ways. This means that there are six permutations.

Quick Check

1. Use a tree diagram to find the number of permutations.
   - a. You arrange five books on a shelf. In how many ways can you arrange the books? 120 ways
   - b. Four geese fly in line. In how many different orders can they fly? 24 orders

The tree diagram in Example 1 illustrates the counting principle.

Differentiated Instruction Solutions for All Learners

Special Needs L1
Students draw tree diagrams with a partner. Students discover that the counting principle is a better way to find the number of permutations when the number gets too large to draw a tree diagram.

learning style: visual

Below Level L2
Students find 5! and 7! by saying, then writing down, the integers that need to be multiplied.
$5 \cdot 4 \cdot 3 \cdot 2 \cdot 1 = 120$;
$7 \cdot 6 \cdot 5 \cdot 4 \cdot 3 \cdot 2 \cdot 1 = 5{,}040$

learning style: verbal

10-5

1. Plan

Objective
To find the number of permutations of a set of objects

Examples
1 Permutations Using a Diagram
2 Using the Counting Principle
3 Permutations Using Factorials

Math Understandings: p. 468C

Professional Development

Math Background

A *permutation* is an arrangement of a set of objects in which the order of the choices makes a difference. The number of permutations of n objects chosen r at a time can be represented by the expression ${}_nP_r$. The *factorial* of a positive integer is the product of all the positive integers less than or equal to that number, so $5! = 5 \cdot 4 \cdot 3 \cdot 2 \cdot 1$ or 120.

More Math Background: p. 468D

Lesson Planning and Resources

See p. 468E for a list of the resources that support this lesson.

PowerPoint

Bell Ringer Practice

Check Skills You'll Need
Use student page, transparency, or PowerPoint. For intervention, direct students to:

Ratios and Probability
Lesson 5-8
Extra Skills and Word Problems Practice, Ch. 5

2. Teach

Activity Lab

Use before the lesson.

All in One Teaching Resources

Activity Lab 10-5: Permutations

Guided Instruction

Alternative Method
In Example 2, have seven volunteers use cards labeled with 1st, 2nd, 3rd, . . . , 7th to model some of these possibilities. Show how there are 7 possible volunteers for the first award, 6 for the second award, and so on.

Connection to Multi-Media
Some students may not be aware that some CD players allow you to choose the track to be played. Have a student explain how to use such a player.

Technology Tip
In *More Than One Way,* point out to students that they enter the first number, 20, *before* they press the nPr key.

Error Prevention!

Remind students that order matters in permutations. Then have them ask: *Am I choosing all or some of the objects?*

KEY CONCEPTS The Counting Principle

Suppose there are m ways of making one choice and n ways of making a second choice. Then there are $m \cdot n$ ways to make the first choice followed by the second choice.

EXAMPLE Using the Counting Principle

2 **Awards** At a school awards ceremony, the principal will present awards to three winners out of seven finalists. How many different ways can the principal give out the awards?

There are seven ways to give out the first award, six ways to give out the second, and five ways to give out the third.

$7 \cdot 6 \cdot 5 = 210$ ← **Use the counting principle.**

There are 210 different ways to give out the awards.

Quick Check

2. Suppose the principal gives out four awards. How does this affect the number of different ways to give out the awards?
There are 4 times as many ways, or 840 ways.

Calculator Tip

Some calculators have a factorial key. Look on the PRB menu for the ! option.

If the principal in Example 2 gave awards to all seven finalists, then there would be $7 \cdot 6 \cdot 5 \cdot 4 \cdot 3 \cdot 2 \cdot 1$ different ways to give out the awards. This solution involves the product of all the integers from 7 to 1.

The product of all positive integers less than or equal to a number is a **factorial.** Write 7!, which you read as "seven factorial."

EXAMPLE Permutations Using Factorials

3 **Music** Many CD players can vary the order in which songs are played. Suppose a CD has eight songs. Find the number of orders in which you can play the songs.

$8! = 8 \cdot 7 \cdot 6 \cdot 5 \cdot 4 \cdot 3 \cdot 2 \cdot 1 = 40{,}320$ ← **Simplify.**

The songs can be played in 40,320 different orders.

Quick Check

3. Simplify each expression.
a. 2! 2 **b.** 6! 720 **c.** 4! 24

If you only want to play three songs from the CD in Example 3, there are $8 \cdot 7 \cdot 6 = 336$ ways to choose any three songs. You can write this as ${}_8P_3$.

Differentiated Instruction Solutions for All Learners

Advanced Learners L4	**English Language Learners** ELL
Students determine if each statement is true. They justify their answer. 3! + 4! = 7! no; 3! + 4! = 30; 7! = 5,040 12! ÷ 3! = 4! no; 12! ÷ 3! = 79,833,600; 4! = 24 **learning style: verbal**	Students distinguish between *factorial* and *factor*. When they calculate a factorial, such as 8!, they do not factor the number. They refer to the counting principle when speaking about factorials. **learning style: verbal**

Vocabulary Tip

The expression $_{25}P_2$ represents the number of ways of arranging, in order, 2 items from a set of 25.

KEY CONCEPTS **Permutation Notation**

The expression $_nP_r$ represents the number of permutations of n objects chosen r at a time.

Example $_{25}P_2 = 25 \cdot 24 = 600$

↑ 25 objects ↑ groups of 2 (two factors)

More Than One Way

At a school science fair, ribbons are given for first, second, and third place. There are 20 exhibits in the fair. How many different arrangements of three winning exhibits are possible?

Tina's Method

I can use permutation notation.

$_nP_r = {}_{20}P_3$ ← There are 20 exhibits; 3 of the exhibits will be selected in order.

$= 20 \cdot 19 \cdot 18$ ← Simplify $_{20}P_3$.

$= 6{,}840$ ← Simplify.

There are 6,840 different arrangements.

Roberto's Method

I can use a calculator.

Enter 20. Find the PRB menu. Select $_nP_r$.

Enter 3. Press ENTER. The display shows 6840.

There are 6,840 different arrangements.

Choose a Method

How many permutations are there if the school also awards fourth place? Explain why you chose the method you used.

116,280 arrangements; check students' work.

Check Your Understanding

1. A permutation is an arrangement of a set of objects in a particular order.

1. **Vocabulary** What is a permutation?

Simplify each expression.

2. $6 \cdot 5 \cdot 4$ 120
3. $10 \cdot 9 \cdot 8$ 720
4. $3!$ 6
5. $_{10}P_2$ 90

PowerPoint

Additional Examples

1. In how many ways can four people form a line? 24
2. Suppose you have six invitations to write. In how many different sequences can you write them? 720
3. A CD has nine songs. In how many different orders could you play these songs? 362,880

All in One Teaching Resources

- Daily Notetaking Guide 10-5 L3
- Adapted Notetaking 10-5 L1

Closure

- *What is a permutation?* an arrangement of a set of objects in a particular order
- *Name two ways to find the number of permutations of a set of objects.* Use a calculator, a tree diagram, or the counting principle.
- *Write the notation you could use to show the permutation of 10 things taken 2 at a time.* $_{10}P_2$

3. Practice

Assignment Guide

Check Your Understanding

Go over Exercises 1–5 in class before assigning the Homework Exercises.

Homework Exercises

A	Practice by Example	6–15
B	Apply Your Skills	16–30
C	Challenge	31
	Test Prep and Mixed Review	32–36

Homework Quick Check

To check students' understanding of key skills and concepts, go over Exercises 7, 15, 16, 27, and 30.

Differentiated Instruction Resources

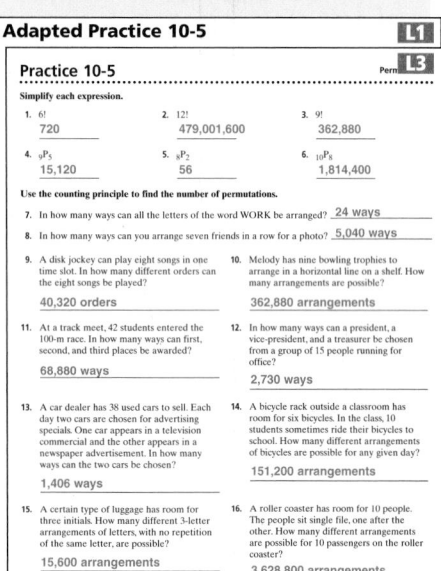

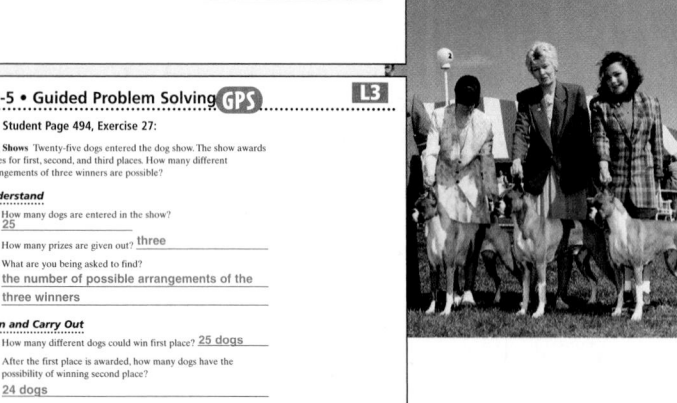

Adapted Practice 10-5 L1

Practice 10-5 Perm L3

Simplify each expression.

1. 6! 720
2. 12! 479,001,600
3. 9! 362,880
4. ${}_9P_5$ 15,120
5. ${}_8P_2$ 56
6. ${}_{10}P_8$ 1,814,400

Use the counting principle to find the number of permutations.

7. In how many ways can all the letters of the word WORK be arranged? 24 ways
8. In how many ways can you arrange seven friends in a row for a photo? 5,040 ways
9. A disk jockey can play eight songs in one time slot. In how many different orders can the eight songs be played? 40,320 orders
10. Melody has nine bowling trophies to arrange in a horizontal line on a shelf. How many arrangements are possible? 362,880 arrangements
11. At a track meet, 42 students entered the 100-m race. In how many ways can first, second, and third places be awarded? 68,880 ways
12. In how many ways can a president, a vice-president, and a treasurer be chosen from a group of 15 people running for office? 2,730 ways
13. A car dealer has 38 used cars to sell. Each day two cars are chosen for advertising specials. One car appears in a television commercial and the other appears in a newspaper advertisement. In how many ways can the two cars be chosen? 1,406 ways
14. A bicycle rack outside a classroom has room for six bicycles. In the class, 10 students sometimes ride their bicycles to school. How many different arrangements of bicycles are possible for any given day? 151,200 arrangements
15. A certain type of luggage has room for three initials. How many different 3-letter arrangements of letters, with no repetition of the same letter, are possible? 15,600 arrangements
16. A roller coaster has room for 10 people. The people sit single file, one after the other. How many different arrangements are possible for 10 passengers on the roller coaster? 3,628,800 arrangements

10-5 • Guided Problem Solving GPS L3

GPS Student Page 494, Exercise 27:

Dog Shows Twenty-five dogs entered the dog show. The show awards prizes for first, second, and third places. How many different arrangements of three winners are possible?

Understand

1. How many dogs are entered in the show? 25
2. How many prizes are given out? three
3. What are you being asked to find? the number of possible arrangements of the three winners

Plan and Carry Out

4. How many different dogs could win first place? 25 dogs
5. After the first place is awarded, how many dogs have the possibility of winning second place? 24 dogs
6. After the first and second places are awarded, how many dogs are left that could win third place? 23 dogs
7. Use the counting principle to find the number of possible arrangements. $25 \cdot 24 \cdot 23$ or 13,800 arrangements

Check

8. Write the problem using permutation notation. Then, solve the problem. ${}_{25}P_3 = 25 \cdot 24 \cdot 23 = 13{,}800$ arrangements

Solve Another Problem

9. A storage company asks you to choose five different digits from 0 to 9 as your personal identification number (PIN) to enter the property after hours. How many possible five-digit numbers can you choose from? $10 \cdot 9 \cdot 8 \cdot 7 \cdot 6 = 30{,}240$ numbers

Homework Exercises

For more exercises, see Extra Skills and Word Problems.

GO for Help

For Exercises	See Examples
6–7	1
8–9	2
10–15	3

A **Use a tree diagram to find the number of permutations.**

6. Four students are in line to see the school nurse. In how many different ways can the students be positioned in the line? 24 ways

7. Suppose you rent a thriller, a drama, and a comedy from a video store. In how many different orders can you watch the videos? 6 orders

Use the counting principle to find the number of permutations.

8. **Education** Your English teacher gives you a summer reading list of ten books. You must read three of them. In how many different orders can you select three books? 720 orders

9. There are six finalists in a poetry contest. In how many different orders can three winning poems be read? 120 orders

Simplify each expression.

10. 5! 120
11. 7! 5,040
12. 9! 362,880
13. 10! 3,628,800
14. 11! 39,916,800

15. An organizer is made up of six sections. If you have six items, in how many different ways can you place them in the organizer? 720 ways

B **GPS** 16. **Guided Problem Solving** From a list of ten artists, students were asked to list their favorite four in order of preference. In how many different ways can the artists be listed? 5,040 ways
- How many choices are there for a student's favorite artist?
- How many choices are there for the second favorite artist?
- Complete this multiplication to solve the problem: ■ · ■ · ■ · ■.

Simplify each expression.

17. ${}_{25}P_3$ 13,800
18. ${}_{18}P_2$ 306
19. ${}_{32}P_3$ 29,760
20. ${}_8P_4$ 1,680
21. ${}_{400}P_2$ 159,600

A bag contains ten blocks. Each block is a different color. Find how many ways you can select each number of blocks.

22. 3 720
23. 5 30,240
24. 7 604,800
25. 9 3,628,800
26. 10 3,628,800

27. **Dog Shows** Twenty-five dogs enter a dog show. The show awards prizes for first, second, and third places. How many different arrangements of three winners are possible? 13,800 arrangements (GPS)

28. A picture frame comes in four colors and three sizes. Use the counting principle to find the number of different styles of frames. 12 frames

29. **Choose a Method** A music class has 21 students. In how many different orders can the teacher choose six students to perform in a concert? Explain why you chose the method you used. 39,070,080 orders; check students' work.

GO Online
Homework Video Tutor
Visit: PHSchool.com
Web Code: ase-1005

30. You can multiply 12 by each positive integer less than 12, or you can use the factorial key.

30. **Writing in Math** Describe two different ways you can use a calculator to compute 12!.

C 31. **Challenge** You color rows of eight squares on graph paper, using a different color for each square in a row. It takes 45 seconds to color a row. You use the same eight colors for each row. How many hours will it take you to color all possible arrangements of colors?
504 hours

Test Prep and Mixed Review

Practice

Multiple Choice

32. A survey of Americans shows that 78% get to work by driving alone, 9% use a carpool, 5% use mass transporation, 5% use other methods such as walking or biking, and 3% work at home. Find the central angle for the carpool sector in a circle graph of the data. C

(A) 9° (B) 24° (C) 32.4° (D) 90°

33. Which graph shows a rhombus with 3 vertices in the second quadrant and a vertex with an x-coordinate of -3? J

(F)
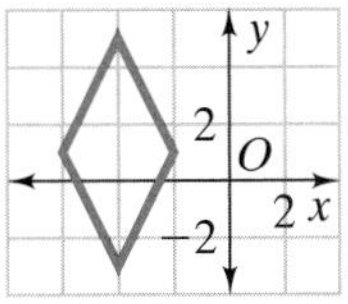

(H)
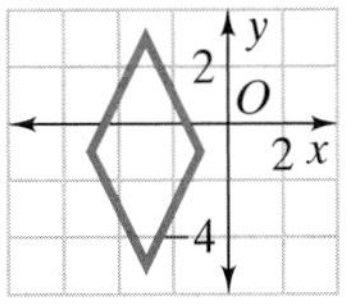

(G)
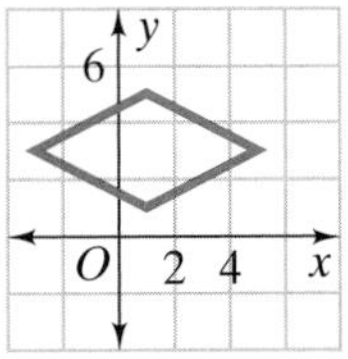

(J)
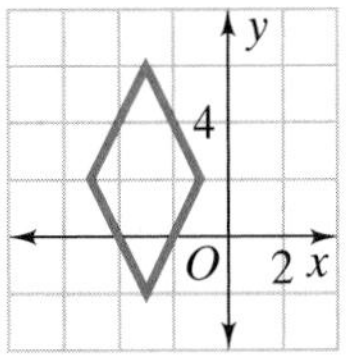

34. Emily borrowed money from her brother for a new CD player with a regular price of $55. The player was on sale for 25% off and the sales tax was 8%. If Emily pays her brother back in four equal payments, what is the approximate amount of each payment? A

(A) $11.00 (B) $12.00 (C) $12.50 (D) $13.75

GO for Help

For Exercises	See Lesson
35–36	9-9

Choose the appropriate graph for each data set. Explain your choice.

35. **Computer Use by 12-Year-Olds**

Types of Use	Time (min)
Games	17
Web sites	13
E-mail	5
Chat rooms	4
Other	22

SOURCE: The Kaiser Family Foundation Report

36. **Florida Orange Production**

Year	Boxes of Oranges (thousands)
1960	82,700
1970	142,300
1980	172,400
1990	151,600
2000	223,300

SOURCE: Florida Agricultural Statistics Service

35. Circle graph; it shows how the total time using computers is broken into parts.

36. Line graph; it shows change over time.

Online lesson quiz, PHSchool.com, Web Code: asa-1005

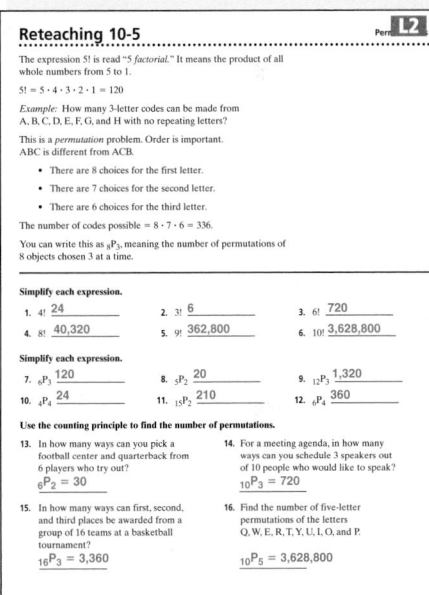

Alternative Assessment

Have students explain whether or not 30! is the solution for the number of ways to choose a president and vice-president from a class of 30 students. Sample: No, the correct answer is 30 × 29, or 870, because you are choosing only two students from the 30.

Test Prep

Resources

For additional practice with a variety of test item formats:

- Test-Taking Strategies, p. 503
- Test Prep, p. 507
- Test-Taking Strategies with Transparencies

4. Assess & Reteach

PowerPoint

Lesson Quiz

1. In how many different ways can you line up a half dollar, quarter, dime, nickel, and penny? 120
2. A CD has 11 songs. Find in how many orders you can play the songs. 39,916,800
3. Find 12! 479,001,600
4. Simplify $_{10}P_3$. 720

Reteaching 10-5

Perm L2

The expression 5! is read "5 *factorial*." It means the product of all whole numbers from 5 to 1.

$5! = 5 \cdot 4 \cdot 3 \cdot 2 \cdot 1 = 120$

Example: How many 3-letter codes can be made from A, B, C, D, E, F, G, and H with no repeating letters?

This is a *permutation* problem. Order is important. ABC is different from ACB.

- There are 8 choices for the first letter.
- There are 7 choices for the second letter.
- There are 6 choices for the third letter.

The number of codes possible $= 8 \cdot 7 \cdot 6 = 336$.

You can write this as $_8P_3$, meaning the number of permutations of 8 objects chosen 3 at a time.

Simplify each expression.

1. 4! 24
2. 3! 6
3. 6! 720
4. 8! 40,320
5. 9! 362,800
6. 10! 3,628,800

Simplify each expression.

7. $_6P_3$ 120
8. $_5P_2$ 20
9. $_{12}P_3$ 1,320
10. $_4P_4$ 24
11. $_{15}P_2$ 210
12. $_6P_4$ 360

Use the counting principle to find the number of permutations.

13. In how many ways can you pick a football center and quarterback from 6 players who try out?
$_6P_2 = 30$

14. For a meeting agenda, in how many ways can you schedule 3 speakers out of 10 people who would like to speak?
$_{10}P_3 = 720$

15. In how many ways can first, second, and third places be awarded from a group of 16 teams at a basketball tournament?
$_{16}P_3 = 3{,}360$

16. Find the number of five-letter permutations of the letters Q, W, E, R, T, Y, U, I, O, and P.
$_{10}P_5 = 3{,}628{,}800$

Enrichment 10-5

Perm L4

Visual Thinking

Rosa's little sister, Maria, makes solid figures by stacking her play cubes. After all the cubes have been stacked, Rosa paints the outside of each figure Maria made.

1. a. Maria made a wall of cubes as shown in the figure. Complete the table to find how many cubes will have the given number of painted faces.

Number of painted faces	6	5	4	3	2	1	0
Number of cubes	0	0	4	32	64	0	0

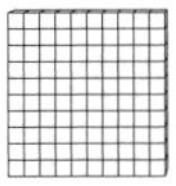

b. Maria has 26 alphabet stickers (one for each letter). She wants to put one sticker on each cube with 4 painted faces. How many ways can the cube be marked?
358,800 ways

2. Next, Maria made a large cube like the one shown. Complete the table to find how many small cubes in the figure will have the given number of painted faces.

Number of painted faces	6	5	4	3	2	1	0
Number of cubes	0	0	0	8	96	384	512

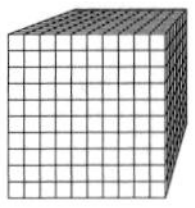

3. Rosa has 5 different colors of paint for the large cube in exercise 2. She wants to paint each group of small cubes with a given number of faces a different color. For example, she may choose to paint all the cubes with 1 painted face green and those with 2 painted faces blue.

a. How many different groups of cubes will Rosa paint?
3 groups

b. Write an expression for the number of ways Rosa can paint the large cube, using permutation notation.
$_5P_3$

c. How many ways can Rosa paint the large cube?
60 ways

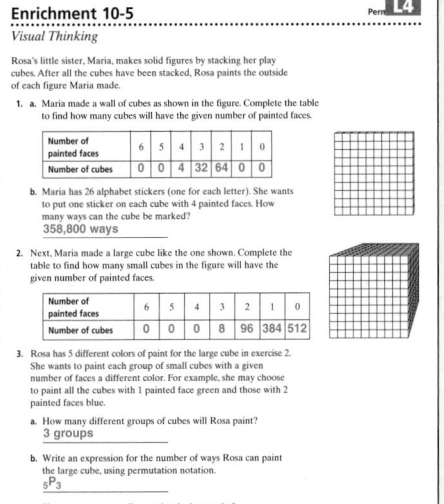

10-6

1. Plan

Objective

To find the number of combinations of a set of objects using lists and combination notation

Examples

1 Finding Combinations
2 Using Combination Notation

Math Understandings: p. 468D

Professional Development

Math Background

A *combination* is a group of items in which the order of the items is *not* considered. One way to find the number of combinations is to make an organized list of all the possibilities and eliminate the duplicates (since, for example, *raisins and nuts* is the same choice as *nuts and raisins*). The expression ${}_nC_r$ is read as "the number of combinations of *n* objects chosen *r* at a time." Another way to find the number of combinations is to use the formula: ${}_nC_r = \frac{{}_nP_r}{r!}$.

More Math Background: p. 468D

Lesson Planning and Resources

See p. 468E for a list of the resources that support this lesson.

PowerPoint

Bell Ringer Practice

Check Skills You'll Need
Use student page, transparency, or PowerPoint. For intervention, direct students to:

Permutations
Lesson 10-5
Extra Skills and Word Problems Practice, Ch. 10

10-6 Combinations

Check Skills You'll Need

1. **Vocabulary Review** An arrangement of objects in a certain order is a _?_. permutation

Simplify each expression.

2. 7 · 6 42
3. 4! 24
4. ${}_{10}P_2$ 90
5. ${}_{101}P_3$ 999,900

GO for Help Lesson 10-5

What You'll Learn

To find the number of combinations of a set of objects using lists and combination notation

New Vocabulary combination

Why Learn This?

The pair of yogurt toppings *raisins and nuts* is the same as the pair of toppings *nuts and raisins*. When you eat them, they form the same combination.

A **combination** is a group of items in which the order of the items is *not* considered. Recall that in permutations, order does matter.

EXAMPLE Finding Combinations

1 Food The table below contains four yogurt toppings. How many different ways can you choose two toppings?

Yogurt Toppings

Topping	Raisins	Nuts	Blueberries	Granola
Letter	R	N	B	G

Use letters to represent the four possible toppings.

Step 1 Make an organized list of all the possible groups of toppings.

RN	RB	RG
NR	NB	NG
BR	BN	BG
GR	GN	GB

Step 2 Cross out any group that is a duplicate of another.

RN	RB	RG
~~NR~~	NB	NG
~~BR~~	~~BN~~	BG
~~GR~~	~~GN~~	~~GB~~

Step 3 Count the number of groups that remain.

There are six different ways to choose two toppings.

Vocabulary Tip

A group of toppings that contains the same items as another group is a *duplicate*. Since NR is the same as RN, NR is a duplicate.

Quick Check

1. Make an organized list to find the number of different groups of three tutors your teacher can choose from four students. 4 groups

Differentiated Instruction Solutions for All Learners

Special Needs L1
Students see that NR is crossed out in Example 1 because it is considered the same as RN. The order of the toppings does not matter in this example—only what toppings are chosen. Students find the number of combinations of toppings.
learning style: visual

Below Level L2
Students find the value of each expression by saying, then writing down, the integers that need to be multiplied and divided.

$\frac{12!}{5!} = \frac{12 \cdot 11 \cdot 10 \cdot 9 \cdot 8 \cdot 7 \cdot 6 \cdot 5 \cdot 4 \cdot 3 \cdot 2 \cdot 1}{5 \cdot 4 \cdot 3 \cdot 2 \cdot 1} = 3{,}991{,}680$

$\frac{(12 \cdot 11 \cdot 10)}{4!} = \frac{12 \cdot 11 \cdot 10}{4 \cdot 3 \cdot 2 \cdot 1} = 55$

learning style: verbal

GO Online

Video Tutor Help
Visit: PHSchool.com
Web Code: ase-0775

In Example 1, you found the number of combinations by using a list. You can also use permutations to find combinations.

Since order does not matter, the permutation *raisins and nuts* and the permutation *nuts and raisins* represent the same group of toppings. To remove all the duplicate groups, divide by 2!, the number of ways to arrange two toppings.

$$\text{combinations} = \frac{\text{total number of permutations}}{\text{number of permutations of 2 toppings}} = \frac{4 \cdot 3}{2 \cdot 1} = 6$$

You can write the number of combinations of four yogurt toppings chosen two at a time as ${}_4C_2$.

KEY CONCEPTS **Combination Notation**

The expression ${}_nC_r$ represents the number of combinations of n objects chosen r at a time.

$${}_nC_r = \frac{{}_nP_r}{r!}$$

Example ${}_7C_3 = \frac{{}_7P_3}{3!} = \frac{7 \cdot 6 \cdot 5}{3 \cdot 2 \cdot 1} = 35$

The notation can look difficult. The next example shows how the numerator counts all possible arrangements and the denominator "divides out" the repeated combinations.

EXAMPLE Using Combination Notation

2 **Fishing** A fishing boat uses 5 fishing lines. Each line holds one lure. There are 12 different lures. How many different combinations of lures can be used at one time on the boat?

Find the number of ways you can choose 5 lures from 12.

$${}_{12}C_5 = \frac{{}_{12}P_5}{5!}$$

← **The numerator shows the number of ways to arrange 5 lures out of 12.**
← **The denominator shows there are 5! arrangements of each group of 5 lures.**

$$= \frac{12 \cdot 11 \cdot 10 \cdot 9 \cdot 8}{5 \cdot 4 \cdot 3 \cdot 2 \cdot 1}$$ ← **Simplify ${}_{12}P_5$ and 5!.**

$$= 792$$ ← **Simplify.**

There are 792 different combinations of lures.

Quick Check

2. Simplify each expression.

a. ${}_7C_5$ 21 **b.** ${}_8C_4$ 70 **c.** ${}_5C_3$ 10

2. Teach

Activity Lab

Use before the lesson.

All in One Teaching Resources

Activity Lab 10-6: Combinations

Guided Instruction

Some students may have trouble remembering the difference between permutations and combinations. Suggest that they associate *prizes* with *permutations*, usually given in the order of first, second, and so forth. They can associate *combos* (as in food choices) with *combinations*, where order does not matter, since a cheese sandwich with milk is the same as milk with a cheese sandwich.

Diversity
In Example 2, ask volunteers to share what they know about fishing lures.

Error Prevention!

Point out that the divisor in a combination is $r!$, not just r.

PowerPoint

Additional Examples

1 How many groups of two can be formed from a committee of six members? 15 groups

2 Find the number of ways you can choose 3 lures from a box of 8 fishing lures. 56 ways

All in One Teaching Resources

- Daily Notetaking Guide 10-6 L3
- Adapted Notetaking 10-6 L1

Closure

- Explain what the formula ${}_nC_r = \frac{{}_nP_r}{r!}$ means. Sample: ${}_nC_r = \frac{{}_nP_r}{r!}$ represents the number of combinations of n objects chosen r at a time.

Advanced Learners L4
Students write a real-world problem that involves evaluating a combination. They challenge classmates to solve the problems.

learning style: verbal

English Language Learners ELL
Students create a compare and contrast chart. They list the differences and similarities between combinations and permutations and include the formulas for finding each.

learning style: visual

3. Practice

Assignment Guide

Check Your Understanding

Go over Exercises 1–6 in class before assigning the Homework Exercises.

Homework Exercises

A	Practice by Example	7–19
B	Apply Your Skills	20–26
C	Challenge	27
Test Prep and Mixed Review		28–33

Homework Quick Check

To check students' understanding of key skills and concepts, go over Exercises 8, 16, 20, 25, and 26.

Differentiated Instruction Resources

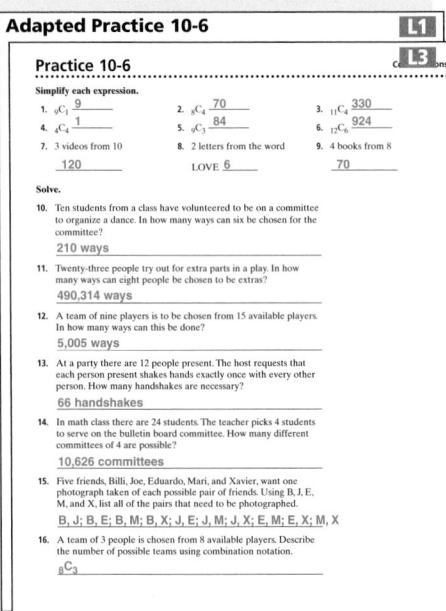

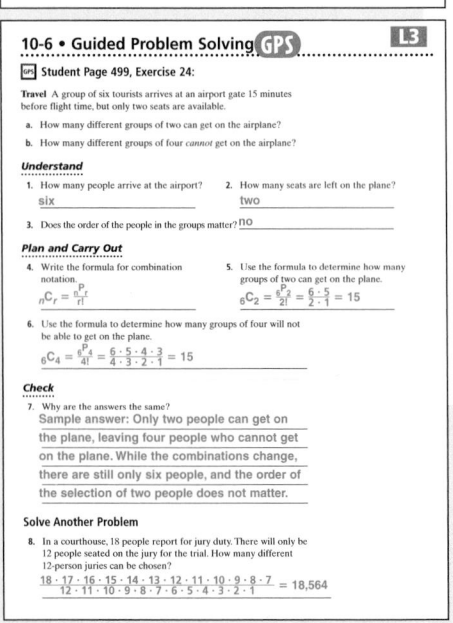

Adapted Practice 10-6 L1

Practice 10-6 L3

Simplify each expression.

1. $_9C_1$ 9
2. $_8C_4$ 70
3. $_{11}C_4$ 330
4. $_4C_4$ 1
5. $_9C_3$ 84
6. $_{12}C_6$ 924
7. 3 videos from 10 120
8. 2 letters from the word LOVE 6
9. 4 books from 8 70

Solve.

10. Ten students from a class have volunteered to be on a committee to organize a dance. In how many ways can six be chosen for the committee? 210 ways
11. Twenty-three people try out for extra parts in a play. In how many ways can eight people be chosen to be extras? 490,314 ways
12. A team of nine players is to be chosen from 15 available players. In how many ways can this be done? 5,005 ways
13. At a party there are 12 people present. The host requests that each person present shakes hands exactly once with every other person. How many handshakes are necessary? 66 handshakes
14. In math class there are 24 students. The teacher picks 4 students to serve on the bulletin board committee. How many different committees of 4 are possible? 10,626 committees
15. Five friends, Billi, Joe, Eduardo, Mari, and Xavier, want one photograph taken of each possible pair of friends. Using B, J, E, M, and X, list all of the pairs that need to be photographed. B, J; B, E; B, M; B, X; J, E; J, M; J, X; E, M; E, X; M, X
16. A team of 3 people is chosen from 8 available players. Describe the number of possible teams using combination notation. $_8C_3$

10-6 • Guided Problem Solving GPS L3

Student Page 499, Exercise 24:

Travel A group of six tourists arrives at an airport gate 15 minutes before flight time, but only two seats are available.

a. How many different groups of two can get on the airplane?
b. How many different groups of four *cannot* get on the airplane?

Understand

1. How many people arrive at the airport? six
2. How many seats are left on the plane? two
3. Does the order of the people in the groups matter? no

Plan and Carry Out

4. Write the formula for combination notation. $_nC_r = \frac{_nP_r}{r!}$
5. Use the formula to determine how many groups of two can get on the plane. $_6C_2 = \frac{_6P_2}{2!} = \frac{6 \cdot 5}{2 \cdot 1} = 15$
6. Use the formula to determine how many groups of four will not be able to get on the plane. $_6C_4 = \frac{_6P_4}{4!} = \frac{6 \cdot 5 \cdot 4 \cdot 3}{4 \cdot 3 \cdot 2 \cdot 1} = 15$

Check

7. Why are the answers the same? Sample answer: Only two people can get on the plane, leaving four people who cannot get on the plane. While the combinations change, there are still only six people, and the order of the selection of two people does not matter.

Solve Another Problem

8. In a courthouse, 18 people report for jury duty. There will only be 12 people seated on the jury for the trial. How many different 12-person juries can be chosen? $\frac{18 \cdot 17 \cdot 16 \cdot 15 \cdot 14 \cdot 13 \cdot 12 \cdot 11 \cdot 10 \cdot 9 \cdot 8 \cdot 7}{12 \cdot 11 \cdot 10 \cdot 9 \cdot 8 \cdot 7 \cdot 6 \cdot 5 \cdot 4 \cdot 3 \cdot 2 \cdot 1} = 18{,}564$

Check Your Understanding

1. **Vocabulary** Explain the difference between a permutation and a combination. In a permutation, the order matters. In a combination, order does not matter.

In each situation, tell whether order matters. Then decide if the situation describes a permutation or a combination.

2. First-, second-, and third-prize winners will be selected. yes; permutation
3. Three types of nuts will be selected to go into a snack mix. no; combination
4. Seven students are chosen to be on the Student Council. no; combination

Find each number of combinations.

5. Ways to choose four of five books 5
6. Ways to choose four of nine colors 126

Homework Exercises

For more exercises, see Extra Skills and Word Problems.

GO for Help

For Exercises	See Examples
7–8	1
9–19	2

A **Make an organized list to find the number of combinations.**

7. **Food** You are buying a pizza with two toppings. The store offers nine toppings. In how many ways can you choose your two toppings? 36 ways
8. **Committees** A school committee has five members. The principal wants to form a subcommittee of three people. How many different groups of three can be formed from the five committee members? 10 groups

Simplify each expression.

9. $_4C_3$ 4
10. $_4C_2$ 6
11. $_4C_1$ 4
12. $_6C_5$ 6
13. $_6C_4$ 15
14. $_{10}C_1$ 10
15. $_{10}C_9$ 10
16. $_7C_4$ 35
17. $_3C_1$ 3
18. $_9C_6$ 84

19. You can bring three people to a party. You have ten friends. How many different groups of three people can you bring? 120 groups

B **GPS** 20. **Guided Problem Solving** Sixteen listeners call a radio station, and each person requests a different song. The disc jockey only has time to play ten songs. How many different groups of ten songs can the disc jockey play? 8,008 groups
- There are ■ songs to choose from. The disc jockey will pick ■.
- Does this situation describe a permutation or a combination?

GO Online
Homework Video Tutor
Visit: PHSchool.com
Web Code: ase-1006

Decide whether the situation describes a permutation or a combination.

21. A president and a vice president will be elected from club members. permutation
22. A salad bar offers eight choices of vegetables. combination

25. The number of combinations is equal to the number of permutations divided by $r!$. The number of permutations is greater.

26. No; Sanjay found the number of permutations instead of combinations. The order of the sweaters does not matter.

23. **Sports** Ten teams enter a volleyball tournament. Each team plays every other team once. How many different games are played? 45 games

24. **Travel** A group of six tourists arrives at an airport gate 15 minutes before flight time, but only two seats are available. 15 groups
    a. How many different groups of two can get on the airplane?
    b. How many different groups of four *cannot* get on the airplane? 15 groups

GPS

25. **Writing in Math** What is the difference between the number of permutations and the number of combinations of n objects chosen r at a time? Explain. See left.

26. **Error Analysis** Sanjay can take two of his five sweaters on a trip. He reasons that he has five choices for his first sweater and four choices for his second. Using the counting principle, he thinks he has 20 ways to choose his sweaters. Is Sanjay correct? Explain. See left.

C 27. **Challenge** A designer chooses three colors from the palette below for a customer's logo. She picks the three colors in a specific order. What is the probability that another customer, choosing at random, picks the same three colors in the same order? $\frac{1}{2{,}184}$

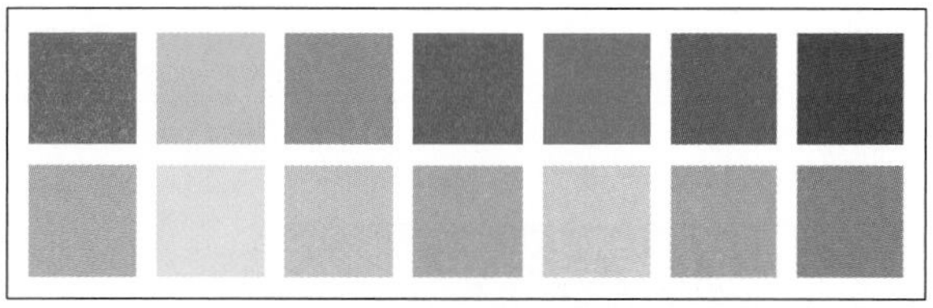

Test Prep and Mixed Review

Practice

Multiple Choice

28. A pack of juice boxes contains 4 apple, 4 cherry, 4 orange, and 4 grape juice boxes. If two people select a juice box at random, what is the probability that they will both get grape? B

    (A) $\frac{3}{64}$ (B) $\frac{1}{20}$ (C) $\frac{1}{16}$ (D) $\frac{1}{4}$

29. The Venn diagram shows how many of the 40 members in a Girl Scout troop can meet on Monday, Wednesday, or Thursday. What is the probability that a member chosen at random will NOT be able to meet on Monday? H

    (F) $\frac{3}{10}$ (H) $\frac{11}{20}$
    (G) $\frac{21}{40}$ (J) $\frac{27}{40}$

Available Meeting Days

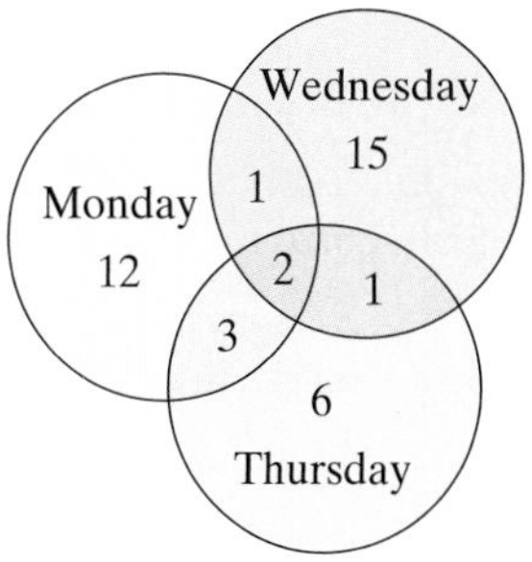

GO for Help

For Exercises	See Lesson
30–33	2-8

Write each number in scientific notation.

30. 153,000 1.53×10^5
31. 45 4.5×10
32. 53,200,000 5.32×10^7
33. 8,693 8.693×10^3

Alternative Assessment

Students use combination notation to solve this problem: There are 13 players on the basketball team. In how many ways can 5 starting players be selected? ${}_{13}C_5 = \frac{{}_{13}P_5}{5!} = \frac{13 \cdot 12 \cdot 11 \cdot 10 \cdot 9}{5!} = 1{,}287$

Test Prep

Resources

For additional practice with a variety of test item formats:

- Test-Taking Strategies, p. 503
- Test Prep, p. 507
- Test-Taking Strategies with Transparencies

4. Assess & Reteach

PowerPoint

Lesson Quiz

1. How many different ways can two dancers be selected for a dance team out of five candidates? 10
2. A hairdresser schedules 10 clients for appointments. Does this situation describe a permutation or a combination? permutation
3. Simplify ${}_{10}C_3$. 120
4. How many teams of 6 players can be formed from a group of 14 players? $\frac{14 \cdot 13 \cdot 12 \cdot 11 \cdot 10 \cdot 9}{6!} = 3{,}003$

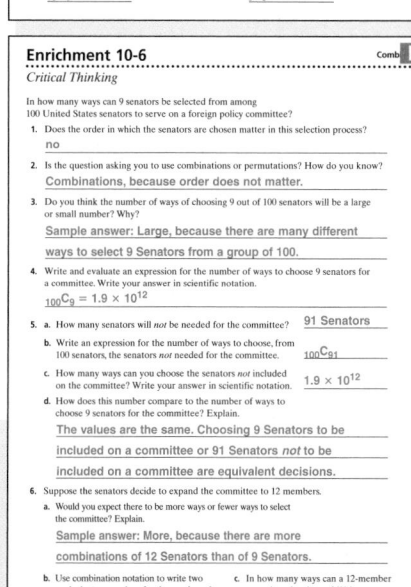

Reteaching 10-6

Com L2

Mr. Wisniewski wants to pick 2 students from Minh, Joan, Jim, Esperanza, and Tina to demonstrate an experiment. How many different pairs of students can he choose?

In this *combination* problem, the order of the choice of students does not matter. These are the possibilities:

Minh-Esperanza			
Minh-Jim	Esperanza-Jim		
Minh-Joan	Esperanza-Joan	Jim-Joan	
Minh-Tina	Esperanza-Tina	Jim-Tina	Joan-Tina

There are 10 possible combinations.

The number of combinations of 5 students taken 2 at a time is ${}_5C_2$ where:

$${}_5C_2 = \frac{{}_5P_2}{2!} = \frac{5 \cdot 4}{2 \cdot 1} = 10$$

In general, the number of combinations of n objects taken r at a time is ${}_nC_r$ where:

$${}_nC_r = \frac{{}_nP_r}{r!}$$

Simplify each expression.

1. ${}_6C_3$ 20
2. ${}_5C_2$ 10
3. ${}_4C_3$ 4
4. ${}_8C_2$ 28
5. ${}_9C_4$ 126
6. ${}_5C_3$ 10
7. ${}_7C_3$ 35
8. ${}_8C_3$ 56

Find the number of combinations.

9. In how many ways can Susie choose 3 of 10 books to take with her on a trip? ${}_{10}C_3 = 120$
10. In how many ways can Rosa select 2 movies to rent out of 6 that she likes? ${}_6C_2 = 15$
11. In how many ways can Bill pick 2 of his 7 trophies to show his grandfather? ${}_7C_2 = 21$
12. In how many ways can Mr. Wu choose 5 tulip bulbs out of 15 to plant in a flower bed? ${}_{15}C_5 = 3{,}003$
13. In how many ways can a town name 5 citizens out of 10 to serve on a committee? ${}_{10}C_5 = 252$
14. In how many ways can Mrs. Harris pick 3 flowers from 8 for a bouquet? ${}_8C_3 = 56$

Enrichment 10-6

Comb L4

Critical Thinking

In how many ways can 9 senators be selected from among 100 United States senators to serve on a foreign policy committee?

1. Does the order in which the senators are chosen matter in this selection process? no
2. Is the question asking you to use combinations or permutations? How do you know? Combinations, because order does not matter.
3. Do you think the number of ways of choosing 9 out of 100 senators will be a large or small number? Why? Sample answer: Large, because there are many different ways to select 9 Senators from a group of 100.
4. Write and evaluate an expression for the number of ways to choose 9 senators for a committee. Write your answer in scientific notation. ${}_{100}C_9 = 1.9 \times 10^{12}$
5. a. How many senators will *not* be needed for the committee? 91 Senators
   b. Write an expression for the number of ways to choose, from 100 senators, the senators *not* needed for the committee. ${}_{100}C_{91}$
   c. How many ways can you choose the senators *not* included on the committee? Write your answer in scientific notation. 1.9×10^{12}
   d. How does this number compare to the number of ways to choose 9 senators for the committee? Explain. The values are the same. Choosing 9 Senators to be included on a committee or 91 Senators *not* to be included on a committee are equivalent decisions.
6. Suppose the senators decide to expand the committee to 12 members.
   a. Would you expect there to be more ways or fewer ways to select the committee? Explain. Sample answer: More, because there are more combinations of 12 Senators than of 9 Senators.
   b. Use combination notation to write two equivalent expressions for the number of ways to choose a committee of 12 senators. ${}_{100}C_{12}$; ${}_{100}C_{88}$
   c. In how many ways can a 12-member committee be chosen? Write your answer in scientific notation. 1.1×10^{15}

Vocabulary Builder

Understanding Vocabulary

Students who grasp the precision of math vocabulary will improve their ability to understand and share mathematical ideas. This feature guides students to use their knowledge of everyday meanings of terms to help them comprehend the mathematical meanings of those terms.

Guided Instruction

Have students work with a partner to complete the table and also come up with some other terms that have a math meaning and a different everyday meaning. Invite pairs to share their terms, everyday meanings, and math meanings.

Teaching Tip
Remind students to refer as needed to the Illustrated English/Spanish Glossary in the back of their textbooks.

Invite students to add new terms, and corresponding examples, to a math journal or to adjust entries that already exist by adding comparisons and other ideas sparked by this feature.

Differentiated Instruction

Visual Learners
Students may benefit by using graphic organizers, such as concept maps, to help them process and use new math vocabulary.

Resources

- Vocabulary and Study Skills Worksheet

Vocabulary Builder

Understanding Vocabulary

Many words have an everyday meaning, as well as a specific meaning in mathematics. Knowing the everyday meaning can help you understand the math meaning.

EXAMPLE

Give the everyday meaning and math meaning of each of the following words: population, sample, and combination.

Word	Everyday Meaning	Math Meaning
Population	The total number of people living in a region	The total group of people or objects being studied
Sample	A representative item from a larger group	A part of the population
Combination	Two or more things put together	A group of items in which the order of items is *not* considered

Exercises

Copy and complete the table below. Use a dictionary to look up the everyday meanings of words, if necessary.

	Word	Everyday Meaning	Math Meaning
1.	Permutation	A complete rearrangement	?
2.	?	?	Based on all the outcomes when the outcomes are equally likely
3.	Independent	?	?
4.	Biased	Having a strong opinion	?
5.	Random	?	Having the same chance of being selected
6.	Experimental	?	Based on a number of trials
7.	?	Relying on something for support	Outcome of one event affects the outcome of the other

1. an arrangement of objects in a particular order
2. theoretical; based on a theory
3. Free from influence; outcome of one event does not affect the other.
4. having hidden assumptions or suggesting a preferred answer
5. by chance
6. based on an experiment
7. dependent

Permutations, Combinations, and Probability

You often need to find the number of permutations or combinations of a set of objects before finding probability.

Teams Cathie, Karla, and Shizuka are on a gymnastics team. There are six members on the team. Three team members are chosen at random to represent the school at the State Olympics. What is the probability that these three girls will be selected?

What You Might Think	What You Might Write
What do I know? What do I want to find out?	Three gymnasts are being selected at random from six gymnasts. I want to find the probability that three specific gymnasts will be selected.
First I need to find how many different groups are possible.	Since the order that the gymnasts are selected does not matter, I want to find the number of combinations. $_6C_3 = \frac{_6P_3}{3!} = \frac{6 \times 5 \times 4}{3 \times 2 \times 1} = 20$ There are 20 ways to select three gymnasts.
I can find the probability.	I only want the probability of selecting Cathie, Karla, and Shizuka. This is just one arrangement out of 20. So, the probability is $\frac{1}{20}$.

Think It Through

1. What does $_6C_3$ mean in this situation? the number of ways you can pick 3 from 6 gymnasts where order does not matter
2. Is the selection of the second gymnast an independent or dependent event? Explain. Dependent; the selection of the second gymnast depends on the selection of the previous gymnast.
3. Why was $6 \cdot 5 \cdot 4$ divided by $3 \cdot 2 \cdot 1$? Because order does not matter, the total number of permutations is divided by the number of ways of arranging three gymnasts in order, to remove the duplicate groups.

Permutations, Combinations, and Probability

Students read a guided real-world problem to develop problem solving and reasoning skills. In the left-hand column, they read questions they could ask themselves to make sense of the problem. In the right-hand column, they read the steps for setting up and solving equations used to describe the situation.

Guided Instruction

Have students work through the example, rather than just read it. Have them identify any steps that are unclear or that don't match their own work. Then have students ask themselves the same or similar questions as in the example as they work through the Exercises.

Error Prevention!

Students may be unsure whether they need to find a permutation or combination. Have students ask themselves: *Does the order in which items are chosen matter? How do I know?*

Teaching Tip

In the second row of the table, make sure students know why $_6P_3$ comes out to $6 \times 5 \times 4$.

Alternative Method

Ask: *Is the number of ways to pick the 3 gymnasts a permutation or combination? What other formula could they have used to solve this?* a combination; $_6C_3 = \frac{6 \times 5 \times 4}{3 \times 2 \times 1} = 20.$

Teaching Tip
Have students ask themselves the same or similar questions as in the example as they work through the Exercises.

Differentiated Instruction

Visual Learners
Have students perform necessary calculations, but allow them to use tree diagrams to verify their results or make predictions.

Exercises

Solve each problem. For Exercises 4 and 5, answer parts (a) and (b) first.

4. Carlos and Kareem are two of five members on a bowling team. Two team members are randomly chosen to compete in a Wednesday night tournament. What is the probability that Carlos and Kareem will be selected? $\frac{1}{10}$
   a. List what you know.
   b. Find the number of combinations.

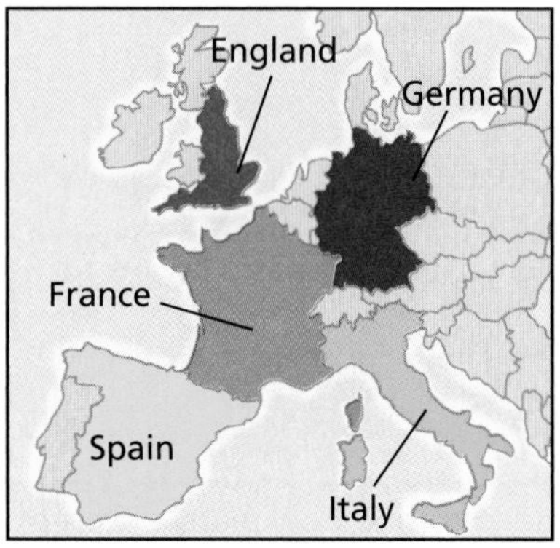

5. Your family makes a list of five European countries to visit on your vacation. You all decide that Italy will be one of the countries you visit. Of the remaining four countries, you decide to choose two at random. What is the probability that you choose to visit Germany? $\frac{1}{2}$
   a. List what you know.
   b. Find the number of combinations.

6. A vendor makes tacos topped with lettuce, tomatoes, cheese, sour cream, and guacamole. If you order a taco with three randomly chosen toppings, what is the probability you will get one with guacamole? $\frac{3}{5}$

7. Ten events in a track and field meet take place over two days.

Track and Field Events

Day 1	Day 2
100-m run	1,500-m run
Shot put	Discus throw
High jump	150-m hurdles
Long jump	Pole vault
400-m run	Javelin throw

   Each event must be completed on the designated day. In how many ways can the meet director arrange the events? 14,400 ways

8. On a certain game show, six numbers are chosen at random from the numbers 1 through 53. Suppose your chances of getting hit by lightning are about 1 in 3,000. Are your chances of getting hit by lightning greater or less than the chances of winning the game show? Explain. Greater; your chance of winning the game show is only 1 out of 22,957,480.

Test-Taking Strategies

Answering the Question Asked

When answering a multiple-choice question, be sure to answer the question asked. Some answer choices may be answers to related questions. Read the question carefully and check that you have answered it.

EXAMPLE

Santo spins the spinner at the right and tosses a coin. What is the probability that he will spin the color blue and the coin will land with tails side up?

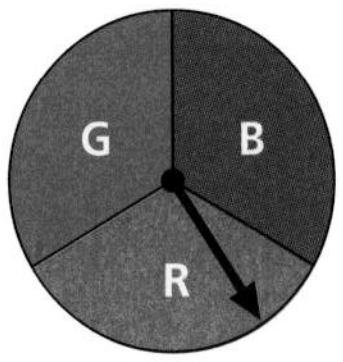

Ⓐ $\frac{1}{6}$ Ⓑ $\frac{1}{3}$ Ⓒ $\frac{1}{2}$ Ⓓ $\frac{2}{3}$

The question is, "What is the probability of spinning blue and getting tails?" The probability of spinning blue is $\frac{1}{3}$. The probability of getting tails is $\frac{1}{2}$. Since the two events are independent, multiply the probabilities.

$P(\text{blue, then tails}) = \frac{1}{3} \cdot \frac{1}{2}$ ← **Since spinning blue and getting tails are independent, multiply the probabilities.**

$= \frac{1}{6}$ ← **Simplify.**

The probability of spinning blue and getting tails is $\frac{1}{6}$. The correct answer is choice A.

Exercises

1. Ty is equally likely to pick any one of his friends to be on his basketball team. He has seven friends who want to play. What is the probability that he will pick Jana first and then Cooper? B

   Ⓐ $\frac{1}{49}$ Ⓑ $\frac{1}{42}$ Ⓒ $\frac{2}{13}$ Ⓓ $\frac{2}{7}$

2. A company makes 8 oz packages of snack mix. The probability of a package being lighter than 8 oz is $\frac{2}{25}$. The company makes 300 packages of snack mix in one day. Predict how many will be underweight. H

   Ⓕ 6 Ⓖ 12 Ⓗ 24 Ⓙ 80

3. If you roll a number cube five times, what is the probability of rolling all ones? A

   Ⓐ $\frac{1}{7{,}776}$ Ⓑ $\frac{1}{3{,}125}$ Ⓒ $\frac{1}{6}$ Ⓓ $\frac{5}{6}$

Answering the Question Asked

This feature alerts students to the importance of reading test questions carefully to make sure that they answer the question asked. It points out the importance of recognizing that some of the answer choices are distractors that answer related questions.

Guided Instruction

Teaching Tip

Students may know that some answer choices on tests are there to catch common mathematical errors. Discuss that other choices are included because they are correct given a *misreading* of the question asked. Stress the importance of reading carefully to avoid this trap. Guide students to reread the question to make sure that they have answered it and not a related one.

Resources

Test-Taking Strategies with Transparencies
- Transparency 8
- Practice sheet, p. 34

Test-Taking Strategies with Transparencies

Test-Taking Strategies: Answering the Question Asked

Incorrect choices may answer related questions.

Example **Midori owes $20 on a restaurant bill, and wants to tip the server 15%. How much should Midori pay altogether?**

A. $3 B. $15 C. $20 D. $23

Calculate the tip: 0.15 × 20 = $3

Choice A is $3, but this is how much Midori should leave for a tip, not how much to pay altogether.

Calculate the total bill: 20 + 3 = 23

The answer is $23, or choice D.

Answer the question asked. Explain your reasoning.

1. **Clarisse earns $10 per hour and works about 25 hours per week. How much could she earn in a year?**

   A. $250 B. $1,000 C. $3,000 D. $13,000

2. **Find the area of the triangle.**

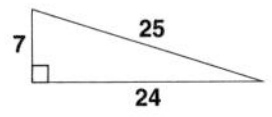

   F. 84 units^2 G. 56 units^2 H. 186 units^2 J. 4,200 units^2

Chapter 10 Review

Resources

Student Edition
Extra Skills and Word Problems Practice, Ch. 10, p. 622
English/Spanish Glossary, p. 650
Formulas and Properties, p. 648
Tables, p. 643

All in One Teaching Resources
- Vocabulary and Study Skills 10F L3

Differentiated Instruction
Spanish Vocabulary Workbook with Study Skills ELL
Interactive Textbook
- Audio Glossary

Online Vocabulary Quiz

Success Tracker™
Online at PHSchool.com

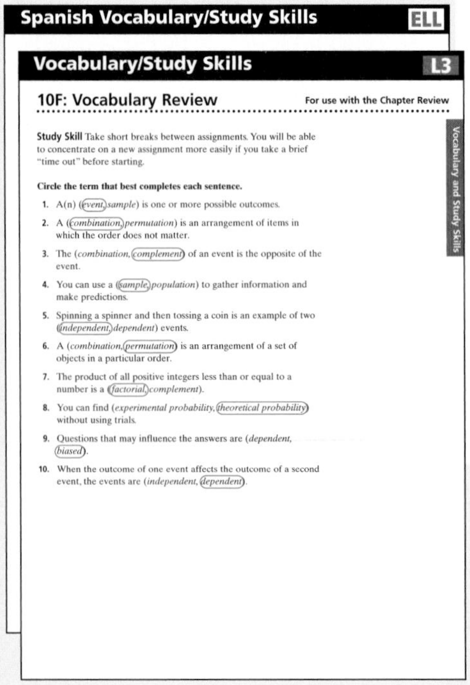
Spanish Vocabulary/Study Skills ELL

Vocabulary/Study Skills L3

10F: Vocabulary Review — For use with the Chapter Review

Study Skill Take short breaks between assignments. You will be able to concentrate on a new assignment more easily if you take a brief "time out" before starting.

Circle the term that best completes each sentence.

1. A(n) (*event*, *sample*) is one or more possible outcomes.
2. A (*combination*, *permutation*) is an arrangement of items in which the order does not matter.
3. The (*combination*, *complement*) of an event is the opposite of the event.
4. You can use a (*sample*, *population*) to gather information and make predictions.
5. Spinning a spinner and then tossing a coin is an example of two (*independent*, *dependent*) events.
6. A (*combination*, *permutation*) is an arrangement of a set of objects in a particular order.
7. The product of all positive integers less than or equal to a number is a (*factorial*, *complement*).
8. You can find (*experimental probability*, *theoretical probability*) without using trials.
9. Questions that may influence the answers are (*dependent*, *biased*).
10. When the outcome of one event affects the outcome of a second event, the events are (*independent*, *dependent*).

Vocabulary and Study Skills

Chapter 10 Review

Vocabulary Review

biased questions (p. 481)
combination (p. 496)
counting principal (p. 492)
dependent events (p. 487)
experimental probability (p. 470)
factorial (p. 492)
independent events (p. 486)
odds in favor (p. 471)
odds against (p. 471)
permutation (p. 491)
population (p. 480)
random sample (p. 480)
sample (p. 480)
theoretical probability (p. 471)

Go Online
PHSchool.com
For: Online Vocabulary Quiz
Web Code: asj-1051

Choose the correct vocabulary term to complete each sentence.

1. (Experimental probability, Theoretical probability) describes how likely it is that an event will happen based on all the possible outcomes. theoretical probability
2. People often conduct surveys using a (population, random sample) so that each object in the population has the same chance of being selected. random sample
3. To calculate the number of ways a class can line up, you need to find the number of possible (permutations, combinations). permutations
4. When the outcome of an event *does* affect the outcome of a second event, the events are (dependent events, independent events). dependent events

Skills and Concepts

Lessons 10-1, 10-2

- To find theoretical probability, experimental probability, and odds
- To make predictions based on theoretical and experimental probabilities

You can find the **experimental probability** of an event with this formula:

$$P(\text{event}) = \frac{\text{number of times event occurs}}{\text{total number of trials}}.$$

You can find the **theoretical probability** of an event with this formula:

$$P(\text{event}) = \frac{\text{number of favorable outcomes}}{\text{total number of possible outcomes}}.$$

You can use probabilities to make predictions.

You have 5 one-dollar bills, 3 five-dollar bills, and 1 ten-dollar bill in your pocket. You select a bill at random. Find the odds in favor of selecting each type of bill.

5. one-dollar bill 5 : 4
6. five-dollar bill 1 : 2
7. ten-dollar bill 1 : 8
8. The probability of a CD case being defective is $\frac{1}{520}$. If the factory makes 7,800 cases per week, how many are likely to be defective? about 15 cases

9. In a random survey, 8 out of 18 students would rather go to an amusement park than to the zoo. In a group of 225 students, how many students can you expect to prefer the amusement park? about 100 students

Lesson 10-3

- To identify random samples and biased questions and to judge conclusions based on survey results

A **sample** is part of the population, or group, being studied. In a **random sample,** each item has the same chance of being selected. **Biased questions** are unfair questions that may influence the answers in a survey.

A mayor wants to see if there is support for building a skate park in the city. Tell whether or not the surveys use random samples.

10. Randomly interview 50 residents walking on the street. random

11. Interview every fifth person who buys a skateboard at a local sporting goods store. not random

Lesson 10-4

- To find the probabilities of independent and dependent events

When the outcome of one event *does not* affect the outcome of a second event, the events are **independent.**

$$P(A, \text{ then } B) = P(A) \cdot P(B)$$

If the outcome of one event *does* affect the outcome of a second event, the events are **dependent.**

$$P(A, \text{ then } B) = P(A) \cdot P(B \text{ after } A)$$

Are the events dependent or independent? Explain.

12. Roll a number cube. Then roll it again. 12–13. See margin.

13. Pick an item from a bag. Without replacing it, pick another item.

Lessons 10-5, 10-6

- To find the number of permutations of a set of objects
- To find the number of combinations of a group of objects using lists and combination notation

A **permutation** is an arrangement of a set of objects in a certain order.

$${}_9P_4 = 9 \cdot 8 \cdot 7 \cdot 6$$

A **combination** is a group of items in which the order of the items is not important.

$${}_9C_4 = \frac{{}_9P_4}{4!}$$

14. If 12 people are playing in a tournament and each person plays every other person, how many games will be played? 66 games

15. In how many different ways can you choose two magazines from a shelf of ten magazines in a convenience store? 45 ways

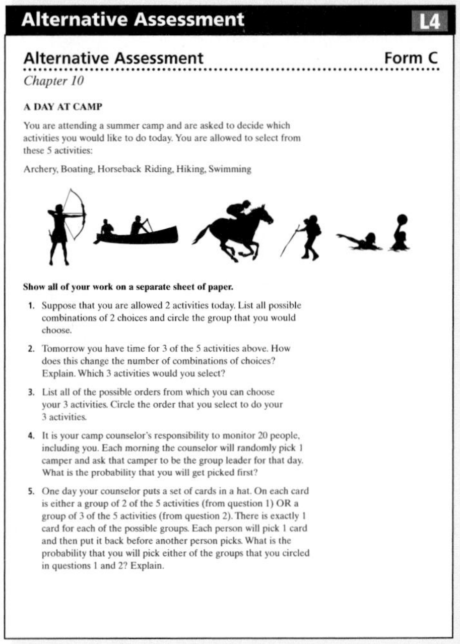
Alternative Assessment L4

Alternative Assessment Form C

Chapter 10

A DAY AT CAMP

You are attending a summer camp and are asked to decide which activities you would like to do today. You are allowed to select from these 5 activities:

Archery, Boating, Horseback Riding, Hiking, Swimming

Show all of your work on a separate sheet of paper.

1. Suppose that you are allowed 2 activities today. List all possible combinations of 2 choices and circle the group that you would choose.
2. Tomorrow you have time for 3 of the 5 activities above. How does this change the number of combinations of choices? Explain. Which 3 activities would you select?
3. List all of the possible orders from which you can choose your 3 activities. Circle the order that you select to do your 3 activities.
4. It is your camp counselor's responsibility to monitor 20 people, including you. Each morning the counselor will randomly pick 1 camper and ask that camper to be the group leader for that day. What is the probability that you will get picked first?
5. One day your counselor puts a set of cards in a hat. On each card is either a group of 2 of the 5 activities (from question 1) OR a group of 3 of the 5 activities (from question 2). There is exactly 1 card for each of the possible groups. Each person will pick 1 card and then put it back before another person picks. What is the probability that you will pick either of the groups that you circled in questions 1 and 2? Explain.

12. Independent; the outcome of the second roll is not affected by the first roll.

13. Dependent; the probability of the second pick is affected by the first pick.

Resources

- ExamView Assessment Suite CD-ROM
  - Chapter 10 Ready-Made Test
  - Make your own Chapter 10 test
- MindPoint Quiz Show CD-ROM
  - Chapter 10 Review

Differentiated Instruction

All in One Teaching Resources
- Below Level Chapter 10 Test L2
- Chapter 10 Test L3
- Chapter 10 Alternative Assessment L4

Spanish Assessment Resources ELL
- Below Level Chapter 10 Test L2
- Chapter 10 Test L3
- Chapter 10 Alternative Assessment L4

ExamView Assessment Suite CD-ROM
- Special Needs Test L1
- Special Needs Practice Bank L1

Online Chapter 10 Test at www.PHSchool.com L3

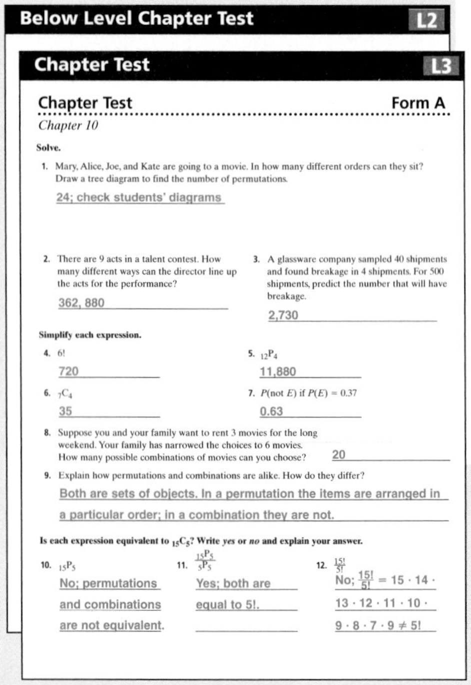

Below Level Chapter Test L2

Chapter Test L3

Chapter Test Form A

Chapter 10

Solve.

1. Mary, Alice, Joe, and Kate are going to a movie. In how many different orders can they sit? Draw a tree diagram to find the number of permutations. 24; check students' diagrams
2. There are 9 acts in a talent contest. How many different ways can the director line up the acts for the performance? 362, 880
3. A glassware company sampled 40 shipments and found breakage in 4 shipments. For 500 shipments, predict the number that will have breakage. 2,730

Simplify each expression.

4. 6! 720
5. $_{12}P_4$ 11,880
6. $_7C_4$ 35
7. $P(\text{not } E)$ if $P(E) = 0.37$ 0.63
8. Suppose you and your family want to rent 3 movies for the long weekend. Your family has narrowed the choices to 6 movies. How many possible combinations of movies can you choose? 20
9. Explain how permutations and combinations are alike. How do they differ? Both are sets of objects. In a permutation the items are arranged in a particular order; in a combination they are not.

Is each expression equivalent to $_{15}C_5$? Write *yes* or *no* and explain your answer.

10. $_{15}P_5$ No; permutations and combinations are not equivalent.
11. $\frac{_{15}P_5}{_5P_5}$ Yes; both are equal to 5!.
12. $\frac{15!}{5!}$ No; $\frac{15!}{5!} = 15 \cdot 14 \cdot 13 \cdot 12 \cdot 11 \cdot 10 \cdot 9 \cdot 8 \cdot 7 \cdot 9 \neq 5!$

Chapter 10 Test

Go Online PHSchool.com For: Online chapter test Web Code: asa-1052

Food **Find each probability.** A supermarket polled its customers to see which brand of salsa they prefer. The table below shows the results from the survey.

Preference	Number of Votes
Brand X	92
Brand Y	80
Brand Z	120
No preference	108
Total	**400**

1. $P(\text{Brand X})$ $\frac{23}{100}$
2. $P(\text{Brand Y})$ $\frac{1}{5}$
3. **Repairs** On a recent day, a mechanic found that out of 126 fenders, 7 had cracks. What is the experimental probability that a fender selected at random does *not* have a crack? $\frac{17}{18}$
4. **School** Every day, Nora's teacher randomly selects a row of students to organize the classroom. There are six rows of students. What is the probability that the teacher selects Nora's row two days in a row? $\frac{1}{36}$

A number from 1 to 100 is selected at random. Find each theoretical probability.

5. $P(85)$ $\frac{1}{100}$
6. $P(105)$ 0
7. $P(\text{number divisible by 9})$ $\frac{11}{100}$
8. $P(\text{number containing a 4})$ $\frac{19}{100}$

Find each probability. Lucinda has 5 yellow pencils, 6 blue pencils, and 9 green pencils. She picks 1 pencil at random and does not replace it. Then she picks another pencil. 9. $\frac{3}{38}$

9. $P(\text{yellow, then blue})$
10. $P(\text{2 green})$ $\frac{18}{95}$
11. $P(\text{green, then blue})$ $\frac{27}{190}$
12. $P(\text{2 yellow})$ $\frac{1}{19}$
13. Suppose you roll a number cube 25 times. Predict the number of times you will roll a 4. about 4 times

Simplify each expression.

14. 8! 40,320
15. 5! 120
16. $_4P_3$ 24
17. $\frac{6!}{2!}$ 360
18. $_{18}C_2$ 153
19. $_{10}C_7$ 120
20. At a school, 50 students were asked whether they brought lunch to school or bought it in the cafeteria. The results are in the table.

Lunch Survey

Response	Number
Bring lunch	17
Buy lunch	33

There are 235 students in the school. About how many of them bring lunch? about 80 students

Determine whether each survey uses a random sample. Describe the population.

21. **Entertainment** A movie theater surveys every tenth person to determine what types of movies its patrons like. See margin.
22. **Games** A computer game company surveys its teenage customers to determine its most popular games. Not random; teenagers do not represent all customers.

Is each expression equivalent to $_{12}C_3$? Write *yes* or *no* and explain your answer. 23–26. See margin.

23. $_{12}C_9$
24. $\frac{12!}{9!}$
25. $\frac{12 \cdot 11 \cdot 10}{3!}$
26. $_{12}P_3$
27. **School Supplies** Suppose you want to buy five different colored notebooks. There are eight colors from which to choose. How many combinations of notebooks are possible? 56 combinations
28. **Writing in Math** Explain why there are fewer combinations than permutations for a group of more than 1. See margin.

21. Random; every patron of the movie theater has the same chance of being asked.
23. Yes; both equal 220.
24. No; $\frac{12!}{9!}$ is equal to $12 \cdot 11 \cdot 10$, or 1,320.
25. Yes; both equal 220.
26. No; $_{12}P_3$ is equal to $12 \cdot 11 \cdot 10$, or 1,320.
28. Answers may vary. Sample: Order does not matter in combinations, so different arrangements of the same outcomes are not counted multiple times.

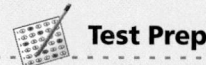

Reading Comprehension

Read each passage and answer the questions that follow.

> **Mathematical Notes** Have you ever wondered how there can still be any songs left to be written? After all, people have been writing music for a very long time, and many songs are limited to the eight notes in the octave of a major or minor scale. Doesn't it seem as though all the new melodies should have been written by now?

For Exercises 1–4, you can use the same note more than once.

1. Suppose you plan to write a song. You use the notes in an octave of a scale. How many different outcomes are there for the first two notes of the song? D

   A 8 B 16 C 56 D 64

2. In how many different ways can you choose the first three notes of a song from the notes in an octave of a scale? J

   F 6 G 24 H 336 J 512

3. What is the general formula for the number of ways you can write n notes of music choosing from the notes in an octave? D

   A $8 \cdot 7 \cdot 6 \cdot 5 \cdot 4 \cdot 3 \cdot 2 \cdot 1$
   B $(n)(n-1) \ldots (3)(2)(1)$
   C n^8
   D 8^n

4. In how many ways can you choose from eight possible notes to write the first ten notes of a song? F

   F 8^{10} H $10 \cdot 9 \cdot 8$
   G 10^8 J 1×10^8

> **Ecology Club** The ecology club at school has 20 members. When the club selects officers, the order of selection matters. When the club selects members to study either recycling, water, land surface, or waste disposal, order does not matter.

5. In how many different ways can the ecology club choose a president, a vice president, and a coordinator? C

   A 380 B 1,140 C 6,840 D 8,000

6. The club plans to go on a field trip. Each member must have a buddy. Which expression represents the number of different ways n members can pair off? J

   F $(n)(n-1)$ H $(n)(n-1) \ldots 1$
   G n^2 J $\frac{(n)(n-1)}{2}$

7. The club selects 4 people to lead the curriculum groups. How many ways can the club select 4 people? B

   A 116,280 B 4,845 C 80 D 5

8. Suppose the club gets four more members. In how many more ways can the club select 4 group leaders than in Exercise 7? H

   F ${}_{24}P_4 - {}_{20}P_4$ H ${}_{24}C_4 - {}_{20}C_4$
   G ${}_{24}C_4 + {}_{20}C_4$ J ${}_{24}P_4 + {}_{20}P_4$

Test Prep

Resources

Test Prep Workbook

All in One Teaching Resources
- Cumulative Review L3

ExamView Assessment Suite CD-ROM
- Standardized Test Practice

Differentiated Instruction

Spanish Assessment Resources
- Spanish Cumulative Review ELL

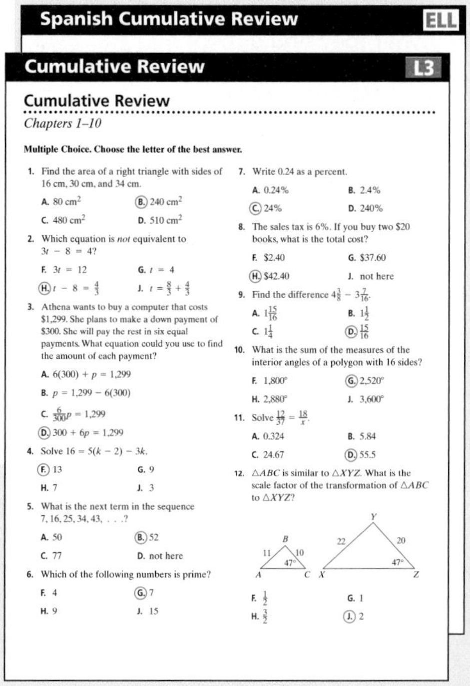
Spanish Cumulative Review ELL

Cumulative Review L3

Cumulative Review

Chapters 1–10

Multiple Choice. Choose the letter of the best answer.

1. Find the area of a right triangle with sides of 16 cm, 30 cm, and 34 cm.
   A. 80 cm² (B.) 240 cm² C. 480 cm² D. 510 cm²
2. Which equation is *not* equivalent to $3t - 8 = 4$?
   F. $3t = 12$ G. $t = 4$ (H.) $t - 8 = \frac{4}{3}$ J. $t = \frac{8}{3} + \frac{4}{3}$
3. Athena wants to buy a computer that costs $1,299. She plans to make a down payment of $300. She will pay the rest in six equal payments. What equation could you use to find the amount of each payment?
   A. $6(300) + p = 1{,}299$
   B. $p = 1{,}299 - 6(300)$
   C. $\frac{6}{300}p = 1{,}299$
   (D.) $300 + 6p = 1{,}299$
4. Solve $16 = 5(k - 2) - 3k$.
   (F.) 13 G. 9 H. 7 J. 3
5. What is the next term in the sequence 7, 16, 25, 34, 43, . . .?
   A. 50 (B.) 52 C. 77 D. not here
6. Which of the following numbers is prime?
   F. 4 (G.) 7 H. 9 J. 15
7. Write 0.24 as a percent.
   A. 0.24% B. 2.4% (C.) 24% D. 240%
8. The sales tax is 6%. If you buy two $20 books, what is the total cost?
   F. $2.40 G. $37.60 (H.) $42.40 J. not here
9. Find the difference $4\frac{3}{8} - 3\frac{7}{16}$.
   A. $1\frac{15}{16}$ B. $1\frac{1}{2}$ C. $1\frac{1}{4}$ (D.) $\frac{15}{16}$
10. What is the sum of the measures of the interior angles of a polygon with 16 sides?
    F. 1,800° (G.) 2,520° H. 2,880° J. 3,600°
11. Solve $\frac{12}{37} = \frac{18}{x}$.
    A. 0.324 B. 5.84 C. 24.67 (D.) 55.5
12. $\triangle ABC$ is similar to $\triangle XYZ$. What is the scale factor of the transformation of $\triangle ABC$ to $\triangle XYZ$?

    F. $\frac{1}{2}$ G. 1 H. $\frac{3}{2}$ (J.) 2

Problem Solving

Applying Probability

Students will use data from these two pages to answer the questions posed here in Put It All Together.

Activating Prior Knowledge

Have students discuss what they know about why and how scientists tag animals in the wild.

Guided Instruction

Have a volunteer read aloud the information about capture-recapture for sea turtles, albatrosses, and king penguins. Tell students that in this activity they are going to simulate the way scientists keep track of animal populations.

Social Studies Connection
Tell students that at one time the North American bison population was dropping precipitously, but now the herds are again thriving in places. Invite interested students to learn more about the decline and re-emergence of these large animals, who were once so very important in many ways to Plains Indians like the Cheyenne, Pawnee, and Sioux. Ask them to share with classmates what they find out.

Science Connection
When people think of game preserves, they may think of the large ones in Africa, where lions, wildebeests, giraffes, and other large animals roam freely. But there are many preserves right here in the United States. Have students do research to find out where these preserves are, what purposes they serve, and who runs them.

Problem Solving Application

Applying Probability

Animal Census Suppose you want to know how many polar bears live in Alaska, or how many cheetahs live in the Serengeti desert. Since it is nearly impossible to count an animal population directly, scientists use a capture–recapture method to estimate populations.

Monitoring the Albatross
Scientists tag albatrosses to study how commercial fishing ventures affect them.

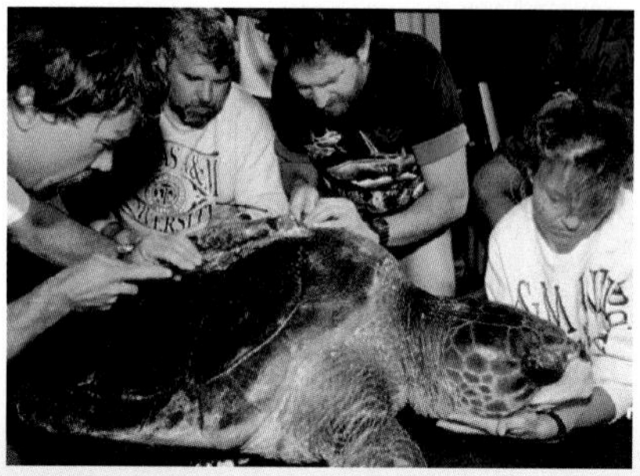

Loggerhead Sea Turtles
Scientists use tags to track sea turtles' movements after nesting, including migration paths and feeding habitats.

King Penguins
Researchers tagged king penguin pairs in a colony of 40,000 penguins to find out how the penguin parents communicated with each other as they incubated their eggs.

1. Check students' work.

2a–c. Check students' work.

2d. Answers may vary. Sample: The differences occur due to the random nature of the recapture. It is unlikely that the same number of beans will be recaptured every time.

3. The population is usually not fixed in the wild, because animals can enter or leave the area and new ones may be born or old ones die. Animals may also lose their tags or markings. Scientists might try to control for these factors by closing the area temporarily or doing the second capture soon after the first, But if the

Put It All Together

Materials paper bag, dried white beans, permanent marker, graph paper

Work with a partner or in a small group.

- Count out between 250 and 400 beans.
- Record the number and place the beans in the paper bag.
- Exchange bags with another group of students.

1. Use the capture–recapture method to sample the population. Copy and extend the table. Record your results.

Trial Number	Sample Size	Number Recaptured	Percent Recaptured
1	10	2	20%
2	10	■	■
3	10	■	■
4	10	■	■
5	10	■	■
6	20	■	■
7	20	■	■

2. a. Make a scatter plot comparing the probability of recapturing a marked bean to the sample size.

b. Based on your graph, what percent of the total population do you think is marked?

c. **Estimation** Estimate the population in the bag.

d. **Writing in Math** Compare your estimate with the number of beans recorded by the group that gave you the bag. Explain any differences.

3. **Reasoning** What real-life factors might make capture–recapture less accurate in the wild? How might scientists control these factors?

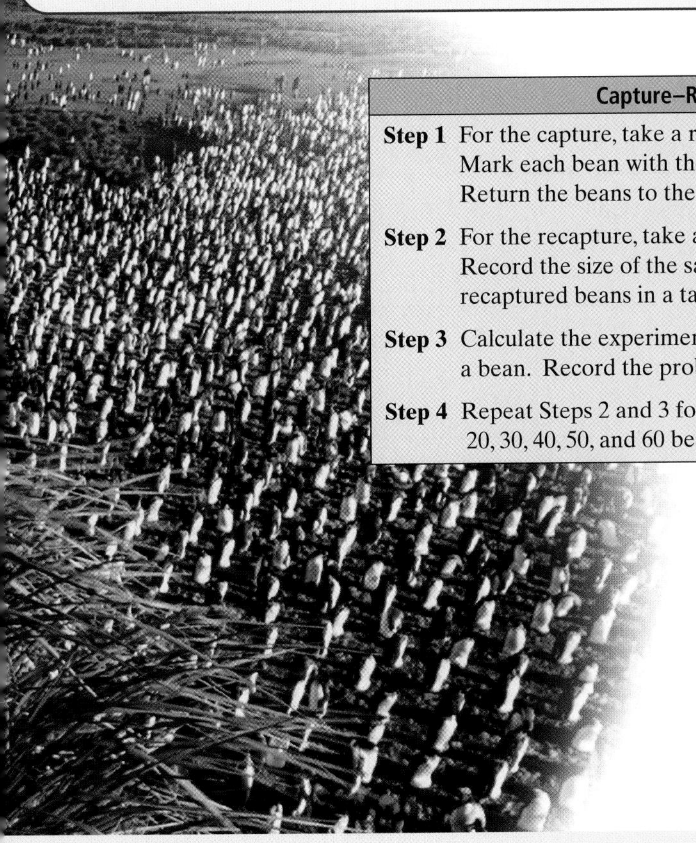

Capture–Recapture	
Step 1	For the capture, take a random sample of 50 beans. Mark each bean with the permanent marker. Return the beans to the bag and shake it.
Step 2	For the recapture, take a random sample of the beans. Record the size of the sample and the number of recaptured beans in a table.
Step 3	Calculate the experimental probability of recapturing a bean. Record the probability as a percent.
Step 4	Repeat Steps 2 and 3 for five samples each of 10, 20, 30, 40, 50, and 60 beans.

Go Online PHSchool.com
For: Information about animal populations
Web Code: ace-1053

second capture is done too soon, the animals will not have had a chance to mix properly and the results will be skewed.

Put It All Together

Have students work in pairs to do the activities and answer the questions. Guide them to record data as they measure and accumulate it.

Discuss with students that the table started at the right is directly related to the capture-recapture method decribed in the box at the bottom of the page. To complete the table, students should follow the steps in the box. Guide them to understand that each trial number in the table refers to a recapture. The first step for the partners to take is to collect a random sample of 50 beans and mark the beans.

Teaching Tip
Tell students that while it is important to use permanent markers on the beans, these markers can stain clothing. Guide students to take care when using them.

Exercise 2 As needed, review what a *scatterplot* is and how to make and interpret one. Discuss how trends can be used to make conjectures about a relationship between two quantities.

Differentiated Instruction

Special Needs L1
Discuss ways to equitably share the work in the activity.

11 Functions

Chapter at a Glance

Lesson Titles, Objectives, and Features	Assessment	NCTM Standards	Local Standards
11-1 Sequences • To write rules for sequences and to use the rules to find terms in a sequence **11-1b Activity Lab, Technology:** Exploring Sequences	Lesson Quiz	1, 2, 5, 6, 7, 8, 9, 10	
11-2 Relating Graphs to Events • To interpret and sketch graphs that represent real-world situations **11-2b Activity Lab, Data Collection:** Line Graphs	Lesson Quiz Checkpoint Quiz 1	1, 2, 5, 6, 7, 8, 9, 10	
11-3 Functions • To represent functions with equations, tables, and function notation	Lesson Quiz	1, 2, 6, 7, 8, 9, 10	
11-4a Activity Lab: Rate of Change **11-4 Understanding Slope** • To find the slope of a line from a graph or table **Extension:** Parallel and Perpendicular Lines	Lesson Quiz	1, 2, 3, 4, 6, 7, 8, 9, 10	
11-5a Activity Lab, Technology: Graphing Equations **11-5 Graphing Linear Functions** • To use tables and equations to graph linear functions	Lesson Quiz Checkpoint Quiz 2	1, 2, 3, 5, 6, 7, 8, 9, 10	
11-6 Writing Rules for Linear Functions • To write function rules from words, tables, and graphs **Guided Problem Solving:** Linear Functions	Lesson Quiz	1, 2, 6, 7, 8, 9, 10	
11-7 Quadratic and Other Nonlinear Functions • To graph and write quadratic functions and other nonlinear functions **11-7b Activity Lab, Data Analysis:** Changing Representations	Lesson Quiz	1, 2, 6, 7, 8, 9, 10	
Problem Solving Application: Applying Polynomials			

NCTM Standards 2000
1 Number and Operations
2 Algebra
3 Geometry
4 Measurement
5 Data Analysis and Probability
6 Problem Solving
7 Reasoning and Proof
8 Communication
9 Connections
10 Representation

Correlations to Standardized Tests

All content for these tests is contained in *Prentice Hall Math*, Course 3. This chart reflects coverage in this chapter only.

	11-1	11-2	11-3	11-4	11-5	11-6	11-7
Terra Nova CAT6 (Level 18)							
Number and Number Relations							
Computation and Numerical Estimation							
Operation Concepts							
Measurement							
Geometry and Spatial Sense							
Data Analysis, Statistics, and Probability							
Patterns, Functions, Algebra	✔	✔	✔	✔	✔	✔	✔
Problem Solving and Reasoning	✔	✔	✔	✔	✔	✔	✔
Communication	✔	✔	✔	✔	✔	✔	✔
Decimals, Fractions, Integers, Percent							
Order of Operations							
Algebraic Operations	✔		✔	✔	✔	✔	✔
Terra Nova CTBS (Level 18)							
Decimals, Fractions, Integers, Percents							
Order of Operations, Numeration, Number Theory			✔				
Data Interpretation		✔					
Measurement							
Geometry							
ITBS (Level 14)							
Number Properties and Operations							
Algebra	✔	✔	✔	✔	✔	✔	✔
Geometry							
Measurement							
Probability and Statistics							
Estimation							
SAT10 (Adv 1 Level)							
Number Sense and Operations							
Patterns, Relationships, and Algebra	✔	✔	✔	✔	✔	✔	✔
Data, Statistics, and Probability							
Geometry and Measurement							
NAEP							
Number Sense, Properties, and Operations	✔						
Measurement							
Geometry and Spatial Sense							
Data Analysis, Statistics, and Probability							
Algebra and Functions	✔	✔	✔	✔	✔	✔	✔

CAT6 California Achievement Test, 6th Ed.
SAT10 Stanford Achievement Test, 10th Ed.
CTBS Comprehensive Test of Basic Skills
NAEP National Assessment of Educational Progress 2005 Mathematics Objectives
ITBS Iowa Test of Basic Skills, Form M

Math Background

Professional Development

Skills Trace

BEFORE Chapter 11

Course 2 introduced function relationships using tables, word statements, and graphs.

DURING Chapter 11

Course 3 reviews and extends work with functions and introduces students to nonlinear relationships.

AFTER Chapter 11

Throughout this course students use patterns in words, tables, algebraic rules, and graphs.

11-1 Sequences

Math Understandings

- To write an arithmetic sequence, you have to know the number to start with and the common difference, which may be a positive or negative number.
- You can use an algebraic expression, such as $n(n - 1)$, to make a sequence by substituting the counting numbers.
- Some sequences, such as 2, 6, 12, 20, . . . , are neither arithmetic nor geometric.

A **sequence** is a set of numbers that follows a pattern. Each number in a sequence is called a **term.** You can find each term of an **arithmetic sequence** by *adding* a fixed number to the previous term. This fixed number is called the **common difference.**

Example: The rule for the arithmetic sequence 2, 6, 10, 14, 18, 22, 26, . . . is: Start with 2 and add 4 repeatedly.

This can be written as an algebraic expression: $2 + 4(n - 1)$.

You can find each term of a **geometric sequence** by multiplying the previous term by a fixed number, called the **common ratio.**

Example: The rule for the geometric sequence 2, 6, 18, 54, . . . is: Start with 2 and multiply by 3 repeatedly.

11-2 Relating Graphs to Events

Math Understandings

- A graph can show complex and changing relationships between variables in a simple, visual way.
- When you draw a graph without actual data, you are making a sketch.

The graph at right shows the speed of a commuter train as it makes a morning run.

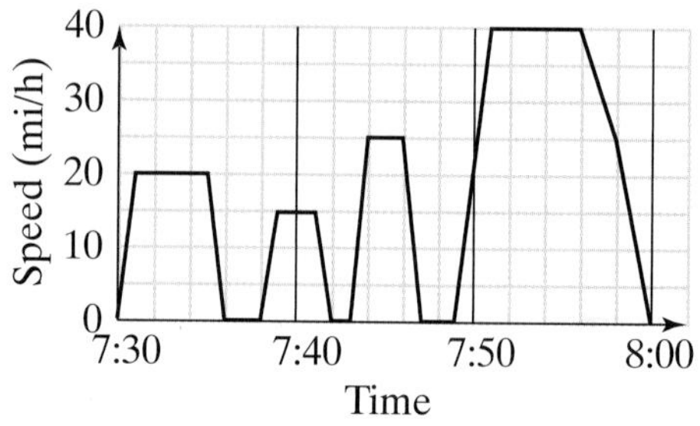

11-3 Functions

Math Understandings

- Some quantities are mathematically related in a special way: for each value of one quantity there is a unique value for the related quantity.

The **function** is a relationship that assigns exactly one output value to each input value. A **function rule** is an equation that describes a function.

Example: Make a table of input/output pairs for $d = \$.05c$.

Input c	6	12	24
Output d	\$.30	\$.60	\$1.20

11-4 Understanding Slope

Math Understandings

- A line that rises from left to right has a positive slope; a line that falls from left to right has a negative slope.
- A vertical line has an undefined slope; a horizontal line has a slope of zero.
- Linear data have the same ratio for $\frac{\text{change in } y}{\text{change in } x}$ between any two points.

Slope is a number indicating the steepness, or ratio of vertical change to horizontal change, of a line.

Slope of a Line
slope $= \dfrac{\text{change in } y\text{-coordinates}}{\text{change in } x\text{-coordinates}}$ ← **rise** / ← **run**

Example: The data in the table below are linear. Find the Slope.

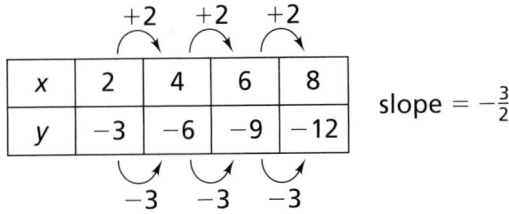

+2 +2 +2

x	2	4	6	8
y	−3	−6	−9	−12

−3 −3 −3

slope $= -\frac{3}{2}$

11-5 Graphing Linear Functions
11-6 Writing Rules for Linear Functions

Math Understandings

- When you graph a function, you place input values along the horizontal axis (x-axis) and output values along the vertical axis (y-axis).
- Discrete data items are separate and values between two data items have no meaning. For example, this list of shoe sizes contains discrete data:

  $4, 4\frac{1}{2}, 5, 5\frac{1}{2}, 6, 6\frac{1}{2}, 7, 7\frac{1}{2}, 8, 8\frac{1}{2}, 9, 9\frac{1}{2}$
- You can write a function rule from a problem stated in words, an equation, values in a table, or in a graph.

Discrete data are data that involve a count of items, such as numbers of people or numbers of cars, and you graph discrete data with a dashed line. **Continuous data** are data where numbers between any two data values have meaning, such as measurements, and you use a solid line to graph continuous data.

A **linear function** is a function whose points lie on a line. The ***y*-intercept** of a non-vertical line is the y-coordinate of the point where the line crosses the y-axis. A linear function written in the form $f(x) = mx + b$ or $y = mx + b$ is in **slope-intercept form.** The graph is a line with slope m and y-intercept b. You can used the slope, m, and the y-intercept, b, to graph the function.

Example: Graph the linear function $y = 2x - 3$.

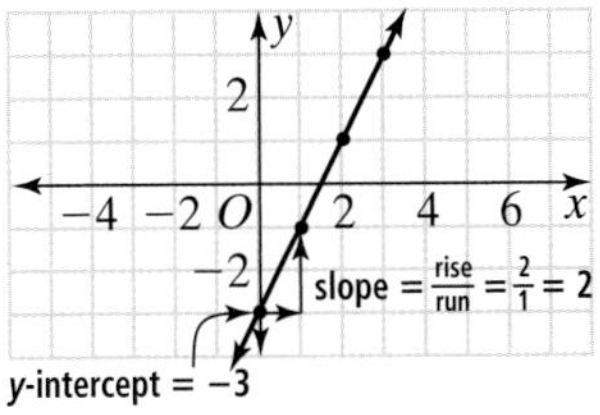

11-7 Quadratic and Other Nonlinear Functions

Math Understandings

- Some functional relationships are not linear.

One type of nonlinear function is a **quadratic function** of the form $y = ax^2 + bx + c$. The graph of a quadratic function is a U-shaped curve called a **parabola,** which may open upwards or downwards.

Additional Professional Development Opportunities

Professional Development

Math Background Notes for Chapter 11: Every lesson has a Math Background in the PLAN section.

Research Overview, Mathematics Strands
Additional support for these topics and more is in the front of the Teacher's Edition.

LessonLab
LessonLab, a Pearson Education company, offers comprehensive, facilitated professional development designed to help teachers to improve student achievement. To learn more, please visit lessonlab.com.

Chapter 11 Resources

	11-1	11-2	11-3	11-4	11-5	11-6	11-7	For the Chapter
Print Resources								
L3 Practice	●	●	●	●	●	●	●	●
L1 Adapted Practice	●	●	●	●	●	●	●	●
L3 Guided Problem Solving	●	●	●	●	●	●	●	●
L2 Reteaching	●	●	●	●	●	●	●	●
L4 Enrichment	●	●	●	●	●	●	●	●
L3 Daily Notetaking Guide	●	●	●	●	●	●	●	●
L1 Adapted Daily Notetaking Guide	●	●	●	●	●	●	●	●
L3 Vocabulary and Study Skills Worksheets	●		●	●	●		●	●
L3 Daily Puzzles	●	●	●	●	●	●	●	●
L3 Activity Labs	●	●	●	●	●	●	●	●
L3 Checkpoint Quiz		●			●			
L3 Chapter Project								●
L2 Below Level Chapter Test								●
L3 Chapter Test								●
L4 Alternative Assessment								●
L3 Cumulative Review								●
Spanish Resources ELL								
L3 Practice	●	●	●	●	●	●	●	●
L3 Vocabulary and Study Skills Worksheets	●		●	●	●		●	
L3 Checkpoint Quiz		●			●			
L2 Below Level Chapter Test								●
L3 Chapter Test								●
L4 Alternative Assessment								●
L3 Cumulative Review								●
Transparencies								
Check Skills You'll Need	●	●	●	●	●	●	●	●
Additional Examples	●	●	●	●	●	●	●	●
Problem of the Day	●	●	●	●	●	●	●	●
Classroom Aid	●	●		●	●		●	●
Student Edition Answers	●	●	●	●	●	●	●	●
Lesson Quiz	●	●	●	●	●	●	●	●
Test-Taking Strategies								●
Technology								
Interactive Textbook Online	●	●	●	●	●	●	●	●
StudentExpress™ CD-ROM	●	●	●	●	●	●	●	●
Success Tracker™ Online Intervention	●	●	●	●	●	●	●	●
TeacherExpress™ CD-ROM	●	●	●	●	●	●	●	●
PresentationExpress™ with QuickTake Presenter	●	●	●	●	●	●	●	●
ExamView® Assessment Suite CD-ROM	●	●	●	●	●	●	●	●
MindPoint® Quiz Show CD-ROM								●
Prentice Hall Web Site: PHSchool.com	●	●	●	●	●	●	●	●

Also available: **Prentice Hall Assessment System**
- Progress Monitoring Assessments
- Skills and Concepts Review
- Test Prep Workbook

Other Resources
Algebra Readiness Tests
All-in-One Student Workbook
All-in-One Student Workbook, Adapted Version
Multilingual Handbook
Solution Key
Math Notes Study Folder
Spanish Cumulative Assessment

Where You Can Use the Lesson Resources

Here is a suggestion, following the four-step teaching plan, for how you can incorporate Differentiated Instruction Resources into your teaching.

	Instructional Resources L3	Differentiated Instruction Resources
1. Plan		
Preparation Read the Math Background in the Teacher's Edition to connect this lesson with students' previous experience. **Starting Class** **Check Skills You'll Need** Assign these exercises to review prerequisite skills. **New Vocabulary** Help students pre-read the lesson by pointing out the new terms introduced in the lesson.	**Math Background** **Math Understandings** **Transparencies & PresentationExpress™ with QuickTake Presenter** Check Skills You'll Need Problem of the Day **Resources** Vocabulary and Study Skills	**Spanish Support** ELL Vocabulary and Study Skills
2. Teach		
L3 **Guided Instruction** Use the Activity Labs to build conceptual understanding. Teach each Example. Use the Teacher's Edition side column notes for specific teaching tips, including Error Prevention notes. Use the Additional Examples found in the side column (and on transparency and PowerPoint) as an alternative presentation for the content. After each Example, assign the Quick Check exercise for that Example to get an immediate assessment of student understanding. Use the Closure activity in the Teacher's Edition to help students attain mastery of lesson content.	**Student Edition** Activity Lab **Resources** Daily Notetaking Guide Activity Lab **Transparencies & PresentationExpress™ with QuickTake Presenter** Additional Examples Classroom Aids **ExamView® Assessment Suite CD-ROM**	**Teacher's Edition** Every lesson includes suggestions for working with students who need special attention. L1 Special Needs L2 Below Level L4 Advanced Learners ELL English Language Learners **Resources** L1 Adapted Daily Notetaking Guide **Multilingual Handbook**
3. Practice		
Assignment Guide **Check Your Understanding** Use these questions to check students' understanding before you assign homework. **Homework Exercises** Assign homework from these leveled exercises in the Assignment Guide. A Practice by Example B Apply Your Skills C Challenge Test Prep and Mixed Review **Homework Quick Check** Use these key exercises to quickly check students' homework.	**Transparencies & PresentationExpress™ with QuickTake Presenter** Student Answers **Resources** Practice Guided Problem Solving Vocabulary and Study Skills Activity Lab Daily Puzzles **ExamView® Assessment Suite CD-ROM**	**Spanish Support** ELL Practice ELL Vocabulary and Study Skills **Resources** L1 Adapted Practice L4 Enrichment
4. Assess & Reteach		
Lesson Quiz Assign the Lesson Quiz to assess students' mastery of the lesson content. **Checkpoint Quiz** Use the Checkpoint Quiz to assess student progress over several lessons.	**Transparencies & PresentationExpress™ with QuickTake Presenter** Lesson Quiz **Resources** Checkpoint Quiz	**Resources** L2 Reteaching ELL Checkpoint Quiz Success Tracker™ Online Intervention **ExamView® Assessment Suite CD-ROM**

KEY L1 Special Needs L2 Below Level L3 For All Students L4 Advanced, Gifted ELL English Language Learners

CHAPTER 11

Functions

Check Your Readiness

Answers for students are in the back of the textbook.

For intervention, direct students to:

Dividing Integers
Lesson 1-4
Extra Skills and Word Problems Practice, Ch. 1

Graphing in the Coordinate Plane
Lesson 3-4
Extra Skills and Word Problems Practice, Ch. 3

Graphing Equations with Two Variables
Lesson 3-5
Extra Skills and Word Problems Practice, Ch. 3

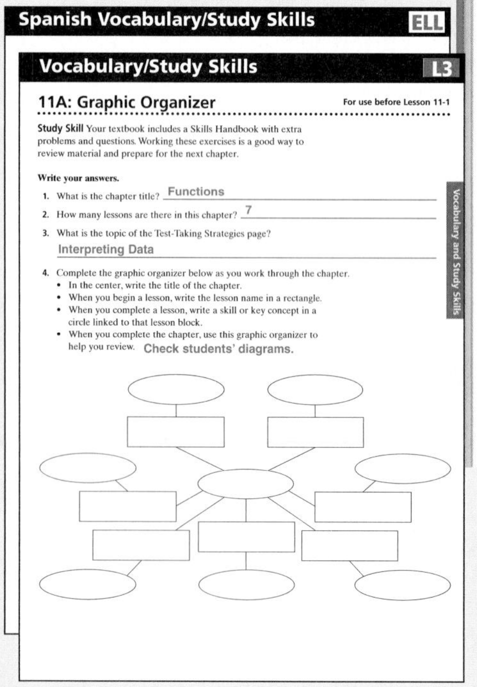
Spanish Vocabulary/Study Skills ELL

Vocabulary/Study Skills L3

11A: Graphic Organizer — For use before Lesson 11-1

Study Skill Your textbook includes a Skills Handbook with extra problems and questions. Working these exercises is a good way to review material and prepare for the next chapter.

Write your answers.

1. What is the chapter title? Functions
2. How many lessons are there in this chapter? 7
3. What is the topic of the Test-Taking Strategies page? Interpreting Data
4. Complete the graphic organizer below as you work through the chapter.
   - In the center, write the title of the chapter.
   - When you begin a lesson, write the lesson name in a rectangle.
   - When you complete a lesson, write a skill or key concept in a circle linked to that lesson block.
   - When you complete the chapter, use this graphic organizer to help you review. Check students' diagrams.

CHAPTER 11 Functions

What You've Learned

- In Chapter 3, you graphed points using ordered pairs of rational numbers.
- You used tables, graphs, and equations to solve problems.
- In Chapter 6, you wrote and solved multi-step equations and inequalities.

Check Your Readiness

GO for Help

For Exercises	See Lessons
1–6	1-4
7–11	3-4
12–14	3-5

Dividing Integers

Simplify each expression.

1. $\frac{35}{-7}$ −5
2. $\frac{-72}{12}$ −6
3. $\frac{-54}{9}$ −6
4. $\frac{-40}{5}$ −8
5. $\frac{-24}{-6}$ 4
6. $\frac{63}{-21}$ −3

Graphing in the Coordinate Plane

Graph each point on the same coordinate plane. 7–9. See margin.

7. $(0, 3)$
8. $(-1, 5)$
9. $(6, -8)$

10. Which vertex of the figure at the right is in the second quadrant? P
11. What are the coordinates of point S? (−3, −2)

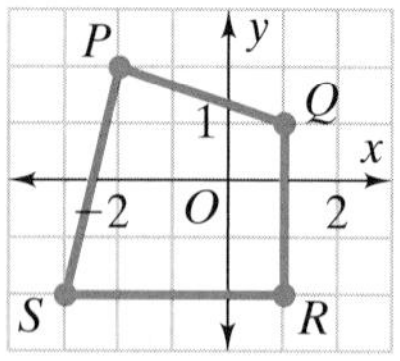

Graphing Equations with Two Variables

Graph each linear equation. 12–14. See margin.

12. $y = \frac{3}{4}x + 2$
13. $y = -7x - 14$
14. $y = \frac{6}{7}x - 4$

7–9. See back of book.

12.

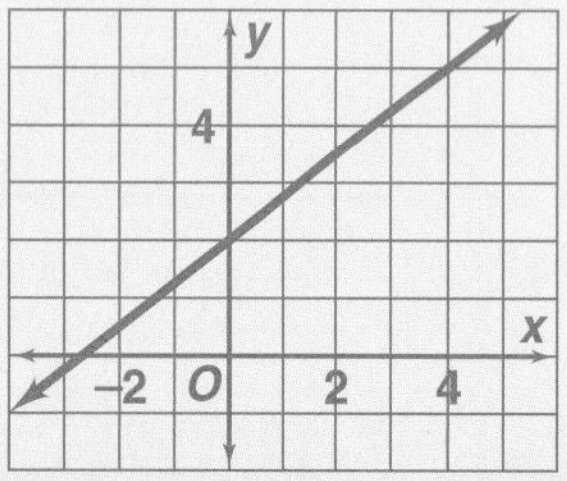

13.

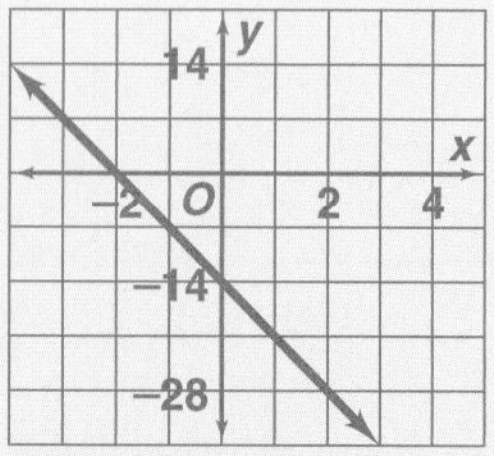

14. See back of book.

Chapter 11 Overview

In this chapter, students investigate sequences and both linear and nonlinear functions. They write function rules and then draw graphs for those rules.

Activating Prior Knowledge

In this chapter, students build on their knowledge of locating points and identifying coordinates and of writing and solving one-step and two-step equations to plot points in the coordinate plane and to graph and solve linear equations. Ask questions such as:

- *What is the solution to the equation* $x + 5 = 12$*?* $x = 7$
- *What is the next number in the following sequence of numbers: 1, 3, 2, 5, 3, 7, 4, _?* 9

What You'll Learn Next

- In this chapter, you will identify types of sequences and describe them using verbal descriptions and algebraic expressions.
- You will calculate the slopes of lines and use slope to write equations and draw graphs.
- You will identify and describe linear and nonlinear functions.

Problem Solving Application On pages 556 and 557, you will work an extended activity on setting prices.

Key Vocabulary

- arithmetic sequence (p. 513)
- common difference (p. 513)
- common ratio (p. 514)
- continuous data (p. 534)
- discrete data (p. 534)
- function (p. 523)
- function rule (p. 523)
- geometric sequence (p. 514)
- linear function (p. 535)
- parabola (p. 546)
- quadratic function (p. 546)
- sequence (p. 512)
- slope (p. 528)
- slope of a line (p. 528)
- slope-intercept form (p. 535)
- term (p. 512)
- *y*-intercept (p. 535)

11-1

1. Plan

Objective
To write rules for sequences and to use the rules to find terms in a sequence

Examples
1 Finding Terms of a Sequence
2 Evaluating Algebraic Expressions
3 Writing an Algebraic Expression
4 Describing a Geometric Sequence

Math Understandings: p. 510C

Professional Development

Math Background

A mathematical *sequence* is a set of numbers, separated by commas, that follows a pattern stated in a rule, such as 2, 5, 8, 11, 14, ... In this sequence, 2 is the first *term*, and each new term is formed by adding 3, the *common difference*, to the previous term. *Arithmetic* sequences have a common difference while *geometric* sequences have a *common ratio*. For example, each term in 5, 10, 20, 40, . . . , is found by multiplying the previous term by 2.

More Math Background: p. 510C

Lesson Planning and Resources

See p. 510E for a list of the resources that support this lesson.

PowerPoint

Bell Ringer Practice

Check Skills You'll Need
Use student page, transparency, or PowerPoint. For intervention, direct students to:

Algebraic Expressions and Order of Operations
Lesson 1-1
Extra Skills and Word Problems Practice, Ch. 1

Algebra

11-1 Sequences

Check Skills You'll Need

1. **Vocabulary Review** How do you *evaluate* an expression? See below.

Write an algebraic expression for each word phrase.

2. 7 more than a number. $n + 7$
3. 5 times a number. $5n$
4. the number of eggs in d dozen. $12d$

GO for Help Lesson 1-1

Check Skills You'll Need

1. Replace each variable with a number and then simplify.

What You'll Learn

To write rules for sequences and to use the rules to find terms in a sequence

New Vocabulary sequence, term, inductive reasoning, arithmetic sequence, common difference, geometric sequence, common ratio

Why Learn This?

You can find patterns in data just as a detective finds patterns in evidence. In some problems, you are given a set of numbers and asked to find the pattern. Once you have found the pattern, you can write an algebraic expression to find other numbers.

A **sequence** is a set of numbers that follows a pattern. Here are three different sequences that begin with the numbers 2 and 6.

2, 6, 10, 14, . . .

2, 6, 18, 54, . . .

2, 6, 8, 14, . . .

Each number in a sequence is called a **term.** You can often find additional terms in a given sequence by figuring out the pattern of the sequence. You are using **inductive reasoning** when you make conclusions based on patterns you observe.

EXAMPLE 1 Finding Terms of a Sequence

Find the next three terms in the sequence 2, 6, 10, 14, . . .

2 → 6 → 10 → 14 → 18 → 22 → 26
(each step +4)

You find each term by adding 4 to the previous term.

The next three terms are 18, 22, and 26.

Quick Check

1. Find the next three terms in each sequence. 1a–c. See left.
   a. 5, 12, 19, 26, . . . b. 4, 9, 14, 19, . . . c. 2, 12, 22, 32, . . .

1a. 33, 40, 47
b. 24, 29, 34
c. 42, 52, 62

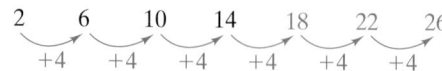

Differentiated Instruction Solutions for All Learners

Special Needs L1
Students determine the common difference in an arithmetic sequence by plotting the terms on a number line. They trace the distance between each term with their finger to find the common difference.

learning style: tactile

Below Level L2
Give students this sequence: 2, 4, 6, 8, 10, ... Ask them to name the pattern used to get from one term to the next. Sample: 2 plus 2 gives 4, 4 plus 2 gives 6, 6 plus 2 gives 8, 8 plus 2 gives 10

learning style: verbal

Vocabulary Tip

You pronounce *arithmetic sequence* as "ar ith MET ik SEE kwuns."

The sequence in Example 1 is an arithmetic sequence. An **arithmetic sequence** is a sequence in which each term differs from the next by a fixed number, called the **common difference.**

You can use an algebraic expression for a sequence. The expression gives the *n*th term, where *n* is the term's position in the sequence.

EXAMPLE Evaluating Algebraic Expressions

2 **Multiple Choice** Find the first four terms of the sequence represented by the expression $4 + 3n$.

Ⓐ 2, 5, 8, 11 Ⓒ 5, 7, 9, 11

Ⓑ 7, 10, 13, 16 Ⓓ 4, 6, 9, 12

Test Prep Tip

Make a table like the one shown here, using the counting numbers 1, 2, 3, and 4.

Position, *n*	1	2	3	4
$4 + 3n$	$4 + 3 \cdot 1$	$4 + 3 \cdot 2$	$4 + 3 \cdot 3$	$4 + 3 \cdot 4$
Term	7	10	13	16

Write the sequence as 7, 10, 13, 16, . . . The correct answer is choice B.

Quick Check

2. Find the first four terms of the sequence represented by $3(n - 1)$. 0, 3, 6, 9

A table can help you write an algebraic expression for a sequence.

EXAMPLE Writing an Algebraic Expression

3 Write an algebraic expression for the sequence 5, 10, 15, . . . Then find the 20th term in the sequence.

Make a table that pairs each term's position with its value.

Position, *n*	1	2	3	. . .	20
	↓·5	↓·5	↓·5	↓·5	↓·5
Term	5	10	15	. . .	■

You find a term in the sequence by multiplying the term's position number by 5. The algebraic expression $5n$ represents the sequence.

$5n = 5(20)$ ← **Substitute 20 for *n* to find the 20th term.**

$= 100$ ← **Simplify.**

The 20th term in the sequence is 100.

Quick Check

3. Write an algebraic expression for the sequence −2, −4, −6, −8, . . . Then find the 20th term. $-2n$; -40

2. Teach

Activity Lab

Use before the lesson.

All in One Teaching Resources

Activity Lab 11-1: Sequencing

Guided Instruction

Error Prevention!

In Exercise 3, help students see why the common difference is negative by reminding them that the common difference is always added to the previous term.

Math Tip

Make sure students realize that a sequence may be neither arithmetic nor geometric. The pattern for such a sequence has no common difference and no common ratio.

PowerPoint

Additional Examples

1 Find the next three terms in the sequence 3, 10, 17, 24, ... 31, 38, 45

2 Find the first four terms of the sequence represented by the expression $3 + 6n$. 9, 15, 21, 27

3 Find an algebraic expression for the sequence −3, 3, 9, 15, ... Use the expression to find the next term in the sequence. $-3 + 6(n - 1)$; 21

Advanced Learners L4

A 5-in. plant grows 1.5 in. each month. Find its height after 3 months. 9.5 in. Write the rule. Start with 5 and add 1.5 repeatedly.

learning style: verbal

English Language Learners ELL

The word *term* has been defined in relation to expressions. Students distinguish between terms in an expression, such as $3b$ *or* $-2y$, and the terms in a sequence such as *2, 4, 6, 8, . . .*

learning style: verbal

PowerPoint
Additional Examples

4 A scientist isolates 10 cells in a dish. The next day there are 40 cells in the dish. The day after there are 160 cells. Write the rule for the geometric sequence and find the next three terms. **Start with 10 and multiply by 4 repeatedly; 640; 2,560; 10,240**

All in One Teaching Resources
- Daily Notetaking Guide 11-1 L3
- Adapted Notetaking 11-1 L1

Closure

- *What is an arithmetic sequence?* **a set of numbers that has a common difference between each term**
- *What is a geometric sequence?* **a set of numbers in which each term is related to the previous term by a common ratio**
- *How do you use an algebraic expression to write a sequence?* **Substitute the term number for the variable and evaluate. Repeat to find the value of each term of the sequence.**
- *How do you find an algebraic expression for a sequence?* **Start by describing the pattern with words. Then replace the term number with *n* and write the expression.**

GO Online

Video Tutor Help
Visit: PHSchool.com
Web Code: ase-0775

The sequence 2, 6, 18, 54, . . . is a geometric sequence. A **geometric sequence** is a set of numbers in which each term is found by *multiplying* the previous term by a fixed number. This fixed number is called the **common ratio.**

The common ratio in the sequence below is 3.

$$2 \xrightarrow{\times 3} 6 \xrightarrow{\times 3} 18 \xrightarrow{\times 3} 54$$

You can describe the sequence as *Start with 2 and multiply by 3 repeatedly.*

EXAMPLE Describing a Geometric Sequence

4 **Sports** The first round of a soccer tournament includes 128 teams. The following rounds have 64 teams, 32 teams, 16 teams, and so on. Describe the geometric sequence formed by the tournament. Then find the next three terms.

$$128 \xrightarrow{\times \frac{1}{2}} 64 \xrightarrow{\times \frac{1}{2}} 32 \xrightarrow{\times \frac{1}{2}} 16 \xrightarrow{\times \frac{1}{2}} 8 \xrightarrow{\times \frac{1}{2}} 4 \xrightarrow{\times \frac{1}{2}} 2$$

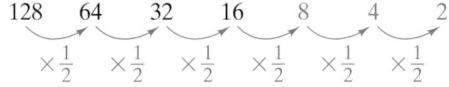

The common ratio is $\frac{1}{2}$. You can describe the sequence as *Start with 128 and multiply by $\frac{1}{2}$ repeatedly.* The next three terms are 8, 4, and 2.

Quick Check

4. Find the common ratio in the sequence 0.1, 1, 10, 100, . . . Describe the sequence and find the next three terms. **10; start with 0.1 and multiply by 10 repeatedly; 1,000; 10,000; 100,000.**

Check Your Understanding

1. **Vocabulary** Explain the difference between a common difference and a common ratio. **A common ratio involves mult. or div. A common difference involves add. or subtr.**

Find the common difference for each arithmetic sequence.

2. 0, 2, 4, 6, . . . **2**
3. 0, −1, −2, −3, . . . **−1**
4. Write a sequence that has the common difference $\frac{1}{2}$. **Answers may vary. Sample: 1, $1\frac{1}{2}$, 2, $2\frac{1}{2}$, . . .**

Find the common ratio for each geometric sequence.

5. 100, 200, 400, 800, . . . **2**
6. 1, 3, 9, 27, . . . **3**
7. A sequence is described as *Start with 2 and multiply by 4 repeatedly.* Write the first three terms in the sequence. **2, 8, 32**

18. Start with 750 and multiply by 0.1 repeatedly; 0.075, 0.0075, 0.00075.
19. Start with 1 and multiply by 4 repeatedly; 256; 1,024; 4,096.
20. Start with 1 and multiply by $\frac{1}{2}$ repeatedly; $\frac{1}{16}$, $\frac{1}{32}$, $\frac{1}{64}$.
21. Start with 3 and multiply by 2 repeatedly; 48, 96, 192.
22. Start with 0.12 and multiply by 3 repeatedly; 3.24, 9.72, 29.16.
23. Start with 125 and multiply by $\frac{1}{5}$ repeatedly; $\frac{1}{5}$, $\frac{1}{25}$, $\frac{1}{125}$.
27. Yes, if the sequence has enough terms; if you start with any number and repeatedly add a negative number, you eventually will end up with a negative answer.

Homework Exercises

For more exercises, see Extra Skills and Word Problems.

GO for Help

For Exercises	See Examples
8–10	1
11–14	2
15–17	3
18–23	4

A **Find the next three terms in each sequence.** 9. $-\frac{1}{4}, -1\frac{1}{4}, -2\frac{1}{4}$

8. 7.5, 11.5, 15.5, . . . 19.5, 23.5, 27.5 **9.** $2\frac{3}{4}, 1\frac{3}{4}, \frac{3}{4}, \ldots$ **10.** 11, 18, 25, . . . 32, 39, 46

Find the first four terms of the sequence represented by each expression.

11. $5 + 2n$ 7, 9, 11, 13 **12.** $2 - 2n$ 0, −2, −4, −6 **13.** $-7n$ −7, −14, −21, −28 **14.** $5n + 6$ 11, 16, 21, 26

Write an algebraic expression for each sequence. Then find the 20th term.

15. 3, 6, 9, 12, . . . $3n$; 60 **16.** $\frac{1}{2}, 1, 1\frac{1}{2}, 2, \ldots$ $\frac{1}{2}n$; 10 **17.** −4, −8, −12, . . . $-4n$; −80

Describe each geometric sequence and find the next three terms. 18–23. See margin.

18. 750, 75, 7.5, 0.75, . . . **19.** 1, 4, 16, 64, . . . **20.** $1, \frac{1}{2}, \frac{1}{4}, \frac{1}{8}, \ldots$

21. 3, 6, 12, 24, . . . **22.** 0.12, 0.36, 1.08, . . . **23.** 125, 25, 5, 1, . . .

B **GPS** **24. Guided Problem Solving** Use the pattern below. Each side of each pentagon is one unit long. Write an algebraic expression to represent the perimeter of each figure in the pattern.

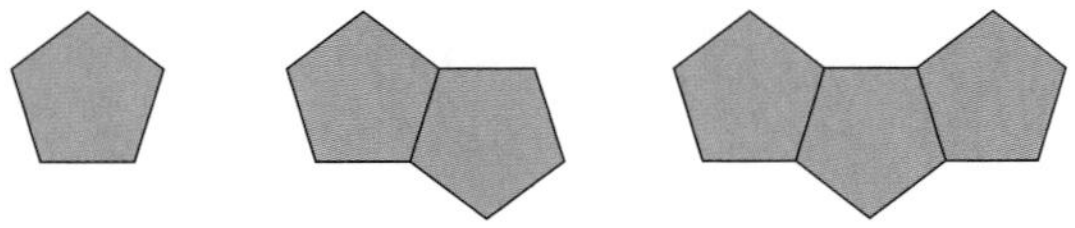

- Write a sequence based on the number of outer edges in each figure. The common difference d is ■.
- How many times do you add d to 5 to get the second term? How many times do you add d to 5 to get the third term?
- How many times should you add d to 5 to get the nth term?

Answers may vary. Sample: $3n + 2$

Tell whether each situation produces an *arithmetic sequence,* a *geometric sequence,* or *neither.*

25. A baby gains 2 oz every week. arithmetic

26. The time a person bikes each day varies between 30 and 45 minutes. neither

27. **Writing in Math** Will an arithmetic sequence that has a negative common difference always contain negative numbers? Explain. See margin.

Identify each sequence as *arithmetic, geometric,* or *neither.* Find the next three terms of the sequence. 28–33. See margin.

28. 2, 2.3, 2.6, 2.9, . . . **29.** 2, 5, 10, 17, . . . **30.** 21, 15, 9, 3, . . .

31. 2, 6, 18, 54, . . . **32.** 1.1, 1.01, 1.001, . . . **33.** 2, 1, 0.5, 0.25, . . .

28. arithmetic; 3.2, 3.5, 3.8
29. neither; 26, 37, 50
30. arithmetic; −3, −9, −15
31. geometric; 162, 486, 1,458
32. neither; 1.0001, 1.00001, 1.000001
33. geometric; 0.125, 0.0625, 0.03125

GO Online
Homework Video Tutor
Visit: PHSchool.com
Web Code: ase-1101

Online lesson quiz, PHSchool.com, Web Code: asa-1101

Che
Go ove
before as
Exercises.

Homework Ex
A Practice by Exam
B Apply Your Skills
C Challenge
Test Prep and
Mixed Review 41–

Homework Quick Check

To check students' understanding of key skills and concepts, go over Exercises 17, 27, 28, 32, and 39.

Differentiated Instruction Resources

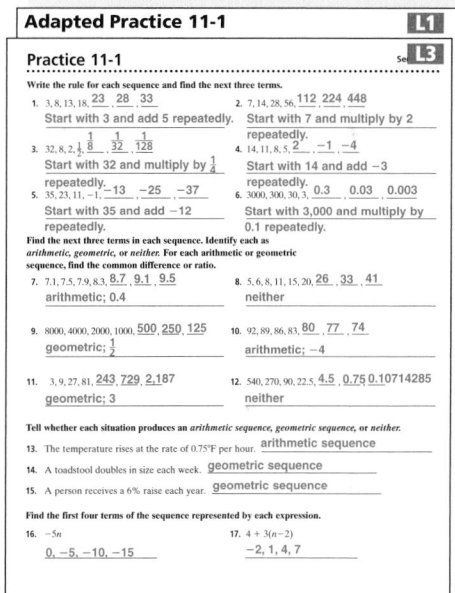

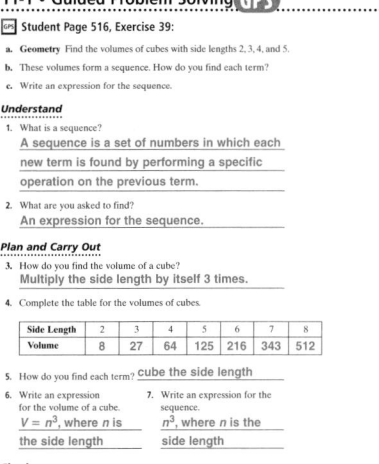

Adapted Practice 11-1 L1

Practice 11-1 Se L3

Write the rule for each sequence and find the next three terms.

1. 3, 8, 13, 18, 23, 28, 33
Start with 3 and add 5 repeatedly.
2. 7, 14, 28, 56, 112, 224, 448
Start with 7 and multiply by 2 repeatedly.
3. $32, 8, 2, \frac{1}{2}$, $\frac{1}{8}$, $\frac{1}{32}$, $\frac{1}{128}$
Start with 32 and multiply by $\frac{1}{4}$ repeatedly.
4. 14, 11, 8, 5, 2, −1, −4
Start with 14 and add −3 repeatedly.
5. 35, 23, 11, −1, −13, −25, −37
Start with 35 and add −12 repeatedly.
6. 3000, 300, 30, 3, 0.3, 0.03, 0.003
Start with 3,000 and multiply by 0.1 repeatedly.

Find the next three terms in each sequence. Identify each as *arithmetic, geometric,* or *neither.* For each arithmetic or geometric sequence, find the common difference or ratio.

7. 7.1, 7.5, 7.9, 8.3, 8.7, 9.1, 9.5
arithmetic; 0.4
8. 5, 6, 8, 11, 15, 20, 26, 33, 41
neither
9. 8000, 4000, 2000, 1000, 500, 250, 125
geometric; $\frac{1}{2}$
10. 92, 89, 86, 83, 80, 77, 74
arithmetic; −4
11. 3, 9, 27, 81, 243, 729, 2,187
geometric; 3
12. 540, 270, 90, 22.5, 4.5, 0.75, 0.10714285
neither

Tell whether each situation produces an *arithmetic sequence, geometric sequence,* or *neither.*

13. The temperature rises at the rate of 0.75°F per hour. arithmetic sequence
14. A toadstool doubles in size each week. geometric sequence
15. A person receives a 6% raise each year. geometric sequence

Find the first four terms of the sequence represented by each expression.

16. $-5n$
0, −5, −10, −15
17. $4 + 3(n-2)$
−2, 1, 4, 7

11-1 • Guided Problem Solving GPS L3

GPS Student Page 516, Exercise 39:

a. **Geometry** Find the volumes of cubes with side lengths 2, 3, 4, and 5.
b. These volumes form a sequence. How do you find each term?
c. Write an expression for the sequence.

Understand

1. What is a sequence?
A sequence is a set of numbers in which each new term is found by performing a specific operation on the previous term.
2. What are you asked to find?
An expression for the sequence.

Plan and Carry Out

3. How do you find the volume of a cube?
Multiply the side length by itself 3 times.
4. Complete the table for the volumes of cubes.

Side Length	2	3	4	5	6	7	8
Volume	8	27	64	125	216	343	512

5. How do you find each term? cube the side length
6. Write an expression for the volume of a cube.
$V = n^3$, where n is the side length
7. Write an expression for the sequence.
n^3, where n is the side length

Check

8. How can you determine if your sequence is reasonable?
Substitute numbers into the expression.

Solve Another Problem

9. Find the areas of squares with side lengths 2, 3, 4, and 5.
Write an expression for the sequence. n^2

3. Practice

Assignment Guide

...ck Your Understanding
...r Exercises 1–7 in class
...signing the Homework

...ercises
...ple 8–23
24–39
40
...47

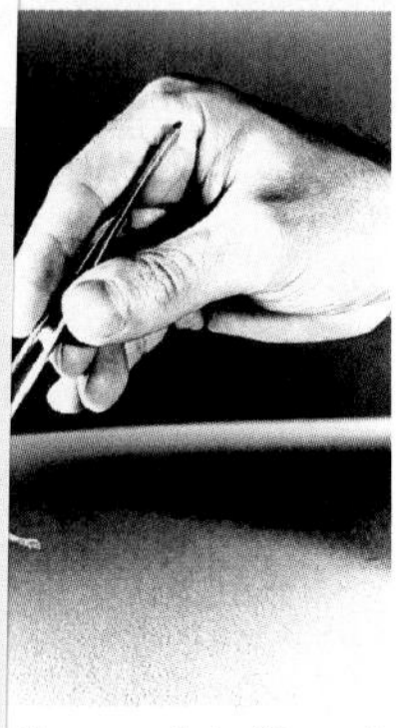

...the special effects in *...edible Shrinking Man* ...ated by using split ...and oversized props.

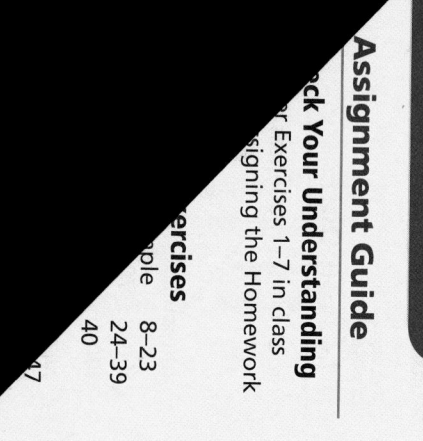

4. Write the first four terms of the sequence represented by $-7n + 21$. 14, 7, 0, −7

37. ...swers may vary. ...mple: ...$5 - 3n$; −44.5

38. Answers may vary. Sample: $3 + 4n$; 83

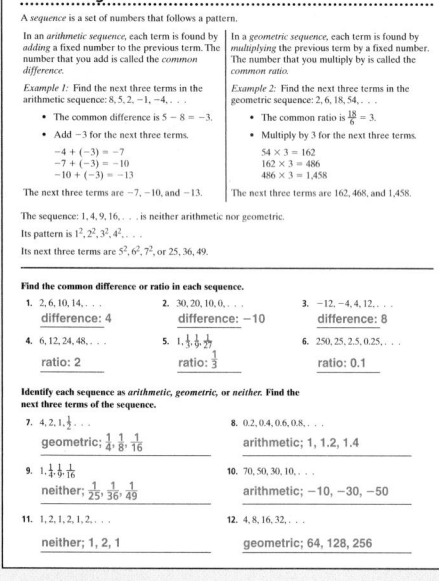

Use the following information for Exercises 34–36. In the 1957 movie *The Incredible Shrinking Man,* the main character mysteriously starts shrinking. Suppose his original height is 6 ft and he shrinks 3 in. every day.

34. How tall is the man at the end of one week? 4 ft 3 in. or 51 in.

35. How many days would it take for the man to shrink to half his original height? 12 days

36. What type of sequence is the series of numbers representing his height? Write a verbal description for the sequence. Arithmetic; start with 72 in. and add −3 repeatedly.

Each table shows four terms of an arithmetic sequence. Write an expression for each sequence. Then find the 20th term in the sequence.

37.

Position, n	1	2	3	4
Term	12.5	9.5	6.5	3.5

38.

Position, n	1	2	4	8
Term	7	11	19	35

37–38. See left.

39. a. **Geometry** Find the volumes of cubes with side lengths of 2, 3, 4, and 5. 39a–c. See margin.
GPS
b. These volumes form a sequence. How do you find each term?
c. Write an expression for the sequence.

C **40.** **Challenge** Evaluate the expression $400 \cdot \left(\frac{1}{2}\right)^{n-1}$ for $n = 1, 2, 3,$ and 4. Is the sequence formed *arithmetic, geometric,* or *neither?* 400, 200, 100, 50; geometric

Test Prep and Mixed Review

Practice

Multiple Choice

41. Which expression represents the sequence 2, 2.3, 2.6, 2.9, . . .? C

A $2(0.3)^n$
B $2 + 0.3n$
C $2 + 0.3(n - 1)$
D $0.3 + 2^{(n-1)}$

42. A number cube has faces labeled 1, 2, and 3, with each number appearing twice. The cube is rolled twice. What is the probability of rolling a 1 and then rolling a 1 or 3? H

F $\frac{1}{18}$ G $\frac{1}{9}$ H $\frac{2}{9}$ J 1

43. The chess club deposits $245 in an account that earns 7.5% simple interest per year. How much interest will be earned in 3 years? B

A $18.38 B $55.13 C $61.25 D $183.75

GO for Help

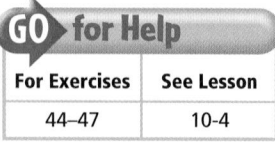

For Exercises	See Lesson
44–47	10-4

Find each probability. A bag contains 7 black paper clips, 2 blue paper clips, and 10 red paper clips. One paper clip is chosen at random and is not replaced. Then a second paper clip is chosen.

44. P(black, then red) $\frac{35}{171}$

45. P(red, then blue) $\frac{10}{171}$

46. P(blue, then blue) $\frac{1}{171}$

47. P(blue, then black) $\frac{7}{171}$

Reteaching 11-1 L2

A *sequence* is a set of numbers that follows a pattern.

In an *arithmetic sequence,* each term is found by *adding* a fixed number to the previous term. The number that you add is called the *common difference.*

Example 1: Find the next three terms in the arithmetic sequence: 8, 5, 2, −1, −4, . . .

- The common difference is $5 - 8 = -3$.
- Add −3 for the next three terms.

$-4 + (-3) = -7$
$-7 + (-3) = -10$
$-10 + (-3) = -13$

The next three terms are −7, −10, and −13.

In a *geometric sequence,* each term is found by *multiplying* the previous term by a fixed number. The number that you multiply by is called the *common ratio.*

Example 2: Find the next three terms in the geometric sequence: 2, 6, 18, 54, . . .

- The common ratio is $\frac{18}{6} = 3$.
- Multiply by 3 for the next three terms.

$54 \times 3 = 162$
$162 \times 3 = 486$
$486 \times 3 = 1{,}458$

The next three terms are 162, 468, and 1,458.

The sequence: 1, 4, 9, 16, . . . is neither arithmetic nor geometric.

Its pattern is $1^2, 2^2, 3^2, 4^2, \ldots$

Its next three terms are $5^2, 6^2, 7^2$, or 25, 36, 49.

Find the common difference or ratio in each sequence.

1. 2, 6, 10, 14, . . . difference: 4
2. 30, 20, 10, 0, . . . difference: −10
3. −12, −4, 4, 12, . . . difference: 8
4. 6, 12, 24, 48, . . . ratio: 2
5. $1, \frac{1}{3}, \frac{1}{9}, \frac{1}{27}$ ratio: $\frac{1}{3}$
6. 250, 25, 2.5, 0.25, . . . ratio: 0.1

Identify each sequence as *arithmetic, geometric,* or *neither.* Find the next three terms of the sequence.

7. $4, 2, 1, \frac{1}{2} \ldots$ geometric; $\frac{1}{4}, \frac{1}{8}, \frac{1}{16}$
8. 0.2, 0.4, 0.6, 0.8, . . . arithmetic; 1, 1.2, 1.4
9. $1, \frac{1}{4}, \frac{1}{9}, \frac{1}{16}$ neither; $\frac{1}{25}, \frac{1}{36}, \frac{1}{49}$
10. 70, 50, 30, 10, . . . arithmetic; −10, −30, −50
11. 1, 2, 1, 2, 1, 2, . . . neither; 1, 2, 1
12. 4, 8, 16, 32, . . . geometric; 64, 128, 256

Enrichment 11-1 L4

Patterns in Numbers

1. Study the triangle of numbers and describe the numbers in the pattern.
The numbers are consecutive odd numbers.

2. Continue the triangle by writing the numbers in the next four rows.

1
3 5
7 9 11
13 15 17 19
21 23 25 27 29
31 33 35 37 39 41
43 45 47 49 51 53 55
57 59 61 63 65 67 69 71
73 75 77 79 81 83 85 87 89
91 93 95 97 99 101 103 105 107 109

3. Find the sum of the numbers in each row. Describe these numbers.
1, 8, 27, 64, 125, 216, 343, 512, 729, and 1,000
They are cubes: $1^3, 2^3, 3^3, 4^3, 5^3, 6^3, 7^3, 8^3, 9^3$, and 10^3.

4. Find the mean (average) of the numbers in each row. Describe these numbers.
1, 4, 9, 16, 25, 36, 49, 64, 81, and 100
They are squares: $1^2, 2^2, 3^2, 4^2, 5^2, 6^2, 7^2, 8^2, 9^2$, and 10^2.

5. Look for the following diagonals in the triangle. List the next four numbers in each sequence.
a. 11, 17, 25, 35, 47, 61, 77, 95
b. 21, 33, 47, 63, 81, 101
c. Describe the pattern. Each number in the sequence increases by two more than the preceding number increased.

6. Does this pattern hold true for the other diagonals in the triangle? yes

Test Prep

Resources
For additional practice with a variety of test item formats:
- Test-Taking Strategies, p. 551
- Test Prep, p. 555
- Test-Taking Strategies with Transparencies

Alternative Assessment

Each student in a pair writes an arithmetic sequence. Partners trade papers and find the next three terms and the algebraic expression for their partner's sequence. Pairs repeat the activity for a geometric sequence.

39. a. 8; 27; 64; 125
b. volume is the length of the side cubed
c. n^3; where n is length of side

Exploring Sequences

You can use a graphing calculator to generate sequences.

EXAMPLE

1 Find the first five terms of this sequence: *Start with 100 and add 0.9 repeatedly.*

Step 1 Press 100 ENTER.

Step 2 Press + 0.9 ENTER.

Step 3 Press ENTER repeatedly.

```
100
                100
Ans+0.9
              100.9
              101.8
              102.7
              103.6
```

The first five terms are 100, 100.9, 101.8, 102.7, and 103.6.

You can use the table feature on a graphing calculator to list the terms of a sequence.

EXAMPLE

2 Find the sequence of y-values for $y = 3x + 2$ and $x = 1, 2, 3, 4,$ and 5. Then write a verbal description for the sequence.

Step 1 Press Y= and enter the formula.

```
Plot1  Plot2  Plot3
\Y1 = 3X+2
\Y2 =
\Y3 =
\Y4 =
```

Step 2 Use the TBLSET feature.

```
TABLE SETUP
 TblStart=1
 ΔTbl=1
Indpnt: Auto Ask
Depend: Auto Ask
```

Step 3 Use the TABLE feature.

X	Y1
1	5
2	8
3	11
4	14
5	17
6	20
7	23

X=1

The sequence is 5, 8, 11, 14, and 17. The verbal description is *Start with 5 and add 3 repeatedly.*

Exercises

Find the first five terms of each sequence.

1. Start with −3.5; add 0.7 repeatedly. −3.5, −2.8, −2.1, −1.4, −0.7
2. Start with 900; subtract 83 repeatedly. 900, 817, 734, 651, 568

For each formula, find the sequence of y values for $x = 1, 2, 3, 4,$ and 5. Then write a verbal description for the sequence. 3–6. See margin.

3. $y = x + 4$
4. $y = 5 \cdot 3^x$
5. $y = -4x + 30$
6. $y = 2x + 4$

3. 5, 6, 7, 8, 9; start with 5 and add 1 repeatedly.
4. 15, 45, 135, 405, 1,215; start with 15 and multiply by 3 repeatedly.
5. 26, 22, 18, 14, 10; start with 26 and add −4 repeatedly.
6. 6, 8, 10, 12, 14; start with 6 and add 2 repeatedly.

11-2 1. Plan

Objective
To interpret and sketch gr... that represent real-worl... situations

Examples
1 Interpretin...
2 Sketchin...

Math Un...

term by a fixed num... common difference).

Technology Tip
Model the specific keystroke sequences presented. Provide time for students to familiarize themselves with these special keys.

Error Prevention!

Students may press the keys in the wrong order. To help remediate this kind of error, have students work through the examples in pairs, together identifying the keys to press before one partner presses them.

Exercises

Have students work in pairs on the exercises. Before they begin work on Exercises 3–6, have them name the keystrokes they will use to find the sequence of y-values. One partner names and the other presses the keys.

Resources

- graphing calculators

aphs
d

g a Graph
g a Graph

derstandings: p. 510C

Professional Development

Math Background

Graphs can show complex relationships between variables. Many graphs use time on the *x*-axis because the other variable depends on time.

More Math Background: p. 510C

Lesson Planning and Resources

See p. 510E for a list of the resources that support this lesson.

PowerPoint

Bell Ringer Practice

Check Skills You'll Need
Use student page, transparency, or PowerPoint. For intervention, direct students to:

Choosing an Appropriate Graph
Lesson 9-9
Extra Skills and Word Problems Practice, Ch. 9

11-2 Relating Graphs to Events

Check Skills You'll Need

1. **Vocabulary Review** What type of data sets do *line graphs* best display?
1–3. See back of book.
Describe a set of data that is appropriate for each graph.
2. line plot
3. bar graph

GO for Help
Lesson 9-9

What You'll Learn

To interpret and sketch graphs that represent real-world situations

Why Learn This?

Newspapers, books, and magazines often use graphs to display data. A graph shows complex relationships between variables in a simple, visual way.

Drawing a graph makes it easier to see trends and changes in data. You can use a line graph to show how data such as speed or distance change over time.

EXAMPLE Interpreting a Graph

1 Transportation The line graph below shows the speed of a commuter train as it makes a morning run.

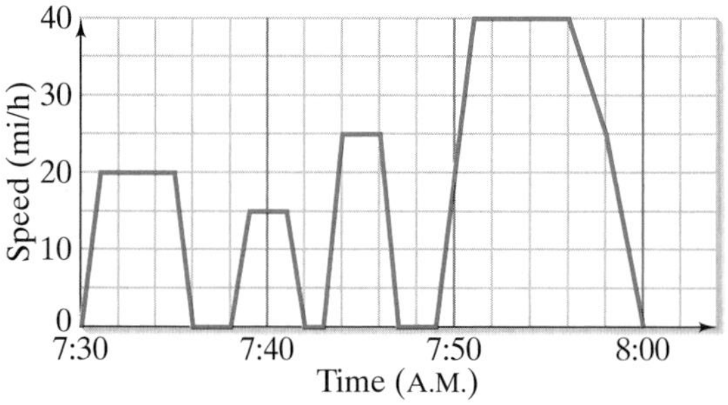

a. How long did the train's trip take?

Time is shown on the *x*-axis. The trip lasted 30 minutes, from 7:30 to 8:00.

b. Between which two times did the speed increase the most?

Between 7:49 and 7:51, the speed increased from 0 to 40 mi/h.

Online active math

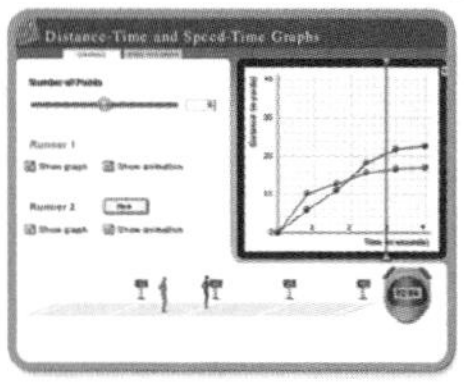

For: Graph Activity
Use: Interactive Textbook, 11-2

Quick Check

40 mi/h

1. Use the graph in Example 1. What was the train's fastest speed?

Differentiated Instruction Solutions for All Learners

Special Needs L1	Below Level L2
Some students may have difficulty sketching a graph. A student who has difficulty with graphing is paired with a student who does not. They check their sketch against the descriptions of the data to make sure it makes sense. **learning style: visual**	Students discuss how to read information from a graph, and identify the importance of the title, the labels, and the scales. **learning style: visual**

When you draw a graph without actual data, you are making a sketch.

EXAMPLE Sketching a Graph

2 **Fitness** Kim measured her pulse rate occasionally during a 45-min workout. The workout included a 10-min warmup period and a 10-min cool-down period. Sketch and label a graph showing her pulse rate during her workout.

The graph below shows that as Kim warmed up, her pulse rate increased. While she was in the middle of her workout, her pulse rate was high, but stable. The cool-down brought her pulse rate down again.

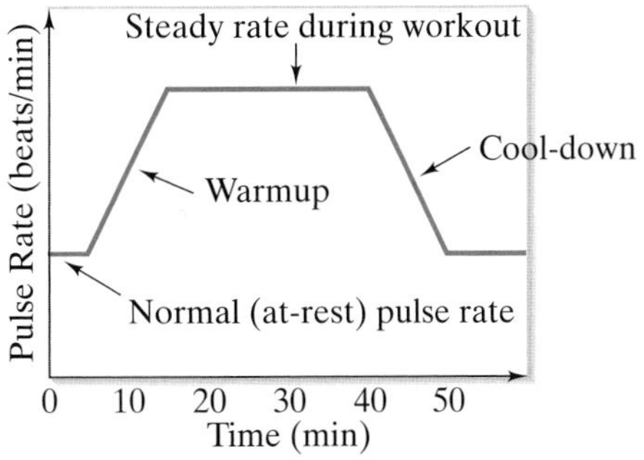

Test Prep Tip

After you sketch a graph, check to be sure it makes sense in relation to the problem.

Quick Check

2. You walk to your friend's house. For the first 10 min, you walk from home to a park. For the next 5 min, you watch a ball game in the park. For the last 5 min, you run to your friend's house. Sketch and label a graph showing your distance from home during your trip.
See back of book.

Check Your Understanding

Use the following information for Exercises 1–5. A student wants to sketch a graph that shows the distance of a bus from the transit center during the morning commute. The trip includes three stops where people get on and a highway where the bus travels at 50 mi/h.

1. **Vocabulary** Why should the student use a line graph? **Line graphs best display changes over time.**
2. What label should the student put on the horizontal scale? What label should be on the vertical scale? **time; distance**
3. When is the line on the graph parallel to the horizontal axis? **when the bus stops**
4. When is the line farthest away from the horizontal axis? **when the bus is farthest from the transit center**
5. **Reasoning** Which section of the graph should be steeper, the section for the bus on the highway or the section for the bus in the city? Explain. **See left.**

5. Highway; the bus travels a greater distance over a shorter period of time on the highway.

Advanced Learners L4	**English Language Learners** ELL
Students explain what it means if the graph of a problem appears only in Quadrant I. **both variables are always positive**	Help students understand the context in Example 1. For example, they may not know what a *commuter* train is, or what a morning run entails. Show them a picture of a commuter train, or spend some time explaining what typical commuter times are.
learning style: verbal	learning style: visual

2. Teach

Activity Lab

Use before the lesson.

All in One Teaching Resources

Activity Lab 11-2: Relating Graphs to Events

Guided Instruction

Error Prevention!

In Example 1, make sure that students recognize which points on the graph mean that the train has stopped.

PowerPoint

Additional Examples

1 Use the graph below.

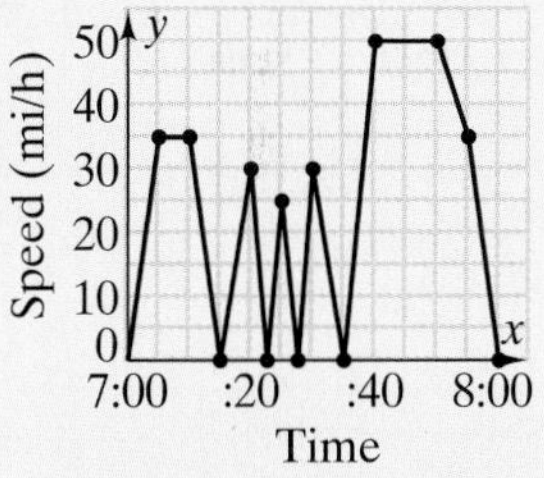

a. How long did the trip take? **1 hr**

b. What was the fastest speed? **50 mi/h**

2 An athlete jogs for 30 min, sprints for 5 min, and walks for 10 min. Sketch and label a graph showing his speed.

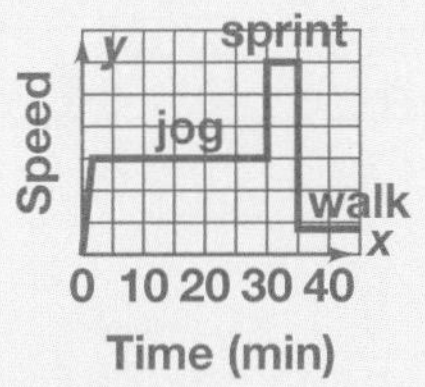

All in One Teaching Resources

- Daily Notetaking Guide 11-2 L3
- Adapted Notetaking 11-2 L1

Closure

- Explain how to interpret and to sketch the graph of a mail truck making deliveries. **Sample: Time is graphed on the *x*-axis; speed on the *y*-axis. Points on the *x*-axis indicate stops. Steep slopes show a rapid increase or decrease in speed.**

3. Practice

Assignment Guide

Check Your Understanding

Go over Exercises 1–5 in class before assigning the Homework Exercises.

Homework Exercises

A	Practice by Example	6–11
B	Apply Your Skills	12–19
C	Challenge	20
Test Prep and Mixed Review		21–27

Homework Quick Check

To check students' understanding of key skills and concepts, go over Exercises 7, 11, 13, 16, and 19.

Differentiated Instruction Resources

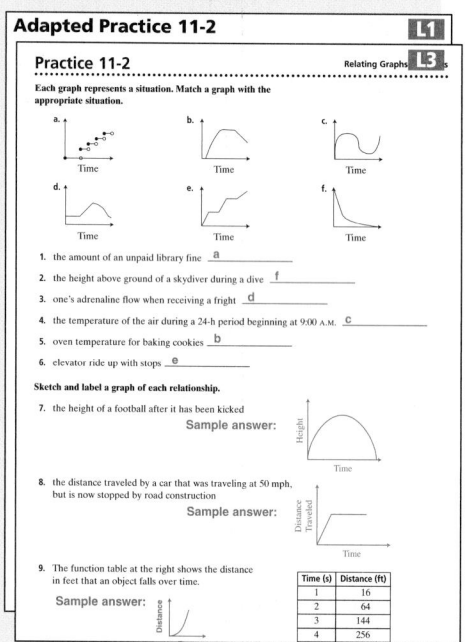

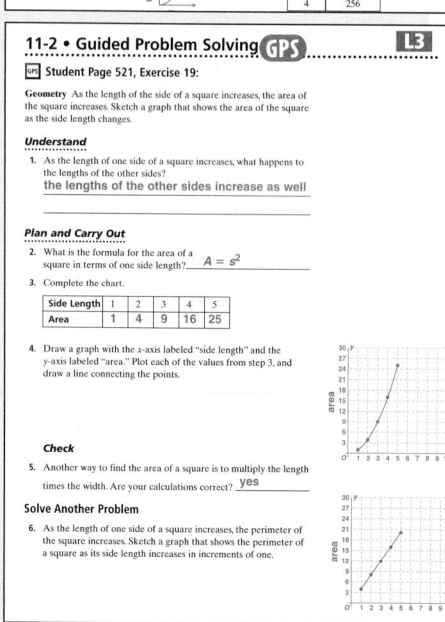

Adapted Practice 11-2 L1

Practice 11-2 — Relating Graphs L3

Each graph represents a situation. Match a graph with the appropriate situation.

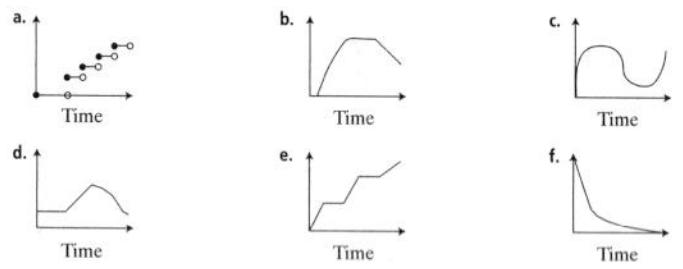

1. the amount of an unpaid library fine a
2. the height above ground of a skydiver during a dive f
3. one's adrenaline flow when receiving a fright d
4. the temperature of the air during a 24-h period beginning at 9:00 A.M. c
5. oven temperature for baking cookies b
6. elevator ride up with stops e

Sketch and label a graph of each relationship.

7. the height of a football after it has been kicked
   Sample answer:

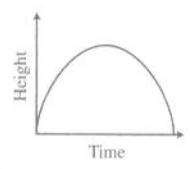

8. the distance traveled by a car that was traveling at 50 mph, but is now stopped by road construction
   Sample answer:

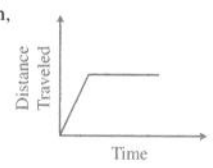

9. The function table at the right shows the distance in feet that an object falls over time.
   Sample answer:

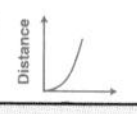

Time (s)	Distance (ft)
1	16
2	64
3	144
4	256

11-2 • Guided Problem Solving GPS L3

GPS Student Page 521, Exercise 19:

Geometry As the length of the side of a square increases, the area of the square increases. Sketch a graph that shows the area of the square as the side length changes.

Understand

1. As the length of one side of a square increases, what happens to the lengths of the other sides?
   the lengths of the other sides increase as well

Plan and Carry Out

2. What is the formula for the area of a square in terms of one side length? $A = s^2$
3. Complete the chart.

Side Length	1	2	3	4	5
Area	1	4	9	16	25

4. Draw a graph with the x-axis labeled "side length" and the y-axis labeled "area." Plot each of the values from step 3, and draw a line connecting the points.

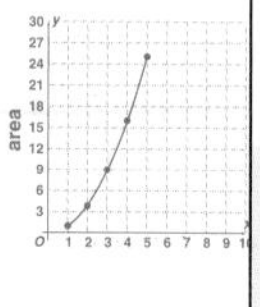

Check

5. Another way to find the area of a square is to multiply the length times the width. Are your calculations correct? yes

Solve Another Problem

6. As the length of one side of a square increases, the perimeter of the square increases. Sketch a graph that shows the perimeter of a square as its side length increases in increments of one.

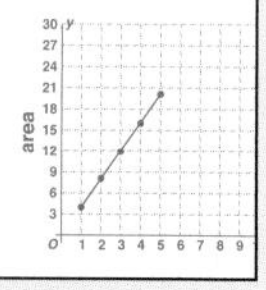

Homework Exercises

For more exercises, see Extra Skills and Word Problems.

GO for Help

For Exercises	See Examples
6–9	1
10–11	2

A **Swimming** **Use the graph below for Exercises 6–9.**

Weekly Swimming Distance During Olympic Training

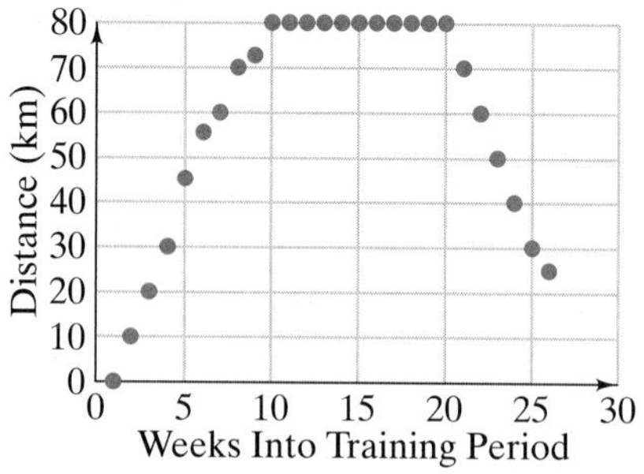

6. For how many weeks is the swimming distance 80 km/wk? 11 weeks
7. How many weeks does it take to reach the peak training level? 10 weeks
8. Between which two weeks does the greatest increase in swimming distance occur? fourth and fifth weeks
9. Find the change in the distance from week 24 to week 25. −10 km
10. **Temperature** In general, air temperature rises during the day and drops during the night. Sketch and label a graph showing the temperature during a 24-hour period. See margin.
11. **Pets** Haley took her dog to the park. She walked slowly to the park and then sat with a friend. Haley and her dog ran home together. Sketch a graph showing their distance from home throughout the trip. See left.

11.

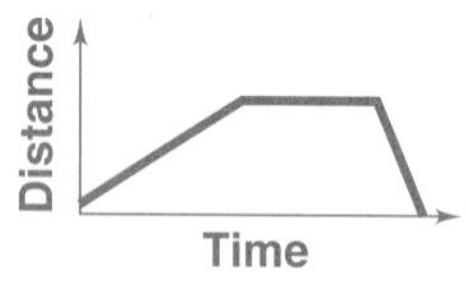

B **GPS**

12. **Guided Problem Solving** Abel, Ben, and Cam left the computer lab at 2:30 P.M. Cam walked the fastest and Abel the slowest. At the same time, Dan and Erin were walking toward the lab. Erin was walking faster than Dan but slower than Cam. Sketch a graph of each student's distance from the computer lab over time. See margin.
    - For which students does distance from the lab increase with time?
    - Which student is represented by the steepest line in the graph?

Use the graph at the right for Exercises 13–16.

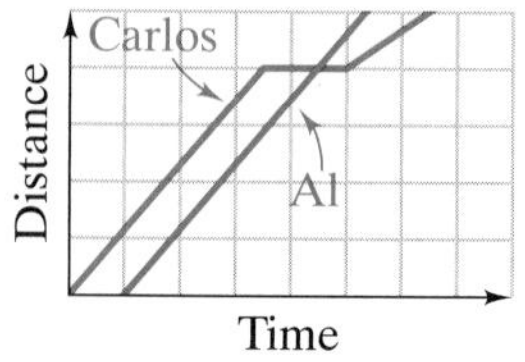

13. Who started the race later? Al
14. Who finished the race first? Al
15. Who stopped to tie his shoe? Carlos
16. **Writing in Math** Describe the outcome of the race. Al ran the same distance in a shorter period of time. Al won.

GO Online
Homework Video Tutor
Visit: PHSchool.com
Web Code: ase-1102

10.

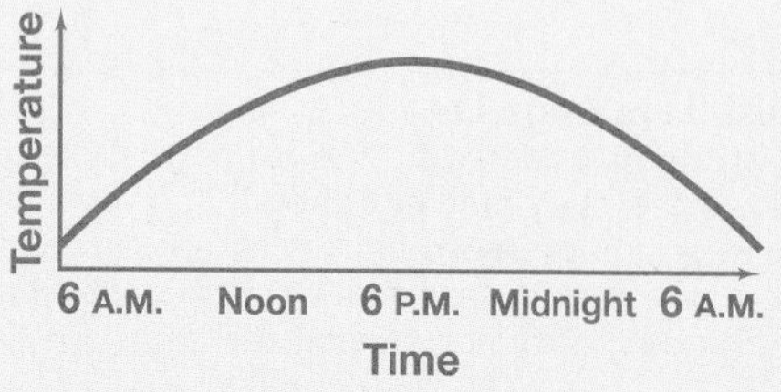

12.

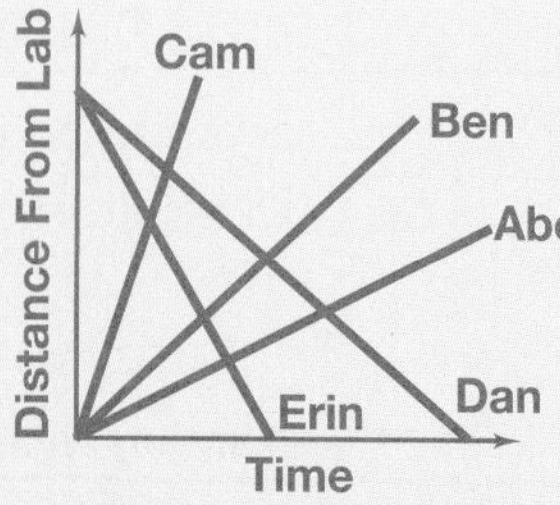

17. **Chemistry** Water is poured at a constant rate into the container at the left. Sketch a graph of the water level as the container is filled. See margin.

18. A boat travels at low speed for 3 min while leaving a harbor. Then it travels at a constant cruising speed for 15 min. Finally, it travels at low speed for 5 min while entering another harbor. Sketch a graph that shows the boat's speed during the trip. See margin.

19. **Geometry** As the length of the side of a square increases, the area (GPS) of the square increases. Sketch a graph that shows the area of the square as the side length changes. See margin.

(C) 20. **Challenge** You throw a ball into the air. It lands four seconds later. Sketch and label a graph showing the ball's height during this time. See margin.

Test Prep and Mixed Review

Practice

Multiple Choice

21. Maritza walks home from school, stopping at a friend's house on the way. Which graph could describe the total distance she walked? B

(A)

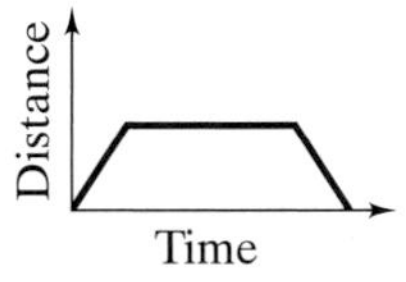

(C)

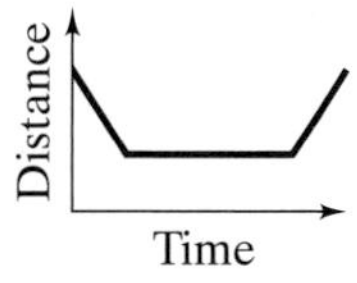

(B)

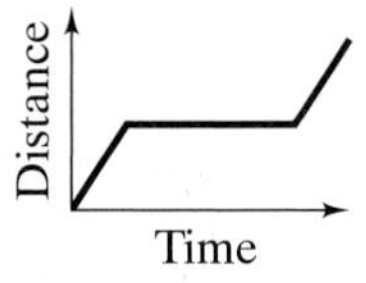

(D)

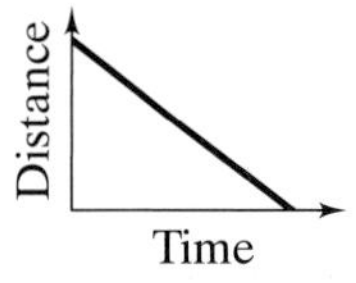

22. Triangle ABC was dilated to make triangle DEF. What is the scale factor used in the dilation? F

(F) $\frac{1}{2}$ (H) $\frac{5}{4}$

(G) $\frac{4}{5}$ (J) 2

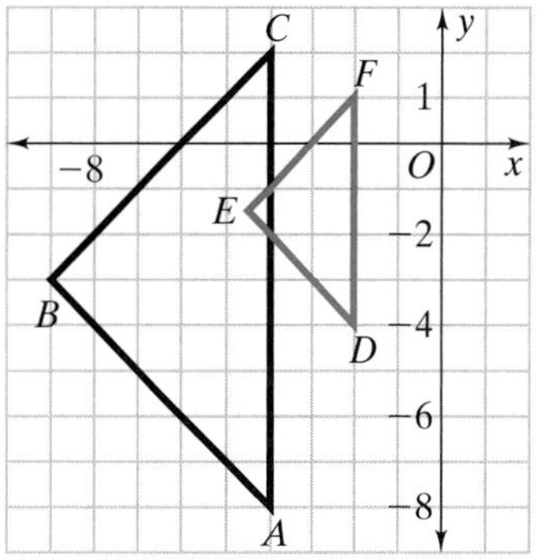

23. The algebraic expression $2 + 3n$ represents a sequence of numbers in which n is the number's position in the sequence. Which sequence does the expression represent? D

(A) 1, 5, 11, 29, 83, . . . (C) 3, 5, 11, 29, 83, . . .

(B) 3, 5, 7, 9, 11, . . . (D) 5, 8, 11, 14, 17, . . .

GO for Help

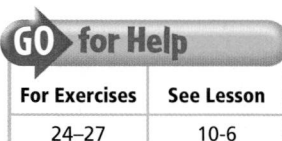

For Exercises	See Lesson
24–27	10-6

Simplify each expression.

24. ${}_9C_3$ 84 25. ${}_7C_5$ 21 26. ${}_5C_2$ 10 27. ${}_7C_3$ 35

4. Assess & Reteach

PowerPoint

Lesson Quiz

1. Water is steadily poured into a cone-shaped vase. Sketch and label a graph for the water level as the vase is filled. See back of book.

2. The graph below describes changes in the water level between low tides at the Bay of Fundy on the east coast of Canada. What is the approximate amount of time between low tides? What is the greatest distance between high tide and low tide? about 12 hours; about 40 feet

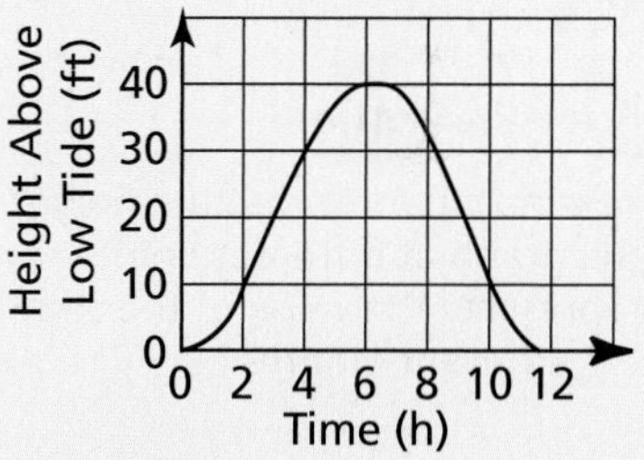

3. An airplane flew from Los Angeles to San Francisco in 70 min. The plane took 20 min to reach its cruising altitude. It took 15 min to descend into San Francisco. Sketch and label a graph that shows the plane's altitude during the flight. See back of book.

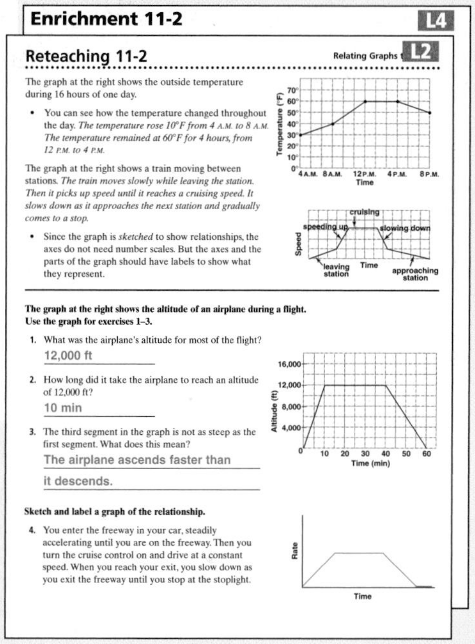
Enrichment 11-2 L4

Reteaching 11-2 Relating Graphs t L2

The graph at the right shows the outside temperature during 16 hours of one day.

- You can see how the temperature changed throughout the day. *The temperature rose 10°F from 4 A.M. to 8 A.M. The temperature remained at 60°F for 4 hours, from 12 P.M. to 4 P.M.*

The graph at the right shows a train moving between stations. *The train moves slowly while leaving the station. Then it picks up speed until it reaches a cruising speed. It slows down as it approaches the next station and gradually comes to a stop.*

- Since the graph is *sketched* to show relationships, the axes do not need number scales. But the axes and the parts of the graph should have labels to show what they represent.

The graph at the right shows the altitude of an airplane during a flight. Use the graph for exercises 1–3.

1. What was the airplane's altitude for most of the flight? 12,000 ft
2. How long did it take the airplane to reach an altitude of 12,000 ft? 10 min
3. The third segment in the graph is not as steep as the first segment. What does this mean? The airplane ascends faster than it descends.

Sketch and label a graph of the relationship.

4. You enter the freeway in your car, steadily accelerating until you are on the freeway. Then you turn the cruise control on and drive at a constant speed. When you reach your exit, you slow down as you exit the freeway until you stop at the stoplight.

Alternative Assessment

Students are shown an unlabeled graph with peaks and dips and horizontal stretches. They write a story to explain the graph.

17–20. See back of book.

Test Prep

Resources

For additional practice with a variety of test item formats:

- Test-Taking Strategies, p. 551
- Test Prep, p. 555
- Test-Taking Strategies with Transparencies

Activity Lab

Line Graphs

Students analyze data in a line graph that represents stock value over time. They also generate and interpret the graph of a simulated stock trend.

Guided Instruction

Ask:
- *What does this graph describe?* the value of a stock over a year
- *How is the stock value measured?* in dollars per share, by month
- *What does the graph tell you about the value of this stock?* Sample: steady and doing well, dropped significantly in August, then rose in October and leveled off

Error Prevention!

Remind students that the height of the graph at different points represents the value of the stock for different months.

Checkpoint Quiz

Use this Checkpoint Quiz to check students' understanding of the skills and concepts of Lessons 11-1 through 11-2.

Resources

- All in One Teaching Resources Checkpoint Quiz 1
- ExamView Assessment Suite CD-ROM
- Success Tracker Online Intervention

11-2b Activity Lab

Data Collection

Line Graphs

One type of line graph is called a "stock chart." It records the value of a company's stock over time.

ACTIVITY

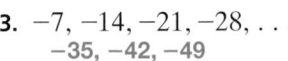

Sample Stock Chart

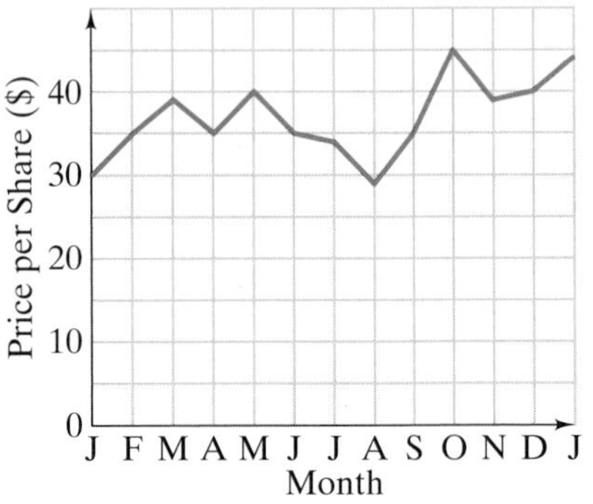

1. The line graph shows the value of a company's stock as it changed over one year.
   a. How much did the value increase in one year? about $15
   b. Between which two consecutive months was the greatest increase? Sept. and Oct.

2. Suppose you buy a share of stock in a company for $30. Toss a coin and roll a number cube to simulate the month-to-month gains and losses in the stock value. Heads represents a loss in the stock value and tails represents a gain. The number on the number cube determines the value of the gain or loss. Record the value of the stock for 12 months. Then make a line graph. 2–3. Check students' work.

3. Write a paragraph summarizing how the stock performed. Would you buy more stock in the company for the next year? Explain.

Checkpoint Quiz 1

Lessons 11-1 through 11-2

Find the next three terms in each sequence.

1. 13, 26, 39, 52, . . . 65, 78, 91

2. $\frac{3}{4}, 1\frac{1}{2}, 2\frac{1}{4}, 3, \ldots$ $3\frac{3}{4}, 4\frac{1}{2}, 5\frac{1}{4}$

3. −7, −14, −21, −28, . . . −35, −42, −49

Use the graph at the right for Exercises 4–8.

Naomi's Car Trip

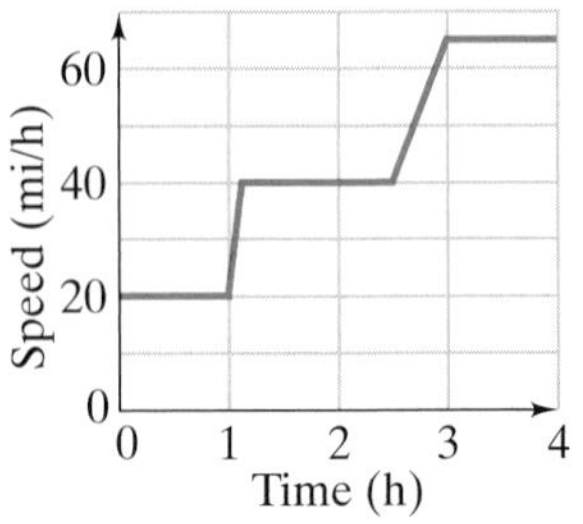

4. How fast was Naomi driving during the first hour of her trip? 20 mi/h
5. How many miles did she travel at this speed? 20 mi
6. When did Naomi's speed first increase? after 1 hour
7. To what speed did it increase? 40 mi/h
8. What was Naomi's final speed at the end of the 4 hours? 65 mi/h

11-3 Functions

Check Skills You'll Need

1. **Vocabulary Review** What is the *variable* in the expression $3a + 7$? *a*

Evaluate each expression for $v = 7$.

2. $2(v - 3)$ 8
3. $7v + 4$ 53
4. $3v - 12$ 9
5. $-5(15 - 2v)$ -5

GO for Help Lesson 1-1

What You'll Learn

To represent functions with equations, tables, and function notation

New Vocabulary function, function rule

Why Learn This?

The time it takes you to get to your destination is a function of how fast you travel. Your speed affects how long the trip will take.

A **function** is a relationship that assigns exactly one output value to each input value. A **function rule** is an equation that describes a function.

To encourage recycling, some states require a five-cent deposit on drink containers. The total deposit you pay depends on how many containers you buy. You can describe this relationship with a function rule.

$d = 0.05c$ ← input variable c = number of containers
↑
output variable d = deposit

EXAMPLE Representing Functions

1 **Recycling** Complete the table of input-output pairs for the function rule $d = 0.05c$, where d represents the deposit in dollars and c represents the number of containers.

Input c (number of containers)	Output d (dollars)	
6	■	← $0.05 \times 6 = 0.30$
12	■	← $0.05 \times 12 = 0.60$
24	■	← $0.05 \times 24 = 1.20$

Quick Check

1. The deposit on a drink container is \$.10 in the state of Michigan. Use the function rule $d = 0.1c$. Make a table of input-output pairs to show the total deposits on 5, 10, and 15 containers. See back of book.

Differentiated Instruction Solutions for All Learners

Special Needs L1
Students visualize examples through drawings of the example and writing the accompanying function. Students draw the fish in Example 3 and place dollar values under each group.

learning style: visual

Below Level L2
Students draw and label familiar relationships that can be expressed as functions. For example, the perimeter of a square depends on the length of its sides.

learning style: visual

11-3

1. Plan

Objective
To represent functions with equations, tables, and function notation

Examples
1 Representing Functions
2 Evaluating a Function Rule
3 Using Function Notation

Math Understandings: p. 510C

Professional Development

Math Background

A function is a relationship between two or more quantities. The value of the function (output) depends on the value of the input. Functions can be represented numerically (as in an input/output table), graphically, symbolically (as in an equation, also called a *function rule*), or verbally (as in a problem that describes a situation). The set of ordered pairs that satisfies a function has exactly one output value for a given input value.

More Math Background: p. 510C

Lesson Planning and Resources

See p. 510E for a list of the resources that support this lesson.

PowerPoint

Bell Ringer Practice

Check Skills You'll Need
Use student page, transparency, or PowerPoint. For intervention, direct students to:
Algebraic Expressions and Order of Operations
Lesson 1-1
Extra Skills and Word Problems Practice, Ch. 1

2. Teach

Activity Lab

Use before the lesson.

All in One Teaching Resources

Activity Lab 11-3: Functions

Guided Instruction

Error Prevention!

Students often mistake function notation $f(x)$ for multiplication, as in f times x. Help students remember its meaning by reading: "f of x" or "f as a function of x" or "the value of the function f."

Example 2

Provide students with a blank grid.

PowerPoint

Additional Examples

1. Complete the table for $p = 4s$.

Input s	3	5	7	9
Output p	12	20	28	36

2. Use the function rule $f(x) = 3x - 1$. Find the output value $f(5)$. Then grid the response. 14

3. Use function notation to show the relationship between the total number of cars and the number of tires. Identify your variables. Sample: $f(t) = t \div 4$ where t is the number of tires and $f(t)$ is the number of cars

All in One Teaching Resources

- Daily Notetaking Guide 11-3 L3
- Adapted Notetaking 11-3 L1

Closure

- *What is a function?* a relationship that assigns exactly one output value to each input value
- *How can you use function notation to write a function rule?* Write an equation in the form $y =$ but use $f(x)$ for y, the output, and x for the input.

Vocabulary Tip

Read $T(s)$ as "T of s."

Function notation is a shorter way of writing word descriptions.

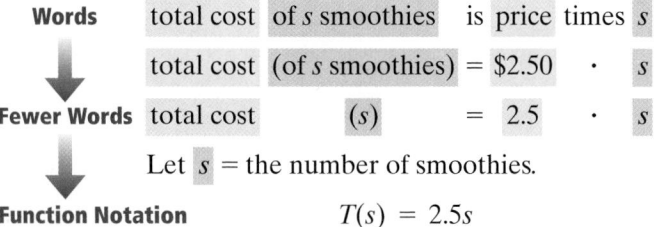

Words	total cost	of s smoothies	is	price	times	s
	total cost	(of s smoothies)	$=$	\$2.50	$\cdot$	s
Fewer Words	total cost	(s)	$=$	2.5	$\cdot$	s

Let s = the number of smoothies.

Function Notation $T(s) = 2.5s$

EXAMPLE Evaluating a Function Rule

2 **Gridded Response** A smoothie costs \$2.50. Use the function rule $T(s) = 2.5s$. Find the total cost of three smoothies by finding the output value $T(3)$.

$T(s) = 2.5s$ ← Write the function rule.

$T(3) = 2.5(3)$ ← Substitute the input value for s.

$= 7.5$ ← Simplify.

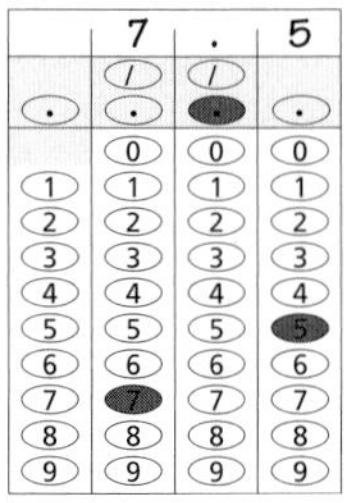

The total cost of three smoothies is \$7.50.

Test Prep Tip

To evaluate a function rule, substitute the input value for the variable inside the parentheses.

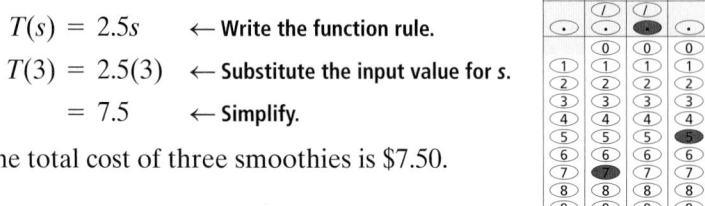

Quick Check

2. Use the function rule $f(x) = -4x + 12$. Find $f(-7)$ and $f(3)$. 40; 0

$T(3)$ means "total cost of 3 smoothies." Notice that $T(3)$ does *not* mean the product of T and 3. It means the output of the function when the input is 3.

EXAMPLE Using Function Notation

3 **Aquariums** Suppose you go to the pet store and buy several fish at \$2 each. Use function notation to show the relationship between the total cost and the number of fish you buy. Identify the variables you use.

Words total cost = \$2 · number of fish bought

Let n = the number of fish bought. ← input

Let $f(n)$ = the total cost. ← output

Function $f(n) = 2 \cdot n$

$f(n) = 2n$

Quick Check

3. Use the function in Example 3. Find $f(6)$. What does $f(6)$ represent? $f(6) = 12$; $f(6)$ is the total cost of buying 6 fish.

Differentiated Instruction Solutions for All Learners

Advanced Learners L4

Students use function notation to write expressions for the perimeter of a regular triangle, a pentagon, and an octagon. $f(s) = 3s$; $5s$; $8s$

learning style: verbal

English Language Learners ELL

In previous lessons, students read $T(s)$ as "the product of T and s" or "T times the number of smoothies." Here they need to read it as a function, "the value of the function T at the input s."

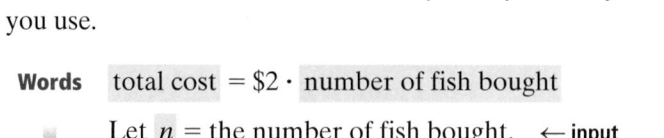

learning style: verbal

Check Your Understanding

1. **Vocabulary** How are a function and a function rule related?

2. If $f(n)$ is a function, can $f(2) = 4$ and $f(2) = 5$ both be true? Explain. No; a function assigns exactly one output value to each input value.

3. **Number Sense** If the input value is negative, is the output value of $f(z) = -4z + 12$ always positive or always negative? Explain.

4. Complete the input-output table for the function $f(n) = 3 + n$. 4; 5; 6

Input n	0	1	2	3
Output $f(n)$	3	■	■	■

1. A function rule is an equation that describes a function.
3. Always positive; the product of two negative numbers is always positive.

Homework Exercises

For more exercises, see Extra Skills and Word Problems.

GO for Help

For Exercises	See Examples
5–6	1
7–12	2–3

A 5. **Hockey** Copy and complete the table of input-output pairs for the function rule $t = \frac{n}{11}$. The variable t represents the number of teams formed in a hockey league. The variable n represents the number of people signed up for the league. See left.

Input n (number of people)	Output t (number of teams)
44	■
132	■
165	■

6. The function rule $p = 1.5 + 2m$ represents the taxi fare p in dollars for a ride that is m miles long. Make a table of input-output pairs to show the fare for rides of 2, 6, and 13 miles. See left.

5.

n	t
44	4
132	12
165	15

6.

m	p
2	5.50
6	13.50
13	27.50

Use the function rule $f(x) = 2x + 3$. Find each output.

7. $f(0)$ 3
8. $f(-2)$ −1
9. $f(2)$ 7
10. $f(10)$ 23
11. $f(-16.7)$ −30.4

12. **Energy** Each hour a stereo is on, it uses 0.4 kilowatt-hours of energy. Complete the function rule $E(h) =$ __?__ to describe the relationship between the total energy $E(h)$ used by the stereo and the number of hours h the stereo is on. $E(h) = 0.4h$

B **GPS** 13. **Guided Problem Solving** Paint brushes cost $1.79 each. Use function notation to show the total cost as a function of the number of paint brushes you buy. Use the rule to find the cost of 27 brushes. $48.33
- Let c represent the total cost and p the number of paint brushes.
- Find c when $p = 27$.

Reasoning **Tell whether the data in each table are values of a function.**

14.

Input	2	3	4	5	6
Output	5	5	5	5	5

yes

15.

Input	1	2	2	3	3
Output	1	3	6	9	12

no

GO Online
Homework Video Tutor
Visit: PHSchool.com
Web Code: ase-1103

Online lesson quiz, PHSchool.com, Web Code: asa-1103

3. Practice

Assignment Guide

Check Your Understanding
Go over Exercises 1–4 in class before assigning the Homework Exercises.

Homework Exercises

A	Practice by Example	5–12
B	Apply Your Skills	13–20
C	Challenge	21
	Test Prep and Mixed Review	22–25

Homework Quick Check
To check students' understanding of key skills and concepts, go over Exercises 6, 8, 12, 17, and 20.

Differentiated Instruction Resources

Adapted Practice 11-3 L1

Practice 11-3 L3

Complete the table of input/output pairs for each function.

1. $y = 3x$

Input x	Output y
4	12
8	24
12	36
16	48

2. $z = 15n$

Input n	Output z
1	15
2	30
3	45
4	60

3. $d = 30 - s$

Input s	Output d
0	30
5	25
10	20
15	15

4. $h = 120 \div g$

Input g	Output h
2	60
6	20
12	10
15	8

5. $r = 2t - 1$

Input t	Output r
3	5
9	17
20	39
50	99

6. $p = 2v - 12$

Input v	Output p
9	6
26	40
43	74
75	138

Does each situation represent a function? Explain.

7. Input: the distance that needs to be biked
   Output: the time it takes if you bike at 5 mph
   yes

8. Input: the time of day you go to the grocery store
   Output: the cost of the groceries
   no

Use the function rule $f(x) = 5x + 1$. Find each output.

9. $f(3)$ 16
10. $f(-6)$ −29
11. $f(8)$ 41
12. $f(1.5)$ 8.5
13. $f(25)$ 126
14. $f(30)$ 151

Use the function rule $f(n) = 4n^2 - 1$. Find each output.

15. $f(0)$ −1
16. $f(1)$ 3
17. $f(-1)$ 3
18. $f(-2)$ 15
19. $f(3)$ 35
20. $f(2.5)$ 24

11-3 • Guided Problem Solving GPS L3

Student Page 526, Exercise 20:

Fruit smoothies cost $1.50 each plus $.50 for each fruit mixed into the smoothie. Use function notation to find the cost of a smoothie with 4 different fruits mixed in.

Understand

1. Which two quantities are related?
   cost and the number of fruits mixed in
2. Circle what you are asked to find.

Plan and Carry Out

3. What two operations are needed to determine the cost?
   addition and multiplication
4. Let n be the number of fruits mixed into the smoothie. Write an expression for the total cost of a smoothie with n fruits mixed in.
   $1.50 + 0.50n$
5. Use the expression you found in step 4 to write a function.
   $f(n) = 1.50 + 0.50n$
6. Use the function to find the cost of a smoothie with 4 fruits mixed in.
   $f(4) = 1.50 + 0.50(4) = 3.50$; $3.50

Check

7. How could you find the answer another way?
   Multiply $.50 times four then add the $1.50; you will get the same answer.

Solve Another Problem

8. You spent $4.50 for admission to the fair. Each ride ticket costs $.75. Use function notation to find the cost of 6 ride tickets.
   $f(x) = 4.5 + 0.75x$; $9

4. Assess & Reteach

PowerPoint

Lesson Quiz

1. A photocopy costs \$.08. Use the function rule $c = \$0.08n$. Make a table of input/output pairs to show the cost for 5, 10, and 15 copies.

Input n	5	10	15
Output c	\$.40	\$.80	\$1.20

Evaluate items 2 and 3 for the function rule $f(x) = 40 - 2x$.

2. $f(12)$ 16 3. $f(-12)$ 64

4. Suppose peaches cost \$.99 per pound. Write a function rule to describe the relationship between the total cost and the number of pounds of peaches you buy. Sample: $C(p) = 0.99p$

Enrichment 11-3 L4

Reteaching 11-3 L2

A *function* describes the relationship between two variables called the *input* and the *output*. In a function, each input value has only one output value.

Function:

$y = 2x + 4$

↑ ↑

output variable y *input variable x*

You can list input/output pairs in a table.

$y = 2x + 4$

Input x	Output y
−10	−16
−5	−6
0	4
1	6

To find output y, substitute values for input x into the function equation.

For $x = -10$: $y = 2(-10) + 4$
$y = -16$

You can also show input/output pairs using *function notation.*

Function rule:

$f(x) = 2x + 4$
$f(-10) = 2(-10) + 4 = -16$

↑ *input* ↑ *output*

Find $f(0)$.

$f(0) = 2(0) + 4$
$f(0) = 4$

Complete the table of input/output pairs for each function.

1. $y = 3x$

Input x	Output y
5	15
7	21
9	27
11	33

2. $d = 20r$

Input r	Output d
1	20
2	40
3	60
8	160

3. $y = 25 - 2x$

Input x	Output y
0	25
1	23
2	21
3	19

Use the function rule $f(x) = 3x + 1$. Find each output.

4. $f(0)$
$= 3(\underline{0}) + 1$
$= \underline{1}$

5. $f(1)$
$= 3(\underline{1}) + 1$
$= \underline{4}$

6. $f(5)$
16

7. $f(-6)$
−17

16. **Water Use** The function $w = 40\ell$ describes the number w of gallons of water used to wash ℓ loads of laundry in a washing machine. 16a–c. See margin.
   a. Find the value of w when $\ell = 6$. What does this represent?
   b. The *domain* of a function is all possible input values. The *range* of a function is all possible output values. Which variable, w or ℓ, represents the domain in part (a)? Explain.
   c. The input variable is also called the *independent variable.* The output variable is the *dependent variable,* because it depends on the input variable. Which is the dependent variable, w or ℓ?

17. **Writing in Math** Find several solutions of the equation $y = 3x - 2$. Explain how these solutions are related to input-output pairs for the function $f(x) = 3x - 2$. Write each solution using function notation. See left.

17. Answers may vary. Sample: (0, −2), (2, 4), (7, 19); each solution (x, y) equals an input-output pair for the function $f(x) = 3x - 2$; $f(0) = -2$, $f(2) = 4$, $f(7) = 19$.

Copy and complete the table of input-output pairs for each function. 18–19. See left.

18. $y = 4x$

Input x	Output y
5	■
7	■
9	■
11	■

19. $d = 50t$

Input t	Output d
1	■
2	■
3	■
■	200

18.

Input x	Output y
5	20
7	28
9	36
11	44

19.

Input t	Output d
1	50
2	100
3	150
4	200

20. Fruit smoothies cost \$1.50 each plus \$.50 for each fruit mixed into the smoothie. Use function notation to find the cost of a smoothie with 4 different fruits mixed in. \$3.50 (GPS)

(C) 21. **Challenge** For each function, find $f(1)$, $f(2)$, $f(3)$, and $f(4)$. Identify each sequence as *arithmetic, geometric,* or *neither.*
   a. $f(n) = 100 - 4n$
   96, 92, 88, 84; arithmetic
   b. $f(n) = n(4 - n)$
   3, 4, 3, 0; neither

Test Prep and Mixed Review

Practice

Gridded Response

22. An ad in the newspaper costs \$52 plus \$2.50 for each line of the ad. What is the cost in dollars of placing a 7-line ad? 69.5

23. Two similar cylinders are shown. The volume of the larger cylinder is 3,375 cubic centimeters. What is the volume of the smaller cylinder in cubic centimeters? 27

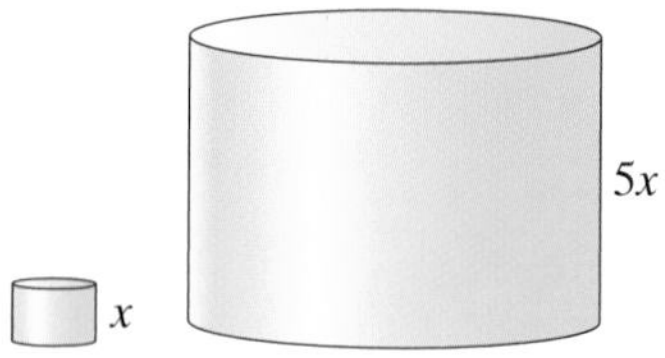

GO for Help

For Exercises	See Lesson
24–25	11-1

Write an algebraic expression for each sequence and find the next three terms. 24–25. See margin.

24. 4, 8, 12, 16, . . .

25. −1, −2, −3, −4, . . .

Test Prep

Resources

For additional practice with a variety of test item formats:

- Test-Taking Strategies, p. 551
- Test Prep, p. 555
- Test-Taking Strategies with Transparencies

Alternative Assessment

Each student in a pair makes a table of values for a function. Partners exchange tables and use function notation to write their partner's function rule.

Rate of Change

You know that in 1 yard, there are 3 feet. In 2 yards, there are 6 feet.

The table at the right shows that the number of feet changes by 3 as the number of yards changes by 1. You can represent this relationship with a ratio:

$$\frac{\text{change in number of feet}}{\text{change in number of yards}} = \frac{3}{1}$$

	+1	+1	+1	+1	+1

Yards, *x*	1	2	3	4	5	6
Feet, *y*	3	6	9	12	15	18

	+3	+3	+3	+3	+3

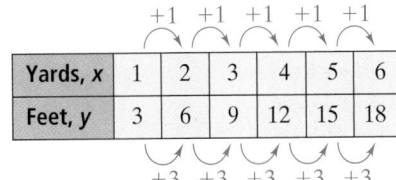

This comparison of two quantities that are changing is called a **rate of change.** As the value of one quantity changes, the value of the other quantity also changes. The rate of change of feet to yards is $\frac{3}{1}$, or 3.

You can find the rate of change from a graph such as the one at the right. Notice that rate of change is the ratio of the vertical change to the horizontal change.

$$\text{rate of change} = \frac{\text{vertical change}}{\text{horizontal change}} = \frac{3}{1}$$

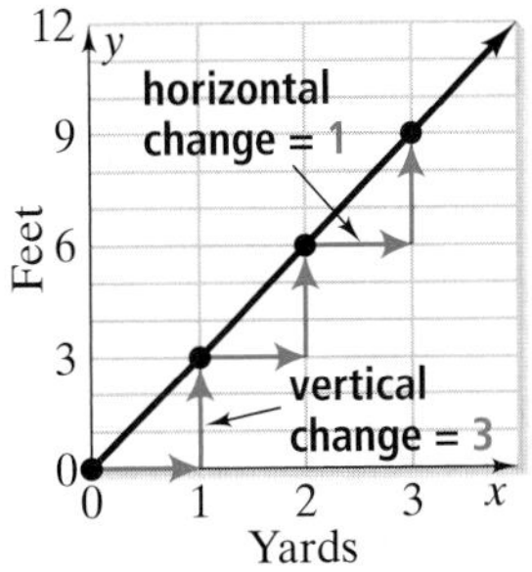

Exercises

1. 2; the person grows 2 in./yr.

Find the rate of change from each table or graph. Explain what the rate of change means in each problem situation.

1.

Age (yr)	8	9	10	11	12
Height (in.)	51	53	55	57	59

See above right.

3; it rains 3 mm/h.

2.

Time (h)	1	2	3	4	5
Rainfall (mm)	3	6	9	12	15

3.

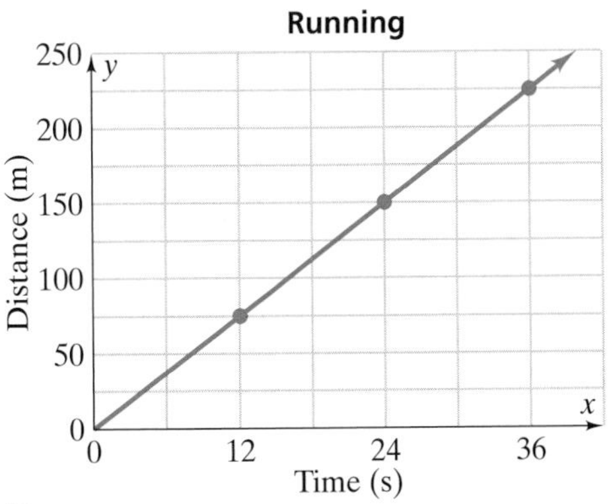

$\frac{25}{4}$; the person runs 25 m every 4 s.

4.

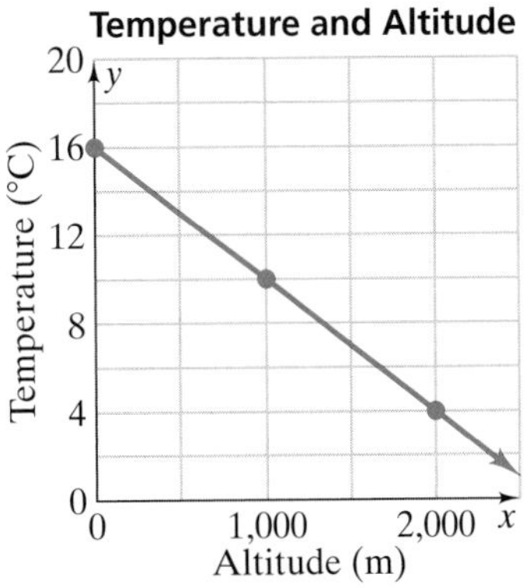

$-\frac{3}{500}$; the temperature drops 3°C every 500 m ascended.

Activity Lab

Rate of Change

Using real-world data, students investigate rate of change as a ratio that underlies linear functions. In the lesson that follows, they will learn that this is the *slope* of the linear function.

Guided Instruction

Before beginning the activity, review the number of feet in a yard and the concept of ratio as a comparison between two quantities.

Teaching Tip
Have students write ratios in words first to keep track of the values they are comparing.

Error Prevention!

Emphasize that a rate of change is a ratio of *changes* between two inputs and two corresponding outputs, not just a ratio of an input and an output. For example, in Exercise 1, the rate of change is the ratio of the *difference* between any two ages to the *difference* between the corresponding heights.

Differentiated Instruction

Visual Learners
Have students draw and label arrows (with the difference) between consecutive input values, then between consecutive output values. See the Example table for a sample.

Resources

- Activity Lab 11-4: Understanding Slope

Exercises, p. 526

16 a. 240; the number of gallons of water used to wash 6 loads of laundry

b. ℓ; the number of loads, which is the input, is the domain.

c. w

24. $4n$; 20, 24, 28

25. $-1n$; −5, −6, −7

11-4

1. Plan

Objective
To find the slope of a line from a graph or table

Examples
1 Finding the Slope of a Line
2 Slopes for Horizontal and Vertical Lines
3 Finding Slope From a Table

Math Understandings: p. 510C

Professional Development

Math Background

Slope is a rate of change. The slope of a non-vertical line is calculated by finding the ratio of the change in *y*-values (or the difference between values of the function at two inputs) to the change in *x*-values (or the difference between the two inputs). The slope of a line is the same (or constant) between any two points on the line.

More Math Background: p. 510C

Lesson Planning and Resources

See p. 510E for a list of the resources that support this lesson.

PowerPoint

Bell Ringer Practice

Check Skills You'll Need
Use student page, transparency, or PowerPoint. For intervention, direct students to:
Adding and Subtracting Integers
Lesson 1-3
Extra Skills and Word Problems Practice, Ch. 1

Algebra

11-4 Understanding Slope

Check Skills You'll Need

1. **Vocabulary Review** Do the *negative integers* include zero? no

Simplify each expression.

2. $-3 - 1$ -4
3. $10 - (-4)$ 14
4. $1 - 7$ -6
5. $-8 - (-6)$ -2

GO for Help Lesson 1-3

Vocabulary Tip
A *ratio* is the comparison of two quantities by division.

What You'll Learn

To find the slope of a line from a graph or table

New Vocabulary slope, slope of a line

Why Learn This?

You can use slope to describe the steepness of an incline or hill. The steepness of a ramp is the ratio of the vertical change to the horizontal change. In math, slope is a number that describes the steepness of a line.

You can also use slope to describe rate of change of a quantity.

$$\textbf{slope} = \frac{\text{vertical change}}{\text{horizontal change}} \quad \begin{matrix}\leftarrow \text{rise} \\ \leftarrow \text{run}\end{matrix}$$

Slope describes the steepness of lines in the coordinate plane. You can find the slope of a line by subtracting the coordinates of any two points on the line.

KEY CONCEPTS **Slope of a Line**

$$\textbf{slope of a line} = \frac{\text{change in } y\text{-coordinates}}{\text{change in } x\text{-coordinates}} \quad \begin{matrix}\leftarrow \text{rise} \\ \leftarrow \text{run}\end{matrix}$$

The direction of the slant of a line indicates a positive or a negative slope.

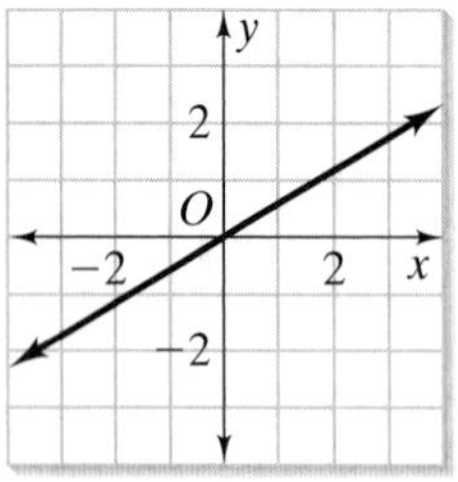

Positive slope

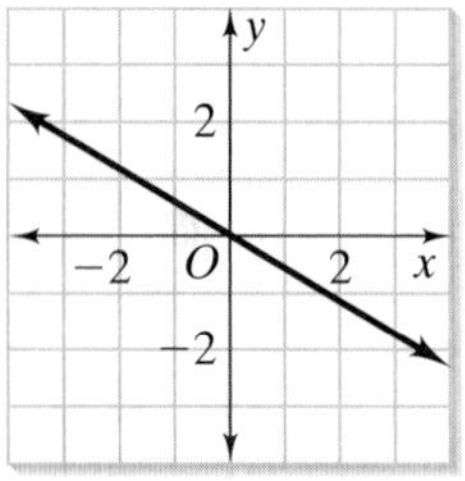

Negative slope

Differentiated Instruction Solutions for All Learners

Special Needs L1
Students trace lines with zero slope, positive slope, and negative slope in the air with their finger. They also use their forearm to show a line that is not very steep, then one that is very steep.
learning style: tactile

Below Level L2
Using Example 3, students find the slope between two other pairs of points on the line. They draw vertical and horizontal lines to represent the change in *y* and the change in *x*, respectively, between each pair of points, finding that the slope is always the same.
learning style: visual

When you find the slope of a line, the first *y*-coordinate you use for the rise must belong to the same point as the first *x*-coordinate you use for the run.

EXAMPLE **Finding the Slope of a Line**

1 Find the slope of the line in the graph below.

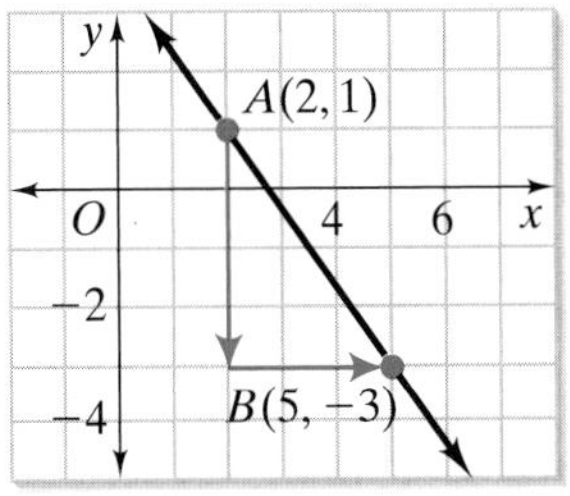

$$\text{slope} = \frac{\text{change in } y\text{-coordinates}}{\text{change in } x\text{-coordinates}}$$

$$= \frac{-3 - 1}{5 - 2} \quad \leftarrow \text{Subtract coordinates of } A \text{ from coordinates of } B.$$

$$= \frac{-4}{3} \text{ or } -\frac{4}{3} \quad \leftarrow \text{Simplify.}$$

Online active math

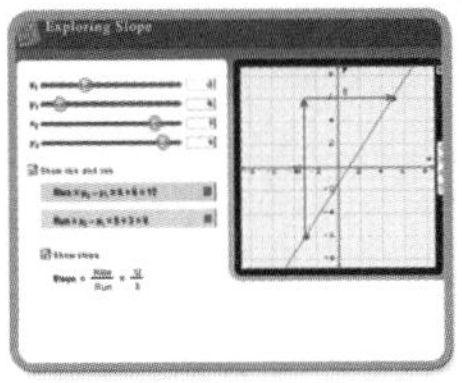

For: Exploring Slope Activity
Use: Interactive Textbook, 11-4

Quick Check

1. Find the slope of each line.

a.

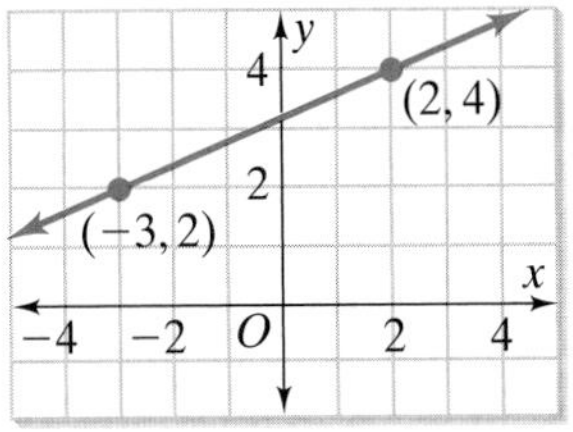

$\frac{2}{5}$

b.

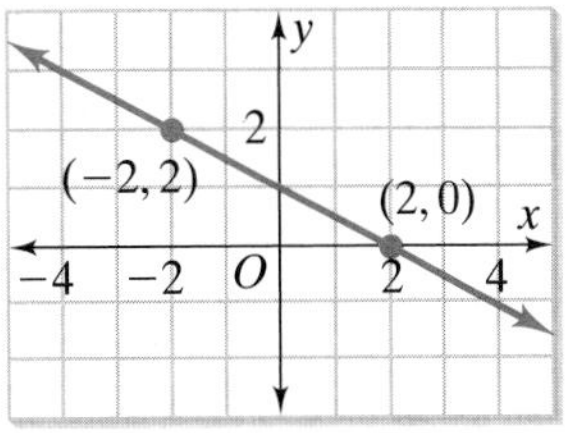

$-\frac{1}{2}$

Some lines have slopes that are neither positive nor negative.

EXAMPLE **Slopes of Horizontal and Vertical Lines**

Vocabulary Tip

Do not confuse the terms *zero* and *undefined*. The slope of a horizontal line is zero. The slope of a vertical line is undefined.

2 Find the slope of each line. State whether the slope is zero or undefined.

a.

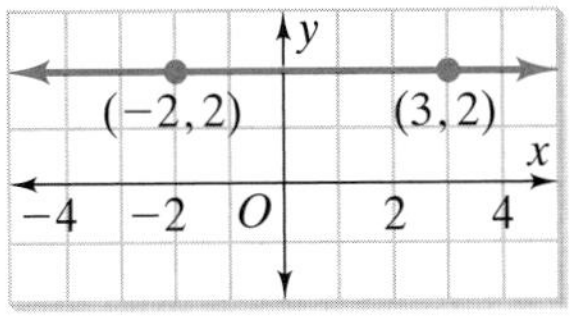

$$\text{slope} = \frac{2 - 2}{3 - (-2)} = \frac{0}{5} = 0$$

The slope of a horizontal line is zero.

b.

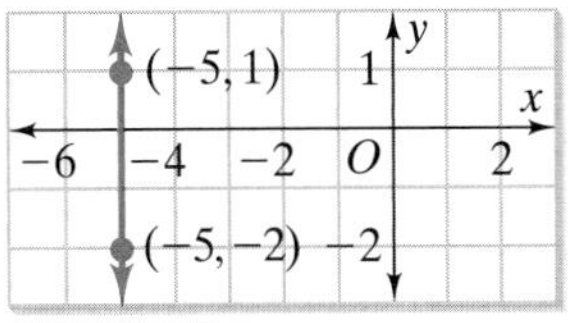

$$\text{slope} = \frac{1 - (-2)}{-5 - (-5)} = \frac{3}{0}$$

Division by zero is undefined. So, the slope of a vertical line is undefined.

Quick Check

2. Find the slope of a line through the points (3, 1) and (3, −2). State whether the slope is zero or undefined. undefined

2. Teach

Activity Lab

Use before the lesson.
Student Edition Activity Lab, 11-4a Rate of Change, p. 527

All in One Teaching Resources

Activity Lab 11-4: Understanding Slope

Guided Instruction

Error Prevention!

Make it clear that when students find the change in *y* by subtracting one *y*-coordinate from the other, they must follow the same order of subtraction for the *x*-coordinates.

PowerPoint

Additional Examples

1 Using coordinates, find the slope of the line between *P*(−2, 3) and *Q*(−1, −1). −4

2 Find the slope of each line. State whether the slope is zero or undefined.

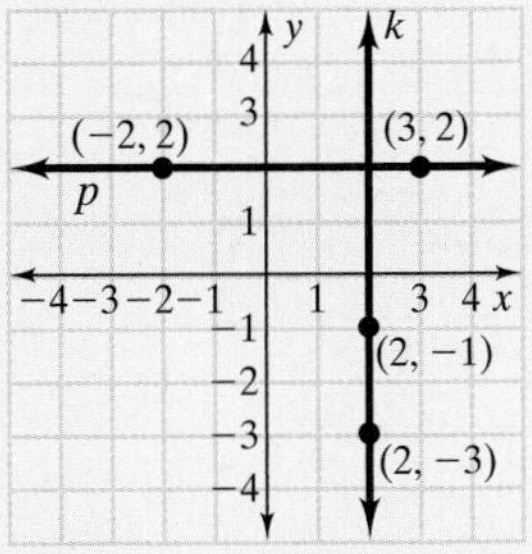

a. line *k* undefined **b.** line *p* 0

3 Graph the distance-cost data below. Connect the points with a line. Then find the rate of change. See back of book.

Distance (mi)	0	100	200	300	400	500
Cost ($)	0	25	50	75	100	125

All in One Teaching Resources

- Daily Notetaking Guide 11-4 L3
- Adapted Notetaking 11-4 L1

Advanced Learners L4

Students form a conjecture about the slope of lines that are parallel. They test their conjectures. Parallel lines have the same slope.

learning style: verbal

English Language Learners ELL

Students sketch a coordinate plane on a note card. Then they sketch a line with a positive slope. They repeat this process three times by sketching a line with a negative slope, an undefined slope, and a slope of zero.

learning style: visual

3. Practice

Assignment Guide

Check Your Understanding

Go over Exercises 1–4 in class before assigning the Homework Exercises.

Homework Exercises

A	Practice by Example	5–9
B	Apply Your Skills	10–13
C	Challenge	14
Test Prep and Mixed Review		15–21

Homework Quick Check

To check students' understanding of key skills and concepts, go over Exercises 6, 9, 12, 13, and 14.

Differentiated Instruction Resources

Adapted Practice 11-4 L1

Practice 11-4 Understanding Slope L3

Find the slope of each line.

1. 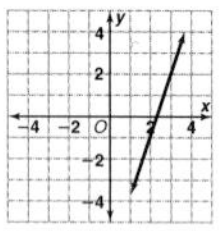
3

2. 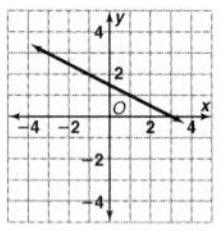
$-\frac{1}{2}$

3. 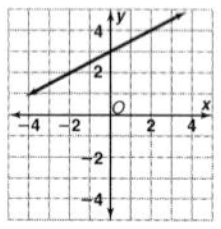
$\frac{1}{2}$

4. 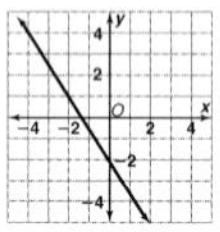
$-\frac{3}{2}$

The points from each table lie on a line. Use the table to find the slope of each line. Then graph the line.

5.

x	0	1	2	3	4
y	−3	−1	1	3	5

slope = 2

6.

x	0	1	2	3	4
y	5	3	1	−1	−3

slope = −2

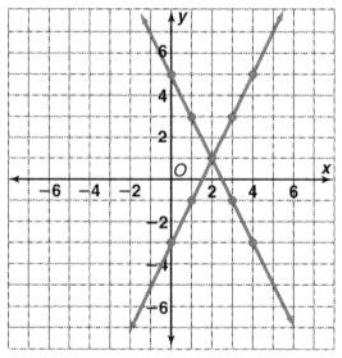

11-4 • Guided Problem Solving GPS L3

Student Page 531, Exercise 12:

Which roof is steeper: a roof with a rise of 12 and a run of 7 or a roof with a rise of 8 and a run of 4?

Understand

1. What are you being asked to do? Determine which roof is steeper.
2. What describes the steepness of a line on a coordinate plane? the slope
3. What is a good way to visualize this problem? graph lines with the given slopes on a coordinate plane.
4. How is slope defined in terms of run and rise? slope = $\frac{\text{rise}}{\text{run}}$

Plan and Carry Out

5. The rise involves the change in the y -coordinates.
6. The run involves the change in the x -coordinates.
7. Graph each slope on the coordinate plane.
8. Which roof is steeper? the one with a rise of 8 and a run of 4

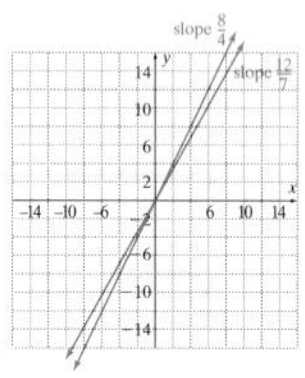

Check

9. What can you determine about the steepness of a line in terms of its slope? the greater the slope the steeper the line

Solve Another Problem

10. Which ramp is steeper: one with a run of 4 and a rise of 6, or one with a run of 7 and a rise of 9? the ramp that has a run of 4 and a rise of 6

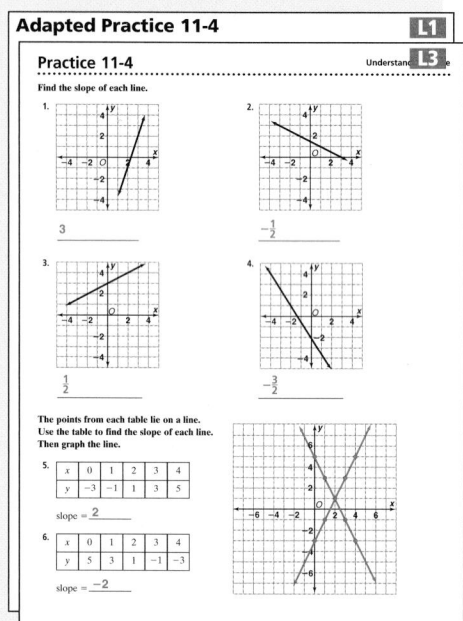

When you graph some data, all the points lie on a line. For such data, you can find slope, or rate of change, using a table.

EXAMPLE Finding Slope From a Table

Miles Traveled	Fuel Used (gallons)
80	4
120	6
160	8
200	10

3 Graph the fuel-usage data at the left. Connect the points with a line. Then find the rate of change.

Fuel Usage

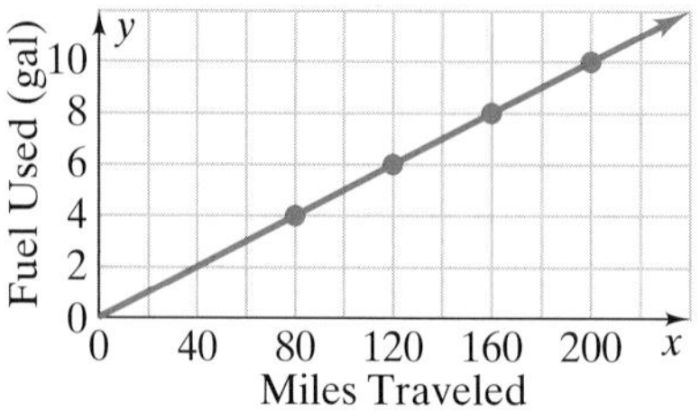

$$\text{rate of change} = \text{slope} = \frac{\text{change in } y}{\text{change in } x} = \frac{10 - 4}{200 - 80} \quad \leftarrow \text{Use coordinates of two points.}$$

$$= \frac{6}{120} = \frac{1}{20} \quad \leftarrow \text{Subtract and simplify.}$$

The amount of fuel used is 1 gallon for every 20 miles traveled.

Quick Check

3. Graph the data in the table and connect the points with a line. Then find the slope. See back of book.

x	−1	0	1	2
y	2	0	−2	−4

Check Your Understanding

1. **Vocabulary** The slope of a line is the rise over the _?_. run
2. Draw one line for each slope: 0, undefined, +1, and −1. Check students' work.

Find the slope of the line that passes through each pair of points.

3. (0, 3) and (6, 1) $-\frac{1}{3}$
4. (2, 2) and (6, −1) $-\frac{3}{4}$

Homework Exercises

For more exercises, see Extra Skills and Word Problems.

GO for Help

For Exercises	See Examples
5–7	1–2
8–9	3

A **Find the slope of each line.** 5. $\frac{3}{5}$ 6. $-\frac{1}{4}$ 7. 2

5. 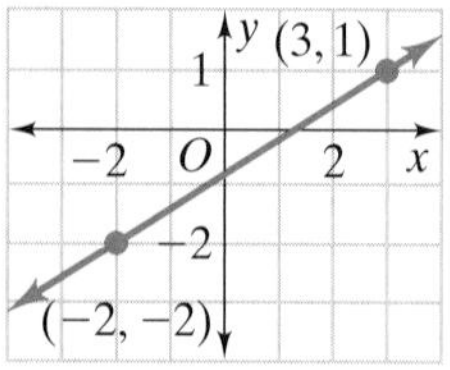

6. 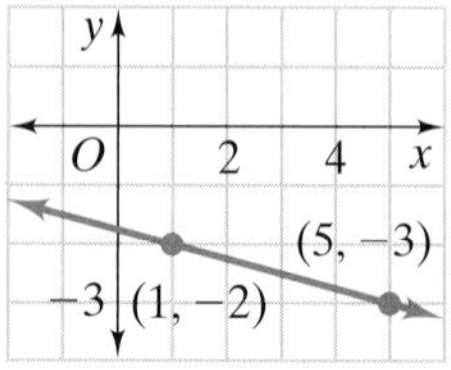

7. 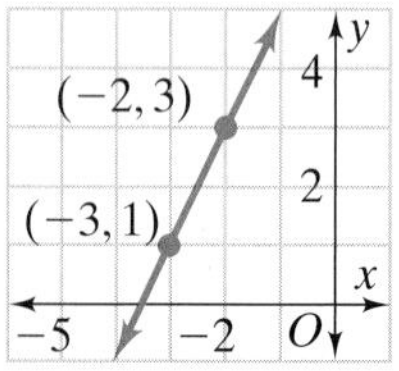

8. 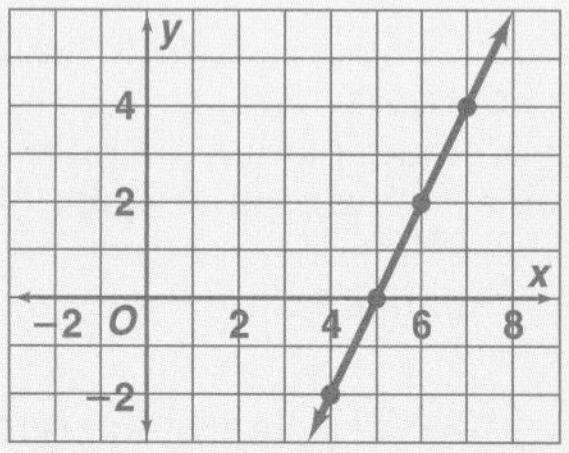

9. 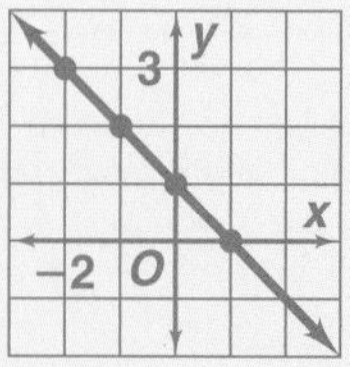

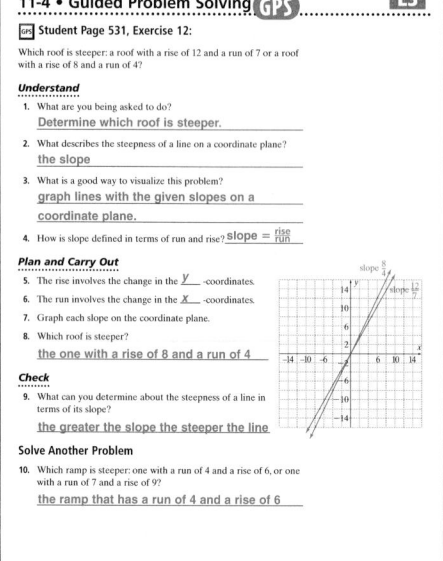

Graph the data in each table and connect the points with a line. Then find the slope of the line. 8–9. See margin for graphs.

8.

x	4	5	6	7
y	−2	0	2	4

2

9.

x	−2	−1	0	1
y	3	2	1	0

−1

B GPS 10. **Guided Problem Solving** The graph at the right shows the amount of rice a store has in stock at different times. Use the slope to describe how the amount of rice changes over time.

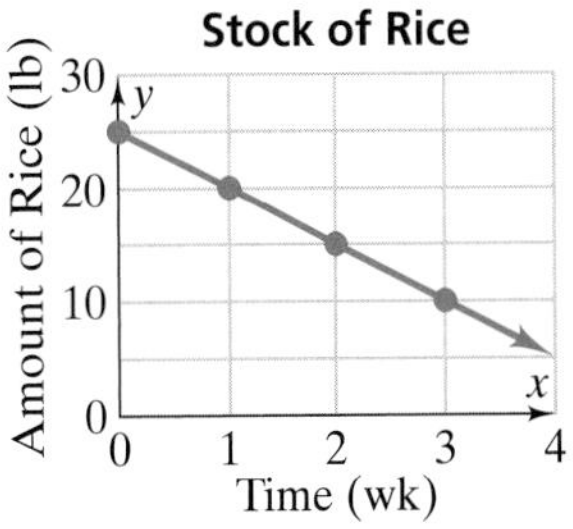

- How is the rate of change related to the slope? −5; the supply of rice decreases by 5 lb/wk.

11. Your classmate found $\frac{\text{run}}{\text{rise}}$ instead of $\frac{\text{rise}}{\text{run}}$.

11. **Error Analysis** Your classmate said that the slope of a line through (1, 3) and (7, 5) is 3. What error did your classmate make? See left.

12. Which roof is steeper: a roof with a rise of 12 and a run of 7 or a roof with a rise of 8 and a run of 4? The roof with a rise of 8 and a run of 4 is steeper.

GPS

13. **Writing in Math** Point $A(-2, 3)$ lies on a line with a slope of 2. Describe how to find two points on the line on either side of A. See margin.

C 14. **Challenge** Determine whether this statement is *true* or *false*. If the statement is false, rewrite it to make it true. If two lines have the same slope, their equations describe the same line. False; if two lines have the same slope, their equations describe the same line or parallel lines.

GO Online
Homework Video Tutor
Visit: PHSchool.com
Web Code: ase-1104

Test Prep and Mixed Review

Practice

Multiple Choice

15. Chloe wants to graph the distance traveled on a bike ride versus time. Which type of graph should she use? A

Ⓐ Line graph
Ⓑ Circle graph
Ⓒ Scatter plot
Ⓓ Bar graph

16. At the end of March, Alvin's bank account balance was $54. He deposited $75 a month in April, May, June, and July. He made a car payment of $94 in each of those months. What was his bank balance at the end of July? F

Ⓕ −$22 Ⓖ −$12 Ⓗ $76 Ⓙ $130

17. A farmer has 35 square miles of land in the shape of a square. Which is closest to the measure of each side of the farm? A

Ⓐ 6 mi Ⓑ 9 mi Ⓒ 18 mi Ⓓ 36 mi

GO for Help

For Exercises	See Lesson
18–21	3-4

Graph each point on the same coordinate plane. 18–21. See margin.

18. $A(6, -4)$ 19. $B(0, -3)$ 20. $C(-2, 5)$ 21. $D(-8, -1)$

4. Assess & Reteach

PowerPoint

Lesson Quiz

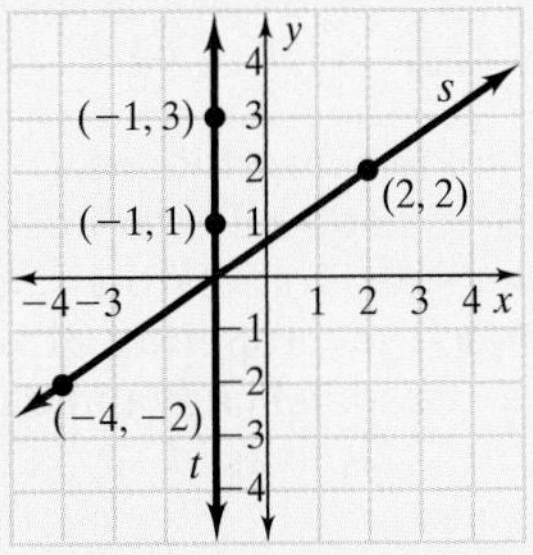

1. Find the slope of line s. $\frac{2}{3}$

2. Find the slope of line t. undefined

3. The data in the table below is linear. Find the slope. 3

x	0	−1	−2	−3
y	0	−3	−6	−9

4. Graph item #3 data and the line. See back of book.

13. See back of book.

18–21.

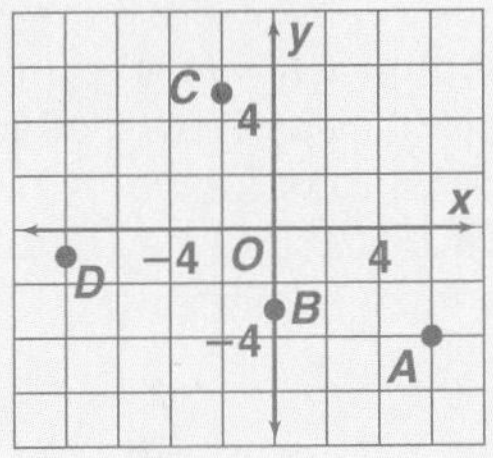

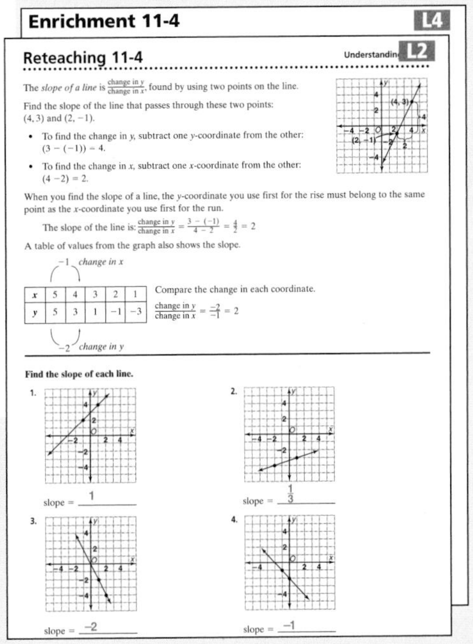
Enrichment 11-4 L4

Reteaching 11-4 Understandin L2

The *slope of a line* is $\frac{\text{change in } y}{\text{change in } x}$, found by using two points on the line.

Find the slope of the line that passes through these two points: (4, 3) and (2, −1).

- To find the change in y, subtract one y-coordinate from the other: $(3 - (-1)) = 4$.
- To find the change in x, subtract one x-coordinate from the other: $(4 - 2) = 2$.

When you find the slope of a line, the y-coordinate you use first for the rise must belong to the same point as the x-coordinate you use first for the run.

The slope of the line is: $\frac{\text{change in } y}{\text{change in } x} = \frac{3 - (-1)}{4 - 2} = \frac{4}{2} = 2$

A table of values from the graph also shows the slope.

−1 change in x

x	5	4	3	2	1
y	5	3	1	−1	−3

−2 change in y

Compare the change in each coordinate.

$\frac{\text{change in } y}{\text{change in } x} = \frac{-2}{-1} = 2$

Find the slope of each line.

1. slope = 1

2. slope = $\frac{1}{3}$

3. slope = −2

4. slope = −1

Alternative Assessment

Each student in a pair writes a two-variable equation. On a separate paper, students make a table of values. Then they find the slope of the data in their partner's table.

Test Prep

Resources

For additional practice with a variety of test item formats:

- Test-Taking Strategies, p. 551
- Test Prep, p. 555
- Test-Taking Strategies with Transparencies

Extension

Parallel and Perpendicular Lines

In earlier lessons, students identified perpendicular lines and parallel lines. This feature focuses on the special properties of the slopes of parallel lines and of perpendicular lines.

Guided Instruction

English Language Learners ELL
Review the meaning of parallel and perpendicular.

Alternative Method
Ask students what they notice when they look at the values $\frac{2}{1}$ and $\frac{1}{2}$. Students may recognize that the values are *reciprocals*. Perpendicular lines have negative reciprocal slopes.

Error Prevention!

To compare slopes of perpendicular lines, remind students to write whole numbers as fractions. This may help them recognize reciprocals.

Teaching Tip
Have students analyze the graphs qualitatively. Ask:

- *What do you notice about the direction of the parallel lines?* They are slanted in the same direction.
- *What do you notice about the perpendicular lines?* Sample: they are slanted in different directions, 90° apart.
- *What are the signs of the slopes of perpendicular lines?* One is positive and one is negative.

Differentiated Instruction

Tactile Learners
Have students trace the lines with their fingers to help them recognize when the slants are the same and when they are different.

Extension — For Use With Lesson 11-4

Parallel and Perpendicular Lines

The slopes of parallel and perpendicular lines have special properties.

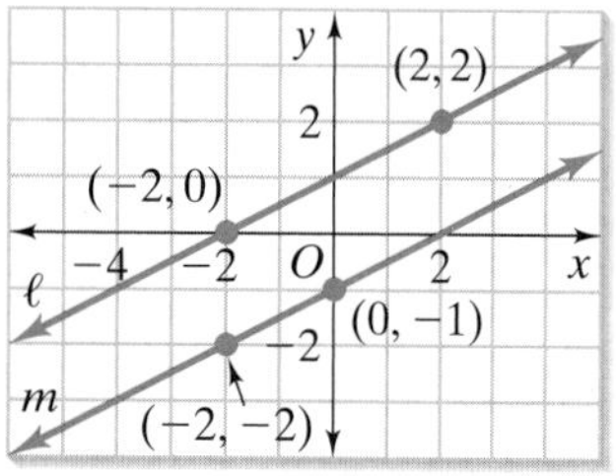

slope of $\ell = \frac{2 - 0}{2 - (-2)} = \frac{2}{4} = \frac{1}{2}$

slope of $m = \frac{-1 - (-2)}{0 - (-2)} = \frac{1}{2}$

Parallel lines have the same slope.

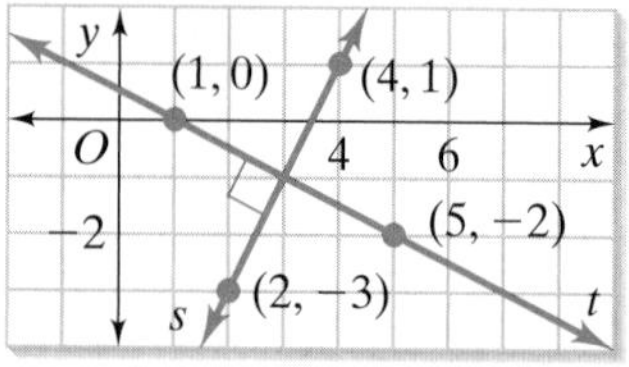

slope of $s = \frac{1 - (-3)}{4 - 2} = \frac{4}{2} = \frac{2}{1}$

slope of $t = \frac{-2 - 0}{5 - 1} = \frac{-2}{4} = -\frac{1}{2}$

product of slopes $= \frac{2}{1} \cdot \left(-\frac{1}{2}\right) = -1$

The product of the slopes of perpendicular lines is -1.

EXAMPLE

Line AB has slope $\frac{1}{3}$. Find the slope of a line that is parallel to $\overleftrightarrow{AB}$ and the slope of a line that is perpendicular to $\overleftrightarrow{AB}$.

A line parallel to $\overleftrightarrow{AB}$ has a slope of $\frac{1}{3}$.

Let m represent the slope of a line perpendicular to $\overleftrightarrow{AB}$.

$\frac{1}{3} \cdot m = -1$ ← The product of the slopes of perpendicular lines is −1.

$m = -3$ ← Multiply each side by 3.

A line perpendicular to $\overleftrightarrow{AB}$ has a slope of -3.

Exercises

Are lines with the given slopes *parallel, perpendicular,* or *neither?*

1. $\frac{2}{3}, -\frac{3}{2}$ perpendicular
2. $5, -5$ neither
3. $\frac{3}{4}, \frac{4}{3}$ neither
4. $\frac{1}{12}, -12$ perpendicular
5. $\frac{3}{9}, \frac{1}{3}$ parallel
6. $\frac{2}{7}, \frac{12}{42}$ parallel

Find the slope of a line parallel to $\overleftrightarrow{PQ}$ and a line perpendicular to $\overleftrightarrow{PQ}$.

7. $P(1, 2), Q(3, 4)$ 1; −1
8. $P(-5, 1), Q(-1, 2)$ $\frac{1}{4}$; −4
9. $P(3, -2), Q(-2, 1)$ $-\frac{3}{5}$; $\frac{5}{3}$

Graphing Equations

You can use a graphing calculator to graph equations and to find solutions.

EXAMPLE

Graph $y = \frac{1}{2}x + 1$. Make a table of solutions for values of x from -3 to 3.

Step 1 Press Y=. Enter $\frac{1}{2}x + 1$.

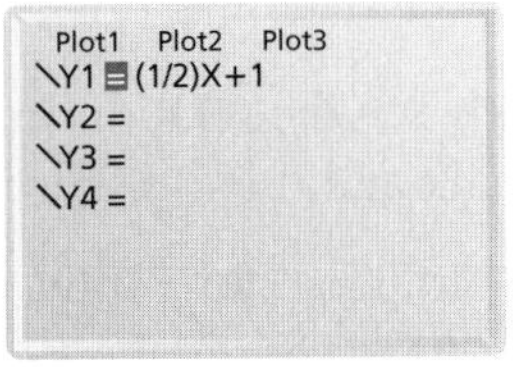

Step 2 Press ZOOM 6 to graph your equation with the standard viewing window.

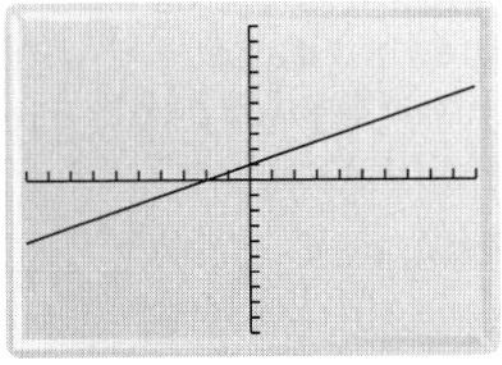

Step 3 Use the TBLSET feature. Set TblStart = -3 and $\triangle$Tbl = 1. The x-values start at -3 and increase by increments of 1.

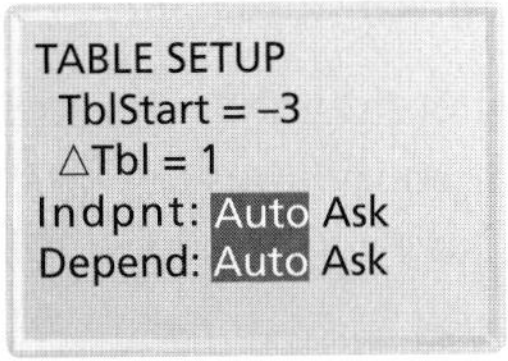

Step 4 Use the TABLE feature to see solutions.

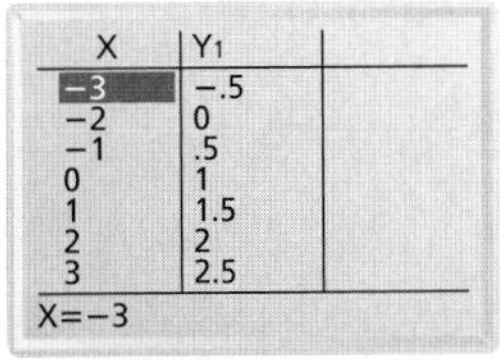

Step 5 Sketch the graph and copy the table of solutions.

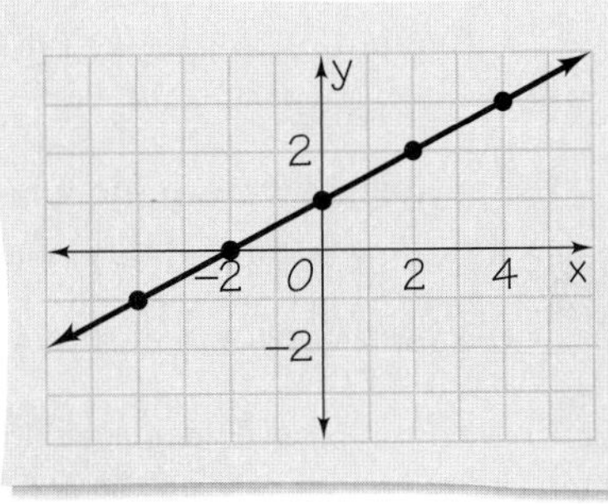

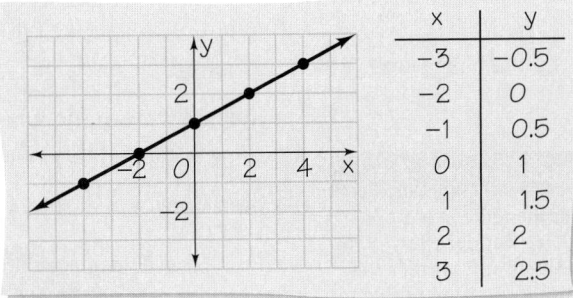

x	y
−3	−0.5
−2	0
−1	0.5
0	1
1	1.5
2	2
3	2.5

Exercises

6. They intersect at the same place on the y-axis but have different slopes.

Graph each equation using a graphing calculator. Sketch the graph and make a table of solutions for values of x from -3 to 3. 1–4. See margin.

1. $y = 2x - 3$
2. $y = 2x + 3$
3. $y = -\frac{2}{3}x - 2$
4. $y = 5x - 2$

5. Compare the graphs of Exercises 1 and 2. What do you notice? The lines are parallel.
6. Explain how the graphs of Exercises 3 and 4 are different. See above.

1–4. See back of book.

Activity Lab

Graphing Equations

Students graph linear functions on graphing calculators. They observe and compare characteristics of the graphs.

Guided Instruction

Connection to Algebra
Point out that this activity enables students to view a function in three different ways—as an equation, a table, and a graph. Using multiple representations is very useful in understanding algebraic concepts such as linear functions.

Exercises
For Exercises 1–4, have students create equations that will form a line perpendicular with the graph of each item. Have them verify their equations by graphing the original equation and the equation of its perpendicular counterpart.

Resources

- Activity Lab 11-5: Graphing Linear Functions
- graphing calculators or any dynamic software tool that can be used to graph equations

11-5

1. Plan

Objective
To use tables and equations to graph linear functions

Examples
1 Graphing Discrete Data
2 Graphing Continuous Data

Math Understandings: p. 510D

Professional Development

Math Background

Discrete data often result from counting and are connected with a dashed line. *Continuous data* often result from measuring and can have values between the graphed points, which are joined with a solid line.

The *slope-intercept form* of a linear equation, $y = mx + b$, describes a line with slope m and y-intercept b.

More Math Background: p. 510D

Lesson Planning and Resources

See p. 510E for a list of the resources that support this lesson.

PowerPoint

Bell Ringer Practice

Check Skills You'll Need
Use student page, transparency, or PowerPoint. For intervention, direct students to:
Understanding Slope
Lesson 11-4
Extra Skills and Word Problems Practice, Ch. 11

Algebra

11-5 Graphing Linear Functions

Check Skills You'll Need

1. **Vocabulary Review** Explain how to find the *slope* of a line. See below.

Find the slope of the line that passes through each pair of points.

2. (2, 4), (−5, 10) $-\frac{6}{7}$
3. (0, 0), (6, 0) 0
4. (2, 1), (1, 2) −1

GO for Help Lesson 11-4

What You'll Learn

To use tables and equations to graph linear functions

New Vocabulary discrete data, continuous data, y-intercept, slope-intercept form, linear function

Why Learn This?

Graphs can help you quickly see the relationship between two sets of data, such as the price of milk and the total cost of milk for your family.

Different types of data are graphed differently. **Discrete data** are data that involve a count of items, such as numbers of people or cars. For discrete data, plot the data points and connect them with a dashed line.

Continuous data are data where numbers between any two data values have meaning. Examples of continuous data include measurements of height, length, or weight. Use a solid line to indicate continuous data.

EXAMPLE Graphing Discrete Data

Check Skills You'll Need
1. Divide the change in y by the change in x.

Vocabulary Tip
A dashed line in a graph means that not every point on the graph satisfies the conditions of the problem.

1 **Groceries** A gallon of milk costs \$2.59. The total cost of g gallons of milk is a function of the price of one gallon. Make a table and graph the function.

Step 1 Determine whether the data are discrete or continuous. You cannot buy part of a gallon container, so the data are discrete.

Step 2 Make a table. Connect the points with a dashed line.

Number of Gallons	Total Cost (dollars)
1	\$2.59
2	\$5.18
3	\$7.77
4	\$10.36

Cost of Milk

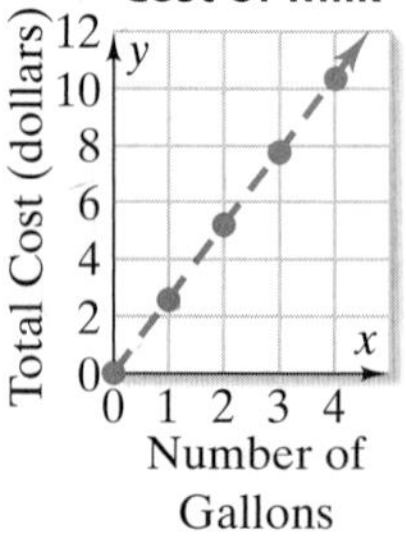

Quick Check

1. **Tickets** The function $c = 15t$ represents the cost (in dollars) of t adult tickets to a museum. Make a table and graph the function. See back of book.

Differentiated Instruction Solutions for All Learners

Special Needs L1
Students pair up to graph the functions. The student in the pair who is less able to graph works on the function table. The other student graphs the data from the table.
learning style: tactile

Below Level L2
Demonstrate that the graph of $y = -\frac{3}{4}x + 5$ remains a line, although a different line, even if the slope is changed to some other value and the y-intercept is changed to some other value.
learning style: visual

EXAMPLE Graphing Continuous Data

2 **Fitness** During one hour of walking, you burn about 257 Calories. The total number of Calories burned is a function of the number of hours walked. Make a table and graph the function.

You can walk for part of an hour, so the data are continuous. Plot the data and connect the data points with a solid line.

Time (hours)	Number of Calories
1	257
2	514
3	771

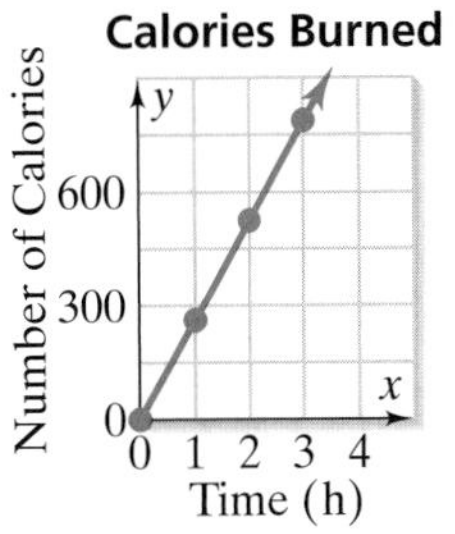

Quick Check

2. **Sky Diving** The function $h = 4{,}000 - 600m$ gives the height h of a sky diver in feet after she has been falling for m minutes. Make a table and graph the function. See back of book.

The **y-intercept** is the point where the graph crosses the y-axis.

$$y = -\frac{3}{4}x + 5$$

↑ slope ↑ y-intercept

Below is the graph of $y = -\frac{3}{4}x + 5$.

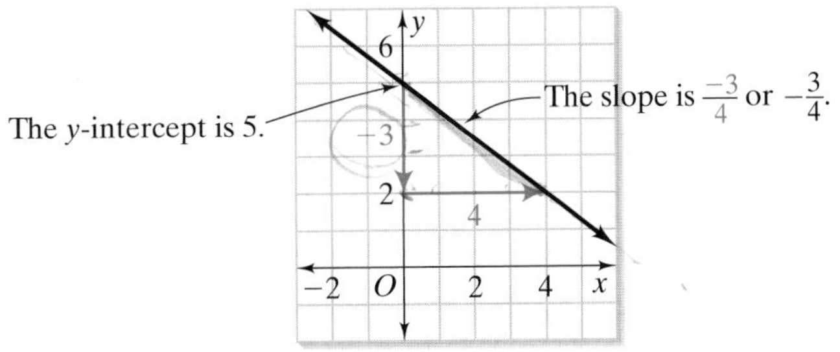

Notice that the slope and y-intercept may be part of the equation of a line.

An equation written in the form $y = mx + b$ is in **slope-intercept form.** The graph is a line with slope m and y-intercept b.

A **linear function** is a function with points that lie on a line. You can write a linear function in the form $f(x) = mx + b$, or $y = mx + b$. Then you can use the slope and y-intercept to graph the function.

Video Tutor Help
Visit: PHSchool.com
Web Code: ase-0775

2. Teach

Activity Lab

Use before the lesson.
Student Edition Activity Lab, Technology 11-5a, Graphing Equations, p. 533

All in One Teaching Resources
Activity Lab 11-5: Graphing Linear Function

Guided Instruction

Explain that *intercept* refers to the meeting point where the graphed line crosses another line. So *y*-intercept refers to the point where the graph of the equation crosses the *y*-axis.

PowerPoint

Additional Examples

1 Juice costs \$2.19 per gallon. The total cost of g gallons is a function of the price of a single gallon. Make a table and graph.

Input g (gal)	1	2	3
Output (\$)	2.19	4.38	6.57

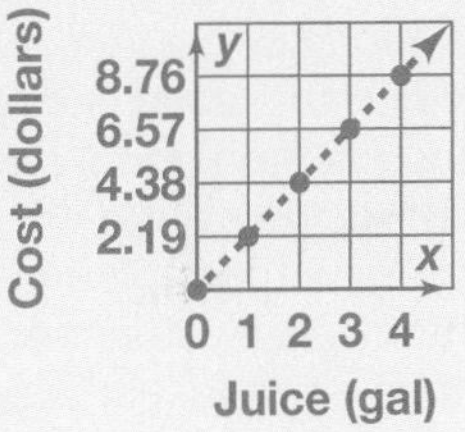

2 Amber earns \$7 per hour. Make a table to describe Amber's earnings (output) as a function of hours she works (input). Graph the function.

Input (hrs)	0	1	2	3	4
Output (\$)	0	7	14	21	28

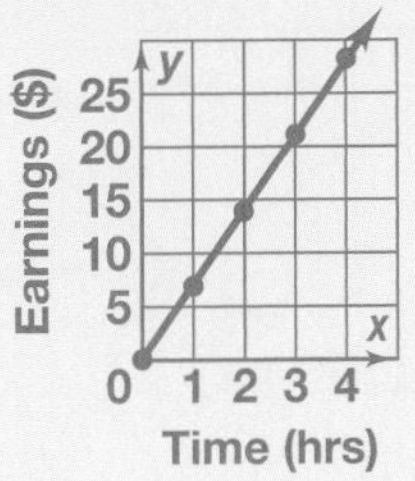

Advanced Learners L4
Students use a graphing calculator to compare the graphs of $y = x$, $y = 3x$, $y = 5x$, $y = 6x$. Each line gets steeper.
learning style: visual

English Language Learners ELL
Discuss the meaning and spelling for *discrete* and *discreet.* Elicit the fact that a discreet person might keep a secret, and discrete points are separate from each other.
learning style: verbal

Guided Instruction

Error Prevention!

Students may confuse the slope and the *y*-intercept. Have them write the equation $y = mx + b$ and then write the word *slope* above the *m* and the word *y*-intercept below the *b*.

Teaching Tip
When using slope-intercept form to graph an equation, or in Sarah's method, use the following steps: locate *b*, the *y*-intercept, on the *y*-axis; write the slope as a fraction; use the numerator of the fraction as the change in *y* and the denominator of the fraction as the change in *x* in order to locate a second point. Then draw the line that connects the points.

All in One Teaching Resources
- Daily Notetaking Guide 11-5 L3
- Adapted Notetaking 11-5 L1

Closure

- Explain how to use a table to graph a function. Plot the input on the *x*-axis and the output on the *y*-axis.
- *How do you decide whether to make a solid or dashed line?* Sample: Use a solid line for continuous data and a dashed line for discrete data.
- Explain how to graph an equation when you know only the slope and the *y*-intercept. Sample: Graph the point (0, *b*) using the *y*-intercept. Write the slope as a fraction. Find a second point. Draw a straight line through these two points.

More Than One Way

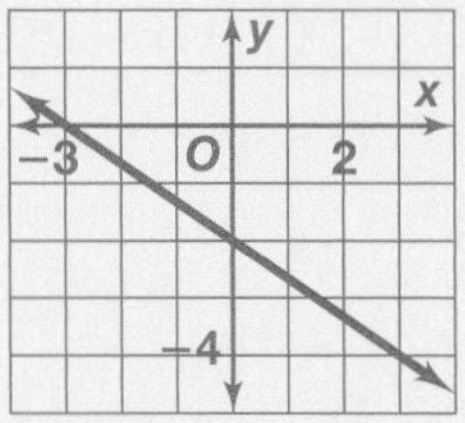

Explanations may vary.

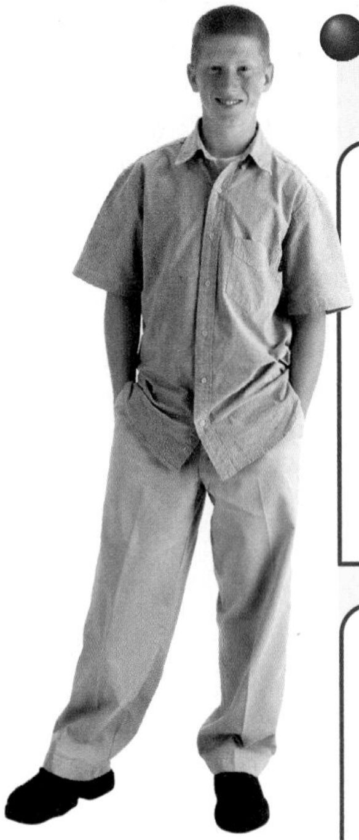

More Than One Way

Graph the function $y = \frac{3}{5}x + 1$.

Kevin's Method

First I will make a table. Then I will graph the points.

x	0	1	2	3	4	5
y	1	1.6	2.2	2.8	3.4	4

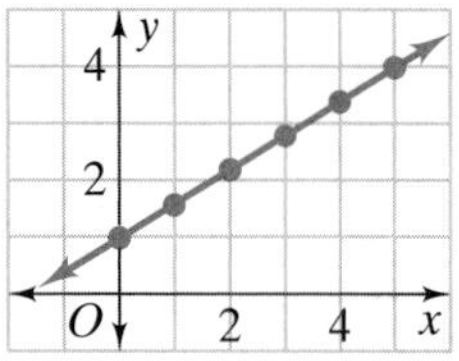

Michelle's Method

I can use slope-intercept form to graph the equation. The *y*-intercept is 1 and the slope is $\frac{3}{5}$.

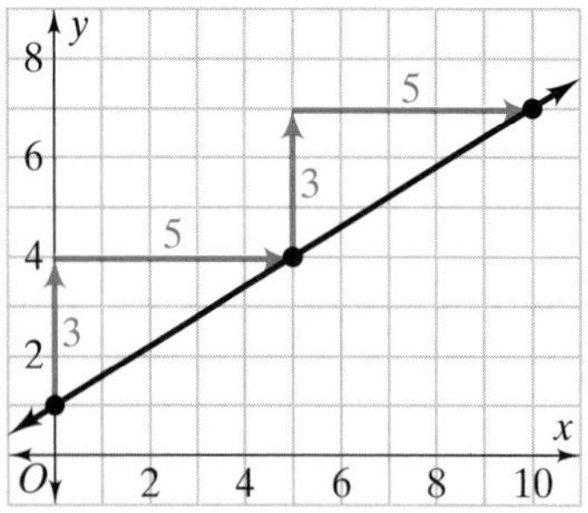

Choose a Method
Graph the function $y = -\frac{2}{3}x - 2$. Explain why you chose the method you used. See margin.

Check Your Understanding

1. **Vocabulary** Explain the difference between discrete data and continuous data. See margin.

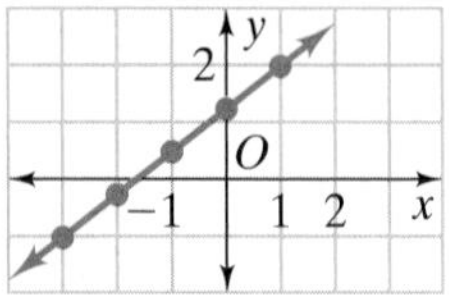

2. Does the graph at the left show discrete data or continuous data? continuous

For each function, find the slope and the *y*-intercept.

3. $y = 4x - 1$ 4; −1
4. $y = x + 4$ 1; 4

5. Make a table for the function $y = 3x$. Then graph the function. See margin.

Check Your Understanding

1. Discrete data involve a count of items. Continuous data are data for which numbers between any two data values have meaning.

5. See back of book.

Homework Exercises

For more exercises, see Extra Skills and Word Problems.

GO for Help

For Exercises	See Examples
6–8	1–2

A **Determine whether the data for each function are *discrete* or *continuous*. Then make a table and graph for the function.** 6–8. See margin.

6. The function $d = 40 - 15x$ represents the amount of money d (in dollars) you have left after buying x CDs.

7. **Scuba Diving** The deeper a scuba diver descends, the more pressure the diver feels. The function $p = 1 + 0.03x$ represents the approximate pressure p (in atmospheres) at x feet below sea level.

8. The function $y = 1.8x + 32$ represents the equivalent temperature y in degrees Fahrenheit for a temperature of x degrees Celsius.

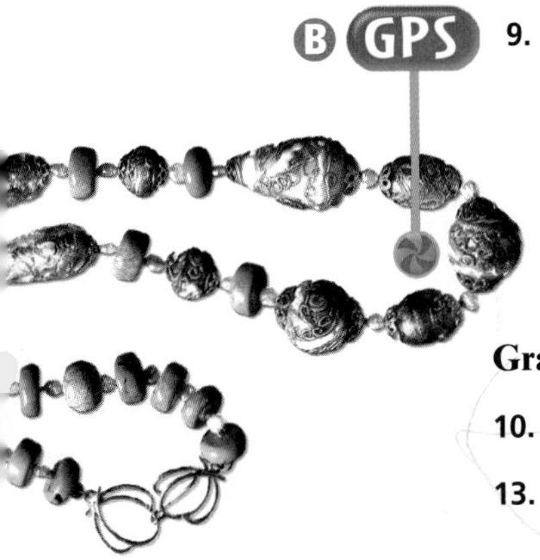

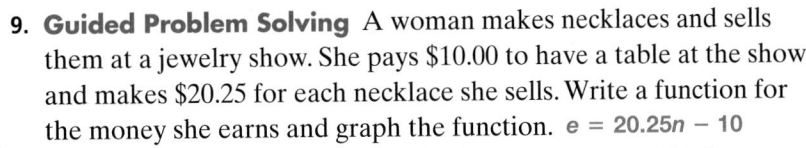

B **GPS** 9. **Guided Problem Solving** A woman makes necklaces and sells them at a jewelry show. She pays \$10.00 to have a table at the show and makes \$20.25 for each necklace she sells. Write a function for the money she earns and graph the function. $e = 20.25n - 10$
- What is the input variable? What is the output variable?
- What is the slope of this function? What is the y-intercept?

Graph each linear function. 10–15. See margin.

10. $y = -2x + 5$
11. $y = \frac{2}{3}x - 1$
12. $y = -\frac{3}{5}x - 2$
13. $y = 3x - 7$
14. $y = -6x - 1$
15. $y = x + 4$

16. **Writing in Math** Describe a relation in your daily life that is a function. Explain why it is a function and define the input and the output. Check students' work.

17. **Science** The height of a burning candle depends on how long the candle has been burning. For one type of candle, the function $h = 8 - \frac{1}{2}t$ gives the candle's height h (in centimeters) as a function of the time t the candle has burned (in hours). 17a–c. See margin.
    a. Graph the function.
    b. What was the original height of the candle?
    c. What is the greatest amount of time the candle can burn?

18. **Nutrition** The label at the right shows the nutrition facts for a package of crackers. Find how many Calories are in one cracker. The number of Calories consumed is a function of the number of crackers eaten. Make a table and a graph for the function. See margin.

Nutrition Facts
Serving Size: 8 crackers (31g)
Servings Per Container: about 15

Amount Per Serving	
Calories 140	Calories from Fat 35
	% Daily Value
Total Fat 4g	6%
Saturated Fat 1g	5%
Monounsaturated Fat 1.5g	

19. Graph the functions $y = 2x + 1$ and $y = 2x - 1$ on the same coordinate grid. What do you notice about the two lines? See margin.

GO Online
Homework Video Tutor
Visit: PHSchool.com
Web Code: ase-1105

Online lesson quiz, PHSchool.com, Web Code: asa-1105

3. Practice

Assignment Guide

Check Your Understanding
Go over Exercises 1–5 in class before assigning the Homework Exercises.

Homework Exercises

A Practice by Example	6–8
B Apply Your Skills	9–20
C Challenge	21
Test Prep and Mixed Review	22–28

Homework Quick Check
To check students' understanding of key skills and concepts, go over Exercises 6, 7, 9, 16, and 17.

Differentiated Instruction Resources

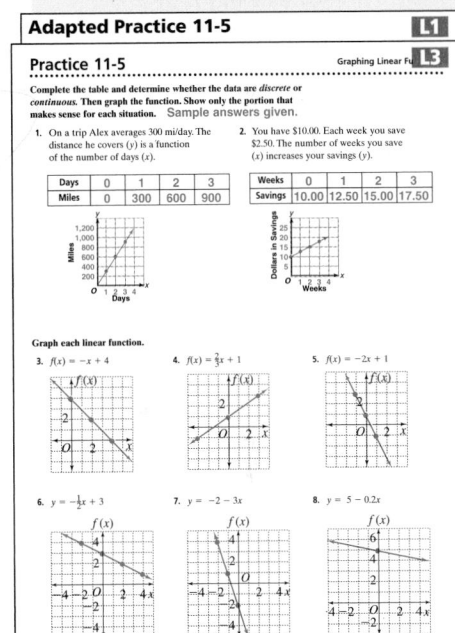

Adapted Practice 11-5 L1

Practice 11-5 Graphing Linear Fu... L3

Complete the table and determine whether the data are *discrete* or *continuous*. Then graph the function. Show only the portion that makes sense for each situation. Sample answers given.

1. On a trip Alex averages 300 mi/day. The distance he covers (y) is a function of the number of days (x).

Days	0	1	2	3
Miles	0	300	600	900

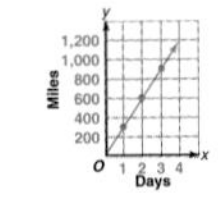

2. You have \$10.00. Each week you save \$2.50. The number of weeks you save (x) increases your savings (y).

Weeks	0	1	2	3
Savings	10.00	12.50	15.00	17.50

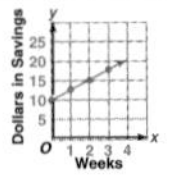

Graph each linear function.

3. $f(x) = -x + 4$
4. $f(x) = \frac{2}{3}x + 1$
5. $f(x) = -2x + 1$

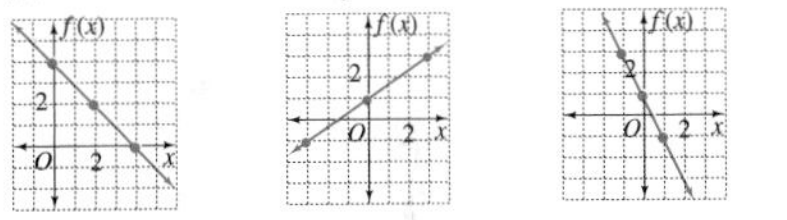

6. $y = -\frac{1}{2}x + 3$
7. $y = -2 - 3x$
8. $y = 5 - 0.2x$

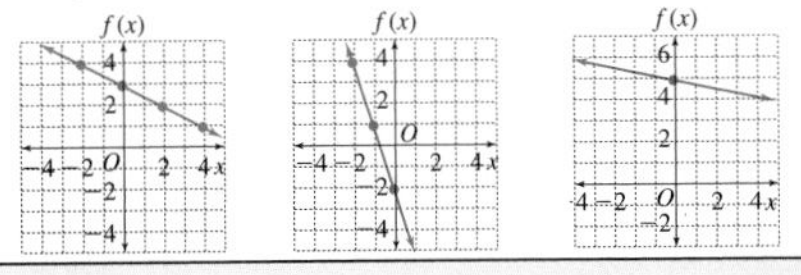

11-5 • Guided Problem Solving GPS L3

GPS Student Page 537, Exercise 17:

Science The height of a burning candle depends on how long the candle has been burning. For one type of candle, the function $h = 8 - \frac{1}{2}t$ gives the candle's height h (in centimeters) as a function of the time t the candle has burned (in hours).

a. Graph the function.
b. What was the original height of the candle?
c. What is the greatest amount of time the candle can burn?

Understand

1. What do the variables h and t represent?
   h = height (in centimeters), t = time (in hours)

Plan and Carry Out

2. Graph the function on a separate sheet of paper. Check students' graphs.
3. What does the x-axis represent?
   How long the candle has burned in hours.
4. What does the y-axis represent?
   How tall the candle is in centimeters.
5. What was the original height of the candle? How can you tell?
   8 centimeters; it is where the graph starts on the y-axis.
6. How long can the candle burn? How can you tell?
   16 hours; it is where the graph crosses the x-axis.

Check

7. How can you check your answer?
   Substitute 16 for h in the, $h = 8 - \frac{1}{2}t = 0$ and solve for t to find out the time when the candle will burn out.

Solve Another Problem

8. The initial payment on a car lease is \$3,000. Each monthly payment is \$300. This can be represented by the function $c = 3{,}000 + 300m$, where c is the cost of the lease after m months. Graph the function on a separate sheet of paper. How many months will it be until the cost of the lease is \$4,800?
   Check students' graphs; 6 months

6. discrete

x	d
0	40
1	25
2	10

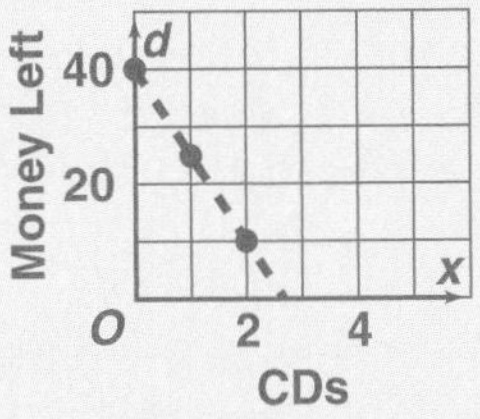

10.

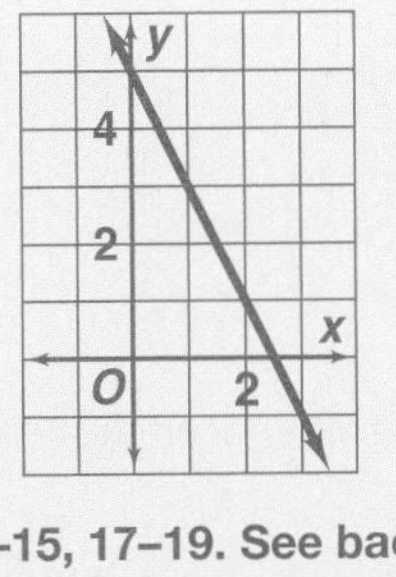

11.

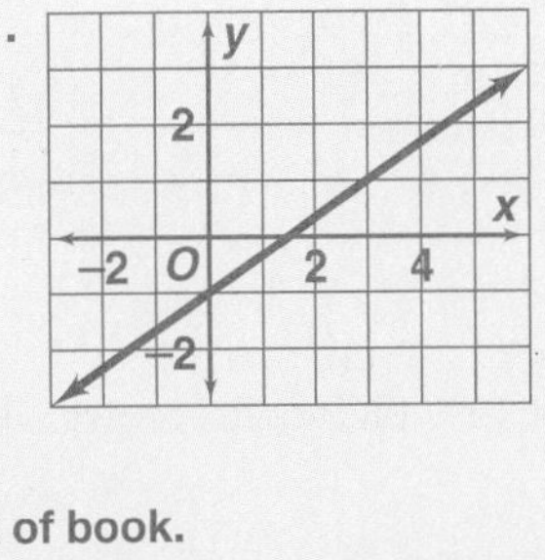

7–8. See back of book.

12–15, 17–19. See back of book.

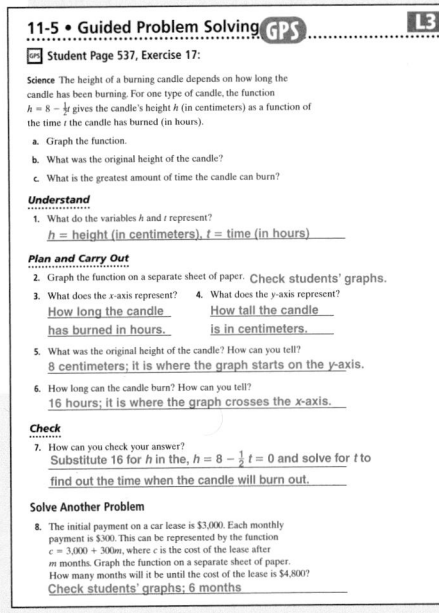

4. Assess & Reteach

PowerPoint

Lesson Quiz

1. A rock climber 150 ft above the base of a cliff climbs at a rate of 5 ft per min. Make a table to describe the climber's height above the cliff base as a function of elapsed time. Graph the function. **1–3. See back of book.**
2. Graph the function $y = -3x - 4$.
3. One kilogram is equivalent to about 2.2 pounds. The weight of an object in pounds is a function of its weight in kilograms. Make a table and graph the function.

20–21. See back of book.

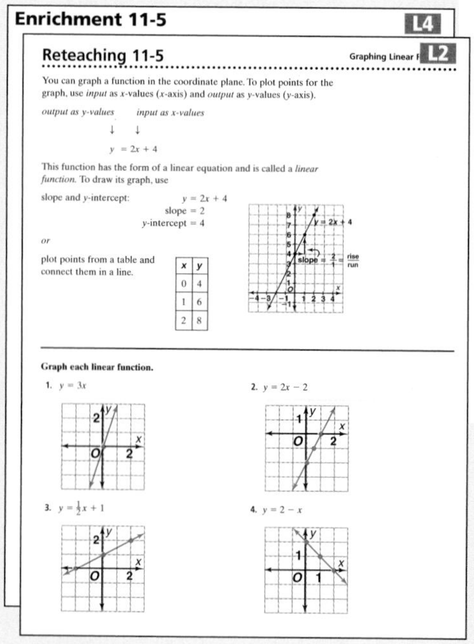

Enrichment 11-5 L4

Reteaching 11-5 Graphing Linear F... L2

You can graph a function in the coordinate plane. To plot points for the graph, use *input* as *x*-values (*x*-axis) and *output* as *y*-values (*y*-axis).

output as y-values *input as x-values*

$y = 2x + 4$

This function has the form of a linear equation and is called a *linear function.* To draw its graph, use

slope and *y*-intercept: $y = 2x + 4$, slope = 2, *y*-intercept = 4

or

plot points from a table and connect them in a line.

x	y
0	4
1	6
2	8

Graph each linear function.

1. $y = 3x$
2. $y = 2x - 2$
3. $y = \frac{1}{2}x + 1$
4. $y = 2 - x$

20. **Internet** Company A charges a fee of \$5.00 per month plus \$2.00 for each hour of Internet use. Company B charges \$10.00 per month plus \$1.00 for each hour of Internet use. Write and graph two functions to show how the total cost each month depends on the hours of usage for each company. **See margin.**

C 21. **Challenge** Suppose gasoline costs \$2.30 per gallon at one gas station and \$2.35 at another. Write and graph two functions showing how the cost to fill a car's gas tank depends on the number of gallons of gas it needs. For how many gallons of gasoline is there a price difference of \$0.30 between the two functions? **See margin.**

Test Prep and Mixed Review

Practice

Multiple Choice

22. Which of the following is a graph of the equation $y = 2x - 1$? **A**

Ⓐ 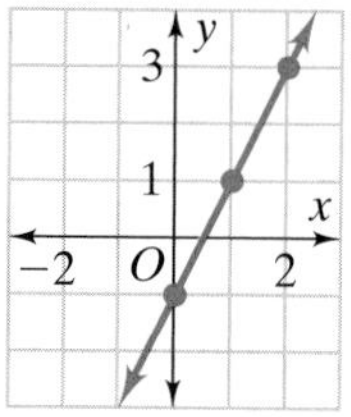

Ⓒ 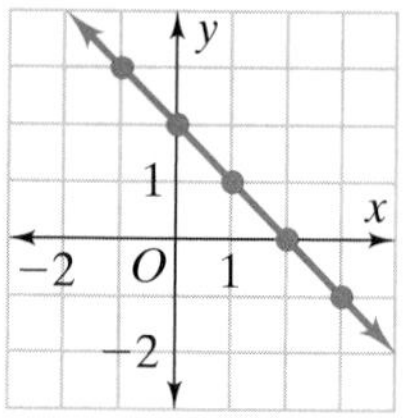

Ⓑ 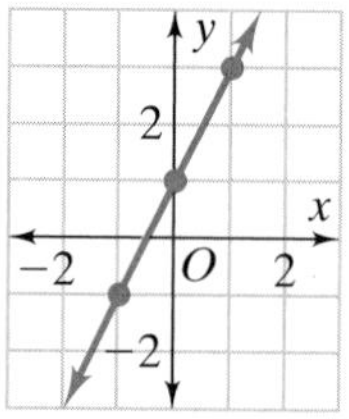

Ⓓ 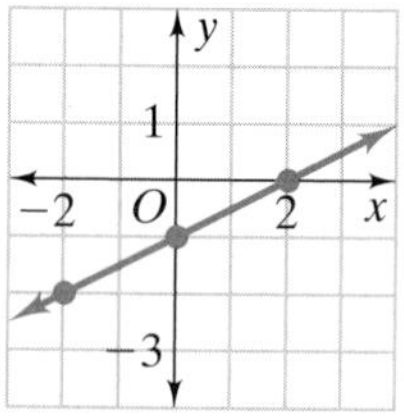

23. A rectangular room that measures 72 inches by 90 inches is to be finished in square tiles. What is the largest size of square tile that can be used without any being cut? **H**

Ⓕ 6 in.^{2} Ⓖ 9 in.^{2} Ⓗ 18 in.^{2} Ⓙ 36 in.^{2}

24. A spinner is spun 50 times. It lands on red 8 times, yellow 12 times, green 20 times, and blue 10 times. Based on the results, what is the experimental probability of landing on green or yellow? **D**

Ⓐ $\frac{6}{25}$ Ⓑ $\frac{2}{5}$ Ⓒ $\frac{3}{5}$ Ⓓ $\frac{16}{25}$

GO for Help

For Exercises	See Lesson
25–28	9-6

Use the box-and-whisker plot below to find each value.

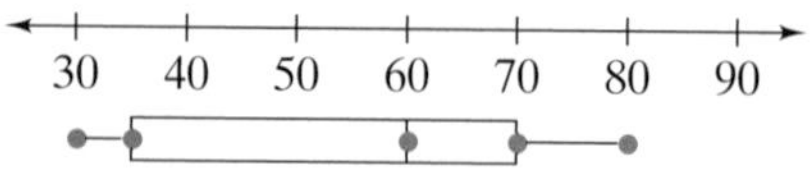

25. the median **60**
26. the lower quartile **35**
27. the upper quartile **70**
28. the least value **30**

Test Prep

Resources

For additional practice with a variety of test item formats:

- Test-Taking Strategies, p. 551
- Test Prep, p. 555
- Test-Taking Strategies with Transparencies

Alternative Assessment

Students work in small groups to list examples of functions. Groups work together to identify whether the data in each example is discrete or continuous.

Checkpoint Quiz 2

Lessons 11-3 through 11-5

Use the function rule $f(x) = -3x - 2$. Find each output.

1. $f(-1)$ 1 **2.** $f(5)$ −17 **3.** $f(0)$ −2 **4.** $f(-10)$ 28

5. Suppose potatoes cost $.99 per pound. Complete the function rule $C(p) =$ _?_ to describe the relationship between the total cost $C(p)$ and the number of pounds of potatoes p you buy. 0.99 p

Find the slope of each line in the graph at the right.

6. line a 0 **7.** line b $\frac{3}{2}$ **8.** line c −1

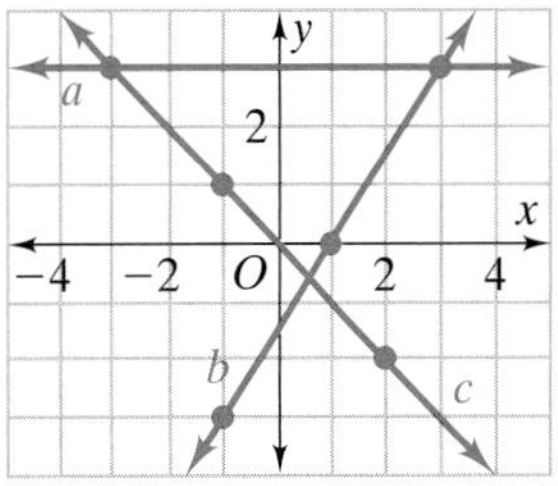

9. **Number Sense** Explain which hill is steeper: a hill with a rise of 5 and a run of 3 or a hill with a rise of 3 and a run of 5. See margin.

10. Your cousin works at a bookstore and earns $7 per hour. Make a table to show your cousin's earnings as a function of the hours she works. Graph the data. See margin.

MATH GAMES

What's My Rule?

How To Play

- Player 1 writes a function rule on paper. The other players are not allowed to see this function.
- Make a table like the one at the right. Player 1 writes an input-output pair in the table for the other players to see.
- In turn, each of the other players gives an input and guesses the corresponding output.
- If a player guesses the output correctly, the player gets a point and is allowed to guess the function.
- If the player guesses the function correctly, the player gets another point and starts a new round of play.
- Player 1 gets one point each time a player makes an incorrect guess at the function.
- The player with the most points wins.

What's My Rule?

Input	Output
■	■
■	■
■	■
■	■

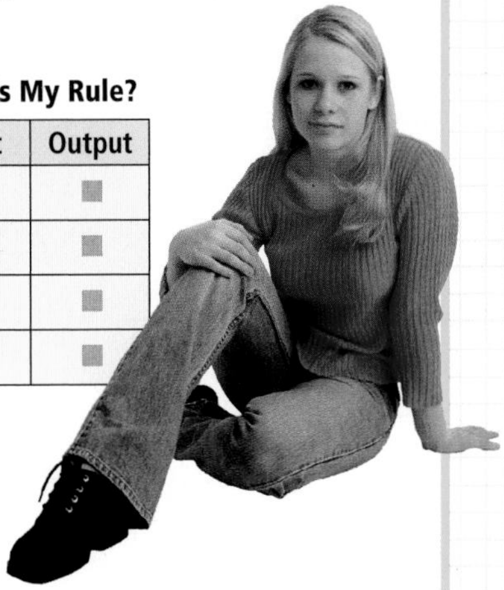

Checkpoint Quiz

Use this Checkpoint Quiz to check students' understanding of the skills and concepts of Lessons 11-3 through 11-5.

Resources

- All in One Teaching Resources Checkpoint Quiz 2
- ExamView Assessment Suite CD-ROM
- Success Tracker Online Intervention

MATH GAMES

What's My Rule?

Given an input/output pair by one student, other students take turns trying to guess more correct input/output pairs and, ultimately, the corresponding function rule.

Guided Instruction

Have students who are guessing draw a table and record their guesses to keep track of input/output pairs that do or do not satisfy the function.

Teaching Tip
When one student guesses the correct output, encourage all students to think about a rule that might apply to their growing collection of input/output pairs.

Checkpoint Quiz 2

9. A hill with a rise of 5 and a run of 3 is steeper because it is rising $1\frac{2}{3}$ units for each horizontal unit. The other hill is rising only $\frac{3}{5}$ unit for each horizontal unit.

10. See back of book.

11-6

1. Plan

Objective
To write function rules from words, tables and graphs

Examples
1 Writing a Function Rule From Words
2 Writing a Rule from a Table
3 Writing an Equation From a Graph

Math Understandings: p. 510D

Professional Development

Math Background
Functions can be described in words, tables, graphs, and in equations or function rules. You can write function rules for linear graphs by reading the y-intercept and slope and using $y = mx + b$. To write a function rule for a table of linear data, use the ratio of the changes in the inputs and outputs for the slope and the data point $(0, b)$ to write the function rule.

More Math Background: p. 510D

Lesson Planning and Resources
See p. 510E for a list of the resources that support this lesson.

PowerPoint

Bell Ringer Practice

Check Skills You'll Need
Use student page, transparency, or PowerPoint. For intervention, direct students to:

Graphing Linear Equations
Lesson 11-5
Extra Skills and Word Problems Practice, Ch. 11

Algebra

11-6 Writing Rules for Linear Functions

Check Skills You'll Need

1. **Vocabulary Review** What is *slope-intercept form?* See below.

For each function, find the slope and y-intercept.

2. $y = 3x - 2$ 3; −2
3. $y = x + 5$ 1; 5
4. $y = 8x$ 8; 0

GO for Help Lesson 11-5

Check Skills You'll Need

1. $y = mx + b$, where m is the slope and b is the y-intercept.

Test Prep Tip

The form of each of these answer choices is similar to slope-intercept form. In order to identify the correct answer easily, write your answer in a similar form.

What You'll Learn
To write function rules from words, tables, and graphs

Why Learn This?
Businesses have toll-free numbers to encourage customers to use their services. A business owner can calculate the cost of a toll-free number if she can write a rule for the function.

Just as you can translate words to an equation, you can also translate words to a function rule. When writing a function rule, be sure to identify the input and the output.

EXAMPLE Writing a Function Rule From Words

1 **Multiple Choice** Suppose the rate for a toll-free telephone number is \$2.95 per month plus \$.10 per minute of use. Which function rule correctly represents the monthly cost?

Ⓐ $y = 0.1 + 2.95x$
Ⓑ $y = 2.95 + 0.1x$
Ⓒ $y = 2.95 - 0.1x$
Ⓓ $y = 0.1x - 2.95$

Words monthly cost = \$2.95 plus \$0.10 times number of minutes

Let x = the number of minutes. ← **input**

Let y = the monthly cost. ← **output**

Function $y = 2.95 + 0.1 \cdot x$

$y = 2.95 + 0.1x$

The function rule $y = 2.95 + 0.1x$ represents the monthly cost for x minutes of use. The correct answer is choice B.

Quick Check

1. A school orchestra is buying music stands. The group has \$298 in its treasury. Each stand costs \$42. Write a function rule to show how the balance in the treasury depends on the number of stands bought.

1. $y = 298 - 42x$

Differentiated Instruction Solutions for All Learners

Special Needs L1
Students examine simple illustrations with pictures to determine the patterns in the tables and the function rules. In Example 1, Quick Check, students draw a series of music stands with a −\$42 next to each when solving the example.

learning style: visual

Below Level L2
Ask: *If a student saves* d *dollars every month, and her grandmother contributes an equal amount, what rule shows her total after 7 months?* $T = 7(2d)$

learning style: visual

If the ratios of the changes in inputs and outputs of a fraction are the same for all values, then the function is linear.

EXAMPLE Writing a Rule From a Table

2 Do the values in the table below represent a linear function? If so, write a function rule.

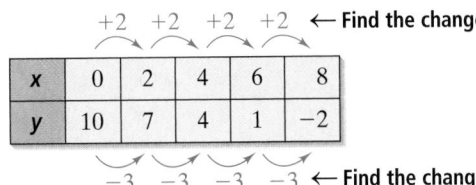

+2 +2 +2 +2 ← **Find the changes in inputs.**

x	0	2	4	6	8
y	10	7	4	1	−2

−3 −3 −3 −3 ← **Find the changes in outputs.**

$\frac{\text{change in } y}{\text{change in } x} \rightarrow \frac{-3}{2} \quad \frac{-3}{2} \quad \frac{-3}{2} \quad \frac{-3}{2}$ ← **Compare the changes as ratios.**

Since each ratio is the same, the function is linear. The slope is $-\frac{3}{2}$.

The point (0, 10) lies on the graph of the function. So the y-intercept is 10. Use slope-intercept form to write a function rule.

$$y = -\frac{3}{2}x + 10 \quad \leftarrow \textbf{Substitute } -\tfrac{3}{2} \textbf{ for } m \textbf{ and 10 for } b.$$

Quick Check

2. Do the values in the table represent a linear function? If so, write a function rule. no

x	0	1	2	3
y	2	4	7	8

The slope of a line can be expressed by the equation $\frac{y - y_1}{x - x_1} = m$. You can rewrite this equation as $y - y_1 = m(x - x_1)$. If you know two points on a line, or the slope and any point, you can find the equation of the line.

EXAMPLE Writing an Equation From a Graph

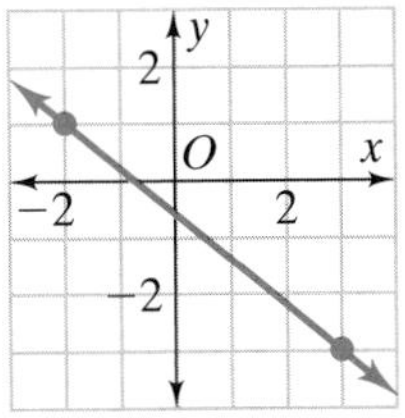

3 Find the equation of the line in the graph at the left.

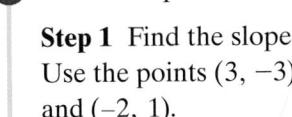

Step 1 Find the slope. Use the points (3, −3) and (−2, 1).

$$\text{slope} = \frac{1 - (-3)}{-2 - 3} = -\frac{4}{5}$$

Step 2 Use the slope and one point to write an equation.

$$y - y_1 = m(x - x_1)$$

$$y - (-3) = -\frac{4}{5}(x - 3) \quad \leftarrow \textbf{Use (3, −3) for } (x_1, y_1).$$

$$y + 3 = -\frac{4}{5}(x - 3)$$

Using the point (3, −3), the equation of the line is $y + 3 = -\frac{4}{5}(x - 3)$.

Quick Check

3. Use the point (−2, 1) to write an equation for the line in Example 3. $y - 1 = -\frac{4}{5}(x + 2)$

GO for Help

For help with slope-intercept form, go to Lesson 11-5, Example 2.

2. Teach

Activity Lab

Use before the lesson.

All in One Teaching Resources

Activity Lab 11-6: Writing Rules for Linear Functions

PowerPoint

Additional Examples

1 A rate for Internet access is $15 per month plus $.25 per hour of use. Write a function rule that shows how the monthly bill depends upon the number of hours used. $y = 15 + 0.25x$

2 Do the data in the table below represent a linear function? If so, write a rule for the function. $y = 2x + 8$

x	−1	0	1	2	3
y	6	8	10	12	14

3 Find the equation of the line in the graph below. $y = 2x + 8$

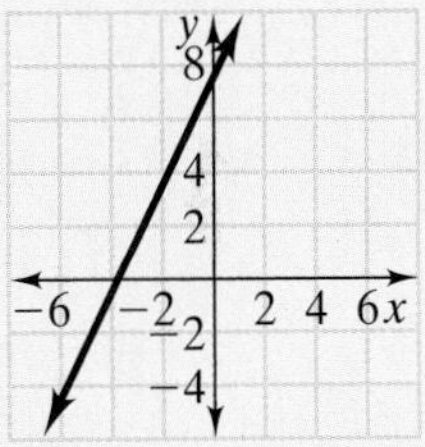

All in One Teaching Resources

- Daily Notetaking Guide 11-6 L3
- Adapted Notetaking 11-6 L1

Closure

- *How can you write a function rule from a table?* Find the slope using a pair of input/output values and use the point (0, *b*) as the *y*-intercept. Write a function rule using the slope-intercept form, $y = mx + b$.
- *How can you write a function rule from a graph?* Find the slope and y-intercept and substitute into $y = mx + b$. Or find the slope and another point and substitute into $y - y_1 = m(x - x_1)$.

Advanced Learners L4

Ask: *In general, in a problem, is the amount that follows the words "depends on" the input or the output?* input

learning style: verbal

English Language Learners ELL

For each function rule, students write the rule in words. Although they are translating words to function rules in this lesson, having them work from functions to words helps them develop mathematical language and conceptual understanding.

learning style: verbal

3. Practice

Assignment Guide

Check Your Understanding

Go over Exercises 1–2 in class before assigning the Homework Exercises.

Homework Exercises

A Practice by Example	3–8
B Apply Your Skills	9–14
C Challenge	15
Test Prep and Mixed Review	16–20

Homework Quick Check

To check students' understanding of key skills and concepts, go over Exercises 4, 8, 9, 10, and 11.

Differentiated Instruction Resources

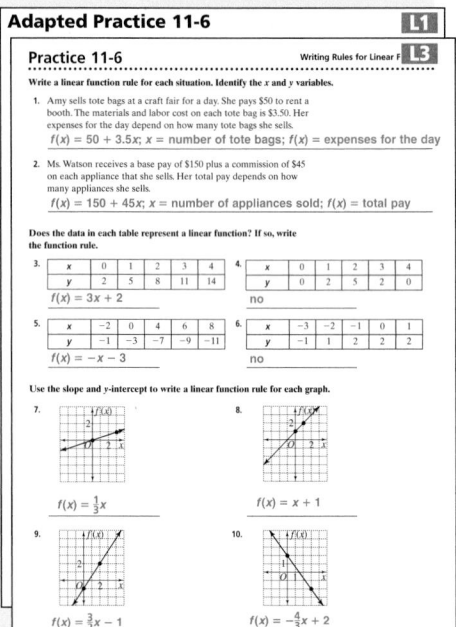

Adapted Practice 11-6 L1

Practice 11-6 Writing Rules for Linear F L3

Write a linear function rule for each situation. Identify the *x* and *y* variables.

1. Amy sells tote bags at a craft fair for a day. She pays $50 to rent a booth. The materials and labor cost on each tote bag is $3.50. Her expenses for the day depend on how many tote bags she sells.
   $f(x) = 50 + 3.5x$; x = number of tote bags; $f(x)$ = expenses for the day
2. Ms. Watson receives a base pay of $150 plus a commission of $45 on each appliance that she sells. Her total pay depends on how many appliances she sells.
   $f(x) = 150 + 45x$; x = number of appliances sold; $f(x)$ = total pay

Does the data in each table represent a linear function? If so, write the function rule.

3.

x	0	1	2	3	4
y	2	5	8	11	14

$f(x) = 3x + 2$

4.

x	0	1	2	3	4
y	0	2	5	2	0

no

5.

x	−2	0	4	6	8
y	−1	−3	−7	−9	−11

$f(x) = -x - 3$

6.

x	−3	−2	−1	0	1
y	−1	1	2	2	2

no

Use the slope and *y*-intercept to write a linear function rule for each graph.

7. 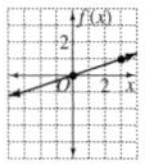

$f(x) = \frac{1}{3}x$

8. 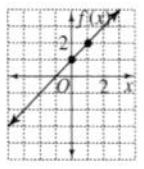

$f(x) = x + 1$

9. 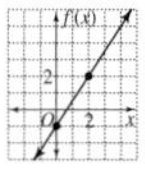

$f(x) = \frac{3}{2}x - 1$

10. 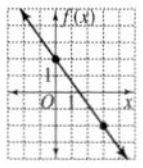

$f(x) = -\frac{4}{3}x + 2$

11-6 • Guided Problem Solving GPS L3

GPS Student Page 543, Exercise 11:

Art At a fair, an artist draws caricatures. He pays the fair $30 for space to set up his table and $2 for each drawing that he sells.

a. Write a function rule to represent his total payment to the fair as a function of the number of drawings he sells.

b. **Reasoning** What input is paired with the output $54? What does this input represent? Express the input/output pair in the form f(□) = □.

Understand

1. What is a caricature?
   A caricature is a cartoon portrait of someone.

Plan and Carry Out

2. How much does the artist pay the fair for space rental and each drawing he sells?
   $30; $2
3. Which expression shows the amount of money the artist will pay the fair if *c* represents the number of caricatures he sells?
   $f(c) = 30 + 2c$
4. Complete the table below.

Number of Caricatures	1	2	3	4	5	6	7	8	9	10	11	12
Total Payment to Fair	$32	$34	$36	$38	$40	$42	$44	$46	$48	$52	$54	$56

5. What input is paired with an output of $54? 12 caricatures; $f(12) = 54$

Check

6. How could you have found the input value another way?
   Substitute $54 into the expression, and solve for *c*.

Solve Another Problem

7. At the craft show, Becky sells small ceramic, painted balls. She pays $25 for booth rental and $.50 for each ceramic ball that she sells. Write a function rule to represent her total payment to the craft show organizers as a function of the number of ceramic balls she sells.
   $f(b) = 25 + 0.50b$

Check Your Understanding

1. **Vocabulary** How is slope-intercept form related to a linear function rule? The slope-intercept form is an example of the linear function rule.
2. Use the graph at the right to find the slope and complete the equation for the line.

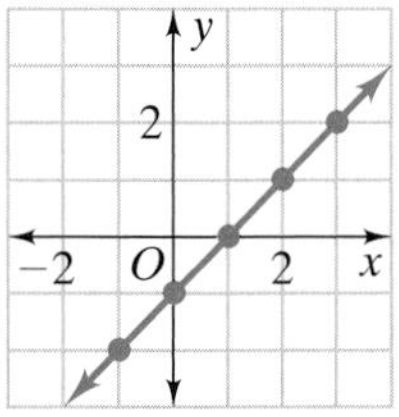

a. slope $= \frac{y_2 - y_1}{x_2 - x_1} = ■$ 1

b. $y - y_1 = m(x - x_1)$
$y - ■ = ■(x - ■)$
Answers may vary. Sample:
$y - 2 = 1(x - 3)$

Homework Exercises

For more exercises, see Extra Skills and Word Problems.

GO for Help

For Exercises	See Examples
3–4	1
5–6	2
7–8	3

A 3. **Sales** Mrs. Savin receives a weekly base salary of $500, plus a commission of $1,200 on each car that she sells. Write a function rule relating her total weekly pay *p* to cars she sells *c*. $p = 1{,}200c + 500$

4. **Ecology** Water flows over a dam at a rate of 500 gallons per minute. Write a function rule relating the amount of water *a* that flows over the dam to the number of minutes *m* that have passed. $a = 500m$

Do the values in each table represent a linear function? If so, write a function rule.

5.

x	−2	−1	0	1
y	8	5	2	−1

yes; $y = -3x + 2$

6.

x	0	1	2	3
y	8	6	4	2

yes; $y = -2x + 8$

Use the slope and two points to write an equation for each line.

7. 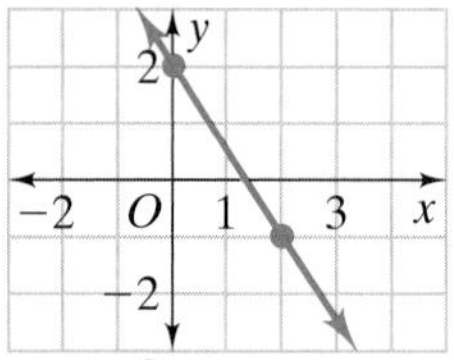

$y = -\frac{3}{2}x + 2$

8. 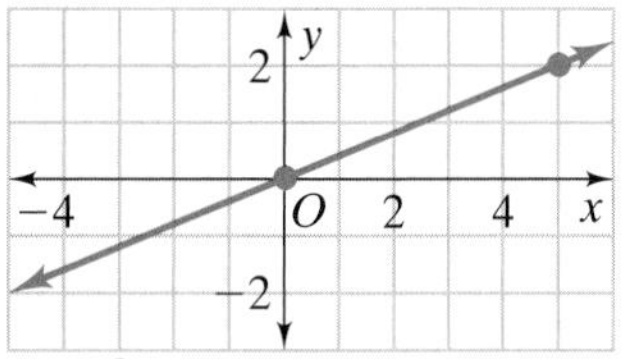

$y = \frac{2}{5}x$

B GPS 9. **Guided Problem Solving** Prices at a laundromat are $1.25 per load of wash and $.75 per 20 minutes of drying time. An average load takes 1 hour to dry. Write a function rule to describe the total cost of washing and drying as a function of the number of loads.
- What is the cost for one load of laundry to be washed and dried?
- Let *n* be the number of loads. Let *C* be the cost of *n* loads.

$C = 3.50n$

10. **Writing in Math** Explain how to determine whether a function is linear by analyzing an input-output table. See margin.

GO Online
Homework Video Tutor
Visit: PHSchool.com
Web Code: ase-1106

10. Determine the change between each pair of inputs and outputs. If the ratios are the same, it is a linear function.

15. See back of book.

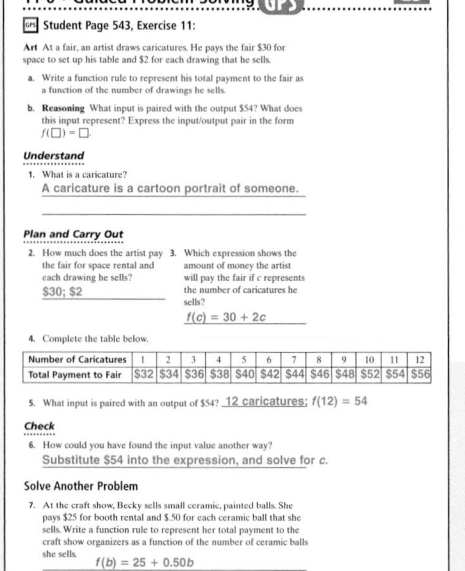

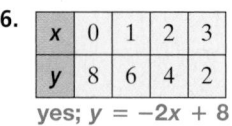

Caricatures are pictures of people in which certain features are exaggerated for comic effect.

14. $y = -\frac{1}{2}x + 1$

11. **Art** At a fair, an artist draws caricatures. He pays the fair \$30 for space to set up his table, and \$2 for each drawing that he sells. GPS
   a. Write a function rule to represent the artist's total payment to the fair as a function of the number of drawings he sells. $y = 30 + 2x$
   b. **Reasoning** What input is paired with the output \$54? What does this input represent? Express the input-output pair in the form $f(\blacksquare) = \blacksquare$. When $x = 12$, $y = 54$; his payment is \$54 for the space and the 12 drawings he sold; $f(12) = 54$.

Find the equation of each line with the given slope and point.

12. slope $= \frac{3}{4}$; $(2, -5)$ $y + 5 = \frac{3}{4}(x - 2)$

13. slope $= -\frac{1}{2}$; $(4, -1)$ $y + 1 = -\frac{1}{2}(x - 4)$

14. Write the equation in Exercise 13 in slope-intercept form. See left.

C 15. **Challenge** A water theme park charges a \$15 entrance fee and \$1 per ride. The park also offers a plan with a \$30 admission fee and a charge of \$.50 per ride. Write and graph a function rule to show the total cost C for r rides for each plan. Which is the best plan for someone who intends to go on many rides? Explain. See margin.

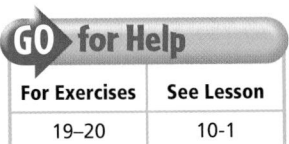

Test Prep and Mixed Review

Practice

Multiple Choice

16. The graph shows the relationship between hours worked h and Gomez Plumbing's total bill b, when materials cost \$100. Which of the following is the equation represented by the graph? D
   A $h = 50b + 100$
   B $h = 100b + 50$
   C $b = 100h + 50$
   D $b = 50h + 100$

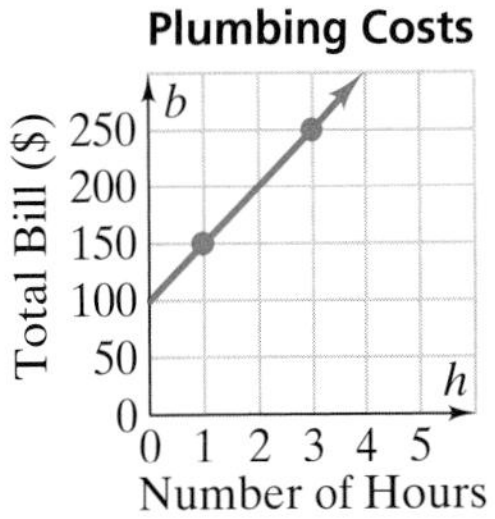

17. A piece of siding is in the shape of a trapezoid that is 6 inches high with bases 18 inches long and 24 inches long. Find the area of the trapezoid. H
   F 54 in.^{2} G 63 in.^{2} H 126 in.^{2} J 252 in.^{2}

18. Which group of numbers lists the integers in order from least to greatest? B
   A $-5, 4, -2, 1$
   B $-5, -2, 1, 4$
   C $1, -2, 4, -5$
   D $1, 4, -2, -5$

GO for Help

For Exercises	See Lesson
19–20	10-1

Decide whether each probability is experimental or theoretical.

19. A six-sided number cube is tossed 250 times. $P(\text{rolling a 4})$ is $\frac{37}{250}$. experimental

20. A bag contains 8 pens and 18 pencils. $P(\text{choosing a pen})$ is $\frac{4}{13}$. theoretical

4. Assess & Reteach

PowerPoint

Lesson Quiz

1. A telephone company charges \$4.95 per month plus \$.10 per minute used. Write the rule to show how the monthly bill depends on the minutes used. $y = 0.1x + 4.95$

2. Write a function rule for the data in the table. $y = -0.5x + 8$

x	0	2	4	6
y	8	7	6	5

3. An electrician charges \$60 for a house call plus \$75 for each hour of work. Write a function rule that shows how the total cost of the electrician's work y depends upon the number of hours x the electrician works. What is the output for an input value of 4, and what does it represent? $y = 75x + 60$; \$360; the electrician's charge for 4 hours of work.

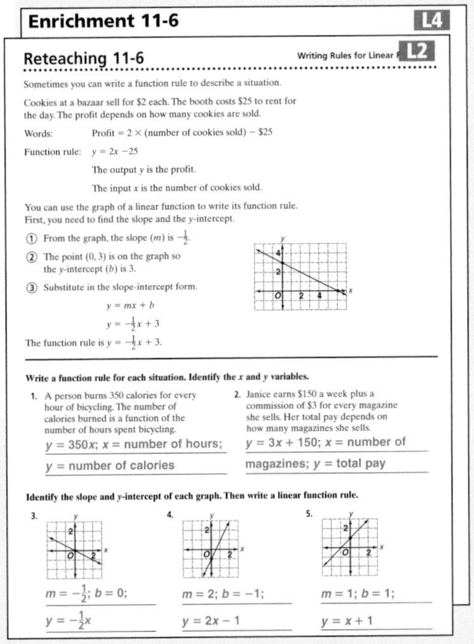
Enrichment 11-6 L4

Reteaching 11-6 Writing Rules for Linear F L2

Sometimes you can write a function rule to describe a situation.

Cookies at a bazaar sell for \$2 each. The booth costs \$25 to rent for the day. The profit depends on how many cookies are sold.

Words: Profit = 2 × (number of cookies sold) − \$25

Function rule: $y = 2x - 25$

The output y is the profit.

The input x is the number of cookies sold.

You can use the graph of a linear function to write its function rule. First, you need to find the slope and the y-intercept.

① From the graph, the slope (m) is $-\frac{1}{2}$.

② The point (0, 3) is on the graph so the y-intercept (b) is 3.

③ Substitute in the slope-intercept form.

$y = mx + b$

$y = -\frac{1}{2}x + 3$

The function rule is $y = -\frac{1}{2}x + 3$.

Write a function rule for each situation. Identify the x and y variables.

1. A person burns 350 calories for every hour of bicycling. The number of calories burned is a function of the number of hours spent bicycling. $y = 350x$; x = number of hours; y = number of calories

2. Janice earns \$150 a week plus a commission of \$3 for every magazine she sells. Her total pay depends on how many magazines she sells. $y = 3x + 150$; x = number of magazines; y = total pay

Identify the slope and y-intercept of each graph. Then write a linear function rule.

3. $m = -\frac{1}{2}$; $b = 0$; $y = -\frac{1}{2}x$

4. $m = 2$; $b = -1$; $y = 2x - 1$

5. $m = 1$; $b = 1$; $y = x + 1$

Alternative Assessment

Each student in a pair writes a function rule and makes a table. Partners trade tables and write the function rule for each other's table.

Test Prep

Resources

For additional practice with a variety of test item formats:

- Test-Taking Strategies, p. 551
- Test Prep, p. 555
- Test-Taking Strategies with Transparencies

GPS Guided Problem Solving

Linear Functions

Students read a real-world problem to develop problem solving and reasoning skills. In the left-hand column, they read questions they could ask themselves to make sense of the problem. In the right-hand column, they read the steps for setting up and solving equations used to describe the situation.

Guided Instruction

Have students work through the problem, rather than just read it. Have them identify any steps that are unclear or that don't match their own work.

Math Tip
Point out that using subscripts is similar to using a different letter.

Error Prevention!

The graph gives a good picture of the intersection point. However, remind students not to guess the actual value from the graph. They must verify that the point is a solution to both functions.

Linear Functions

For each rental plan, represent the relationship between the number of miles (from 20 to 45) and the cost. Use a linear function, a table of ordered pairs, and a graph (using the same coordinate grid). What conclusions can you draw about these plans?

What You Might Think

What do I know? What do I want to find out?

How can I write a function rule for each plan?

How can I make a table and graph?

What conclusions can be stated?

What You Might Write

Plan 1 costs $15 plus $.25 per mile. Plan 2 costs $8 plus $.45 per mile. I want to compare the two plans using function rules, tables, and graphs.

Let m = the number of miles driven. Let C = the cost of the rental in dollars.

Plan 1: $C_1 = \$.25m + 15$

Plan 2: $C_2 = \$.45m + 8$

I can use the function rule to get data points for the table. Then I can graph those points.

m	C_1	C_2
20	20	17
30	22.5	21.5
35	23.75	23.75
45	26.25	28.25

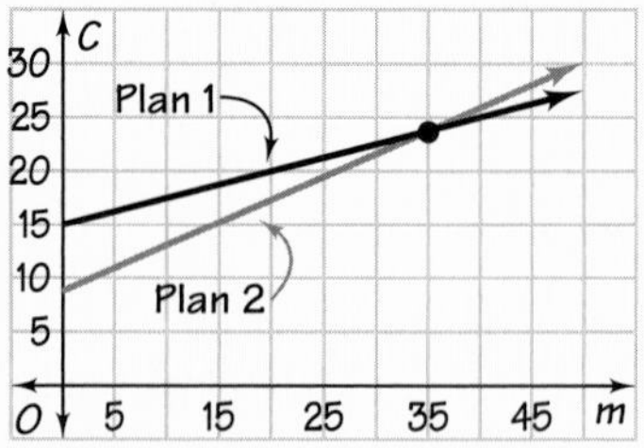

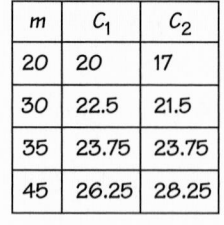

The lines intersect at (35, 23.75). Plan 2 is better if you drive less than 35 miles; otherwise, Plan 1 is better.

Think It Through

1. Could you have used other values for m in the table? Explain.
   Yes; the function rule works for any positive number.
2. How was the conclusion arrived at? Are there other conclusions?
   The conclusion was made by using a table and graph; there are no other conclusions.

Exercises

Solve each problem. For Exercises 3 and 4, answer the questions first.

3. **Population** Assume the relationship between the year and number of senior citizens is a linear function. Use the data at the right to predict the number of senior citizens in the United States in 2020. about 53 million senior citizens
   a. Using the ordered pairs in the graph as endpoints, make a line graph showing years and number of senior citizens. See margin.
   b. Find the slope of the line and then write a function rule for the line. Use the rule to solve the problem. $y = 1.1x + 31.9$

U.S. Senior Population

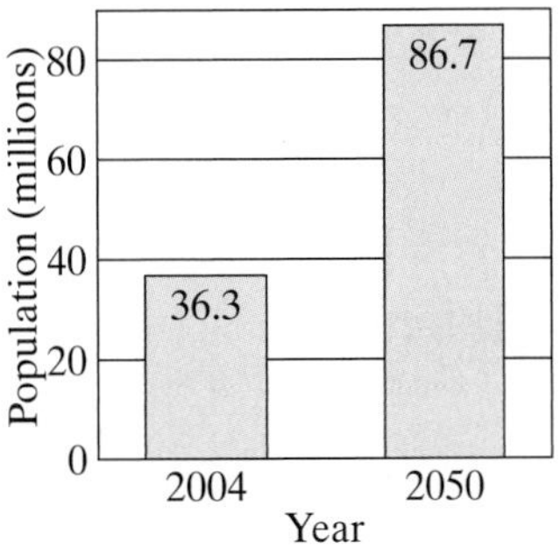

4. A certain airplane can climb 3,000 feet for every mile it travels horizontally. If it maintains this rate of ascent, how far will the plane have traveled horizontally when it reaches 5 miles in altitude? 8.8 mi
   a. What is the rate of ascent in feet per mile? 3,000 ft/mi
   b. Let m be the number of miles traveled horizontally and A be the altitude. Write a function rule relating the number of miles traveled and the altitude. Be sure to use the correct units. $A = 3{,}000\,m$

5. Student council members are raising funds by selling hats. They take a survey to see how many students will buy the hats at different prices. The results are below.

Price (dollars)	2	4	6	8	10	12
Number of Buyers	400	325	250	175	100	25

   Graph the data. Use the graph to estimate the number of hats that will be sold at $5. See margin.

6. **Landfill** A county landfill already contains 20,000 tons of trash. It is gaining 500 tons per month. How many months will it be until the landfill contains 50,000 tons of trash? Write a function rule and make a graph to solve the problem. $t = 20{,}000 + 500m$; 60 months

3a.

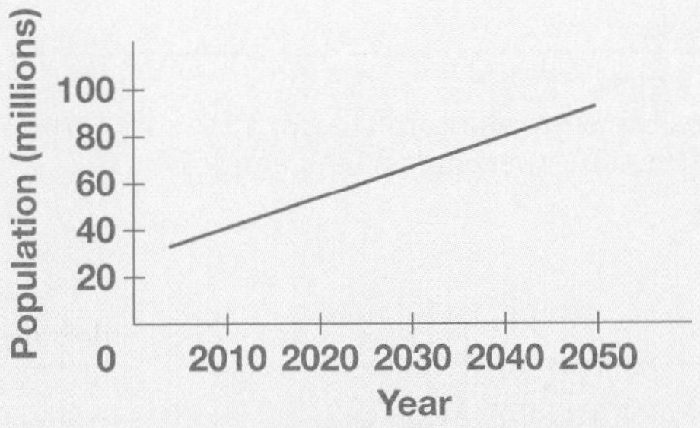

Teaching Tip
Have students ask themselves the same or similar questions as in the example as they work through the Exercises.

Alternative Method
It is not always necessary to begin with the same representation. Encourage students to start with a representation that helps them make sense of the problem. For example, graphing data may help them analyze one situation but writing an equation and generating a table might help them analyze another.

5.

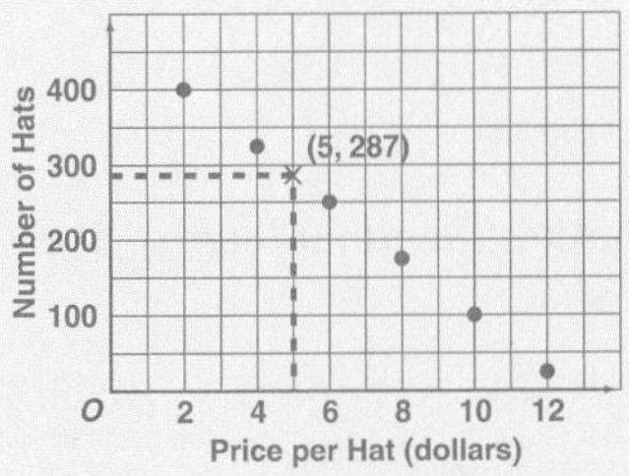

About 287 hats will sell if hats are priced at $5 each.

11-7

1. Plan

Objective
To graph and write quadratic functions and other non-linear functions

Examples
1 Graphing a Quadratic Function
2 Graphing Other Nonlinear Functions
3 Writing a Quadratic Function Rule

Math Understandings: p. 510D

Professional Development

Math Background

Equations of the form $y = mx + b$ always have a graph that is a straight line. Equations of the form $y = ax^2 + bx + c$ $(a \neq 0)$ are called *quadratic equations* and have a U-shaped curve called a *parabola*. A parabola opens upward, like a drinking glass, if the coefficient of x^2 is positive $(a > 0)$ and opens downward if the coefficient is negative $(a < 0)$.

More Math Background: p. 510D

Lesson Planning and Resources

See p. 510E for a list of the resources that support this lesson.

PowerPoint

Bell Ringer Practice

Check Skills You'll Need
Use student page, transparency, or PowerPoint. For intervention, direct students to:
Graphing Linear Equations
Lesson 11-5
Extra Skills and Word Problems Practice, Ch. 11

Algebra

11-7 Quadratic and Other Nonlinear Functions

Check Skills You'll Need

1. **Vocabulary Review** How do you know if a function is *linear*?
1–5. See back of book.

Graph each function.

2. $y = 3x - 1$
3. $y = x + 7$
4. $y = -2x - 5$
5. $y = -4x + 2$

GO for Help Lesson 11-5

What You'll Learn

To graph and write quadratic functions and other nonlinear functions

New Vocabulary quadratic function, parabola

Why Learn This?

Think of a juggler's ball being tossed up in the air and falling back down. As the ball rises, its speed decreases. Then it falls, and the speed increases. The relationship between speed and time is not always the same.

In cases like this, nonlinear functions are needed to describe how variables are related. Nonlinear functions are functions whose graphs are not straight lines. A **quadratic function** is a function in which the greatest exponent of a variable is 2.

The graph of a quadratic function is a U-shaped curve called a **parabola.** The curve may open upward or downward. When you throw a ball into the air, the path it follows is a parabola.

EXAMPLE Graphing a Quadratic Function

1 Make a table and graph the quadratic function $y = 4t - t^2$. Use integers from 0 to 4 for inputs. Connect the points with a smooth curve.

t	$4t - t^2$			=	y
0	$4(0) - (0)^2$	=	$0 - 0$	=	0
1	$4(1) - (1)^2$	=	$4 - 1$	=	3
2	$4(2) - (2)^2$	=	$8 - 4$	=	4
3	$4(3) - (3)^2$	=	$12 - 9$	=	3
4	$4(4) - (4)^2$	=	$16 - 16$	=	0

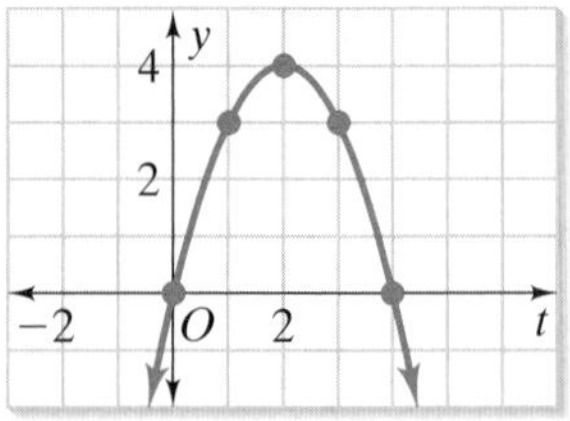

Online active math

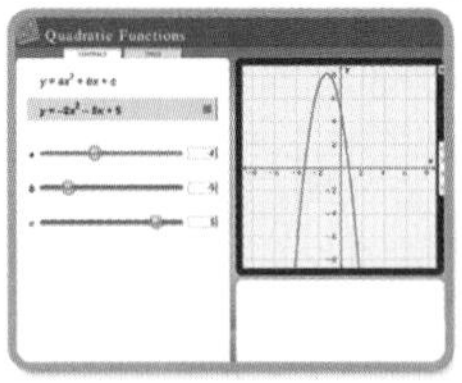

For: Quadratic Functions Activity
Use: Interactive Textbook, 11-7

Quick Check

See back of book.

1. Make a table and a graph for the function $y = 2x^2 - 5$.

Differentiated Instruction Solutions for All Learners

Special Needs L1	**Below Level** L2
Students trace lines and parabolas in the air with their finger based on a table of values or situation. For example, say: *Show me a line with a negative slope,* or *Show me a parabola.* learning style: tactile	Students use a graphing calculator to see the graphs of the functions (parabolas) in Examples 1 and 3. learning style: visual

Other types of nonlinear functions also have curved graphs.

EXAMPLE Graphing Other Nonlinear Functions

Careers Animal rescue workers go to the aid of wildlife and pets.

2 **Animal Rescue** Suppose it takes a total of 60 hours of work to clean wildlife damaged by an oil spill. The function $y = \frac{60}{x}$ represents the number of hours y each person must work if x people work to clean the animals. Make a table and graph the function.

Number of People, *x*	Hours per Person, *y*
3	60 ÷ 3 = 20
4	60 ÷ 4 = 15
5	60 ÷ 5 = 12
6	60 ÷ 6 = 10
10	60 ÷ 10 = 6

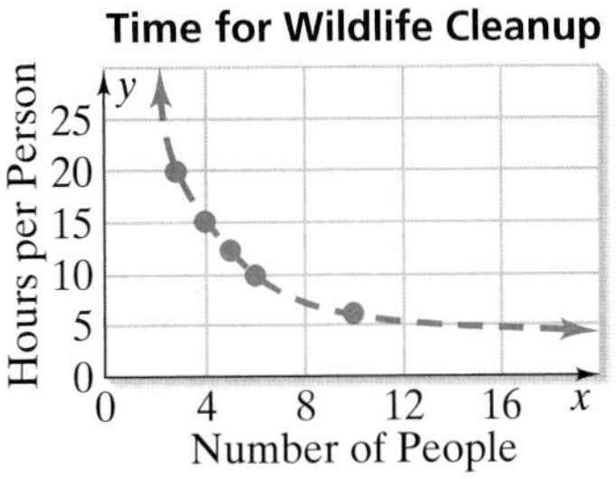

The data are discrete, so the curve is dashed.

Quick Check

2. The function $y = \frac{200}{s}$ relates the time y (in hours) for a 200-mile trip to the speed traveled s (in miles per hour). Make a table showing speed and number of hours traveled. Then graph the data.
See back of book.

You can write function rules for quadratic functions and other nonlinear functions.

EXAMPLE Writing a Quadratic Function Rule

x	*y*
0	3
2	7
3	12
5	28

3 Write a rule for the quadratic function shown in the table at the left.

Input x	$(\text{Input})^2$ x^2	Output y
0	0	3
2	4	7
3	9	12
5	25	28

← Compare each output to $(\text{input})^2$. Each output is greater than $(\text{input})^2$ by 3.

So the function rule is $y = x^2 + 3$.

Quick Check

3. Write a quadratic function rule for the data in the table below.

x	−3	−1	0	2	4
y	7	−1	−2	2	14

$y = x^2 - 2$

Advanced Learners L4
Students find points for the graph of $xy = 12$.
Sample:
(3, 4), (4, 3), (−4, −3),(−2, −6), (12, 1), . . .

learning style: visual

English Language Learners ELL
Pairs of students write a definition of, illustrate, and give an example of a quadratic function as compared to a linear function.

learning style: visual

2. Teach

Activity Lab

Use before the lesson.

All in One Teaching Resources

Activity Lab 11-7: Quadratic and Other Nonlinear Functions

Guided Instruction

Teaching Tip
In Example 3, point out that the words *quadratic function* in the instructions give you a hint that x may be squared.

PowerPoint

Additional Examples

1 Make a table and graph the quadratic function $f(x) = x^2 - 2x$. Use integers from −2 to 4 for inputs.
1–2. See back of book.

2 Suppose a driver is making a 120 mile trip. Make a table and graph this situation using the relationship that 120 ÷ hours for trip = speed for trip. Use 2, 3, 4, 5, and 6 hours for input.

3 Write a quadratic function rule for the data in the table below. $f(x) = x^2 - 3$

Input *x*	−2	−1	0	1	2
Output *y*	1	−2	−3	−2	1

All in One Teaching Resources
- Daily Notetaking Guide 11-7 L3
- Adapted Notetaking 11-7 L1

Closure

- Define a parabola. a U-shaped curve formed by the graph of a quadratic function
- *How do you write a function rule for a quadratic function represented in a function table?* Find the relationship between each input value and the input value squared and write the corresponding function rule.
- *How do you graph nonlinear functions?* Substitute values for x and make a table. Then graph the ordered pairs and connect them in a curve.

3. Practice

Assignment Guide

Check Your Understanding

Go over Exercises 1–3 in class before assigning the Homework Exercises.

Homework Exercises

A	Practice by Example	4–17
B	Apply Your Skills	18–29
C	Challenge	30
Test Prep and Mixed Review		31–36

Homework Quick Check

To check students' understanding of key skills and concepts, go over Exercises 9, 12, 18, 19, and 23.

Differentiated Instruction Resources

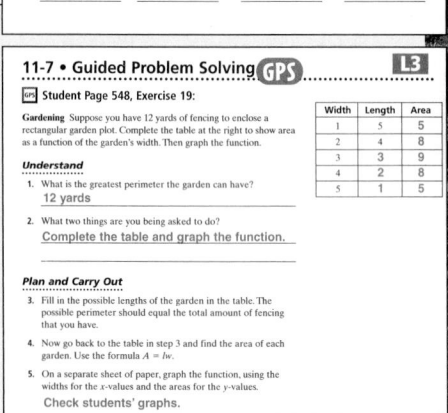

Adapted Practice 11-7 L1

Practice 11-7 Quadratic and Other Nonlinear... L3

Write a quadratic function rule for the data in each table.

1.

x	0	1	2	3	4
f(x)	3	4	7	12	19

$f(x) = x^2 + 3$

2.

x	−2	−1	0	1	2
f(x)	−8	−2	0	−2	−8

$f(x) = -2x^2$

3.

x	−1	0	1	2	3
f(x)	4	0	4	16	36

$f(x) = 4x^2$

4.

x	−10	−5	0	5	10
f(x)	95	20	−5	20	95

$f(x) = x^2 - 5$

Complete the table for each function. Then graph the function.

5. $f(x) = x^2 + 1$

x	$x^2 + 1 = f(x)$
−3	10
−2	5
−1	2
0	1
1	2
2	5
3	10

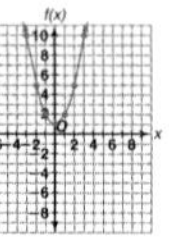

6. $f(x) = 4 - x^2$

x	$4 - x^2 = f(x)$
−3	−5
−2	0
−1	3
0	4
1	3
2	0
3	−5

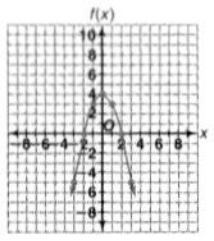

7. $f(x) = \frac{20}{x}$

x	f(x)
2	10
4	5
5	4
10	2

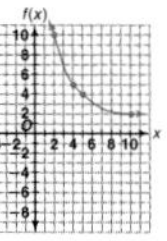

8. $f(x) = 2^x - 1$

x	f(x)
−1	$-\frac{1}{2}$
0	0
1	1
2	3
3	7

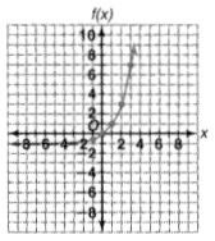

Does the point (2, 2) lie on the graph of each function?

9. $f(x) = 2x - 2$ yes
10. $f(x) = \left(\frac{1}{2}\right)^x$ no
11. $f(x) = x^2 - x$ yes
12. $f(x) = \frac{4}{x}$ yes

11-7 • Guided Problem Solving GPS L3

Student Page 548, Exercise 19:

Gardening Suppose you have 12 yards of fencing to enclose a rectangular garden plot. Complete the table at the right to show area as a function of the garden's width. Then graph the function.

Width	Length	Area
1	5	5
2	4	8
3	3	9
4	2	8
5	1	5

Understand

1. What is the greatest perimeter the garden can have? 12 yards
2. What two things are you being asked to do? Complete the table and graph the function.

Plan and Carry Out

3. Fill in the possible lengths of the garden in the table. The possible perimeter should equal the total amount of fencing that you have.
4. Now go back to the table in step 3 and find the area of each garden. Use the formula $A = lw$.
5. On a separate sheet of paper, graph the function, using the widths for the x-values and the areas for the y-values. Check students' graphs.

Check

6. Is your graph reasonable? Using a width of 3.5 yards, what is the area? Does this data fall on the curve? Yes, the point (3.5, 8.75) is on the curve.

Solve Another Problem

7. You are building a rectangular patio and would like to outline the perimeter in brick. If the bricks you have total 40 feet in length, what would the area of the patio be for the following widths: 6 ft, 8 ft, 10 ft, 12 ft, and 14 ft? 6 ft: 84ft²; 8 ft: 96 ft²; 10 ft: 100 ft²; 12ft: 96 ft²; 14 ft: 84 ft²

Check Your Understanding

1. Graphs of linear functions are straight lines, and graphs of quadratic functions are parabolas.

1. **Vocabulary** Explain how a quadratic function differs from a linear function.
2. Sketch a parabola. See margin.
3. Make a table of values for the function $y = 2x^2 - 1$. Use only positive values for x. See margin.

Homework Exercises

For more exercises, see Extra Skills and Word Problems.

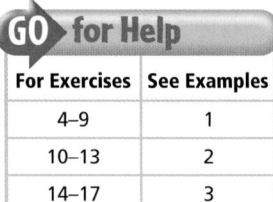

GO for Help

For Exercises	See Examples
4–9	1
10–13	2
14–17	3

A **Make a table and graph each quadratic function. Use integers from −3 to 3 for inputs.** 4–9. See margin.

4. $y = -x^2$
5. $y = 2x^2$
6. $y = -8x^2$
7. $y = x^2 + 2$
8. $y = -4x^2$
9. $y = 9 + 2x^2$

Make a table and a graph for each function. Use only positive values for x. 10–13. See margin.

10. $y = \frac{10}{x}$
11. $y = \frac{8}{x}$
12. $y = \frac{20}{x}$
13. $y = \frac{16}{x}$

Write a quadratic function rule for the data in each table. 14–17. See left.

14. $y = x^2 - 20$
15. $y = -x^2$
16. $y = x^2 + 5$
17. $y = x^2 - 4$

14.

x	−10	−5	0	5	10
y	80	5	−20	5	80

15.

x	0	1	2	3	4
y	0	−1	−4	−9	−16

16.

x	0	1	2	3	4
y	5	6	9	14	21

17.

x	−2	−1	0	1	4
y	0	−3	−4	−3	12

B **GPS** 18. **Guided Problem Solving** The number of bushels of walnuts y that one acre of trees produces (output) is a function of the number of trees x planted per acre (input). The function rule is $y = -0.01x^2 + 0.8x$. Graph the function and use the graph to explain how the number of trees planted per acre affects walnut production.
- Complete a table of input-output pairs to represent the data.
- Graph the data in the table.

See margin.

19. **Gardening** Suppose you have 12 yards of fencing to enclose a rectangular garden plot. Complete the table at the right to show area as a function of the garden's width. Then graph the function. See margin.

Width w	Length	Area A
1	5	■
2	4	■
3	■	■
4	■	■
5	■	■

2.

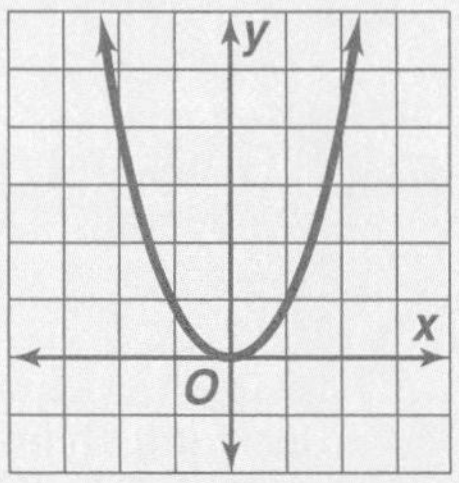

3.

x	0	1	2	3	4
y	−1	1	7	17	31

4. See back of book.

5.

x	−3	−2	−1	0	1	2	3
y	18	8	2	0	2	8	18

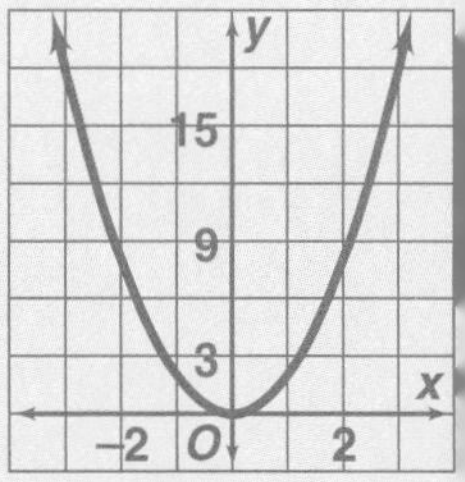

6–13, 18–19. See back of book.

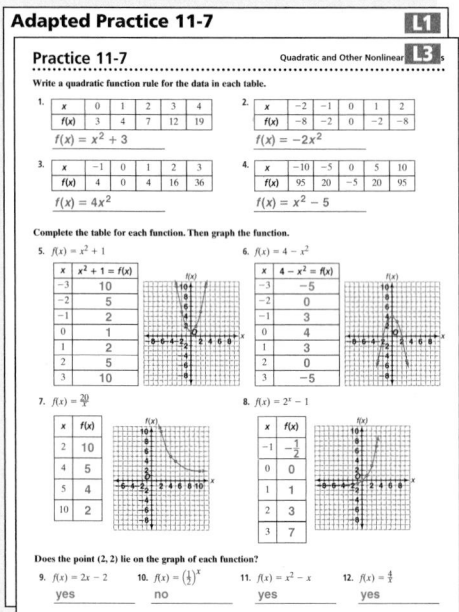

Go Online
Homework Video Tutor
Visit: PHSchool.com
Web Code: ase-1107

Make a table and a graph for each quadratic function. 20–22. See margin.

20. $y = -x - 3x^2$ 21. $y = 2x^2 + 2x + 2$ 22. $y = x - x^2$

23. a. Graph $y = n^2$ and $y = n^3$ on the same coordinate grid.
b. **Writing in Math** Describe the similarities and differences between the graphs of the two functions. 23a–b. See margin.

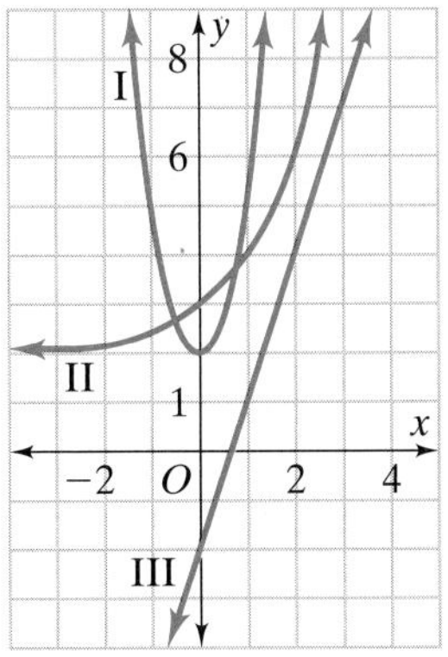

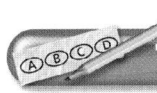

For Exercises 24–26, match each function to its graph at the left.

24. $y = 3x - 2$ III 25. $y = 3x^2 + 2$ I 26. $y = 2 + 2^x$ II

Copy and complete the table for each function. Then graph the data.

27. $y = x^2 - 2$

x	$x^2 - 2 = y$
0	■
1	■
2	■
3	■

28. $y = \frac{7}{x} + 2$

x	$\frac{7}{x} + 2 = y$
1	■
2	■
3	■
4	■

29. $y = 3 \cdot 2^x$

x	$3 \cdot 2^x = y$
1	■
2	■
3	■
4	■

27–29. See margin.

C 30. **Challenge** Make a table and a graph for each function. Then compare the graphs. 30a–d. See margin.
a. $y = 3^x$ b. $y = 3^{x-2}$ c. $y = 3^{x+2}$ d. $y = -3^x$

Test Prep and Mixed Review — Practice

Multiple Choice

31. Which graph best represents the equation $d = -16s + 125$? D

A
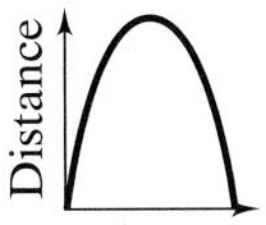

C
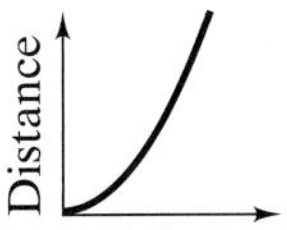

B
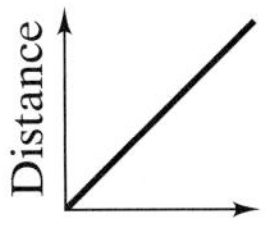

D
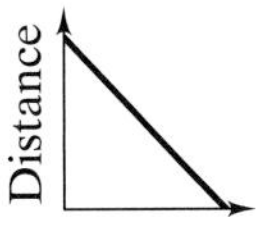

32. A house includes a rectangular door that is 3 ft wide and 7 ft tall and a window of the same width above the door in the shape of a semicircle. Which is closest to the area of the door and the window? G
F 14 ft^2 G 24.5 ft^2 H 28 ft^2 J 74 ft^2

GO for Help

For Exercises	See Lesson
33–36	11-3

Use the function rule $f(x) = 2x + 5$. Find each output.

33. $f(2)$ 9 34. $f(-2)$ 1 35. $f(13)$ 31 36. $f(27)$ 59

Online lesson quiz, PHSchool.com, Web Code: asa-1107

4. Assess & Reteach

PowerPoint Lesson Quiz

For items 1–2, use the function rule $y = -x^2 + 4x$.

1. Make a table for the function.

x	0	1	2	3	4
y	0	3	4	3	0

2. Graph the function.

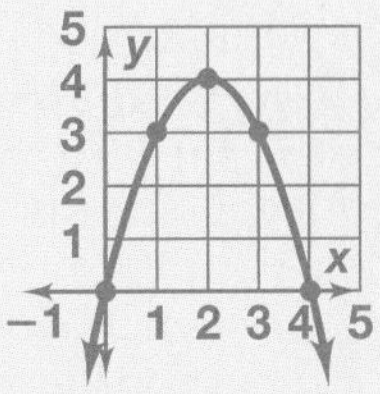

For items 3–4, use the function rule $y = x + \frac{1}{x}$.

3. Make a table for the function.

x	1	2	3	4	5
y	2	2.5	3.3	4.25	5.2

4. Graph the function.

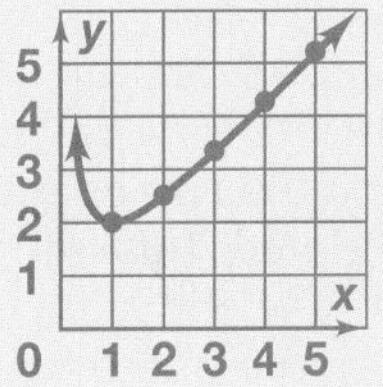

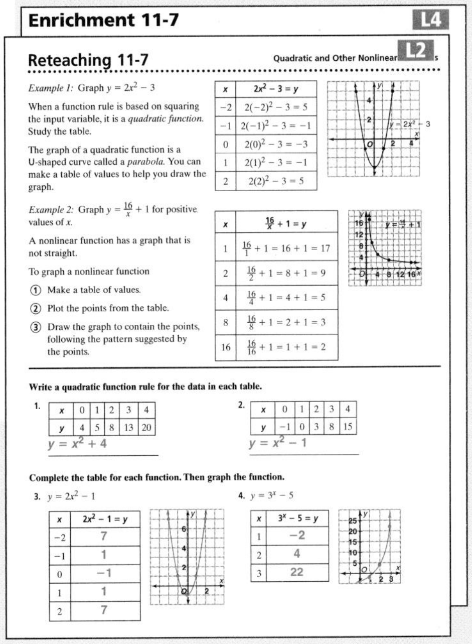

Enrichment 11-7 L4

Reteaching 11-7 Quadratic and Other Nonlinear ...s L2

Example 1: Graph $y = 2x^2 - 3$

When a function rule is based on squaring the input variable, it is a *quadratic function.* Study the table.

The graph of a quadratic function is a U-shaped curve called a *parabola.* You can make a table of values to help you draw the graph.

x	$2x^2 - 3 = y$
−2	$2(-2)^2 - 3 = 5$
−1	$2(-1)^2 - 3 = -1$
0	$2(0)^2 - 3 = -3$
1	$2(1)^2 - 3 = -1$
2	$2(2)^2 - 3 = 5$

Example 2: Graph $y = \frac{16}{x} + 1$ for positive values of x.

A nonlinear function has a graph that is not straight.

To graph a nonlinear function
① Make a table of values.
② Plot the points from the table.
③ Draw the graph to contain the points, following the pattern suggested by the points.

x	$\frac{16}{x} + 1 = y$
1	$\frac{16}{1} + 1 = 16 + 1 = 17$
2	$\frac{16}{2} + 1 = 8 + 1 = 9$
4	$\frac{16}{4} + 1 = 4 + 1 = 5$
8	$\frac{16}{8} + 1 = 2 + 1 = 3$
16	$\frac{16}{16} + 1 = 1 + 1 = 2$

Write a quadratic function rule for the data in each table.

1.

x	0	1	2	3	4
y	4	5	8	13	20

$y = x^2 + 4$

2.

x	0	1	2	3	4
y	−1	0	3	8	15

$y = x^2 - 1$

Complete the table for each function. Then graph the function.

3. $y = 2x^2 - 1$

x	$2x^2 - 1 = y$
−2	7
−1	1
0	−1
1	1
2	7

4. $y = 3^x - 5$

x	$3^x - 5 = y$
1	−2
2	4
3	22

Alternative Assessment

Each student writes a simple quadratic function and makes a table on a separate piece of paper. Partners exchange tables, graph the data, and write the function rule for each other's functions.

Test Prep

Resources
For additional practice with a variety of test item formats:
- Test-Taking Strategies, p. 551
- Test Prep, p. 555
- Test-Taking Strategies with Transparencies

20–23. See back of book.
27–30. See back of book.

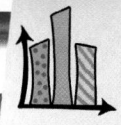

Changing Representations

You can use words, graphs, tables, or equations to show algebraic relationships. Learning how to translate among these representations can help solve problems.

EXAMPLE

Food Drive A class collected cans for a food drive for a local shelter. The teacher brought in 15 cans to start the collection. Beginning the next day, the class brought in 6 cans every day. The table below shows the number of cans collected for the first week. Use these data to make a graph and write an equation describing the number of cans c collected in d days.

Number of Days, d	0	1	2	3	4	5
Number of Cans, c	15	21	27	33	39	45

Graph: Make a graph of the data with the number of days on the horizontal axis and the number of cans on the vertical axis.

Since the number of cans must be a whole number, the data are discrete. Connect the points with a dashed line.

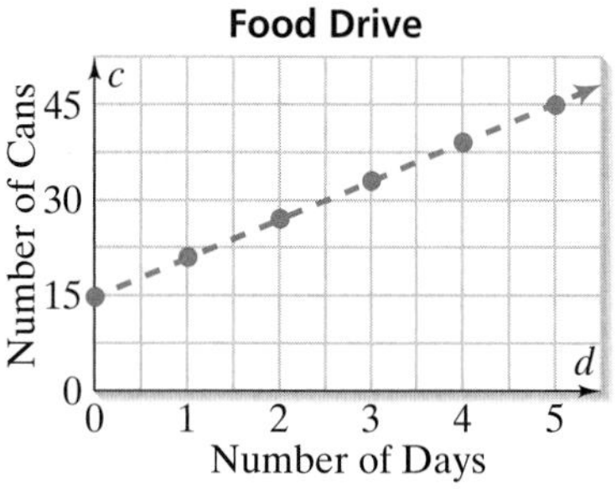

Function Rule: The function is linear because the graph is a line. The y-intercept is 15, and the slope is $\frac{21 - 15}{1 - 0} = 6$. So the linear function rule is $c = 6d + 15$.

Exercises

In Exercises 1–3, one representation of a relation is given. Translate each relation by representing it as a table, as a graph, and as a function rule. 1–4. See margin.

1. 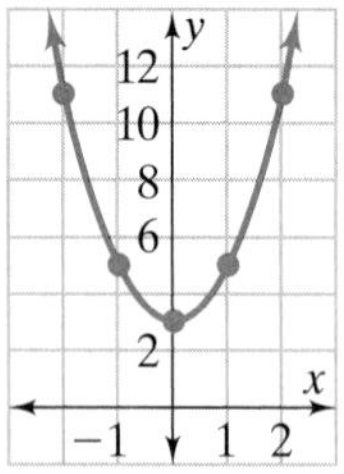

2. $P = 5 \cdot 3^n$

3.

Input	Output
0	10
1	18
2	26
3	34

4. **Reasoning** When might it be more useful to use a graph rather than a function rule? A function rule rather than a graph?

Activity Lab

Changing Representations

Viewing a function in different forms can help students understand the relationship that the function describes. In this activity, students translate between verbal, tabular, graphical, and symbolic representations of linear functions.

Guided Instruction

After the function rule is determined, have the students reread the problem. Have them make the connection between the known elements in the problem and the resulting function rule. Ask them to predict how the function rule changes with various changes to the number of cans the teacher brings in and/or changes to the number of cans brought in each day. Have students check their predictions.

Error Prevention!

For each representation, make sure students clearly describe and understand the two quantities that are related. This will help them translate between representations of the function.

Exercises

In Exercise 2, remind students to draw a smooth curve between a few points. In Exercise 4, discuss the purposes of the different representations and the type of information that each gives you about the function (relationship).

Resources

- graph paper (optional)

1. Function Rule: $y = 3 + 2x^2$

x	y
−2	11
−1	5
0	3
1	5
2	11

2.

n	P
0	5
1	15
2	45
3	135
4	405
5	1,215

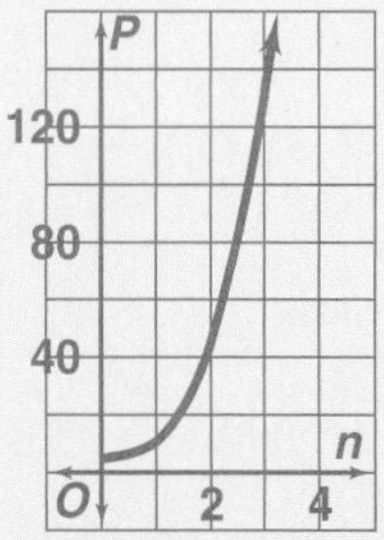

3. Function Rule: $y = 10 + 8x$

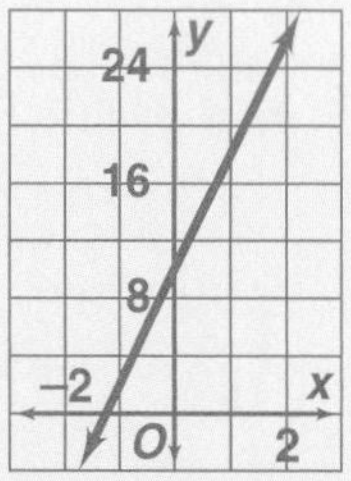

4. Answers may vary. Sample: It is easier to use a graph when looking for an estimate or prediction, and it is easier to use a function rule when you have a known value.

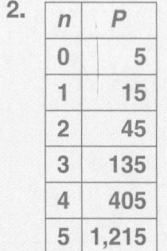

Interpreting Data

Many questions involve interpreting data in a table or a graph. Before you answer the question, be sure you understand the information the graph or table is displaying.

EXAMPLE

1 The circle graph shows Traci's monthly budget. If Traci earns \$500 a month, how much does she spend on bills each month?

(A) \$150 (B) \$600 (C) \$750 (D) \$2,500

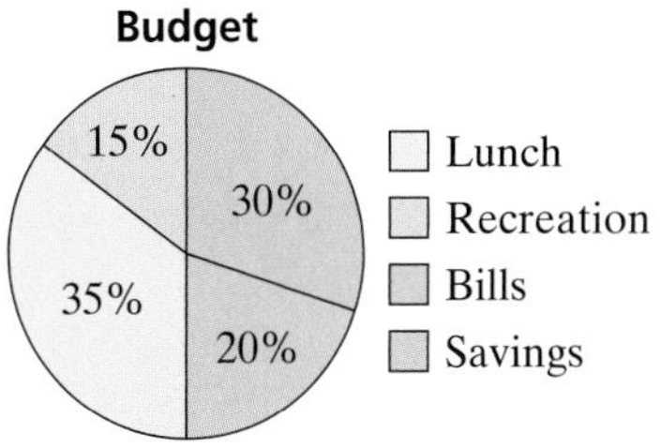

The circle graph shows the percent of her budget that Traci spends on different categories. Notice that the answer choices are all dollar amounts, not percents. To calculate the dollar amount she spends on bills, b, find 30% of \$500.

b = 30% of 500

= 0.3 · 500 ← **Change the percent to a decimal. Then multiply by 500.**

= 150

Traci spends \$150 on bills each month. The correct answer is choice A.

Exercises

Use the scatter plot below for Exercises 1–3.

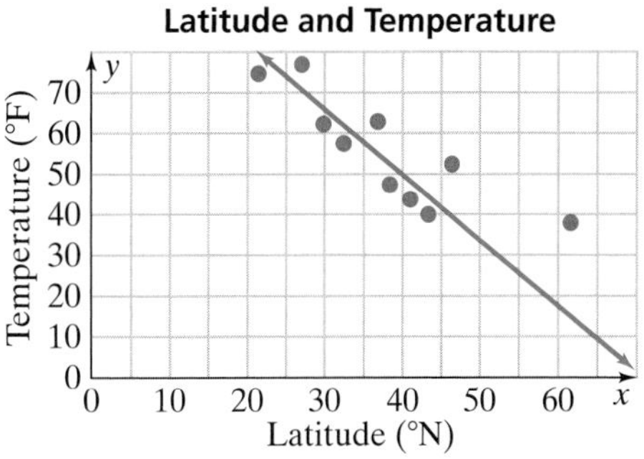

1. Predict the mean temperature for a city at 25° north latitude. **D**

(A) 45°F (C) 65°F
(B) 55°F (D) 75°F

2. Which of the following is NOT supported by the data in the graph? **F**

(F) As latitude increases, so does temperature.
(G) As latitude increases, temperature decreases.
(H) This graph has a negative trend.
(J) The temperature is higher at lower latitudes.

3. At approximately what latitude is the temperature 60°F? **C**

(A) 0° N (B) 15° N (C) 35° N (D) 40° N

Interpreting Data

Understanding the information that is given in a graph is an important skill. Students build reasoning skills as they interpret data in charts.

Guided Instruction

Error Prevention!

In Exercise 1, ask students to recall the definition of *mean.* Show students that reading the graph is different from actually finding (or calculating) the mean. Instead, they should interpret what the graph is telling them about data.

Resources

Test-Taking Strategies with Transparencies
- Transparency 12
- Practice sheet, p. 35

Test-Taking Strategies with Transparencies

Test-Taking Strategies: Interpreting Data

Before you answer a question that involves interpreting data from a table, graph, or plot, make sure that you understand the information displayed.

Example The bar graph below shows the favorite fruit choices of a class of students. Which statement is best supported by the graph?

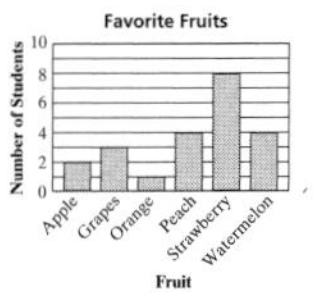

A. More students chose grapes than chose apple and orange combined.

B. The fewest students chose apple.

C. The same number of students chose peach as chose watermelon.

D. More than half the students chose strawberry.

- 3 students chose grapes, 2 students chose apple, and 1 chose orange. Since 3 ≯ 2 + 1, eliminate choice A.
- 2 students chose apple. This is not the fewest, since only 1 student chose orange. Eliminate choice B.
- The total number of students choosing was 2 + 3 + 1 + 4 + 8 + 4 = 22. 8 is not more than half of 22, so eliminate choice D.
- 4 students chose peach, and 4 students chose watermelon. This is the same number, so the correct answer is choice C.

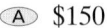

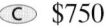

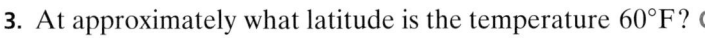

Chapter 11 Review

Resources

Student Edition
Extra Skills and Word Problems Practice, Ch. 11, p. 624
English/Spanish Glossary, p. 650
Formulas and Properties, p. 648
Tables, p. 643

All-in-One Teaching Resources
- Vocabulary and Study Skills 11F L3

Differentiated Instruction
Spanish Vocabulary Workbook with Study Skills ELL
Interactive Textbook
- Audio Glossary

Online Vocabulary Quiz

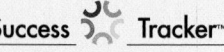

Success Tracker™
Online at PHSchool.com

Vocabulary Review

arithmetic sequence (p. 513)
common difference (p. 513)
common ratio (p. 514)
continuous data (p. 534)
discrete data (p. 534)
function (p. 523)
function rule (p. 523)
geometric sequence (p. 514)
inductive reasoning (p. 512)
linear function (p. 535)
parabola (p. 546)
quadratic function (p. 546)
sequence (p. 512)
slope (p. 528)
slope of a line (p. 528)
slope-intercept form (p. 535)
term (p. 512)
***y*-intercept** (p. 535)

Choose the vocabulary term from the column on the right that completes the sentence.

1. The U-shaped graph of an equation like $y = x^2 - 2$ is a _?_. E
2. A function whose points lie on a line is a _?_. D
3. A _?_ is a set of numbers that follows a pattern. A
4. Each number in a sequence is called a _?_. C
5. A _?_ is a relationship that assigns exactly one output to each input value. B

A. sequence
B. function
C. term
D. linear function
E. parabola

Go Online
PHSchool.com
For: Online Vocabulary Quiz
Web Code: asj-1151

Skills and Concepts

Lesson 11-1
- To write rules for sequences and to use the rules to find terms in a sequence

Each term of an **arithmetic sequence** is found by *adding* a fixed number to the previous term. This fixed number is called the **common difference.**

Each term of a **geometric sequence** is found by *multiplying* the previous term by a fixed number. This fixed number is called the **common ratio.**

Find the common difference or ratio in each sequence. Write an algebraic expression for the sequence and find the next three terms.
6–9. See margin.

6. 160, 40, 10, 2.5, . . .
7. 14, 21, 28, 35, . . .
8. −1, 2, −4, 8, . . .
9. 13, 17, 21, 25, . . .

Find the first four terms of the sequence represented by each expression.

10. $14 - 11n$ 3, −8, −19, −30
11. $\frac{1}{4}n$ $\frac{1}{4}, \frac{1}{2}, \frac{3}{4}, 1$
12. $23 + n$ 24, 25, 26, 27

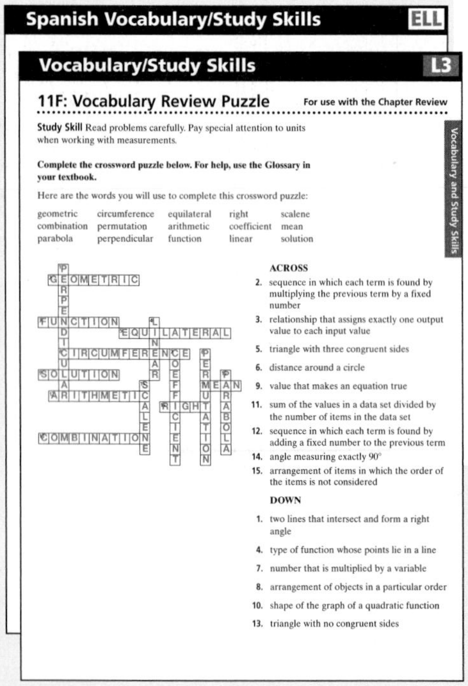
Spanish Vocabulary/Study Skills ELL
Vocabulary/Study Skills L3
11F: Vocabulary Review Puzzle For use with the Chapter Review
Study Skill Read problems carefully. Pay special attention to units when working with measurements.
Complete the crossword puzzle below. For help, use the Glossary in your textbook.
Here are the words you will use to complete this crossword puzzle:
geometric, circumference, equilateral, right, scalene, combination, permutation, arithmetic, coefficient, mean, parabola, perpendicular, function, linear, solution

ACROSS
2. sequence in which each term is found by multiplying the previous term by a fixed number
3. relationship that assigns exactly one output value to each input value
5. triangle with three congruent sides
6. distance around a circle
9. value that makes an equation true
11. sum of the values in a data set divided by the number of items in the data set
12. sequence in which each term is found by adding a fixed number to the previous term
14. angle measuring exactly 90°
15. arrangement of items in which the order of the items is not considered

DOWN
1. two lines that intersect and form a right angle
4. type of function whose points lie in a line
7. number that is multiplied by a variable
8. arrangement of objects in a particular order
10. shape of the graph of a quadratic function
13. triangle with no congruent sides

6. $\frac{1}{4}$; start with 160 and multiply by $\frac{1}{4}$ repeatedly; 0.625, 0.15625, 0.0390625.
7. 7; start with 14 and add 7 repeatedly; 42, 49, 56.
8. −2; start with −1 and multiply by −2 repeatedly; −16, 32, −64.
9. 4; start with 13 and add 4 repeatedly; 29, 33, 37.

Lessons 11-2, 11-3

- To interpret and sketch graphs that represent real-world situations
- To represent functions with equations, tables, and function notation

A graph can show complex relationships between variables in a simple, visual way. A **function** is a relationship that assigns exactly one output value to each input value. In **function notation,** $f(3)$ represents the output of function f when the input is 3.

13. Baseball A baseball player gets a hit and runs to second base. The next two batters strike out. When the next player hits the ball, the player on second base runs home. Sketch a graph showing the first player's distance from home plate during the inning. See margin.

Use the function rule $f(x) = 4x - 7$. Find each output.

14. $f(3)$ 5 **15.** $f(0)$ −7 **16.** $f(-5)$ −27 **17.** $f\left(\frac{1}{2}\right)$ −5

Lessons 11-4, 11-5

- To find the slope of a line from a graph or table
- To use tables and equations to graph linear functions

The **slope of a line** is the steepness of the line. An equation written in the form $y = mx + b$ is in **slope-intercept form.** The graph is a line with **slope** m and **y-intercept** b. A **linear function** is a function whose points lie on a line.

Find the slope of the line that passes through each pair of points.

18. $(1, 2)$ and $(-3, 2)$ 0

19. $(5, 1)$ and $(0, -7)$ $\frac{8}{5}$

20. $(-4, 9)$ and $(10, 6)$ $-\frac{3}{14}$

21. $(8, -2)$ and $(-2, 8)$ −1

Graph each linear function. 22–23. See margin.

22. $y = 2x - 5$

23. $y = -4x + 7$

Lessons 11-6, 11-7

- To write function rules from words, tables, and graphs
- To graph and write quadratic functions and other nonlinear functions

You can write a rule for linear and nonlinear functions from words, a table, or a graph. A **quadratic function** is a function in which the greatest exponent of a variable is 2. Its graph is a U-shaped curve called a **parabola.** Other nonlinear functions also have curved graphs.

Do the data in each table represent a linear function? If so, write a rule for the function.

24.

x	−4	−2	0	2	4
y	−1	0	1	2	3

yes; $y = \frac{1}{2}x + 1$

25.

x	0	1	2	3	4
y	10	7	4	1	−2

yes; $y = -3x + 10$

Make a table and a graph for each function. Use only positive values for x in Exercises 28 and 29. 26–29. See margin.

26. $y = 2x^2 - 4$

27. $y = -x^2 + 2$

28. $y = \frac{7}{x}$

29. $y = \frac{5}{x} + 2$

Alternative Assessment L4

Alternative Assessment Form C

Chapter 11

SELL IT IN THE CLASSIFIEDS

Trina decided to place a classified advertisement in a newspaper to sell her bike. Trina's red mountain bike has 21 speeds and is in good condition. She bought the bike new less than two months ago. Trina has a water bottle and a handlebar pack that she will include with the bike. She wants to sell all three items for at least $180. Trina's phone number is 555-4313.

One of Trina's friends recently placed a similar advertisement, and he received 8 calls the first day of the ad. Therefore, Trina expects to get many calls on the first day that her ad is placed.

Show all of your work on a separate sheet of paper.

1. Trina called the *Daily News* classified advertising department to find out about advertising costs. Trina was told that the cost for one ad is a function of the number of lines in the ad and the number of days the ad appears in the paper. There is a 3-line minimum and a 3-day minimum. Explain what this means.
2. Trina then called the *City Times* to find out what that paper charges for advertising. There is no minimum number of lines. Below is the function that represents that paper's advertising costs. The total cost, c, in dollars, is written as a function of the number of lines, ℓ, and the number of days, d. Describe these rates in words.

RATES AT THE *CITY TIMES*	
for $d \leq 5$,	$c = (0.90\ell)d$
for $5 < d < 10$,	$c = (0.88\ell)d$
for $d \geq 10$	$c = (0.86\ell)d$

3. Trina decided on a 3-line ad. The *Daily News* ad costs $7.65 if Trina runs the ad for 3 or fewer days. If she runs it for 4 or 5 days, it costs $.83 per line each day. If she runs the ad for 6 or more days, it costs $.81 per line each day.

Write a function definition for the *Daily News* charges, using c for the total cost in dollars and d for the number of days.

26.

x	−2	−1	0	1	2
y	4	−2	−4	−2	4

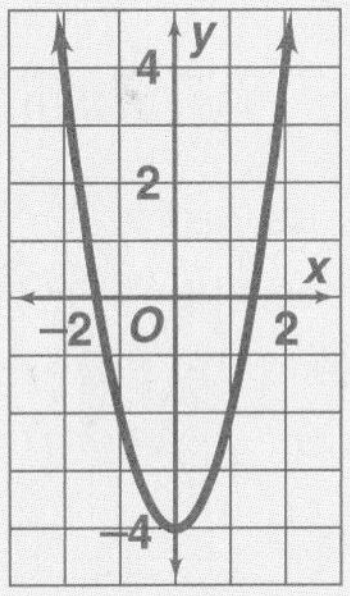

27.

x	−2	−1	0	1	2
y	−2	1	2	1	−2

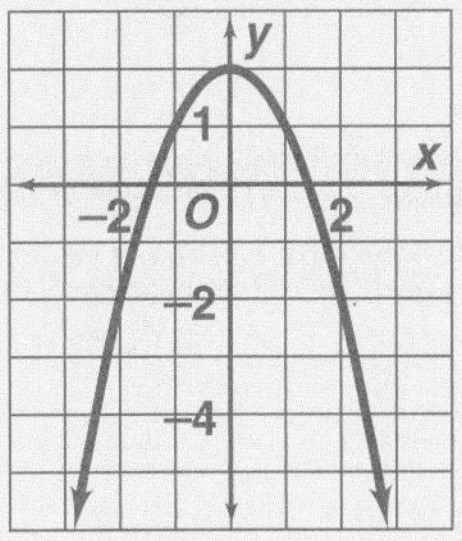

28–29. See back of book.

13.

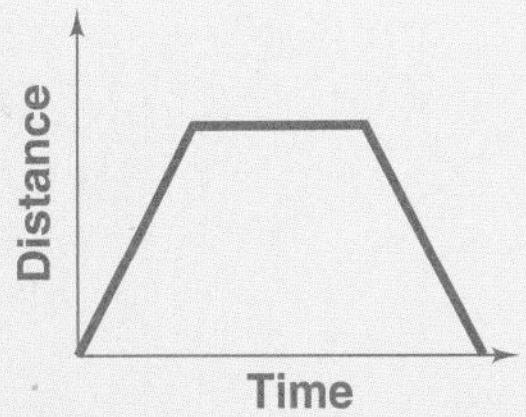

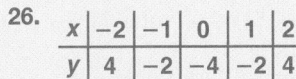

22–23. See back of book.

Resources

- ExamView Assessment Suite CD-ROM
  - Chapter 11 Ready-Made Test
  - Make your own Ch. 11 test
- MindPoint Quiz Show CD-ROM
  - Chapter 11 Review

Differentiated Instruction Resources

All in One Teaching Resources
- Below Level Chapter 11 Test L2
- Chapter 11 Test L3
- Chapter 11 Alternative Assessment L4

Spanish Assessment Resources ELL
- Below Level Chapter 11 Test L2
- Chapter 11 Test L3
- Chapter 11 Alternative Assessment L4

ExamView Assessment Suite CD-ROM
- Special Needs Test L1
- Special Needs Practice Bank L1

Online Chapter 11 Test at www.PHSchool.com

8.

t	0	1	2	5	10
p	5,000	5,400	5,800	7,000	9,000

; 9,000

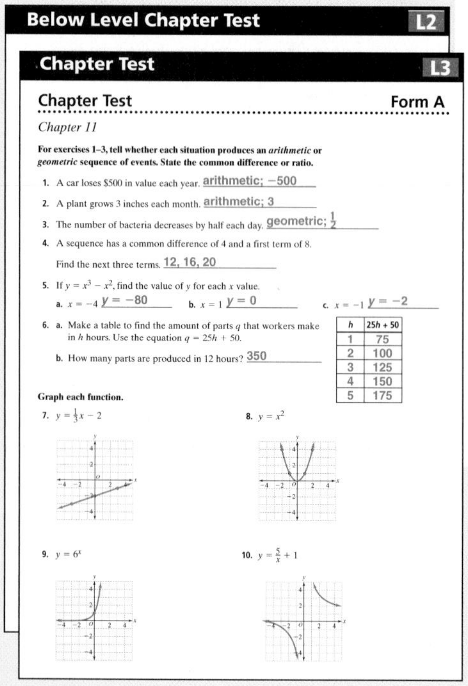
Below Level Chapter Test L2

Chapter Test L3

Chapter Test Form A

Chapter 11

For exercises 1–3, tell whether each situation produces an *arithmetic* or *geometric* sequence of events. State the common difference or ratio.

1. A car loses $500 in value each year. arithmetic; −500
2. A plant grows 3 inches each month. arithmetic; 3
3. The number of bacteria decreases by half each day. geometric; $\frac{1}{2}$
4. A sequence has a common difference of 4 and a first term of 8. Find the next three terms. 12, 16, 20
5. If $y = x^3 - x^2$, find the value of y for each x value.
   a. $x = -4$ $y = -80$ b. $x = 1$ $y = 0$ c. $x = -1$ $y = -2$
6. a. Make a table to find the amount of parts q that workers make in h hours. Use the equation $q = 25h + 50$.
   b. How many parts are produced in 12 hours? 350

h	$25h + 50$
1	75
2	100
3	125
4	150
5	175

Graph each function.

7. $y = \frac{1}{3}x - 2$
8. $y = x^2$
9. $y = 6^x$
10. $y = \frac{5}{x} + 1$

Chapter 11 Test

Go Online PHSchool.com For: Online chapter test Web Code: asa-1152

For Exercises 1–3, tell whether each situation produces an *arithmetic* or *geometric sequence.* Give the *common difference* or *ratio.*

1. A house gains $4,500 in value each year. arithmetic; 4,500
2. A clock loses 30 seconds each hour. arithmetic; −30
3. The number of bacteria in a pond triples each day. geometric; 3
4. A sequence has a common difference of $-\frac{1}{2}$ and a first term of 125. Find the next three terms. $124\frac{1}{2}$, 124, $123\frac{1}{2}$

For Exercises 5–7, find each output for the equation $f(x) = -x^2 - 3x$.

5. $f(-6)$ −18
6. $f(3)$ −18
7. $f(0)$ 0
8. The population of a town is described by $p = 400t + 5{,}000$. The population is p and the time in years is t. Make a table and find the population after 10 years. See margin.

Graph each function. For Exercise 12, use only positive integers as input values. 9–12. See margin.

9. $y = \frac{1}{2}x - 3$
10. $y = x^2$
11. $y = 5 - x^2$
12. $y = \frac{12}{x} + 2$

Match each function with its graph.

13. $y = -x - 1$ IV
14. $y = x^2 + 1$ III
15. $y = x - 1$ II
16. $y = \frac{1}{2}x$ I

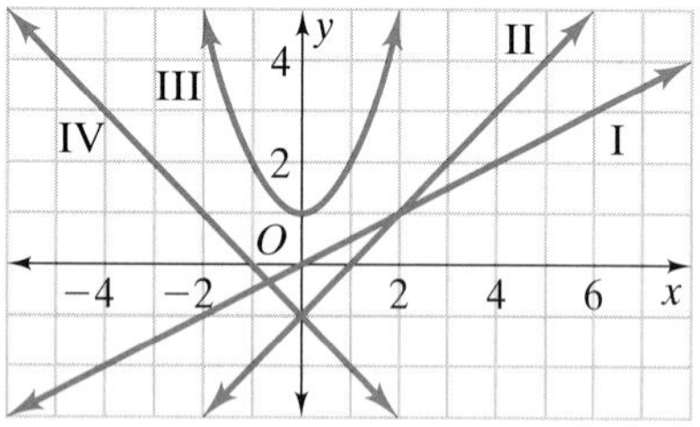

17. Which is steeper, a line with a slope of 7 or a line with a slope of −10? Explain. See margin.
18. a. A nickel's mass is about 5 grams. Write a function rule for the mass of n nickels.
    b. What is the mass of $1.00 in nickels?
    18a–b. See margin.
19. **Writing in Math** Describe a situation that the following graph could represent.

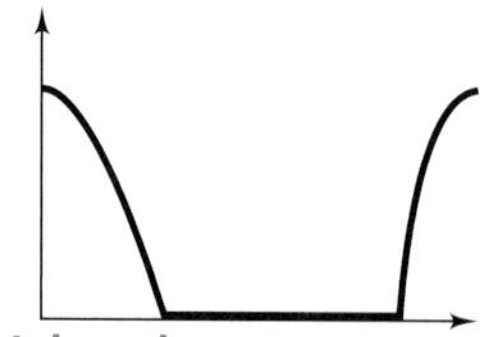

Check students' work.

Find the slope of the line that passes through each pair of points. 20. $\frac{3}{10}$ 21. $-\frac{6}{7}$

20. (−4, 10) and (6, 13)
21. (2, 3) and (9, −3)
22. (5, 7) and (−12, 4) $\frac{3}{17}$
23. (1, −1) and (5, 6) $\frac{7}{4}$
24. Write a rule for the quadratic function in the table below. $y = x^2 + 1$

x	−2	−1	0	1	2
y	5	2	1	2	5

25. A person drops a stone from 40 feet above ground. The equation $d = -16t^2 + 40$ describes the distance in feet the stone is from the ground after t seconds. Make a table, graph the equation, and find how long it takes the stone to hit the ground. See margin.

Find the slope of each line

26. 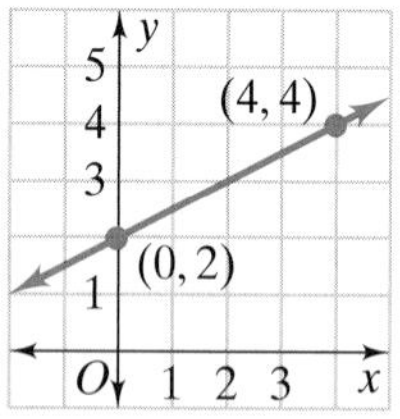

$\frac{1}{2}$

27. 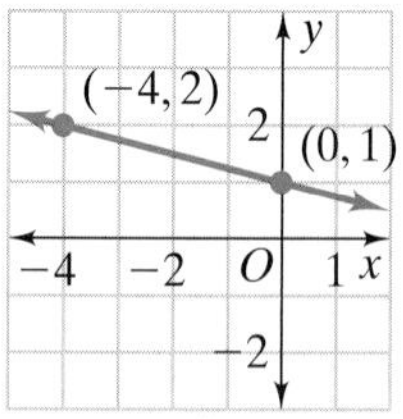

$-\frac{1}{4}$

28. Does the data in the table below represent a function? Explain. See margin.

Input	0	8	5	3	8
Output	−1	4	7	9	−2

9. 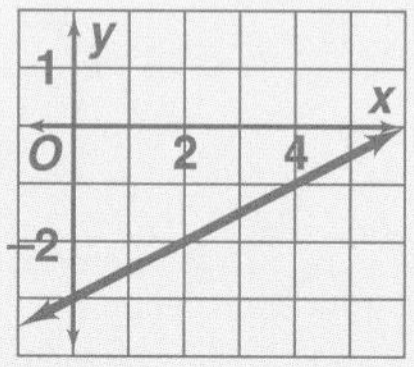

10. 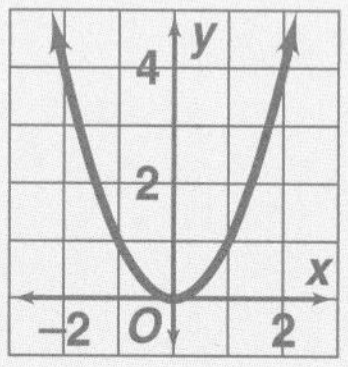

11. 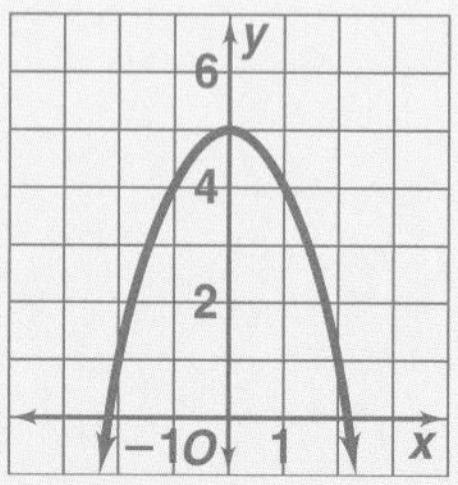

12. 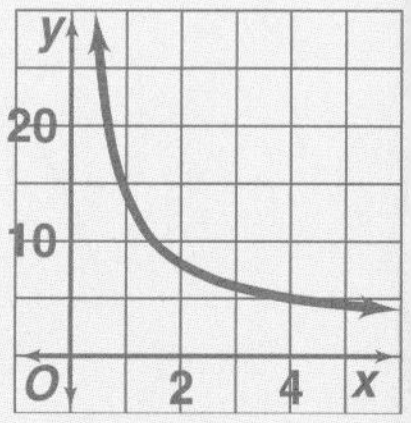

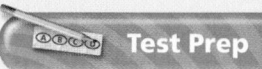

Reading Comprehension

Read each passage and answer the questions that follow.

Our Changing America The 1990 U.S. Census gave the populations of the four largest racial groups as White: 199,686,000; African American: 29,986,000; Latino: 22,354,000; and Asian American: 6,909,000. By 2000, the White population increased to 211,461,000, the African American population increased to 34,658,000, the Latino population increased to 35,306,000, and the Asian American population increased to 10,243,000. The entire population of the United States in 2000 was about 2.82×10^8 people.

1. How would you write the 2000 Latino population in scientific notation? B
   - (A) $3 \times 10^8 + 5 \times 10^7 + 3 \times 10^6 + 6 \times 10^4$
   - (B) 3.5306×10^7
   - (C) 35.306×10^6
   - (D) 3.5306×10^6

2. In 2000, about what percent of the population was non-White? H
   (F) 2.5 (G) 7.5 (H) 25 (J) 75

3. What was the approximate percent of increase in the Asian American population from 1990 to 2000? C
   (A) 4 (B) 29 (C) 48 (D) 71

4. About what percent of the population was Latino in 2000? G
   - (F) 1.25
   - (G) 12.5
   - (H) 25
   - (J) 1.25×10^7

What a Difference! The tides in the Bay of Fundy are world famous. The difference between the water level at low tide and at high tide averages 39.4 ft, but it can be as much as 53 ft. Situated in Canada between New Brunswick and Nova Scotia, the Bay of Fundy is about 170 mi long and is about 35 mi wide on average. Scientists believe that the bay's long, narrow shape accounts for the extreme variation in its tidal range.

5. Which type of graph would best describe the height of the water throughout the day? D
   - (A) circle graph
   - (B) scatter plot
   - (C) bar graph
   - (D) line graph

6. Which of the following is the best approximation of the area of the Bay of Fundy? G
   - (F) 215 mi^2
   - (G) 5,950 mi^2
   - (H) 7,092 mi^2
   - (J) 12,600 mi^2

7. Which equation can be used to find the percent of increase from the average tidal range to the maximum tidal range? D
   - (A) $\frac{39.4 - 53}{39.4} \times 100$
   - (B) $\frac{39.4 - 53}{53} \times 100$
   - (C) $\frac{53 - 39.4}{53} \times 100$
   - (D) $\frac{53 - 39.4}{39.4} \times 100$

Test Prep

Resources

Test Prep Workbook

All in One Teaching Resources
- Cumulative Review L3

ExamView Assessment Suite CD-ROM
- Standardized Test Practice

Differentiated Instruction

Spanish Assessment Resources
- Spanish Cumulative Review ELL

Chapter 11 Test

25.

x	0	0.5	1	1.5	2
y	40	36	24	4	−24

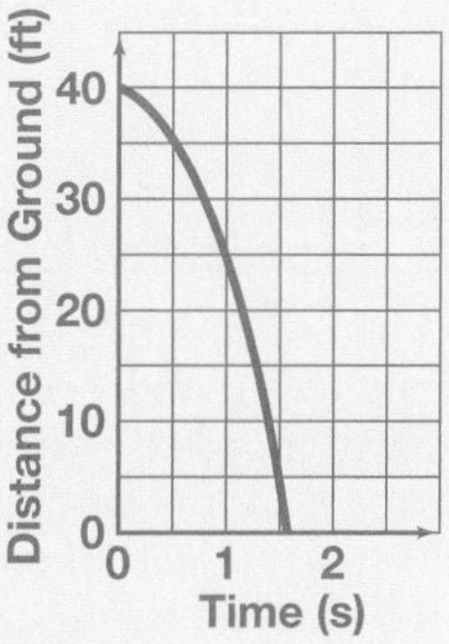

about 1.6 s

28. No; a function has exactly one output value for each input.

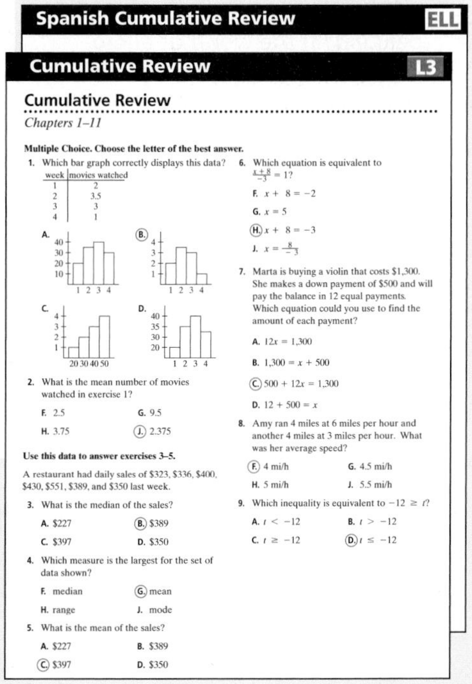
Spanish Cumulative Review ELL

Cumulative Review L3

Cumulative Review

Chapters 1–11

Multiple Choice. Choose the letter of the best answer.

1. Which bar graph correctly displays this data?

week	movies watched
1	2
2	3.5
3	3
4	1

A. B. C. D.

2. What is the mean number of movies watched in exercise 1?
   F. 2.5 G. 9.5 H. 3.75 (J.) 2.375

Use this data to answer exercises 3–5.

A restaurant had daily sales of $323, $336, $400, $430, $551, $389, and $350 last week.

3. What is the median of the sales?
   A. $227 (B.) $389 C. $397 D. $350
4. Which measure is the largest for the set of data shown?
   F. median (G.) mean H. range J. mode
5. What is the mean of the sales?
   A. $227 B. $389 (C.) $397 D. $350
6. Which equation is equivalent to $\frac{x+8}{-3} = 1$?
   F. $x + 8 = -2$ G. $x = 5$ (H.) $x + 8 = -3$ J. $x = \frac{8}{-3}$
7. Marta is buying a violin that costs $1,300. She makes a down payment of $500 and will pay the balance in 12 equal payments. Which equation could you use to find the amount of each payment?
   A. $12x = 1{,}300$ B. $1{,}300 = x + 500$ (C.) $500 + 12x = 1{,}300$ D. $12 + 500 = x$
8. Amy ran 4 miles at 6 miles per hour and another 4 miles at 3 miles per hour. What was her average speed?
   (F.) 4 mi/h G. 4.5 mi/h H. 5 mi/h J. 5.5 mi/h
9. Which inequality is equivalent to $-12 \geq t$?
   A. $t < -12$ B. $t > -12$ C. $t \geq -12$ (D.) $t \leq -12$

Chapter 11 Test

17. Slope of −10; it decreases more sharply than the line with a slope of 7 increases.

18a. $f(n) = 5n$

18b. about 100 grams

Applying Quadratic Functions

Students will use data from these two pages to answer the questions posed here in Put It All Together.

Activating Prior Knowledge

How do your students listen to music? How do they watch their favorite TV shows and movies? Initiate a class discussion about the distinctions between CDs and cassette tapes, and between DVDs and video tape. Have students compare quality of sound and/or picture, prices, options, product availability, and so on.

Guided Instruction

Have a volunteer read the opening paragraph about interpreting functions to choose the right price to charge for CD players. Invite students to act as consumer advocates and rate today's popular CD players. Which one do students rate as the best? Which is their best buy?

Science Connection
Have interested students find out about the following: What is next on the horizon, technologically speaking, in the world of audio and video? What companies and organizations are leaders in this field? What magazines focus on this kind of data?

Language Art Connection
Invite students to write a compare/contrast essay to summarize their views on (1) whether CDs are better than audio tapes or vinyl records, or (2) whether DVDs are an improvement upon video tapes.

Applying Quadratic Functions

Product Pricing Suppose you make and sell portable CD/DVD players. You want the price to be high enough for you to make a profit, yet low enough that people will want to buy. Interpreting functions can come in handy when choosing the right price.

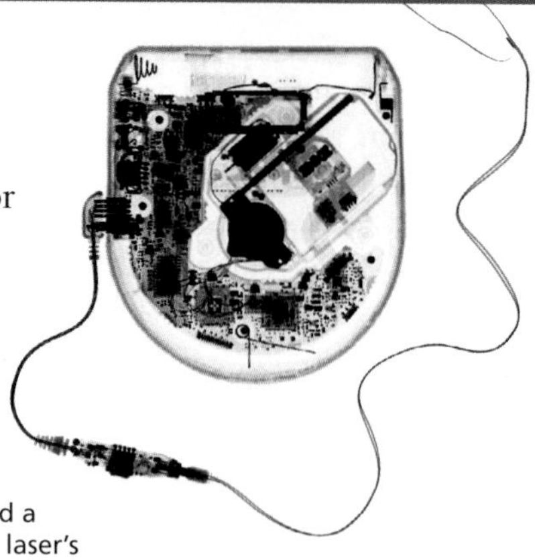

Portable Drive
In a CD player, a drive motor spins the disc. A laser system reads the bumps on the CD, and a tracking mechanism moves the laser's beam along the spiral track.

TV Bank
People use banks of TVs to monitor more than one TV station at a time or to see one enlarged image.

Put It All Together

1. The equation $n = -2.5p^2 + 39{,}400$ models the relationship between the price, p, of each CD/DVD player and the number sold, n. Copy and extend the table to a price of \$100. Complete the table.

Price p	Number Sold n	Sales Income s
\$30	37,150	\$1,114,500
\$35	■	■
\$40	■	■

2. Add a column to your table for income from sales, $s = p \times n$, for each price in the table. Record the income for each price.
3. Make a scatter plot comparing the number sold to income.
4. **Writing in Math** Decide on the best price to charge for your CD/DVD player. Find the number you can expect to sell and the income at that price. Explain your choice.
5. **a.** The prices your competitors charge affect your sales. Make adjustments to the price you chose in Exercise 4 based on the prices you think two competitors will charge. Write down your final price.
   b. Exchange prices with two classmates. Calculate the mean of the three prices.
   c. Use your answer to part (b) and the function from Exercise 1. Find the total number of CD/DVD players your three companies will sell.
   d. Assume that the company with the lowest price makes 40% of the sales from part (c), the company with the highest price makes 25% of the sales, and the third company makes 35% of the sales. Calculate the units sold and the total sales for each company. Which company is the most successful? Explain.

Go Online
PHSchool.com
For: Information about product pricing
Web Code: ase-1153

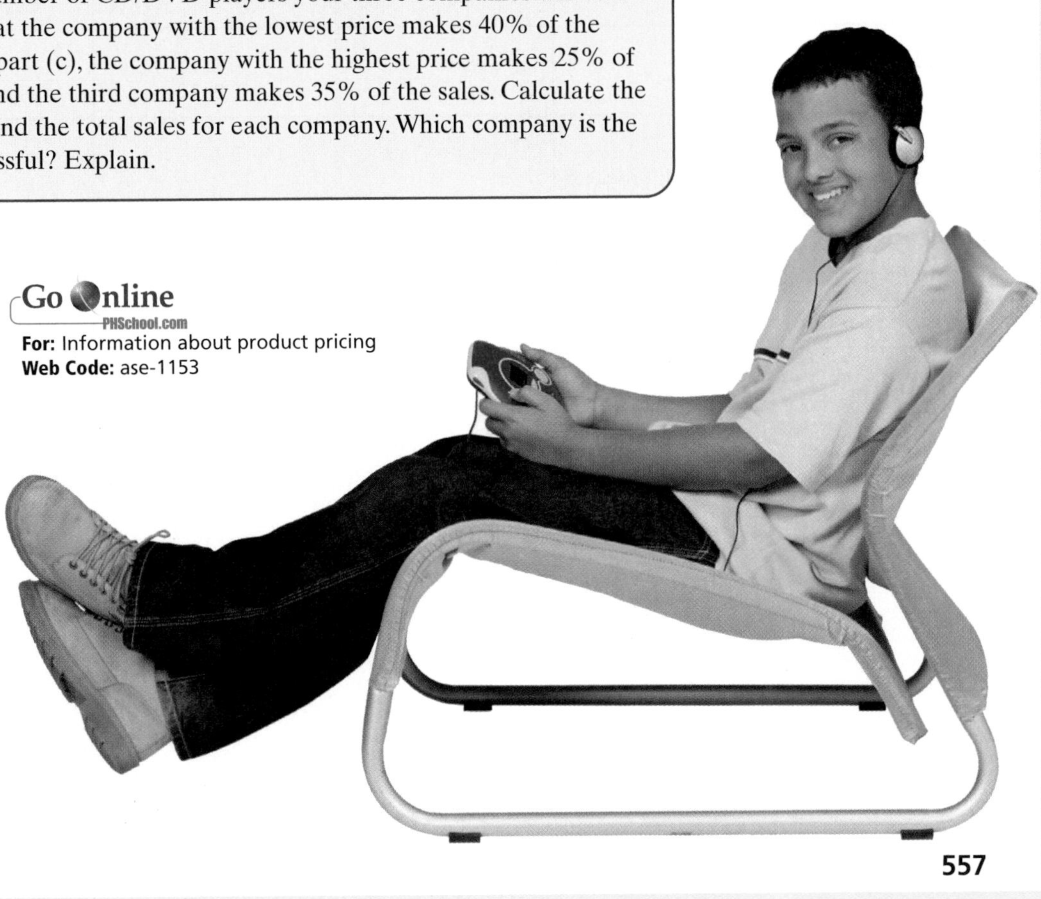

Put It All Together

Have students work in pairs to complete the table, make the scatterplot, and complete the activity.

You may wish to work through the first row in the table with the class. Point out to students that they should continue the first column by writing multiples of \$5. Encourage pairs to work with calculators.

Exercise 5 Have an extended class discussion about this activity. Elicit that students who choose a price much higher than the optimum will probably find that they have the lowest sales. Discuss that the company with the lowest prices will likely get the most sales but may be hurt if their price is too low compared with the next lowest price.

Differentiated Instruction

Below Level
Remind students of the order of operations: PEMDAS. Emphasize, accordingly, that in the equation for modeling the relationship between the price of the CD/DVD player and the number sold, students should square the price, p, before multiplying it by -2.5.

1–2.

Price (p)	Number of Sales (n)	Sales in Dollars) (s)
30	37,150	1,114,500
35	36,338	1,271,813
40	35,400	1,416,000
45	34,338	1,545,188
50	33,150	1,657,500
55	31,838	1,751,063
60	30,400	1,824,000
65	28,838	1,874,438
70	27,150	1,900,500
75	25,338	1,900,313
80	23,400	1,872,000
85	21,338	1,813,688
90	19,150	1,723,500
95	16,838	1,599,563
100	14,400	1,440,000

3. Check students' work.

4. Answers may vary. Sample: The best price is about \$72.50, which yields an income of about \$1,900,400. Prices that are higher or lower than that yield a lower income.

5. Check students' work.

12 Polynomials and Properties of Exponents

Chapter at a Glance

Lesson Titles, Objectives, and Features	Assessment	NCTM Standards	Local Standards
12-1a Activity Lab: Writing Expressions **12-1 Exploring Polynomials** • To write variable expressions and to simplify polynomials	Lesson Quiz	1, 2, 5, 6, 7, 8, 9, 10	
12-2 Adding and Subtracting Polynomials • To add and subtract polynomials	Lesson Quiz Checkpoint Quiz 1	1, 2, 6, 7, 8, 9, 10	
12-3a Activity Lab: Exploring Exponents **12-3 Exponents and Multiplication** • To multiply powers with the same base and to multiply numbers in scientific notation **12-3b Activity Lab, Technology:** Scientific Notation	Lesson Quiz	1, 2, 6, 7, 8, 9, 10	
12-4 Multiplying Polynomials • To multiply monomials and binomials	Lesson Quiz Checkpoint Quiz 2	1, 2, 3, 6, 7, 8, 9, 10	
12-5 Exponents and Division • To divide powers with the same base and to simplify expressions with negative exponents **Extension:** Power Rules **Guided Problem Solving:** Solving Equations	Lesson Quiz	1, 2, 4, 6, 7, 8, 9, 10	
Problem Solving Application: Applying Scientific Notation			

NCTM Standards 2000
1 Number and Operations
2 Algebra
3 Geometry
4 Measurement
5 Data Analysis and Probability
6 Problem Solving
7 Reasoning and Proof
8 Communication
9 Connections
10 Representation

Correlations to Standardized Tests

All content for these tests is contained in *Prentice Hall Math*, Course 3. This chart reflects coverage in this chapter only.

	12-1	12-2	12-3	12-4	12-5
Terra Nova CAT6 (Level 18)					
Number and Number Relations			✔		✔
Computation and Numerical Estimation			✔		✔
Operation Concepts			✔		✔
Measurement					
Geometry and Spatial Sense					
Data Analysis, Statistics, and Probability					
Patterns, Functions, Algebra	✔	✔	✔	✔	✔
Problem Solving and Reasoning	✔	✔	✔	✔	✔
Communication	✔	✔	✔	✔	✔
Decimals, Fractions, Integers, Percent					
Order of Operations					
Algebraic Operations	✔	✔	✔	✔	✔
Terra Nova CTBS (Level 18)					
Decimals, Fractions, Integers, Percents					
Order of Operations, Numeration, Number Theory	✔	✔	✔	✔	✔
Data Interpretation					
Measurement					
Geometry					
ITBS (Level 14)					
Number Properties and Operations			✔		✔
Algebra	✔	✔	✔	✔	✔
Geometry					
Measurement					
Probability and Statistics					
Estimation					
SAT10 (Adv 1 Level)					
Number Sense and Operations			✔		✔
Patterns, Relationships, and Algebra	✔	✔	✔	✔	✔
Data, Statistics, and Probability					
Geometry and Measurement					
NAEP					
Number Sense, Properties, and Operations			✔		✔
Measurement					
Geometry and Spatial Sense					
Data Analysis, Statistics, and Probability					
Algebra and Functions	✔	✔	✔	✔	✔

CAT6 California Achievement Test, 6th Ed.
CTBS Comprehensive Test of Basic Skills
ITBS Iowa Test of Basic Skills, Form M
SAT10 Stanford Achievement Test, 10th Ed.
NAEP National Assessment of Educational Progress 2005 Mathematics Objectives

Math Background

Professional Development

Skills Trace

BEFORE Chapter 12

Course 2 introduced powers and monomials and binomials.

DURING Chapter 12

Course 3 reviews and extends work with powers to include power rules and introduces polynomials and operations with polynomials.

AFTER Chapter 12

Throughout this course, students use, simplify, and solve algebraic expressions and equations.

12-1 12-2 Adding and Subtracting Polynomials

Math Understandings

- We can use models to make sense of adding and subtracting polynomials.
- The variables and their degrees in a term determine whether terms are like or unlike.
- Polynomials can be simplified by combining like terms.

A **polynomial** is one term, or the sum or difference of two or more terms. For example, $-x^2 + 3x - 4$ is a polynomial in three terms. Each term is separated by a + or a −. A term that does not contain a variable, such as −4, is a **constant**. A **coefficient** is a number that is multiplied by a variable, such as 3 in $3x$.

12-3 Exponents and Multiplication

Math Understandings

- Exponential notation with positive exponents is a mathematical shorthand for repeated multiplication.
- A positive exponent tells how many times the base is used as a factor.
- An exponent applies only to its base and not to the coefficient in front of the base, so -3^2 is $-(3 \cdot 3)$ or −9 but $(-3)^2$ is $(-3) \cdot (-3)$ or 9.
- To multiply two powers with the same base, you keep the common base and add the exponents to find the new exponent.

Multiplying Powers With the Same Base	
To multiply numbers or variables with the same base, add the exponents.	
Arithmetic	**Algebra**
$3^2 \cdot 3^7 = 3^{(2+7)} = 3^9$	$a^m \cdot a^n = a^{(m+n)}$

You can apply the rule for multiplying powers with the same base when you multiply numbers in scientific notation.

Example:
$$\begin{aligned}(7 \times 10^5)(8 \times 10^6) &= (7 \times 8) \times (10^5 \times 10^6)\\ &= 56 \times (10^5 \times 10^6)\\ &= 56 \times 10^{11}\\ &= 5.6 \times 10^1 \times 10^{11}\\ &= 5.6 \times 10^{12}\end{aligned}$$

12-4 Multiplying Polynomials

Math Understandings

- You can use an area model to show the product of a monomial and a binomial or the product of two binomials.

A polynomial that has only one term, such as $4a^3$, is a **monomial**. A **binomial** is a polynomial with two terms. You can model the product of two binomials by forming a rectangular array of tiles. The model below shows that $(2x + 1)(3x + 2) = 6x^2 + 7x + 2$.

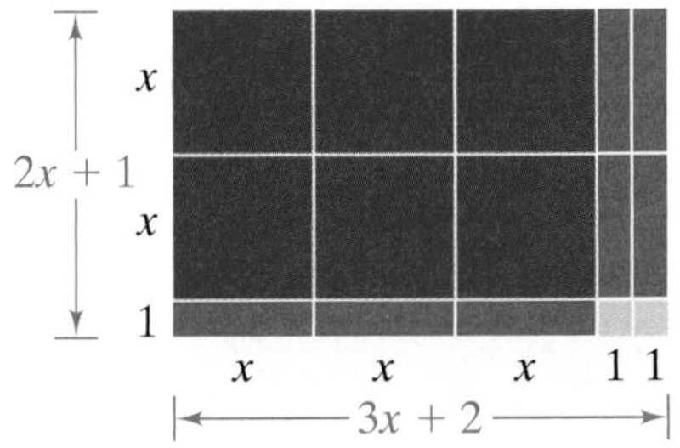

12-5 Exponents and Division

Math Understandings

- An exponent that is a negative number indicates that you are to take a reciprocal.
- A zero exponent on a nonzero base means the power has a value of 1.
- To divide two powers with the same base, you keep the common base and subtract the exponent of the divisor from the exponent of the dividend to find the new exponent.

Just as you can multiply powers with the same base, you can divide powers with the same base. So, numbers expressed in scientific notation can be divided as well as multiplied.

Dividing Powers With the Same Base

To divide nonzero numbers or variables with the same nonzero base, subtract the exponents.

Arithmetic	**Algebra**
$\frac{8^5}{8^3} = 8^{(5-3)} = 8^2$	$\frac{a^m}{a^n} = a^{(m-n)}$, where $a \neq 0$

Zero as an Exponent

For any nonzero number a, $a^0 = 1$
Example: $9^0 = 1$ because $1 = \frac{x^a}{x^a} = x^{a-a} = x^0$, $x \neq 0$.

Negative Exponents

For any nonzero number a and integer n, $a^{-n} = \frac{1}{a^n}$.
Example: $8^{-5} = \frac{1}{8^5}$

Numbers in scientific notation can have negative exponents. Multiplying a number by 10^n when n is negative moves the decimal point n places to the left. To write a number that is less than 1 in scientific notation, determine the first factor by moving the decimal point. Then write the second factor as a negative power of ten.

Example:	**Standard Form**	**Scientific Notation**
	1.483	1.483×10^0
	0.1483	1.483×10^{-1}
	0.01483	1.483×10^{-2}

Additional Professional Development Opportunities

Professional Development

Math Background Notes for Chapter 12: Every lesson has a Math Background in the PLAN section.

Research Overview, Mathematics Strands
Additional support for these topics and more is in the front of the Teacher's Edition.

LessonLab
LessonLab, a Pearson Education company, offers comprehensive, facilitated professional development designed to help teachers to improve student achievement. To learn more, please visit lessonlab.com.

Chapter 12 Resources

	12-1	12-2	12-3	12-4	12-5	For the Chapter
Print Resources						
L3 Practice	●	●	●	●	●	
L1 Adapted Practice	●	●	●	●	●	
L3 Guided Problem Solving	●	●	●	●	●	
L2 Reteaching	●	●	●	●	●	
L4 Enrichment	●	●	●	●	●	
L3 Daily Notetaking Guide	●	●	●	●	●	
L1 Adapted Daily Notetaking Guide	●	●	●	●	●	
L3 Vocabulary and Study Skills Worksheets	●	●	●	●	●	●
L3 Daily Puzzles	●	●	●	●	●	
L3 Activity Labs	●	●	●	●	●	
L3 Checkpoint Quiz		●		●		
L3 Chapter Project						●
L2 Below Level Chapter Test						●
L3 Chapter Test						●
L4 Alternative Assessment						●
L3 Cumulative Review						●
Spanish Resources ELL						
L3 Practice	●	●	●	●	●	
L3 Vocabulary and Study Skills Worksheets	●	●	●	●	●	●
L3 Checkpoint Quiz		●		●		
L2 Below Level Chapter Test						●
L3 Chapter Test						●
L4 Alternative Assessment						●
L3 Cumulative Review						●
Transparencies						
Check Skills You'll Need	●	●	●	●	●	
Additional Examples	●	●	●	●	●	
Problem of the Day	●	●	●	●	●	
Classroom Aid	●	●	●	●		
Student Edition Answers	●	●	●	●	●	●
Lesson Quiz	●	●	●	●	●	
Test-Taking Strategies						●
Technology						
Interactive Textbook Online	●	●	●	●	●	●
StudentExpress™ CD-ROM	●	●	●	●	●	●
Success Tracker™ Online Intervention	●	●	●	●	●	●
TeacherExpress™ CD-ROM	●	●	●	●	●	●
PresentationExpress™ with QuickTake Presenter CD-ROM	●	●	●	●	●	●
ExamView® Assessment Suite CD-ROM	●	●	●	●	●	●
MindPoint® Quiz Show CD-ROM						●
Prentice Hall Web Site: PHSchool.com	●	●	●	●	●	●

Also available: **Prentice Hall Assessment System**
- Progress Monitoring Assessments
- Skills and Concepts Review
- Test Prep Workbook

Other Resources
Algebra Readiness Tests
All-in-One Student Workbook
All-in-One Student Workbook, Adapted Version
Multilingual Handbook
Solution Key
Math Notes Study Folder
Spanish Cumulative Assessment

Where You Can Use the Lesson Resources

Here is a suggestion, following the four-step teaching plan, for how you can incorporate Differentiated Instruction Resources into your teaching.

	Instructional Resources L3	Differentiated Instruction Resources
1. Plan		
Preparation Read the Math Background in the Teacher's Edition to connect this lesson with students' previous experience. **Starting Class** **Check Skills You'll Need** Assign these exercises to review prerequisite skills. **New Vocabulary** Help students pre-read the lesson by pointing out the new terms introduced in the lesson.	**Math Background** **Math Understandings** **Transparencies & PresentationExpress™ with QuickTake Presenter** Check Skills You'll Need Problem of the Day Daily Review **Resources** Vocabulary and Study Skills	**Spanish Support** ELL Vocabulary and Study Skills
2. Teach		
L3 **Guided Instruction** Use the Activity Labs to build conceptual understanding. Teach each Example. Use the Teacher's Edition side column notes for specific teaching tips, including Error Prevention notes. Use the Additional Examples found in the side column (and on transparency and PowerPoint) as an alternative presentation for the content. After each Example, assign the Quick Check exercise for that Example to get an immediate assessment of student understanding. Use the Closure activity in the Teacher's Edition to help students attain mastery of lesson content.	**Student Edition** Activity Lab a **Resources** Daily Notetaking Guide Activity Lab **Transparencies & PresentationExpress™ with QuickTake Presenter** Additional Examples Classroom Aids **ExamView® Assessment Suite CD-ROM**	**Teacher's Edition** Every lesson includes suggestions for working with students who need special attention. L1 Special Needs L2 Below Level L4 Advanced Learners ELL English Language Learners **Resources** L1 Adapted Daily Notetaking Guide **Multilingual Handbook**
3. Practice		
Assignment Guide **Check Your Understanding** Use these questions to check students' understanding before you assign homework. **Homework Exercises** Assign homework from these leveled exercises in the Assignment Guide. A Practice by Example B Apply Your Skills C Challenge Test Prep and Mixed Review **Homework Quick Check** Use these key exercises to quickly check students' homework.	**Transparencies & PresentationExpress™ with QuickTake Presenter** Student Answers **Resources** Practice Guided Problem Solving Vocabulary and Study Skills Activity Lab Daily Puzzles **ExamView® Assessment Suite CD-ROM**	**Spanish Support** ELL Practice ELL Vocabulary and Study Skills **Resources** L1 Adapted Practice L4 Enrichment
4. Assess & Reteach		
Lesson Quiz Assign the Lesson Quiz to assess students' mastery of the lesson content. **Checkpoint Quiz** Use the Checkpoint Quiz to assess student progress over several lessons.	**Transparencies & PresentationExpress™ with QuickTake Presenter** Lesson Quiz **Resources** Checkpoint Quiz	**Resources** L2 Reteaching ELL Checkpoint Quiz Success Tracker™ Online Intervention **ExamView® Assessment Suite CD-ROM**

KEY L1 Special Needs L2 Below Level L3 For All Students L4 Advanced, Gifted ELL English Language Learners

Algebra

CHAPTER 12 Polynomials and Properties of Exponents

What You've Learned

- In Chapter 2, you used exponents and the order of operations to evaluate expressions.
- You wrote numbers in scientific notation.
- In Chapter 6, you wrote and simplified algebraic expressions.

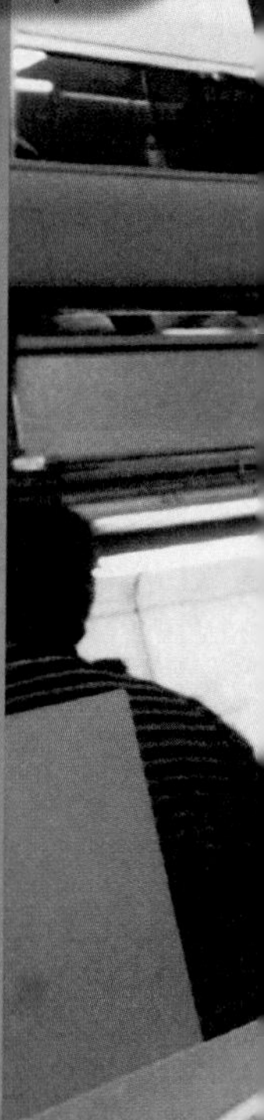

Check Your Readiness

GO for Help

For Exercises	See Lesson
1–12	6-2
13–24	2-7

Simplifying Algebraic Expressions

Simplify each expression.

1. $13d + 9d - 4$ $22d - 4$
2. $4v + 65 - 11v + 8$ $-7v + 73$
3. $2w - 42 - 7(1 - 9w)$ $65w - 49$
4. $6f - 23g + 3 + 37f$ $43f - 23g + 3$
5. $8r + 34 - 2r + 30r$ $36r + 34$
6. $7t - 6 - 15t + x$ $-8t + x - 6$
7. $5 + 4(a - 3)$ $4a - 7$
8. $-2b - 7(b - 3)$ $-9b + 21$
9. $-8(f + 11) + 44f$ $36f - 88$
10. $6x - 9(2x + 5)$ $-12x - 45$
11. $7.3(2.8 + c) - 13c$ $20.44 - 5.7c$
12. $20y - (15y + 5)$ $5y - 5$

Using Exponents

Write using exponents.

13. $7 \cdot 7 \cdot 7 \cdot 7 \cdot 7$ 7^5
14. $5 \cdot 5 \cdot c \cdot c$ $5^2 \cdot c^2$
15. $a \cdot a \cdot b \cdot b \cdot b$ a^2b^3
16. $x \cdot y \cdot x \cdot y \cdot x$ x^3y^2
17. $(3x) \cdot (3x) \cdot (3x)$ $(3x)^3$
18. $c \cdot d \cdot g \cdot d \cdot g$ $c \cdot d^2 \cdot g^2$

Simplify each expression.

19. 4^2 16
20. $(-4)^2$ 16
21. -4^2 -16
22. $-(-2)^5$ 32
23. 10^2 100
24. 10^3 $1{,}000$

Polynomials and Properties of Exponents

Check Your Readiness

Answers for students are in the back of the textbook.

For intervention, direct students to:

Simplifying Algebraic Expressions
Lesson 6-2
Extra Skills and Word Problems Practice, Ch. 6

Using Exponents
Lesson 2-7
Extra Skills and Word Problems Practice, Ch. 2

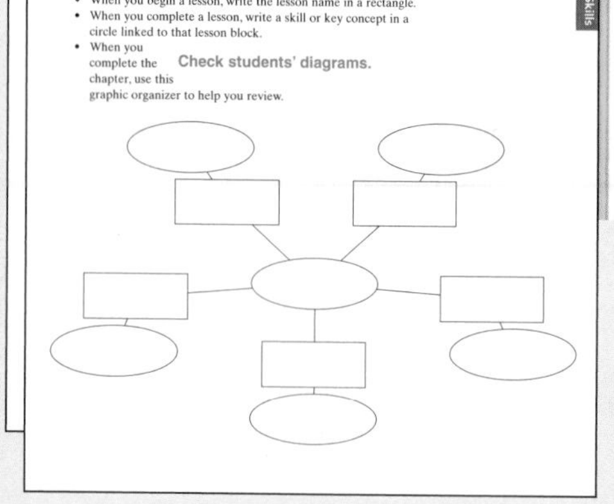

Spanish Vocabulary/Study Skills ELL

Vocabulary/Study Skills L3

12A: Graphic Organizer — For use before Lesson 12-1

Study Skill Your textbook includes a Skills Handbook with extra problems and questions. Working these exercises is a good way to review material and prepare for the next chapter.

Write your answers.

1. What is the chapter title? Polynomials and Properties of Exponents
2. How many lessons are there in this chapter? 5
3. What is the topic of the Test-Taking Strategies page? Working Backward
4. Complete the graphic organizer below as you work through the chapter.
   - In the center, write the title of the chapter.
   - When you begin a lesson, write the lesson name in a rectangle.
   - When you complete a lesson, write a skill or key concept in a circle linked to that lesson block.
   - When you complete the chapter, use this graphic organizer to help you review.

Check students' diagrams.

Vocabulary and Study Skills

What You'll Learn Next

- In this chapter, you will write and simplify polynomial expressions.
- You will add, subtract, and multiply polynomials.
- You will use exponent rules to simplify expressions involving powers with the same base.

Key Vocabulary

- binomial (p. 576)
- coefficient (p. 566)
- constant (p. 561)
- monomial (p. 576)
- polynomial (p. 561)

Problem Solving Application On pages 596 and 597, you will work an extended activity on sizes of animals.

Chapter 12 Overview

In this chapter, students learn to add, subtract, and multiply polynomials. They also learn how to multiply and divide powers, including zero and negative exponents.

Activating Prior Knowledge

In this chapter, students build on their knowledge of decimal place value, the order of operations, and exponents. They also apply their experience with simplifying algebraic expressions. Ask students questions such as:

- *How can you simplify:* $24 - 10t + 3(t - 1)$? $21 - 7t$
- *How can you simplify:* $(2x)(3x)$? $6x^2$
- *How can you simplify:* -5^3? -125

Activity Lab

Writing Expressions

In this activity, students perform specific sequences of operations—here called "number tricks"—on their own ages. Then they write algebraic expressions representing their answers and compare these to their ages to understand how the tricks work.

Guided Instruction

Activity

For each trick, ask students to describe the relationship between the "secret" age and the number that results after Step 6. Ask:

- *What happens when you let x be the age, perform the operations on x, and then simplify the polynomial?* **Sample: When you simplify the polynomial, the answer has the same relationship to the number you started with, such as 1 more for the first number trick and 1 less for the second number trick.**
- *What would you have to do to make up your own number trick so you would divide the last number by 2 to guess the correct age?* **Sample: Use operations on the variable that, when simplified, give the result of $2x$. When this expression is divided by 2, the result will be x.**

Resources

- Activity Lab 12-1: Exploring Polynomials

Writing Expressions

ACTIVITY

Kwame loves number tricks. Below is a number trick he uses to guess his friends' ages.

Number Trick 1

1. Start with your age.
2. Multiply your age by 3.
3. Add 4 to the result.
4. Multiply the result by 2.
5. Subtract 2 from the result.
6. Divide the result by 6. Tell me your answer.

1. How is your age related to the result in Step 6? How is Kwame able to tell his friends' ages from the answer they tell him? **Your age is one less than the answer; Kwame subtracts one from the answer.**
2. Let x be your age. Use x to write an algebraic expression for the answer you get in Step 6. **$x + 1$**

Here is another number trick Kwame uses to guess his friends' ages.

Number Trick 2

1. Start with your age.
2. Multiply your age by 4.
3. Subtract 6 from the result.
4. Multiply the result by 2.
5. Add 4 to the result.
6. Divide the result by 8. Tell me your answer.

3. How is your age related to the result in Step 6? How is Kwame able to tell his friends' ages from the answer they tell him? **Your age is one more than the answer; Kwame adds one to the answer.**
4. Let x be your age. Use x to write an algebraic expression for the answer you get in Step 6. **$x - 1$**

Exercises

1–3. Check students' work.

1. Write instructions for another number trick with 6 steps. Trade tricks with a partner.
2. How does the number you chose for Step 1 in your partner's trick compare to the result in Step 6?
3. Use x to write an algebraic expression for the answer you got in Step 6 of your partner's trick.

Algebra

12-1 Exploring Polynomials

Check Skills You'll Need

1. **Vocabulary Review** Are x, $\frac{1}{2}x$, and $-4x$ *like terms*? Explain.

1–4. See below.

Simplify each expression.

2. $-2 + 2t - 3t$
3. $7w - 10 + 5w$
4. $3k + 32k - 5$

GO for Help Lesson 6-2

What You'll Learn

To write algebraic expressions and to simplify polynomials

New Vocabulary polynomial, constant

Why Learn This?

Calculating area and volume often involves using expressions with exponents. Understanding polynomials can help you write and simplify such expressions.

You can use algebra tiles like those shown below to model algebraic expressions.

▫ represents 1.	▮ represents x.	■ represents x^2.
▪ represents -1.	▮ represents $-x$.	■ represents $-x^2$.

EXAMPLE 1 Writing Algebraic Expressions

Write an algebraic expression for the model below.

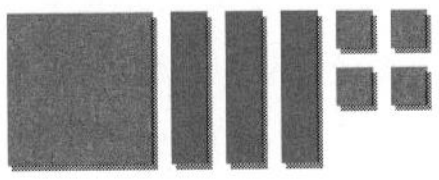

The model shows the expression $-x^2 + 3x - 4$.

Quick Check

1. Write an algebraic expression for each model.

a. 

$x^2 - 2x + 2$

b. 

$-2x^2 + 2x - 3$

The expression $-x^2 + 3x - 4$ has three terms: $-x^2$, $3x$, and -4. A **polynomial** is one term or the sum or difference of two or more terms. A term that does not contain a variable, such as -4, is a **constant.**

Check Skills You'll Need

1. yes; all the terms include the same variable, x.
2. $-2 - t$
3. $12w - 10$
4. $35k - 5$

12-1

1. Plan

Objective

To write variable expressions and to simplify polynomials

Examples

1 Writing Algebraic Expressions
2 Simplifying Polynomials
3 Using Properties to Simplify Polynomials

Math Understandings: p. 558C

Professional Development

Math Background

The *terms* in a variable expression are separated by + or −, so $-2x + 5 - x^2$ has 3 terms. A *polynomial* has one or more terms. A term with no variable, such as 5 in Example 2, is called a *constant* or *constant term.*

Like terms have exactly the same variable, or are constant terms, so $-3x$ and $2x$ are like terms and can be combined. However, $3x$ and $3x^2$ are not like terms and cannot be combined.

More Math Background: p. 558C

Lesson Planning and Resources

See p. 558E for a list of the resources that support this lesson.

PowerPoint

Bell Ringer Practice

Check Skills You'll Need
Use student page, transparency, or PowerPoint. For intervention, direct students to:

Simplifying Algebraic Expressions
Lesson 6-2
Extra Skills and Word Problems Practice, Ch. 6

Differentiated Instruction Solutions for All Learners

Special Needs L1
Write a polynomial on the board. Have students copy this expression onto a piece of paper. Then, have them highlight each term of the polynomial with a different color. Also have them label the constant.

learning style: visual

Below Level L2
Students review the Commutative, Associative, and Distributive Properties and give examples of each.

learning style: verbal

2. Teach

Activity Lab

Use before the lesson.
Student Edition
Activity Lab 12-1a, Writing Expressions, p. 560

All in One Teaching Resources
Activity Lab 12-1: Exploring Polynomials

Guided Instruction

Example 3
After completing the Example, have students discuss whether they prefer to use tiles or the properties. Ask them to explain their reasons.
Point out that students who find that tiles help them can sketch tiles (or even just picture them in their minds) when they are simplifying an expression.

Error Prevention!

Demonstrate to students that a zero pair consists of two tiles that are the same size but opposite in sign (indicated by a different color).

GO for Help
For help combining like terms, go to Lesson 6-2, Example 1.

To simplify a polynomial, combine like terms.

EXAMPLE Simplifying Polynomials

2 Use tiles to simplify the polynomial $2x^2 - 3x - x^2 + 2x + 5$.

Step 1 Model each term.

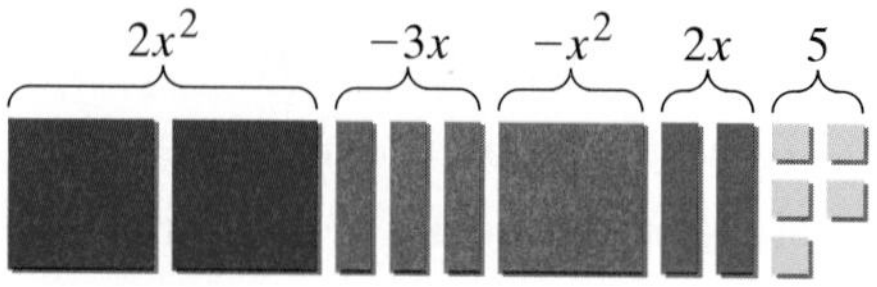

Step 2 Group like terms together. Remove zero pairs. Recall that a zero pair is a pair of algebra tiles whose sum is zero.

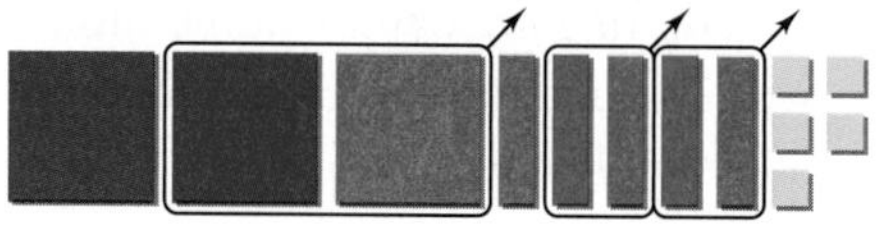

The simplified polynomial is $x^2 - x + 5$.

Quick Check

2. Draw or use tiles to simplify each polynomial.

a. $5x^2 - 4x + 3x - 7x^2 + 6$ $-2x^2 - x + 6$

b. $8x^2 + 7 - 3x - 2x^2 - 5$ $6x^2 - 3x + 2$

You can also use properties of numbers to simplify polynomials.

EXAMPLE Using Properties to Simplify Polynomials

3 The plans for a new neighborhood show housing lots of various sizes. You can use the polynomial $4t^2 + 6t + 9 - 2t^2 - t$ to represent the total area of the lots minus the area of the road. Use properties of numbers to simplify the polynomial.

$4t^2 + 6t + 9 - 2t^2 - t$

$4t^2 - 2t^2 + 6t - t + 9$	← **commutative property**
$(4t^2 - 2t^2) + (6t - t) + 9$	← **associative property**
$(4 - 2)t^2 + (6 - 1)t + 9$	← **Distributive Property**
$2t^2 + 5t + 9$	← **Simplify.**

The total area of the lots can be represented by $2t^2 + 5t + 9$.

Quick Check

3. The polynomials below represent the areas of two neighborhoods. Use properties of numbers to simplify each polynomial. 3a–b. See left.

a. $4g^2 - 5g - 2g^2 + 7g$

b. $3y - 5y^2 - y + 7$

3a. $2g^2 + 2g$
b. $2y - 5y^2 + 7$

Differentiated Instruction Solutions for All Learners

Advanced Learners L4
Students simplify the following polynomial:
$2y^2 + 8xy + 3 + 4x^2 + 2xy + 5$.
$2y^2 + 10xy + 4x^2 + 8$

learning style: verbal

English Language Learners ELL
Tell students to write a few examples of terms, constants, polynomials, expressions, and like terms on index cards. Then label their examples. Students work in pairs to review each example and assign additional labels.

learning style: verbal

More Than One Way

Simplify the polynomial $m^2 - 3m + m^2 + 2m - 1$.

Daryl's Method

I can model the polynomial with algebra tiles.

$m^2 \quad - 3m \quad + m^2 \quad + 2m - 1$

I can group like terms together and remove zero pairs.

$2m^2 \quad - m - 1$

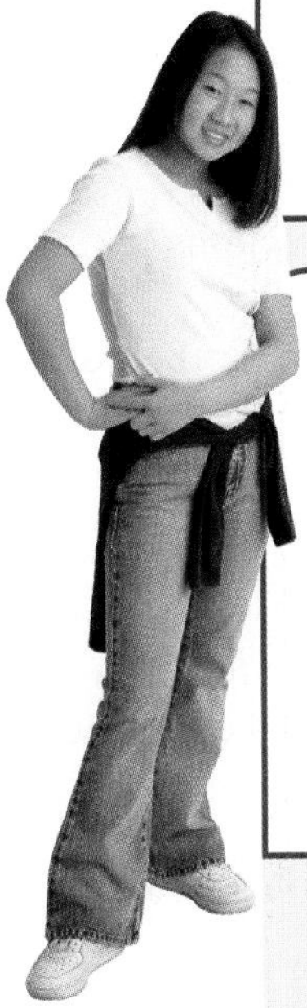

Michelle's Method

I can simplify the polynomial using properties of numbers.

$m^2 - 3m + m^2 + 2m - 1$

$m^2 + m^2 - 3m + 2m - 1$ ← **commutative property**

$(m^2 + m^2) + (-3m + 2m) - 1$ ← **associative property**

$(1 + 1)m^2 + (-3 + 2)m - 1$ ← **Distributive Property**

$2m^2 - m - 1$ ← **Simplify.**

Choose a Method

Simplify the polynomial $-2x^2 + 5x - 6x + 5 - 2x^2$. Explain why you chose the method you used. $-4x^2 - x + 5$; check students' work.

Check Your Understanding

1. **Vocabulary** Name the constant term(s) in the polynomial $11x^2 + 47x + 63 + 23x^2 + 35$. 63, 35

Match each step taken to simplify $3x^2 + 6x - 2 - 4x$ with the appropriate property.

2. $3x^2 + 6x - 4x - 2$ B
3. $3x^2 + (6x - 4x) - 2$ A
4. $3x^2 + (6 - 4)x - 2$ C

A. associative property
B. commutative property
C. Distributive Property

PowerPoint

Additional Examples

1. Write a variable expression for this model. $x^2 - 2x + 3$

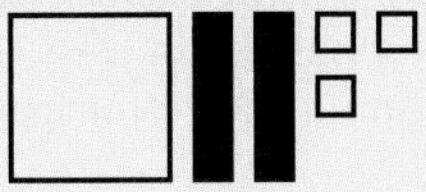

2. Use tiles to simplify the polynomial $-x^2 + 3x + 2x^2 + 3 - x - 4$
$x^2 + 2x - 1$

3. A playground has areas of grass and sand. The polynomial $2x^2 + 3x + 3 - x^2 - x - 4$ represents the total area of the grass minus the sandy areas. Use properties of numbers to simplify the polynomial. $x^2 + 2x - 1$

All in One Teaching Resources

- Daily Notetaking Guide 12-1 L3
- Adapted Notetaking 12-1 L1

Closure

- Explain the parts of a variable expression. Sample: The terms are separated by + or −, and any term that does not contain a variable is a constant.
- *How do you simplify a polynomial?* Sample: Rearrange the terms so the like terms (with the same form of the variable) are together and then combine like terms.

3. Practice

Assignment Guide

Check Your Understanding
Go over Exercises 1–4 in class before assigning the Homework Exercises.

Homework Exercises

A	Practice by Example	5–14
B	Apply Your Skills	15–27
C	Challenge	28
Test Prep and Mixed Review		29–34

Homework Quick Check
To check students' understanding of key skills and concepts, go over Exercises 11, 13, 18, 26, and 27.

Differentiated Instruction Resources

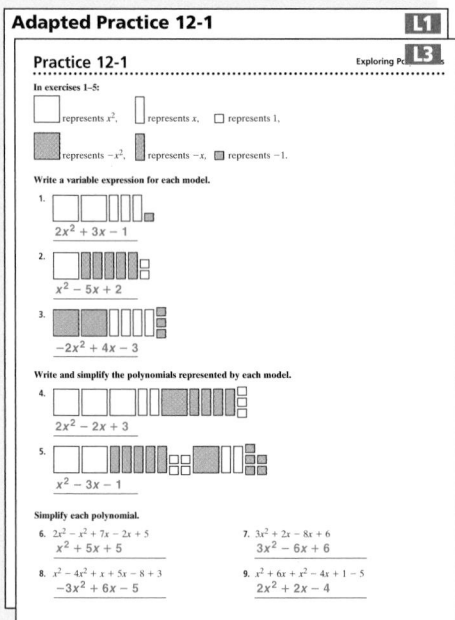

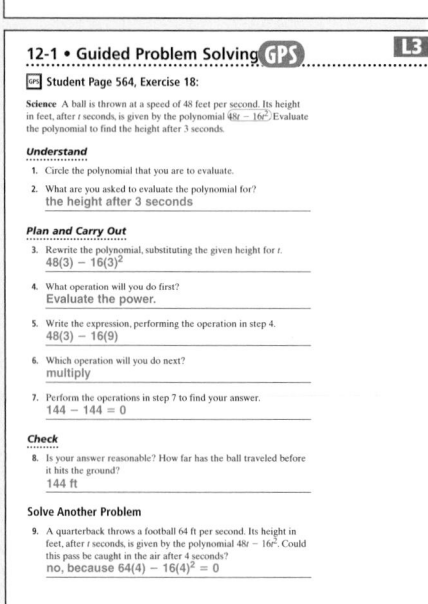

Adapted Practice 12-1 L1

Practice 12-1 L3 Exploring Polynomials

In exercises 1–5:

represents x^2, represents x, represents 1,

represents $-x^2$, represents $-x$, represents -1.

Write a variable expression for each model.

1. 
$2x^2 + 3x - 1$

2. 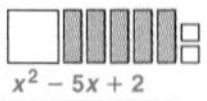
$x^2 - 5x + 2$

3. 
$-2x^2 + 4x - 3$

Write and simplify the polynomials represented by each model.

4. 
$2x^2 - 2x + 3$

5. 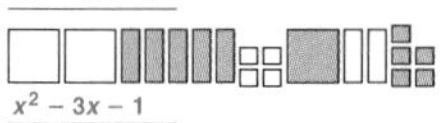
$x^2 - 3x - 1$

Simplify each polynomial.

6. $2x^2 - x^2 + 7x - 2x + 5$
$x^2 + 5x + 5$

7. $3x^2 + 2x - 8x + 6$
$3x^2 - 6x + 6$

8. $x^2 - 4x^2 + x + 5x - 8 + 3$
$-3x^2 + 6x - 5$

9. $x^2 + 6x + x^2 - 4x + 1 - 5$
$2x^2 + 2x - 4$

12-1 • Guided Problem Solving GPS L3

GPS **Student Page 564, Exercise 18:**

Science A ball is thrown at a speed of 48 feet per second. Its height in feet, after t seconds, is given by the polynomial $48t - 16t^2$. Evaluate the polynomial to find the height after 3 seconds.

Understand

1. Circle the polynomial that you are to evaluate.
2. What are you asked to evaluate the polynomial for?
the height after 3 seconds

Plan and Carry Out

3. Rewrite the polynomial, substituting the given height for t.
$48(3) - 16(3)^2$
4. What operation will you do first?
Evaluate the power.
5. Write the expression, performing the operation in step 4.
$48(3) - 16(9)$
6. Which operation will you do next?
multiply
7. Perform the operations in step 7 to find your answer.
$144 - 144 = 0$

Check

8. Is your answer reasonable? How far has the ball traveled before it hits the ground?
144 ft

Solve Another Problem

9. A quarterback throws a football 64 ft per second. Its height in feet, after t seconds, is given by the polynomial $48t - 16t^2$. Could this pass be caught in the air after 4 seconds?
no, because $64(4) - 16(4)^2 = 0$

Homework Exercises

For more exercises, see Extra Skills and Word Problems.

GO for Help

For Exercises	See Examples
5–7	1
8–11	2
12–14	3

8. $2x^2 + 5x + 1$

A **Write an algebraic expression for each model.**

5. 
$2x^2 - x + 3$

6. 
$x^2 + 3x - 5$

7. 
$-2x^2 + x - 2$

Draw or use tiles to simplify each polynomial.

8. $x^2 + 3x + x^2 + 1 + 2x$

9. $x + 3x^2 + x - 4$ $3x^2 + 2x - 4$

10. $-2 - 2x - 2x^2 + 3x + 3 + 3x^2$ $x^2 + x + 1$

11. $7x - x^2 - 5x + 3x^2$ $2x^2 + 2x$

Use properties of numbers to simplify each polynomial.

12. $3x^2 - 8 + 2x - 4x + 3 - 5x^2$ $-2x^2 - 2x - 5$

13. $-1 + 2x^2 - 2x + 2 + 3x$ $2x^2 + x + 1$

14. You are planning a park that will have sections of grass as well as walking trails. The polynomial $3 - 7x + 3x^2 + 2x^2 + 2x$ represents the area that will be grass minus the area for the trails. Use properties of numbers to simplify the polynomial. $5x^2 - 5x + 3$

B GPS 15. **Guided Problem Solving** Write and simplify an expression for the total area of the two rectangles at the right.

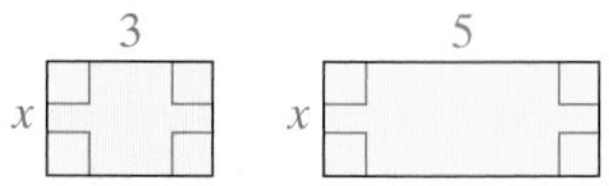

- What expression can you write for the area of each rectangle?
- What do you get if you add the two area expressions and simplify? $8x$

GO Online
Homework Video Tutor
Visit: PHSchool.com
Web Code: ase-1201

Write and simplify the polynomial represented by each model.

16. 
$-x^2 + 3$

17. 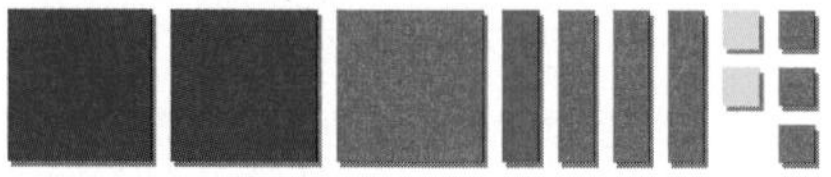
$x^2 - 2x - 1$

18. **Science** A ball is projected upward at a speed of 48 feet per second. Its height in feet, after t seconds, is given by the polynomial $48t - 16t^2$. Evaluate the polynomial to find the height after 3 seconds. 0 ft

Simplify each polynomial.

19. $-5n + 2n + k + k + 10n$ $7n + 2k$

20. $13 + g - 3r + 10g + 14r$ $11g + 11r + 13$

21. Evaluate $2y^2 - y + 3$ for $y = 4$. 31

27. Answers may vary. Sample: The prefix *poly* means "several" or "many." This meaning can be combined with the meaning of the root word, as in *polygon*, which means "many sided."

32–34. See back of book.

Find the degree of each polynomial. The degree of a polynomial with one variable is the value of the greatest exponent of the variable that appears in any term. The polynomial $3x^2 + 5x - 6$ has degree 2, since the greatest exponent of x is 2.

22. $-4x^2 + 5x + 1$ 2

23. $3x^3 + 2x^2 - 3x$ 3

24. $2x + 1$ 1

25. $x^5 + 2x^3 - 3x + 1$ 5

The Crystal Bridge Tropical Conservatory is a cylinder of acrylic and steel, 244 ft long and 70 ft across.

26. **Geometry** To find the surface area of a cylinder, you can use the polynomial $\pi r^2 + \pi r^2 + \pi dh$, where r is the radius, d is the diameter, and h is the height of the cylinder. Simplify the polynomial. $2\pi r^2 + \pi dh$

27. **Writing in Math** Explain how knowing the meaning of the prefix *poly-* can help you understand the meanings of words with the prefix *poly-*. See margin.

Ⓒ **28.** **Challenge** Simplify the polynomial.

$-3x^3 + 2x - 9xy - z^5y^5 + 1 - 4y^2 + 5yx + x^3 - 6y + y^5z^5$

$-2x^3 - 4y^2 - 4xy + 2x - 6y + 1$

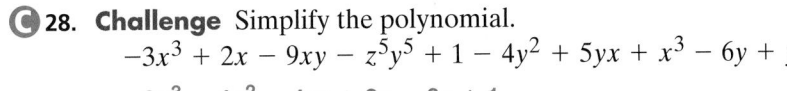

Test Prep and Mixed Review

Practice

Multiple Choice

29. Using the graph at the right, about how many hours per week do women ages 18–24 watch television? C

Ⓐ 18 Ⓒ 22
Ⓑ 20 Ⓓ 25

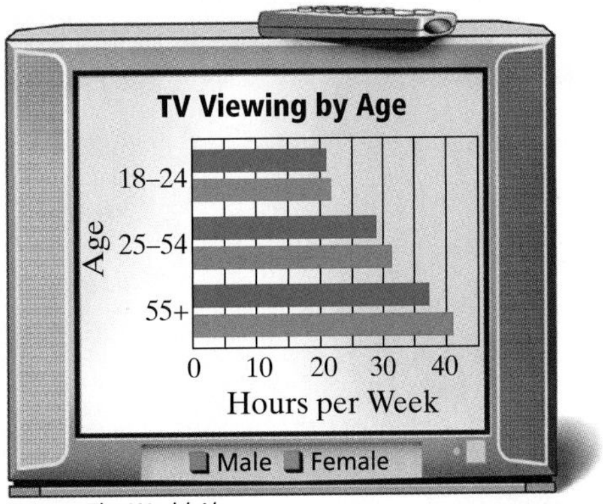

SOURCE: *The World Almanac*

30. Kita bought a laptop computer for $1,295 and extra programs for $74.99. If Kita paid 8% tax on the laptop and the upgrade, what is a reasonable amount for her total cost? G

Ⓕ $1,525 Ⓖ $1,485 Ⓗ $1,400 Ⓙ $1,375

31. Which is the best description of the relationship of the data in the scatter plot at the right? B

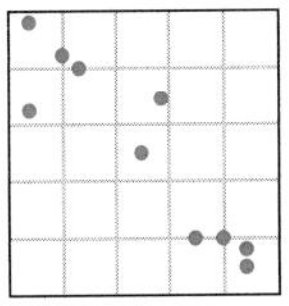

Ⓐ Positive trend
Ⓑ Negative trend
Ⓒ Opposite trend
Ⓓ No trend

GO for Help

For Exercises	See Lesson
32–34	11-7

Make a table and graph each quadratic function. Use integers from −3 to 3 for inputs. 32–34. See margin.

32. $y = 3t^2 - 12$

33. $y = m^2 - m$

34. $y = 2x^2 - 2$

4. Assess & Reteach

PowerPoint

Lesson Quiz

1. Write a variable expression for the model. $x^2 - 2x + 4$

2. Write a variable expression for the model. $-x^2 + 3x - 1$

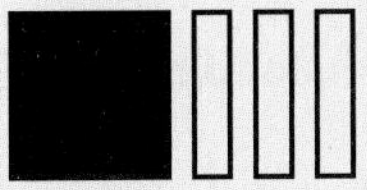

3. Use properties to simplify the polynomial $4x^2 + 9x - x^2 - 10x - 2$. $3x^2 - x - 2$

4. Use properties to simplify the polynomial $5a^2 - 7a + 4 + a - 7a^2 + 6$. $-2a^2 - 6a + 10$

Alternative Assessment

Each student in a pair writes a 3-term polynomial in terms of x. Partners work together to combine and simplify their polynomials.

Test Prep

Resources

For additional practice with a variety of test item formats:

- Test-Taking Strategies, p. 589
- Test Prep, p. 593
- Test-Taking Strategies with Transparencies

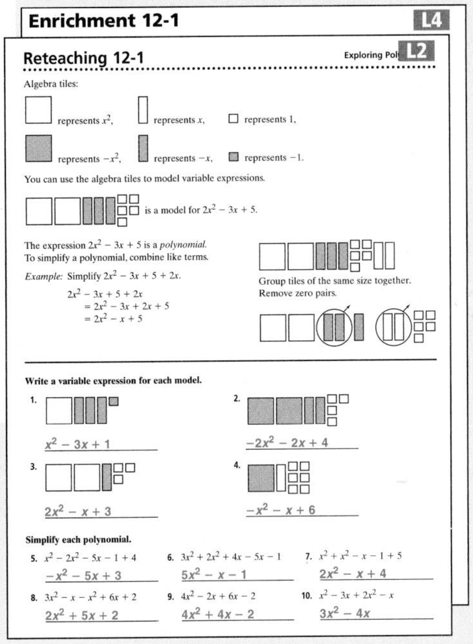

Enrichment 12-1 L4

Reteaching 12-1 Exploring Pol L2

Algebra tiles:

□ represents x^2, ▯ represents x, □ represents 1,

■ represents $-x^2$, ▮ represents $-x$, ■ represents −1.

You can use the algebra tiles to model variable expressions.

is a model for $2x^2 - 3x + 5$.

The expression $2x^2 - 3x + 5$ is a *polynomial*.
To simplify a polynomial, combine like terms.

Example: Simplify $2x^2 - 3x + 5 + 2x$.

$2x^2 - 3x + 5 + 2x$
$= 2x^2 - 3x + 2x + 5$
$= 2x^2 - x + 5$

Group tiles of the same size together.
Remove zero pairs.

Write a variable expression for each model.

1. $x^2 - 3x + 1$
2. $-2x^2 - 2x + 4$
3. $2x^2 - x + 3$
4. $-x^2 - x + 6$

Simplify each polynomial.

5. $x^2 - 2x^2 - 5x - 1 + 4$ $-x^2 - 5x + 3$
6. $3x^2 + 2x^2 + 4x - 5x - 1$ $5x^2 - x - 1$
7. $x^2 + x^2 - x - 1 + 5$ $2x^2 - x + 4$
8. $3x^2 - x - x^2 + 6x + 2$ $2x^2 + 5x + 2$
9. $4x^2 - 2x + 6x - 2$ $4x^2 + 4x - 2$
10. $x^2 - 3x + 2x^2 - x$ $3x^2 - 4x$

12-2

1. Plan

Objective
To add and subtract polynomials

Examples
1 Adding Polynomials
2 Application: Advertising
3 Subtracting Polynomials

Math Understandings: p. 558C

Professional Development

Math Background

The word *coefficient* is most often used to refer to a numerical factor, such as 3 in $3xy^2$.

A term such as x^2 has an understood coefficient of 1, and the term $-x$ has an understood coefficient of -1.

In the variable expression $-(x^2 - 4)$, the entire parentheses has an understood multiplier, or coefficient, of -1. To simplify $-(x^2 - 4)$, take the opposite of every term within the parentheses, resulting in $-x^2 + 4$.

More Math Background: p. 558C

Lesson Planning and Resources

See p. 558E for a list of the resources that support this lesson.

PowerPoint

Bell Ringer Practice

Check Skills You'll Need
Use student page, transparency, or PowerPoint. For intervention, direct students to:
Exploring Polynomials
Lesson 12-1
Extra Skills and Word Problems Practice, Ch. 12

Algebra

12-2 Adding and Subtracting Polynomials

Check Skills You'll Need

1. **Vocabulary Review** Name the *constant* in the polynomial $1 - p + 2p$. 1

Simplify. 2–4. See below.

2. $2y^2 + 3y + (-5y)$
3. $-x + x + 6x^2 - 1$
4. $7z - 8z^2 + z + 3z^2$

GO for Help Lesson 12-1

Check Skills You'll Need
2. $2y^2 - 2y$
3. $6x^2 - 1$
4. $8z - 5z^2$

GO for Help
For help using algebra tiles, go to Lesson 12-1, Example 2.

What You'll Learn

To add and subtract polynomials

New Vocabulary coefficient

Why Learn This?

You can solve perimeter problems using addition and subtraction. You may need to add or subtract polynomials when a problem involves variables.

A **coefficient** is a number that is multiplied by a variable. In the polynomial $-2y^2 + y - 3$, the coefficients are -2 and 1. To add polynomials, combine the like terms by adding the coefficients.

EXAMPLE 1 Adding Polynomials

Add $(3n^2 + 3n + 4) + (n^2 - n + 5)$.

Method 1 Add using tiles.

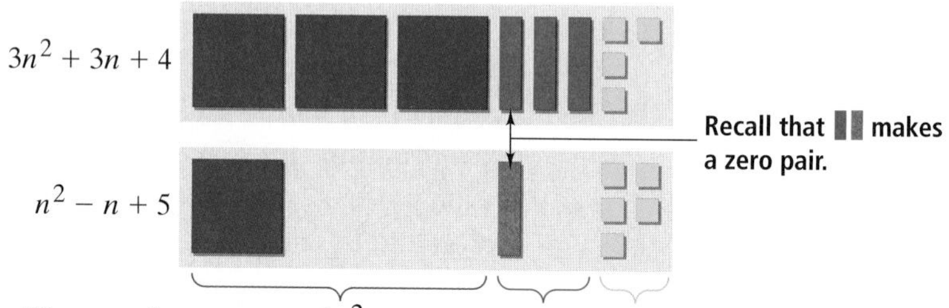

The sum is $4n^2 + 2n + 9$.

Method 2 Add using properties of numbers.

$(3n^2 + 3n + 4) + (n^2 - n + 5)$
$= (3n^2 + n^2) + (3n - n) + (4 + 5)$ ← **Group like terms.**
$= (3 + 1)n^2 + (3 - 1)n + (4 + 5)$ ← **Use the Distributive Property.**
$= 4n^2 + 2n + 9$ ← **Simplify.**

Quick Check

1. Find each sum. 1a–b. See left.
   a. $(c^2 + 3c - 5) + (4c^2 - c + 7)$ b. $(x^2 + 3x - 1) + (2x^2 - 6)$

1a. $5c^2 + 2c + 2$
b. $3x^2 + 3x - 7$

Differentiated Instruction Solutions for All Learners

Special Needs L1	Below Level L2
Write a list of terms on the board. Have students write the opposite of each term. Have them explain how they know the terms are opposites. learning style: verbal	Students review how to add integers, such as $-3 + 5$, $4 - 7$, $-1 + (-3)$. 2, −3, −4 learning style: verbal

EXAMPLE Application: Advertising

2 The owner of a store wants to put a string of lights around the store sign he is designing. The diagram at the left shows the dimensions of the sign in feet. Use it to write the perimeter of the sign as a polynomial. Then simplify the polynomial to find the length of the string of lights he would need to go around the sign.

To find the perimeter of the sign, find the sum of the side lengths.

$P = (5g - 2) + (5g - 2) + (6g + 3) + (6g + 3)$

$= (5g + 5g + 6g + 6g) + (-2 - 2 + 3 + 3)$ ← **Group like terms.**

$= 22g + 2$ ← **Add the coefficients.**

The perimeter of the sign is $(22g + 2)$ ft. The string of lights must be $(22g + 2)$ ft long to go around the sign.

Quick Check

2. Write the perimeter of each figure below as a polynomial. Simplify.

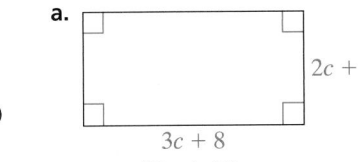

a.

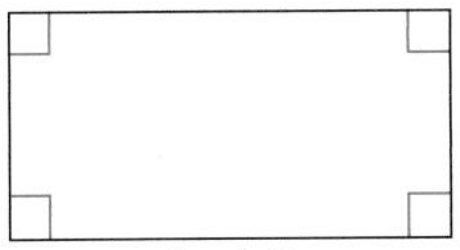

$10c + 24$

b.

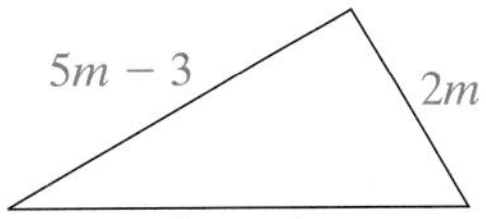

$10m - 2$

To subtract a polynomial, add the opposite of the second polynomial.

EXAMPLE Subtracting Polynomials

3 Subtract $(p^2 - 2p + 5) - (2p^2 + p - 4)$.

$(p^2 - 2p + 5) - (2p^2 + p - 4)$

$(p^2 - 2p + 5) + (-2p^2 - p + 4)$ ← **Add the opposite of each term in the second polynomial.**

$(p^2 - 2p^2) + (-2p - p) + (5 + 4)$ ← **Group like terms.**

$(1 - 2)p^2 + (-2 - 1)p + (5 + 4)$ ← **Use the Distributive Property.**

$-p^2 - 3p + 9$ ← **Simplify.**

Check Check the solution by substituting 1 for p.

$(p^2 - 2p + 5) - (2p^2 + p - 4) \stackrel{?}{=} -p^2 - 3p + 9$

$(1^2 - 2 \cdot 1 + 5) - (2 \cdot 1^2 + 1 - 4) \stackrel{?}{=} -1^2 - 3 \cdot 1 + 9$ ← **Substitute.**

$(1 - 2 + 5) - (2 + 1 - 4) \stackrel{?}{=} -1 - 3 + 9$ ← **Multiply.**

$5 = 5$ ✔ ← **Add.**

Quick Check

3. Subtract $(4y^2 - 3y + 1) - (6y^2 - 3y + 3)$. Check the solution. **$-2y^2 - 2$**

Online active math

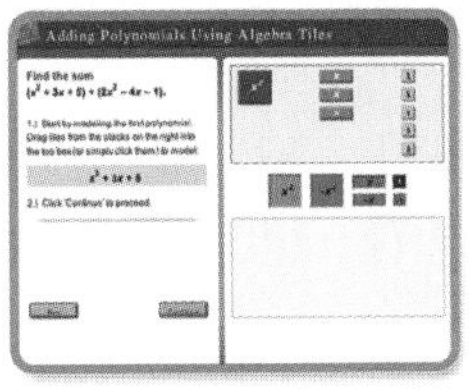

For: Polynomials Activity
Use: Interactive Textbook, 12-2

2. Teach

Activity Lab

Use before the lesson.

All in One Teaching Resources

Activity Lab 12-2: Adding and Subtracting Polynomials

Guided Instruction

Alternative Method

Some students prefer to perform the subtraction in the vertical format. Make sure they change the subtraction to addition as shown below for Example 3.

Subtraction	→ *Addition*
$p^2 - 2p + 5$ →	$p^2 - 2p + 5$
$-(2p^2 + p - 4)$ →	$-2p^2 - p + 4$
	$-p^2 - 3p + 9$

Additional Examples

1 Add: $(5p^2 + 2p + 7) + (2p^2 - p - 5)$. $7p^2 + p + 2$

2 A garden has sides of $3x + 5$, $4x - 2$, $5x + 2$, and $7x - 6$. Write a polynomial to express the length of edging that is needed to go around the garden. $19x - 1$

3 Subtract: $(3q^2 - 2q + 4) - (2q^2 - 2q + 3)$. $q^2 + 1$

All in One Teaching Resources

- Daily Notetaking Guide 12-2 L3
- Adapted Notetaking 12-2 L1

Closure

- Explain how subtracting polynomials differs from adding polynomials. **Rewrite, changing the subtraction to adding the opposite of each term in the polynomial you are subtracting, then combine like terms.**

Advanced Learners L4

Students explain, using examples, why $y + y^2$ cannot be further simplified. **Sample: y and y^2 are not like terms. For instance, you cannot combine inches and square inches.**

learning style: verbal

English Language Learners ELL

Using a copy of Example 1, students circle like terms with the same colors and label the constants and coefficients. Students should understand that terms, such as $3n$ and $-n$, are considered like terms.

learning style: tactile

3. Practice

Assignment Guide

Check Your Understanding

Go over Exercises 1–6 in class before assigning the Homework Exercises.

Homework Exercises

A	Practice by Example	7–18
B	Apply Your Skills	19–27
C	Challenge	28
	Test Prep and Mixed Review	29–34

Homework Quick Check

To check students' understanding of key skills and concepts, go over Exercises 10, 16, 19, 25, and 27.

Differentiated Instruction Resources

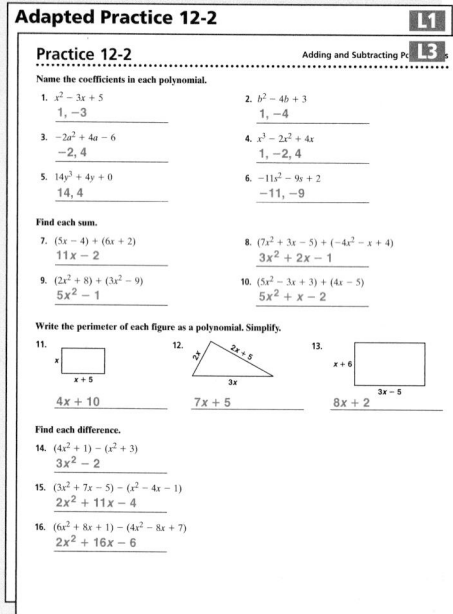

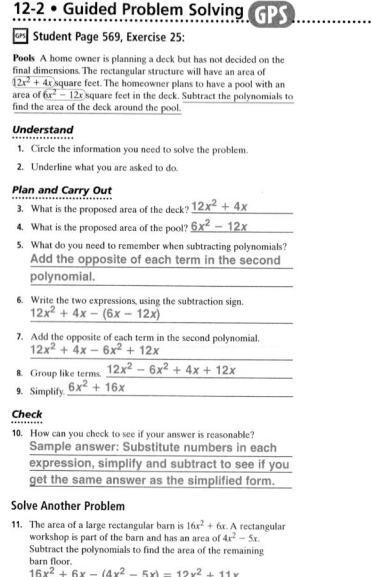

Adapted Practice 12-2 L1

Practice 12-2 — Adding and Subtracting Polynomials L3

Name the coefficients in each polynomial.

1. $x^2 - 3x + 5$ — 1, −3
2. $b^2 - 4b + 3$ — 1, −4
3. $-2a^2 + 4a - 6$ — −2, 4
4. $x^3 - 2x^2 + 4x$ — 1, −2, 4
5. $14y^3 + 4y + 0$ — 14, 4
6. $-11s^2 - 9s + 2$ — −11, −9

Find each sum.

7. $(5x - 4) + (6x + 2)$ — $11x - 2$
8. $(7x^2 + 3x - 5) + (-4x^2 - x + 4)$ — $3x^2 + 2x - 1$
9. $(2x^2 + 8) + (3x^2 - 9)$ — $5x^2 - 1$
10. $(5x^2 - 3x + 3) + (4x - 5)$ — $5x^2 + x - 2$

Write the perimeter of each figure as a polynomial. Simplify.

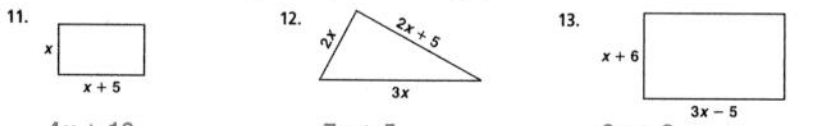

11. $4x + 10$
12. $7x + 5$
13. $8x + 2$

Find each difference.

14. $(4x^2 + 1) - (x^2 + 3)$ — $3x^2 - 2$
15. $(3x^2 + 7x - 5) - (x^2 - 4x - 1)$ — $2x^2 + 11x - 4$
16. $(6x^2 + 8x + 1) - (4x^2 - 8x + 7)$ — $2x^2 + 16x - 6$

12-2 • Guided Problem Solving GPS L3

GPS **Student Page 569, Exercise 25:**

Pools A home owner is planning a deck but has not decided on the final dimensions. The rectangular structure will have an area of $12x^2 + 4x$ square feet. The homeowner plans to have a pool with an area of $6x^2 - 12x$ square feet in the deck. Subtract the polynomials to find the area of the deck around the pool.

Understand

1. Circle the information you need to solve the problem.
2. Underline what you are asked to do.

Plan and Carry Out

3. What is the proposed area of the deck? $12x^2 + 4x$
4. What is the proposed area of the pool? $6x^2 - 12x$
5. What do you need to remember when subtracting polynomials? Add the opposite of each term in the second polynomial.
6. Write the two expressions, using the subtraction sign. $12x^2 + 4x - (6x - 12x)$
7. Add the opposite of each term in the second polynomial. $12x^2 + 4x - 6x^2 + 12x$
8. Group like terms. $12x^2 - 6x^2 + 4x + 12x$
9. Simplify. $6x^2 + 16x$

Check

10. How can you check to see if your answer is reasonable? Sample answer: Substitute numbers in each expression, simplify and subtract to see if you get the same answer as the simplified form.

Solve Another Problem

11. The area of a large rectangular barn is $16x^2 + 6x$. A rectangular workshop is part of the barn and has an area of $4x^2 - 5x$. Subtract the polynomials to find the area of the remaining barn floor. $16x^2 + 6x - (4x^2 - 5x) = 12x^2 + 11x$

Check Your Understanding

1. **Vocabulary** A coefficient is a number that is multiplied by a __?__. variable

Name the coefficients in each polynomial.

2. $2x^2 + 3x - 5$ — 2, 3
3. $-c^2 - c - 1$ — −1, −1
4. $-4x^2 + 3$ — −4

Fill in the blank.

5. $(3m - 7) + (5m + 9)$
   $= (3m + \blacksquare) + (-7 + 9)$ — $5m$
6. $(x^2 - 4x) + (3x^2 - 2x)$
   $= (x^2 + 3x^2) + (\blacksquare - 2x)$ — $-4x$

Homework Exercises

For more exercises, see Extra Skills and Word Problems.

GO for Help

For Exercises	See Examples
7–10	1
11–14	2
15–18	3

A **Find each sum.** 7. $8p^2 + 2p + 1$ 8. $t^2 + t$

7. $(3p^2 - 2p + 1) + (5p^2 + 4p)$
8. $(7t^2 + t - 3) + (-6t^2 + 3)$
9. $(k^2 + 3k) + (3k^2 - 2k)$ — $4k^2 + k$
10. $(2b^2 + b - 3) + (2b^2 - b - 3)$ — $4b^2 - 6$

Write the perimeter of each figure as a polynomial. Simplify.

11.
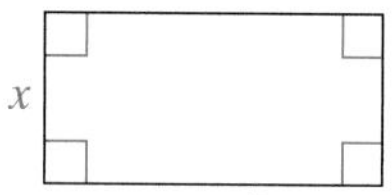

$4x + 6$

12.
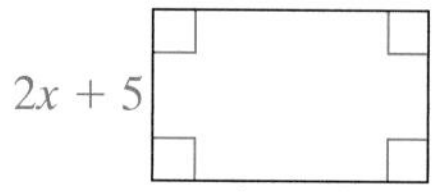

$12x + 26$

13.
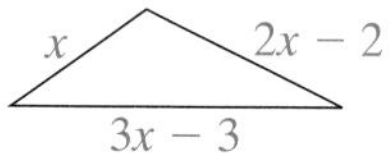

$6x - 5$

14. A town is planning a rectangular playground but has not decided on the final dimensions. The length will be $(4x - 4)$ ft and the width will be $(2x + 5)$ ft. The value of the variable x is not yet known. Find and simplify an expression for the length of fence needed to go around the playground. $(4x - 4) + (2x + 5) + (4x - 4) + (2x + 5)$; $(12x + 2)$ ft

Find each difference. 15–16. See left.

15. $(2x^2 + 5x + 7) - (3x^2 + 7x)$
16. $(2a^2 + 5a + 7) - (a^2 - 3a - 1)$
17. $(g^2 + 7) - (3g^2 + 2g + 1)$ — $-2g^2 - 2g + 6$
18. $(3r^2 - 4r - 1) - (2r^2 + r - 4)$ — $r^2 - 5r + 3$

15. $-x^2 - 2x + 7$
16. $a^2 + 8a + 8$

B GPS 19. **Guided Problem Solving** The polynomial $13x + 400$ represents the expense, in dollars, of producing x items. The polynomial $25x - 30$ represents the income, in dollars, from selling x items. The profit is the amount of money made and is equal to income minus expenses. Find the profit on 45 items. $110

- Translate the words into an equation.
  Words: income minus expenses equals __?__.
  Equation: $(25x - 30) - \blacksquare = \blacksquare$

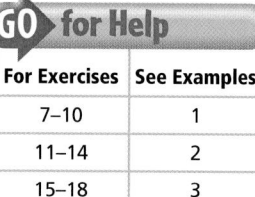

20. $12x^3 + 11x^2 + 5x - 4$
21. $x^3 - 9x + 1$
22. $3x^3 - 5x^2 + 2x + 3$
23. $-x^3 - 2x^2 + 2x + 5$

Online
Homework Video Tutor
Visit: PHSchool.com
Web Code: ase-1202

Add or subtract. 20–23. See margin.

20. $(12x^3 + 2x^2 - 4) + (9x^2 + 5x)$ **21.** $(x^3 + x^2 + 1) - (x^2 + 9x)$

22. $(3x^3 - 1) - (5x^2 - 2x - 4)$ **23.** $(-3x^3 - 2x^2 + 5) + (2x^3 + 2x)$

24. Write the addition problem modeled below. Then find the sum.

$(2x^2 - 2x + 3) +$
$(-x^2 + x + 2) =$
$x^2 - x + 5$

25. Pools A homeowner is planning a deck but has not decided on the final dimensions. The rectangular structure will have an area of $12x^2 + 4x$ square feet. The homeowner plans to have a pool with an area of $6x^2 - 12x$ square feet in the deck. Subtract the polynomials to find the area of the deck around the pool. $6x^2 + 16x$

26. Find the perimeter of the figure at the right. $7a + 4b$

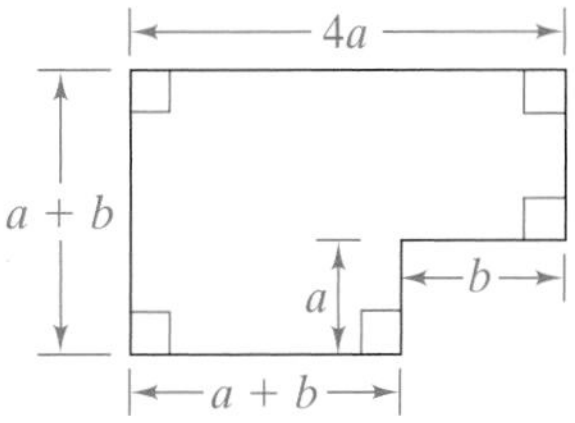

27. Writing in Math How is the process for adding two polynomials like the process for adding two integers? How is it different? See left.

C 28. Challenge Write and simplify an expression for the total area of the two figures below. $2.5x^2 + x^2; \frac{7}{2}x^2$

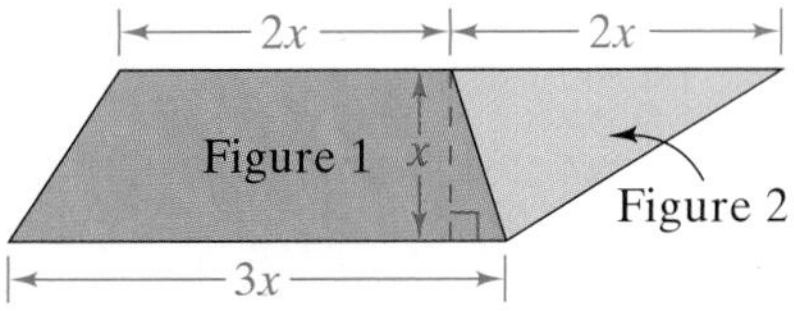

27. As in adding integers, you add the coefficients of like terms; however, unlike adding integers, there are different kinds of terms—some with variables of differing powers and some without variables.

Test Prep and Mixed Review

Practice

Multiple Choice

29. Let x represent the position of a number in the following arithmetic sequence: $\frac{1}{3}, \frac{2}{3}, 1, \frac{4}{3}, \ldots$

Which expression can be used to find any term in the sequence? B

A $3x$ B $\frac{1}{3}x$ C $\frac{2}{3}x$ D $\frac{4}{3}x$

30. Five houses in a development have sold for \$127,000; \$156,000; \$127,000; \$164,000; and \$170,000. Which of the following measures makes the homes appear to be the most expensive? F

F median G mode H mean J range

GO for Help

For Exercises	See Lesson
31–34	10-5

Simplify each expression.

31. ${}_{20}P_5$ 1,860,480 **32.** ${}_{8}P_3$ 336 **33.** ${}_{4}P_2$ 12 **34.** ${}_{12}P_4$ 11,880

4. Assess & Reteach

PowerPoint

Lesson Quiz

Simplify each polynomial.

1. $(4n^2 + n + 1) + (n^2 + 3n + 1)$
   $5n^2 + 4n + 2$
2. $(x^2 - 2x + 6) + (x^2 + 2x - 2)$
   $2x^2 + 4$
3. $(a^2 - 7) - (a^2 + 4a - 4)$
   $-4a - 3$
4. $(m - 5) + (m^2 - 12) + (6m^2 - 9m)$ $7m^2 - 8m - 17$

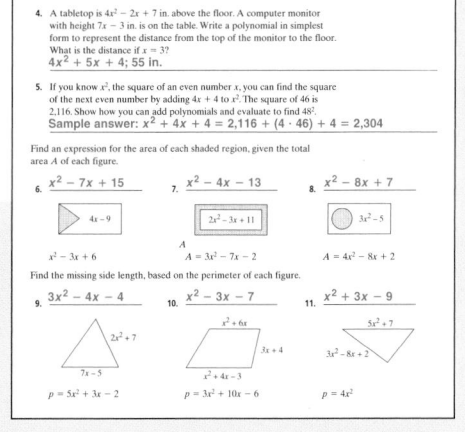

Reteaching 12-2 Adding and Subtracting Po[lynomials] **L2**

To add polynomials, combine like terms. Add the *coefficients* in the like terms.

Example 1: Add $(3x^2 - 5x - 1)$ and $(x^2 - 6x + 3)$.

$3x^2 - 5x - 1 + x^2 - 6x + 3$ ← Write the sum.
$= (3x^2 + x^2) + (-5x - 6x) + (-1 + 3)$ ← Group like terms.
$= (3 + 1)x^2 + (-5 - 6)x + (-1 + 3)$ ← Use the Distributive Property.
$= 4x^2 - 11x + 2$ ← Add and subtract.

To subtract a polynomial, rewrite the second polynomial to be the opposite and add to the first polynomial.

Example 2: Subtract $(2x^2 + x - 3)$ from $(x^2 - 3x + 1)$.

$(x^2 - 3x + 1) - (2x^2 + x - 3)$
$= (x^2 - 3x + 1) + (-2x^2 - x + 3)$ ← Add the opposite of each term in the second polynomial.
$= (x^2 - 2x^2) + (-3x - x) + (1 + 3)$ ← Group like terms.
$= (1 - 2)x^2 + (-3 - 1)x + (1 + 3)$ ← Use the Distributive Property.
$= -x^2 - 4x + 4$ ← Add and subtract.

Add.

1. $(x^2 + 4x) + (2x^2 - 6x)$ $-3x^2 - 2x$
2. $(3x^2 - x - 1) + (2x^2 + 2x - 1)$ $5x^2 + x - 2$
3. $(y^2 - y - 1) + (y^2 + y + 3)$ $2y^2 + 2$
4. $(2k^2 + 1) + (k^2 - 2k + 5)$ $3k^2 - 2k + 6$

Subtract.

5. $(2x^2 + 3x) - (x^2 + x)$ $x^2 + 2x$
6. $(3l^2 - 2l + 1) - (2l^2 + l - 3)$ $l^2 - 3l + 4$
7. $(x^2 + 1) - (2x^2 + x - 1)$ $-x^2 - x + 2$
8. $(z^2 - 4z) - (3z^2 + 2z + 1)$ $-2z^2 - 6z - 1$

Enrichment 12-2 Adding and Subtracting Po[lynomials] **L4**

Geometric Reasoning

Find the total area of each figure.

1. $3x^2 - 3x + 7$ (figure: $x^2 + 5$; $2x^2 - 3x + 2$)
2. $5x^3 + 23x + 7$ (figure: $5x^3 - 2x + 7$; $25x$)
3. $3x^2 - 21x + 22$ (figure: $2x^2 - 21x + 5$; $x^2 + 17$)

4. A tabletop is $4x^2 - 2x + 7$ in. above the floor. A computer monitor with height $7x - 3$ in. is on the table. Write a polynomial in simplest form to represent the distance from the top of the monitor to the floor. What is the distance if $x = 3$?
   $4x^2 + 5x + 4$; 55 in.

5. If you know x^2, the square of an even number x, you can find the square of the next even number by adding $4x + 4$ to x^2. The square of 46 is 2,116. Show how you can add polynomials and evaluate to find 48^2.
   Sample answer: $x^2 + 4x + 4 = 2{,}116 + (4 \cdot 46) + 4 = 2{,}304$

Find an expression for the area of each shaded region, given the total area A of each figure.

6. $x^2 - 7x + 15$ (figure: $4x - 9$; $x^2 - 3x + 6$)
7. $x^2 - 4x - 13$ (figure: $2x^2 - 3x + 11$; A; $A = 3x^2 - 7x - 2$)
8. $x^2 - 8x + 7$ (figure: $3x^2 - 5$; $A = 4x^2 - 8x + 2$)

Find the missing side length, based on the perimeter of each figure.

9. $3x^2 - 4x - 4$ (figure: $2x^2 + 7$; $7x - 5$; $p = 5x^2 + 3x - 2$)
10. $x^2 - 3x - 7$ (figure: $x^2 + 6x$; $3x + 4$; $x^2 + 4x - 3$; $p = 3x^2 + 10x - 6$)
11. $x^2 + 3x - 9$ (figure: $5x^2 + 7$; $3x^2 - 8x + 2$; $p = 4x^2$)

Alternative Assessment

Each student in a pair writes a polynomial with three terms: an x^2 term, an x term, and a constant term. Partners work together to find the sum and the differences of their polynomials.

Test Prep

Resources

For additional practice with a variety of test item formats:

- Test-Taking Strategies, p. 589
- Test Prep, p. 593
- Test-Taking Strategies with Transparencies

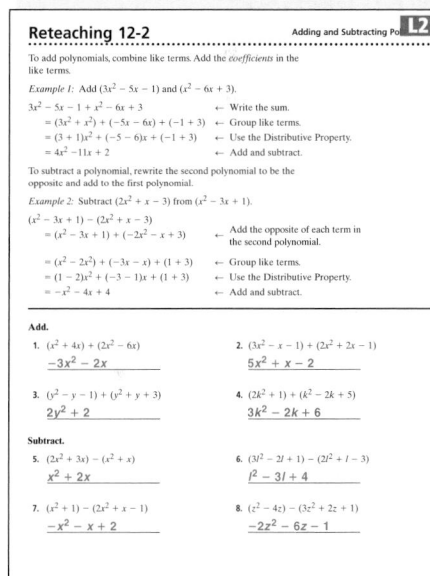

Checkpoint Quiz

Use this Checkpoint Quiz to check students' understanding of the skills and concepts of Lessons 12-1 through 12-2.

Resources

- All in One Teaching Resources Checkpoint Quiz 1
- ExamView Assessment Suite CD-ROM
- Success Tracker Online Intervention

Activity Lab

Exploring Exponents

Students study and complete a table showing products of powers of 2. They generalize the rule: when powers with the same base are multiplied, the product is the base raised to the sum of the exponents of the powers.

Guided Instruction

Error Prevention!

Some students may think incorrectly that, for example, $2^2 \times 2^3$ should be 4^5. Have them write $(2 \times 2) \times (2 \times 2 \times 2)$ and compare it to $4 \times 4 \times 4 \times 4 \times 4$.

Differentiated Instruction

Auditory Learners
Have students read aloud the expressions in the first and last columns of the table. This way they learn to say correctly, for example, "2 to the 1st power; 2 to the 2nd power, or 2 squared; 2 to the 3rd power, or 2 cubed."

Resources

- Activity Lab 12-3: Exponents and Multiplication

Checkpoint Quiz 1

Lessons 12-1 through 12-2

Write an algebraic expression for each model.

1. 
$-x - 2$

2. 
$x^2 + 2x + 2$

3. 
$x^2 + 2x$

Use properties to simplify each polynomial.

4. $-2 - 6x + 5x^2 - 2x + 6$ $5x^2 - 8x + 4$

5. $9x^2 + 3 - 10x - 3 + 7x^2$ $16x^2 - 10x$

Add or subtract.

6. $(3a^2 + 2a - 1) + (-3a^2 - 9)$ $2a - 10$

7. $(11b^2 - 7) + (15b^2 - b)$ $26b^2 - b - 7$

8. $(c^2 - 9c - 5) - (-c^2 - 8c - 10)$
$2c^2 - c + 5$

9. $(2d^2 - 9d) - (-4d^2 + 20d + 17)$
$6d^2 - 29d - 17$

Write the perimeter of each figure as a polynomial. Simplify.

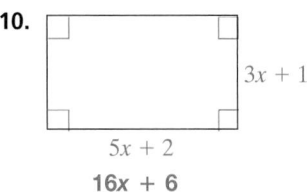

10. 

$16x + 6$

11. 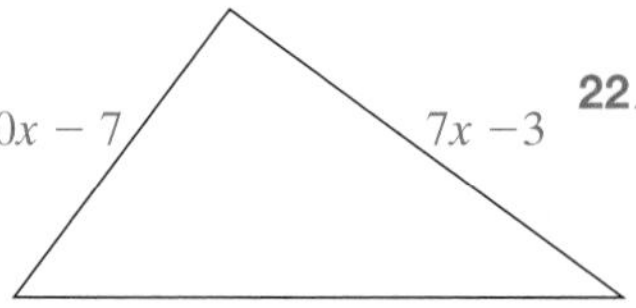

$22x - 10$

12-3a Activity Lab

Exploring Exponents

1. Copy and complete the table. See margin.

2. a. **Patterns** Look at the first row in the table. What relationship do you see between the sum of the exponents in the first cell and the exponent in the last cell?
2a. The sum of the exponents in the first cell is equal to the exponent in the last
b. Does this relationship hold for the other rows in the table? yes

Two Exponents	Product as a Repeated Factor	Standard Form	Single Exponent
$2^1 \cdot 2^1$	$2 \cdot 2$	4	2^2
$2^1 \cdot 2^2$	■	■	■
$2^2 \cdot 2^2$	$2 \cdot 2 \cdot 2 \cdot 2$	16	■
$2^2 \cdot 2^3$	■	■	■

3. Write a rule that you can use to find the product of two exponents such as $a^m \cdot a^n$. $a^m \cdot a^n = a^{m+n}$

Activity Lab

1.

Two Exponents	Product as a Repeated Factor	Standard Form	Single Exponent
$2^1 \cdot 2^1$	$2 \cdot 2$	4	2^2
$2^1 \cdot 2^2$	$2 \cdot 2 \cdot 2$	8	2^3
$2^2 \cdot 2^2$	$2 \cdot 2 \cdot 2 \cdot 2$	16	2^4
$2^2 \cdot 2^3$	$2 \cdot 2 \cdot 2 \cdot 2 \cdot 2$	32	2^5

Algebra

12-3 Exponents and Multiplication

Check Skills You'll Need

1. **Vocabulary Review** What is the *base* of the exponential expression x^y? x

Simplify each expression.

2. $(-1)^4$ 1
3. $(-3)^2$ 9
4. -3^2 −9
5. -1^4 −1

GO for Help Lesson 2-7

What You'll Learn

To multiply powers with the same base and to multiply numbers in scientific notation

Why Learn This?

Astronomers use scientific notation when they work with very large numbers. To calculate using scientific notation, you must know how to multiply with exponents.

You can write the expression $3^2 \cdot 3^4$ using a single exponent.

$$3^2 \cdot 3^4 = (3 \cdot 3)(3 \cdot 3 \cdot 3 \cdot 3) = 3^6$$

The two factors of 3 together with four factors of 3 give a total of six factors of 3. Notice that the exponent 6 is equal to the sum of the exponents 2 and 4.

Vocabulary Tip

The word *power* can be used in two ways. The expression a^n is a power. You can also read a^n as "*a* to the *n*th power."

KEY CONCEPTS Multiplying Powers With the Same Base

To multiply numbers or variables with the same base, add the exponents

Arithmetic	Algebra
$3^2 \cdot 3^7 = 3^{(2+7)} = 3^9$	$a^m \cdot a^n = a^{(m+n)}$

EXAMPLE Multiplying Powers

1 Write the expression $(-2)^3 \cdot (-2)^5$ using a single exponent.

$(-2)^3 \cdot (-2)^5 = (-2)^{(3+5)}$ ← Add the exponents.

$= (-2)^8$ ← Simplify the exponent.

Quick Check

1. Write each expression using a single exponent.
   a. $6^2 \cdot 6^3$ 6^5 b. $(-4) \cdot (-4)^7$ $(-4)^8$ c. $m^1 \cdot m^{11}$ m^{12}

12-3

1. Plan

Objective

To multiply powers with the same base and to multiply numbers in scientific notation

Examples

1 Multiplying Powers
2 Multiplying With Scientific Notation
3 Application: Science

Math Understandings: p. 558C

Professional Development

Math Background

Two exponential expressions with different exponents can be combined only when the bases are identical. So x^3 and y^2 cannot be combined unless you have values for the variables.

On the other hand, x^3 and x^2 can be multiplied (or divided) by adding (or subtracting) the exponents. But the quantities x^3 and x^2 cannot be added or subtracted.

More Math Background: p. 558C

Lesson Planning and Resources

See p. 558E for a list of the resources that support this lesson.

PowerPoint

Bell Ringer Practice

Check Skills You'll Need
Use student page, transparency, or PowerPoint. For intervention, direct students to:

Powers and Exponents
Lesson 2-7
Extra Skills and Word Problems Practice, Ch. 2

Differentiated Instruction Solutions for All Learners

Special Needs L1
Remind students **not** to add the bases when they multiply powers with the same base. They are to add the exponents but keep the base the same, for example, $3^3 \times 3^2 = (3 \times 3 \times 3) \times (3 \times 3) = 3 \times 3 \times 3 \times 3 \times 3 = 3^5$.
learning style: verbal

Below Level L2
Students review the vocabulary for powers by naming the parts of 2^5 and finding the value. 2 is the base; 5 is the exponent; the value is 32.
learning style: verbal

2. Teach

Activity Lab

Use before the lesson.
Student Edition Activity Lab 12-3a, Exploring Exponents, p. 570

All in One Teaching Resources

Activity Lab 12-3: Exponents and Multiplication

Guided Instruction

Error Prevention!

Use Example 1 to show that, when powers having the same base are multiplied, the base, including its sign, does not change.

PowerPoint

Additional Examples

1. Write the expression using a single exponent.
$(-3)^2 \cdot (-3)^4$ $(-3)^6$

2. Multiply $(3 \times 10^3)(7 \times 10^5)$. Write the product in scientific notation. 2.1×10^9

3. A light-year is 5.9×10^{12} miles. A mile is 1.609×10^3 meters. In scientific notation, how many meters are in a light year? 9.5×10^{15}

All in One Teaching Resources

- Daily Notetaking Guide 12-3 L3
- Adapted Notetaking 12-3 L1

Closure

- *How do you multiply powers with the same base?* Add the exponents.
- *What are the steps in multiplying numbers in scientific notation?* Sample: First, group the numbers and the powers of ten; second, multiply the numbers and multiply the powers by adding the exponents; third, write the product in scientific notation.

The rule for multiplying powers with the same base applies to multiplying numbers in scientific notation.

GO for Help
For help with scientific notation, go to Lesson 2-8, Example 2.

EXAMPLE Multiplying With Scientific Notation

2 Multiply $(5 \times 10^6)(9 \times 10^3)$. Write the product in scientific notation.

$(5 \times 10^6)(9 \times 10^3) = (5 \times 9) \times (10^6 \times 10^3)$ ← Use the associative and commutative properties.
$= 45 \times (10^6 \times 10^3)$ ← Multiply 5 and 9.
$= 45 \times 10^9$ ← Add the exponents of the powers of 10.
$= 4.5 \times 10^1 \times 10^9$ ← Write 45 in scientific notation.
$= 4.5 \times 10^{10}$ ← Add the exponents.

Quick Check

2. Multiply. Write each product in scientific notation.
a. $(2 \times 10^6)(4 \times 10^3)$ 8×10^9
b. $(3 \times 10^5)(2 \times 10^8)$ 6×10^{13}
c. $12(8 \times 10^{20})$ 9.6×10^{21}

You can multiply numbers in scientific notation to find solutions to real-world problems. Multiplying large or small numbers in scientific notation is easier than multiplying the same numbers in standard form.

EXAMPLE Application: Science

GO Online

Video Tutor Help
Visit: PHSchool.com
Web Code: ase-0775

3 **Multiple Choice** A light-year, the distance light travels in one Earth year, is about 5.9×10^{12} miles. A mile is 5.28×10^3 feet. How many feet are in a light-year?

Ⓐ 31.2×10^{15} Ⓒ 3.12×10^{15}
Ⓑ 31.2×10^{16} Ⓓ 3.12×10^{16}

$(5.9 \times 10^{12})(5.28 \times 10^3)$ ← Multiply by the conversion factor.
$(5.9 \times 5.28) \times (10^{12} \times 10^3)$ ← associative and commutative properties
$31.2 \times (10^{12} \times 10^3)$ ← Multiply 5.9 and 5.28. Round to the nearest tenth.
31.2×10^{15} ← Add the exponents of the powers of 10.
$(3.12 \times 10^1) \times 10^{15}$ ← Write 31.2 in scientific notation.
3.12×10^{16} ← Add the exponents.

Since there are about 3.12×10^{16} feet in a light-year, the correct answer is choice D.

Quick Check

3. Astronomy The speed of light is about 3.0×10^5 kilometers/second. Use the formula $d = r \cdot t$ to find the distance light travels in an hour, which is 3.6×10^3 seconds. about 1.08×10^9 km

Differentiated Instruction Solutions for All Learners

Advanced Learners L4

Students prove that $\frac{2^7}{2^5} = 2^2$.

$\frac{2^7}{2^5} = \frac{2 \cdot 2 \cdot 2 \cdot 2 \cdot 2 \cdot 2 \cdot 2}{2 \cdot 2 \cdot 2 \cdot 2 \cdot 2} = \frac{2 \cdot 2}{1} = 2^2$

learning style: verbal

English Language Learners ELL

Remind students that a conversion factor is a fraction, such as $\frac{5.28 \times 10^3 \text{ feet}}{1 \text{ mile}}$, in Example 3, that contains two equivalent values. Emphasize that the unit they are converting to is in the numerator and the unit they are converting from is in the denominator.

learning style: verbal

Check Your Understanding

For Exercises 1 and 2, fill in the blank.

1. $(8)^3 \cdot (\blacksquare^4) = 8^7$ 8
2. $5^3 \cdot 5^{\blacksquare} = 5^6$ 3

Write each expression using a single exponent.

3. $(-6)^2 \cdot (-6)^2$ $(-6)^4$
4. $(-2)^8 \cdot (-2)^3$ $(-2)^{11}$
5. $7^2 \cdot 7^8$ 7^{10}
6. $4^5 \cdot 4^6$ 4^{11}
7. **Error Analysis** A student simplified $5^2 \cdot 5^4$ as 25^6. Explain the student's error. See left.
8. **Mental Math** Multiply 4.17×10^{20} by 10^3. 4.17×10^{23}

7. Instead of just adding the exponents, the student multiplied the bases and then added the exponents.

Homework Exercises

For more exercises, see Extra Skills and Word Problems.

GO for Help

For Exercises	See Examples
9–16	1
17–22	2
23	3

A **Write each expression using a single exponent.** 9–12. See left.

9. $y^3 \cdot y^5$
10. $m^{10} \cdot m^{100}$
11. $3.4^3 \cdot 3.4^{10}$
12. $12^5 \cdot 12^{50}$
13. $4.5^{10} \cdot 4.5^{10}$ 4.5^{20}
14. $(-5)^5 \cdot (-5)$ $(-5)^6$
15. $0.4^5 \cdot 0.4^{10}$ 0.4^{15}
16. $x \cdot x^0$ x^1

9. y^8
10. m^{110}
11. 3.4^{13}
12. 12^{55}

Multiply. Write each product in scientific notation.

17. $(2 \times 10^3)(4 \times 10^6)$ 8×10^9
18. $(7 \times 10^2)(9 \times 10^5)$ 6.3×10^8
19. $90(8 \times 10^9)$ 7.2×10^{11}
20. $(3 \times 10^5)(5 \times 10^7)$ 1.5×10^{13}
21. $(9 \times 10^5)(5 \times 10^9)$ 4.5×10^{15}
22. $(5.1 \times 10^4)(2 \times 10^7)$ 1.02×10^{12}
23. **Earth Science** There are about 4.8×10^{19} ft^3 of water on Earth. One cubic foot of water contains about 9.47×10^{26} water molecules. Approximately how many water molecules are there on Earth? about 4.55×10^{46} molecules

24. 9×10^{16} joules

B **GPS** 24. **Guided Problem Solving** Einstein's famous equation states that $E = mc^2$. E represents energy, m represents mass, and c represents the speed of light. Find the value of E (in joules) when m is equal to 1 kilogram and c is equal to 3.0×10^8 meters per second. See left.
- How can you write Einstein's law without using exponents?
- Evaluate c^2 for $c = 3.0 \times 10^8$.

25. **Open-Ended** Give three different ways to write 4^{12} as the product of two powers. Answers may vary. Sample: $4 \cdot 4^{11}$; $4^2 \cdot 4^{10}$; $4^6 \cdot 4^6$
26. **Writing in Math** Explain why you *cannot* write $5^3 \cdot 7^9$ as $(35)^{12}$. The bases are not the same.
27. Double the number 3.4×10^{12}. Write the answer in scientific notation. 6.8×10^{12}

3. Practice

Assignment Guide

Check Your Understanding

Go over Exercises 1–8 in class before assigning the Homework Exercises.

Homework Exercises

A	Practice by Example	9–23
B	Apply Your Skills	24–44
C	Challenge	45
	Test Prep and Mixed Review	46–50

Homework Quick Check

To check students' understanding of key skills and concepts, go over Exercises 14, 21, 24, 26, and 40.

Differentiated Instruction Resources

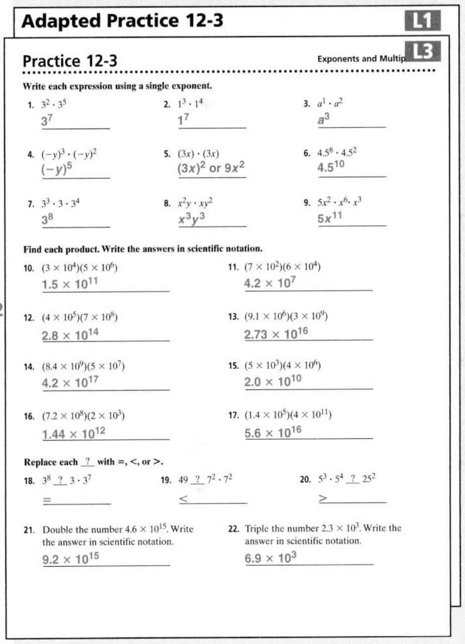

Adapted Practice 12-3 L1

Practice 12-3 Exponents and Multip L3

Write each expression using a single exponent.

1. $3^2 \cdot 3^5$ 3^7
2. $1^3 \cdot 1^4$ 1^7
3. $a^1 \cdot a^2$ a^3
4. $(-y)^3 \cdot (-y)^2$ $(-y)^5$
5. $(3x) \cdot (3x)$ $(3x)^2$ or $9x^2$
6. $4.5^8 \cdot 4.5^2$ 4.5^{10}
7. $3^3 \cdot 3 \cdot 3^4$ 3^8
8. $x^2y \cdot xy^2$ x^3y^3
9. $5x^2 \cdot x^6 \cdot x^3$ $5x^{11}$

Find each product. Write the answers in scientific notation.

10. $(3 \times 10^4)(5 \times 10^6)$ 1.5×10^{11}
11. $(7 \times 10^2)(6 \times 10^4)$ 4.2×10^7
12. $(4 \times 10^5)(7 \times 10^8)$ 2.8×10^{14}
13. $(9.1 \times 10^6)(3 \times 10^9)$ 2.73×10^{16}
14. $(8.4 \times 10^9)(5 \times 10^7)$ 4.2×10^{17}
15. $(5 \times 10^3)(4 \times 10^6)$ 2.0×10^{10}
16. $(7.2 \times 10^8)(2 \times 10^3)$ 1.44×10^{12}
17. $(1.4 \times 10^5)(4 \times 10^{11})$ 5.6×10^{16}

Replace each _?_ with =, $<$, or $>$.

18. 3^8 _?_ $3 \cdot 3^7$ =
19. 49 _?_ $7^2 \cdot 7^2$ $<$
20. $5^3 \cdot 5^4$ _?_ 25^2 $>$
21. Double the number 4.6×10^{15}. Write the answer in scientific notation. 9.2×10^{15}
22. Triple the number 2.3×10^3. Write the answer in scientific notation. 6.9×10^3

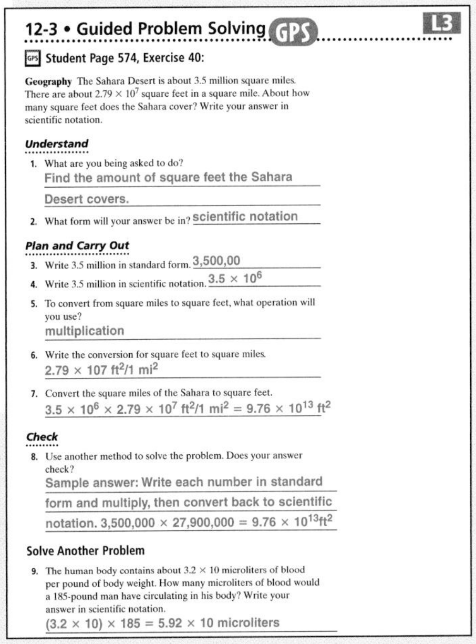

12-3 • Guided Problem Solving GPS L3

Student Page 574, Exercise 40:

Geography The Sahara Desert is about 3.5 million square miles. There are about 2.79×10^7 square feet in a square mile. About how many square feet does the Sahara cover? Write your answer in scientific notation.

Understand

1. What are you being asked to do? Find the amount of square feet the Sahara Desert covers.
2. What form will your answer be in? scientific notation

Plan and Carry Out

3. Write 3.5 million in standard form. 3,500,00
4. Write 3.5 million in scientific notation. 3.5×10^6
5. To convert from square miles to square feet, what operation will you use? multiplication
6. Write the conversion for square feet to square miles. 2.79×107 $ft^2/1$ mi^2
7. Convert the square miles of the Sahara to square feet. $3.5 \times 10^6 \times 2.79 \times 10^7$ $ft^2/1$ $mi^2 = 9.76 \times 10^{13}$ ft^2

Check

8. Use another method to solve the problem. Does your answer check? Sample answer: Write each number in standard form and multiply, then convert back to scientific notation. $3{,}500{,}000 \times 27{,}900{,}000 = 9.76 \times 10^{13} ft^2$

Solve Another Problem

9. The human body contains about 3.2×10 microliters of blood per pound of body weight. How many microliters of blood would a 185-pound man have circulating in his body? Write your answer in scientific notation. $(3.2 \times 10) \times 185 = 5.92 \times 10$ microliters

4. Assess & Reteach

PowerPoint

Lesson Quiz

1. Write $(-8)^4 \cdot (-8)^5$ using a single exponent. $(-8)^9$
2. Write the product of (8.2×10^6) and (5×10^2) in scientific notation. 4.1×10^9
3. The speed of light is 3.00×10^5 km/s. Find the distance light travels in 8×10^2 seconds. 2.4×10^8 km
4. A light-year is 5.9×10^{12} miles. A mile is approximately 6.34×10^4 inches. About how many inches are in a light-year? 3.74×10^{17}

Reteaching 12-3

Exponents and Mult L2

- To multiply numbers or variables with the same base, add the exponents.

Simplify $3^2 \cdot 3^4$: $3^2 \cdot 3^4 = 3^{(2+4)} = 3^6$

Simplify $n^3 \cdot n^4$: $n^3 \cdot n^4 = n^{(3+4)} = n^7$

Simplify $(-4)^3 \cdot (-4)^5$: $(-4)^3 \cdot (-4)^5 = (-4)^{(3+5)} = (-4)^8$

- To multiply numbers in scientific notation.

Find the product $(5 \times 10^4)(7 \times 10^5)$. Write the result in scientific notation.

$(5 \times 10^4)(7 \times 10^5)$

$(5 \cdot 7)(10^4 \cdot 10^5)$ ← Use the Associative and Commutative properties.

$35 \times (10^4 \cdot 10^5)$ ← Multiply 5 and 7.

$35 \times 10^{4+5}$ ← Add the exponents for the powers of 10.

35×10^9

$3.5 \times 10^1 \times 10^9$ ← Write 35 in scientific notation.

3.5×10^{10} ← Add the exponents.

Write each expression using a single exponent.

1. $5^3 \cdot 5^4$ — 5^7
2. $a^2 \cdot a^5$ — a^7
3. $(-8)^4 \cdot (-8)^5$ — $(-8)^9$
4. $n^6 \cdot n^2$ — n^8
5. $m^3 \cdot m^6$ — m^9
6. $(-7)^4 \cdot (-7)^2$ — 7^6
7. $(-3)^2 \cdot (-3)^2$ — $(-3)^4$
8. $2^5 \cdot 2^2$ — 2^7
9. $c^5 \cdot c^3$ — c^8

Find each product. Write the answer in scientific notation.

10. $(3 \times 10^4)(5 \times 10^3)$ — 1.5×10^8
11. $(2 \times 10^3)(7 \times 10^6)$ — 1.4×10^{10}
12. $(8 \times 10^2)(5 \times 10^2)$ — 4.0×10^5
13. $(9 \times 10^4)(7 \times 10^4)$ — 6.3×10^9
14. $(4 \times 10^2)(7 \times 10^5)$ — 2.8×10^8
15. $(8 \times 10^3)(4 \times 10^5)$ — 3.2×10^9

Enrichment 12-3

Exponents and Mul L4 n

Critical Thinking

Arrange each of the following numbers from greatest to least. Explain your answer.

a. 1.24×10^{-3} b. 2.24×10^{-2} c. 1.89×10^{-4} d. 2.6×10^{-2}

1. Are these numbers written in standard or scientific notation? scientific
2. Which of the numbers are positive? All of the numbers are positive.
3. Compare 10^{-4} and 10^{-3}. Which number is greater? $10^{-3} > 10^{-4}$
4. How can you use the exponents to compare powers of ten? The number with the larger exponent is the greater number.
5. Compare 1.6×10^{-2} and 2.6×10^{-2}. Which number is greater? 2.6×10^{-2}
6. When the powers of 10 of two numbers written in scientific notation are the same, how can you compare the numbers? The number with the greater first factor is the greater number.
7. Use your insights from exercises 2, 4, and 6 to order the numbers. 2.6×10^{-2}, 2.24×10^{-2}, 1.24×10^{-3}, 1.89×10^{-4}
8. How could you have found the answer using a different method? Change all numbers to standard notation before comparing.
9. Arrange these numbers from least to greatest.
   a. 1.9×10^{-3} b. 2.5×10^{-4} c. 1.2×10^{-2} d. 2.8×10^{-4}
   2.5×10^{-4}, 2.8×10^{-4}, 1.9×10^{-3}, 1.2×10^{-2}

GO Online
Homework Video Tutor
Visit: PHSchool.com
Web Code: ase-1203

31. $(-4)^{x+y}$

Write each expression using a single exponent.

28. $4^x \cdot 4^t$ 4^{x+t}
29. $3^m \cdot 3^n$ 3^{m+n}
30. $1.5^8 \cdot 1.5^t$ 1.5^{8+t}
31. $(-4)^x \cdot (-4)^y$
32. $2^3 \cdot 2 \cdot 2^8$ 2^{12}
33. $a^5 \cdot a^4 \cdot a$ a^{10}
34. $9^{12} \cdot 9^6 \cdot 9^3$ 9^{21}
35. $3^a \cdot 3^{2a} \cdot 3^{3a}$ 3^{6a}
36. $xy \cdot x^2y^3$ x^3y^4
37. $c^2d \cdot cd^3$ c^3d^4
38. $x \cdot x^3 \cdot x^5$ x^9
39. $3x^2 \cdot x^5 \cdot x$ $3x^8$

40. **Geography** The Sahara is a desert of about 3.5 million square miles. There are about 2.79×10^7 square feet in a square mile. About how many square feet does the Sahara cover? Write your answer in scientific notation. about 9.77×10^{13} ft^2 (GPS)

Use <, >, or = to complete each statement.

41. 4^6 ■ $4^3 \cdot 4^2$ >
42. 36 ■ $6^2 \cdot 6^2$ <
43. 5^{16} ■ $5^8 \cdot 5^2$ >

44. The radius of Venus is about 6.05×10^3 km. Use the formula S.A. $= 4\pi r^2$ to approximate the surface area of Venus. about 4.60×10^8 km^2

45. **Challenge** If $(h + h) \cdot (h \cdot h) = 16$, what is the value of h? 2

Test Prep and Mixed Review

Practice

Multiple Choice

46. Look for a pattern in the table at the right. Based on the pattern in the table, what value of x makes the statement $4^{15} = 2^x$ true? C

Powers of 4	Powers of 2
$4^2 = 16$	$2^4 = 16$
$4^3 = 64$	$2^6 = 64$
$4^4 = 256$	$2^8 = 256$
$4^5 = 1024$	$2^{10} = 1024$

   A 15 C 30
   B 20 D 7.5

47. On a typing test, Lana typed 900 words in 5 minutes. Sierra typed 980 words in 7 minutes. Which of the following statements is true? H
   F Lana's average typing rate was 67 words per minute faster than Sierra's average rate.
   G Sierra's average typing rate was 80 words per minute faster than Lana's average rate.
   H Lana's average typing rate was 40 words per minute faster than Sierra's average rate.
   J Lana's average typing rate was the same as Sierra's average typing rate.

GO for Help

For Exercises	See Lesson
48–50	4-1

Find each unit rate.

48. \$75 for 15 books \$5/book
49. 150 mi in 3.5 h about 43 mi/hr
50. \$150 for 250 lb \$.60/lb

Test Prep

Resources

For additional practice with a variety of test item formats:

- Test-Taking Strategies, p. 589
- Test Prep, p. 593
- Test-Taking Strategies with Transparencies

Alternative Assessment

Each student in a pair writes a number in scientific notation. Then partners together find the product of their numbers.

Scientific Notation

Calculators use scientific notation as a shorthand way to write very large numbers. If you enter a number with too many digits for a calculator to display, the calculator will use scientific notation to display the rounded number.

2346549887051 ENTER 2.346549887E12 ← The display shows the number rounded.

The number in the display is $2.346549887 \times 10^{12}$. The 12 after the E is the exponent on 10.

You can use your calculator to simplify expressions in scientific notation.

EXAMPLES Calculating With Scientific Notation

1 Use a calculator to find $(7.6 \times 10^6)(3.52 \times 10^3)$.

$(7.6 \times 10^6)\ (3.52 \times 10^3)$

7.6 EE 6 × 3.52 EE 3 ← Use EE to enter the exponent of the power of 10.

2.6752E10

The product is 2.6752×10^{10}.

2 Use a calculator to find $(2.8 \times 10^{12}) + (4.9 \times 10^{15})$.

2.8 EE 12 + 4.9 EE 15

4.9028E15

The sum is 4.9028×10^{15}.

Exercises

Use a calculator to simplify. Write your answer in scientific notation.

1. $(3.5 \times 10^{12})(2.3 \times 10^9)$ 8.05×10^{21}
2. $(2.99 \times 10^{16})(4.36 \times 10^{12})$ 1.30364×10^{29}
3. $(2.75 \times 10^4)^2$ 7.5625×10^8
4. $(5.54 \times 10^6) + (1.38 \times 10^6)$ 6.92×10^6
5. $(4.02 \times 10^{13}) - (2.01 \times 10^{13})$ 2.01×10^{13}
6. $(9.22 \times 10^{11})^3$ 7.84×10^{35}
7. **Mental Math** Simplify 10^{20}. Check your answer with a calculator. 1.0×10^{20}
8. Find the area of a square with side length 1.5×10^4 units. 2.25×10^8

Activity Lab

Scientific Notation

Students have worked with exponents and scientific notation in Lesson 12-3. In this activity, they are introduced to how to use a calculator to read, display, and calculate with numbers expressed in scientific notation.

Guided Instruction

Discuss the opening information about how and when calculators will display a number in scientific notation. Invite students to enter additional great numbers into the display to verify this calculator feature.

Error Prevention!

Remind students to be careful to enter the correct operation symbol when simplifying expressions with their calculators.

Example 1

Review the rule for multiplying powers with the same base (add the exponents). Ask: *If $10^6 \times 10^3 = 10^9$, then why doesn't the calculator display the answer as the product of 7.6 and 3.52, or 26.752, times 10^9?* The first factor of a number in scientific notation must be greater than or equal to 1 and less than 10; 7.6×3.52 is greater than 10.

Resources

- any scientific or graphing calculator

12-4

1. Plan

Objective
To multiply monomials and binomials

Examples
1 Multiplying Monomials
2 Multiplying a Monomial and Binomial
3 Using Area Models to Multiply Binomials

Math Understandings: p. 558D

Professional Development

Math Background

Polynomials can be named according to the number of terms they have. A polynomial with only one term, such as $5xy^2$ or $-b$, is called a *monomial.* Polynomials with two terms, such as $x + 3$ or $y^2 - 3y$, are called *binomials.*

More Math Background: p. 558D

Lesson Planning and Resources

See p. 558E for a list of the resources that support this lesson.

PowerPoint

Bell Ringer Practice

Check Skills You'll Need
Use student page, transparency, or PowerPoint. For intervention, direct students to:
Exponents and Multiplication
Lesson 12-3
Extra Skills and Word Problems Practice, Ch. 12

Algebra

12-4 Multiplying Polynomials

Check Skills You'll Need

1. **Vocabulary Review** The expression $2^3 \cdot 2^5$ can be simplified by adding the _?_. exponents

Simplify using a single exponent.

2. $x^4 \cdot x^5 \cdot x^6$ x^{15}
3. $(-a)^3 \cdot (-a)^7$ $(-a)^{10}$ or a^{10}

GO for Help Lesson 12-3

What You'll Learn

To multiply monomials and binomials

New Vocabulary monomial, binomial

Why Learn This?

Builders use formulas to find quantities such as the area of a foundation. When formulas involve more than one unknown value, you may need to multiply polynomials.

A polynomial with only one term, such as $4a^3$, is a **monomial.** To multiply monomials, multiply the coefficients and use the properties of exponents.

EXAMPLE Multiplying Monomials

1 Simplify $(4a^3)(-5a^2)$.

$$(4a^3)(-5a^2) = (4)(-5) \cdot a^3 \cdot a^2$$ ← Use the Commutative Property of Multiplication to rearrange the factors.

$$= -20 \cdot a^3 \cdot a^2$$ ← Multiply coefficients.

$$= -20 \cdot a^5$$ ← Add exponents.

Quick Check

1. Simplify $(2y^3)(4y)$. $8y^4$

Vocabulary Tip
The prefix *mono-* means "one." The prefix *bi-* means "two."

A **binomial** is a polynomial with two terms. You can use an area model to find the product of a monomial and a binomial.

This model shows the product of $3x$ and $2x + 3$.

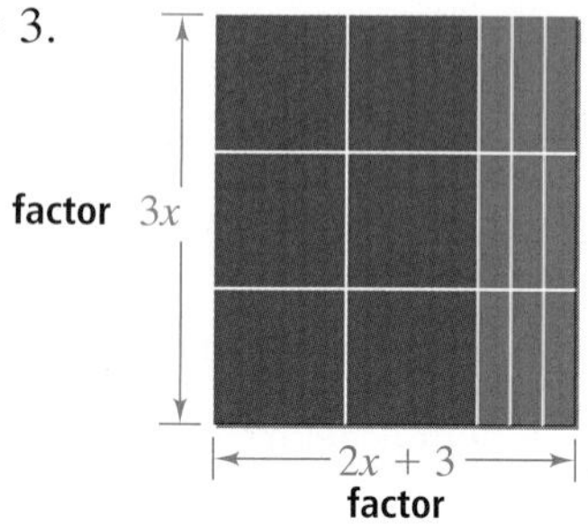

Since the array of tiles forms a rectangle, the area is the product of the height and the base, or $3x(2x + 3)$. The area is also the sum of the tiles, or $6x^2 + 9x$.

So $3x(2x + 3) = 6x^2 + 9x$.

Differentiated Instruction Solutions for All Learners

Special Needs L1	**Below Level** L2
Some students find it easier to draw the area models rather than manipulate tiles, while other students find the reverse to be true. Provide both grid paper and algebra tiles for students to use to make their models. learning style: tactile	Review the names of the algebra tile models: x^2, x, and 1, and emphasize that the long side of the x tile does NOT equal a whole number. learning style: verbal

You can also use the Distributive Property to find the product of a monomial and a binomial.

EXAMPLE Multiplying a Monomial and Binomial

2 **Multiple Choice** An architect is planning the foundation of a new house. The house must have certain dimensions to fit on the home lot. Which expression can he use to find the area of the foundation?

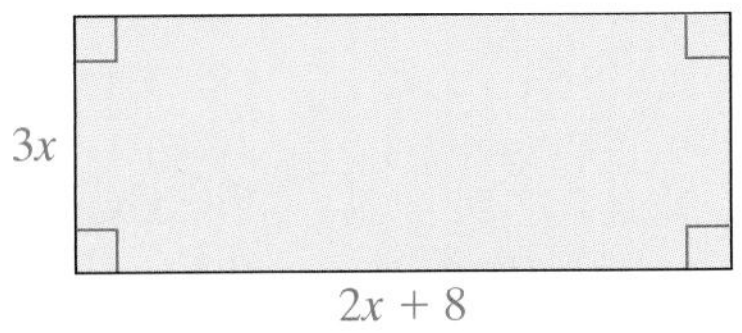

(A) $5x^2 + 8$ (B) $5x^2 + 24x$ (C) $6x + 24$ (D) $6x^2 + 24x$

To find the area, multiply the length, $3x$, times the width, $2x + 8$.

$A = \ell \cdot w = 3x(2x + 8)$

$= 3x \cdot 2x + 3x \cdot 8$ ← **Use the Distributive Property.**

$= 6x^2 + 24x$ ← **Simplify.**

Since $3x(2x + 8) = 6x^2 + 24x$, the correct answer is choice D.

Quick Check

2. Your neighbor is building an addition to her house. The expression $3r(5r + 5)$ represents the planned area of the house after it is remodeled. Simplify the polynomial to find the total area of the house, including the addition. $15r^2 + 15r$

You can use an area model to find the product of two binomials.

EXAMPLE Using Area Models to Multiply Binomials

3 Simplify $(2x + 1)(3x + 2)$.

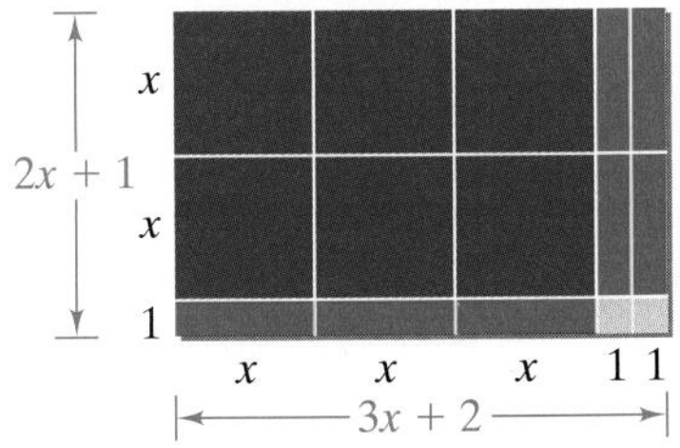

Count each type of tile.

There are six x^2 tiles.

There are seven x tiles.

There are two unit tiles.

So $(2x + 1)(3x + 2) = 6x^2 + 7x + 2$.

Quick Check 3a–c. See left.

3. Draw an area model or use algebra tiles to simplify each expression.

a. $(x + 2)(2x + 3)$ **b.** $(3x + 4)(2x + 1)$ **c.** $(x + 1)(2x + 5)$

GO Online

Video Tutor Help

Visit: PHSchool.com

Web Code: ase-0775

3a. $2x^2 + 7x + 6$

b. $6x^2 + 11x + 4$

c. $2x^2 + 7x + 5$

2. Teach

Activity Lab

Use before the lesson.

All in One Teaching Resources

Activity Lab 12-4: Multiplying Polynomials

Guided Instruction

Error Prevention!

Watch for students who may multiply rather than add exponents when multiplying powers having the same base. Review the multiplication of $y^2 \cdot y^3$ by writing

$y^2 \cdot y^3 = (y \cdot y) \cdot (y \cdot y \cdot y)$

$= y^{2+3}$ or y^5.

Alternative Method

In Example 3, show students that these tiles can be arranged in a different way, as long as they make a rectangle. Make sure that students relate building this rectangle and finding the product to finding the area of a rectangle with dimensions that equal the two binomial expressions.

PowerPoint

Additional Examples

1 Simplify $(3x^2)(-4x^3)$. $-12x^5$

2 If the width of a new house foundation is represented by $2x$ and the length is represented by $4x + 6$, which expression represents the area of the foundation? $8x^2 + 12x$

3 Use an area model to simplify $(x + 1)(3x + 1)$. $3x^2 + 4x + 1$

All in One Teaching Resources

- Daily Notetaking Guide 12-4 L3
- Adapted Notetaking 12-4 L1

Closure

- *How do you multiply two monomials?* Multiply the coefficients and multiply like variables by adding exponents.

Advanced Learners L4

Students relate multiplying 12(13) with $(x + 2)(x + 1)$ to develop a method of multiplying binomials.

learning style: verbal

English Language Learners ELL

Students are often confused by the word *monomial* because monomials have three parts: a coefficient, a variable (or variables), and an exponent (or exponents). Explain that *monomial* refers to a single term and review the definition of a *term*.

learning style: verbal

3. Practice

Assignment Guide

Check Your Understanding

Go over Exercises 1–6 in class before assigning the Homework Exercises.

Homework Exercises

A	Practice by Example	7–21
B	Apply Your Skills	22–31
C	Challenge	32
Test Prep and Mixed Review		33–37

Homework Quick Check

To check students' understanding of key skills and concepts, go over Exercises 7, 18, 22, 25, and 29.

Differentiated Instruction Resources

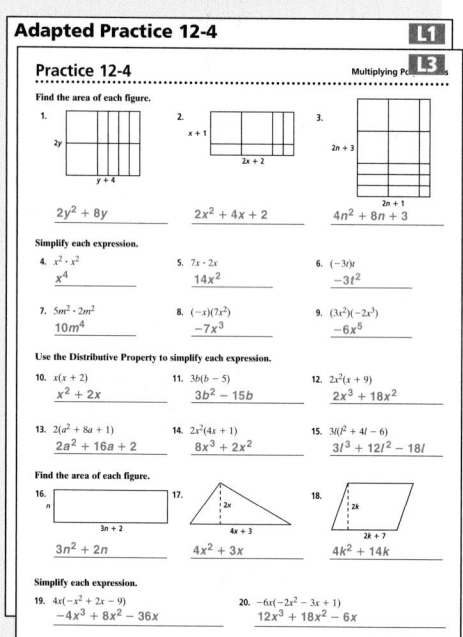

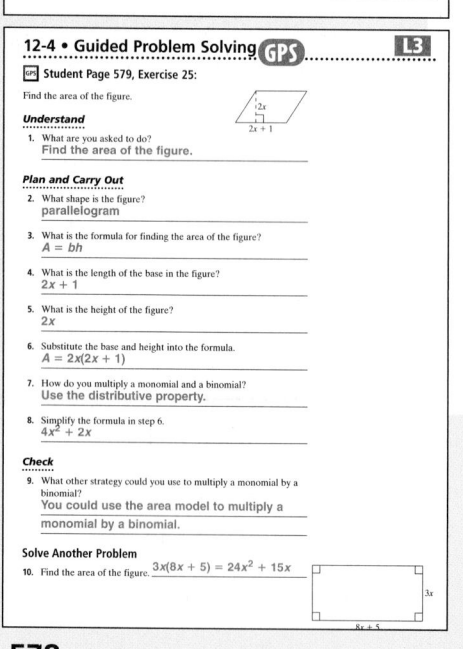

Adapted Practice 12-4 L1

Practice 12-4 L3 Multiplying Po[lynomial]s

Find the area of each figure.

1. 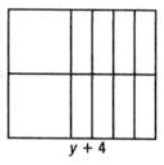
2y, y + 4
$2y^2 + 8y$

2. 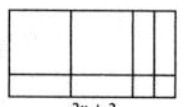
x + 1, 2x + 2
$2x^2 + 4x + 2$

3. 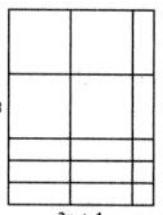
2n + 3, 2n + 1
$4n^2 + 8n + 3$

Simplify each expression.

4. $x^2 \cdot x^2$ x^4
5. $7x \cdot 2x$ $14x^2$
6. $(-3t)t$ $-3t^2$
7. $5m^2 \cdot 2m^2$ $10m^4$
8. $(-x)(7x^2)$ $-7x^3$
9. $(3x^2)(-2x^3)$ $-6x^5$

Use the Distributive Property to simplify each expression.

10. $x(x + 2)$ $x^2 + 2x$
11. $3b(b - 5)$ $3b^2 - 15b$
12. $2x^2(x + 9)$ $2x^3 + 18x^2$
13. $2(a^2 + 8a + 1)$ $2a^2 + 16a + 2$
14. $2x^2(4x + 1)$ $8x^3 + 2x^2$
15. $3l(l^2 + 4l - 6)$ $3l^3 + 12l^2 - 18l$

Find the area of each figure.

16. 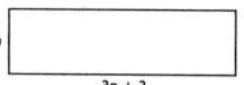
n, 3n + 2
$3n^2 + 2n$

17. 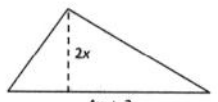
2x, 4x + 3
$4x^2 + 3x$

18. 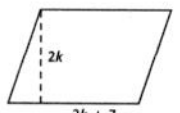
2k, 2k + 7
$4k^2 + 14k$

Simplify each expression.

19. $4x(-x^2 + 2x - 9)$ $-4x^3 + 8x^2 - 36x$
20. $-6x(-2x^2 - 3x + 1)$ $12x^3 + 18x^2 - 6x$

12-4 • Guided Problem Solving GPS L3

GPS Student Page 579, Exercise 25:

Find the area of the figure.

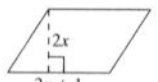
2x, 2x + 1

Understand

1. What are you asked to do?
Find the area of the figure.

Plan and Carry Out

2. What shape is the figure?
parallelogram
3. What is the formula for finding the area of the figure?
$A = bh$
4. What is the length of the base in the figure?
$2x + 1$
5. What is the height of the figure?
$2x$
6. Substitute the base and height into the formula.
$A = 2x(2x + 1)$
7. How do you multiply a monomial and a binomial?
Use the distributive property.
8. Simplify the formula in step 6.
$4x^2 + 2x$

Check

9. What other strategy could you use to multiply a monomial by a binomial?
You could use the area model to multiply a monomial by a binomial.

Solve Another Problem

10. Find the area of the figure. $3x(8x + 5) = 24x^2 + 15x$

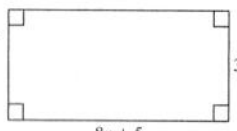
3x, 8x + 5

Check Your Understanding

1. **Vocabulary** How are a monomial and a binomial different?
A monomial has one term, whereas a binomial has two terms.

Simplify each expression.

2. $(-8y)(2y)$ $-16y^2$
3. $5a \cdot 3a$ $15a^2$
4. $x^5 \cdot x$ x^6

For Exercises 5–6, use the area model at the right.

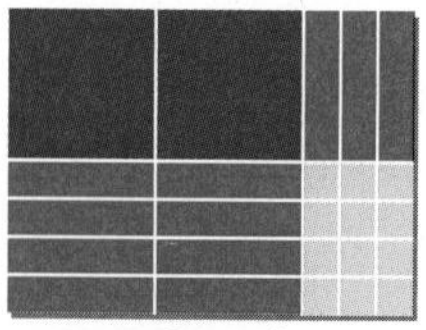
x + 4
2x + 3

5. Write the factors shown in the model. $(x + 4)(2x + 3)$
6. Find the product of these factors.
$2x^2 + 11x + 12$

Homework Exercises

For more exercises, see Extra Skills and Word Problems.

GO for Help

For Exercises	See Examples
7–12	1
13–19	2
20–21	3

A Simplify each expression.

7. $(-3t^2)(-4t^3)$ $12t^5$
8. $4g^4 \cdot 3g^3$ $12g^7$
9. $(-z^3)(6z^2)$ $-6z^5$
10. $(7x^2)(-2x^3)$ $-14x^5$
11. $(10s^2)(-4s)$ $-40s^3$
12. $(5c^3)(-4c^4)$ $-20c^7$

Simplify each expression.

13. $a(a - 3)$ $a^2 - 3a$
14. $2m(m - 7)$ $2m^2 - 14m$
15. $7(3s^2 + 1)$ $21s^2 + 7$
16. $-3y(y^2 - 6y)$ $-3y^3 + 18y^2$
17. $2k(5k - 1)$ $10k^2 - 2k$
18. $-3d^2(d - 4)$ $-3d^3 + 12d^2$

19. The length of a rectangle is four more than twice the width. The product $x(2x + 4)$ represents the area of the figure. Simplify this product. $2x^2 + 4x$

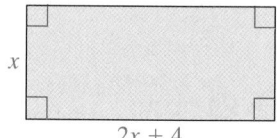
x
2x + 4

Use the area model to find each product.

20. 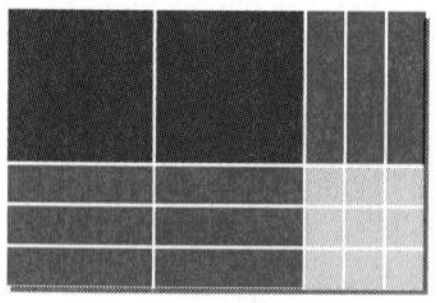
x + 3
2x + 3
$2x^2 + 9x + 9$

21. 
2x + 1
2x + 2
$4x^2 + 6x + 2$

B GPS 22. **Guided Problem Solving** An architect is planning a deck. It will be $2(2x + 4)$ ft long and $3(x - 4)$ ft wide. Write an expression for the area of the deck when it is completed. $(12x^2 - 24x - 96)$ ft^2
- Use the area formula $A = \ell w$.
- Simplify the expression.

35–37. See back of book.

Go Online
Homework Video Tutor
Visit: PHSchool.com
Web Code: ase-1204

Find the area of each figure.

23. 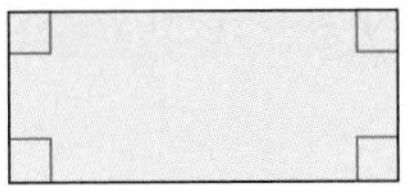

$6x^2 + 4x$

24. 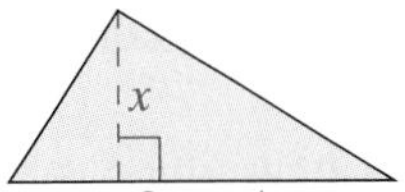

$\frac{3}{2}x^2 - 2x$

25. GPS 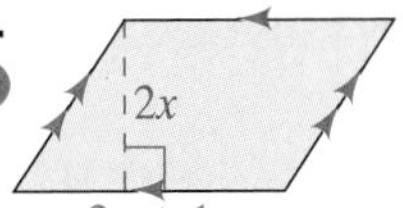

$4x^2 + 2x$

26. Use the Distributive Property to simplify $-w^2(w^2 + 2w - 4)$. $-w^4 - 2w^3 + 4w^2$

27. **Writing in Math** Explain how to multiply $(x + 1)$ and $(x + 2)$ using an area model. See left.

27. Model $x + 1$ along the vertical and model $x + 2$ along the horizontal. Since length times width is the area of a rectangle, complete the rectangle. The area of the array of tiles is $x^2 + 3x + 2$.

State whether each expression is best described as a *monomial*, a *binomial*, a *polynomial*, or *none of these*.

28. $2n^4 + 3n$ binomial

29. $-5n^4$ monomial

30. $6n^2 + n - 2$ polynomial

31. 5 monomial

Ⓒ 32. **Challenge** Find the factors of each polynomial by finding the GCF of the terms of the polynomial.

Sample $2a^2 + 6a = 2a \cdot a + 2a \cdot 3 = 2a(a + 3)$

a. $3x^2 + 9$ $3(x^2 + 3)$

b. $5y^2 + 10y$ $5y(y + 2)$

c. $8a^3 + 4a^2 + 12a$ $4a(2a^2 + a + 3)$

Test Prep and Mixed Review

Practice

Multiple Choice

33. Andrea is twice as tall as Jordan. Caitlin is half as tall as Harry. Harry is 4 inches taller than Alec. Alec is 5 feet 10 inches tall. Jordan is 2 inches shorter than Caitlin. How tall is Andrea? D

Ⓐ 4 ft 5 in. Ⓑ 4 ft 6 in. Ⓒ 5 ft 5 in. Ⓓ 5 ft 10 in.

34. The top and side views of a solid figure are shown. Which of the following is the solid figure represented by these views? F

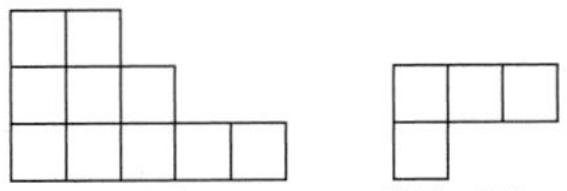

Ⓕ 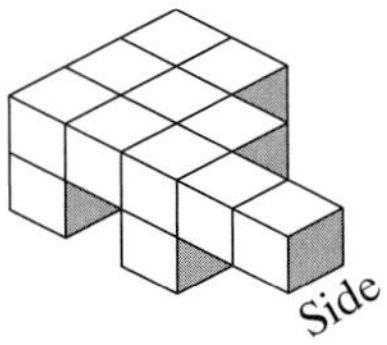

Ⓗ 

Ⓖ 

Ⓙ 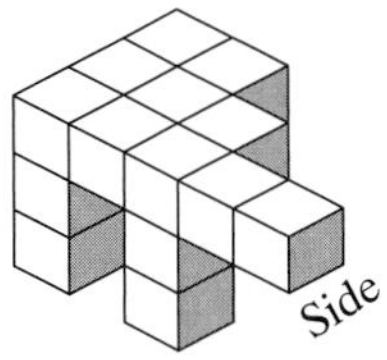

Graph each linear function. 35–37. See margin.

35. $y = 7 - 3x$

36. $y = 8x + 10$

37. $y = -x + 2$

Go for Help

For Exercises	See Lesson
35–37	11-5

Online lesson quiz, PHSchool.com, Web Code: asa-1204

Alternative Assessment

Together partners decide who writes a binomial in terms of x and who writes a monomial in terms of x. Partners together find the product of the monomial and binomial.

Test Prep

Resources

For additional practice with a variety of test item formats:

- Test-Taking Strategies, p. 589
- Test Prep, p. 593
- Test-Taking Strategies with Transparencies

4. Assess & Reteach

PowerPoint

Lesson Quiz

Simplify each expression in 1–3.

1. $(-7c^3)(4c)$ $-28c^4$
2. $x(3x + 2)$ $3x^2 + 2x$
3. $-2m^2(m - 1)$ $-2m^3 + 2m^2$
4. If the base of a parallelogram-shaped playground is represented by $6y$, and the height is represented by $4y - 3$, which expression represents the area? $24y^2 - 18y$

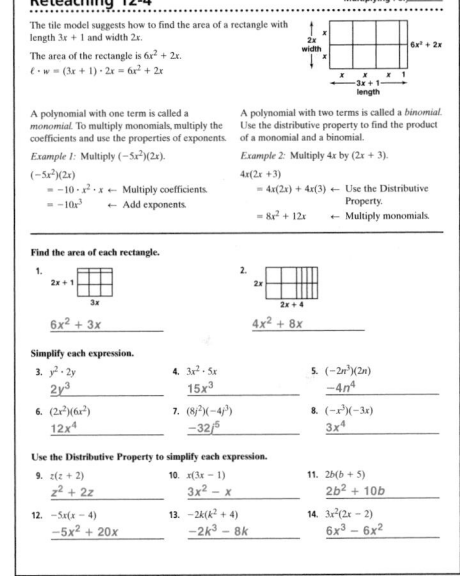

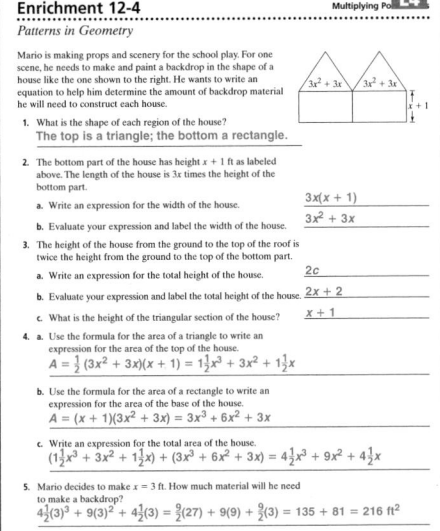

Reteaching 12-4 Multiplying Poly L2

The tile model suggests how to find the area of a rectangle with length $3x + 1$ and width $2x$.

The area of the rectangle is $6x^2 + 2x$.

$\ell \cdot w = (3x + 1) \cdot 2x = 6x^2 + 2x$

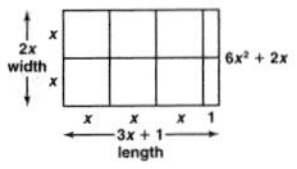

A polynomial with one term is called a *monomial*. To multiply monomials, multiply the coefficients and use the properties of exponents.

Example 1: Multiply $(-5x^2)(2x)$.

$(-5x^2)(2x)$
$= -10 \cdot x^2 \cdot x$ ← Multiply coefficients.
$= -10x^3$ ← Add exponents.

A polynomial with two terms is called a *binomial*. Use the distributive property to find the product of a monomial and a binomial.

Example 2: Multiply $4x$ by $(2x + 3)$.

$4x(2x + 3)$
$= 4x(2x) + 4x(3)$ ← Use the Distributive Property.
$= 8x^2 + 12x$ ← Multiply monomials.

Find the area of each rectangle.

1. 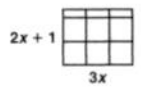

$6x^2 + 3x$

2. 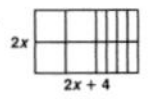

$4x^2 + 8x$

Simplify each expression.

3. $y^2 \cdot 2y$ $2y^3$
4. $3x^2 \cdot 5x$ $15x^3$
5. $(-2n^3)(2n)$ $-4n^4$
6. $(2x^2)(6x^2)$ $12x^4$
7. $(8j^2)(-4j^3)$ $-32j^5$
8. $(-x^3)(-3x)$ $3x^4$

Use the Distributive Property to simplify each expression.

9. $z(z + 2)$ $z^2 + 2z$
10. $x(3x - 1)$ $3x^2 - x$
11. $2b(b + 5)$ $2b^2 + 10b$
12. $-5x(x - 4)$ $-5x^2 + 20x$
13. $-2k(k^2 + 4)$ $-2k^3 - 8k$
14. $3x^2(2x - 2)$ $6x^3 - 6x^2$

Enrichment 12-4 Multiplying Po L4

Patterns in Geometry

Mario is making props and scenery for the school play. For one scene, he needs to make and paint a backdrop in the shape of a house like the one shown to the right. He wants to write an equation to help him determine the amount of backdrop material he will need to construct each house.

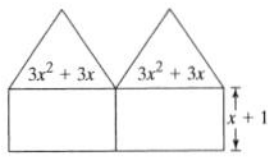

1. What is the shape of each region of the house?
The top is a triangle; the bottom a rectangle.

2. The bottom part of the house has height $x + 1$ ft as labeled above. The length of the house is $3x$ times the height of the bottom part.
   a. Write an expression for the width of the house. $3x(x + 1)$
   b. Evaluate your expression and label the width of the house. $3x^2 + 3x$

3. The height of the house from the ground to the top of the roof is twice the height from the ground to the top of the bottom part.
   a. Write an expression for the total height of the house. $2c$
   b. Evaluate your expression and label the total height of the house. $2x + 2$
   c. What is the height of the triangular section of the house? $x + 1$

4. a. Use the formula for the area of a triangle to write an expression for the area of the top of the house.
   $A = \frac{1}{2}(3x^2 + 3x)(x + 1) = 1\frac{1}{2}x^3 + 3x^2 + 1\frac{1}{2}x$
   b. Use the formula for the area of a rectangle to write an expression for the area of the base of the house.
   $A = (x + 1)(3x^2 + 3x) = 3x^3 + 6x^2 + 3x$
   c. Write an expression for the total area of the house.
   $(1\frac{1}{2}x^3 + 3x^2 + 1\frac{1}{2}x) + (3x^3 + 6x^2 + 3x) = 4\frac{1}{2}x^3 + 9x^2 + 4\frac{1}{2}x$

5. Mario decides to make $x = 3$ ft. How much material will he need to make a backdrop?
$4\frac{1}{2}(3)^3 + 9(3)^2 + 4\frac{1}{2}(3) = \frac{9}{2}(27) + 9(9) + \frac{9}{2}(3) = 135 + 81 = 216\ ft^2$

Checkpoint Quiz

Use this Checkpoint Quiz to check students' understanding of the skills and concepts of Lessons 12-3 through 12-4.

Resources

- All in One Teaching Resources Checkpoint Quiz 2
- ExamView Assessment Suite CD-ROM
- Success Tracker Online Intervention

MATH AT WORK

Video Game Programmers

This feature describes some ways that video game programmers use math.

Guided Instruction

After students finish reading the selection, ask questions such as:

- *What kind of math do video game programmers use?* **Sample: logic, algebra, geometry**
- *What math skills do you use when you **play** video games? Explain.* **Sample: geometry—being able to visualize spatial relationships; arithmetic—keeping score**

Checkpoint Quiz 2

Lessons 12-3 through 12-4

Write each expression using a single exponent.

1. $4.7^6 \cdot 4.7^{15}$ 4.7^{21}
2. $(-4a)^2(-4a)^2$ $(-4a)^4$
3. $xy^5 \cdot x^3y^7$ x^4y^{12}

Multiply. Write each product in scientific notation.

4. $50(6 \times 10^3)$ 3.0×10^5
5. $(3 \times 10^7)(5 \times 10^4)$ 1.5×10^{12}
6. $(4 \times 10^4)(9 \times 10^2)$ 3.6×10^7

Simplify each expression.

7. $7f^5 \cdot 4f^3$ $28f^8$
8. $(3.1g^6)(5g^2)$ $15.5g^8$
9. $(-8h^8)(2.2h^{10})$ $-17.6h^{18}$
10. $-5j(j^2 - 9j)$ $-5j^3 + 45j^2$
11. $6k(k - 1)$ $6k^2 - 6k$
12. $10m^2(3m - 4)$ $30m^3 - 40m^2$

Use the area model to find each product.

13.

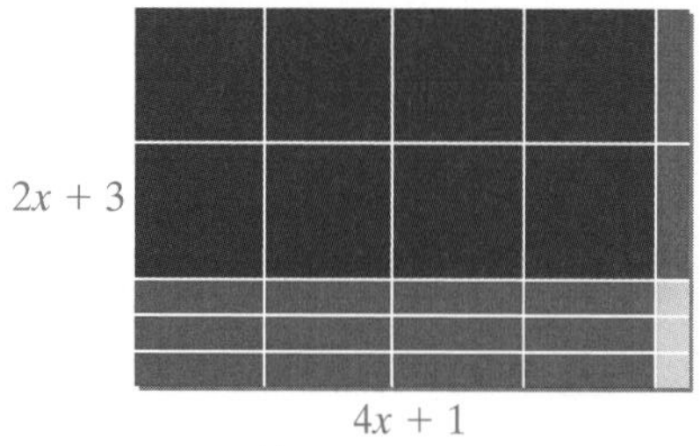

$8x^2 + 14x + 3$

14.

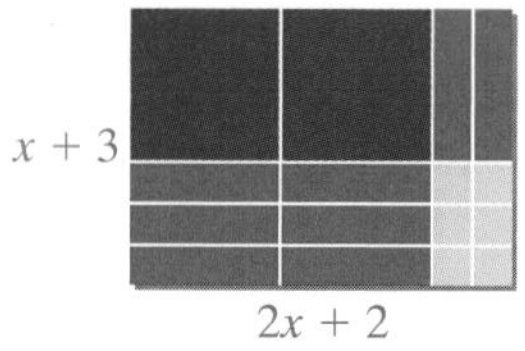

$2x^2 + 8x + 6$

MATH AT WORK

Video Game Programmers

Video game programmers write the code that drives the actions in video games.

Video game programmers need a strong background in mathematics and computer programming. They use logic to design their programs. Then they use algebra to write the detailed instructions that the computer understands. The result is a game that is fun to play.

Go Online PHSchool.com **For:** Information about video game programmers
Web Code: asb-2031

12-5 Exponents and Division

Check Skills You'll Need

1. **Vocabulary Review** Is the expression x^5 an *exponent* or a *power*? power

Write each expression using exponents.

2. $7 \cdot 7 \cdot 7 \cdot 7$ 7^4
3. $4 \cdot 4 \cdot 4$ 4^3
4. $5 \cdot 5$ 5^2
5. $1 \cdot 1 \cdot 1 \cdot 1 \cdot 1$ 1^5

GO for Help Lesson 2-7

What You'll Learn

To divide powers with the same base and to simplify expressions with negative exponents

Why Learn This?

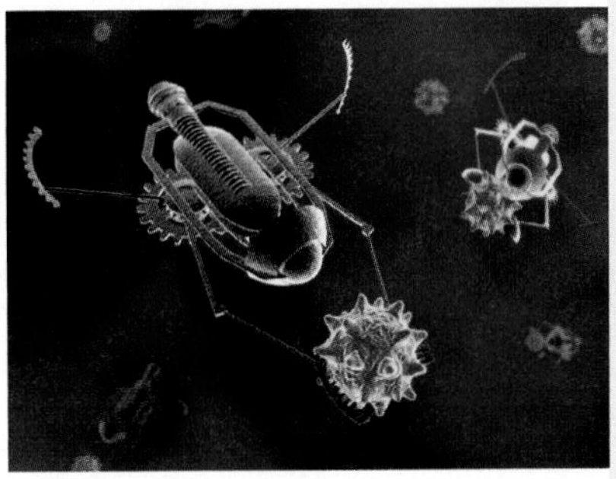

Nanorobots are microscopic machines that may soon be used to fight illness inside the human body. When working with very small numbers, such as the length of a nanorobot, you often divide expressions with exponents.

You can divide powers with the same base by writing out all the factors.

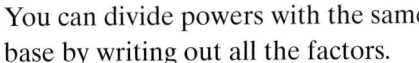

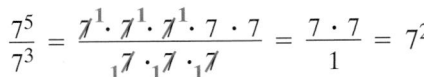

$$\frac{7^5}{7^3} = \frac{\overset{1}{\cancel{7}} \cdot \overset{1}{\cancel{7}} \cdot \overset{1}{\cancel{7}} \cdot 7 \cdot 7}{\underset{1}{\cancel{7}} \cdot \underset{1}{\cancel{7}} \cdot \underset{1}{\cancel{7}}} = \frac{7 \cdot 7}{1} = 7^2$$

Notice that $5 - 3 = 2$. This example suggests the following rule.

KEY CONCEPTS Dividing Powers With the Same Base

To divide nonzero numbers or variables with the same nonzero base, subtract the exponents.

Arithmetic	Algebra
$\frac{8^5}{8^3} = 8^{(5-3)} = 8^2$	$\frac{a^m}{a^n} = a^{(m-n)}$, where $a \neq 0$

EXAMPLE Dividing Powers

1 Write $\frac{m^{12}}{m^5}$ using a single exponent.

$\frac{m^{12}}{m^5} = m^{(12-5)}$ ← Subtract exponents with the same base.

$= m^7$ ← Simplify.

Quick Check

1. Write $\frac{w^8}{w^5}$ using a single exponent. w^3

12-5

1. Plan

Objective

To divide powers with the same base and to simplify expressions with negative exponents

Examples

1. Dividing Powers
2. Dividing Numbers in Scientific Notation
3. Expressions With a Zero Exponent
4. Expressions With Negative Exponents

Math Understandings: p. 558D

Professional Development

Math Background

Just as you can multiply powers with the same base by adding the exponents, you can divide powers with the same base by subtracting the exponents. Division of powers requires two important rules: For any nonzero number, x, $x^0 = 1$ and $x^{-1} = \frac{1}{x}$. Negative exponents can be used to write numbers which are less than 1 and greater than 0 in scientific notation. So, for example, 0.0035 is written as 3.5×10^{-3}.

More Math Background: p. 558D

Lesson Planning and Resources

See p. 558E for a list of the resources that support this lesson.

PowerPoint

Bell Ringer Practice

Check Skills You'll Need
Use student page, transparency, or PowerPoint. For intervention, direct students to:

Powers and Exponents
Lesson 2-7
Extra Skills and Word Problems Practice, Ch. 2

Differentiated Instruction Solutions for All Learners

Special Needs L1
After writing out the factors of a quotient of powers with the same base, students may cancel too few or too many factors. Remind them that they can only cancel pairs of the same factors (one from the numerator and one from the denominator).
learning style: tactile

Below Level L2
Students write as a product of factors and find the value of $(-2)^2$, $(-2)^3$, -2^2, -2^3. $(-2)(-2) = 4$; $(-2)(-2)(-2) = -8$; $-(2)(2) = -4$; $-(2)(2)(2) = -8$
learning style: verbal

2. Teach

Activity Lab

Use before the lesson.

All in One Teaching Resources

Activity Lab 12-5: Exponents and Division

Guided Instruction

Error Prevention!

In Example 1, remind students that subtracting exponents is the method for dividing powers, and that the numerical bases are *not* divided.

Alternative Method

After Example 1, remind students how to multiply powers by having them find $2^3 \cdot 2^4$. Then ask:

- *Since $2^7 = 2^3 \cdot 2^4$, what must be the quotient of $2^7 \div 2^4$?* 2^3
- *What method does this suggest for dividing powers?* subtracting the exponents

Example 2

Provide students with a blank grid.

Teaching Tip

After Example 2, ask:

- *Is 7.14×10^{-3} a positive or a negative number?* positive
- *What does the exponent of −3 tell you about the number?* The number is between 0 and 1.

PowerPoint

Additional Examples

1 Write $\frac{x^{14}}{x^9}$ using a single exponent. x^5

2 The distance between the sun and Jupiter is about 4.84×10^8 miles. Light travels at about 1.1×10^7 miles per minute. Use the formula time $= \frac{\text{distance}}{\text{speed}}$ to estimate how long it takes sunlight to reach Jupiter. Write your answer in standard form. 44 minutes

The rule for dividing powers with the same base applies to dividing numbers in scientific notation.

EXAMPLE Dividing Numbers in Scientific Notation

2 **Gridded Response** The distance between the sun and a comet is about 2.79×10^8 miles. Light travels about 1.1×10^7 miles per minute.

Use the formula time $= \frac{\text{distance}}{\text{speed}}$ to estimate how many minutes sunlight takes to reach the comet. Write your answer in standard form and round to the nearest tenth.

$\text{time} = \frac{\text{distance}}{\text{speed}}$ ← **Use the formula for time.**

$= \frac{2.79}{1.1} \times \frac{10^8}{10^7}$ ← **Substitute. Write as a product of quotients.**

$= \frac{2.79}{1.1} \times 10^1$ ← **Subtract exponents.**

$\approx 2.54 \times 10^1$ ← **Divide.**

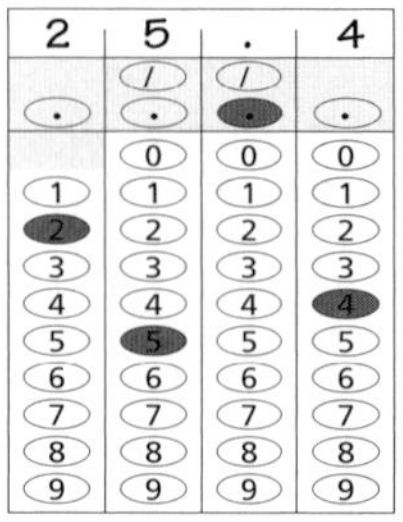

Sunlight takes about 2.54×10^1 minutes, or 25.4 minutes, to reach the comet.

Quick Check

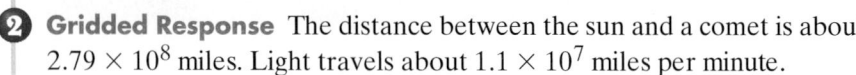

2. Astronomy The distance between the sun and Earth is about 9.3×10^7 miles. Light travels about 1.1×10^7 miles per minute. Use the formula time $= \frac{\text{distance}}{\text{speed}}$ to estimate how long sunlight takes to reach Earth. Write your answer in standard form and round to the nearest tenth. 8.5 min

What does the exponent 0 mean? Consider finding the quotient $\frac{3^5}{3^5}$.

If you subtract exponents, $\frac{3^5}{3^5} = 3^{(5-5)} = 3^0$.

If you write factors, $\frac{3^5}{3^5} = \frac{\cancel{3}^1 \cdot \cancel{3}^1 \cdot \cancel{3}^1 \cdot \cancel{3}^1 \cdot \cancel{3}^1}{{}_1\cancel{3} \cdot {}_1\cancel{3} \cdot {}_1\cancel{3} \cdot {}_1\cancel{3} \cdot {}_1\cancel{3}}$

$= \frac{1}{1} = 1.$

Vocabulary Tip

Read 3^0 as "3 to the zero power."

Notice that $\frac{3^5}{3^5} = 3^0$ and $\frac{3^5}{3^5} = 1$. This suggests the following rule.

KEY CONCEPTS Zero as an Exponent

For any nonzero number a, $a^0 = 1$.

Example $9^0 = 1$

Differentiated Instruction Solutions for All Learners

Advanced Learners L4

Students compare the value of $-x^0$ and $(-x)^0$. −1 and 1

learning style: verbal

English Language Learners ELL

Remind students that *inverse operations* undo each other. Show by an example that if exponents are added when powers with the same base are multiplied, they must be subtracted when powers with the same base are divided since multiplication and division are inverse operations.

learning style: verbal

EXAMPLE Expressions With a Zero Exponent

3 Simplify each expression.

a. $(-8)^0$ **b.** $3m^0$

$(-8)^0 = 1$ ← **Simplify.** → $3m^0 = 3 \cdot 1 = 3$

Quick Check

3. Simplify each expression.

a. $(-9)^0$ 1 **b.** $(2r)^0$ 1 **c.** $2r^0$ 2

To understand negative exponents, consider finding the quotient $\frac{6^2}{6^5}$.

If you subtract exponents, $\frac{6^2}{6^5} = 6^{(2-5)} = 6^{-3}$.

If you write factors, $\frac{6^2}{6^5} = \frac{\cancel{6}^1 \cdot \cancel{6}^1}{{}_1\cancel{6} \cdot {}_1\cancel{6} \cdot 6 \cdot 6 \cdot 6}$

$= \frac{1}{6 \cdot 6 \cdot 6} = \frac{1}{6^3}$.

Notice that $\frac{6^2}{6^5} = 6^{-3}$ and $\frac{6^2}{6^5} = \frac{1}{6^3}$. This suggests the following rule.

KEY CONCEPTS **Negative Exponents**

For any nonzero number a and integer n, $a^{-n} = \frac{1}{a^n}$.

Example $8^{-5} = \frac{1}{8^5}$

To simplify an expression with negative exponents, first write the expression with a positive exponent.

EXAMPLE Expressions With Negative Exponents

4 Simplify each expression.

a. 3^{-2} **b.** $(y)^{-6}$

$3^{-2} = \frac{1}{3^2}$ ← **Use a positive exponent.** → $(y)^{-6} = \frac{1}{y^6}$

$= \frac{1}{9}$ ← **Simplify.**

Quick Check

4. Simplify each expression.

a. 3^{-1} $\frac{1}{3}$ **b.** w^{-4} $\frac{1}{w^4}$ **c.** $(-2)^{-3}$ $-\frac{1}{8}$

Guided Instruction

Example 4

Some students may read 3^{-2} as $3 - 2$ or $3(-2)$. Have students read the problem aloud as "3 to the negative 2."

PowerPoint

Additional Examples

3 Simplify each expression.

a. $(-5)^0$ 1 **b.** $5y^0$ 5

4 Simplify each expression.

a. 2^{-3} $\frac{1}{8}$ **b.** $(p)^{-8}$ $\frac{1}{p^8}$

All in One Teaching Resources

- Daily Notetaking Guide 12-5 L3
- Adapted Notetaking 12-5 L1

Closure

- *How do you divide powers with the same base?* Subtract the exponents.
- *What is the value of any nonzero number with a zero exponent?* 1

3. Practice

Assignment Guide

Check Your Understanding

Go over Exercises 1–5 in class before assigning the Homework Exercises.

Homework Exercises

A	Practice by Example	6–22
B	Apply Your Skills	23–38
C	Challenge	39
	Test Prep and Mixed Review	40–44

Homework Quick Check

To check students' understanding of key skills and concepts, go over Exercises 11, 17, 24, 33, and 35.

Differentiated Instruction Resources

Adapted Practice 12-5 L1

Practice 12-5 Exponents an[d Division] L3

Simplify each expression.

1. 8^{-2} $\frac{1}{64}$
2. $(-3)^0$ 1
3. 5^{-1} $\frac{1}{5}$
4. 18^0 1
5. 2^{-5} $\frac{1}{32}$
6. 3^{-3} $\frac{1}{27}$
7. 2^{-3} $\frac{1}{8}$
8. 5^{-2} $\frac{1}{25}$
9. $\frac{4^4}{4}$ 64
10. $8^6 \div 8^8$ $\frac{1}{64}$
11. $\frac{(-3)^6}{(-3)^8}$ $\frac{1}{9}$
12. $\frac{8^4}{8^0}$ 4,096
13. $1^{15} \div 1^{18}$ 1
14. $7 \div 7^4$ $\frac{1}{343}$
15. $\frac{(-4)^8}{(-4)^4}$ 256
16. $\frac{10^9}{10^{12}}$ $\frac{1}{1{,}000}$
17. $\frac{b^{12}}{b^4}$ b^8
18. $\frac{g^9}{g^{15}}$ $\frac{1}{g^6}$
19. $x^{16} \div x^7$ x^9
20. $v^{20} \div v^{25}$ $\frac{1}{v^5}$

Complete each equation.

21. $\frac{1}{3^5} = 3^{?}$ −5
22. $\frac{1}{(-2)^7} = -2^{?}$ −7
23. $\frac{1}{x^2} = x^{?}$ −2
24. $\frac{1}{-125} = (-5)^{?}$ −3
25. $\frac{1}{1{,}000} = 10^{?}$ −3
26. $\frac{5^{10}}{?} = 5^5$ 5^5
27. $\frac{z}{z^{?}} = z^{-3}$ 5
28. $\frac{q^5}{?} = q^{-7}$ q^{12}

Is each statement true or false? Explain your reasoning.

29. $(-1)^3 = 1^{-3}$ false: $(-1)^3 = -1$, but $1^{-3} = 1$
30. $3^{-1} \cdot 3^{-1} = 3^1$ false: $3^{-1} \cdot 3^{-1} = \frac{1}{3^2}$ or 3^{-2}
31. $2^2 \cdot 2^{-2} = 1$ true: $2^2 \cdot 2^{-2} = 2^0 = 1$
32. $7^2 \cdot (-7)^3 = (-7)^{-6}$ false: $7^2 \cdot (-7)^3 = (-7)^5$

12-5 • Guided Problem Solving GPS L3

GPS Student Page 584, Exercise 24:

Astronomy The Sun's diameter is 1.39×10^6 kilometers. Earth's diameter is 1.28×10^4 kilometers. How many times greater is the Sun's diameter than Earth's diameter?

Understand

1. Which diameter is larger? the sun's
2. What are you being asked to find? how many times larger the sun's diameter is than the Earth's diameter

Plan and Carry Out

3. The diameters are in scientific notation, and the numbers 1.28 and 1.39 are close in value, so what do you need to compare? the exponents
4. When dividing powers with the same base, what do you do to the exponents? subtract
5. Subtract the exponents and write the power in standard form. $10^6 - 10^4 = 10^2$; $10^2 = 100$
6. How many times greater is the Sun's diameter than Earth's? 100

Check

7. What other strategy could you use to find the answer? Find the exact number of times the sun's diameter is greater than the Earth's. 1.08×10^2, or 108, is approximately 100.

Solve Another Problem

8. When you donate a pint of blood, you lose about 2.3×10^{12} red blood cells. If your body can produce about 2×10^6 red blood cells per second, about how many seconds would it take for your body to replenish the red blood cells lost through donation? Write your answer in standard form. $10^{12} \div 10^6 = 10^6$; $10^6 = 1{,}000{,}000$ s

Check Your Understanding

1. Positive; any nonzero number to the power zero is equal to one.

3. $\frac{2 \cdot 2 \cdot 2 \cdot 2 \cdot 2 \cdot 2}{2 \cdot 2 \cdot 2 \cdot 2 \cdot 2} = 2^1$
4. $\frac{3 \cdot 3 \cdot 3 \cdot 3}{3 \cdot 3} = 3^2$
5. $\frac{8 \cdot 8 \cdot 8 \cdot 8 \cdot 8}{8 \cdot 8} = 8^3$

1. **Reasoning** Is $(-1)^0$ a positive or a negative number? Explain.
2. **Mental Math** Find the value of $\frac{123^5}{123^4}$. 123

Write out the factors of each expression. Then simplify using a single exponent. Exercise 3 has been started for you. 3–5. See left.

3. $\frac{2^6}{2^5} = \frac{2 \cdot 2 \cdot 2 \cdot 2 \cdot 2 \cdot 2}{2 \cdot 2 \cdot 2 \cdot 2 \cdot 2}$
4. $\frac{3^4}{3^2}$
5. $\frac{8^5}{8^2}$

Homework Exercises

For more exercises, see Extra Skills and Word Problems.

GO for Help

For Exercises	See Examples
6–13	1
14	2
15–22	3–4

A **Write each expression using a single exponent.**

6. $\frac{a^5}{a^3}$ a^2
7. $\frac{x^9}{x^5}$ x^4
8. $\frac{c^7}{c^2}$ c^5
9. $\frac{(-1)^5}{(-1)^4}$ $(-1)^1$
10. $\frac{23^{12}}{23^8}$ 23^4
11. $\frac{135^{10}}{135^1}$ 135^9
12. $\frac{(-7)^{99}}{(-7)^{98}}$ $(-7)^1$
13. $\frac{(-9)^{32}}{(-9)^{15}}$ $(-9)^{17}$

14. **Astronomy** The distance from the sun to Saturn is about 8.88×10^8 miles. The speed of light is about 1.1×10^7 miles per minute. Use the formula time $= \frac{\text{distance}}{\text{speed}}$ to estimate how long sunlight takes to reach Saturn. Round the answer to the nearest tenth. 80.7 min

Simplify each expression.

15. 4^0 1
16. $(-3)^0$ 1
17. u^0 1
18. $(3t)^0$ 1
19. 10^{-2} $\frac{1}{100}$
20. b^{-6} $\frac{1}{b^6}$
21. x^{-4} $\frac{1}{x^4}$
22. 7^{-1} $\frac{1}{7}$

B **GPS**

23. **Guided Problem Solving** China has about 1.3×10^9 people. One of the world's smallest nations, the Marshall Islands, has a population of just 5.9×10^4 people. How many times greater is China's population than the Marshall Islands' population?
    - **Make a Plan** Write a ratio comparing China's population to the Marshall Islands' population.
    - **Carry Out the Plan** Divide and write the quotient in scientific notation. Simplify. 2.2×10^4 times greater

24. GPS The sun's diameter is 1.39×10^6 kilometers. Earth's diameter is 1.28×10^4 kilometers. How many times greater is the sun's diameter than Earth's diameter? 1.09×10^2 times greater

GO Online
Homework Video Tutor
Visit: PHSchool.com
Web Code: ase-1205

Complete each equation.

25. $\frac{4^{\blacksquare}}{4^2} = 4^{10}$ 12
26. $\frac{x^6}{x^{\blacksquare}} = x^4$ 2
27. $\frac{14x^5}{7x^3} = 2x^{\blacksquare}$ 2
28. $\frac{1}{c^7} = c^{\blacksquare}$ −7

34. False; $4^0 = 1$ and $4^{-1} = \frac{1}{4}$.
35. False; $8^{-1} = \frac{1}{8}$ and $(-8)^1 = -8$.
36. True; $2^1 \cdot 2^{-1} = 2^{1 + -1} = 2^0 = 1$.
37. False; $(-2)^{-1} = \frac{1}{-2} = -\frac{1}{2}$ and $-\frac{1}{2} \neq 2$.

Use $w = -1$ and $x = 2$. Simplify each expression.

29. $(w + x)^{-4}$ 1 **30.** x^w $\frac{1}{2}$ **31.** $-2^{w + 2x}$ -8 **32.** $(2x)^{w + 1}$ 1

33. Speed of Sound At sea level, the speed of sound is about 761 miles per hour, or $\frac{4.02 \times 10^6 \text{ feet}}{3.6 \times 10^3 \text{ seconds}}$. What is this speed in feet per second? Write your answer in scientific notation. 1.12×10^3 ft/s

Careers Test pilots often fly airplanes faster than the speed of sound. When they fly near the speed of sound, a cloud of condensation may form because of a rapid drop in air pressure and temperature.

Writing in Math **Is each statement *true* or *false*? Explain your reasoning.** 34–37. See margin.

34. $4^0 = 4^{-1}$ **35.** $8^{-1} = (-8)^1$ **36.** $2^1 \cdot 2^{-1} = 2^0$ **37.** $(-2)^{-1} = 2$

38. Space Travel The space probe *Pioneer 10* was 12.1×10^9 km from Earth in 2002. Its radio signal traveled at 3.0×10^5 km/s. How many hours did its signal take to reach Earth? 11.2 hr

C **39. Challenge** You can divide a polynomial by a monomial by dividing each term of the numerator by the denominator.

Sample $\frac{6x^4 + 10x^3}{2x^2} = \frac{6x^4}{2x^2} + \frac{10x^3}{2x^2}$
$= 3x^2 + 5x$

a. $\frac{6n^5 - 12n^2}{3n^2}$ $2n^3 - 4$

b. $\frac{4m^9 + 6m^6 + 2m^3}{2m^3}$ $2m^6 + 3m^3 + 1$

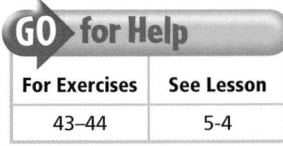

Test Prep and Mixed Review

Practice

Gridded Response

40. The net for a square pyramid is shown at the right. Use a centimeter ruler to measure the dimensions. Find the lateral surface area of the pyramid in square centimeters. 4.5

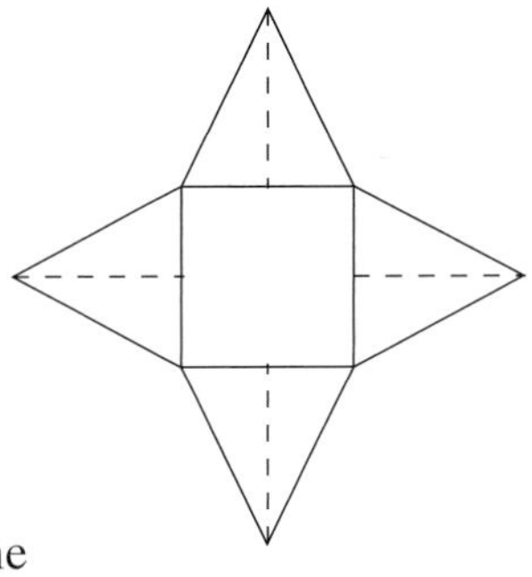

41. Lola's monthly charge for downloading music from the Internet can be found using the equation $c = 8.95 + 0.95s$, where s represents the number of songs she downloaded that month. Find the charges in dollars on her monthly bill if she downloads 23 songs this month. 30.8

42. A square is dilated with a scale factor of 3. If the area of the original square is 12 square inches, how many square inches is the area of the dilated square? 108

GO for Help

For Exercises	See Lesson
43–44	5-4

Use an equation to solve each problem. Round to the nearest hundredth.

43. What percent of 58 is 17? $58x = 17$; 29.31%

44. What is 12.5% of 34.50? $x = 0.125 \cdot 34.5$; 4.31

Online lesson quiz, PHSchool.com, Web Code: asa-1205

4. Assess & Reteach

PowerPoint

Lesson Quiz

1. Write $\frac{9^7}{9^4}$ using a single exponent. 9^3

Simplify each expression.

2. 6^0 1
3. 4^{-2} $\frac{1}{16}$
4. Jupiter's diameter is about 1.43×10^5 kilometers. Earth's diameter is about 1.28×10^4 kilometers. How many times greater is Jupiter's diameter than Earth's diameter? Round the answer to the nearest tenth. 11.2 times greater

Reteaching 12-5 Exponents and ... L2

To divide powers with the same base, subtract exponents.

$\frac{8^6}{8^4} = 8^{6-4} = 8^2 = 64$ $\frac{a^5}{a^3} = a^{5-3} = a^2$

- For any nonzero number a, $a^0 = 1$.

$3^0 = 1$ $(-6)^0 = 1$ $4t^0 = 4(1) = 4$

- For any nonzero number a and any integer n, $a^{-n} = \frac{1}{a^n}$.

$2^{-4} = \frac{1}{2^4} = \frac{1}{16}$ $3c^{-2} = \frac{3}{c^2}$ $\frac{5^3}{5^6} = 5^{3-6} = 5^{-3} = \frac{1}{5^3} = \frac{1}{125}$ $\frac{10z^3}{5z} = 2z^{3-1} = 2z^2$

Simplify each expression.

1. $\frac{6^5}{6^3} =$ 36
2. $(-4)^5 \div (-4)^3 =$ 16
3. $(-3)^{-2} =$ $\frac{1}{9}$
4. $\frac{2^5}{2^7} =$ $\frac{1}{4}$
5. $(-8)^0 =$ 1
6. $\frac{5^0}{5^2} =$ $\frac{1}{25}$
7. $\frac{(-6)^4}{(-6)^6} =$ $\frac{1}{36}$
8. $7^3 \div 7^5 =$ $\frac{1}{49}$
9. $9^8 \div 9^{10} =$ $\frac{1}{81}$

Simplify each expression. Write your answer using only positive exponents.

10. $w^8 \div w^3 =$ w^5
11. $x^6 \div x^1 =$ x^5
12. $\frac{d^7}{d^3} =$ d^4
13. $\frac{w^2}{w^6} =$ $\frac{1}{w^4}$
14. $4c^5 \div c^8 =$ $\frac{4}{c^3}$
15. $\frac{8x^2}{4x^5} =$ $\frac{2}{x^3}$
16. $8a^4 \div 2a^2 =$ $4a^2$
17. $6w^2 \div 2w^5 =$ $\frac{3}{w^3}$
18. $\frac{6x^6}{3x^9} =$ $\frac{2}{x^3}$

Enrichment 12-5 Exponents and ... L4

Patterns in Numbers

1. You know that you add exponents when you multiply two expressions with the same base. For example: $7^2 \times 7^3 = 7^{2+3} = 7^5$. Make a conjecture about what you should do with the exponents when you divide expressions with the same base.
Check students' answers.
2. Study the example below. What is the value of $\frac{7 \times 7 \times 7}{7 \times 7 \times 7}$? 1
$7^7 \div 7^3 = \frac{7 \times 7 \times 7 \times 7 \times 7 \times 7 \times 7}{7 \times 7 \times 7} = 7 \times 7 \times 7 \times 7 \times \frac{7 \times 7 \times 7}{7 \times 7 \times 7}$
$= 7 \times 7 \times 7 \times 7$
$= 7^4$
3. Study and continue the pattern below.
$7^9 \div 7^3 = 7^{9-3} = 7^6$ $= 7 \times 7 \times 7 \times 7 \times 7 \times 7$
$7^9 \div 7^4 = 7^{9-4} = 7^5$ $= 7 \times 7 \times 7 \times 7 \times 7$
$7^9 \div 7^5 = 7^{9-5} = 7^4$ $= 7 \times 7 \times 7 \times 7$
$7^9 \div 7^6 = 7^{9-6} = 7^3$ $= 7 \times 7 \times 7$
$7^9 \div 7^7 = 7^{9-7} = 7^2$ $= 7 \times 7$
$7^9 \div 7^8 = 7^{9-8} = 7^1$ $= 7$
4. Describe the pattern that you see.
Sample answer: When you divide expressions with the same base, you subtract the exponents.
5. Extend the pattern for $7^9 \div 7^9$.
$7^9 \div 7^9 = \frac{7 \times 7 \times 7 \times 7 \times 7 \times 7 \times 7 \times 7 \times 7}{7 \times 7 \times 7 \times 7 \times 7 \times 7 \times 7 \times 7 \times 7} =$ 1
6. What do you think a^0 means? Explain.
$a^0 = 1$. To get zero as an exponent, you are dividing a number by itself, such as $7^9 \div 7^9 = 7^{9-9} = 7^0 = 1$.

Alternative Assessment

Each student in a pair writes a number in scientific notation. Partners compare numbers, divide the larger number by the smaller number, and write the result in scientific notation.

Test Prep

Resources

For additional practice with a variety of test item formats:

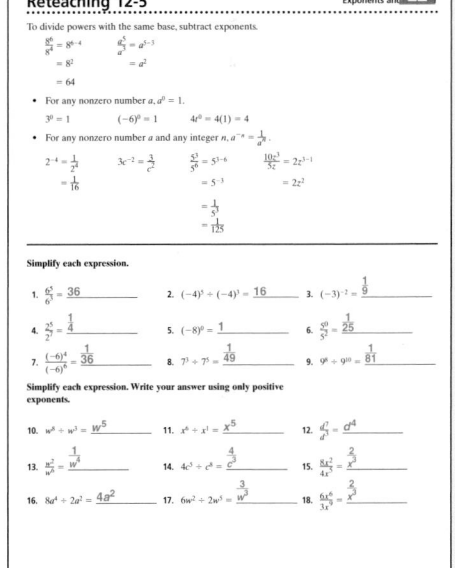

- Test-Taking Strategies, p. 589
- Test Prep, p. 593
- Test-Taking Strategies with Transparencies

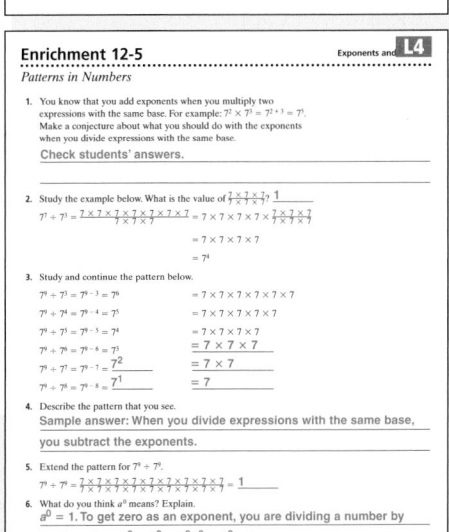

Extension

Power Rules

In previous lessons, students learned to multiply and divide expressions with exponents. This feature focuses on rules for finding powers of expressions with exponents. Students learn to raise a power to a power and raise a product to a power.

Guided Instruction

Read through the lesson with students. Help students understand, and not just memorize, the power rules by asking questions such as:

What's another way to show that $(3^{-4})^5 = 3^{-20}$? Write the expression in factored form and apply the rule for multiplying powers with the same base: $(3^{-4})(3^{-4})(3^{-4})(3^{-4})(3^{-4}) = 3^{-20}$

In what other ways can you write (4a)(4a)(4a)? $(4a)^3$ or $4^3 \cdot a^3$ or $64a^3$

Exercises

If students have difficulty with the exercises, have them write each expression in factored form as an intermediate step before writing the expression using a single exponent.

Differentiated Instruction

Auditory Learners

To help students remember that the exponent applies to each factor within the parentheses, have them read the expression inside the parentheses aloud, followed by the word "quantity." For example, in Exercise 7, students should say "ten times *x* to the fifth power, quantity squared".

Power Rules

You can use the rules for multiplying exponents to simplify an expression such as $(4^3)^2$.

$$(4^3)^2 = 4^3 \cdot 4^3 = 4^{(3+3)} = 4^6$$

Since $6 = 3 \cdot 2$, $(4^3)^2 = 4^{(3 \cdot 2)} = 4^6$. This suggests that to raise a power to a power, you multiply the exponents.

EXAMPLE 1 Raising a Power to a Power

Write each expression using a single exponent.

a. $(3^{-4})^5$

$(3^{-4})^5 = 3^{(-4 \cdot 5)} = 3^{-20}$

b. $(x^{-2})^{-3}$

$(x^{-2})^{-3} = x^{(-2 \cdot -3)} = x^6$

You can raise a product to a power using repeated multiplication.

$(2w)^3 = (2w) \cdot (2w) \cdot (2w)$ ← Write out the factors of the power.

$= 2 \cdot 2 \cdot 2 \cdot w \cdot w \cdot w$ ← Use the commutative property to rearrange the factors.

$= 2^3 \cdot w^3 = 2^3w^3$ ← Write the factors as a product.

Notice that $(2w)^3 = 2^3w^3$. This suggests that to raise a product to a power, you raise each factor to the power.

EXAMPLE 2 Raising a Product to a Power

Simplify $(3y^3)^2$.

$$(3y^3)^2 = 3^2(y^3)^2 = 3^2y^6 = 9y^6$$

Exercises

Write each expression using a single exponent.

1. $(3^3)^7$ 3^{21}
2. $(9^2)^{-5}$ 9^{-10}
3. $(w^{-2})^{-6}$ w^{12}
4. $(r^2)^3$ r^6

Simplify each expression.

5. $(3x)^2$ $9x^2$
6. $(a^2b^3)^4$ a^8b^{12}
7. $(10x^5)^2$ $100x^{10}$
8. $(y^2 \cdot 2^2)^4$ $256y^8$

GPS Guided Problem Solving

Solving Equations

Rectangles based on the Golden Ratio ($1.618w : w$, where w is the width of the rectangle) are pleasing to the eye. Suppose you want a rectangular tiled patio using the Golden Ratio for a circular hot tub with a diameter that is one half of the rectangle's width. How many square feet of patio will be tiled if the patio's width is 25 feet?

1. Yes; 10% of 889 is 88.9, 88.9 + 889 = 977.9. Since 977.9 < 1,000, 1,000 will be enough.

What You Might Think

What do I know? What am I trying to find out?

How can I visualize the problem?

How can I write an equation for the area of the patio that needs to be tiled?

What is the area when $w = 25$?

What You Might Write

The patio has a length to width ratio of $1.618w : w$. A circle with diameter $\frac{1}{2}w$ is removed. I want to find the area of the patio when $w = 25$ feet.

Draw a diagram.

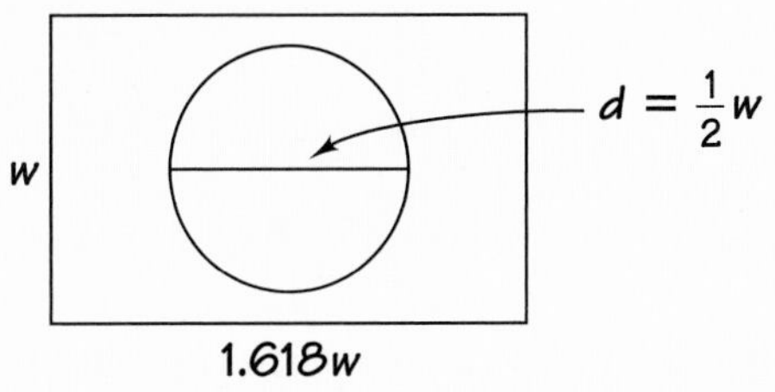

Find the rectangle's area and subtract the circle's area. The radius of the circle is half the diameter. Use 3.14 for π.

$$\ell w - \pi r^2 = (1.618w)(w) - \pi(\tfrac{1}{4}w)^2$$
$$= 1.618w^2 - (3.14)\frac{w^2}{16}$$

$$1.618(25)^2 - (3.14)\frac{25^2}{16} = 888.59375$$

I will need about 889 square feet of tile.

Think It Through

1. In buying tile, you should buy 10% more than the area to be covered. Will 1,000 square feet be enough? Explain. See above.

GPS Guided Problem Solving

Solving Equations

It is important for students to be able to use their understanding of polynomials, equations, and algebraic relationships to solve real-world problems. In this feature, they use area formulas, distance formulas, and other equations to solve problems.

Guided Instruction

Have a volunteer read aloud the problem. Then guide students to notice the careful step-by-step problem solving process used to answer the question the problem asks.

Teaching Tip
Work through the solution strategy beginning with the key steps of identifying what you know and what you want to find out.

Ask:
- *If the length to width ratio is 1.612w : w, what expression represents the length?* 1.612*w*
- *How does the diagram help you see how to find the area of the patio that needs to be tiled?* Sample: The diagram shows that you need to subtract the area of the circle from the area of the rectangle.

Review the formulas for area of a rectangle and area of a circle. Then, allow pairs of students a few minutes to work through the steps in the solution and verify that the results are correct.

Error Prevention!

Emphasize the fact that the **diameter** of the hot tub equals half of the width of the patio, while the **radius** of the hot tub equals half of the diameter. Emphasize that the formula for area of a circle is π times the square of the radius.

Ask: *How do you determine the radius of the circular hot tub?* The diameter of the circle is half the width of the patio or $\frac{1}{2}w$. The radius is half the diameter or $\frac{1}{2}\left(\frac{1}{2}w\right) = \frac{1}{4}w$.

Exercises

Have students use the steps in the example as a general guide. Remind them to use order of operations and rules for powers when they replace variables in the equations with numbers.

Differentiated Instruction

Special Needs L1

Review the meaning of the symbol π. Remind students that the number 3.14 can be used to estimate π in calculations. In Exercise 5, remind students that the symbol $\sqrt{\ }$ means "the square root of."

Exercises

Solve each problem. For Exercises 2 and 3, answer the questions first.

2. Wanda likes to set up and knock down dominoes arranged as shown at the right. She says you can find out how many dominoes you need for n rows by adding $1 + 2 + 3 + \ldots + n$. Jake says you can find it by evaluating $\frac{1}{2}(n^2 + n)$. Who is correct?
   a. What are you trying to find? Both Wanda and Jake are correct.
   b. Try both expressions for the first ten rows. What do you notice?

3. **Science** Gravitational pull varies among the different planets in our solar system. Since your weight depends on gravitational pull, it also varies from planet to planet. Use the table below to find your weight on Jupiter if you weigh 110 lbs on Earth. 259.6 lb

Planet	Gravitational Pull (compared to Earth)
Mercury	0.38
Venus	0.91
Mars	0.38
Jupiter	2.36
Saturn	0.91
Uranus	0.89
Neptune	1.12

   a. What do you know? What do you want to find out?
   b. How is your weight on Jupiter related to your weight on Earth? It is 2.36 times your weight on Earth.

4. On a clear day, the distance d in miles you can see across the ocean from a height of h feet is given by $h = \frac{2}{3}d^2$. Jaime is learning to parasail with his friends. If beginning parasailers usually go up about 150 feet, how far can Jaime see when he is in the air? 15 miles

5. Suppose your father goes skydiving for his birthday. He jumps from a plane at 10,000 feet and opens his parachute at 5,000 feet. How much time passes before he opens his parachute? Use the equation $t = 0.25\sqrt{d}$, where t is the time in seconds a falling object takes to fall d feet. 17.7 seconds

Working Backward

In multiple-choice tests, the correct answer is among the choices. To determine which answer is correct, you can use the problem-solving strategy *Work Backward.*

EXAMPLES

1 A bus can hold 72 passengers. A school uses the equation $b = \frac{n}{72}$ to calculate the number of buses needed to transport n students. What is the greatest number of students 6 buses can hold?

(A) 288 (B) 360 (C) 432 (D) 504

You can answer the question without solving the equation. Substitute each answer choice for the variable until you find the solution.

Let $n = 288$. Then $\frac{288}{72} = 4$. Since $4 \neq 6$, choice A is wrong.

Let $n = 360$. Then $\frac{360}{72} = 5$. Since $5 \neq 6$, choice B is wrong.

Let $n = 432$. Then $\frac{432}{72} = 6$. Since $6 = 6$, the correct answer is choice C.

You do not need to try choice D.

2 Which expression is equivalent to $12x^2 - 28x$?

(A) $12x(x - 2)$ (B) $4x(3x - 7)$ (C) $4x^2(3 - 7)$ (D) $6(2x^2 - 4)$

You can multiply each of the answer choices to answer the question.

$12x(x - 2) = 12x^2 - 24x$ This is not equal to $12x^2 - 28x$, so choice A is wrong.

$4x(3x - 7) = 12x^2 - 28x$ Choice B is correct.

You do not need to test the other two choices.

Exercises

Solve each of the following by working backward.

1. The equation $m = 33g$ describes the number of miles m a car can travel on g gallons of gas. For which value of g does $m = 297$? C

   (A) 4 (B) 6 (C) 9 (D) 14

2. Jorge wants to run a half-marathon (13.1 miles). About how many miles per hour should he run to complete the half-marathon in 1.5 hours? Use the equation $d = rt$. G

   (F) 5.2 (G) 8.7 (H) 9.6 (J) 19.6

Working Backward

In general, students can use the work backward strategy effectively when they know a solution but need to find information that led to that solution. This feature guides students to work backward to solve multiple-choice questions.

Guided Instruction

Emphasize that students should stop checking answer choices once their substitution results in the desired result.

Discuss that eliminating some answer choices, by estimating or by using number sense, will increase their chances of success on that test question, whether they work backward or apply any other test-taking strategy.

Resources

Test-Taking Strategies with Transparencies
- Transparency 7
- Practice sheet, p. 36

Test-Taking Strategies with Transparencies

Test-Taking Strategies: Working Backward

Sometimes it is easier to start with an end result and work backward.

Example What is the prime factorization of 48?

A. 6×2^3 B. $2^4 \times 3$ C. 4×12 D. 2^5

Try each choice:

Since 6 is not a prime number, choice A is wrong.

Since 4 is not a prime number, choice C is wrong.

Compare choice B and choice D. Is 48 divisible by 3? Yes. So, choice D is wrong.

The answer is $2^4 \times 3$, or choice B.

Work backward to find the answer. Explain your reasoning.

1. Which number is composite, less than 50, and has a tens digit greater than its ones digit?

   A. 51 B. 13 C. 28 D. 32

2. Carlos has $\frac{2}{3}$ of a bushel of apples, weighing 26 pounds. How much does a bushel of apples weigh?

   F. 20 pounds G. 50 pounds
   H. 39 pounds J. 33 pounds

Chapter 12 Review

Resources

Student Edition
Extra Skills and Word Problems Practice, Ch. 12, p. 626
English/Spanish Glossary, p. 650
Formulas and Properties, p. 648
Tables, p. 643

All in One Teaching Resources
- Vocabulary and Study Skills 12F L3

Differentiated Instruction
Spanish Vocabulary Workbook with Study Skills ELL
Interactive Textbook
- Audio Glossary

Online Vocabulary Quiz

Success Tracker™
Online at PHSchool.com

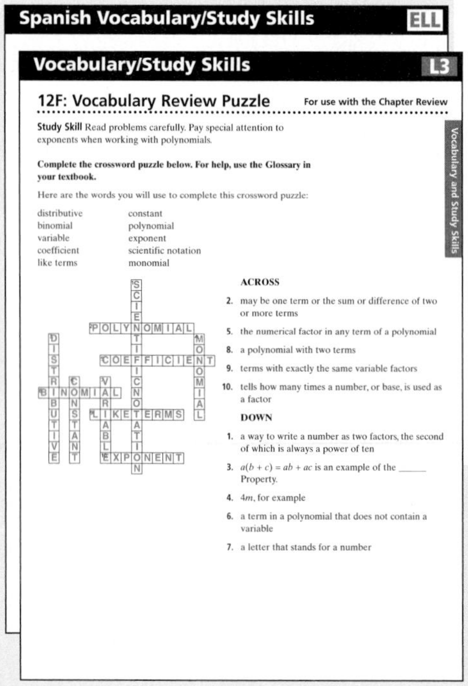
Spanish Vocabulary/Study Skills ELL

Vocabulary/Study Skills L3

12F: Vocabulary Review Puzzle For use with the Chapter Review

Study Skill Read problems carefully. Pay special attention to exponents when working with polynomials.

Complete the crossword puzzle below. For help, use the Glossary in your textbook.

Here are the words you will use to complete this crossword puzzle:

distributive	constant
binomial	polynomial
variable	exponent
coefficient	scientific notation
like terms	monomial

ACROSS
2. may be one term or the sum or difference of two or more terms
5. the numerical factor in any term of a polynomial
8. a polynomial with two terms
9. terms with exactly the same variable factors
10. tells how many times a number, or base, is used as a factor

DOWN
1. a way to write a number as two factors, the second of which is always a power of ten
3. $a(b + c) = ab + ac$ is an example of the _____ Property.
4. $4m$, for example
6. a term in a polynomial that does not contain a variable
7. a letter that stands for a number

Vocabulary and Study Skills

Chapter 12 Review

Vocabulary Review

binomial (p. 576)
coefficient (p. 566)
constant (p. 561)
monomial (p. 576)
polynomial (p. 561)

Go Online PHSchool.com
For: Online Vocabulary Quiz
Web Code: asj-1251

Choose the correct vocabulary term above to complete each sentence.

1. $6x^2 + 3x - 2$ is an example of a __?__. polynomial
2. A term that does not contain a variable is a __?__. constant
3. A polynomial such as $4y$ is called a __?__. monomial
4. In the polynomial $5z^2 + 2$, 5 is a __?__. coefficient
5. A __?__ is a polynomial with two terms. binomial

Skills and Concepts

Lessons 12-1, 12-2
- To write algebraic expressions and to simplify polynomials
- To add and subtract polynomials

A **polynomial** is an expression such as $2x^2 - 3x$. A term in a polynomial that does not contain a variable is a **constant.**

To simplify a polynomial, combine like terms. You can use algebra tiles or the properties of numbers to simplify a polynomial.

Write a variable expression for each model.

6. 
$2x^2 + 8$

7. 
$x^2 + 3x + 4$

Use properties of numbers to simplify each polynomial.

8. $5x^2 + 6 - 4x + 9x^2 + 17x$ See left.
9. $8 - 3x + 11x^2 + 2x^2 - 10 + 7x$ $13x^2 + 4x - 2$
10. $4 - 3x^2 + 2x - x^2 + 3$ $-4x^2 + 2x + 7$
11. $-x^2 + 4x + 7 - 2x + 9x$ $-x^2 + 11x + 7$

8. $14x^2 + 13x + 6$

Find each sum.

12. $(2x - 5) + (14x + 10)$ $16x + 5$
13. $(-4x^2 + 7x) + (x^2 - 7x + 3)$ $-3x^2 + 3$
14. $(8x^2 - 7x + 3) + (3x^2 + x - 5)$ $11x^2 - 6x - 2$
15. $(5x^2 + 3) + (2x^2 - 3x - 1)$ $7x^2 - 3x + 2$

Find each difference.

16. $(5x - 4) - (9x + 3)$ $-4x - 7$
17. $(2x^2 - 4x - 8) - (x^2 - 5x + 3)$ $x^2 + x - 11$
18. $(7x^2 + 6) - (2x - 7)$ $7x^2 - 2x + 13$
19. $(5x^2 + 9x - 7) - (2x^2 + 3x)$ $3x^2 + 6x - 7$

Lesson 12-3

- To multiply powers with the same base and to multiply numbers in scientific notation

To multiply numbers with the same base, add the exponents. Use this same property to multiply numbers in scientific notation.

Write each expression using a single exponent.

20. $8^{10} \cdot 8^9$ 8^{19}

21. $(-3)^4 \cdot (-3)^9$ $(-3)^{13}$

22. $2.6^{12} \cdot 2.6^{12}$ 2.6^{24}

23. $11^5 \cdot 11^6$ 11^{11}

Multiply. Write each product in scientific notation.

24. $(3 \times 10^6)(2 \times 10^{12})$ 6×10^{18}

25. $5(1.4 \times 10^6)$ 7×10^6

26. $(6 \times 10^9)(5 \times 10^4)$ 3×10^{14}

27. $(2.1 \times 10^7)(7 \times 10^{12})$

27. 1.47×10^{20}

Lesson 12-4

- To multiply monomials and binomials

To multiply **monomials,** rearrange the factors and use the properties of exponents. To multiply a monomial and a **binomial,** use the Distributive Property. Use an area model to find the product of two binomials.

Simplify each expression.

28. $(-6x)(3x^3)$ $-18x^4$

29. $(-2x)(-7x)$ $14x^2$

30. $-10x(3x - 2)$ $-30x^2 + 20x$

31. $5x(x^2 - 3x)$ $5x^3 - 15x^2$

Use the area model to find each product.

32.

$2x + 1$

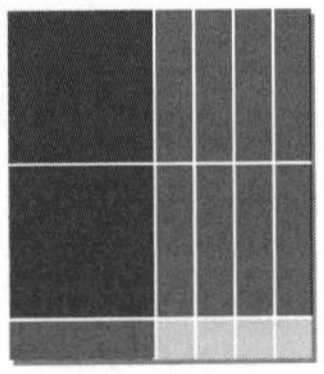

$x + 4$

33.

$x + 1$

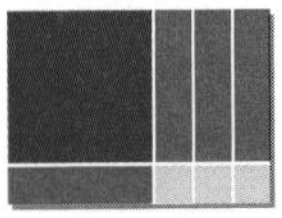

$x + 3$

$x^2 + 4x + 3$

32. $2x^2 + 9x + 4$

Lesson 12-5

- To divide powers with the same base and to simplify expressions with negative exponents

To divide numbers with the same base, subtract the exponents. Any nonzero number with a zero exponent equals 1. For any nonzero number a and integer n, $a^{-n} = \frac{1}{a^n}$.

Write each expression using a single exponent.

34. $\frac{5^{10}}{5^7}$ 5^3

35. $\frac{(-8)^{12}}{(-8)^2}$ $(-8)^{10}$

36. $\frac{76^{11}}{76^5}$ 76^6

37. $\frac{1.8^6}{1.8^5}$ 1.8^1

Simplify each expression.

38. 8^0 1

39. $(-16)^0$ 1

40. g^0 1

41. $(8b)^0$ 1

42. 5^{-4} $\frac{1}{625}$

43. x^{-9} $\frac{1}{x^9}$

44. 9^{-2} $\frac{1}{81}$

45. h^{-8} $\frac{1}{h^8}$

Alternative Assessment L4

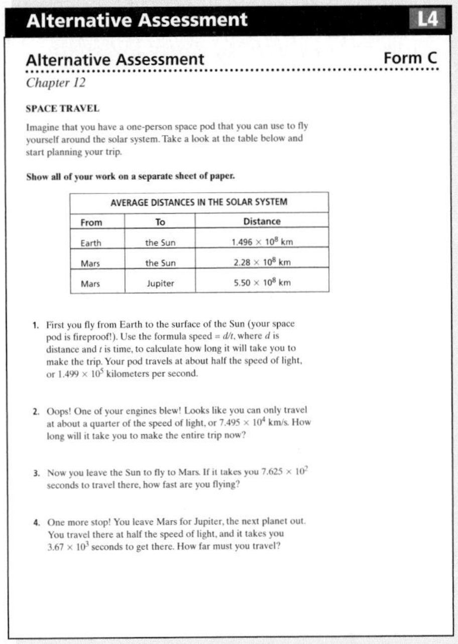

Alternative Assessment Form C

Chapter 12

SPACE TRAVEL

Imagine that you have a one-person space pod that you can use to fly yourself around the solar system. Take a look at the table below and start planning your trip.

Show all of your work on a separate sheet of paper.

AVERAGE DISTANCES IN THE SOLAR SYSTEM		
From	To	Distance
Earth	the Sun	1.496×10^8 km
Mars	the Sun	2.28×10^8 km
Mars	Jupiter	5.50×10^8 km

1. First you fly from Earth to the surface of the Sun (your space pod is fireproof!). Use the formula speed = d/t, where d is distance and t is time, to calculate how long it will take you to make the trip. Your pod travels at about half the speed of light, or 1.499×10^5 kilometers per second.

2. Oops! One of your engines blew! Looks like you can only travel at about a quarter of the speed of light, or 7.495×10^4 km/s. How long will it take you to make the entire trip now?

3. Now you leave the Sun to fly to Mars. If it takes you 7.625×10^2 seconds to travel there, how fast are you flying?

4. One more stop! You leave Mars for Jupiter, the next planet out. You travel there at half the speed of light, and it takes you 3.67×10^3 seconds to get there. How far must you travel?

Spanish Quarter 4 Test - Forms A, B ELL

Quarter 4 Test Forms D, E L2

Quarter 4 Test - Forms A, B L3

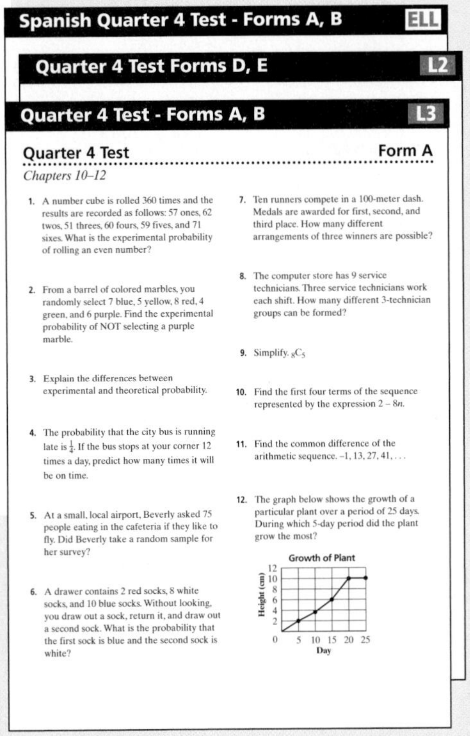

Quarter 4 Test Form A

Chapters 10–12

1. A number cube is rolled 360 times and the results are recorded as follows: 57 ones, 62 twos, 51 threes, 60 fours, 59 fives, and 71 sixes. What is the experimental probability of rolling an even number?

2. From a barrel of colored marbles, you randomly select 7 blue, 5 yellow, 8 red, 4 green, and 6 purple. Find the experimental probability of NOT selecting a purple marble.

3. Explain the differences between experimental and theoretical probability.

4. The probability that the city bus is running late is $\frac{1}{4}$. If the bus stops at your corner 12 times a day, predict how many times it will be on time.

5. At a small, local airport, Beverly asked 75 people eating in the cafeteria if they like to fly. Did Beverly take a random sample for her survey?

6. A drawer contains 2 red socks, 8 white socks, and 10 blue socks. Without looking, you draw out a sock, return it, and draw out a second sock. What is the probability that the first sock is blue and the second sock is white?

7. Ten runners compete in a 100-meter dash. Medals are awarded for first, second, and third place. How many different arrangements of three winners are possible?

8. The computer store has 9 service technicians. Three service technicians work each shift. How many different 3-technician groups can be formed?

9. Simplify. ${}_8C_5$

10. Find the first four terms of the sequence represented by the expression $2 - 8n$.

11. Find the common difference of the arithmetic sequence. $-1, 13, 27, 41, \ldots$

12. The graph below shows the growth of a particular plant over a period of 25 days. During which 5-day period did the plant grow the most?

Resources

- ExamView Assessment Suite CD-ROM
  - Chapter 12 Ready-Made Test
  - Make your own Chapter 12 test
- MindPoint Quiz Show CD-ROM
  - Chapter 12 Review

Differentiated Instruction

All in One Teaching Resources
- Below Level Chapter 12 Test L2
- Chapter 12 Test L3
- Chapter 12 Alternative Assessment L4

Spanish Assessment Resources ELL
- Below Level Chapter 12 Test L2
- Chapter 12 Test L3
- Chapter 12 Alternative Assessment L4

ExamView Assessment Suite CD-ROM
- Special Needs Test L1
- Special Needs Practice Bank L1

Online Chapter 12 Test at www.PHSchool.com L3

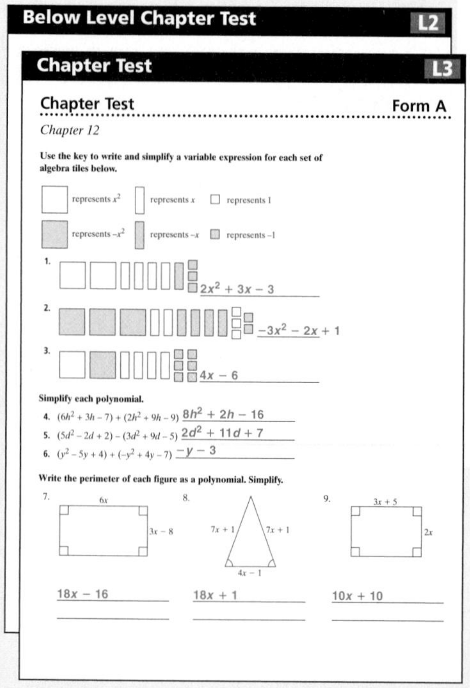
Below Level Chapter Test L2

Chapter Test L3

Chapter Test Form A

Chapter 12

Use the key to write and simplify a variable expression for each set of algebra tiles below.

represents x^2 represents x represents 1

represents $-x^2$ represents $-x$ represents -1

1. $2x^2 + 3x - 3$
2. $-3x^2 - 2x + 1$
3. $4x - 6$

Simplify each polynomial.

4. $(6h^2 + 3h - 7) + (2h^2 + 9h - 9)$ $8h^2 + 2h - 16$
5. $(5d^2 - 2d + 2) - (3d^2 + 9d - 5)$ $2d^2 + 11d + 7$
6. $(y^2 - 5y + 4) + (-y^2 + 4y - 7)$ $-y - 3$

Write the perimeter of each figure as a polynomial. Simplify.

7. $18x - 16$
8. $18x + 1$
9. $10x + 10$

Chapter 12 Test

Go Online PHSchool.com For: Online chapter test Web Code: asa-1252

For Exercises 1–4, use tiles or properties of numbers to simplify each polynomial.

1. $3x + 12 - 4 + 9x$ $12x + 8$
2. $4x^2 - 6 + x^2 + 5x - 10$ $5x^2 + 5x - 16$
3. $4 - 2x + 9 + 3x^2 + 7x - 6x^2$
4. $14x - 1 + 5x^2 + 10x^2 - 4$ 3–4. See margin.
5. Write and simplify the polynomial represented by the model below.

$x^2 - 2x + 3$

Find each sum.

6. $(5x^2 - 4x + 2) + (3x^2 - 3x - 5)$ $8x^2 - 7x - 3$
7. $(x^2 - 3x + 5) + (-x^2 + 4x + 4)$ $x + 9$
8. $(2x^2 + 7x - 6) + (4x^2 + 3x - 2)$ $6x^2 + 10x - 8$

Find each difference.

9. $(7x^2 - x + 2) - (x^2 + 4x - 4)$ $6x^2 - 5x + 6$
10. $(2x^2 + 3x + 4) - (2x - 7)$ $2x^2 + x + 11$
11. $(9x^2 + 5x - 10) - (-2x^2 + 4x + 3)$ $11x^2 + x - 13$
12. a. Find the perimeter of the figure below.

b. Find the area of the figure. $2x^2 - 3x$

Write each expression using a single exponent.

13. $10^7 \cdot 10^6$ 10^{13}
14. $a^5 \cdot a^2$ a^7
15. $3.4^3 \cdot 3.4^6$ 3.4^9
16. $(-h)^5 \cdot (-h)^8$ $(-h)^{13}$
17. $2^3 \cdot 2^6 \cdot 2^5$ 2^{14}
18. $r^3 \cdot r^4 \cdot r^{10}$ r^{17}

Simplify each expression.

19. $(-9x)(2x)$ $-18x^2$
20. $x(3x + 5)$ $3x^2 + 5x$
21. $x^2(x + 17)$ $x^3 + 17x^2$
22. $2x(x^2 - 6x)$ $2x^3 - 12x^2$

Multiply. Write each product in scientific notation.

23. $5(7 \times 10^4)$ 3.5×10^5
24. $11(8 \times 10^2)$ 8.8×10^3
25. $(9 \times 10^5)(3 \times 10^{12})$ 2.7×10^{18}
26. $(12 \times 10^7)(2 \times 10^6)$ 2.4×10^{14}
27. $(6 \times 10^3)(6 \times 10^{10})$ 3.6×10^{14}

Write each expression using a single exponent.

28. $t^{23} \cdot t^0$ t^{23}
29. $\frac{(-3)^5}{(-3)^2}$ $(-3)^3$
30. $\frac{14^8}{14^4}$ 14^4
31. $\frac{c^6}{c^2}$ c^4
32. Use the area model below to find the product. $4x^2 + 6x + 2$

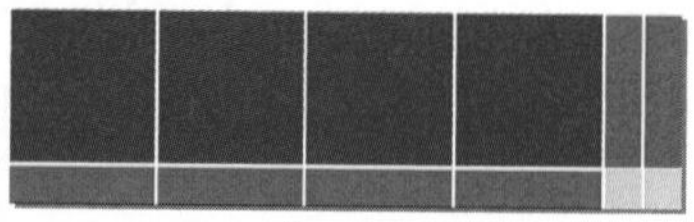

Simplify each expression.

33. 2^0 1
34. r^0 1
35. 7^0 1
36. d^0 1
37. 4^{-5} $\frac{1}{1024}$
38. a^{-8} $\frac{1}{a^8}$
39. r^{-2} $\frac{1}{r^2}$
40. 9^{-4} $\frac{1}{6561}$
41. x^{-6} $\frac{1}{x^6}$
42. 6^{-3} $\frac{1}{216}$
43. **Writing in Math** Write what you would say to a classmate who asked you to explain why 5^0 is equal to 1. 43–44. See margin.
44. **Biology** The human eye blinks about 4.2×10^6 times each year. About how many times has the eye of a 14-year-old blinked? Write your answer in scientific notation.

3. $-3x^2 + 5x + 13$
4. $15x^2 + 14x - 5$
43. Answers may vary. Sample: Since you subtract exponents to find the quotient of two numbers with the same base, any nonzero number divided by itself will give you a number to the zero power, and any nonzero number divided by itself is always 1. For example, $\frac{5^4}{5^4} = 5^0 = 1$.
44. 5.88×10^7

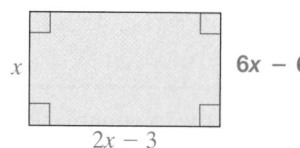

Multiple Choice

Choose the correct letter.

1. You have a set of data that has five items. The median is 14, the mean is 14.8, the mode is 14, and the range is 4. Which could be the correct data set? B
   - A 14, 14, 14, 16, 18
   - C 13, 14, 14, 16, 17
   - B 12, 14, 14, 15, 20
   - D 12, 13, 14, 16, 16

2. Which proportion could NOT be represented by the model at the right? H

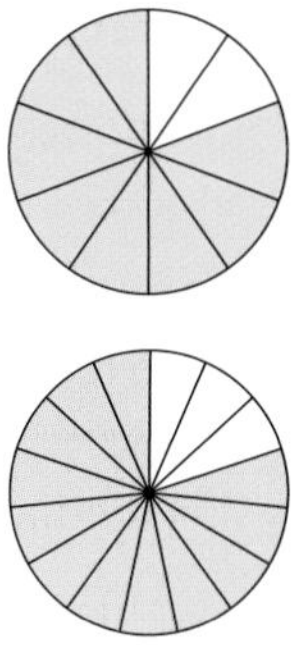

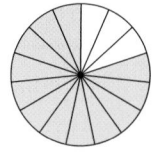

   - F $\frac{12}{15} = \frac{8}{10}$
   - G $\frac{2}{8} = \frac{3}{12}$
   - H $\frac{3}{10} = \frac{2}{15}$
   - J $\frac{4}{5} = \frac{8}{10}$

3. Which number could NOT be a value of y if $y = 2x^2 - 3$? D
   - A 15
   - B 5
   - C −3
   - D −5

4. The graph below represents which inequality? F

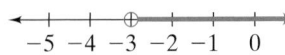

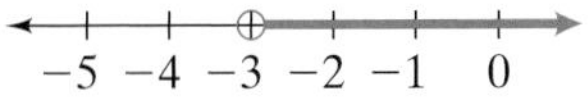

   - F $-\frac{x}{3} < 1$
   - H $2 + y \leq -1$
   - G $6z > 18$
   - J $-2w \geq -6$

5. Tia has art class every 6th day of school (Monday through Friday). How often does she have art class on Monday? B
   - A every week
   - C every 6th week
   - B every 5th week
   - D every 7th week

6. Tate bought 500 grams of hamburg. How many kilograms is this? G
   - F 0.05 kg
   - H 5 kg
   - G 0.5 kg
   - J 50 kg

7. A right triangle has legs of lengths 3 and 4. What is the length of the hypotenuse? D
   - A 2
   - B 4
   - C 5
   - D 7

Go Online PHSchool.com **For:** Online end-of-chapter test **Web Code:** asa-1254

8. Which algebraic expression is NOT equivalent to $2(x - 3)$? J
   - F $2(x) - 2(3)$
   - H $(x - 3) + (x - 3)$
   - G $2(-3) + 2x$
   - J $2x - 3$

9. Which set of ordered pairs describes the image of the vertices of $\triangle ABC$ after a translation 2 units left and 3 units down? A

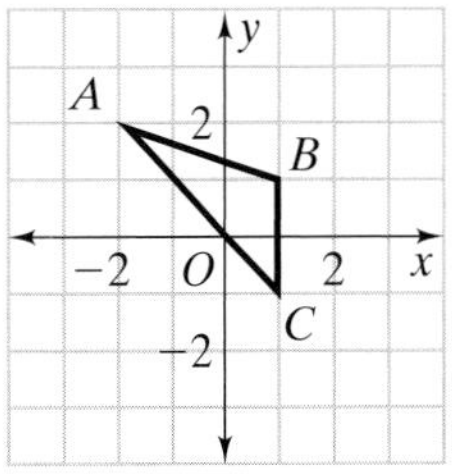

   - A $A'(-4, -1), B'(-1, -2), C'(-1, -4)$
   - B $A'(0, -1), B'(3, -2), C'(3, -4)$
   - C $A'(0, 5), B'(3, 4), C'(3, 2)$
   - D $A'(-4, 5), B'(-1, 4), C'(-1, 2)$

10. How many integers have an absolute value less than 3? H
    - F 3
    - G 4
    - H 5
    - J 6

11. Deidre has 4 red shirts, 3 blue shirts, and 2 green shirts. If she chooses a shirt at random, what is the probability it is green? C
    - A $\frac{7}{9}$
    - B $\frac{2}{7}$
    - C $\frac{2}{9}$
    - D $\frac{1}{9}$

12. Estimate the shaded area. G

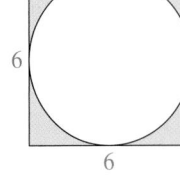

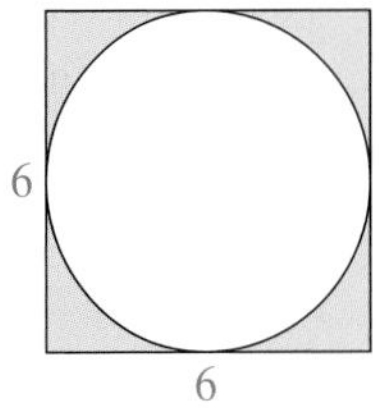

    - F 0.7 units^2
    - G 7 units^2
    - H 17 units^2
    - J 27 units^2

13. There are about 10,550 radio stations in the United States. How is this number written in scientific notation? B
    - A 1.055×10^3
    - C 10.55×10^3
    - B 1.055×10^4
    - D 10.55×10^4

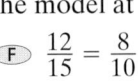

Item	1	2	3	4	5	6	7	8	9	10	11	12	13	14	15
Lesson	9-1	4-3	11-7	6-6	Problem Solving Handbook	4-2	3-3	6-2	3-6	1-2	5-8	7-7	2-8	10-5	9-8

Test Prep

Resources

Test Prep Workbook

All in One **Teaching Resources**
- Cumulative Review L3

ExamView Assessment Suite CD-ROM
- Standardized Test Practice

Differentiated Instruction

Spanish Assessment Resources
- Spanish Cumulative Review ELL

31. [2] 192 ft^2, 336 ft^2
    [1] only one answer correct

32. [2] markup = selling price − store's cost, \$11.08 = \$15.95 − \$4.87, percent of markup = markup ÷ store's cost, 2.275 ≈ 11.08 ÷ 4.87, the percent of markup is about 227.5%.
    [1] appropriate method with one computational error OR correct answer without work shown

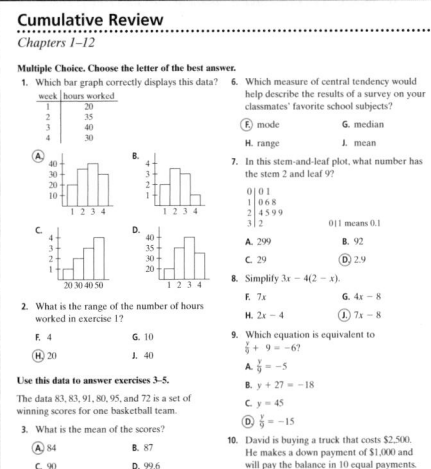

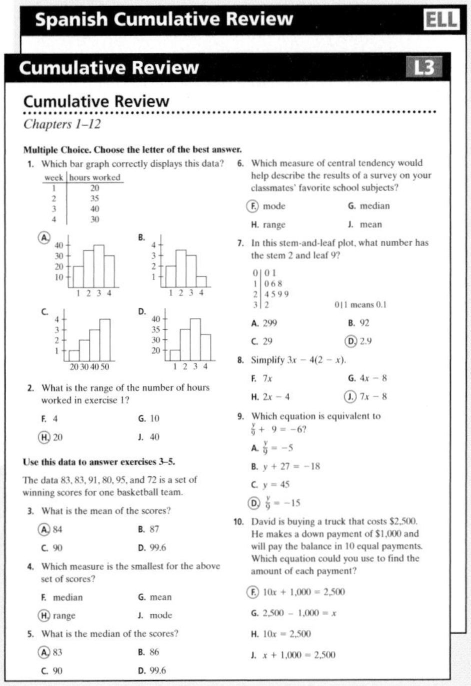
Spanish Cumulative Review ELL

Cumulative Review L3

Cumulative Review

Chapters 1–12

Multiple Choice. Choose the letter of the best answer.

1. Which bar graph correctly displays this data?

week	hours worked
1	20
2	35
3	40
4	30

A. B. C. D.

2. What is the range of the number of hours worked in exercise 1?
F. 4 G. 10 H. 20 J. 40

Use this data to answer exercises 3–5.

The data 83, 83, 91, 80, 95, and 72 is a set of winning scores for one basketball team.

3. What is the mean of the scores?
A. 84 B. 87 C. 90 D. 99.6

4. Which measure is the smallest for the above set of scores?
F. median G. mean H. range J. mode

5. What is the median of the scores?
A. 83 B. 86 C. 90 D. 99.6

6. Which measure of central tendency would help describe the results of a survey on your classmates' favorite school subjects?
F. mode G. median H. range J. mean

7. In this stem-and-leaf plot, what number has the stem 2 and leaf 9?
0 | 0 1
1 | 0 6 8
2 | 4 5 9 9
3 | 2
0|1 means 0.1
A. 299 B. 92 C. 29 D. 2.9

8. Simplify $3x - 4(2 - x)$.
F. $7x$ G. $4x - 8$ H. $2x - 4$ J. $7x - 8$

9. Which equation is equivalent to $\frac{y}{9} + 9 = -6$?
A. $\frac{y}{9} = -5$
B. $y + 27 = -18$
C. $y = 45$
D. $\frac{y}{9} = -15$

10. David is buying a truck that costs \$2,500. He makes a down payment of \$1,000 and will pay the balance in 10 equal payments. Which equation could you use to find the amount of each payment?
F. $10x + 1{,}000 = 2{,}500$
G. $2{,}500 - 1{,}000 = x$
H. $10x = 2{,}500$
J. $x + 1{,}000 = 2{,}500$

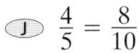

33. [2] a.

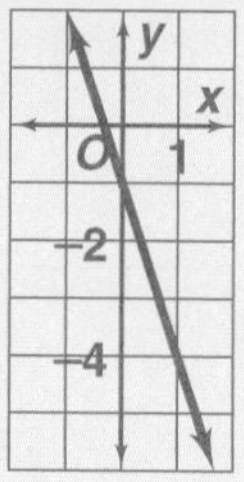

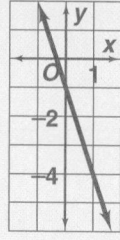

b. $11 = -3x - 1$
$12 = -3x$
$-4 = x$

[1] correct graph OR correct value of x

34. [2] The stock fund earned the most at about 1.8 years because that is the peak or highest point on the graph.

[1] correct answer without explanation

35. [2] The cone with height 2 cm and radius 6 cm has the greater volume, since $\frac{1}{3}\pi \cdot 6^2 \cdot 2 > \frac{1}{3}\pi \cdot 2^2 \cdot 6$.

[1] correct answer with inadequate explanation

36. [2] a. 324
b. 3

[1] correct term OR correct ratio

37. [2] 44.0 cm; 153.9 cm^2

[1] only one answer correct

38. [2] $30 + 4m = 60$
$4m = 30$
$m = 7.5$
She increased her daily workout by 7.5 minutes.

[1] appropriate procedure with one computational error OR correct answer without work shown

14. In how many different orders can 5 out of 8 people be seated in a row of 5 chairs? G

(F) 40,320 (G) 6,720 (H) 120 (J) 56

15. In a circle graph, what is the measure of the central angle of a sector that represents 24% of the whole? D

(A) 2.4° (B) 8.64° (C) 24° (D) 86.4°

16. Which of the following CANNOT be found by looking at a box-and-whisker plot? G

(F) range (H) median
(G) mode (J) upper quartile

17. In the figure below, the triangles are similar. Find the unknown length h. B

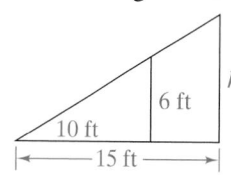

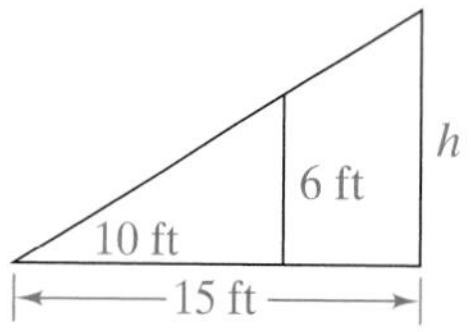

(A) 30 ft (B) 9 ft (C) 6 ft (D) 3 ft

18. Jim had $500 in his bank account on Monday. He wrote checks for $200 and $400 on Tuesday and Wednesday. Which of these amounts represents the balance in his account on Thursday? F

(F) −$100 (H) $300
(G) $100 (J) $1,100

19. Which of the following is NOT an example of a prism? D

(A) a shoe box (C) a domino
(B) a file cabinet (D) a soup can

20. Describe the relationship in the scatter plot at the right. G

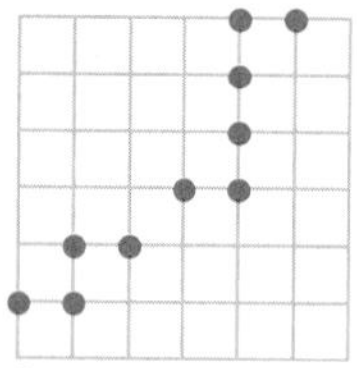

(F) no trend
(G) positive trend
(H) negative trend
(J) positive and negative trend

Gridded Response

Use the table below for Exercises 21–23.

How Long Students Studied Last Night

Number of Hours	Less than 1	1	2	3	More than 3
Number of Students	15	12	8	3	5

21. How many students were surveyed? 43

22. How many students studied 1 hour or less? 27

23. What percent of the students surveyed studied more than 2 hours? Round to the nearest tenth of a percent. 18.6

24. Jake received these grades on his math tests: 83, 86, 95, 95, 90, 82, 85, 82, 87, 82. What is his median test score? 88.5

25. Evaluate $-3 + x - y$ for $x = -4$ and $y = -8$. 1

26. An equilateral triangle has a perimeter of $5\frac{1}{4}$ cm. What is the length of one side in centimeters? 1.75

27. Find the area of the figure below in mm^2. 41

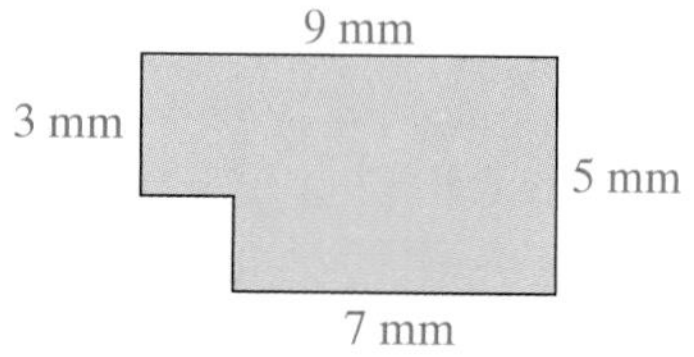

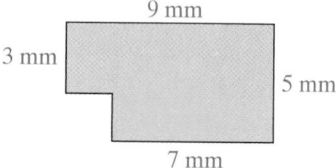

28. A diving board is 4 ft above a pool that is 15 ft deep. The total vertical distance of a person's dive is 10 ft. How many feet below the surface of the water did the person dive? 6

29. A copy center charges $.08 per copy. How much would it cost in dollars to make a copy of a one-page song for 250 students? 20

30. A rectangular pyramid has a base area of 126 cm^2 and a height of 23 cm. Find the volume of the pyramid in cm^3. 966

Item	16	17	18	19	20	21	22	23	24	25	26	27	28	29	30
Lesson	9-6	4-4	1-3	8-1	9-7	9-2	9-2	5-4	9-1	1-3	2-5	7-7	1-3	Skills Handbook p. 632	8-7

Short Response

31–32. See margin p. 593.

31. Find the lateral area of the square pyramid below. Then find the surface area.

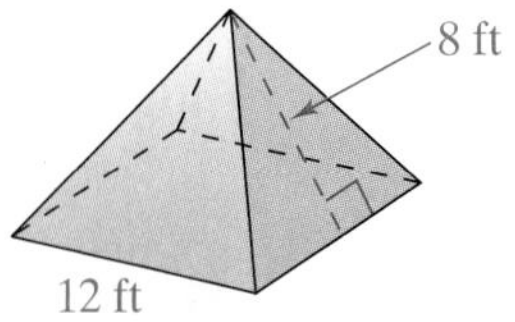

32. Find the percent of markup on a T-shirt that has a store cost of $4.87 and a selling price of $15.95. Show your work.

33–43. See margin.

33. a. Graph the function $y = -3x - 1$.

b. What value of x will give $y = 11$?

34. According to the graph shown, when did the stock fund earn the most? Explain.

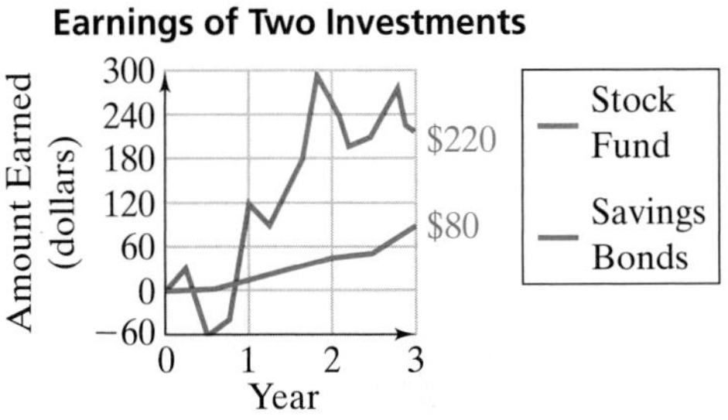

35. Which has a greater volume: a cone with radius 2 cm and height 6 cm, or a cone with height 2 cm and radius 6 cm? Explain.

36. a. What is the next term in the sequence 4, 12, 36, 108, . . . ?

b. What is the common ratio?

37. Find the circumference and the area of the circle. Round to the nearest tenth.

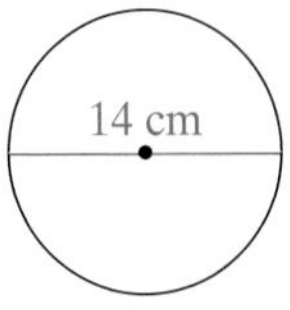

38. Karen swam for a half hour on Monday. She increased her workout by the same number of minutes each day. On Friday, she swam for one hour. Write and solve an equation to find the number of minutes by which Karen increased her workout each day.

Extended Response

39. It costs $3.99 to connect and $3.99 per minute to use an in-flight phone.

a. Write a function rule for the cost of a call using an in-flight phone.

b. Find the cost of a 10-minute in-flight call. Explain your work.

c. Graph the function.

40. a. Draw a net for a cylinder that has a diameter of 4 yd and a height of 7 yd. Label the diameter and height.

b. Find the surface area of the cylinder to the nearest yd^2. Show your work.

41. Boise wants to buy a scanner for $349. He has $34 and plans to save $15 each week.

a. Write an equation to show how many weeks Boise must save before he can buy the scanner. Define the variables you use.

b. How long will Boise need to save money for the scanner? Justify your reasoning.

42. The diagram below is a plan for a room. The scale is 1 in. = 20 ft.

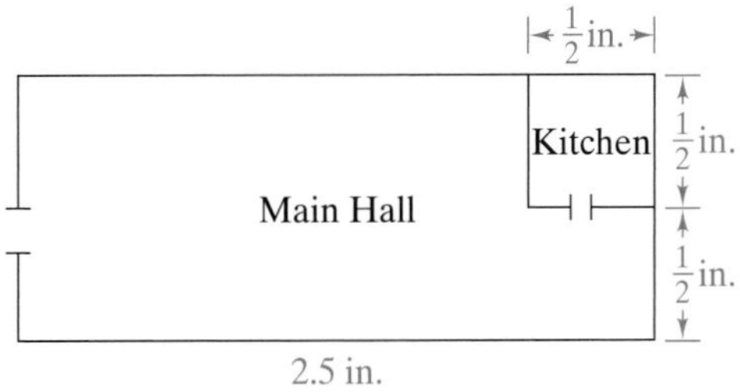

a. How long will the 2.5-in. side be in the real building? Justify your reasoning.

b. Find the area of the actual floor. Show your work.

43. A store pays $3.50 for a water bottle. The store sells each water bottle for $6.00.

a. Find the percent of markup on the water bottle. Show your work.

b. How many water bottles can you buy with $15.00? Show your work.

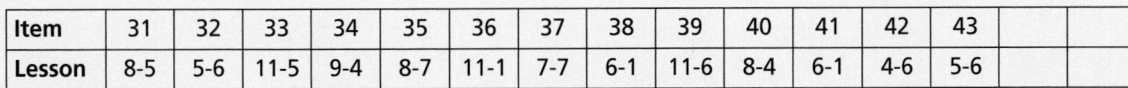

Item	31	32	33	34	35	36	37	38	39	40	41	42	43		
Lesson	8-5	5-6	11-5	9-4	8-7	11-1	7-7	6-1	11-6	8-4	6-1	4-6	5-6		

39. [4] a. $C = 3.99 + 3.99x$, where x is the number of minutes and C is the total cost.

b. $C = 3.99 + 3.99(10) = 43.89$

c.

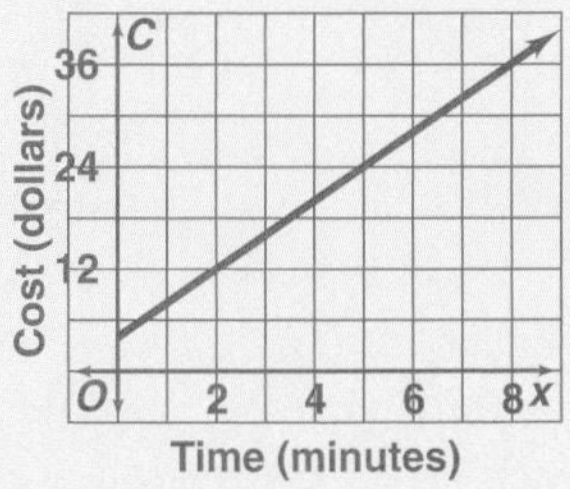

[3] appropriate methods with one error

[2] correct function evaluated correctly OR correct function graphed correctly but evaluated incorrectly

[1] correct solution without work shown

40. [4] a.

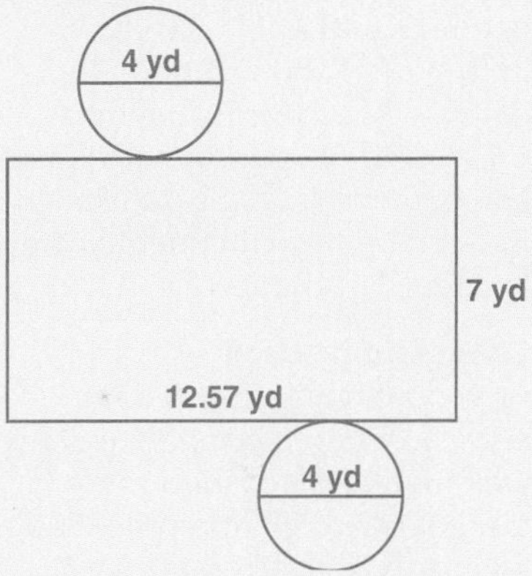

b. S.A. = $2(\pi r^2) + 2\pi rh$
$2(\pi \cdot 2^2) + 2\pi(2)(7)$
$25.13 + 87.964$
113.097
The surface area is 113 yd^2.

[3] appropriate methods with one computational error

[2] correct net OR correct surface area

[1] correct solution without work shown

41–43. See back of book.

Problem Solving

Applying Scientific Notation

Students will use data from these two pages to complete the activities posed here in Put It All Together.

Activating Prior Knowledge

Have students brainstorm a list of the tallest, shortest, longest, heaviest, lightest, fastest, and slowest animals. Then have volunteers do research on this topic to compare the names on the list with actual animal data.

Guided Instruction

Have volunteers read aloud the opening paragraph with the information about various animals. Then discuss the data presented. Have a student explain and demonstrate how to express in standard form numbers written in scientific notation.

Science Connection
How do the giants of today's animal kingdom compare in size, weight, and speed with the dinosaurs and giant reptiles and mammals of the distant past? Have interested students find out. Ask them to share what they have learned with classmates. Invite them to present their findings in a table and graph.

Careers
What kinds of jobs are there, other than as pet store owners, zoo keepers, or veterinarians, for those wishing to work with or learn more about animals? What skills, interests, and aptitudes should those interested in the field possess? What education is required? Have them put together an annotated list of interesting job opportunities.

Problem Solving Application

Applying Scientific Notation

Wild Exponents Would a giraffe 5.79×10^3 mm tall fit in your bedroom? Should you be afraid of a lobster that weighs 7.5×10^{-4} t? Could you outrun a rabbit that hopped 5.55×10^9 ft per decade? Scientific notation is convenient for expressing and comparing numbers, but it can also mislead you into thinking the numbers are wilder than they actually are. Often you can tame them by turning them back into a more familiar form.

Average Heights
Middle school boy: 156 cm
Middle school girl: 157 cm
Male giraffe: 530 cm
Female giraffe: 430 cm

Small Packages
Amoebas, small, transparent organisms, flow outward to move. It's easy to overlook them because they're only about 0.003 mm long!

How Many Is That?
A blue whale can be 33.5 m long—about the length of 18 scuba divers, including their flippers.

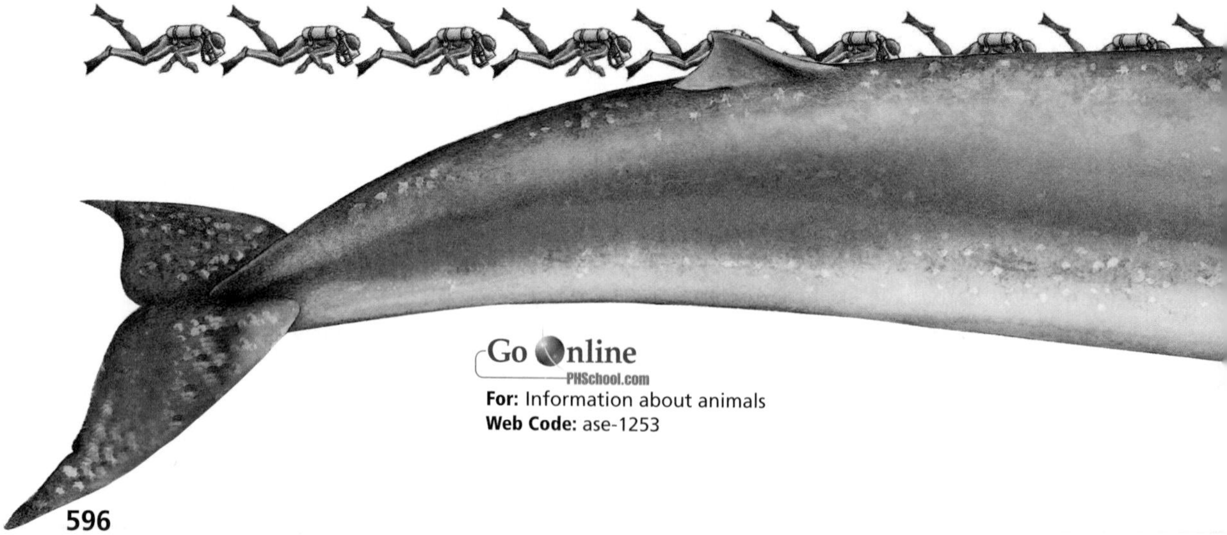

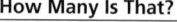

Go Online
PHSchool.com
For: Information about animals
Web Code: ase-1253

596

1a. 5.79 m
b. 1.5 lb
c. 12 mi/h
2–3. Check students' work.

Put It All Together

1. **Warm Up** Use the information in the introductory paragraph.
   a. How tall is the giraffe in meters?
   b. How much does the lobster weigh in pounds?
   c. How fast does the rabbit hop in miles per hour?

The goal of this game is to identify an animal when given its common dimensions in uncommon ways.

What You'll Need

- 3 to 5 index cards per student
- **Research** Choose an animal for each card. Consider animals that range in size from microscopic to gigantic. Find three numerical facts about each animal.
- Convert each fact to scientific notation, using units of measure that make the animal look especially large or small. Some numbers should have positive exponents and others should have negative exponents.
- Write these facts, or clues, on the front of the card.
- Illustrate the back of the card with a picture of the animal.

How to Play

2. Exchange cards with another student. Looking only at the clues, and *not* at the back of the card, change each into standard notation. Write your answers on a piece of paper.
3. Check your partner's answers while he or she checks yours. Correct any mistakes. Take turns asking questions about each animal until you guess what it is.

Sample Card (Zebra)

Who Am I?

1. Shoulder height up to 1.5×10^{-2} km
2. Weight up to 4×10^{5} g
3. Adult female has 1×10^{0} foal per year.

Length Conversions
1 micron = 1×10^{-6} m
1 mm = 1×10^{-3} m
1 km = 1×10^{3} m
1 ft = 3.048×10^{-1} m
1 mi = 5.28×10^{3} ft
1 light-year = 5.879×10^{12} mi

Weight Conversions
1 mg = 1×10^{-3} g
1 kg = 1×10^{3} g
1 kg = 2.2 lb
1 oz = 28.35 g
1 lb = 16 oz
1 t = 2×10^{3} lb

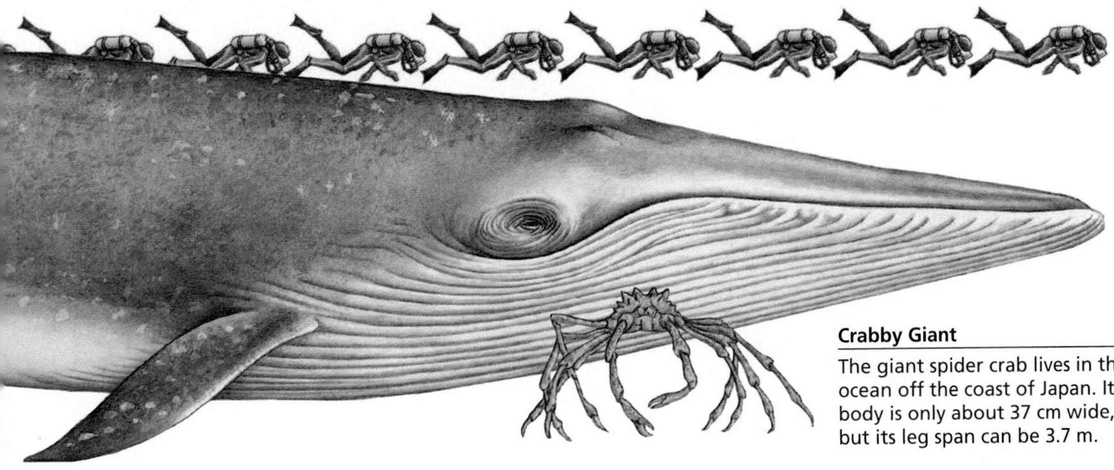

Crabby Giant

The giant spider crab lives in the ocean off the coast of Japan. Its body is only about 37 cm wide, but its leg span can be 3.7 m.

Put It All Together

Work through the Warm Up exercises together. Then discuss the rules and goals of the game that students will play. You may wish to have students work in pairs to create their cards. Refer all students to the conversion charts.

Teaching Tip
Using the sample card for the zebra as a guide, emphasize the importance of using the correct language when describing characteristics of a particular kind of animal. Point out, for instance, that a *foal* is a baby zebra.

Differentiated Instruction

Special Needs L1
As needed, have students help one another compute with or convert the numbers expressed in scientific notation, particularly with those containing negative powers of ten. Review the abbreviations for the different customary units of measure.

Visual Learners
Invite students to tape photos of the animals on the back of the cards instead of creating drawings of them.

Chapter Projects

Weather or Not

Students apply their knowledge of algebraic expressions to report on weather temperature data.

Resources

All in One Teaching Resources

- Chapter 1 Project Support

Guided Instruction

Activating Prior Knowledge
Have students develop a few benchmarks for identifying common Celsius temperatures. Ask:

- *What formula can you use to express Fahrenheit temperatures in degrees Celsius?* **Sample:** $C = (F - 32) \div 1.8$

Science Connection
Our ability to forecast weather is constantly improving. Ask students to predict the advantages of knowing with confidence what the weather will be weeks rather than hours in advance.

A New New Year

Students apply their knowledge of real numbers to invent a new calendar.

Resources

All in One Teaching Resources

- Chapter 2 Project Support

Guided Instruction

Activating Prior Knowledge
Explain to students that the calendar we use, the Gregorian calendar, dates from 1582. It was an improvement over the Julian calendar that it replaced because it took leap years into account. Ask:

- *What are the origins of the names of our days and months?* **They come from celestial bodies and from mythological gods and goddesses.**

Chapter Projects

WEATHER or NOT

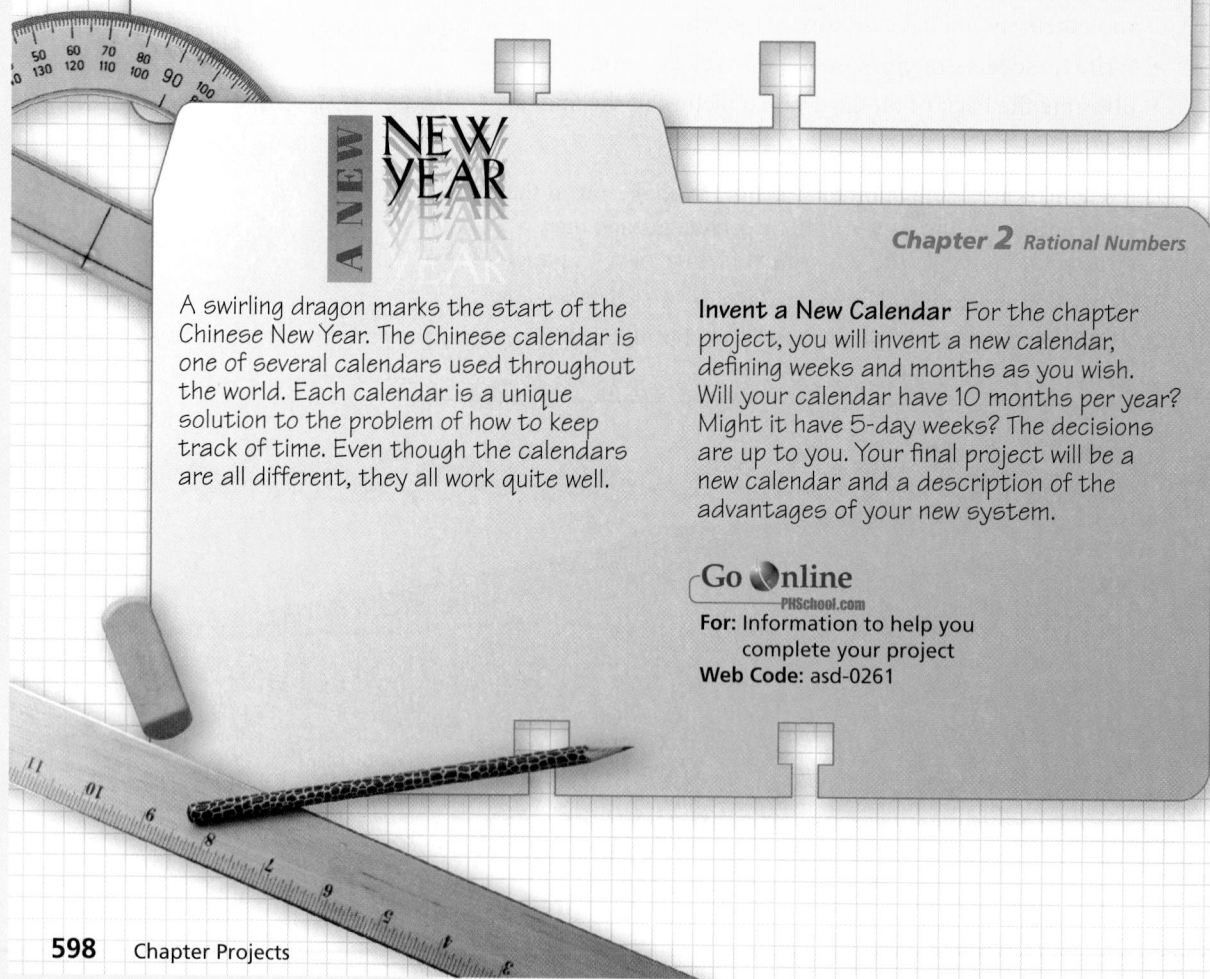

Chapter 1 *Integers and Algebraic Expressions*

Would you go swimming in 32° water? Is −2° a good temperature setting for a home freezer? The answer to both questions is "That depends!"

Are you using the Celsius or Fahrenheit scale? Water at 32°C feels like a bath! As for a freezer, −2°C is barely below freezing, while −2°F is a deep freeze! People living in North America use both the Fahrenheit and the Celsius scales, so it pays to know the difference.

Prepare a Report For the chapter project, you will examine weather data for a state or region of your choice. Your final project will be a report on temperature data, using both scales.

Go Online PHSchool.com
For: Information to help you complete your project
Web Code: asd-0161

A NEW NEW YEAR

Chapter 2 *Rational Numbers*

A swirling dragon marks the start of the Chinese New Year. The Chinese calendar is one of several calendars used throughout the world. Each calendar is a unique solution to the problem of how to keep track of time. Even though the calendars are all different, they all work quite well.

Invent a New Calendar For the chapter project, you will invent a new calendar, defining weeks and months as you wish. Will your calendar have 10 months per year? Might it have 5-day weeks? The decisions are up to you. Your final project will be a new calendar and a description of the advantages of your new system.

Go Online PHSchool.com
For: Information to help you complete your project
Web Code: asd-0261

Diversity
The origin of the *day* is a natural consequence of the rising and setting of the sun. However, Native Americans determine a day as the time from one dawn to the next.

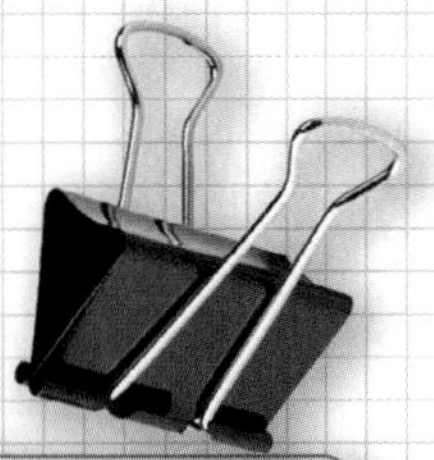

Step Right Up!

Chapter 3 Real Numbers and the Coordinate Plane

Have you ever been to a carnival or fair? "Hit the bull's-eye and win a prize!" Is it skill? Or is it luck?

Design a Game Suppose your class is putting on a fair to raise money for a class trip. For the chapter project, you will invent a game in which a ball rolls down a ramp and comes to rest in a target area of your own design. Does a bull's-eye score 10, or maybe 100? Can the players vary the slope of the ramp? You decide, since you make up the rules! Your final project will be the game, along with written rules to play by.

Go Online
PHSchool.com
For: Information to help you complete your project
Web Code: asd-0361

Larger Than Life

Chapter 4 Applications of Proportions

Mount Rushmore is an example of a scale model that is larger than the objects on which it is based—much larger! Other types of scale models, such as toy trains, dollhouses, and other toys, are smaller than the objects on which they are based.

Build a Scale Model For the chapter project, you will build your own scale model. First, you will choose an object to model. Use your imagination! Your model can be larger or smaller than the actual object—you choose the scale. Then you will select building materials and assemble the model. Your final project will be to present the model to your class, explaining the scale and how you chose the item to model.

Go Online
PHSchool.com
For: Information to help you complete your project
Web Code: asd-0461

Step Right Up!

Students apply their knowledge of slope to design a game in which a ball rolls down a ramp.

Resources

All in One Teaching Resources
- Chapter 3 Project Support

Guided Instruction

Activating Prior Knowledge
Ask students to suggest ways to start this project. Ask:
- *What features of your game can you vary as you try to improve the design so that the game will work as you wish it to?* **Sample: the slope and length of the ramp, the size and number of targets, the size of the ball, and so on**

Larger Than Life

Students apply their knowledge of proportions to make a scale model.

Resources

All in One Teaching Resources
- Chapter 4 Project Support

Guided Instruction

Activating Prior Knowledge
Discuss with students what factors they would consider and what tools they would use if they were to make a scale model of the classroom. Ask:
- *How could you use graph paper to help you make a scale model?* **Sample: Draw a floor plan on it using a scale in which an increment on the grid (cm, $\frac{1}{4}$-in., and so on) equals an actual distance.**

Careers
Architects draw and revise floor plans (carefully drawn to scale), or make accurate scale models.

Invest in a Winner

Students apply their knowledge of percents to plan investments.

Resources

All in One Teaching Resources

- Chapter 5 Project Support

Guided Instruction

Activating Prior Knowledge
Elicit from students what they know about different kinds of investments. Discuss that most investing involves risk. Ask:

- *Why would someone invest in a higher risk investment?* **Sample: Higher risk investments generally offer higher returns.**

English Language Learners ELL
Pair English language learners with native speakers to help the former with the terms associated with investments.

Balancing Act

Students apply their knowledge of equations to explore ways to make a mobile.

Resources

All in One Teaching Resources

- Chapter 6 Project Support

Guided Instruction

Activating Prior Knowledge
Have students share any experiences they have had constructing mobiles. Ask:

- *What did you do to keep your sculpture in motion?* **Answers will vary.**

English Language Learners ELL
Help students understand the meanings of the terms *mobile*, *kinetic*, and *in balance*.

Invest in a Winner

Chapter 5 *Applications of Percent*

You've won! You entered a quiz contest thinking you didn't have a chance, and now you're $5,000 richer! You are looking for a way to double your money in five years. Is that possible?

Explore Ways to Invest Money For the chapter project, you will explore different investments, looking for the best one for your money. Your final project will be to prepare an oral and visual presentation describing your investment choice.

Go Online PHSchool.com
For: Information to help you complete your project
Web Code: asd-0561

Balancing Act

Chapter 6 *Equations and Inequalities*

Mobiles are a popular form of art that you may see anywhere: in people's homes, in large office buildings, and in parks. The objects on a mobile float gently on currents of air. American sculptor Alexander Calder (1898–1976) first popularized mobiles. Calder is considered the founder of kinetic art, or art that is in motion.

Make a Mobile For the chapter project, you will explore techniques for constructing a mobile and use equations to model the relationships involved in the mobile. Your final project will be a finished mobile, along with a written summary telling what you have learned.

Go Online PHSchool.com
For: Information to help you complete your project
Web Code: asd-0661

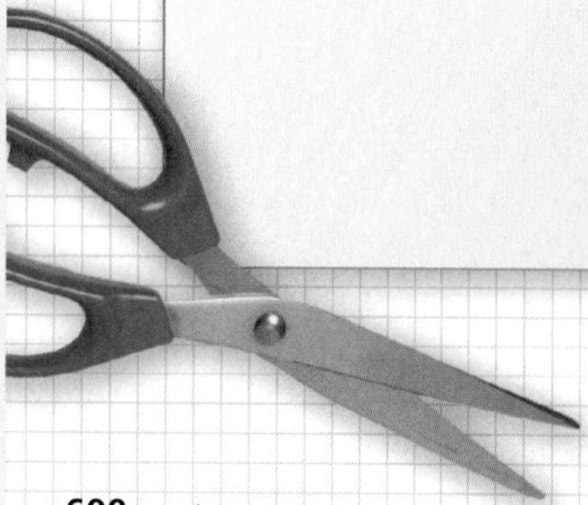

Great Escape

Chapter 7 Geometry

As the summer sun goes down on another hot day, you just have to get outside. Where do you go? To the park! For generations, people in towns and cities have used parks as places to escape. When properly planned, a park can be the perfect place to relax, meet friends, skate, and be surrounded by natural beauty.

Design a Park For the chapter project, you will design a small park and be prepared to present your plan to the town council. Your final project will be a detailed plan of the park.

Go Online
PHSchool.com
For: Information to help you complete your project
Web Code: asd-0761

A Better Way

Chapter 8 Measurement

Stop by the cereal section of your local supermarket. There are dozens of brands! Now check out the packaging. Most cereals are packaged in the same way: in cardboard rectangular boxes that are high and wide, but not deep.

Is this a waste of cardboard? Can you design a better package? You can . . . because now, you're in charge!

Design Packaging for Cereal For the chapter project, you will redesign the packaging of your favorite cereal. Your final project will be a new and different-shaped cardboard package that still holds the same volume as the original.

Go Online
PHSchool.com
For: Information to help you complete your project
Web Code: asd-0861

Great Escape

Students apply their knowledge of geometry to design a park.

Resources

All in One Teaching Resources

- Chapter 7 Project Support

Guided Instruction

Activating Prior Knowledge
Have students brainstorm a list of features and facilities they would want a park to have. Ask:

- *What would be a reasonable scale to use for a 8″ by 11″ drawing of a park the same size as your school's grounds?* Sample: 1 in. = 40 ft

Careers
Landscape architects are trained to design and oversee the construction of parks and other public spaces.

A Better Way

Students apply their knowledge of geometry and measurement to design a cereal package.

Resources

All in One Teaching Resources

- Chapter 8 Project Support

Guided Instruction

Activating Prior Knowledge
Initiate a discussion of what food manufacturers consider when designing packages for their product. Ask:

- *What purposes does packaging serve other than to hold a product and display or stack it?* Sample: to provide advertising space and space for required nutritional information and other information

News Flash

Students apply their knowledge of using graphs to illustrate a news story.

Resources

All in One Teaching Resources
- Chapter 9 Project Support

Guided Instruction

Activating Prior Knowledge
Discuss what kinds of news stories benefit by having a graph accompany them. Ask:
- *What kind of graph might you use to accompany a story about budget problems a city faces? Explain.* **Sample: circle graph, which shows how parts relate to a whole**

English Language Learners ELL
Invite students acquiring English to use a newspaper written in their native language. Pair them with native English speakers who can help them interpret a news story.

Start With the Stats

Students apply their knowledge of probability to prepare a statistical report for a coach.

Resources

All in One Teaching Resources
- Chapter 10 Project Support

Guided Instruction

Activating Prior Knowledge
Have students discuss key basketball statistics for the level of the sport they choose. Ask:
- *Which statistical information would the coach most want to know?* **Accept any answers students can justify.**

Physical Education Connection
Discuss that, with the advent of the computer, statistics have played an increasingly important role in collegiate and professional sports.

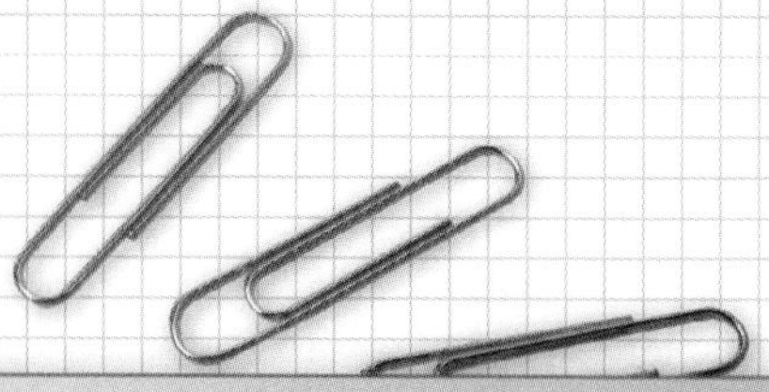

NEWS Flash

Chapter 9 Using Graphs to Analyze Data

What type of news catches your eye? Do you notice graphs and charts in news magazines and newspapers? If a picture is worth a thousand words, a graph is worth a thousand numbers! Reporters use graphs to summarize data and to tell a story clearly and simply. Do they always do it accurately?

Make a Graph for a News Article For the chapter project, you will analyze graphs and charts that appear in the news. For your final project, using a topic that you choose, you will write a news article and illustrate it with an appropriate graph.

Go Online PHSchool.com
For: Information to help you complete your project
Web Code: asd-0961

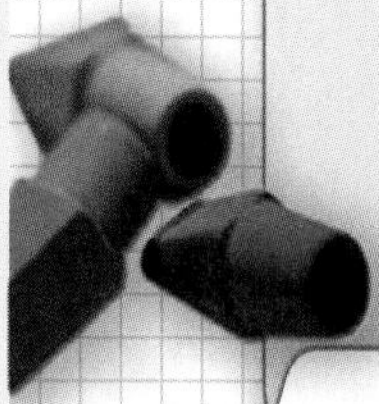

Start With the STATS

Chapter 10 Probability

There are fifteen seconds to go in a close basketball game. Should you foul intentionally? What is the probability that the player you foul will make both free throws? Statistics are everywhere in sports: field-goal percentages, batting averages, and so on. Coaches and players use these statistics to assess probabilities and make decisions.

Prepare a Stat Sheet Suppose you are a statistician for a basketball team. Pick any team—school, professional, or even fictional.

For the chapter project, you will gather data on five key players from the team. For your final project, you will present a statistical report that summarizes these basketball players' season last year.

Go Online PHSchool.com
For: Information to help you complete your project
Web Code: asd-1061

How Much Dough?

Chapter 11 Functions

How much should a pizza cost? Many restaurants sell pizzas in a variety of sizes and types, with many different kinds of toppings. Do restaurants base their prices on what they think their customers will be willing to pay for different sizes? Or do they take a mathematical approach and figure their costs using area formulas?

Set Prices for a Product For the chapter project, you will investigate prices for a product that is available in many sizes. You will look for patterns in the prices and describe the patterns mathematically. Then you will use this analysis to decide on prices for new products. Your final project will be a written proposal for setting pizza prices.

Go Online
PHSchool.com
For: Information to help you complete your project
Web Code: asd-1161

One Small STEP

Chapter 12 Polynomials and Properties of Exponents

"That's one small step for man, one giant leap for mankind." In July of 1969, Neil Armstrong was the first man to touch the moon's surface. Since then, space travel has exploded, with new missions being launched almost monthly.

Can you even imagine what the space program will be like in 30 more years? How about in 100 years? Take a small step into the future. Pretend you are a travel agent—one who specializes in space travel!

Create a brochure For the chapter project, you will collect information about two planets, including travel between them, and calculate the approximate distance from Earth to each of them. Your final project will be to design a space-travel brochure that includes interesting and enticing information about travel between the two planets.

Go Online
PHSchool.com
For: Information to help you complete your project
Web Code: asd-1261

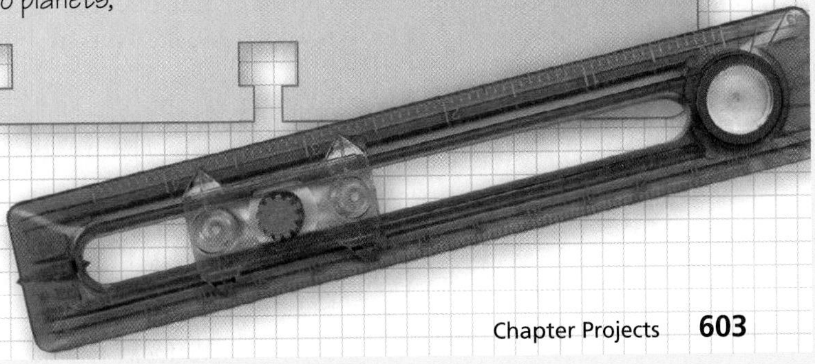

How Much Dough?

Students apply their knowledge of algebraic relationships to analyze product pricing.

Resources

All in One Teaching Resources
- Chapter 11 Project Support

Guided Instruction

Activating Prior Knowledge
Have students brainstorm a list of products they buy that are sold in different sizes. Ask:
- *What size/price patterns might you expect to find for foods that come in different sizes?* **Sample: unit prices based on volume or weight**

Consumer Connection
Initiate a class discussion about factors they, as shoppers, consider when making purchases.

One Small Step . . .

Students apply their knowledge of scientific notation to design a travel brochure.

Resources

All in One Teaching Resources
- Chapter 12 Project Support

Guided Instruction

Activating Prior Knowledge
Initiate a discussion of potential space travel destinations. Ask:
- *Where can you find the information you need to design your space travel brochure?* **Sample: almanacs, NASA, Internet, science texts, or magazines**

Science Connection
Some planets or moons are likely to be somewhat more hospitable than others for human visits. Have students do research to come up with a preferred list of human-friendly galactic destinations.

21. Distr. Prop.
22. Assoc. Prop. of Add.
23. Comm. Prop. of Add.
24. Distr. Prop.
25. Assoc. Prop. of Mult.
26. Ident. Prop. of Add.

CHAPTER 1

Extra Practice

Skills

Lesson 1-1 **Evaluate each expression for $n = 2$, $m = 3$, and $t = 5$.**

1. $3t - 4n$ 7
2. $13 - (m + n)$ 8
3. $\frac{m+t}{n}$ 4
4. $4.7 + mt$ 19.7

Lesson 1-2 **Compare. Write <, =, or >.**

5. -7 ■ 7 <
6. 32 ■ $|-32|$ =
7. $|-9|$ ■ -3 >
8. $|-8|$ ■ $|-6|$ >

Lessons 1-3 and 1-4 **Simplify each expression.**

9. $-6 + 4$ −2
10. $-4 + (-5)$ −9
11. $-2 - 6$ −8
12. $-8 - (-5)$ −3
13. $15 - (-8)$ 23
14. $99 + (-101)$ −2
15. $-3 \cdot 4$ −12
16. $-15 \cdot (-5)$ 75
17. $2 \cdot (-7) \cdot 5$ −70
18. $\frac{-12}{6}$ −2
19. $\frac{-80}{-16}$ 5
20. $\frac{16}{-8}$ −2

Lesson 1-5 **Identify each property.** 21–26. See margin.

21. $2(11) + 2(4) = 2(11 + 4)$
22. $(3 + 4) + 5 = 3 + (4 + 5)$
23. $2n + p = p + 2n$
24. $(3 + m)(-7) = -21 - 7m$
25. $(12 \cdot 5) \cdot 100 = 12 \cdot (5 \cdot 100)$
26. $c + 0 = c$

Lessons 1-6 and 1-7 **Solve each equation.**

27. $x - 6 = -15$ −9
28. $-12 = m + 8$ −20
29. $1.5 = m - 3.2$ 4.7
30. $x + 10 = 10$ 0
31. $\frac{b}{7} = 9$ 63
32. $-3w = 360$ −120
33. $144 = 6k$ 24
34. $20 = \frac{h}{-10}$ −200

Word Problems

Lesson 1-1

35. The depth of Lake Huron is 855 ft less than the depth of Lake Chelan. Lake Chelan is 1,605 ft deep. How deep is Lake Huron? 750 ft

36. **Sales** A store sells one model of bicycle for $250. If you buy more than one bicycle, the store will take $10 off the price of the first bicycle, $20 off the price of the second, $30 off the price of the third, and so on. If you buy 5 bicycles, how much will you pay? $1,100

Lesson 1-2

37. A teacher asks 15 students to estimate an answer to a question. The answers are 1, 5, 5, 6, 7, 8, 10, and 12. The correct estimate is 7. The teacher wants to calculate how far off the estimates were by finding the absolute value of the difference between each estimate and the answer. Which estimate was off by the most? The student who answered 1

Lessons 1-3 and 1-4

38. Stock Market A stock worth $34 at the beginning of the day lost $15 in value by the end of the day. What was the price at the end of the day? $19

39. A balloon is floating 47 feet above a lake. The bottom of the lake is 128 ft below the surface. How high above the lake bottom is the balloon? 175 ft

40. Coupons A store sells 12 shirts for $20.00 each. Seven of the shirts are purchased with $5 coupons. Use the equation $20s - 5c$, where s is the number of shirts sold and c is the number of coupons to find the total cost. Evaluate the expression for $s = 12$ and $c = 7$. $205

41. Over a 3-hour period a subway line carries 7,200 passengers. What is the number of passengers per hour? 2,400 passengers per hour

Lesson 1-5 **In Exercises 42–45, use the Distributive Property to find each total cost.**

42. 3 loaves of bread at $1.99 each $5.97

43. 6 cans of tuna at $.97 each $5.82

44. 4 bags of berries at $1.98 each $7.92

45. 5 boxes of rice at $2.95 each $14.75

Lesson 1-6

46. School Between 7:30 A.M. and 8:00 A.M. the number of students in a school increased by 73. There were 152 students in the school at 8:00 A.M. How many students were in school at 7:30 A.M.? 79 students

47. The movie *Antz* has a run time that is 33 minutes shorter than *Fantasia*'s run time. *Fantasia*'s run time is 120 minutes. Find the run time of *Antz*. $m + 33 = 120$; $m = 87$ minutes

Lesson 1-7 **Write and solve an equation for each situation.**

48. Three students eat lunch five days in a row. They spend a total of $60. The students spend the same amount of money for each lunch. What is the cost of one lunch? $4

49. A group of twelve volunteers raises $144 for three charities. Each charity gets the same amount. How much money does each charity get? $48

Extra Skills and Word Problems

CHAPTER 2

Extra Practice

Skills

Lesson 2-1 **Find the GCF of each pair of numbers using prime factorization.**

1. 9, 33 3
2. 7, 15 1
3. 6, 24 6
4. 4, 18 2
5. 22, 121 11
6. 17, 51 17
7. 42, 165 3
8. 18, 60 6

Lesson 2-2 **Write each fraction in simplest form.**

9. $\frac{20}{25}$ $\frac{4}{5}$
10. $\frac{7}{77}$ $\frac{1}{11}$
11. $\frac{40}{48}$ $\frac{5}{6}$
12. $-\frac{15}{35}$ $-\frac{3}{7}$
13. $-\frac{9}{42}$ $-\frac{3}{14}$
14. $\frac{36}{63}$ $\frac{4}{7}$
15. $-\frac{26}{65}$ $-\frac{2}{5}$
16. $\frac{34}{51}$ $\frac{2}{3}$

Write each decimal as a mixed number or fraction in simplest form.

17. 0.45 $\frac{9}{20}$
18. 12.2 $12\frac{1}{5}$
19. 8.6 $8\frac{3}{5}$
20. $0.\overline{8}$ $\frac{8}{9}$

Lesson 2-3 **Compare. Write <, =, or >.**

21. $\frac{25}{36}$ ■ $0.69\overline{4}$ =
22. 2.7 ■ $\frac{10}{3}$ <
23. −4.3 ■ −4.2 <
24. $-\frac{17}{5}$ ■ −15.9 >

Lessons 2-4 and 2-5 **Simplify. Write each answer in simplest form.**

25. $-\frac{3}{8} + \frac{7}{8}$ $\frac{1}{2}$
26. $-\frac{5}{18} + \left(-\frac{1}{6}\right)$ $-\frac{4}{9}$
27. $12\frac{1}{3} - 6\frac{2}{3}$ $5\frac{2}{3}$
28. $3\frac{1}{2} - \left(-\frac{11}{14}\right)$ $4\frac{2}{7}$
29. $-\frac{3}{7} \cdot \frac{5}{9}$ $-\frac{5}{21}$
30. $-4\frac{5}{24} \cdot (-6)$ $25\frac{1}{4}$
31. $-2\frac{1}{2} \div 6$ $-\frac{5}{12}$
32. $-25 \div \frac{5}{7}$ −35

Lesson 2-6 **Solve each formula for the variable indicated in red.**

33. $V = \frac{1}{3}Bh$ $h = \frac{3V}{B}$
34. $I = prt$ $\frac{I}{pt} = r$
35. $C = 44a + b$ $b = C - 44a$
36. $E = mc^2$ $m = \frac{E}{c^2}$

Lesson 2-7 **Simplify or evaluate each expression.**

37. $-3^2 - (-8)$ −1
38. $(-2)^3 + 4 \div 2 - 3$ −9
39. $(3 - 4)^5 - 17 + 1^{12}$ −17
40. $2r^2 + 6r + 3$ for $r = -6$ 39
41. $-c^3 + 2c^2 - c + 8$ for $c = 3$ −4

Lesson 2-8 **Write each number in scientific notation.**

42. 400,000,000 4×10^8
43. 8,750,000 8.75×10^6
44. 40,000 4×10^4
45. 19,000,000 1.9×10^7

606

Word Problems

Lesson 2-1

46. Two frogs hop around a circular track that is 60 inches around. First the larger frog jumps 13 in. and then the smaller frog jumps 11 in. If they take turns jumping, how many inches from the start will they be when they once again are at the same point? 23 inches

Lesson 2-2

47. A bag of beads for a craft project weighs 6 oz. The project uses 5 bags. Express the total weight of the beads in pounds as a decimal. 1.875 lbs

Lesson 2-3

48. Science Two students are measuring the amount of water in 2 liquids. One student finds that $\frac{10}{17}$ of the first liquid is water. The other finds that 0.6 of the second liquid is water. Which of the two liquids has the higher fraction of water? The second liquid

Lessons 2-4 and 2-5

49. Find the perimeter of a square whose sides measure $4\frac{7}{8}$ in. 19.5 inches

50. A small room has a floor space that measures 48.75 square feet. In one corner of the room a cabinet will be set. The rest of the room will be carpeted. If the cabinet takes up $4\frac{2}{3}$ square feet, how much carpeting is needed? $44\frac{1}{12}$ ft^2

51. Three quarters of a pound of honey sold at a roadside stand costs \$4. How much honey can you get for \$6? 1.125 lbs

52. A bag of nuts weighs $2\frac{1}{4}$ oz. In making a recipe a chef uses $3\frac{1}{2}$ bags. How many ounces of nuts are used in the recipe? $7\frac{7}{8}$ oz

Lessons 2-6 and 2-7

53. An African driver ant queen can lay as many as 4 million eggs in a 25-day period. What is this rate in eggs per hour? $6{,}666\frac{2}{3}$ eggs per hour

54. Geometry The formula for the area of a square is $A = s^2$. What is the area of a square whose sides measure 12 cm? 144 cm^2

Lesson 2-8

55. An electronic counter increases by 1 every second. If it starts at 0, what will the count be after 50 days? Express your answer in scientific notation. 4.32×10^6

Extra Skills and Word Problems

607

CHAPTER 3 Extra Practice

Skills

Lesson 3-1 **Identify each number as *rational* or *irrational*.**

1. 1.020304 . . . irrational
2. $\sqrt{25}$ rational
3. $\sqrt{26}$ irrational
4. $5.63\overline{663}$ rational

Lessons 3-2 and 3-3 **Use the Pythagorean Theorem to find the hypotenuse of the right triangle from the given lengths of the two legs.**

5. 3, 4 5
6. 10, 24 26
7. 7, 13 $\sqrt{218}$
8. 6, 11 $\sqrt{157}$
9. $\sqrt{2}$, $\sqrt{7}$ 3
10. 1.2, 1.6 2
11. 21, 22 $\sqrt{925}$
12. 13, 31 $\sqrt{1{,}130}$

Given leg ℓ and hypotenuse h determine the length of the missing leg of the right triangle.

13. $\ell = 7$, $h = 25$ 24
14. $\ell = 7.5$, $h = 12.5$ 10
15. $\ell = 23$, $h = 44$ $\sqrt{1{,}407}$
16. $\ell = 50$, $h = 76$ $\sqrt{3{,}276}$

Lesson 3-4 **Name the coordinates of each point in the graph.**

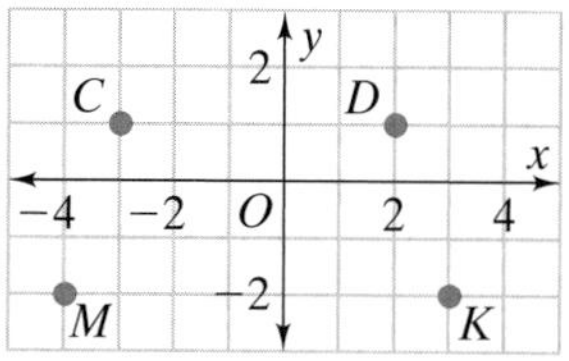

17. C (−3, 1)
18. D (2, 1)
19. K (3, −2)
20. M (−4, −2)

Lesson 3-5 **Graph each linear equation.** 21–24. See margin.

21. $y = 3x + 3$
22. $y = -2x + 3$
23. $y = \frac{1}{3}x - \frac{2}{3}$
24. $y = -\frac{3}{4}x + 1$

Lessons 3-6 to 3-8 **Copy the figure shown below for Exercises 25–27. Then draw its image after each transformation.** 25–27. See margin.

25. translation 3 units right and 1 unit down
26. reflection over the y-axis
27. rotation 270° about the origin

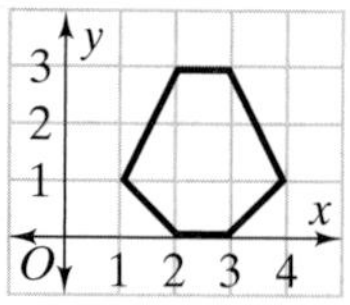

Word Problems

Lesson 3-1

28. **Open-Ended** Name a rational number whose square root is a number between 0 and 1. Answers may vary. Sample: $\frac{1}{2}$
29. A square has an area of 240.25 in.^{2}. What are the lengths of its sides? 15.5 in.

21.
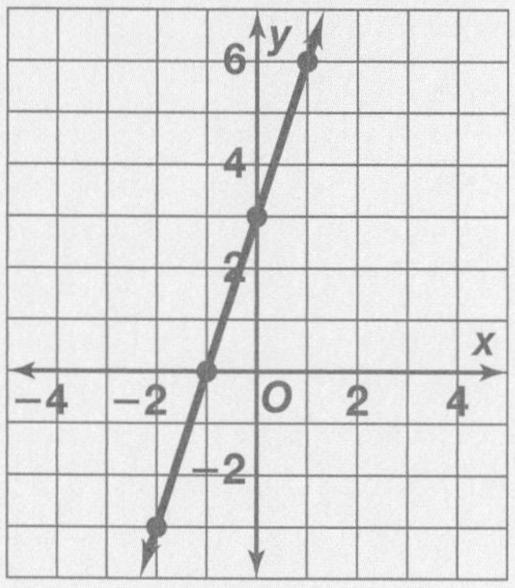

22.
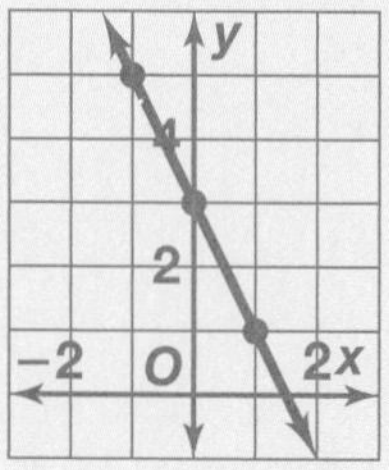

23.
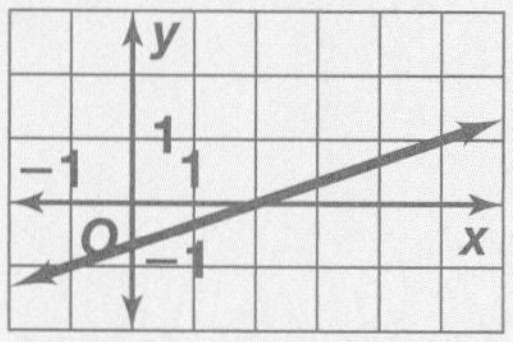

24.
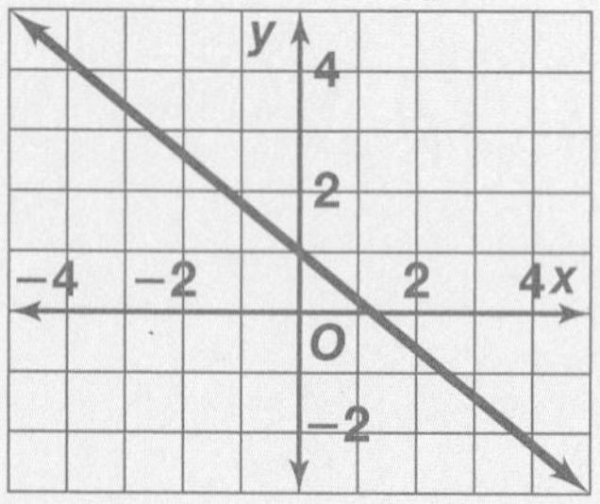

25.
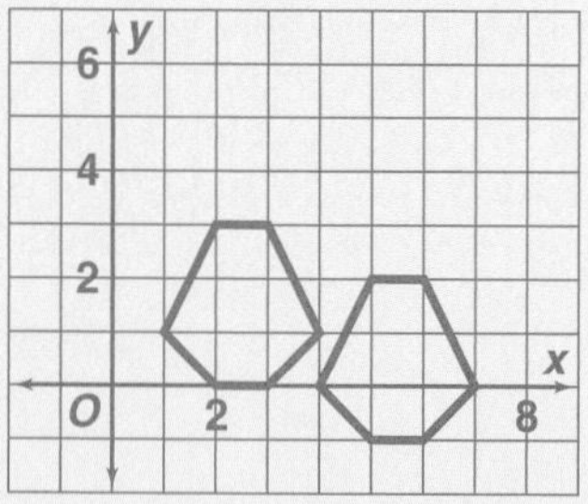

26.
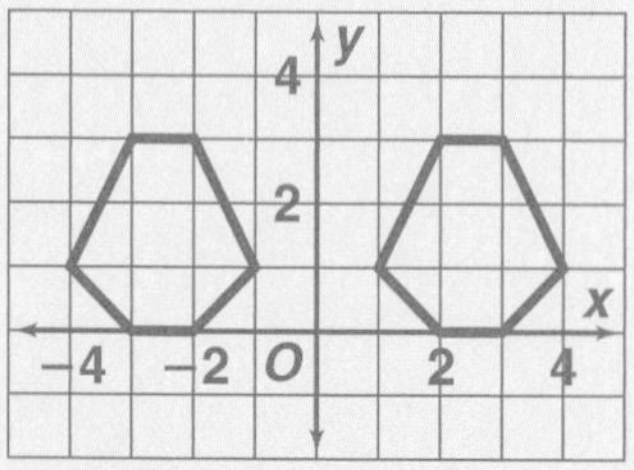

27.
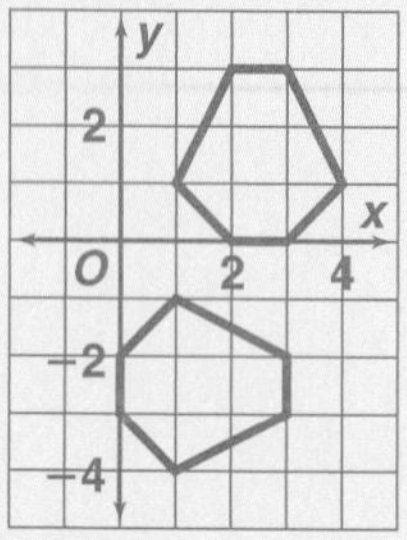

Lessons 3-2 and 3-3

30. The hypotenuse of a right triangle is 5 cm. The lengths of both legs are equal. Find the lengths of the legs. Round to the nearest tenth. 3.5 cm

31. A tree forms a right angle with the ground. If you place the base of a 12-ft ladder 3 ft from the tree, how high up the tree will it reach? $\sqrt{135}$

Lesson 3-4

32. Designers use coordinates to make graphics. On a computer screen a point is called a pixel. Name the coordinates of each orange pixel shown below. What do these coordinates have in common?
(4, 8), (6, 8), (9, 8), (13, 8), (17,8), (20, 8), (22, 8); same *y*-coordinate

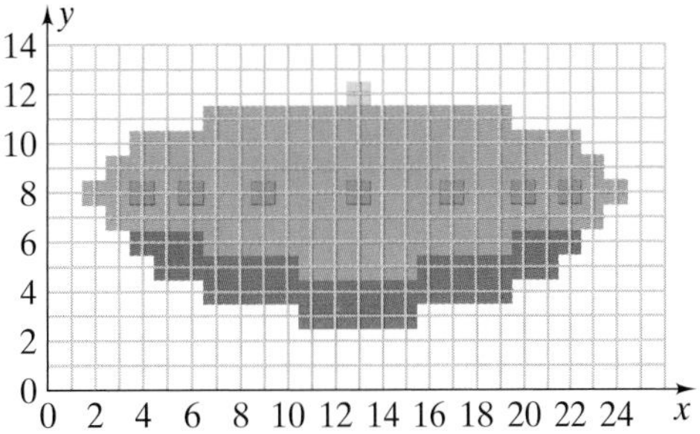

Lesson 3-5

33. Population A country's population is currently about 20 million. The population increases by about 1.2 million people per year. The equation for the population p in millions after y years is $p = 1.2y + 20$. Graph the equation and predict how many people there will be in 19 years. See margin.

Lesson 3-6

34. Point Z is translated using the rule $(x, y) \rightarrow (x - 4, y + 11)$. The coordinates of Z' are $(4, -11)$. What are the coordinates of point Z? (8, −22)

Lesson 3-7

35. The vertices of $\triangle RST$ are $R(0, 4)$, $S(0, 0)$, and $T(-4, 0)$. Graph $\triangle RST$ on a coordinate plane. What are the coordinates after a reflection over the y-axis? $R'(0, 4)$, $S'(0, 0)$, $T'(4, 0)$

Lesson 3-8

36. Rotate the figure at the right 90° clockwise about the origin. What are the coordinates of point Q'? (−5, 6)

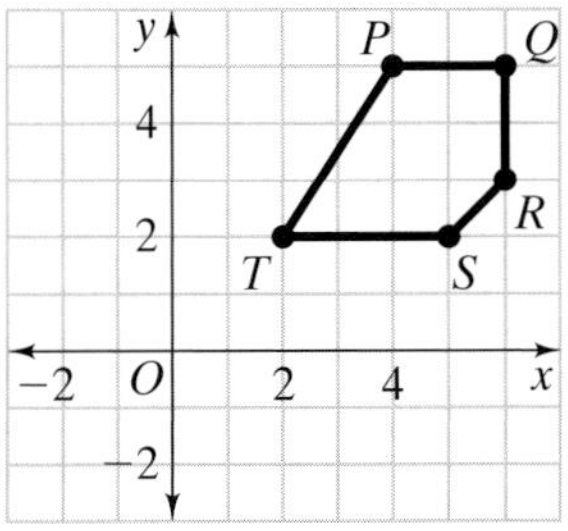

37. Geometry A regular polygon has all sides and all angles equal. All regular polygons have rotational symmetry. A certain regular polygon has an angle of rotation of 72°. How many sides does this polygon have?
5 sides

33.

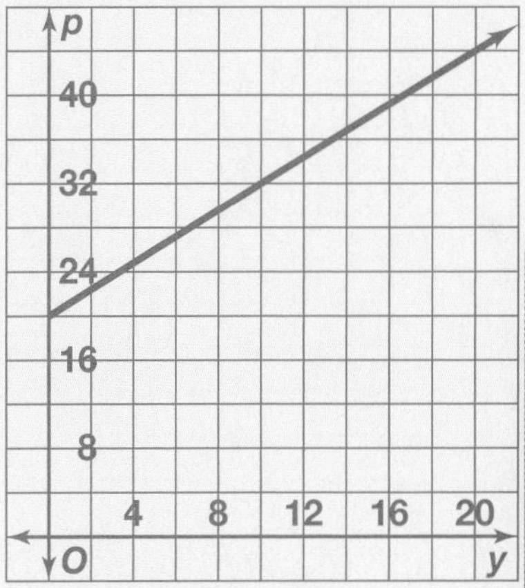

about 42.8 million people

16.

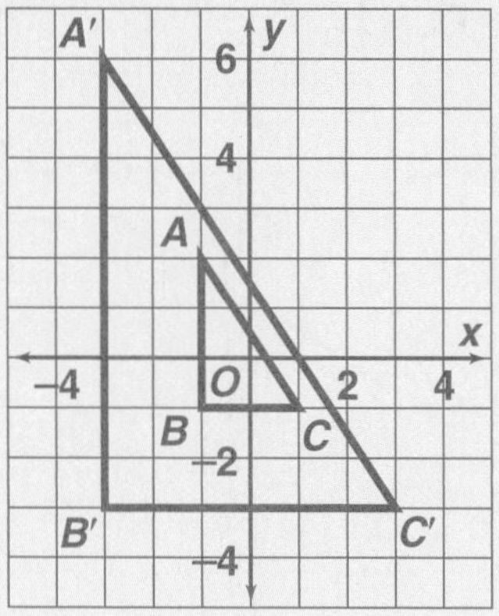

17.

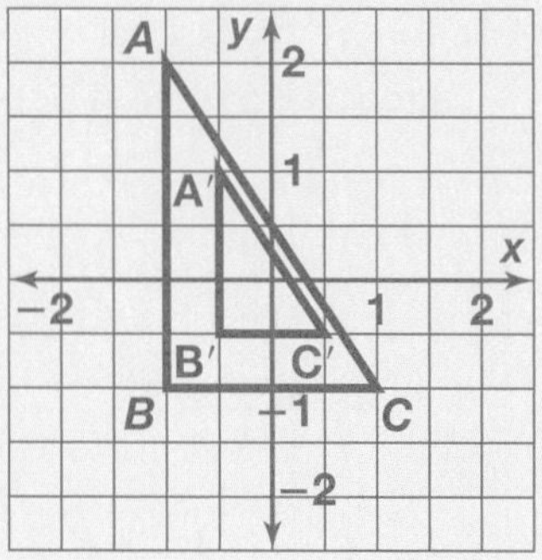

CHAPTER 4 Extra Practice

Skills

Lesson 4-1 **Find each unit rate.**

1. 240 mi on 8 gal 30 mi/gal
2. \$3.50 for 10 oz \$.35/oz
3. 450 mi in 9 h 50 mph
4. \$18 for 12 cans \$1.50/can

Lesson 4-2 **Convert each measure.**

5. 3.5 mi = ■ ft 18,480
6. 7.2 km = ■ m 7,200
7. 80 oz = ■ lb 5
8. 120 fl oz = ■ gal 0.9375

Lesson 4-3 **Solve each proportion.**

9. $\frac{4}{7} = \frac{x}{21}$ 12
10. $\frac{3}{x} = \frac{18}{9}$ $1\frac{1}{2}$
11. $\frac{x}{10} = \frac{8}{15}$ $5\frac{1}{3}$
12. $\frac{3}{5} = \frac{2}{x}$ $3\frac{1}{3}$

Lesson 4-4 **Exercises 13–15 show pairs of similar polygons. Find the unknown lengths.**

13. 10.5

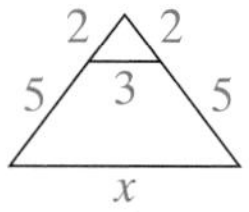

14. 6.75

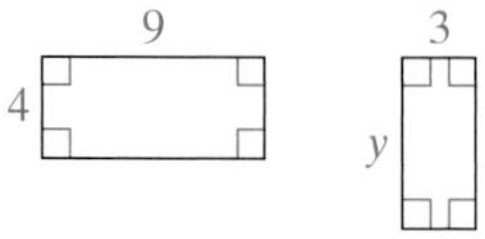

15. y = 1.5, z = 4

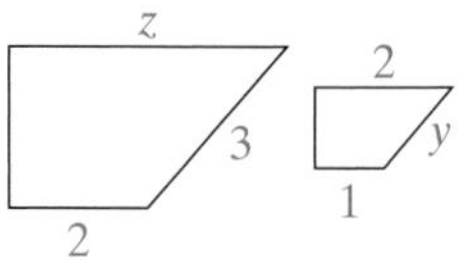

Lesson 4-5 **Find the image of △ABC at the right after a dilation with the given center and scale factor.**

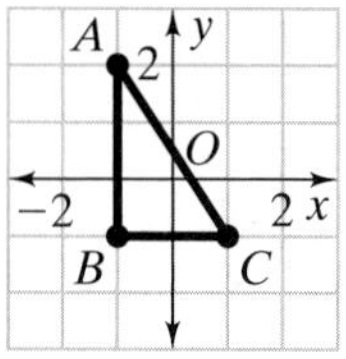

16. center B, scale factor of 3 See margin.
17. center A, scale factor of $\frac{1}{2}$ See margin.

Lesson 4-6 **The scale of a map is 1 in. : 30 mi. How many actual miles does each measurement on the map represent?**

18. 3 in. 90 mi
19. $2\frac{2}{3}$ in. 80 mi
20. $\frac{1}{4}$ in. 7.5 mi
21. 5 in. 150 mi
22. $6\frac{1}{2}$ in. 195 mi

Lesson 4-7

23. A student is 5 ft tall and casts a shadow 12 ft long. A flagpole casts a shadow 25 ft long. Find the height of the flagpole to the nearest tenth. 10.4 ft

Word Problems

Lesson 4-1

24. Shampoo A 12-oz bottle of shampoo costs \$3.99. A 25.4-oz bottle of the same shampoo costs \$7.49. Find the unit cost of each bottle. Which bottle of shampoo is the better buy? The 25.4 oz bottle is a better buy.

Lesson 4-2

25. The world's fastest elevators are located in a building in Taiwan. At top speed, the elevators can go as fast as 37.6 mph. What is this rate in feet per second? $55.14\overline{6}$ ft/s

Lesson 4-3

26. Florence can knit 3 scarves in 7 days. Write a proportion to find how long it will take her to knit 10 scarves for a school fundraiser. $23\frac{1}{3}$ days

Lesson 4-4 **An Antonov An-225 airplane model has a wingspan of 22.5 cm. The actual wingspan of an An-225 is 88.4 m.**

27. If the actual length of an An-225 is 84 m, what is the length of the airplane model in decimal form? 21.38 cm

28. Suppose another model of the An-225 has a scale of 1 cm to 36 m. What is the wingspan of this model in cm? $2.\overline{45}$ cm

Lesson 4-5

29. **Photography** Jorge is enlarging a digital photo that is 4 in. high by 6 in. wide. If the enlarged photo is $18\frac{1}{2}$ in. high, find its width. 27.75 in.

Lesson 4-6

30. **Sports** A tennis court is 36 ft wide and 78 ft long. A scale drawing of the court is 1 in. wide and 2 in. long. Find the scale used. 1 in. : 36 ft

Lesson 4-7

31. The tallest unsupported flagpole in the world is in Amman, Jordan. It casts a shadow 550.6 ft long. At the same time, a nearby man who is 6 ft tall casts a shadow 8 ft long. How tall is the flagpole? Round to the nearest foot. 413 ft

Extra Skills and Word Problems

CHAPTER 5

Extra Practice

Skills

Lesson 5-1 Write each number as a decimal, a fraction, and a percent.

1. 0.3 0.3, $\frac{3}{10}$, 30%
2. 21% 0.21, $\frac{21}{100}$, 21%
3. 3.47 3.47, $3\frac{47}{100}$, 347%
4. 0.004 0.004, $\frac{1}{250}$, 0.40%
5. $\frac{3}{20}$ 0.15, $\frac{3}{20}$, 15%
6. $\frac{1}{3}$ $0.\overline{3}$, $\frac{1}{3}$, $33\frac{1}{3}$%
7. 0.62% 0.0062, $\frac{31}{5{,}000}$, 0.62%
8. $2\frac{1}{2}$ 2.5, $2\frac{1}{2}$, 250%

Lesson 5-2 Estimate each percent.

9. 28% of 99 about 28
10. 7% of 93 about 7
11. 48% of 32 about 16
12. 125% of 84 about 105

Estimate a 15% tip for each restaurant bill.

13. $15.50 $2.40
14. $27.89 $4.50
15. $33.07 $5.25
16. $52.31 $7.50

Lessons 5-3 and 5-4 Solve each problem.

17. 6% of 51 3.06
18. 117% of 22 25.74
19. 2.5% of 78 1.95
20. 145 is 15% of ■. $966.\overline{6}$
21. 0.4 is ■% of 5. 8
22. 215% of 20 is ■. 43

Lesson 5-5 Find each percent of change. Round your answer to the nearest tenth of a percent where necessary.

23. 16 to 20 25%
24. 320 to 542 69.4%
25. 1 to 4 300%
26. 13 ft 5 in. to 17 ft 4 in. 29.2%
27. 8 qt 3 pt to 6 qt 6 pt −5.3%
28. 10 lb 4 oz to 14 lb 1 oz 37.2%

Lesson 5-6 Find each percent of markup.

29. store's cost: $16; selling price: $20 25%
30. store's cost: $43; selling price: $57.19 33%
31. store's cost: $24.50; selling price: $34.79 42%

Find each sale price. Round to the nearest cent.

32. regular price: $14.49, percent of discount: 6% $13.62
33. regular price: $28, percent of discount: 11% $24.92
34. regular price: $61.25, percent of discount: 18% $50.23

Lesson 5-7 Find the balance in each account to the nearest cent.

35. $165 at $4\frac{1}{2}$% simple interest for 2 years $179.85
36. $350 at $5\frac{1}{4}$% simple interest for 3 years $405.13

Lesson 5-8 Suppose you toss a coin twice. Find each probability.

37. P(no heads) $\frac{1}{4}$
38. P(exactly one head) $\frac{1}{2}$
39. P(at least one head) $\frac{3}{4}$

Word Problems

Lesson 5-1

Household Pets

Animal	Number of Students
Bird	3
Cat	35
Dog	42
Rabbit	8

40. **Pets** The table at the right shows the results of a survey asking students what pets they have at home. What percent of students have a dog at home? 47.7%

Lesson 5-2

41. **Food** A restaurant's appetizers are $\frac{1}{3}$ off on Thursdays. Your bill comes to $17.25. About how much should you leave for a 15% tip if you base your tip on the cost before the discount? $3.75

Lessons 5-3 and 5-4

42. **States** The area of Iowa is about 55,869 square miles. Missouri's area is about 123.3% of Iowa's area. What is the area of Missouri? about 68,886 square miles

43. **Cars** Suppose a car salesperson makes a $3\frac{1}{2}$% commission on each car she sells. What is the salesperson's commission on a $34,285 car? about $1,200

Lesson 5-5

44. **Weather** During January 2005, 2.27 inches of precipitation fell in Maine. Only 0.90 inches of precipitation fell in Maine during January 2004. Find the percent of change. Round your answer to the nearest tenth of a percent if necessary. 152.2%

Lesson 5-6

45. Daniel ordered a shipment of $18.00 sunglasses for his store. He marked them up 50%. After a few weeks, he marked them down to $22.95. What was the percent of discount? 15%

Lesson 5-7

46. **Fundraising** Your track team deposits money they make from fundraisers during the school year. The team deposits $250 in September at 2.3% simple interest. What is the balance nine months later? $254.31

Lesson 5-8

47. **Bowling** The probability of a professional bowler getting a perfect score of 300 in one year of bowling is 1 out of 4,001. Express this probability as a percent. 0.025%

Extra Skills and Word Problems

613

28. $x \le 12$;

29. $f \le -9$;

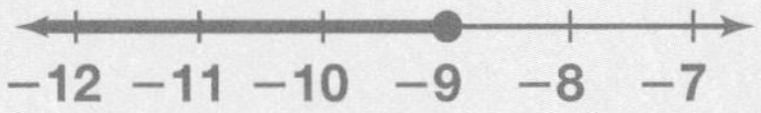

30. $p > 0$;

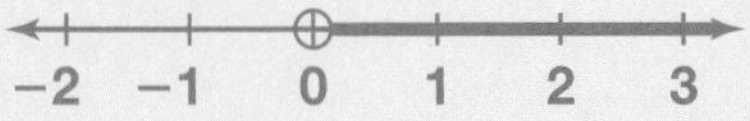

31. $a \ge -10$;

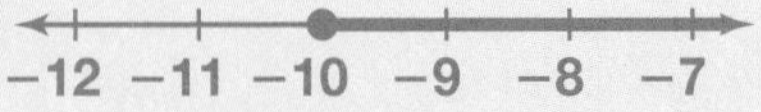

32. $-10 \ge y$;

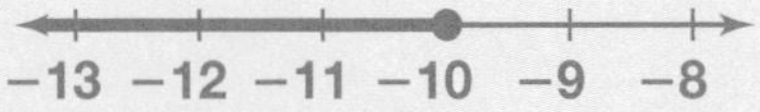

33. $m < 12$;

CHAPTER 6 Extra Practice

Skills

Lesson 6-1 Write an equation for each model.

1. 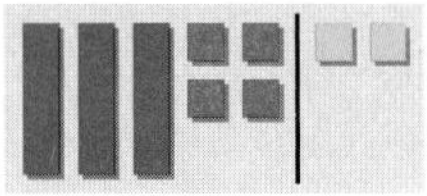 $3x - 4 = 2$

2.  $5 - 4x = -1$

Solve each equation.

3. $6n + 3 = 21$ 3
4. $10 = \frac{m}{5} + 2$ 40
5. $-b + 2 = -\frac{1}{2}$ $2\frac{1}{2}$
6. $7g - 4 = 10$ 2
7. $-10 = 2 + 6w$ −2
8. $5d + 10 = 25$ 3
9. $15 = -k + 18$ 3
10. $4x - 2 = 8$ $2\frac{1}{2}$

Lesson 6-2 Simplify each expression.

11. $6x + 4 - 3x$ $3x + 4$
12. $7(h - 5)$ $7h - 35$
13. $2(x + 1) + 5$ $2x + 7$
14. $-5 + 3p - p$ $-5 + 2p$
15. $13q + 91 - 13q$ 91
16. $-(8z + 2z - 1)$ $-10z + 1$
17. $47 - 11r - 7r$ $47 - 18r$
18. $-15h - (23 - 9h)$ $-6h - 23$

Lessons 6-3 and 6-4 Solve each equation.

19. $16 = -(2 - 2b)$ 9
20. $k = 1.5(7 - k)$ 4.2
21. $-8(3a - 5) = 56a$ $\frac{1}{2}$
22. $123 = 9y + 4 - 7y$ $59\frac{1}{2}$
23. $-9 - 3y = 19 + y$ −7
24. $30 - 5(p - 10) = 11p$ 5
25. $14 - 2w = 18w - 26$ 2
26. $4(2.2d - 1) - 0.8d = 23$ $3\frac{3}{8}$
27. $4.1x + 1.4 - 5.1x = 6.6$ −5.2

Lesson 6-5 Solve each inequality. Graph the solution. 28–33. See margin.

28. $x - 2 \le 10$
29. $f + 21 \le 12$
30. $p - 1 > -1$
31. $5 + a \ge -5$
32. $-12 \ge -2 + y$
33. $m + 4 < 16$

Write an inequality for each graph.

34. 

$x \le 1$

35. 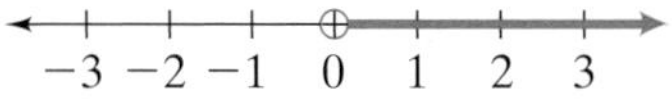

$x > 0$

Lesson 6-6 Solve each inequality.

36. $7p \le -35$ $p \le -5$
37. $-4y < 28$ $y > -7$
38. $\frac{q}{-6} < 3.1$ $q > -18.6$
39. $\frac{x}{3} < 0$ $x < 0$
40. $\frac{z}{-1} > -11$ $z < 11$
41. $26 \ge -2.5t$ $-10.4 \le t$

Word Problems

Lesson 6-1

42. Claudia bought 3 movie passes and a large box of popcorn. The total cost was \$33.49. The popcorn cost \$4.99. How much did each movie pass cost? \$9.50

43. Clothes You bought socks for \$4.99 a pair and a belt for \$29.99. The total cost was \$59.93. How many pairs of socks did you buy? 6 pairs

Lesson 6-2

44. Seth bought lunch three times and breakfast twice last week. This week Seth bought lunch four times and breakfast once. Define and use variables to represent the total cost. b = breakfast cost
ℓ = lunch cost
$(3\ell + 2b) + (4\ell + b) = 4\ell + 3b$

Lessons 6-3 and 6-4

45. Fruit You buy 5 pounds of Bartlett pears and some Bosc pears. Each variety of pears costs \$1.09 per pound. The total cost is \$10.36. About how many pounds of Bosc pears did you buy? about $4\frac{1}{2}$ lbs

46. Boats A marina charges \$175 for materials and \$15 per foot to paint the bottom of a boat. It cost \$595 to paint a boat. What is the length of the boat? 28 ft

47. Savings Hugo received \$100 for his birthday. He then saved \$20 each week until he had a total of \$460. How many weeks did it take him to save the money? 18 weeks

Lesson 6-5

48. You have only \$100 spending money this week. You put \$39.85 worth of gas into your car. You spend \$56.14 at the grocery store. Do you have enough money to get an oil change for \$24.99? Write and solve an inequality to solve this problem. $39.85 + 56.14 + m \leq 100$;
$m \leq 4.01$; No

Lesson 6-6

49. There are 47 children going to a birthday party at a family entertainment center. If a minivan can transport 6 children in a vehicle, how many vans are needed to transport all the children? 8 vans

50. A school rowing team needs to earn at least \$1,250 for new equipment. The team decides to sell raffle tickets for \$7 per ticket. How many tickets must the team sell in order to meet their goal? 179 tickets

Extra Skills and Word Problems

615

1. 37°
2. Answers may vary. Sample: ∠LPM and ∠KPN
3. 115°, 65°
4. Answers may vary. Sample: ∠3 and ∠6
5. ∠2 = 72°, ∠3 = 72°, ∠4 = 108°, ∠5 = 108°, ∠6 = 72°, ∠7 = 72°, ∠8 = 108°
6. △RST ≅ △NMQ by SAS
7. △ABC ≅ △FDE by ASA
8. △KLM ≅ △GHK by SSS

CHAPTER 7 Extra Practice

Skills

Lesson 7-1 **For Exercises 1–3, use the diagram at the right.** 1–3. See margin.

1. Find the measure of the complement of ∠PLK.
2. Name a pair of vertical angles.
3. Find the measures of ∠LPM and ∠MPN.

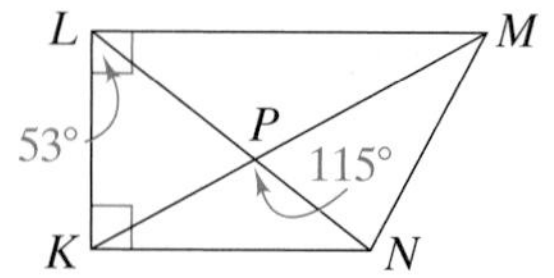

Lesson 7-2 **In the diagram at the right, $\ell \parallel m$.** 4–5. See margin.

4. Identify a pair of alternate interior angles.
5. If $m\angle 1 = 108°$, find the measure of each numbered angle.

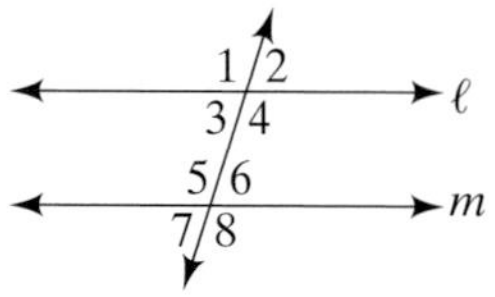

Lesson 7-3 **Explain why each pair of triangles is congruent.** 6–8. See margin.

6. 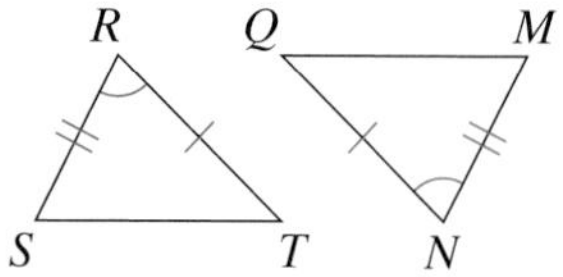

7. 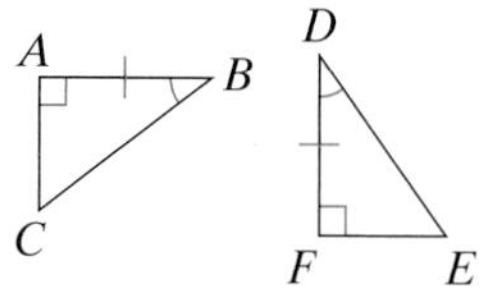

8. 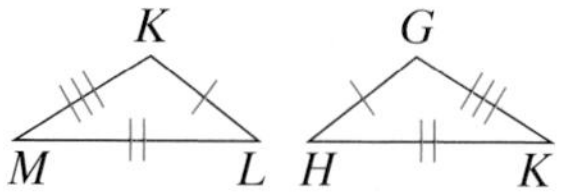

Lesson 7-4 **Determine the best name for each quadrilateral.**

9. 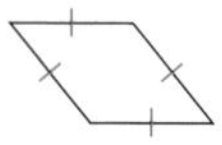 rhombus
10. 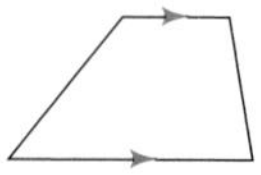 trapezoid
11. 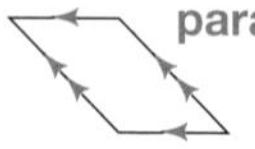 parallelogram
12. 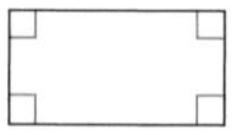 rectangle

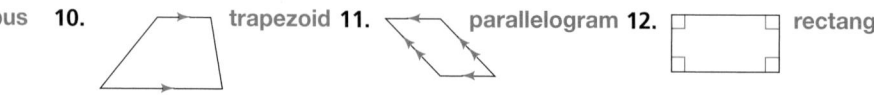

Lesson 7-5 **Find the sum of the measures of the interior angles of each polygon.**

13. rhombus 360°
14. hexagon 720°
15. triangle 180°
16. pentagon 540°
17. trapezoid 360°

Lessons 7-6 and 7-7 **Find the area of each figure. Round to the nearest tenth.**

18. 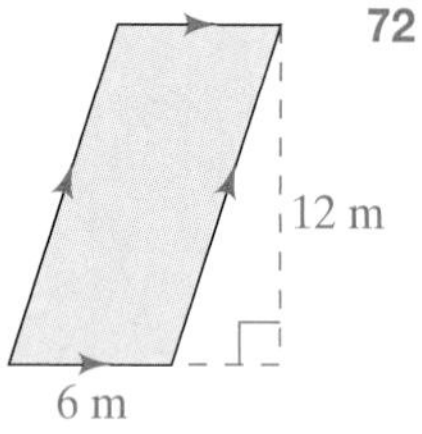

72 m²

19. 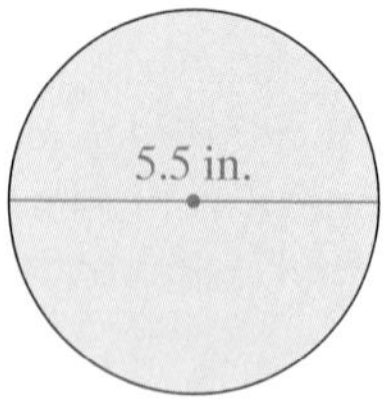

23.8 in.²

Lesson 7-8

20. Draw an angle and label it ∠A. Construct ∠B congruent to ∠A. Check students' work.

Word Problems

Lesson 7-1

21. Trees Suppose a leaning tree makes an angle of 88.5° with the ground as shown in the diagram at the right. What is the measure of angle 1?
91.5°

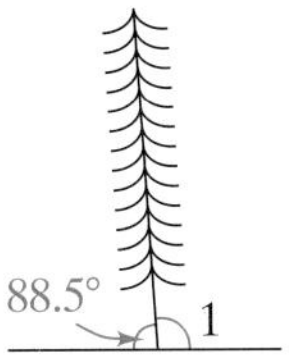

Lesson 7-2 **Which pairs of lines, if any, are parallel? Explain.**

22.

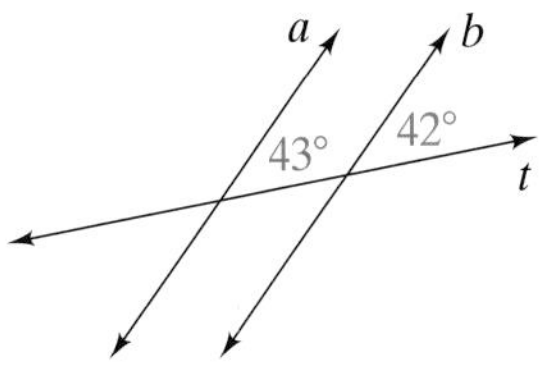

none

23.

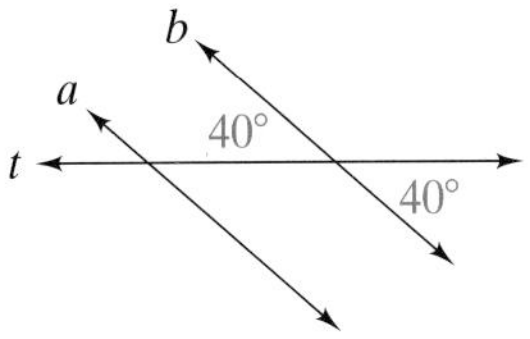

none

24.

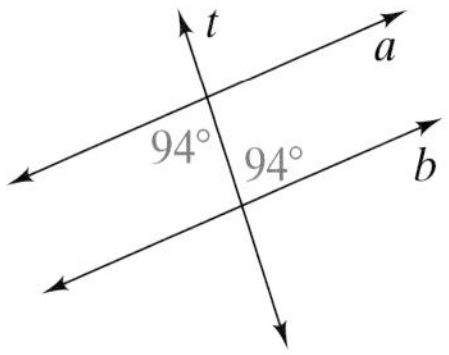

a and b

Lesson 7-3

25. Use rotations and translations to find a point P such that $\triangle ABC \cong \triangle MNP$ in the figure at the right.
C(5, 3)

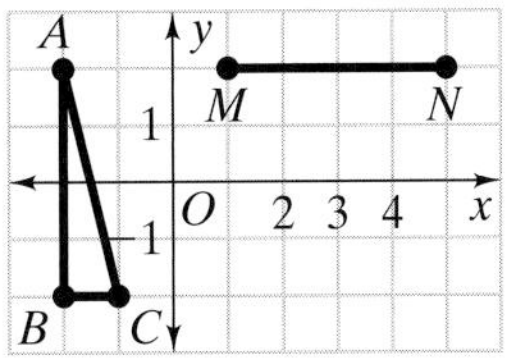

Lesson 7-4

26. Jewelry Andrea has a piece of paper with a green shape on it. The shape has exactly two parallel sides. Name the shape. trapezoid

Lesson 7-5

27. Find the measure of each of the interior angles of an octagonal stop sign. 135°

Lessons 7-6 and 7-7

28. Wallpaper Two walls on the top floor of Louis' house are trapezoidal in shape. The walls are 10 feet wide at the floor and 8.5 feet wide at the ceiling. The walls are 8 feet high. How much wallpaper would Louis need to cover these two walls? 148 ft^2

29. A circular sports arena has a diameter of 710 feet. As a security guard, Farrah patrols around the outside edges of the arena. If she walks around the entire stadium three times during each shift, how far has she walked? 6,691.6 ft

Lesson 7-8

30. Describe how to construct two parallel lines. Check students' work.

Extra Skills and Word Problems

Extra Skills and Word Problems

1. circle; cone; diameter
2. circle; cylinder; diameter
3. triangle; triangular prism; edge
4.

Top Front Right

5.

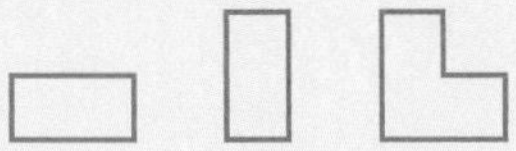

Top Front Right

6.

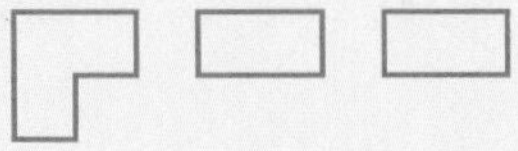

Top Front Right

CHAPTER 8 Extra Practice

Skills

Lesson 8-1 **For each figure, describe the base(s), name the figure, and name the part labeled $\overline{PQ}$.** 1–3. See margin.

1. 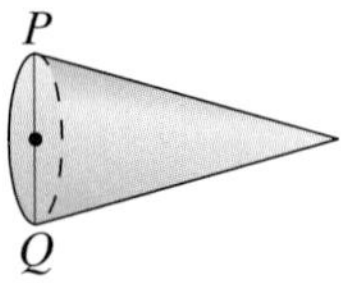

2. 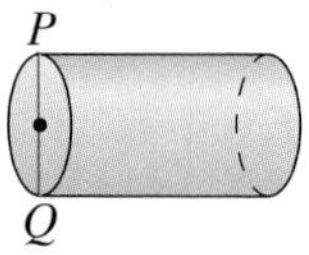

3. 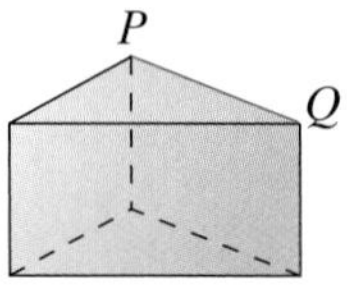

Lesson 8-2 **Draw the top, front, and right views of each figure.** 4–6. See margin.

4. 

5. 

6. 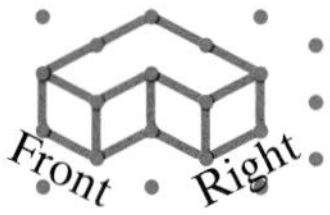

Lesson 8-3

7. Identify the solid that the net at the right forms. cone

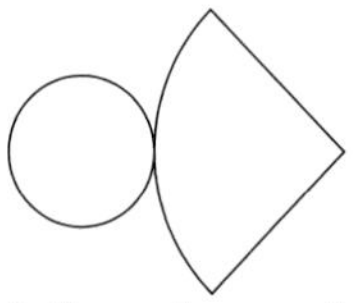

Lessons 8-4 and 8-6 **Find (a) the surface area and (b) the volume of each figure. Round to the nearest whole unit.**

8. cube with edge length 1.2 m 9 m^2; 2 m^3
9. rectangular prism 10 cm × 15 cm × 18 cm $1{,}200 \text{ cm}^2$; $2{,}700 \text{ cm}^3$
10. cylinder with radius 1 ft and height 8 ft 57 ft^2; 25 ft^3
11. cylinder with diameter 6 in. and height 4 in. 132 in.^2; 113 in.^3

Lessons 8-5 and 8-7 **Find (a) the surface area and (b) the volume of each figure with the given characteristics. Round to the nearest whole unit.**

12. a square pyramid with a height of 4 in., a slant height of 5 in., and a base area of 36 in.^2 96 in.^2; 48 in.^3
13. a cone with a diameter of 12 cm, a height of 8 cm, and a slant height of 10 cm. 302 cm^2; 302 cm^3

Lesson 8-8

14. Find the surface area and volume of a sphere with diameter 18.2 cm. Round to the nearest whole unit. $S.A. = 1{,}041 \text{ cm}^2$
$V = 3{,}157 \text{ cm}^3$

Lesson 8-9

15. Find the volume of the smaller similar solid at the right. 446.25 m^3

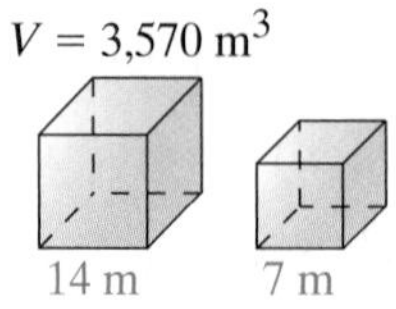

Word Problems

Lesson 8-1

16. Name the common solids that make up the structure at the right. See margin.

Lesson 8-2

17. Describe a situation in which drawing the base plan of an object would be more useful than drawing the top, front, or right view. See margin.

Lesson 8-3

18. **Moving** Gwen is moving to college. She has boxes that are 24 in. wide by 18 in. long by 18 in. high. Draw a net to represent one of the boxes. See margin.

Lessons 8-4 and 8-6

19. **Baking** For a cake recipe, Donnie needs to cover the inside of the cake pan at the right with parchment paper. How much parchment paper will he need to cover the inside of the cake pan (including the bottom)? Round to the nearest square inch. 120 $in.^2$

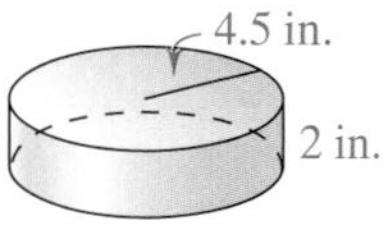

20. If the cake batter exactly fills the cake pan, what is the volume of cake batter Donnie has before baking the cake? Round to the nearest cubic inch. 127 $in.^3$

Lessons 8-5 and 8-7 **Jai's office has a water cooler that dispenses conical paper cups like the one at the right.**

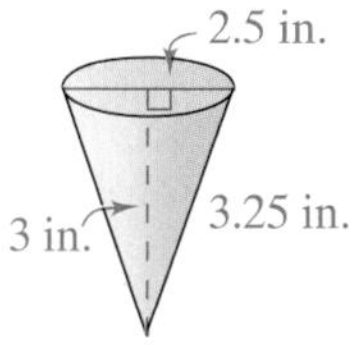

21. How much paper is used in creating one of the paper cups? 12.7 $in.^2$

22. How much water can each of the paper cups hold? Round to the nearest cubic inch. 5 $in.^3$

Lessons 8-8 and 8-9

23. Mercury has a radius of about 2,440 km. Find the volume and surface area to the nearest unit. $S.A.$ = 74,815,144 km^2, V = 60,849,650,530 km^3

24. A can of tomatoes has a volume of 245 mL and a diameter of 5 cm. Find the volume of a similar can with a diameter of 6 cm. about 423 mL

25. A cone has a radius of 4 ft and a surface area of 150 ft^2. Find the surface area of a similar cone with a radius of 7 ft. about 459 ft^2

16. rectangular prism, triangular prism, cylinder, cone

17. Answers may vary. Sample: A base plan would be more useful if you were going to use the plan to construct something, such as the set for a school play.

18.

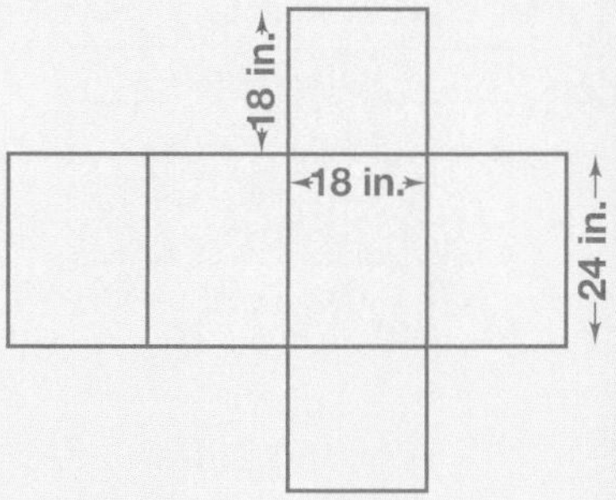

CHAPTER 9 Extra Practice

Skills

Lesson 9-1 **Find the mean, median, mode, and range of each data set. Where necessary, round to the nearest hundredth.**

1. goals per game: 1 1 1 2 2 2 4 4
   2.13, 2, 1 and 2, 3

2. golf scores: −2 −3 2 5 0 3 7
   1.71, 2, none, 10

Lessons 9-2 and 9-3 3–4. See margin.

3. Make a frequency table, histogram, and line plot for the data set.
   Minutes spent waiting: 1.8 1.7 1.4 1.2 1.7 1.7 1.7 1.7 1.5 1.9 1.6 1.6 1.5 1.3 1.4

4. Draw a Venn diagram for the situation: 10 blue shapes, 5 circles, 2 blue circles.

Lesson 9-4 **Use the graph below for Exercises 5–6.**

Favorite Fruits

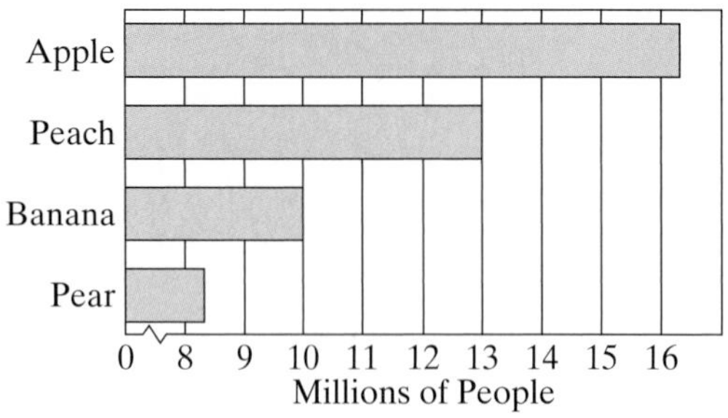

5. Which fruit appears to have about half the popularity of a banana? Pear

6. Explain why the graph gives a misleading visual impression of the data.
   The line break does not show all of the data proportionally.

Lessons 9-5 and 9-6 **Use the stem-and-leaf plot for Exercises 7–8.**

7. Find the mode and median of the data set. 71 mi/h; 68 mi/h

8. Make a box-and-whisker plot for the data set. See margin.

Average Speed

5	8 9 9 9
6	0 0 0 2 2 5 6 7 8 8 9
7	0 0 0 1 1 1 1 2 2 3 5

Key: 5 | 8 means 58 mi/h

Lesson 9-7 **In each scatter plot, describe the type of trend.**

9. 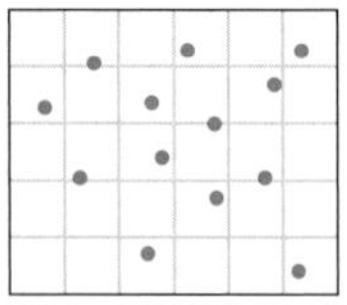 no trend

10. 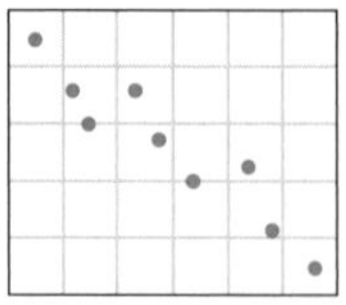 negative

11. 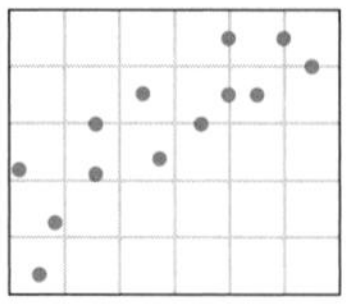 positive

3.

Waiting Time

Minutes	Tally	Frequency
1.2–1.3	II	2
1.4–1.5	IIII	4
1.6–1.7	~~IIII~~ II	7
1.8–1.9	II	2

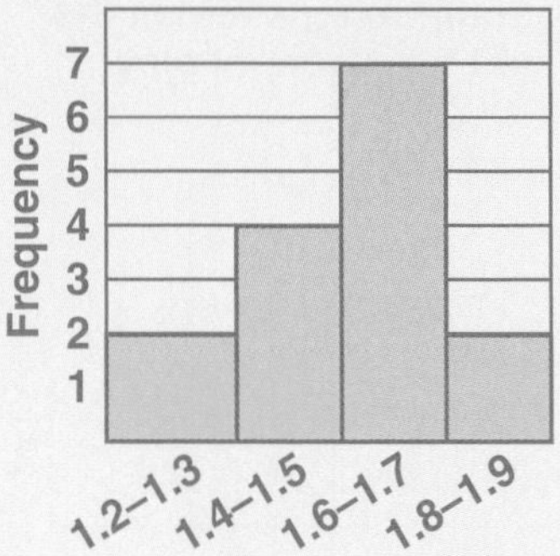

Waiting Time

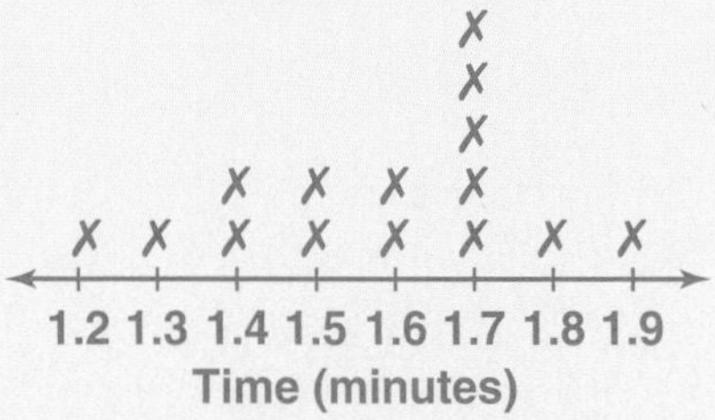

4.

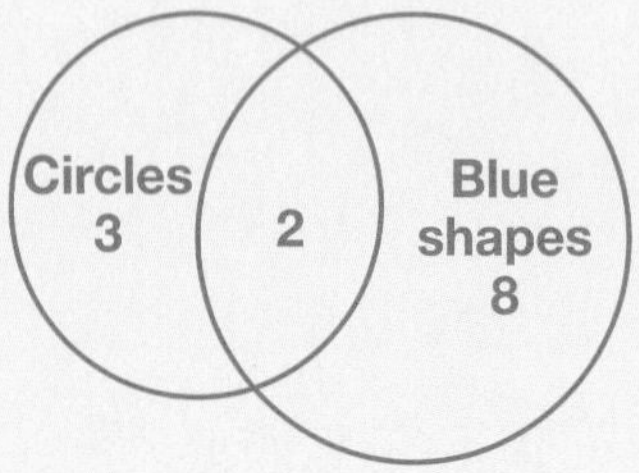

8.

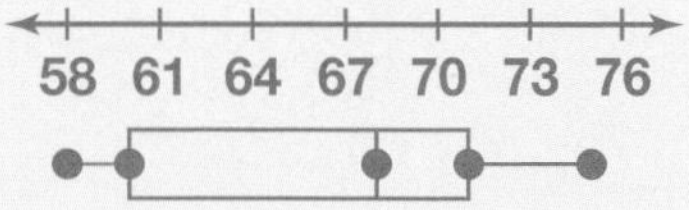

Lesson 9-8

12. Make a circle graph for the set of data at the right. See margin.

U.S. Service Academy 2001 Enrollment

School	Enrollment
Army	4,152
Navy	4,297
Air Force	4,365
Coast Guard	919
Merchant Marine	931

SOURCE: *College Board Handbook*

Lesson 9-9 **Choose the appropriate graph to display each set of data.**

13. circle graph or scatter plot? parts of a monthly budget circle graph

14. box-and-whisker plot or double bar graph? number of girls and number of boys in three classes double bar graph

Word Problems

Lessons 9-1, 9-2, 9-3, and 9-4

15. A student bused tables for the summer. His tips for one week were $15, $45, $51, $66, $39, $49, and $78. How does the outlier affect the mean?
It lowers the mean by about $5.66.

16. Make a frequency table and histogram to diaplay the data. Ages of members of the ski team: 17 15 14 15 16 14 17 14 13 14 See margin.

17. In a class of 21 students, 14 take Spanish, 10 take French, and 5 take both languages. Use a Venn diagram to find how many students do not take either language. 2 students

18. Make two bar graphs for the data at the right. Use a break symbol in only one graph. Explain which graph shows the data more clearly.
The graph with the break; check students' graphs.

Farm Animals

Type of Animals	Number of Animals
Cow	12
Pig	38
Horse	5
Chicken	100

Lessons 9-5, 9-6, and 9-7 19–20. See margin.

19. Make a stem-and-leaf plot and a box-and-whisker plot for the data set. gymnastics scores: 6.9 9.1 2.7 7.5 6.6 8.3 7.2 10.0 5.4 6.3

20. Make a scatter plot for the minimum wage data shown at the right. If possible, draw a trend line.

Minimum Wage (1975–2005)

Year	1975	1980	1985	1990	1995	2000	2005
Minimum Wage	$2.10	$3.10	$3.35	$3.80	$4.25	$5.15	$5.15

SOURCE: U.S. Dept. of Labor. Go to **PHSchool.com** for a data update. Web Code: asg-9041

Lesson 9-8

21. Dana surveyed 125 students about their favorite subject in school. Display the results, shown at the right, in a circle graph. See margin.

Favorite Academic Subject

Subject	Number of Students
English	30
Math	15
Science	23
Social Studies	57

Lesson 9-9

22. Is a stem-and-leaf plot or a bar graph appropriate to display the number of students at three schools? Explain your choice.
Bar graph; it shows the comparison of sets of data.

12.

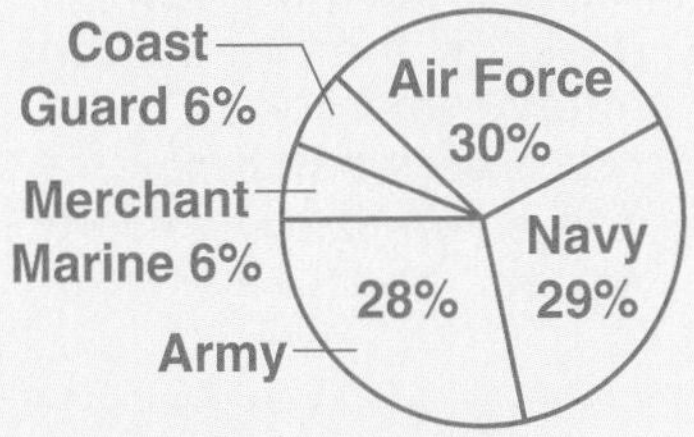

Source: *2003 College Board Handbook*

16.

Age of Ski Team Members

Ages	Tally	Frequency
13–14	𝍸	5
15–16	III	3
17–18	II	2

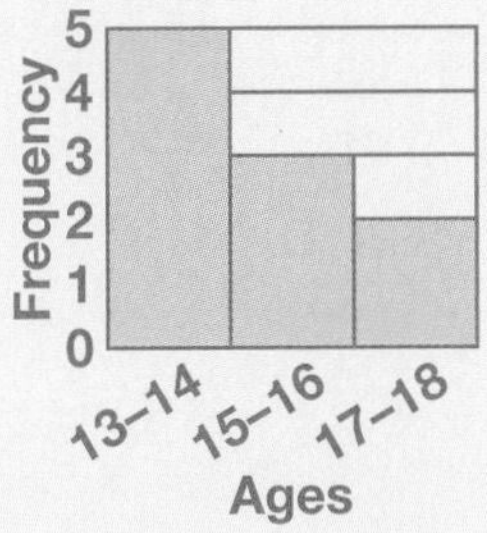

19.

2	7
5	4
6	3 6 9
7	2 5
8	3
9	1
10	0

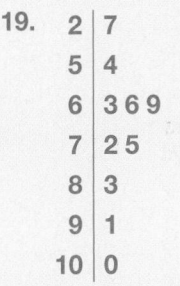

Key: 2 | 7 means 2.7

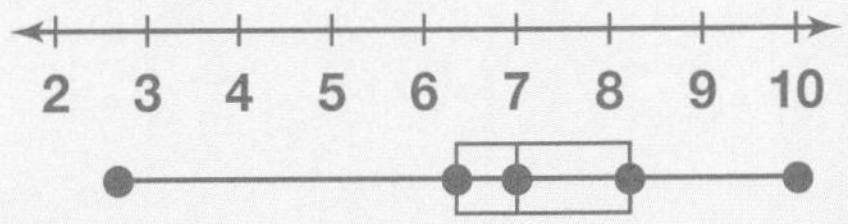

20.

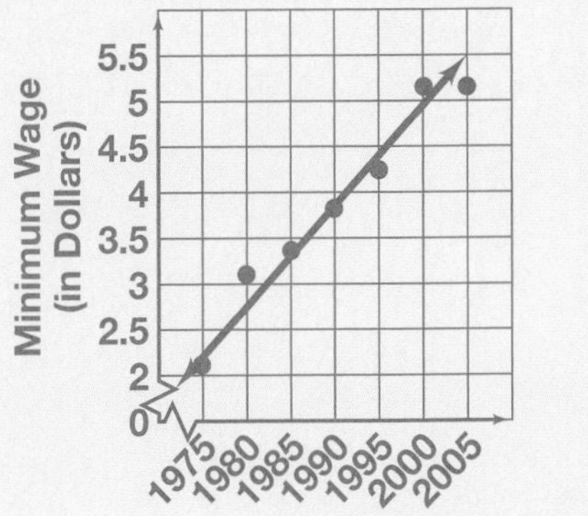

21.

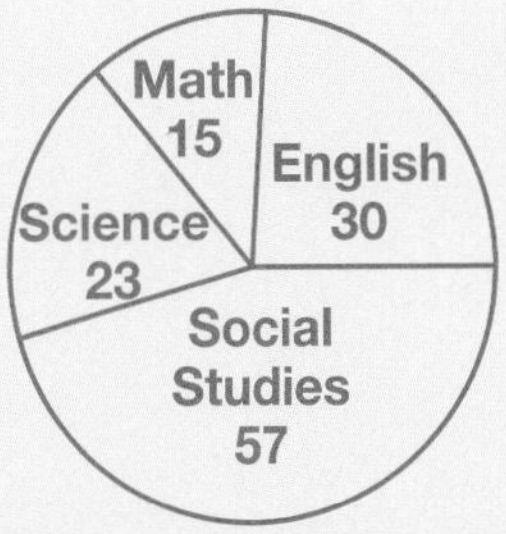

Extra Skills and Word Problems

9. Unbiased; the question does not favor an answer.

10. Biased; the question assumes that the person interviewed does homework and that homework is done every night.

CHAPTER 10 Extra Practice

Skills

Lesson 10-1 Find each experimental probability. Suppose you write North, South, East, and West on separate pieces of paper and put them in a hat. You select a piece of paper at random, record the result, replace the paper, and select again. The results of 20 trials are shown.

Location	Number Selected
North	7
South	5
East	3
West	5

1. $P(\text{West})$ $\frac{1}{4}$
2. $P(\text{South or East})$ $\frac{2}{5}$
3. $P(\text{not North})$ $\frac{13}{20}$
4. What is the theoretical probability of selecting North? $\frac{1}{4}$
5. Which event or events have the same experimental probability as the theoretical probability? South and West

Lesson 10-2 The table shows the results from a survey of 50 students at Green Middle School. The school has 670 students.

Favorite Elective Class	Number of Students
Music	12
Art	8
Woodshop	7
Graphic Design	23

6. Predict how many students in the school enjoy music class the most. 161 students
7. About how many students in the school would choose art class as their favorite elective? 107 students
8. Predict how many students in the school like either wood shop or graphic design class the best. 402 students

Lesson 10-3 Determine whether each question is biased or not. Explain. 9–10. See margin.

9. What is your favorite food?
10. How much homework do you do each night?

Lesson 10-4 Find each probability. A spinner is divided into 26 equal sections. Each section is labeled with a letter of the alphabet. Suppose you spin the spinner once and then roll a number cube. Assume Y is a consonant.

11. $P(\text{M, then 2})$ $\frac{1}{156}$
12. $P(\text{C, then prime})$ $\frac{1}{52}$
13. $P(\text{vowel, then odd})$ $\frac{5}{52}$
14. $P(\text{consonant, then 5})$ $\frac{7}{52}$

Lessons 10-5 and 10-6 Simplify each expression.

15. $4!$ 24
16. $8!$ 40,320
17. ${}_6P_3$ 120
18. ${}_{17}P_2$ 272
19. ${}_{24}P_4$ 255,024
20. ${}_{18}P_5$ 1,028,160
21. ${}_7C_4$ 35
22. ${}_{16}C_2$ 120
23. ${}_{19}C_7$ 50,388
24. ${}_{24}C_2$ 276
25. You need to choose a team of 5 players from 15 potential players. In how many ways can you do this? 3,003 ways

Word Problems

Lesson 10-1 **A bag contains 33 green marbles and 25 blue marbles. You select a marble at random from the bag.**

26. Find the theoretical probability of selecting a green marble. $\frac{33}{58}$

27. Find the theoretical probability of selecting a blue marble. $\frac{25}{58}$

28. The table at the right shows the results of selecting a marble from the bag, recording the color, and returning the marble to the bag. Find the experimental probability of each color based on the table.

P(green) = $\frac{41}{76}$; P(blue) = $\frac{35}{76}$

Outcome	Occurrences
Green	41
Blue	35

Lessons 10-2 and 10-3 **A company surveys 100 bicycle riders and asks whether they would be more likely to purchase a mountain bicycle, a road bicycle, or a hybrid bicycle. According to the survey, 67 people would buy a mountain bicycle, and 11 would buy a road bicycle.**

29. If the company sells 500 bikes per month, predict how many of those customers will purchase a mountain bicycle. 335 customers

30. The company sells 750 bicycles one busy July. About how many of those bikes should be hybrid bicycles? 165 bikers

31. Transportation A company is doing a survey on the satisfaction of people who use public transportation. The company surveys every sixth customer at a gas station. Is this a random sample? Explain.
Not random; the gas station customers may not represent all those who use public transportation.

Lesson 10-4 **Jacques has 9 brothers and sisters. His mother makes 5 turkey, 2 roast beef, 2 tuna fish, and 1 cheese sandwiches for lunch.**

32. If Jacques chooses a sandwich at random, what is the probability he will get a roast beef sandwich? $\frac{1}{5}$

33. Suppose Jacques takes a roast beef sandwich, and then his sister Eva selects her sandwich. What is the probability that she will choose a tuna fish sandwich? $\frac{2}{9}$

Lesson 10-5 **An eighth-grade class of 144 students elects a president, a vice-president, and a treasurer.**

34. In how many different ways can the class officers be chosen? 2,924,064 ways

35. What is the probability of a teacher choosing the same officers at random? $\frac{1}{2,924,064}$

Lesson 10-6

36. Research You have 12 Web sites you can use to write a research paper. How many different combinations of 3 sites can you select? 220 combinations

Extra Skills and Word Problems

Extra Skills and Word Problems

623

1. 4; start with 4 and multiply by 4 repeatedly; 256, 1,024, 4,096

2. 2; start with −5 and add 2 repeatedly; 1, 3, 5

3. $-\frac{1}{6}$; start with 1 and add $-\frac{1}{6}$ repeatedly; $\frac{1}{3}$, $\frac{1}{6}$, 0

4. $\frac{1}{2}$; start with 12 and multiply by $\frac{1}{2}$ repeatedly; $\frac{3}{2}$, $\frac{3}{4}$, $\frac{3}{8}$

12. 2;

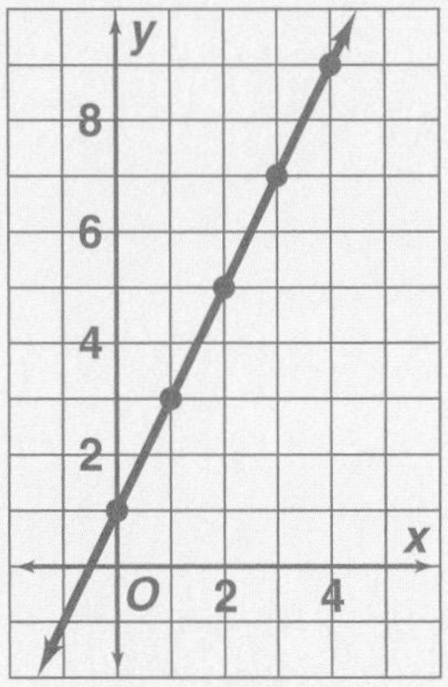

13. $-\frac{3}{2}$;

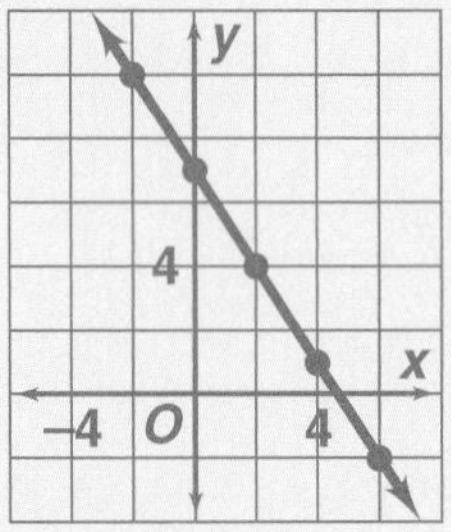

14. $\frac{5}{3}$;

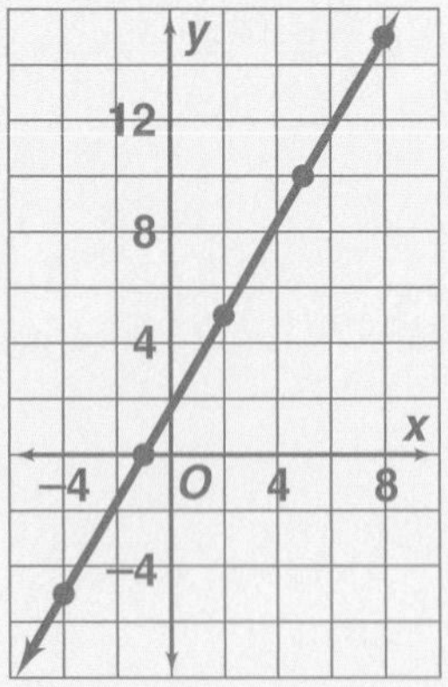

CHAPTER 11 Extra Practice

Skills

Lesson 11-1 Find the common difference or ratio in each sequence. Write the rule for each sequence and find the next three terms. 1–4. See margin.

1. 4, 16, 64, . . .
2. −5, −3, −1, . . .
3. $1, \frac{5}{6}, \frac{2}{3}, \frac{1}{2}, \ldots$
4. 12, 6, 3, . . .

Lesson 11-2 Use the graph at the right for Exercises 5–7.

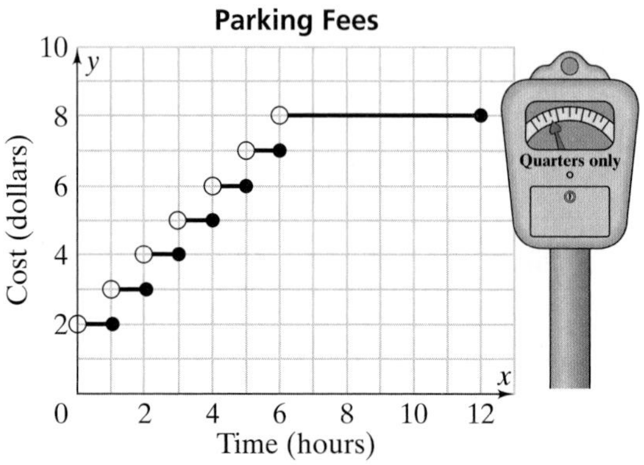

5. What is the rate for the first hour of parking? $2
6. What is the cost to park for $3\frac{1}{2}$ hours? $5
7. What is the maximum cost to park for up to 12 hours? $8

Lesson 11-3 Use the function rule $f(x) = 2x - 1$. Find each output.

8. $f(1)$ 1
9. $f(0)$ −1
10. $f(-3)$ −7
11. $f\left(\frac{1}{2}\right)$ 0

Lesson 11-4 Use the table to find the slope. Then graph the data and each line. 12–14. See margin.

12.

x	0	1	2	3	4
y	1	3	5	7	9

13.

x	−2	0	2	4	6
y	10	7	4	1	−2

14.

x	−4	−1	2	5	8
y	−5	0	5	10	15

Lesson 11-5 Make a table of input-output pairs for each function. Then graph the function. 15–18. See margin.

15. $y = 3x$
16. $y = -2x + 3$
17. $y = \frac{3}{5}x + 1$
18. $y = x + 5$

Lesson 11-6 Do the data in each table represent a linear function? If so, write a rule for the function.

19.

x	0	1	2	3	4
y	8	6	4	2	0

yes; $f(x) = -2x + 8$

20.

x	−3	−1	1	3	5
y	0	1	2	3	4

yes; $f(x) = \frac{1}{2}x + \frac{3}{2}$

21.

x	0	3	6	9	12
y	0	2	4	7	10

no

Lesson 11-7 Make a table and a graph for each quadratic function. Use integers from −4 to 4 for inputs. 22–25. See margin.

22. $y = x^2 + 2$
23. $y = -2x^2$
24. $y = 3x^2$
25. $y = -x^2 + 3$

Word Problems

Lesson 11-1 **Tell whether each situation produces an *arithmetic sequence*, *a geometric sequence*, or *neither*.**

26. A tree grows 1 foot each year. arithmetic

27. The distance a person jogs daily varies between 3 and 5 miles. neither

Lesson 11-2

28. A library charges 25 cents for each day a book is overdue. After 5 days, the library charges 50 cents per day. Sketch and label a graph that shows the total charge each day a book is overdue. See margin.

Lesson 11-3

29. Potatoes cost \$.99 per pound. Use function notation to show the relationship between the total cost and the number of pounds you buy. Use the rule to find the cost of 6 pounds of potatoes. $f(x) = .99x$; $f(6) = \$5.94$

Lesson 11-4

30. Suppose a wheelchair ramp has a slope of $\frac{1}{15}$. If it reaches a doorway that is 2 ft above ground, how far from the doorway does the ramp begin? 30 ft

Lesson 11-5

31. Agriculture A bamboo plant is 23 cm high and grows 16 cm a day. The plant's height (output) depends on the number of days that have passed (input). Make a table and graph the function. See margin.

Lesson 11-6

32. Plumbing A plumber charges \$60 for a house call, plus \$75 for each hour of work. Write a function rule that shows how the total cost of the plumber's work y depends on the number of hours x the plumber works. $y = 75x + 60$

Lesson 11-7

33. Construction Suppose it takes a total of 225 workdays to build a house. With more workers, the number of days to finish the house decreases. The function $y = \frac{225}{x}$ describes the number of days (y) it will take x people to build the house. Make a table and graph the function. See margin.

15. Answers may vary. Sample:

x	−1	0	1	2
y	−3	0	3	6

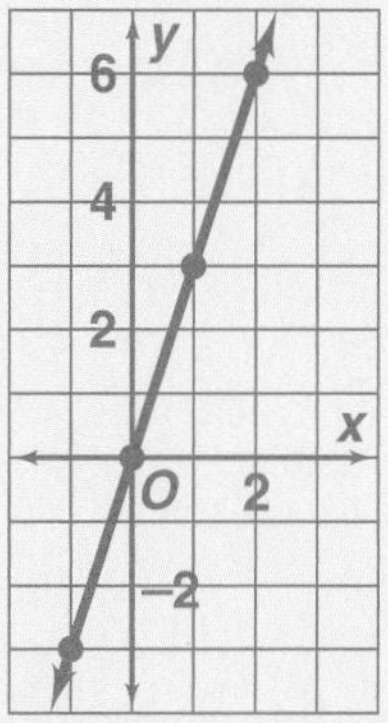

16. Answers may vary. Sample:

x	−1	0	1	2
y	5	3	1	−1

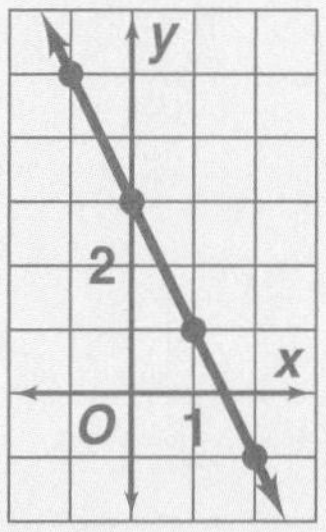

17. Answers may vary. Sample:

x	−5	0	5
y	−2	1	4

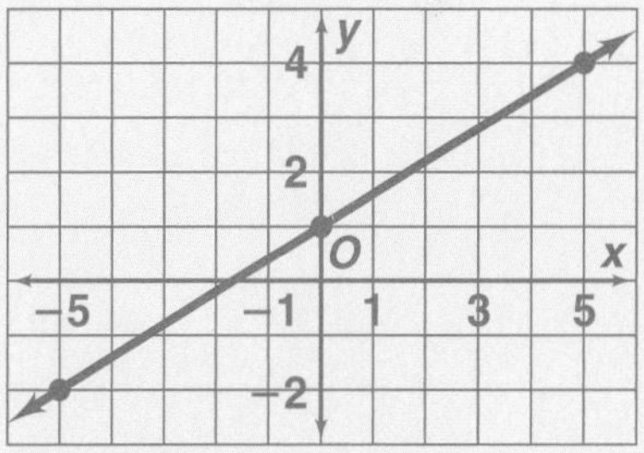

18. Answers may vary. Sample:

x	−3	−2	0	1
y	2	2	5	6

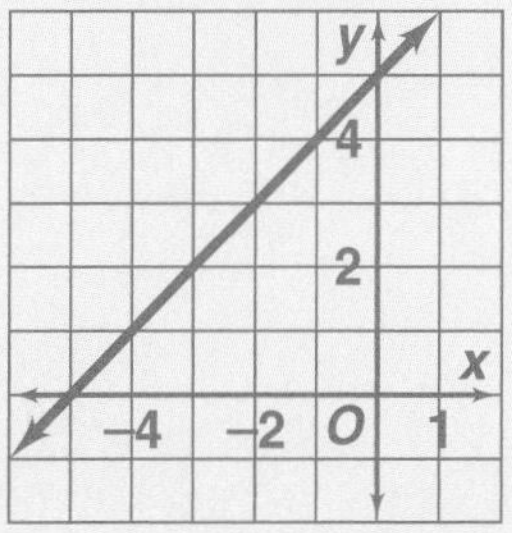

22–25, 28, 31, 33. See back of book.

Extra Skills and Word Problems

CHAPTER 12 Extra Practice

Skills

Lesson 12-1 Simplify each polynomial.

1. $3x - 5 + 23x - 9$ $26x - 14$
2. $-x^2 + 2x^2 - 6x + 3 - 2$ $x^2 - 6x + 1$
3. $x^2 - 5x + 3x + 4$ $x^2 - 2x + 4$
4. $-4 + x - 13x + 10 - 5 + 20x$ $8x + 1$
5. Write and simplify the polynomial represented by the model below.

$4x^2 + 3x - 2$

Lesson 12-2 Add or subtract.

6. $(2x^2 - x + 1) - (4x^2 - 3)$ $-2x^2 - x + 4$
7. $(3x + 2) + (2x^2 + 5x - 7)$ $2x^2 + 8x - 5$
8. $(5x^2 + 2x - 10) + (-3x^2 - 2)$ $2x^2 + 2x - 12$
9. $(x^2 + 6x + 4) - (4x - 9)$ $x^2 + 2x + 13$

Lesson 12-3 Write each expression using a single exponent.

10. $4^8 \cdot 4^{10}$ 4^{18}
11. $(-9)^2 \cdot (-9)^4$ $(-9)^6$
12. $3.2^8 \cdot 3.2^3$ $(3.2)^{11}$
13. $7^t \cdot 7^{3t}$ 7^{4t}

Multiply. Write each product in scientific notation.

14. $(3 \times 10^4)(2 \times 10^{12})$ 6×10^{16}
15. $(5 \times 10^9)(7 \times 10^3)$ 3.5×10^{13}
16. $(1 \times 10^3)(2.6 \times 10^8)$ 2.6×10^{11}
17. $(7 \times 10^2)(8 \times 10^{10})$ 5.6×10^{13}

Lesson 12-4 Simplify each expression.

18. $(-4x^2)(3x^4)$ $-12x^6$
19. $(6x)(-2x)$ $-12x^2$
20. $4x^2(2x - 7)$ $8x^3 - 28x^2$
21. $-6x(x^2 - 5)$ $-6x^3 + 30x$
22. Use the area model below to find the product.

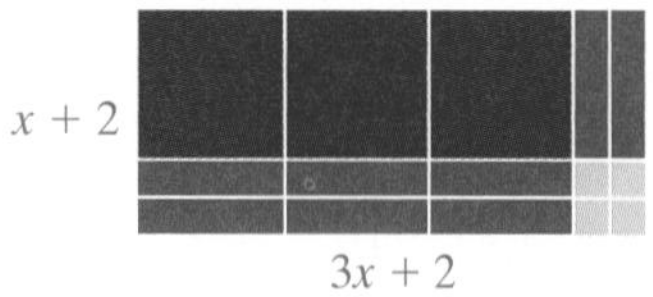

$3x^2 + 8x + 4$

Lesson 12-5 Write each expression using a single exponent.

23. $\frac{4^7}{4^5}$ 4^2
24. $\frac{8.1^{15}}{8.1^{12}}$ $(8.1)^3$
25. $\frac{(-654)^{20}}{(-654)^1}$ $(-654)^{19}$
26. $\frac{2^{3x}}{2^x}$ 2^{2x}

626

Simplify each expression.

27. $(-142)^0$ 1

28. $(4c)^{-1}$ $\frac{1}{4c}$

29. 7^{-w} $\frac{1}{7^w}$

30. $(-3)^{-5}$ $\frac{1}{-243}$

Word Problems

Lesson 12-1

31. Geometry To find the surface area of the prism shown at the right, you can use the polynomial $x^2 + 2x + 2x + 2x + 2x + x^2$. Simplify the polynomial. $2x^2 + 8x$

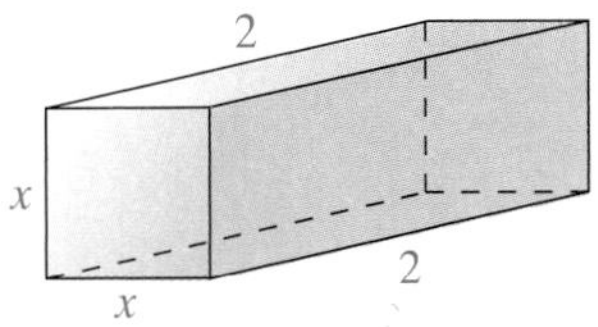

Lesson 12-2

32. City Planning A town is planning the hexagonal park shown below. Write the perimeter of the park as a polynomial and simplify.

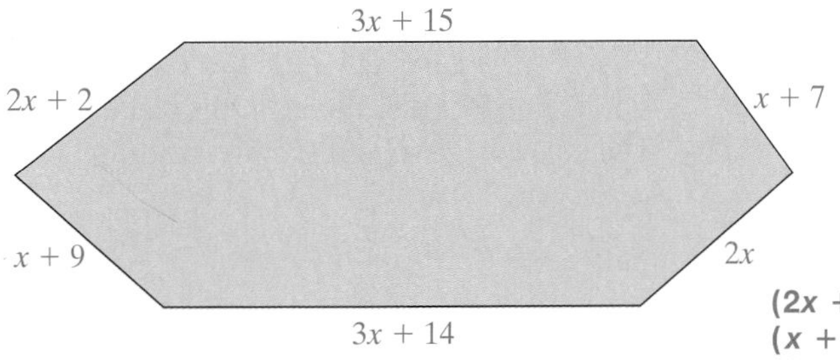

$(2x + 2) + (3x + 15) + (x + 7) + (x + 9) + (3x + 14) + (2x)$; $12x + 47$

Lesson 12-3

33. Biology There are about 5×10^{10} white blood cells and about 500 times as many red blood cells in a human's bloodstream. Find the number of red blood cells. Write your answer in scientific notation. 2.5×10^{13}

34. Sports There are about 2.65×10^{32} possible ways a 30-player football team can form a line to run onto the field. When a thirty-first player is included, there will be about $31 \cdot (2.65 \times 10^{32})$ possible ways. Write this number in scientific notation. 8.215×10^{33}

Lesson 12-4

35. A middle school art class is painting a mural on the side of the school building. They plan to use a rectangular area that is $(3x + 5)$ ft long and $8x$ ft wide. Write an expression for the area of the completed mural. $(24x^2 + 40x)$ ft^2

Lesson 12-5

36. Physics The wavelength of red light is 0.0000076 meters. Write this number in scientific notation. 7.6×10^{-6}

Extra Skills and Word Problems

Extra Skills and Word Problems

Decimals and Place Value

Each digit in a whole number or a decimal has both a place and a value. The value of any place is one tenth the value of the place to its left. The chart below can help you read and write decimals. It shows the place and value of the number 2,401,262,830.750191.

billions	hundred millions	ten millions	millions	hundred thousands	ten thousands	thousands	hundreds	tens	ones	.	tenths	hundredths	thousandths	ten-thousandths	hundred-thousandths	millionths
2	4	0	1	2	6	2	8	3	0	.	7	5	0	1	9	1

EXAMPLE

a. What is the value of the digit 8 in the number above?

The digit 8 is in the hundreds place. So its value is 8 hundreds.

b. Write 2.006 in words.

The digit 6 is in the thousandths place. The answer is two and six thousandths.

c. Write five and thirty-four ten-thousandths as a decimal.

Ten-thousandths is 4 places to the right of the decimal point. So the decimal will have 4 places after the decimal point. The answer is 5.0034.

Exercises

Use the chart above. Write the value of each digit.

1. the digit 9 hundred-thousandths

2. the digit 7 tenths

3. the digit 5 hundredths

4. the digit 6 ten thousands

5. the digit 4 hundred millions

6. the digit 3 tens

Write a decimal for the given words.

7. forty-one ten-thousandths 0.0041

8. eighteen and five hundred four thousandths 18.504

9. eight millionths 0.000008

10. seven and sixty-three hundred-thousandths 7.00063

11. twelve thousandths 0.012

12. sixty-five and two hundred one thousandths 65.201

Write each decimal in words.

13. 0.06 six hundredths

14. 4.7 four and seven tenths

15. 0.00011 eleven hundred-thousandths

16. 0.9 nine tenths

17. 0.012 twelve thousandths

18. 0.000059 fifty-nine millionths

19. 0.0042 forty-two ten-thousandths

20. 6.029186 six and twenty-nine thousand one hundred eighty-six millionths

Comparing and Ordering Decimals

To compare two decimals, use the symbols < (is less than), > (is greater than), or = (is equal to). When you compare, start at the left and compare the digits.

EXAMPLE

1 Use <, >, or = to compare the decimals.

a. 0.1 ■ 0.06

1 tenth > 0 tenths, so
0.1 > 0.06

b. 2.4583 ■ 2.48

5 hundredths < 8 hundredths,
so 2.4583 < 2.48

c. 0.30026 ■ 0.03026

3 tenths > 0 tenths, so
0.30026 > 0.03026

EXAMPLE

2 Draw number lines to compare the decimals.

a. 0.1 ■ 0.06

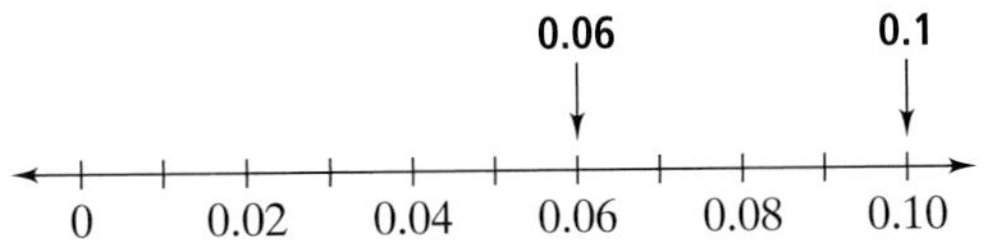

0.1 > 0.06

b. 2.4583 ■ 2.48

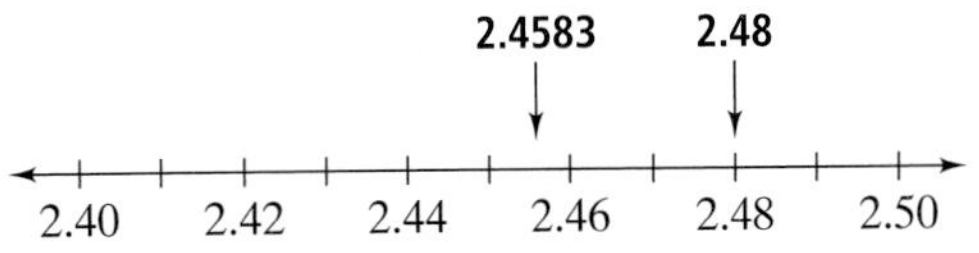

2.4583 < 2.48

Exercises

Use <, >, or = to compare the decimals. Draw number lines if you wish.

1. 0.003 ■ 0.02 <
2. 84.2 ■ 842 <
3. 0.162 ■ 0.106 >
4. 0.0659 ■ 0.6059 <
5. 2.13 ■ 2.99 <
6. 3.53 ■ 3.529 >
7. 2.01 ■ 2.010 =
8. 0.00072 ■ 0.07002 <
9. 0.458 ■ 0.4589 <
10. 8.627 ■ 8.649 <
11. 0.0019 ■ 0.0002 >
12. 0.19321 ■ 0.19231 >

Write the decimals in order from least to greatest.

13. 2.31, 0.231, 23.1, 0.23, 3.21 — **0.23, 0.231, 2.31, 3.21, 23.1**
14. 1.02, 1.002, 1.2, 1.11, 1.021 — **1.002, 1.02, 1.021, 1.11, 1.2**
15. 0.02, 0.002, 0.22, 0.222, 2.22 — **0.002, 0.02, 0.22, 0.222, 2.22**
16. 55.5, 555.5, 55.555, 5.5555 — **5.5555, 55.5, 55.555, 555.5**
17. 7, 7.3264, 7.3, 7.3246, 7.0324 — **7, 7.0324, 7.3, 7.3246, 7.3264**
18. 0.0101, 0.0099, 0.011, 0.00019 — **0.00019, 0.0099, 0.0101, 0.011**
19. 0.8, 0.83, 0.08, 0.083, 0.082 — **0.08, 0.082, 0.083, 0.8, 0.83**
20. 4.6, 4.61, 4.601, 4.602, 4.6002, 4.62 — **4.6, 4.6002, 4.601, 4.602, 4.61, 4.62**

Rounding

When you round to a particular place, look at the digit to the right of that place. If it is 5 or more, the digit in the place you are rounding to will increase by 1. If it is less than 5, the digit in the place you are rounding to will stay the same.

EXAMPLE

a. Round 1.627 to the nearest whole number.

The digit to the right of the ones place is 6, so 1.627 rounds up to 2.

b. Round 12,034 to the nearest thousand.

The digit to the right of the thousands place is 0, so 12,034 rounds down to 12,000.

c. Round 2.7195 to the nearest hundredth.

The digit to the right of the hundredths place is 9, so 2.7195 rounds up to 2.72.

d. Round $0.060\underline{5}21$ to the place of the underlined digit.

The digit to the right of $\underline{5}$ is 2, so 0.060521 rounds down to 0.0605.

Exercises

Round to the nearest thousand.

1. 105,099 105,000 **2.** 10,400 10,000 **3.** 79,527,826 79,528,000 **4.** 79,932 80,000 **5.** 4,312,349 4,312,000

Round to the nearest whole number.

6. 135.91 136 **7.** 3.001095 3 **8.** 96.912 97 **9.** 101.167 101 **10.** 299.9 300

Round to the nearest tenth.

11. 82.01 82.0 **12.** 4.67522 4.7 **13.** 20.397 20.4 **14.** 399.95 400.0 **15.** 129.98 130.0

Round to the nearest hundredth.

16. 13.458 13.46 **17.** 96.4045 96.40 **18.** 0.699 0.70 **19.** 4.234 4.23 **20.** 12.09531 12.10

Round to the place of the underlined digit.

21. $7.0\underline{6}15$ 7.06 **22.** $\underline{5}.77125$ 6 **23.** $1{,}5\underline{2}2$ 1,520 **24.** $0.919\underline{5}2$ 0.9195 **25.** $4.\underline{2}43$ 4.2

26. $2\underline{3}6.001$ 240 **27.** $\underline{3}52$ 400 **28.** $3.4953\underline{6}6$ 3.49537 **29.** $8.\underline{0}7092$ 8.1 **30.** $\underline{0}.6008$ 1

31. $\underline{9}18$ 900 **32.** $7{,}\underline{7}35$ 7,700 **33.** $25.66\underline{0}47$ 25.660 **34.** $9\underline{8}3{,}240{,}631$ 980,000,000 **35.** $\underline{2}7$ 30

Adding and Subtracting Decimals

You add or subtract decimals just as you do whole numbers. You line up the decimal points and then add or subtract. If you wish, you can use zeros to make the columns even.

EXAMPLE

Find each sum or difference.

a. 37.6 + 8.431

$$\begin{array}{r} 37.6 \\ +\ 8.431 \\ \hline \end{array} \rightarrow \begin{array}{r} 37.600 \\ +\ 8.431 \\ \hline 46.031 \end{array}$$

b. 8 − 4.593

$$\begin{array}{r} 8. \\ -\ 4.593 \\ \hline \end{array} \rightarrow \begin{array}{r} 8.000 \\ -\ 4.593 \\ \hline 3.407 \end{array}$$

c. 8.3 + 2.99 + 17.5

$$\begin{array}{r} 8.3 \\ 2.99 \\ +\ 17.5 \\ \hline \end{array} \rightarrow \begin{array}{r} 8.30 \\ 2.99 \\ +\ 17.50 \\ \hline 28.79 \end{array}$$

Exercises

Find each sum or difference.

1. $\begin{array}{r} 39.7 \\ -\ 36.03 \\ \hline \end{array}$ **3.67**

2. $\begin{array}{r} 1.08 \\ -\ 0.9 \\ \hline \end{array}$ **0.18**

3. $\begin{array}{r} 6.784 \\ +\ 0.528 \\ \hline \end{array}$ **7.312**

4. $\begin{array}{r} 5.01 \\ -\ 0.87 \\ \hline \end{array}$ **4.14**

5. $\begin{array}{r} 13.02 \\ +\ 23.107 \\ \hline \end{array}$ **36.127**

6. $\begin{array}{r} 8.634 \\ +\ 1.409 \\ \hline \end{array}$ **10.043**

7. $\begin{array}{r} 2.1 \\ -\ 0.5 \\ \hline \end{array}$ **1.6**

8. $\begin{array}{r} 8.23 \\ -\ 3.1 \\ \hline \end{array}$ **5.13**

9. $\begin{array}{r} 1.05 \\ +\ 12.9 \\ \hline \end{array}$ **13.95**

10. $\begin{array}{r} 2.60 \\ +\ 23.107 \\ \hline \end{array}$ **25.707**

11. $\begin{array}{r} 0.1 \\ 58.21 \\ +\ 1.9 \\ \hline \end{array}$ **60.21**

12. $\begin{array}{r} 12.2 \\ 3.06 \\ +\ 0.5 \\ \hline \end{array}$ **15.76**

13. $\begin{array}{r} 9.42 \\ 3.6 \\ +\ 21.003 \\ \hline \end{array}$ **34.023**

14. $\begin{array}{r} 15.22 \\ 7.4 \\ +\ 8.125 \\ \hline \end{array}$ **30.745**

15. $\begin{array}{r} 3.7 \\ 20.06 \\ +\ 16.19 \\ \hline \end{array}$ **39.95**

16. $\begin{array}{r} 12.22 \\ 9.8 \\ +\ 2.375 \\ \hline \end{array}$ **24.395**

17. 76.39 − 8.47 **67.92**

18. 8.7 + 17.03 **25.73**

19. 32.403 + 12.06 **44.463**

20. 20.5 + 11.45 **31.95**

21. 8.9 − 4.45 **4.45**

22. 1.245 + 5.8 **7.045**

23. 3.9 + 6.57 **10.47**

24. 14.81 − 8.6 **6.21**

25. 11.9 − 2.06 **9.84**

26. 3.45 + 4.061 **7.511**

27. 8.29 + 4.3 **12.59**

28. 7.06 − 4.235 **2.825**

29. 5.002 − 3.45 **1.552**

30. 6.8 + 3.57 **10.37**

31. 0.23 + 0.091 **0.321**

32. 0.5 − 0.18 **0.32**

33. 8.3 + 2.99 + 17.52 **28.81**

34. 9.5 + 12.32 + 6.4 **28.22**

35. 4.521 + 1.8 + 3.07 **9.391**

36. 57 + 0.6327 + 189.007 **246.6397**

37. 741 + 6.08 + 0.0309 **747.1109**

38. 0.045 + 16.32 + 8.6 **24.965**

39. 4.27 + 6.18 + 0.91 **11.36**

40. 3.856 + 14.01 + 1.72 **19.586**

41. 11.45 + 3.79 + 23.861 **39.101**

Multiplying Decimals

Multiply decimals as you would whole numbers. Then place the decimal point in the product. To do this, add the number of decimal places in the factors.

EXAMPLE

1 Multiply 0.068×2.3.

Step 1 Multiply decimals without the decimal point.

$$\begin{array}{r} 0.068 \\ \times\ 2.3 \\ \hline \end{array} \qquad \begin{array}{r} 68 \\ \times\ 23 \\ \hline 204 \\ +\ 1360 \\ \hline 1564 \end{array}$$

Step 2 Place the decimal point.

$$\begin{array}{rl} 0.068 & \leftarrow \text{three decimal places} \\ \times\ 2.3 & \leftarrow \text{one decimal place} \\ \hline 204 & \\ +\ 1360 & \\ \hline 0.1564 & \leftarrow \text{four decimal places} \end{array}$$

EXAMPLE

2 Find each product.

a. 3.12×0.9

$$\begin{array}{r} 3.12 \\ \times\ 0.9 \\ \hline 2.808 \end{array}$$

b. 5.75×42

$$\begin{array}{r} 5.75 \\ \times\ 42 \\ \hline 1150 \\ +\ 23000 \\ \hline 241.50 \end{array}$$

c. 0.964×0.28

$$\begin{array}{r} 0.964 \\ \times\ 0.28 \\ \hline 7712 \\ +\ 19280 \\ \hline 0.26992 \end{array}$$

Exercises

Multiply.

1. 1.48×3.6 **5.328**
2. 191.1×3.4 **649.74**
3. 0.05×43 **2.15**
4. 0.27×5 **1.35**
5. 1.36×3.8 **5.168**

6. 6.23×0.21 **1.3083**
7. 0.512×0.76 **0.38912**
8. 0.04×7 **0.28**
9. 0.136×8.4 **1.1424**
10. 3×0.05 **0.15**

11. 2.07×1.004 **2.07828**
12. 0.12×61 **7.32**
13. 3.2×0.15 **0.48**
14. 0.74×0.23 **0.1702**

15. 0.42×98 **41.16**
16. 6.3×85 **535.5**
17. 45×0.028 **1.26**
18. 76×3.3 **250.8**

19. 8.003×0.6 **4.8018**
20. 42.2×0.9 **37.98**
21. 0.6×30.02 **18.012**
22. 0.05×11.8 **0.59**

Zeros in a Product

When you multiply with decimals, you may have to write one or more zeros to the left of a product before you can place the decimal point.

EXAMPLE

1 Multiply 0.06×0.015.

Step 1 Multiply.

$$\begin{array}{r} 0.015 \\ \times\ 0.06 \\ \hline 90 \end{array}$$

Step 2 Place the decimal point.

$$\begin{array}{r} 0.015 \\ \times\ 0.06 \\ \hline 0.00090 \end{array}$$

← three decimal places
← two decimal places
← The product should have five decimal places, so you must write three zeros before placing the decimal point.

EXAMPLE

2 **a.** 0.02×1.3

$$\begin{array}{r} 1.3 \\ \times\ 0.02 \\ \hline 0.026 \end{array}$$

b. 0.012×2.4

$$\begin{array}{r} 2.4 \\ \times\ 0.012 \\ \hline 48 \\ +\ 240 \\ \hline 0.0288 \end{array}$$

c. 0.022×0.051

$$\begin{array}{r} 0.051 \\ \times\ 0.022 \\ \hline 102 \\ +\ 1020 \\ \hline 0.001122 \end{array}$$

Exercises

Multiply.

1. 0.03×0.9 0.027

2. 0.06×0.5 0.03

3. 2.4×0.03 0.072

4. 7×0.01 0.07

5. 0.05×0.05 0.0025

6. 0.016×0.12 0.00192

7. 0.031×0.08 0.00248

8. 0.03×0.2 0.006

9. 0.27×0.033 0.00891

10. 0.014×0.25 0.0035

11. 0.003×0.55 0.00165

12. 0.01×0.74 0.0074

13. 0.47×0.08 0.0376

14. 0.76×0.1 0.076

15. 0.3×0.27 0.081

16. 0.19×0.05 0.0095

17. 0.018×0.04 0.00072

18. 0.43×0.2 0.086

19. 0.03×0.03 0.0009

20. 4.003×0.02 0.08006

21. 0.5×0.08 0.04

22. 0.06×0.7 0.042

23. 0.3×0.24 0.072

24. 0.67×0.09 0.0603

25. 3.02×0.006 0.01812

26. 0.31×0.08 0.0248

27. 0.14×0.05 0.007

28. 0.07×0.85 0.0595

Skills Handbook

Dividing Decimals by Whole Numbers

When you divide a decimal by a whole number, the decimal point in the quotient goes directly above the decimal point in the dividend. You may need extra zeros to place the decimal point.

EXAMPLE 1

Divide 2.432 ÷ 32.

Step 1 Divide.

$$\begin{array}{r} 76 \\ 32\overline{)2.432} \\ -\ 2\ 24 \\ \hline 192 \\ -\ 192 \\ \hline 0 \end{array}$$

Step 2 Place the decimal point.

$$\begin{array}{r} 0.076 \\ 32\overline{)2.432} \\ -2\ 24 \\ \hline 192 \\ -192 \\ \hline 0 \end{array}$$

← **You need two extra zeros to get the decimal point in the correct place.**

EXAMPLE 2

a. 37.6 ÷ 8

$$\begin{array}{r} 4.7 \\ 8\overline{)37.6} \\ -\ 32 \\ \hline 5\ 6 \\ -\ 5\ 6 \\ \hline 0 \end{array}$$

b. 39.33 ÷ 69

$$\begin{array}{r} 0.57 \\ 69\overline{)39.33} \\ -\ 34\ 5 \\ \hline 4\ 83 \\ -\ 4\ 83 \\ \hline 0 \end{array}$$

c. 4.482 ÷ 54

$$\begin{array}{r} 0.083 \\ 54\overline{)4.482} \\ -\ 4\ 32 \\ \hline 162 \\ -\ 162 \\ \hline 0 \end{array}$$

Exercises

Divide.

1. 17.92 ÷ 7 2.56
2. 16.5 ÷ 5 3.3
3. 6.984 ÷ 9 0.776
4. 91.44 ÷ 6 15.24
5. 35.16 ÷ 4 8.79
6. 8.848 ÷ 56 0.158
7. 2.42 ÷ 22 0.11
8. 1,723.8 ÷ 26 66.3
9. 17.52 ÷ 2 8.76
10. 37.14 ÷ 6 6.19
11. 0.1352 ÷ 8 0.0169
12. 0.0324 ÷ 9 0.0036
13. 0.0882 ÷ 6 0.0147
14. 0.8682 ÷ 6 0.1447
15. 12.342 ÷ 22 0.561
16. 29.792 ÷ 32 0.931
17. 22.568 ÷ 26 0.868
18. 11.340 ÷ 36 0.315
19. 45.918 ÷ 18 2.551
20. 79.599 ÷ 13 6.123
21. 0.0672 ÷ 48 0.0014
22. 171.031 ÷ 53 3.227
23. 79.53 ÷ 11 7.23
24. 3.2 ÷ 8 0.4
25. 0.378 ÷ 5 0.0756
26. 9.76 ÷ 32 0.305
27. 0.133 ÷ 7 0.019
28. 61.915 ÷ 35 1.769

634

Multiplying and Dividing by Powers of Ten

You can use shortcuts to multiply or divide by powers of ten.

When you multiply by...	Move the decimal point ...
10,000	4 places to the right.
1,000	3 places to the right.
100	2 places to the right.
10	1 place to the right.
0.1	1 place to the left.
0.01	2 places to the left.
0.001	3 places to the left.

When you divide by...	Move the decimal point ...
10,000	4 places to the left.
1,000	3 places to the left.
100	2 places to the left.
10	1 place to the left.
0.1	1 place to the right.
0.01	2 places to the right.
0.001	3 places to the right.

EXAMPLE

1 Multiply.

a. 0.7×0.001

Move the decimal point three places to the left. 0.000.7

$0.7 \times 0.001 = 0.0007$

b. 0.934×100

Move the decimal point two places to the right. 0.93.4

$0.934 \times 100 = 93.4$

EXAMPLE

2 Divide.

a. $0.605 \div 100$

Move the decimal point two places to the left. 0.00.605

$0.605 \div 100 = 0.00605$

b. $0.38 \div 0.001$

Move the decimal point three places to the right. 0.380.

$0.38 \div 0.001 = 380$

Exercises

Multiply or divide.

1. $10{,}000 \times 0.056$ 560
2. 0.001×0.09 0.00009
3. 5.2×10 52
4. $0.03 \times 1{,}000$ 30
5. $236.7 \div 0.1$ 2,367
6. $45.28 \div 10$ 4.528
7. $0.9 \div 1{,}000$ 0.0009
8. $1.07 \div 0.01$ 107
9. 100×0.08 8
10. $1.03 \times 10{,}000$ 10,300
11. 1.803×0.001 0.001803
12. 4.1×100 410
13. $13.7 \div 0.001$ 13,700
14. $203.05 \div 0.01$ 20,305
15. $4.7 \div 10$ 0.47
16. $0.05 \div 100$ 0.0005

Skills Handbook

Dividing Decimals by Decimals

To divide by a decimal divisor, multiply it by the smallest power of ten that will make the divisor a whole number. Then multiply the dividend by that same power of ten.

EXAMPLE

Find each quotient.

a. 3.348 ÷ 6.2

Multiply by 10.

$$\begin{array}{r} 0.54 \\ 6.2\overline{)3.3\,48} \\ \underline{-3\,1\,0} \\ 2\,48 \\ \underline{-2\,48} \\ 0 \end{array}$$

b. 2.4885 ÷ 0.35

Multiply by 100.

$$\begin{array}{r} 7.11 \\ 0.35\overline{)2.48\,85} \\ \underline{-2\,45} \\ 3\,8 \\ \underline{-3\,5} \\ 35 \\ \underline{-35} \\ 0 \end{array}$$

c. 0.0576 ÷ 0.012

Multiply by 1000.

$$\begin{array}{r} 4.8 \\ 0.012\overline{)0.057\,6} \\ \underline{-48} \\ 9\,6 \\ \underline{-9\,6} \\ 0 \end{array}$$

Exercises

Divide.

1. 268.8 ÷ 3.2 **84**	**2.** 123.5 ÷ 1.9 **65**	**3.** 135.6 ÷ 0.3 **452**
4. 170.2 ÷ 2.3 **74**	**5.** 252.8 ÷ 7.9 **32**	**6.** 10.26 ÷ 5.7 **1.8**
7. 71.53 ÷ 2.3 **31.1**	**8.** 16.12 ÷ 3.1 **5.2**	**9.** 24.18 ÷ 7.8 **3.1**
10. 14.49 ÷ 6.3 **2.3**	**11.** 134.42 ÷ 5.17 **26**	**12.** 89.96 ÷ 3.46 **26**
13. 160.58 ÷ 5.18 **31**	**14.** 106.59 ÷ 6.27 **17**	**15.** 62.4 ÷ 3.9 **16**
16. 260.4 ÷ 8.4 **31**	**17.** 316.8 ÷ 7.2 **44**	**18.** 162.4 ÷ 2.9 **56**
19. 1.512 ÷ 0.54 **2.8**	**20.** 3.225 ÷ 0.43 **7.5**	**21.** 2.484 ÷ 0.69 **3.6**
22. 511.5 ÷ 5.5 **93**	**23.** 0.992 ÷ 0.8 **1.24**	**24.** 4.53 ÷ 0.05 **90.6**
25. 3.498 ÷ 0.06 **58.3**	**26.** 59.2 ÷ 0.8 **74**	**27.** 2.198 ÷ 0.07 **31.4**
28. 14.28 ÷ 0.7 **20.4**	**29.** 1.98 ÷ 0.5 **3.96**	**30.** 26.36 ÷ 0.04 **659**
31. 3.922 ÷ 7.4 **0.53**	**32.** 23.52 ÷ 0.98 **24**	**33.** 71.25 ÷ 7.5 **9.5**
34. 114.7 ÷ 3.7 **31**	**35.** 0.832 ÷ 0.52 **1.6**	**36.** 1.125 ÷ 0.09 **12.5**
37. 9.666 ÷ 2.7 **3.58**	**38.** 1.456 ÷ 9.1 **0.16**	**39.** 0.4374 ÷ 1.8 **0.243**

636

Zeros in Decimal Division

When you are dividing by a decimal, sometimes you need to use extra zeros in the dividend or the quotient, or both.

EXAMPLE

1 Divide 0.045 ÷ 3.6.

Step 1 Multiply by 10.

$3.6\overline{)0.045}$

Step 2 Divide.

```
      125
36)0.4500
  − 36
     90
  − 72
    180
  − 180
      0
```

Step 3 Place the decimal point.

```
   0.0125
36)0.4500
  − 36
     90
  − 72
    180
  − 180
      0
```

EXAMPLE

2 Find each quotient.

a. 0.4428 ÷ 8.2

Multiply by 10.

$8.2\overline{)0.4428}$ = 0.054

b. 0.00434 ÷ 0.07

Multiply by 100.

$0.07\overline{)0.00434}$ = 0.062

c. 0.00306 ÷ 0.072

Multiply by 1,000.

$0.072\overline{)0.0030600}$ = 0.0425

Exercises

Divide.

1. 0.0023 ÷ 0.05 0.046
2. 0.000162 ÷ 0.02 0.0081
3. 0.009 ÷ 0.12 0.075
4. 0.021 ÷ 2.5 0.0084
5. 0.0019 ÷ 0.2 0.0095
6. 0.9 ÷ 0.8 1.125
7. 0.000175 ÷ 0.07 0.0025
8. 0.142 ÷ 0.04 3.55
9. 0.0017 ÷ 0.02 0.085
10. 0.003 ÷ 0.6 0.005
11. 0.0105 ÷ 0.7 0.015
12. 0.034 ÷ 0.05 0.68
13. 0.00056 ÷ 0.16 0.0035
14. 0.0612 ÷ 7.2 0.0085
15. 0.217 ÷ 3.1 0.07
16. 0.052 ÷ 0.8 0.065
17. 0.000924 ÷ 0.44 0.0021
18. 0.05796 ÷ 0.63 0.092
19. 0.00123 ÷ 8.2 0.00015
20. 0.0954 ÷ 0.09 1.06
21. 0.0084 ÷ 1.4 0.006
22. 0.259 ÷ 3.5 0.074
23. 0.00468 ÷ 0.52 0.009
24. 0.104 ÷ 0.05 2.08
25. 0.00063 ÷ 0.18 0.0035
26. 0.011 ÷ 0.25 0.044
27. 0.3069 ÷ 9.3 0.033
28. 0.00045 ÷ 0.3 0.0015

Skills Handbook

637

Mixed Numbers and Improper Fractions

A fraction such as $\frac{10}{7}$, in which the numerator is greater than or equal to the denominator, is an improper fraction. You can write an improper fraction as a mixed number that shows the sum of a whole number and a fraction.

Sometimes it is necessary to do the opposite and write a mixed number as an improper fraction.

EXAMPLE

a. Write $\frac{11}{5}$ as a mixed number.

$$\frac{11}{5} \rightarrow \begin{array}{r} 2 \\ 5\overline{)11} \\ -10 \\ \hline 1 \end{array}$$

2 ← **whole number**

1 ← **remainder**

$\frac{11}{5} = 2\frac{1}{5}$ ← **whole number +** $\frac{\textbf{remainder}}{\textbf{denominator}}$

b. Write $2\frac{5}{6}$ as an improper fraction.

$2\frac{5}{6} = 2 + \frac{5}{6}$

$= \frac{12}{6} + \frac{5}{6}$ ← **Write 2 as $\frac{12}{6}$.**

$= \frac{12 + 5}{6}$ ← **Add the numerators.**

$= \frac{17}{6}$

$2\frac{5}{6} = \frac{17}{6}$ ← **Simplify.**

Exercises

Write each improper fraction as a mixed number.

1. $\frac{7}{5}$ $1\frac{2}{5}$ **2.** $\frac{9}{2}$ $4\frac{1}{2}$ **3.** $\frac{13}{4}$ $3\frac{1}{4}$ **4.** $\frac{21}{5}$ $4\frac{1}{5}$ **5.** $\frac{13}{10}$ $1\frac{3}{10}$

6. $\frac{49}{5}$ $9\frac{4}{5}$ **7.** $\frac{21}{8}$ $2\frac{5}{8}$ **8.** $\frac{13}{7}$ $1\frac{6}{7}$ **9.** $\frac{17}{5}$ $3\frac{2}{5}$ **10.** $\frac{49}{6}$ $8\frac{1}{6}$

11. $\frac{17}{4}$ $4\frac{1}{4}$ **12.** $\frac{5}{2}$ $2\frac{1}{2}$ **13.** $\frac{27}{5}$ $5\frac{2}{5}$ **14.** $\frac{12}{9}$ $1\frac{1}{3}$ **15.** $\frac{30}{8}$ $3\frac{3}{4}$

16. $\frac{37}{12}$ $3\frac{1}{12}$ **17.** $\frac{8}{6}$ $1\frac{1}{3}$ **18.** $\frac{19}{12}$ $1\frac{7}{12}$ **19.** $\frac{45}{10}$ $4\frac{1}{2}$ **20.** $\frac{15}{12}$ $1\frac{1}{4}$

21. $\frac{11}{2}$ $5\frac{1}{2}$ **22.** $\frac{20}{6}$ $3\frac{1}{3}$ **23.** $\frac{34}{8}$ $4\frac{1}{4}$ **24.** $\frac{21}{9}$ $2\frac{1}{3}$ **25.** $\frac{42}{4}$ $10\frac{1}{2}$

Write each mixed number as an improper fraction.

26. $1\frac{1}{2}$ $\frac{3}{2}$ **27.** $2\frac{2}{3}$ $\frac{8}{3}$ **28.** $1\frac{1}{12}$ $\frac{13}{12}$ **29.** $3\frac{1}{5}$ $\frac{16}{5}$ **30.** $2\frac{2}{7}$ $\frac{16}{7}$

31. $4\frac{1}{2}$ $\frac{9}{2}$ **32.** $2\frac{7}{8}$ $\frac{23}{8}$ **33.** $1\frac{2}{9}$ $\frac{11}{9}$ **34.** $5\frac{1}{5}$ $\frac{26}{5}$ **35.** $4\frac{7}{9}$ $\frac{43}{9}$

36. $9\frac{1}{4}$ $\frac{37}{4}$ **37.** $2\frac{3}{8}$ $\frac{19}{8}$ **38.** $7\frac{7}{8}$ $\frac{63}{8}$ **39.** $1\frac{5}{12}$ $\frac{17}{12}$ **40.** $3\frac{3}{7}$ $\frac{24}{7}$

41. $6\frac{1}{2}$ $\frac{13}{2}$ **42.** $3\frac{1}{10}$ $\frac{31}{10}$ **43.** $4\frac{6}{7}$ $\frac{34}{7}$ **44.** $8\frac{1}{8}$ $\frac{65}{8}$ **45.** $6\frac{1}{3}$ $\frac{19}{3}$

Adding and Subtracting Fractions With Like Denominators

When you add or subtract fractions with the same denominator, add or subtract the numerators and then write the answer over the denominator.

EXAMPLE

1 Add or subtract. Write the answers in simplest form.

a. $\frac{5}{8} + \frac{7}{8}$

$\frac{5}{8} + \frac{7}{8} = \frac{5+7}{8} = \frac{12}{8} = 1\frac{4}{8} = 1\frac{1}{2}$

b. $\frac{11}{12} - \frac{2}{12}$

$\frac{11}{12} - \frac{2}{12} = \frac{11-2}{12} = \frac{9}{12} = \frac{3}{4}$

To add or subtract mixed numbers, add or subtract the fractions first. Then add or subtract the whole numbers.

EXAMPLE

2 Add or subtract. Write the answers in simplest form.

a. $3\frac{4}{6} + 2\frac{5}{6}$

$$\begin{array}{r} 3\frac{4}{6} \\ +\ 2\frac{5}{6} \\ \hline 5\frac{9}{6} \end{array} = 5 + 1 + \frac{3}{6} = 6\frac{1}{2}$$

b. $6\frac{1}{4} - 1\frac{3}{4}$ ← Rewrite 6 as $5\frac{4}{4}$ and add it to $\frac{1}{4}$.

$$\begin{array}{r} 6\frac{1}{4} \\ -1\frac{3}{4} \\ \hline \end{array} \rightarrow \begin{array}{r} 5\frac{5}{4} \\ -1\frac{3}{4} \\ \hline 4\frac{2}{4} \end{array} = 4\frac{1}{2}$$

Exercises

Add or subtract. Write the answers in simplest form.

1. $\frac{4}{5} + \frac{3}{5}$ $1\frac{2}{5}$
2. $\frac{2}{6} - \frac{1}{6}$ $\frac{1}{6}$
3. $\frac{2}{7} + \frac{2}{7}$ $\frac{4}{7}$
4. $\frac{7}{8} + \frac{2}{8}$ $1\frac{1}{8}$
5. $1\frac{2}{5} - \frac{1}{5}$ $1\frac{1}{5}$
6. $\frac{3}{6} - \frac{1}{6}$ $\frac{1}{3}$
7. $\frac{6}{8} - \frac{3}{8}$ $\frac{3}{8}$
8. $\frac{2}{9} + \frac{1}{9}$ $\frac{1}{3}$
9. $\frac{4}{5} - \frac{1}{5}$ $\frac{3}{5}$
10. $\frac{5}{9} + \frac{7}{9}$ $1\frac{1}{3}$
11. $9\frac{1}{3} - 8\frac{1}{3}$ 1
12. $8\frac{6}{7} - 4\frac{2}{7}$ $4\frac{4}{7}$
13. $3\frac{1}{10} + 1\frac{3}{10}$ $4\frac{2}{5}$
14. $2\frac{2}{9} + 3\frac{4}{9}$ $5\frac{2}{3}$
15. $4\frac{5}{12} - 3\frac{1}{12}$ $1\frac{1}{3}$
16. $9\frac{5}{9} + 6\frac{7}{9}$ $16\frac{1}{3}$
17. $5\frac{7}{8} + 2\frac{3}{8}$ $8\frac{1}{4}$
18. $4\frac{4}{7} - 2\frac{1}{7}$ $2\frac{3}{7}$
19. $9\frac{3}{4} + 1\frac{3}{4}$ $11\frac{1}{2}$
20. $8\frac{2}{3} - 4\frac{1}{3}$ $4\frac{1}{3}$
21. $8\frac{7}{10} + 2\frac{3}{10}$ 11
22. $1\frac{4}{5} + 3\frac{3}{5}$ $5\frac{2}{5}$
23. $7\frac{1}{5} - 2\frac{3}{5}$ $4\frac{3}{5}$
24. $4\frac{1}{3} - 1\frac{2}{3}$ $2\frac{2}{3}$
25. $4\frac{3}{8} - 3\frac{5}{8}$ $\frac{3}{4}$
26. $5\frac{1}{12} - 2\frac{7}{12}$ $2\frac{1}{2}$

Skills Handbook

Skills Handbook

Classifying and Measuring Angles

Recall that an angle is a geometric figure formed by two rays with a common endpoint. The rays are sides of the angle and the endpoint is the vertex of the angle. You can name the angle at the right in three different ways: $\angle A$, $\angle BAC$, or $\angle CAB$.

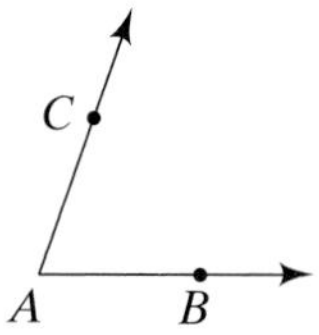

Classify angles by their measures.

Acute angle	**Right angle**	**Obtuse angle**	**Straight angle**
less than 90°	90°	greater than 90° but less than 180°	180°
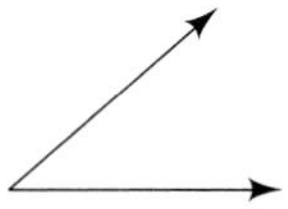	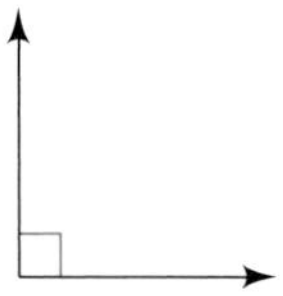	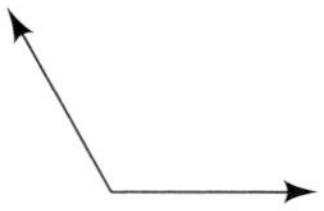	

EXAMPLE

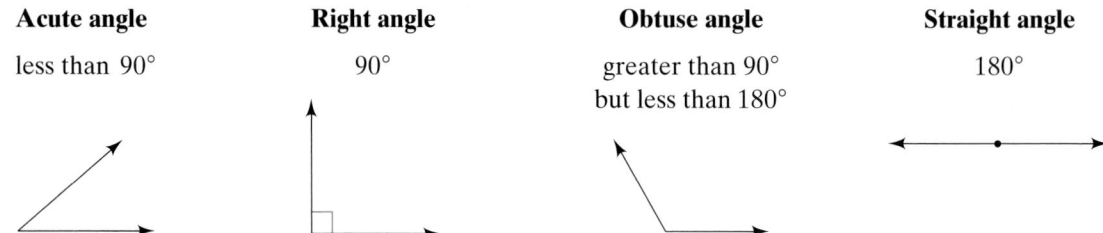

Measure the angle. Classify it as *acute, right, obtuse,* or *straight.*

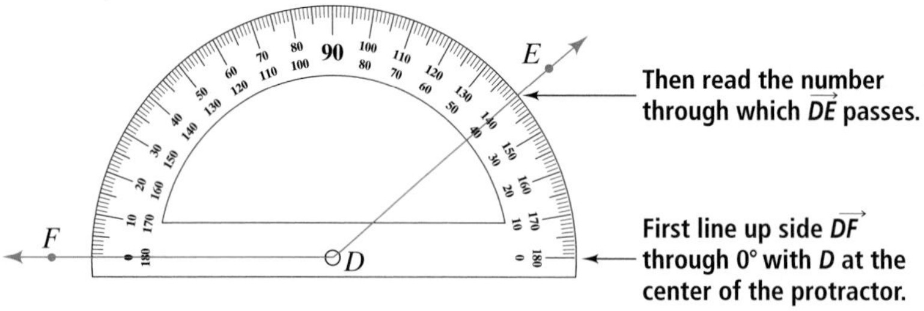

The measure of the angle is 140°. The angle is obtuse.

Exercises

Measure each angle. Classify it as *acute, right, obtuse,* or *straight.*

1. 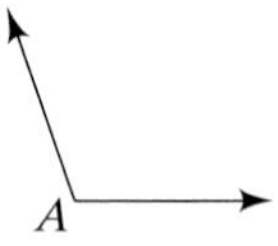

110°; obtuse

2. 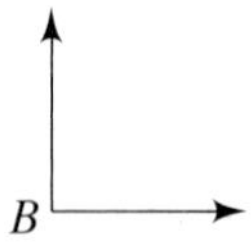

90°; right

3. 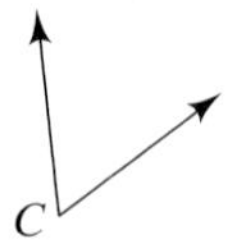

60°; acute

4. 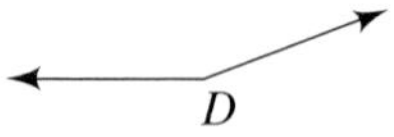

160°; obtuse

Classify each angle as *acute, right, obtuse,* or *straight.*

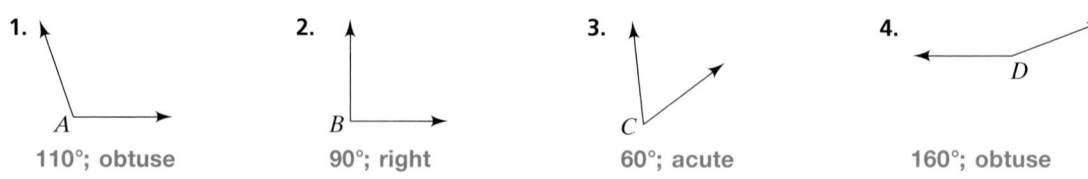

5. 30° acute 6. 45° acute 7. 95° obtuse 8. 180° straight 9. 140° obtuse 10. 170° obtuse

Bar Graphs

Use bar graphs to compare amounts. The horizontal axis shows the categories and the vertical axis shows the amounts. A multiple bar graph includes a key.

EXAMPLE

Draw a bar graph for the data in the table at the right.

List and Sale Prices

Item	List	Sale
Pocket PC	$450	$400
Digital Camera	$500	$350
Minidisc Player/Recorder	$230	$180

Place the categories (in the first column) on the horizontal scale. Place the amounts (in the second and third columns) on the vertical scale. Include a key to the two price categories.

List and Sale Prices

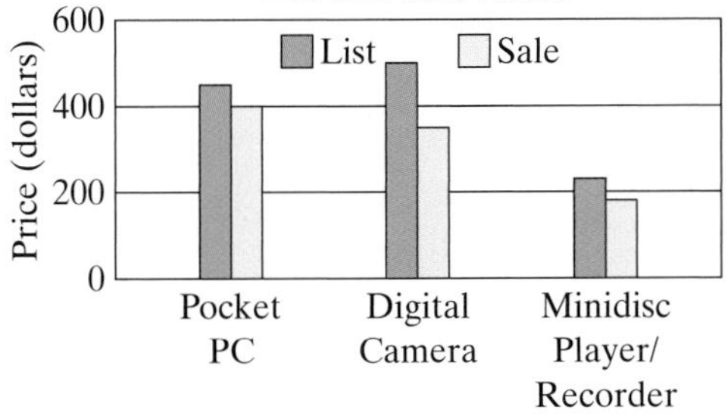

Exercises

Draw a bar graph for each set of data. 1–4. See margin.

1. **Meat Consumption (pounds per person per year)**

Beef	Chicken	Pork	Turkey
62.9	53.9	46.7	13.7

SOURCE: U.S. Department of Agriculture. Go to **PHSchool.com** for a data update. Web Code: asg-9041

2. **Pets in Students' Homes**

Number of Pets	0	1	2	3	more than 3
Number of Students	11	16	9	11	6

Draw a multiple bar graph for the set of data.

3. **Weekly Leisure Time (hours)**

Activity	Sports	Reading	Working
Anna	12	8	12
Tobi	6	12	10

4. **Average SAT Math and Verbal Scores**

Year	1	2	3
Math	514	514	516
Verbal	505	506	504

SOURCE: U.S. Dept. of Education. Go to **PHSchool.com** for a data update. Web Code: asg-9041

1.

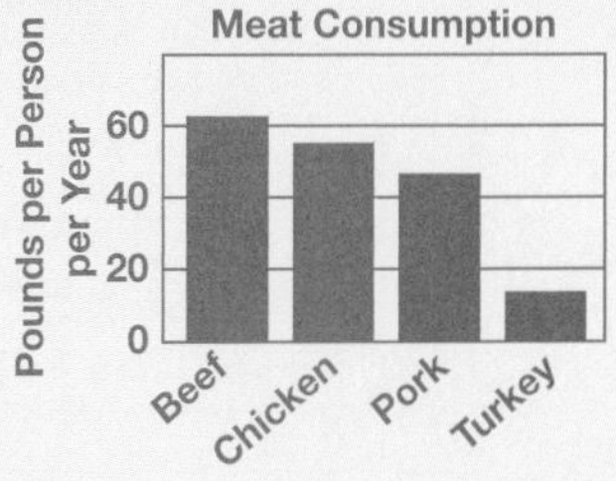

2.

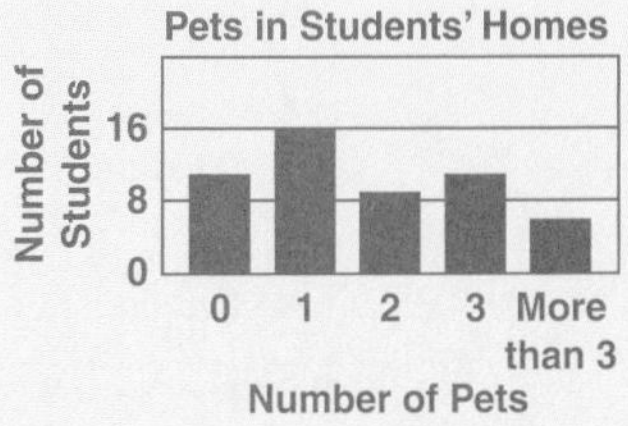

3.

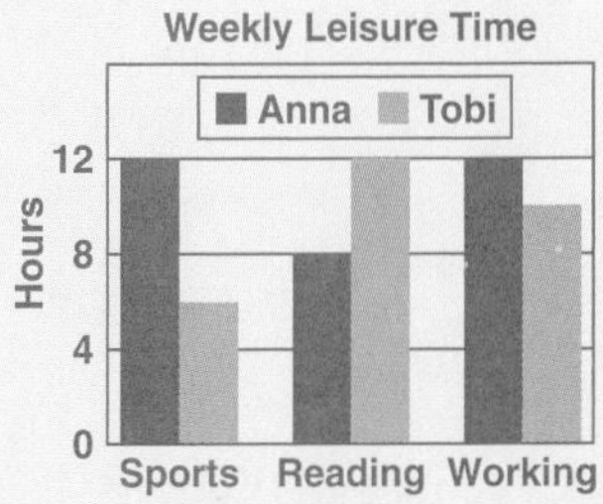

4.

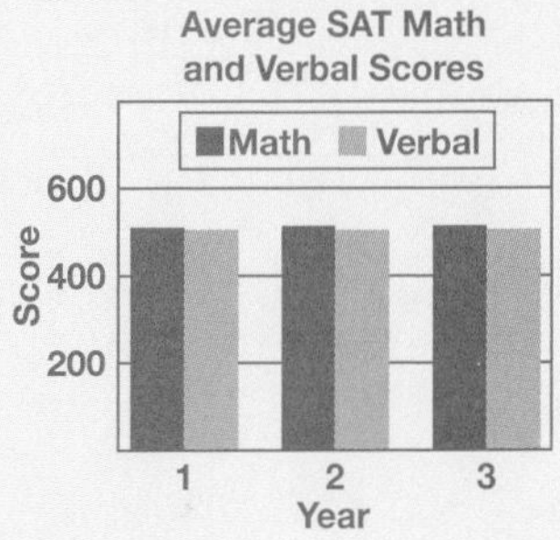

641

1.

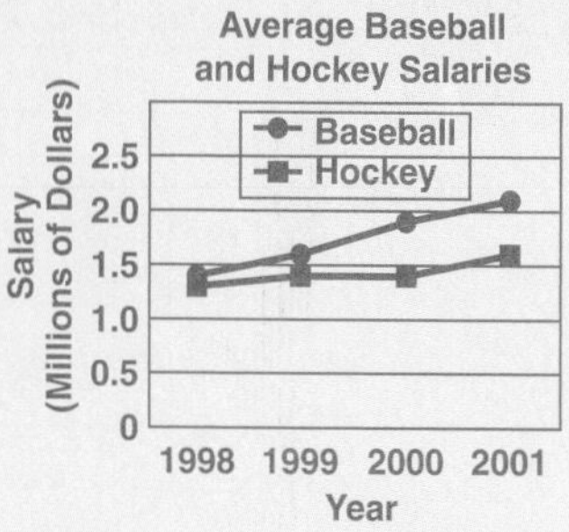

2.

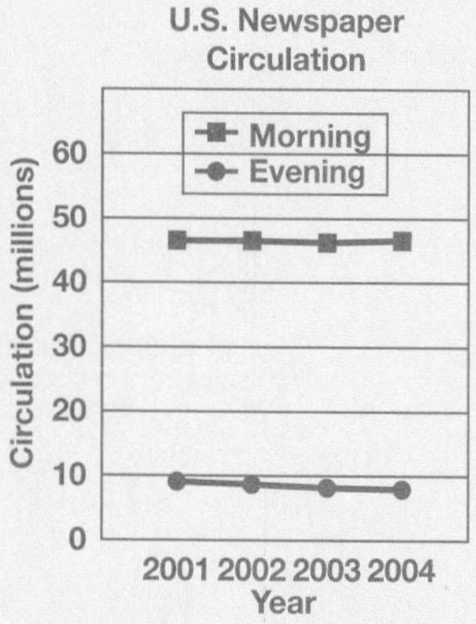

3.

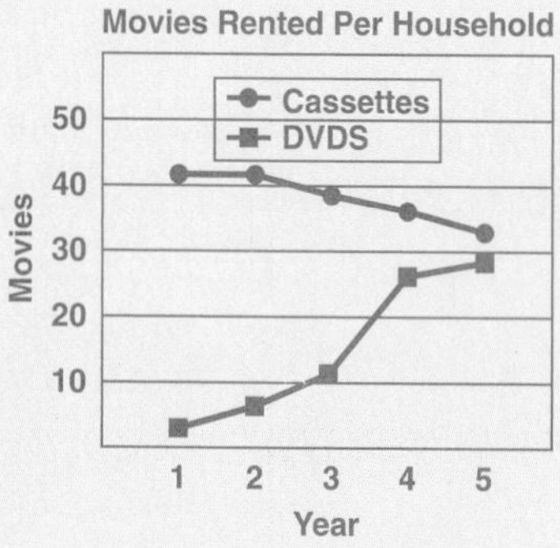

4.

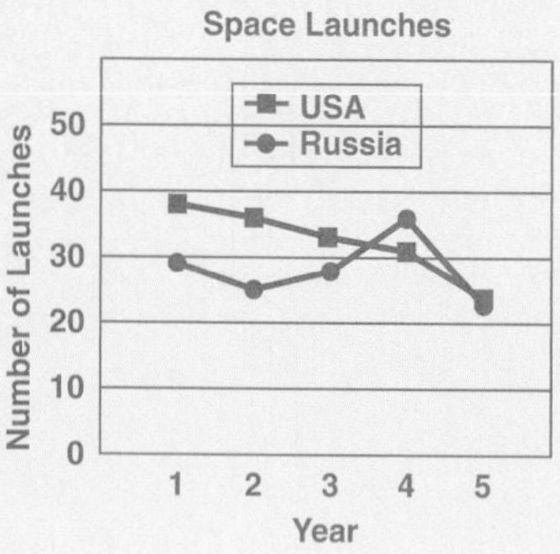

Line Graphs

Use line graphs to show changes over time. A multiple line graph shows more than one category changing over time.

EXAMPLE

Display the data in the table below in a line graph.

Monthly Average Temperatures (°F)

Month	J	F	M	A	M	J	J	A	S	O	N	D
Houston, Texas	50	54	61	68	75	80	83	82	78	70	61	54
Chicago, Illinois	21	25	37	49	59	69	73	72	64	53	40	27

SOURCE: National Climatic Data Center. Go to **PHSchool.com** for a data update. Web Code: asg-9041

Monthly Average Temperatures

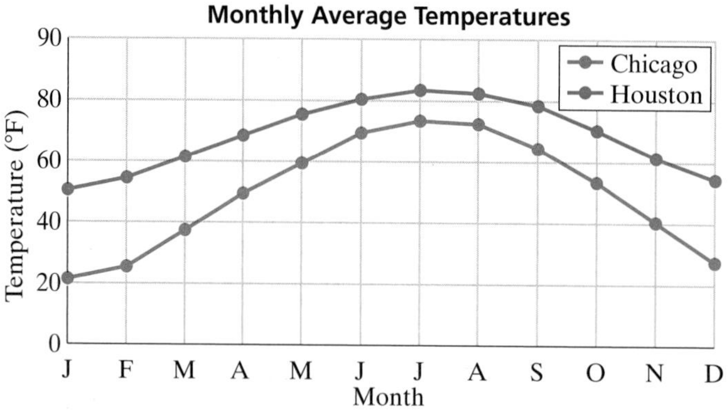

Exercises

Draw multiple line graphs for the data below. 1–4. See margin.

1. **Average Baseball and Hockey Salaries (millions of dollars)**

Year	1998	1999	2000	2001
Baseball	1.4	1.6	1.9	2.1
Hockey	1.3	1.4	1.4	1.6

SOURCE: Major League Baseball Players Association and National Hockey League

2. **U.S. Newspaper Circulation (millions)**

Year	2000	2001	2002	2003
Morning	46.8	46.8	46.6	46.9
Evening	9.0	8.8	8.6	8.3

SOURCE: U.S. Census Bureau. Go to **PHSchool.com** for a data update. Web Code: asg-9041

3. **Movies Rented per Household**

Year	1	2	3	4	5
Videos	40.8	40.1	38.9	35.2	33.8
DVDs	3.1	8.5	10.9	25.4	29.9

4. **Space Launches**

Year	1	2	3	4	5
United States	38	36	33	31	24
Russia	29	25	28	36	23

Tables

Table 1 Measures

Metric	Customary
Length	**Length**
10 millimeters (mm) = 1 centimeter (cm) 100 cm = 1 meter (m) 1,000 m = 1 kilometer (km)	12 inches (in.) = 1 foot (ft) 36 in. = 1 yard (yd) 3 ft = 1 yd 5,280 ft = 1 mile (mi) 1,760 yd = 1 mi
Area	**Area**
100 square millimeters (mm^2) = 1 square centimeter (cm^2) 10,000 cm^2 = 1 square meter (m^2)	144 square inches ($in.^2$) = 1 square foot (ft^2) 9 ft^2 = 1 square yard (yd^2) 4,840 yd^2 = 1 acre
Volume	**Volume**
1,000 cubic millimeters (mm^3) = 1 cubic centimeter (cm^3) 1,000,000 cm^3 = 1 cubic meter (m^3)	1,728 cubic inches ($in.^3$) = 1 cubic foot (ft^3) 27 ft^3 = 1 cubic yard (yd^3)
Mass	**Mass**
1,000 milligrams (mg) = 1 gram (g) 1,000 g = 1 kilogram (kg)	16 ounces (oz) = 1 pound (lb) 2,000 lb = 1 ton (t)
Capacity	**Capacity**
1,000 milliliters (mL) = 1 liter (L)	8 fluid ounces (fl oz) = 1 cup (c) 2 c = 1 pint (pt) 2 pt = 1 quart (qt) 4 qt = 1 gallon (gal)

Time
1 minute (min) = 60 seconds (s) 1 hour(h) = 60 min 1 day(d) = 24 h 1 year(yr) = 365 d

Table 2 Math Symbols

+	plus (addition)	p. 4
−	minus (subtraction)	p. 4
×, ·	times (multiplication)	p. 4
÷, $\overline{)\ }$	divide (division)	p. 4
=	is equal to	p. 5
( )	parentheses for grouping	p. 6
[ ]	brackets for grouping	p. 6
$-a$	opposite of a	p. 10
. . .	and so on	p. 10
°	degrees	p. 10
$\lvert a \rvert$	absolute value of a	p. 10
$\stackrel{?}{=}$	Is the statement true?	p. 34
≈	is approximately equal to	p. 63
$\frac{b}{a}$	reciprocal of $\frac{a}{b}$	p. 73
A	area	p. 81
ℓ	length	p. 81
w	width	p. 81
h	height	p. 81
b_1, b_2	base lengths of a trapezoid	p. 81
d	distance	p. 82
r	rate	p. 82
t	time	p. 82
P	perimeter	p. 82
a^n	nth power of a	p. 86
$\sqrt{x}$	nonnegative square root of x	p. 106
π	pi, an irrational number approximately equal to 3.14	p. 108
(a, b)	ordered pair with x-coordinate a and y-coordinate b	p. 124
$\overline{AB}$	segment AB	p. 128
A'	image of A, A prime	p. 136
$\triangle ABC$	triangle with vertices A, B, and C	p. 136
→	arrow notation	p. 137
$a : b$, $\frac{a}{b}$	ratio of a to b	p. 160
≅	is congruent to	p. 181
~	is similar to	p. 181
$\angle A$	angle with vertex A	p. 181
AB	length of segment $\overline{AB}$	p. 181
$\overrightarrow{AB}$	ray AB	p. 186
%	percent	p. 210
P(event)	probability of an event	p. 246
<	is less than	p. 281
>	is greater than	p. 281
≤	is less than or equal to	p. 281
≥	is greater than or equal to	p. 281
≠	is not equal to	p. 282
$\angle ABC$	angle with sides $\overrightarrow{BA}$ and $\overrightarrow{BC}$	p. 303
$m\angle ABC$	measure of angle ABC	p. 303
⊥	is perpendicular to	p. 304
$\overleftrightarrow{AB}$	line AB	p. 308
$\parallel$	is parallel to	p. 308
b	base length	p. 328
C	circumference	p. 336
d	diameter	p. 336
r	radius	p. 336
S.A.	surface area	p. 368
B	area of base	p. 369
L.A.	lateral area	p. 369
ℓ	slant height	p. 374
V	volume	p. 380
$n!$	n factorial	p. 492
$_nP_r$	permutations of n things taken r at a time	p. 493
$_nC_r$	combinations of n things taken r at a time	p. 497
$f(n)$	the function value at n, f of n	p. 524
b	y-intercept	p. 535
m	slope of a line	p. 535
sin A	sine of $\angle A$	p. 646
cos A	cosine of $\angle A$	p. 646
tan A	tangent of $\angle A$	p. 646

Table 3 Squares and Square Roots

Number n	Square n^2	Positive Square Root $\sqrt{n}$	Number n	Square n^2	Positive Square Root $\sqrt{n}$
1	1	1.000	**51**	2,601	7.141
2	4	1.414	**52**	2,704	7.211
3	9	1.732	**53**	2,809	7.280
4	16	2.000	**54**	2,916	7.348
5	25	2.236	**55**	3,025	7.416
6	36	2.449	**56**	3,136	7.483
7	49	2.646	**57**	3,249	7.550
8	64	2.828	**58**	3,364	7.616
9	81	3.000	**59**	3,481	7.681
10	100	3.162	**60**	3,600	7.746
11	121	3.317	**61**	3,721	7.810
12	144	3.464	**62**	3,844	7.874
13	169	3.606	**63**	3,969	7.937
14	196	3.742	**64**	4,096	8.000
15	225	3.873	**65**	4,225	8.062
16	256	4.000	**66**	4,356	8.124
17	289	4.123	**67**	4,489	8.185
18	324	4.243	**68**	4,624	8.246
19	361	4.359	**69**	4,761	8.307
20	400	4.472	**70**	4,900	8.367
21	441	4.583	**71**	5,041	8.426
22	484	4.690	**72**	5,184	8.485
23	529	4.796	**73**	5,329	8.544
24	576	4.899	**74**	5,476	8.602
25	625	5.000	**75**	5,625	8.660
26	676	5.099	**76**	5,776	8.718
27	729	5.196	**77**	5,929	8.775
28	784	5.292	**78**	6,084	8.832
29	841	5.385	**79**	6,241	8.888
30	900	5.477	**80**	6,400	8.944
31	961	5.568	**81**	6,561	9.000
32	1,024	5.657	**82**	6,724	9.055
33	1,089	5.745	**83**	6,889	9.110
34	1,156	5.831	**84**	7,056	9.165
35	1,225	5.916	**85**	7,225	9.220
36	1,296	6.000	**86**	7,396	9.274
37	1,369	6.083	**87**	7,569	9.327
38	1,444	6.164	**88**	7,744	9.381
39	1,521	6.245	**89**	7,921	9.434
40	1,600	6.325	**90**	8,100	9.487
41	1,681	6.403	**91**	8,281	9.539
42	1,764	6.481	**92**	8,464	9.592
43	1,849	6.557	**93**	8,649	9.644
44	1,936	6.633	**94**	8,836	9.695
45	2,025	6.708	**95**	9,025	9.747
46	2,116	6.782	**96**	9,216	9.798
47	2,209	6.856	**97**	9,409	9.849
48	2,304	6.928	**98**	9,604	9.899
49	2,401	7.000	**99**	9,801	9.950
50	2,500	7.071	**100**	10,000	10.000

Table 4 Trigonometric Ratios

Angle	Sine	Cosine	Tangent	Angle	Sine	Cosine	Tangent
1°	0.0175	0.9998	0.0175	**46°**	0.7193	0.6947	1.0355
2°	0.0349	0.9994	0.0349	**47°**	0.7314	0.6820	1.0724
3°	0.0523	0.9986	0.0524	**48°**	0.7431	0.6691	1.1106
4°	0.0698	0.9976	0.0699	**49°**	0.7547	0.6561	1.1504
5°	0.0872	0.9962	0.0875	**50°**	0.7660	0.6428	1.1918
6°	0.1045	0.9945	0.1051	**51°**	0.7771	0.6293	1.2349
7°	0.1219	0.9925	0.1228	**52°**	0.7880	0.6157	1.2799
8°	0.1392	0.9903	0.1405	**53°**	0.7986	0.6018	1.3270
9°	0.1564	0.9877	0.1584	**54°**	0.8090	0.5878	1.3764
10°	0.1736	0.9848	0.1763	**55°**	0.8192	0.5736	1.4281
11°	0.1908	0.9816	0.1944	**56°**	0.8290	0.5592	1.4826
12°	0.2079	0.9781	0.2126	**57°**	0.8387	0.5446	1.5399
13°	0.2250	0.9744	0.2309	**58°**	0.8480	0.5299	1.6003
14°	0.2419	0.9703	0.2493	**59°**	0.8572	0.5150	1.6643
15°	0.2588	0.9659	0.2679	**60°**	0.8660	0.5000	1.7321
16°	0.2756	0.9613	0.2867	**61°**	0.8746	0.4848	1.8040
17°	0.2924	0.9563	0.3057	**62°**	0.8829	0.4695	1.8807
18°	0.3090	0.9511	0.3249	**63°**	0.8910	0.4540	1.9626
19°	0.3256	0.9455	0.3443	**64°**	0.8988	0.4384	2.0503
20°	0.3420	0.9397	0.3640	**65°**	0.9063	0.4226	2.1445
21°	0.3584	0.9336	0.3839	**66°**	0.9135	0.4067	2.2460
22°	0.3746	0.9272	0.4040	**67°**	0.9205	0.3907	2.3559
23°	0.3907	0.9205	0.4245	**68°**	0.9272	0.3746	2.4751
24°	0.4067	0.9135	0.4452	**69°**	0.9336	0.3584	2.6051
25°	0.4226	0.9063	0.4663	**70°**	0.9397	0.3420	2.7475
26°	0.4384	0.8988	0.4877	**71°**	0.9455	0.3256	2.9042
27°	0.4540	0.8910	0.5095	**72°**	0.9511	0.3090	3.0777
28°	0.4695	0.8829	0.5317	**73°**	0.9563	0.2924	3.2709
29°	0.4848	0.8746	0.5543	**74°**	0.9613	0.2756	3.4874
30°	0.5000	0.8660	0.5774	**75°**	0.9659	0.2588	3.7321
31°	0.5150	0.8572	0.6009	**76°**	0.9703	0.2419	4.0108
32°	0.5299	0.8480	0.6249	**77°**	0.9744	0.2250	4.3315
33°	0.5446	0.8387	0.6494	**78°**	0.9781	0.2079	4.7046
34°	0.5592	0.8290	0.6745	**79°**	0.9816	0.1908	5.1446
35°	0.5736	0.8192	0.7002	**80°**	0.9848	0.1736	5.6713
36°	0.5878	0.8090	0.7265	**81°**	0.9877	0.1564	6.3138
37°	0.6018	0.7986	0.7536	**82°**	0.9903	0.1392	7.1154
38°	0.6157	0.7880	0.7813	**83°**	0.9925	0.1219	8.1443
39°	0.6293	0.7771	0.8098	**84°**	0.9945	0.1045	9.5144
40°	0.6428	0.7660	0.8391	**85°**	0.9962	0.0872	11.4301
41°	0.6561	0.7547	0.8693	**86°**	0.9976	0.0698	14.3007
42°	0.6691	0.7431	0.9004	**87°**	0.9986	0.0523	19.0811
43°	0.6820	0.7314	0.9325	**88°**	0.9994	0.0349	28.6363
44°	0.6947	0.7193	0.9657	**89°**	0.9998	0.0175	57.2900
45°	0.7071	0.7071	1.0000	**90°**	1.0000	0.0000	

Table 5 For Use With Problem Solving Applications

Chapter 6

Animated Movies

Movie	Year Released	Budget (millions of dollars)	Run Time (minutes)
Snow White and the Seven Dwarfs	1937	1.5	83
Fantasia	1940	2.3	120
The Lion King	1994	79.3	89
Hercules	1997	70.0	92
A Bug's Life	1998	45.0	96
Toy Story 2	1999	90.0	92
Chicken Run	2000	42.0	84
Lilo & Stitch	2002	80.0	85

SOURCE: The Internet Movie Database

Chapter 8

Typical Measurements of Bird Species and Nest Sizes

Species	Typical Wingspan (in.)	Typical Length (in.)	Typical Nest Diameter (in.)
Bald Eagle	84	38.5	60
Red-Tailed Hawk	52	22	29
Scarlet Ibis	38	25	10
American Crow	36.5	17.5	24
Blue Jay	16	11	7.5
Ruby-Throated Hummingbird	4.25	3.5	1.5

SOURCES: *A Field Guide to the Birds' Nests: United States East of the Mississippi River*; *Birds of North America*

Tables

Formulas and Properties

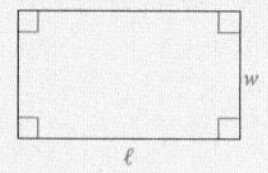

$P = 2\ell + 2w$
$A = \ell w$

Rectangle

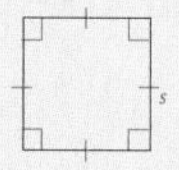

$P = 4s$
$A = s^2$

Square

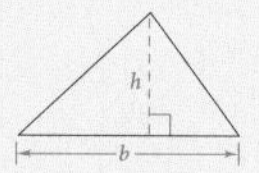

$A = \frac{1}{2}bh$

Triangle

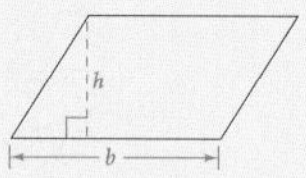

$A = bh$

Parallelogram

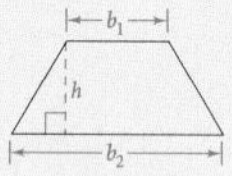

$A = \frac{1}{2}(b_1 + b_2)h$

Trapezoid

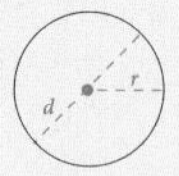

$C = 2\pi r$ or $C = \pi d$
$A = \pi r^2$

Circle

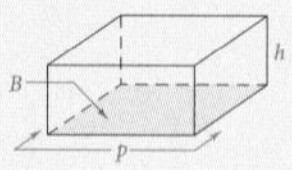

$V = Bh$
$L.A. = ph$
$S.A. = L.A. + 2B$

Rectangular Prism

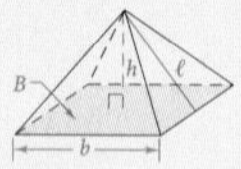

$V = \frac{1}{3}Bh$
$L.A. = 2b\ell$
$S.A. = L.A. + B$

Square Pyramid

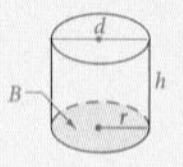

$V = Bh$
$L.A. = 2\pi rh$
$S.A. = L.A. + 2B$

Cylinder

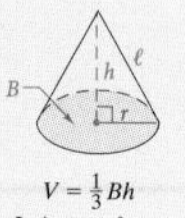

$V = \frac{1}{3}Bh$
$L.A. = \pi r\ell$
$S.A. = L.A. + B$

Cone

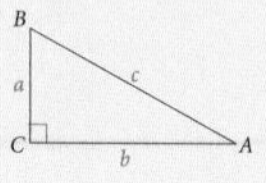

$a^2 + b^2 = c^2$

Pythagorean Theorem

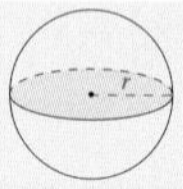

$V = \frac{4}{3}\pi r^3$
$S.A. = 4\pi r^2$

Sphere

Properties of Real Numbers

Unless otherwise stated, the variables *a*, *b*, *c*, and *d* used in these properties can be replaced with any number represented on a number line.

Identity Properties

Addition $a + 0 = a$ and $0 + a = a$
Multiplication $a \cdot 1 = a$ and $1 \cdot a = a$

Commutative Properties

Addition $a + b = b + a$
Multiplication $a \cdot b = b \cdot a$

Associative Properties

Addition $(a + b) + c = a + (b + c)$
Multiplication $(a \cdot b) \cdot c = a \cdot (b \cdot c)$

Inverse Properties

Addition
$a + (-a) = 0$ and $-a + a = 0$
Multiplication
$a \cdot \frac{1}{a} = 1$ and $\frac{1}{a} \cdot a = 1$ $(a \neq 0)$

Distributive Properties

$a(b + c) = ab + ac$ $(b + c)a = ba + ca$
$a(b - c) = ab - ac$ $(b - c)a = ba - ca$

Properties of Equality

Addition If $a = b$, then $a + c = b + c$.
Subtraction If $a = b$, then $a - c = b - c$.
Multiplication If $a = b$, then $a \cdot c = b \cdot c$.
Division If $a = b$, and $c \neq 0$, then $\frac{a}{c} = \frac{b}{c}$.
Substitution If $a = b$, then b can replace a in any expression.
Reflexive $a = a$
Symmetric If $a = b$, then $b = a$.
Transitive If $a = b$ and $b = c$, then $a = c$.

Cross Products Property

$\frac{a}{c} = \frac{b}{d}$ is equivalent to $ad = bc$.

Zero-Product Property

If $ab = 0$, then $a = 0$ or $b = 0$.

Closure Property

$a + b$ is a unique real number.
ab is a unique real number.

Density Property

Between any two rational numbers, there is at least one other rational number.

Properties of Inequality

Addition If $a > b$, then $a + c > b + c$.
If $a < b$, then $a + c < b + c$.
Subtraction If $a > b$, then $a - c > b - c$.
If $a < b$, then $a - c < b - c$.

Multiplication
If $a > b$ and $c > 0$, then $ac > bc$.
If $a < b$ and $c > 0$, then $ac < bc$.
If $a > b$ and $c < 0$, then $ac < bc$.
If $a < b$ and $c < 0$, then $ac > bc$.

Division
If $a > b$ and $c > 0$, then $\frac{a}{c} > \frac{b}{c}$.
If $a < b$ and $c > 0$, then $\frac{a}{c} < \frac{b}{c}$.
If $a > b$ and $c < 0$, then $\frac{a}{c} < \frac{b}{c}$.
If $a < b$ and $c < 0$, then $\frac{a}{c} > \frac{b}{c}$.

Transitive
If $a > b$ and $b > c$, then $a > c$.

Comparative
If $a = b + c$ and $c > 0$, then $a > b$.

Properties of Exponents

For any nonzero number a and any integers m and n:
Zero Exponent $a^0 = 1$
Negative Exponent $a^{-n} = \frac{1}{a^n}$
Product of Powers $a^m \cdot a^n = a^{m+n}$
Quotient of Powers $\frac{a^m}{a^n} = a^{m-n}$

Formulas and Properties

English/Spanish Illustrated Glossary

A

EXAMPLES

Absolute value (p. 10) The absolute value of a number is its distance from 0 on a number line.

Valor absoluto (p. 10) El valor absoluto de un número es su distancia del 0 en una recta numérica.

-7 is 7 units from 0, so $|-7| = 7$.

Acute angle (p. 640) An acute angle is an angle with a measure between 0° and 90°.

Ángulo agudo (p. 640) Un ángulo agudo es un ángulo que mide entre 0° y 90°.

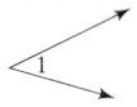

$0° < m\angle 1 < 90°$

Acute triangle (p. 318) An acute triangle has three acute angles.

Triángulo acutángulo (p. 318) Un triángulo acutángulo tiene tres ángulos agudos.

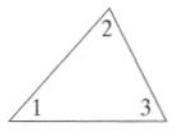

$\angle 1$, $\angle 2$, and $\angle 3$ are acute.

Addition Property of Equality (p. 33) The Addition Property of Equality states that if you add the same value to each side of an equation, the results are equal.

Propiedad Aditiva de la Igualdad (p. 33) La Propiedad Aditiva de la Igualdad establece que si se suma el mismo valor a cada lado de una ecuación, los resultados son iguales.

If $a = b$, then $a + c = b + c$.
Since $\frac{20}{2} = 10$, $\frac{20}{2} + 3 = 10 + 3$.

Addition Property of Inequality (p. 282) The Addition Property of Inequality states that if you add the same value to each side of an inequality, the relationship between the two sides does not change.

Propiedad Aditiva de la Desigualdad (p. 282) La Propiedad Aditiva de la Desigualdad establece que si sumas el mismo valor a cada lado de una desigualdad, la relación entre los dos lados no cambia.

If $a > b$, then $a + c > b + c$.
Since $4 > 2$, $4 + 11 > 2 + 11$.
If $a < b$, then $a + c < b + c$.
Since $4 < 9$, $4 + 11 < 9 + 11$.

Additive inverses (p. 16) Two numbers whose sum is 0 are additive inverses.

Inversos aditivos (p. 16) Dos números cuya suma es 0 son inversos aditivos.

$-a + a = 0$
$(-5) + 5 = 0$

EXAMPLES

Adjacent angles (p. 303) Adjacent angles share a vertex and a side but have no interior points in common.

Ángulos adyacentes (p. 303) Los ángulos adyacentes comparten un vértice y un lado, pero no tienen puntos interiores en común.

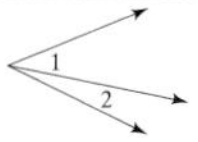

$\angle 1$ and $\angle 2$ are adjacent angles.

Algebraic expression (p. 4) An algebraic expression is a mathematical phrase that contains variables, numbers, and operation symbols.

Expresión algebraica (p. 4) Una expresión algebraica es un enunciado matemático que contiene variables, números y símbolos de operaciones.

$2x - 5$ is an algebraic expression.

Alternate exterior angles (p. 310) Alternate exterior angles lie outside a pair of lines and on opposite sides of a transversal.

Ángulos alternos externos (p. 310) Los ángulos alternos externos se ubican fuera de un par de rectas y a lados opuestos de la secante.

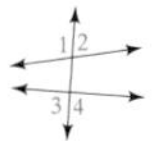

$\angle 2$ and $\angle 3$ are alternate exterior angles. $\angle 1$ and $\angle 4$ are also alternate exterior angles.

Alternate interior angles (p. 307) Alternate interior angles lie within a pair of lines and on opposite sides of a transversal.

Ángulos alternos internos (p. 307) Los ángulos alternos internos están ubicados entre un par de rectas y a lados opuestos de la secante.

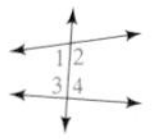

$\angle 2$ and $\angle 3$ are alternate interior angles. $\angle 1$ and $\angle 4$ are also alternate interior angles.

Angle (p. 640) An angle is formed by two rays with a common endpoint called a vertex.

Ángulo (p. 640) Un ángulo está formado por dos rayos que tienen un punto final común llamado vértice.

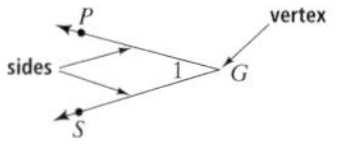

$\angle 1$ is made up of $\overrightarrow{GP}$ and $\overrightarrow{GS}$ with the common endpoint G.

Angle bisector (p. 344) An angle bisector is a ray that divides an angle into angles of equal measure.

Bisectriz de un ángulo (p. 344) La bisectriz de un ángulo es un rayo que divide un ángulo en ángulos de igual medida.

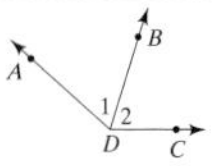

$\overrightarrow{DB}$ bisects $\angle ADC$, so $\angle 1 \cong \angle 2$.

EXAMPLES

Angle of rotation (p. 146) The angle of rotation is the number of degrees that a figure rotates.

Ángulo de rotación (p. 146) El ángulo de rotación es el número de grados que se rota una figura.

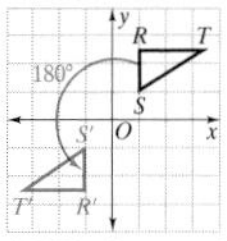

$\triangle RST$ has been rotated 180° to $\triangle R'S'T'$.

Arc (p. 340) An arc is part of a circle.

Arco (p. 340) Un arco es parte de un círculo.

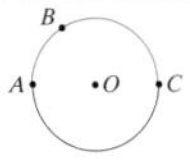

$\widehat{AB}$ is an arc of circle O. $\widehat{ABC}$ is a semicircle of circle O.

Area (p. 328) The area of a figure is the number of square units it encloses.

Área (p. 328) El área de una figura es el número de unidades cuadradas que contiene.

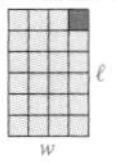

Each square equals 1 ft^2. $\ell = 6$ ft, and $w = 4$ ft, so the area is $6 \cdot 4 = 24$ ft^2.

Arithmetic sequence (p. 513) In an arithmetic sequence, each term is the result of adding the same number to the previous term.

Progresión aritmética (p. 513) En una progresión aritmética, cada término es el resultado de sumar el mismo número al término anterior.

The sequence 4, 10, 16, 22, 28, . . . is an arithmetic sequence. You add 6 to each term to find the next term.

Associative Property of Addition (p. 26) The Associative Property of Addition states that changing the grouping of the addends does not change the sum.

Propiedad Asociativa de la Suma (p. 26) La Propiedad Asociativa de la Suma establece que cambiar la agrupación de los sumandos no cambia la suma.

$(a + b) + c = a + (b + c)$
$(2 + 3) + 7 = 2 + (3 + 7)$

Associative Property of Multiplication (p. 26) The Associative Property of Multiplication states that changing the grouping of factors does not change the product.

Propiedad Asociativa de la Multiplicación (p. 26) La Propiedad Asociativa de la Multiplicación establece que cambiar la agrupación de los factores no altera el producto.

$(a \cdot b) \cdot c = a \cdot (b \cdot c)$
$(3 \cdot 4) \cdot 5 = 3 \cdot (4 \cdot 5)$

B

EXAMPLES

Balance (p. 243) The balance of an account is the principal plus the interest earned.

Saldo (p. 243) El saldo de una cuenta es el capital más los intereses ganados.

You deposit $100 into a bank account and earn $5 interest. Your balance is $105.

Base (p. 86) When a number is written in exponential form, the number that is used as a factor is the base.

Base (p. 86) Cuando un número se escribe en forma exponencial, el número que se usa como factor es la base.

$5^4 = 5 \times 5 \times 5 \times 5$
↑ base

Base plan (p. 358) A base plan shows the shape of the base and indicates the height of each part of a solid.

Plano base (p. 358) Un plano base muestra la forma de la base e indica la altura de cada parte de una figura tridimensional.

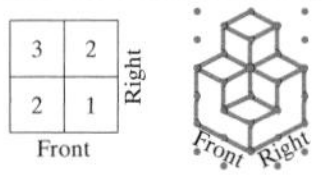

The first drawing is a base plan; the second drawing is an isometric drawing using the base plan.

Biased questions (p. 481) Unfair questions in a survey are biased questions. They can make assumptions that may or may not be true. Biased questions can also make one answer seem better than another.

Preguntas tendenciosas (p. 481) Las preguntas injustas de una encuesta son preguntas tendenciosas. Pueden hacer suposiciones que pueden o no ser verdaderas. Las preguntas tendenciosas hacen que una respuesta parezca mejor que otra.

"Do you prefer good food or junk food?"

Binomial (p. 576) A polynomial that has two terms is called a binomial.

Binomio (p. 576) Se llama binomio a un polinomio que tiene dos términos.

$3x^2 - 1$ is a binomial.

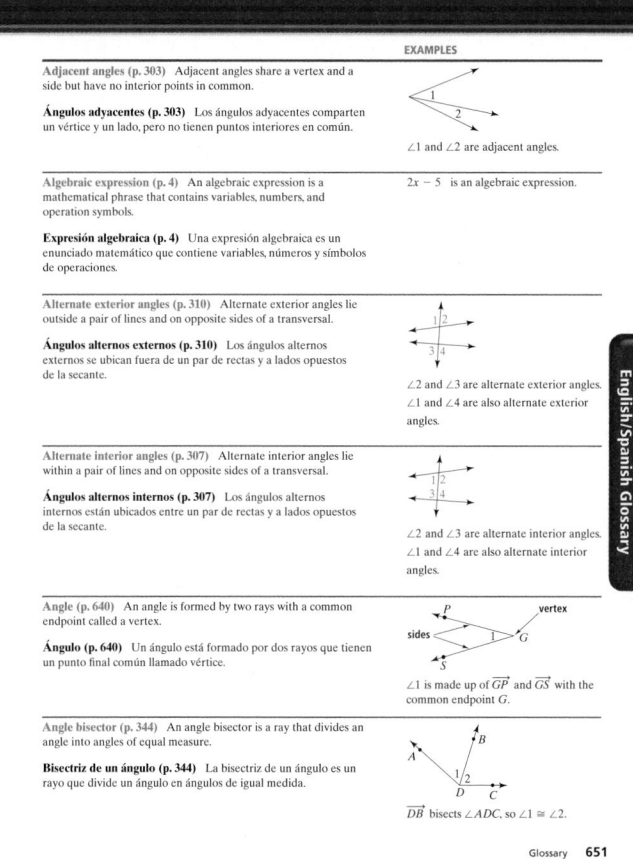

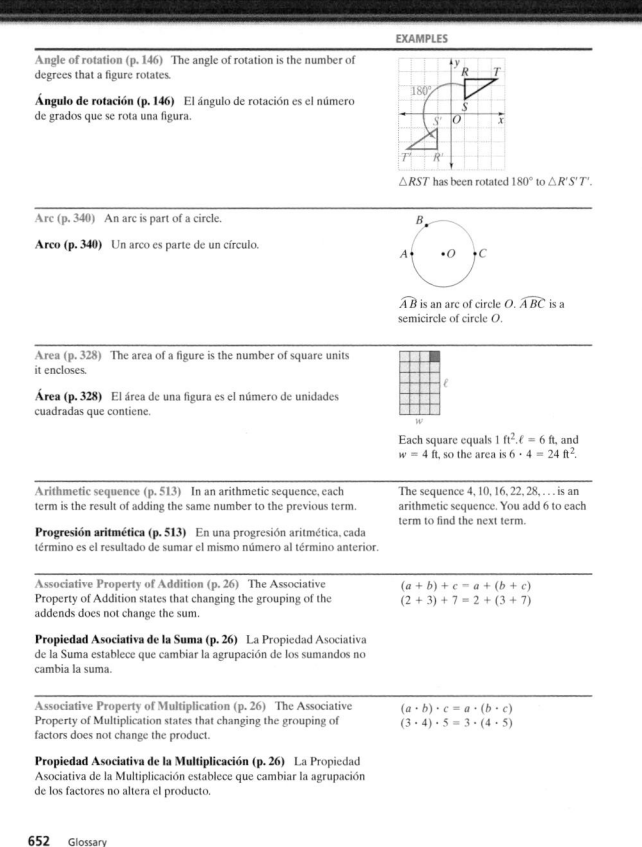

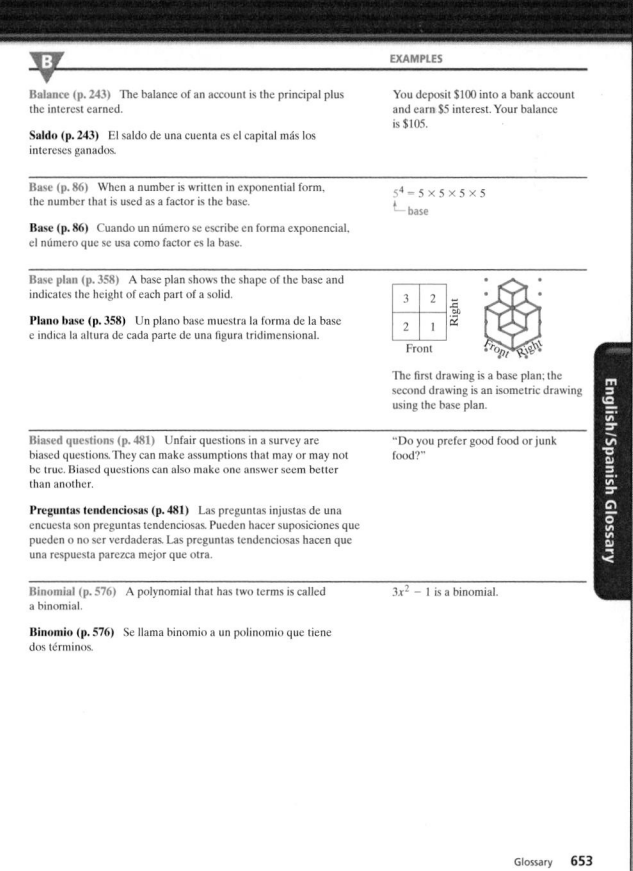

EXAMPLES

Box-and-whisker plot (p. 438) A box-and-whisker plot is a graph that summarizes a data set using five key values. There is a box in the middle and "whiskers" at either side. The quartiles divide the data into four equal parts.

Gráfica de caja y brazos (p. 438) Una gráfica de caja y brazos es un diagrama que resume un conjunto de datos usando cinco valores clave. Hay una caja en el centro y extensiones a cada lado. Los cuartiles se dividen los datos en cuartas partes iguales.

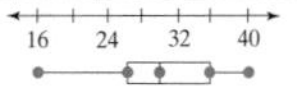

The box-and-whisker plot above uses these data:
16 19 26 26 27 29 30 31 34 34 38 39 40

C

Center of a circle (p. 336) A circle is named by its center.

Centro de un círculo (p. 336) Un círculo es denominado por su centro.

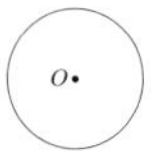

Circle O

Center of a sphere (p. 393) See *Sphere*.

Centro de una esfera (p. 393) Ver *Sphere*.

Center of rotation (p. 146) The center of rotation is a fixed point about which a figure is rotated.

Centro de rotación (p. 146) El centro de rotación es un punto fijo alrededor del cual se rota una figura.

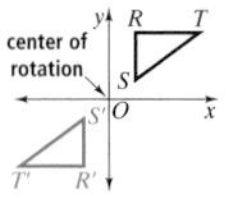

O is the center of rotation.

Central angle (p. 451) A central angle is an angle whose vertex is the center of a circle. The sum of the measures of the central angles is 360°.

Ángulo central (p. 451) Un ángulo central es un ángulo cuyo vértice es el centro de un círculo. La suma de las medidas de los ángulos centrales es 360°.

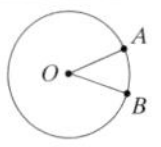

$\angle AOB$ is a central angle of circle O.

EXAMPLES

Chord (pp. 336, 340) A chord is a segment that has both endpoints on the circle.

Cuerda (pp. 336, 340) Una cuerda es un segmento que tiene ambos extremos sobre un círculo.

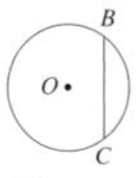

$\overline{CB}$ is a chord of circle O.

Circle (p. 336) A circle is the set of points in a plane that are all the same distance from a given point called the center.

Círculo (p. 336) Un círculo es el conjunto de puntos de un plano que están a la misma distancia de un punto dado llamado centro.

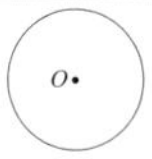

Circle graph (p. 450) A circle graph is a graph of data where the entire circle represents the whole. Each wedge, or sector, in the circle represents part of the whole.

Gráfica circular (p. 450) Una gráfica circular es una gráfica de datos donde el círculo completo representa el todo. Cada cuña o sector del círculo representa una parte del todo.

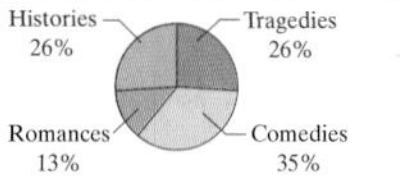

The circle graph represents the types of plays William Shakespeare wrote.

Circumference (p. 336) Circumference is the distance around a circle. You calculate the circumference of a circle by multiplying the diameter by π.

Circunferencia (p. 336) La circunferencia es la distancia alrededor de un círculo. La circunferencia de un círculo se calcula multiplicando el diámetro por π.

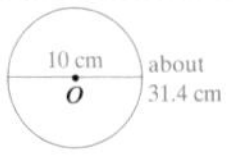

The circumference of a circle with a diameter of 10 cm is approximately 31.4 cm.

Closure Property (p. 109) A set of numbers is closed under an arithmetic operation if the answer of the operation is unique and in the same set as the original numbers.

Propiedad de Cerradura (p. 109) Un conjunto de números está cerrado bajo una operación metemática si la respuesta de la operación es única y está en el mismo conjunto de números originales.

Rational numbers are closed under addition because the sum of two rational numbers is a rational number.

Coefficient (p. 566) A coefficient is the numerical factor in any term of a polynomial.

Coeficiente (p. 566) Un coeficiente es un factor numérico en cualquier término de un polinómio.

In the expression $2x + 3y - 16$, the coefficient of x is 2 and the coefficient of y is 3.

English/Spanish Glossary

EXAMPLES

Combination (p. 496) A combination is a group of items in which the order of the items is not considered.

Combinación (p. 496) Una combinación es una agrupación de objetos en donde el orden de los objetos no tiene importancia.

You choose two vegetables from carrots, peas, and spinach. The possible combinations are: carrots and peas, carrots and spinach, and peas and spinach.

Commission A commission is a percent of sales.

Comisión Una comisión es un porcentaje de las ventas.

A salesperson receives a 6% commission on sales of $200. Her commission is $12.

Common difference (p. 513) Each term of an arithmetic sequence is found by *adding* a fixed number (called the common difference) to the previous term.

Diferencia común (p. 513) Cada término de una progresión aritmética se halla al *sumar* un número fijo (llamado diferencia común) al término anterior.

In the arithmetic sequence $-2, -4, -6, -8, \dots$, the common difference is -2.

Common ratio (p. 514) Each term of a geometric sequence is found by *multiplying* the previous term by a fixed number (called the common ratio).

Razón común (p. 514) Cada término de una progresión geométrica se halla al *multiplicar* el término anterior por un número fijo (llamado razón común).

In the geometric sequence 3, 18, 108, 648, . . . , the common ratio is 6.

Commutative Property of Addition (p. 26) The Commutative Property of Addition states that changing the order of the addends does not change the sum.

Propiedad Conmutativa de la Suma (p. 26) La Propiedad Conmutativa de la Suma establece que al cambiar el orden de los sumandos no se altera la suma.

$a + b = b + a$
$3 + 1 = 1 + 3$

Commutative Property of Multiplication (p. 26) The Commutative Property of Multiplication states that changing the order of the factors does not change the product.

Propiedad Conmutativa de la Multiplicación (p. 26) La Propiedad Conmutativa de la Multiplicación establece que al cambiar el orden de los factores no se altera el producto.

$a \cdot b = b \cdot a$
$6 \cdot 3 = 3 \cdot 6$

Compass (p. 341) A compass is a geometric tool used to draw circles or arcs.

Compás (p. 341) Un compás es una herramienta que se usa en geometría para dibujar círculos o arcos.

EXAMPLES

Compatible numbers (pp. 168, 214) Compatible numbers are numbers that are easy to compute mentally.

Números compatibles (pp. 168, 214) Los números compatibles son números con los que se puede calcular mentalmente con facilidad.

Estimate $151 \div 14.6$.
$151 \approx 150$, $14.6 \approx 15$
$150 \div 15 = 10$
$151 \div 14.6 \approx 10$

Complement (p. 479) The complement of an event is the collection of outcomes not contained in the event.

Complemento (p. 479) El complemento de un suceso es la colección de resultados que el suceso no incluye.

The event *no rain* is the complement of the event *rain*.

Complementary (p. 304) Two angles are complementary if the sum of their measures is 90°.

Complementario (p. 304) Dos ángulos son complementarios si la suma de sus medidas es 90°.

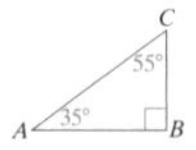

$\angle BCA$ and $\angle CAB$ are complementary angles.

Composite number (p. 52) A composite number is a whole number greater than 1 with more than two factors.

Número compuesto (p. 52) Un número compuesto es un número entero mayor que 1, que tiene más de dos factores.

24 is a composite number that has 1, 2, 3, 4, 6, 8, 12, and 24 as factors.

Compound event (p. 486) A compound event is an event that consists of two or more events. The probability of a compound event can be found by multiplying the probability of one event by the probability of a second event.

Suceso compuesto (p. 486) Un suceso compuesto es un suceso que está formado por dos o más sucesos. La probabilidad de un suceso compuesto se puede hallar al multiplicar la probabilidad de un suceso por la probabilidad de un segundo suceso.

If $P(A) = \frac{1}{3}$ and $P(B) = \frac{1}{2}$, then $P(A \text{ and } B) = \frac{1}{3} \cdot \frac{1}{2} = \frac{1}{6}$, when A and B are independent events.

Compound interest Compound interest is interest paid on the original principal and on any interest that has been left in the account. You can use the formula $B = p(1 + r)^n$ where B is the balance in the account, p is the principal, r is the annual interest rate, and n is the number of years that the account earns interest.

Interés compuesto El interés compuesto es el interés que se paga sobre el principal original y sobre cualquier interés que ha quedado en la cuenta. Se puede usar la fórmula $S = p(1 + i)^t$ donde S es el saldo en la cuenta, p es el principal, i es la tasa de interés anual y t es el tiempo en años en que la cuenta gana interés.

You deposit $500 in an account earning 5% annual interest.
The balance after six years is $500(1 + 0.05)^6$, or $670.05.

English/Spanish Glossary

EXAMPLES

Cone (p. 354) A cone has exactly one circular base and one vertex.

Cono (p. 354) Un cono tiene exactamente una base circular y un vértice.

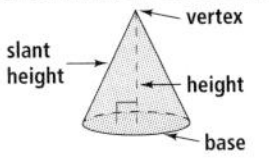

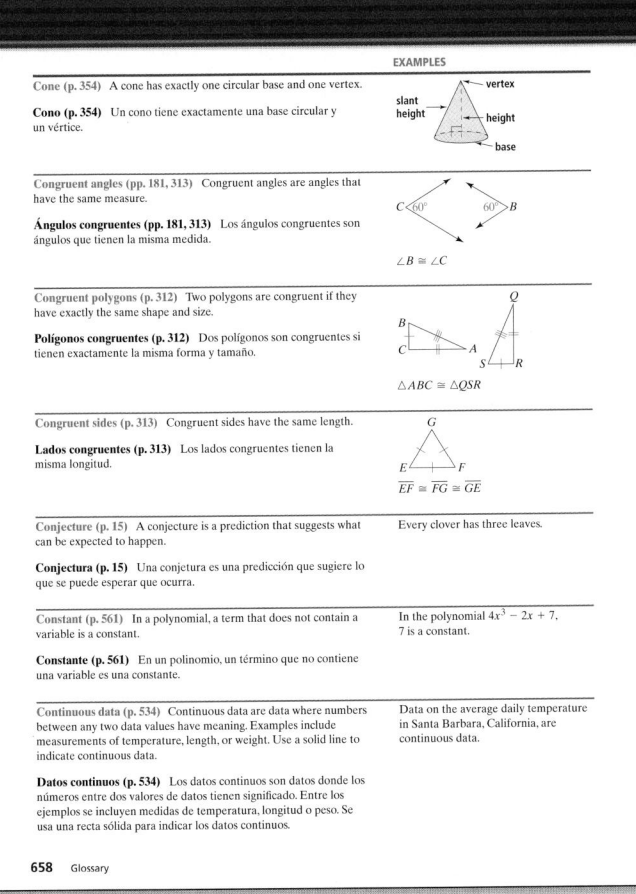

Congruent angles (pp. 181, 313) Congruent angles are angles that have the same measure.

Ángulos congruentes (pp. 181, 313) Los ángulos congruentes son ángulos que tienen la misma medida.

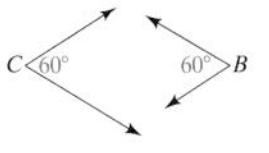

$\angle B \cong \angle C$

Congruent polygons (p. 312) Two polygons are congruent if they have exactly the same shape and size.

Polígonos congruentes (p. 312) Dos polígonos son congruentes si tienen exactamente la misma forma y tamaño.

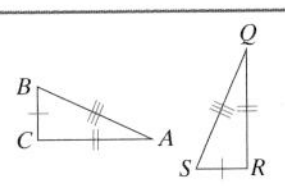

$\triangle ABC \cong \triangle QSR$

Congruent sides (p. 313) Congruent sides have the same length.

Lados congruentes (p. 313) Los lados congruentes tienen la misma longitud.

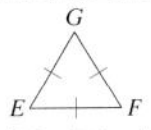

$\overline{EF} \cong \overline{FG} \cong \overline{GE}$

Conjecture (p. 15) A conjecture is a prediction that suggests what can be expected to happen.

Conjectura (p. 15) Una conjetura es una predicción que sugiere lo que se puede esperar que ocurra.

Every clover has three leaves.

Constant (p. 561) In a polynomial, a term that does not contain a variable is a constant.

Constante (p. 561) En un polinomio, un término que no contiene una variable es una constante.

In the polynomial $4x^3 - 2x + 7$, 7 is a constant.

Continuous data (p. 534) Continuous data are data where numbers between any two data values have meaning. Examples include measurements of temperature, length, or weight. Use a solid line to indicate continuous data.

Datos continuos (p. 534) Los datos continuos son datos donde los números entre dos valores de datos tienen significado. Entre los ejemplos se incluyen medidas de temperatura, longitud o peso. Se usa una recta sólida para indicar los datos continuos.

Data on the average daily temperature in Santa Barbara, California, are continuous data.

EXAMPLES

Conversion factor (p. 167) Rates equal to 1.

Factor de conversión (p. 167) Las razones dan igual a 1.

$\frac{3 \text{ ft}}{1 \text{ yd}}$ and $\frac{1 \text{ yd}}{3 \text{ ft}}$ are conversion factors.

Coordinate plane (p. 124) A coordinate plane is formed by the intersection of a horizontal number line called the *x*-axis and a vertical number line called the *y*-axis.

Plano de coordenadas (p. 124) Un plano de coordenadas está formado por la intersección de una recta numérica horizontal llamada eje de *x* y por una recta numérica vertical llamada eje de *y*.

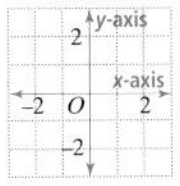

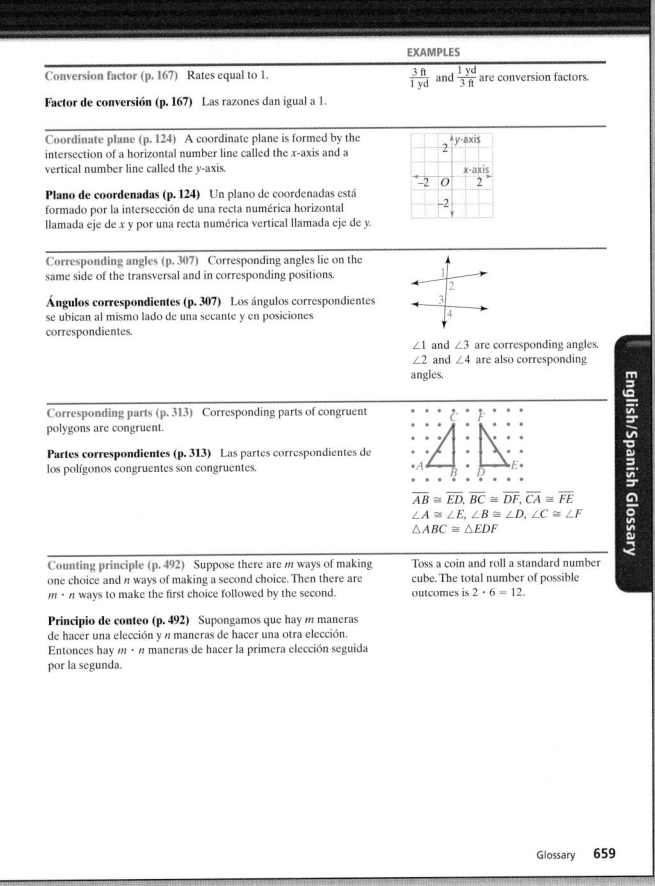

Corresponding angles (p. 307) Corresponding angles lie on the same side of the transversal and in corresponding positions.

Ángulos correspondientes (p. 307) Los ángulos correspondientes se ubican al mismo lado de una secante y en posiciones correspondientes.

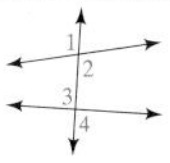

$\angle 1$ and $\angle 3$ are corresponding angles. $\angle 2$ and $\angle 4$ are also corresponding angles.

Corresponding parts (p. 313) Corresponding parts of congruent polygons are congruent.

Partes correspondientes (p. 313) Las partes correspondientes de los polígonos congruentes son congruentes.

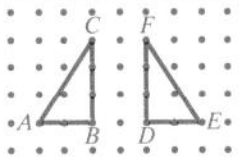

$\overline{AB} \cong \overline{ED}$, $\overline{BC} \cong \overline{DF}$, $\overline{CA} \cong \overline{FE}$
$\angle A \cong \angle E$, $\angle B \cong \angle D$, $\angle C \cong \angle F$
$\triangle ABC \cong \triangle EDF$

Counting principle (p. 492) Suppose there are *m* ways of making one choice and *n* ways of making a second choice. Then there are $m \cdot n$ ways to make the first choice followed by the second.

Principio de conteo (p. 492) Supongamos que hay *m* maneras de hacer una elección y *n* maneras de hacer una otra elección. Entonces hay $m \cdot n$ maneras de hacer la primera elección seguida por la segunda.

Toss a coin and roll a standard number cube. The total number of possible outcomes is $2 \cdot 6 = 12$.

English/Spanish Glossary

English/Spanish Glossary

EXAMPLES

Cross products (p. 175) For two ratios, the cross products are found by multiplying the denominator of one ratio by the numerator of the other ratio.

Productos cruzados (p. 175) En dos razones, los productos cruzados se hallan al multiplicar el denominador de una razón por el numerador de la otra razón.

In the proportion $\frac{2}{5} = \frac{10}{25}$, the cross products are $2 \cdot 25$ and $5 \cdot 10$.

Cube (p. 358) A cube is a rectangular prism whose faces are all squares.

Cubo (p. 358) Un cubo es un prisma rectangular cuyas caras son todas cuandras.

Cylinder (p. 354) A cylinder has two bases that are parallel, congruent circles.

Cilindro (p. 354) Un cilindro tiene dos bases congruentes paralelas que son círculos.

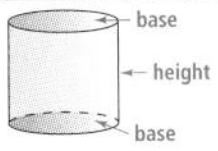

D

Deductive reasoning (p. 308) A process of reasoning logically from given facts to a conclusion is called deductive reasoning.

Razonamiento deductivo (p. 308) El proceso de razonar lógicamente para llegar a una conclusión a partir de datos dados se llama razonamiento deductivo.

Dependent events (p. 487) When the outcome of one event *does* affect the outcome of a second event, the events are dependent events.

Sucesos dependientes (p. 487) Cuando el resultado de un suceso afecta el resultado de un segundo suceso, los sucesos son dependientes.

Suppose you remove two marbles, one after the other, from a bag. If you do not replace the first marble before removing the second marble, the events are dependent.

EXAMPLES

Diameter (p. 336) A diameter is a segment that passes through the center of a circle and has both endpoints on the circle.

Diámetro (p. 336) Un diámetro es un segmento que pasa por el centro de un círculo y que tiene ambos extremos sobre el círculo.

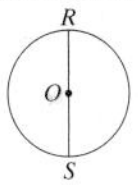

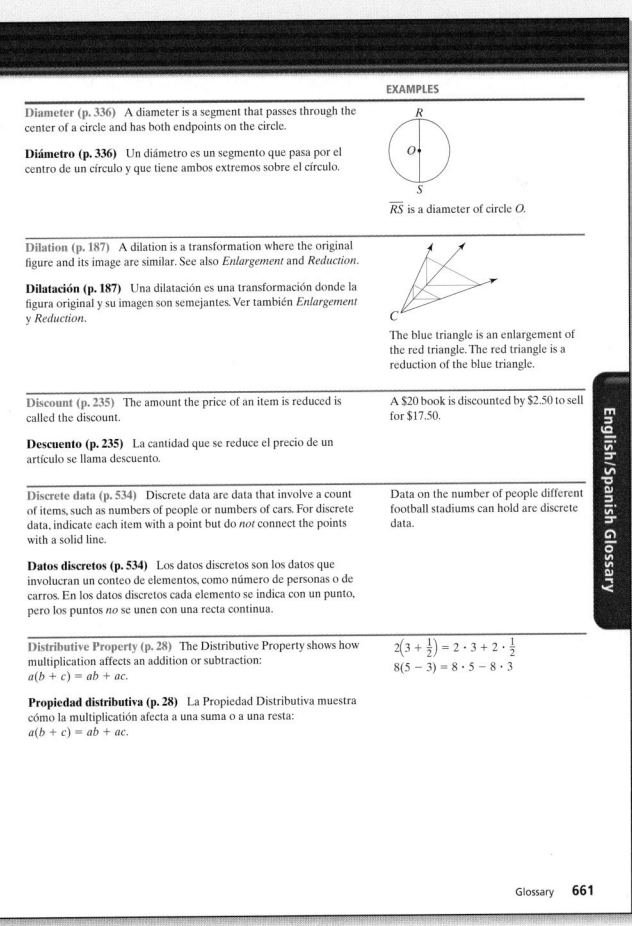

$\overline{RS}$ is a diameter of circle *O*.

Dilation (p. 187) A dilation is a transformation where the original figure and its image are similar. See also *Enlargement* and *Reduction*.

Dilatación (p. 187) Una dilatación es una transformación donde la figura original y su imagen son semejantes. Ver también *Enlargement* y *Reduction*.

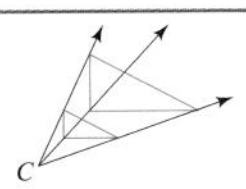

The blue triangle is an enlargement of the red triangle. The red triangle is a reduction of the blue triangle.

Discount (p. 235) The amount the price of an item is reduced is called the discount.

Descuento (p. 235) La cantidad que se reduce el precio de un artículo se llama descuento.

A $20 book is discounted by $2.50 to sell for $17.50.

Discrete data (p. 534) Discrete data are data that involve a count of items, such as numbers of people or numbers of cars. For discrete data, indicate each item with a point but do *not* connect the points with a solid line.

Datos discretos (p. 534) Los datos discretos son los datos que involucran un conteo de elementos, como número de personas o de carros. En los datos discretos cada elemento se indica con un punto, pero los puntos *no* se unen con una recta continua.

Data on the number of people different football stadiums can hold are discrete data.

Distributive Property (p. 28) The Distributive Property shows how multiplication affects an addition or subtraction: $a(b + c) = ab + ac$.

Propiedad distributiva (p. 28) La Propiedad Distributiva muestra cómo la multiplicación afecta a una suma o a una resta: $a(b + c) = ab + ac$.

$2\left(3 + \frac{1}{2}\right) = 2 \cdot 3 + 2 \cdot \frac{1}{2}$
$8(5 - 3) = 8 \cdot 5 - 8 \cdot 3$

English/Spanish Glossary

EXAMPLES

Divisible (p. 52) A number is divisible by a second whole number if the first number can be divided by the second number with a remainder of 0.

Divisible (p. 52) Un número es divisible por un segundo número entero si el primer número se puede dividir por el segundo número y el residuo es 0.

16 is divisible by 1, 2, 4, 8, and 16.

Division Property of Equality (p. 39) The Division Property of Equality states that if you divide each side of an equation by the same nonzero number, the sides remain equal.

Propiedad de División de la Igualdad (p. 39) La Propiedad de División de la Igualdad establece que si cada lado de una ecuación se divide por el mismo número distinto de cero, los dos lados se mantienen iguales.

If $a = b$ and $c \neq 0$, then $\frac{a}{c} = \frac{b}{c}$.
Since $3 \cdot 2 = 6$, $\frac{3 \cdot 2}{2} = \frac{6}{2}$.

Division Property of Inequality (p. 288) The Division Property of Inequality states that if you divide an inequality by a positive number, the direction of the inequality is unchanged. If you divide an inequality by a negative number, *reverse* the direction of the inequality sign.

Propiedad de División de la Desigualdad (p. 288) La Propiedad de División de la Desigualdad establece que si se divide una desigualdad por un número positivo, la dirección de la desigualdad no cambia. Si se divide una desigualdad por un número negativo, se *invierte* la dirección del signo de desigualdad.

If $a > b$ and $c > 0$, then $\frac{a}{c} > \frac{b}{c}$.
Since $2 > 1$ and $3 > 0$, $\frac{2}{3} > \frac{1}{3}$.
If $a < b$ and $c > 0$, then $\frac{a}{c} < \frac{b}{c}$.
Since $2 < 4$ and $3 > 0$, $\frac{2}{3} < \frac{4}{3}$.
If $a > b$ and $c < 0$, then $\frac{a}{c} < \frac{b}{c}$.
Since $2 > 1$ and $-4 < 0$, $\frac{2}{-4} < \frac{1}{-4}$.
If $a < b$ and $c < 0$, then $\frac{a}{c} > \frac{b}{c}$.
Since $2 < 4$ and $-4 < 0$, $\frac{2}{-4} > \frac{4}{-4}$.

E

Edge (p. 354) An edge is a segment formed by the intersection of two faces of a three-dimensional figure.

Arista (p. 354) Una arista es un segmento formado por la intersección de dos caras de una figura tridimensional.

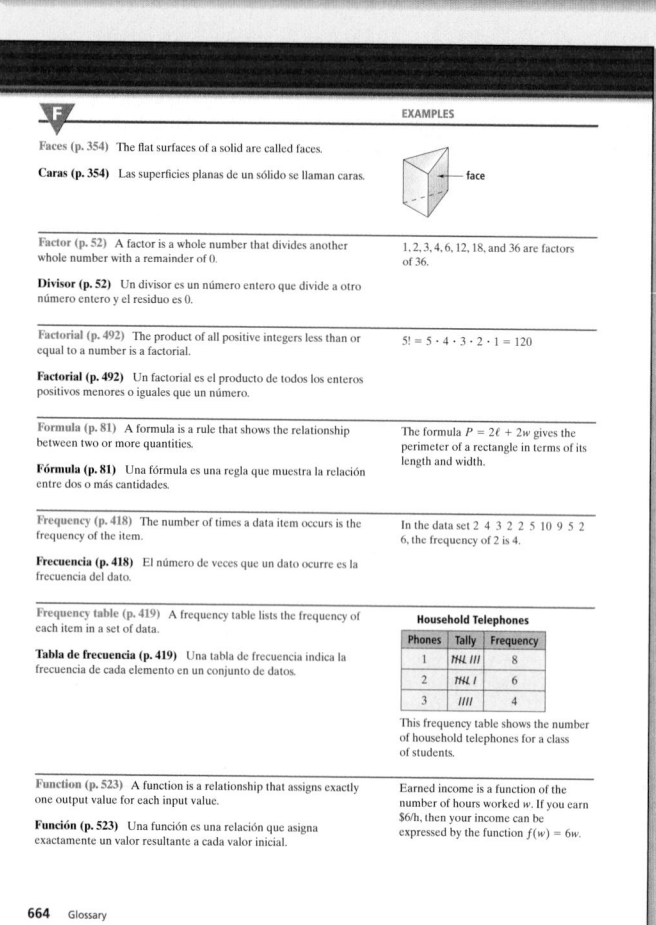

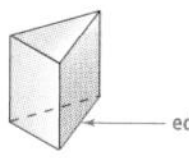

Enlargement (p. 188) A dilation with a scale factor greater than 1 is an enlargement.

Aumento (p. 188) Una dilatación con un factor de escala mayor que 1 es un aumento.

See *Dilation*.

Equation (p. 33) An equation is a mathematical sentence with an equal sign.

Ecuación (p. 33) Una ecuación es una oración matemática con un signo igual.

$2(3 + 5) = 16$ and $x + 10 = 8$ are examples of equations.

EXAMPLES

Equilateral triangle (p. 318) An equilateral triangle is a triangle with three congruent sides.

Triángulo equilátero (p. 318) Un triángulo equilátero es un triángulo que tiene tres lados congruentes.

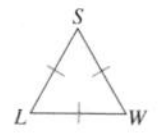

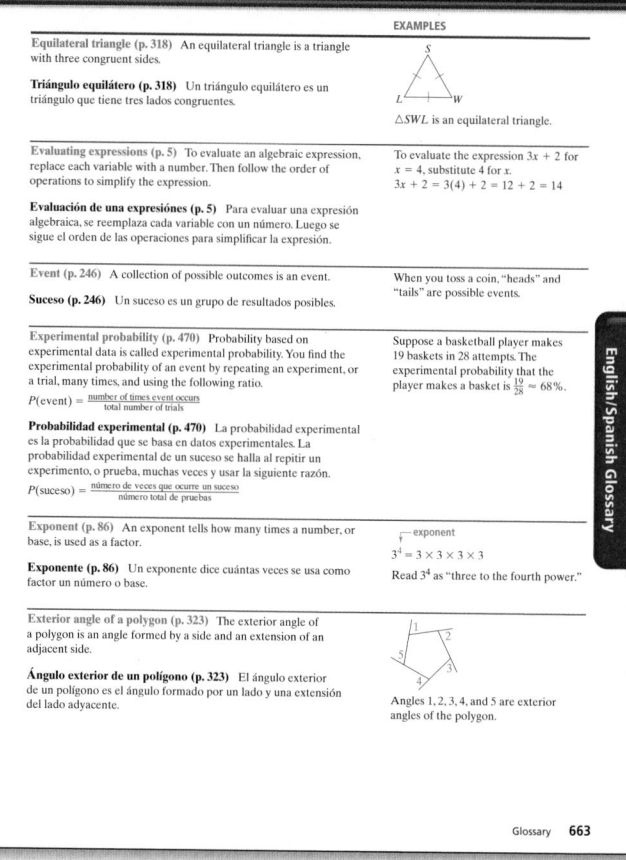

$\triangle SWL$ is an equilateral triangle.

Evaluating expressions (p. 5) To evaluate an algebraic expression, replace each variable with a number. Then follow the order of operations to simplify the expression.

Evaluación de una expresiónes (p. 5) Para evaluar una expresión algebraica, se reemplaza cada variable con un número. Luego se sigue el orden de las operaciones para simplificar la expresión.

To evaluate the expression $3x + 2$ for $x = 4$, substitute 4 for x.
$3x + 2 = 3(4) + 2 = 12 + 2 = 14$

Event (p. 246) A collection of possible outcomes is an event.

Suceso (p. 246) Un suceso es un grupo de resultados posibles.

When you toss a coin, "heads" and "tails" are possible events.

Experimental probability (p. 470) Probability based on experimental data is called experimental probability. You find the experimental probability of an event by repeating an experiment, or a trial, many times, and using the following ratio.

$P(\text{event}) = \frac{\text{number of times event occurs}}{\text{total number of trials}}$

Probabilidad experimental (p. 470) La probabilidad experimental es la probabilidad que se basa en datos experimentales. La probabilidad experimental de un suceso se halla al repitir un experimento, o prueba, muchas veces y usar la siguiente razón.

$P(\text{suceso}) = \frac{\text{número de veces que ocurre un suceso}}{\text{número total de pruebas}}$

Suppose a basketball player makes 19 baskets in 28 attempts. The experimental probability that the player makes a basket is $\frac{19}{28} \approx 68\%$.

Exponent (p. 86) An exponent tells how many times a number, or base, is used as a factor.

Exponente (p. 86) Un exponente dice cuántas veces se usa como factor un número o base.

exponent
$3^4 = 3 \times 3 \times 3 \times 3$
Read 3^4 as "three to the fourth power."

Exterior angle of a polygon (p. 323) The exterior angle of a polygon is an angle formed by a side and an extension of an adjacent side.

Ángulo exterior de un polígono (p. 323) El ángulo exterior de un polígono es el ángulo formado por un lado y una extensión del lado adyacente.

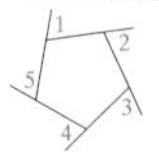

Angles 1, 2, 3, 4, and 5 are exterior angles of the polygon.

English/Spanish Glossary

F

EXAMPLES

Faces (p. 354) The flat surfaces of a solid are called faces.

Caras (p. 354) Las superficies planas de un sólido se llaman caras.

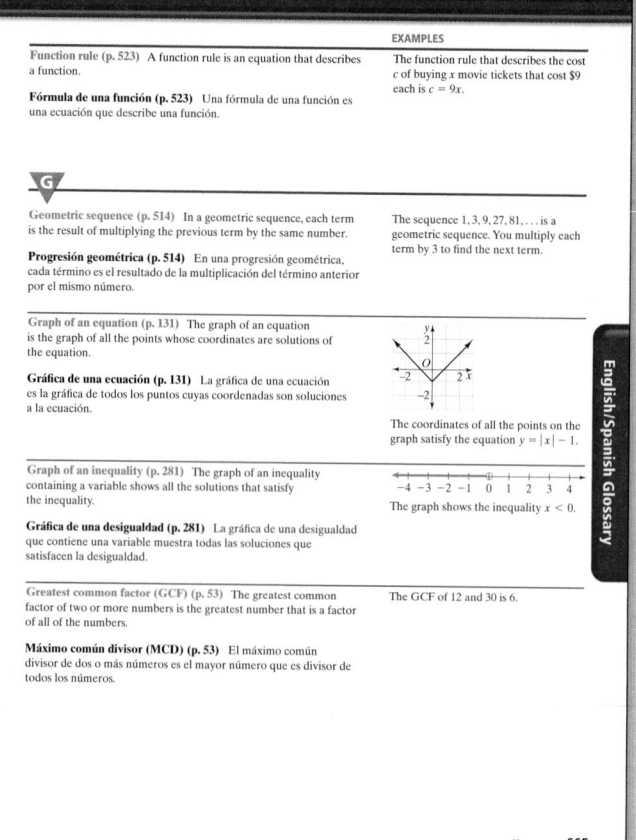

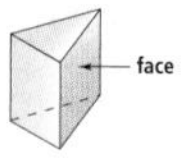

Factor (p. 52) A factor is a whole number that divides another whole number with a remainder of 0.

Divisor (p. 52) Un divisor es un número entero que divide a otro número entero y el residuo es 0.

1, 2, 3, 4, 6, 12, 18, and 36 are factors of 36.

Factorial (p. 492) The product of all positive integers less than or equal to a number is a factorial.

Factorial (p. 492) Un factorial es el producto de todos los enteros positivos menores o iguales que un número.

$5! = 5 \cdot 4 \cdot 3 \cdot 2 \cdot 1 = 120$

Formula (p. 81) A formula is a rule that shows the relationship between two or more quantities.

Fórmula (p. 81) Una fórmula es una regla que muestra la relación entre dos o más cantidades.

The formula $P = 2\ell + 2w$ gives the perimeter of a rectangle in terms of its length and width.

Frequency (p. 418) The number of times a data item occurs is the frequency of the item.

Frecuencia (p. 418) El número de veces que un dato ocurre es la frecuencia del dato.

In the data set 2 4 3 2 2 5 10 9 5 2 6, the frequency of 2 is 4.

Frequency table (p. 419) A frequency table lists the frequency of each item in a set of data.

Tabla de frecuencia (p. 419) Una tabla de frecuencia indica la frecuencia de cada elemento en un conjunto de datos.

Household Telephones

Phones	Tally	Frequency
1	卌 III	8
2	卌 I	6
3	IIII	4

This frequency table shows the number of household telephones for a class of students.

Function (p. 523) A function is a relationship that assigns exactly one output value for each input value.

Función (p. 523) Una función es una relación que asigna exactamente un valor resultante a cada valor inicial.

Earned income is a function of the number of hours worked w. If you earn \$6/h, then your income can be expressed by the function $f(w) = 6w$.

EXAMPLES

Function rule (p. 523) A function rule is an equation that describes a function.

Fórmula de una función (p. 523) Una fórmula de una función es una ecuación que describe una función.

The function rule that describes the cost c of buying x movie tickets that cost \$9 each is $c = 9x$.

G

Geometric sequence (p. 514) In a geometric sequence, each term is the result of multiplying the previous term by the same number.

Progresión geométrica (p. 514) En una progresión geométrica, cada término es el resultado de la multiplicación del término anterior por el mismo número.

The sequence 1, 3, 9, 27, 81, . . . is a geometric sequence. You multiply each term by 3 to find the next term.

Graph of an equation (p. 131) The graph of an equation is the graph of all the points whose coordinates are solutions of the equation.

Gráfica de una ecuación (p. 131) La gráfica de una ecuación es la gráfica de todos los puntos cuyas coordenadas son soluciones a la ecuación.

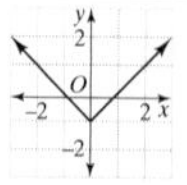

The coordinates of all the points on the graph satisfy the equation $y = |x| - 1$.

Graph of an inequality (p. 281) The graph of an inequality containing a variable shows all the solutions that satisfy the inequality.

Gráfica de una desigualdad (p. 281) La gráfica de una desigualdad que contiene una variable muestra todas las soluciones que satisfacen la desigualdad.

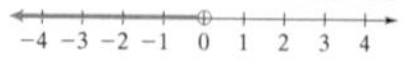

The graph shows the inequality $x < 0$.

Greatest common factor (GCF) (p. 53) The greatest common factor of two or more numbers is the greatest number that is a factor of all of the numbers.

Máximo común divisor (MCD) (p. 53) El máximo común divisor de dos o más números es el mayor número que es divisor de todos los números.

The GCF of 12 and 30 is 6.

English/Spanish Glossary

H

EXAMPLES

Histogram (p. 419) A histogram is a bar graph with no spaces between the bars. The height of each bar shows the frequency of data within that interval.

Histograma (p. 419) Un histograma es una gráfica de barras sin espacio entre las barras. La altura de cada barra muestra la frecuencia de los datos dentro del intervalo.

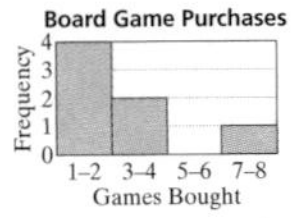

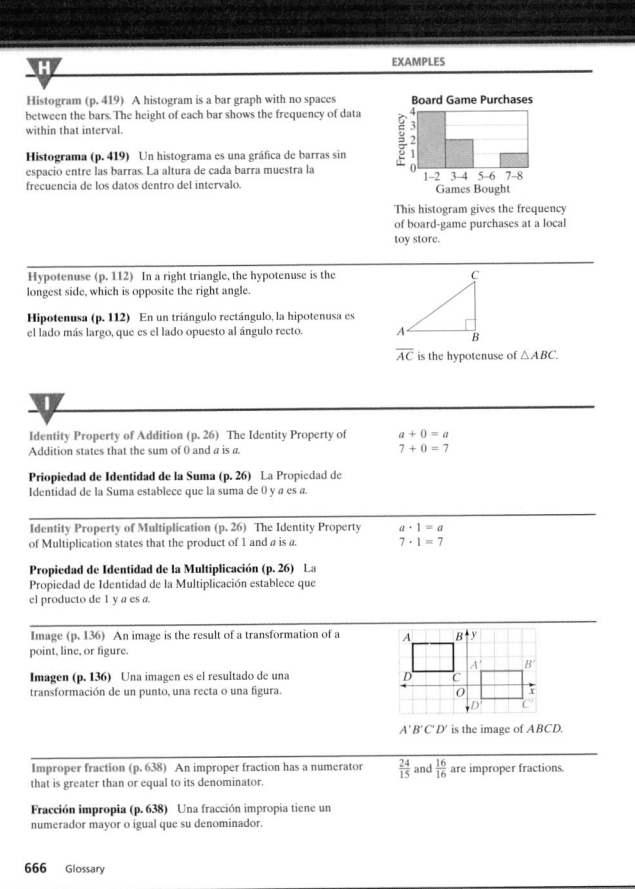

This histogram gives the frequency of board-game purchases at a local toy store.

Hypotenuse (p. 112) In a right triangle, the hypotenuse is the longest side, which is opposite the right angle.

Hipotenusa (p. 112) En un triángulo rectángulo, la hipotenusa es el lado más largo, que es el lado opuesto al ángulo recto.

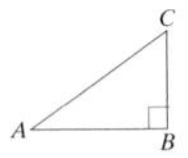

$\overline{AC}$ is the hypotenuse of $\triangle ABC$.

I

Identity Property of Addition (p. 26) The Identity Property of Addition states that the sum of 0 and a is a.

Propiedad de Identidad de la Suma (p. 26) La Propiedad de Identidad de la Suma establece que la suma de 0 y a es a.

$a + 0 = a$
$7 + 0 = 7$

Identity Property of Multiplication (p. 26) The Identity Property of Multiplication states that the product of 1 and a is a.

Propiedad de Identidad de la Multiplicación (p. 26) La Propiedad de Identidad de la Multiplicación establece que el producto de 1 y a es a.

$a \cdot 1 = a$
$7 \cdot 1 = 7$

Image (p. 136) An image is the result of a transformation of a point, line, or figure.

Imagen (p. 136) Una imagen es el resultado de una transformación de un punto, una recta o una figura.

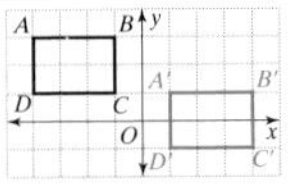

$A'B'C'D'$ is the image of $ABCD$.

Improper fraction (p. 638) An improper fraction has a numerator that is greater than or equal to its denominator.

Fracción impropia (p. 638) Una fracción impropia tiene un numerador mayor o igual que su denominador.

$\frac{24}{15}$ and $\frac{16}{16}$ are improper fractions.

EXAMPLES

Independent events (p. 486) Two events are independent events if the occurrence of one event does not affect the probability of the occurrence of the other.

Sucesos independientes (p. 486) Dos sucesos son independientes si el acontecimiento de uno no afecta la probabilidad de que el otro suceso ocurra.

Suppose you remove two marbles, one after the other, from a bag. If you replace the first marble before removing the second marble, the events are independent.

Indirect measurement (p. 197) Indirect measurement uses proportions and similar triangles to measure distances that would be difficult to measure directly.

Medición indirecta (p. 197) La medición indirecta usa proporciones y triángulos semejantes para medir las distancias que serían difíciles de medir directamente.

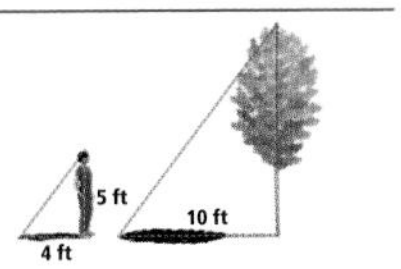

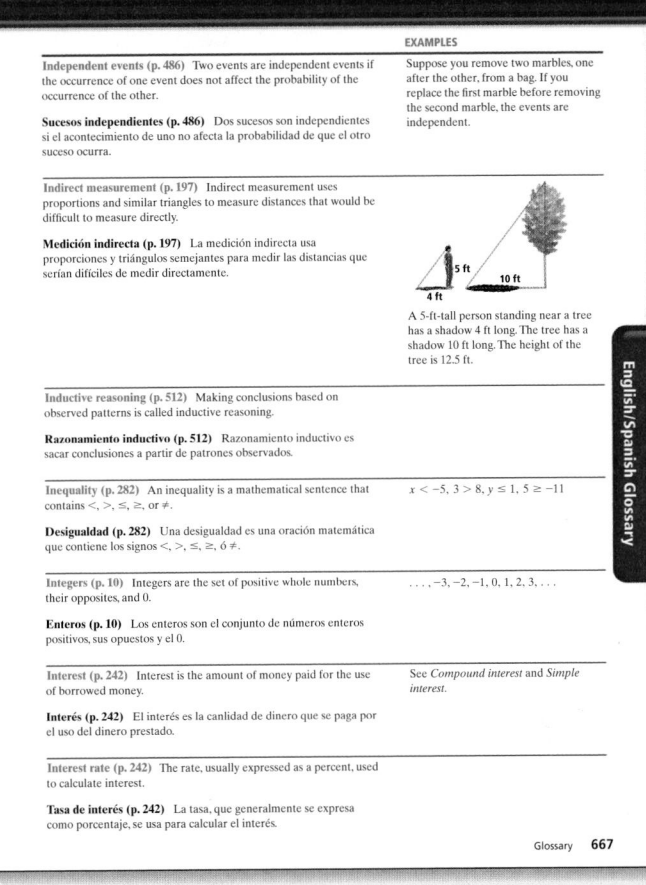

A 5-ft-tall person standing near a tree has a shadow 4 ft long. The tree has a shadow 10 ft long. The height of the tree is 12.5 ft.

Inductive reasoning (p. 512) Making conclusions based on observed patterns is called inductive reasoning.

Razonamiento inductivo (p. 512) Razonamiento inductivo es sacar conclusiones a partir de patrones observados.

Inequality (p. 282) An inequality is a mathematical sentence that contains $<$, $>$, $\le$, $\ge$, or $\ne$.

Desigualdad (p. 282) Una desigualdad es una oración matemática que contiene los signos $<$, $>$, $\le$, $\ge$, ó $\ne$.

$x < -5$, $3 > 8$, $y \le 1$, $5 \ge -11$

Integers (p. 10) Integers are the set of positive whole numbers, their opposites, and 0.

Enteros (p. 10) Los enteros son el conjunto de números enteros positivos, sus opuestos y el 0.

$\ldots, -3, -2, -1, 0, 1, 2, 3, \ldots$

Interest (p. 242) Interest is the amount of money paid for the use of borrowed money.

Interés (p. 242) El interés es la cantidad de dinero que se paga por el uso del dinero prestado.

See *Compound interest* and *Simple interest.*

Interest rate (p. 242) The rate, usually expressed as a percent, used to calculate interest.

Tasa de interés (p. 242) La tasa, que generalmente se expresa como porcentaje, se usa para calcular el interés.

EXAMPLES

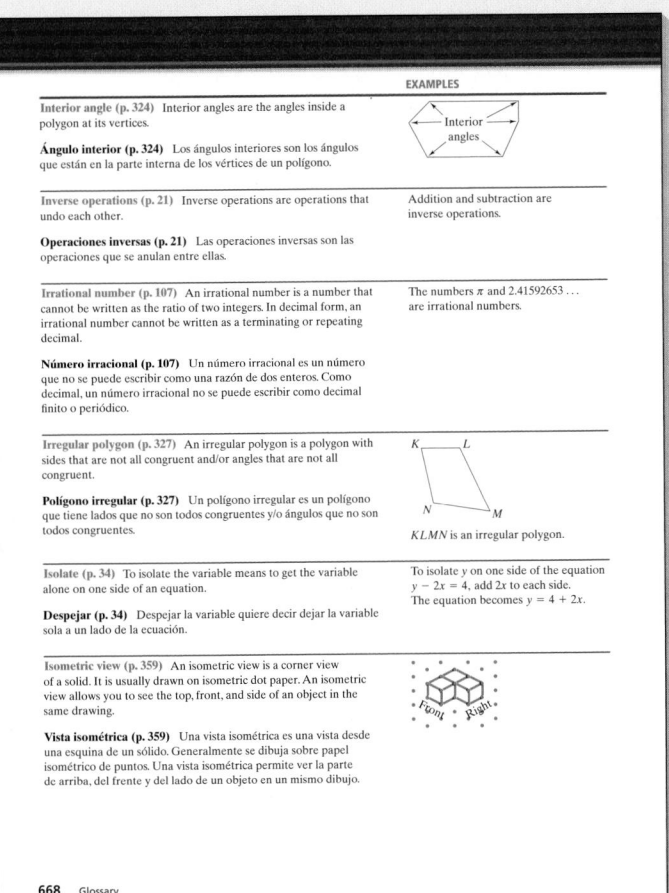

Interior angle (p. 324) Interior angles are the angles inside a polygon at its vertices.

Ángulo interior (p. 324) Los ángulos interiores son los ángulos que están en la parte interna de los vértices de un polígono.

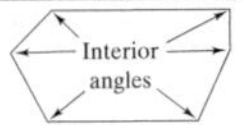

Inverse operations (p. 21) Inverse operations are operations that undo each other.

Operaciones inversas (p. 21) Las operaciones inversas son las operaciones que se anulan entre ellas.

Addition and subtraction are inverse operations.

Irrational number (p. 107) An irrational number is a number that cannot be written as the ratio of two integers. In decimal form, an irrational number cannot be written as a terminating or repeating decimal.

Número irracional (p. 107) Un número irracional es un número que no se puede escribir como una razón de dos enteros. Como decimal, un número irracional no se puede escribir como decimal finito o periódico.

The numbers π and 2.41592653 . . . are irrational numbers.

Irregular polygon (p. 327) An irregular polygon is a polygon with sides that are not all congruent and/or angles that are not all congruent.

Polígono irregular (p. 327) Un polígono irregular es un polígono que tiene lados que no son todos congruentes y/o ángulos que no son todos congruentes.

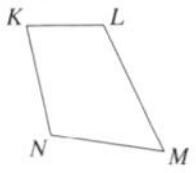

$KLMN$ is an irregular polygon.

Isolate (p. 34) To isolate the variable means to get the variable alone on one side of an equation.

Despejar (p. 34) Despejar la variable quiere decir dejar la variable sola a un lado de la ecuación.

To isolate y on one side of the equation $y - 2x = 4$, add $2x$ to each side. The equation becomes $y = 4 + 2x$.

Isometric view (p. 359) An isometric view is a corner view of a solid. It is usually drawn on isometric dot paper. An isometric view allows you to see the top, front, and side of an object in the same drawing.

Vista isométrica (p. 359) Una vista isométrica es una vista desde una esquina de un sólido. Generalmente se dibuja sobre papel isométrico de puntos. Una vista isométrica permite ver la parte de arriba, del frente y del lado de un objeto en un mismo dibujo.

EXAMPLES

Isosceles triangle (p. 318) An isosceles triangle is a triangle with at least two congruent sides.

Triángulo isósceles (p. 318) Un triángulo isósceles es un triángulo que tiene al menos dos lados congruentes.

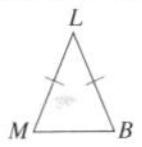

$\overline{LM} \cong \overline{LB}$

L

Lateral area (p. 369) Lateral area is the sum of the areas of the lateral surfaces of a solid.

Área lateral (p. 369) La suma de las áreas de las superficies laterales de un sólido es el área lateral de la figura.

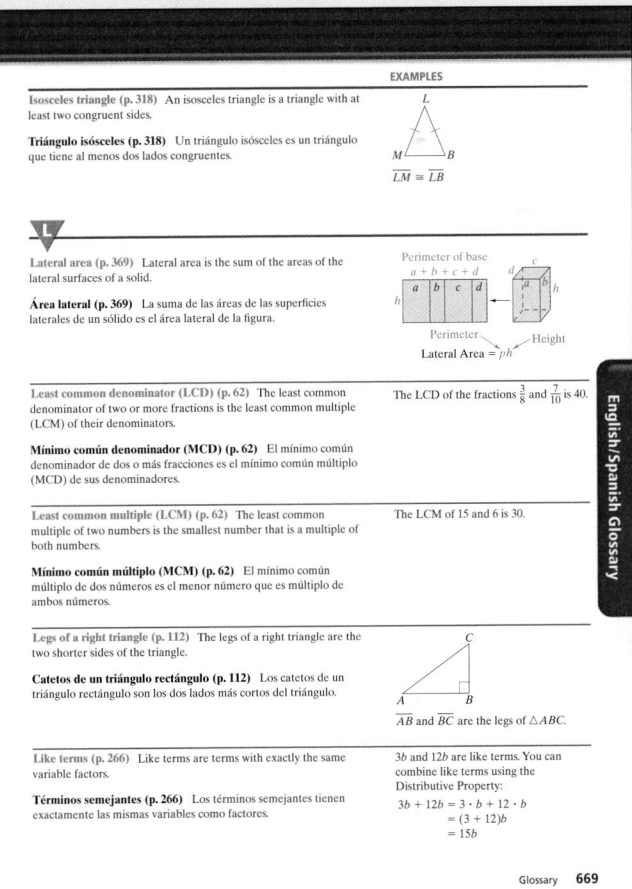

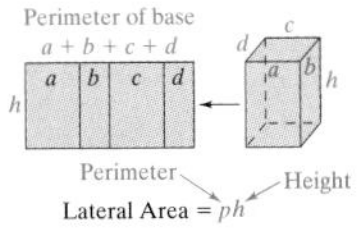

Least common denominator (LCD) (p. 62) The least common denominator of two or more fractions is the least common multiple (LCM) of their denominators.

Mínimo común denominador (MCD) (p. 62) El mínimo común denominador de dos o más fracciones es el mínimo común múltiplo (MCD) de sus denominadores.

The LCD of the fractions $\frac{3}{8}$ and $\frac{7}{10}$ is 40.

Least common multiple (LCM) (p. 62) The least common multiple of two numbers is the smallest number that is a multiple of both numbers.

Mínimo común múltiplo (MCM) (p. 62) El mínimo común múltiplo de dos números es el menor número que es múltiplo de ambos números.

The LCM of 15 and 6 is 30.

Legs of a right triangle (p. 112) The legs of a right triangle are the two shorter sides of the triangle.

Catetos de un triángulo rectángulo (p. 112) Los catetos de un triángulo rectángulo son los dos lados más cortos del triángulo.

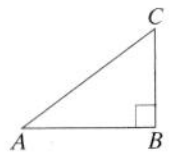

$\overline{AB}$ and $\overline{BC}$ are the legs of $\triangle ABC$.

Like terms (p. 266) Like terms are terms with exactly the same variable factors.

Términos semejantes (p. 266) Los términos semejantes tienen exactamente las mismas variables como factores.

$3b$ and $12b$ are like terms. You can combine like terms using the Distributive Property:

$$3b + 12b = 3 \cdot b + 12 \cdot b = (3 + 12)b = 15b$$

EXAMPLES

Line (p. 131) A line is a series of points that extends in two opposite directions without end.

Recta (p. 131) Una recta es una serie de puntos que se extiende indefinidamente en dos direcciones opuestas.

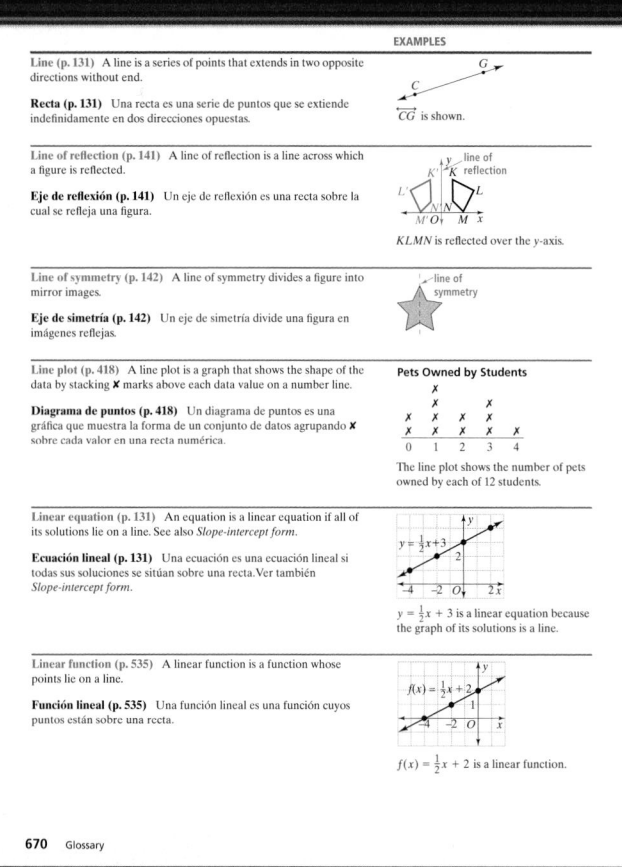

$\overleftrightarrow{CG}$ is shown.

Line of reflection (p. 141) A line of reflection is a line across which a figure is reflected.

Eje de reflexión (p. 141) Un eje de reflexión es una recta sobre la cual se refleja una figura.

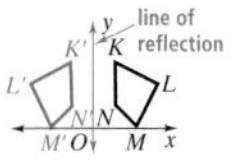

KLMN is reflected over the *y*-axis.

Line of symmetry (p. 142) A line of symmetry divides a figure into mirror images.

Eje de simetría (p. 142) Un eje de simetría divide una figura en imágenes reflejas.

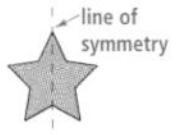

Line plot (p. 418) A line plot is a graph that shows the shape of the data by stacking ✗ marks above each data value on a number line.

Diagrama de puntos (p. 418) Un diagrama de puntos es una gráfica que muestra la forma de un conjunto de datos agrupando ✗ sobre cada valor en una recta numérica.

Pets Owned by Students

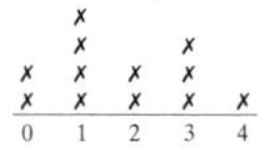

The line plot shows the number of pets owned by each of 12 students.

Linear equation (p. 131) An equation is a linear equation if all of its solutions lie on a line. See also *Slope-intercept form*.

Ecuación lineal (p. 131) Una ecuación es una ecuación lineal si todas sus soluciones se sitúan sobre una recta. Ver también *Slope-intercept form*.

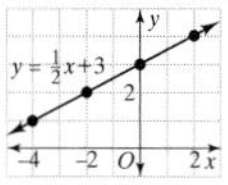

$y = \frac{1}{2}x + 3$ is a linear equation because the graph of its solutions is a line.

Linear function (p. 535) A linear function is a function whose points lie on a line.

Función lineal (p. 535) Una función lineal es una función cuyos puntos están sobre una recta.

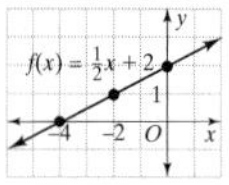

$f(x) = \frac{1}{2}x + 2$ is a linear function.

M

EXAMPLES

Markup (p. 234) The markup is the difference between the selling price and the original cost of an item.

Sobrecosto (p. 234) El sobrecosto es la diferencia entre el precio de venta y el costo original de un objeto.

A store buys a shirt for \$15 and sells it for \$25. The markup is \$25 − \$15 = \$10.

Mean (p. 412) The mean of a set of data values is the sum of the data divided by the number of data items.

Media (p. 412) La media de un conjunto de valores de datos es la suma de los datos dividida por el número de datos.

The mean temperature (°F) for the set of temperatures 44, 52, 48, 55, 61, and 67 is $\frac{44 + 52 + 48 + 55 + 61 + 67}{6} = 54.5$°F.

Measure of central tendency (p. 412) A measure of central tendency is a single, central value that summarizes a set of data.

Medida de tendencia central (p. 412) Una medida de tendencia central es un valor único y central que resume un conjunto de datos.

See *Mean*, *Median*, and *Mode*.

Median (p. 412) The median of a data set is the middle value when the data are arranged in numerical order. When there is an even number of data values, the median is the mean of the two middle values.

Mediana (p. 412) La mediana de un conjunto de datos es el valor del medio cuando los datos están organizados en orden numérico. Cuando hay un número par de valores de datos, la mediana es la media de los dos valores del medio.

Temperatures (°F) for one week arranged in order are 44, 48, 52, 55, and 58. The median temperature is 52°F because it is the middle number in the set of data.

Midpoint (p. 128) The midpoint of a segment is the point that divides the segment into two segments of equal length.

Punto medio (p. 128) El punto medio de un segmento es el punto que divide el segmento en dos segmentos de igual longitud.

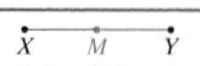

$\overline{XM} = \overline{YM}$
M is the midpoint of $\overline{XY}$.

Mixed number (p. 638) A mixed number is the sum of a whole number and a fraction.

Número mixto (p. 638) Un número mixto es la suma de un número entero y una fracción.

$3\frac{11}{16}$ is a mixed number.

$3\frac{11}{16} = 3 + \frac{11}{16}$

Mode (p. 412) The mode of a data set is the item that occurs with the greatest frequency.

Moda (p. 412) La moda de un conjunto de datos es el dato que sucede con mayor frecuencia.

The mode of the set of prices \$2.50, \$2.75, \$3.60, \$2.75, and \$3.70 is \$2.75.

EXAMPLES

Monomial (p. 576) A polynomial that has only one term is called a monomial.

Monomio (p. 576) Un polinomio que sólo tiene un término se llama monomio.

$5x$, -4, and y^3 are all monomials.

Multiplication Property of Equality (p. 38) The Multiplication Property of Equality states that if each side of an equation is multiplied by the same number, the two sides remain equal.

Propiedad Multiplicativa de la Igualdad (p. 38) La Propiedad Multiplicativa de la Igualdad establece que si cada lado de una ecuación se multiplica por el mismo número, los dos lados se mantienen iguales.

If $a = b$, then $a \cdot c = b \cdot c$.
Since $\frac{12}{2} = 6$, $\frac{12}{2} \cdot 2 = 6 \cdot 2$.

Multiplication Property of Inequality (p. 288) The Multiplication Property of Inequality states that if you multiply an inequality by a positive number, the direction of the inequality is unchanged. If you multiply an inequality by a negative number, *reverse* the direction of the inequality sign.

Propiedad Multiplicativa de la Desigualdad (p. 288) La Propiedad Multiplicativa de la Desigualdad establece que cuando se multiplica una desigualdad por un número positivo, la dirección de la desigualdad no cambia. Si se multiplica una desigualdad por un número negativo, se *invierte* la dirección del signo de la desigualdad.

If $a > b$ and $c > 0$, then $ac > bc$.
Since $3 > 2$ and $7 > 0$, $3 \cdot 7 > 2 \cdot 7$.
If $a < b$ and $c > 0$, then $ac < bc$.
Since $3 < 5$ and $7 > 0$, $3 \cdot 7 < 5 \cdot 7$.
If $a > b$ and $c < 0$, then $ac < bc$.
Since $3 > 2$ and $-6 < 0$,
$3 \cdot -6 < 2 \cdot -6$.
If $a < b$ and $c < 0$, then $ac > bc$.
Since $3 < 5$ and $-6 < 0$,
$3 \cdot -6 > 5 \cdot -6$.

Multiplicative inverse (p. 73) The reciprocal of a number is called its multiplicative inverse.

Inverso multiplicativo (p. 73) El recíproco de un número se llama su inverso multiplicativo.

The multiplicative inverse of $\frac{4}{9}$ is $\frac{9}{4}$.

N

Negative trend (p. 445) There is a negative trend between two sets of data if one set of values tends to increase while the other set tends to decrease.

Tendencia negativa (p. 445) Hay una tendencia negativa entre dos conjuntos de datos si un conjunto de valores tiende a aumentar mientras el otro conjunto tiende a disminuir.

EXAMPLES

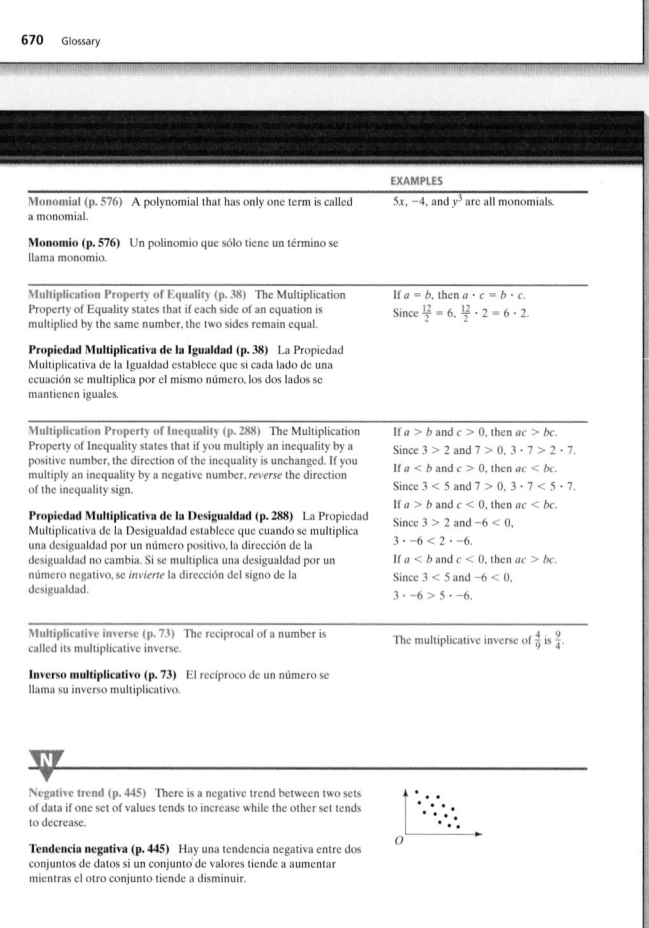

Net (p. 364) A net is a pattern that can be folded to form a solid. A figure's net shows all the faces of that figure in one view.

Plantilla (p. 364) Una plantilla es un patrón bidimensional que se puede doblar para formar un sólido. La plantilla de una figura muestra todas las caras de esa figura en una vista.

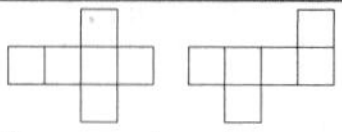

These are nets for a cube.

Nonlinear function (p. 546) The graph of a nonlinear function is not a straight line.

Función no lineal (p. 546) La gráfica de una función no lineal no es una recta.

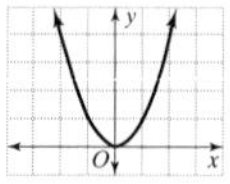

$y = x^2$ is an example of a nonlinear function.

No trend (p. 445) There is no trend between two sets of data if the points show no relationship to each other.

Sin tendencia (p. 445) No hay tendencia entre dos conjuntos de datos si no hay relación alguna entre los puntos.

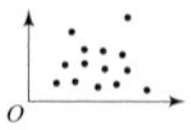

O

Obtuse angle (p. 640) An obtuse angle is an angle with a measure greater than 90° and less than 180°.

Ángulo obtuso (p. 640) Un ángulo obtuso es un ángulo que mide más de 90° y menos de 180°.

Obtuse triangle (p. 318) An obtuse triangle is a triangle with one obtuse angle.

Triángulo obtusángulo (p. 318) Un triángulo obtusángulo es un triángulo que tiene un ángulo obtuso.

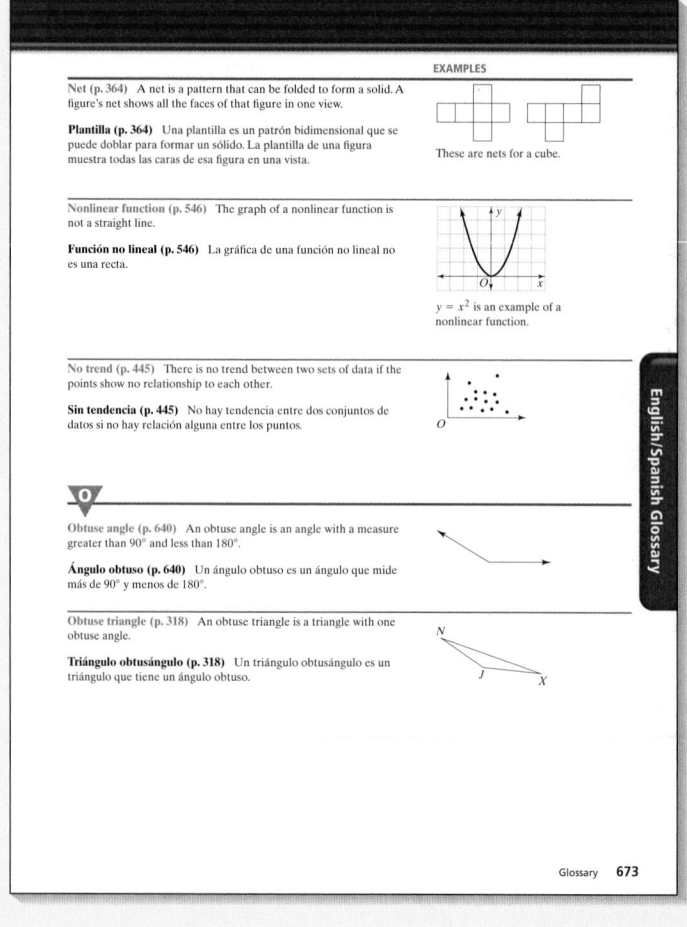

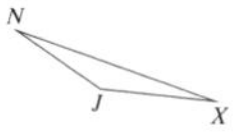

EXAMPLES

Odds (p. 471) When outcomes are equally likely, odds are expressed as the following ratios:

odds *in favor* of an event = the ratio of the number of favorable outcomes *to* the ratio of the number of unfavorable outcomes

odds *against* an event = the ratio of the number of unfavorable outcomes *to* the ratio of the number of favorable outcomes

Posibilidades (p. 471) Cuando los resultados son igualmente posibles, las posibilidades se expresan como las siguientes razones:

posibilidades *en favor* de un suceso = la razón del número de resultados favorables *al* número de resultados desfavorables

posibilidades *en contra* de un suceso = la razón del número de resultados desfavorables *al* número de resultados favorables

If you roll a standard number cube, the odds in favor of getting a 4 are 1 : 5.

Opposites (p. 10) Opposites are two numbers that are the same distance from 0 on a number line, but in opposite directions.

Opuestos (p. 10) Opuestos son dos números que están a la misma distancia del 0 en una recta numérica, pero en direcciones opuestas.

17 and −17 are opposites.

Ordered pair (p. 124) An ordered pair identifies the location of a point. The *x*-coordinate shows a point's position left or right from the origin. The *y*-coordinate shows a point's position up or down from the *x*-axis.

Par ordenado (p. 124) Un par ordenado identifica la ubicación de un punto. La coordenada *x* muestra la posición de un punto a la izquierda o derecha del origen. La coordenada *y* muestra la posición de un punto arriba o abajo del eje de *x*.

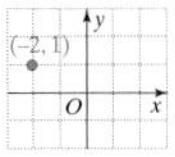

The *x*-coordinate of the point (−2, 1) is −2, and the *y*-coordinate is 1.

Order of operations (pp. 5, 86)
1. Work inside grouping symbols.
2. Simplify the exponents.
3. Multiply and divide in order from left to right.
4. Add and subtract in order from left to right.

Orden de las operaciones (pp. 5, 86)
1. Trabaja dentro de los signos de agrupación.
2. Simplifica los exponentes.
3. Multiplica y divide en orden de izquierda a derecha.
4. Suma y resta en orden de izquierda a derecha.

$2^3(7 - 4) = 2^3 \cdot 3 = 8 \cdot 3 = 24$

Origin (p. 124) The origin is the point of intersection of the *x*- and *y*-axes in a coordinate plane.

Origen (p. 124) El origen es el punto de intersección de los ejes de *x* y de *y* en un plano de coordenadas.

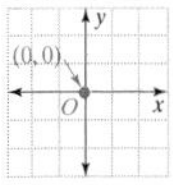

The ordered pair that describes the origin is (0, 0).

EXAMPLES

Outcome (p. 246) An outcome is any of the possible results that can occur in an experiment.

Resultado (p. 246) Un resultado es cualquiera de los posibles desenlaces que pueden ocurrir en un experimento.

The outcomes of rolling a standard number cube are 1, 2, 3, 4, 5, and 6.

Outlier (p. 413) An outlier is a data item that is much higher or much lower than the other items in a data set.

Valor extremo (p. 413) Un valor extremo es un dato que es mucho más alto o más bajo que los demás datos de un conjunto de datos.

An outlier in the data set 6, 7, 9, 10, 11, 12, 14, and 52 is 52.

P

Parabola (p. 546) The graph of a quadratic function is a U-shaped curve, called a parabola.

Parábola (p. 546) La gráfica de una función cuadrática es una curva en forma de U llamada parábola.

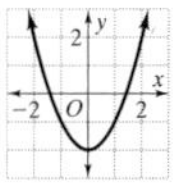

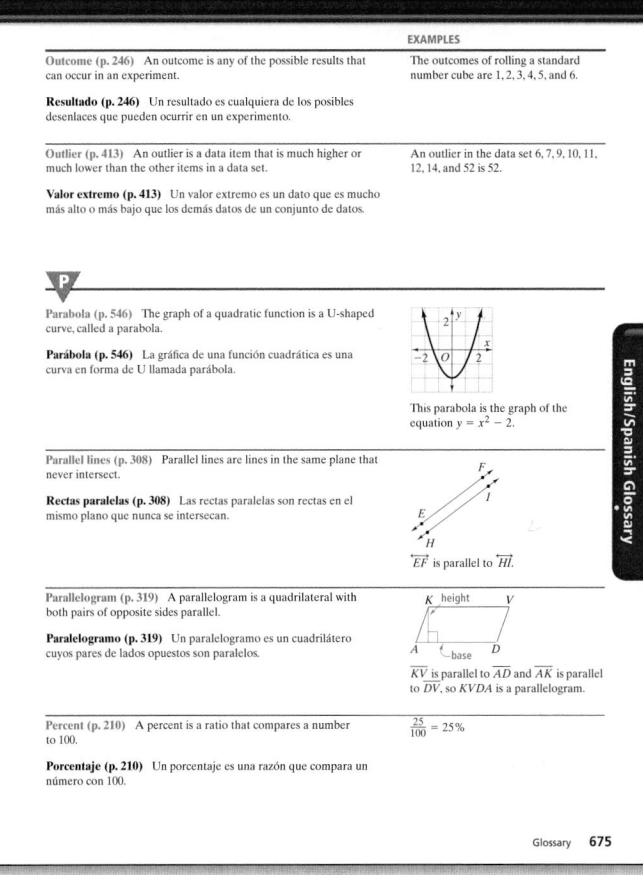

This parabola is the graph of the equation $y = x^2 - 2$.

Parallel lines (p. 308) Parallel lines are lines in the same plane that never intersect.

Rectas paralelas (p. 308) Las rectas paralelas son rectas en el mismo plano que nunca se intersecan.

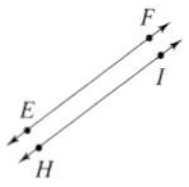

$\overleftrightarrow{EF}$ is parallel to $\overleftrightarrow{HI}$.

Parallelogram (p. 319) A parallelogram is a quadrilateral with both pairs of opposite sides parallel.

Paralelogramo (p. 319) Un paralelogramo es un cuadrilátero cuyos pares de lados opuestos son paralelos.

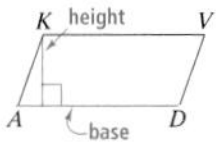

$\overline{KV}$ is parallel to $\overline{AD}$ and $\overline{AK}$ is parallel to $\overline{DV}$, so *KVDA* is a parallelogram.

Percent (p. 210) A percent is a ratio that compares a number to 100.

Porcentaje (p. 210) Un porcentaje es una razón que compara un número con 100.

$\frac{25}{100} = 25\%$

EXAMPLES

Percent of change (p. 230) The percent of change is the percent a quantity increases or decreases from its original amount.

Porcentaje de cambio (p. 230) El porcentaje de cambio es el porcentaje que aumenta o disminuye una cantidad a partir de su cantidad original.

The number of employees increases from 14 to 21. The percent of change is $\frac{21 - 14}{14} = 50\%$.

Perfect square (p. 106) A perfect square is a number that is the square of an integer.

Cuadrado perfecto (p. 106) Un cuadrado perfecto es un número que es el cuadrado de un entero.

Since $25 = 5^2$, 25 is a perfect square.

Perimeter (p. 81) The perimeter of a figure is the distance around the figure.

Perímetro (p. 81) El perímetro de una figura es la distancia alrededor de la figura.

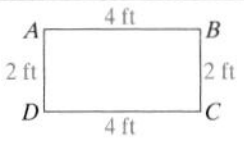

The perimeter of rectangle *ABCD* is 12 ft.

Permutation (p. 491) A permutation is an arrangement of objects in a particular order.

Permutación (p. 491) Una permutación es un arreglo de objetos en un orden particular.

The permutations of the letters W, A, and X, are WAX, WXA, AXW, AWX, XWA, and XAW.

Perpendicular bisector (p. 344) A perpendicular bisector is a segment bisector that is perpendicular to the segment.

Mediatriz (p. 344) Una mediatriz es una bisectriz de un segmento que es perpendicular a ese segmento.

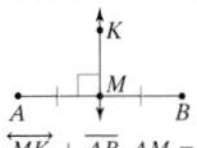

$\overleftrightarrow{MK} \perp \overline{AB}$, $AM = MB$. $\overleftrightarrow{MK}$ is the perpendicular bisector of $\overline{AB}$.

Perpendicular lines (p. 304) Perpendicular lines intersect to form right angles.

Rectas perpendiculares (p. 304) Las rectas perpendiculares se intersecan para formar ángulos rectos.

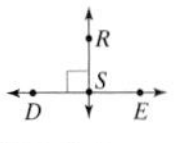

$\overleftrightarrow{DE} \perp \overleftrightarrow{RS}$

Pi (p. 336) Pi (π) is the ratio of the circumference *C* of any circle to its diameter *d*.

Pi (p. 336) Pi (π) es la razón de la circunferencia *C* de cualquier círculo a su diámetro *d*.

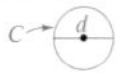

$\pi = \frac{C}{d}$

EXAMPLES

Plane (p. 124) A plane is a flat surface that extends indefinitely in all directions.

Plano (p. 124) Un plano es la superficie plana que se extiende indefinidamente en todas las direcciones.

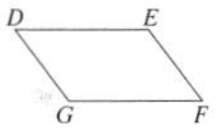

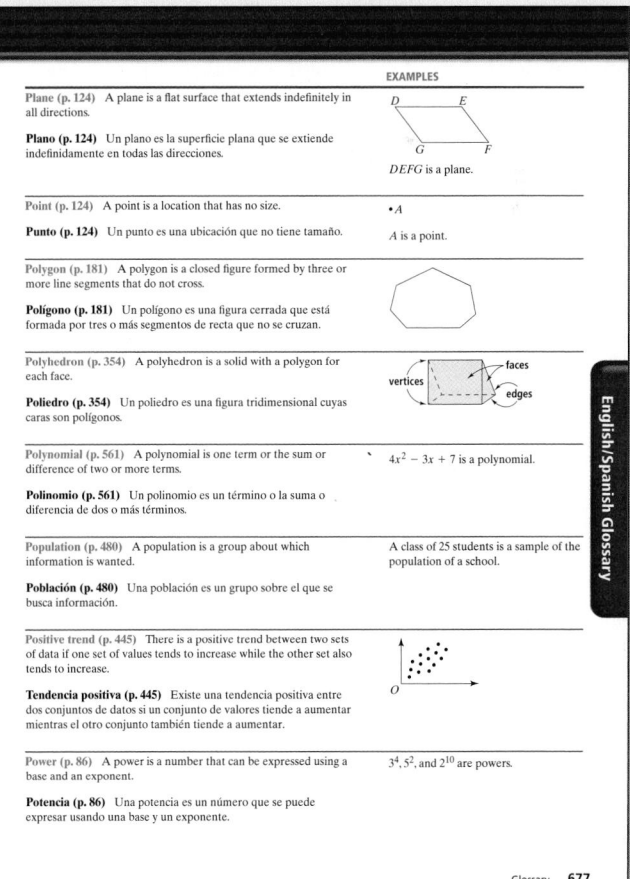

DEFG is a plane.

Point (p. 124) A point is a location that has no size.

Punto (p. 124) Un punto es una ubicación que no tiene tamaño.

•*A*

A is a point.

Polygon (p. 181) A polygon is a closed figure formed by three or more line segments that do not cross.

Polígono (p. 181) Un polígono es una figura cerrada que está formada por tres o más segmentos de recta que no se cruzan.

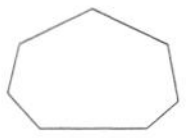

Polyhedron (p. 354) A polyhedron is a solid with a polygon for each face.

Poliedro (p. 354) Un poliedro es una figura tridimensional cuyas caras son polígonos.

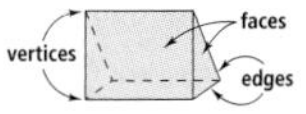

Polynomial (p. 561) A polynomial is one term or the sum or difference of two or more terms.

Polinomio (p. 561) Un polinomio es un término o la suma o diferencia de dos o más términos.

$4x^2 - 3x + 7$ is a polynomial.

Population (p. 480) A population is a group about which information is wanted.

Población (p. 480) Una población es un grupo sobre el que se busca información.

A class of 25 students is a sample of the population of a school.

Positive trend (p. 445) There is a positive trend between two sets of data if one set of values tends to increase while the other set also tends to increase.

Tendencia positiva (p. 445) Existe una tendencia positiva entre dos conjuntos de datos si un conjunto de valores tiende a aumentar mientras el otro conjunto también tiende a aumentar.

Power (p. 86) A power is a number that can be expressed using a base and an exponent.

Potencia (p. 86) Una potencia es un número que se puede expresar usando una base y un exponente.

3^4, 5^2, and 2^{10} are powers.

EXAMPLES

Precision (p. 402) Precision refers to the exactness of a measurement, as determined by the unit of measure.

Precisión (p. 402) La precisión se refiere a la exactitud de una medida, según está determinada por la unidad de medida.

$\frac{1}{16}$ in. is a smaller unit than $\frac{1}{4}$ in., so $\frac{1}{16}$ in. is more precise than $\frac{1}{4}$ in.

Prime factorization (p. 53) Writing a composite number as the product of its prime factors is the prime factorization of the number.

Descomposición en factores primos (p. 53) Escribir un número compuesto como el producto de sus factores primos es la descomposición en factores primos del número.

The prime factorization of 12 is $2 \cdot 2 \cdot 3$, or $2^2 \cdot 3$.

Prime notation (p. 136) Prime notation is used to identify an image point.

Notación prima (p. 136) La notación prima se usa para identificar un punto de imagen.

Point $F'(4, 1)$ is the image of point $F(4, 3)$ after a translation.

Prime number (p. 52) A prime number is a whole number with exactly two factors, 1 and the number itself.

Número primo (p. 52) Un número primo es un entero que tiene exactamente dos factores, 1 y el mismo número.

13 is a prime number because its only factors are 1 and 13.

Principal (p. 242) Principal is the original amount deposited or borrowed.

Capital (p. 242) El capital es el monto original que se deposita o se toma prestado.

You deposit $500 in a savings account. Your principal is $500.

Prism (p. 354) A prism is a solid with two parallel and congruent polygonal faces called bases. A prism is named for the shape of its base.

Prisma (p. 354) Un prisma es un sólido que tiene dos caras poligonales paralelas y congruentes llamadas bases. Un prisma recibe su nombre por la forma de su base.

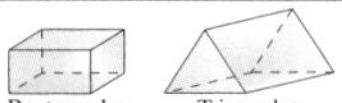

Rectangular Prism   Triangular Prism

Probability of an event (p. 246) When outcomes are equally likely: $P(E) = \frac{\text{number of favorable outcomes}}{\text{total number of possible outcomes}}$.

Probabilidad de un suceso (p. 246) Cuando los resultados son igualmente posibles: $P(E) = \frac{\text{número de resultados favorables}}{\text{número total de resultados posibles}}$.

The probability of rolling a 4 on a number cube is $\frac{1}{6}$.
See also *Experimental probability* and *Theoretical probability*.

EXAMPLES

Proportion (p. 174) A proportion is an equation stating that two ratios are equal.

Proporción (p. 174) Una proporción es una ecuación que establece que dos razones son iguales.

$\frac{3}{12} = \frac{9}{36}$ is a proportion.

Pyramid (p. 354) A pyramid is a solid with triangular faces that meet at a vertex and a base that is a polygon. A pyramid is named for the shape of its base.

Pirámide (p. 354) Una pirámide es una figura tridimensional que tiene caras triangulares que coinciden en un vértice y una base que es un polígono. Una pirámide recibe su nombre por la forma de su base.

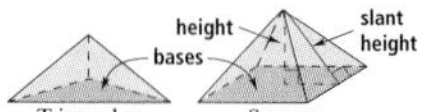

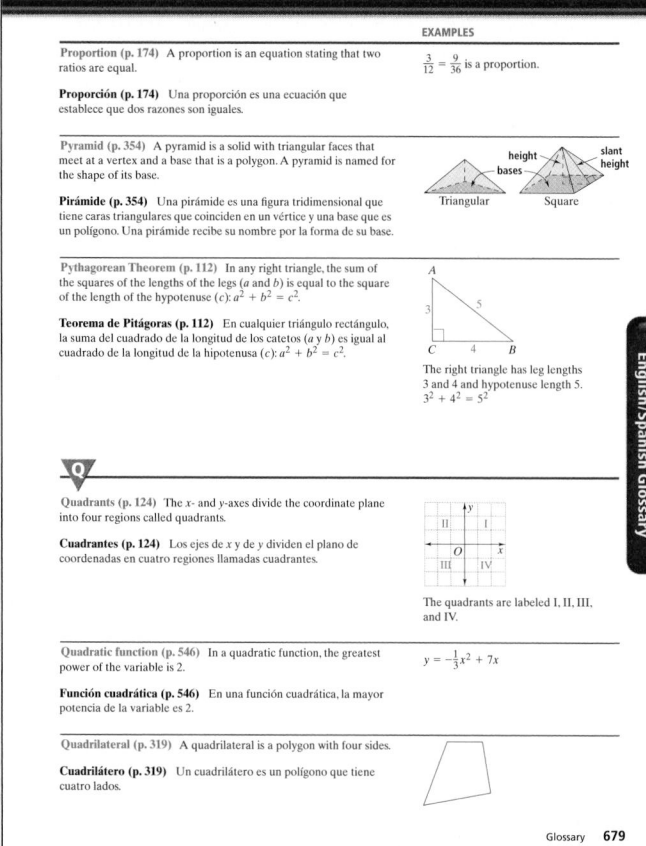

Triangular   Square

Pythagorean Theorem (p. 112) In any right triangle, the sum of the squares of the lengths of the legs (a and b) is equal to the square of the length of the hypotenuse (c): $a^2 + b^2 = c^2$.

Teorema de Pitágoras (p. 112) En cualquier triángulo rectángulo, la suma del cuadrado de la longitud de los catetos (a y b) es igual al cuadrado de la longitud de la hipotenusa (c): $a^2 + b^2 = c^2$.

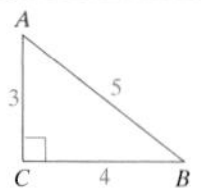

The right triangle has leg lengths 3 and 4 and hypotenuse length 5.
$3^2 + 4^2 = 5^2$

Q

Quadrants (p. 124) The x- and y-axes divide the coordinate plane into four regions called quadrants.

Cuadrantes (p. 124) Los ejes de x y de y dividen el plano de coordenadas en cuatro regiones llamadas cuadrantes.

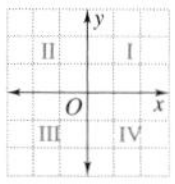

The quadrants are labeled I, II, III, and IV.

Quadratic function (p. 546) In a quadratic function, the greatest power of the variable is 2.

Función cuadrática (p. 546) En una función cuadrática, la mayor potencia de la variable es 2.

$y = -\frac{1}{3}x^2 + 7x$

Quadrilateral (p. 319) A quadrilateral is a polygon with four sides.

Cuadrilátero (p. 319) Un cuadrilátero es un polígono que tiene cuatro lados.

EXAMPLES

Quartiles (p. 438) Quartiles are numbers that divide data into four equal parts.

Cuartiles (p. 438) Los cuartiles son números que dividen los datos en cuatro partes iguales.

See *Box-and-whisker plot*.

R

Radius (p. 336) A radius of a circle is a segment that connects the center to the circle.

Radio (p. 336) Un radio de un círculo es un segmento que conecta el centro con el círculo.

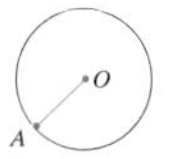

$\overline{OA}$ is a radius of circle O.

Random sample (p. 480) In a random sample, each member in the population has an equal chance of being selected.

Muestra aleatoria (p. 480) En una muestra aleatoria, cada miembro de la población tiene la misma posibilidad de ser elegido.

For the population *customers at a mall*, a random sample would be every 20th customer entering during a 2-hour period.

Range (p. 413) The range of a data set is the difference between the greatest and the least values.

Rango (p. 413) El rango de un conjunto de datos es la diferencia entre los valores mayor y menor.

Data set: 62, 109, 234, 35, 96, 49, 201
Range: $234 - 35 = 199$

Rate (p. 161) A rate is a ratio that compares two quantities measured in different units.

Tasa (p. 161) Una tasa es una razón que compara dos cantidades medidas en diferentes unidades.

You read 116 words in 1 min. Your reading rate is $\frac{116 \text{ words}}{1 \text{ min}}$.

Rate of change (p. 527) A rate of change is a comparison between two quantities that are changing.

rate of change $= \frac{\text{change in one quantity}}{\text{change in another quantity}}$

Tasa de cambio (p. 527) Una tasa de cambio es una comparación entre dos cantidades que cambian. La tasa de cambio se llama también pendiente.

tasa de cambio $= \frac{\text{cambio en una cantidad}}{\text{cambio en otra cantidad}}$

Video rental for 1 day is $1.99. Video rental for 2 days is $2.99.

$$\text{rate of change} = \frac{2.99 - 1.99}{2 - 1} = \frac{1.00}{1} = 1$$

Ratio (p. 160) A ratio is a comparison of two quantities by division.

Razón (p. 160) Una razón es una comparación de dos cantidades mediante la división.

There are three ways to write a ratio: 9 to 10, 9 : 10, and $\frac{9}{10}$.

EXAMPLES

Rational number (p. 57) A rational number is any number written as a quotient of two integers where the denominator is not 0.

Número racional (p. 57) Un número racional es cualquier número escrito como cociente de dos enteros, donde el denominador es diferente de 0.

$\frac{1}{3}$, -5, 6.4, 0.666 . . . , $-2\frac{4}{5}$, 0, and $\frac{7}{3}$ are rational numbers.

Ray (p. 640) A ray has endpoint and all the points of the line on one side of the point.

Rayo (p. 640) Un rayo tiene un extremo y todos los puntos de la recta a un lado del punto.

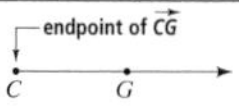

$\overrightarrow{CG}$ represents a ray.

Real numbers (p. 107) Together, rational and irrational numbers form the set of real numbers.

Números reales (p. 107) Juntos, los números rationales e irracionales forman el conjunto de los números reales.

3, -5.25, 3.141592653 . . . , and $\frac{7}{8}$ are real numbers.

Reciprocals (p. 73) Two numbers are reciprocals if their product is 1.

Recíprocos (p. 73) Dos números son recíprocos si su producto es 1.

The numbers $\frac{4}{9}$ and $\frac{9}{4}$ are reciprocals.

Rectangle (p. 319) A rectangle is a parallelogram with four right angles.

Rectángulo (p. 319) Un rectángulo es un paralelogramo que tiene cuatro ángulos rectos.

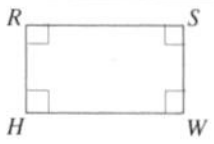

Reduction (p. 188) A dilation with a scale factor less than 1 is a reduction.

Reducción (p. 188) Una dilatación con un factor de escala menor que 1 es una reducción.

See *Dilation*.

Reflection (p. 141) A reflection is a transformation that flips a figure over a line of reflection.

Reflexión (p. 141) Una reflexión es una transformación que voltea una figura sobre un eje de reflexión.

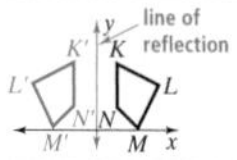

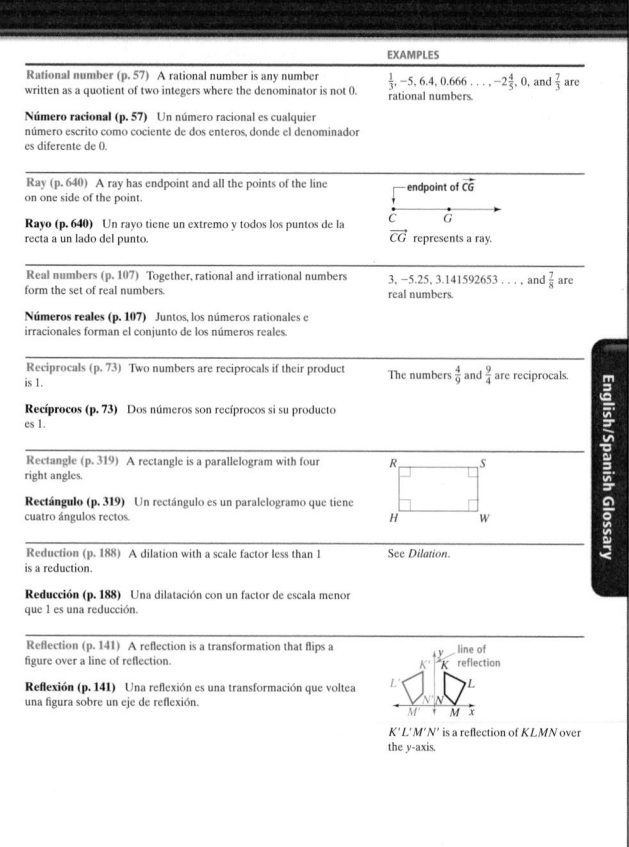

$K'L'M'N'$ is a reflection of $KLMN$ over the y-axis.

EXAMPLES

Reflectional symmetry (p. 142) If a figure can be reflected over a line so that its image matches the original figure, the figure has reflectional symmetry.

Simetría por reflexión (p. 142) Si una figura se puede reflejar sobre una recta de modo que su imagen coincida con la figura original, la figura tiene simetría por reflexión.

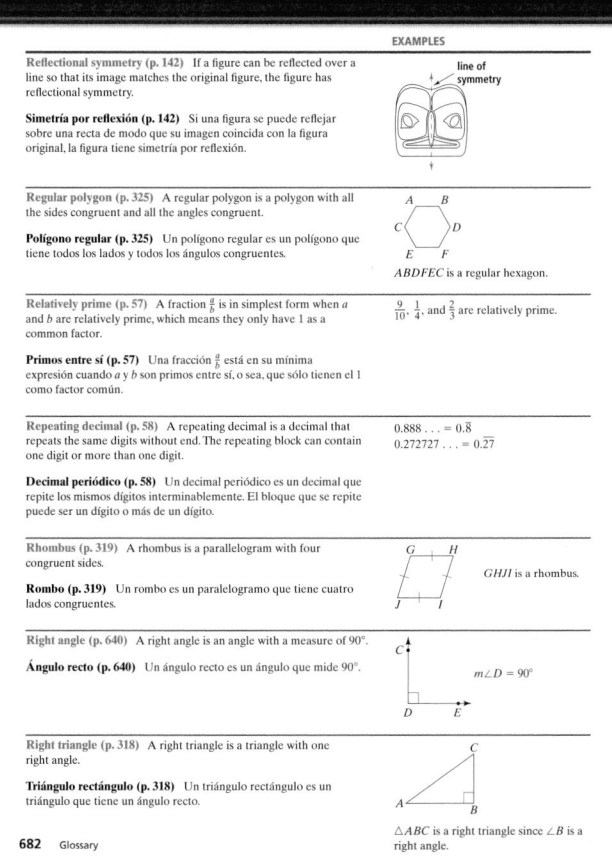

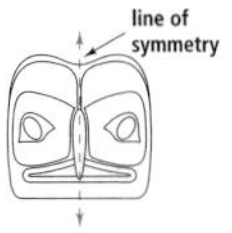

Regular polygon (p. 325) A regular polygon is a polygon with all the sides congruent and all the angles congruent.

Polígono regular (p. 325) Un polígono regular es un polígono que tiene todos los lados y todos los ángulos congruentes.

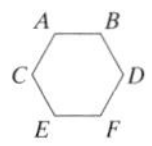

$ABDFEC$ is a regular hexagon.

Relatively prime (p. 57) A fraction $\frac{a}{b}$ is in simplest form when a and b are relatively prime, which means they only have 1 as a common factor.

Primos entre sí (p. 57) Una fracción $\frac{a}{b}$ está en su mínima expresión cuando a y b son primos entre sí, o sea, que sólo tienen el 1 como factor común.

$\frac{9}{10}$, $\frac{1}{4}$, and $\frac{2}{3}$ are relatively prime.

Repeating decimal (p. 58) A repeating decimal is a decimal that repeats the same digits without end. The repeating block can contain one digit or more than one digit.

Decimal periódico (p. 58) Un decimal periódico es un decimal que repite los mismos dígitos interminablemente. El bloque que se repite puede ser un dígito o más de un dígito.

$0.888\ldots = 0.\overline{8}$
$0.272727\ldots = 0.\overline{27}$

Rhombus (p. 319) A rhombus is a parallelogram with four congruent sides.

Rombo (p. 319) Un rombo es un paralelogramo que tiene cuatro lados congruentes.

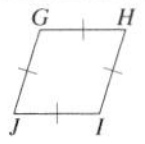

$GHJI$ is a rhombus.

Right angle (p. 640) A right angle is an angle with a measure of 90°.

Ángulo recto (p. 640) Un ángulo recto es un ángulo que mide 90°.

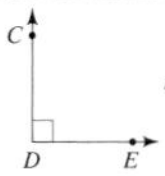

$m\angle D = 90°$

Right triangle (p. 318) A right triangle is a triangle with one right angle.

Triángulo rectángulo (p. 318) Un triángulo rectángulo es un triángulo que tiene un ángulo recto.

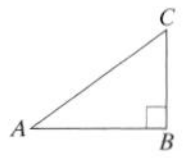

$\triangle ABC$ is a right triangle since $\angle B$ is a right angle.

EXAMPLES

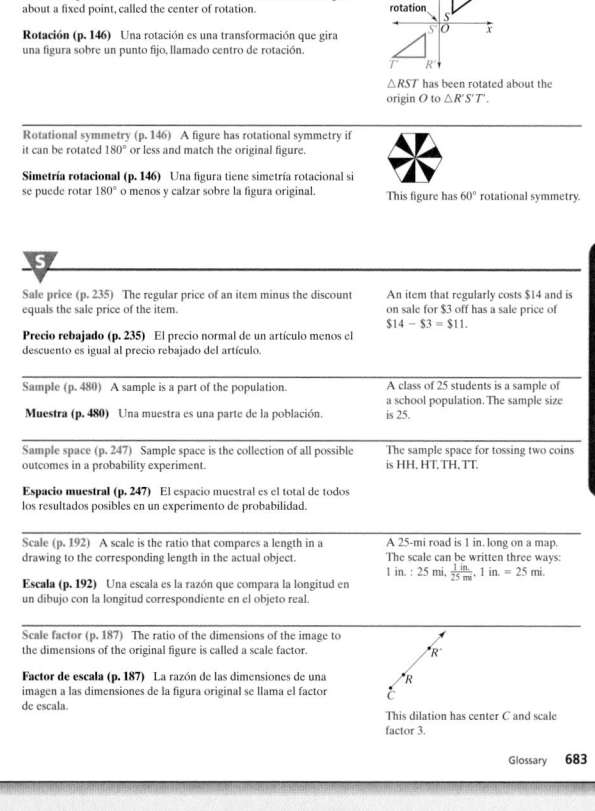

Rotation (p. 146) A rotation is a transformation that turns a figure about a fixed point, called the center of rotation.

Rotación (p. 146) Una rotación es una transformación que gira una figura sobre un punto fijo, llamado centro de rotación.

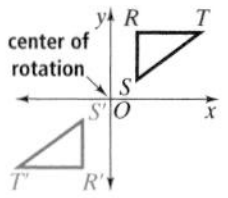

$\triangle RST$ has been rotated about the origin O to $\triangle R'S'T'$.

Rotational symmetry (p. 146) A figure has rotational symmetry if it can be rotated 180° or less and match the original figure.

Simetría rotacional (p. 146) Una figura tiene simetría rotacional si se puede rotar 180° o menos y calzar sobre la figura original.

This figure has 60° rotational symmetry.

S

Sale price (p. 235) The regular price of an item minus the discount equals the sale price of the item.

Precio rebajado (p. 235) El precio normal de un artículo menos el descuento es igual al precio rebajado del artículo.

An item that regularly costs \$14 and is on sale for \$3 off has a sale price of \$14 − \$3 = \$11.

Sample (p. 480) A sample is a part of the population.

Muestra (p. 480) Una muestra es una parte de la población.

A class of 25 students is a sample of a school population. The sample size is 25.

Sample space (p. 247) Sample space is the collection of all possible outcomes in a probability experiment.

Espacio muestral (p. 247) El espacio muestral es el total de todos los resultados posibles en un experimento de probabilidad.

The sample space for tossing two coins is HH, HT, TH, TT.

Scale (p. 192) A scale is the ratio that compares a length in a drawing to the corresponding length in the actual object.

Escala (p. 192) Una escala es la razón que compara la longitud en un dibujo con la longitud correspondiente en el objeto real.

A 25-mi road is 1 in. long on a map. The scale can be written three ways: 1 in. : 25 mi, $\frac{1 \text{ in.}}{25 \text{ mi}}$, 1 in. = 25 mi.

Scale factor (p. 187) The ratio of the dimensions of the image to the dimensions of the original figure is called a scale factor.

Factor de escala (p. 187) La razón de las dimensiones de la imagen a las dimensiones de la figura original se llama el factor de escala.

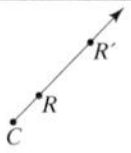

This dilation has center C and scale factor 3.

EXAMPLES

Scale model (p. 192) A scale model is an enlarged or reduced model of an object that is similar to the actual object.

Dibujo a escala (p. 192) Un dibujo a escala es un dibujo aumentado o reducido de un objeto que es semejante al objeto real.

Maps and floor plans are scale models.

Scalene triangle (p. 318) A scalene triangle is a triangle with no congruent sides.

Triángulo escaleno (p. 318) Un triángulo escaleno es un triángulo cuyos lados no son congruentes.

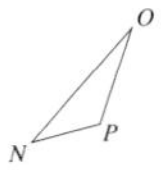

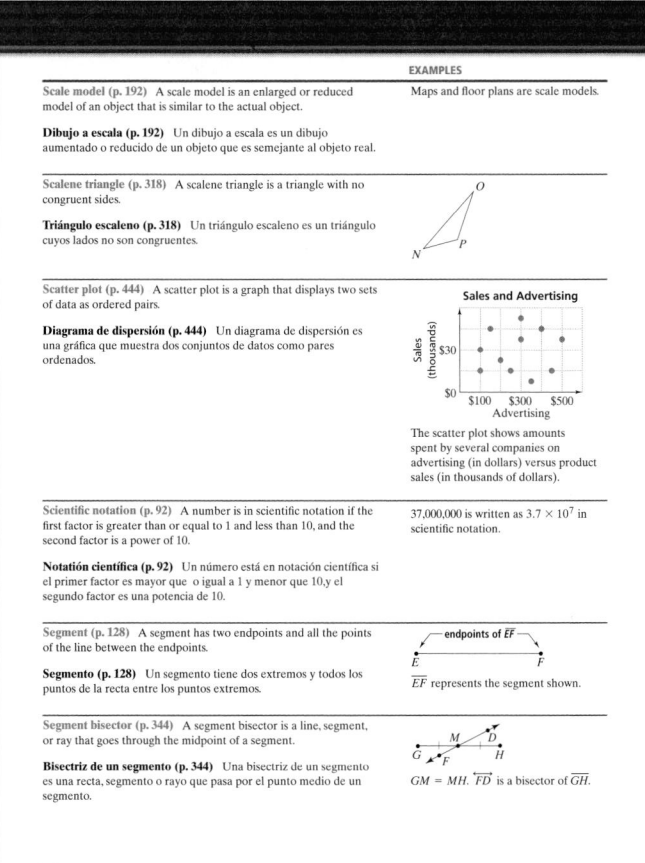

Scatter plot (p. 444) A scatter plot is a graph that displays two sets of data as ordered pairs.

Diagrama de dispersión (p. 444) Un diagrama de dispersión es una gráfica que muestra dos conjuntos de datos como pares ordenados.

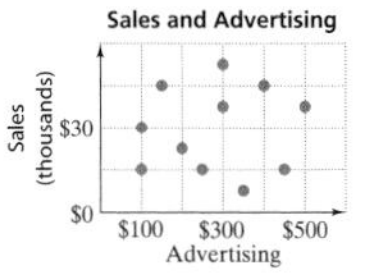

The scatter plot shows amounts spent by several companies on advertising (in dollars) versus product sales (in thousands of dollars).

Scientific notation (p. 92) A number is in scientific notation if the first factor is greater than or equal to 1 and less than 10, and the second factor is a power of 10.

Notación científica (p. 92) Un número está en notación científica si el primer factor es mayor que o igual a 1 y menor que 10,y el segundo factor es una potencia de 10.

37,000,000 is written as 3.7×10^7 in scientific notation.

Segment (p. 128) A segment has two endpoints and all the points of the line between the endpoints.

Segmento (p. 128) Un segmento tiene dos extremos y todos los puntos de la recta entre los puntos extremos.

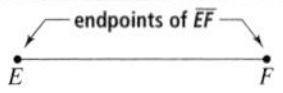

$\overline{EF}$ represents the segment shown.

Segment bisector (p. 344) A segment bisector is a line, segment, or ray that goes through the midpoint of a segment.

Bisectriz de un segmento (p. 344) Una bisectriz de un segmento es una recta, segmento o rayo que pasa por el punto medio de un segmento.

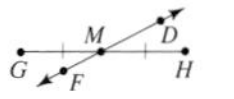

$GM = MH$. $\overleftrightarrow{FD}$ is a bisector of $\overline{GH}$.

EXAMPLES

Selling price (p. 234) Markup is added to the cost of merchandise to arrive at the selling price.

Precio de venta (p. 234) Se agrega el sobrecosto al costo de la mercadería para llegar al precio de venta.

An item that costs a store \$15 and is marked up \$7 has a selling price of \$15 + \$7 = \$22.

Semicircle (p. 340) A semicircle is half a circle.

Semicírculo (p. 340) Un semicírculo es la mitad de un círculo.

See *Arc*.

Sequence (p. 512) A sequence is a set of numbers that follows a pattern.

Secuencia (p. 512) Una secuencia es un conjunto de números que sigue un patrón.

3, 6, 9, 12, 15, . . . is a sequence.

Significant digits (p. 402) Use significant digits to determine how precise the answer should be when you multiply or divide measurements. Nonzero digits (1–9) are always significant. Zero digits are only significant in certain places.

Dígitos significativos (p. 402) Se usan dígitos significativos para determinar cuán precisa debe ser una respuesta cuando se multiplican or dividen medidas. Los dígitos distintos de cero (1–9) siempre son significativos. Los ceros son significativos sólo en ciertos lugares.

0.007500 has four significant digits.
19,200 has three significant digits.
40.290 has five significant digits.

Similar figures (p. 181) Similar figures have the same shape, but not necessarily the same size.

Figuras semejantes (p. 181) Las figuras semejantes tienen la misma forma, pero no necesariamente el mismo tamaño.

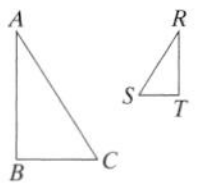

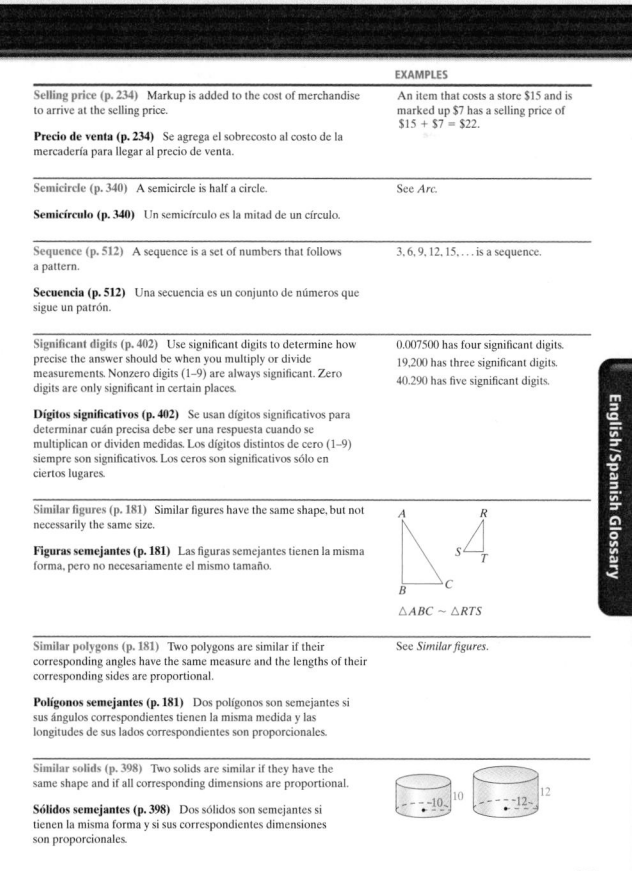

$\triangle ABC \sim \triangle RTS$

Similar polygons (p. 181) Two polygons are similar if their corresponding angles have the same measure and the lengths of their corresponding sides are proportional.

Polígonos semejantes (p. 181) Dos polígonos son semejantes si sus ángulos correspondientes tienen la misma medida y las longitudes de sus lados correspondientes son proporcionales.

See *Similar figures*.

Similar solids (p. 398) Two solids are similar if they have the same shape and if all corresponding dimensions are proportional.

Sólidos semejantes (p. 398) Dos sólidos son semejantes si tienen la misma forma y si sus correspondientes dimensiones son proporcionales.

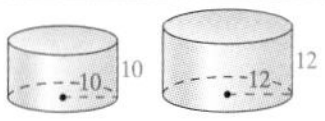

EXAMPLES

Simple interest (p. 242) Simple interest is interest calculated only on the principal. Use the formula $I = p \cdot r \cdot t$ where I is the interest, p is the principal, r is the annual interest rate, and t is time in years.

Interés simple (p. 242) El interés simple se calcula sólo en relación al principal. Se usa la fórmula $I = p \cdot i \cdot t$ donde I es el interés, p es el principal, i es la tasa de interés anual y t es el tiempo en años.

The simple interest earned on \$200 invested at 5% annual interest for three years is $\$200 \cdot 0.05 \cdot 3 = \$30$.

Simplest form (p. 57) A fraction is in simplest form when the numerator and denominator have no common factors other than 1.

Mínima expresión (p. 57) Una fracción está en su mínima expresión cuando el numerador y el denominador no tienen otro factor común más que el 1.

The simplest form of $\frac{3}{9}$ is $\frac{1}{3}$.

Simplify (p. 5) To simplify a numerical expression, replace it with its simplest name.

Simplificar (p. 5) Para simplificar una expresión numérica, se reemplaza con su mínima expresión.

$8 + 3x - 2$ simplifies to $6 + 3x$.

Simulation (p. 484) A simulation is a model of a real-world situation used to find probability.

Simulación (p. 484) Una simulación es un modelo de una situación real que se usa para hallar la probabilidad.

A baseball team has an equal chance of winning or losing its next game. You can toss a coin to simulate the situation.

Skew lines (p. 355) Skew lines lie in different planes. They are neither parallel nor intersecting

Rectas cruzadas (p. 355) Las rectas cruzadas están en planos diferentes. No son paralelas ni se intersecan.

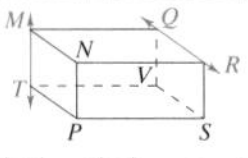

$\overleftrightarrow{MT}$ and $\overleftrightarrow{QR}$ are skew lines.

Slant height (p. 374) The height of a pyramid's lateral faces is called the slant height and is indicated by the symbol ℓ.

Altura inclinada (p. 374) La altura de las caras laterales de una pirámide se llama altura inclinada y se indica con el símbolo ℓ.

See *Cone, Pyramid.*

Slope (p. 528) Slope is a ratio that describes steepness.

$$\text{Slope} = \frac{\text{vertical change}}{\text{horizontal change}} = \frac{\text{rise}}{\text{run}}$$

Pendiente (p. 528) La pendiente es la razón que describe la inclinación.

$$\text{Pendiente} = \frac{\text{cambio vertical}}{\text{cambio horizontal}} = \frac{\text{elevación}}{\text{desplazamiento}}$$

EXAMPLES

Slope of a line (p. 528)

$$\text{Slope} = \frac{\text{change in } y \text{ coordinates}}{\text{change in } x \text{ coordinates}} = \frac{\text{rise}}{\text{run}}$$

Pendiente de una recta (p. 528)

$$\text{Pendiente} = \frac{\text{cambio en la coordenada } y}{\text{cambio en la coordenada } x} = \frac{\text{elevación}}{\text{desplazamiento}}$$

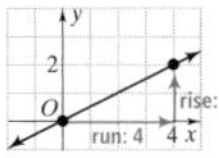

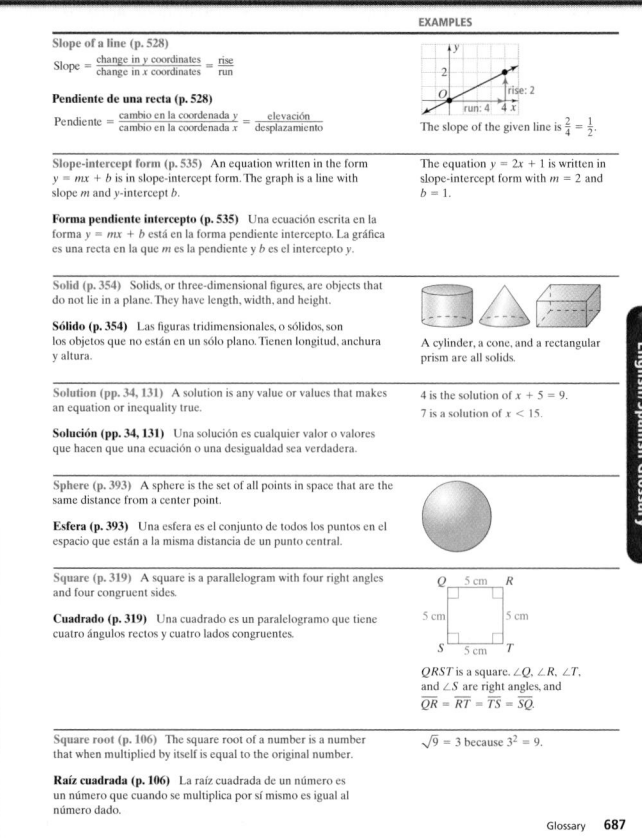

The slope of the given line is $\frac{2}{4} = \frac{1}{2}$.

Slope-intercept form (p. 535) An equation written in the form $y = mx + b$ is in slope-intercept form. The graph is a line with slope m and y-intercept b.

Forma pendiente intercepto (p. 535) Una ecuación escrita en la forma $y = mx + b$ está en la forma pendiente intercepto. La gráfica es una recta en la que m es la pendiente y b es el intercepto y.

The equation $y = 2x + 1$ is written in slope-intercept form with $m = 2$ and $b = 1$.

Solid (p. 354) Solids, or three-dimensional figures, are objects that do not lie in a plane. They have length, width, and height.

Sólido (p. 354) Las figuras tridimensionales, o sólidos, son los objetos que no están en un sólo plano. Tienen longitud, anchura y altura.

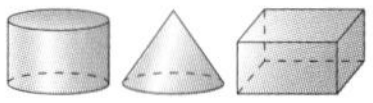

A cylinder, a cone, and a rectangular prism are all solids.

Solution (pp. 34, 131) A solution is any value or values that makes an equation or inequality true.

Solución (pp. 34, 131) Una solución es cualquier valor o valores que hacen que una ecuación o una desigualdad sea verdadera.

4 is the solution of $x + 5 = 9$.

7 is a solution of $x < 15$.

Sphere (p. 393) A sphere is the set of all points in space that are the same distance from a center point.

Esfera (p. 393) Una esfera es el conjunto de todos los puntos en el espacio que están a la misma distancia de un punto central.

Square (p. 319) A square is a parallelogram with four right angles and four congruent sides.

Cuadrado (p. 319) Una cuadrado es un paralelogramo que tiene cuatro ángulos rectos y cuatro lados congruentes.

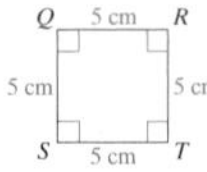

$QRST$ is a square. $\angle Q$, $\angle R$, $\angle T$, and $\angle S$ are right angles, and $\overline{QR} = \overline{RT} = \overline{TS} = \overline{SQ}$.

Square root (p. 106) The square root of a number is a number that when multiplied by itself is equal to the original number.

Raíz cuadrada (p. 106) La raíz cuadrada de un número es un número que cuando se multiplica por sí mismo es igual al número dado.

$\sqrt{9} = 3$ because $3^2 = 9$.

English/Spanish Glossary

EXAMPLES

Standard form (p. 92) A number written using digits and place value is in standard form. See also *Expanded form.*

Forma normal (p. 92) Un número escrito usando dígitos y valor posicional está en forma normal. Ver también *Expanded form.*

The standard form of 8.9×10^5 is 890,000.

Stem-and-leaf plot (p. 433) A stem-and-leaf plot is a display that shows numeric data arranged in order. Each data item is broken into a stem (digit or digits on the left) and a leaf (digit on the right).

Diagram a de tallo y hojas (p. 433) Un diagrama de tallo y hojas es una muestra de datos numéricos arreglados en orden. Cada dato se divide en un tallo (dígito o dígitos a la izquierda) y hoja (dígito a la derecha).

stem	leaves
27	7
28	5 6 8
29	6 9
30	8

Key: 27 | 7 means 27.7

This stem-and-leaf plot displays recorded times in a race. The stems represents the whole number of seconds. The leaves represent tenths of a second.

Straight angle (p. 640) A straight angle is an angle with a measure of 180°.

Ángulo llano (p. 640) Un ángulo llano es un ángulo que mide 180°.

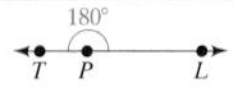

$m\angle TPL = 180°$

Subtraction Property of Equality (p. 33) The Subtraction Property of Equality states that if the same number is subtracted from each side of an equation, the results are equal.

Propiedad Sustractiva de la Igualdad (p. 33) La Propiedad Sustractiva de la Igualdad establece que si se resta el mismo número a cada lado de una ecuación, los resultados son iguales.

If $a = b$, then $a - c = b - c$.
Since $\frac{20}{2} = 10$, $\frac{20}{2} - 3 = 10 - 3$.

Subtraction Property of Inequality (p. 282) When you subtract the same number from each side of an inequality, the relationship between the two sides does not change.

Propiedad Sustractiva de la Desigualdad (p. 282) Cuando se resta el mismo número a cada lado de una desigualdad, la relación entre los dos lados no cambia.

If $a > b$, then $a - c > b - c$.
Since $9 > 6$, $9 - 2 > 6 - 2$.
If $a < b$, then $a - c < b - c$.
Since $9 < 13$, $9 - 2 < 13 - 2$.

Supplementary (p. 304) Supplementary angles are two angles whose measures add to 180°.

Suplementario (p. 304) Los ángulos suplementarios son dos ángulos cuyas medidas suman 180°.

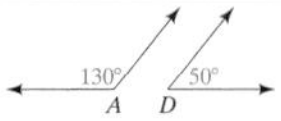

$\angle A$ and $\angle D$ are supplementary angles.

EXAMPLES

Surface area (p. 368) The surface area of a solid is the sum of the areas of its surfaces.

Área total (p. 368) El área total de un sólido es la suma de las áreas de todas sus caras.

Each square = 1 in.^{2}.

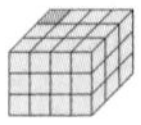

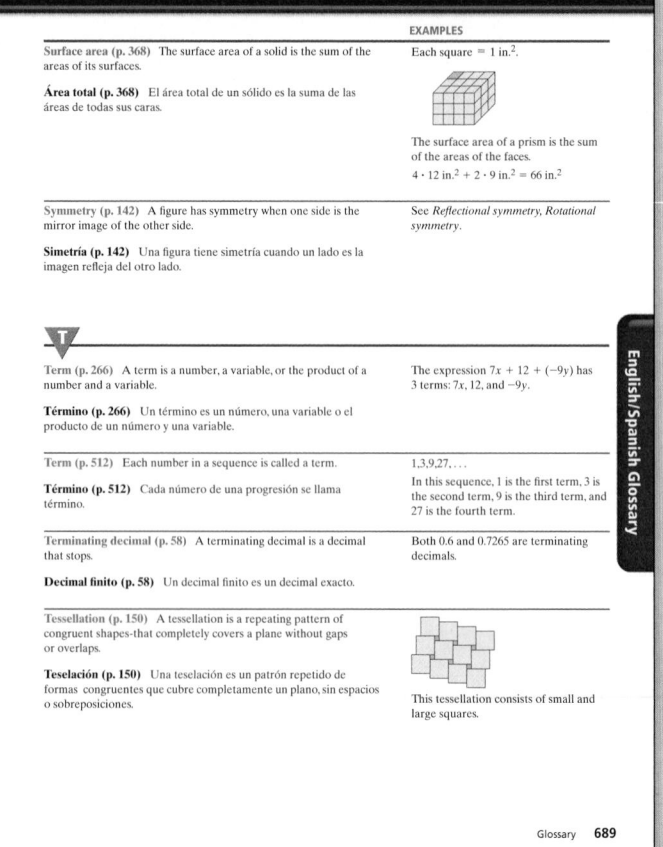

The surface area of a prism is the sum of the areas of the faces.

$4 \cdot 12 \text{ in.}^2 + 2 \cdot 9 \text{ in.}^2 = 66 \text{ in.}^2$

Symmetry (p. 142) A figure has symmetry when one side is the mirror image of the other side.

Simetría (p. 142) Una figura tiene simetría cuando un lado es la imagen refleja del otro lado.

See *Reflectional symmetry, Rotational symmetry.*

T

Term (p. 266) A term is a number, a variable, or the product of a number and a variable.

Término (p. 266) Un término es un número, una variable o el producto de un número y una variable.

The expression $7x + 12 + (-9y)$ has 3 terms: $7x$, 12, and $-9y$.

Term (p. 512) Each number in a sequence is called a term.

Término (p. 512) Cada número de una progresión se llama término.

1,3,9,27, . . .

In this sequence, 1 is the first term, 3 is the second term, 9 is the third term, and 27 is the fourth term.

Terminating decimal (p. 58) A terminating decimal is a decimal that stops.

Decimal finito (p. 58) Un decimal finito es un decimal exacto.

Both 0.6 and 0.7265 are terminating decimals.

Tessellation (p. 150) A tessellation is a repeating pattern of congruent shapes that completely covers a plane without gaps or overlaps.

Teselación (p. 150) Una teselación es un patrón repetido de formas congruentes que cubre completamente un plano, sin espacios o sobreposiciones.

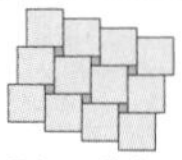

This tessellation consists of small and large squares.

English/Spanish Glossary

EXAMPLES

Theoretical probability (p. 471) Theoritical probability describes how likely it is that an event will happen. This probability is based on all the outcomes when the outcomes are equally likely.

Probabilidad teórica (p. 471) La probabilidad teórica describe cuán posible es que ocurra un suceso. Esta probalidad está basada en todos los resultados cuando los resultados son igualmente probables.

Suppose you select a letter from the letters H, A, P, P, and Y. The theoretical probability of selecting a P is $\frac{2}{5}$.

Three-dimensional figure (p. 354) Three-dimensional figures are figures that do not lie in a plane. They are also known as solids.

Figura tridemensional (p. 354) Las figuras tridimensionales son figuras que no están en un solo plano. También se llaman sólidos.

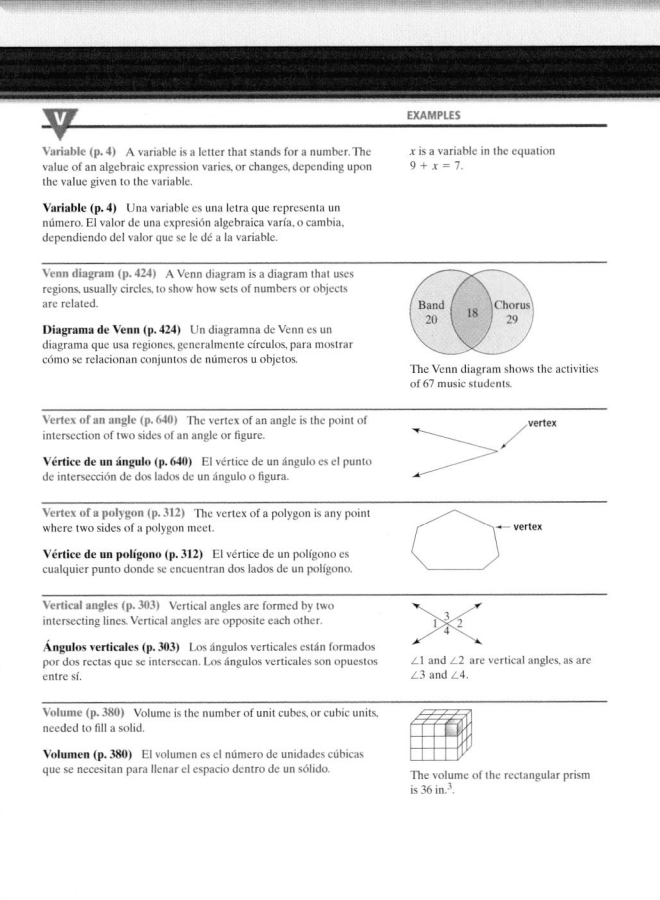

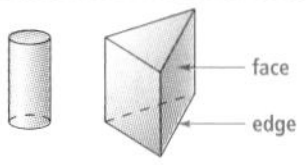

Tip (p. 215) A tip is a percent of a bill given to a person for providing a service.

Propina (p. 215) Una propina es un porcentaje de una cuenta que se le da a una persona por el servicio prestado.

A lunch bill is $18.00. You leave a 20% tip of $3.60.

Transformation (p. 136) A transformation is a change in position, shape, or size of a figure. Three types of transformations that change position only are translations, reflections, and rotations.

Transformación (p. 136) Una transformación es un cambio de posición, forma o tamaño de una figura. Los tres tipos de transformaciones que cambian la posición son las traslaciones, las reflexiones y las rotaciones.

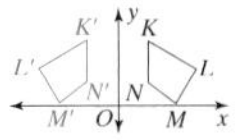

K'L'M'N' is a reflection, or flip, of *KLMN* across the *y*-axis.

Translation (p. 136) A translation is a transformation that moves each point of a figure the same distance and in the same direction.

Traslación (p. 136) Una traslación es una transformación que mueve cada punto de una figura la misma distancia y en la misma dirección.

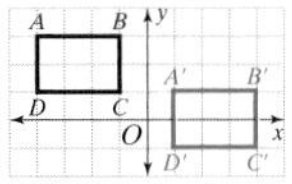

A'B'C'D' is a translation image of *ABCD*.

Transversal (p. 307) A transversal is a line that intersects two or more lines at different points.

Secante (p. 307) Una secante es una recta que corta dos o más rectas en puntos diferentes.

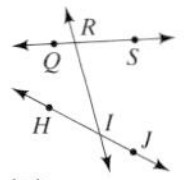

$\overleftrightarrow{RI}$ is a transversal of $\overleftrightarrow{QS}$ and $\overleftrightarrow{HJ}$.

EXAMPLES

Trapezoid (p. 319) A trapezoid is a quadrilateral with exactly one pair of parallel sides.

Trapecio (p. 319) Un trapecio es un cuadrilátero que tiene exactamente un par de lados paralelos.

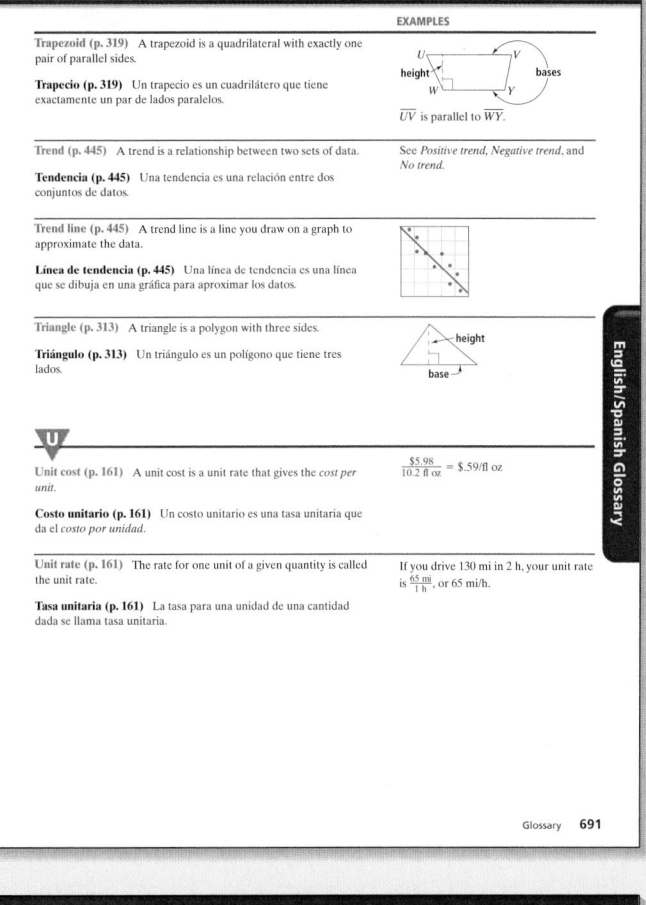

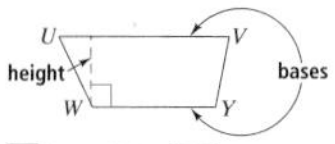

$\overline{UV}$ is parallel to $\overline{WY}$.

Trend (p. 445) A trend is a relationship between two sets of data.

Tendencia (p. 445) Una tendencia es una relación entre dos conjuntos de datos.

See *Positive trend*, *Negative trend*, and *No trend*.

Trend line (p. 445) A trend line is a line you draw on a graph to approximate the data.

Línea de tendencia (p. 445) Una línea de tendencia es una línea que se dibuja en una gráfica para aproximar los datos.

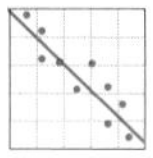

Triangle (p. 313) A triangle is a polygon with three sides.

Triángulo (p. 313) Un triángulo es un polígono que tiene tres lados.

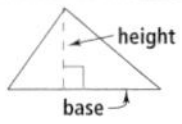

U

Unit cost (p. 161) A unit cost is a unit rate that gives the *cost per unit*.

Costo unitario (p. 161) Un costo unitario es una tasa unitaria que da el *costo por unidad*.

$\frac{\$5.98}{10.2 \text{ fl oz}} = \$.59/\text{fl oz}$

Unit rate (p. 161) The rate for one unit of a given quantity is called the unit rate.

Tasa unitaria (p. 161) La tasa para una unidad de una cantidad dada se llama tasa unitaria.

If you drive 130 mi in 2 h, your unit rate is $\frac{65 \text{ mi}}{1 \text{ h}}$, or 65 mi/h.

English/Spanish Glossary

V

EXAMPLES

Variable (p. 4) A variable is a letter that stands for a number. The value of an algebraic expression varies, or changes, depending upon the value given to the variable.

Variable (p. 4) Una variable es una letra que representa un número. El valor de una expresión algebraica varía, o cambia, dependiendo del valor que se le dé a la variable.

x is a variable in the equation $9 + x = 7$.

Venn diagram (p. 424) A Venn diagram is a diagram that uses regions, usually circles, to show how sets of numbers or objects are related.

Diagrama de Venn (p. 424) Un diagramna de Venn es un diagrama que usa regiones, generalmente círculos, para mostrar cómo se relacionan conjuntos de números u objetos.

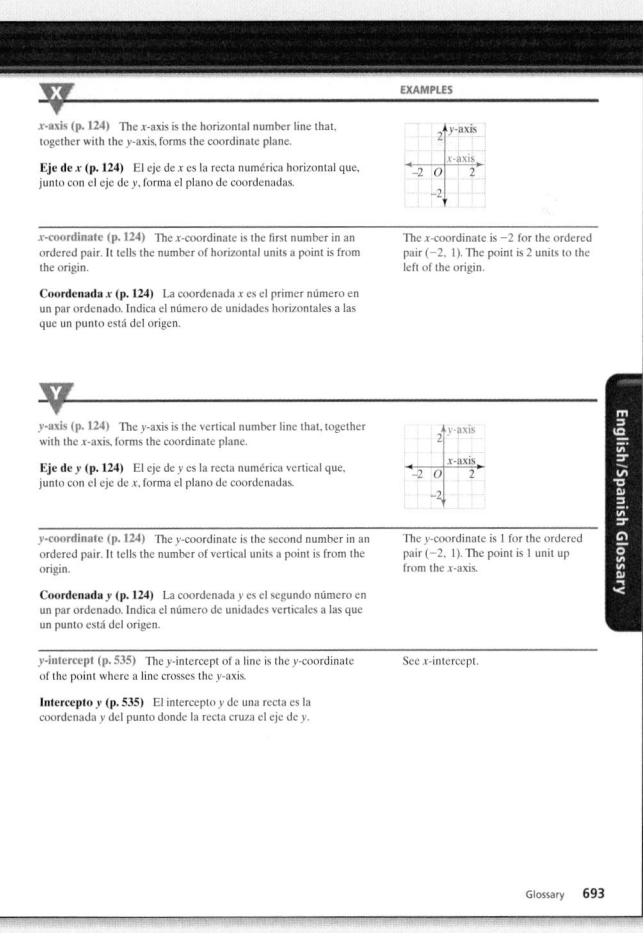

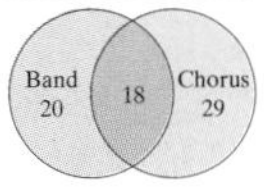

The Venn diagram shows the activities of 67 music students.

Vertex of an angle (p. 640) The vertex of an angle is the point of intersection of two sides of an angle or figure.

Vértice de un ángulo (p. 640) El vértice de un ángulo es el punto de intersección de dos lados de un ángulo o figura.

Vertex of a polygon (p. 312) The vertex of a polygon is any point where two sides of a polygon meet.

Vértice de un polígono (p. 312) El vértice de un polígono es cualquier punto donde se encuentran dos lados de un polígono.

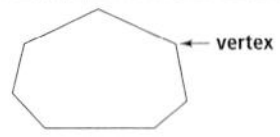

Vertical angles (p. 303) Vertical angles are formed by two intersecting lines. Vertical angles are opposite each other.

Ángulos verticales (p. 303) Los ángulos verticales están formados por dos rectas que se intersecan. Los ángulos verticales son opuestos entre sí.

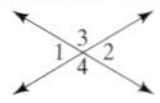

$\angle 1$ and $\angle 2$ are vertical angles, as are $\angle 3$ and $\angle 4$.

Volume (p. 380) Volume is the number of unit cubes, or cubic units, needed to fill a solid.

Volumen (p. 380) El volumen es el número de unidades cúbicas que se necesitan para llenar el espacio dentro de un sólido.

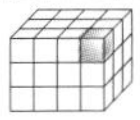

The volume of the rectangular prism is 36 in.^{3}.

X

EXAMPLES

***x*-axis (p. 124)** The *x*-axis is the horizontal number line that, together with the *y*-axis, forms the coordinate plane.

Eje de *x* (p. 124) El eje de *x* es la recta numérica horizontal que, junto con el eje de *y*, forma el plano de coordenadas.

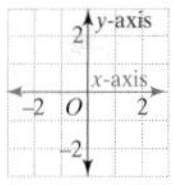

***x*-coordinate (p. 124)** The *x*-coordinate is the first number in an ordered pair. It tells the number of horizontal units a point is from the origin.

Coordenada *x* (p. 124) La coordenada *x* es el primer número en un par ordenado. Indica el número de unidades horizontales a las que un punto está del origen.

The *x*-coordinate is −2 for the ordered pair (−2, 1). The point is 2 units to the left of the origin.

Y

***y*-axis (p. 124)** The *y*-axis is the vertical number line that, together with the *x*-axis, forms the coordinate plane.

Eje de *y* (p. 124) El eje de *y* es la recta numérica vertical que, junto con el eje de *x*, forma el plano de coordenadas.

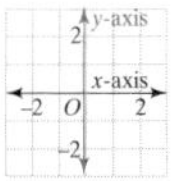

***y*-coordinate (p. 124)** The *y*-coordinate is the second number in an ordered pair. It tells the number of vertical units a point is from the origin.

Coordenada *y* (p. 124) La coordenada *y* es el segundo número en un par ordenado. Indica el número de unidades verticales a las que un punto está del origen.

The *y*-coordinate is 1 for the ordered pair (−2, 1). The point is 1 unit up from the *x*-axis.

***y*-intercept (p. 535)** The *y*-intercept of a line is the *y*-coordinate of the point where a line crosses the *y*-axis.

Intercepto *y* (p. 535) El intercepto *y* de una recta es la coordenada *y* del punto donde la recta cruza el eje de *y*.

See *x*-intercept.

English/Spanish Glossary

English/Spanish Glossary

Z

EXAMPLES

Zero pair (p. 32) The pairing of one positive tile with one negative tile is called a zero pair.

a zero pair

Par cero (p. 32) El emparejamiento de una ficha positiva con una ficha negativa se llama par cero.

Zero Product Property (p. 649) The Zero Product Property states that the product of 0 and any number is 0.

$a \cdot 0 = 0$
$6 \cdot 0 = 0$

Propiedad del cero (p. 649) La Propiedad del Cero establece que el producto de 0 y cualquier número es 0.

Answers to Instant Check System™

Chapter 1

Check Your Readiness p. 2

1. < **2.** = **3.** < **4.** > **5.** 1.234 **6.** 0.96 **7.** 7.29 **8.** 47.3 **9.** 1.88 **10.** 10.16 **11.** 0.68 **12.** 14.7 **13.** 15.52 **14.** 0.0138 **15.** 22.53 **16.** 8.512 **17.** 5.68 **18.** 8.95 **19.** 0.092

Lesson 1-1 pp. 4–6

Check Skills You'll Need **1.** $\frac{3}{4}$ **2.** 96 **3.** 10 **4.** 44.4 **5.** 3

Quick Check **1.** $15n$ **2.** 5 **3.** 40 **4.** $100 + 35m$; \$520

Lesson 1-2 pp. 10–11

Check Skills You'll Need **1.** An algebraic expression is a mathematical phrase that uses numbers, variables, and operation symbols. **2.** 11 **3.** 15 **4.** 12

Quick Check **1.** 7, 7 **2.** −5, 0, 4 **3.** Asia **4.** 15

Checkpoint Quiz 1 p. 14 **1.** $-3s$ **2.** $v \div 12$ or $\frac{v}{12}$ **3.** $m \div 10$ or $\frac{m}{10}$ **4.** $4 + f$ **5.** 304 **6.** 15 **7.** 16 **8.** 3 **9.** 10.5 **10.** 28 **11.** 7.2 **12.** $168 + 35h$; \$273

Lesson 1-3 pp. 16–17

Check Skills You'll Need **1.** Answers may vary. Sample: When you simplify an expression, you write its simplest name. When you evaluate an expression, you replace each variable with a number and then simplify. **2.** 19 **3.** 2 **4.** 38 **5.** 3

Quick Check **1a.** 18 **b.** −15 **2a.** 12 **b.** −12 **c.** −200 **3.** −181 ft, or 181 ft below the surface

Lesson 1-4 pp. 20–21

Check Skills You'll Need **1.** opposites **2.** −6 **3.** −15 **4.** −6

Quick Check **1.** 144 **2.** −18 ft/min **3.** −36

Lesson 1-5 pp. 26–28

Check Skills You'll Need **1.** To simplify an expression means to replace it with its simplest name. **2.** 99 **3.** 100 **4.** −21 **5.** 32

Quick Check **1.** 48 **2.** −46 **3.** 2,420 **4.** $6m + 18$ **5.** \$162

Checkpoint Quiz 2 p. 31 **1.** −64 **2.** 37 **3.** −43 **4.** 4 **5.** 5 **6.** 25 **7.** 119 **8.** 410 **9.** \$63.92 **10.** $-37 - 16.5$ or $-37 + (-16.5)$

Lesson 1-6 pp. 33–34

Check Skills You'll Need **1.** inverses **2.** −11 **3.** 0 **4.** −7 **5.** −6

Quick Check **1.** −3 **2.** $x + 8 = 52$; 44

Lesson 1-7 pp. 38–39

Check Skills You'll Need **1.** undo **2.** 24 **3.** −21 **4.** −2 **5.** 3

Quick Check **1.** −40 **2.** −4

Chapter 2

Check Your Readiness p. 50

1. 14 **2.** 22 **3.** 2 **4.** 2 **5.** −11, −4, 0, 3 **6.** −9, −6, 8, 13 **7.** −21, −8, 9, 16 **8.** −35, −17, −3, 22 **9.** 3 **10.** −13 **11.** −37 **12.** −25 **13.** −48 **14.** −6 **15.** 42 **16.** 9

Lesson 2-1 pp. 52–54

Check Skills You'll Need **1.** product **2.** −100 **3.** 56 **4.** 40 **5.** 0

Quick Check **1.** composite; divisible by 2 **2a.** $2 \cdot 2 \cdot 2 \cdot 2 \cdot 2 \cdot 3$ **b.** $2 \cdot 2 \cdot 2 \cdot 2 \cdot 3 \cdot 5$ **3a.** 9 **b.** 6 **4.** 21 ft

Lesson 2-2 pp. 57–58

Check Skills You'll Need **1.** $2 \cdot 2 \cdot 5 \cdot 5$ **2.** 6 **3.** 4 **4.** 25 **5.** 4

Quick Check **1.** $\frac{12 \div 4}{20 \div 4} = \frac{3}{5}$ **2.** $\frac{3 \cdot 3 \cdot 3}{3 \cdot 3 \cdot 5} = \frac{3}{5}$ **3.** .459 **4.** $1\frac{21}{50}$

Lesson 2-3 pp. 62–63

Check Skills You'll Need **1.** The numerator represents a part of the whole. **2.** $\frac{3}{5}$ **3.** $\frac{3}{11}$ **4.** $\frac{1}{4}$ **5.** $\frac{1}{11}$

Quick Check **1.** $\frac{3}{18}, \frac{2}{18}; \frac{1}{6}$ is greater. **2.** dogs; $\frac{12}{17} > \frac{7}{10}$ **3.** $-\frac{7}{8}$, −0.625, $1\frac{1}{2}$, $\frac{8}{5}$, 1.61

Lesson 2-4 pp. 66–67

Check Skills You'll Need **1.** 2, 0, −6 **2.** −10 **3.** −90 **4.** 10

Quick Check **1.** $\frac{7}{30}$ **2.** $-\frac{3}{20}$ **3.** $6\frac{19}{20}$ **4.** $17\frac{4}{5} + x = 20\frac{3}{10}$; $x = 2\frac{1}{2}$ in.

Checkpoint Quiz 1 p. 70 **1.** $2 \cdot 2 \cdot 2 \cdot 3 \cdot 3 \cdot 7$ **2.** 33

3. .296 **4.** $\frac{14}{25}$ **5.** −2.6, $-\frac{15}{7}$, $\frac{8}{25}$, 0.35, 2 **6.** $\frac{7}{9}$ **7.** $4\frac{3}{5}$ **8.** $-1\frac{23}{24}$ **9.** $-2\frac{9}{20}$ **10.** $1\frac{1}{8}$ cups

Lesson 2-5 pp. 72–73

Check Skills You'll Need **1.** $\frac{a}{b}$ **2.** $\frac{1}{3}$ **3.** $\frac{3}{5}$ **4.** $\frac{1}{9}$ **5.** $\frac{6}{11}$

Quick Check **1.** $\frac{3}{10}$ **2.** $-2\frac{47}{50}$ **3.** 5 lengths **4.** $8\frac{1}{6}$

Lesson 2-6 pp. 81–82

Check Skills You'll Need **1.** add; subtract **2.** 5 **3.** −4 **4.** −4 **5.** 10

Quick Check **1a.** 12.6 cm^2 **b.** 2 yd^2 **2.** 1.58 mi/h **3.** $w = A + 5$

Lesson 2-7 pp. 86–87

Check Skills You'll Need **1.** factor **2.** 4 **3.** 6 **4.** 16 **5.** 24 **6.** 16

Quick Check **1.** $6^2 \cdot 7^6$ **2.** −343 **3.** −343 **4.** 50 **5.** $5\frac{2}{3}$ m

Checkpoint Quiz 2 p. 91 **1.** $-2\frac{4}{5}$ **2.** $1\frac{7}{9}$ **3.** $\frac{7}{15}$ **4.** $-\frac{2}{57}$ **5.** −38 **6.** −71 **7.** 100 **8.** 93 **9.** $b = \frac{3T}{a}$ **10.** $A = 10\frac{1}{72}$ cm^2 **11.** $h = \frac{4}{\pi}$ cm

Lesson 2-8 pp. 92–93

Check Skills You'll Need **1.** power **2.** 20 **3.** 451 **4.** 1,500 **5.** 18,030 **6.** 2,390,000

Quick Check **1.** 7,660,000 km^2 **2.** 3.476×10^6 m **3.** 0.00025 in. **4.** 3.5×10^{-6}

Chapter 3

Check Your Readiness p. 104

1. −28 **2.** 68 **3.** −9 **4.** 13 **5.** 10 **6.** 0.833 **7.** 0.4 **8.** 1.615 **9.** 0.864 **10.** $b = c - a$ **11.** $t = \frac{d}{16}$ **12.** $T = s - 200$ **13.** 25 **14.** 21 **15.** 181

Lesson 3-1 pp. 106–108

Check Skills You'll Need **1.** exponent **2.** 4 **3.** 4 **4.** 36 **5.** 100

Quick Check **1a.** 6, −6 **b.** 1, −1 **c.** $\frac{1}{4}, -\frac{1}{4}$ **2.** 6 **3a.** 5.5 s **b.** 6.3 s **4.** Rational; the decimal repeats.

Lesson 3-2 pp. 112–113

Check Skills You'll Need **1.** a number that when multiplied by itself is equal to the given number **2.** 8 **3.** 11 **4.** 9 **5.** 5

Quick Check **1.** 20 cm **2.** 33 ft

Lesson 3-3 pp. 118–119

Check Skills You'll Need **1.** The Pythagorean Theorem states that in any right triangle, the sum of the squares of the lengths of the legs (a and b) is equal to the square of the length of the hypotenuse: $a^2 + b^2 = c^2$. **2.** 5 **3.** 8.6

Quick Check **1.** 15.8 ft **2.** 17.3 ft

Checkpoint Quiz 1 p. 123 **1.** 9 **2.** Irrational; 13 is not a perfect square. **3.** Rational; the number is a ratio of two integers. **4.** Irrational; the decimal does not terminate or repeat. **5.** 15 cm **6.** 22.5 ft **7.** 24 in. **8.** 24.2 m **9.** 8.9 m

Lesson 3-4 pp. 124–125

Check Skills You'll Need **1.** They are the same distance from zero on a number line but on opposite sides of zero. **2.** −5, −3, −1, 3 **3.** −6, −4, 2, 9 **4.** −10, −8, 0, 6 **5.** −5, −2, 4, 7

Quick Check **1.**

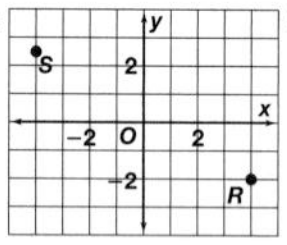

2. 6 mi

Lesson 3-5 pp. 130–131

Check Skills You'll Need **1.** variable **2.** 3 **3.** 21 **4.** 28

Quick Check **1.**

Number of CDs	Expression	Total Cost (dollars)
0	15(0)	0
1	15(1)	15
2	15(2)	30
3	15(3)	45
c	15(c)	t

$t = 15c$, where t represents total cost and c represents number of CDs.

2.

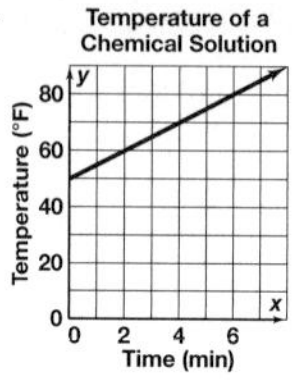

Lesson 3-6 pp. 136–137

Check Skills You'll Need **1.** Quadrant II **2.** (4, 2) **3.** (2, 1) **4.** $4 + f$ **5.** (1, −1)

Quick Check **1.**

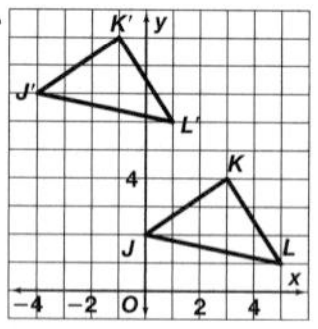

$J'(-4, 7)$ **2.** $(x, y) \rightarrow (x + 6, y + 2)$

Checkpoint Quiz 2 p. 140 **1–5.**

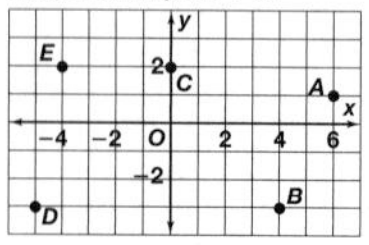

6.

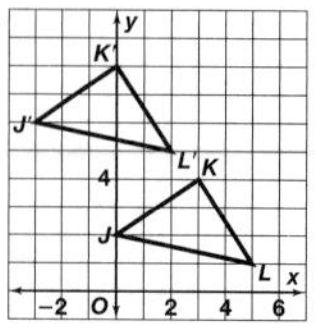

$J'(-3, 6)$, $K'(0, 8)$, $L'(2, 5)$

7. $(x, y) \rightarrow (x - 3, y + 4)$

8.

Number of Exercises	Expression	Workout Time (min)
0	3(0) + 5	5
1	3(1) + 5	8
2	3(2) + 5	11
3	3(3) + 5	14
x	3(x) + 5	w

$w = 3x + 5$

Lesson 3-7 pp. 141–142

Check Skills You'll Need **1.** distance **2.**

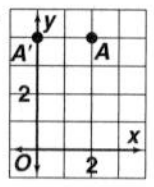

3.

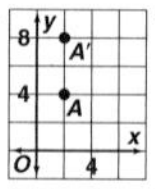

4.

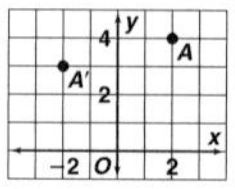

5.

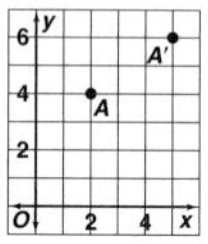

Quick Check **1.**

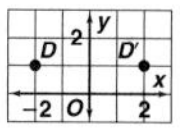

$D'(2, 1)$

2.

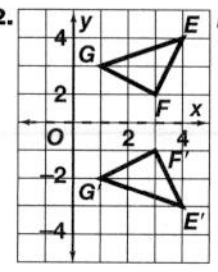

$E'(4, -3)$, $F'(3, -1)$, $G'(1, -2)$

3.

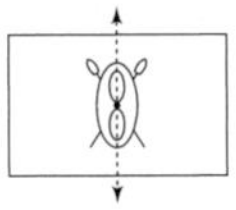

Lesson 3-8 pp. 146–147

Check Skills You'll Need **1.** matches **2.** straight **3.** obtuse **4.** obtuse **5.** acute **6.** acute **7.** right

Quick Check **1.** 72°

2a.

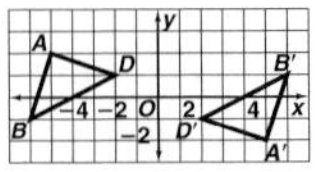

b.

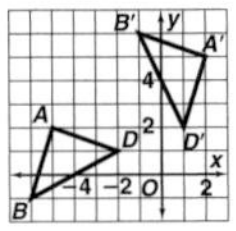

Chapter 4

Check Your Readiness p. 158

1. $\frac{1}{2}$ **2.** $\frac{2}{7}$ **3.** $\frac{5}{7}$ **4.** $\frac{11}{20}$ **5.** 0.630 **6.** 4.083 **7.** 0.323 **8.** 2.714 **9.** 0.514 **10.** 56 **11.** $\frac{1}{4}$ **12.** $\frac{5}{6}$ **13.** $\frac{9}{16}$ **14.** $4\frac{1}{5}$ **15.** 30 **16.** 36.1 in. **17.** 10.1 m **18.** 28.8 cm

Lesson 4-1 pp. 160–161

Check Skills You'll Need **1.** The least common denominator is the smallest multiple the denominators have in common. **2.** $\frac{3}{9}$ **3.** $\frac{4}{5}$ **4.** $\frac{45}{54}$ **5.** $\frac{7}{12}$

Quick Check **1.** $\frac{1}{6}$ **2.** 6.5 deliveries/h **3.** the 20-oz box

Lesson 4-2 pp. 166–168

Check Skills You'll Need **1.** 1 **2.** $\frac{5}{6}$ **3.** $\frac{5}{9}$ **4.** $\frac{2}{3}$ **5.** $2\frac{2}{7}$

Quick Check **1.** 11,880 ft **2.** 13.2 ft/s **3a.** 7 **b.** 5 **4.** 16.0 qt

Checkpoint Quiz 1 p. 171 **1.** $\frac{1}{15}$ **2.** $\frac{1}{4}$ **3.** 6 : 1 **4.** $\frac{3}{4}$ **5.** $12/book **6.** 12 m/s **7.** 3 gal/min **8.** 8 mi/h

9. 0.20 **10.** 20 **11.** 17.0 **12.** 7.9 **13.** 104.7 km/h **14.** $4.75/page **15.** 12.2 km/min

Lesson 4-3 pp. 174–175

Check Skills You'll Need **1.** Yes; there is no common factor between the numerator and denominator. **2.** $\frac{10}{33}$ **3.** $3\frac{1}{2}$ **4.** $\frac{66}{301}$ **5.** $2\frac{4}{5}$

Quick Check **1.** no; $\frac{6}{7} \neq \frac{23}{28}$ **2.** $240.96

Lesson 4-4 pp. 181–182

Check Skills You'll Need **1.** $10 \cdot 3 = 15 \cdot 2$ **2.** 39 **3.** 110 **4.** $506\frac{1}{4}$

Quick Check **1.** Yes; the corresponding angles are congruent and the corresponding side lengths are proportional. **2.** 11.2 in. **3.** 21 ft

Checkpoint Quiz 2 p. 186 **1.** 38 **2.** 21 **3.** 8 **4.** 52 **5.** 6 **6.** 2.8 **7.** about $19.80 **8.** 49.5 **9.** $n = 30$; $y = 12$ **10.** 51 ft

Lesson 4-5 pp. 187–188

Check Skills You'll Need **1.** x **2-5.**

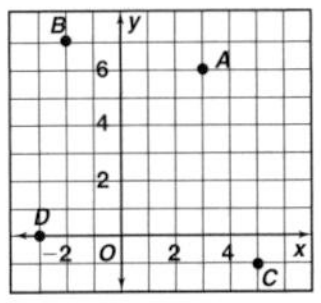

Quick Check **1.**

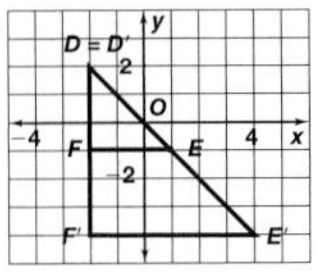

2. $A'(0, 0)$, $B'(0, 4)$, $C'(4, 4)$, $D'(4, 0)$ **3.** 3; enlargement

Lesson 4-6 pp. 192–193

Check Skills You'll Need **1.** multiplication **2.** 12.8 **3.** 44.84 **4.** 39.6 **5.** 84.5

Quick Check **1.** $2\frac{13}{16}$ in. **2.** about 140 mi

Lesson 4-7 pp. 197–198

Check Skills You'll Need **1.** shape **2.** $\angle Y$

Quick Check **1.** 52.5 ft **2.** about 460.7 m

Chapter 5

Check Your Readiness p. 208

1. 20 **2.** 15.91 **3.** 237.5 **4.** 1.75 **5.** $\frac{1}{2}$ **6.** $\frac{5}{8}$ **7.** $\frac{1}{12}$ **8.** $\frac{9}{16}$ **9.** 30 **10.** $8\frac{1}{2}$ **11.** 100 **12.** 36 **13.** 2 **14.** 32 **15.** 100 **16.** 19 **17.** 85.5

Lesson 5-1 pp. 210–212

Check Skills You'll Need **1.** $\frac{a}{b}, b \neq 0$ **2.** $\frac{9}{10}$ **3.** $\frac{4}{5}$ **4.** $\frac{7}{20}$ **5.** $\frac{1}{4}$

Quick Check **1.** 55% **2.** 8% **3.** $\frac{3}{2}$ **4.** 0.73, $\frac{3}{4}$, 76%

Lesson 5-2 pp. 214–215

Check Skills You'll Need **1.** $\frac{7}{3}$ **2.** 27 **3.** 8 **4.** 54 **5.** 45

Quick Check **1.** about 20 **2.** about 8 students **3.** about $10.80

Lesson 5-3 pp. 218–220

Check Skills You'll Need **1.** proportion **2.** 20 **3.** $66\frac{2}{3}$ **4.** 100 **5.** 3 **6.** 25

Quick Check **1.** 70.3 **2.** 199.75 **3.** 275 students **4.** 20%

Lesson 5-4 pp. 224–225

Check Skills You'll Need **1.** Equation; it contains an = sign. **2.** 40 **3.** 1.25 **4.** 15 **5.** 0.03125

Quick Check **1.** $11.76 **2.** 90

Checkpoint Quiz 1 p. 229 **1.** 50% **2.** 9.09% **3.** 37.5% **4.** 250% **5.** 40% **6.** about 12 **7.** about 0.24 **8.** about 11 **9.** about 0.04 **10.** about 1,300,000 people **11.** 50 **12.** 5% **13.** 0.78 **14.** 0.25

Lesson 5-5 pp. 230–231

Check Skills You'll Need **1.** percent **2.** 112.5% **3.** 27.3% **4.** 26.7% **5.** 366.7%

Quick Check **1.** 19.4% **2.** 5.3% **3.** 57.2%

Lesson 5-6 pp. 234–236

Check Skills You'll Need **1.** percent **2.** 4 **3.** 200 **4.** 1,100 **5.** 14,000

Quick Check **1.** 90% **2.** $161.80 **3.** $100.51 **4.** $116.47

Lesson 5-7 pp. 242–243

Check Skills You'll Need **1.** formula **2.** $w = \frac{V}{\ell h}$ **3.** $r = \frac{d}{t}$ **4.** $b = y - x$ **5.** $B = \frac{3v}{h}$

Quick Check **1.** $630 **2.** $369

Checkpoint Quiz 2 p. 245 **1.** 1,000% increase **2.** 1.6% decrease **3.** 80% decrease **4.** 270.7% increase **5.** 3.4% **6.** $23.06 **7.** 15% **8.** $43.75 **9.** $17.10

Lesson 5-8 pp. 246–248

Check Skills You'll Need **1.** ratio **2.** 1 : 2 **3.** $\frac{2}{25}$ **4.** $\frac{1}{3}$ **5.** $\frac{5}{9}$ **6.** 1 : 4

Quick Check **1.** $\frac{3}{8}$ **2.** 28% **3.** $\frac{1}{2}$ **4.** $\frac{3}{8}$

Chapter 6

Check Your Readiness p. 258

1. −2 **2.** −2 **3.** 14 **4.** 123 **5.** −4 **6.** 3 **7.** −3 **8.** 1 **9.** −1 **10.** 1 **11.** 3 **12.** $5c - 15$ **13.** $-2w - 16$ **14.** $-54 + 9t$ **15.** $-10 + 2a$ **16.** $44 - 11b$ **17.** $-x + 2$

Lesson 6-1 pp. 261–262

Check Skills You'll Need **1.** to get the variable alone on one side of the equation **2.** −7 **3.** 6 **4.** 30

Quick Check **1.** −8.7 **2.** $0.5 + 0.85c = 3.90$; 4 min

Lesson 6-2 pp. 266–267

Check Skills You'll Need **1.** No; 15 can be subtracted from 5. The simplest form is $3a - 10$. **2.** $-8r - 24$ **3.** $-7s + 35$ **4.** $70 - 35t$

Quick Check **1.** $-14t$ **2.** Let b = the cost of a board. Let n = the cost of a box of nails. Let h = the cost of a hammer. $26b + 3n + h$ **3.** $9 - 6b$

Checkpoint Quiz 1 p. 270 **1.** 5.5 **2.** 9 **3.** 1 **4.** 3 **5.** 15 **6.** −28 **7.** $56.\overline{6}$ **8.** −26.65 **9.** −3 **10.** $1.50 **11.** $-8m + p + 4$ **12.** $8.1g - 13.65$ **13.** $-2h + 20$ **14.** $10k + 0.11$ **15.** $-4.81j - 18.27$ **16.** $168 - 3a$ **17.** Let s = the cost of a sleeping bag. Let f = the cost of a flashlight. $11s + 7f$

Lesson 6-3 pp. 271–272

Check Skills You'll Need **1.** $3x$, $2x$, $-x$ **2.** $12 - 26m$ **3.** $28 - 12r$ **4.** $8q + 5$

Quick Check **1.** −11 **2.** 17 boys

Lesson 6-4 pp. 276–277

Check Skills You'll Need **1.** inverse operations **2.** $9t + 47$ **3.** $60 - 12r$ **4.** $-3x - 7$

Quick Check **1.** 2 **2.** 61 text messages

Lesson 6-5 pp. 282–283

Check Skills You'll Need **1.** equation **2.** −18 **3.** −13 **4.** 24

Quick Check **1.** $5 \leq u$

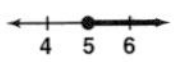

2. At most, 211 more people can attend.

Checkpoint Quiz 2 p. 287 **1.** $x \geq -2$ **2.** $x < 1$ **3.** −9 **4.** −1 **5.** −28 **6.** $a \geq -6$ **7.** $g \leq 1$ **8.** $y < -23$ **9.** Let b = the cost of a banana. $4.99 + b = 13b$; $b = \$.42$ **10.** Let x = the load weight. $28{,}500 + x = 64{,}000$; $x = 35{,}500$ lb

Lesson 6-6 pp. 288–290

Check Skills You'll Need **1.** No; zero is not a negative number. **2.** −4 **3.** −101 **4.** 6.2 **5.** −8

Quick Check **1.** up to 12 passengers

2. $b \leq -4$

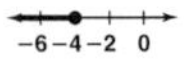

3. $p \leq -17$

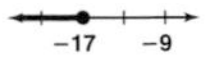

Chapter 7

Check Your Readiness p. 300

1. 36 **2.** 100.48 **3.** 40 **4.** 8 **5.** 43 **6.** −3 **7.** 32 **8.** 15 **9.** $1\frac{1}{7}$ **10.** 84 **11.** 35.7 **12.** 216 m^2 **13.** 28 $in.^2$ **14.** 169 ft^2

Lesson 7-1 pp. 303–304

Check Skills You'll Need **1.** subtraction **2.** 18 **3.** 31 **4.** −41 **5.** −29

Quick Check **1.** $\angle DBJ$ and $\angle YBT$; adjacent angles may vary. Sample: $\angle DBJ$ and $\angle DBY$ **2.** 133° **3.** 58°; 90°

Lesson 7-2 pp. 307–308

Check Skills You'll Need **1.** 120° and 60° **2.** 132° **3.** 61° **4.** 113° **5.** 49°

Quick Check **1a.** alternate interior **b.** corresponding **c.** neither **2.** $m\angle 6 = m\angle 7 = 117°$ **3.** The measure of each angle formed by lines t and ℓ and lines t and m is 90°. Since pairs of corresponding angles are congruent, the lines are parallel.

Lesson 7-3 pp. 312–314

Check Skills You'll Need **1.** equal **2.** Not similar; corresponding sides are not in proportion.

Quick Check **1.** $\triangle TRS \cong \triangle KJL$ **2a.** $\triangle XYZ \cong \triangle RQP$ by SSS **b.** $\triangle KLM \cong \triangle JLM$ by SAS **3a.** 40° **b.** 50°

Checkpoint Quiz 1 p. 317 **1.** vertical **2.** alternate interior **3.** corresponding **4.** adjacent **5.** corresponding **6.** adjacent **7.** Answers may vary. Sample: SAS, ASA, or SSS; $\triangle JKD \cong \triangle WTB$. **8.** 23°; 113° **9.** 100° **10.** 90° **11.** 120° **12.** 0.9 m **13.** 1.6 m **14.** 1.7 m

Lesson 7-4 pp. 318–319

Check Skills You'll Need **1.** 90° **2.** acute **3.** obtuse

Quick Check **1a.** isosceles obtuse **b.** equilateral acute **2a.** Rectangle; the quadrilateral has four right angles. **b.** Trapezoid; the quadrilateral has exactly one pair of parallel sides.

Lesson 7-5 pp. 324–325

Check Skills You'll Need **1.** You replace each variable in the expression with a number and then simplify. **2.** 27 **3.** 6 **4.** 36

Quick Check **1.** 900° **2.** 151° **3.** 108°

Lesson 7-6 pp. 328–330

Check Skills You'll Need **1.** A formula is a rule that shows the relationship between two or more quantities. **2.** 80 cm^2 **3.** 49 ft^2

Quick Check **1.** 10.5 cm^2 **2.** 15 yd^2

Checkpoint Quiz 2 p. 335 **1.** parallelogram; 100.86 cm^2 **2.** isosceles triangle; 1.7 $in.^2$ **3.** trapezoid; 43.35 m^2 **4.** 133° **5–6.** Answers may vary. Samples are given.

5.

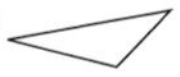

6.

Lesson 7-7 pp. 336–337

Check Skills You'll Need **1.** Perimeter is the distance around a figure. Area is the number of square units a figure encloses. **2.** 45.5 ft^2

Quick Check **1.** 78.5 in.; 490.9 $in.^2$ **2.** 193.0 m^2

Lesson 7-8 pp. 341–342

Check Skills You'll Need **1.** Congruent polygons have the same size and shape.

2. $\angle P \cong \angle T$; $\angle Q \cong \angle U$; $\angle R \cong \angle V$; $\overline{PQ} \cong \overline{TU}$; $\overline{QR} \cong \overline{UV}$; $\overline{RP} \cong \overline{VT}$

3. $\angle A \cong \angle L$; $\angle B \cong \angle M$; $\angle C \cong \angle N$; $\angle D \cong \angle O$; $\overline{AB} \cong \overline{LM}$; $\overline{BC} \cong \overline{MN}$; $\overline{CD} \cong \overline{NO}$; $\overline{DA} \cong \overline{OL}$

Quick Check **1.**

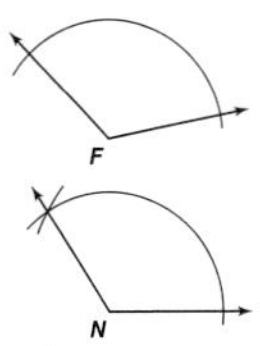

2.

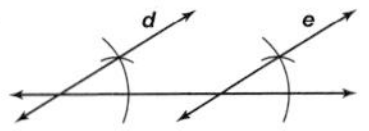

Chapter 8

Check Your Readiness p. 352

1. 7 ft^2 **2.** 13 m^2 **3.** 96 cm^2 **4.** 54 mm^2 **5.** 20 $in.^2$ **6.** 22 cm^2 **7.** 3 **8.** 7 **9.** 2.5 **10.** 12

Lesson 8-1 pp. 354–355

Check Skills You'll Need **1.** Congruent triangles have the same shape and size. **2.** scalene triangle **3.** parallelogram

Quick Check **1.** The figure is a pentagonal prism. $\overline{JK}$ is a lateral edge. Points J and K are vertices of the prism. **2.** a trapezoidal prism; a rectangular prism **3.** Answers may vary. Sample: $\overline{AB}$ and $\overline{BC}$ are intersecting line segments; no.

Lesson 8-2 pp. 358–359

Check Skills You'll Need **1.** parallelograms **2.** rectangular prisms

Quick Check **1.**

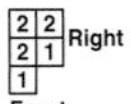

2.

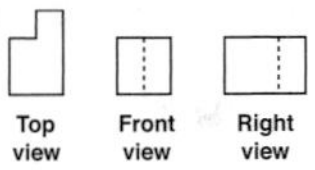

3.

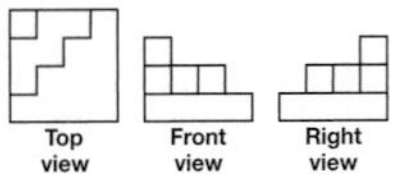

Lesson 8-3 pp. 364–365

Check Skills You'll Need **1.** isometric **2.**

Quick Check **1.** six congruent squares **2.** pentagonal pyramid

Lesson 8-4 pp. 368–370

Check Skills You'll Need **1.** Multiply the length times the width. **2.** 16.5 cm^2 **3.** 12.6 ft^2

Quick Check **1.** 936 cm^2 **2.** about 392 $in.^2$ **3.** 151 m^2

Checkpoint Quiz 1 p. 373 **1.** triangular prism **2.** rectangles **3.**

4.

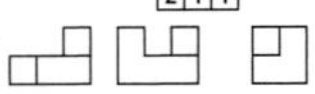

5. 468 ft^2

Lesson 8-5 pp. 374–376

Check Skills You'll Need **1.** hypotenuse **2.** 10 ft^2

Quick Check **1.** 224 cm^2

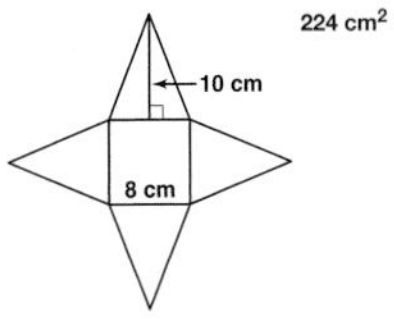

2. 922,610 ft^2 **3.** 1,492,635 ft^2 **4.** 113 yd^2

Lesson 8-6 pp. 380–381

Check Skills You'll Need **1.** No; the base of a cylinder is a circle, not a polygon. **2.** 105 ft^2 **3.** 207 m^2

Quick Check **1.** 52.5 ft^3 **2a.** about 2,025 mm^3 **b.** 2,120 mm^3

Lesson 8-7 pp. 388–389

Check Skills You'll Need **1.** The base of a pyramid is a polygon, whereas the base of a cone is a circle. **2.** 429 $in.^2$

Quick Check **1.** 19,200 $in.^3$ **2.** 113 m^3 **3.** $r \approx 6.2$ cm

Checkpoint Quiz 2 p. 392 **1.** 1,155 cm^2; 1,911 cm^3 **2.** 1,759 $in.^2$; 4,516 $in.^3$ **3.** 6,552 cm^2; 31,164 cm^3 **4.** 126 m^3 **5.** 324 $in.^3$ **6.** 40,000 cm^3 **7.** about 1 ft **8.** about 42 ft^3

Lesson 8-8 pp. 393–394

Check Skills You'll Need **1.** The radius is half the diameter. **2.** about 48 cm^2 **3.** about 108 m^2 **4.** about 27 ft^2 **5.** about 217 $in.^2$

Quick Check **1.** 616 ft^2 **2.** 33,510 $in.^3$

Lesson 8-9 pp. 398–399

Check Skills You'll Need **1.** A proportion is an equation stating that two ratios are equal. **2.** 1.75 **3.** 43.2 **4.** 9

Quick Check **1.** 8.8 m **2.** 486 $in.^2$; 729 $in.^3$

Chapter 9

Check Your Readiness p. 410

1–9.

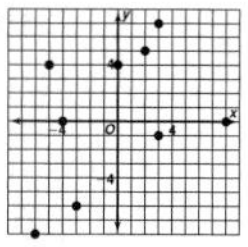

10. 18 **11.** 28 **12.** 24 **13.** 5 **14.** $\frac{13}{50}$ **15.** $\frac{12}{25}$ **16.** $\frac{13}{100}$ **17.** $\frac{18}{25}$ **18.** $\frac{1}{5}$ **19.** $\frac{47}{100}$ **20.** $\frac{1}{2}$ **21.** $\frac{1}{10}$ **22.** $\frac{1}{20}$

Lesson 9-1 pp. 412–414

Check Skills You'll Need **1.** subtraction **2.** 18 **3.** 31 **4.** −41 **5.** −29

Quick Check **1.** 14; 15; 11 **2.** 8.9 **3a.** 1; it lowers the mean about 1.4. **b.** −18; it lowers the mean about 1.8. **4.** median

Lesson 9-2 pp. 418–419

Check Skills You'll Need **1.** range **2.** 7.9; 8; 7 and 8; 4 **3.** 0.875; 1; no mode; 9

Quick Check **1.** Human Body Temperatures

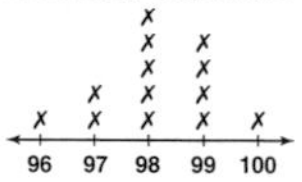

2. 101.5°; 101° **3.** Answers may vary. Sample:

Cost (Dollars)	Frequency
4–5.99	4
6–7.99	6
8–9.99	4

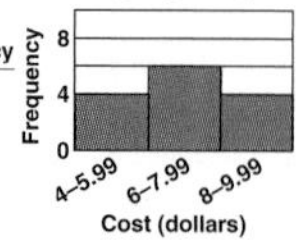

Lesson 9-3 p. 424

Check Skills You'll Need **1.** additive inverses **2.** 16 **3.** −1 **4.** 7

Quick Check **1.**

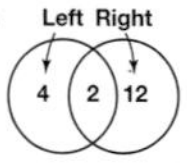

Lesson 9-4 pp. 428–429

Check Skills You'll Need **1.** A bar graph compares amounts. **2.**

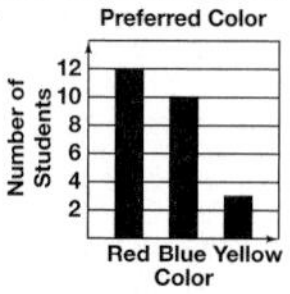

Quick Check **1.** The graph starts at 0 on the vertical axis, so the difference between the airports is portrayed more accurately. **2.** The second graph with the break symbol shows the data more clearly because the scale is more spread out.

Checkpoint Quiz 1 p. 432 **1.** 94.5 **2.** 90 **3.** 88 **4.** 30

5.

Scores	Frequency
61–70	1
71–80	5
81–90	5
91–100	6

6.

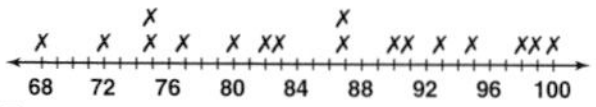

7.

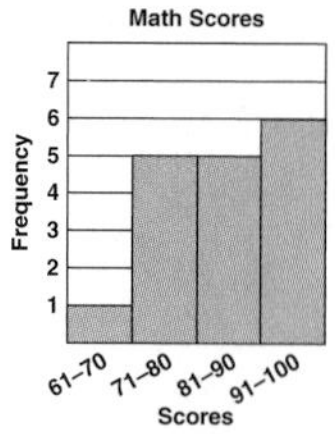

8.

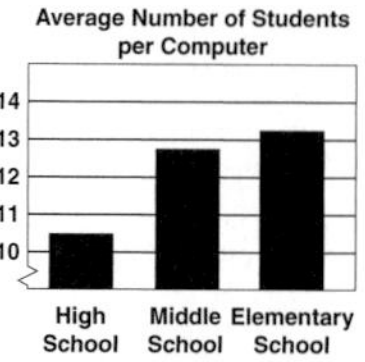

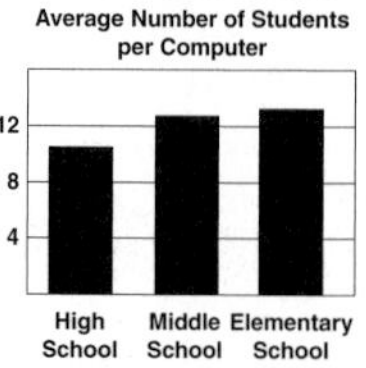

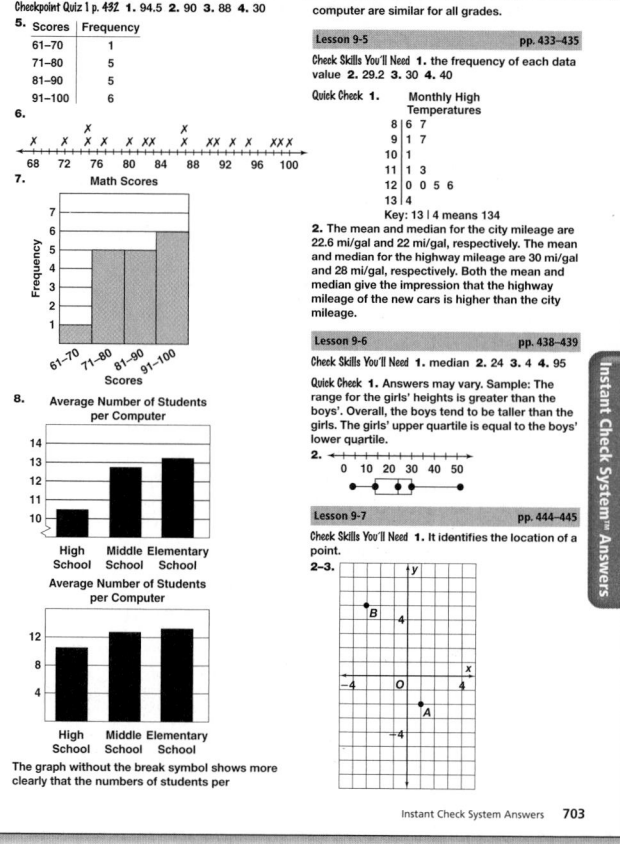

The graph without the break symbol shows more clearly that the numbers of students per computer are similar for all grades.

Lesson 9-5 pp. 433–435

Check Skills You'll Need **1.** the frequency of each data value **2.** 29.2 **3.** 30 **4.** 40

Quick Check **1.** Monthly High Temperatures

8	6 7
9	1 7
10	1
11	1 3
12	0 0 5 6
13	4

Key: 13 | 4 means 134

2. The mean and median for the city mileage are 22.6 mi/gal and 22 mi/gal, respectively. The mean and median for the highway mileage are 30 mi/gal and 28 mi/gal, respectively. Both the mean and median give the impression that the highway mileage of the new cars is higher than the city mileage.

Lesson 9-6 pp. 438–439

Check Skills You'll Need **1.** median **2.** 24 **3.** 4 **4.** 95

Quick Check **1.** Answers may vary. Sample: The range for the girls' heights is greater than the boys'. Overall, the boys tend to be taller than the girls. The girls' upper quartile is equal to the boys' lower quartile.

2.

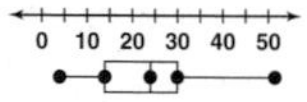

Lesson 9-7 pp. 444–445

Check Skills You'll Need **1.** It identifies the location of a point.

2–3.

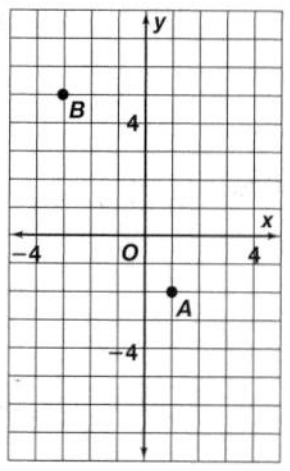

Instant Check System™ Answers

Quick Check **1.**

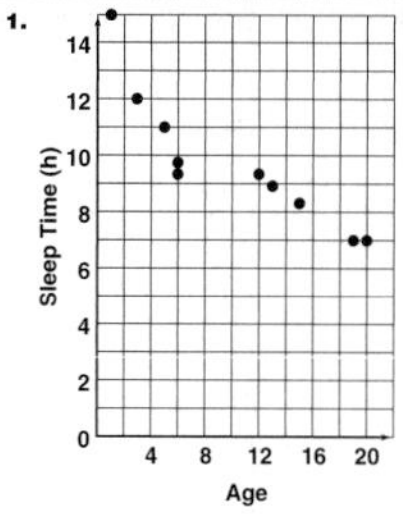

2.

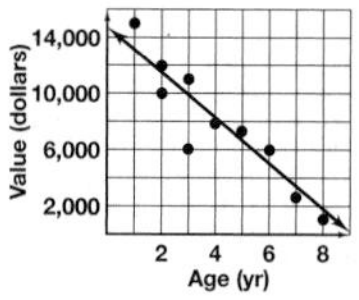

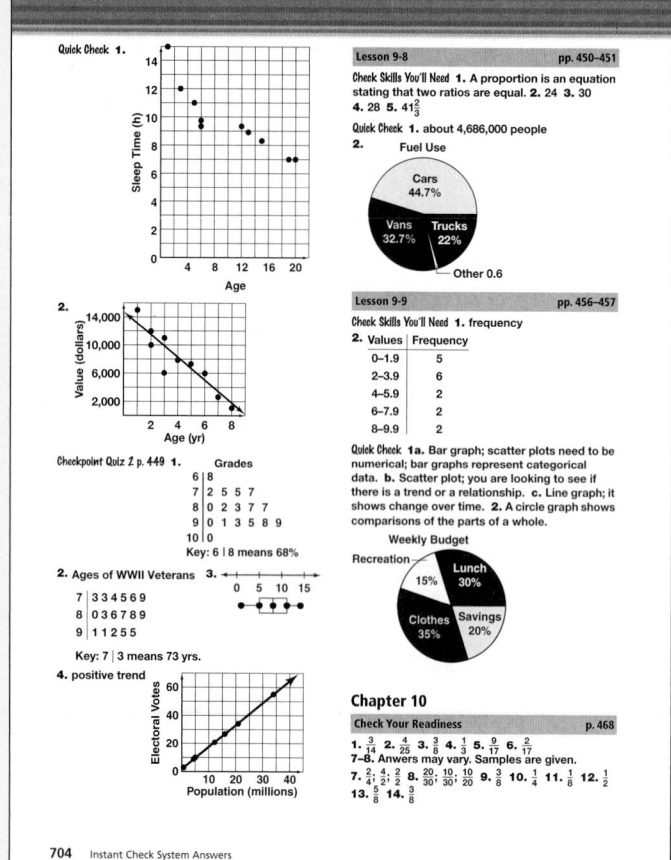

Checkpoint Quiz 2 p. 449 **1.** Grades

6	8
7	2 5 5 7
8	0 2 3 7 7
9	0 1 3 5 8 9
10	0

Key: 6 | 8 means 68%

2. Ages of WWII Veterans

7	3 3 4 5 6 9
8	0 3 6 7 8 9
9	1 1 2 5 5

Key: 7 | 3 means 73 yrs.

3.

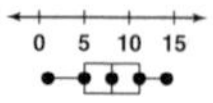

4. positive trend

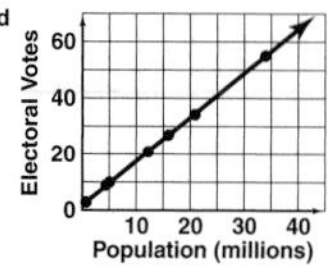

Lesson 9-8 pp. 450–451

Check Skills You'll Need **1.** A proportion is an equation stating that two ratios are equal. **2.** 24 **3.** 30 **4.** 28 **5.** $41\frac{2}{3}$

Quick Check **1.** about 4,686,000 people

2.

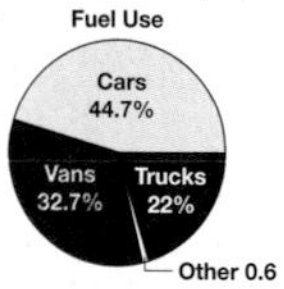

Lesson 9-9 pp. 456–457

Check Skills You'll Need **1.** frequency

2.

Values	Frequency
0–1.9	5
2–3.9	6
4–5.9	2
6–7.9	2
8–9.9	2

Quick Check **1a.** Bar graph; scatter plots need to be numerical; bar graphs represent categorical data. **b.** Scatter plot; you are looking to see if there is a trend or a relationship. **c.** Line graph; it shows change over time. **2.** A circle graph shows comparisons of the parts of a whole.

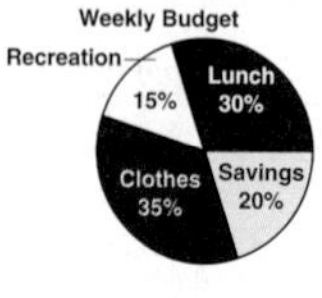

Chapter 10

Check Your Readiness p. 468

1. $\frac{3}{14}$ **2.** $\frac{4}{25}$ **3.** $\frac{3}{8}$ **4.** $\frac{1}{3}$ **5.** $\frac{9}{17}$ **6.** $\frac{2}{17}$
7–8. Anwers may vary. Samples are given.
7. $\frac{2}{4}$; $\frac{4}{2}$; $\frac{2}{2}$ **8.** $\frac{20}{30}$; $\frac{10}{30}$; $\frac{10}{20}$ **9.** $\frac{3}{8}$ **10.** $\frac{1}{4}$ **11.** $\frac{1}{8}$ **12.** $\frac{1}{2}$ **13.** $\frac{5}{8}$ **14.** $\frac{3}{8}$

Lesson 10-1 pp. 470–471

Check Skills You'll Need **1.** sample space **2.** 1, 2, 3, 4, 5, 6 **3.** $\frac{1}{6}$ **4.** $\frac{1}{2}$ **5.** $\frac{1}{3}$

Quick Check **1.** 0.4 **2.** Theoretical; the result is based on the number of possible outcomes. **3.** 5 : 2

Lesson 10-2 pp. 475–476

Check Skills You'll Need **1.** cross **2.** 135 **3.** 136 **4.** 4.5

Quick Check **1.** about 13 winning caps **2.** 380 votes

Checkpoint Quiz 1 p. 479 **1.** 0.95 **2.** 0.94 **3.** 0.77 **4.** Experimental; the results are based on a survey. **5.** 10 heads **6.** 9 toys

Lesson 10-3 pp. 480–481

Check Skills You'll Need **1.** Experimental probability is based on running numerous trials or experiments, whereas theoretical probability is based on the mathematical likelihood of events. **2.** $\frac{1}{2}$ **3.** $\frac{2}{9}$ **4.** $\frac{5}{18}$

Quick Check **1.** Not a random sample; people who are 18–30 years old may not represent all people. **2.** It assumes you either in-line skate or ice skate; answers may vary. Sample: Do you like to in-line skate or ice skate, or neither? **3.** No; she would not get a random sample of all shoppers.

Lesson 10-4 pp. 486–487

Check Skills You'll Need **1.** You can set up a proportion to solve, or you can multiply the theoretical probability by the population size. **2.** about 8 **3.** about 8 **4.** 0 **5.** about 25

Quick Check **1.** $\frac{21}{400}$ or 0.0525 **2.** $\frac{3}{10}$ **3a.** Independent; the outcome of the first coin flip does not affect the outcome of the second coin flip. **b.** Dependent; since you do not replace the name after you pick it, the outcome of the first pick affects the outcome of the second pick.

Checkpoint Quiz 2 p. 490 **1.** No; people at the music store are not representative of all the people who read. **2.** Yes; it makes watching a movie seem more appealing than reading a book. **3.** $\frac{1}{50}$ **4.** $\frac{1}{10}$ **5.** $\frac{1}{20}$ **6.** $\frac{9}{100}$ **7.** $\frac{1}{182}$ **8.** $\frac{1}{26}$ **9.** $\frac{3}{91}$ **10.** $\frac{6}{91}$

Lesson 10-5 pp. 491–492

Check Skills You'll Need **1.** a collection of all possible outcomes **2.** 12 **3.** 36 **4.** 4

Quick Check **1a.** 120 ways **b.** 24 orders **2.** There are 4 times as many ways, or 840 ways. **3a.** 2 **b.** 720 **c.** 24

Lesson 10-6 pp. 496–497

Check Skills You'll Need **1.** permutation **2.** 42 **3.** 24 **4.** 90 **5.** 999,900

Quick Check **1.** 4 groups **2a.** 21 **b.** 70 **c.** 10

Chapter 11

Check Your Readiness p. 510

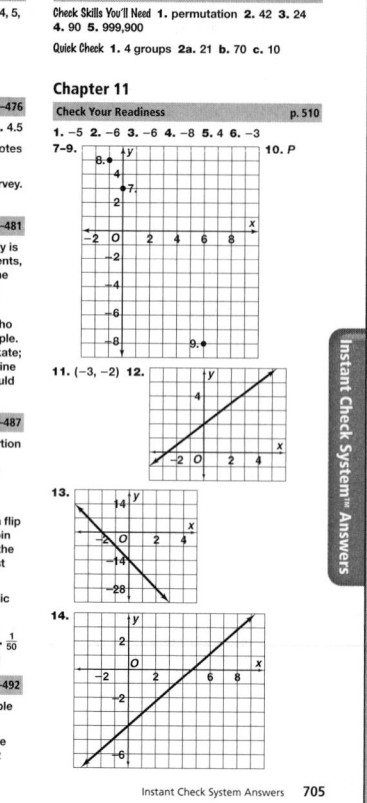

1. −5 **2.** −6 **3.** −6 **4.** −8 **5.** 4 **6.** −3

7–9.

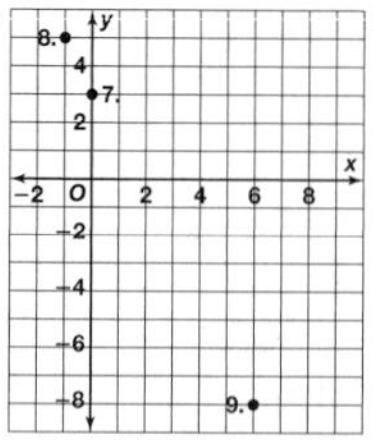

10. *P*

11. (−3, −2) **12.**

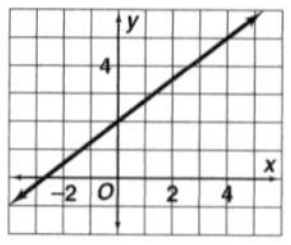

13.

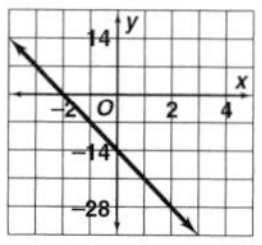

14.

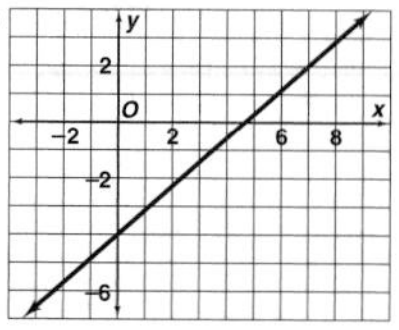

Instant Check System™ Answers

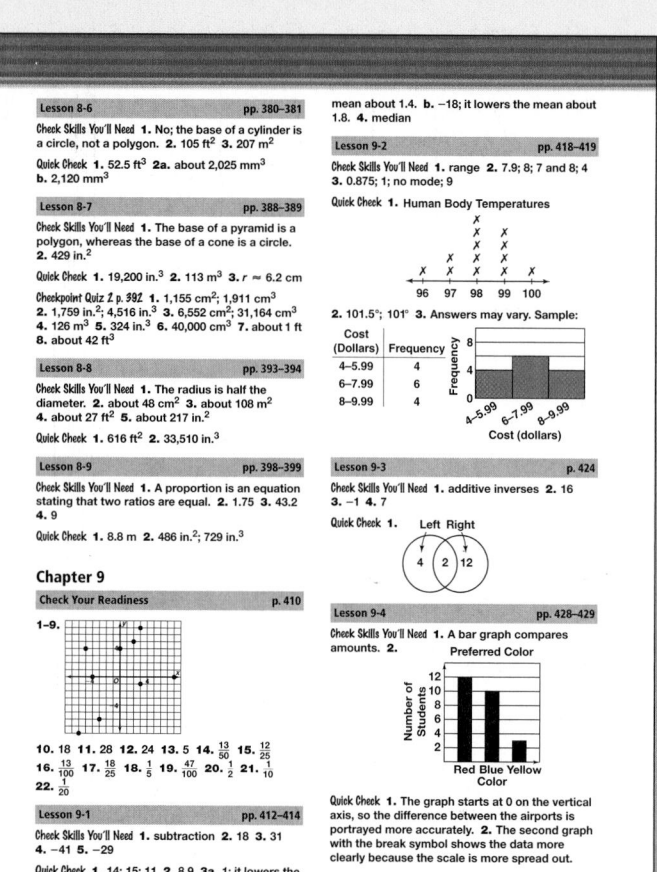

Lesson 11-1 pp. 512–514

Check Skills You'll Need **1.** Replace each variable with a number and then simplify. **2.** $n + 7$ **3.** $5n$ **4.** $12d$

Quick Check **1a.** 33, 40, 47 **b.** 24, 29, 34 **c.** 42, 52, 62 **2.** 0, 3, 6, 9 **3.** $-2n$; -40 **4.** 10; start with 0.1 and multiply by 10 repeatedly; 1,000; 10,000; 100,000.

Lesson 11-2 pp. 518–519

Check Skills You'll Need **1.** Line graphs best display changes over time. **2–3.** Answers may vary. Samples are given. **2.** Line plots best display frequency of data—for example, displaying the number of siblings each class member has. **3.** Bar graphs compare amounts in different categories—for example, the number of students in each grade.

Quick Check **1.** 40 mi/h

2.

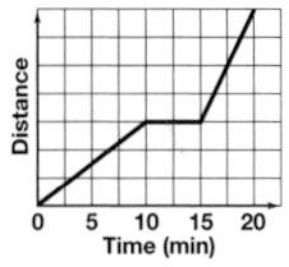

Checkpoint Quiz 1 p. 522 **1.** 65, 78, 91 **2.** $3\frac{3}{4}, 4\frac{1}{2}, 5\frac{1}{4}$ **3.** $-35, -42, -49$ **4.** 20 mi/h **5.** 20 mi **6.** after 1 hour **7.** 40 mi/h **8.** 65 mi/h

Lesson 11-3 pp. 523–524

Check Skills You'll Need **1.** a **2.** 8 **3.** 53 **4.** 9 **5.** -5

Quick Check **1.**

c	d
5	$.50
10	$1.00
15	$1.50

2. 40; 0

3. $f(6) = 12$; $f(6)$ is the total cost of buying 6 fish.

Lesson 11-4 pp. 528–530

Check Skills You'll Need **1.** no **2.** -4 **3.** 14 **4.** -6 **5.** -2

Quick Check **1a.** $\frac{2}{5}$ **b.** $-\frac{1}{2}$ **2.** undefined

3. -2

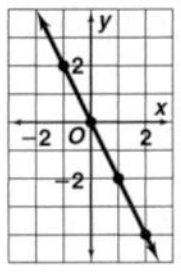

Lesson 11-5 pp. 534–535

Check Skills You'll Need **1.** Divide the change in y by the change in x. **2.** $-\frac{6}{7}$ **3.** 0 **4.** -1

Quick Check **1.**

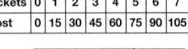

Tickets	0	1	2	3	4	5	6	7
Cost	0	15	30	45	60	75	90	105

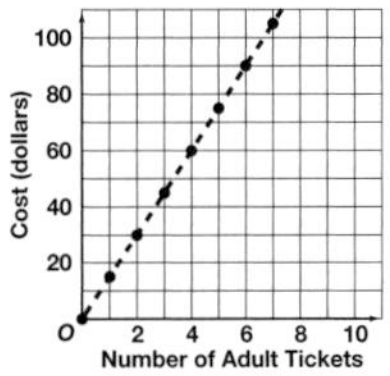

2.

Time	0	1	2	3	4	5	6
Height	4,000	3,400	2,800	2,200	1,600	1,000	400

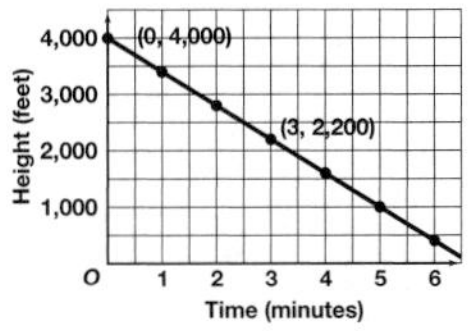

Checkpoint Quiz 2 p. 539 **1.** 1 **2.** -17 **3.** -2 **4.** 28 **5.** 0.99 p **6.** 0 **7.** $\frac{3}{2}$ **8.** -1 **9.** A hill with a rise of 5 and a run of 3 is steeper because it is rising $1\frac{2}{3}$ units for each horizontal unit. The other hill is rising only $\frac{3}{5}$ unit for each horizontal unit.

10.

Hours Worked	Money Earned
0	0
1	7
2	14
3	21
4	28
5	35
6	42
7	49
8	56

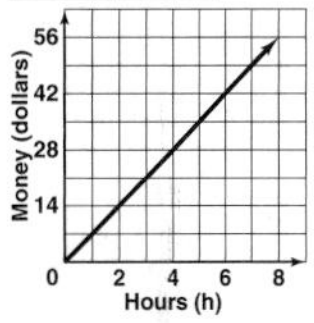

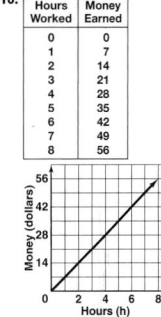

Lesson 11-6 pp. 540–541

Check Skills You'll Need **1.** $y = mx + b$, where m is the slope and b is the y-intercept **2.** 3; -2 **3.** 1; 5 **4.** 8; 0

Quick Check **1.** $y = 298 - 42x$ **2.** no **3.** $y - 1 = -\frac{4}{5}(x + 2)$

Lesson 11-7 pp. 546–547

Check Skills You'll Need **1.** The rate of change is constant.

2.

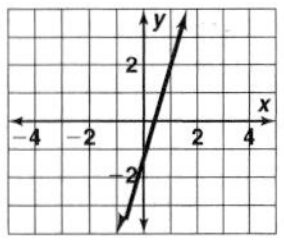

3.

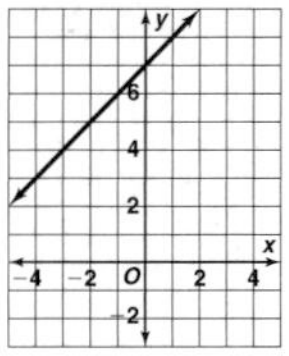

4.

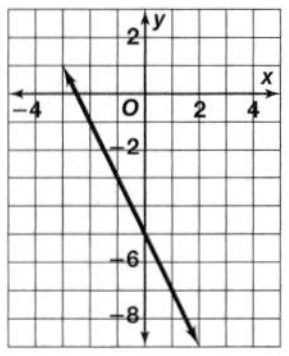

5.

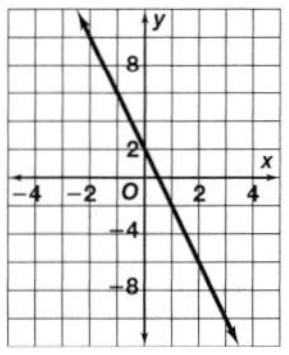

Quick Check **1.**

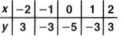

x	-2	-1	0	1	2
y	3	-3	-5	-3	3

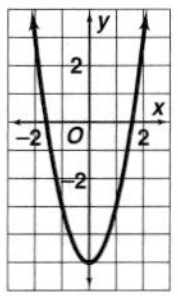

2.

s	10	20	30	40	50	60
y	20	10	$6\frac{2}{3}$	5	4	$3\frac{1}{3}$

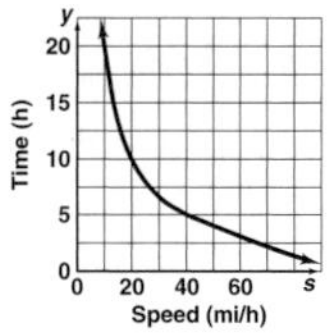

3. $y = x^2 - 2$

Chapter 12

Check Your Readiness p. 558

1. $22d - 4$ **2.** $-7v + 73$ **3.** $65w - 49$ **4.** $43f - 23g + 3$ **5.** $36r + 34$ **6.** $-8t + x - 6$ **7.** $4a - 7$ **8.** $-9b + 21$ **9.** $36f - 88$ **10.** $-12x - 45$ **11.** $20.44 - 5.7c$ **12.** $5y - 5$ **13.** 7^5 **14.** $5^2 \cdot c^2$ **15.** a^2b^3 **16.** x^3y^2 **17.** $(3x)^3$ **18.** $c \cdot d^2 \cdot g^2$ **19.** 16 **20.** 16 **21.** -16 **22.** 32 **23.** 100 **24.** 1,000

Lesson 12-1 pp. 561–562

Check Skills You'll Need **1.** Yes; all the terms include the same variable, x. **2.** $-2 - t$ **3.** $12w - 10$ **4.** $35k - 5$

Quick Check **1a.** $x^2 - 2x + 2$ **b.** $-2x^2 + 2x - 3$ **2a.** $-2x^2 - x + 6$ **b.** $6x^2 - 3x + 2$ **3a.** $2g^2 + 2g$ **b.** $2y - 5y^2 + 7$

Lesson 12-2 pp. 566–567

Check Skills You'll Need **1.** 1 **2.** $2y^2 - 2y$ **3.** $6x^2 - 1$ **4.** $8z - 5z^2$

Quick Check **1a.** $5c^2 + 2c + 2$ **b.** $3x^2 + 3x - 7$ **2a.** $10c + 24$ **b.** $10m - 2$ **3.** $-2y^2 - 2$

Checkpoint Quiz 1 p. 570 **1.** $-x - 2$ **2.** $x^2 + 2x + 2$ **3.** $x^2 + 2x$ **4.** $5x^2 - 8x + 4$ **5.** $16x^2 - 10x$ **6.** $2a - 10$ **7.** $26b^2 - b - 7$ **8.** $2c^2 - c + 5$ **9.** $6d^2 - 29d - 17$ **10.** $16x + 6$ **11.** $22x - 10$

Lesson 12-3 pp. 571–572

Check Skills You'll Need **1.** x **2.** 1 **3.** 9 **4.** -9 **5.** -1

Quick Check **1a.** 6^5 **b.** $(-4)^8$ **c.** m^{12} **2a.** 8×10^9 **b.** 6×10^{13} **c.** 9.6×10^{21} **3.** about 1.08×10^9 km

Lesson 12-4 pp. 576–577

Check Skills You'll Need **1.** exponents **2.** x^{15} **3.** $(-a)^{10}$ or a^{10}

Quick Check **1.** $8y^4$ **2.** $15r^2 + 15r$ **3a.** $2x^2 + 7x + 6$ **b.** $6x^2 + 11x + 4$ **c.** $2x^2 + 7x + 5$

Checkpoint Quiz 2 p. 580 **1.** 4.7^{21} **2.** $(-4a)^4$ **3.** x^4y^{12} **4.** 3.0×10^5 **5.** 1.5×10^{12} **6.** 3.6×10^7 **7.** $28f^8$ **8.** $15.5g^8$ **9.** $-17.6h^{18}$ **10.** $-5j^3 + 45j^2$ **11.** $6k^2 - 6k$ **12.** $30m^3 - 40m^2$ **13.** $8x^2 + 14x + 3$ **14.** $2x^2 + 8x + 6$

Lesson 12-5 pp. 581–583

Check Skills You'll Need **1.** power **2.** 7^4 **3.** 4^3 **4.** 5^2 **5.** 1^5

Quick Check **1.** w^3 **2.** 8.5 min **3a.** 1 **b.** 1 **c.** 2 **4a.** $\frac{1}{3}$ **b.** $\frac{1}{w^4}$ **c.** $-\frac{1}{8}$

Selected Answers

Chapter 1

Lesson 1-1 pp. 7–8

EXERCISES **1.** Answers may vary. Sample: An algebraic expression may use variables. A numerical expression does not. **3.** C **5.** A **7.** $7w$ **9.** 3, 5, 8 **13.** 3 **19.** $37b + 205$ **21.** 46.82 **25.** B **31.** 18.89

Lesson 1-2 pp. 12–13

EXERCISES **1.** Answers may vary. Sample: Integers include whole numbers and their opposites. **3.** A **5.** B **7.** 26 **11.** $-16, -13, -6, -4, 2, 7, 11$ **15.** 48 **21.** $5|-x|$ **23.** Yes; the record in Kansas is -40°C, which is colder than -38°C. **25.** < **27.** < **31.** for all non-positive values of x

Lesson 1-3 pp. 18–19

EXERCISES **1.** 0; $0 + 0 = 0$ **3.** negative **5.** 8 **7.** -2 **9.** 1 **11.** -8 **13.** -1 **31.** sometimes; $2 - (-2) = 4$ and $-2 - 2 = -4$ **35.** all integers greater than 1 or less than -3 **39.** <

Lesson 1-4 pp. 22–23

EXERCISES **1.** three **3.** < **5.** > **7.** -35 **9.** 4 **11.** 160 **13.** 36 **23.** -35 **25.** 2 **31.** -25 points **35.** 300 **37.** negative **41a.** $-40,230$ **b.** Answers may vary. Sample: 8 mi **47.** -6

Lesson 1-5 pp. 29–30

EXERCISES **1.** 1 **3.** Comm. Prop. of Mult. **5.** Comm. Prop. of Add. **7.** Ident. Prop. of Mult. **9.** -17 **11.** $(27 + 73)2$ **13.** 132 **15.** -54 **21.** $5a + 30$ **23.** $-4t - 12$ **35.** Answers may vary. Sample: mental math; $4(5.98) = 4(6 - 0.02) = 24 - 0.08 = 23.92$ **37.** 23,200 **41.** No; 20 lb is 320 oz. Two dozen cans weigh 360 oz. **45.** 36

Lesson 1-6 pp. 35–36

EXERCISES **1.** Answers may vary. Sample: An equation has an equal sign, but an expression does not. **3.** $y - 4 = 8$ **5.** yes **7.** no **9.** yes **11.** 54 **13.** 0 **31.** $-3, 3$ **35.** 13 lb **37.** 5.55 **45.** -21

Lesson 1-7 pp. 40–41

EXERCISES **1.** A value is a solution if it makes the equation true. **3.** Add. Prop. of Eq. **5.** Subtr. Prop. of Eq. **7.** yes **9.** yes **11.** no **13.** -5 **15.** 572 **35.** $5.34 **37.** 7 **41.** 360 tickets **47.** 8.4

Chapter Review pp. 44–45

1. simplify **2.** absolute value **3.** Distributive Property **4.** solution **5.** inverse operations **6.** variable **7.** integers **8.** equation **9.** 6 **10.** -15.5 **11.** -5.6 **12.** $27 + g$ **13.** $\frac{y}{4}$ **14.** $500r$ **15.** < **16.** < **17.** > **18.** = **19.** North America **20.** -12 **21.** -6 **22.** 17 **23.** -40 **24.** -7 **25.** -13 **26.** $263 **27.** $-16,800$ **28.** 1,094 **29.** $-1,800$ **30.** $3p - 21$ **31.** $8m + 32$ **32.** $10 + 5k$ **33.** 30 **34.** 3 **35.** 11 **36.** 7 **37.** 48 **38.** 2

Chapter 2

Lesson 2-1 pp. 54–56

EXERCISES **1.** GCF **3.** No; the ones digit is not 0, 2, 4, 6, or 8. **5.** Yes; the sum of the digits is 6, which is divisible by 3. **7.** composite; $2 \cdot 2 \cdot 2 \cdot 2 \cdot 3$ **9.** prime **15.** $2 \cdot 2 \cdot 5$ **17.** $2 \cdot 2 \cdot 2 \cdot 2$ **23.** 6 **25.** 6 **31.** 7 **33.** 15 **45.** 9 **47.** Answers may vary. Samples are given. $7 + 53$; $13 + 47$; $17 + 43$; $19 + 41$; $23 + 37$; $29 + 31$ **49.** It is also divisible by 2. **51.** 7, 17, and 19 are prime. **57.** -210

Lesson 2-2 pp. 59–60

EXERCISES **1.** $\frac{123}{1}$ **3.** D **5.** A **7.** $\frac{3}{4}$ **9.** $-\frac{2}{3}$ **15.** 0.667 **17.** 1.063 **25.** $\frac{33}{100}$ **27.** $4\frac{11}{25}$ **35.** $-\frac{2}{5}$ **43.** 9

Lesson 2-3 pp. 64–65

EXERCISES **1.** The LCM is the smallest number that is a multiple of both numbers. **3.** $\frac{2}{9}$ **5.** $\frac{4}{5}$ **7.** $\frac{4}{25}$ **9.** $-\frac{5}{14}$ **17.** $\frac{19}{11}$ **21.** $0.03, \frac{3}{10}, 0.33, \frac{1}{3}$ **27.** = **31.** your friend **33.** Maria **39.** $48 - 8b$

Lesson 2-4 pp. 68–69

EXERCISES **1.** 10 **3.** 28 **5.** $\frac{1}{2}$ **7.** Positive; $51 > 50$, so $\frac{1}{51} < \frac{1}{50}$, and $\frac{1}{50} - \frac{1}{51}$ is positive. **9.** $1\frac{3}{40}$ **11.** $1\frac{1}{15}$ **21.** $3\frac{1}{6}$ **23.** $-6\frac{3}{8}$ **31.** $2\frac{1}{2}$ **33.** $-\frac{1}{8}$ **37.** $\frac{8}{21}$ **39.** Answers may vary. Sample: $\frac{1}{2} + \frac{1}{3} = \frac{5}{6}$; $\frac{1}{2 + 3} = \frac{1}{5}$ **41.** $a - \frac{2}{3}$ **45.** $\frac{1}{125}, 0.8, 0.808, \frac{22}{25}$

Lesson 2-5 pp. 74–76

EXERCISES **1.** multiplicative inverse **3.** 1 **5.** –5 **7.** $-\frac{3}{5}$ **9.** $-\frac{5}{24}$ **15.** $-\frac{2}{3}$ **17.** 17 **27.** $\frac{3}{5}$ **29.** $-3\frac{3}{4}$ **35.** 6 **39.** Dividing by a fraction is the same as multiplying by its reciprocal. The reciprocal of a number less than 1 is a number greater than 1, so the answer will be greater. **41.** $10\frac{5}{8}$ yd **47.** 7

Lesson 2-6 pp. 83–84

EXERCISES **1.** ℓ is the length; w is the width. **3.** $\frac{7}{8}$ cm^2 **5.** Area of a trapezoid; h is the height; b_1 and b_2 are the bases. **7.** Perimeter of a square; s is the side length. **9.** 24 m^2 **15.** $t = \frac{d}{r}$ **17.** $C = K - 273$ **21.** 24 mi/h **23.** $\frac{9}{\pi}$ ft **25a.** 2,220 ft **b.** The difference between the dew point and air temperature will grow larger, and the height of the base of the cloud will increase. Examples: H = 222(80 – 70) = 2,220 ft H = 222(80 – 60) = 4,440 ft **31.** 17

Lesson 2-7 pp. 88–89

EXERCISES **1.** C **3.** B **5.** $9^3 \cdot x$ **7.** z^6 **9.** 64 **11.** $4^2 \cdot 8^4$ **13.** $5^2 \cdot x^3 \cdot y$ **17.** –32 **19.** –216 **33.** –360 **37.** 112 ft **41.** yes; when $a = 0$ or $b = 0$, and when $a = 1$ **47.** $6\frac{9}{25}$

Lesson 2-8 pp. 94–95

EXERCISES **1.** 1 **3.** greater than 0, because the number remains positive even though the decimal point moves 5 places to the left **5.** 3,200 **11.** 1.72×10^4 **15.** 0.0025 **21.** 1.05×10^{-3} **23.** 2.7×10^{-5} **27.** 8 **31.** 3.92×10^8 **33.** 1.5×10^6 km **35a.** 2,750,000 calories **b.** 2.75×10^6 calories **37.** 9×10^{28} **41.** –135

Chapter Review pp. 98–99

1. scientific notation **2.** reciprocals or multiplicative inverses **3.** LCM **4.** prime factorization **5.** power **6.** formula **7.** relatively prime **8.** terminating decimal **9.** GCF **10.** exponent; base **11.** $2^2 \cdot 5 \cdot 13$ **12.** $2^2 \cdot 5^2 \cdot 7$ **13.** $2 \cdot 3^3 \cdot 7$ **14.** $1 \cdot 139$ **15.** $2^2 \cdot 3^3 \cdot 5 \cdot 13$ **16.** $\frac{4}{25}$ **17.** < **18.** > **19.** = **20.** $-\frac{1}{8}$ **21.** $-1\frac{1}{2}$ **22.** $-\frac{2}{3}$ **23.** $\frac{1}{16}$ **24.** $3\frac{1}{4}$ **25.** $-2\frac{1}{10}$ **26.** 3 **27.** 45 mi/h **28.** $b = \frac{2A}{h}$ **29.** $b = y - mx$ **30.** $r = \frac{d}{t}$ **31.** 61 **32.** 54 **33.** 24 **34.** 3.5×10^3 **35.** 8.01×10^5 **36.** 2.05×10^{-4} **37.** 8.1×10^{-8} **38.** 380,000,000

Chapter 3

Lesson 3-1 pp. 108–110

EXERCISES **1.** irrational, real **3.** rational, real **5.** 2, –2 **7.** 10, –10 **9.** 7, –7 **11.** $\frac{1}{6}, -\frac{1}{6}$ **15.** 3 **17.** 9 **23.** 342 m/s **27.** Irrational; 40 is not a perfect square. **29.** Rational; 144 is a perfect square. **33.** 88 ft **35.** Answers may vary. Sample: $\sqrt{3}$; 3 is not a perfect square. **37a.** Yes; the sum of even numbers is an even number. **b.** Yes; the sum of two irrational numbers is an irrational number. **c.** No; the sum of two prime numbers can be a composite number. **39.** 10 **43.** 4 **47.** 26.1 mi **49.** The student took the square root of 4 and added it to the square root of 9. You must add 4 + 9 first and then take the square root. **55.** 6.038×10^6

Lesson 3-2 pp. 114–115

EXERCISES **1.** The hypotenuse is the longest side. **3.** 17 cm **5.** 7.1 cm **7.** 5 **15a.** 27 in. **b.** Answers may vary. Sample: 20 in. by 18 in. **17.** 2.8 cm **19.** 17.0 m **23.** yes; $3^2 + (3 + 1)^2 \stackrel{?}{=} (3 + 2)^2$ **29.** 102,000

$$3^2 + 4^2 \stackrel{?}{=} 5^2$$
$$9 + 16 \stackrel{?}{=} 25$$
$$25 = 25$$

Lesson 3-3 pp. 120–121

EXERCISES **1.** $\overline{PR}$ and $\overline{RQ}$; $\overline{PQ}$ **3.** 16 in. **5.** 6.7 ft **13.** 8.7 ft **15.** 6 **17.** 19.8 **19.** The student added 3^2 to 4^2 instead of subtracting it from 4^2. You must find $\sqrt{4^2 - 3^2}$. **21.** no; $(a + b)^2 \neq a^2 + b^2$ **25.** >

Lesson 3-4 pp. 126–127

EXERCISES **1.** B **3.** D **5.** (–4, 3) **7.** (–3, 0) **9.** (0, –1) **19.** C

25a.

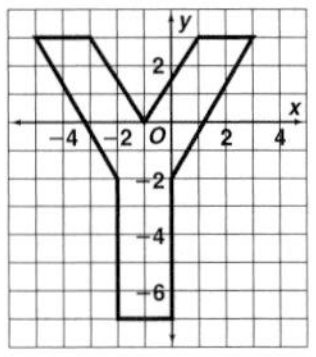

b. the letter Y **27.** 93° W, 45° N; 97° W, 41° N **29.** Quadrant I

31.

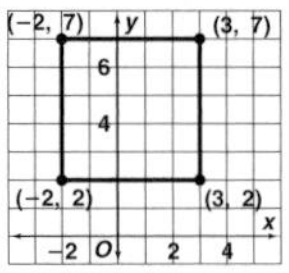

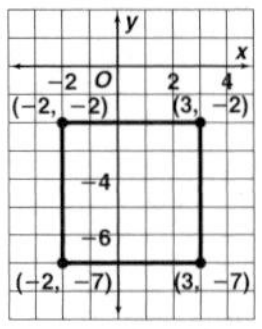

The square is reflected over the x-axis. **35.** 7.1

Lesson 3-5 pp. 132–134

EXERCISES **1.** C **3.** $g = 0.75t$

11.

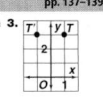

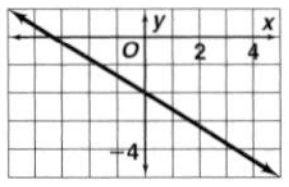

15. 6 letters;

Number of Letters	Expression	Total Cost (dollars)
0	1.50(0) + 10	10.00
1	1.50(1) + 10	11.50
2	1.50(2) + 10	13.00
3	1.50(3) + 10	14.50
ℓ	1.50(ℓ) + 10	c

$c = 1.50\ell + 10$ **17.** Gina; the graph drawn by Gina's father shows the amount owed after Gina gives him $40 each week, not $20. **23.** 25

Lesson 3-6 pp. 137–139

EXERCISES **1.** transformation **3.**

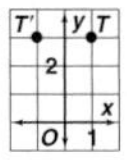

5.

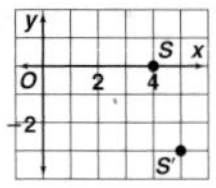

7.

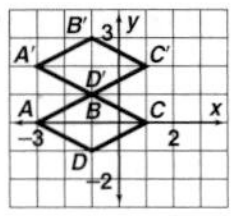

11. $(x, y) \rightarrow (x + 4, y + 3)$ **17.** C **19.** Answers may vary. Sample:

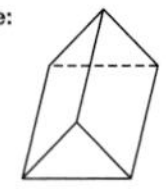

25.

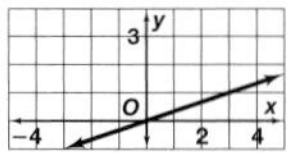

Lesson 3-7 pp. 143–144

EXERCISES **1.** Line a is a line of symmetry if one half of the figure matches the other half exactly when the figure is reflected over line a. **3.** G **5.** G **7.** F

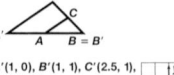

15.

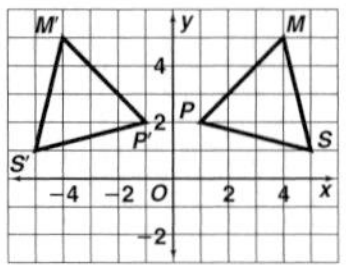

$M'(-4, 5)$, $P'(-1, 2)$, $S'(-5, 1)$

17.

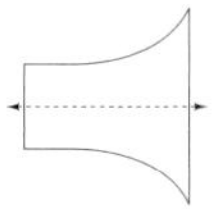

Selected Answers

23.

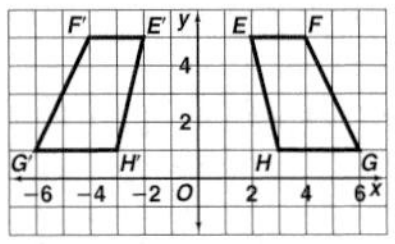

$E'(-2, 5)$, $F'(-4, 5)$, $G'(-6, 1)$, $H'(-3, 1)$

25.

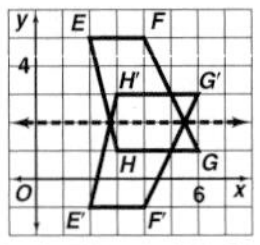

$E'(2, -1)$, $F'(4, -1)$, $G'(6, 3)$, $H'(3, 3)$ **33.** 13

Lesson 3-8 pp. 148–149

EXERCISES **1.** 180 **5.** yes; 45°

9.

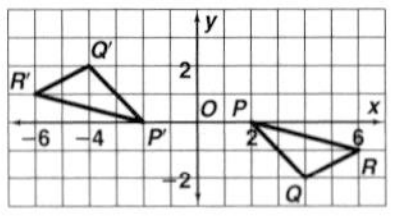

13. A complete rotation has 360°. A square can be rotated 360° ÷ 4 or 90°.

Chapter Review pp. 152–153

1. y-axis; origin; quadrants **2.** translations; reflections; rotations **3.** angle of rotation; rotational symmetry **4.** perfect square **5.** hypotenuse **6.** 2.6 ft **7.** 8.9 ft **8.** 13.8 ft **9.** Rational; 196 is a perfect square. **10.** Rational; $\frac{25}{36}$ is a perfect square. **11.** Irrational; 57 is not a perfect square. **12.** Irrational; 1.6 is not a perfect square. **13.** Rational; 225 is a perfect square. **14.** 10 **15.** 13.4 **16.** 46.6 **17.** 23.2 ft **18.** (–3, –2) **19.** (–2, 3) **20.** (1, –3) **21.** Quadrant IV **22.** y-axis **23.** Quadrant II

24.

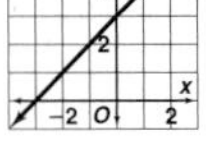

25.

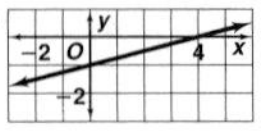

26.

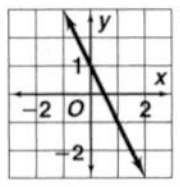

27.

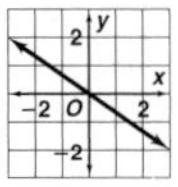

28.

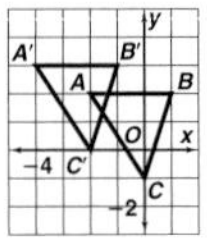

29.

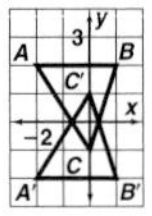

30.

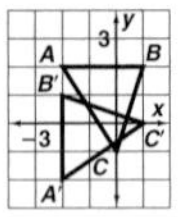

Chapter 4

Lesson 4-1 pp. 162–163

EXERCISES **1.** A rate is a ratio that compares quantities measured in different units. The quantities 6 and 23 have the same unit: students. **3.** 3 : 4 **5.** $\frac{2}{1}$ **7.** $\frac{2}{3}$ **9.** $\frac{7}{30}$ **11.** $\frac{11}{18}$ **15.** $14/book **17.** $1.80/rose **23.** –0.007°C/m **25.** $\frac{21}{83}$ **27.** 56 mi/h **35.** $\frac{1}{25}$

Lesson 4-2 pp. 169–170

EXERCISES **1.** $\frac{12 \text{ in.}}{1 \text{ ft}}$ **3.** A **5.** B **7.** 2.7 **11.** 0.45 **15.** 12 **19.** 9.8 **21.** 24.8 **27.** 190,080 **29.** 82.4°F **31.** 0°C **33.** swimming **35.** dancing **39.** 3 ft 3 in.

43.

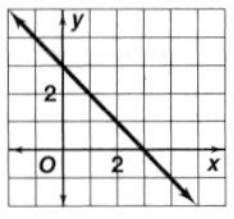

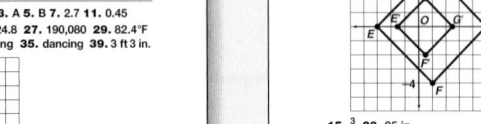

Lesson 4-3 pp. 176–178

EXERCISES **1.** cross products **3.** yes; $\frac{6}{27} = \frac{2}{9}$ **5.** no; $\frac{1}{4} \neq \frac{2}{10}$ **7.** yes; $\frac{7}{6} = \frac{28}{24}$ **13.** 45 **15.** 3 **23.** 48,387 yen **25.** 22,581 yen **27.** $\frac{x + 3}{2} = \frac{5}{4}$; Write the cross products: $(x + 3)4 = 5 \cdot 2$. Multiply: $4x + 12 = 10$. Subtract 12 from each side: $4x = -2$. Divide each side by 4: $\frac{4x}{4} = \frac{-2}{4}$. Simplify: $x = -\frac{1}{2}$. **29.** h and 25 are reversed. **31.** about 3 grams; methods may vary. **33.** Answers may vary. Sample: 2 **35.** about $85 **37.** 15 **45.** –19

Lesson 4-4 pp. 183–184

EXERCISES **1.** No; similar figures must have the same shape. **3.** D **5.** Yes; the angles are all congruent and the sides are proportional. **7.** 5 **11.** 48 **13.** $x = 8$, $y = 14.4$ **15.** about 19 inches **17.** D **19.** They are the same. **23.** =

Lesson 4-5 pp. 189–190

EXERCISES **1.** Reduction; the dilation has a scale factor less than 1. **3.** 3

5.

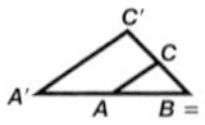

7. $A'(1, 0)$, $B'(1, 1)$, $C'(2.5, 1)$, $D'(2.5, 0)$

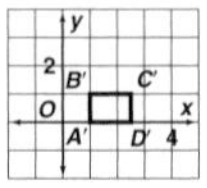

9. $\frac{1}{2}$; reduction

13.

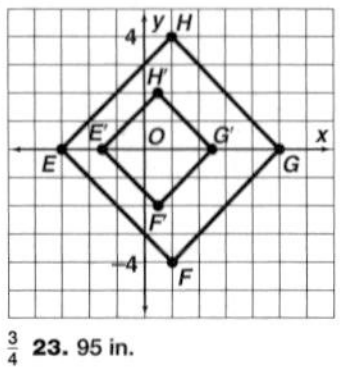

15. $\frac{3}{4}$ **23.** 95 in.

Lesson 4-6 pp. 193–195

EXERCISES **1.** The scale is the ratio of map distance to actual distance. **3.** 1 : 2; the model is half as large as the object, compared to a third as large. **5.** 2.3; 5.75 ft **7.** 15 in.; 3 in. **11.** 25 mi **15.** 21.5 in. **19.** 300 mi **23.** 2.5 ft **31.** 21

Lesson 4-7 pp. 198–200

EXERCISES **1.** indirect **3.** indirect **5.** 8 **7.** 8 m **9.** 360 m **11.** 1,269.7 m **13.** 27.1 ft **17.** 34 ft **19.** about 617 ft **21.** Answers may vary. Sample: Stand where you can see the basketball hoop in the mirror. **25.** 0.05

Chapter Review pp. 202–203

1. unit rate **2.** proportion **3.** scale factor **4.** indirect measurement **5.** reduction **6.** conversion factor **7.** $\frac{1}{8}$ **8.** $3\frac{1}{3}$ **9.** $\frac{1}{3}$ **10.** $28/h **11.** 59 mi/h **12.** 6.25 km/L **13.** Neither, the unit rate for each container is about $.07. **14.** 3,300 cm/h **15.** 256 oz/ft **16.** $16\frac{2}{3}$ mL/s **17.** 380,160 ft/day **18.** 50 cm/min **19.** $18/h **20.** 16 **21.** 1 **22.** 12 **23.** 72 **24.** 810 euros **25.** 10 cm **26.** 7.5 cm **27.** 4.5 cm **28.** 4; enlargement **29.** 43.4 mi **30.** 66.5 mi **31.** 32.7 mi **32.** 57.4 mi **33.** $2\frac{1}{4}$ in. by $1\frac{3}{4}$ in. **34.** 14.4 **35.** 13.6 **36.** 11 ft 9 in.

Chapter 5

Lesson 5-1 pp. 212–213

EXERCISES **1.** 100 **3.** B **5.** A **7.** 40% **9.** 96% **13.** 0.3% **15.** 90% **17.** $\frac{21}{20}$ **19.** $\frac{2}{9}$ **23.** 0.09%, 0.01, 1.01%, $\frac{1}{99}$ **27.** $\frac{5}{6}$, $0.8\overline{3}$, $83\frac{1}{3}$% **29.** $\frac{3}{4}$, $\frac{29}{50}$ **31.** 84% **37.** 3

Lesson 5-2 pp. 216–217

EXERCISES **1.** B **3.** C **5.** Answers may vary. Sample: 0.25 × 200 = 50 **7.** about 36 **9.** about 250 **13.** about 90 **17.** about $1.80 **19.** about $4.50 **25.** about $23 **27.** about $22.40 **29.** > **31.** > **33.** about 121,000,000 Americans **35.** about 240 Calories **39.** $(x, y) \rightarrow (x + 4, y + 5)$

Lesson 5-3 pp. 220–222

EXERCISES **1.**

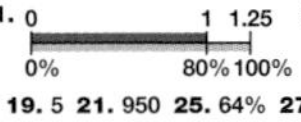

3. C **5.** 57.6 **7.** 33 **19.** 5 **21.** 950 **25.** 64% **27.** 4%

Selected Answers

33. Answers may vary. Sample: A "whole" is an arbitrary number, and you can have a "part" that is more than that arbitrary number. **37.** 76,198.76 **39.** 6 **41.** 1,095.12 **43.** No; for example, if the two numbers are 100 and 200, then (40% of 100) + (30% of 200) = 40 + 60 = 100, but 70% of 300 = 210. **45.** 10,000% **49.** 1 cm : 250 cm

Lesson 5-4 pp. 226–227

EXERCISES **1.** 24 **3.** 1.4 **5.** 6% **9.** 70 **11.** 445 **17.** \$2,650,000 **19.** \$946.65 **21.** \$943.95 **23.** 15,996,000 people **25.** $0.75(0.8x)(1.065)$ **29.** $\frac{15}{12}$

Lesson 5-5 pp. 232–233

EXERCISES **1.** original **3.** 25% increase **5.** 200% increase **7.** 130% **9.** 40% **13.** 3.4% **17.** 33.3% **19.** 26.4% **25.** 75% decrease **27.** 75% decrease **29.** 86.7% decrease **37.** 24

Lesson 5-6 pp. 237–238

EXERCISES **1.** C **3.** B **5.** 50% **9.** \$188.99 **13.** \$73.15 **15.** \$189.43 **19.** \$119.98 **21.** No difference; the final cost is \$192.50 either way. **29.** 187.2

Lesson 5-7 pp. 243–244

EXERCISES **1.** C **3.** A **5.** \$82.45 **7.** \$1,312.50 **9.** \$856 **13.** The account that pays 1.3% simple interest, because 747(1 + 0.013) = \$756.71 and 747(1 + 0.02) − 12 = \$749.94. **19.** 102.6 ft^2

Lesson 5-8 pp. 248–250

EXERCISES **1.** Answers may vary. Sample: An outcome is any of the possible results that can occur. An event is the collection of possible outcomes in an experiment. An outcome can be an event if there is only one possible result of the experiment. **3.** $\frac{1}{3}$ **5.** $\frac{1}{6}$ **7.** $\frac{1}{8}$ **9.** $\frac{3}{8}$ **13.** 10% **15.** $\frac{3}{16}$ **17.** $\frac{1}{4}$

21. Toss 1 Toss 2 Toss 3 Outcome

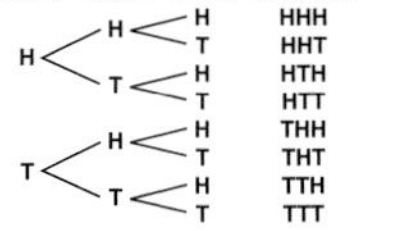

23. $\frac{3}{8}$ **27.** $\frac{1}{5}$ **29.** $\frac{1}{5}$ or 20% **31.** $\frac{2}{9}$ or 22.2% **33.** $\frac{1}{12}$ **37.** 30 lb : 1 lb

Chapter Review pp. 252–253

1. markup **2.** principal **3.** outcome **4.** discount **5.** simple interest **6.** 87.5% **7.** 108.33% **8.** 31.25% **9.** 450% **10.** $\frac{9}{25}$ **11.** $\frac{1}{3}$ **12.** $1\frac{6}{25}$ **13.** $\frac{27}{100}$ **14–16.** Answers may vary. Samples are given. **14.** about 25 **15.** about \$5.25 **16.** about 63 **17.** about 3 students **18.** 200 **19.** 40% **20.** 18 **21.** 150 **22.** 160 students **23.** 30.8% decrease **24.** 4,300% increase **25.** 0.6% increase **26.** 83.3% decrease **27.** \$199.99 **28.** \$574.75 **29.** \$809.40 **30.** \$4,725 **31.** $\frac{5}{9}$

Chapter 6

Lesson 6-1 pp. 262–264

EXERCISES **1.** $3x - 2 = 7$ **3.** Answers may vary. Sample: Add 8 to each side. **5.** Answers may vary. Sample: Add 12 to each side. **7.** about 56 **9.** −4 **11.** 4 **17.** $4x + 5 = 68.96$; \$15.99 **21.** 11 mg **23.** $7b + 3 = 24$; Subtr. Prop. of Eq.: $7b + 3 - 3 = 24 - 3$; Div. Prop. of Eq.: $\frac{7b}{7} = \frac{21}{7}$; $b = 3$ **25.** 12.6 **27.** −6 **31.** $x = 7$; It is the same. You could avoid working with decimals. **35.** 22.8 m

Lesson 6-2 pp. 268–269

EXERCISES **1.** No; the variable factors $x^2y^5z^{11}$ and $x^2z^5y^{11}$ are different. **3.** $4x + 7y - 6$ **5.** $8a + 15$ **7.** $11b$ **9.** $31x$ **17.** $5x + 1$ **19.** $9n - 3r$ **23.** $23 - 5a$ **25.** $-27m - 16$ **31.** Let b = the cost of a barrette. Let h = the cost of a headband. $5b + 3h$ **33.** $3x - 2y$ **35.** $x + y + 9$ **37.** $31.66y + 8.4$ **39.** $12x$ **41.** Answers may vary. Sample: $2m + m + 8$; $4m + 2 - m + 6$ **43.** $0.5t - 29v$ **47.** 20

Lesson 6-3 pp. 273–275

EXERCISES **1.** like **3.** C **5.** B **7.** −2 **9.** 7 **23.** $n + n + 1 = -45$; −23 and −22

25. $n + (n + 1) + (n + 2) = -255$;
−86, −85, −84

27. −1 **29.** 10 **31.** $4m + 5 = 21$; $m = 4$ ft **39.** −75

Lesson 6-4 pp. 277–278

EXERCISES **1.** all of them **3.** 11 a and a, $-4.1a^2$ and a^2 **5.** The student added x to the left side but subtracted x from the right side.

$$3x + 4 - x = 7 + x$$
$$2x + 4 = 7 + x$$
$$2x - x + 4 = 7 + x - x$$
$$x + 4 = 7$$
$$x + 4 - 4 = 7 - 4$$
$$x = 3$$

7. −2 **9.** 21 **17.** at about 9:57 A.M. **19.** 0.15 **23.** 3

Lesson 6-5 pp. 284–285

EXERCISES **1.** An equation states that two expressions are equal; an inequality compares two expressions that are not usually equal. **3.** $0.6 \leq x$ **5.** $y - 4 < 0$ **7.** $x \geq 65$

9. $m < -2$ 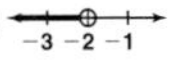

11. $7 \leq n$ 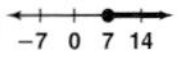

25. $x \leq 0$ **27.** > **29.** 6 **31.** 5 **37.** $\frac{5}{12}$

Lesson 6-6 pp. 291–292

EXERCISES **1.** When you multiply or divide each side of an inequality by a positive number, the relationship between the two sides does not change. When you multiply or divide by a negative number, the direction of the inequality sign reverses. **3.** $d > 12$ **5.** $y > 0$ **7.** $c < 2$ **11.** $4.89s \leq 23.50$; 4 specials

13. $r \geq -6$ 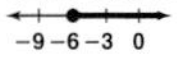

15. $z \geq 96$ 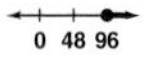

25. a and b must have opposite signs. **27.** a can be positive or negative, but b must be positive. **29.** 4 teachers **31.** No; it is only true if b is positive. If $b = 0$, the problem is undefined. If b is negative, the inequality sign needs to change.

35. $y \leq 26$ 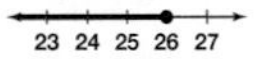

Chapter Review pp. 294–295

1. like terms **2.** inequality **3.** term **4.** Mult. Prop. of Ineq. **5.** Add. Prop. of Ineq. **6.** 12 **7.** $-\frac{11}{3}$ **8.** −15 **9.** −9 **10.** $-\frac{5}{6}$ **11.** 40 **12.** 15 cans **13.** 3 shirts **14.** $7 - 3f$ **15.** $3a + 11$ **16.** $11x - 12$ **17.** −4 **18.** 5 **19.** $\frac{16}{5}$ or 3.2

20. −5 **21.** 2.5 lb **22.** $g > 19$ 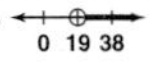

23. $u \leq 2$ 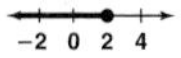

24. $t \geq -11$ 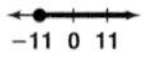

25. $c < 75$ **26.** $x \geq 150$

27. $x < -3$ 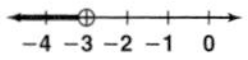

28. $y \leq -2$ 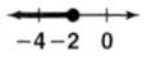

29. $a < 7$ 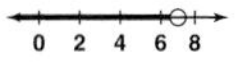

30. $w \leq 128$ 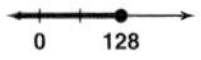

31. $c < -20$ 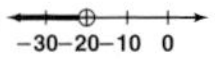

32. $z > 12$ 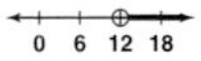

Chapter 7

Lesson 7-1 pp. 305–306

EXERCISES **1.** No; they do not share a common side. **3.** No; they do not share a common vertex. **5.** Answers may vary. Sample: ∠MRQ and ∠NRP; ∠NRP and ∠QRP; 80° **9.** 156° **13.** $m\angle 1 = 152°$; $m\angle 2 = 28°$; $m\angle 3 = 62°$; $m\angle 4 = 90°$ **17.** 58°; 148° **19.** 4.1°; 94.1° **23.** No; they are adjacent. **25.** Answers may vary. Sample: ∠5 and ∠7 **29.** ∠KBL **31.** 76°

Lesson 7-2 pp. 309–310

EXERCISES **1.** Answers may vary. Sample: ∠2 and ∠4 **3.** $\overleftrightarrow{UV}$ **5.** False; corresponding angles lie on the same side of a transversal, but alternate interior angles do not. **7.** corresponding **9.** alternate interior **15.** 122° **17.** 122° **21.** Alternate interior angles are congruent. **25.** No parallel lines; alternate interior angles are not congruent.

29. $m\angle 1 = 70°$; $m\angle 2 = 70°$;
$m\angle 3 = 110°$; $m\angle 4 = 110°$

31a. $m\angle 1 = 80°$; $m\angle 2 = 40°$; $m\angle 3 = 60°$ **b.** 180° **37.** 31.98

Lesson 7-3 pp. 314–316

EXERCISES **1.** size and shape **3.** SAS **5.** $\overline{EH} \cong \overline{GF}$; $\angle EHF \cong \angle GFH$; $\overline{FH} \cong \overline{FH}$; $\angle FEH \cong \angle HGF$; $\overline{EF} \cong \overline{GH}$; $\angle EFH \cong \angle GHF$ **7.** $PALK \cong PSNK$ **9.** SAS **11.** 104° **13.** 0.9 cm **21.** congruent; SAS using vertical angles **23.** no; $\triangle ABC \ncong \triangle DEF$

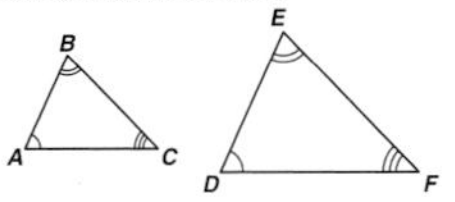

25.

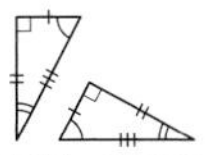

27. 0.09 km **33.** 0.0372

Lesson 7-4 pp. 320–321

EXERCISES **1.** C **3.** D **5.** B **9.** isosceles obtuse **11.** parallelogram **17.** Answers may vary. Sample:

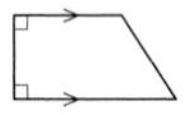

23. If a quadrilateral has two pairs of opposite sides that are parallel, then it is a parallelogram; true. **25.** If a triangle is isosceles, then it is equilateral; not true. **31.** 63.6% increase

Lesson 7-5 pp. 326–327

EXERCISES **1.** A regular polygon is a polygon with all sides congruent and all angles congruent. **3.** heptagon **5.** octagon **7.** 540° **9.** 720° **13.** 83° **17.** 128.6° **19.** 154.3° **23.** square **25.** $a = 105°$; $b = 106°$ **29.** 135° **35.** 132°

Lesson 7-6 pp. 331–332

EXERCISES **1.** C **3.** triangle **5.** 50 cm^2 **7.** 96 m^2 **9.** 84 m^2 **13.** Each area is 135 ft^2; 120 ft^2. **15.** 34 m^2 **19.** Answers may vary. Sample: about 81,000 km^2 **21.** 1 : 2 **25.** 1,080°

Lesson 7-7 pp. 338–339

EXERCISES **1.** circumference

3. $C = \pi d = \pi(2r) = 2\pi r$

5. 44 km **7.** 88 in. **9.** 15.7 cm; 19.6 cm^2

11. 28.9 in.; 66.5 $in.^2$ **17.** 22.3 ft^2 **19.** 1,253.4 ft^2 **27.** 0.27 in.; 0.54 in. **31.** 40.8 $in.^2$ **33.** 12 ft **39.** \$9.60

Lesson 7-8 pp. 342–343

EXERCISES **1.** circles and arcs **3.** Place the compass tip at A and draw an arc that intersects the sides of ∠A. Label the points of intersection C and D.

5.

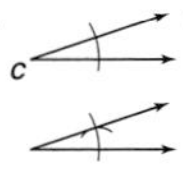

7.

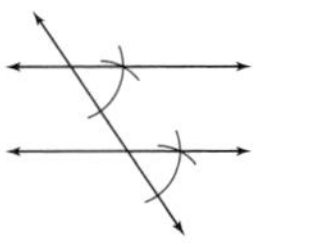

17. $\frac{4}{13}$

Chapter Review pp. 346–347

1. transversal **2.** scalene **3.** supplementary **4.** rhombus **5.** regular polygon **6.** 35°; 55° **7.** 48°; 132° **8.** isosceles, acute **9.** scalene, obtuse **10.** equilateral, acute **11.** $\triangle CDE \cong \triangle HGF$; SAS **12.** $\triangle JLK \cong \triangle OMN$; SSS **13.** 120° **14.** 135° **15.** 150° **16.** 160° **17.** 540 ft^2 **18.** 24 cm^2 **19.** 124.7 cm^2

20.

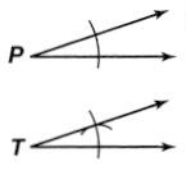

21.

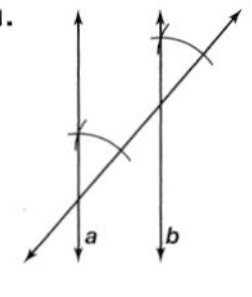

Chapter 8

Lesson 8-1 pp. 356–357

EXERCISES **1.** Parallel lines lie in the same plane; skew lines do not. **3.** triangular **5.** cylinder **7.** The base is a square. The figure is a square pyramid. $\overline{PQ}$ is a lateral edge. **11.** $\overline{DE}$ and $\overline{FH}$, $\overline{GD}$ and $\overline{EF}$ **15.** skew **19.** triangular prism **25.** 24

Lesson 8-2 pp. 360–361

EXERCISES **1.** isometric view **3.** rectangle

5.

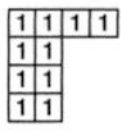

9.

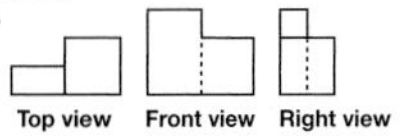

13.

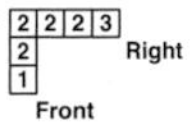

15.

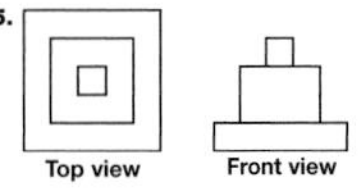

17. cone **19.** 6, 8; 6, 8, 10 **23.** 11.9 $in.^2$

Lesson 8-3 pp. 365–366

EXERCISES **1.** A net is a two-dimensional pattern, whereas a prism is a three-dimensional solid. **3.** circles **5.** C **7.** cone

13.

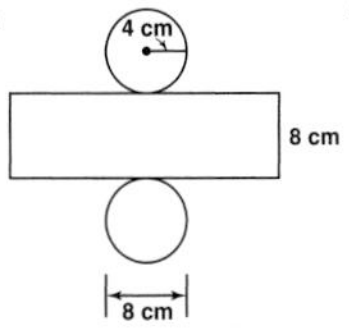

17. 60°

Lesson 8-4 pp. 371–372

EXERCISES **1.** The lateral area of a prism is the sum of the areas of the lateral faces. The surface area includes the lateral area plus the area of the two bases. **3.** 384 $in.^2$ **5.** 2,304 $in.^2$ **7.** 96 cm^2 **9.** 600 cm^2 **13.** 275 cm^2 **15.** The 9 cm-by-5.5 cm-by-11.75 cm box will require more cardboard because it has a greater surface area. **17a.** Treat the lighthouse as a cylinder. Multiply 3 × 30 × 150 to estimate the lateral area. L.A. ≈ 13,500 ft^2 **b.** about 20 gallons of black paint and 20 gallons of white paint

19. L.A. = 675 m^2
S.A. = 1.045 m^2

21. None; the area of the three new surfaces of figure A is exactly the same as the area of three surfaces of cube B. **25.** 118°

Lesson 8-5 pp. 377–378

EXERCISES **1.** Lateral area is less than surface area because it does not include the area of the square base. **3.** 14 **5.** S.A. = $56\pi + 16\pi = 72\pi$ **7.** 3.4 yd^2 **9.** L.A. = 3,000 $in.^2$; S.A. = 3,900 $in.^2$ **13.** 104 m^2 **17a.** 856 ft **b.** 248,240 ft^2 **19.** 628 cm^2 **21.** yes, because it is equivalent to $\pi r^2 + \pi r\ell$ **23.** Answers may vary. Sample: 270 m^2; 268 m^2.

27.

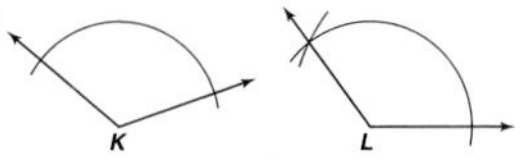

Lesson 8-6 pp. 382–384

EXERCISES **1.** Answers may vary. Sample: ft^3, $in.^3$, cm^3 **3.** B **5.** C **7.** 3,900 mm^3 **9.** 20 ft^3 **13.** 302 m^3 **17.** 589 ft^3 **19.** doubling the radius, since the radius is squared in calculating the volume **21.** 1,800 m^3 **25.** 539 ft^3 **29.** 35.3%

Lesson 8-7 pp. 390–391

EXERCISES **1.** 15 m^3 **3.** B **5.** 72 $in.^3$ **9.** 13 ft^3 **13.** 603 cm^3 **15.** no; because the radius is squared in the formula, and the height is not **17.** 1.67 ft

Lesson 8-8 pp. 395–396

EXERCISES **1.** C **3.** B **5.** 12.6 m^2 **7.** 1,810 cm^2; 7,238 cm^3 **9.** 95 m^2; 87 m^3 **15.** about 1.5 $in.^2$ **17.** She forgot to divide by 3. **19.** 5,027 mm^2; 33,510 mm^3 **21.** 5 cm^2; 1 cm^3 **23.** 83 $in.^2$; 64 $in.^3$ **25.** about 3,397 km **29.** 14 $in.^3$

Lesson 8-9 pp. 400–401

EXERCISES **1.** Two solids are similar if they have the same shape and all their corresponding lengths are proportional. **3.** 54 cm^2 **5.** 8.4 in. **7.** 1,008 m^2; 2,074 m^3 **11.** 5 m **13.** 1,274 ft^2; 2,382 ft^3 **17.** 10.1 cm **21.** 7.5×10^4

Chapter Review pp. 404–405

1. volume **2.** cone **3.** lateral, surface **4.** cylinder, prism **5.** isometric view **6.** rectangle, parallelograms **7.** square, triangles **8.** circle, curved surface

9.

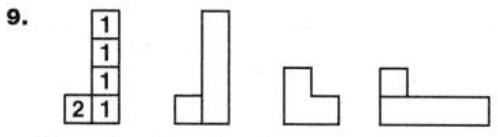

10.

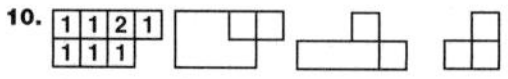

11.

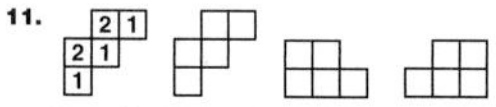

12. cone **13.** triangular prism **14.** cube **15.** 24 m^2; 6 m^3 **16.** 196 cm^2; 196 cm^3 **17.** 1,014 in.^{2}; 2,197 in.^{3} **18.** 90 m^2; 48 m^3 **19.** 258 cm^2; 268 cm^3 **20.** 190 ft^2; 131 ft^3 **21.** 5.3×10^8 km^2; 1.15×10^{12} km^3 **22.** 444 yd^2; 651 yd^3 **23.** 108 in.^{2}; 74 in.^{3} **24.** 87 m^2; 53 m^3

Chapter 9

Lesson 9-1 pp. 414–416

EXERCISES 1. No; because none of the data values are repeated, there is no mode. **3.** 12 **5.** −9, −8, −3, −2, 0, 1, 2, 6, 7, 11, 11, 15; median: 1.5; mode: 11 **7.** 1; 1; 0; 3 **9.** 8.7; 9; 9; 3 **13.** 10; it raises the mean about 1.05. **19.** 8 **25.** 6, 7, 20 **29.** −300

Lesson 9-2 pp. 420–422

EXERCISES 1. A histogram is a bar graph with no spaces between the bars. **3.** 27.4

5.

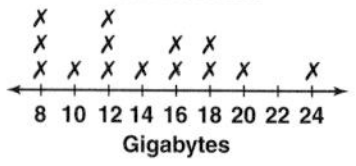

7. 0.7; 1; 0, 1, and 3 **11.** Answers may vary. Sample: 50–59, 60–69, 70–79, 80–89, 90–99, 100–109

13.

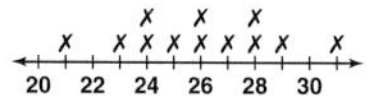

26; 26; 24; 26 and 28

17. Answers may vary. Sample:

Score	Frequency
(−5)–(−3)	1
(−2)–0	15
1–3	11
4–6	5

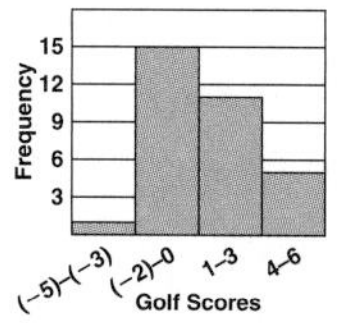

21. the Bakers **27.** $\frac{1}{3}$

Lesson 9-3 pp. 425–426

EXERCISES 1. objects or people that fall into both categories **3.** 60 students

5.

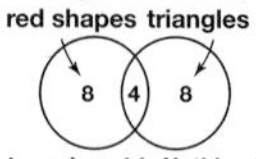

9. 1 number **11.** Nothing falls in both categories. **13.** $\frac{105}{580}$ or 0.181 or 18.1%

Lesson 9-4 pp. 429–431

EXERCISES 1. Answers may vary. Sample: not starting at zero on the vertical scale; using intervals that are too small, too large, or unequal **3.** No; the break in the scale makes the differences appear greater than they are. **5.** *Sports Fan*

9.

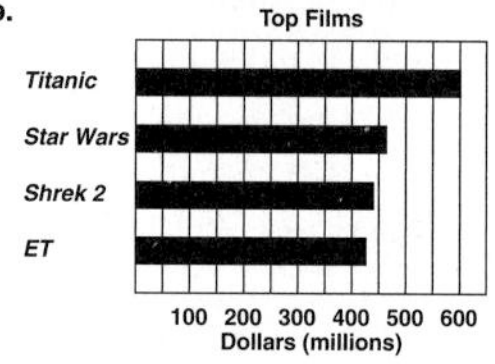

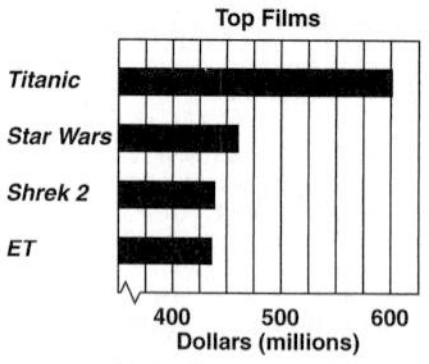

You can approximate the amounts better on the graph with the break, but the differences are exaggerated.

11.

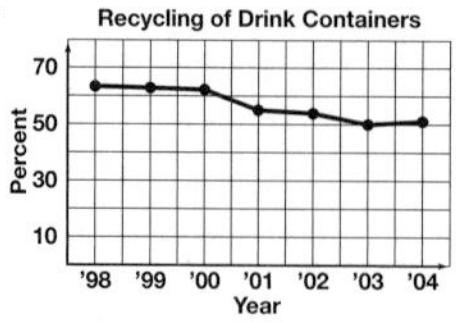

17a. 5; 10; 20; 40 **b.** No; the time differences are not the same, which is misleading. **c.** Yes; each interval is twice the size of the interval before it. **21.** 615.8 in.^{2}

Lesson 9-5 pp. 435–437

EXERCISES 1. 6 is the stem; 7 is the leaf. **3.** 8, 8 **5.** median: 84%, mode: 78%

7.

4	0 8 9
5	0 2 3 4
6	1 7 8 9
7	3 4 6 8

Key: 4 | 8 means 48

11. Both measures of central tendency indicate that the women's blood pressure in the survey was considerably less than the men's blood pressure. **13.** The mean, median, and mode for the men's golf scores are around 278 strokes, while the women's scores were around 280. This indicates that the difference in scores isn't very large. However, the fact that one of the modes for the women's scores was 290 shows that women frequently do have a higher number of strokes. **19.** 180.3; 180; 180; 8

Lesson 9-6 pp. 440–441

EXERCISES 1. median **3.** E **5.** Answers may vary. Sample: the range of percents of on-time arrivals is about the same for Atlanta and Denver. Overall, Denver had a greater percent of on-time arrivals per day in 2004 than Atlanta. The median for Denver is about the same as the upper quartile for Atlanta.

7.

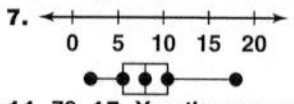

11. 70 **15.** Yes; the upper quartile would move from 162 to 167.5, and the lower quartile would move from 139 to 149.5.

Lesson 9-7 pp. 446–447

EXERCISES 1. scatter plot **3.** no trend

5.

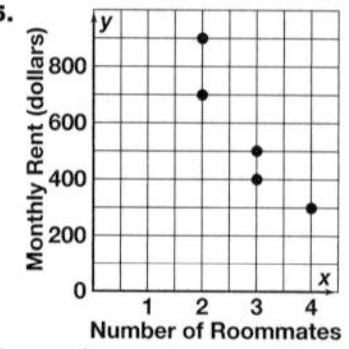

7. negative trend

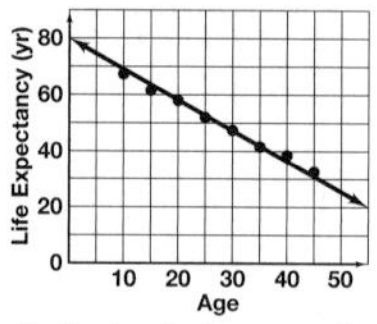

11. Negative trend; as the temperature increases, you wear fewer layers of clothing.

13a–b.

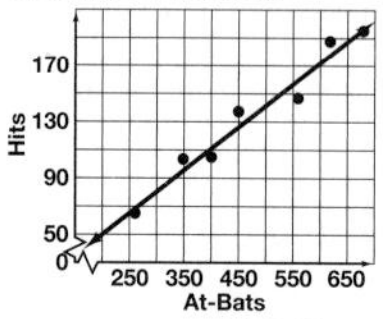

Selected Answers

13c. about 140 **d.** about 800

Lesson 9-8 pp. 452–453

EXERCISES 1. 360° **3.** It identifies each sector. **5.** football: 60; baseball: 54; soccer: 42; basketball: 24; swimming: 12; tennis: 8

9.

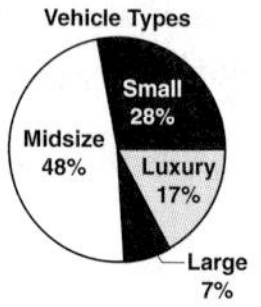

13a.

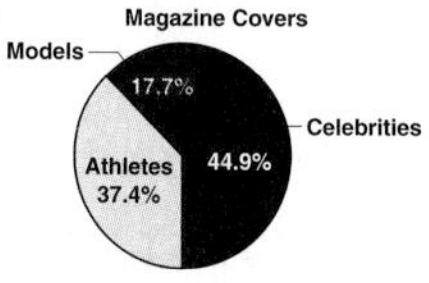

b. 150 women **c.** 220 women

Lesson 9-9 pp. 457–459

EXERCISES 5. Line graph; this graph is better for showing data over time. **9.** Box-and-whisker plot; it gives a good summary of data, including high and low, median, and upper and lower quartiles.

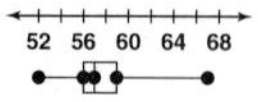

15a. The data are not parts of a whole.

b.

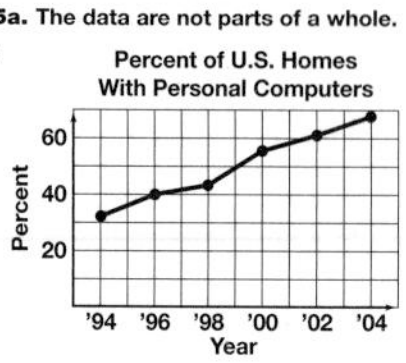

A line graph shows change over time. **17.** Answers may vary. Sample: You could choose a histogram with intervals. **21.** 85°

Chapter Review pp. 462–463

1. quartiles **2.** scatter plot **3.** central angle **4.** stem-and-leaf plot **5.** 15.18; 15; 15; 14 **6.** 9.82; 9.85; 9.1 and 10.3; 1.7 **7.** Answers may vary. Sample:

Number	Frequency
50–54	2
55–59	3
60–64	3
65–69	2
70–74	2
75–79	4
80–84	2

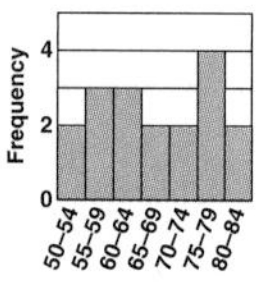

8. 5 artists

9.

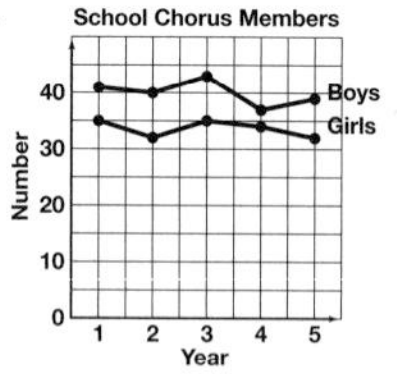

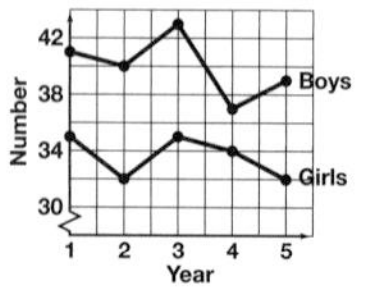

The graph with the break symbol tends to exaggerate the changes.

10.

6	3 5 7	79; 79
7	2 5 8 8 9 9 9	
8	5 5 9	
9	0 9	

Key: 9 | 0 means 90

11. 72; 85

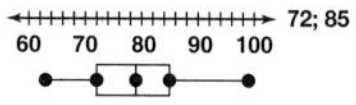

12.

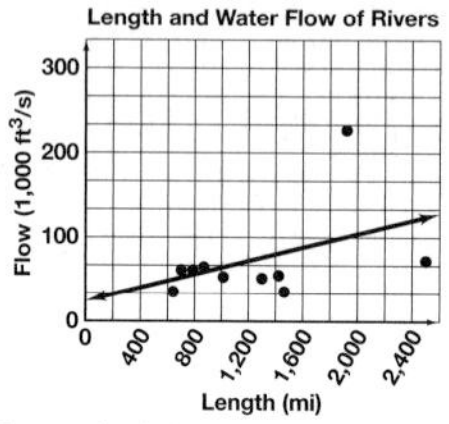

13. Scatter plot; it shows the relationship between two sets of data.

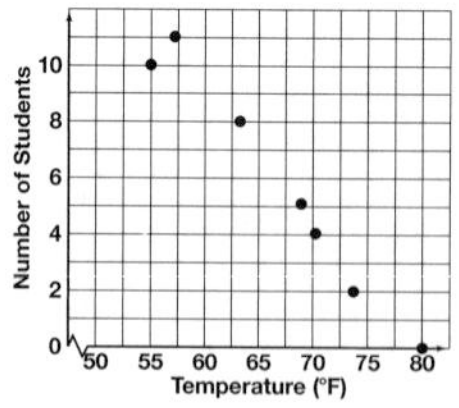

14. Stem-and-leaf plot; it shows numerical data arranged in order.

1	5 6 7
2	0 1 3 9
3	0 3

Key: 3 | 0 means 30

Chapter 10

Lesson 10-1 pp. 472–473

EXERCISES 1. experimental **3.** $\frac{3}{10}$ **5.** 0.272 **9.** theoretical **15.** $\frac{38}{171}$ **17.** $\frac{129}{171}$ **19.** $\frac{135}{171}$ **25.** 36°

Lesson 10-2 pp. 476–478

EXERCISES 1. 18 cars **3.** 30 **5.** 300 **7.** 90 **9.** 8 **13.** 2,400 people **15.** 1,440 people **19.** about 6 bats **21.** 3,000 votes **23.** 3,480 votes **25.** 96 students **27.** 288 students **29.** 60 students **33.** 14 ft^2

Lesson 10-3 pp. 482–483

EXERCISES 1. Researchers use samples because there are usually too many objects or people in a population to survey. **3.** Answers may vary. Sample: Do you like reality television or homework, or neither? **5.** This is a random sample; the population is the students in the class. **9.** Biased; it makes roses sound more appealing than carnations. **15a.** people who register a car **b.** $\frac{12}{41}$ **17.** Answers may vary. Sample: Do you prefer to swim in a pool or in the ocean, or neither?

Lesson 10-4 pp. 488–489

EXERCISES 1. If the outcome of the first event affects the outcome of the second event, the events are dependent. If the outcome of the first event has no effect on the outcome of the second event, the events are independent. **3.** Dependent; after the first card is chosen, the remaining collection of cards has changed. **5.** $\frac{1}{36}$ **7.** $\frac{1}{676}$ **11.** $\frac{9}{190}$ **15.** Independent; the first spin does not affect the second spin. **19.** $\frac{5}{32}$ **21.** 0 **23.** $\frac{1}{36}$ **25.** $\frac{2}{5}$

29.

5	0 2 5 5 6 7 7
6	1 1 4 5 8
7	0

Key: 5 | 0 means 5.0

Lesson 10-5 pp. 493–495

EXERCISES 1. A permutation is an arrangement of a set of objects in a particular order. **3.** 720 **5.** 90 **7.** 6 orders **9.** 120 orders **11.** 5,040 **13.** 3,628,800 **17.** 13,800 **19.** 29,760 **21.** 159,600 **23.** 30,240 **25.** 3,628,800 **27.** 13,800 arrangements **29.** 39,070,080 orders **31.** 504 hours **35.** Circle graph; it shows how the total time using computers is broken into parts.

Lesson 10-6 pp. 498–499

EXERCISES 1. In a permutation, the order matters. In a combination, order does not matter. **3.** no; combination **5.** 5 **7.** 36 ways **9.** 4 **11.** 4 **21.** permutation **23.** 45 games **27.** $\frac{1}{2,184}$ **31.** 4.5×10

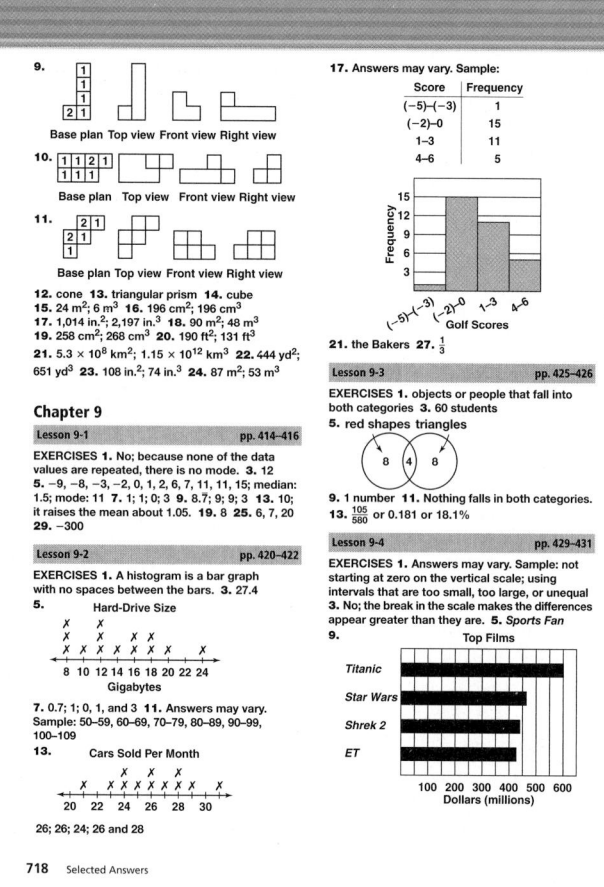

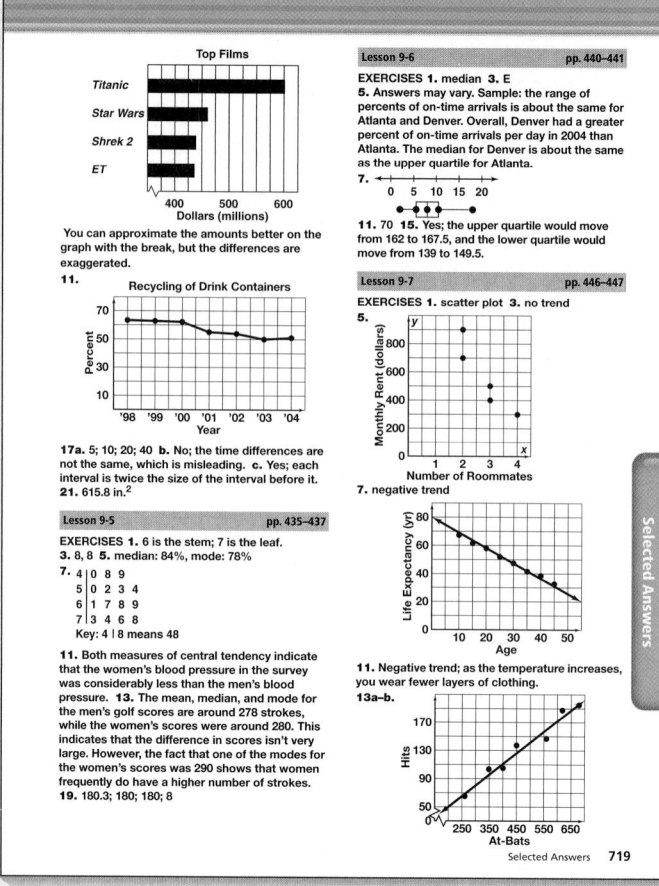

Selected Answers

Chapter Review pp. 504–505

1. theoretical probability **2.** random sample **3.** permutations **4.** dependent events **5.** 5 : 4 **6.** 1 : 2 **7.** 1 : 8 **8.** about 15 cases **9.** about 100 students **10.** random **11.** not random **12.** Independent; the outcome of the second roll is not affected by the first roll. **13.** Dependent; the probability of the second pick is affected by the first pick. **14.** 66 games **15.** 45 ways

Chapter 11

Lesson 11-1 pp. 514–516

EXERCISES **1.** A common ratio involves mult. or div. A common difference involves add. or subtr. **3.** −1 **5.** 2 **7.** 2, 8, 32 **9.** $-\frac{1}{4}, -1\frac{1}{4}, -2\frac{1}{4}$ **11.** 7, 9, 11, 13 **15.** $3n$; 60 **19.** Start with 1 and multiply by 4 repeatedly; 256; 1,024; 4,096. **21.** Start with 3 and multiply by 2 repeatedly; 48, 96, 192. **25.** arithmetic **29.** neither; 26, 37, 50 **31.** geometric; 162, 486, 1,458 **33.** geometric; 0.125, 0.625, 0.3125 **35.** 12 days **37.** Answers may vary. Sample: $15.5 - 3n$; −44.5 **39a.** 8; 27; 64; 125 **b.** Volume is the length of the side cubed. **c.** n^3, where n is length of side **45.** $\frac{10}{171}$

Lesson 11-2 pp. 519–521

EXERCISES **1.** Line graphs best display changes over time. **3.** when the bus stops **5.** Highway; the bus travels a greater distance over a shorter period of time on the highway. **7.** 10 weeks **9.** −10 km **13.** Al **15.** Carlos

17.

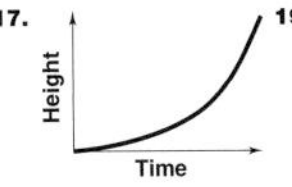

19.

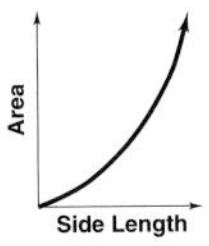

25. 21

Lesson 11-3 pp. 525–526

EXERCISES **1.** A function rule is an equation that describes a function. **3.** Always positive; the product of two negative numbers is always positive.

5.

n	t
44	4
132	12
165	15

7. 3 **9.** 7 **15.** no

19.

Input t	Output d
1	50
2	100
3	150
4	200

21a. 96, 92, 88, 84; arithmetic **b.** 3, 4, 3, 0; neither **25.** $-1n$; −5, −6, −7

Lesson 11-4 pp. 530–531

EXERCISES **1.** run **3.** $-\frac{1}{3}$ **5.** $\frac{3}{5}$

9. −1

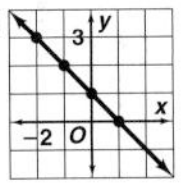

11. Your classmate found $\frac{\text{run}}{\text{rise}}$ instead of $\frac{\text{rise}}{\text{run}}$.

Lesson 11-5 pp. 536–538

EXERCISES **1.** Discrete data involve a count of items. Continuous data are data for which numbers between any two data values have meaning. **3.** 4; −1

5.

x	−3	−2	−1	0	1	2	3
y	−9	−6	−3	0	3	6	9

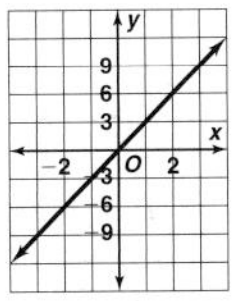

7. continuous

x	p
0	1
10	1.3
20	1.6
30	1.9

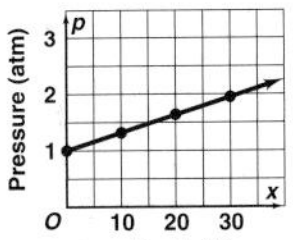

11.

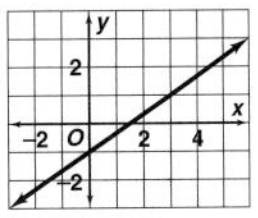

13.

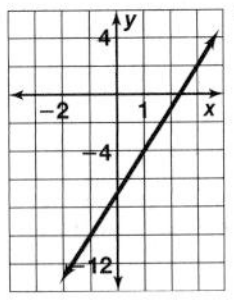

15.

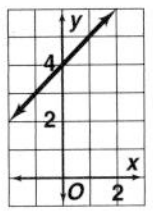

17a.

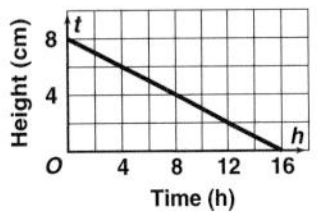

b. 8 cm **c.** 16 h

19.

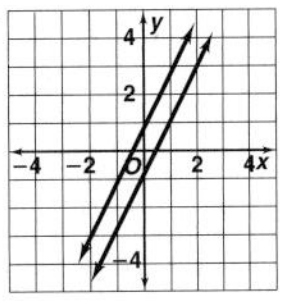

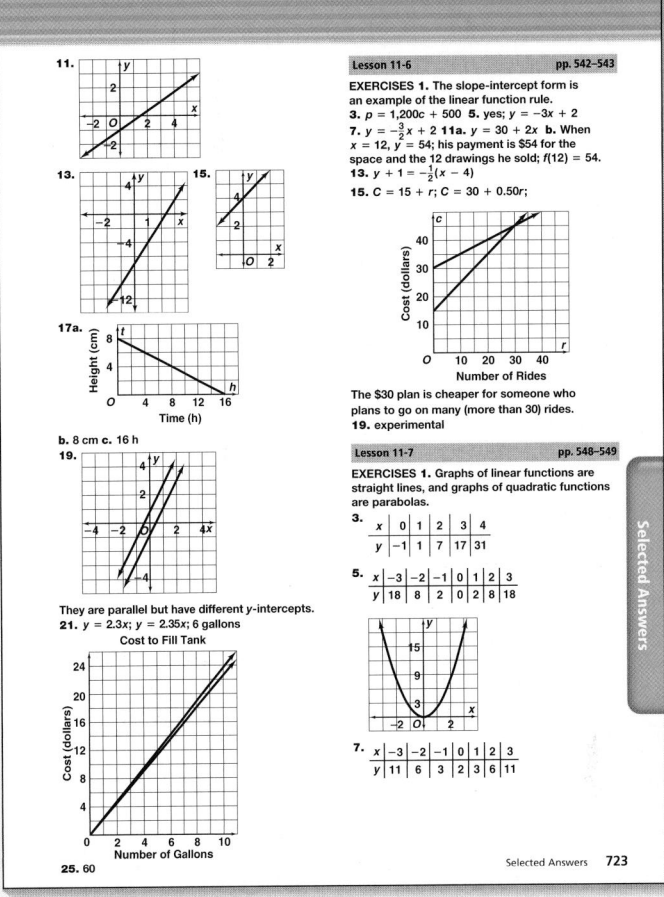

They are parallel but have different y-intercepts.

21. $y = 2.3x$; $y = 2.35x$; 6 gallons

Cost to Fill Tank

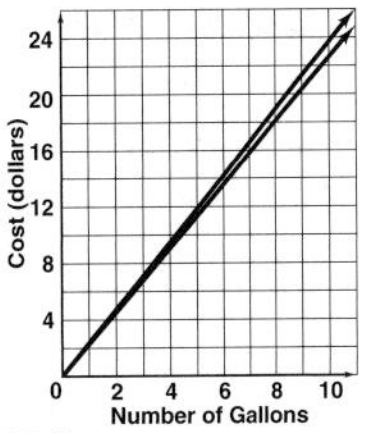

25. 60

Lesson 11-6 pp. 542–543

EXERCISES **1.** The slope-intercept form is an example of the linear function rule. **3.** $p = 1{,}200c + 500$ **5.** yes; $y = -3x + 2$ **7.** $y = -\frac{3}{2}x + 2$ **11a.** $y = 30 + 2x$ **b.** When $x = 12$, $y = 54$; his payment is $54 for the space and the 12 drawings he sold; $f(12) = 54$. **13.** $y + 1 = -\frac{1}{2}(x - 4)$

15. $C = 15 + r$; $C = 30 + 0.50r$;

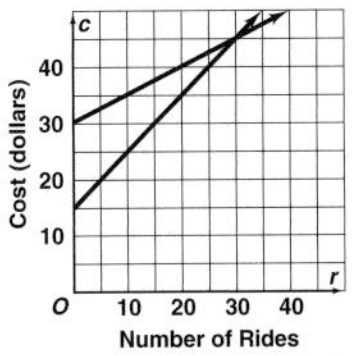

The $30 plan is cheaper for someone who plans to go on many (more than 30) rides. **19.** experimental

Lesson 11-7 pp. 548–549

EXERCISES **1.** Graphs of linear functions are straight lines, and graphs of quadratic functions are parabolas.

3.

x	0	1	2	3	4
y	−1	1	7	17	31

5.

x	−3	−2	−1	0	1	2	3
y	18	8	2	0	2	8	18

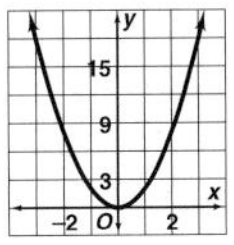

7.

x	−3	−2	−1	0	1	2	3
y	11	6	3	2	3	6	11

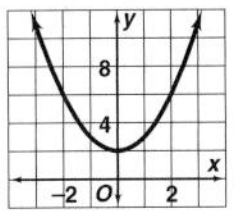

11.

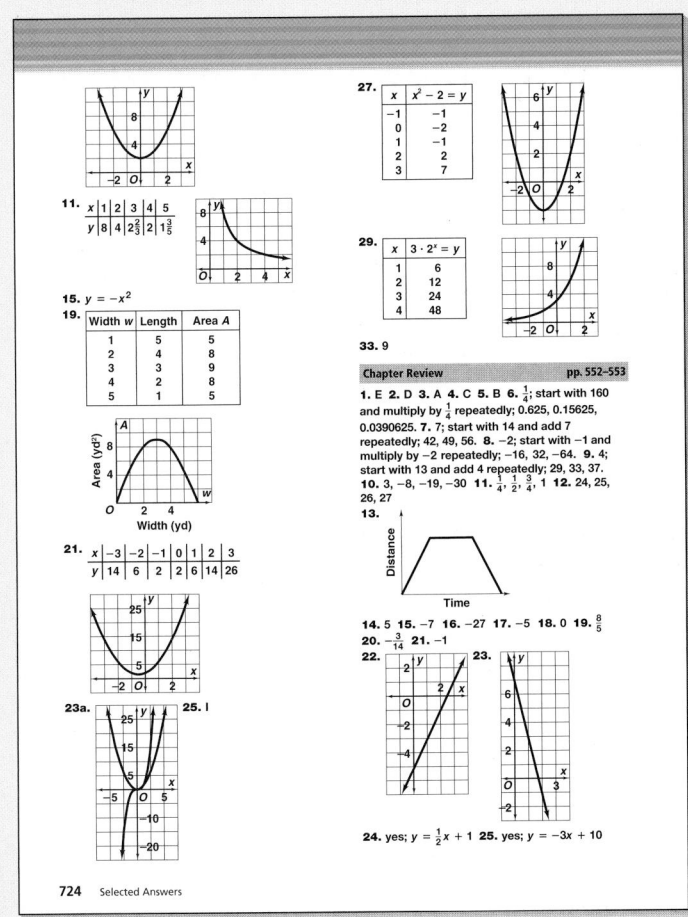

x	1	2	3	4	5
y	8	4	$2\frac{2}{3}$	2	$1\frac{3}{5}$

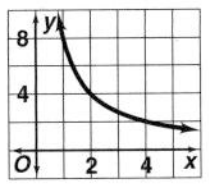

15. $y = -x^2$

19.

Width w	Length	Area A
1	5	5
2	4	8
3	3	9
4	2	8
5	1	5

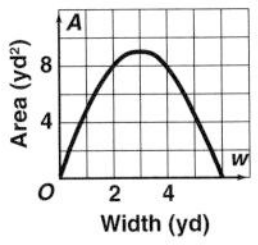

21.

x	−3	−2	−1	0	1	2	3
y	14	6	2	2	6	14	26

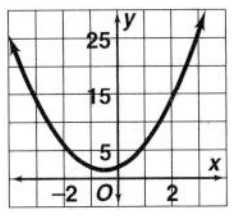

23a.

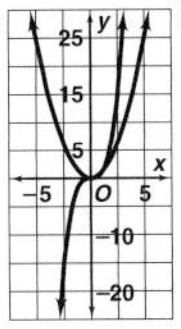

25. I

27.

x	$x^2 - 2 = y$
−1	−1
0	−2
1	−1
2	2
3	7

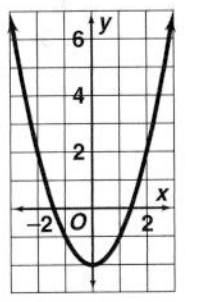

29.

x	$3 \cdot 2^x = y$
1	6
2	12
3	24
4	48

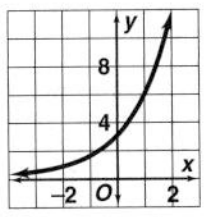

33. 9

Chapter Review pp. 552–553

1. E **2.** D **3.** A **4.** C **5.** B **6.** $\frac{1}{4}$; start with 160 and multiply by $\frac{1}{4}$ repeatedly; 0.625, 0.15625, 0.0390625. **7.** 7; start with 14 and add 7 repeatedly; 42, 49, 56. **8.** −2; start with −1 and multiply by −2 repeatedly; −16, 32, −64. **9.** 4; start with 13 and add 4 repeatedly; 29, 33, 37. **10.** 3, −8, −19, −30 **11.** $\frac{1}{4}, \frac{1}{2}, \frac{3}{4}$, 1 **12.** 24, 25, 26, 27

13.

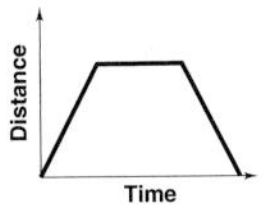

14. 5 **15.** −7 **16.** −27 **17.** −5 **18.** 0 **19.** $\frac{8}{5}$ **20.** $-\frac{3}{14}$ **21.** −1

22.

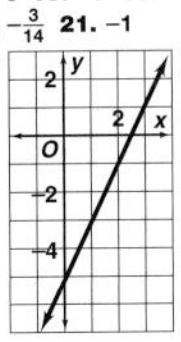

23.

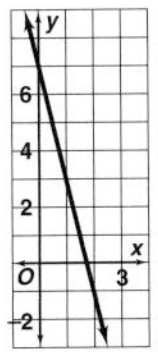

24. yes; $y = \frac{1}{2}x + 1$ **25.** yes; $y = -3x + 10$

26.

x	−2	−1	0	1	2
y	4	−2	−4	−2	4

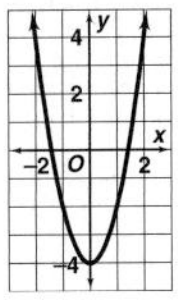

27.

x	−2	−1	0	1	2
y	−2	1	2	1	−2

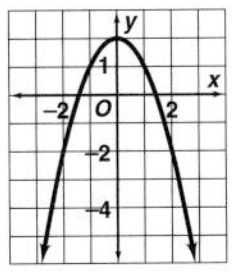

28.

x	1	7	14	21
y	7	1	$\frac{1}{2}$	$\frac{1}{3}$

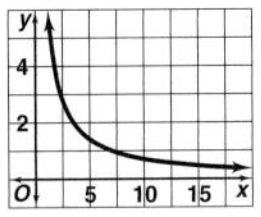

29.

x	1	2	3	4	5
y	7	$\frac{9}{2}$	$\frac{11}{3}$	$\frac{13}{4}$	3

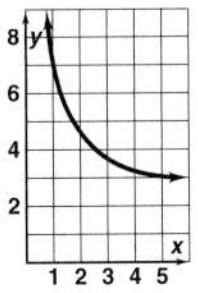

Chapter 12

Lesson 12-1 pp. 563–565

EXERCISES **1.** 63, 35 **3.** A **5.** $2x^2 - x + 3$ **9.** $3x^2 + 2x - 4$ **13.** $2x^2 + x + 1$ **17.** $x^2 - 2x - 1$ **19.** $7n + 2k$ **21.** 31 **23.** 3 **25.** 5

Lesson 12-2 pp. 568–569

EXERCISES **1.** variable **3.** −1, −1 **5.** $5m$ **7.** $8p^2 + 2p + 1$ **11.** $4x + 6$ **15.** $-x^2 - 2x + 7$ **21.** $x^3 - 9x + 1$ **23.** $-x^3 - 2x^2 + 2x + 5$ **25.** $6x^2 + 16x$ **31.** 1,860,480

Lesson 12-3 pp. 573–574

EXERCISES **1.** 8 **3.** $(-6)^4$ **5.** 7^{10} **7.** Instead of just adding the exponents, the student multiplied the bases and then added the exponents. **9.** y^8 **11.** 3.4^{13} **17.** 8×10^9 **19.** 7.2×10^{11} **25.** Answers may vary. Sample: $4 \cdot 4^{11}$; $4^2 \cdot 4^{10}$; $4^6 \cdot 4^6$ **27.** 6.8×10^{12} **29.** 3^{m+n} **31.** $(-4)^{x+y}$ **33.** a^{10} **35.** 3^{6a} **37.** c^3d^4 **39.** $3x^8$ **41.** > **43.** > **45.** 2 **49.** about 43 mi/hr

Lesson 12-4 pp. 578–579

EXERCISES **1.** A monomial has one term, whereas a binomial has two terms. **3.** $15a^2$ **5.** $(x + 4)(2x + 3)$ **7.** $12t^5$ **9.** $-6z^5$ **13.** $a^2 - 3a$ **15.** $21s^2 + 7$ **21.** $4x^2 + 6x + 2$ **23.** $6x^2 + 4x$ **25.** $4x^2 + 2x$ **29.** monomial **31.** monomial

Lesson 12-5 pp. 584–585

EXERCISES **1.** Positive; any nonzero number to the power zero is equal to one. **3.** $\frac{2 \cdot 2 \cdot 2 \cdot 2 \cdot 2 \cdot 2}{2 \cdot 2 \cdot 2 \cdot 2 \cdot 2} = 2^1$ **5.** $\frac{8 \cdot 8 \cdot 8 \cdot 8 \cdot 8}{8 \cdot 8} = 8^3$ **7.** x^4 **9.** −1 **15.** 1 **17.** 1 **25.** 12 **27.** 2 **29.** 1 **31.** −8 **33.** 1.12×10^3 ft/s **35.** False; $8^{-1} = \frac{1}{8}$ and $(-8)^1 = -8$. **37.** False; $(-2)^{-1} = \frac{1}{-2} = -\frac{1}{2}$ and $-\frac{1}{2} \neq 2$. **39 a.** $2n^3 - 4$ **b.** $2m^6 + 3m^3 + 1$ **43.** $58x = 17$; 29.31%

Chapter Review pp. 590–591

1. polynomial **2.** constant **3.** monomial **4.** coefficient **5.** binomial **6.** $2x^2 + 8$ **7.** $x^2 + 3x + 4$ **8.** $14x^2 + 13x + 6$ **9.** $13x^2 + 4x - 2$ **10.** $-4x^2 + 2x + 7$ **11.** $-x^2 + 11x + 7$ **12.** $16x + 5$ **13.** $-3x^2 + 3$ **14.** $11x^2 - 6x - 2$ **15.** $7x^2 - 3x + 2$ **16.** $-4x - 7$ **17.** $x^2 + x - 11$ **18.** $7x^2 - 2x + 13$ **19.** $3x^2 + 6x - 7$ **20.** 8^{19} **21.** $(-3)^{13}$ **22.** 2.6^{24} **23.** 11^{11} **24.** 6×10^{18} **25.** 7×10^6 **26.** 3×10^{14} **27.** 1.47×10^{20} **28.** $-18x^4$ **29.** $14x^2$ **30.** $-30x^2 + 20x$ **31.** $5x^3 - 15x^2$ **32.** $2x^2 + 9x + 4$ **33.** $x^2 + 4x + 3$ **34.** 5^3 **35.** $(-8)^{10}$ **36.** 76^6 **37.** 1.8^1 **38.** 1 **39.** 1 **40.** 1 **41.** 1 **42.** $\frac{1}{625}$ **43.** $\frac{1}{x^9}$ **44.** $\frac{1}{81}$ **45.** $\frac{1}{h^8}$

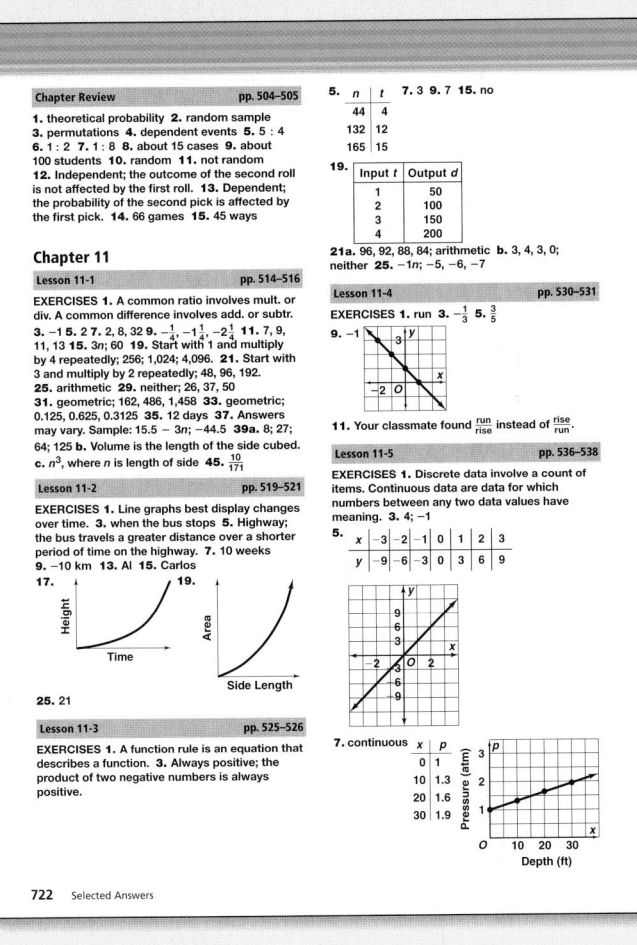

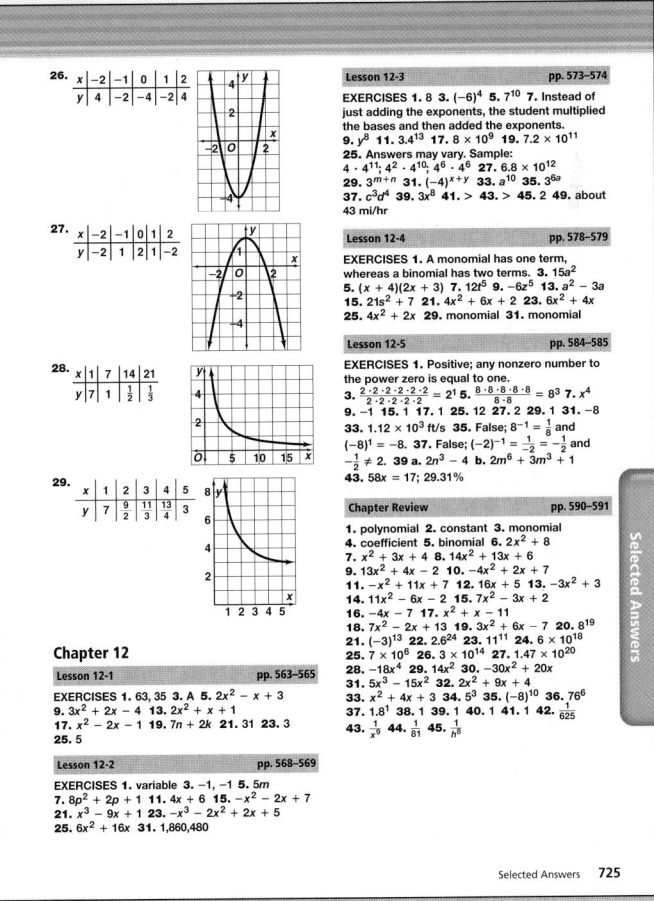

Additional Answers

CHAPTER 3

Lesson 3-2

page 115

21. Answers may vary. Sample: I would create a right triangle by drawing a line from point B to line segment below it and by drawing a hypotenuse, AB. The legs of the triangle are 100 ft and $200 - 50 = 150$ ft. Using the Pythagorean Theorem, I would find the square root of the sum of 100^2 and 150^2. The distance across the length is about 180.3 ft.

Lesson 3-4

page 125 Quick Check

1.

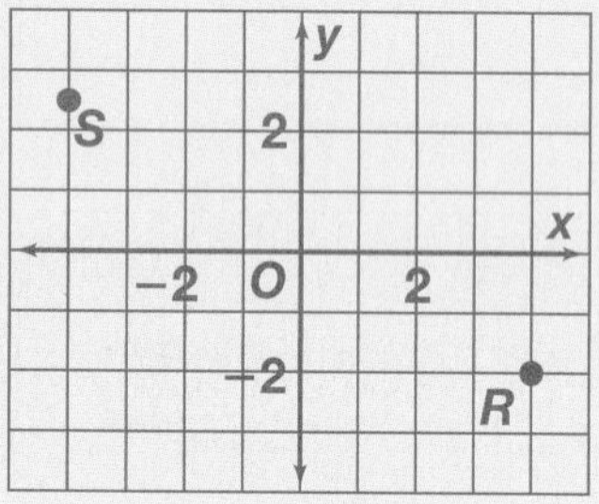

page 126

11–18.

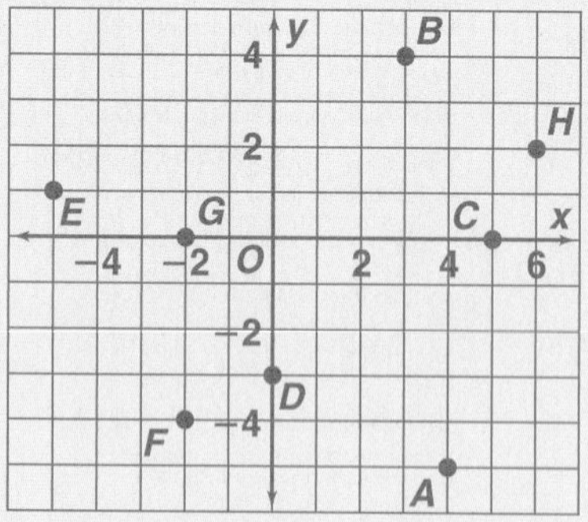

25a.

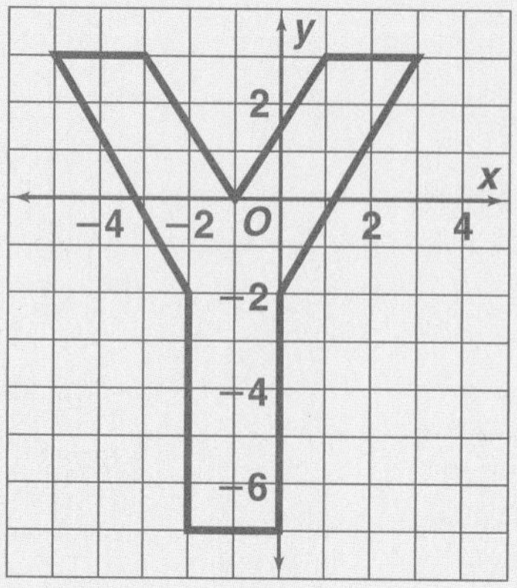

b. the letter Y

page 127

30. Start at (−5, −3).
Then move to
(−4, −3), (−4, 1), (−3, 1),
(−3, −2), (−2, −2), (−2, −3),
(4, −3), (4, 3), (1, 3), (1, 1), (3, 1), and
(3, 2) in that order.

31.

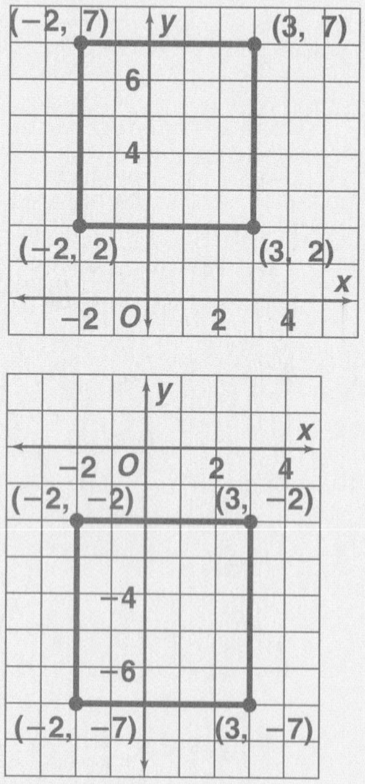

The square is reflected over the *x*-axis.

page 129 Activity Lab

3a.

Number of Days	0	1	2	3	20
Tickets Remaining	180	171	162	153	0

b.

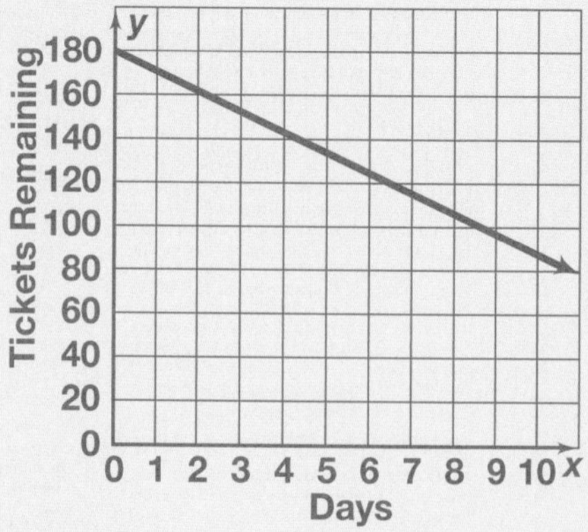

Lesson 3-5

pages 130–131 Quick Check

1.

Number of CDs	Expression	Total Cost (dollars)
0	15(0)	0
1	15(1)	15
2	15(2)	30
3	15(3)	45
c	15(*c*)	*t*

$t = 15c$, where *t* represents total cost and *c* represents number of CDs.

2.

Temperature of a Chemical Solution

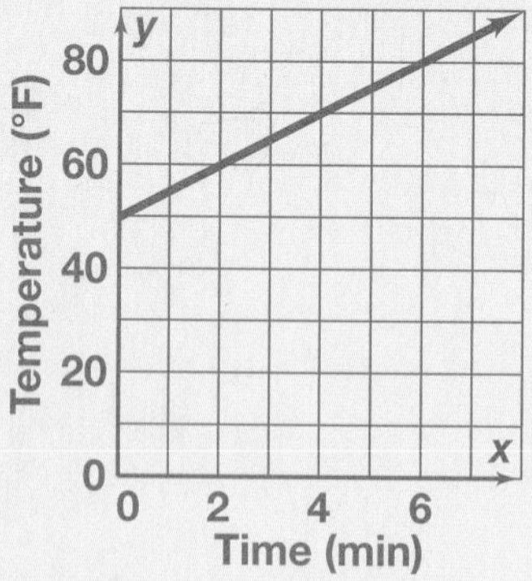

pages 133–134 Exercises

5.

Time (seconds)	Expression	Total Number of Babies
0	4(0)	0
1	4(1)	4
2	4(2)	8
3	4(3)	12
s	4(*s*)	*b*

$b = 4s$

6.

Time (hours)	Expression	Temperature Drop (°F)
0	−2(0)	0
1	−2(1)	−2
2	−2(2)	−4
3	−2(3)	−6
h	−2(h)	t

$t = -2h$

7.

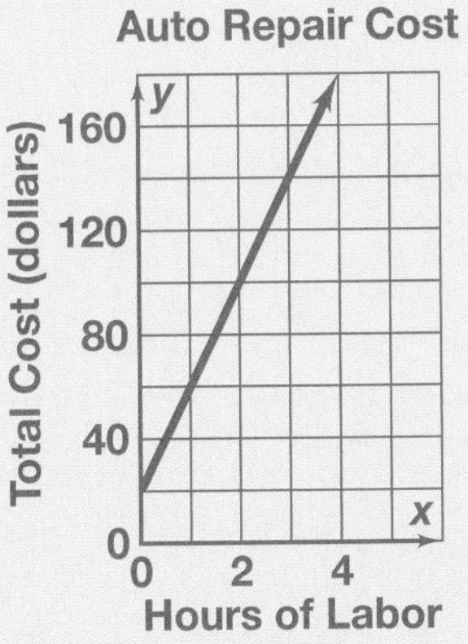

8.

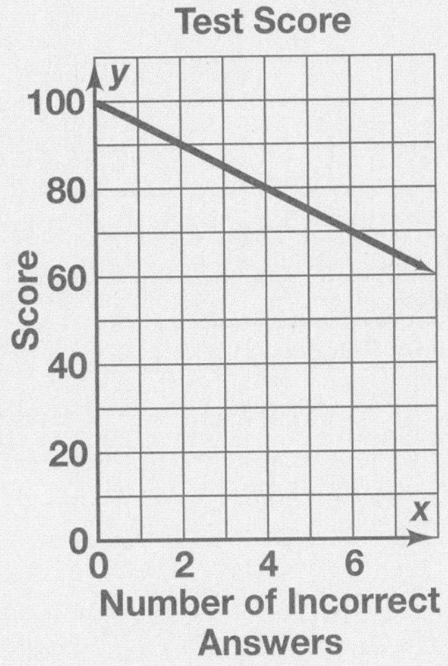

10.

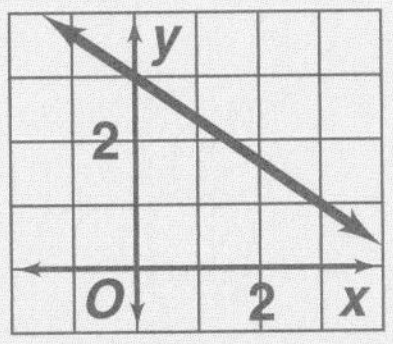

11.

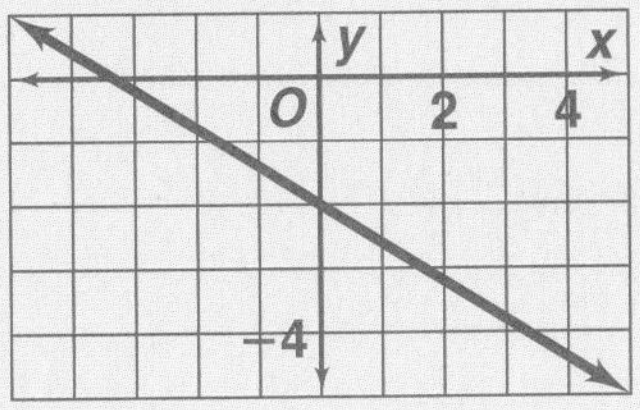

12.

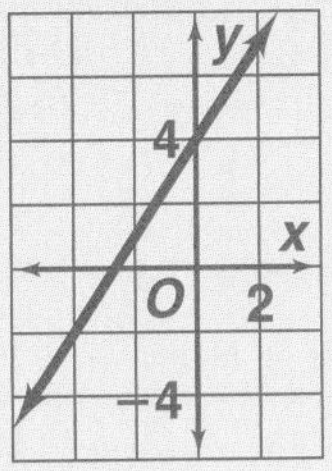

15. 6 letters;

Number of Letters	Expression	Total Cost (dollars)
0	1.50(0) + 10	10.00
1	1.50(1) + 10	11.50
2	1.50(2) + 10	13.00
3	1.50(3) + 10	14.50
ℓ	1.50(ℓ) + 10	c

$c = 1.50\ell + 10$

18. Let y = income or expenses. Let x = the number of calendars sold.
Income: $y = 4x$
Expenses: $y = 2x + 20$

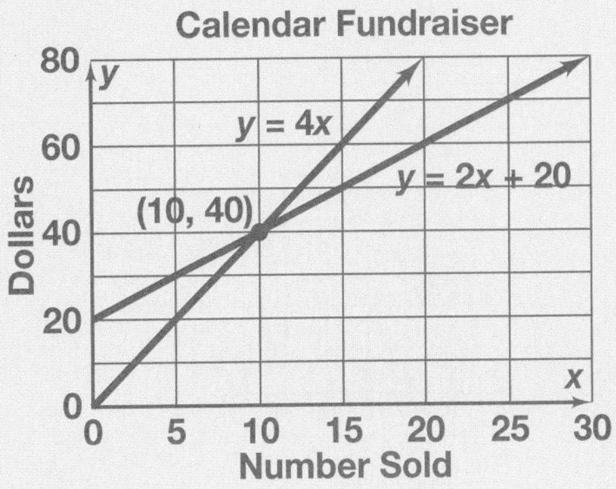

page 134 TE Lesson Quiz

1. Sample: $p = 8h$;

Hours	1	2	3	4	5	6
Pay ($)	8	16	24	32	40	48

2.

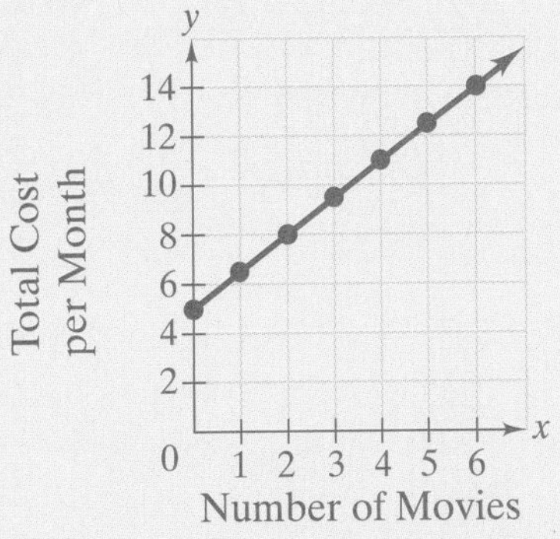

3.

Number of Movies	0	1	2	3	4	5	6
Total Cost ($)	5	6.50	8	9.50	11	12.50	14

Lesson 3-6

page 136 Quick Check

1.

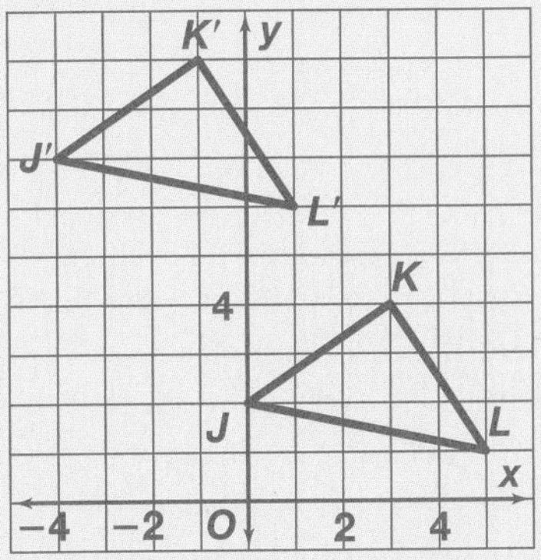

$J'(-4, 7)$

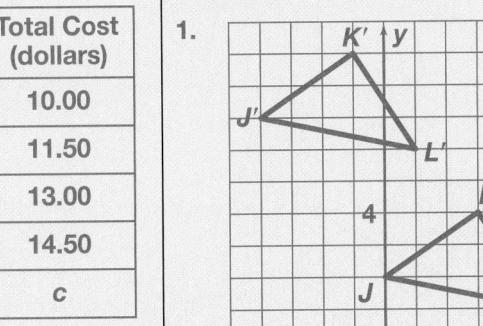

page 137 TE Additional Examples

1.

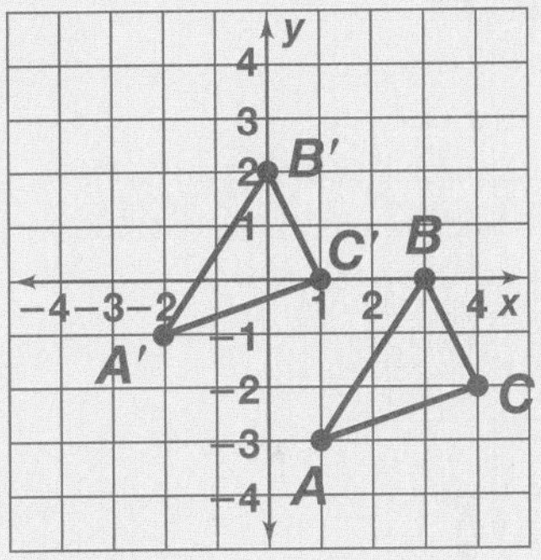

$A'(-2, -1)$, $B'(0, 2)$, $C'(1, 0)$

page 137 Exercises

3.

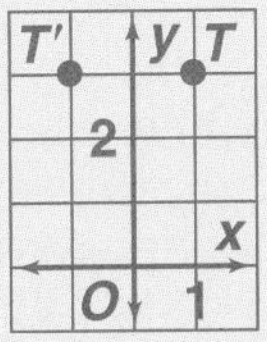

4.

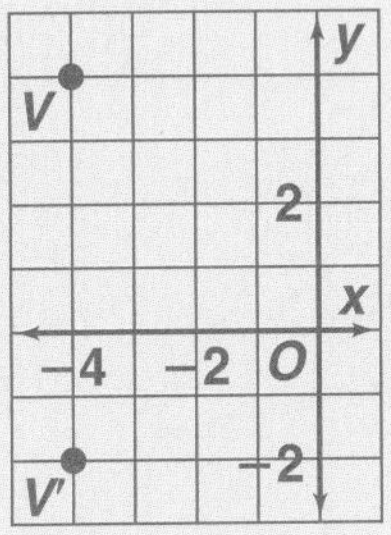

5.

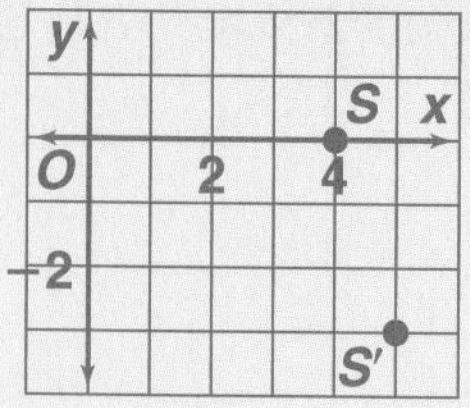

6.

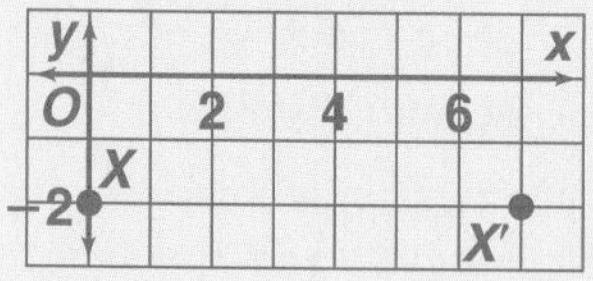

page 139

22.

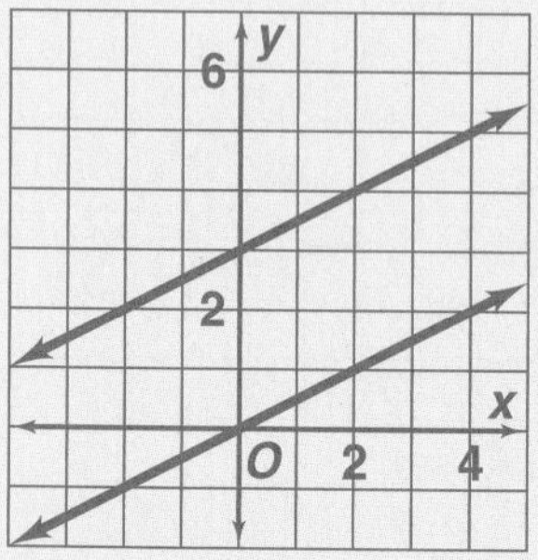

25.

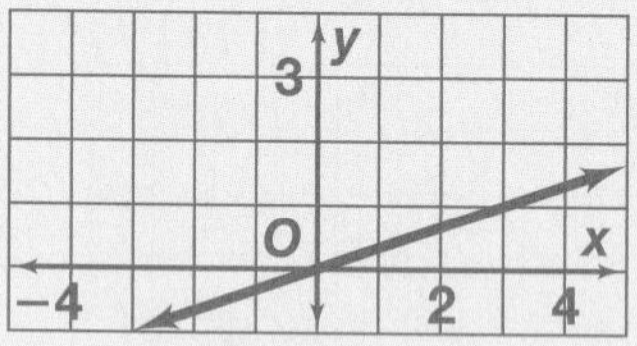

26.

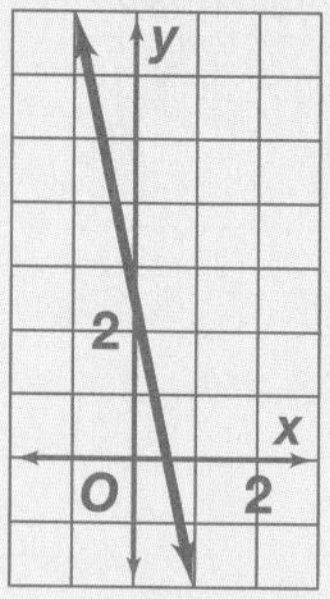

page 140 Checkpoint Quiz

6.

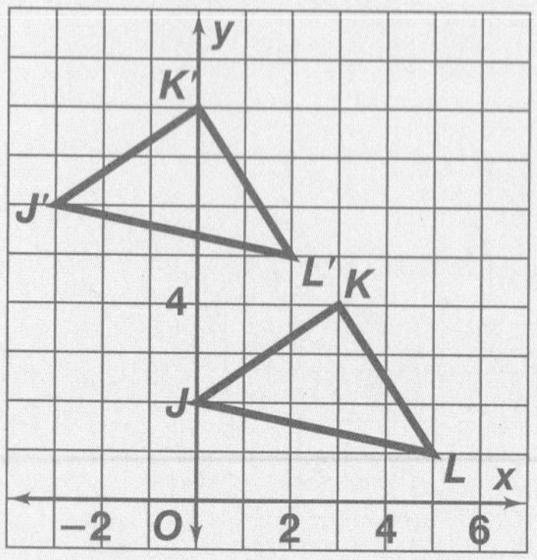

$J'(-3, 6)$, $K'(0, 8)$, $L'(2, 5)$

7. $(x, y) \rightarrow (x - 3, y + 4)$

8.

Number of Exercises	Expression	Workout Time (min)
0	3(0) + 5	5
1	3(1) + 5	8
2	3(2) + 5	11
3	3(3) + 5	14
x	3(*x*) + 5	*w*

$w = 3x + 5$

Lesson 3-7

page 141 Check Skills You'll Need

2.

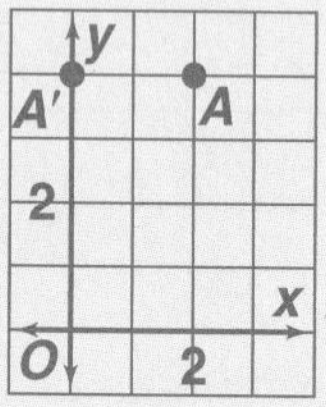

3.

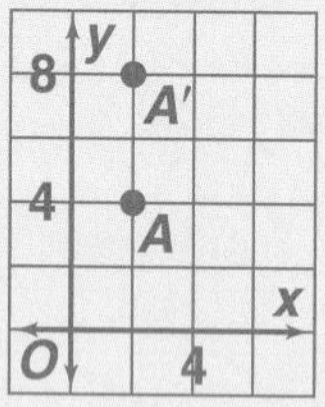

4.

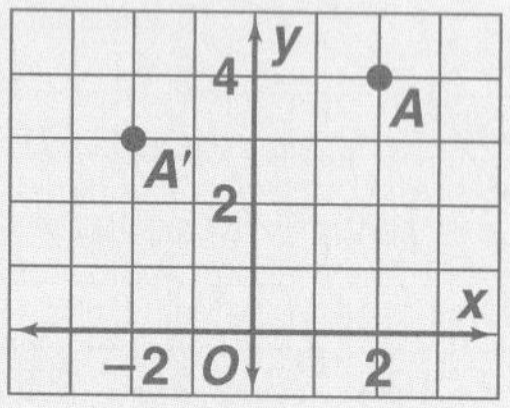

5.

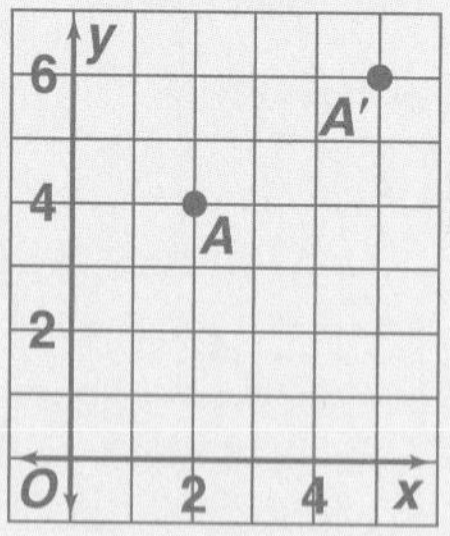

page 142 Quick Check

2.

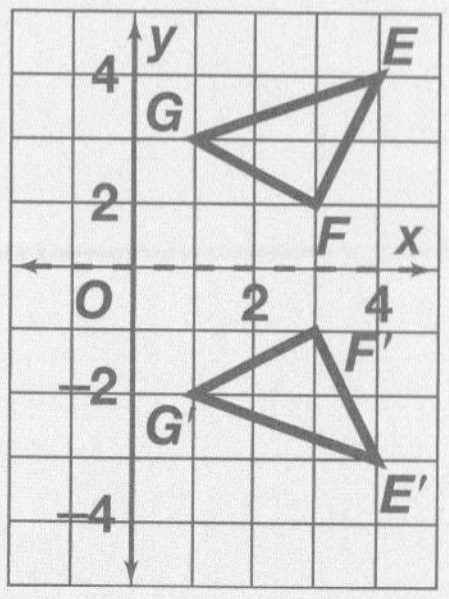

$E'(4, -3)$, $F'(3, -1)$, $G'(1, -2)$

3.

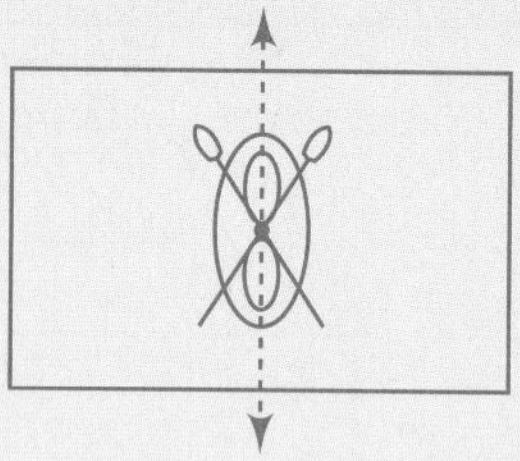

page 142 TE Additional Examples

2.

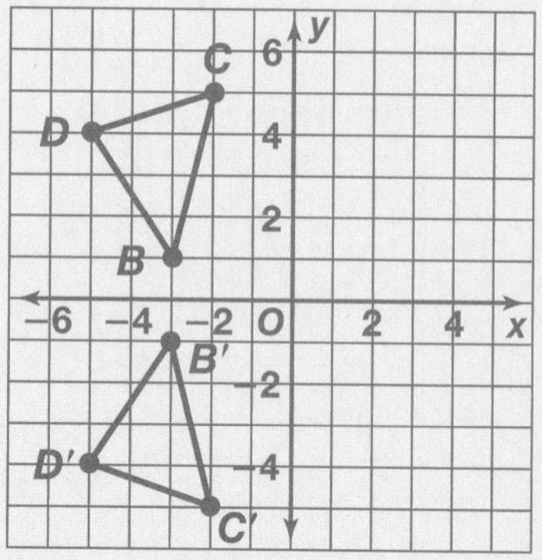

$B'(-3, -1)$, $C'(-2, -5)$, $D'(-5, -4)$

page 143 Exercises

8–13.

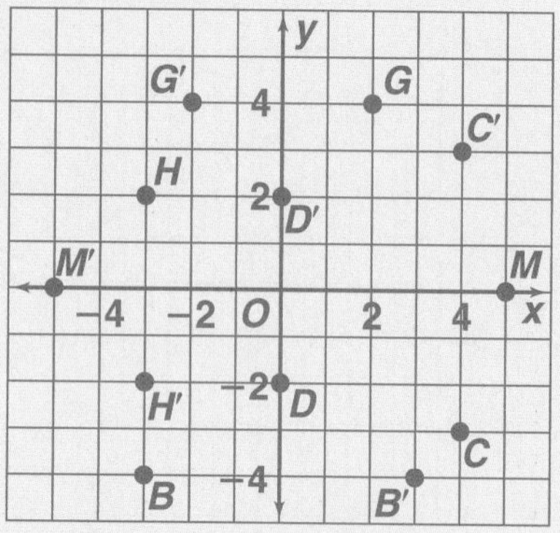

$H'(-3, -2)$, $G'(-2, 4)$,
$B'(3, -4)$, $D'(0, 2)$,
$C'(4, 3)$, $M'(-5, 0)$

14.

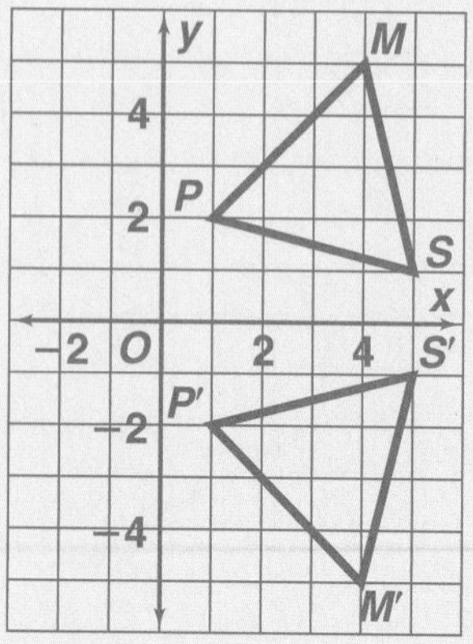

$M'(4, -5)$, $P'(1, -2)$, $S'(5, -1)$

15.

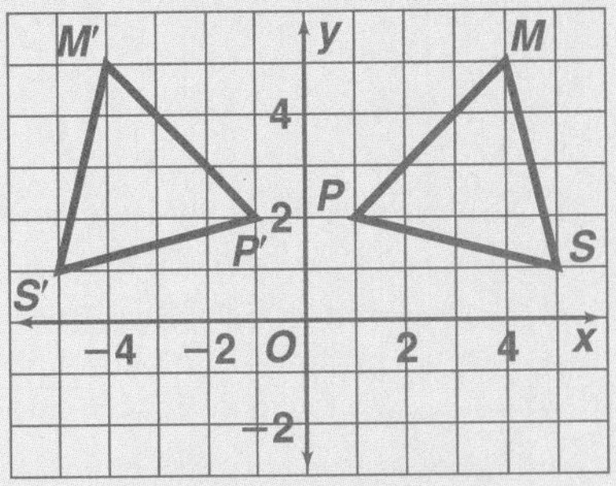

$M'(-4, 5)$, $P'(-1, 2)$, $S'(-5, 1)$

16.

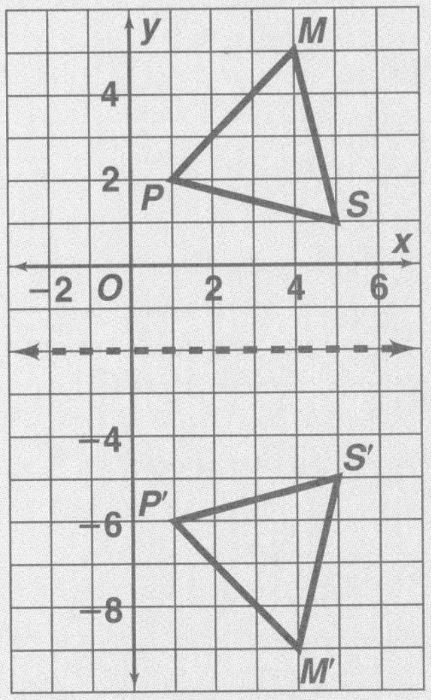

$M'(4, -9)$, $P'(1, -6)$, $S'(5, -5)$

page 144

22a.

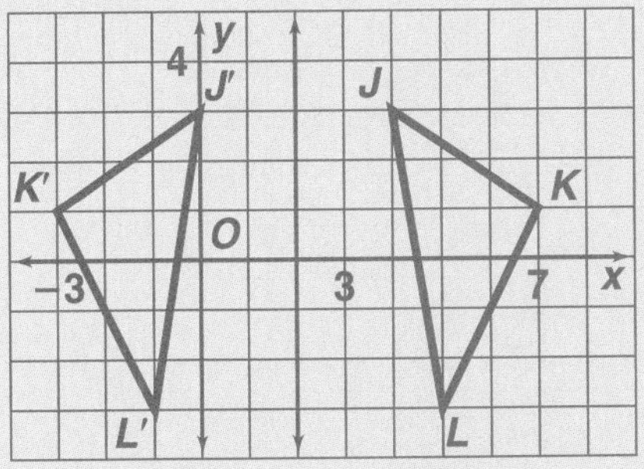

$J'(0, 3)$, $K'(-3, 1)$, $L'(-1, -3)$; the y-coordinates did not change.

b. $J''(-3, 3)$, $K''(-6, 1)$, $L''(-4, -3)$

23.

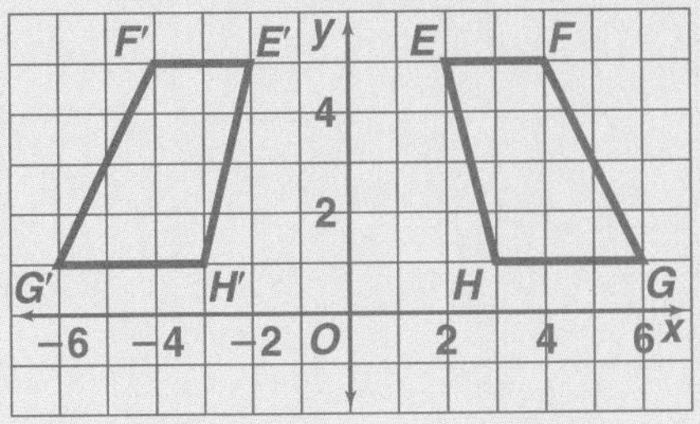

$E'(-2, 5)$, $F'(-4, 5)$, $G'(-6, 1)$, $H'(-3, 1)$

24.

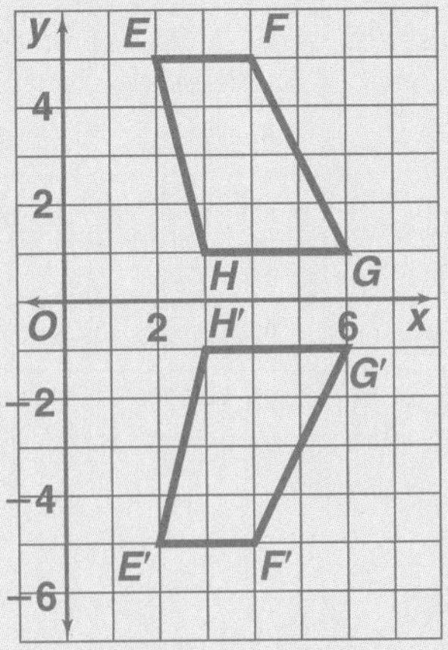

$E'(2, -5)$, $F'(4, -5)$, $G'(6, -1)$, $H'(3, -1)$

25.

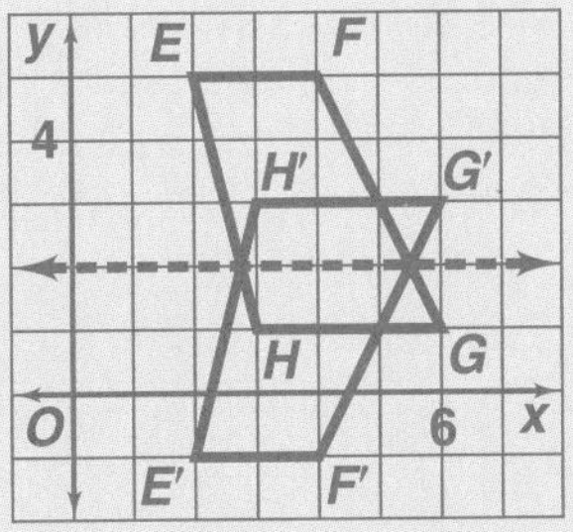

$E'(2, -1)$, $F'(4, -1)$, $G'(6, 3)$, $H'(3, 3)$

28.

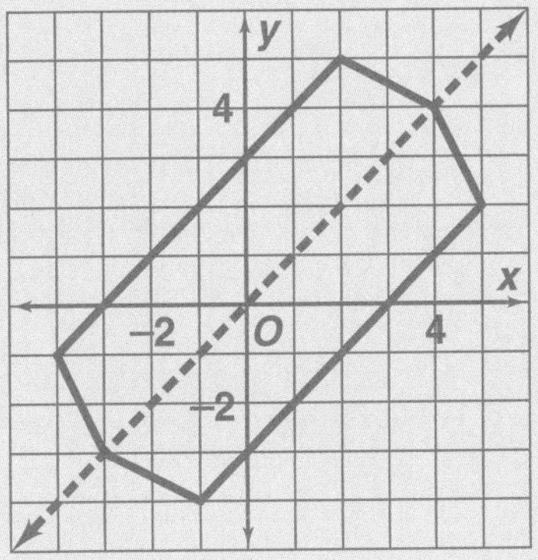

Lesson 3-8

page 147 Quick Check

2a.

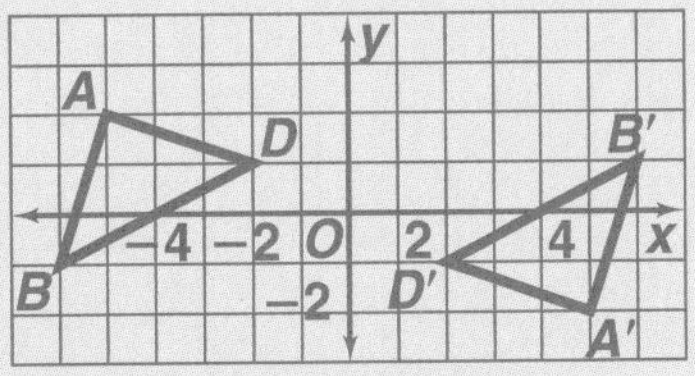

b.

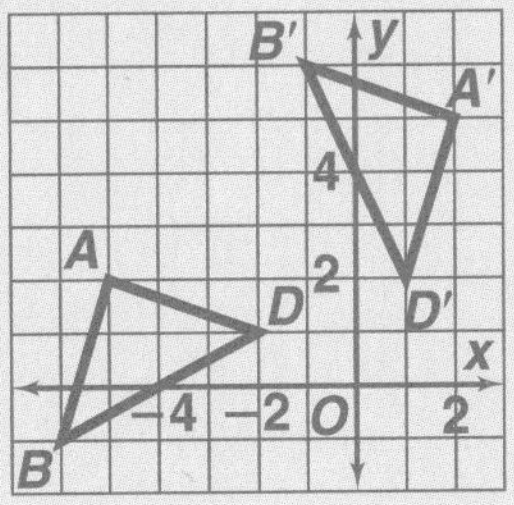

page 148 Exercises

2–4.

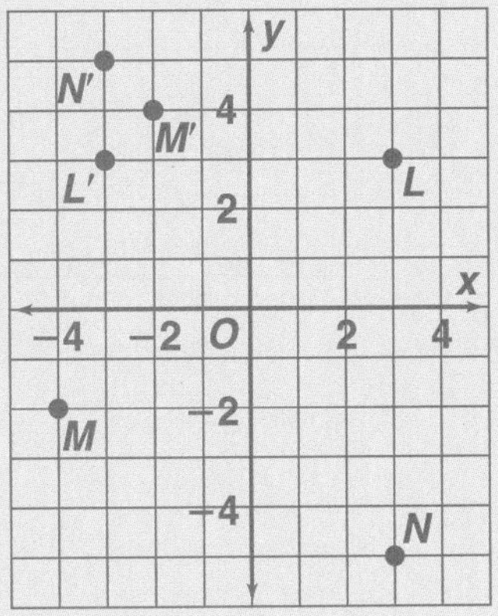

8.

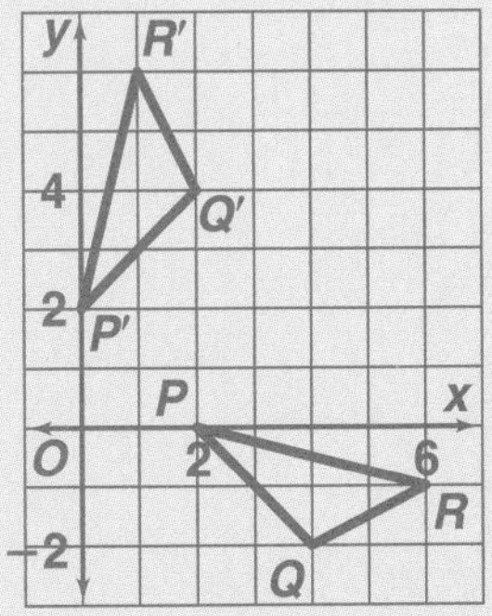

9.

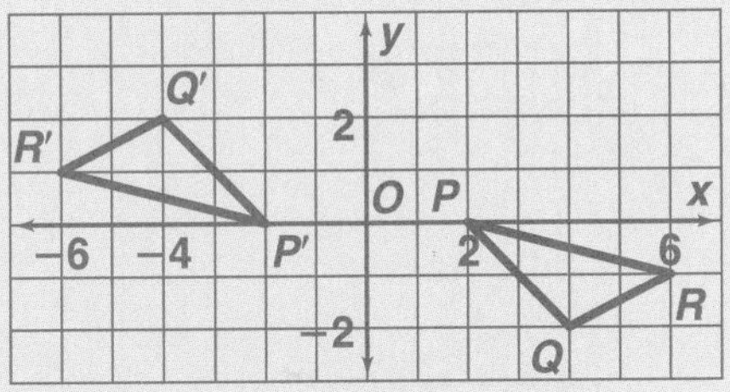

10.

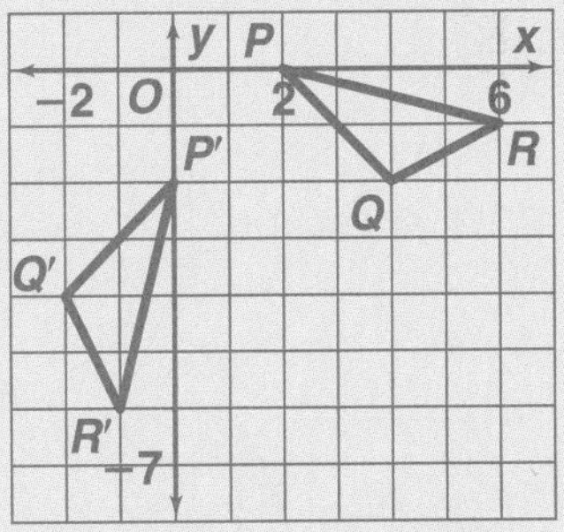

12.

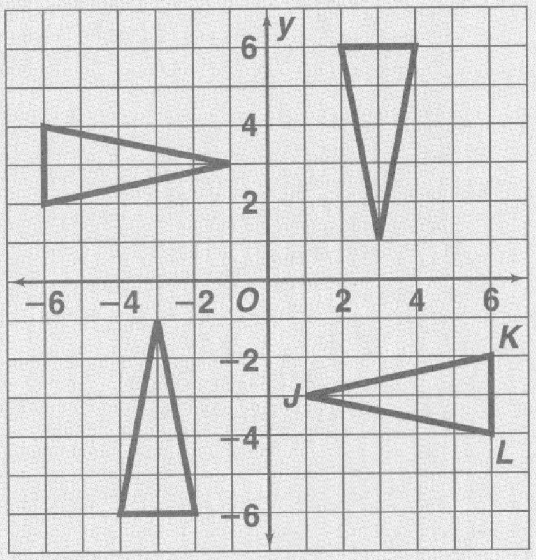

20.

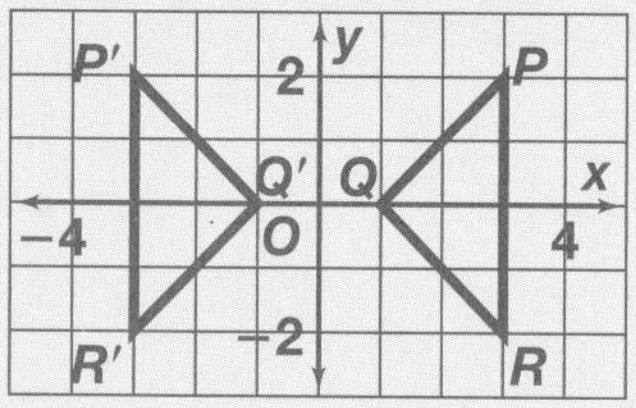

Rotate △*PQR* 180° about the origin.

page 153 Chapter Review

28.

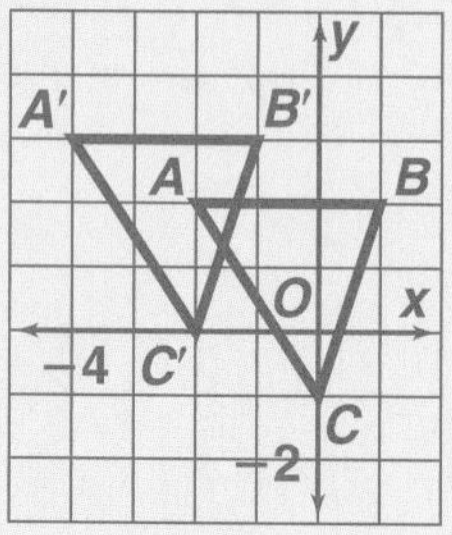

29.

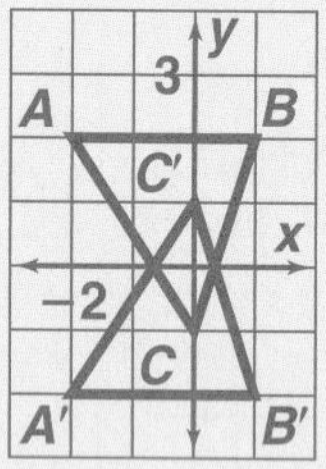

30.

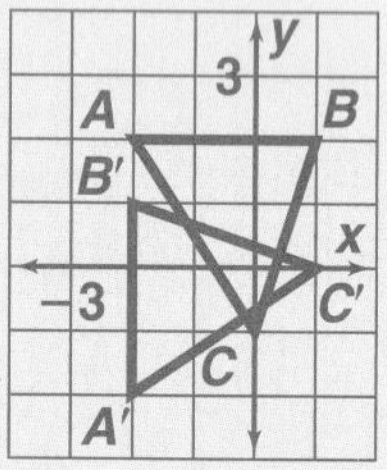

page 154 Chapter Test

27. $y = 4x + 2$;

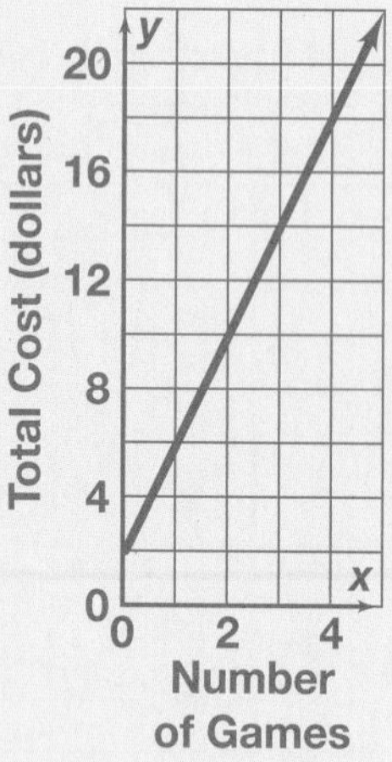

28.

Number of Games	Expression	Total Cost (dollars)
1	5(1) + 20	25
2	5(2) + 20	30
3	5(3) + 20	35
4	5(4) + 20	40
g	5(*g*) + 20	*c*

$c = 5g + 20$

29.

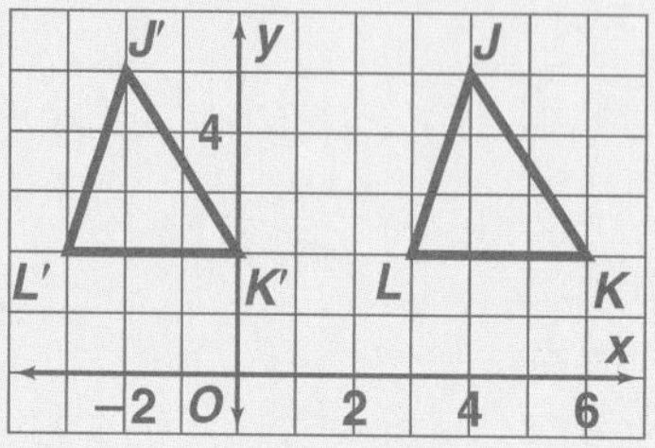

30.

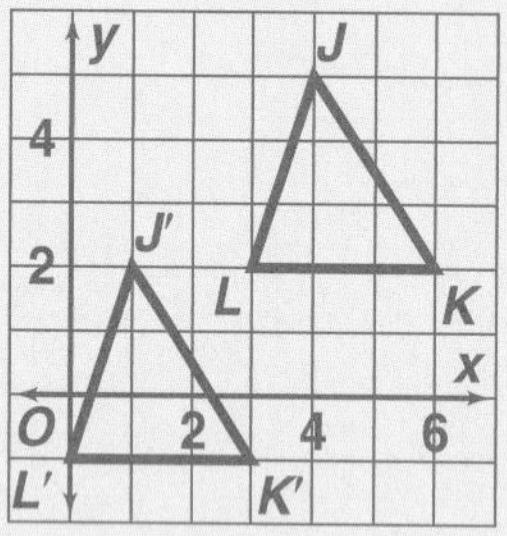

31.

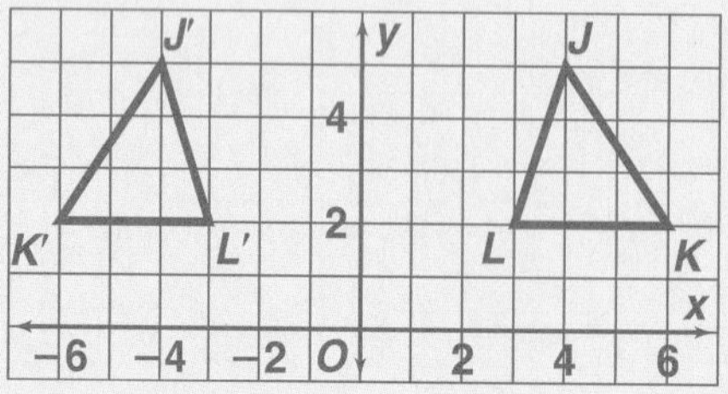

32.

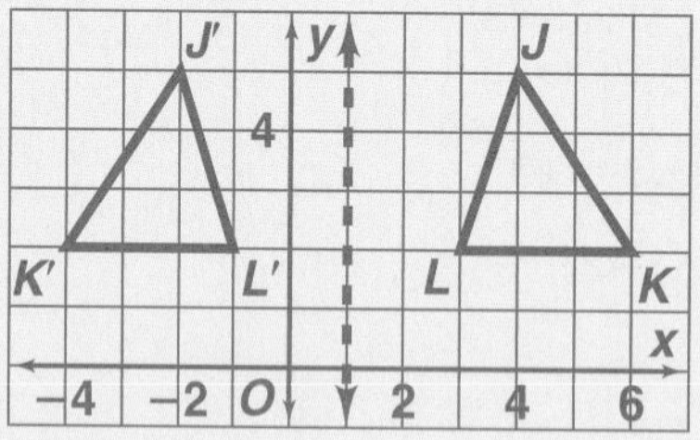

33.

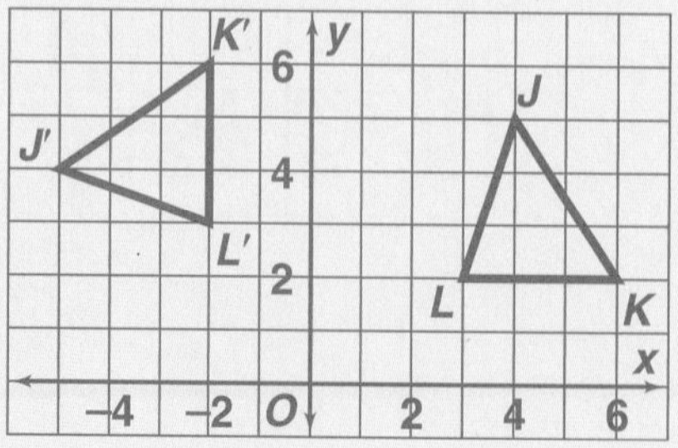

34.

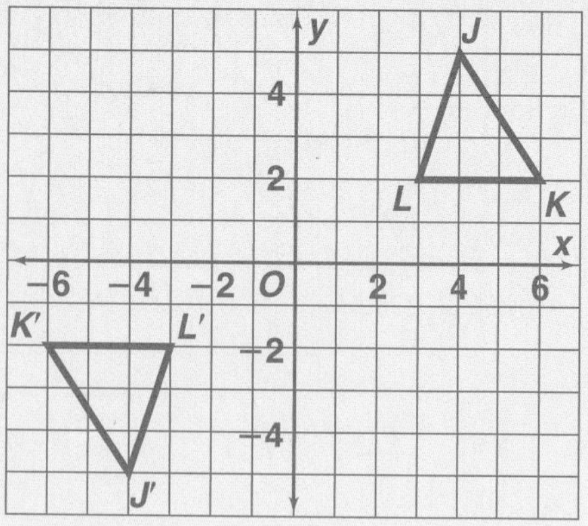

CHAPTER 4

Lesson 4-2

page 170 Exercises

43.

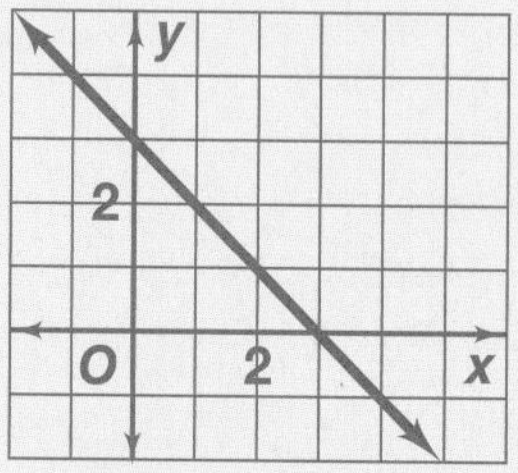

44.

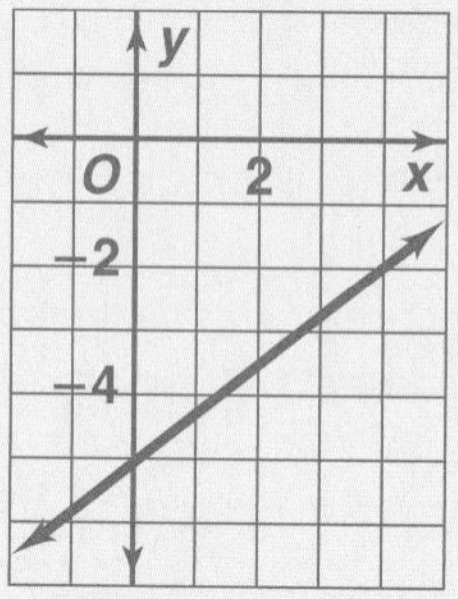

45.

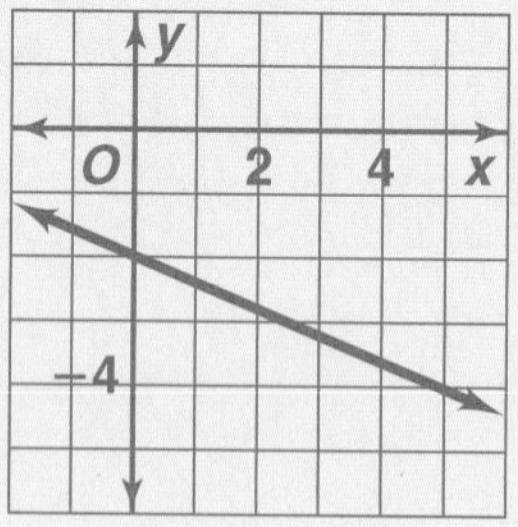

page 172 Activity Lab

4.

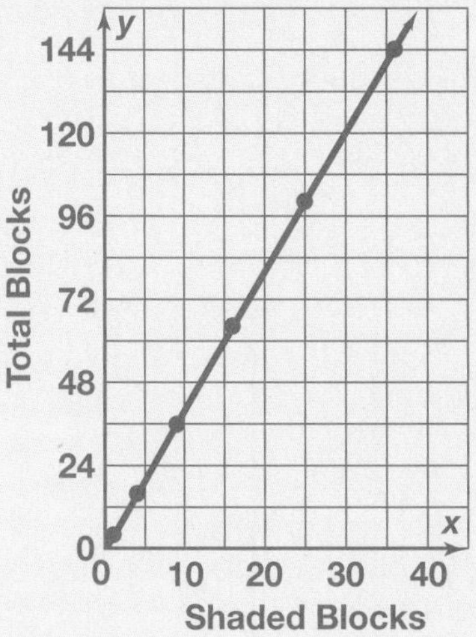

Lesson 4-4

page 182 TE Additional Examples

1. Yes; the corresponding angles are equal, and the corresponding side lengths are proportional.

Lesson 4-5

page 187 Check Skills You'll Need

2–5.

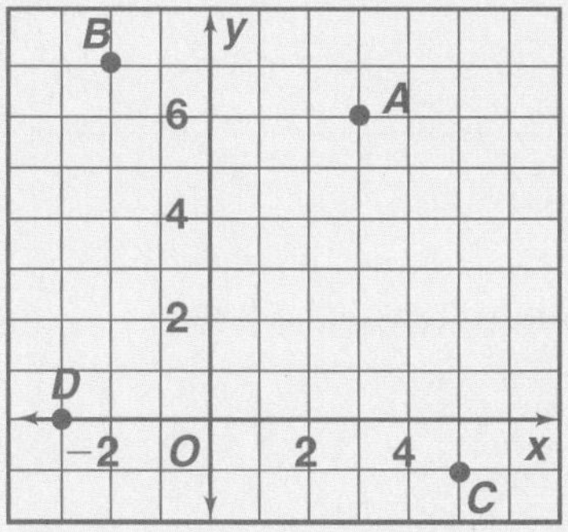

page 187 Quick Check

1.

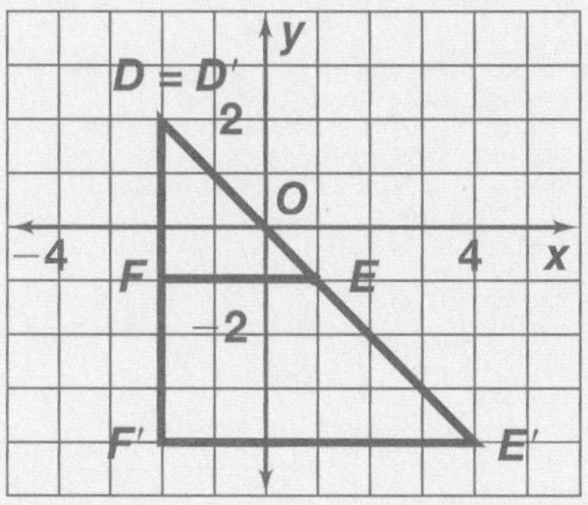

page 188 TE Additional Examples

1.

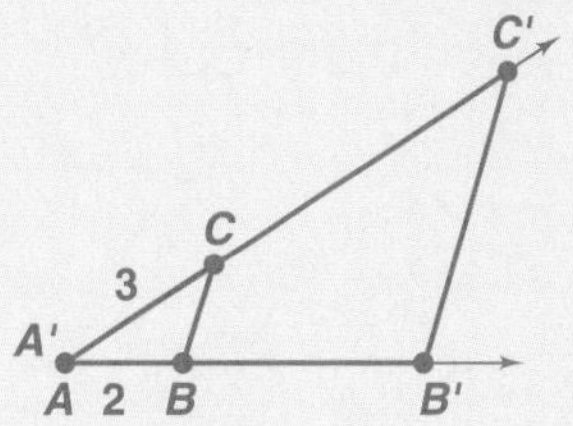

page 190 Exercises

12.

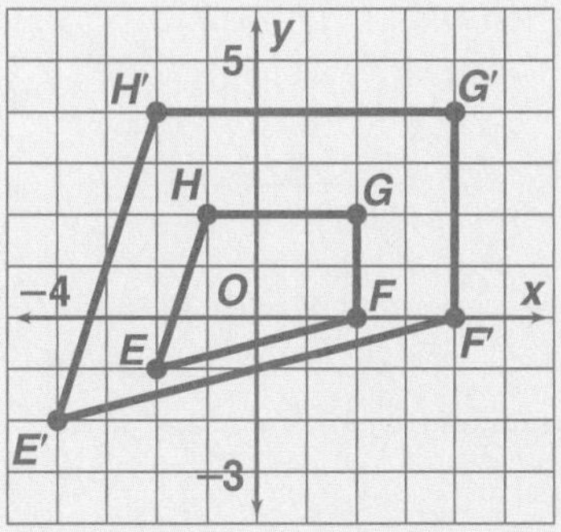

13.

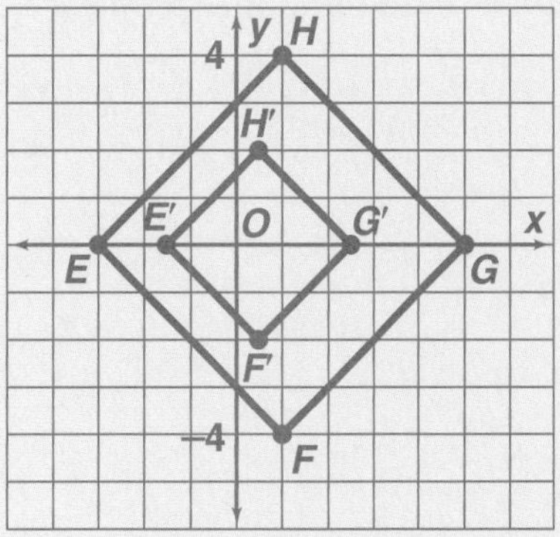

14.

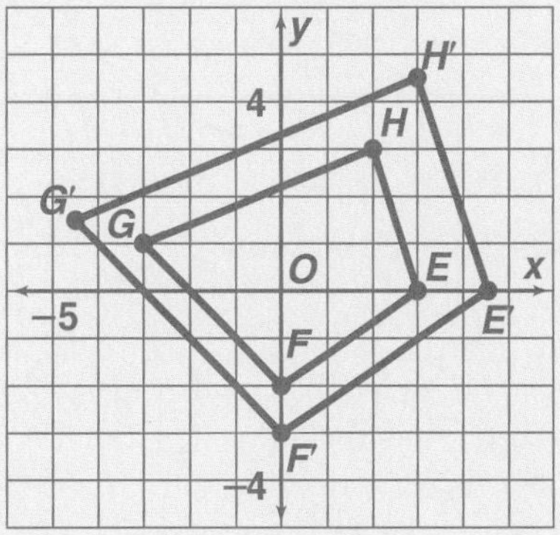

CHAPTER 5

Lesson 5-3

page 223 Activity Lab

1.

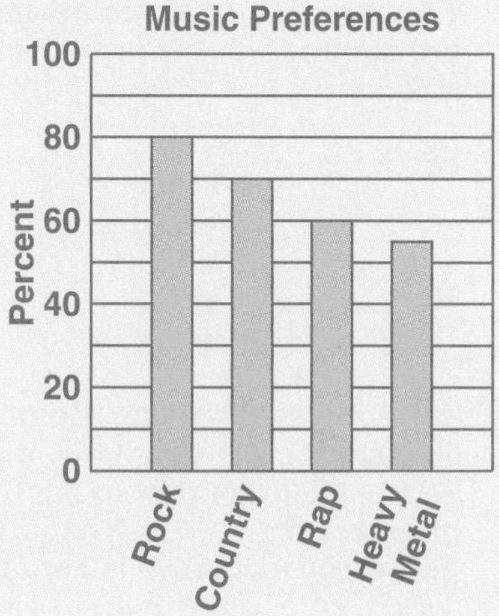

3. yes: $51\frac{2}{3}$%; maybe: $26\frac{2}{3}$%; no: $21\frac{2}{3}$%.

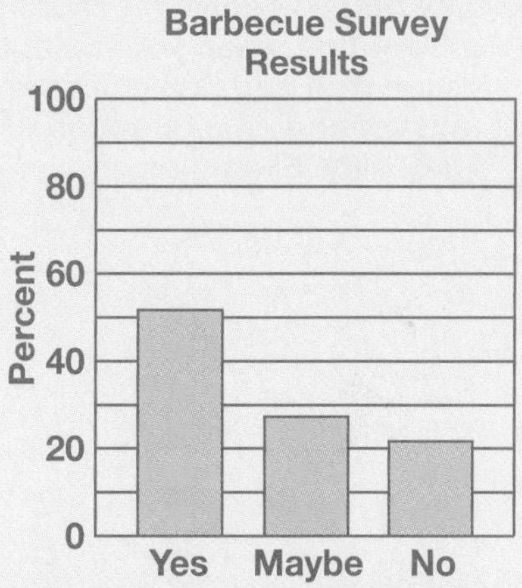

6. Anna: 70%, Carla: 60%, Nikki: 80%, Raylene: 75%

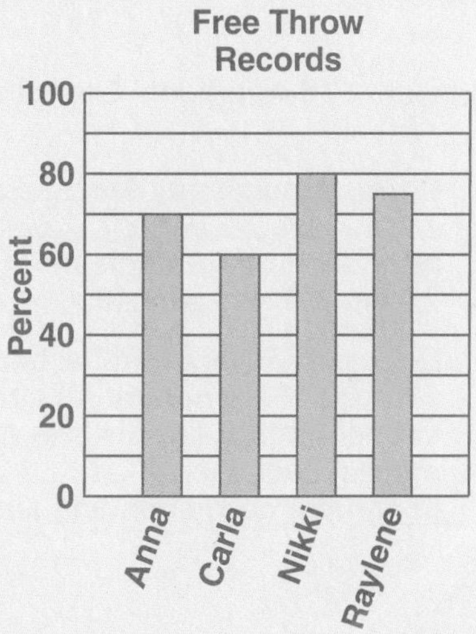

CHAPTER 6

Lesson 6-4

page 277 Exercises

5. The student added x to the left side but subtracted x from the right side.

$$\begin{aligned} 3x + 4 - x &= 7 + x \\ 2x + 4 &= 7 + x \\ 2x - x + 4 &= 7 + x - x \\ x + 4 &= 7 \\ x + 4 - 4 &= 7 - 4 \\ x &= 3 \end{aligned}$$

6. It is a negative integer. Combining like terms on the right gives you $-2x - 12$. Adding $2x$ to each side gives you $4x = -12$. A negative divided by a positive is negative.

page 296 Chapter 6 Test

40. You solve an inequality the same way that you solve an equation, except that when you multiply or divide by a negative number, you must change the direction of the inequality. Examples:

$$\begin{aligned} -3x + 4 &= 10 \\ -3x &= 6 \\ x &= -2 \\ -3x + 4 &\geq 10 \\ -3x &\geq 6 \\ x &\leq -2 \end{aligned}$$

CHAPTER 7

Lesson 7-2

page 308 TE Additional Examples

1. Corresponding angles: $\angle 1$ and $\angle 3$, $\angle 2$ and $\angle 4$, $\angle 5$ and $\angle 7$, $\angle 6$ and $\angle 8$
Alternate interior angles: $\angle 2$ and $\angle 7$, $\angle 3$ and $\angle 6$

3. Lines p and q are parallel because $\angle 5$ and $\angle 7$ are congruent alternate interior angles. Lines s and t are parallel because $\angle 6$ and $\angle 7$ are congruent corresponding angles.

Lesson 7-8

pages 341–342 Quick Check

1.

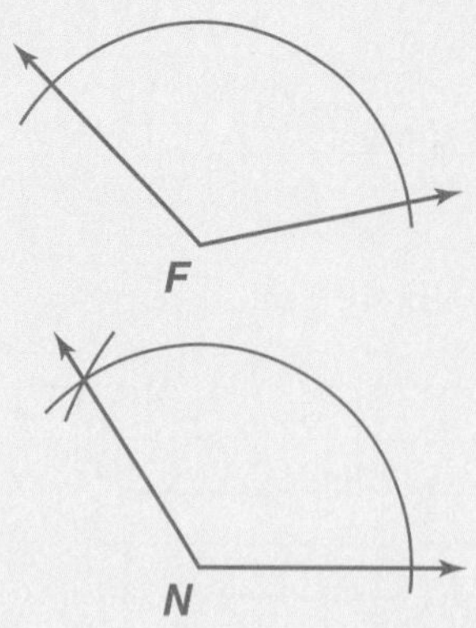

2.

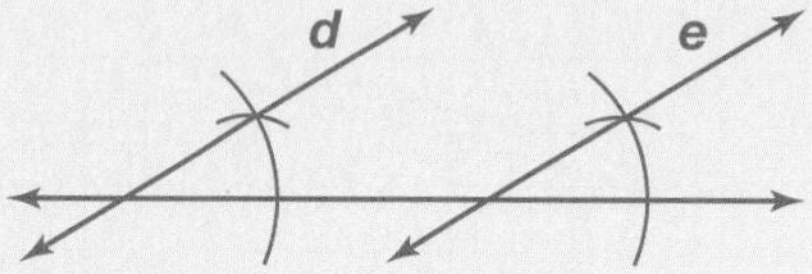

page 342 Additional Examples

1.

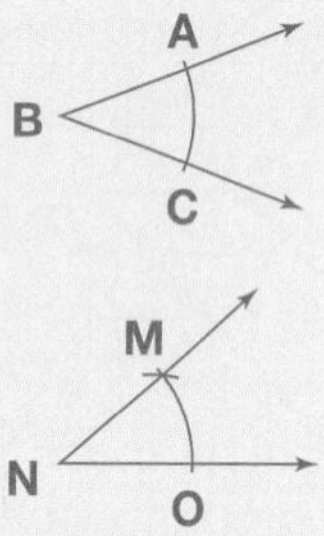

2.

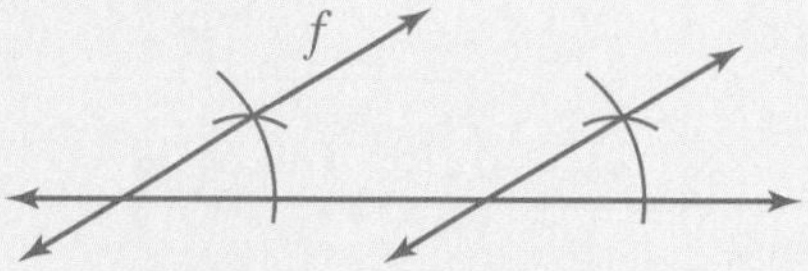

page 342 Exercises

5.

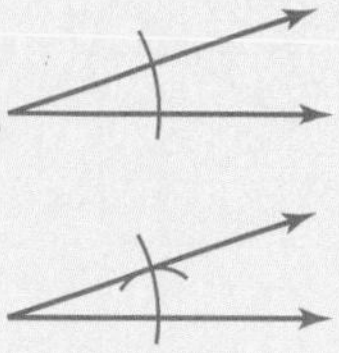

6.

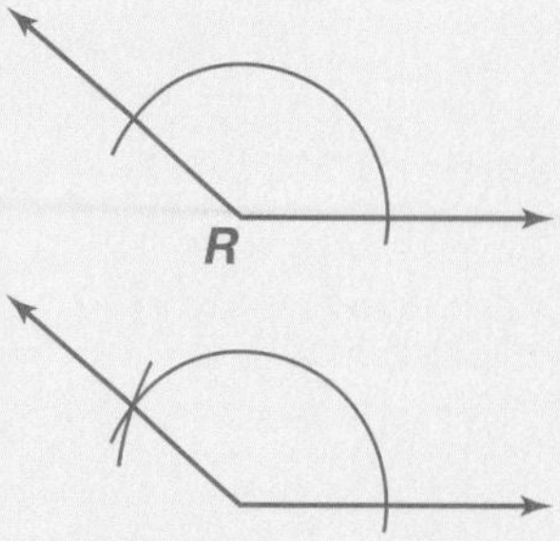

7.

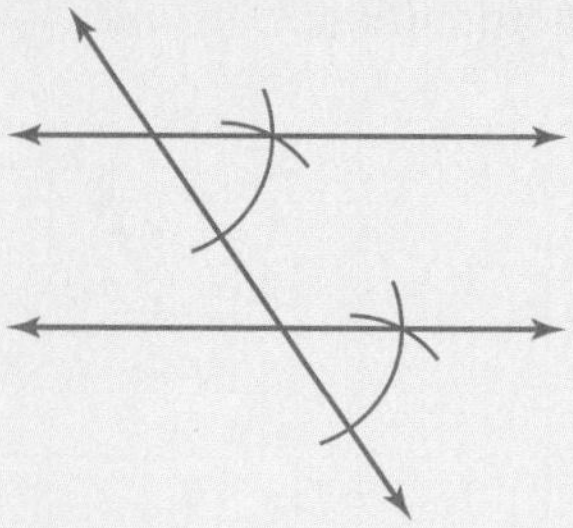

8.

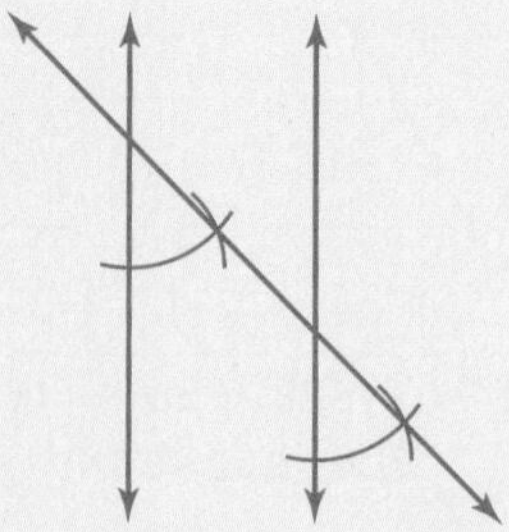

page 343 TE Lesson Quiz

1.

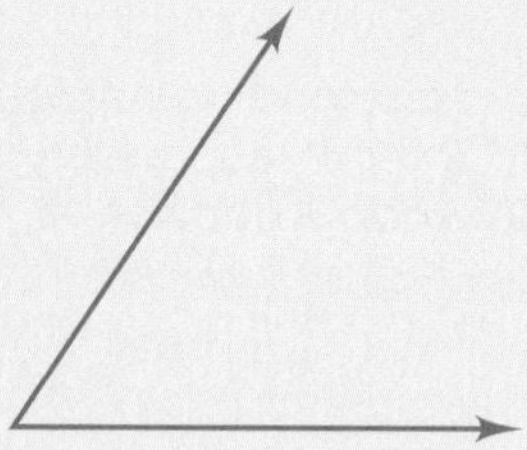

2.

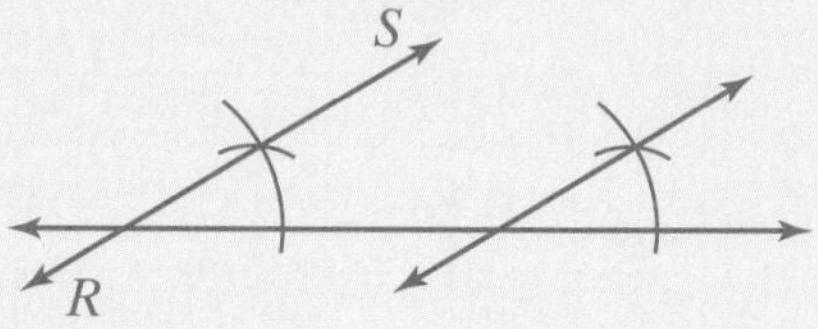

page 348 Chapter 7 Test

29.

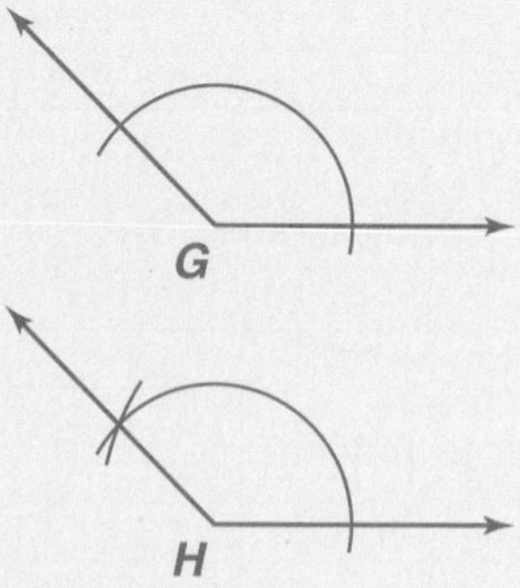

CHAPTER 8

Lesson 8-2

page 359 Quick Check

2. 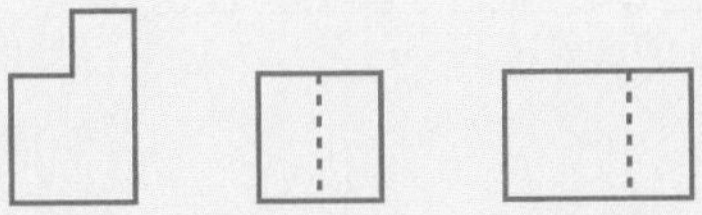

Top view | Front view | Right view

3. 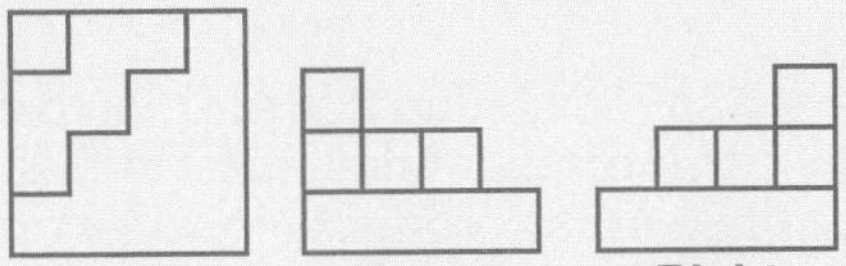

Top view | Front view | Right view

page 359 TE Additional Examples

1. 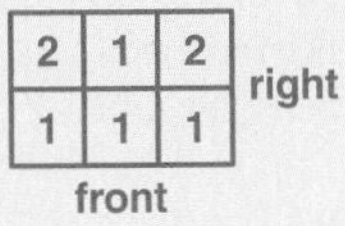

2, 3. 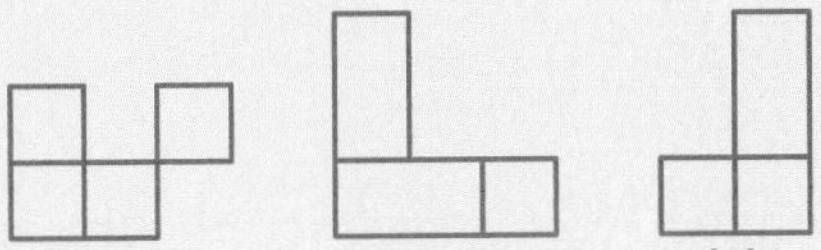

top | front | right

pages 360–361 Exercises

9. 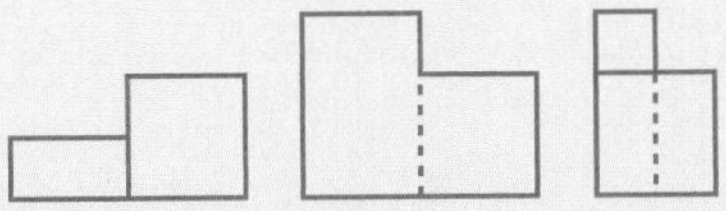

Top view | Front view | Right view

10. 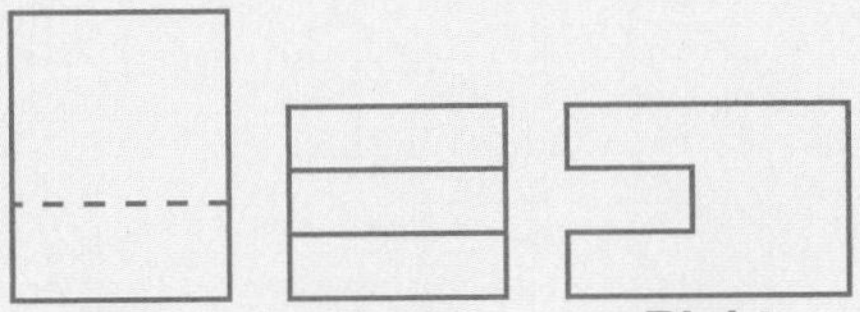

Top view | Front view | Right view

12. 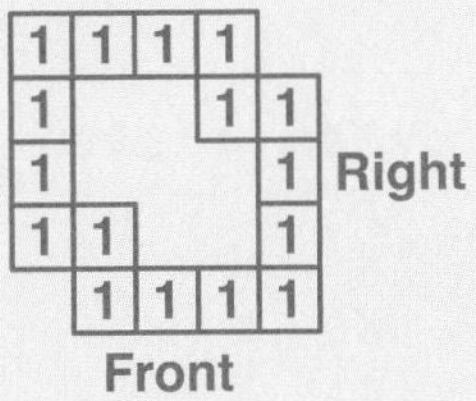

13. 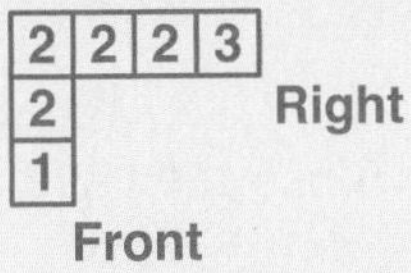

14. 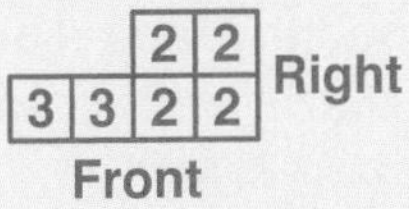

15. 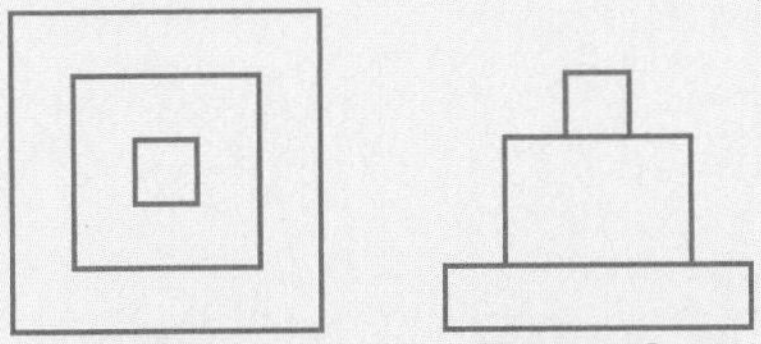

Top view | Front view

16. A plane that cuts parallel to the bases will make a circle. A plane that cuts perpendicular to the bases will make a rectangle.

page 361 TE Lesson Quiz

1. 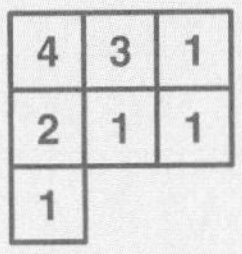

2. 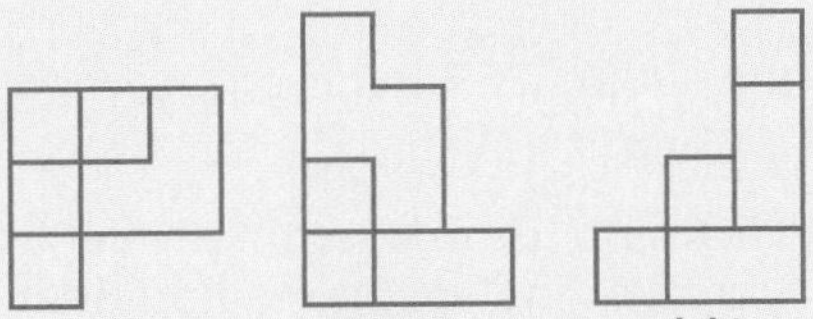

top | front | right

3. 

4. 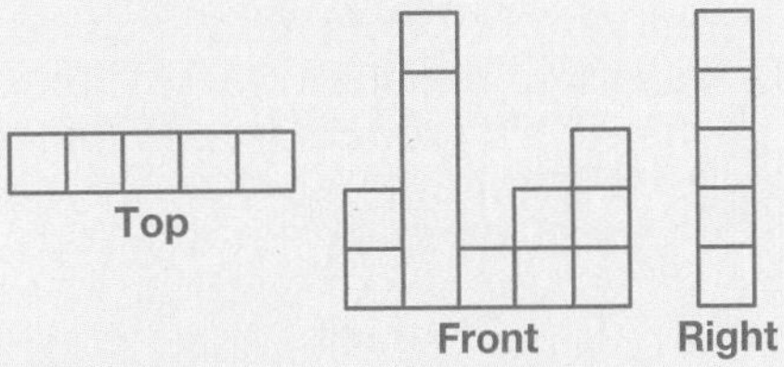

page 362 Activity Lab Exercises

6–11. Answers may vary. Samples are given.

6. 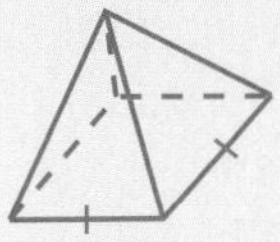

7. 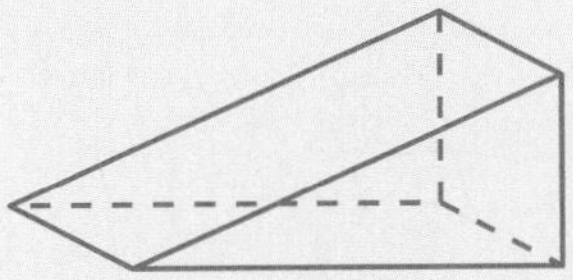

8. 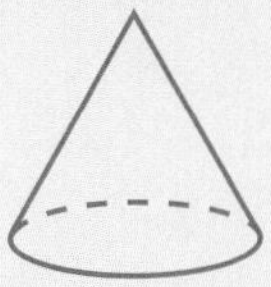

9. 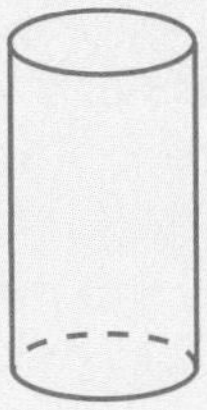

10. 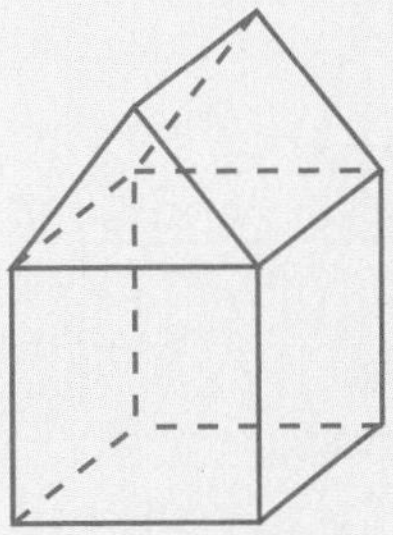

11. 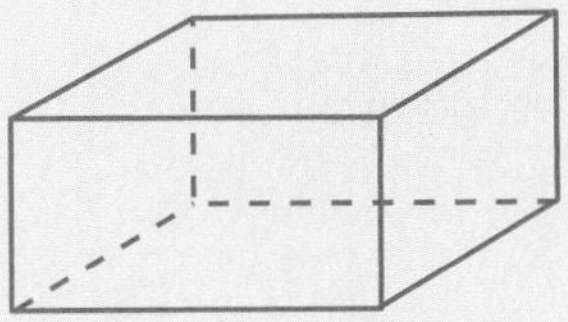

Lesson 8-3

page 364 Check Skills You'll Need

2. 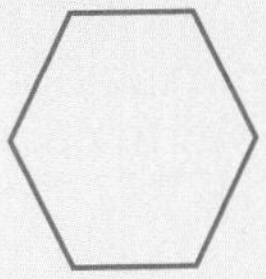

page 365 TE Lesson Quiz

2. 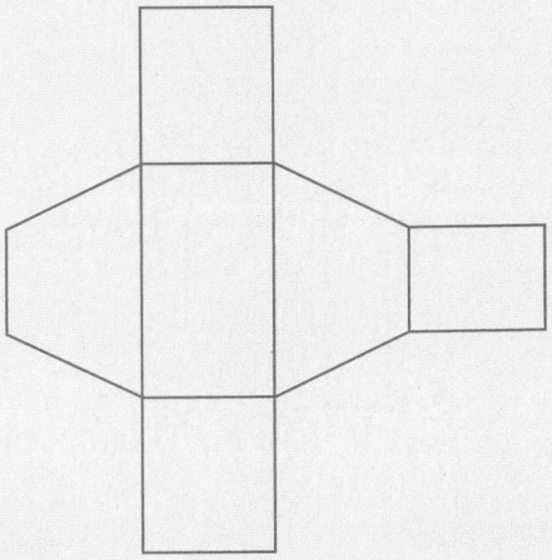

page 366 Exercises

10.

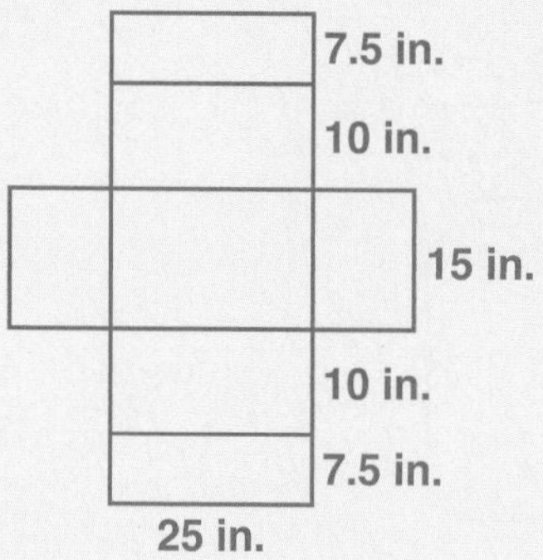

13.

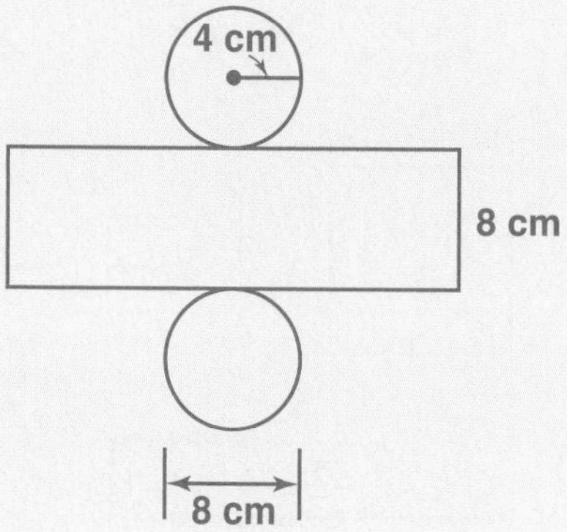

Lesson 8-4

page 372 Exercises

17a. Treat the lighthouse as a cylinder. Multiply $3 \times 30 \times 150$ to estimate the lateral area. L.A. $\approx 13{,}500$ ft^2

b. about 20 gallons of black paint and 20 gallons of white paint

Lesson 8-5

page 374 Quick Check

1.

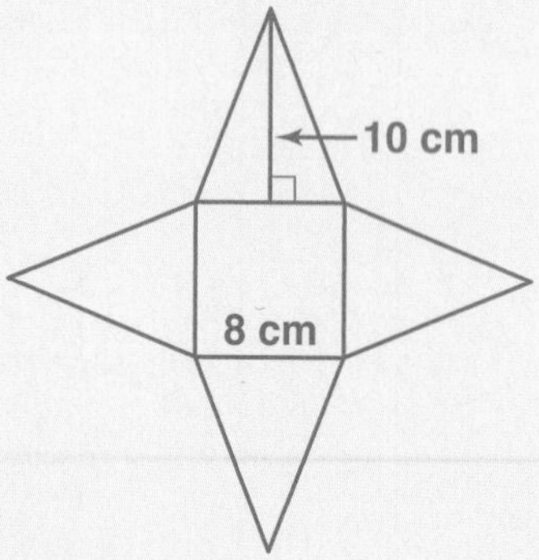

224 cm^2

page 378 Exercises

24. The pyramid; since the base areas are the same, $\pi r^2 = b^2$ or $b = r\sqrt{\pi}$. The lateral area of the cone is $\pi r\ell$, and the lateral area of the pyramid is $2b\ell$ or $2(r\sqrt{\pi})\ell$. Therefore, $\pi r\ell < 2\sqrt{\pi}r\ell$, because $\pi < 2\sqrt{\pi}$.

27.

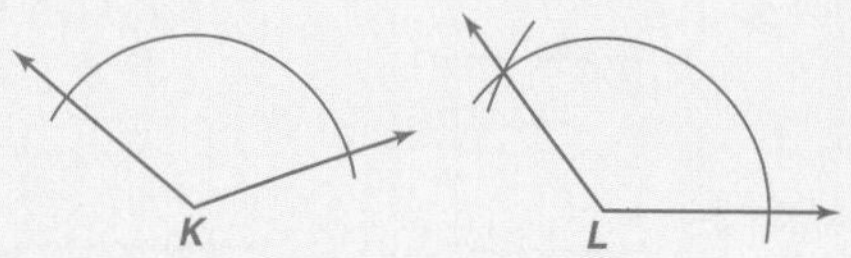

Lesson 8-6

page 379 Activity Lab

3.

Height	Base area	Volume
3	6	18
3	14	42
2	12.6	25.2

Lesson 8-7

page 389 TE Closure

- Sample: Both use the product of the area of the base times the height to find the volume, but, for the pyramid, this product is also multiplied by one-third.
- Sample: Both use the product of the area of the circular base times the height to find the volume, but, for the cone, this product is also multiplied by one-third.

page 391 Exercises

19. Each volume formula involves the product of the height h and the base area B. You can substitute the appropriate area formula for B when finding the volume. For cones and pyramids, you must also multiply the product by $\frac{1}{3}$.

Lesson 8-8

page 394 TE Closure

Surface area squares the radius and multiplies by 4 (S.A. = $4\pi r^2$); volume cubes the radius and multiplies by $\frac{4}{3}$ ($V = \frac{4}{3}\pi r^3$).

Lesson 8-9

page 399 TE Closure

- Sample: Set up a proportion between the corresponding dimensions and use cross products to solve for the missing measurement.
- Sample: Set up a proportion using the fact that the ratio of the surface areas equals the ratio of the squares of the linear measurements and the ratio of the volumes equals the ratio of the cubes of the linear dimensions.

CHAPTER 9

page 410 Check Your Readiness

1–9.

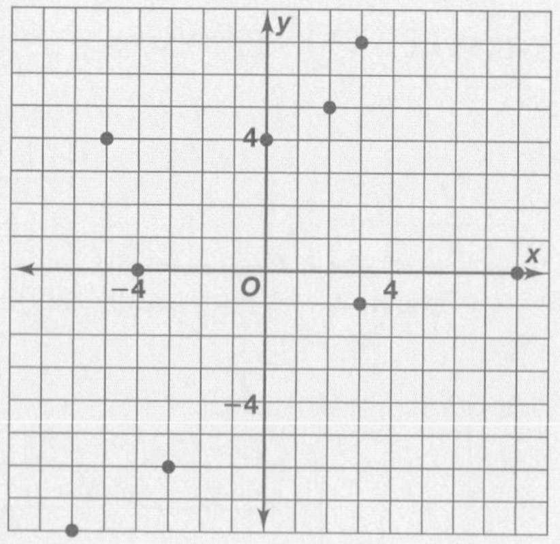

Lesson 9-2

pages 418–419 Quick Check

1. Human Body Temperatures

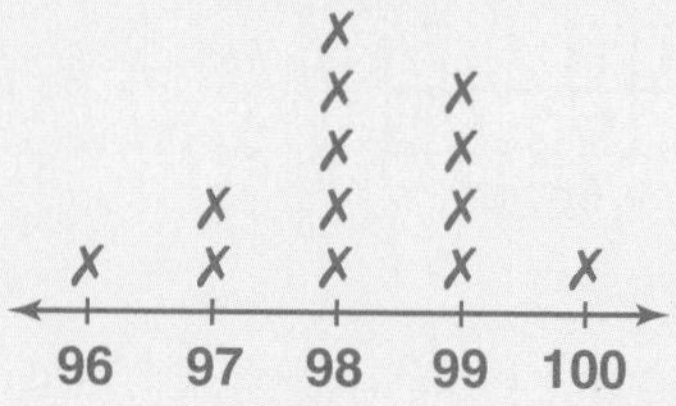

3. Answers may vary. Sample:

Cost (Dollars)	Frequency
4–5.99	4
6–7.99	6
8–9.99	4

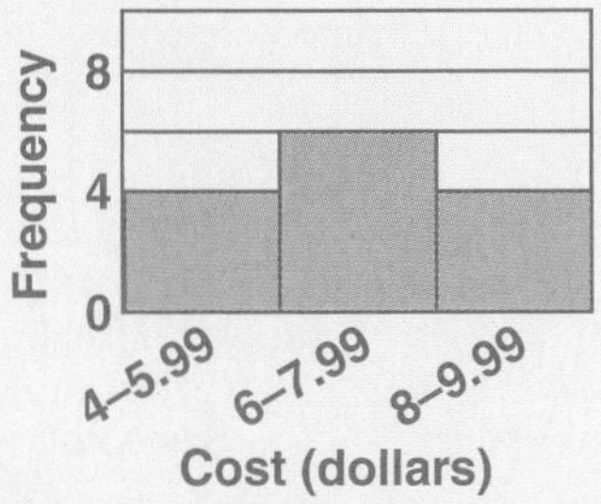

page 419 TE Additional Examples

1.

3.

Goals	Tally	Freq.
0-1	卌 IIII	9
2-3	III	3
4-5	I	1
6-7	II	2

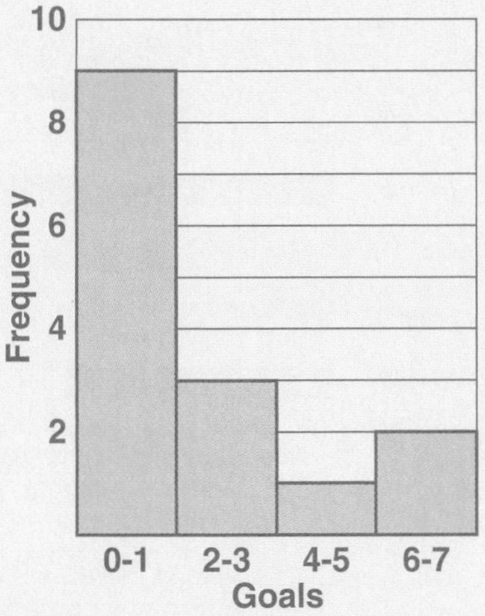

page 421 Exercises

16–17. Answers may vary. Samples are given.

16.

TVs Sold	Frequency
0–4	1
5–9	10
10–14	6
15–19	2
20–24	1

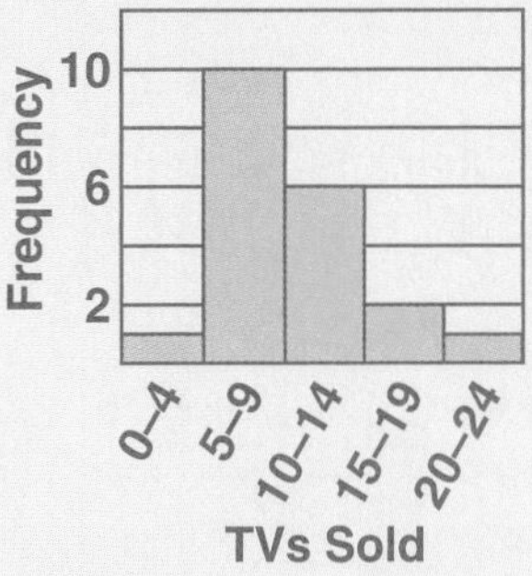

17.

Score	Frequency
(−5)–(−3)	1
(−2)–0	15
1–3	11
4–6	5

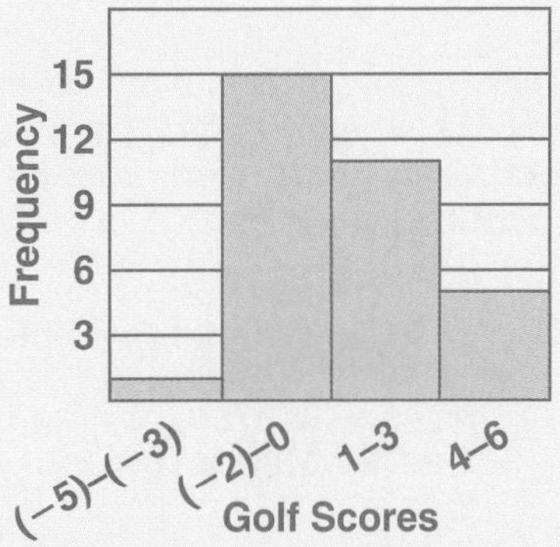

18. Answers may vary. Sample:

Monthly Car Payment	Frequency
0–99	0
100–199	2
200–299	3
300–399	7
400–499	1
500–599	1

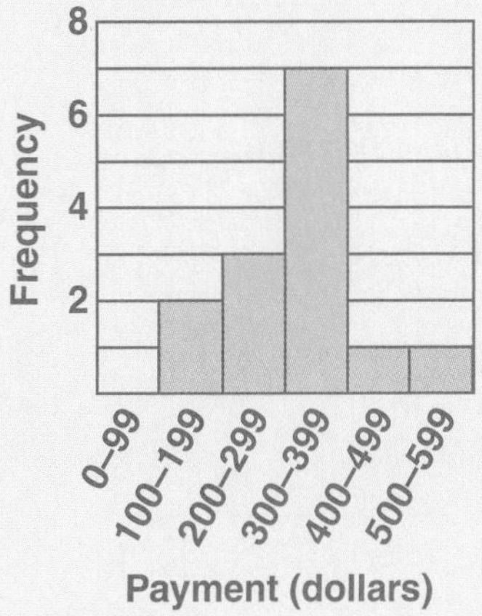

Lesson 9-3

pages 425 TE Additional Examples

1. Nine children used both red & blue crayons

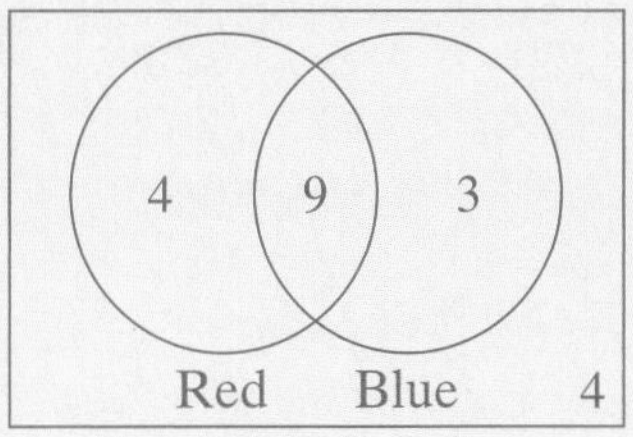

page 425 TE Lesson Quiz

1. 26 students

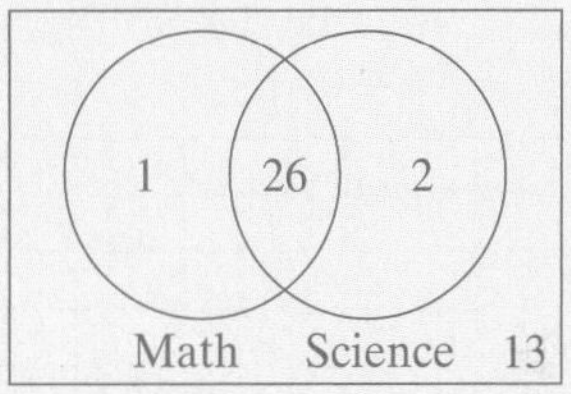

pages 426 Exercises

17–18. Answers may vary. Samples are given.

17.

Lengths of Wood	Frequency
21–22	3
23–24	4
25–26	5

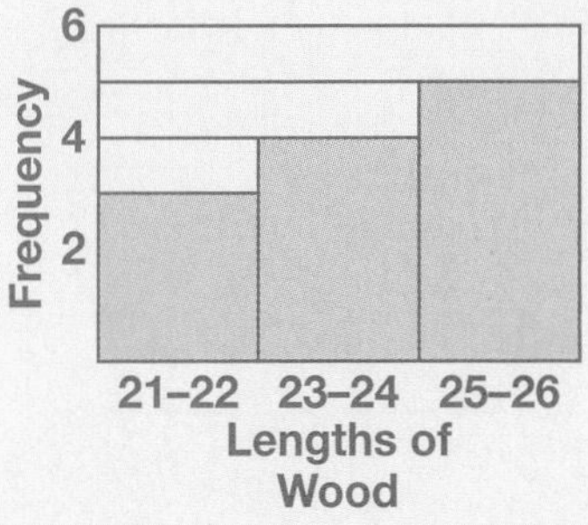

18.

Weekly Earnings	Frequency
250–274	6
275–299	1
300–324	3

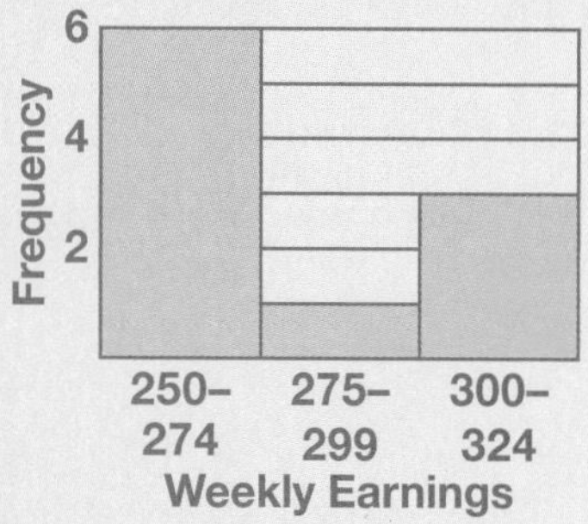

page 427 Activity Lab

5. Answers may vary. Sample: While the monthly sales only increased by 2.5%, the operating expenses went up 100%. The business is not doing well.

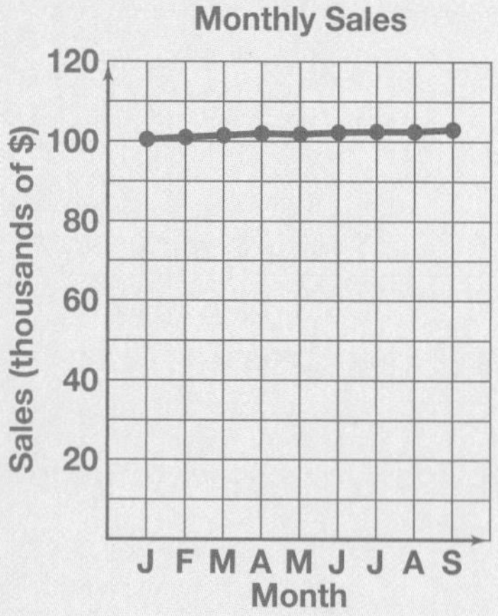

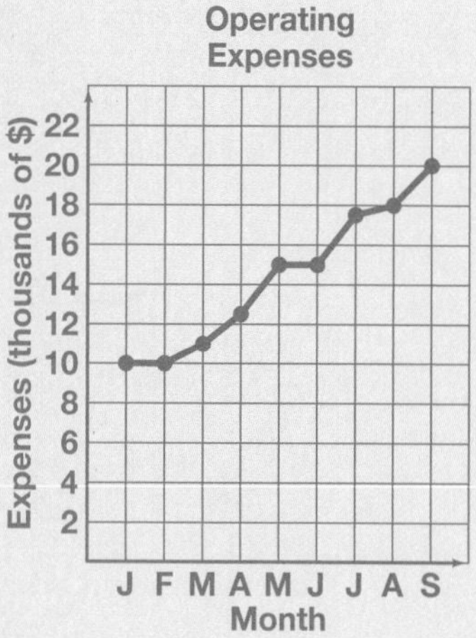

Lesson 9-4

page 428 Check Skills You'll Need

2.

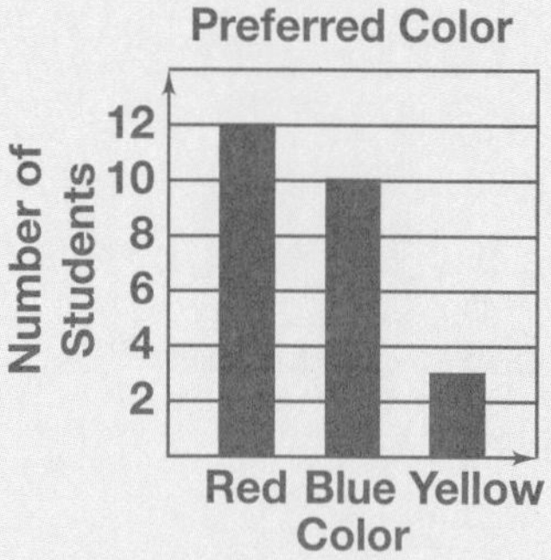

page 428 Quick Check

1. The graph starts at 0 on the vertical axis, so the difference between the airports is portrayed more accurately.

page 429 TE Additional Examples

2.

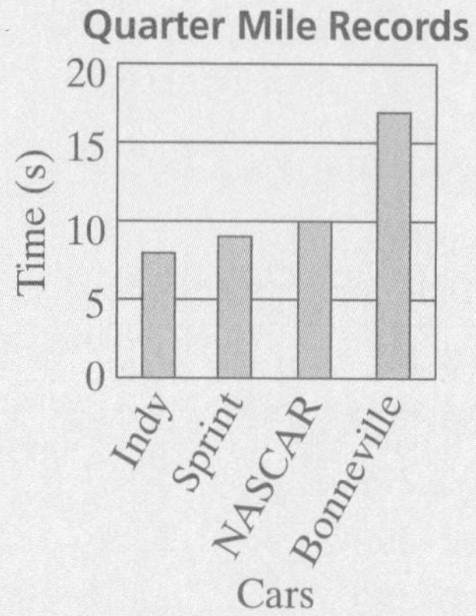

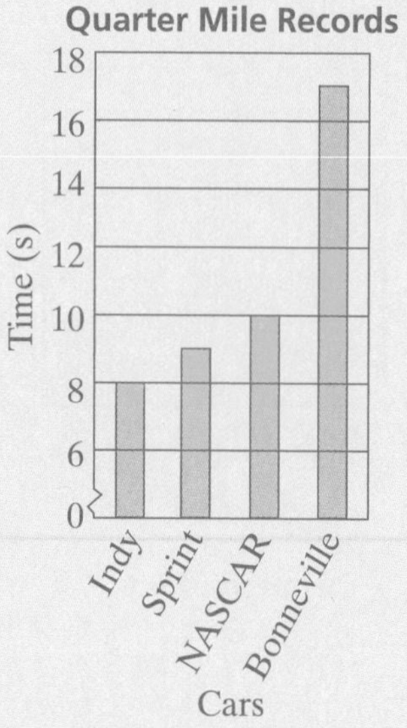

pages 430–431 Exercises

7.

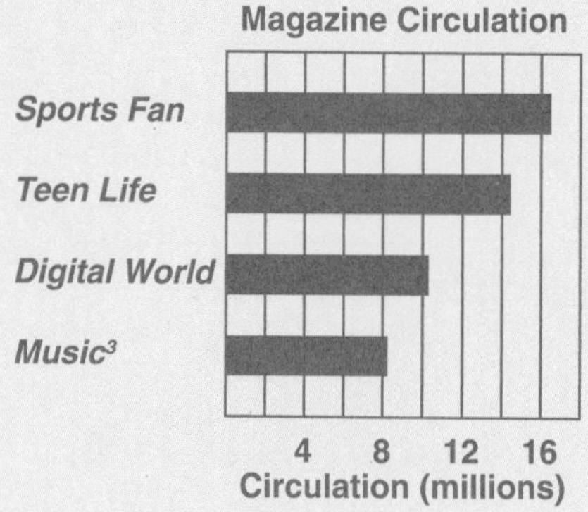

8. Answers may vary. Sample:

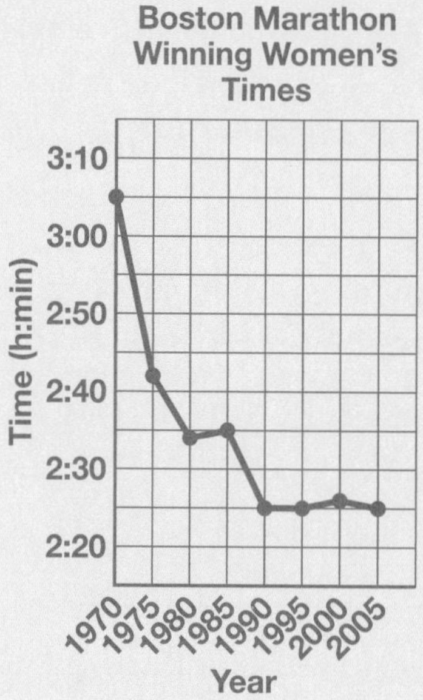

9.

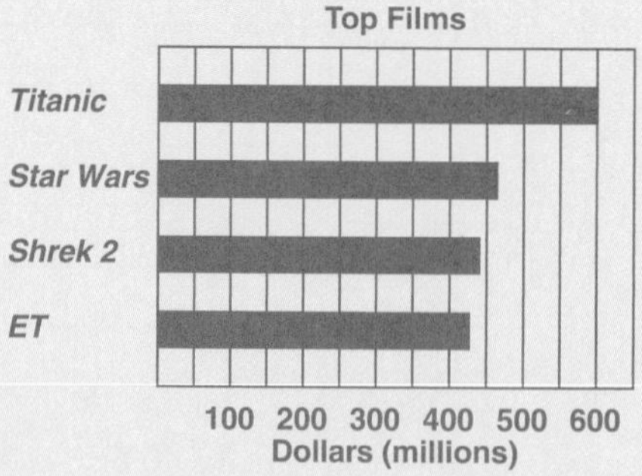

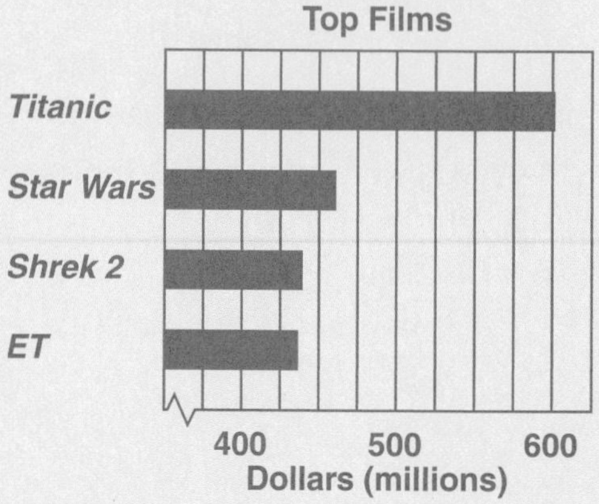

You can approximate the amounts better on the graph with the break, but the differences are exaggerated.

10.

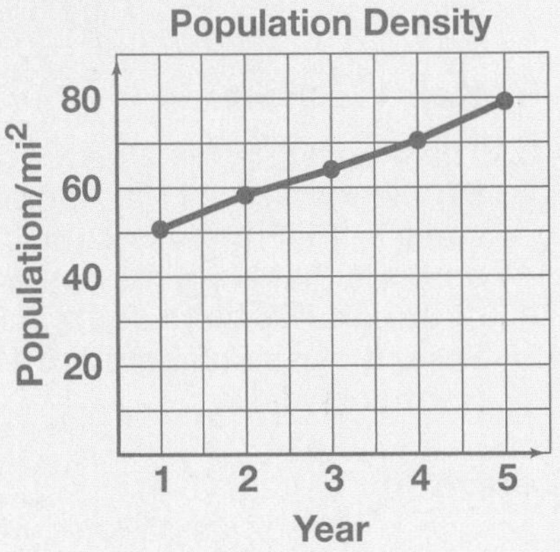

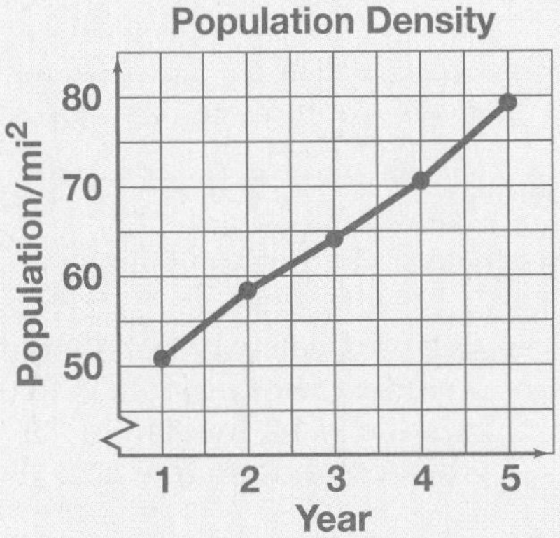

The graph with the break allows you to approximate the population more closely, but the changes are exaggerated.

11.

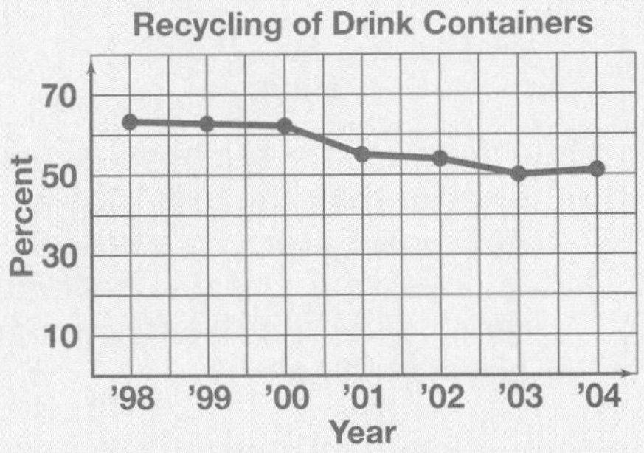

12.

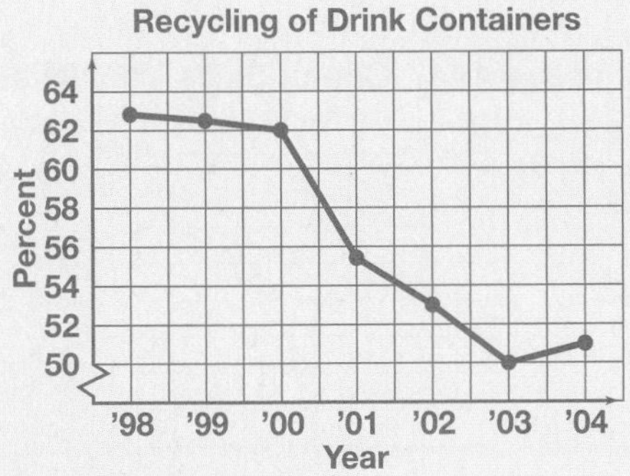

14.

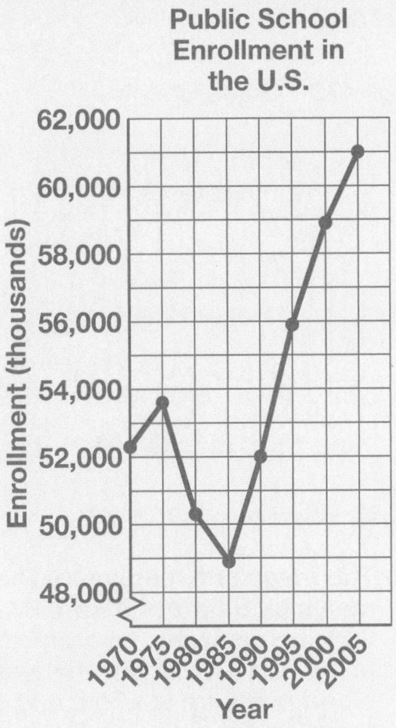

15.

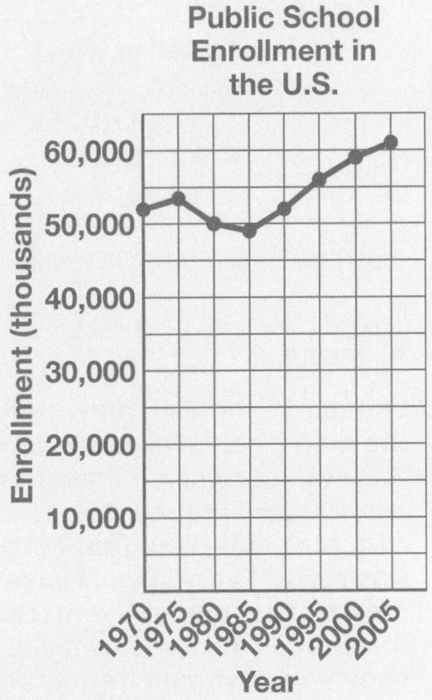

16. The second graph is more accurate because the enrollment only grew about 17%. The first graph makes this difference look much larger.

17a. 5; 10; 20; 40

b. No; the time differences are not the same, which is misleading.

c. Yes; each interval is twice the size of the interval before it.

page 431 TE Lesson Quiz

2. Sample: Use intervals of 5 from 0 to 30.

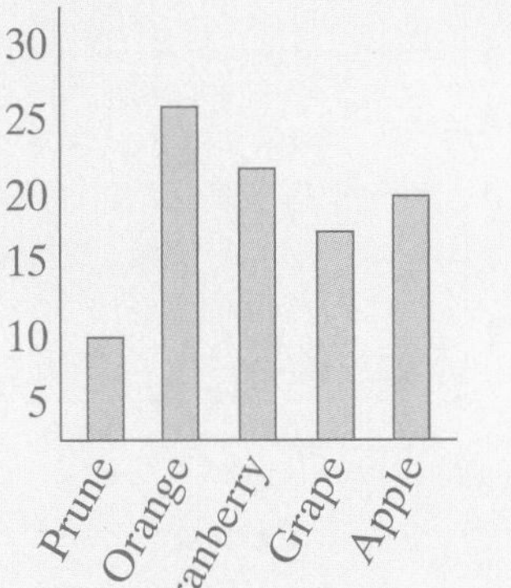

page 432 Activity Lab

1.

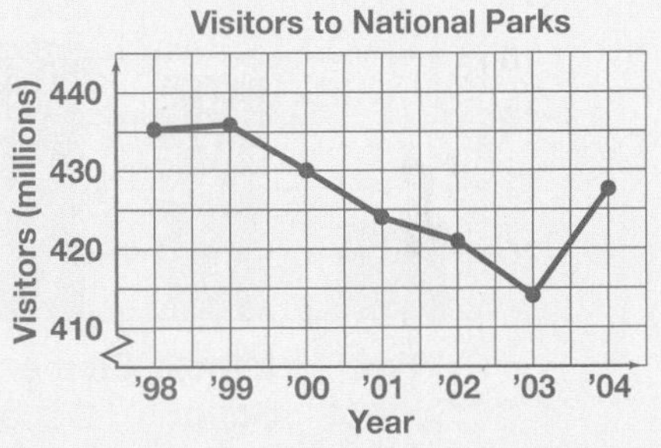

2.

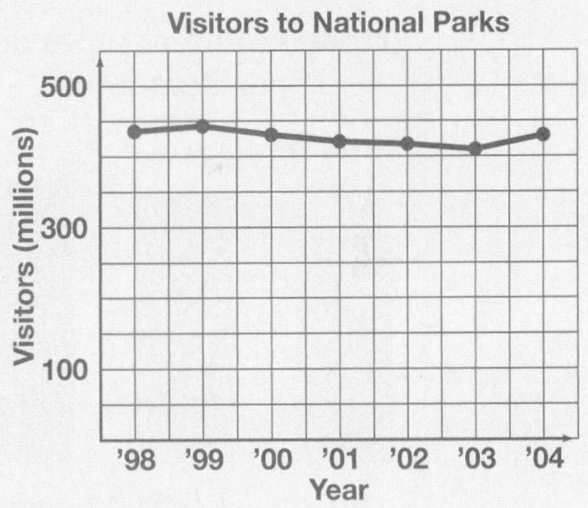

page 432 Checkpoint Quiz 1

6.

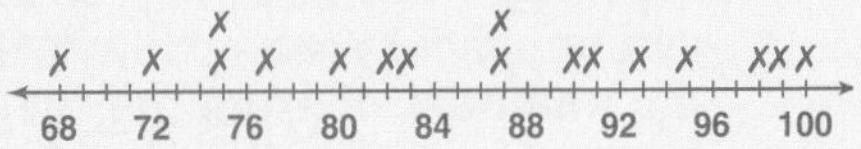

7. Math Scores

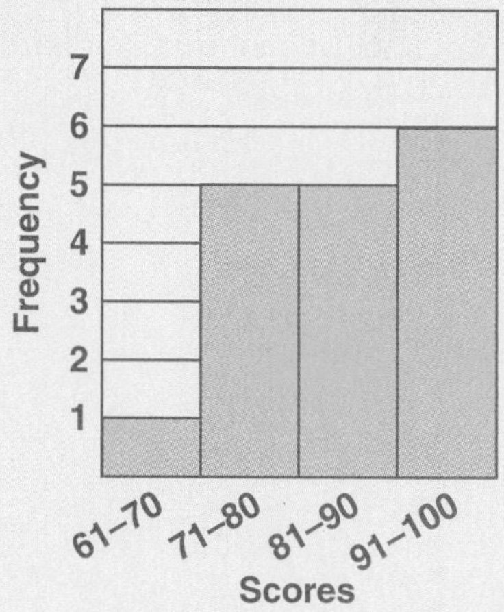

8. Average Number of Students per Computer

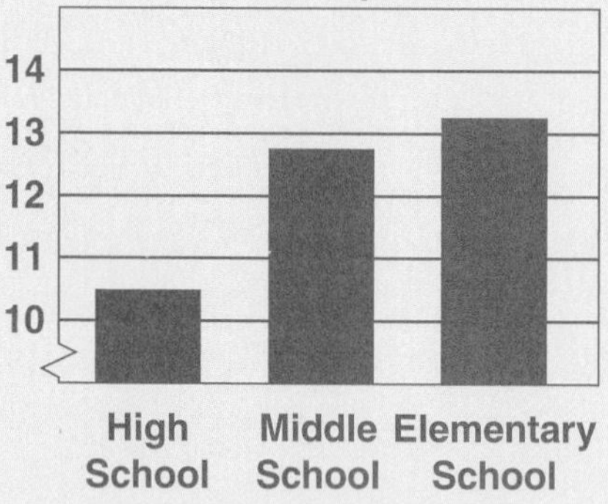

Average Number of Students per Computer

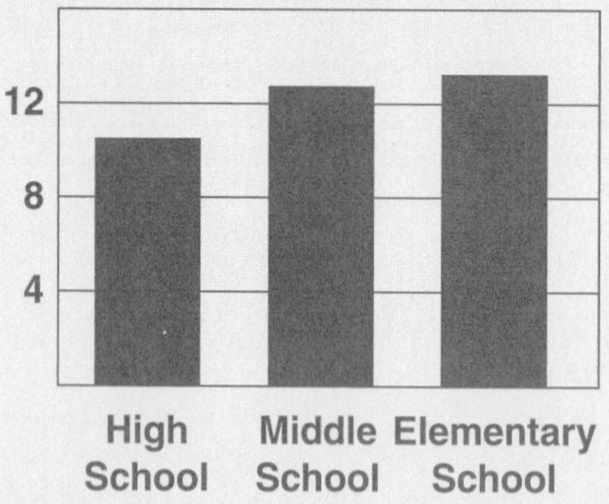

The graph without the break symbol shows more clearly that the numbers of students per computer are similar for all grades.

Lesson 9-5

page 433 Quick Check

1. Monthly High Temperatures

8	6 7
9	1 7
10	1
11	1 3
12	0 0 5 6
13	4

Key: 13 | 4 means 134

pages 436-437 Exercises

10. The mean and median for the men's blood pressure are 87 and 88.5, respectively, whereas the mean and median for the women's blood pressure are 76.5 and 77, respectively.

12. Length of Wood

Saw A		Saw B
	4	3 5 9
8 7 4 4 2	5	2 7
4 3 1	6	3 4
	7	2

Key: 61 ← means 1 | 6 | 3 means → 63

Saw A: 57.5; 54 Saw B: 54.5; no mode

13. The mean, median, and mode for the men's golf scores are around 278 strokes, while the women's scores were around 280. This indicates that the difference in scores isn't very large. However, the fact that one of the modes for the women's scores was 290 shows that women frequently do have a higher number of strokes.

14a. Life Spans of Different Animals

0	1 3 4 5 6 7 7
1	0 0 0 2 2 3 5 5 5 5 5 8
2	0 0 0 0 2 5 5
3	
4	0

Key: 1 | 3 means 13 years

b. Answers may vary. Sample: The new data include decimal values. You might choose to use the integer part as stems to avoid decimals in the leaves.

page 437 TE Lesson Quiz

1.

2	0 1 2 2
3	1 3 9
4	0

Key: 4 | 0 means 40

3. The median for Ms. Perez's class is 67; the median for Mr. Harmon's class is 45. From this data, it appears that students earned better grades on the quiz in Ms. Perez's class compared to Mr. Harmon's class.

Lesson 9-6

page 439 Quick Check

2.

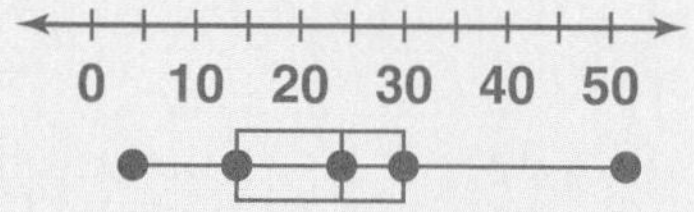

page 441 TE Lesson Quiz

1. Answers will vary but should include: lower quartile is 8, upper quartile is 14, median is 10, whiskers extend to 6 and 18.

2. Individual Points Scored

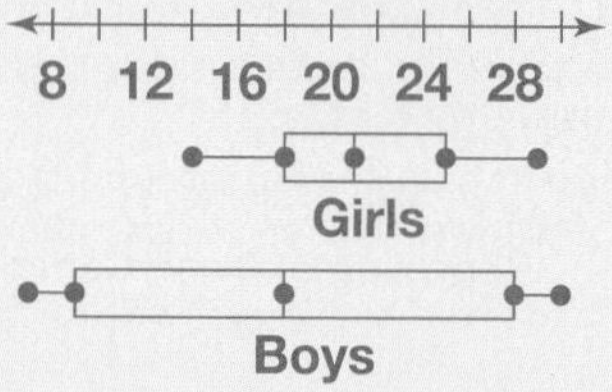

3. The range for the boys' scores is greater than the girls' scores. The girls' shorter box means that their scores were more consistent. The girls' lower quartile is equal to the boys' median.

Lesson 9-7

page 444 Check Skills You'll Need

2–3.

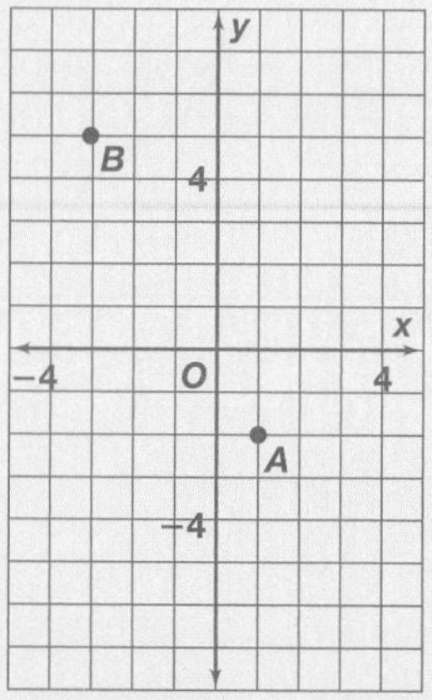

pages 444–445 Quick Check

1.

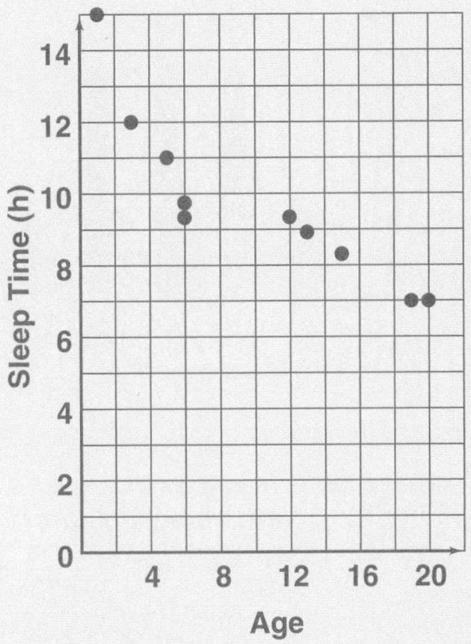

2.

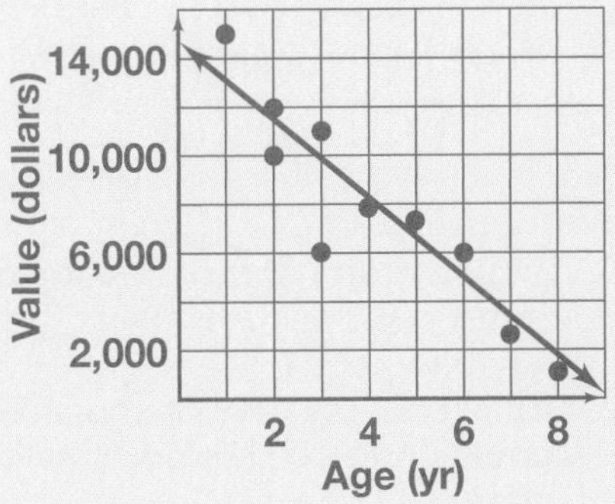

page 445 TE Additional Examples

1.

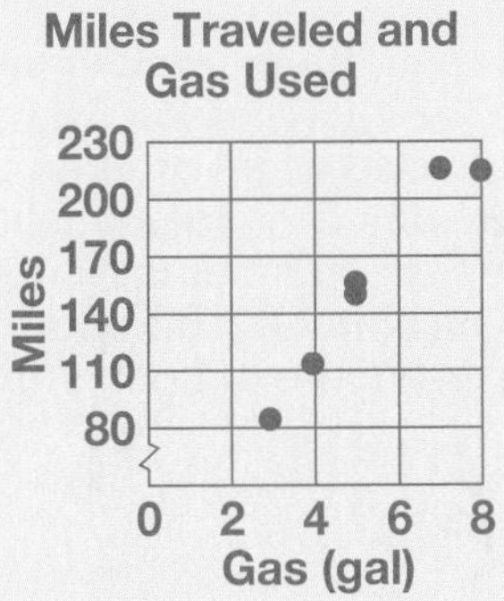

2. a positive trend; about 185 miles;

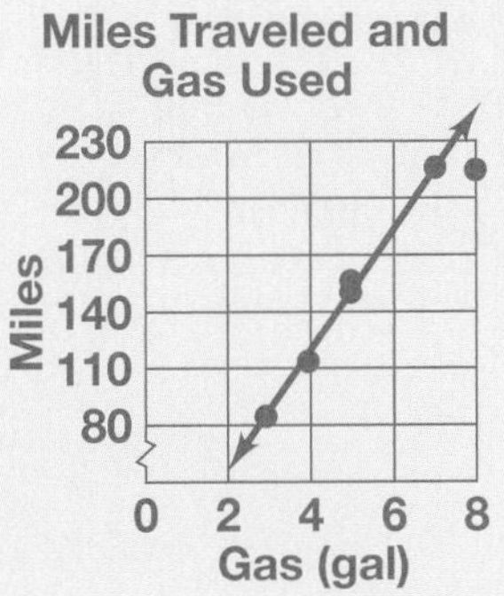

page 446 Exercises

5.

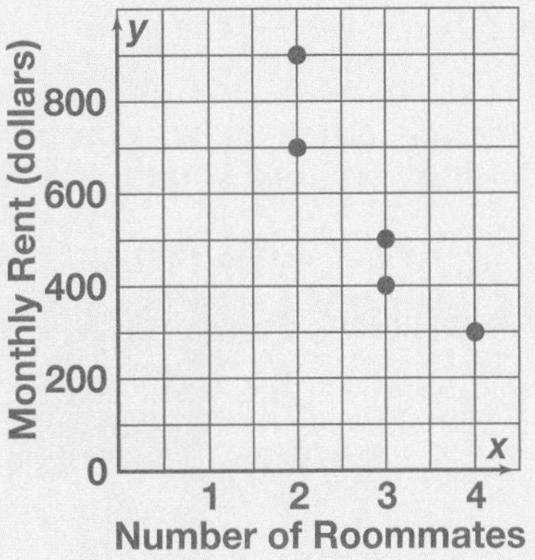

6.

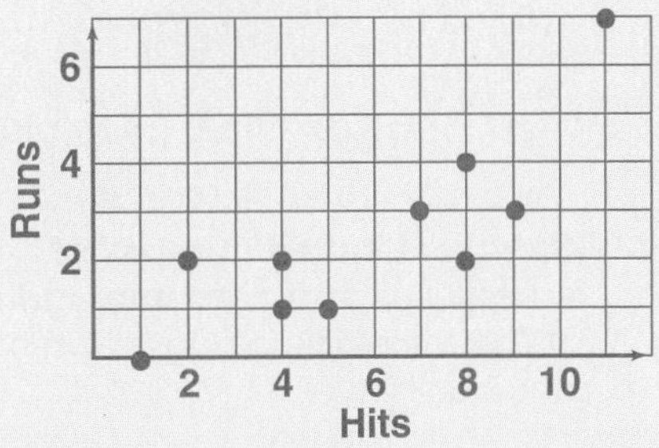

7. negative trend

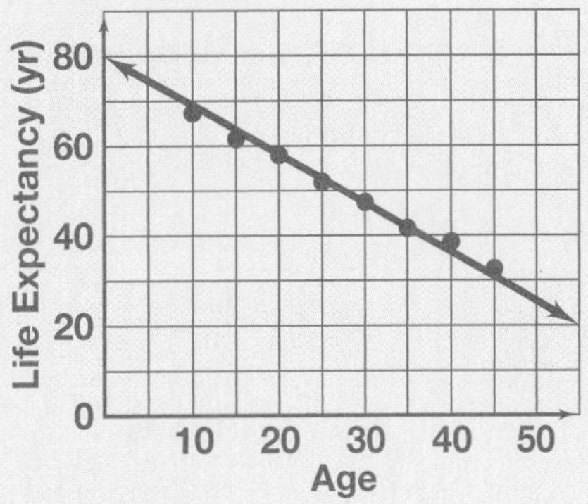

8. negative trend

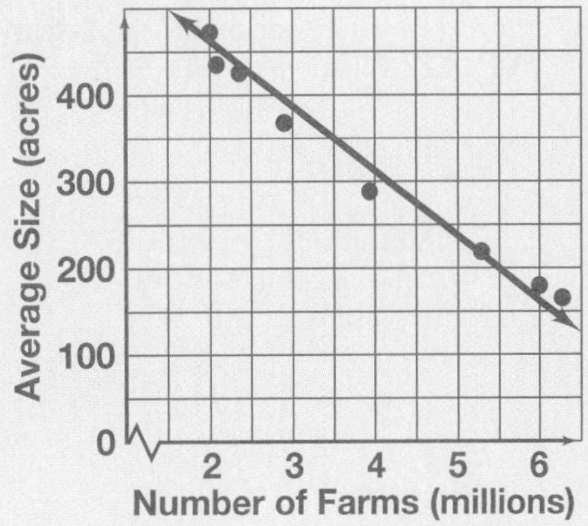

page 447 TE Lesson Quiz

1.

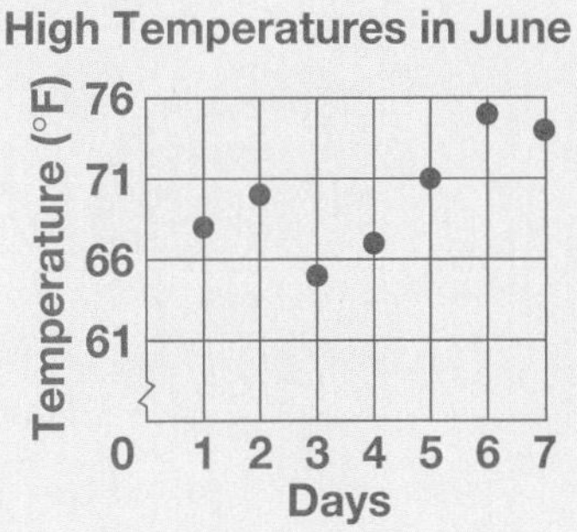

2. positive trend

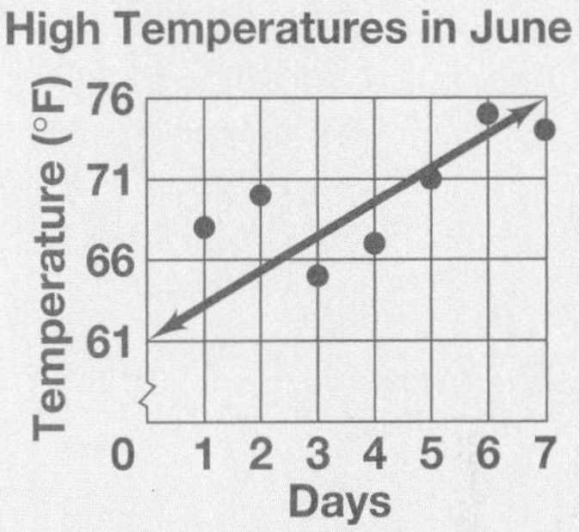

Lesson 9-8

page 451 Quick Check

2.

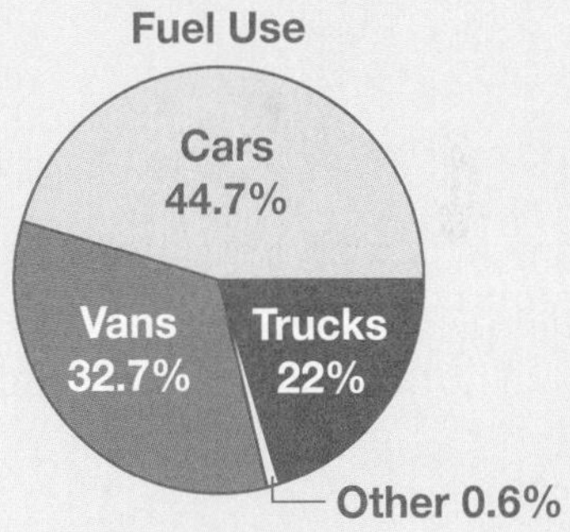

page 451 TE Additional Examples

2.

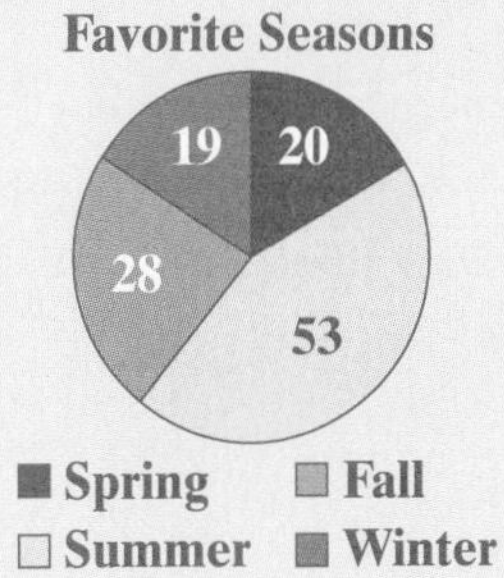

page 453 Exercises

11.

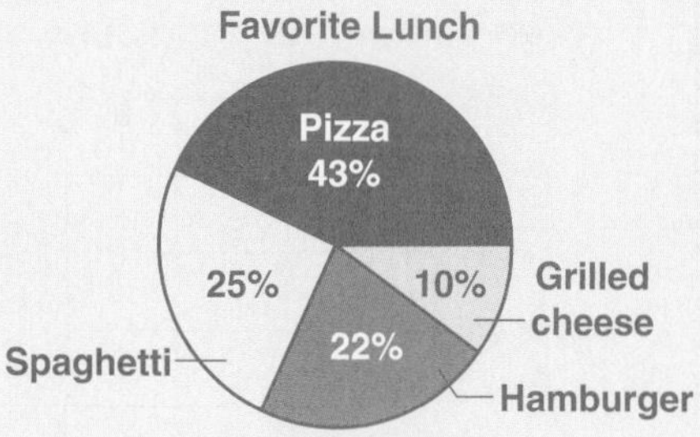

13a.

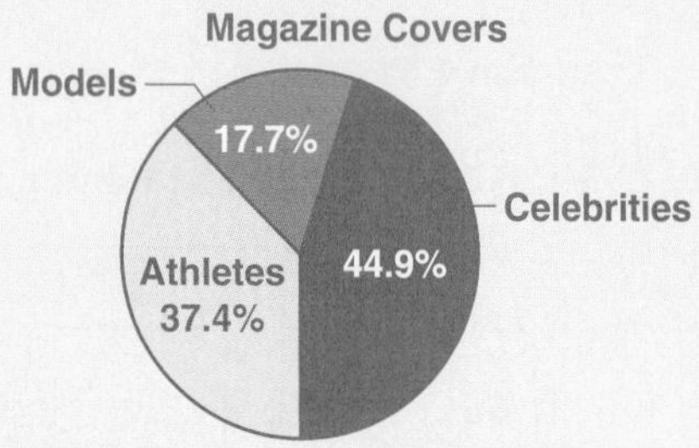

b. 150 women

c. 220 women

14. Color of Cell Phones

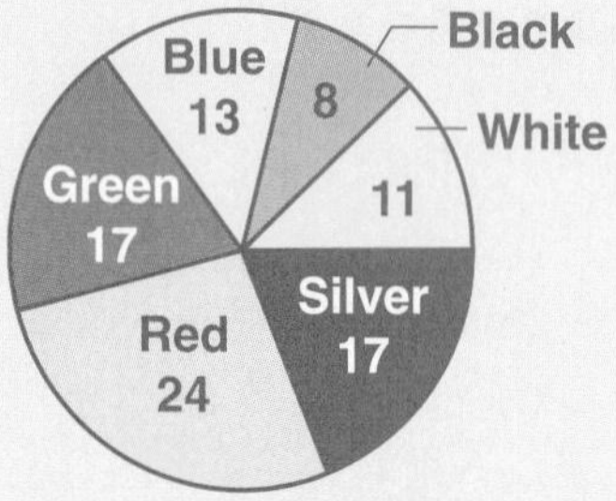

The circle graph; it shows the proportions clearly.

17.

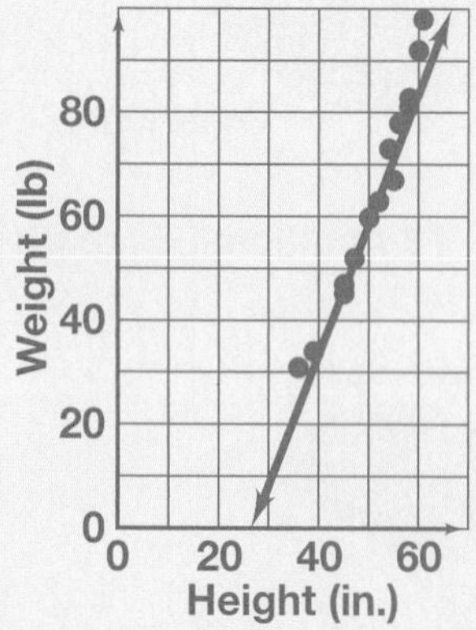

page 453 TE Lesson Quiz

3. Mango, 33.3%, 120°; Banana 37.5%, 135°; Pear 16.7%, 60°; Papaya 12.5%, 45°.

Lesson 9-9

page 457 Quick Check

2. A circle graph shows comparisons of the parts of a whole.

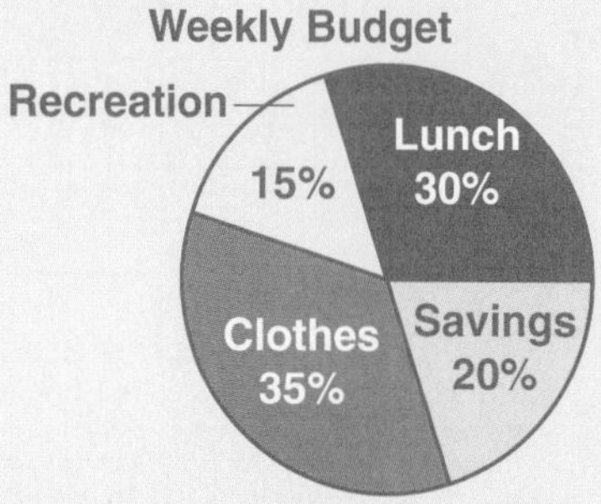

page 457 TE Additional Examples

1. Sample: Limited number of categories and percents adding to 100% make the circle graph a good choice.

2. Sample: Since the data show a change over time, a line graph is appropriate.

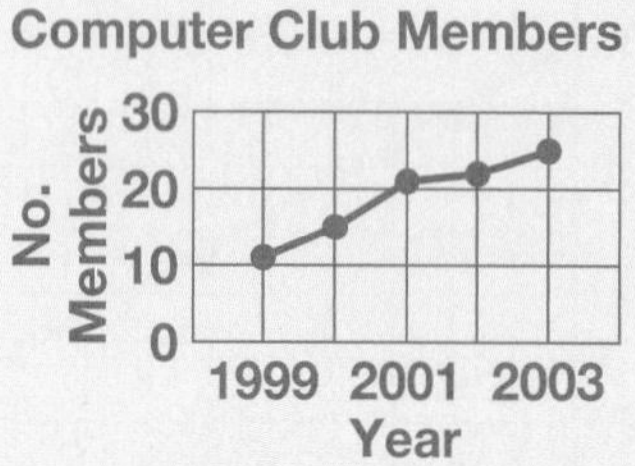

pages 458–459 Exercises

8. Line graph; it shows data over time well.

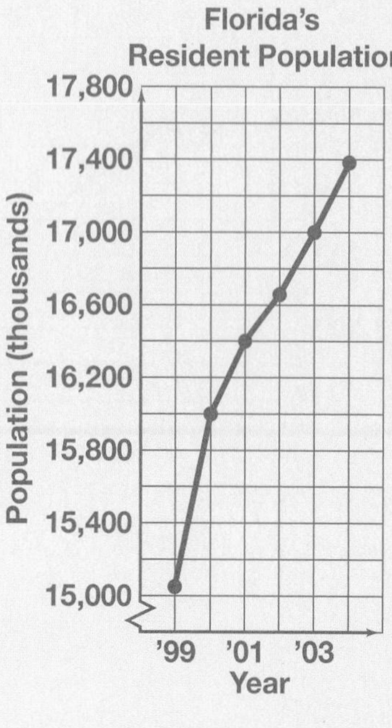

11.

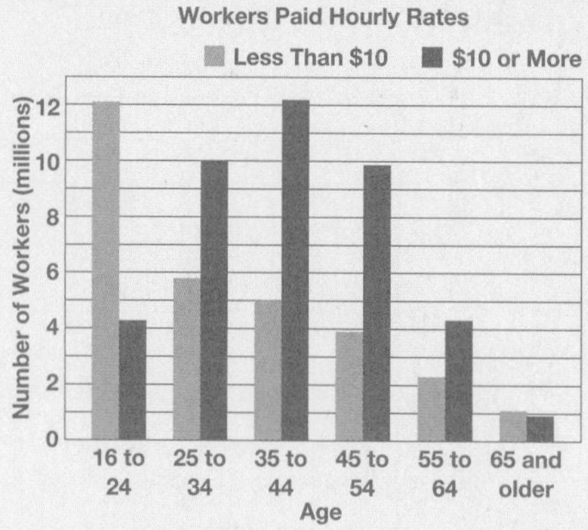

15a. The data are not parts of a whole.

b.

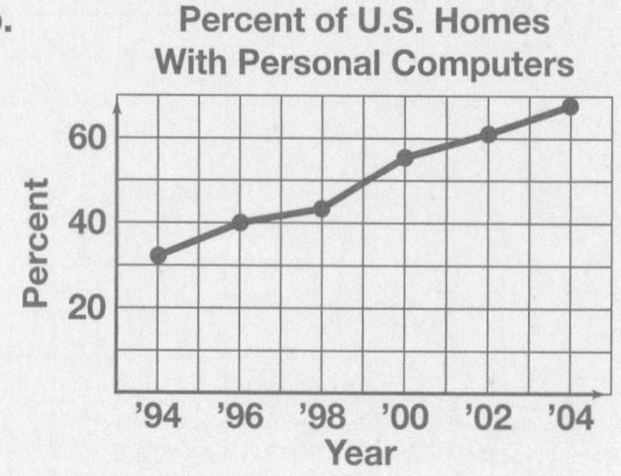

A line graph shows change over time.

17. Answers may vary. Sample: You could choose a histogram with intervals.

page 459 TE Lesson Quiz

2. Scatter plot; there are two pieces of data for each person, which can be expressed as an ordered pair. You can look for a relationship between the number of hours of television watching and the number of hours of homework.

3.

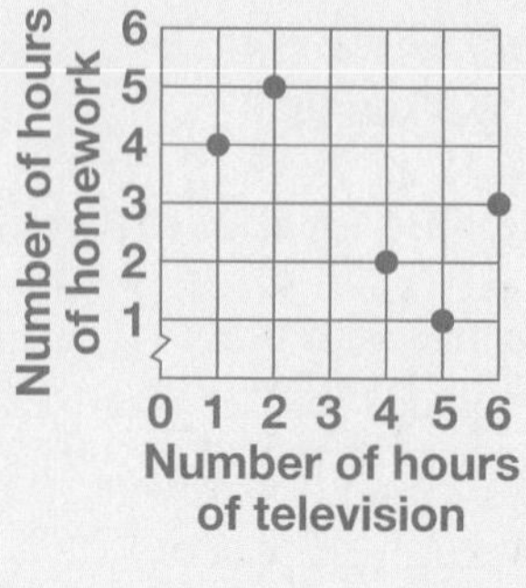

page 463 Chapter Review

9.

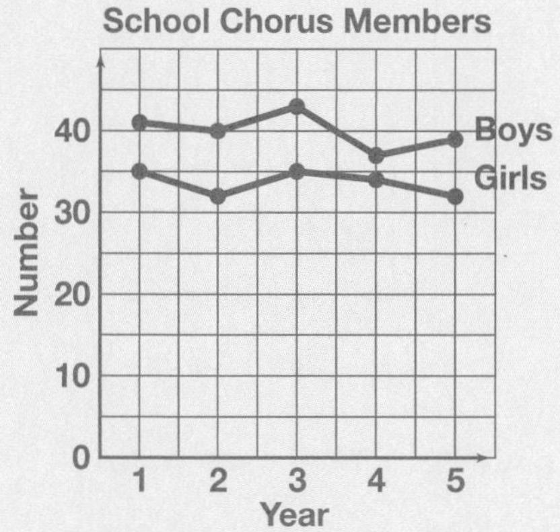

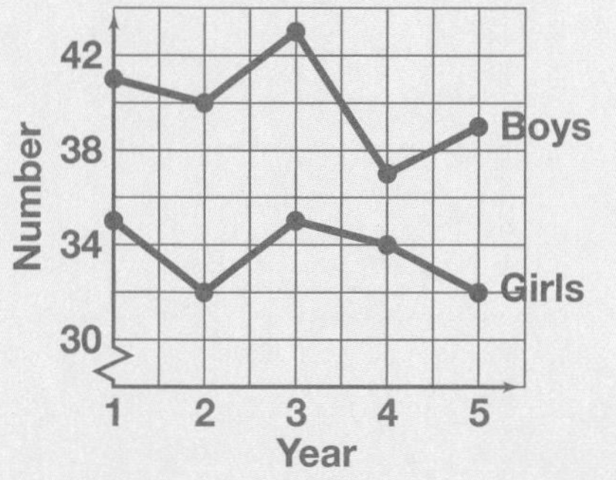

The graph with the break symbol tends to exaggerate the changes.

12.

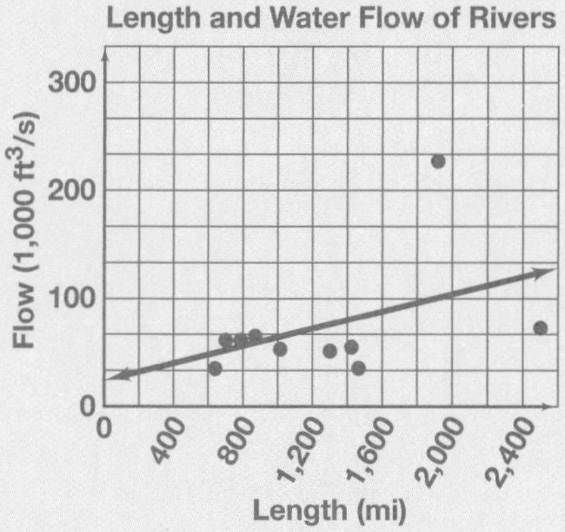

13. Scatter plot; it shows the relationship between two sets of data.

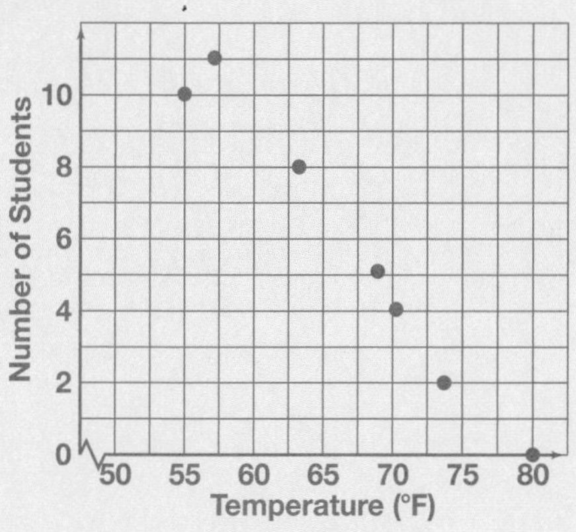

page 464 Chapter 9 Test

7.

Hours	Frequency
5–6	3
7–8	9
9–10	4
11–12	1

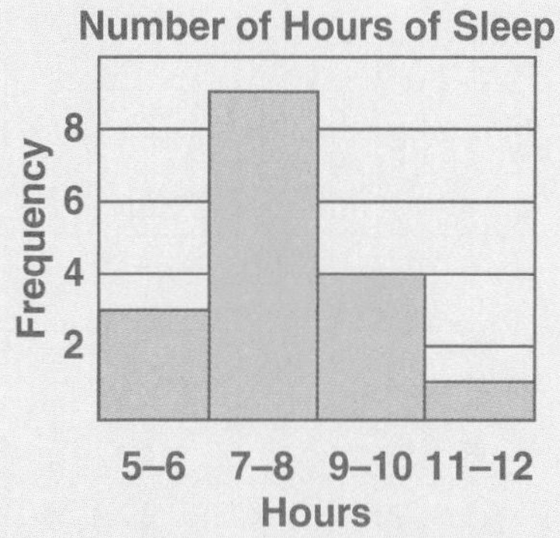

8.

Salary	Frequency
400–699	2
700–999	7
1,000–1,299	4
1,300–1,599	1

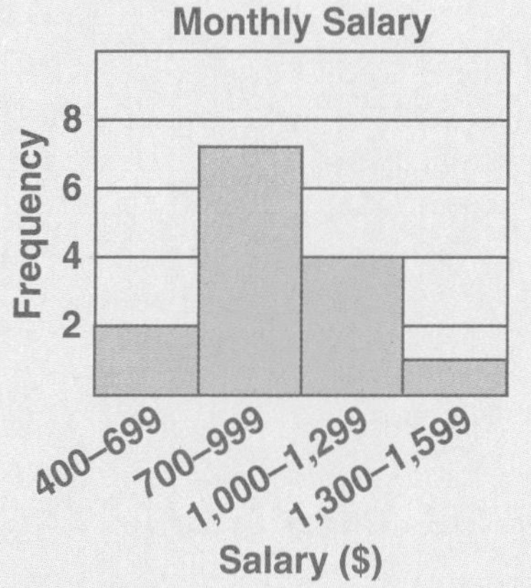

14. Bar graph; it shows the relative size of categories.

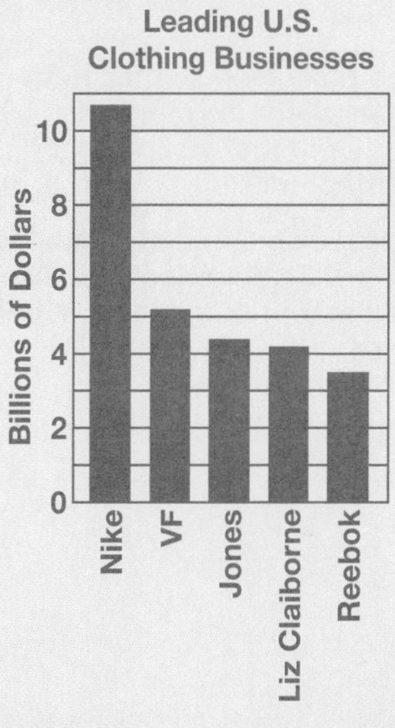

15. Line graph; it shows changes over time.

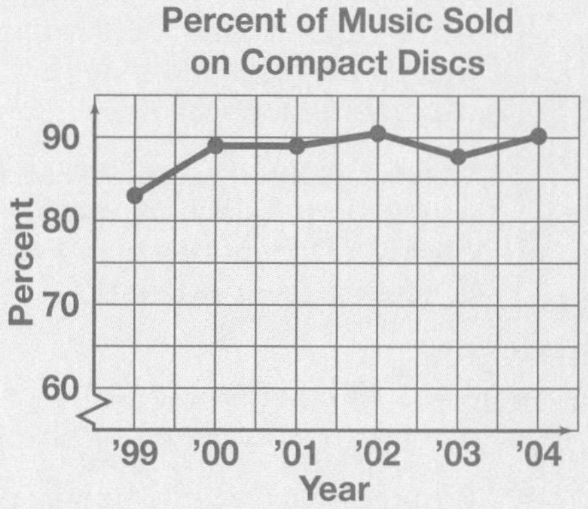

16. Bar graph; it shows the relative size of categories.

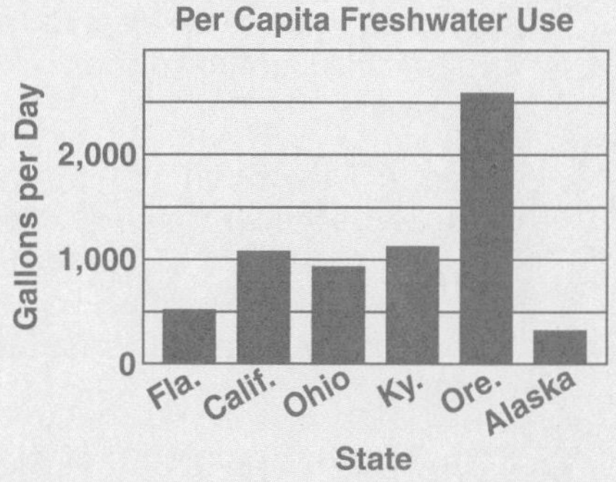

CHAPTER 10

Lesson 10-2

page 474 Activity Lab

5.

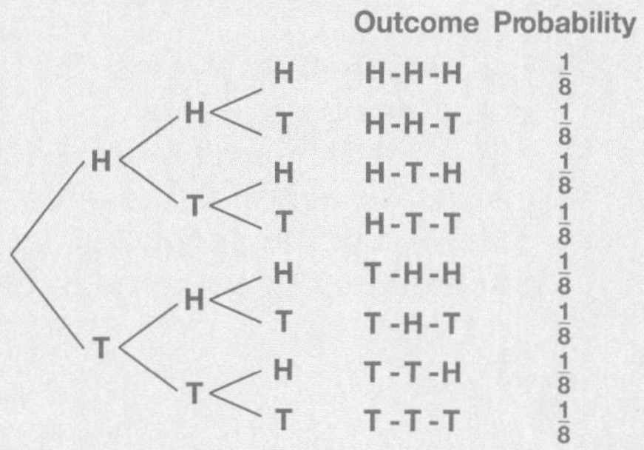

Lesson 10-3

page 480 Check Skills You'll Need

1. Experimental probability is based on running numerous trials or experiments, whereas theoretical probability is based on the mathematical likelihood of events.

pages 480–481 Quick Check

1. Not a random sample; people who are 18–30 years old may not represent all people.
2. It assumes you either in-line skate or ice skate; answers may vary. Sample: Do you like to in-line skate or ice skate, or neither?

page 483 TE Lesson Quiz

1. Sample: Your science class does not include students from other grades.
2. Sample: The question implies that staying home might be a more acceptable choice to the interviewer.
3. Sample: The conclusions may not be valid because these students who are members of the football team may be more likely to attend the pep rally than students in general.
4. Sample: No. Recipients of the questionnaire are current members who are more likely to be satisfied with the facility than any ex-members.

Lesson 10-4

page 489 Exercises

24. For independent events, the outcome of the first event does not affect the outcome of the second event. For dependent events, the outcome of the second event is affected by the outcome of the first event.

CHAPTER 11

Lesson 11-1

page 510 Check Your Readiness

7–9.

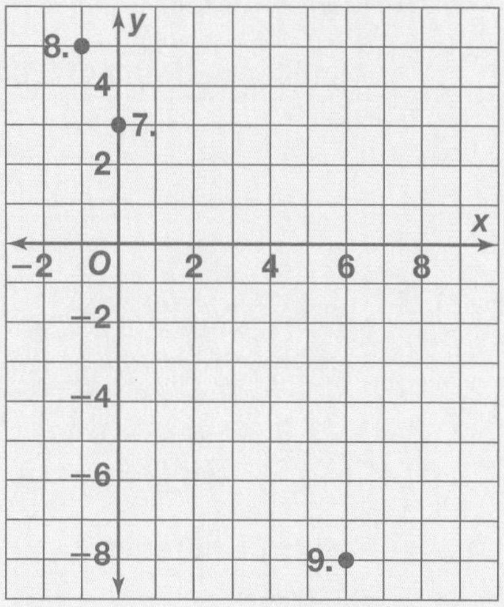

14.

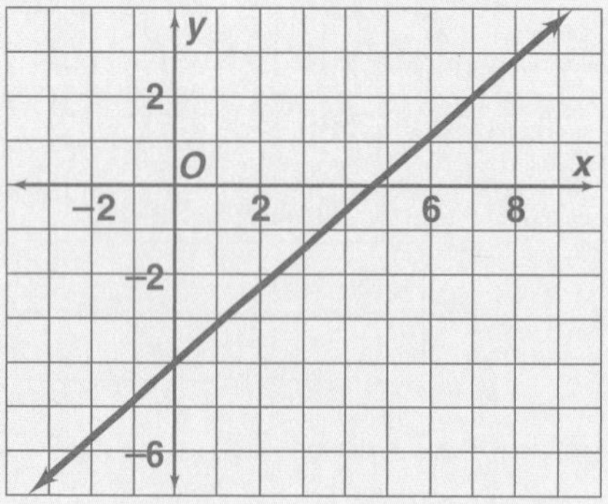

Lesson 11-2

page 518 Check Skills You'll Need

1. Line graphs best display changes over time.

2–3. Answers may vary. Samples are given.

2. Line plots best display frequency of data—for example, displaying the number of siblings each class member has.
3. Bar graphs compare amounts in different categories—for example, the number of students in each grade.

page 519 Quick Check

2.

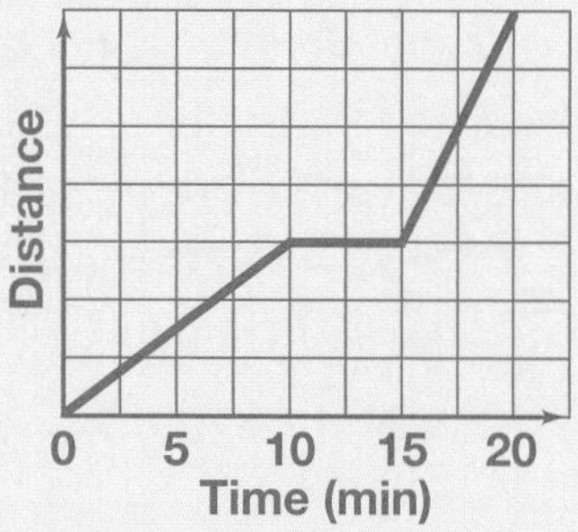

page 521 TE Lesson Quiz

1.

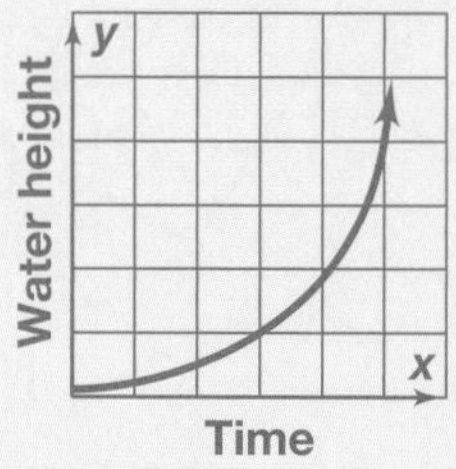

3.

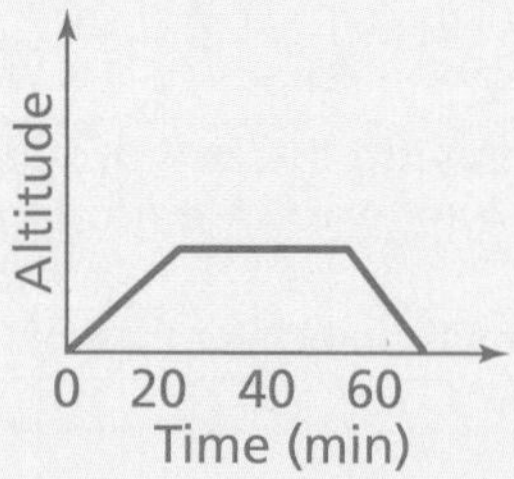

page 521 Exercises

17.

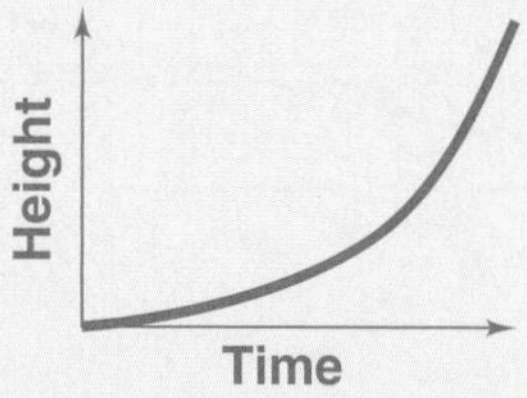

18.

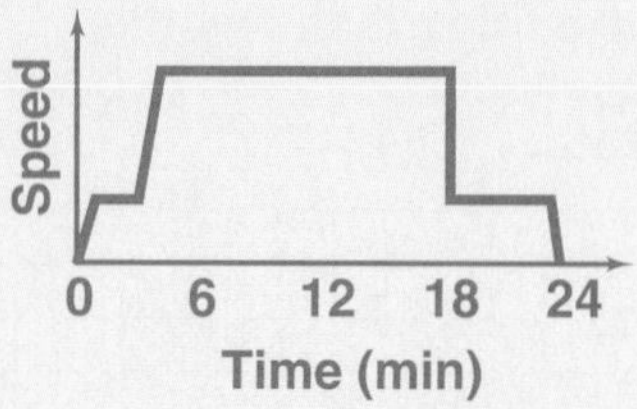

19.

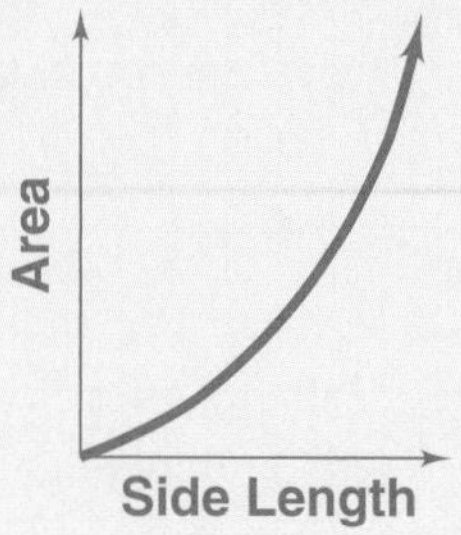

20.

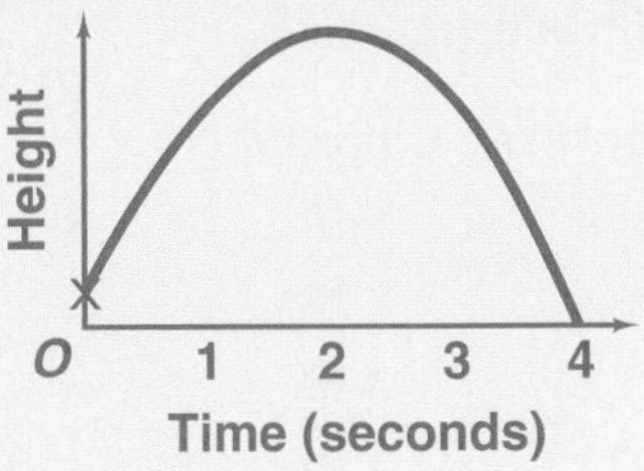

Lesson 11-3

page 523 Quick Check

1.

c	*d*
5	$.50
10	$1.00
15	$1.50

Lesson 11-4

page 529 TE Additional Examples

3.

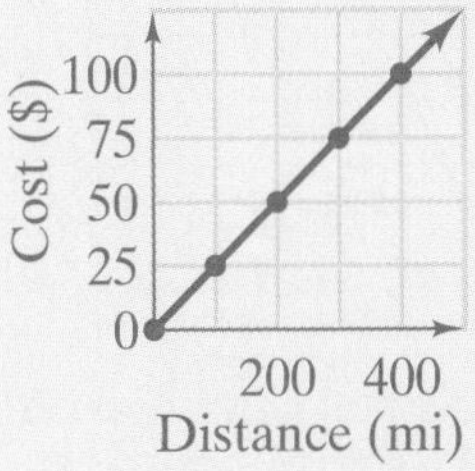

The amount spent on fuel increases $1 for every 4 miles driven.

page 530 Quick Check

3. −2

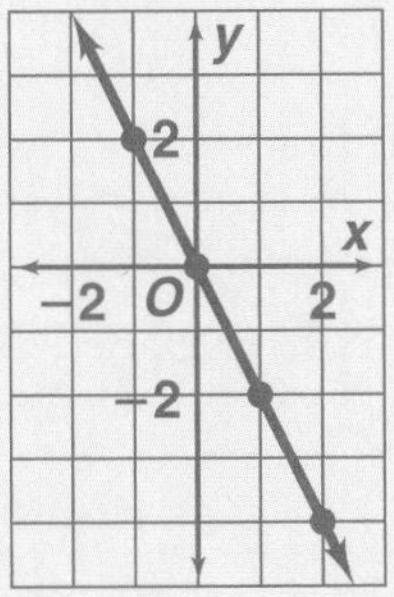

page 531 Exercises

13. Answers may vary. Sample: Add 2 to or subtract 2 from the *y*-coordinate and add 1 to or subtract 1 from the *x*-coordinate.

page 531 TE Lesson Quiz

4.

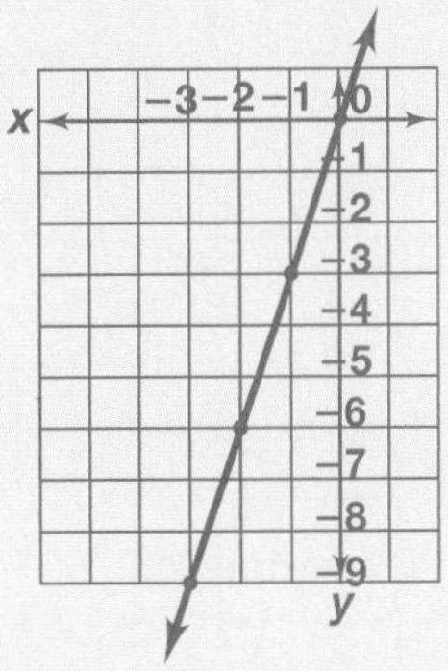

page 533 Activity Lab

1.

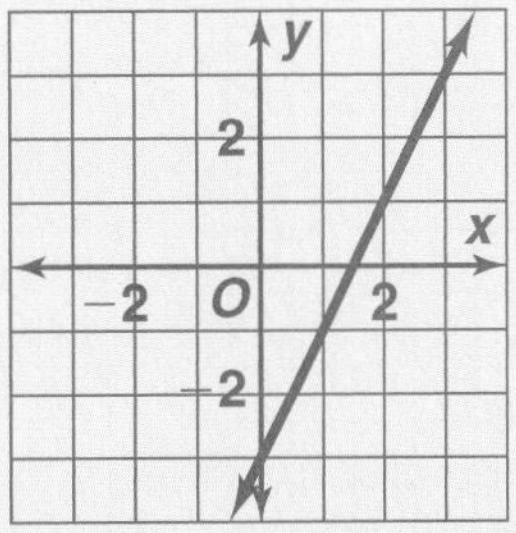

x	−3	−2	−1	0	1	2	3
y	−9	−7	−5	−3	−1	1	3

2.

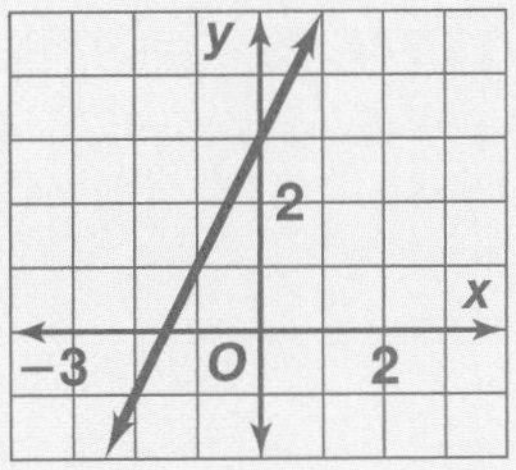

x	−3	−2	−1	0	1	2	3
y	−3	−1	1	3	5	7	9

3.

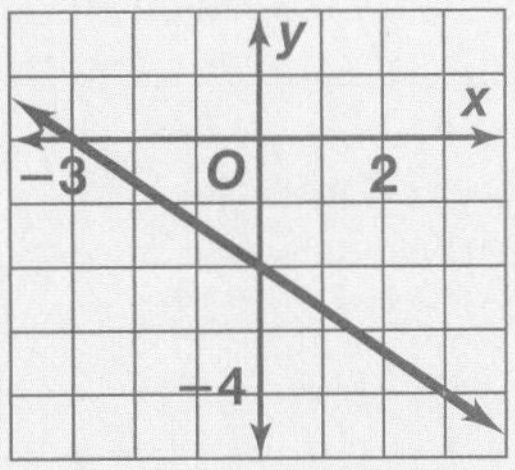

x	−3	−2	−1	0	1	2	3
y	0	$-\frac{2}{3}$	$-\frac{4}{3}$	−2	$-\frac{8}{3}$	$-\frac{10}{3}$	−4

4.

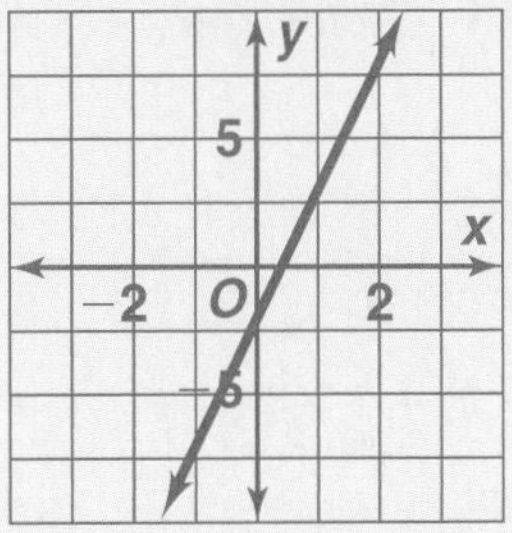

x	−3	−2	−1	0	1	2	3
y	−17	−12	−7	−2	3	8	13

Lesson 11-5

pages 534–535 Quick Check

1.

Tickets	0	1	2	3	4	5	6	7
Cost	0	15	30	45	60	75	90	105

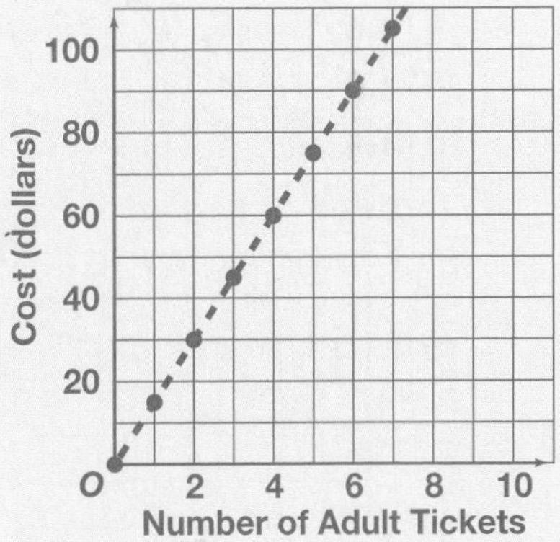

2.

Time	0	1	2	3	4	5	6
Height	4,000	3,400	2,800	2,200	1,600	1,000	400

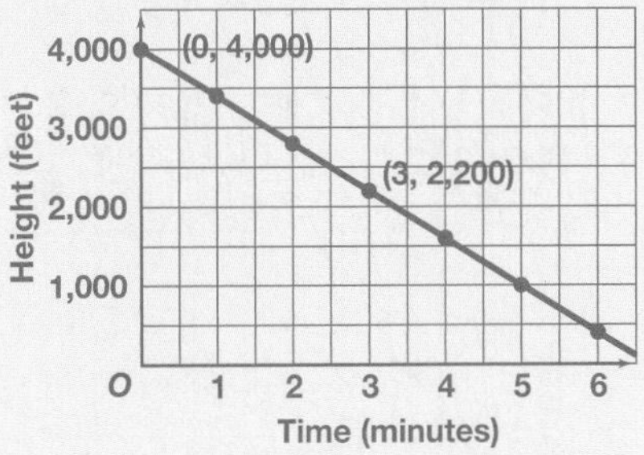

pages 536–538 Exercises

5.

x	−3	−2	−1	0	1	2	3
y	−9	−6	−3	0	3	6	9

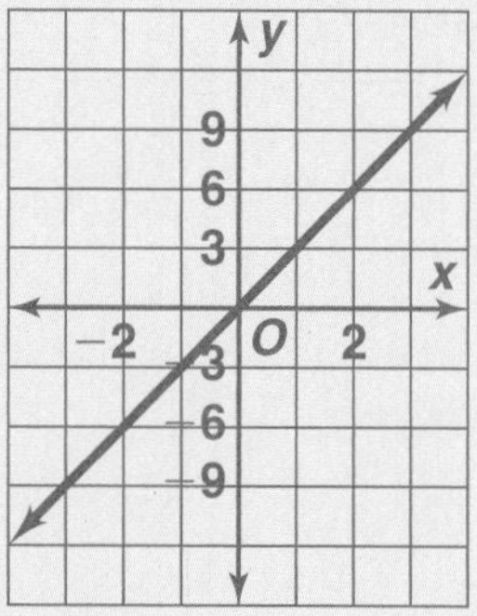

7. continuous

x	p
0	1
10	1.3
20	1.6
30	1.9

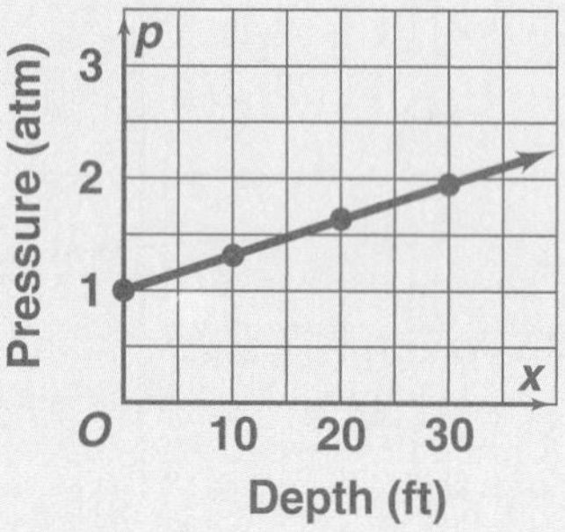

8. continuous

x	y
0	32
50	122
100	212

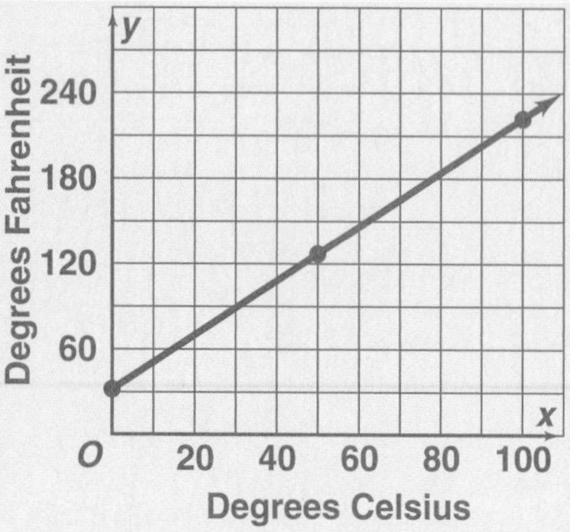

12.

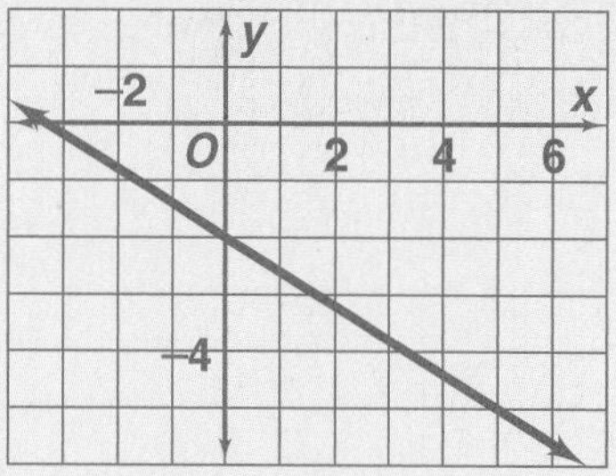

13.

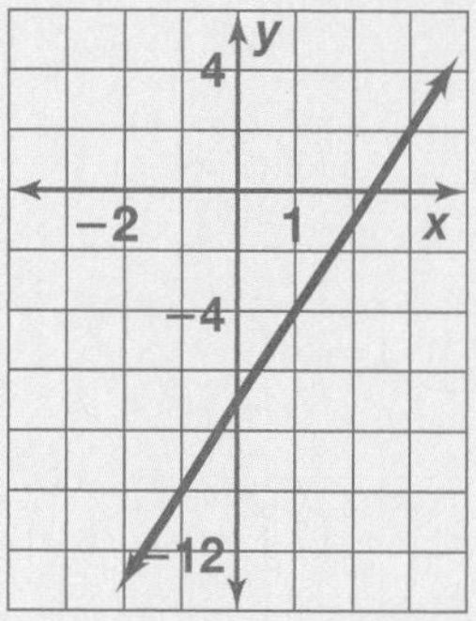

14.

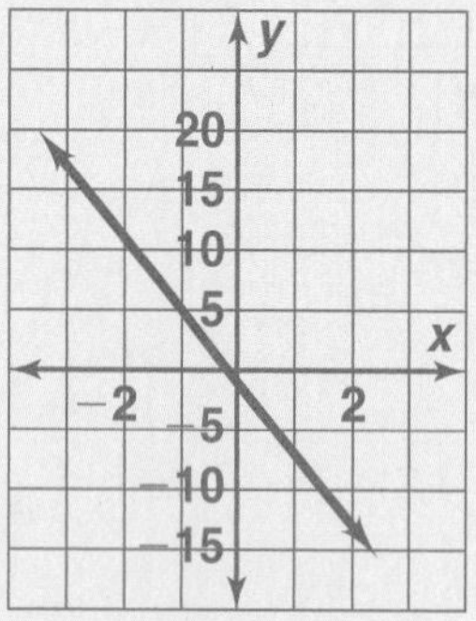

15.

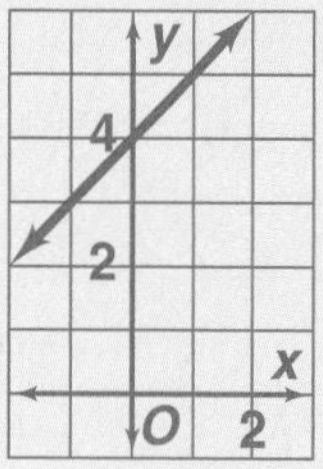

17a.

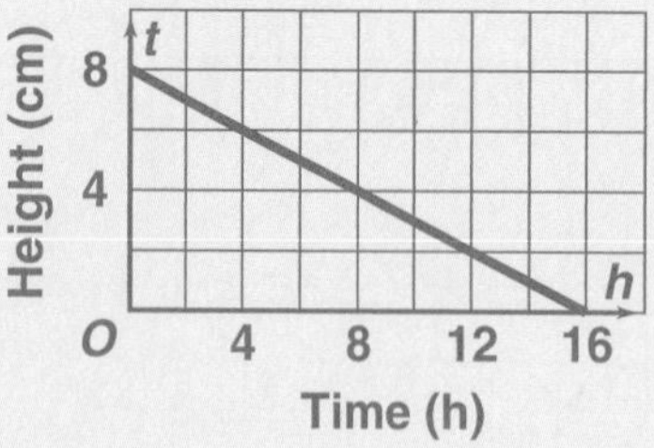

b. 8 cm

c. 16 h

18. 17.5 Calories

Crackers	Calories
0	0
4	70
8	140
12	210
16	280

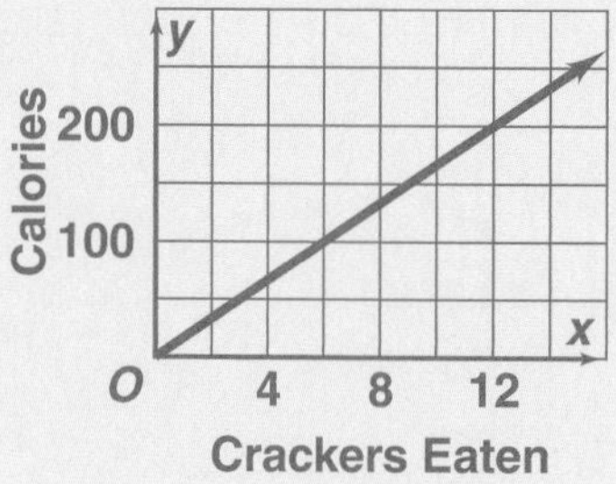

19.

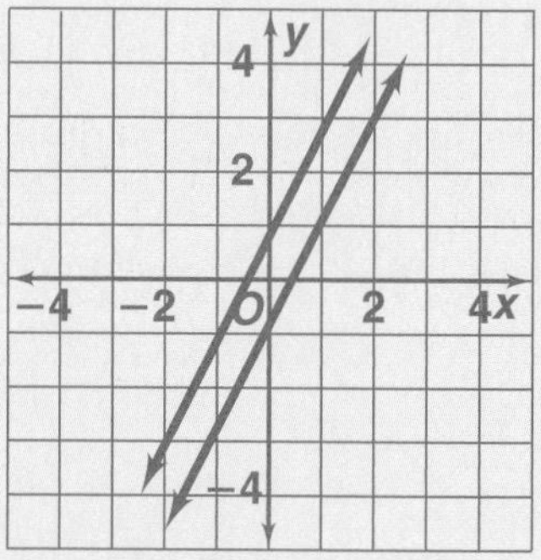

They are parallel but have different y-intercepts.

20. A: $y = 5 + 2x$;
B: $y = 10 + x$

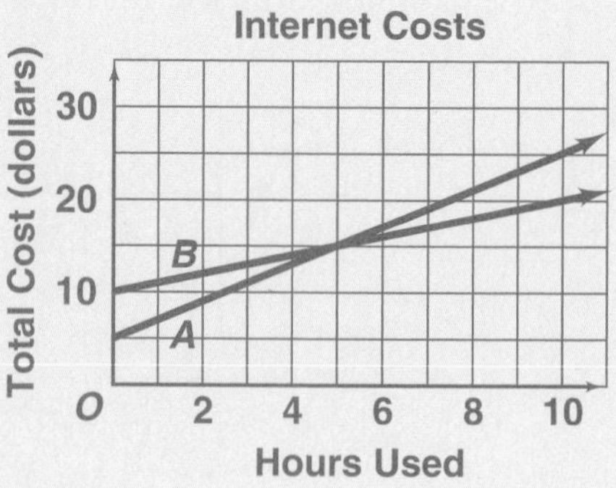

21. $y = 2.3x$; $y = 2.35x$; 6 gallons

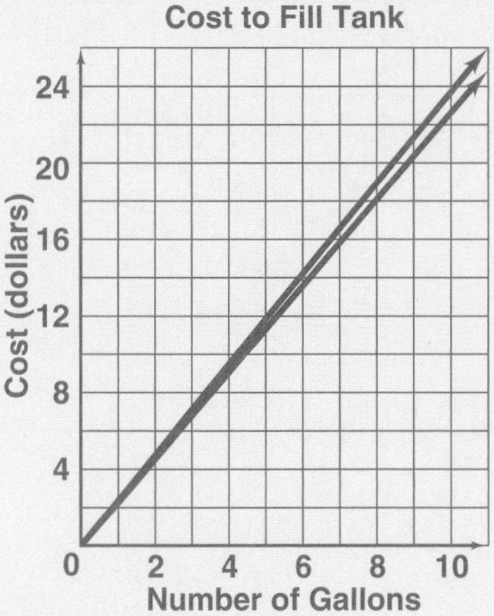

page 538 TE Lesson Quiz

1.

Time (min)	0	1	2
Height (ft)	150	155	160

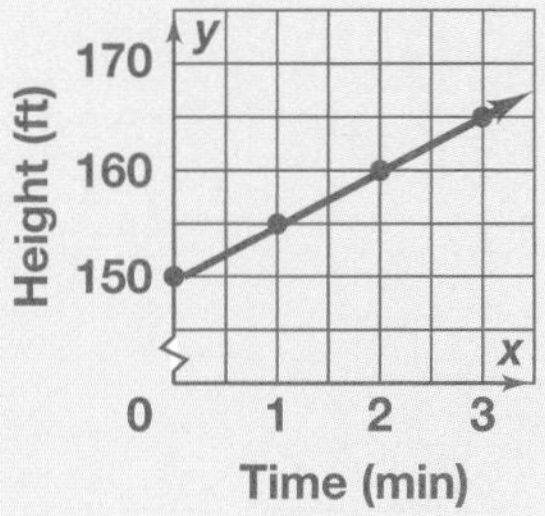

2.

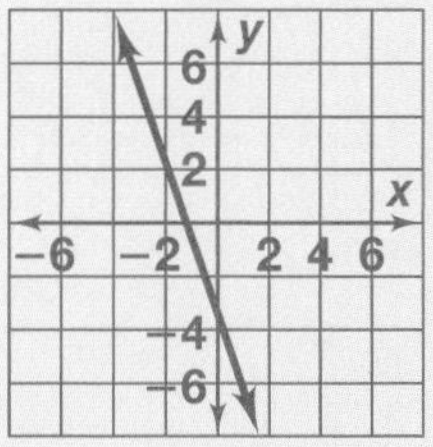

3.

Kilograms (kg)	0	1	2	3
Pounds (lb)	0	2.2	4.4	6.6

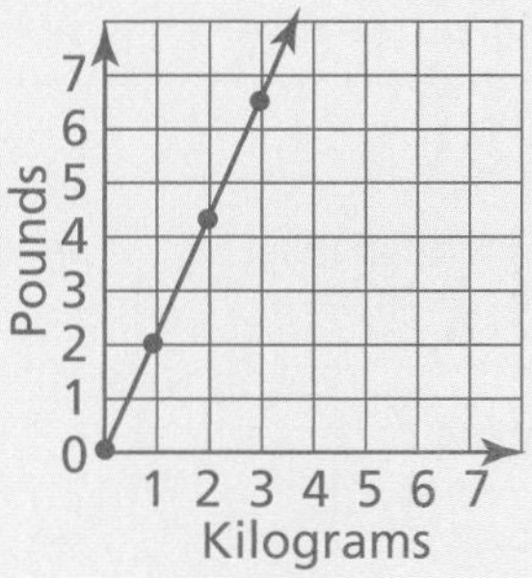

page 539 Checkpoint Quiz

10.

Hours Worked	Money Earned
0	0
1	7
2	14
3	21
4	28
5	35
6	42
7	49
8	56

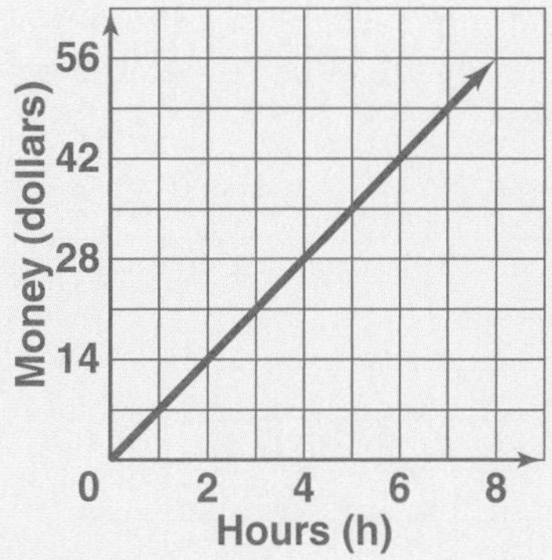

Lesson 11-6

page 543 Exercises

15. $C = 15 + r$;

$C = 30 + 0.50r$;

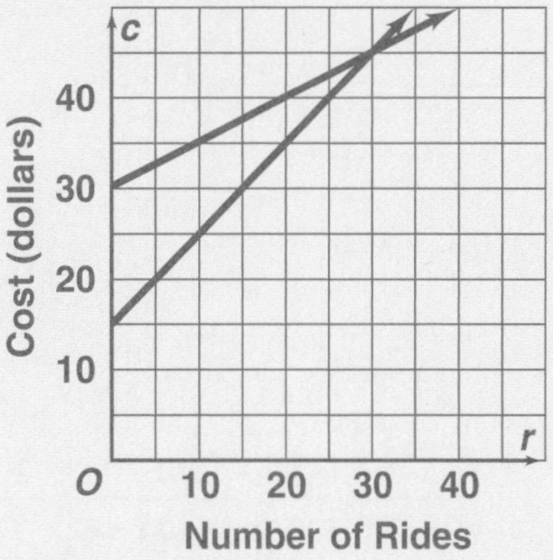

The $30 plan is cheaper for someone who plans to go on many (more than 30) rides.

Lesson 11-7

page 546 Check Skills You'll Need

1. The rate of change is constant.

2.

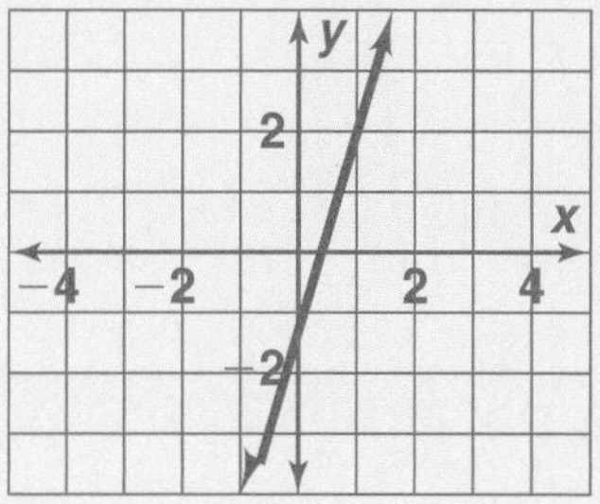

3.

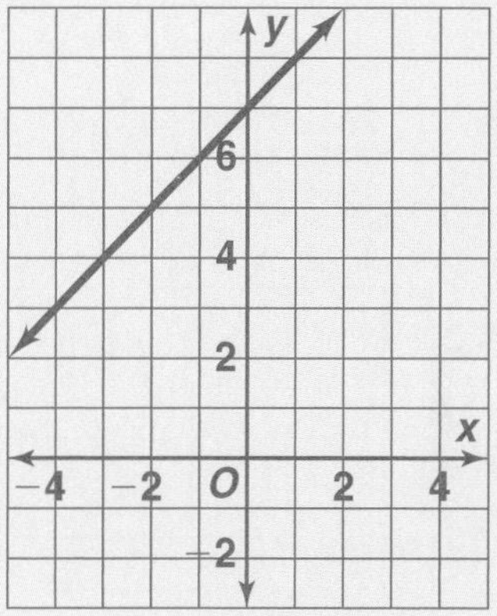

4.

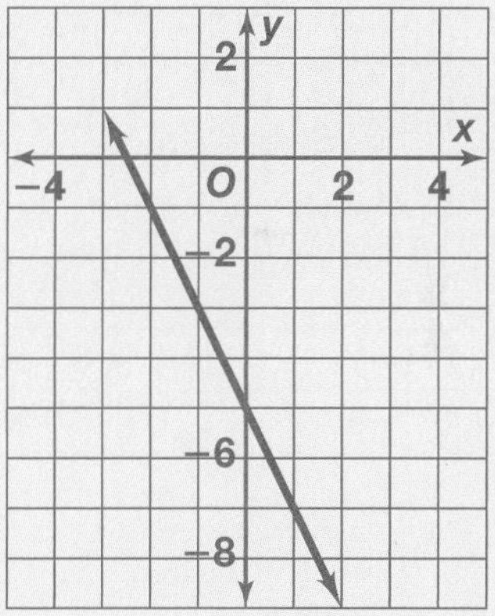

5.

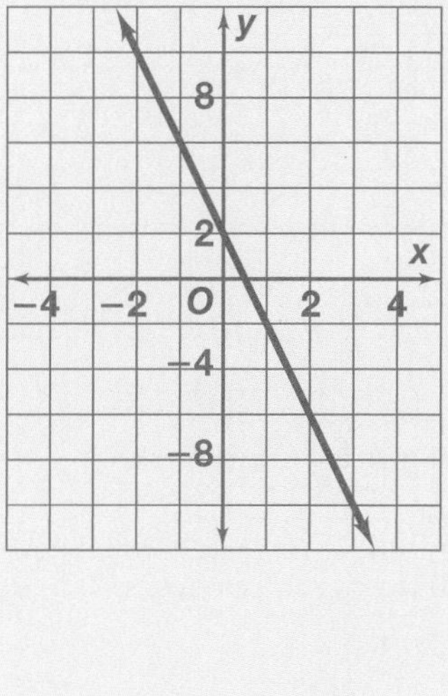

pages 546–547 Quick Check

1.

x	−2	−1	0	1	2
y	3	−3	−5	−3	3

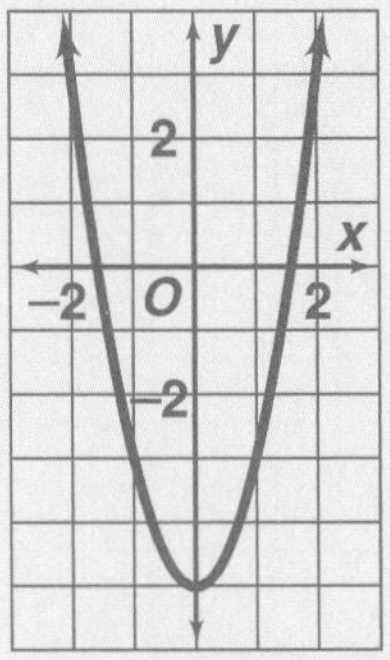

2.

s	10	20	30	40	50	60
y	20	10	$6\frac{2}{3}$	5	4	$3\frac{1}{3}$

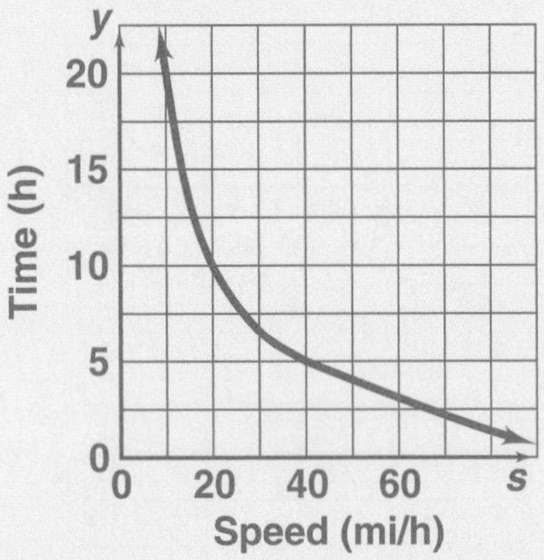

page 547 TE Additional Examples

1.

x	−2	−1	0	1	2	3	4
y	8	−3	0	−1	0	3	8

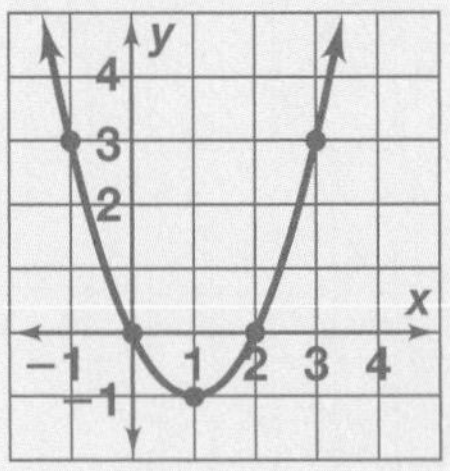

2.

Input *t*	2	3	4	5	6
Output *y*	60	40	30	24	20

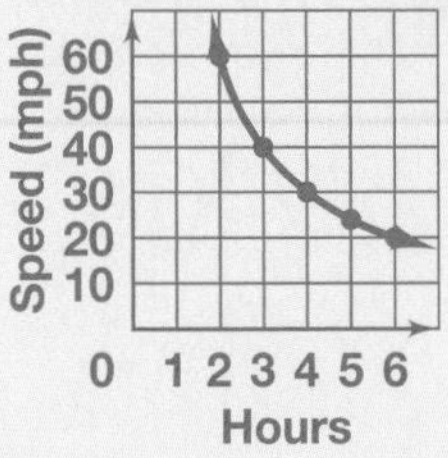

pages 548–549 Exercises

4.

x	−3	−2	−1	0	1	2	3
y	−9	−4	−1	0	−1	−4	−9

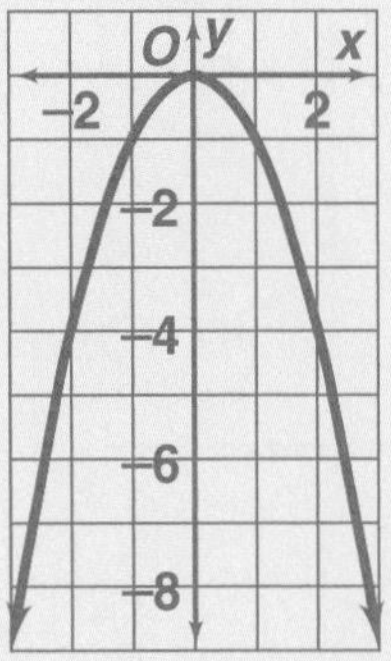

6.

x	−3	−2	−1	0	1	2	3
y	−72	−32	−8	0	−8	−32	−72

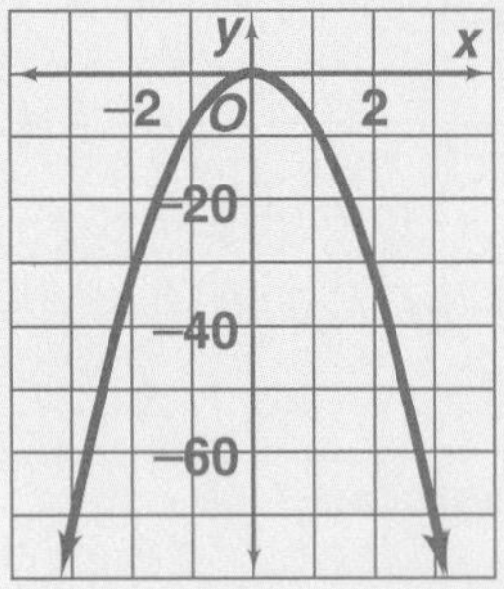

7.

x	−3	−2	−1	0	1	2	3
y	11	6	3	2	3	6	11

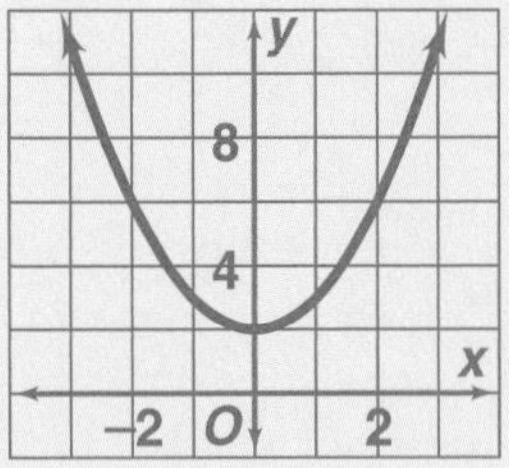

8.

x	−3	−2	−1	0	1	2	3
y	−36	−16	−4	0	−4	−16	−36

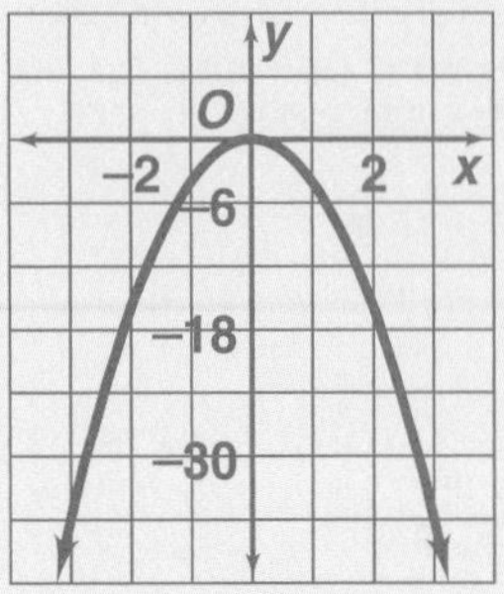

9.

x	−3	−2	−1	0	1	2	3
y	27	17	11	9	11	17	27

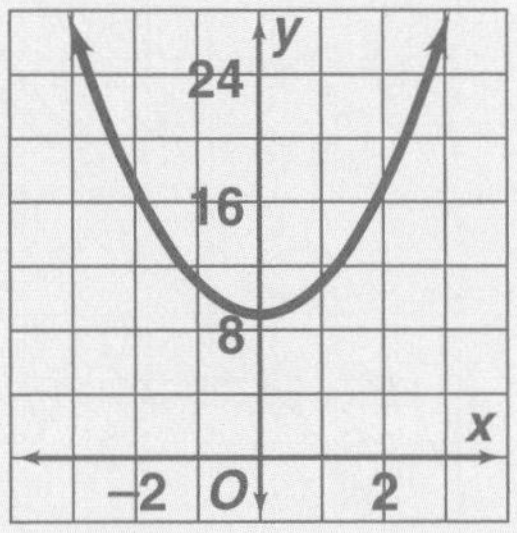

10.

x	1	2	3	4	5
y	10	5	$3\frac{1}{3}$	$2\frac{1}{2}$	2

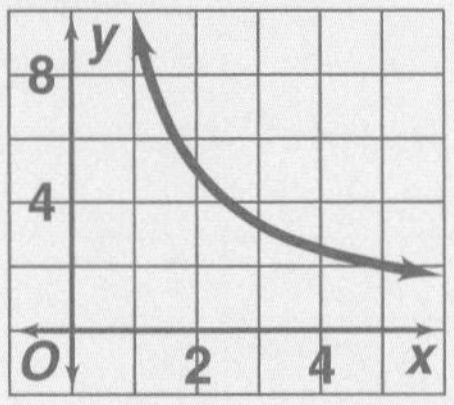

11.

x	1	2	3	4	5
y	8	4	$2\frac{2}{3}$	2	$1\frac{3}{5}$

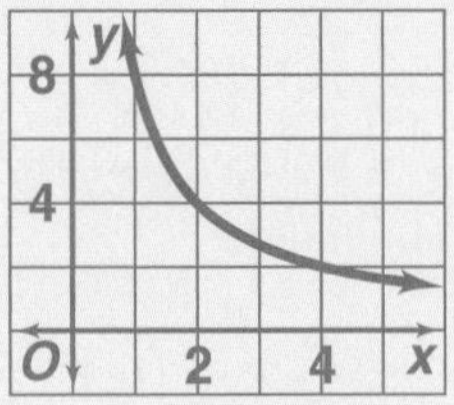

12.

x	1	2	3	4	5
y	20	10	$6\frac{2}{3}$	5	4

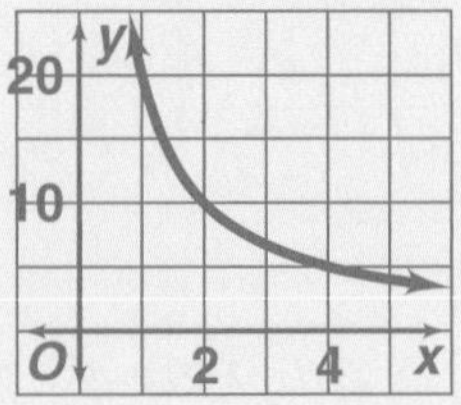

13.

x	1	2	3	4	5
y	16	8	$5\frac{1}{3}$	4	$3\frac{1}{5}$

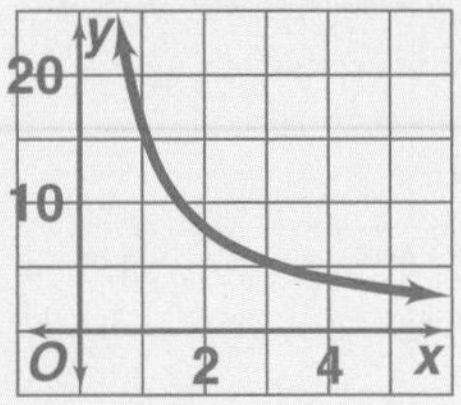

18.

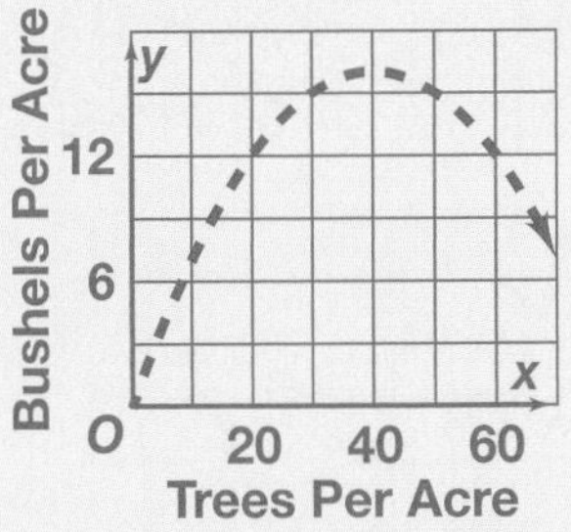

When too many trees are planted per acre, production decreases.

19.

Width x	Length	Area A
1	5	5
2	4	8
3	3	9
4	2	8
5	1	5

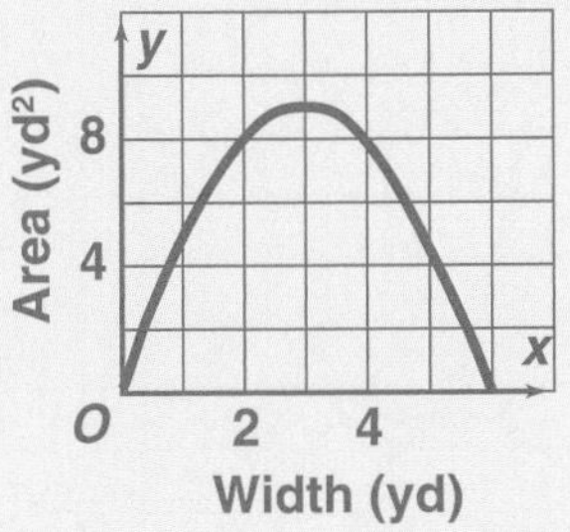

20.

x	−3	−2	−1	0	1	2	3
y	−24	−10	−2	0	−4	−14	−30

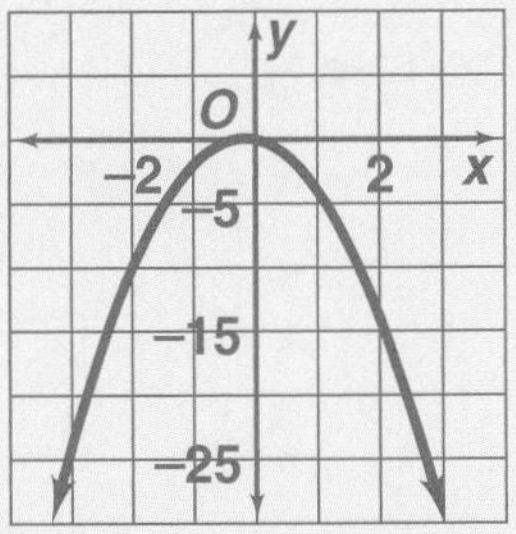

21.

x	−3	−2	−1	0	1	2	3
y	14	6	2	2	6	14	26

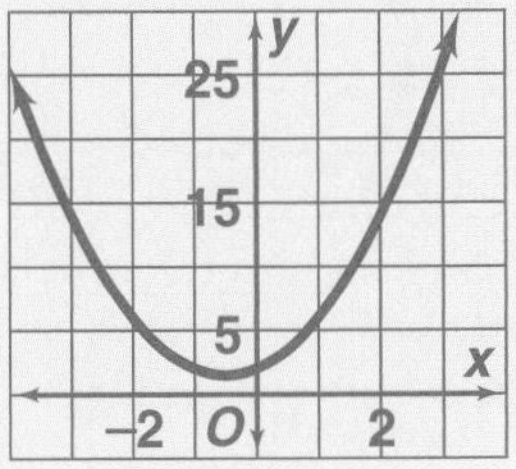

22.

x	−3	−2	−1	0	1	2	3
y	−12	−6	−2	0	0	−2	−6

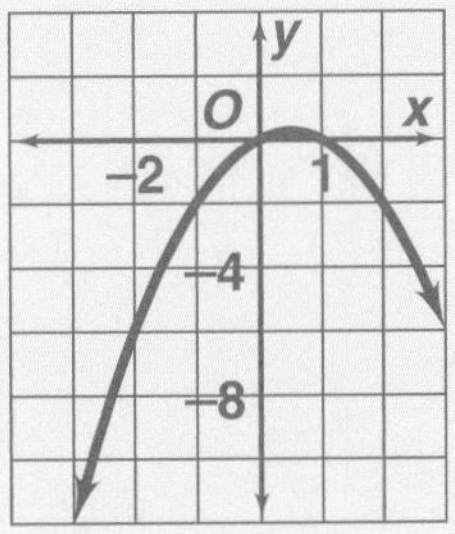

23a.

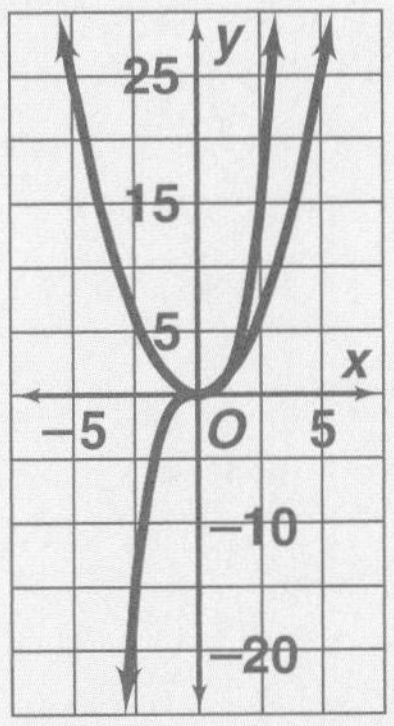

b. Answers may vary. Sample: Both graphs are nonlinear and have positive y values for positive x values. The graph of $y = n^2$ is a parabola, but the graph of $y = n^3$ is not.

27.

x	$x^2 - 2 = y$
−1	−1
0	−2
1	−1
2	2
3	7

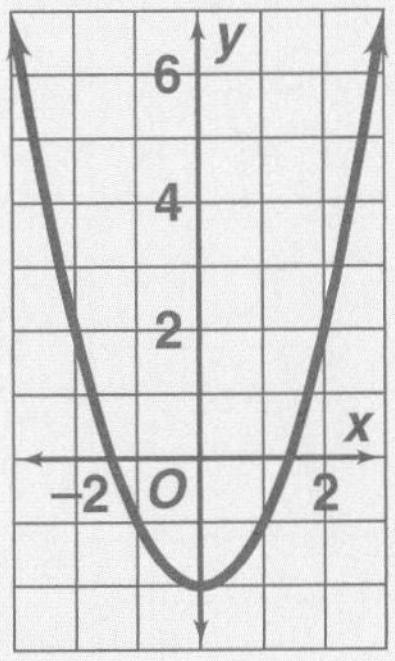

28.

x	$\frac{7}{x} + 2 = y$
1	9
2	5.5
3	4.3
4	3.75

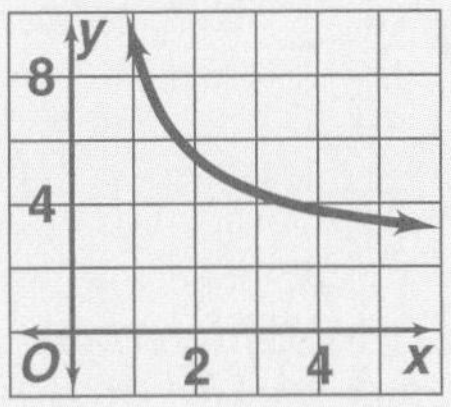

29.

x	$3 \cdot 2^x = y$
1	6
2	12
3	24
4	48

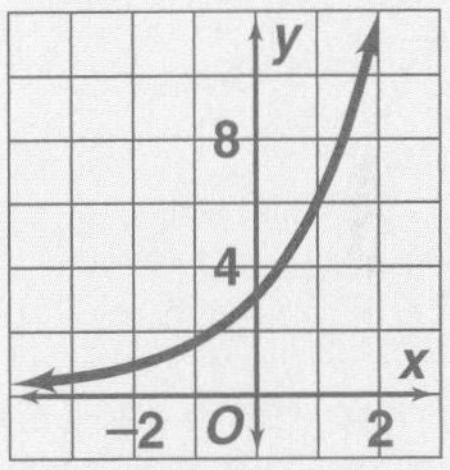

30a.

x	−3	−2	−1	0	1	2	3
y	$\frac{1}{27}$	$\frac{1}{9}$	$\frac{1}{3}$	1	3	9	27

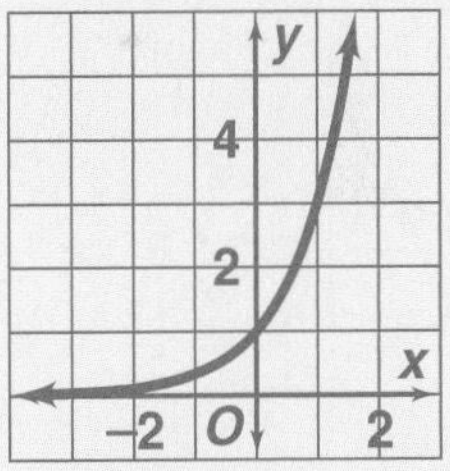

b.

x	−1	0	1	2	3	4	5
y	$\frac{1}{27}$	$\frac{1}{9}$	$\frac{1}{3}$	1	3	9	27

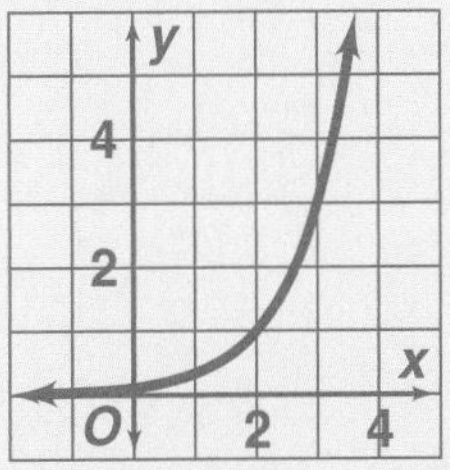

The graph is the same shape as the graph in part (a), but it is shifted two units to the right.

c.

x	-4	-3	-2	-1	0	1
y	$\frac{1}{9}$	$\frac{1}{3}$	1	3	9	27

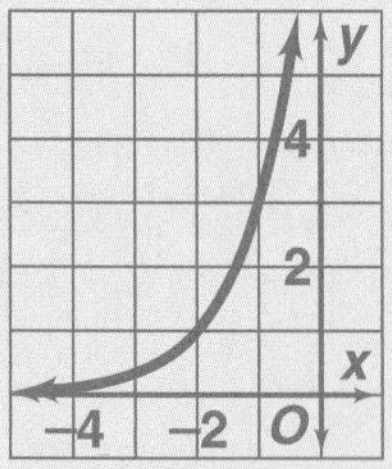

The graph is the same shape as the graphs in parts (a) and (b), but it is shifted two units to the left from part (a).

d.

x	-3	-2	-1	0	1	2
y	$-\frac{1}{27}$	$-\frac{1}{9}$	$-\frac{1}{3}$	-1	-3	-9

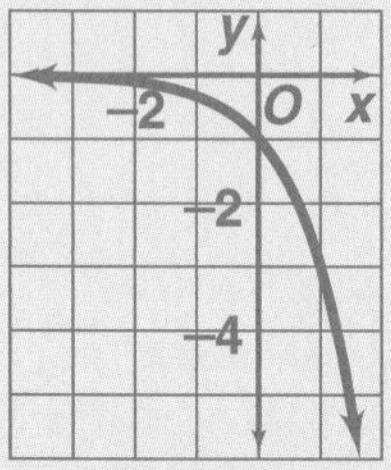

The graph is the same shape as the graph in part (a), but it is reflected through the *x*-axis.

page 553 Chapter 11 Review

22.

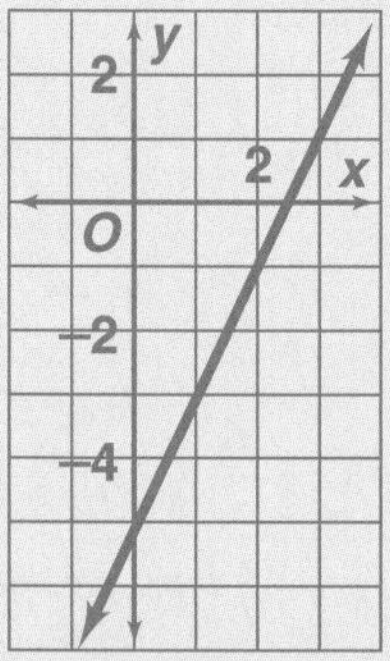

23.

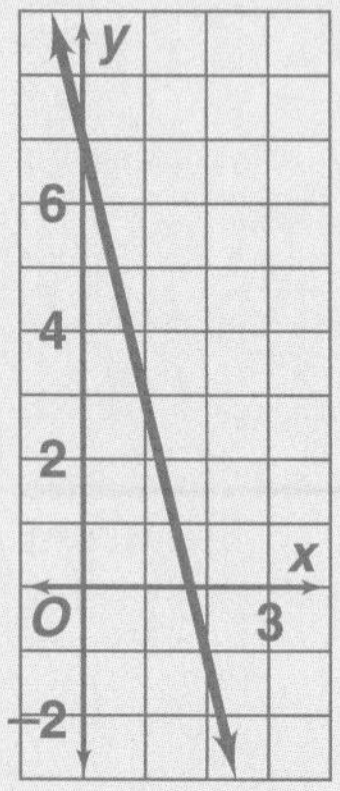

28.

x	1	7	14	21
y	7	1	$\frac{1}{2}$	$\frac{1}{3}$

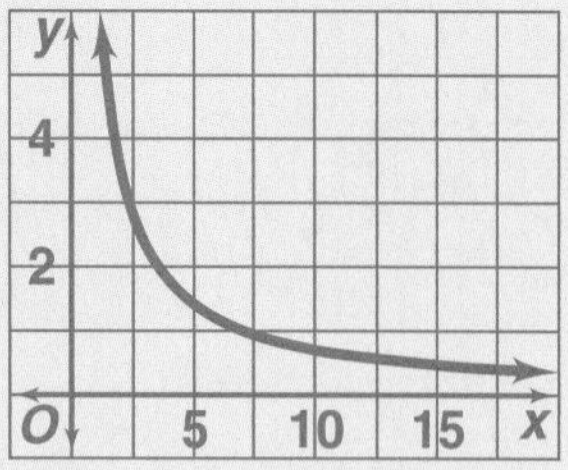

29.

x	1	2	3	4	5
y	7	$\frac{9}{2}$	$\frac{11}{3}$	$\frac{13}{4}$	3

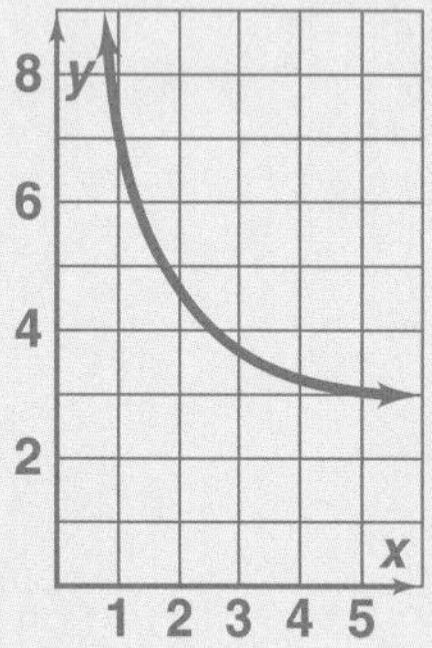

CHAPTER 12

Lesson 12-1

page 565 Exercises

32.

t	-3	-2	-1	0	1	2	3
y	15	0	-9	-12	-9	0	15

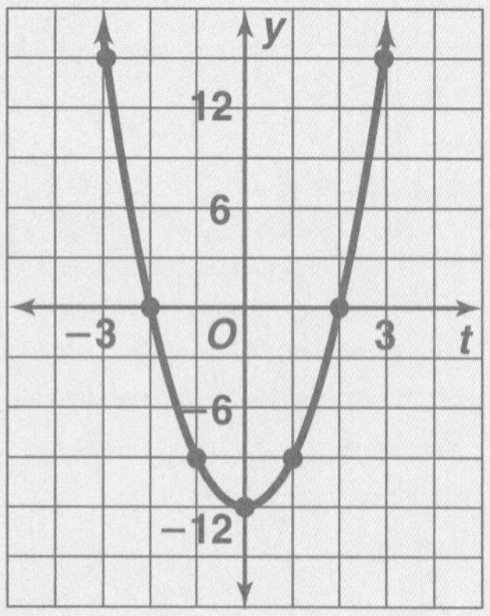

33.

m	-3	-2	-1	0	1	2	3
y	12	6	2	0	0	2	6

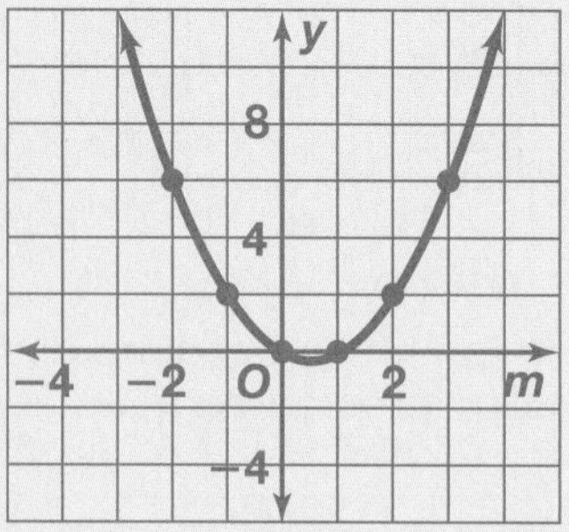

34.

x	-3	-2	-1	0	1	2	3
y	16	6	0	-2	0	6	16

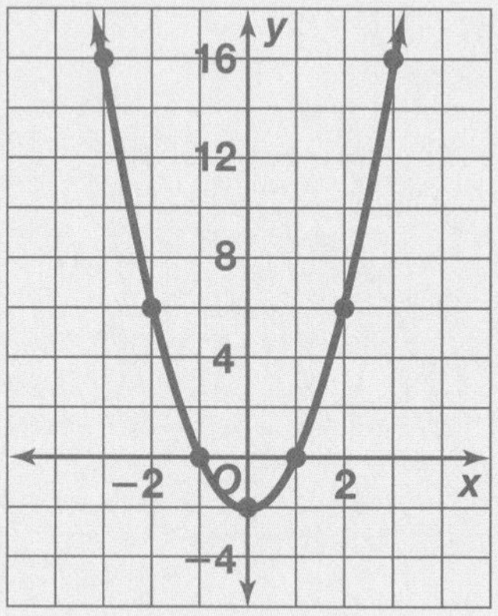

Lesson 12-4

page 579 Exercises

35.

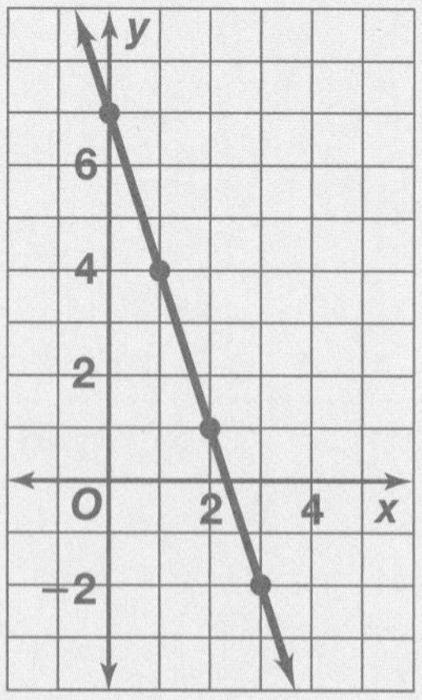

36.

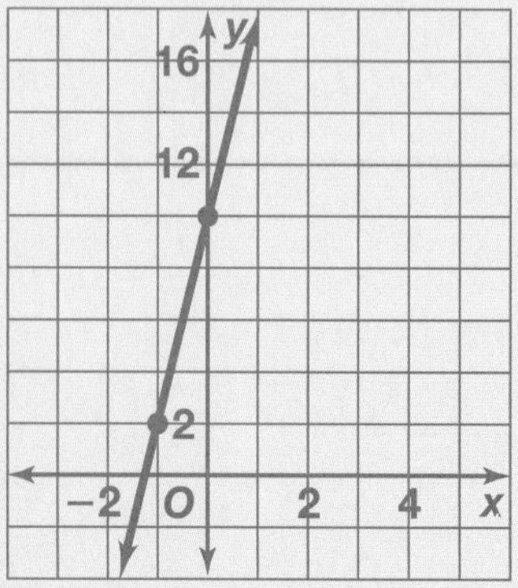

37.

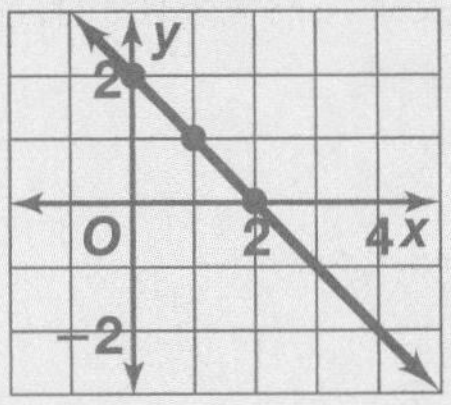

page 595 Test Prep

41. [4] a. $34 + 15w = 349$
where w is the amount of weeks he must save.

b. $34 + 15w = 349$
$15w = 315$
$w = 21$
He needs to save for 21 weeks.

[3] appropriate equation with one computational error

[2] correct equation solved incorrectly

[1] correct solution without work shown

42. [4] a. $2.5 \times 20 = 50$
The side will be 50 ft.

b. $0.5 \times 20 = 10$ ft
$A = S^2 = 10^2 = 100$
The area will be 100 ft^2.

[3] appropriate methods with one computational error

[2] correct lengths of sides but incorrect area

[1] correct solution without work shown

43. [4] a. markup $= 6 - 3.50 = 2.50$
$P \cdot 3.50 = 2.50;$
$P = 0.71428;$
The percent of markup is about 71.4%.

b. $15 \div 6 = 2.5;$
you can buy 2 bottles.

[3] correct procedure with one computational error

[2] correct percent of markup OR correct number of bottles

[1] correct answers without work shown

EXTRA PRACTICE

page 624 and 625

22.

x	−4	−3	−2	−1	0	1	2	3	4
y	18	11	6	3	2	3	6	11	18

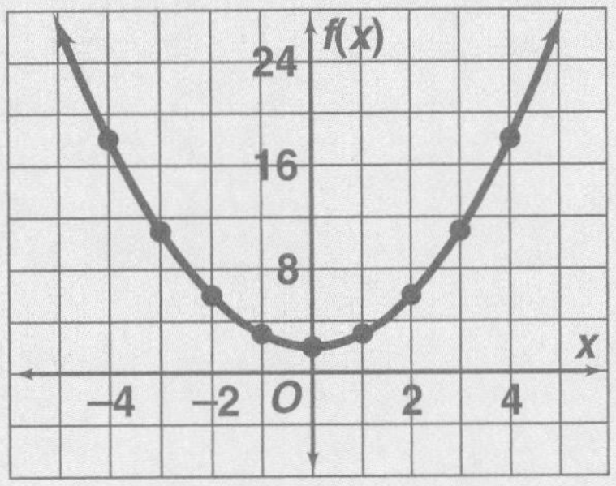

23.

x	−4	−3	−2	−1	0	1	2	3	4
y	−32	−18	−8	−2	0	−2	−8	−18	−32

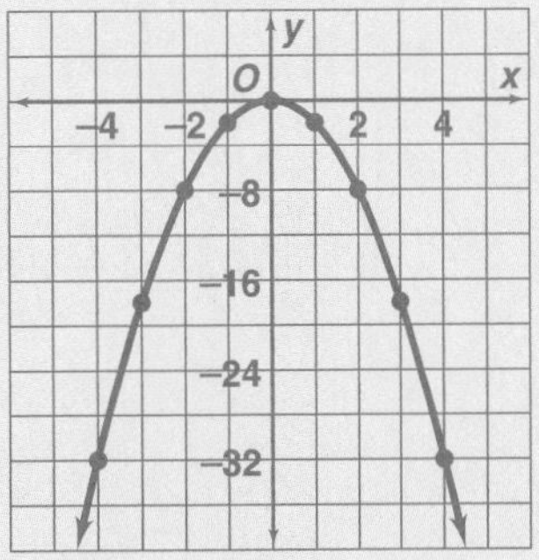

24.

x	−4	−3	−2	−1	0	1	2	3	4
y	48	27	12	3	0	3	12	27	48

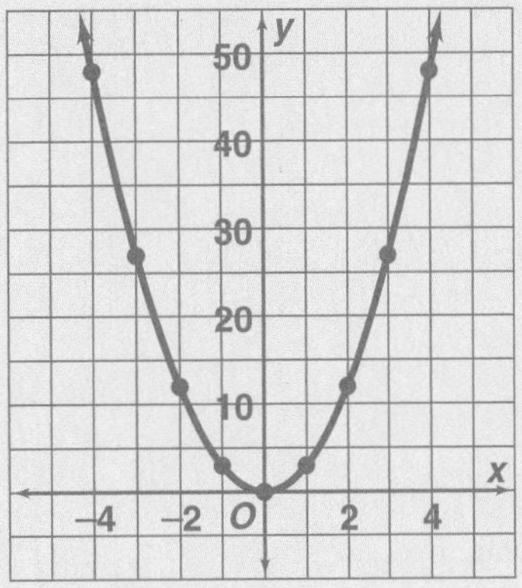

25.

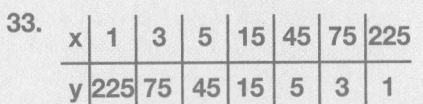

x	−4	−3	−2	−1	0	1	2	3	4
y	−13	−6	−1	2	3	2	−1	−6	−13

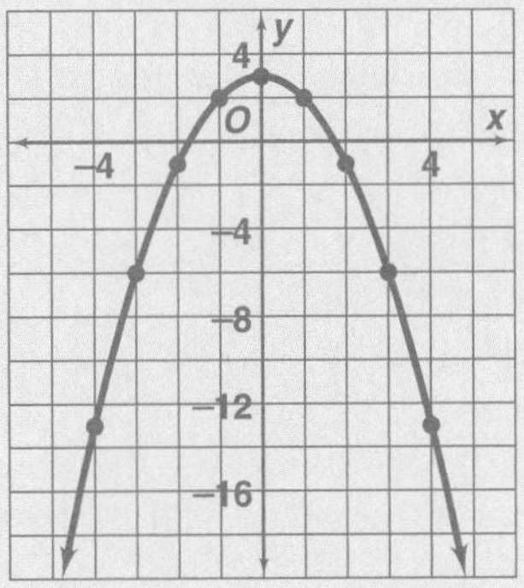

28.

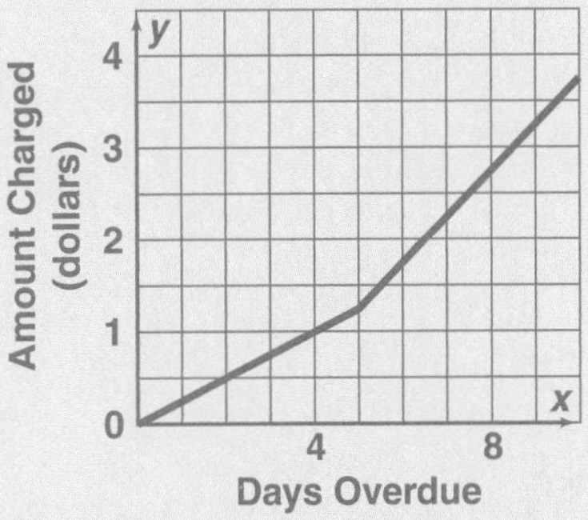

31.

Days	0	1	2	3	4	5
Height	23	39	55	71	87	103

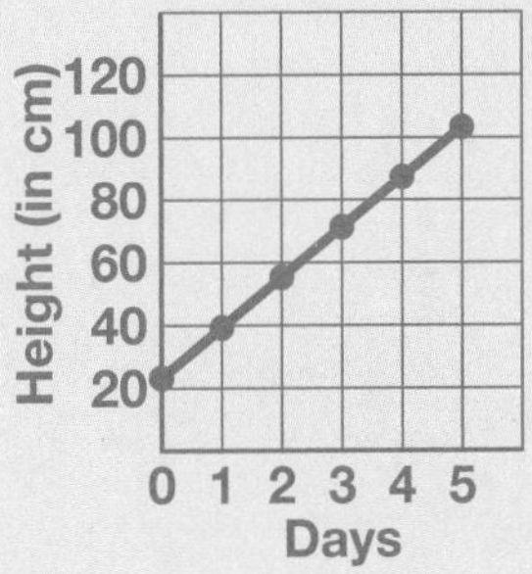

33.

x	1	3	5	15	45	75	225
y	225	75	45	15	5	3	1

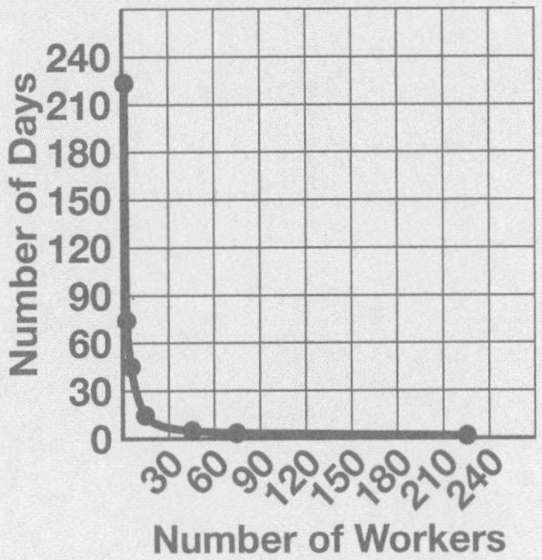

Index

Teacher's Edition entries appear in blue type.

A

D

E

Index

F

G

H

I

N

O

Index

R

S

T

W

X

Y

Z

Staff Credits

The people who make up the **Prentice Hall Math** team—representing design services, editorial, editorial services, educational technology, marketing, market research, photo research and art development, production services, publishing processes, and rights & permissions—are listed below. Bold type denotes core team members.

Dan Anderson, Carolyn Artin, Nick Blake, **Stephanie Bradley,** Kyla Brown, Patrick Culleton, Kathleen J. Dempsey, **Frederick Fellows, Suzanne Finn,** Paul Frisoli, Ellen Granter, **Richard Heater,** Betsy Krieble, Lisa LaVallee, Christine Lee, Kendra Lee, Cheryl Mahan, **Carolyn McGuire,** Eve Melnechuk, Terri Mitchell, Jeffrey Paulhus, Mark Roop-Kharasch, Marcy Rose, Rashid Ross, Irene Rubin, Siri Schwartzman, Vicky Shen, **Dennis Slattery,** Elaine Soares, Dan Tanguay, Tiffany Taylor, Mark Tricca, Paula Vergith, Kristin Winters, Helen Young

Additional Credits

Paul Astwood, Sarah J. Aubry, Jonathan Ashford, Peter Chipman, Patty Fagan, Tom Greene, Kevin Keane, Mary Landry, Jon Kier, Dan Pritchard, Sara Shelton, Jewel Simmons, Ted Smykal, TechBooks/GTS Publishing Services, Steve Thomas, Michael Torocsik, Maria Torti

Illustration Credits

Additional artwork:
Rich McMahon, Ted Smykal

Kenneth Batelman: **11, 246;**
Trevor Johnston: **230;**
Brucie Rosch: **10, 13, 162, 235, 238;**
JB Woolsey: **121, 197, 198, 199, 200, 201, 226;**
XNR Productions: **127, 193, 194, 222**

Photography

Front Cover, Boden/Ledingham/Masterfile
Back Cover, Gary Randall/Getty Images.

Title page: tl, Bob Daemmrich Photography; **tr**, Williamson Edwards/The Image Bank; **bl**, David Muench; **br**, Bob Daemmrich Photography.

Front matter Pages x, Frans Lanting/Minden Pictures; **xi**, Michael Newman/Photo Edit; **xii**, WiteLite/Alamy; **xiii**, Michael Newman/PhotoEdit; **xiv**, Jim West Photography; **xv**, Silver Burdett Ginn; **xvi**, Andrew Laker/AP Wide World; **xvii**, Steve Vidler/Superstock; **xviii**, Joseph Sohm/Chromo Sohm Inc./Corbis; **xix**, Bill Howes; Frank Lane Picture Agency/Corbis; **xx**, Getty Images, Inc; **xxi**, U.S. Navy by Ensign John Gay. **l**, Jack Fields/Corbis; **li**, David Young-Wolff/Getty Images, Inc.; **lii**, Bill Pugliano/Getty Images; **liv**, Phillippe Colombi/Getty Images, Inc.; **lvii**, Kindra Clineff/Index Stock Imagery, Inc.; **xlviii**, Richard Haynes; **xlix**, Richard Haynes

Chapter 1 Pages 3, Miles Ertman/Masterfile; **4**, NASA; **5**, NASA; **6**, Lori Adamski Peek/Getty Images, Inc.; **7**, Ron Behrmann/International Stock/ImageState; **9 t**, Richard Haynes; **11**, Frans Lanting/Minden Pictures; **16**, Tom Hauck/Getty Images, Inc.; **17**, Richard Haynes; **19**, *CALVIN AND HOBBES* ©1990 WATTERSON. Reprinted with permission of Universal Press Syndicate; **20**, Andre Jenny/Alamy; **21**, Photo courtesy Big Bend National Park; **22**, S. Frink/Zefa/Corbis; **26**, Chuck Savage/Corbis; **28**, Michelle Bridwell/PhotoEdit; **30**, Lon C. Diehl/PhotoEdit; **31**, Richard Haynes; **32 t**, Richard Haynes; **34**, Margot Granitsas; **36**, Tony Freeman/PhotoEdit; **38**, Getty Images; **39 ml & br**, Richard Haynes; **49 tl**, Frank Greenaway/Dorling Kindersley; **49 tr**, Dorling Kindersley

Chapter 2 Pages 51, Gary Conner/PhotoEdit; **52**, Tom Carter/Photo Edit; **54**, A. Ramey/PhotoEdit; **55**, Michael Newman/Photo Edit; **58**, David Young-Wolff/Photo Edit; **60**, 1993 King Features Syndicate, Inc. World rights reserved.; **62**, David Young-Wolff/Photo Edit; **65**, Chuck Savage/Corbis; **66**, Don Smetzer/Getty Images; **67**, Tony Freeman/PhotoEdit **69**, Bob Daemmrich/Photo Edit; **70**, Richard Haynes; **73**, Richard Haynes; **74 mr**, Richard Haynes; **76**, David Young-Wolff/Photo Edit; **77**, Richard Haynes; **81**, Paul A. Souders/Corbis; **82**, Frank Flavin/AccentAlaska.com; **83**, George Grall/National Geographic Image Collection/Getty Images; **84**, Dennis Hallinan/FPG International/Getty Images, Inc.; **86**, William Manning/Corbis; **87**, Esbin-Anderson/Photo Network/ PictureQuest; **89**, Jeff Greenberg/PhotoEdit; **92**, NASA; **93**, Strauss/Curtis/Corbis; **94**, Omnikron/Photo Researchers, Inc; **95**, NSO/SEL/Roger Ressmeyer/Corbis; **102 b**, Dorling Kindersley; **102 ml**, Martin Bough/Fundamental Photographs; **102 tr**, Michael Melford/Getty Images; **103 r**, Royalty Free/Corbis

Chapter 3 Pages 105, Chris Noble/Getty Images, Inc.; **106**, Spencer Grant/ PhotoEdit; **109**, National Postal Museum, Smithsonian Institution; **110**, Walker/Index Stock; **111 t**, Richard Haynes; **112**, Deborah Davis/ PhotoEdit; **113**, Richard Haynes; **115**, age fotostock/Superstock; **118**, NASA; **123 bl**, Poulides/Thatcher/Getty Images, Inc.; **123 br**, Lester Lefkowitz/ Corbis; **125**, Vincent Hobbs/SuperStock; **127**, age fotostock/SuperStock; **128**, Douglas Kirkland/Corbis; **130**, WiteLite/Alamy; **131**, Richard Haynes; **132**, Richard Haynes **134**, Bob Daemmrich Photography/Stock Boston; **136**, Koji Sasahara/AP/Wide World Photos; **140 ml, m & br**, Russ Lappa; **140 mr**, Richard Haynes; **141**, Theo Allofs/Corbis; **142**, Russ Lappa; **145**, Richard Haynes; **146 mr**, Runk/Schoenberger/Grant Heilman Photography, Inc.; **146 br**, Andrew J. Martinez/Photo Researchers, Inc.; **148 ml**, Larry Grant/Getty Images, Inc.; **148 mr**, Eric Neurath/Stock Boston; **149**, Russ Lappa; **150**, M. C. Escher's "Symmetry Drawing E25"©1997 Cordon Art-Baarn, Holland. All rights reserved. **156 t**, Alan Kearney/Getty Images, Inc.; **156 ml**, Jonathan Kannair/Index Stock Imagery, Inc.; **156–157 b**, Micheal Orton/Getty Images, Inc.; **157 br**, James Kay/Stock Connection/PictureQuest

Chapter 4 Pages 159, Michael Geissinger/The Image Works; **161**, Richard Haynes; **163**, Robert Maass/Corbis; **166**, NASA; **167**, Kevin Fleming/Corbis; **168**, Jay Penni; **170**, Comstock Images; **171**, Bob Daemmrich/Stock Boston; **175**, Bob Daemmrich/Photo Edit; **176 mr & ml**, Richard Haynes; **178**, Robin Smith/Getty Images, Inc.; **187**, Francisco Cruz/SuperStock; **192 tr**, Dana Hursey/Masterfile; **192 bl**, Cameramann/The Image Works; **194**, Michael Newman/PhotoEdit; **196 t**, Richard Haynes; **197**, Chrstoph Burkl/Getty Images; **197 ml**, Richard Haynes; **206 tr**, Brian Hagiwara/Foodpix/Getty Images, Inc.; **206 ml**, Paul Taylor/Getty Images, Inc.; **206 bl**, Paul Taylor/ Getty Images, Inc.; **207 t & b**, NASA Dryden Flight Research Center

Chapter 5 Pages 209, AP Wide World; **210 mr**, Jim West Photography; **210 ml**, Richard Haynes; **212**, Dana White/PhotoEdit; **213**, Tom McCarthy/ PhotoEdit; **214**, Stewart Cohen/Getty Images; **215**, Ronnie Kamin/ PhotoEdit; **218**, Reuters/Corbis; **219**, Tony Freeman/PhotoEdit; **219 tl**, Richard Haynes; **221**, Comstock Images/Getty Images; **224**, Spencer Grant/ PhotoEdit; **225 ml**, Richard Haynes; **225 mr**, Richard Haynes; **227**, Rick Bostick/Index Stock; **228**, Richard Haynes; **230**, U.S. Census Bureau; **231**, E.L. Miller/Stock Boston; **232**, Royalty Free/Corbis; **234**, H. Huntley Hersch **242**, Robert Llewllyn/Imagestate; **245 m**, Richard Haynes; **246**, Courtesy of the U.S. Mint; **248**, Tom Stewart/Corbis; **256 t**, Getty Images; **256–257 b**, Ken Fisher/Getty Images; **257 t**, Getty Images

Chapter 6 Pages 259, Simon Jauncey/Getty Images, Inc.; **260**, Richard Haynes; **261**, Jerry Shulman/SuperStock; **264**, Kathy McLaughlin/The Image Works; **265**, Richard Haynes; **267 tl**, Spencer Grant/PhotoEdit; **267 bl**, Richard Haynes; **270**, Frans Lanting/Minden Pictures; **272**, David Young-Wolff/PhotoEdit; **273**, Richard Haynes; **274**, Silver Burdett Ginn; **276**, Tony Freeman/PhotoEdit Inc.; **283 tl**, Richard Haynes; **284**, NovaStock/Alamy; **286**, Richard Haynes; **288**, Matthias Tunger/Getty Images; **291**, Ellen Senisi/ The Image Works; **298 tr**, Courtesy MGM/RGA; **298 ml, & br**, With permission Universal Studios Media Licensing, Matte World Digital and Amblin Entertainment; **299 tr, mr, br**, Matte World Digital and the National Park Service

Chapter 7 Pages 301, Roger Ressmeyer/Corbis; **302**, Richard Haynes; **303**, David Frazier; **306**, Joy Franklin; **307**, Tony Freeman/PhotoEdit; **308**, Russ Lappa/Prentice Hall; **310**, Richard Bryant/ARCAID; **312**, Tony Freeman/PhotoEdit; **317**, Dorling Kindersley; **318 mr**, Bonnie Kamin/ PhotoEdit; **318 br**, Courtesy of Irene Rubin; **323**, Ryan McVay/Getty Images, Inc.; **325**, Sandy Felsenthal/Corbis; **326**, Photo courtesy of Royal Australian Mint; **327**, Dusty Willison/ International Stock/ImageState; **328**, Bill Aron/ PhotoEdit; **329**, Joyce Photographics/Photo Researchers, Inc.; **330 br & bl**, Richard Haynes; **330 ml**, Stephen Simpson/Getty Images, Inc.; **330 tl**, Richard Haynes; **335 mr**, Richard Haynes; **335 m**, Carol Lee/The Picture Cube; **336**, Richard Haynes; **337**, Andrew Laker/AP/Wide World Photos; **341**, Richard Wood/Index Stock Imagery, Inc.; **350 b & t**, Dorling Kindersley; **351 b**, Neil Rabinowitz/Corbis; **351 t**, Ryan McVay/Photodisc/Getty Images

Chapter 8 Pages 353, Pepe Diaz/The Image Works; **354**, ©Judith Miller/ Dorling Kindersley/Freeman's; **355**, Fotopic/Omni-Photo Communications, Inc.; **357**, Ryan McVay/Getty Images, Inc.; **358 ml & br**, Russ Lappa; **360**, Steve Vidler/SuperStock; **363**, Richard Haynes; **364**, Stockbyte; **367**, Richard Haynes; **368**, James D. Wilson/Getty Images, Inc.; **372**, Rob Crandall/The Image Works; **373**, Richard Haynes; **375 br**, Dave G. Houser/ Corbis; **375 mr**, Pictor/ImageState; **378**, Craig Lovell/Corbis; **379**, Richard Haynes; **380 mr**, Russ Lappa; **380 bl**, David J. Sams/Stock Boston; **381 bl**, Peer Grimm/dpa/Landov; **381 tl**, Richard Haynes; **382 tl & mr**, Richard Haynes; **384**, Stockdisc; **387**, Richard Haynes; **389**, Richard Haynes; **391**, Adam Woolfitt/Corbis; **392**, Cindy Charles/PhotoEdit; **393**, Courtesy of Drs. Foster & Smith, Rhineland, WI; **394**, A Dressler/Getty Images; **396**, David Stoecklein/Corbis; **397, tl, tr, & mr**, Russ Lappa; **398**, Dorling Kindersley; **399**, Phil Cantor/SuperStock; **401**, Nancy Sheehan/PhotoEdit; **408 tr**, Tim Davis/Getty Images, Inc.; **408 ml**, Simone End/Dorling Kindersley; **408 m**, Dave King/Dorling Kindersley; **409 tr**, Kenneth Lilly/DK Picture Library; **409 mr**, George Bernard/Photo Researchers, Inc.

Chapter 9 Pages 411, Roland Seitre/Peter Arnold, Inc.; **412**, Corbis; **415**, Tom and Pat Leeson; **418 mr**, G. K. & Vikki Hart/Getty Images, Inc.; **418 bl**, Richard Haynes; **424**, Dennis MacDonald/Alamy; **428**, David Young-Wolff/ PhotoEdit; **430**, Reuters NewMedia Inc./Corbis; **434 ml & mr**, Richard Haynes; **437**, F. Gohier/Photo Researchers, Inc.; **438**, Mark Harmel/Getty Images; **440**, Duomo/Corbis; **441 tm**, Ken O'Donoghue; **444**, Russ Lappa; **450**, Jeff Greenberg/Visuals Unlimited; **451**, Kennan Ward/Corbis; **453**, Stephen Frisch/Stock Boston; **456**, Joseph Sohm/ChromoSohm Inc./Corbis; **457**, Getty Images; **466 tr**, Richard Morrell/Corbis; **466 t**, Royalty Free/ Corbis; **467 mr**, Dorling Kindersley; **467 br**, Andy Crawford/Dorling Kindersley

Chapter 10 Pages 469, Doug Dreyer/AP/Wide World Photos; **470**, Ian Shaw/ Getty Images, Inc.; **471**, Richard Haynes; **472**, Keren Su/Getty Images, Inc.; **474 mr**, Pearson Education; **474 tl**, Richard Haynes; **475**, Gabe Palmer III/ Alamy; **480**, Toshiba America Products Inc. ©2002. All Rights Reserved; **480 Inset**, Corel; **481**, Bob Daemmrich/The Image Works; **483**, Spencer Grant PhotoEdit; **485 mr**, Russ Lappa **485 tr**, Richard Haynes; **486**, Annebicque Bernard/Corbis SYGMA; **487**, Royalty Free/Corbis; **489**, Skjold Photographs; **491**, Joseph Sohm, Chromosohm Inc./Corbis; **493 ml**, Richard Haynes; **493 mr**, Richard Haynes; **494**, Ellen Bradley/Brush Hill Boxers; **497 bl**, Bill Howes; Frank Lane Picture Agency/Corbis; **497 tl**, Richard Haynes; **499**, David Young-Wolff/PhotoEdit; **500 t**, Richard Haynes; **508 tr**, Hank Morgan/Photo Researchers; **508 ml**, Flip Nicklin/Minden Pictures; **508–509 b**, Joseph Van Os/Getty Images

Chapter 11 Pages 511, Art Wolfe/Photo Researchers, Inc.; **514 ml**, Getty Images, Inc.; **514**, Richard Haynes; **516**, Kobal Collection; **518**, Laima Druskis/Prentice Hall; **523**, Annette Coolidge/PhotoEdit; **524**, G. K. & Vikki Hart/Getty Images; **526**, Tom Stewart/Corbis; **528**, Ryan McVay/Getty Images, Inc.; **535**, Paul Barton/Corbis; **535**, Richard Haynes; **536 mr & tl**, Richard Haynes; **537**, The Art Archive/Dagli Orti; **539 b**, Richard Haynes; **540**, International Stock/ImageState; **543**, Courtesy of Stewart Wood; **546**, Ken O'Donoghue; **547**, AFP/Getty; **548**, Catherine BIBOLLET/TOP/ Imagestate; **556 b**, Jon Riley/Getty Images, Inc.; **556 t**, Digital Vision/Getty Images; **557 br**, C Squared Studios/Photodisc/Getty Images

Chapter 12 Pages 559, Hillary Smith Garrison/AP/Wide World Photos; **563 ml & tr**, Richard Haynes; **565**, Tom Dietrich/Getty Images, Inc; **569**, Tony Freeman/PhotoEdit; **571**, Alan Carey/The Image Works; **572**, Richard Haynes; **573**, Albert Einstein™ Licensed by The Hebrew University of Jerusalem, Represented by The Roger Richman Agency, Inc. Photo courtesy of the Archives, California Institute of Technology.; **576**, Holloway/Getty Images; **577**, Richard Haynes; **580**, Dennis O'Clair/Getty Images Inc.; **581**, Hybrid Medical Animation; **582**, photo by Peter Stättmayer, Bayerische Volkssternwarte München (Bavarian Public Observatory, Munich, Germany); **585**, U.S. Navy by Ensign John Gay; **588**, John Neubauer/ PhotoEdit; **596 ml**, Adamsmith/Getty Images; **596 ml(inset)**, Photo Researchers; **596 mr**, Amos Morgan Getty Images, Giraffe, DK Images/ Paignton Zoo

TE Design

Susan Gerould/Perspectives

Teacher's Edition

Editional Services: TechBooks/GTS Publishing Services
Production Services: TechBooks/GTS

Acknowledgments